THE OFFICIAL FOOTBALL ASSOCIATION

NON-LEAGUE CLUB DIRECTORY 2001

(24th Edition)

EDITOR TONY WILLIAMS

ISBN 0.9539111-1.X

Published by Non-League Club Directory Ltd
Printed by Biddles of Guildford
Typesetting by Nina Whatmore and George Brown
All distributing queries to Pat Vaughan
Tel: 01823 490080 or 01458 241592

Front Cover:
England internationals clash at Nene Park.
Yeovil Town's skipper Terry Skivington shadows
Rushden & Diamonds striker
Justin Jackson in their first top of the table
Conference meeting.
Photo: Peter Barnes

INTRODUCTION

We have now enjoyed our first year working together as Non-League Media Plc.

The Non-League Paper has been a terrific success.

Team Talk Magazine has moved up market to give our level of football a lift of image through the new 'Non-League Magazine' and, of course, extra television coverage, an exciting new 'She Kicks' magazine for women, the website (www.thenon-leaguepaper.com), James Wright's Non-League Newsdesk and Annual plus our new Non-League Diary, all add up to give a very comprehensive service.

Yes it's been a busy year and as the 'senior' member of the family 'The F.A. Non-League Club Directory' enjoyed another successful edition and is here again as a record of the 2000-2001 season with even more pages.

Last year when first published, the Directory topped both Steve Redgrave and David Beckham in the Sports Books ratings on consecutive weeks, which must have given just a little clue to the sporting public that our level of football is a lot more popular than a lot of people realise!

Another season will be under way by the time you read this and the build up to the season has been as exciting as ever before. Football has never been more popular so let's hope the bubble doesn't burst through too much exposure, but develops with many new converts joining the game as players, supporters and administrators.

Editorial Team

Tony Williams (Editor)
George Brown (House Editor)
Steve Whitney, James Wright, Michael Williams
Jenny Gullick and Nina Whatmore

Editorial Address: Non-League Club Directory Ltd.,
Helland, North Curry, Taunton, Somerset, TA3 6DU
Tel: 01823 490080 Fax: 01823 490281
Email: tony.williams12@virgin.net

ACKNOWLEDGEMENTS

As we edge towards our 'quarter century' the compilation of the Directory still throws up new challenges and this season we tried (without complete success) to include team photos of all the senior clubs who qualify to play in the F.A. Umbro Trophy.

The idea being, that we would include a photo of every senior non-League player if we were successful. However the target is there again for next season and although our team of honorary photographers may not be seeing so many of their photos in the magazine in future, their work for the Directory will still be very welcome.

The team was impressive once again last season and I must emphasise how important their dedicated contributions have been during the years when it was difficult to keep Team Talk and the Directory going.

So a very big thank you once again to:

Paul Barber, Peter Barnes, Graham Brown, Paul Carter, Andrew Chitty, Keith Clayton, Alan Coomes, Graham Cotterill, Paul Dennis, Tim Edwards, Keith Gillard, Ken Gregory, Tim Lancaster, Garry Letts, Peter Lirettoc, Eric Marsh, Ian Morsman, Dennis Nicholson, Jen O'Neill, Ray Pruden, Mark Sandon, Francis Short, Peter Singh, Colin Stevens, Neil Thaler, Darren Thomas, Roger Turner, Alan Watson, Dave Whatmore, Bill Wheatcroft, Gordon Whittington and Martin Wray. What stars!

Valuable contributions of the written word and statistics from all levels of the game have also been magnificent once again and our thanks go to:

Mike Amos, John Anderson, Jeremy Biggs, Bill Berry, Albert Cole, Stewart Davidson (editor of the Scottish Non League Review - Contact 0141 5662 5721), Arthur Evans, Mike Ford, Rob Grillo, Wally Goss, William Hughes, Tony Incenzo, Alan Meadows, Dave Phillips, Mike Simmonds, Michael Williams (Cornish Stats) and Mike Wilson.

The end of the season finds most league, club and county officials quite exhausted and we do appreciate their willingness to ensure that their information is sent to us in time for us to prepare their allocated section to the best of our ability. Ninety-one percent of officials could not be more helpful. Thank you all very much.

I'm glad to say that two of non-League football's real experts, James Wright (General Stats) and Steve Whitney (Player Details) are well and truly part of the new Non-League Media team and once again their particular skills have been greatly appreciated.

The home squad of George Brown, Jenny Gullick, Nina Whatmore and Michael Williams has absorbed the pressure as well as could be expected and at least they are still willing to work together next year!

They have been magnificent and if you wonder what it's like to compile 1,088 pages from so many sources, then just try putting a match day programme together for a cup replay on a Monday and multiply it by a few hundred pages!

The whole point is that we all consider it a `labour of love' and I suppose that also sums up the people for whom we are producing the book.

The supporters, club officials, coaches, trainers, groundsmen, refreshment servers and all involved in non-League football are very rarely in it for the money!

And that's exactly why this level of the game is special - thank you one and all!

TONY WILLIAMS

CONTENTS

Only the major leagues are listed in this section. The full list will be found in the index of leagues on page 1043

This county section starts at page 921 and runs through the various county associations in alphabetical order

Editorial

When we introduced the Non League Football Annual in 1978 as a little 252 page pocket book, who would have thought that 23 years later the massive world of non-League would be promoted so comprehensively by a company such as Non-League Media Plc?

I had struggled on, with the Directory developing into a best seller and a series of magazines eventually settling down as Team Talk with a life span of ten years. But it was always financially difficult to promote and market our ideas and, of course, to find the time to attract financial support from advertisers and sponsors.

The emergence of the Non-League Media anchored by The Non-League paper, an original brain child of David Emery, previously the Sports Editor of the Daily Express and Editor of Sport First, enabled a massive educational operation to click into action.

The paper published on Sundays regularly sells 40,000 in the Summer and is expected to top 70,000 in the present season, while Team Talk has been given a new look and adds the monthly glamour to the paper's weekly news under the new title of 'The Non-League Magazine'.

Obviously the Directory is the annual that records the year's statistics and photographic coverage for 'the national game' and the website will be developing fast throughout the season to give daily coverage.

James Wright's weekly Non-League Newsdesk and his statistical Cherry Red Records' Annual gives even more information, while the women's game is being promoted by 'She Kicks', a monthly magazine previously know as 'On the Ball'.

Last season also saw Sky TV include a weekly half hour magazine programme covering the senior levels of the non-League game thanks to the sponsorship of the Non-League Paper, and for the first time the massive 96 per cent of football played outside the Premier and Football League competitions received coverage of which their following could be justly proud.

From a personal point of view it was great to be involved in a company that was dedicated to the success of the level of the game which I had championed for a life time, so the whole operation has been very satisfying indeed.

However, just as we originally survived thanks to the loyal support of the non-League enthusiasts, who recognised and appreciated our efforts, so we need support on an even larger scale to ensure our services grow every year.

If indeed you approve of our efforts please take on the responsibility of supporting us with your friends and colleagues by:

1. Buying the paper each Sunday
2. Taking out a subscription for the magazine at your newsagents or by post from us
3. Telling everyone you know who is interested in football about these publications;
   for example did you know you can buy this book at a £5 discount if you are a magazine subscriber?
4. Writing or Emailing us with suggestions and ideas to improve our efforts.
5. Passing the word around about our new 'Non-League Diary' and 'The Non-League Poster'.

If your club officials are worried about ordering books in bulk for the club discounts, you can explain that costs can always be covered by using them as raffle prizes, should there not be enough members willing to buy copies.

In general please act as our publicists and agents as we are concentrating our efforts for you and your fellow enthusiasts. and you are the ones who will benefit if we are successful.

Finally, why not buy some shares in the company or encourage your friends to do the same? This really will help the cause and will hopefully reward you in the future as well!

It's been a great first year for the company and the year 2002 will also see this directory celebrate its 25th Anniversary. A special milestone for a special book!

The new look Football Association certainly gives the impression that the game at our levels will be in good hands. Careful negotiations and well thought out planning will eventually produce a more balanced pyramid of leagues geographically and the wonderful work of The Football Foundation and The Football Stadia Improvement Fund have already produced the much needed financial assistance to enable massive ground improvements throughout the country. (Enquiries 0207 534 4210)

Readers of Team Talk and the Directory will know how seriously we have campaigned to encourage the installation of a competitive international tournament for the cream of our players, and now, with the leadership of Frank Pattison, Steve Parkin and Greg Fee at the F.A., we have three senior executives, who are really looking into the situation seriously and searching for the best way to re-introduce the much missed international competition.

The football itself was badly effected by the consistent rainfall throughout the season and the competitions for the smaller clubs suffered badly.

However, the battle for The Conference Championship certainly gripped the football world right up to the last week, when Rushden & Diamonds just pulled ahead of Yeovil Town and achieved their ambition by winning promotion to Division Three.

Both sets of players should be praised for a terrific battle fought out over a long season.

Max Griggs had seen his club overtaken in past seasons, but had kept his cool, his composure and his faith. Sadly his counterpart could not show the same qualities and, after a display of embarrassing temperament that showed a lack of understanding for the game and indeed his manager Colin Addison, who had shown wonderful sportsmanship and dignity throughout the pressure of the run in, the neutrals in the game were united in their conclusion that the right club had won the battle.

Meanwhile we were led to believe the campaign for two up, two down was as good as won and next season could also see play-offs to keep most of the Conference clubs on their toes until the final matches.

But once again The Football League clubs bonded together and, with a vote of 71-1 (thank you Wycombe Wanderers), they complained that only a huge pay off for a second relegated club could alter their minds. It's strange to think of a massive prize being given to a failure, but I suppose in the business world we see many a sacked executive handsomely paid off, despite a lack of success.

The Conference chairmen immediately voted for play-offs anyway, despite the fact that the Champions could well be prevented from promotion, especially if the winners of the play-off then faced the champions, who could have come right off the boil after a couple of weeks of inactivity.

I suppose the majority of chairmen thought their clubs had a better chance of finishing in the top five than in top place and of course there would be bigger crowds. But the F.A.'s appropriate committee considered that the champions and the champions alone should qualify to win promotion to The Football League, so there is even more pressure on everyone to introduce two up and two down.

One of the big successes of the season was the presentation by The Football Association of the F.A. Umbro Trophy and F.A. Carlsberg Vase Finals at Villa Park. Obviously the image and thrill of playing at Wembley was missing but that was all!

The atmosphere created even by comparatively small attendances was excellent and the comfort and view of the spectators was magnificent. The entertainment and facilities in general could not have been improved upon and there is no doubt that all future finalists will enjoy their outings if Villa Park is chosen again.

The presentation of the Trophy and Vase draws held all round the country also reflect very well on the F.A. competitions department, the sponsors and the organisers.

So in every way the so called 'grass roots' of our nation's winter sport is getting the greatly improved image it deserves.

We are very pleased to be part of this revolution and if, when we publish our 25th Directory, we can report the successful launching of a Home International Tournament, well that would just be the icing on a very satisfying cake!

TW

Peter Barraclough discusses the Non League Directory with the Editor on Sky World News at the Reebok Stadium

NON-LEAGUE MEDIA Plc

Elvin House, Stadium Way, Wembley, Middlesex, HA9 0DW
Tel: 020 8900 9021 Fax: 020 8900 9023
Email: info@nlfootball.com

Chairman: Graham Gutteridge - Chief Executive: Steve Ireland
Directors: David Emery, Fiaz Ur Rehman, Barry Gold, Bobby Robson CBE

THE NON-LEAGUE PAPER (Sundays)

Hill House, (2nd Floor), Highgate Hill, London, N19 5NA
Tel: 020 7687 7687 Fax: 020 7687 7688
Email: info@nlfootball.com

Editor in Chief: David Emery - Editor:
Editot: Ian Cole Production Editor: John Cleal News Editor: David Watters

THE NON-LEAGUE MAGAZINE (Monthly)

Hill House (2nd floor), Highgate Hill, London, N19 5NA
Tel: 020 7687 7687 Fax: 020 7687 7688
Email: info@nlfootball.com

Managing Editor: Tony Williams - Editor: Stuart Hammonds

THE F.A. NON-LEAGUE CLUB DIRECTORY (Annual)

Helland, North Curry, Taunton, Somerset, TA3 6DU
Tel: 01823 490080 Fax: 01823 490281
Email: tony.williams12@virgin.net

Editor: Tony Williams

'SHE KICKS' (Women's Football Monthly)

Design Works, William Street, Gateshead, Tyne & Wear, NE10 0JP
Tel: 0191 420 8383 Fax: 0191 420 4950
Email: info@shekicks.net

Editor: Jennifer O'Neill

NON-LEAGUE WEEKLY NEWSDESK & ANNUAL

13 Northfield Avenue, Taunton, Somerset, TA1 1XF
Tel: 01823 254071 Fax: 01823 327720
Email: nlnewsdesk@zetnet.co.uk

Editor: James Wright

THE NON-LEAGUE WEBSITE

Rippleffect Studios Ltd., 68A Rodney Street, Liverpool, L1 9AF
Tel: 0151 7096848 Website: www.rippleffect.com
www.thenon-league paper.com (previously www.nlfootball.com)
News Media Manager: Andrew Mullan
News Editor: Steve Whitney - Tel: 01536 515398 Email: stevewhitney@btconnect.com

ADDITIONAL EXECUTIVES FOR ALL PUBLICATONS

Administration: Blanche Dalton (Office) 020 8900 90221
Advertising (Sponsors): Forbes Chapman 07802 237646 or 020 8367 0910
Advertising (General): Launch Pad (Office) 020 7734 7739
Circulation Manager: Brian King (Mobile) 07775 734107
Public Relations: Graham Courtney (Mobile) 07801 833500

Tony Williams

Educated at Malvern College, one of the country's best football schools in the late sixties, he represented England Under 18 against Scotland at Celtic Park before serving as an administrative officer in the Royal Air Force for five years.

He was on Reading's books from the age of 16-22, but also represented F.A. Amateur XI's and the R.A.F. while playing mainly in the old Isthmian League for Corinthian Casuals, Dulwich Hamlet and Kingstonian joining Hereford United and Grantham during R.A.F. postings.

After taking an F.A. Coaching badge he coached at Harrow Borough, Epsom & Ewell and Hungerford Town and was asked to edit Jimmy Hill's Football Weekly after initial experience with the Amateur Footballer. Monthly Soccer and Sportsweek followed before he had the idea for a football Wisdens and was helped by The Bagnall Harvey Agency to find a suitable sponsor in Rothmans.

After launching the Rothmans Football Yearbook in 1970 as its founder and co- compiler with Roy Peskett, he was asked to join Rothmans (although a non-smoker!) in the company's public relations department and was soon able to persuade the Marketing Director that Rothmans should become the first ever sponsor of a football league.

After a season's trial with the Hellenic and Isthmian Leagues, it was decided to go national with the Northern and Western Leagues and for four years he looked after the football department at Rothmans, with Jimmy Hill and Doug Insole presenting a brilliant sponsorship package which amongst many other innovations included three points for a win and goal difference.

So Non-League football led the way with sponsorship and two, now well accepted, innovations.

Sportsmanship and goals were also rewarded in a sponsorship that proved a great success for football and for Rothmans.

After the cigarette company pulled out of their sports sponsorship Tony launched the first Non-League Annual and later The Football League Club Directory, launching `Non-League Football' with The Mail on Sunday and then Team Talk which has now changed its name to The Non-League Magazine after ten years.

After his ten years with Hungerford Town, he moved West and served Yeovil Town as a Director for seven years but was thrilled when David Emery's plans for the exciting Non-League Media emerged and came into reality, thus giving the Non-League game the publicity and promotion that he and his team had been attempting to set up since the Annual (now Directory) was launched in 1978.

Non-League Football
welcomes
BURTON
for a second year

Kit 4 Clubs celebrates 1st year Anniversary

Leading its way into a 2nd successful year Burton's Kit 4 Clubs has proven to be a resounding success and pioneer for investment in football at a grass-roots level.

Kit 4 Clubs, created last year by Official F.A. Sponsor Burton was devised to provide non-league, school and youth club teams with vital football kit and training equipment. As a pioneering scheme and now celebrating it's 1st Anniversary, and with over 4,000 teams currently registered, support has been immense

Endorsed by the F.A., the scheme has received pledges of support from many high profile figures including Sports Minister **Richard Caborn**, F.A. Chief Executive **Adam Crozier** and the best in British football.

England Captain **David Beckham** said; *"Kit 4 Clubs is a fantastic opportunity for our kids. It's good to see Burton investing time and money in helping kids take up the game. I am sure the scheme will encourage a lot of young talent by creating this opportunity for them."*

Scotland Manager **Craig Brown** said; *"The Kit 4 Clubs scheme is an excellent way of investing something back into the game of football in Scotland and allowing every supporter to make a difference to the successful future of the game."*

Sol Campbell said; *"Kit 4 Clubs is an easy and affordable way for every school and club to benefit. It will help players at all levels participate in the national game. It is encouraging to see players coming through the ranks and playing top-flight football. Burton's Kit 4 Clubs scheme will ensure that players are getting the right support to compete."*

Joe Cole said; *"Kit 4 Clubs is a great initiative that invests in the future of football. It supports the game at a grassroots level and will help make a difference to the future of football and the stars of tomorrow."*

This unique initiative allows the entire nation to help make a difference to club and school teams. For every £10 / IR£12 spent at Burton, customers receive a Kit 4 Clubs token to give to the school or club of their choice (schools and clubs must be registered to the Kit 4 Clubs scheme in advance). These tokens can then be exchanged for quality tailor made football strips in the most popular styles and colours and top brand football equipment from the Kit 4 Clubs catalogue.

Last year Kit 4 Clubs received vociferous support across the board with local communities realising the importance of such a campaign. Amongst the pledges of support received were messages from local media, teams and high profile figures including **Kevin Keegan**, **Tony Adams** and **Kate Hoey**. As a token of their support Darlington F.C. sent two of their brightest stars down to local school Branksome Comprehensive. Signing autographs and giving stars of tomorrow a few pointers epitomised what the campaign represents.

Teams participating in the scheme have eagerly expressed their support:

"May I say what an excellent scheme this is, at a time when so many teams do not receive funding from other sources. thank you very much for your effort in this matter." **Banbury F.C. Under 14s Manager.**

"Some of our students have real talent and the Kit 4 Clubs scheme is enabling them to take it one step further." **Head of PE, St. Richard Gwyn Catholic School in Clydebank**.

This September sees the launch of Kit 4 Clubs for 2002 with many high profile young players looking to pledge their support to the campaign. Three talented young stars of international calibre will publicly launch the scheme with a national photo-call, officially leading the campaign into another successful year.

Sports Minister Richard Caborn said; *"I would like to congratulate Burton on their continued involvement with Kit 4 Clubs. I am sure that Kit 4 Clubs will encourage many more youngsters to participate in football. I am pleased to see major companies supporting football at grass roots level. Burton's committed enthusiasm for the scheme demonstrates an adversary commitment to grass roots football."*

BURTON

Official Sponsor of The Football Association

THANK YOU BURTON

The first year of Burton's sponsorship of the F.A. Non-League Directory was a great success as it was the anchor for their exciting 'Kit 4 Clubs' scheme and, of course, they provided a tremendous reward for the F.A. Trophy level clubs with an excellent Sportsmanship Award for season 2000-01.

The Kit 4 Clubs idea provided tokens to be saved and exchanged for kit for clubs in return for every £10 spent on products by club supporters at the Burton stores throughout the country. Schools, youth and senior clubs all benefited and a massive 4,000 teams have registered with the sponsor's generous scheme.

The Directory was a great success backed by their sponsorship last season and early in October, Histon Football Club will be off to Gatwick Airport after their Dr. Martens Eastern League match at Tonbridge. They are due to arrive in Guernsey in time for a relaxing evening before facing the Island Representative side the following day.

This will be the last game for Guernsey, the present Island Games Football Champions, before they begin their South Western Counties Championship fixtures and a special reception is planned after the game which will be played at St. Martins Blanche Pierre ground.

Histon finished with the best league sportsmanship record of all the clubs who competed in last season's F.A. Trophy with 24 cautions and two dismissals. They were equal with Rocester Football Club, but having scored more goals they clinched the prize.

This year the sportsmanship challenge will be held again and, of course, the Kit 4 Clubs scheme is still in full swing. Team officials wanting to register with the scheme should enquire at their local Burton store for further details.

We all appreciate the magnificent support of one of The Football Association's valued 'Associates' and from all of us we offer a big thank you to Burton for all their efforts that benefit the game at so many levels.

TONY WILLIAMS

The Non-League Club Directory

2000-2001
AWARDS

• ROLL OF HONOUR •

FOOTBALLER OF THE YEAR
Ray Warburton (Rushden & Diamonds Captain)

MANAGER OF THE YEAR
Jeff King (Canvey Island)

ENGLAND PLAYER OF THE YEAR
Tim Ryan (Doncaster Rovers)

F.A. CUP
Dagenham & Redbridge

INDIVIDUAL MERIT AWARDS
Lee Matthews
Colin Addison
Alvin McDonald
Mick Brady
Geoff Butler

REGIONAL AWARDS
Emley
Stalybridge Celtic
Rushden & Diamonds
Canvey Island
Worksop Town
Farnborough Town
Taunton Town

• INDIVIDUAL MERIT AWARDS 2000-01 •

LEE MATTHEWS

(Dagenham & Redbridge)

After the excitement of the F.A. Cup run and two very close encounters with Charlton Athletic, Lee led his side on a superb run in to the Conference season. Sensibly using the cup excitement as an inspiration, which had proved to the squad just how good they could be, Yeovil Town were beaten twice in this spell and third place was achieved just three points behind the Somerset club, Lee won the award from Match magazine for the most consistent match rating in the Conference over the whole season, and this fine contribution to his club's good season underlines that the skipper deserves this merit award.

COLIN ADDISON

(Manager - Yeovil Town 2000-2001)

When your club achieves its best ever season in the Conference and an F.A. Cup run giving a 5-1 home victory of a Division Two club (Colchester United) and a televised 1-0 away win at Blackpool (Div.3) before losing 1-2 away in injury time to Bolton Wanderers (promoted from Div.1 to the Premier League), a manager has every right to feel pleased with life. Especially as his young team had everything to look forward to as they matured and could look forward to building during their exciting season. Sadly, the club didn't appreciate the situation in the same way, but the rest of non-League football certainly did and for his achievements with Yeovil last season the merit award goes to Colin Addison.

ALVIN McDONALD

(Manager of Vauxhall Motors FC)

The spectacular progress of Vauxhall Motors Football Club has been quite outstanding in the last couple of seasons as the disappointment of a semi-final defeat in the F.A. Vase in 2000 was eased by promotion from The North West Counties League to Unibond's Division One. Their manager Alvin McDonald couldn't relay on much income from very sparse support and his quality players were obviously the targets for bigger clubs. But success on the field has lifted everyone at the club and a second promotion to the Premier Division of the Unibond League is an outstanding achievement which deserves national recognition with a merit award.

MICK BRADY

(Chairman of Leamington FC)

AFC Leamington were founder members of the Alliance Football League, but sadly they soon disappeared from the pyramid altogether, when the club lost its membership of the Midland Combination thirteen years ago. The fact that they are back, attracting crowds of about 500 with top attendances over 1,000 and have won promotion to Division One of the Combination says a great deal for the loyalty, determination and obvious enthusiasm of chairman Mick Brady. His loyal band of helpers have kept all developments under strict financial control, but are busy raising money for floodlights and a clubhouse. The town has its football club back and on behalf of all who have helped the chairman he is presented with his merit award.

GEOFF BUTLER

(Manager of Salisbury City 1983-2001)

Was the longest serving manager in football, when the new board of directors at Salisbury City decided to make him redundant. For eighteen years he had looked after playing matters at City and for many of these he also doubled up in charge of commercial matters. He took his club to two promotions to the Premier Division of the Southern League and in his second spell was able to consolidate as one of the Division's top clubs. He also saw the club move from the old Victorian Park to a new, smart home in Old Sarum. Geoff is another example of an experienced and respected football man moved on by the new business men infiltrating the non-League boardrooms.

• REGIONAL CLUB AWARDS 2000-01 •

North West

EMLEY

In the first season in their impressive new home, Emley were involved in the Unibond Championship race until the last weeks of the season. They amassed a creditable 101 points and were desperately unlucky not to win promotion to the Conference as their F.A. Cup and F.A. Trophy performances in recent seasons have proved they are ready for the challenge at the senior level.

North West

STALYBRIDGE CELTIC

To score 96 goals and gain 102 points in a senior competition as good as the Unibond Premier Division is a sign of quality in itself. Celtic also won the Cheshire Senior Cup against Stockport County and their all round development on and off the field showed them to be ready to reclaim their place in the Conference.

Midlands

RUSHDEN & DIAMONDS

Have proved to the football world that if the basics are right and built on sound foundations, success will come, providing patience and standards are kept. Three years of challenging without success, developed the character and development of a club whose principles kept them well respected and Diamonds became popular champions after a terrific season long battle with Yeovil Town.

Home Counties East

CANVEY ISLAND

Completed an outstanding season with an F.A. Trophy success at Villa Park. The huge back log of fixtures amassed by the bad weather probably robbed them of a battle to the end of the season with eventual Ryman champions Farnborough Town and, of course, Canvey's F.A. Cup run including a spectacular 2-1 victory at Port Vale also added to an outstanding season.

Eastern Counties

WORKSOP TOWN

Inspired by the free scoring Kirk Jackson and skills of Chris Waddle, Worksop's cavalier approach to their football produced wonderful entertainment and excitement for their fans. The club scored 102 League goals, gaining fifth position in the Unibond Premier and a place in the F.A. Trophy Quarter Finals. Though Jackson was missed after his transfer to Darlington, their supporters enjoyed a glorious season's entertainment

Home Counties West

FARNBOROUGH TOWN

The steady re-development on and off the field saw Colin Westley's club pull away from all opposition to cruise to the Ryman Championship. They will be the first to admit that their success may have been a little tougher if Canvey Island hadn't fallen behind so far with fixtures, but this won't worry the Conference club one jot this season, as they build a squad to challenge at the top of the Conference.

South West

TAUNTON TOWN

Following the incredibly unlucky circumstances that saw a Vase victory snatched from them in 1994, their F.A. Vase success was especially acceptable for all those at the Somerset club who could also remember the eighteen consecutive cup final losses since 1953. Another Screwfix Western League success just gives them the award from the strong challenges of Tiverton Town and Yeovil Town in the West Country.

FA Cup

DAGENHAM & REDBRIDGE

Having beaten Lincoln City away in the Second Round from home, the Daggers faced the daunting task of a local Derby at Premiership Charlton Athletic. With just four minutes to go the Conference club was deservedly leading by the only goal, and although a late equaliser gave Charlton a replay, Dagenham stayed loyal to their fans and their players by hosting the game at Victoria Road, missing out on a £150,000 TV fee when the replay was delayed by the weather, and although they just lost in extra time, the club cover themselves in glory for their play, their attitude and spirit. Indeed, Dagenham & Redbridge underlined everything that is good about the AXA sponsored F.A. Cup and the contribution of non-League clubs to the competition.

ENGLAND PLAYER OF THE YEAR

TIM RYAN

Photo: Andrew Chitty

Tim Ryan has been an ever present in manager John Owens nine internationals, playing at centre back, on the left side of a back three, or indeed an anchor man in midfield. His sturdy defensive performances have also been highlighted by two goals for the England squad when disguised as an FAXI and he has been one of the important factors behind his manager's unbeaten record.

NON LEAGUE MANAGER OF THE YEAR

JEFF KING

(Canvey Island)

Photo: Darren C Thomas

Having held the reigns at Canvey Island Football Club since moving into the Ryman League from the Essex Senior League in 1993, Jeff King has sensibly strengthened his coaching staff and found the funds to justify a quality squad. Last season saw Canvey beat Port Vale 2-1 away after a 4-4 home draw and then lose a close encounter at Southend, which attracted a crowd of 11,402. They were the first club outside the Conference to reach the Trophy Final for years and, of course, they beat three Conference clubs (Stevenage Borough, Telford United & Chester City), on the way to winning the Trophy against Forest Green Rovers. Canvey also completed their Ryman League programme with nine fixtures in ten days, including a 2-1 victory at champions Farnborough Town. Jeff King masterminded an outstanding all round season, and built a superb squad who were a credit to the Ryman League from which they must be hot favourites to gain promotion this season.

PAST WINNERS

1999-00 Jan Molby (Kidderminster Harr.)
1998-99 Brendan Phillips (Nuneaton Boro)
1997-98 Steve Cotterill (Cheltenham Town)
1996-97 Paul Futcher (Southport)
1995-96 Paul Fairclough (Stevenage Boro)
1994-95 Sammy McIlroy (Macclesfield T)
1993-94 Bill Punton (Diss Town)
1992-93 Martin O'Neill (Wycombe Wndrs)

NON LEAGUE FOOTBALLER OF THE YEAR

RAY WARBURTON

(Rushden & Diamonds)

Photo: Garry Letts

The constant pressure of leading a club such as Rushden & Diamonds into match after match is character testing of the highest order. Supporters and club officials expect success, the opposition are just as determined to topple you as a glamourous and high profile club, so the job of the skipper to carry out his manager's instuctions and drive his players forward each week is a huge responsibility. Ray Warburton is a combative centre half, but his own game had to be without fault each week as the battle at the top of the Conference ebbed and flowed with Yeovil Town and Rushden locked together. The chairman can set the club up in the right way, the manager hopes he has collected a squad with the right balance, and given them the correct instructions, match by match, but the leader on the field takes the responsibility where it matters most, and Ray saw his club safely into Division Three and deserves the ultimate reward as Non-League Footballer of the Season.

PAST WINNERS

1999-00 Gary Abbott (Aldershot Town)
1998-99 Neil Grayson (Cheltenham Town)
1997-98 Phil Everett (Tiverton Town)
1996-97 Howard Forinton (Yeovil Town)
1995-96 Barry Hayes (Stevenage Boro)
1994-95 Kevan Brown (Woking)
1993-94 Chris Brindley (Kidderminster H.)
1992-93 Steve Guppy (Wycombe Wndrs)
1991-92 Tommy Killick (Wimborne Town)
1990-91 Mark West (Wycombe Wndrs)
1989-90 Phil Gridelet (Barnet)
1988-89 Steve Butler (Maidstone Utd)
1987-88 David Howell (Enfield)
1986-87 Mark Carter (Runcorn)
1985-86 Jeff Johnson (Altrincham)
1984-85 Alan Cordice (Wealdstone)
1983-84 Brian Thompson (Maidstone Utd)

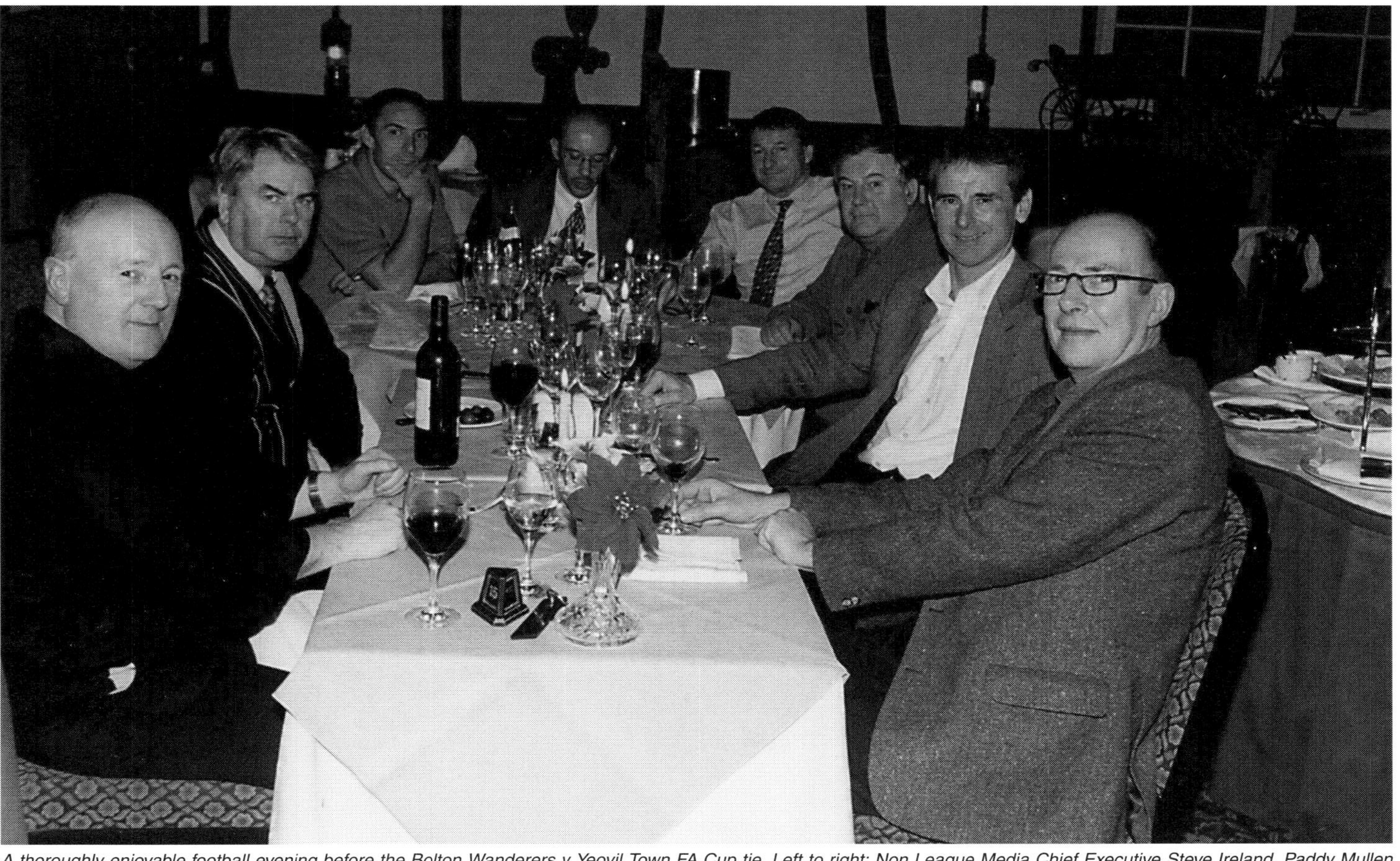

A thoroughly enjoyable football evening before the Bolton Wanderers v Yeovil Town FA Cup tie. Left to right: Non League Media Chief Executive Steve Ireland, Paddy Mullen (Yeovil Town Scout), Steve Thompson (Yeovil Town Coach), Simon Marland (Bolton Wanderers Chief Executive), Roger Hunt, Tony Williams, Colin Addison (Yeovil Town Manager), Brian King (Non League Media Distribution Manager)

PECKING ORDER 2000-2001

A J Sarnecki

97-8	98-9	99-00	00-01	Code	League	FA Cup ent	FA Cup xmt	FA Cup won	FA Trophy ent	FA Trophy xmt	FA Trophy won	FA Vase ent	FA Vase xmt	FA Vase won	C pts	T pts	V pts	Total pts
1	1	1	1	ap	CONFERENCE	22	176	31	22	88	31	0	0	0	229	207	0	436
2	3	2	2	npp	NORTHERN PREMIER Premier	23	92	24	23	8	30	0	0	0	139	130	0	269
3	2	4	3	isp	ISTHMIAN Premier	22	88	34	22	8	26	0	0	0	144	122	0	266
4	4	3	4	sop	SOUTHERN Premier	22	88	26	22	8	28	0	0	0	136	124	0	260
7	7	5	5	is1	ISTHMIAN First	22	0	34	22	0	17	0	0	0	56	105	0	161
6	5	7	6	np1	NORTHERN PREMIER First	21	4	32	22	0	15	0	0	0	57	103	0	160
5	8)	9	7	sow	SOUTHERN Western	22	0	29	22	0	19	0	0	0	51	107	0	158
9	9	8	8	is2	ISTHMIAN Second	22	0	23	0	0	0	22	48	41	45	0	111	156
8	6)	6	9	soe	SOUTHERN Eastern	22	0	32	22	0	11	0	0	0	54	99	0	153
10	10	11	10	nor1	NORTHERN First	21	0	30	0	0	0	21	30	36	51	0	87	138
13=	11=	10	11	nwc1	NORTH WEST COUNTIES First	22	0	15	0	0	0	22	36	35	37	0	93	130
11	11=	12	12	ecop	EASTERN COUNTIES Premier	22	0	29	0	0	0	22	20	23	51	0	65	116
16	19	16=	13	mda	MIDLAND ALLIANCE	21	0	14	0	0	0	22	22	27	35	0	71	106
19	20	14	14	wsx1	WESSEX	20	0	16	0	0	0	21	28	19	36	0	68	104
13=	13=	13	15	ncep	NORTHERN COUNTIES EAST Premier	19	0	16	0	0	0	20	22	21	35	0	63	98
12	13=	16=	16	wesp	WESTERN Premier	18	0	16	0	0	0	19	18	22	34	0	59	93
18	15	15	17	is3	ISTHMIAN Third	22	0	19	0	0	0	22	0	28	41	0	50	91
15	17=	21	18	ucop	UNITED COUNTIES Premier	21	0	12	0	0	0	21	16	14	33	0	51	84
17	17=	19	19	ssx1	SUSSEX COUNTY First	17	0	13	0	0	0	19	18	13	30	0	50	80
	16	20	20	ssmp	SPARTAN SOUTH MIDLANDS Premier	16	0	12	0	0	0	19	6	21	28	0	46	74
20	21	18	21	ken1	KENT	16	0	6	0	0	0	16	16	17	22	0	49	71
26	23	23	22	cocp	COMBINED COUNTIES	15	0	8	0	0	0	17	4	15	23	0	36	59
24	22	22	23	help	HELLENIC Premier	8	0	7	0	0	0	18	8	17	15	0	43	58
22	28=	24	24	nce1	NORTHERN COUNTIES EAST First	13	0	5	0	0	0	16	6	16	18	0	38	56
31=	30=	27	25	nwc2	NORTH WEST COUNTIES Second	9	0	5	0	0	0	11	4	9	14	0	24	38
21	25	25=	26	nor2	NORTHERN Second	12	0	5	0	0	0	15	0	4	17	0	19	36
25	24	25=	27	esxs	ESSEX Senior	10	0	1	0	0	0	13	0	7	11	0	20	31
31=	28=	29	28	wes1	WESTERN First	4	0	1	0	0	0	10	0	13	5	0	23	28
28	30=	28	29	eco1	EASTERN COUNTIES First	0	0	0	0	0	0	15	0	7	0	0	22	22
30	26	30	30	lesp	LEICESTERSHIRE SENIOR Premier	0	0	0	0	0	0	11	0	9	0	0	20	20
29	27	31	31=	swe	SOUTH-WESTERN	2	0	0	0	0	0	3	6	8	2	0	17	19
33	34	33=	31=	wmrp	WEST MIDLAND REGIONAL Premier	0	0	0	0	0	0	12	0	7	0	0	19	19
39=	36	33=	33=	ssms	SPARTAN SOUTH MIDLANDS Senior	0	0	0	0	0	0	8	6	4	0	0	18	18
24=	32	32	33=	cmsu	CENTRAL MIDLANDS Supreme	0	0	0	0	0	0	8	6	4	0	0	18	18
36	35	36	33=	mdcp	MIDLAND COMBINATION Premier	0	0	0	0	0	0	12	0	6	0	0	18	18
34=	33	33=	36	ssx2	SUSSEX COUNTY Second	4	0	0	0	0	0	6	0	1	4	0	7	11
39=	38=	37=	37=	nalp	NORTHERN ALLIANCE Premier	0	0	0	0	0	0	2	0	2	0	0	4	4
		40=	37=	smsp	SOMERSET SENIOR Premier	0	0	0	0	0	0	2	0	2	0	0	4	4
	41=	37=	39	dvc	DEVON COUNTY LEAGUE	0	0	0	0	0	0	2	0	1	0	0	3	3
		40=	40=	hel1w	HELLENIC First West	0	0	0	0	0	0	1	0	0	0	0	1	1
37	37	40=	40=	wch1	WEST CHESHIRE First	0	0	0	0	0	0	1	0	0	0	0	1	1
43=	38=	40=	40=	ntas	NOTTS ALLIANCE Senior	0	0	0	0	0	0	1	0	0	0	0	1	1

(figures in parentheses refer to slightly different leagues: SOUTHERN South and Midland) With apologies to the current year's sponsors.

Points are given for status (acceptance into each of the three competitions), for prestige (exemption from early rounds) and performance (number of wins, however achieved, even by walkover). Entry to the Vase is valued at one point, that to the Trophy at 4. Cup entry gives a further bonus of one point. The number of entries from each league is shown in the appropriate column. Points for exemptions are valued at two for each round missed. The entry in the table is of the total points so gained by the given league, not the number of teams given exemptions. Finally, all wins are valued at one point, regardless of opposition: giving extra points for defeating 'stronger' opponents would be too arbitrary. After all, if they lost then they were not stronger on the day!

F.A. CHALLENGE CUP

sponsored by AXA

2000 - 2001 REVIEW

510 clubs

NON LEAGUE HONOURS BOARD 2000-2001

FIRST ROUND PROPER (32)

NATIONWIDE CONFERENCE (16)
Chester City
Dagenham & Redbridge
Forest Green Rovers
Hayes
Hednesford Town
Kettering Town
Kingstonian
Leigh RMI
Morecambe
Northwich Victoria
Nuneaton Borough
Rushden & Diamonds
Southport

CONFERENCE cont.
Telford United
Woking
Yeovil Town

RYMAN (7)
Aldershot Town
Canvey Island
Grays Athletic
Gravesend & Northfleet
Hampton & Richmond Borough
Harrow Borough
Bracknell Town (Div 3)

DR MARTENS (4)
Burton Albion
Dorchester Town
Havant & Waterlooville
Ilkeston Town

UNIBOND (4)
Barrow
Frickley Athletic
Gateshead
Radcliffe Borough (Div 1)

JEWSON EASTERN
AFC Sudbury

SECOND ROUND (11)

Canvey Island
Gateshead
Chester City
Dagenham & Redbridge
Kettering Town
Kingstonian
Morecambe
Northwich Victoria
Nuneaton Borough
Southport
Yeovil Town

THIRD ROUND (5)

Blackburn Rovers	2	v	0	**Chester City**
Bolton Wanderers	2	v	1	**Yeovil Town**
Morecambe	0	v	3	Ipswich Town
Charlton Athletic	1	v	1	**Dagenham & Redbridge**
Dagenham & Redbridge	0	*	1	Charlton Athletic
Southend United	0	v	1	**Kingstonian**

FOURTH ROUND (1)

Bristol City (Div 2)	1	v	1	**Kingstonian**
Kingstonian	0	v	1	Bristol City

EXTRA PRELIMINARY ROUND

No	Home	Score	Away	Att
1	Brigg Town	3 v 0	Willington	141
2	Eccleshill United	2 v 3	Sheffield	66
3	South Shields	2 v 1	Garforth Town	75
4	Tow Law Town	2 v 0	St Helens Town	181
5	Squires Gate	1 v 2	West Auckland Town	130
6	Guisborough Town	1 v 1	Chadderton	138
R	Chadderton	4 v 1	Guisborough Town	146
7	Armthorpe Welfare	0 v 1	Penrith	103
8	Pelsall Villa	1 v 1	Kidsgrove Athletic	142
R	Kidsgrove Athletic	1 v 3*	Pelsall Villa	204
9	Holbeach United	1 v 0	Halesowen Harriers	123
10	Royston Town	0 v 5	Newmarket Town	87
11	Haringey Borough	4 v 1	Concord Rangers	77
12	Raunds Town	2 v 3	Soham Town Rngrs	121
13	Buckingham Town	4 v 1	Halstead Town	102
14	Lowestoft Town	2 v 3	Fakenham Town	203
15	Yate Town	0 v 3	Brislington	126
16	Melksham Town	1 v 0	Falmouth Town	146
17	Wimborne Town	2 v 0	Bridport	189

PRELIMINARY ROUND

No	Home	Score	Away	Att
1	Louth United	1 v 5	North Ferriby United	
	Bailey 65		*Flounders 9, Blythe 15, 89, Lowthorpe 31, Phillips 51*	
2	Witton Albion	4 v 3	Oldham Town	309
	Bishop 9, 58, Anane 25 Boyd 60		*Lambert 34, 39 (2 pens), Orme 85*	
3	Trafford	1 v 0	Flixton	278
	Patterson 52			
4	Marske United	3 v 1	South Shields	163
	Woods 37, 69, Hampton 51		*Thompson 36*	
5	Consett	2 v 1	Hallam	107
	Halliday 51, Brown 43		*Holmes 76*	
6	Yorkshire Amateur	5 v 0	Parkgate	64
	Zoll 30, Bond 51, Downes 65 Sheridan 73, Tabor 80			
7	Workington	0 v 1	Farsley Celtic	405
			Reagan 13	
8	Bradford (Park Avenue)	1 v 0	Brandon United	256
	Thompson 28			
9	Kennek Ryhope CA	0 v 5	Salford City	84
			Lomas 6, 18, Whittle 74, 84, Giggs 90	
10	Whitley Bay	2 v 1	Ashington	291
	Livermore 47, Cuggy 50		*Hogg 6*	
11	Gretna	0 v 0	Ramsbottom United	108
R	Ramsbottom United	3 v 2	Gretna	227
	Brierley 6, 76, Heyes 41		*Manson 25, Henderson 87*	
12	Glasshoughton Welfare	0 v 2	West Auckland Town	82
			Beasley 55, Stranger 61	
13	Billingham Synthonia	1 v 1	Brigg Town	121
	Wood 38		*Buckley 17*	
R	Brigg Town	1 v 0	Billingham Synthonia	141
	Stead 12			
14	Goole	3 v 0	Jarrow Roofing Boldon CA	206
	Saville, Jefferson, Freeman			
15	Castleton Gabriels	2 v 3	Harrogate Railway	64
	Molyneux 5, McKenna 15		*Gardham 38, 67, Smith 24*	
16	Tow Law Town	2 v 2	Newcastle Blue Star	173
	Bolton 70, 77		*Thompson 5, Beech 25*	
R	Newcastle Blue Star	2 v 1	Tow Law Town	255
	Hirst 15, Brett 27		*Innes 80*	
17	Chadderton	2 v 3	Hebburn	114
	Ferguson 68, Barlow 87		*Laidler 37, Scott 50, Donnelly 76*	
18	Prescot Cables	0 v 2	Bedlington Terriers	168
			Milner 35, 89	
19	Maine Road	2 v 2	Easington Colliery	83
	Russell 41, 75		*Allen 36, Davies 87*	
R	Easington Colliery	3 v 2	Maine Road	52
	Geraldie 65, Robson 76 Allen 85		*Russell 41, 75*	
20	Bacup Borough	0 v 4	Harrogate Town	74
			Simon 23, Smith 30, Osborne 37, Tudor 66	
21	Shotton Comrades	1 v 2	Atherton LR	43
	Christie 13		*Entwistle 17, Meredith 80*	
22	Clitheroe	4 v 1	Shildon	207
	Denny32, Webster 37, 45 Anderton 68		*Stones 27*	
23	Mossley	4 v 1	Hatfield Main	223
	Willcock 20, Garside 50 Murphy 75, Ashcroft 90		*Downring 14*	
24	Winsford United	1 v 1	Selby Town	136
	Rendell 46		*Morley 18*	
R	Selby Town	2 v 0	Winsford United	80
	Shiel 40, Forrest 61			
25	Durham City	4 v 0	Thackley	174
	Dilella 18, Alderson 42 Irvine 62, Outhwaite 88			
26	Skelmersdale United	1 v 1	Guiseley	164
	Murphy 45		*Wilkes 75*	
R	Guiseley	4 v 0	Skelmersdale United	255
	Shuttleworth 22, 36 Agana 26, Evangelatos 67			
27	Brodsworth	2 v 2	Blackpool Mechanics	81
	Hoyle 52, Hughes 77		*Guest 65, Laidlaw 54*	
R	Blackpool Mechanics	3 v 2	Brodsworth	120
	Murphy 9, Ormrod 45, 64		*Hoyle, Hughes*	
28	Horden CW	3 v 0	Crook Town	85
	Bryce 23, Hampshire 38 Stephens 75			
29	Darwen	2 v 2	Penrith	68
	Haywood (og) 53, Khan 55		*Bateman 75, Greenan 89*	
R	Penrith	0 v 1	Darwen	119
			Baker 85	
30	Dunston Fed. Brewery	2 v 0	Curzon Ashton	162
	Forbes 14, Fletcher 44			
31	Great Harwood Town	2 v 0	Northallerton Town	102
	Thompson (og) 69, Peake 84			
32	Radcliffe Borough	2 v 1	Rossington Main	267
	Lunt 13, Carden 59		*Dempsey 64, Dixon 88*	
33	Denaby United	0 v 2	Warrington Town	60
			Holden 48, Barr 66	
34	Ossett Town	0 v 1	Chorley	
			Swailes 41	
35	Atherton Collieries	2 v 0	Morpeth Town	58
	Hardman 10, Jones 61			
36	Evenwood Town	1 v 2	Tadcaster Albion	44
	Patterson		*Bardy 15, 80*	
37	Woodley Sports	0 v 3	Ashton United	163
			Toronczak 22, 53, Riordon 88	
38	Sheffield	2 v 1	Rossendale United	292
	Pickess 6, Godber 75		*Sargeson 54*	
39	Seaham Red Star	3 v 1	Pontefract Collieries	108
	Newham 5, Innes 64 Adamson 80		*Boland 48*	
40	Peterlee Newtown	4 v 4	Fleetwood Freeport	52
	Routledge 7, Holt 48 Creamer 66, Fairhurst 90		*Trainer 45, Smith 52, Taylor 54, Baldwin 90*	
R	Fleetwood Freeport	3 v 0	Peterlee Newtown	235
	Smith 16, 35, Diggle 58			
41	Thornaby-on-Tees	4 v 0	Esh Winning	20
	Crawford 3, Woodhouse 6,69 Newell 22			
42	Abbey Hey	1 v 2	Stocksbridge Pk Steels	150
	Pickering 86		*Fethergill 3, Fidler 88*	

*Top:
Danny Graystone (Witton Albion) takes on Lee Stott (Oldham Town)
Photo: Keith Clayton*

*Centre:
Paul Scott (Whyteleafe) climbs above the Hailsham Town defence and heads towards goal.
Photo: Roger Turner*

*Bottom:
Ramsbottom's Dave Roach wins the ball from Gretna's Craig Potts.
Photo: Alan Watson*

No	Home				Away	Att
43	Liversedge	1	v	1	Chester-le-Street Tn	101
	Ryan 90				*McDonald 35*	
R	Chester-le-Street Tn	0	v	3	Liversedge	116
					Payne 73, 88, Lawford 60	
44	Billingham Town	2	v	0	Ossett Albion	54
	Tucker 52, Rowntree 67					
45	Cheadle Town	0	v	1	Bridlington Town	78
					Harper 29	
46	Kendal Town	3	v	1	Pickering Town	78
	Kent 22, Courtney 40 O'Keefe 59				*Reid 69*	
47	Boston Town	2	v	3	Leek CSOB	79
	Price 12, Scotney 65				*Robindon 67, 69, Stevens 66*	
48	Spalding United	4	v	0	Glossop North End	182
	Sedlan 14, 39, Gilbert 64 Wilkins 86					
49	Bilston Town	3	v	0	Sandwell Borough	138
	Young 11, Voice 41 Rollason 70					
50	Staveley MW	1	v	2	Belper Town	193
	White 30				*Cunningham 25, 61*	
51	Gedling Town	5	v	1	Boldmere St Michaels	84
	Manners 40, Hollis-Smith 48 Limb 54, Frawley 68 Carruthers 73				*Quiggin 26*	
52	Oadby Town	2	v	1	Willenhall Town	202
53	Redditch United	3	v	2	Arnold Town	267
	Knight 38, 83, Myers 77				*Bolan 35, Vitale 78*	
54	Newcastle Town	2	v	0	Buxton	155
	Cunningham 9, Woodvine 34					
55	Stamford	2	v	0	Rushall Olympic	139
	Challinor 2, Staff 15					
56	Holbeach United	2	v	1	Glapwell	113
	Dunn, Eadie				*Smith*	
57	Atherstone United	2	v	1	Pelsall Villa	253
	Higos 9, Kelly 45				*Donovan 60*	
58	Bourne Town	1	v	2	Shepshed Dynamo	131
	Ainsley 28				*Cox 22, Rainford 52*	
59	Corby Town	1	v	0	Knypersley Victoria	75
	Mintus 20					
60	Cradley Town	1	v	2	Paget Rangers	73
	Hammond 71				*Smith 13, McColgan 31*	
61	Gresley Rovers	1	v	1	Matlock Town	320
	Allsop 57				*Simpson 12*	
R	Matlock Town	4	v	1	Gresley Rovers	310
	Kingsey 10, Taylor 12, 51 Francis 45				*Peters 83*	
62	Racing Club Warwick	1	v	2	Stourport Swifts	73
	Eden 5				*Booth 2, Marsh 90*	
63	West Midlands Police	1	v	1	Bedworth United	105
	Bellingham 35				*Drewitt*	
R	Bedworth United	2	v	0	West Midlands Police	135
	Bradder 50, 65					
64	Eastwood Town	3	v	1	Rocester	175
	Bradshaw 7, Warboys 15 Kennerdale 26				*Woolley 60*	
65	Hinckley United	7	v	0	Nantwich Town	257
	Lucas 3 (55, 61, 77) *Hunter 10, 67, Madland 84 Williams 88*					
66	Stapenhill	1	v	0	Bridgnorth Town	73
	Eaton 88					
67	Stratford Town	1	v	1	Stafford Town	138
	Allen 84				*Stark 37*	
R	Stafford Town	0	v	0*	Stratford Town	161
	Stafford Town won 5-4 after penalties					

No	Home				Away	Att
68	Blakenall	0	v	1	Oldbury United	148
					Aldridge 28	
69	Borrowash Victoria	0	v	3	Grantham Town	234
					Gray 64, 69, Ranshaw 89	
70	Barwell	0	v	0	Lincoln United	128
70	Lincoln United	2	v	4*	Barwell	104
	Drinkell 46, Blake 85				*Johnson 19, Percival 65, Marsh 108, Holmes 116*	
71	Blackstone	4	v	1	Shifnal Town	59
	Graham 12,80, Smith 50,62				*Smith*	
72	Congleton Town	0	v	0	Wednesfield	142
R	Wednesfield	0	v	1	Congleton Town	80
					Dodd 57	
73	Solihull Borough	2	v	1	Mickleover Sports	273
	Pippard 61, Russell 88				*Hudson 66*	
74	Stourbridge	0	v	0	Rugby United	199
R	Rugby United	2	v	2*	Stourbridge	190
	Stourbridge won 5-4 after penalties					
	O'Brien 16, Beard 54				*Briscoe 45, Moore 72*	
75	Chasetown	0	v	1	Alfreton Town	146
					Brady 23	
76	Sutton Coldfield Town	1	v	1	Bromsgrove Rovers	144
	Mitchell 37				*Burgess 37*	
R	Bromsgrove Rovers	3	v	2	Sutton Coldfield Town	227
	Burrow 17, Burgess 24 Sutton 65				*Began 25, Judd 89*	
77	Saffron Walden Town	1	v	2	Histon	134
	Riches 73				*Salmon 8, Kennedy 83*	
78	Tiptree United	6	v	2	Buckingham Town	84
	Brady 3 (23, 53, 85) *French 90, Parnell 70 McGrory 56*				*Cole 42, Aluro 75*	
79	Flackwell Heath	0	v	2	Bishop's Stortford	98
					Sedgwick 53, John 67	
80	Wroxham	0	v	3	Ford United	166
					Allen 6, 28, Aransiaia 85	
81	Felixstowe & Walton U	2	v	3	Waltham Abbey	145
	Bloomfield 28, 90				*Campbell 74, 76, Fitzrand 67*	
82	Edgware Town	2	v	2	Stowmarket Town	
	Vincent 29, Gladdy 90				*Jopling 68, Yeomans 90*	
R	Stowmarket Town	1	v	0	Edgware Town	124
	Aldis 19					
83	Chelmsford City	3	v	1	Sawbridgeworth Tn	356
	Portway, Fuller, Berquez				*Hunt 56*	
84	Northampton Spencer	0	v	0	Southall	68
R	Southall	0	v	2	Northampton Spencer	30
					Foster 18, 55	
85	Basildon U (withdrawn)		w.o.		Yeading	
86	Boreham Wood	3	v	0	Great Wakering Rvrs	203
	Lawford 9, Talbot 66 Hutchings 70					
87	Bugbrooke St Michaels	0	v	3	Newmarket Town	118
					Shaw 15, Storey 45, 70	
88	Potters Bar Town	2	v	1	Leighton Town	86
	Chalkley 81, 90				*Tatham 2*	
89	Cogenhoe United	4	v	1	Desborough Town	99
90	Bowers United	1	v	1	Bedford United	51
	Hope 21				*Batt 60*	
R	Bedford United	3	v	1	Bowers United	62
91	Chalfont St Peter	1	v	1	Harwich & Parkeston	50
	Haick 62				*Heath 14*	
R	Harwich & Parkeston	1	v	1*	Chalfont St Peter	89
	Harwich won 4-3 after penalties					
	Allen 9				*Middleton 56*	

No.	Home	Score	Away	Att.
92	Ware	3 v 2	Yaxley	
93	Romford	1 v 6	Hemel Hempstead Tn	204
	Abraham 30		***Durkin 3 (45, 48, 65),*** *Butler 12, Somers 27, Pedder 23*	
94	Wingate & Finchley	2 v 1	Wivenhoe Town	130
	Brady 43, Baum 77		*Clewley 80*	
95	Woodbridge Town	3 v 0	Marlow	102
	Dearsley 16, 84, Wallis 90			
96	Baldock Town	2 v 0	Ruislip Manor	
	Dellar 25, Bignall 80			
97	Uxbridge	6 v 1	Holmer Green	114
	Tunnell 4, 64, Moore 9, 23 Gill 51, Cleary 69		*Scholes 79*	
98	Barking	2 v 1	Haringey Borough	112
	Thomas 78, Sussex 79		*Morton 72*	
99	Wootton Blue Cross	2 v 2	London Colney	105
	Downer 32, Justin 65		*Jones 22, Sippetts 42*	
R	London Colney	2 v 2*	Wootton Blue Cross	35
	Jones 40, Rogers 45		*Jozwiak 26, 53*	
	London Colney won 4-2 after penalties			
100	Ilford	1 v 4	Mildenhall Town	197
	Connelly 59		*Godard 7, Ogilvie 38, 81, Pope 63*	
101	Wellingborough Town	0 v 0	Tring Town	54
R	Tring Town	2 v 1*	Wellingborough Town	35
	Beamish 78, Hall 117		*Jameson 16*	
102	Great Yarmouth Town	4 v 1	Kempston Rovers	134
	Roach 33, 47, McIntosh 58 Turner 64		*Fisher 26*	
103	Braintree Town	6 v 0	Banbury United	212
	Cowan 33, 60, Gutzmore 42 Quinton 55, Noble 85, 89			
104	Witney Town	0 v 3	Beaconsfield SYCOB	82
			Gilder 10, Webb 80, Lamb 90	
105	Harlow Town	2 v 3	Diss Town	172
	Salmon 46, Ridout 85		*Hardy 1, Bartley 40, Fox 90*	
106	Burnham Ramblers	1 v 0	Burnham	86
	Down 75			
107	Hanwell Town	1 v 2	Stotfold	55
	Rowlands 65		*Badland 85, Gadd 87*	
108	Hullbridge Sports	0 v 1	Welwyn Garden City	25
			Miles 22	
109	Witham Town	0 v 3	Bedford Town	197
110	Southend Manor	1 v 4	AFC Sudbury	130
	Barnett 1		***Day 4 (8, 45, 51, 83)***	
111	St Neots Town	5 v 0	Milton Keynes City	116
	McCreanor 11, Byrne 15 Caroy 50, Atkins 56, Hurst 88			
112	Tilbury	1 v 0	Fakenham Town	80
	Martin 91			
113	Rothwell Town	0 v 2	Northwood	136
			Sargent 24, 63	
114	Leyton Pennant	2 v 2	East Thurrock United	105
	Mitchell 32, Notley 34		*Winney 43, Cox 44*	
R	East Thurrock United	3 v 0	Leyton Pennant	147
	Finning 64, Burns 84 Cartlidge 29			
115	Eynesbury Rovers	2 v 4	Stewarts & Lloyds	22
	Lynch 24, Goodall 45		*Hall 19, Byrne 32, Fraser 34, Farr 75*	
116	Arlesey Town	7 v 1	Aveley	153
	Kelly 3 (16, 49p, 55p) *Lynch 53, 58, Tekell 87, 89*		*Fulling 19 (pen)*	
117	Brackley Town	0 v 3	Wealdstone	272
			Tilbury 33, Carter 50, 73	
118	Long Buckby	0 v 1	Clapton	53
			Taylor (og) 15	
119	Ford Sports Daventry	1 v 1	Hertford Town	50
	Jennings 75		*Davis 35*	
R	Hertford Town	2 v 3	Ford Sports Daventry	67
	Hall 40, Moran 85			

No.	Home	Score	Away	Att.
120	Maldon Town	3 v 3	Bury Town	100
	Francis 15, 44, Witney 75		*Ince 40, Vince 59, Newman 85*	
R	Bury Town	0 v 2	Maldon Town	194
			Heaseman 58, Mayes 83	
121	Berkhamsted Town	4 v 1	Hornchurch	140
	Foley 3 (44, 74, 90) *Richardson 90*		*Lowery 34*	
122	Wembley	1 v 1	Gorleston	75
	Tie awarded to Wembley: Gorleston removed - ineligible player			
	Harewood 6		*Ottley 70*	
123	Potton United	0 v 2	Ely City	67
			Hipwell 68, 87	
124	Ipswich Wanderers	3 v 1	Wisbech Town	247
	Rowe 6, Wosakio 8, Brown 88		*Ruscillo 46*	
125	Brentwood	2 v 4	Staines Town	108
	Allen 18, 35		*Butler 5, Terry 38, Everitt 43, Tarboys 64*	
126	Brook House	6 v 0	Kingsbury Town	76
	Flaherty 3 (9, 15, 35) *Yates 75, Lynn 86, 90*			
127	Cheshunt	2 v 2*	Clacton Town	71
	Cox 41, Wilkie 63		*Miller 22, Hanney 43*	
R	Clacton Town	2 v 3*	Cheshunt	135
	Bailey 62, Braybrook 85		*Fenton 6, Gregorio 73, Cox 109*	
128	AFC Wallingford	2 v 1	Warboys Town	120
	Allum 67, Mullaney 50		*Bohonis 25*	
129	Hoddesdon Town	1 v 2	St Margaretsbury	67
	Negus 31		*Pullen 8, 35*	
130	Barton Rovers	0 v 2	Soham Town Rngrs	137
			Docking 28, Atkins 63	
131	Moneyfields	0 v 2	Epsom & Ewell	99
			Morris 75, Marvell 83	
132	Sandhurst Town	0 v 4	Andover	108
			Forbes 3, Powers 42, Rusher 56, Dyke 58	
133	Chertsey Town	3 v 1	Abingdon Town	120
	Marlow 3 (9, 47, 87)		*Atkins 79*	
134	Thatcham Town	2 v 0	Corinthian Casuals	134
	Grist 2, 4			
135	Eastbourne Town	1 v 1	Selsey	149
	Henderson 18		*Lee 33*	
R	Selsey	3 v 1	Eastbourne Town	139
	Hurst 58, Ford 80, Bines 85		*Veroe 70*	
136	Camberley Town	0 v 1	Saltdean United	
137	Bashley	3 v 0	North Leigh	128
	Anderson 23, Pickett 84 Marwood 87			
138	Littlehampton Town	2 v 0	Peacehaven & Tels.	138
	Lloyd 10, Woods 86			
139	Beckenham Town	0 v 1	Aylesbury United	108
			Wotton 65	
140	Walton & Hersham	3 v 1	Croydon Athletic	112
	Harrison 31, Phillips 40 Pearson 44		*Stassinos 6*	
141	Chichester City Utd	2 v 2	Abingdon United	81
	Laidlaw 24, Moore 73		*Simms 29, Harbert 67*	
R	Abingdon United	2 v 1	Chichester City United	95
	Hooper 6, Simms 62		*Moore 82*	
142	Lordswood	1 v 3	Horsham	102
	Gooding 20		*Clark 43, 70, Geddes 60*	
143	Cowes Sports	1 v 0	Cray Wanderers	70
	Jones 68			
144	Burgess Hill Town	4 v 1	Brockenhurst	171
	Simmons 15, Lament 40 Newman 84, Carr 87		*Leigh-Bryant 82*	
145	Banstead Athletic	4 v 0	Farnham Town	40
	Webb 43, 54, Langford 9, Ferguson 81			
146	St Leonards	1 v 1	Three Bridges	179
	Baker 27		*Cashman 15*	
R	Three Bridges	2 v 3	St Leonards	117
	Marsh 65, Massaro 86		*Baker 45, 83, O'Callaghan 81*	

147	Lewes	3 v 0	Dorking	124
	Lieghton 49, 85, Hack 67			
148	Tooting & Mitcham U	3 v 0	Worthing	177
	Brady 18, Rootes 76, Webb 87			
149	Southwick	0 v 5	Langney Sports	126
			Allen 3 (8, 11, 16), *Snelgrove 6, Agutter 39*	
150	Viking Greenford	1 v 4	Merstham	25
	Cargill 65		*Mitchell 57, 65, Watts 47, Eldrid 75*	
151	Sittingbourne	2 v 0	Godalming & G'ford	210
	Russell 29, King 89			
152	Whitchurch United	0 v 2	AFC Newbury	123
			Alleyne 43, 48	
153	Thamesmead Town	1 v 2	Herne Bay	69
	Heselden 44		*Jones 62, Jeffrey 79*	
154	Greenwich Borough	1 v 0	Hythe United	57
	Tie awarded Hythe Utd.: Greenwich removed - ineligible player			
155	Shoreham	1 v 10	Oxford City	91
	Carter 25		***Wise 5 (32, 65, 74, 81, 88)***, ***Pierson 3 (14, 50, 86)***, *Emsden 4, Hulbert 74*	
156	Erith Town	2 v 2	Hassocks	104
	Blyther 37, Bowey 45		*Laing 30, 55*	
R	Hassocks	3 v 1	Erith Town	171
	Laing 3 (13p, 50, 68)		*Mitchell 58*	
157	Ashford Town	4 v 1	Walton Casuals	298
	Monteith 3, Peachey 18, Lovell 78, 90		*D'Rozario 15*	
158	Wokingham Town	0 v 3	Bedfont	114
			Jenkins 36, 51, Logie 81	
159	Dartford	3 v 1	Deal Town	231
	Arnold 42, Guiver 44, 65		*Ingram 53*	
160	Chipstead	0 v 1	Ashford Town (Middx)	74
			Canning 77	
161	Fareham Town	1 v 1	Ringmer	111
	Chamberlain 70		*Reid 26*	
R	Ringmer	0 v 2	Fareham Town	124
			Reed 11, Franklin 17	
162	Gosport Borough	1 v 1	Slade Green	115
	Wallsgrove 65		*Brown 20*	
R	Slade Green	1 v 2	Gosport Borough	110
	Wilson 12		*Mann 50, Fitt 71*	
163	Windsor & Eton	1 v 0	Whitstable Town	159
	Crittendon 35			
164	Portsmouth R N	1 v 4	Ash United	54
	O'Connor 40		*Joyce 7, 68, Keane 10, Brophy 84*	
165	Reading Town	2 v 0	Lancing	58
	Wylie 9, Broad 90			
166	Newport (IW)	5 v 2	Arundel	329
	Wright 14, 46, Wilson 89 Betteridge 17, Gibbons 13		*Sokoras 41, Scerri 82*	
167	Metropolitan Police	2 v 1	Leatherhead	155
	Batten 56, Dunn 84		*Ottley 39*	
168	Hungerford Town	0 v 2	Bromley	148
			Tompkins 22, Bartley 90	
169	East Preston	1 v 0	Redhill	73
	Quigg 40			
170	Tunbridge Wells	1 v 2	VCD Athletic	104
	Walmsley 38		*Warrilow 61, Davis 79*	
171	Carterton Town	1 v 1	Thame United	94
	Mortimer-Jones 27		*Brown 80*	
R	Thame United	0 v 0*	Carterton Town	115
	Carterton Town won 3-1 after penalties			
172	Hillingdon Borough	1 v 3	Bracknell Town	71
			Frank 12, Smith 55, Havermans 88	
173	Eastbourne United	1 v 4	Egham Town	133
	Harris 82		*Wilmore 12, Powell 18, Nicholls 59, Mitchell 60*	
174	Horsham YMCA	2 v 0	Cobham	85
	Churchill 29, Tilley 56			
175	Wick	1 v 0	Erith & Belvedere	120
	Thorpe 8			
176	Tonbridge Angels	0 v 0	Eastleigh	394
R	Eastleigh	0 v 1	Tonbridge Angels	162
			Elliott 31	
177	Lymington & New M.	2 v 1	Didcot Town	183
	Smith 31, Morris 88		*Kelly 38*	
178	Hailsham Town	1 v 2	Whyteleafe	150
	Adams 67		*Mason 51, Lunn 89*	
179	Chatham Town	3 v 1	Molesey	98
	Miles 2, Jones 23, Hearn 29		*Wilfort 30*	
180	Ch'ington & Hook U	1 v 6	Hastings Town	267
	Moorhouse 70		*Burt 2, Simmonds 20, 62, Jones 29, White 42, 83*	
181	Bognor Regis Town	2 v 3	Cove	240
	Scammell 31, Russell 80		*Willes 13 (p), Manley 57, Osbourne 90*	
182	BAT Sports	0 v 0	Sheppey United	70
R	Sheppey United	2 v 2*	BAT Sports	49
	Sheppey United won 5-4 after penalties			
	Brown 85, 96		*Chalke 45, 116*	
183	Fleet Town	1 v 0	Ramsgate	68
	Frampton 87			
184	Whitehawk	0 v 3	AFC Totton	70
			Totten 21, 60, Sherrington 28	
185	Paulton Rovers	4 v 0	Street	114
	Cook 18, 70, Tovey 87 Bennett 89			
186	Westbury United	1 v 3	Bristol Manor Farm	56
	Ranger 79		*Bannerman 21, Whelan 58, Burnett 60*	
187	Downton	4 v 0	Bournemouth	81
	Parkin 4, O'Magan 50 Guy 67, 70			
188	Bemerton Heath Hquns	0 v 4	Tiverton Town	254
			Rees 22, Everett 28, Marker 70, Ovens 72	
189	Cinderford Town	0 v 3	Bridgwater Town	96
			Spence 46, Graddon 54, Francis 60	
190	Devizes Town	1 v 1	Melksham Town	212
	Flippance 90		*Lunt 72*	
R	Melksham Town	0 v 1	Devizes Town	272
			Alexander 89	
191	Chippenham Town	3 v 3	St Blazey	449
	Tiley 32		*Waters 65*	
R	St Blazey	0 v 3	Chippenham Town	268
			Tweddle 3 (8, 18, 49)	
192	Tuffley Rovers	4 v 1	Taunton Town	90
	Patterson 50, Roberts 60, 80 Knight 75		*Hapgood 87*	
193	Brislington	3 v 2	Calne Town	48
	Brown 30, Whitcliff 47, 89		*Bush 29, Colbaine 55*	
194	Weston Super Mare	2 v 1	Wimborne Town	174
	Pritchard 65, Cheeseman 67		*Jones 33*	
195	Welton Rovers	1 v 1	Shortwood United	85
	Porter 44		*Cole 55*	
R	Shortwood United	1 v 0	Welton Rovers	129
	Walker 71			
196	Elmore	3 v 4	Barnstaple Town	195
	Woon 37, 51, Harvey 82		*Blurton 11, 79, Cole 27 + 1*	
197	Frome Town	2 v 0	Bishop Sutton	146
	Ashton 21, Thorpe 78			
198	Evesham United	3 v 1	Bideford	135
	Bowen 50, Roberts 60 Powell 89		*Joslin 78*	
199	Odd Down	0 v 2	Gloucester City	108
			Tucker 2, John Stone 72	
200	Cirencester Town	1 v 0	Minehead Town	98
	Dunton 63			
201	Mangotsfield United	4 v 2	Christchurch	205
	Edwards 3 (12, 26, 89) *Elsey 5*		*Dear 54, Spackman 85*	
202	Backwell United	5 v 2	Torrington	32
	King 75, 87, Hewitt 29, 66 Haynes 64		*Madge 44, Bater 47*	

Top:
Arlesley's Dave Kilson (white) and Histon's James Saddington jump clear of the rest.
Photo: Steve Ayre

Centre:
Trafford keeper Andy Merrick punches clear during his team's visit to Chorley.
Photo: Colin Stevens

Bottom:
Potters Bar Town keeper John Leahy gathers the ball despite the 'distraction' of his fellow defender, against Uxbridge.
Photo: Gordon Whittington

FIRST QUALIFYING ROUND

No.	Home	Score	Away	Att.
1	Warrington Town	0 - 2	Clitheroe	119
			Spencer 40, Sculpher 60	
2	Tadcaster Town	0 - 1	Horden CW	81
3	Stocksbridge Pk Steels	1 - 0	Darwen or Penrith	158
	Flynn 57			
4	Harrogate Railway	1 - 5	Bedlington Terriers	175
	Smith 70		*Milner 29, 71, Locker 24, Chapman 86, Gibb 90*	
5	West Auckland T	3 - 1	Selby Town	80
	Beasley 4, Anderson 17 Milroy 19		*Cygan 27*	
6	Guisley	0 - 1	Farsley Celtic	233
			Whellans 75	
7	Thornaby-on-Tees	0 - 1	Marske United	125
			Hodgson 36	
8	Seaham Red Star	7 - 0	Great Harwood Town	85
	Newham 4 (25, 60, 75, 85) *Ross 15, Adamson 35 Innes 50*			
9	Easington Colliery	2 - 1	Yorkshire Amateur	54
	Allen 33, Robson 81		*Zoll 12*	
10	Blackpool Mechanics	0 - 1	Radcliffe Borough	140
			Lunt 2	
11	Goole	2 - 1	Ramsbottom United	268
	Saville 38, Lanaghan 65		*Vaughan 22*	
12	Durham City	3 - 1	Newcastle Blue Star	142
	Dilella 42, 70, Canavan 1		*Beech 25*	
13	Chorley	3 - 2	Trafford	259
	Mills 26, Eatock 77, Smyth 90		*Pannett 66, Emmett 84*	
14	North Ferriby United	2 - 2	Ashton United	147
	Riordan 22, Blythe 43		*Adams 80, Toronczak 86*	
R	Ashton United	4 - 3*	North Ferriby United	157
	Miller 3 (30, 103, 119) *Connally 90*		*Phillips 68, Flounders 75, Botham 117*	
15	Witton Albion	1 - 0	Atherton Collieries	295
	Anane 74			
16	Mossley	2 - 0	Hebburn	299
	Dicken 17, Garside 88			
17	Harrogate Town	0 - 2	Billingham Town	172
			Rowntree 65, 90	
18	Dunston Fed. Brewery	1 - 2	Fleetwood Freeport	169
	Fletcher 44		*Baldwin 45, Smith 60*	
19	Atherton LR	1 - 5	Sheffield	61
	Massey 62		***Pickess 4 (2, 14, 55, 63)****, Godber 41*	
20	Whitley Bay	3 - 1	Consett	215
	Dawson 10, Nash 25, 87		*Halliday 22*	
21	Brigg Town	5 - 1	Liversedge	152
	Borman 45, Moore 55 Buckley 60, Raspin 75 Cadman 80		*Lawford 64*	
22	Bradford (Pk Avenue)	0 - 1	Salford City	209
			O'Giggs 53	
23	Bridlington Town	3 - 1	Kendal Town	113
	Edeson 46, 76, Burdick 24		*Hodgson 36*	
24	Redditch United	2 - 3	Belper Town	263
	Myers 16, 36		*Cunningham 65, 83, Turner 28*	
25	Hinckley United	3 - 0	Gedling Town	265
	Lewton 13, Lucas 61, 72			
26	Bromsgrove Rovers	1 - 1	Oldbury United	241
	McWilliams 89		*Rutter 90*	
R	Oldbury United	2 - 0	Bromsgrove Rovers	83
	Hesson 16, Banner 34			
27	Bilston Town	1 - 5	Solihull Borough	170
	Rollason 70		*Smith 15, 53, Lovelock 22, Pippard 75, 86*	
28	Grantham Town	3 - 1	Bedworth United	432
	Ranshaw 48, 83, Wright 62		*Webster 25*	
29	Paget Rangers	0 - 2	Stafford Town	118
			Stark 52, Smith 73	
30	Atherstone United	0 - 1	Stourport Swifts	222
			Booth 60	
31	Stourbridge	2 - 3	Stamford	121
	Robinson 33, 41		*Staffs 4, 87, Ashby 79*	
32	Leek CSOB	1 - 1	Holbeach United	120
	Baker 51		*Eady 83*	
R	Holbeach United	3 - 1	Leek CSOB	74
	Dunn 32, 35, Gray 43		*Cooney 85*	
33	Stapenhill	1 - 1	Barwell	102
	Taylor 1		*Holmes 70*	
R	Barwell	5 - 1	Stapenhill	136
	Morris 25, Wittall 47 Stanborough 62, Finlay 80 Grassby 85		*Allum 36*	
34	Shepshed Dynamo	4 - 2	Oadby Town	341
	McGlinchey 26, 83, Ball 37 Davies 67		*Tiday 6, Walker 17*	
35	Newcastle Town	2 - 1	Corby Town	114
	O'Reilly 34, 42		*Mintus 20*	
36	Congleton Town	4 - 3	Eastwood Town	200
	Johnson 23, 89 Thornley 56, 89		*Wright 30, Castledine 33, Warboys 61*	
37	Blackstone	2 - 3	Matlock Town	108
	Graham 64, Smith 89		*Paul 4, Francis 45, 90*	
38	Alfreton Town	3 - 2	Spalding United	186
	Brady 28, 54, Fretwell 77		*Torino 11, Wilson 61*	
39	Cogenhoe United	2 - 3	Maldon Town	66
	Anderson 10, Westley 57		*Mayes 34, Francis 55, Moss 80*	
40	Northampton Spencer	0 - 2	Mildenhall Town	70
			Tuck 49, Goddard 65	
41	Waltham Abbey	4 - 2	St Neots Town	115
	Campbell 4 (40, 45, 48, 78)		*Meeds 62,70*	
42	Wealdstone	4 - 0	Ware	240
	Swaysland 12 (p), 29 Murphy 59, Holmes 66			
43	Stewarts & Lloyds	1 - 3	Baldock Town	30
	Fraser 80			
44	Ford United	3 - 0	Welwyn Garden City	154
	Aransiba 58, Allen 83 Holding 88			
45	Tilbury	1 - 3	Chelmsford City	293
	Mold 77		***Portway 3 (40, 42, 47)***	
46	Stotfold	1 - 1	London Colney	90
	Reynolds 62		*Dean 56*	
R	London Colney	2 - 3	Stotfold	54
	Doctor 45, Rogers 79		*Buckland 1, Davidson 4, Griffiths 50*	
47	Uxbridge	5 - 1	Potters Bar Town	132
	Ryder 5, Clark 33, Jordan 74 Tunnell 47, 80		*Chalkley 61*	
48	Braintree Town	5 - 0	Clapton	201
	Noble 24, Howard 26 Stanley 48, Gutzmore 76 Smith 82			
49	St Margaretsbury	1 - 0	Boreham Wood	128
	Winger 55			
50	Soham Town R	3 - 1	Ford Sports Daventry	104
	Docking 17, Davis 24, Coe 78		*McGuiness 30*	
51	Ely City	2 - 2	Tring Town	101
	Hipwell 43, Egan 85		*Kinsley 33, Boad 74*	
R	Tring Town	3 - 2*	Ely City	46
	Kinsley 3 (22, 105, 107)		*Baker 37, Saberton 118*	
52	Newmarket Town	3 - 3	Wingate & Finchley	99
	Stokes 22, Crisp 26, Long 51		*Wilson 33, Hakim 66, Brady 75*	
R	Wingate & Finchley	4 - 1	Newmarket Town	95
	Myers 10, Brady 15 Hakim 41 + 1		*Crawford 70*	
53	Yeading	2 - 3	Beaconsfield SYCOB	81
	Denton 23, Woodruffe 35		*Polidere 60, Callender 75, 88*	
54	Arlesey Town	1 - 2	Histon	167
	Terell 89		*Potter 33, Chattoe 37*	

No	Home	Score	Away	Att
55	Bedford Town	3 - 1	Staines Town	442
	Drew 7, Slinn 27, Wilson 89		*Everitt 74*	
56	Woodbridge Town	3 - 1	Burnham Ramblers	122
	Dearsley 43, Fryatt 75		*Dolby 66*	
	David 88			
57	AFC Sudbury	5 - 1	Brook House	226
	Cornish 55, Devereaux 71, 90		*Xalin 85*	
	Claydon 80, 90			
58	Barking	2 - 3	Berkhamsted Town	141
	Rose 86, 90		*Cooper 26, 89, Nightingale 65*	
59	Ipswich Wanderers	1 - 0	Bedford United	96
	Bell 63			
60	Hemel Hempstead T	3 - 0	Cheshunt	141
	Redder 48, 61, Durkin 70			
61	Diss Town	0 - 5	Bishop's Stortford	256
			Ball 3 (39, 81, 89)	
			John 43, Lanser 90	
62	East Thurrock United	1 - 4	Northwood	106
	Bauckham 74		*Hale 4, Gill 15, Yaku 60, 85*	
63	Tiptree United	1 - 3	Stowmarket Town	73
	Parnell 1		*Haygreen 48, Gedney 74, 84*	
64	Harwich & Parkestopn	1 - 2	AFC Wallingford	81
	English 63		*Brayan 17, Stevens 86*	
65	Wembley	2 - 0	Great Yarmouth Town	67
	Dyer 37, Newman 85			
66	Cowes Sports	1 - 1	Horsham YMCA	103
	Barsdale 73		*Churchill 80*	
R	Horsham YMCA	6 - 0	Cowes Sports	94
	Churchill 4 (3, 63, 78, 90)			
	Butcher 48			
67	Littlehampton Town	1 - 1	Greenwich Borough	106
	Woods 67			
R	Hythe United	0 - 1*	Littlehampton Town	102
			Thornton 114	
68	Selsey	4 - 0	Reading Town	130
	Ford 3 (75, 76, 88)			
	Morey 87			
69	Carterton Town	3 - 1	St Leonards	74
	Jones 24, Sherwood 28		*Baker 55*	
	Cook 75			
70	East Preston	3 - 3	Merstham	81
	Liversidle 8, Hearn 76		*Eldred 62, 66, Mitchell 90*	
	Huckett 80			
R	Merstham	3 - 1	East Preston	79
71	Thatcham Town	1 - 1	Gosport Borough	102
	Worsfold 38		*Reid 68*	
R	Gosport Borough	1 - 1*	Thatcham Town	85
	Thatcham win 3-2 after penalties			
	Wallsgrove 65		*Dornan 67*	
72	Newport (I. o .W.)	1 - 1	Bashley	397
	Gibbons 31		*Gee 75*	
R	Bashley	0 - 2	Newport (I. o .W.)	230
73	Fareham Town	0 - 0	Herne Bay	120
R	Herne Bay	2 - 1	Fareham Town	201
	Appleton 18, 1 og		*Brown 22*	
74	Sittingbourne	0 - 3	Horsham	287
			Geddes 71, 80, Moore 90	
75	Ashford Town	1 - 2	Bracknell Town	294
	Frost 64		*Hollman 12, Smith 51*	
76	Fleet Town	3 - 1	Walton & Hersham	146
	Dadson 69, Miller 79		*Ellington 84*	
	Smith 90			
77	AFC Totton	0 - 0	Egham Town	74
R	Egham Town	1 - 3	AFC Totton	72
	Bennett 75		*Hussey 78, 89 (2 pens), 1 og*	
78	Lymington & New M.	0 - 1	Oxford City	229
			Pierson 49	

No	Home	Score	Away	Att
79	Abingdon United	4 - 1	Tooting & Mitcham U	156
	Maciar 42, Smith 52		*Read 39*	
	Morton 65, Hooper 89			
80	Aylesbury United	4 - 3	Bedfont	259
	Rondel 22, 68, Hill 48, 70		*Jenkin 26, Fossey 73,*	
			Honeyball 85	
81	VCD Athletic	4 - 4	Epsom & Ewell	84
	Hannon 6, Warrilow 30		***Nimmo 3 (21, 38 (p), 84),***	
	Davis 33, Winchcombe 87		*Hall 51*	
R	Epsom & Ewell	2 - 0	VCD Athletic	56
	Nimmo 31, 49			
82	Windsor & Eton	1 - 0	Chatham Town	127
	Fiore 26			
83	Langney Sports	3 - 2	Ashtead Town (Mx)	275
	Allen 21, 43, Stevens 69		*Frost 64, 76*	
84	Ash United	2 - 4	Hastings Town	174
	Calvert 35, Joyce 36		*Yates 2, McArthur 36,*	
			Simmonds 81, 86	
85	AFC Newbury	2 - 0	Wick	100
	Whorriskey 33, Nancarrow 43			
86	Whyteleafe	4 - 0	Burgess Hill Town	215
	Mtungwazi 11, Dillon 51			
	Lock 85, Elliott 88			
87	Lewes	2 - 2	Cove	88
	Pattenden 12, Stokes 65		*Cooke 9, Willes 79*	
R	Cove	1 - 2	Lewes	
	Mancey 90		*Stokes 63, Pattendon 90*	
88	Dartford	1 - 1	Chertsey Town	175
	Guiver 43		*Marshall 29*	
R	Chertsey Town	0 - 2	Dartford	95
			Roberts 1, 14	
89	Bromley	1 - 2	Metropolitan Police	107
	Cooksey 50		*Prins 61, Service 85*	
90	Andover	2 - 3	Saltdean United	139
	Whale 41, Forbes 74		*Cooper 78, Townsend 90,*	
			Costello 90	
91	Banstead Athletic	3 - 1	Sheppey United	49
	Ward 21, York 54, Huckle 46		*Battin 32*	
92	Tonbridge Angels	5 - 0	Hassocks	455
	Bates 33, Falana 37, 54			
	Robertson 43, Arter 80			
93	Weston Super Mare	0 - 0	Shortwoood Rovers	142
R	Shortwoood Rovers	3 - 2	Weston Super Mare	225
	Ward 29, Evans 44, Green 65		*Bevan 29, 75*	
94	Bridgwater Town	2 - 1	Downton	227
	Bowering 68, Spence 73		*Guy 86*	
95	Tuffley Rovers	0 - 1	Chippenham Town	135
			Charity 82	
96	Backwell United	1 - 2	Devizes Town	44
	Gwyther 69		*Flippance 26, 45*	
97	Gloucester City	2 - 1	Evesham United	403
	Bayliss 12, Tucker 76		*Bowen 37*	
98	Barnstaple Town	1 - 5	Cirencester Town	201
	Blurton 75		*Griffin 44, 47, Harris 90*	
99	Brislington	2 - 3	Paulton Rovers	120
	Sullivan 6, Brown 28		*Smart 48, 60, Buxton 75*	
100	Mangotsfield United	4 - 2	Frome Town	227
	Seal 10, Edwards 25		*Fricker 85, Salter 87*	
	Churchill 55, Pendry 75			
101	Tiverton Town	1 - 0	Bristol Manor Farm	547
	Match ordered to be replayed, Tiverton fielded a player without International Clearance			
R	Bristol Manor Farm	1 v 4	Tiverton Town	130
	Edwards 47		*Everett 25, Saunders 38,*	
			Richardson 28, Marker 65	

SECOND QUALIFYING ROUND

No	Home				Away	Att
1	Emley	3	v	1	Salford City	261
	Tonks 73, Nicholson 88				*Vaughan 83*	
	Bambrook 90					
2	Gateshead	2	v	1	Bishop Auckland	255
	Bowey 31, Thompson 90				*Dunwell 85*	
3	Stalybridge Celtic	2	v	0	Blyth Spartans	523
	McNeil 27, Evans 87					
4	Witton Albion	1	v	1	Fleetwood Freeport	296
	Anane 74				*Smith 60*	
R	Fleetwood Freeport	1	v	2	Witton Albion	277
	Smith 45				*Hennin 9, Pritchard 41*	
5	Durham City	2	v	2	Accrington Stanley	299
	Irvine 59, Outhwaite 85				*Ceradlo 69, Brennan 81*	
R	Accrington Stanley	4	v	2	Durham City	597
	Mullin 3, Ceraolo 46				*Canavan 5, 24*	
	Mullin 48, 87					
6	Bamber Bridge	1	v	1	Marske United	229
	Aspinall 35 (pen)				*Sankey 1*	
R	Marske United	0	v	2	Bamber Bridge	238
					Burton 28, 29	
7	Spennymoor United	0	v	3	Belington Terriers	286
					Rowe 26, Moat 56,	
					Chapman 65	
8	Marine	4	v	3	Colwyn Bay	366
	Robinson 25, 60, Schofield 90				*Graham 62, 88*	
9	Sheffield	2	v	1	Farsley Celtic	128
	Baker 33 (og), Godber 83				*Blackstone 16*	
10	Barrow	3	v	0	Droylsden	1153
	Doherty 37, Housham 42					
	Peel 74					
11	Ashton United	1	v	1	Goole	207
	Royle 77				*Severn 32*	
R	Goole	2	v	3	Ashton United	
	Harrison 45, Jefferson 82				***Carty 3 (15, 31, 80)***	
12	Altrincham	0	v	3	Mossley	705
					Dicken 17, Burns 62,	
					Garside 88	
13	Frickley Athletic	1	v	0	Stocksbridge Pk Steels	167
	Beckett 80					
14	Clitheroe	1	v	2	Hyde United	408
	Jones 83				*Yeo 44, Taylor 48 (pen)*	
15	Horden C.W.	1	v	3	Gainsborough Trinity	135
	Stephens 9				*Watts 15, Allison 43, Limber 71*	
16	Bridlington Town	1	v	1	Billingham Town	153
	Burdick 3				*Rowntree 65 (pen)*	
R	Billingham Town	3	v	1	Bridlington Town	139
	Chapman 2, Tucker 17				*Foot 60*	
	Hutchinson 43					
17	Whitley Bay	2	v	1	Worksop Town	620
	Cuggy 47, Bowman 53				*Johnson 67*	
18	Burscough	2	v	1	Runcorn	346
	McEvilly 69, Talbot 90				*Brunskill 17*	
19	Brigg Town	2	v	2	Lancaster City	189
	Massingham 25, Ward 86				*Barnes 90, Haddow 93*	
R	Lancaster City	3	v	4*	Brigg Town	185
	Ward 31, 93, Haddow 90				*Roach 36, 57, Borman 107,*	
					Cadman 111	
20	Radcliffe Borough	4	v	1	West Auckland Town	204
	Collins 22, Bean 33				*Anderson 55*	
	Carden 41, Dempsey 90					
21	Chorley	0	v	2	Whitby Town	269
					Ludlow 77, Ure 87	

No	Home				Away	Att
22	Seaham Red Star	0	v	3	Easington Colliery	105
					Naylor 37, 48, Matthews 78	
23	Alfreton Town	1	v	1	Hinckley United	260
	Tomlinson 44				*Lenton 59*	
R	Hinckley United	2	v	1*	Alfreton Town	273
	Lucas 28, George 118				*Fretwell 19*	
24	Holbeach United	1	v	3	Belper Town	190
	Andy 32				*Smithurst 37, Payne 45,*	
					Cunningham 56	
25	Oldbury Utd	2	v	3	Stourport Swifts	107
	Dunn 60, Hesson 65				***Marsh 3 (3, 73, 78)***	
26	Stamford	1	v	1	Tamworth	362
	Staff 66				*Foy 33*	
R	Tamworth	1	v	1*	Stamford	447
	Hallam 63				*Staff 87*	
	Tamworth won 3-2 after penalties					
27	Stafford Town	2	v	1	Moor Green	238
	Stark 52, Smith 73				*Baddams 41*	
28	Shepshed Dynamo	0	v	3	Ilkeston Town	479
					Helliwell 23, Eshelby 42,	
					Kirkwood 88	
29	Hucknall Town	4	v	0	Congleton Town	211
	Mayman 15, Roberts 37					
	Cooke 44, Morris 67					
30	Barwell	0	v	3	Grantham Town	247
					Renshaw 9, Neil 67,	
					Wilkes 74	
31	Matlock Town	1	v	2	Kings Lynn	364
	Kingsley 10				*Nwadike 2, Fuff 15*	
32	Solihull Borough	1	v	1	Stafford Rangers	513
	Penny 88				*Craven 46*	
R	Stafford Rangers	0	v	0*	Solihull Borough	432
	Stafford Rangers won 4-3 after penalties					
33	Halesowen Town	0	v	2	Burton Albion	668
					Kavanagh 27, Stride 51	
34	Newcastle Town	1	v	1	Leek Town	402
	Cunningham 39				*Marrow 54*	
R	Leek Town	3	v	2*	Newcastle Town	397
	Marrow 29, Callan 45				*Woodvine 47, Beasley 90*	
	Sandeman 95					
35	Histon	1	v	2	Bishop's Stortford	211
	Kennedy 54				*John 78, Hayes 82 (pen)*	
36	Hendon	3	v	2	St Margaretsbury	236
	Clarke 18, Pickett 37, 79				*Winger 14, Pullen 75*	
37	Ford United	3	v	1	Soham Town Rangers	99
	Bejeda 24, 69, Allen 85				*Leete 73*	
38	Heybridge Swifts	1	v	1	AFC Sudbury	278
	Lee 22				*Cheetham 13*	
R	AFC Sudbury	3	v	2	Heybridge Swifts	409
	Devereux 76, 83, Owen 87				*Haydon 58, Tomlinson 62*	
39	Chesham United	3	v	2	AFC Wallingford	290
	Stephenson 40, Campbell 49				*Mulvaney 1, Parr 89*	
	Harland 61					
40	Hitchin Town	1	v	1	Maidenhead United	336
	Dixon 84 (pen)				*Channell 82*	
R	Maidenhead United	1	v	1*	Hitchin Town	190
	Arkins 36				*Parker 90*	
	Maidenhead Utd. won 7-6 after penalties					

No.	Home	Score	Away	Att.
41	Cambridge City	3 v 0	Stotfold	285
	Wilkin 7, 90, Bramble 35			
42	Chelmsford City	1 v 1	Grays Athletic	674
	Berquez 44		*Hazle 4*	
R	Grays Athletic	2 v 1	Chelmsford City	331
	???		*???*	
43	Purfleet	3 v 1	Ipswich Wanderers	108
	Georgiou 30,46, Coombs 60		*Miller 43*	
44	Canvey Island	1 v 1	Braintree Town	240
	Crome 43		*Gutzmore 90*	
R	Braintree Town	2 v 3	Canvey Island	242
	Reinelt 89, Noble 80		*Gregory 4, Tilson 26, 44*	
45	Hemel Hempstead Tn	3 v 4	Northwood	217
	Durkin 3 (10, 35, 53)		*Sherry 42, Yaku 85, Hale 87, Hook 91*	
46	Mildenhall Town	3 v 0	Beaconsfield SYCOB	157
	Goddard 50, Moore 73 Pope 76			
47	Harrow Borough	3 v 0	Tring Town	190
	Lund 52, Gavin 58, Xavier 59			
48	Stowmarket Town	1 v 2	Wealdstone	224
	Ratcliffe 30		*Carter 48, 52*	
49	Woodbridge Town	0 v 0	Wembley	141
R	Wembley	1 v 4	Woodbridge Town	99
	Sogbodjor 80		*Wallis 17, Curtis 45, 65, David 87*	
50	Baldock Town	0 v 0	St Albans City	432
R	St Albans City	1 v 2*	Baldock Town	185
	Evans 29		*???*	
51	Uxbridge	3 v 2	Berkhampstead Town	162
	Gill 32, 89, Jordan 68		*Lowe 39, Cooper 45*	
52	Waltham Abbey	1 v 3	Maldon Town	70
	Shaw 45		*Heasman 45, 57, Mayes 44*	
53	Billericay Town	5 v 1	Wingate & Finchley	278
	Linger 53, 67, Gentle 54 Spencer 72, Shires 88		*Down 87*	
54	Bedford Town	0 v 0	Enfield	804
R	Enfield	1 v 1*	Bedford Town	289
	Enfield won 4-3 after penalties			
	Flemming 79		*Drew 89*	
55	Farnborough Town	3 v 3	Oxford City	539
	Crawshaw 48, Piper 61 Hooper 90		*Strong 1, 86, Pierson 52*	
R	Oxford City	1 v 2	Farnborough Town	347
	Elmsdon 88		*Piper 4, Baird 52*	
56	Fisher Athletic	4 v 2	Newport (IW)	121
	Nowson 2, Higgins 17, 39 Barr 42		*Gibbons 31, Rew 65*	
57	Dartford	3 v 2	Abingdon United	167
	Guiver 2, 52, Arnold 52		*Watkins 28, Harbert 45*	
58	Windsor & Eton	0 v 3	Hampton & Richmond B	165
			Maskell 59, Green 70, 73	
59	Carshalton Athletic	1 v 1	Croydon	312
	Thomas 16		*Coleman 11*	
R	Croydon	2 v 2*	Carshalton Athletic	194
	Croydon won 5-3 after penalties			
	???		*???*	
60	Margate	0 v 1	Banstead Athletic	300
			Whelan 90	
61	Herne Bay	0 v 5	Aylesbury United	366
			Honeyball 39 ***Callinan 3 (42, 49, 84)*** *Grieves 57*	

No.	Home	Score	Away	Att.
62	Carterton Town	1 v 4	Havant & Waterlooville	160
	Rodney 44		*Leworthy 30, O'Rourke 36, 50, Daish 57*	
63	Saltdean United	4 v 2	AFC Totton	139
	Costello 39, Corlett 61 Grice 61, Bean 85		*Hussey 78, 79 (2 pens)*	
64	Tonbridge Angels	2 v 0	Slough Town	578
	Bates 33, Robertson 43			
65	Crawley Town	1 v 2	Aldershot Town	2504
	Carroll 42		*Ullathorne 48, Abbott 78*	
66	Gravesend & Northfleet	4 v 0	AFC Newbury	254
	Lee 12, Jackson 41, 74 Stadmart 72			
67	Lewes	2 v 0	Langney Sports	322
	Pattenden 7, Arscott 75			
68	Fleet Town	1 v 2	Thatcham Town	93
	Rampton 73		*Anderson 5, Dornay 70*	
69	Whyteleafe	2 v 1	Horsham YMCA	164
	Dillon 61, Elliott 76		*Churchill 54*	
70	Metropolitan Police	1 v 4	Welling United	170
	Morris 67		*Edwards 2, Glover 42, Carter 73, Side 81*	
71	Horsham	5 v 1	Epsom & Ewell	235
	Flain 4 (19, 24, 76, 89) *Payne 23*		*Ford 72*	
72	Folkestone Invicta	1 v 1	Hastings Town	500
	Chambers 53		*Jones 58*	
R	Hastings Town	2 v 0	Folkestone Invicta	485
	White 34, Simmonds 75			
73	Bracknell Town	3 v 1	Merstham	92
	Smith 19, 75, Haverman 90		*Watts 45*	
74	Littlehampton Town	0 v 5	Sutton United	396
			Forrester 46, Thompson 48, 89, Bolt 73 (pen), Sears 86	
75	Selsey	1 v 2	Dulwich Hamlet	310
	Rishman 67		*Garland 32, Perkins 34*	
76	Basingstoke Town	1 v 1	Bath City	522
	Mings 8		*Holloway 58*	
R	Bath City	2 v 0*	Basingstoke Town	606
	Davis 106, McLean 114			
77	Gloucester City	1 v 1	Chippenham Town	565
	Rawlings 53		*Hughes 9*	
R	Chippenham Town	3 v 5	Gloucester City	785
	Cutler 2, 55, Dix 89		*Meadows 7, Marshall 17, Rawlings 43, Griffiths 80, Cox 86*	
78	Mangotsfield United	4 v 2	Paulton Rovers	252
	Edwards 13, Seal 42, 75 Claridge 88		*Buxton 41, Cook 31*	
79	Worcester City	2 v 1	Cirencester Town	689
	Heeley 60, Jones 89		*Bennett 29*	
80	Newport County	0 v 4	Merthyr Tydfil	728
			Summers 22, Ryan 26, Baddeley 45, Mitchell 90	
81	Clevedon Town	2 v 4	Salisbury City	302
	Mainwaring 14, Mehew 45		*Emms 1, Smith 49, 81 (pen), Skidmore (og) 51*	
82	Tiverton Town	2 v 0	Shortwood United	433
	Everett 60, Ovens 70			
83	Weymouth	0 v 1	Dorchester Town	1830
			O'Hagen 1	
84	Devizes Town	2 v 1	Bridgwater Town	12
	Pope 2, Lloyd 84		*Bowering 34*	

Top:
Emley v Salford City 3-1
Simeon Bambrook's header is knocked onto the bar by Salford keeper Phil Melville.
Photo: Bill Wheatcroft

Centre:
Stuart Anderson (10) heads home the first in Thatcham's 2-1 victory over Fleet.
Photo: Andrew Chitty

Bottom:
Crawley v Aldershot
Andy Little saves from Olie Adedeti.
Photo: Ian Morsman

THIRD QUALIFYING ROUND

1	Sheffield	3 v 0	Ashton United	194
	Godber 60, 82, Pickers 75			
2	Marine	0 v 2	Radcliffe Borough	325
			Dempsey 31, Hardy 70	
3	Mossley	1 v 1	Frickley Athletic	373
	Dickens 84		*McAreavey 62*	
R	Frickley Athletic	3 v 0*	Mossley	286
	Hanby 97 McAreavey 105, 109			
4	Stalybridge Celtic	1 v 1	Billingham Town	479
	Pickford 58		*Jackson 40*	
R	Billingham Town	3 v 0	Stalybridge Celtic	188
	Clarke 6, Jackson 24 Rowntree 89			
5	Hyde United	2 v 1	Brigg Town	422
	Taylor 38, Yeo 78		*Borman 83*	
6	Witton Albion	0 v 0	Burscough	335
R	Burscough	6 v 1	Witton Albion	253
	McEvilly 4, Talbot 28, 70 McMullen 50,Stanton 65 Birch 79			
7	Bamber Bridge	1 v 1	Gateshead	255
	Pates 29		*Thompson 33*	
R	Gateshead	3 v 1	Bamber Bridge	231
	Dalton 58, Bowey 68 Ross 81		*Willoughby 85*	
8	Emley	1 v 2	Barrow	586
	Nazba 49		*Hume 31, Peverell 74*	
9	Bedlington Terriers	5 v 2	Accrington Stanley	515
	Kirkay 23, Milner 47 Lockyer 64, Chapman 88 Gibbs 90.		*Mullin 2, Flannery 89*	
10	Easington Colliery	1 v 0	Whitby Town	192
	Matthew 30			
11	Gainsborough Trinity	0 v 0	Whitley Bay	371
R	Whitley Bay	2 v 0	Gainsborough Trinity	339
	Cuddy 15, Bowman 53			
12	AFC Sudbury	1 v 1	Leek Town	425
	Day 37		*Twigg 56 (p)*	
R	Leek Town	1 v 2	AFC Sudbury	281
	Sandeman 65		*Claydon 53, Deverill 85*	
13	Harrow Borough	0 v 0	Stafford Town	184
R	Stafford Town	1 v 3	Harrow Borough	321
	Stark 16		*OG (Walters) 50 Hurlock 54 (p), Roberts 88*	
14	Mildenhall Town	0 v 2	Grays Athletic	343
			OG 67 (Critoph), O'Sullivan 89	
15	Purfleet	2 v 2	Grantham Town	207
	Georgiou 18 (p), Coombs 35		*Wilkins 1, Bull 82 (p)*	
R	Grantham Town	1 v 0*	Purfleet	506
	Wilkes 97			
16	Bishop's Stortford	1 v 2	Billericay Town	636
	Southam 4		*Linger 77, Baker 90 (p)*	
17	Enfield	3 v 1	Stourport Swifts	247
	McDonald 12, Morgan 35 Bunn 57		*Marsh 70*	
18	Stafford Rangers	0 v 2	Chesham United	616
			Campbell 51, Simpson 90	

19	Wealdstone	2 v 3	Belper Town	290
	Jones 2, Swaysland 10		*Kennedy 47, Payne 67, Morgan 90*	
20	Hendon	2 v 1	Ford United	242
	Adekola 12, 72		*Read 49*	
21	Canvey Island	2 v 1	Kings Lynn	306
	Parmenter 35, Vaughan 44		*Pitham 78*	
22	Tamworth	1 v 1	Burton Albion	1456
	Hallam 59		*Rennie 43*	
R	Burton Albion	3 v 1	Tamworth	1579
	Anderson 45, Stride 49, Webster 58		*Smith 63*	
23	Ilkeston Town	3 v 0	Baldock Town	500
	Kirkwood 37, Challinor 58 (p) Kiwomya 89			
24	Northwood	5 v 1	Uxbridge	358
	Yaku 3 (39, 83, 90) *Hale 41, Street 45*		*Moore 56*	
25	Cambridge City	3 v 2	Maldon Town	336
	Bramble 3, Wilkin 52, 73		*Witney 28, 70*	
26	Hucknall Town	3 v 2	Maidenhead United	380
	Martin 5, Taylor 35, Morris 42		*Atkins 25, Brown 81*	
27	Woodbridge Town	0 v 2	Hinckley United	228
			Hunter 4, Lucas 89	
28	Bracknell Town	1 v 0	Banstead Athletic	164
	Smith 75			
29	Welling United	1 v 0	Tonbridge Angels	716
	Rowe 34			
30	Hastings Town	2 v 3	Horsham	626
	Jones 2, Myall 87		*Plain 41, 50. Smart 53*	
31	Saltdean United	1 v 2	Devizes Town	219
	Randall 45		*Mooney, Cutis*	
32	Bath City	3 v 0	Sutton United	897
	Colbourne 34, Holloway 65 Walker 90			
33	Tiverton Town	1 v 3	Gloucester City	676
	Everitt 66		*Bayliss 21, 90 (p), Rawlins 45*	
34	Dartford	0 v 4	Havant & Waterlooville	302
			O'Rourke 9, Hambley 24, 56, Taylor 90	
35	Fisher Athletic	1 v 2	Aldershot Town	514
	Barr 90 (p)		*Abbott 13, 26 (p)*	
36	Merthyr Tydfil	0 v 3	Hampton & R'mond B.	569
			Green 10, Griffiths 21, 85	
37	Farnborough Town	0 v 2	Aylesbury United	699
			Highton 20, Joe 65	
38	Worcester City	3 v 1	Thatcham Town	805
	Cottrill 10, Lutz 20, Owen 79		*OG (Greenman) 72*	
39	Gravesend & Northfleet	4 v 1	Croydon	402
	Wilkins 21, Spiller 44 Booth 60, Stadhart 67		*McDonnell 89*	
40	Dulwich Hamlet	1 v 1	Lewes	245
	P Garland 53		*Dicker 21*	
R	Lewes	0 v 0*	Dulwich Hamlet	228
	Dulwich Hamlet won 3-1 after penalties			
41	Dorchester Town	4 v 3	Salisbury City	818
	Harris 27, Lonnon 68, 76 Pickard 77		*Sales 19, 61, Smith 24*	
42	Whyteleafe	1 v 3	Mangotsfield United	300
	Lock 1		*Seal 16, 64, Claridge 32*	

Above left: Veli Hakki (Dulwich) pulls away to set up a Dulwich attack v Lewes. Photo: Peter Singh

Above right: Bath v Sutton. Stuart Hammonds wins his tackle! Photo: Garry Letts

Below: Northwood's Lawrence Yaku scores again to seal an impressive win against Uxbridge. Photo: Steve Ayre

FOURTH QUALIFYING ROUND

No.	Home		Score		Away	Att.
1	Gateshead	4	v	2	Billingham Town	380
	Preen 2, 83, Bowey 41 Ross 63				*Rowntree 48, Clarke 65*	
2	Easington Colliery	0	v	2	Chester City	478
					Whitehall 7, Beazley 83	
3	Barrow	6	v	1	Whitley Bay	1714
	Housham 14, Maxfield 32 Ellison 44, Peverill 55, 67 Peel 76				*Nash 56*	
4	Burscough	1	v	1	Radcliffe Borough	459
	Leahy 32				*Dempsey 61*	
R	Radcliffe Borough	2	v	1	Burscough	789
	Carden 39, Hardy 67				*Talbot 29*	
5	Sheffield	1	v	5	Northwich Victoria	761
	Davenport 32				*Mike 39, Fletcher 42, 80, Davis 60, Norris 84*	
	(at Sheffield United F.C.)					
6	Bedlington Terriers	1	v	3	Morecambe	912
	Milner 9				*Hardicker 30, Thompson 41, Black 89*	
7	Scarborough	3	v	4	Leigh RMI	853
	Diallo 52, Betts 73 (p) Rennison 80				***Black 3 (4, 5, 54)**, Jones 43*	
8	Doncaster Rovers	2	v	2	Southport	1886
	Marples 50, Patterson 88				*Marsh 55 (p), Elam 73*	
R	Southport	1	v	0	Doncaster Rovers	1354
	Marsh 38 (p)					
9	Frickley Athletic	1	v	0	Hyde United	330
	Hanby 39					
10	Boston United	1	v	1	Burton Albion	2144
	Charlery 8				*Glasser 22*	
R	Burton Albion	3	v	2	Boston United	2299
	Starbuck 57 (p), 68 Anderson 78				*Charlery 17, 87*	
11	Hinckley United	1	v	1	Telford United	675
	Lucas 20				*Gayle 48*	
R	Telford United	4	v	1	Hinckley United	1254
	Moore 39, Edwards 54, 63 Palmer 75				*Lucas 41*	
12	Nuneaton Borough	1	v	1	Stevenage Borough	1554
	Francis 73				*Leadbeater 29*	
R	Stevenage Borough	1	v	2	Nuneaton Borough	1219
	Trott 45				*OG (Smith), Sykes 78*	
13	Hucknall Town	0	v	1	Ilkeston Town	1436
					Timons 3	
14	Harrow Borough	2	v	1	Enfield	504
	Oktay 75, Lund 88				*Bunn 87*	
15	Hendon	1	v	3	Dagenham & Redbridge	519
	Pickett 26				*Broughton 30, Matthews 66 Terry 69*	
16	Rushden & Diamonds	5	v	4	Grantham Town	2685
	McElhatton 18, 36 Underwood 29 (p) Jackson 58, Setchell 64				*Ranshaw 10, Neil 21, Wilkes 57, Taylor 83*	
17	Cambridge City	0	v	2	Canvey Island	575
					Tilson 37 (p), Wardley 83	
18	Belper Town	2	v	3	AFC Sudbury	810
	Payne 38, Gummer 44				*Cheetham 20, R Deveraux 35 B Deveraux 65*	
19	Billericay Town	0	v	0	Hednesford Town	721
R	Hednesford Town	2	v	1*	Billericay Town	450
	Lake 33, OG (Penn) 96				*Baker 57*	
20	Northwood	1	v	1	Grays Athletic	467
	Hale 66				*Dickinson 90*	
R	Grays Athletic	1	v	0	Northwood	313
	O'Sullivan 48					
21	Chesham United	0	v	2	Kettering Town	736
					Adams 4, Lenagh 38	
22	Forest Green Rovers	3	v	1	Bath City	977
	Bennett 3 (28, 48, 90)				*OG (Cousins) 23*	
23	Havant & Waterlooville	1	v	1	Gloucester City	724
	Connelly 27				*Moore 14*	
R	Gloucester City	2	v	3	Havant & Waterlooville	321
	Cox 21, Johnstone 40				*Taylor 16, 74, Wood 47*	
24	Aylesbury United	0	v	1	Bracknell Town	654
					Holzman 39 (p)	
25	Gravesend & Northfleet	4	v	0	Mangotsfield United	736
	Duku 9, Stadhart 34, 78 Restarick 83					
26	Dorchester Town	1	v	1	Welling United	759
	Harris 84				*Rowe 71*	
R	Welling United	2	v	4*	Dorchester Town	459
	Riviere 72, 90				*Sullivan 34, Pickard 55, Groves 99, 101*	
27	Yeovil Town	1	v	1	Horsham	1966
	OG (Kirby) 69				*Charman 34*	
R	Horsham	0	v	2	Yeovil Town	1907
					Way 57, Piper 87 (p)	
28	Hayes	4	v	2	Dulwich Hamlet	464
	Preston 24, 65, Boylon 86 Telemaque 90				*Perkins 45, Fowler 45*	
29	Aldershot Town	1	v	0	Dover Athletic	2873
	Abbott 52					
30	Kingstonian	5	v	2	Devizes Town	619
	Allan 12, 73 ***Pitcher 3 (37, 82, 86 (p))***				*Flippance 45, Wicks 81*	
31	Hampton & Richmond B.	5	v	0	Worcester City	619
	Flitter 2, Holloway 54, 86, Griffiths 80, Williams 89					
32	Woking	1	v	0	Hereford United	2076
	Pitman 30					

Top: Nicolas Lund scores the winning goal for Harrow Borough against Enfield.
Photo: Paul Carter

Centre: Grantham keeper Mario Ziccardi makes an excellent save to deny Diamonds captain Ray Warburton from scoring in the first half at Nene Park.
Photo: Peter Barnes

Bottom: Lockyer (raised arm) celebrates as Jonathon Milner (10) scores with a header to give Bedlington Terriers a ninth minute lead over Morecambe.
Photo: Graham Brown

FIRST ROUND PROPER

1 Wycombe Wndrs 3 v 0 Harrow Borough
Bates 8, 68 *2681*
Simpson 28 (p)

HARROW: Hook, Rose, Nwaokolo, Lewis (sub Hurlock 69), Cooper, Lyons (sub Protain 32), Roberts, Lund, Gavin, Xavier (sub Silkman 75), Payne. Subs: McCormack, Oktay

2 Lincoln City 4 v 0 Bracknell Town
Gain 7, Peacock 16 *2387*
OG (Bere) 43, Gordon 60

BRACKNELL: Cobby, Edwards, Bere, Skerrett, Brown, Franks (sub Havermans 71), Osgood, Pennicott-Bowen (sub Page 46), Holzman (sub Parker 87), Smith, Oliphant. Subs: Day, Nebbett

3 Northampton Tn 4 v 0 Frickley Athletic
Frain 19 *3896*
Forrester 56,81, Hunt 83

FRICKLEY: M Wilkinson, Hilton, Jones, West, Lafferty, Hanby, Morris, Price, Hurst, Duffy (sub M Wilkinson 75), Edge (sub Brooks 87). Subs: Burton, Fox, Collins

4 Kidderminster H 0 v 0 Burton Albion
3384

BURTON: Duke, Kavanagh, Blount, Wassall, Henshaw, Stride, Clough, Glasser, Starbuck, Webster, Anderson. Subs: Lyons, Moore, Davies, Garner, Goodwin.

R Burton Albion 2 v 4 Kidderminster H
Blount 71, Wassall 84 *Bogie 22, Hadley 27, 34*
Bird 90

BURTON: Matt Duke: Jason Kavanagh, Terry Henshaw, Neil Glasser, Mark Blount, Darren Wassall, Darren Stride (sub Christian Moore 66), Aaron Webster (sub Pat Lyons 66), Dale Anderson, Nigel Clough, Phil Starbuck. Subs: Alan Davies, Andy Garner, Nick Goodwin

5 Barnet 2 v 1 Hampton & R. B.
Richards 84, Currie 90 *2340* *Maskell 21*

HAMPTON: Talbot, Flitter, Wood, Burton (sub Girvan 22), Barnsby, Shaw, Manuella, Green, Williams (sub Russell 86), Maskell, Griffiths. Subs: Simpson, Carter, Holloway.

6 Havant & W'ville 1 v 2 Southport
Wood 4 *1118* *Stuart 45, Arnold 74*

HAVANT: Nicholls, Connolly, Cook, MacDonald, Gale, Daish, Wood, Hambley, O'Rourke, Taylor, Anstey. Subs: Leworthy, May, Champion, Jones, Blake.

SOUTHPORT: Dickinson, Clark, Stuart, Teale, Guyett, Bolland, Grayston, Gouck, Arnold, Parke, Furlong. Subs: Linighan, MacAuley, Maamria, Whittaker, Elam.

Right: An early Sudbury attack is dealt with by Liddle of Darlington who began his career in the Northern League Photo: Graham Brown

7 Gravesend & Nflt 1 v 2 Notts County
Jackson 75 *2376* *Stallard 3, Hughes 63*

GRAVESEND: Turner, Lee (sub Hegley 60), Jackson, Lindsey, Duku, Wilkins, D Smith, Spiller (sub Crawley 88), Booth (sub Restarick 54), Stadhart, Owen. Subs: Barnett, Smith

10 Brentford 1 v 3 Kingstonian
Pinamonte 90 *4544* *Pitcher 46,*
Winston 62, 77

KINGSTONIAN: Farrelly, Beard, Luckett, Allan, Saunders, Harris, Patterson, Pitcher, Winston (sub Green 90), Wingfield (sub Bass 88), Akuamoah. Subs: Stewart, Jones, Allen, Boyce

11 Forest Grn Rvrs 0 v 3 Morecambe
1023 OG (Hatswell) 40,
Norman 65, Thompson 81

FOREST GREEN: Perrin, Cousins, Hatswell, Norton, Clark, Burns (sub Campbell 68), Daley, Drysdale, Slater, Foster (sub Bailey 75), Kilgour (sub Bennett 46). Subs: Hedges, Spink.

MORECAMBE: Smith, Fensome, Lyons, McKearney, Hardiker, Walters (sub Knowles 76), Thompson, Drummond, Black, Dowe (sub Quayle 77), Norman. Subs: McGuire, Rigoglioso, Banks

12 Kettering Town 0 v 0 Hull City
2831

KETTERING: Bowling, Inman, Adams (sub Watkins 79), Perkins, McNamara, Norman, Codner, Brown, Llenagh, Hudson, Fisher. Subs: Matthews, Cowling, Diuk, Wilson

R Hull City 0 v 1 Kettering Town
3858 *Fisher 57*

KETTERING: Ian Bowling: Robert Codner, Steve Lenagh, Chris Perkins, Craig Norman, Brett McNamara, Matt Fisher, Phil Brown, Lee Hudson (sub Carl Shutt 69), Niall Inman, Dale Watkins (sub Wayne Duik 80). Subsd: Carl Adams, Lee Cowling, Steve Wilson

16 Swindon Town 4 v 1 Ilkeston Town
Willis 44, Williams 63 *4406* *Cox 87*
Howe 79, Young 89

ILKESTON: Love, Gould, Whitehead, Timons, Middleton, Clifford, Challinor, Knapper, Helliwell (sub Clarke 69), Kiwomya (sub Todd 77), Eshelby (sub Cox 73). Subs: Hopkins, Poppleton.

18 Canvey Island 4 v 4 Port Vale
Smith 48, Tilson 52 (p) *2100* *Minton 7, 76,*
Jones 89, Vaughan 90 *Brammer 35,*
Bridge-Wilkinson 49

CANVEY ISLAND: Ashley Harrison; Peter Smith, Craig Davidson (sub: Sam Cooper 85m), Mickey Bennett (sub: Andy Jones 68m), Mick Bodley, Steve Ward, Steve Tilson, John Kennedy, Neil Gregory, Wayne Vaughan, Steve Parmenter (sub: Ashley Miller 55m); Subs: Steve Clark, Mark Stimson

R Port Vale 1 v 2* Canvey Island
Naylor 120 *3566* *Gregory 105,*
Vaughan 119

CANVEY ISLAND: Ashley Harrison: Paul Smith, Mark Stimpson (sub Steve Clark 114), Mike Bennett, Mick Bodley, Steve Ward, Steve Tilson, John Kennedy, Neil Gregory (sub Ashley Miller 109), Wayne Vaughan, Sam Cooper (sub Andy Jones 87). Subs: Steve Parmenter, Craig Davidson

19 Chester City 1 v 1 Plymouth Argyle
Wright 78 *2393* *Peake 87*

CHESTER: Brown, Fisher (sub Ruscoe 70, sub Gaunt 85), Doughty, Lancaster, Ruffer, P Beesley, Carden, Blackburn,

R Plymouth Argyle 1 v 2* Chester City
McGregor 73 *3264* *Whitehall 42, Ruscoe 107*

CHESTER: Wayne Brown: Neil Fisher (sub Scott Ruscoe 93), Neil Doughty, Martin Lancaster, Carl Ruffer, Paul Beesley, Paul Carden, Chris Blackburn (sub Matt Woods 76), Mark Beesley, Steve Whitehall (sub Darren Wright 101), Andy Porter. Subs: Darren Moss, Craig Gaunt

20 Dagenham & R. 3 v 1 Hayes
Keith 16, OG (Watts) 61 *1150* *Boylan 45*
Jones 71

DAGENHAM: Roberts, Cole, Vickers, Keen, Matthews, Broom (sub Forbes 87), Janney, Terry, Broughton (sub Shipp 79), McDougald (sub Cobb 88), Jones. Subs: Haworth, Rust.

HAYES: Hodson, Bezhadi (sub Barnes 46), Flynn, Watts, Coppard, Pluck, McKimm, Moore, Stevens (sub Sterling 74), Boylan (sub Telemaque 74), Molesley. Subs: Preston

21 Aldershot Town 2 v 6 Brighton & Hove Alb
Abbott 26, 88(p) *7500* *Carpenter 2,*
Watson 43 (p), 60 (p)
Oatway 53, Zamora 75,
Wicks 77

ALDERSHOT: Page, Protheroe, Chewins, Crossley, Blake, Ullathorne, Graham, Pye, Abbott, Andrews, Gell. Subs: Coll, Adedeji, Browne, Bentley, Searle

22 Blackpool 3 v 1 Telford United
Murphy 8 2780 Martindale 65
Ormerod 45, 66

TELFORD: Price, Travis (sub Malkin 52 sub Murphy 85), Davies, Moore, Gayle, Bentley, Preece, Jobling, Martindale, Edwards, Palmer. Subs: Bray, Sandwith, McGorry

23 Stoke City 0 v 0 Nuneaton Borough
8437

NUNEATON: Mackenzie, Sykes, Love, Crowley, Weaver, Angus, Wray (sub Taylor 90), Charles, McGregor (sub Williams 59), King, Francis. Subs: Bacon, Young, Simpson

R Nuneaton Boro 1 v 0 Stoke City
McGregor 90 *4477*

NUNEATON: Chris Mackenzie; Simon Weaver, Terry Angus, Mickey Love, Shaun Wray, Dave Crowley, Lee Charles (sub: Mark Taylor 60m), Alex Sykes, Marc McGregor, Delton Francis, Ian King; Subs: Carl Bacon, Ryan Young, Barry Williams, Richard Mitchell

24 Halifax Town 0 v 2 Gateshead
1902 *Hall 45, Dalton 84*

GATESHEAD: Swan, Pepper, Watson, Kitchen, Hall, Talbot, Proudlock (sub Thompson 63), Bowey, Dalton, Preen (sub Edgcumbe 90), McAlindon (sub Bates 90). Subs: Tremble, Gray

25 Hednesford Tn 2 v 4 Oldham Athletic
Pointon 19, Davis 58 *2053* *Duxbury 4, Dudley 41,*
Corrazin 46, Tipton 90

HEDNESFORD: Gayle, Robinson, Lake, Bradley, Pointon, Airdrie, Sedgemore, Cooper (sub Owen 77), Bonsall (sub Colkin 69), Davis, Bagshaw (sub Norbury 55). Subs: Haran, Goodwin.

26 Barrow 0 v 2 Leyton Orient
3608 *Griffiths 52, Watts 73*

BARROW: Bishop, Warren, Maxfield, Hume, Waller, Anthony, Housham, Ellison, Peverill, Bullimore, Bennett. Subs: Rogers, Roberts, Doherty, Peel, Heritage.

28 Yeovil Town 5 v 1 Colchester United
Patmore 50, 85 *4552* *Duguid 69*
Belgrave 53
Skiverton 57, Way 80 (p)

YEOVIL: Pennock, Piper, Skiverton, White, Tonkin, Lindegaard (sub O'Brien, 76), Way, Smith, Crittenden, Belgrave, Patmore (sub Bent 85). Subs: Poole, Thompson, Weale

Top:
Otis Roberts against Jamie Bates.
Photo: Paul Carter

Centre:
The penalty that brought the Shots back to 1-1 against Brighton.
Photo: Wayne Andrews

Bottom:
Sykes (Nuneaton) finds a gap in the Stoke wall but misses the target.
Photo: Keith Clayton

29	Carlisle United	5	v	1	Woking
	Stevens 14, 23, 31, 68		*2647*		*West 72*
	Dobie 69				

WOKING: Matassa, Wye, Hollingdale, West, Smith, Pitman, Hayfield, Roddis, Brown (sub Perkins 46), Randall (sub Teague 75), Griffin (sub Ruggles 75). Subs: Kamara-Taylor, Aligheri.

30	Leigh RMI	0	v	3	Millwall (At Milwall)
			6907		*Harris 1 (p), Bircham 67, Moody 75*

LEIGH: David Felgate; Robert Trees, David German, Neil Durkin, Andy Farrell, Ian Swan, Ian Monk (sub: Neil Matthews 75m), David Ridings, Ged Kielty (Sub: Richard Harris 83m), Ton Black, Steve Jones; Subs: Neil Critchley, Nicky Spooner, Craig Dootson

31	Darlington	6	v	1	AFC Sudbury
	Naylor 31, 64, 76		*2462*		*Claydon 27*
	Hodgson 51, 87, Kyle 55				

SUDBURY: Walton, Stratton (sub Sallis 80), Cornish, Tracey, Sims (sub Hyde 68), Rayner, Cheetham, R Deveraux, B Deveraux, Claydon, Betson. Subs: Gardiner, Day.

33	Radcliffe Boro	1	v	4	York City
	Hardy 69		*2495*		*Potter 3, Bullock 10, McNiven 15, Jordan 28*

RADCLIFFE: Danny Hurst; Richard Battersby, Tony Whealing (sub: Levi Edwards 85m), Simon Kelly, David Bean, Mark Dempsey, Ian Lunt (sub: David Collins 79m), Paul Carden, Wilson, Neil Hardy, James Price; Subs: Eamonn Kelly, Ian Senior

35	Luton Town	1	v	0	Rushden & Dia.
	George 55		*5771*		

RUSHDEN: Turley, Peters (sub Setchell 90), Rodwell, Warburton, Mustafa, Brady, Mills (sub Wormull 82), Burgess, Underwood, Jackson, Sigere. Subs: Town, Stowell, Naylor

37	Wigan Athletic	3	v	1	Dorchester Town
	Roberts 7, Bidstrup 36		*3883*		*Pickard 7*
	OG (McIver) 80				

DORCHESTER: Ormerod, Cannie (sub Groves 72), Sullivan, White, McIvor (sub Radcliffe 86), Harris, Lonnon, Ferrett, O'Hagan (sub Jermyn 86), Pickard, Holmes. Subs: Baines, Elm

38	Reading	4	v	0	Grays Athletic
	Hodges 16, Cureton 60		*5643*		
	Butler 72, Jones 87				

GRAYS: Desborough, Risley, Taylor, Moseley, O'Sullivan (sub Blaney 68), Dickinson, Feddis (sub Snowsill 76), Hazle, Wright, Wallace (sub Nestling 78), Hazelden. Subs: Prudance, Baker

39	Bury	1	v	1	Northwich Victoria
	Daws 55		*2844*		*Fletcher 72*

NORTHWICH: Key, Bailey, Barnard, Davis, Robertson, Burke, Norris, Simpson, Devlin, Fletcher, Mike. Subs: Rigby, Cooke, Holcroft, Poland, Walsh

R	Northwich Vic.	1	v	0	Bury
	Mike 72		*2869*		

NORTHWICH: Lance Key: Mike Bailey, Mark Barnard, Steve Davis, John Robertson, Jamie Burke, Richard Norris, Wes Simpson, Gary Fletcher, Adie Mike, Mark Devlin. Subs not used: Ian Cooke, Malcolm Rigby, Peter Holcroft, Lee Poland, Steve Walsh

Left:
Woking's Rob Hollingdale evades Mark Birch's (Carlisle) challenge.
Photo: Alan Watson

Right:
John Frain (Northampton Town) with Chris Hurst (Frickley Athletic).
Photo: Peter Barnes

Danny Coid clears before either Barrington Belgrave or Nick Crittenden can tackle. Photo: Garry Letts

Yeovil Town players Nick Crittenden, Warren Patmore, Darren Way, Andy Lindegaard and Roy O'Brien celebrate at Blackpool. Photo: Garry Letts

Above: Morecambe v Cambridge. Another scramble in the Cambridge goalmouth. Photo: Garry Letts

Below: Morecambe celebrate. Photo: Garry Letts

SECOND ROUND

1 Swindon Town 5 v 0 Gateshead
O'Halloran 16, 51 *3,907*
Cowe 84, 89, Howe 87

GATESHEAD: Adrian Swan; Ritchie Watson, Sam Kitchen, Tony Hall, Paul Talbot (sub: Simon Bates 84m), Paul Proudlock, Steve Bowey, Graham Pepper (sub: Wayne Edgcumbe 61m), Paul Dalton, Steve Preen, Gareth McAlinden (sub: Paul Thompson 73m). Subs not used: Iain Gray, David Tremble.

3 AFC Bournemouth 3 v 0 Nuneaton Borough
Hughes 34, Elliott 47 *5,835*
O'Connor 89

NUNEATON: Chris Mackenzie; Alex Sykes, Mickey Love, Dave Crowley, Simon Weaver, Terry Angus, Andy Thackeray (sub: Carl Bacon 44m), Mark Taylor (sub: Barry Williams 46m), Marc McGregor, Ian King, Delton Francis (sub: Richard Mitchell 64m). Subs not used: Lee Charles, Ryan Young.

8 Chester City 3 v 2 Oxford United
Beesley 35 *2,798* *Gray 23, Murphy 25*
Whitehall 54, 60

CHESTER: Wayne Brown; Neil Fisher (sub: Darren Wright 52m), Neil Doughty, Martin Lancaster, Carl Ruffer, Paul Beesley (sub: Scott Ruscoe 75m), Paul Carden, Andy Porter, Mark Beesley, Steve Whitehall, Chris Blackburn. Subs not used: Craig Gaunt, David Moss, Matt Woods.

9 Canvey Island 1 v 2 Southend United
11,402
(at Southend United FC)

CANVEY ISLAND: Ashley Harrison; Peter Smith (sub: Sam Cooper 46m), Craig Davidson, Mickey Bennett, Mark Stimson, Steve Ward, Steve Tilson, John Kennedy (sub: Andy Jones 83m), Neil Gregory, Wayne Vaughan, Alex Inglethorpe (sub: Adam Miller 73m). Subs not used: Steve Clark, Steve Parmenter

10 Blackpool 0 v 1 Yeovil Town
3,757 *Crittenden 45*

YEOVIL: Tony Pennock; David Piper, Tom White, Terry Skiverton, Anthony Tonkin, Andy Lindegaard (sub: Roy O'Brien 77m), Darren Way, Ben Smith, Nick Crittenden, Warren Patmore, Barrington Belgrave (sub: James Bent 90m). Subs not used: Glenn Poole, Chris Weale, Alex Meechan.

15 Bristol City 3 v 1 Kettering Town
Peacock 55, Clist 65 *7,641* *Collins 29*
Thorpe 83

KETTERING: Ian Bowling; Chris Perkins, Colin Vowden, Craig Norman, Phil Brown, Matt Fisher (sub: Wayne Duik 73m), Robert Codner, Niall Inman (sub: Carl Shutt 82m), Brett McNamara, Amara Simba (sub: Dale Watkins 71m), Darren Collins. Subs: Carl Adams, Steve Wilson.

16 Northwich Victoria 3 v 3 Leyton Orient
Fletcher 51, 62, Mike 70 *2,703* *Griffiths 25, 50, Tate 82*

NORTHWICH: Lance Key; John Robertson, Steve Davis, Garry Burke, Mark Bailey, Richard Norris, Wes Simpson, Mark Devlin, Mark Barnard, Adie Mike, Gary Fletcher. Subs: Peter Holcroft, Malcolm Rigby, Lee Poland, Ian Cooke, Neil Ellis.

R Leyton Orient 3 v 2 Northwich Victoria
Griffiths 48 *4,028* *Cooke 10, Mike 12*
OG (Simpson) 70
Houghton 117

NORTHWICH: Lance Key, Mark Bailey, Mark Barnard, Wes Simpson, John Robertson, Garry Burke, Richard Norris, Ian Cooke (sub Walsh 76), Gary Fletcher (sub Lee Poland 107), Adie Mike, Mark Devlin. Subs: Halcroft, Rigby, Bates.

17 Southport 1 v 2 Kingstonian
Maamria 39 *3,659* *Harris 20, Pitcher 33*

SOUTHPORT: Steve Dickinson; Scott Guyett, Phil Bolland, Shaun Teale, Martin Clark (sub: Lee Elam 80m), Mike Marsh, Andy Gouck, Neil Grayston, Lee Furlong (Sub: Stuart Whittaker 50m), Ian Arnold, Dino Maamria. Subs not used: David Linighan, Carl Maculey, Robert Pell.

KINGSTONIAN: Gavin Kelly; Mark Beard, Derek Allan, Eddie Saunders, Mark Harris, Colin Luckett (sub: David Bass 90m), Gary Patterson, Geoff Pitcher, Phil Wingfield, Sammy Winston, Eddie Akuamoah (sub: Simon Stewart 87m). Subs not used: Ronnie Green, Robert Boyce.

19 Lincoln City 0 v 1 Dag. & Redbridge
2,823 *Janney 90*

DAGENHAM & REDBRIDGE: Tony Roberts; Tim Cole, Ashley Vickers, Lee Goodwin, Lee Matthews, Paul Terry, Mark Janney, Steve Heffer (sub: Drew Broughton 90m), Danny Shipp, Junior McDougald, Jason Broom. Subs not used: Nicky Rust, Matt Jones, Paul Cobb, Steve Forbes.

20 Morecambe 2 v 1 Cambridge United
Hardicker 7, Quayle 74 *3,427* *Youngs 10*

MORECAMBE: Mark Smith; Andy Fensome, Dave Perkins, Dave McKearney, John Hardiker, Steve Walters, Gary Thompson (sub: Michael Knowles 57m), Stuart Drummond, Julian Dowe (sub: Mark Quayle 60m), John Norman, Ryan Zico-Black (sub: Adriano Rigoglioso 60m). Subs not used: James Murphy, Steve McIlhargey.

OTHER SECOND ROUND RESULTS

2	Walsall	v	Barnet
4	Scunthorpe United	2 v 1	Brighton & Hove Albion
5	Kidderminster Harriers	0 v 2	Carlisle United
6	Cardiff City	3 v 1	Cheltenham Town
7	York City	2 v 2	Reading
11	Wigan Athletic	p	Notts Co.
12	Darlington	0 v 0	Luton Town
13	Millwall	0 v 0	Wycombe Wanderers
14	Rotherham United	1 v 0	Northampton Town
18	Peterborough Utd	1 v 1	Oldham Athletic

THIRD ROUND

Blackburn Rovers 2 v 0 Chester City
Taylor 71, Bent 84 *15,223*

CHESTER CITY
Wayne Brown; Neil Fisher (sub: Matt Woods 75m), Matt Doughty (sub: Darren Moss 68m), Martin Lancaster, Carl Ruffer, Paul Beesley, Paul Carden, Andy Porter, Mark Beesley, Steve Whitehall, Chris Blackburn (sub: Darren Wright 79m). Subs not used: Lee Woodyatt, Scott Ruscoe.

Southend United 0 v 1 Kingstonian
7,270 *Akuamoah 8*

KINGSTONIAN
Gavin Kelly; Mark Beard, Colin Luckett, Derek Allan, Eddie Saunders, Mark Harris, Garry Patterson, Geoff Pitcher, Sammy Winston (sub: David Bass 46m), Eddie Akuamoah (sub: Ronnie Green 90m), Phil Wingfield (sub: Simon Stewart 90m). Subs not used: Mark Boyce, Mark Jones.

Morecambe 0 v 3 Ipswich Town
5,923 *Stewart 14, Armstrong 65, Wright J 74*

MORECAMBE
Mark Smith; Andy Fensome, Andy Lyons (sub: Paul McGuire 67m), Dave McKearney, John Hardiker, Steve Walters, Gary Thompson, Stuart Drummond, Mark Quayle (sub: Adriano Rigoglioso 65m), John Norman, Ryan-Zico Black (sub: Phil Eastwood 65m). Subs not used: James Murphy, Andy Banks.

Charlton Athletic 1 v 1 Dag. & Redbridge
Salako 86 *19,059* *McDougald 41*

DAGENHAM
Tony Roberts; Tim Cole, Ashley Vickers, Lee Goodwin, Lee Matthews, Paul Terry (sub: Matt Jones 74m), Mark Janney (sub: John Hamsher 90m), Steve Heffer, Danny Shipp, Junior McDougald (sub: Rob Haworth 78m), Jason Broom. Subs not used: Paul Cobb, Andy Lomas

REPLAY

Dag. & Redbridge 0 v 1* Charlton Athletic
5,500 *Newton 92*

DAGENHAM:
Tony Roberts, Tim Cole, Ashley Vickers, Lee Goodwin, Lee Matthews, Paul Terry (sub Matt Jones 67), Mark Janney, Steve Heffer, Danny Shipp (sub Paul Cobb 109), Junior McDougald, Jason Broom (sub Rob Haworth 101). Unused subs: Mark Keen, Andy Lomas.

Bolton Wanderers 2 v 1 Yeovil Town
O'Kane 44 *11,161* *Patmore 24*
Ricketts 90

YEOVIL TOWN
Tony Pennock; David Piper, Anthony Tonkin, Terry Skiverton, Tom White, Darren Way, Ben Smith, Nick Crittenden, Andy Lindegaard (sub: Roy O'Brien 65m), Barrington Belgrave (sub: James Bent 86m), Warren Patmore. Subs not used: Chris Weale, Glenn Poole, Gary Risbridger.

Charlton's John Robinson finds no way past Dagenham's Ashley Vickers (3) and Matt Jones at the Valley.
Photo: Alan Coomes

Top: Dagenham keeper Tony Roberts saves this spectacular effort from Charlton's Martin Pringle at the Valley.

Centre: Dagenham's Tim Cole clears a Charlton corner with a powerful header before a packed Valley.

Bottom: Dagenham players thank the fans after holding Charlton to a draw.

Photos: Alan Coomes

Above:
Eddie Akuamoah causing problems for Southend defenders in an excellent game at Roots Hall.
Photo: Peter Barnes

Left: Kingstonian celebrate a famous victory at Roots Hall.
Photo: Peter Barnes

Above: Bolton Wanderers v Yeovil Town. Warren Patmore fires in a shot at goal. Photo: Garry Letts

Below: Yeovil celebrate the goal. Photo: Garry Letts

FOURTH ROUND

Bristol City	1	v	1	Kingstonian
Thorpe 90		*14,787*		*Wingfield 57*

KINGSTONIAN: Gavin Kelly, Mark Beard, Derek Allan, Eddie Saunders, Mark Harris, Colin Luckett, Geoff Pitcher, Gary Patterson, Phil Wingfield (sub David Bass 85), Eddie Akuamoah, Ian Duerden (sub Sammy Winston 89). Unused subs: Simon Stewart, Mark Boyce, Ronnie Green.

Replay

Kingstonian	0	v	1	Bristol City
		3,341		*Murray 88*

KINGSTONIAN: Gavin Kelly, Mark Beard, Derek Allan, Eddie Saunders, Mark Harris, Colin Luckett, Geoff Pitcher, Gary Patterson, Mark Boyce (sub Sammy Winston 90), Eddie Akuamoah, Ian Duerden. Unused subs: Simon Stewart, Luke Basford, Ronnie Green.

AXA F.A. CUP LEADING GOALSCORERS

9	Lucas	Hinckley United
7	Churchill	Horsham YMCA
	Durkin	Hemel Hempstead Town
	Ackess	Sheffield
6	Abbott	Aldershot Town
	Campbell	Waltham Abbey
	Devereux	AFC Sudbury
	Earnshaw	Cardiff City
	Flain	Horsham
	Milner	Bedlington Terriers
	Rountree	Billingham Town
	Wiltord	Arsenal
5	Allen	Langney Sports
	Cunningham	Belper Town
	Day	AFC Sudbury
5	Donovan	Pelsall Villa
	Edwards	Mangotsfield United
	Fletcher	Northwich Victoria
	Godber	Sheffield
	Guiver	Dartford
	Heshey	Liverpool
	Laing	Hassocks
	Marsh	Stourport Swifts
	Newham	Seaham Red Star
	Nimmo	Epsom & Ewell
	Pitcher	Kingstonian
	Portway	Chelmsford City
	Ranshaw	Grantham Town
	Seal	Mangotsfield United
	Simmonds	Hastings Town
	Smith	Bracknell Town
	Smith	Fleetwood Freeport
	Wise	Oxford City

MOST F.A. CUP GOALS IN A MATCH

4	Day	AFC Sudbury
	Campbell	Waltham Abbey
	Flain	Horsham
	Ackess	Sheffield
	Stevens	Carlisle United

AXA LAST MAN IN AWARD 2000-2001

An award was offered to the last remaining non-exempt team in the competition.

The prize will be shared between
Bracknell Town
AFC Sudbury
and
Radcliffe Borough

NON-LEAGUE LEADING SCORER

Andy Lucas (Hinckley United) - 9 goals

AXA RESULTS OF THE ROUNDS

FIRST QUALIFYING ROUND

North East

Seaham Red Star	7	v	0	Great Harwood Town
The Albany Northern Div 1				*North West Counties Div 1*

North West

Dunston Fed Brewery	1	v	2	**Fleetwood Freeport**
The Albany Northern Div 1				*North West Counties Div 1*
Arlesey Town	1	v	2	**Histon**
Ryman Div 3				*Dr Martens Eastern Div 1*

Midlands

Atherstone United	0	v	1	**Stourport Swifts**
Dr Martens Western Div 1				*Midland Alliance*

South East

St Margaretsbury	1	v	0	Borehamwood
Spartan South Mids				*Ryman Div 1*

South West

West Super Mare	0	v	0	Shortwood United
Dr Martens Western Div 1				*Cherry Red Music Hellenic League*
Shortwood United	3	v	2	Weston Super Mare

SECOND QUALIFYING ROUND

North East

Brigg Town	2	v	2	Lancaster City
N.C.E. Premier Div				*Unibond Premier Div*
Lancaster City	3	v	4	**Brigg Town**

North West

Altrincham	0	v	3	**Mossley**
Unibond Premier Div				*North West Counties Div 1*

Midlands

Stafford Town	2	v	1	Moor Green
Midland Alliance				*Dr Martens Premier*

South East

Margate	0	v	1	**Banstead Athletic**
Dr Martens Premier				*Ryman Div 2*

South West

Newport County	0	v	4	**Merthyr Tydfil**
Dr Martens Premier				*Dr Martens Premier*

THIRD QUALIFYING ROUND

North East

Bedlington Terriers	5	v	2	Accrington Stanley
Albany Northern League Div 1				*Unibond Premier Div*

North West

Marine	0	v	2	**Radcliffe Borough**
Unibond Premier Div				*Unibond Div 1*

Midlands

Purfleet	2	v	2	Grantham Town
Ryman Premier Div				*Dr Martens Eastern*
Grantham Town	1	v	0	Purfleet
AFC Sudbury	1	v	1	Leek Town
Jewson Eastern Premier Div				*Unibond Premier Div*
Leek Town	1	v	2	**AFC Sudbury**

South East

Hastings Town	2	v	3	**Horsham**
Dr Martens Eastern				*Ryman Div 2*

South West

Whyteleafe	1	v	3	Mangotsfield Utd
Ryman Div 1				*Dr Martens Western*

FOURTH QUALIFYING ROUND

North East

Frickley Athletic	1	v	0	Hyde United
Unibond Premier Premier Div				*Unibond Premier Premier Div*

North West

Radcliffe Borough	2	v	1	Burscough
Unibond Premier Div 1				*Unibond Premier Premier Div*

Midlands

Boston United	1	v	1	Burton Albion
Nationwide Conf.				*Dr Martens Premier*
Burton Albion	3	v	2	Boston United

South East

Hampton & Rich. B	5	v	0	Worcester City
Ryman Premier				*Dr Martens Premier*

South West

Dorchester Town	1	v	1	Welling United
Dr Martens Premier				*Dr Martens Premier*
Welling United	2	v	4	**Dorchester Town**

F.A. UMBRO TROPHY

2000-2001 REVIEW

Happy?
Canvey goalscorer Ben Chenery and manager Jeff King cannot quite believe it!

FIRST ROUND

Saturday 4th November 2000

No.	Home	Score	Away	Att.
1	Belper Town	4 v 1	Blakenall	224
	Payne 3 (17, 70 (p), 84)		*Round 28*	
	Gummer 53			
2	North Ferriby United	2 v 3	Gresley Rovers	196
	OG (Doughty) 28, Blythe 89		*Gardner 25, Reynolds 33,*	
			Tucker 85	
3	Gainsborough Trinity	3 v 2	Bradford Pk Avenue	392
	Linighan 50, Ellington 21, 53		*Quinn 74, Maxwell 46*	
4	Droylsden	0 v 0	Bromsgrove Rovers	199
R	Bromsgrove Rovers	1 v 0	Droylsden	185
	OG (Stannard) 40			
5	Kendal Town	2 v 2	Stamford	99
	Hodgson 71, Shaw 86		*Ndekwe 14, Rhule 29*	
R	Stamford	1 v 1*	Kendal Town	162
	Ndkewe 34		*Skeoch 73*	
	Stamford won 3-2 after penalties			
6	Bishop Auckland	1 v 1	Whitby Town	175
	OG (Rennison) 64		*Chillingworth 28*	
R	Whitby Town	2 v 2*	Bishop Auckland	324
	Logan 30, G Robinson 48		*Mellanby 44, 68*	
	Bishop Auckland won 5-4 after penalties			
7	Guiseley	4 v 1	Eastwood Town	202
	Cooke 30, 77, Atkinson 68		*Warboys 5*	
	Wilkes 86			
8	Stalybridge Celtic	4 v 1	Bedworth United	196
	Jones 8, McNeil 12, Parr 58		*Barber 44*	
	Sullivan 70			
9	Harrogate Town	3 v 3	Witton Albion	242
	Couzens 49, 54, Roden 86		*Hennin 2, 73, Anana 43 (p)*	
R	Witton Albion	3 v 2	Harrogate Town	221
	Gleghorn 37, Anane 51		*Dunn 9, Wrigley 11*	
	Hennin 62			
10	Ilkeston Town	1 v 1	Altrincham	597
	Knapper 42 (p)		*Thomas 82*	
R	Altrincham	4 v 3*	Ilkeston Town	323
	Hay 22, Landon 24, 92 (p)		*Whitehead 54, 68, Clark 116*	
	Talbot 98			
11	Bamber Bridge	1 v 3	Atherstone United	211
	Carey 72		*Seddon 48, Casson 79, Kelly 83*	
12	Corby Town	3 v 5	Matlock Town	108
	Mawby 12, Miller 21		***Taylor 3 (7, 55, 90)**,*	
	T Mintus 62		*Tilley 63, Davis 72*	
13	Winsford United	2 v 4	Congleton Town	45
	Birmingham 45, Hayder 67		*Weston 9, OG (Shiel) 50,*	
			Dodd 84 (p), Washington 88	
14	Shepshed Dynamo	2 v 3	Burscough	142
	McGlinchy 5, 74		*Talbot 16, Wilde 87, 90*	
15	Halesowen Town	1 v 3	Bilston Town	323
	Owen 40		*Manton 37, Voice 53, 87*	
16	Colwyn Bay	3 v 3	Tamworth	321
	D Graham 58,79, G Graham 62		*Turner 1, Hallam 41, 45*	
R	Tamworth	2 v 1	Colwyn Bay	362
	Hudson 41, Turner 83		*Cross 65*	
17	Blyth Spartans	2 v 0	Hinckley United	330
	Forster 81 (p), Pepper 88			
18	Stafford Rangers	3 v 1	Ossett Town	267
	Middleton 17, O'Connor 52		*Annan 72*	
	Kiely 62			
19	Spennymoor United	3 v 1	Frickley Athletic	125
	Veart 8, 11, Shalwell 42		*Hurst 44 (p)*	
20	Barrow	0 v 1	Runcorn	1327
			McAlister 60	
21	Trafford	5 v 1	Farsley Celtic	72
	McCartney 68, Pannett 71		*Blackstone 79*	
	Diacuk 74, Whitehead 77			
	Emmett 81			
22	Spalding United	2 v 0	Sutton Coldfield Tn	164
	Vince 29, Henderson 41			
23	Rocester	3 v 1	Stocksbridge P. Stls	108
	Bott 14, 32, Hobby 79		*Earlstone 60*	
24	Chorley	1 v 1	Accrington Stanley	377
	Challender12		*Williams 48*	
R	Accrington Stanley	2 v 1	Chorley	443
	Mullin 29, Patterson 75		*Eatock 13*	
25	Paget Rangers	1 v 2	Worksop Town	249
	Maragh 4		*Jackson 20, Betney 65*	
26	Ashton United	5 v 0	Solihull Borough	172
	Illingworth 26, Connelly 53			
	McDonald 66,84, Jeverson 75			
27	Moor Green	0 v 1	Hucknall Town	246
			Cooke 25	
28	Vauxhall Motors	4 v 0	Lincoln United	183
	Blundell 3 (6, 19, 68)			
	Young 71			
29	Racing Club Warwick	0 v 4	Lancaster City	91
			Graham 30, Haddow 33,	
			Welch 54, 83	
30	Leek Town	2 v 2	Radcliffe Borough	217
	Marrow 32, Houghton 38		*Hardy 27, Wilson 83*	
R	Radcliffe Borough	2 v 1*	Leek Town	178
	Collins 75, 105		*Marrow 5*	
31	Gretna	2 v 1	Workington	262
	Lea 80, Mawson 90		*Holt 33*	
32	Redditch United	3 v 1	Grantham Town	267
	Danks 30,81, OG (Halcrow) 90		*Furnell 6*	
33	Romford	2 v 2	Braintree Town	226
	Leary 21, Ray 23		*Reinelt 15 (p), Noble 73*	
R	Braintree Town	2 v 0	Romford	183
	Jones 27, Stanley 78			

No.	Home	Score	Away	Att.
34	Ford United	4 v 2	St Leonards	92
	Bejada 14, Lord 18, Cove 49 Holding 56		*Chatelier 39, Fletcher 84*	
35	Grays Athletic	3 v 4	Ashford Town	209
	Hazel 37, Wright 41 Wallace 45		*Seagar 65 (p), Peachey 74, 80 Arundel 84*	
36	Tiverton Town	3 v 0	Sittingbourne	656
	Rogers 12, Varley 25 Marker 53			
37	Welling United	0 v 2	Uxbridge	361
			Banford 62, OG (Riviere) 90	
38	Billericay Town	2 v 0	Farnborough Town	453
	Linger 29, Baker 46 (p)			
39	Yeading	2 v 1	Bromley	91
	OG (Rawlings) 17, Tucker 52		*Tompkins 59*	
40	Chelmsford City	0 v 2	St Albans City	504
			Simba 25, 32	
41	Baldock Town	1 v 1	Staines Town	127
	Walker 19		*Talboys 47*	
R	Staines Town	2 v 1	Baldock Town	148
	Talboys 8, Everitt 43		*Fenton 69*	
42	Langney Sports	0 v 1	Histon	241
			Kennedy 2	
43	Cirencester Town	0 v 1	Clevedon Town	120
			Mainwaring 27	
44	Newport (IW)	2 v 2	Hitchin Town	370
	Gibbons 19, Riley 87		*Parker 49, 83*	
R	Hitchin Town	4 v 1	Newport (IW)	241
	Parker 37, 44, Scott 59 Williams 90		*Rofe 51*	
45	Worthing	2 v 2	Thame United	283
	Webber 31, Carrington 76		*Abery 57, Louis 61*	
R	Thame United	0 v 0*	Worthing	500
	Worthing won 4-2 after penalties			
46	Aylesbury United	1 v 1	Rugby United	341
	Joe 42		*Evans 37*	
R	Rugby United	1 v 3	Aylesbury United	210
	Marsdon 87		*Joe 3, Mason 56 (p), 88*	
47	Barton Rovers	2 v 1	Banbury United	127
	Tayne 49, Coughlin 67		*Gooderick 60*	
48	Crawley Town	2 v 1	Heybridge Swifts	698
	Anderson 89, Hynes 90		*Lee 59*	
49	Worcester City	3 v 0	Mangotsfield Utd	623
	Owen 3 (38, 57 (p), 62)			
50	Folkestone Invicta	2 v 2	Oxford City	123
	Dent 37, 50		*Strong 44, Wise 76*	
R	Oxford City	3 v 4	Folkestone Invicta	109
	Thorpe 3, Wise 65, 87		*Lawrence 6, Ponsford 22, Dryden 52, Chambers 81*	
51	Bashley	1 v 0	Salisbury City	257
	Gee 87			

No.	Home	Score	Away	Att.
52	Harlow Town	2 v 1	Basingstoke Town	179
	Coley 8, Hooker 16		*Corman 24 (p)*	
53	Hampton & R.Bor.	1 v 4	Maidenhead Utd	278
	Simpson 27		*Channell 57, 89, Croxford 75, Domingos 90*	
54	Hendon	2 v 0	Tonbridge Angels	195
	Duncan 10, OG (Clout) 42			
55	Weymouth	2 v 1	Sutton United	734
	Robinson 39, Hale 45		*Booth 66*	
56	Fisher Athletic	3 v 2	Burnham	101
	Barr 15, Overton 24, 83		*Howell 52, Tomlinson 86*	
57	Dorchester Town	2 v 1	Boreham Wood	329
	O'Hagan 82, 84		*Lawford 4*	
58	Leatherhead	1 v 2	Evesham United	145
	Harkness 1		*McCarthen 45, Preedy 56*	
59	Bognor Regis Tn	0 v 0	Whyteleafe	201
R	Whyteleafe	0 v 1	Bognor Regis Tn	110
			Wright 75	
60	Gravesend & N'fleet	0 v 1	Hastings Town	232
			Ferguson 19	
61	Slough Town	5 v 0	Bishop's Stortford	426
	Marshall 3 (27, 65, 67) *Hall 31, 49*			
62	Wisbech Town	1 v 2	Carshalton Athletic	253
	OG (Daly) 22		*Liddle 32, Page 51*	
63	Cinderford Town	1 v 1	Dulwich Hamlet	131
	Macklin 85		*Webb 65*	
R	Dulwich Hamlet	1 v 2*	Cinderford Town	137
	Fowler 58		*OG (Chin) 80, Addis 96*	
64	Rothwell Town	2 v 1	Merthyr Tydfil	175
	Turner 21, Morris 28		*Thomas 45*	
65	Havant & W'ville	2 v 1	Croydon	248
	Wakefield 33, McDonald 70		*McDonnell 17*	
66	Cambridge City	1 v 0	Gloucester City	257
	Wilkin 72			
67	Dartford	0 v 3	Northwood	185
			Hart 37, Yaku 55, Hale 60	
68	Bedford Town	1 v 2	Newport County	713
	Drew 11		*Shephard 72, Morgans 90*	
69	Witney Town	2 v 3	Harrow Borough	75
	Murphy 5, Bourne 83		***Gavin 3 (37, 41, 90)***	
70	Wealdstone	3 v 3	Weston Super Mare	234
	Reeve 1 (p), Carter 13 Jones 30		*OG (Lamb) 26, Watts 43, Wharton 70*	
R	Weston s Mare	2 v 0	Wealdstone	140
	McConnell 35 (p), Hunt 44			
71	Enfield	4 v 2	Erith & Belvedere	179
	Allen 39, Bunn 45 (p) Hammett 76, 90		*Dimmock 5, 68*	

Bye:- Walton & Hersham

FIRST ROUND STATISTICS

Home Victories 42

Away Victories 27

Replays 17

Best Attendance
1327 - Barrow v Runcorn

Average Attendance
264

Best Home Victory
Ashton United 5 v 0 Solihull Borough
Slough Town 5 v 0 Bishop's Stortford

Best Away Victory
Racing Club Warwick 0 v 4 Lancaster City

Hat Tricks
3 Payne (Belper Town)
3 Taylor (Matlock Town)
3 Blundell (Vauxhall Motors)
3 Owen (Worcester City)
3 Marshall (Slough Town)
3 Gavin (Harrow Borough)

Top: Romford keeper Jason White punches clear from Braintree's Courtney Naylor in the FA Trophy First Round. Photo: Alan Coomes

Bottom: Stamford's Malcolm Ndekwe pounces on a fumble by Kendal keeper Greg Price to open the scoring. Photo: Alan Watson

SECOND ROUND

Saturday 2nd December 2001

No.	Home	Score	Away	Att.
1	Gresley Rovers	4 v 0	Rocester	335
	Tucker 40, Warren 42, Wardle 80, Allsop 85			
2	Hyde United	1 v 0	Spalding United	339
	Yeo 78			
3	Matlock Town	3 v 1	Gretna	209
	Davies 3, 50, Tilly 57		*Mawson 37*	
4	Marine	2 v 1	Gateshead	209
	Thompson 63, Courtney 82		*Edgcumbe 34*	
5	Ashton United	2 v 2	Bilston Town	201
	Hamlet 63, OG (Harvey) 73		*Smith 27, Wilcox 45*	
R	Bilston Town	3 v 1	Ashton United	115
	Voice 53, 57, Rollason 70		*Connelly 35*	
6	Altrincham	2 v 2	Bishop Auckland	437
	Murphy 1, Ward 60		*Gallagher 45, Lee 50*	
R	Bishop Auckland	3 v 1	Altrincham	235
	Shaw 9 (p), Mellamby 64, Milroy 70		*Maddox 74*	
7	Stalybridge Celtic	2 v 0	Witton Albion	552
	McNeil 6, Parr 80			
8	Blyth Spartans	3 v 0	Stafford Rangers	480
	Innes 10, Robson 14, 20			
9	Hucknall Town	1 v 0	Redditch United	231
	Wright 17			
10	Runcorn	2 v 1	Guiseley	302
	Price 16, Robonson 88		*Trevitt 21*	
11	Emley	5 v 3	Vauxhall Motors	256
	Hatto 28, Bambrook 44, 59, Nazha 68, 75		*Wright 23, Cuminskey 36, Rigby 42*	
12	Radcliffe Borough	0 v 3	Accrington Stanley	407
			Williams 36, Payne 72, 86	
13	Burscough	1 v 0	Gainsborough Trinity	229
	Clandon 64			
14	Congleton Town	3 v 1	Stamford	134
	Weston 14, Johnson 6, Thornley 88		*Kebble 60*	
15	Tamworth	1 v 1	Belper Town	445
	Hallam 76		*Butler 38*	
R	Belper Town	0 v 5	Tamworth	291
			Haughton 3 (35, 81, 86), *Hallam 48, Foy 63*	
16	Worksop Town	4 v 2	Atherstone United	392
	Jackson 12, 25, Johnson 45, Whitehead 75		*Seddon 74, OG (Davis) 90*	
17	Lancaster City	0 v 1	Bromsgrove Rovers	161
			Bedward 44	
18	Trafford	2 v 0	Spennymoor United	104
	Murray 50, 70			
19	Bashley	1 v 7	St Albans City	283
	Gee 90		*Ansell 3 (p), 58, Piper 31, 56, Wraight 60, Knight 70, Pratt 83*	
20	Kings Lynn	2 v 0	Chesham United	731
	Palmer 35, Bush 87			
21	Hendon	1 v 1	Worcester City	122
	Binns 68		*Owen 36*	
	Worcester City	2 v 3	Hendon	610
	Carty 2, 90		*OG (Heeley) 46, Binns 54, Kippitt 89*	
22	Maidenhead United.	1 v 0	Enfield	182
	Narty 21			
23	Carshalton Athletic	3 v 4	Histon	237
	Bartley 36, 66, Tanner 87		*Harrington 33, 46, Kennedy 50, Cambridge 73*	
24	Braintree Town	1 v 1	Rothwell Town	210
	Reinelt 55		*Morris 17*	
R	Rothwell Town	2 v 2*	Braintree Town	167
	Turner 30, OG (Reinelt) 120		*Gutzmore 4, Reinelt 96*	
25	Folkestone Invicta	4 v 0	Worthing	174
	Daniels 20, Lawrence 27, 70, Dent 50			
26	Staines Town	1 v 1	Walton & Hersham	153
R	Walton & Hersham	2 v 3*	Staines Town	152
	Craker 52, Cory 66		*Reilly 45, Terry 90, Sullivan 119*	
27	Tiverton Town	2 v 1	Aylesbury United	699
	Everitt 15, Speakman 44		*Callinan 53*	
28	Barton Rovers	3 v 2	Uxbridge	143
	Donnelly 4, Jones 12 (p), Buckland 47		*Tunnell 22, Moore 31*	
29	Aldershot Town	1 v 0	Havant & W'looville	1887
	Browne 37			
30	Burton Albion	4 v 1	Yeading	784
	Moore 3 (52, 73, 81) *Lyons 72*		*Blount 57*	
31	Northwood	3 v 1	Purfleet	218
	Hook 45, 58, Yaku 90		*Pashley 80*	
32	Ashford Town	4 v 2	Weston Super Mare	195
	Marshall 3 (2, 27, 85(p)) *Edwards 31*		*Bevan 35, 64*	
33	Cinderford Town	0 v 2	Evesham United	92
			Wolsey 27, Roberts 84	
34	Newport County	2 v 1	Slough Town	627
	Thorne 48, Scouter 61		*Black 34*	
35	Harlow Town	2 v 2	Canvey Island	327
	McNally 45, 89		*Bennett 6, Parmenter 61*	
R	Canvey Island	2 v 0	Harlow Town	238
	OG (Drury) 46, Tilson 81			
36	Cambridge City	1 v 1	Bath City	185
	Wardley 11		*McLean 90*	
R	Bath City	1 v 0	Cambridge City	403
	Paul 43			
37	Billericay Town	2 v 2	Hastings Town	401
	Baker 35, Moore 73		*Simmonds 6, 55*	
R	Hastings Town	1 v 2	Billericay Town	317
	Ferguson 36		*Baker 10 (p), Gentle 80*	
38	Ford United	1 v 3	Bognor Regis Town	97
	Lay 22		*Russell 33, Birmingham 60, Miles 85*	
39	Fisher Athletic	2 v 3	Crawley Town	159
	Barr 2, 7		*Mean 17, Hynes 70, 81*	
40	Harrow Borough	3 v 0	Dorchester Town	256
	Payne 42, Hurlock 71, Xavier 76			
41	Margate	2 v 1	Clevedon Town	340
	Porter 53, Munday 85		*Mainwaring 88*	
42	Weymouth	2 v 0	Hitchin Town	681
	Robinson 77, Laws 90			

SECOND ROUND STATISTICS

Home Victories 30

Away Victories 12

Replays 8

Best Attendance

1887 - Aldershot Town v Havant & Waterlooville

Average Attendance 336

Best Home Victory

Gresley Rovers 4-0 Rocester

Folkestone Invicta 4-0 Worthing

Best Away Victory

Bashley 1-7 St Albans City

Hat Tricks

3 Marshall (Ashford Town)

3 Moore (Burton Albion)

3 Haughton (Tamworth)

Top:
Blyth striker Glen Robson chips the ball over Stafford keeper Richard Williams to give Blyth a 2-0 lead.
Photo: Bill Broadley

Centre:
Chris James (Matlock) has his header turned round the post by Gretna keeper Stephen Pape.
Photo: Keith Clayton

Bottom:
Mark Xavier with Dorchester's Steve Cannie and Martyn Sullivan.
Photo: Paul Carter

THIRD ROUND

Saturday 13th January 2001

No	Home				Away	Att
1	Matlock Town	2	v	0	Northwich Victoria	784
	Simpson 13, Shaw 32 (p)					
2	Runcorn	0	v	4	Scarborough	420
					Stoker 53, Pounder 70, Ingram 74, Russell 77	
3	Congleton Town	2	v	0	Gresley Rovers	313
	Borg 60, Thornley 84					
4	Trafford	1	v	1	Telford United	435
	Emmett 18 (p)				*Sandwith 56*	
R	Telford United	7	v	1	Trafford	788
	Edwards 5, 71 Martindale 46, 67 Moore 19, Palmer 57 Huckerby 70				*Emmett 25*	
5	Bilston Town	3	v	2	Nuneaton Borough	806
	Voice 20, 64, Rollason 56				*B Williams 15, Charles 27*	
6	Leigh RMI	1	v	0	Hucknall Town	235
	Spooner 90					
7	Emley	3	v	0	Accrington Stanley	494
	Hatto 5, Thorpe 22, Day 75					
8	Marine	2	v	0	Stalybridge Celtic	441
	Gamble 57, Randles 84					
9	Southport	3	v	0	Hednesford Town	1091
	Arnold 57, Lane 65 Marsh 90 (p)					
10	Worksop Town	3	v	2	Bromsgrove Rovers	586
	Townsend 37, Ludlam 49 (p) Jackson 90				*Burgess 15, Crawford 73.*	
11	Burscough	3	v	3	Morecambe	582
	Talbot 8, Farrell 56, Wilde 77				*Black 13, Hardiker 29, Quayle 51*	
R	Morecambe	3	v	0	Burscough	585
	Walters 29, Black 33 Norman 48					
12	Tamworth	0	v	3	Boston United	846
					Norris 3 (15, 20, 27)	
13	Burton Albion	2	v	0	Bishop Auckland	1173
	Moore 28, Stride 45					
14	Hyde United	0	v	0	Blyth Spartans	556
R	Blyth Spartans	2	v	1	Hyde United	561
	Pepper 27, Innes 61				*Banin 90*	
15	Chester City	2	v	0	Doncaster Rovers	1479
	Whitehall 29, 35					

No	Home				Away	Att
16	Hendon	1	v	2	Tiverton Town	346
	Adekola 17				*Everett 36, 52*	
17	Folkestone Invicta	1	v	3	Kings Lynn	342
	White 55				***Rowland 3 (43, 75, 82)***	
18	Woking	1	v	2	Margate	1542
	Perkins 46				*Collins 20, Brathwaite 31*	
19	Crawley Town	1	v	2	Ashford Town	708
	Carroll 38				*Elles 72, Marshall 77 (p)*	
20	Bognor Regis Town	0	v	2	Billericay Town	411
					Woolsey 45, Baker 78	
21	Aldershot Town	1	v	5	Stevenage Boro	2965
	Browne 23				*Clark 17, Hay 59, Phillips 62 Illman 66, 68*	
22	St Albans City	1	v	0	Newport County	604
	Stevens 13					
23	Forest Green Rvrs	6	v	1	Barton Rovers	654
	Hedges 15, Clark 37 Campbell 60 Meecham 74, 85 (p) Cousins 90				*Jones 27*	
24	Canvey Island	5	v	1	Northwood	302
	Tilson 7, Kennedy 52 Gregory 55, 60, Jones 79				*Yaku 83*	
25	Histon	3	v	0	Kettering Town	837
	Barker 17, Goddard 39 I Cambridge 60					
26	Yeovil Town	2	v	1	Bath City	3507
	Way 71, Bent 74				*Paul 50*	
27	Braintree Town	1	v	2	Maidenhead United	403
	Stanley 19				*Ulasi 39, Nartey 89*	
28	Evesham United	4	v	2	Harrow Borough	154
	McCartan 12, Pratt 71, 75 Wolsey 77				*Petersen 70, Xavier 80 (p)*	
29	Hayes	0	v	1	Rushden & Diamonds	842
					Darby 40	
30	Staines Town	2	v	2	Kingstonian	767
	Talboys 14, Butler 65				*Pitcher 46, 86*	
R	Kingstonian	2	v	0	Staines Town	426
	Luckett 56, Pitcher 90					
31	Dagenham & Red.	0	v	1	Weymouth	1784
					Phillips 90	
32	Hereford United	1	v	0	Dover Athletic	1294

THIRD ROUND STATISTICS

Home Victories 21
Away Victories 11
Replays 4

Best Attendance
3507 Yeovil Town v Bath City

Average Attendance 835

Best Home Victory
Telford United 7 v 1 Trafford

Best Away Victory
Aldershot Town 1 v 5 Stevenage Borough
Runcorn 0 v 4 Scarborough

Hat Tricks
3 Rowland (Kings Lynn)
3 Norris (Boston United)

Accrington Stanley's Russell Payne beats Emley skipper Steve Nicholson to the ball during his side's 0-3 exit from the FA Trophy at Bell Vue, Wakefield. Photo: Darren Thomas

Staines' David Everitt looks to escape from the crowd as Colin Luckett (Kingstonian) prepares to challenge.

Photo: Francis Short

Bognor's Matt Russell is beaten to this cross by Billericay's centre half

Photo: Graham Cotterill

Hendon desperately seek an equaliser at home to Tiverton

Photo: Steve Ayre

FA Trophy Fourth Round. L-R: Linden Whitehead (Worksop), Mr S Chatwin, Mr K Wright, Mr J Brandon and Wayne Johnson (Congleton). Photo: Arthur Evans

Ben Smith of Yeovil Town tries to escape the attention of Emley striker Simeon Bambrook. Photo: Darren Thomas

Morecambe keeper Steve McIlhergey is challenged by Evesham's Steve Taylor. Photo: Gordon Whittington

Maidenhead keeper Richard Barnard watches helplessly as the ball heads goalwards but this effort was marginally wide. Photo: Graham Brown

FOURTH ROUND

Saturday 3rd February 2001

No.	Home	Score	Away	Att.
1	Worksop Town (P)	6 v 2	Congleton Town (1)	724
	Jackson 7,66, Whitehead 17, Johnson 24, Townsend 27(p), G Smith 41		*Thornley 32, Borg 87*	
2	Blyth Spartans (P)	2 v 1	Maidenhead Utd (P)	902
	Stewart 32, Hay 86		*Glynn 21*	
3	Scarborough	0 v 1	Burton Albion (P)	1462
			Stride 55	
4	Histon (E)	0 v 3	Billericay Town (P)	433
			Gentle 3, 32, Baker 90	
5	Bilston Town (W)	0 v 1	Canvey Island (P)	536
			Parmenter 32	
6	Chester City	3 v 2	St. Albans City (P)	1442
	Ruffer 13, Ruscoe 55, Blackburn 77		*Simba 25, Strevens 89*	
7	Kingstonian	0 v 1	Southport	1245
			Gouck 52	
8	Hereford United	0 v 0	Leigh RMI	1491
R	Leigh RMI	1 2	Hereford United	441
	Black 87		*Williams 41, Elmes 79*	
9	Weymouth (P)	3 v 1	Ashford Town (E)	1144
	Laws 24, D Rowbotham 81, Phillips 88		*Webster 69*	
10	Tiverton Town (W)	2 v 1	Boston United	1436
	Toomey 20, 61		*Charlery 70 (p)*	
11	Stevenage Borough	2 v 1	Margate (P)	1515
	Illman 45, Phillips 76		*O'Connell 80*	
12	Kings Lynn (P)	1 v 2	Telford United	1357
	March 30		*OG (Robinson) 8, Jobling 60*	
13	Emley (P)	2 v 4	Yeovil Town	1754
	Day 29, Bambrook 64 (p)		*OG (Nicholson) 3, Poole 28, Betts 34, Smith 88*	
14	Matlock Town (1)	2 v 2	Forest Green Rvrs	802
	Tilley 65, Taylor 84		*A Foster 6, Meechan 60*	
R	Forest Green Rvrs	3 v 1	Matlock Town (1)	425
15	Evesham Utd (W)	0 v 0	Morecambe	738
R	Morecambe	4 v 1	Evesham Utd (W)	634
	Norman 3 (50, 57, 90), *Lee 83*		*Taylor 18*	
16	Marine (P)	0 v 6	Rushden & Dia.	965
			Darby 21, 76, Jackson 60, Burgess 80, Essendon 90, Rodwell 90	

FOURTH ROUND STATISTICS

Home Victories 8

Away Victories 8

Replays 3

Best Attendance
1754 Emley v Yeovil Town

Average Attendance 1023

Best Home Victory
Worksop Town 6 v 2 Congleton Town

Best Away Victory
Marine 0 v 6 Rushden & Diamonds

Hat Tricks
3 Norman (Morecambe)

FIFTH ROUND

Burton Albion 2 v 1 Yeovil Town
Moore 64(p) 2,469 *Lindegaard 90*
Anderson 87

Burton Albion: Duke; Rennie, Henshaw, Glasser, Blount, Wassall, Stride, Anderson, Moore, Lyons, Webster. Subs not used: Starbuck, Kavanagh, Holmes, Garner, Goodwin

Yeovil Town: Pennock; Betts, Tonkin, Skiverton (sub Jones 81m), O'Brien, Way, Bent (sub Belgrave 84m), Smith, Patmore, Crittenden, Poole (sub Lindegaard 81m). Subs not used: Piper, Weal

Weymouth 1 v 2 Southport
Laws 17 1,839 *Guyett 2, Marsh 35(p)*

Weymouth: Potter; Hare, Hale, Browne (sun Hutchinson 68m), Waldock, Cross, Robinson, J.Rowbotham (sub Gammon 77m), D.Rowbotham, Laws, Phillips. Subs not used: Dean, Funnell, Claxton

Southport: Dickinson; Lane, Clark, Teale, Guyett, Bolland, Marsh, Gouck, Arnold, Grayston, Elam (sub Furlong 35m). Subs not used: Linighan, Morgan, O'Brien, Whittaker

Morecambe 0 v 0 Hereford United
1,150

Morecambe: Smith; Fensome (sub Murphy 87m), McKearney, Hardiker, Lyons, Zico-Black, Drummond, Walters, Lee (sub Eastwood 80m), Norman, Quayle (sub Thompson 65m). Subs not used: Rigoglioso, Banks.

Hereford United: Cooksey; Clarke, Sturgess (sub Gardiner 46m), Robinson, James, Wall, Quiggan, Snape, Rodgerson (sub Bull 84m), Elmes, Williams. Subs not used: Baker, Giddings, Shirley

R Hereford United 1 v 1* Morecambe
Williams 45 1,372 *Drummond 71*

Hereford United won 3-1 after kicks from the penalty spot.

Hereford United: S Cooksey, M Clarke, P Sturgess, P Robinson, T James, J Wall, J Quiggin, J Snape, R Elmes, G Williams, I Rodgerson (sub Bull 77m). Subs not used: M Gardiner, M Baker, K Giddings, J Shirley.

Morecambe: M Smith, A Fensome, A Lyons, D McKearney, J Hardiker, J Murphy, D Lee, S Drummond, M Quayle, J Norman, G Thompson (sub Zico-Black 79m, sub Hunter 102m). Subs not used: P Eastwood, A Rigoglioso, A Banks.

Canvey Island 1 v 1 Stevenage Borough
Vaughan 7 1,010 *Illman 20*

Canvey Island: Harrison; Kennedy, Duffy, Chenery, Bodley, Ward, Tilson, Stimson, Gregory, Vaughan, Parmenter. Subs not used: Bennett, Clark, Davidson, A.Miller, Tanner

Stevenage Borough: Wilkerson; Hamsher, Trott, Smith, Bradshaw, D.Phillips, Martin, McMahon, Hay, Illman, Clarke. Subs not used: Armstrong, Brissett, J.Miller, G.Phillips, Metcalfe

R Stevenage Boro 0 v 0* Canvey Island

Canvey Island won 4-2 after kicks from the penalty spot.

Stevenage Borough: Wilkerson, Hamsher, Trott, Smith, Bradshaw, D.Phillips, Martin, McMahon, Clarke, Hay, Brissett (sub Illman 62m). Subs not used: Leadbeater, R.Miller, G.Phillips, Metcalfe

Canvey Island: Harrison, Kennedy, Duffy, Chenery, Bodley, Ward, Tilson, Stimson (sub Tanner 89m), Gregory, Vaughan, Parmenter (sub Miller 112m). Subs not used: Bennett, Clark, Davidson

Glen Robson (Blyth Spartans) scores v Chester City (Wayne Brown)

Billericay Town	2	v	3	Telford United
Moore 23, Spencer 86		709		*Palmer 10, Martindale 43*
				Edwards 52

Billericay Town: King; Penn, Culverhouse, Linger, C.Moore, Baker, Gentle, L.Williams, Gentle, Parratt, Woolsey. Subs not used: Morris, Spencer, Henty, Shiret, T.Baker
Telford United: D.Williams; Travis, Davies, N.Moore, Adams, Bentley, Allbrighton, Goodwin, Jobling, Martindale, Edwards. Subs not used: Palmer, Murphy, Bray, Malkin, Huckerby, Sandwith

Chester City	4	v	2	Blyth Spartans
Haarhoff 6, M Beesley 23		1,831		*Parry 64, Robson 67*
P Beesley 81, Whitehall 90				

Chester City: Brown; Fisher, Doughty, Lancaster, Gaunt (sub Moss 54m), M.Beesley, Carden, Haarhoff (sub Wright 68m), Woods (sub Whitehall 79m), P.Beesley, Ruscoe. Subs not used: Proce, Berry
Blyth Spartans: Burke; Little, Martin, Williams (sub Hay 62m), Forster, Keegan, Dixon, Pepper, Robson, Perry, Stewart. Subs not used: Dunkersley, Collins, Heppell, Cottrill

Tiverton Town	1	v	2	Worksop Town
Everett 80		1,937		*Jackson 4, Townsend 35*

Tiverton Town: Edwards; Pears, Saunders, Tatterton, Marker, Rogers, Nancekivell, Toomey, Everett, Daly, Smith. Subs not used: Conning, Ovens, Vinnicombe, Grimshaw, Winter
Worksop Town: Holmshaw; Ludlam, Mason, Davis, Pearce, Johnson, G.Smith, Waddle, Whitehead, Townsend, Jackson. Subs not used: Bettany, C.Smith, Brookes, Goddard, Hirst

Forest Green Rovers	2	v	0	Rushden & Diamonds
Lightbody 25, M Foster 33		1,018		

Forest Green Rovers: Perrin; Cousins, Cort, M.Foster (sub Drysdale 78m), Clark, Burns, Lightbody, Daley, Hedges, Meechan, Slater. Subs not used: A.Foster, Prince, Hunt, Jell
Rushden & Diamonds: Turley; Mustafa, Setchell, Carey, Peters, Warburton, Butterworth (sub Duffy 68m), Brady (sub Wormull 54m), Jackson (sub Butcher 82m), Darby, Burgess. Subs not used: Rodwell, Naylor

FIFTH ROUND STATISTICS

Home Victories 4

Away Victories 4

Replays 2

Best Attendance
2469 Burton Albion v Yeovil Town

Average Attendance 1481

Jimmy Haarhoff (Chester City) shields the ball from Richard Forster (Blyth Spartans)

Chester's Martyn Lancaster plunges into the air. Photo: Lee Thompson

QUARTER-FINALS

Canvey Island	1	v	0	Telford United
Jones 20		Att: 807		

Canvey Island: Harrison, Kennedy, Duffy, Chenery, Bodley, Ward, Tilson, Stimson, Gregory, Jones, Parmenter. Subs: Clark, Davidson, Miller, Tanner, Thompson

Telford United: Williams, Travis, Davies, Moore, Bentley, Fowler, McGorry, Jobling, Edwards, Malkin, Palmer. Subs: Murphy, Bray, Martindale, Sandwith, Fitzpatrick

Chester City	1	v	0	Southport
Woods 88		Att: 3,204		

Chester City: Brown, Moss (sub J Haarhoff 49, sub Porter 88), Doughty, Woods, Ruffer, Gaunt, Carden, Fisher, Beesley, Whitehall (sub Wright 90), Ruscoe. Subs: Able, Woodyatt

Southport: Dickinson, lane, O'Brien (sub Grayston 55), Clark, Guyett, Bolland, Marsh, Gouck, Arnold, Parke (sub Maamria 84), Elam (sub Furlong 84). Subs: Teale, Morgan

Hereford United	1	v	0	Burton Albion
Elmes 8		Att: 3,238		

Hereford United: Cooksey, Clarke, James, Wright, Sturgess, Quiggin, Snape, Robinson, Rodgerson (sub Giddings 78), Elmes, Williams. Subs: Wall, Baker, Parry, Bull.

Burton Albion: Duke, Davis, Kavanagh, Rennie (sub Holmes 85), Henshaw, Lyons, Stride, Glasser, Webster, Moore (sub Starbuck 72), Anderson. Subs: Garner, Crosby, Goodwin.

Forest Green Rovers	2	v	1	Worksop Town
Clark 12, Lightbody 49		Att: 1,448		*Townsend 90*

Forest Green: Perrin, Cousins, Cort, M Foster, Clark, Burns, Lghtbidy, Hedges (sub Drysdale 90), Meecham (sub A Foster 83), Daley (sub Prince 77), Slater. Subs: Hunt, Ghent.

Worksop Town: Holmshaw, Gray, Mason, Davis, Pearce, Johnson, G Smith, waddle, Whitehead, Townsend, Muller. Subs: Bettany, C Smith, Brookes, Goddard, Hurst.

QUARTER FINAL STATISTICS

Home Victories 4

Away Victories 4

Replays 0

Best Attendance
3238 - Hereford United v Burton Albion

Average Attendance 2174

Top:
Chris Waddle (Forest Green Rovers) and Tony Daley (Worksop Town).
Photo: Bruce Fenn, Freelance Photos

Below:
Burton Albion's Pat Lyons and Hereford United's James Quiggan.
Photo: Nigel Hill

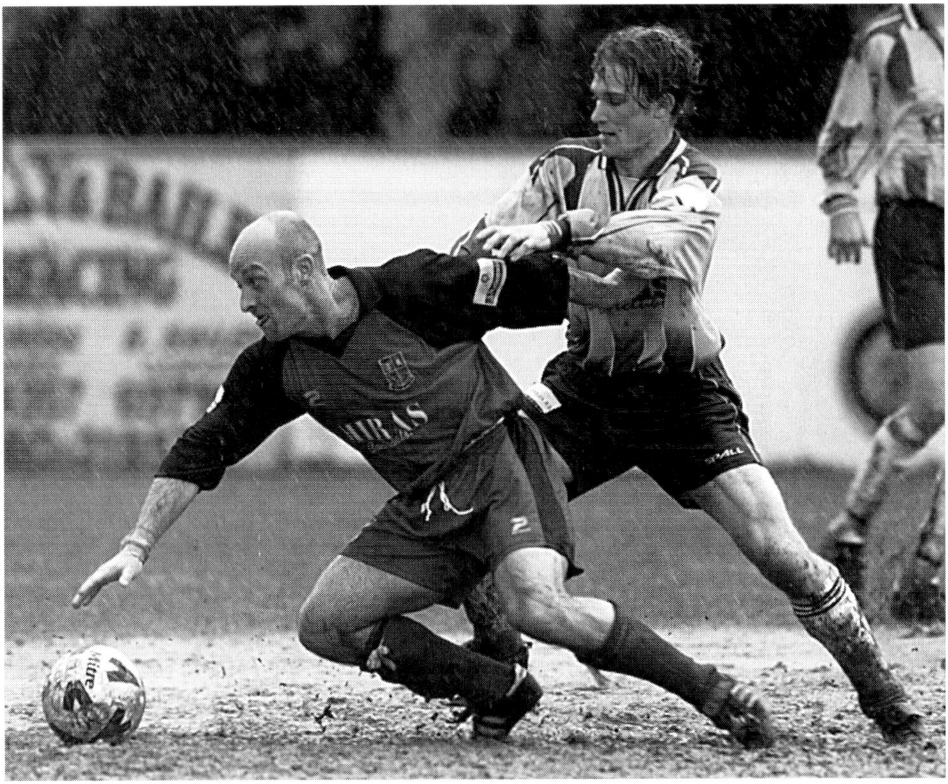

Steve Parmenter gets hold of Telford's Fowler. Photo: Arfa

Andy Jones has this effort beaten away by Telford keeper Dean Williams. Photo: Arfa

SEMI-FINALS

FIRST LEG

Forest Green Rovers 2 v 2 Hereford United

Bennett 62, Meechan 80 (pen) — *Elmes 27, 78*

Att: 2,711

Forest Green Rovers: Perrin, Cousins, Lockwood, A Foster, Clark, Burns, Daley, Drysdale, M Foster, Meechan, Prince (Bennett 46). Subs not used: Allen, Hunt, Adams, Ghent

Hereford United: Cooksey, Clarke, Sturgess (Shirley 67), Robinson, Wright, James, Rodgerson, Snape, Elmes, Williams, Parry (Bull 83). Subs not used: Crowe Baker Wall

Referee: R Oliver

SECOND LEG

Hereford United 1 v 4 Forest Green Rovers

Wright 62 — *Bennett 14, Meechan 28, Burns 59, A Foster 81*

Att: 4,175

Hereford United: Cooksey, Clarke, Wright, James, Sturgess, Quiggin, Robinson, Snape, Parry (Bull 64), Elmes, Williams. Subs not used: Wall, Baker, Shirley, Giddings

Forest Green Rovers: Perrin, Cousins, Lockwood, Clark, Drysdale, M Foster, Burns, Slater, Meechan, A Foster (Daley 83), Bennett. Subs not used: Prince, Allen, Hunt, Ghent

Referee: D Pugh

FIRST LEG

Canvey Island 2 v 0 Chester City

Tilson 28, Vaughan 73

Att: 1,221

Canvey Island: Harrison, Kennedy, Duffy, Chenery, Bodley, Ward, Tilson, Stimson (Tanner 84), Gregory, Jones (Vaughan 71), Parmenter. Subs no used: Clark, Miller, Thompson

Chester City: Brown, Fisher, Doughty, Lancaster, Ruffer (Moss 24), P Beesley, Carden, Porter, Woods, M Beesley (Whitehall 55), Ruscoe (Priestley 46). Subs not used: Guant, Haarhoff.

Referee: S Tomlin

SECOND LEG

Chester City 0 v 2 **Canvey Island**

Parmenter 30, Stimson 60

Att: 2,647

Chester City: Brown, Fisher (Haarhoff 46), Doughty, Lancaster, Woods, P Beesley (Gaunt 65), Carden, Blackburn, M Beesley, Whitehall, Ruscoe. Subs not used: Priestley, Moss, Wright

Canvey Island: Harrison, Kennedy, Duffy, Chenery, Bodley, Ward, Tilson, Stimson, Gregory, Vaughan (Jones 67), Parmenter. Subs not used: Bennett, Miller, Smith, Tanner

Referee: M Warren

Jubilant Jeff King, Canvey Island manager, with Craig Davidson and goalkeeper Ashley Harrison after their First Leg Semi Final win over Chester City.
Photo: Roger Turner

Neil Gregory, Canvey Island, takes on the Chester City defence in the FA Trophy Semi-Final.
Photo: Roger Turner

Goalkeeper Wayne Brown, Chester City, stops a Canvey Island attack during their Semi Final First Leg match.
Photo: Roger Turner

FINAL

CANVEY ISLAND (1)1 v 0 (0) FOREST GREEN ROVERS

Plans to cut the Ryman League's standing by removing its Premier League victors from the present tripartite promotion arrangement to the Conference could not have been more forcefully answered than by Canvey Island's triumph in the 32nd FA Trophy final. A competition set up by the FA for the top Non-League teams, the winners usually come from the Conference, Bishop's Stortford being the last interlopers in 1981.

Playing against their fourth Conference opponents in the competition, the Essex side were worthy winners over Forest Green, displaying the same competitive strengths they had shown in victories over Stevenage Borough, Telford United and Chester City.

A solitary goal - his first for the club - came from a 16th minute header bulleted into the net by Ben Chenery, Mark Stimson's corner finding him in a desert island of space. Shortly after Steve Parmenter nearly made it two when he and Wayne Vaughan combined. Steve Perrin had to dive smartly to his left to hold the shot.

Adrian Foster, set up by Rob Cousins with a long ball over the defence, gave Ashley Harrison no trouble with a weak shot, otherwise it was territorially all Canvey in the attacking stakes. Perrin had to rush to the edge of his area to prevent John Kennedy fastening on to a high bouncing ball, and 19-year-old Adam Lockwood, a player for the future, headed just wide of his own post to thwart another sally. Adrian Foster also had to head clear from his own area and Vaughan could have done better with an opening created by Parmenter.

Back in his attacking role, Adrian Foster's shot was going in until a defender's foot took the sting out of it and allowed Harrison to gather. A well-timed tackle from Chris Duffy then robbed Foster as he threatened to break through but despite the drumming support from Rovers' fans, Canvey ended the half with their narrow lead intact.

Re-organising for the second half, Rovers brought on Frankie Bennett on the right, switching Tony Daley - back on his old stamping ground from where he had earned his seven England caps - to the left. This did produce some threats as Daley went on several speedy, twisting, trademark runs, a foul sometimes being the defenders' only recourse. Occasionally the cross was made, as when one low delivery enabled Martin Foster a chance. Unfortunately two of his own players robbed one another of the resulting loose ball. Adrian Foster then grazed the bar with a header and a Daley zipping shot brought Perrin to his knees.

For the Islanders, substitute Adam Tanner put John Kennedy free and his accurate pass to Nigel Gregory on the penalty spot saw the latter drive over. There was a frenzied macho scuffle in the Canvey area, as a result of which Bennett, Mick Bodley and Duffy were all booked but otherwise the game fizzled out. Forest's woes were complete when Martin Foster's free kick was scooped off Lockwood's head by Harrison just before the final whistle.

A delighted Canvey manager, Jeff King, although deservedly beaming widely in exultation, declared: 'We can play better than that.' A sentiment echoed by his counterparts, Nigel Spink and David Norton. No one could deny, however, that, on the day, Canvey did sufficient to merit victory and prevent Forest Green's second chance in a final of becoming the first double winners of Trophy and Vase.

Arthur Evans

Canvey Island: Ashley Harrison, John Kennedy (MoM), Chris Duffy, Ben Chenery (scored 16mins), Mick Bodley, Steve Ward, Steve Tilson, Mark Stimson (sub Adam Tanner 83rd min), Neil Gregory, Wayne Vaughan (sub Andy Jones 76th min), Steve Parmenter
Subs not used: Micky Bennett, Adam Miller, Ian Thompson

Forest Green Rovers: Steve Perrin, Rob Cousins, Adam Lockwood, Martin Foster, Billy Clark, Chris Burns, Tony Daley, Jason Drysdale (sub Frankie Bennett 46th min), Adrian Foster (sub Paul Hunt 75th min), Alex Meecham, Stuart Slater
Subs not used: Ian Hedges, Luke Prince and Matthew Ghent

Referee: Mr A G Wiley (Staffordshire) assisted by Mr M L Short (Lincolnshire) and Mr T M Kettle (RAF)

FA UMBRO TROPHY AT A GLANCE

THIRD ROUND

Canvey Island 5
Northwood 1

Bilston Town 3
Nuneaton Borough 2

Aldershot Town 1
Stevenage Boro 5

Woking 1
Margate 2

Histon 3
Kettering Town 0

Bognor Regis T 0
Billericay Town 2

Folkestone Invicta 1
Kings Lynn 3

Telford United 7
Trafford 1

Chester City 2
Doncaster Rovers 0

St Albans City 1
Newport County 0

Hyde Utd 0, 1
Blyth Spartans 0, 2

Braintree Town 1
Maidenhead U 2

Dagenham & R. 0
Weymouth 1

Crawley Town 1
Ashford Town 2

Staines Town 2, 0
Kingstonian 2, 2

Southport 3
Hednesford T 0

Hereford Utd 1
Dover Athletic 0

Leigh RMI 1
Hucknall Town 0

Evesham Utd 4
Harrow Borough 2

Burscough 3, 0
Morecambe 3, 3

Runcorn 0
Scarborough 4

Burton Albion 2
Bishop Auckland 0

Emley 3
Accrington Stanley 0

Yeovil Town 2
Bath City 1

Hendon 1
Tiverton Town 2

Tamworth 0
Boston United 3

Workson Town 3
Bromsgrove R 2

Congleton Town 2
Gresley Rovers 0

Marine 2
Stalybridge Celtic 0

Hayes 0
Rushden & Dia. 1

Matlock Town 2
Northwich Vic. 0

Forest Green Rvrs 6
Barton Rovers 1

FOURTH ROUND

Bilston Town 0
Canvey Island 1

Stevenage Boro 2
Margate 1

Histon 0
Billericay Town 3

Kings Lynn 1
Telford Utd 2

Chester City 3
St Albans City 2

Blyth Spartans 2
Maidenhead U 1

Weymouth 3
Ashford Town 1

Kingstonian 0
Southport 1

Hereford Utd 0, 2
Leigh RMI 0, 1

Evesham Utd 0, 1
Morecambe 0, 4

Scarborough 0
Burton Albion 1

Emley 2
Yeovil Town 4

Tiverton Town 2
Boston United 1

Worksop Town 6
Congleton Town 2

Marine 0
Rushden & Dia. 6

Matlock Town 2, 1
Forest Green R 2, 3

FIFTH ROUND

Canvey I. 1, 0, 4p
Stevenage B 1, 0, 2p

Billericay Town 2
Telford United 3

Chester City 4
Blyth Spartans 2

Weymouth 1
Southport 2

Hereford Utd 0, 1,3p
Morecambe 0, 1, 1p

Burton Albion 2
Yeovil Town 1

Tiverton Town 1
Worksop Town 2

Forest Green R 2
Rushden & Dia. 0

SIXTH ROUND

Canvey Island 1
Telford United 0

Chester City 1
Southport 0

Hereford United 1
Burton Albion 0

Forest Green Rvrs 2
Worksop Town 1

SEMI FINALS

Chester City 0 0
Canvey Island 2 2

Forest Green R 2 4
Hereford United 2 1

FINAL

Canvey Island 1
Forest Green Rovers 0

PAST F.A. TROPHY FINALS

1970 MACCLESFIELD TOWN 2 (Lyond, B Fidler) TELFORD UNITED 0 Att: 28,000
Macclesfield: Cooke, Sievwright, Bennett, Beaumont, Collins, Roberts, Lyons, B Fidler,Young, Corfield, D Fidler.
Telford: Irvine, Harris, Croft, Flowers, Coton, Ray,Fudge, Hart, Bentley, Murray, Jagger. Ref: K Walker

1971 TELFORD UTD 3 (Owen, Bentley, Fudge) HILLINGDON BORO. 2 (Reeve, Bishop)
Telford: Irvine, Harris, Croft, Ray, Coton, Carr, Fudge, Owen, Bentley, Jagger ,Murray. Att: 29,500
Hillingdon B.: Lowe, Batt, Langley, Higginson, Newcombe, Moore, Fairchild,Bishop, Reeve, Carter, Knox. Ref: D Smith

1972 STAFFORD RANGERS 3 (Williams 2, Cullerton) BARNET 0 Att: 24,000
Stafford R.: Aleksic, Chadwick, Clayton, Sargeant, Aston, Machin, Cullerton, Chapman,Williams, Bayley, Jones.
Barnet: McClelland, Lye, Jenkins, Ward, Embrey, King,Powell, Rerry, Flatt, Easton, Plume . Ref: P Partridge

1973 SCARBOROUGH 2 (Leask, Thompson) WIGAN ATHLETIC 1 (Rogers) aet Att:23,000
Scarborough: Garrow, Appleton, Shoulder, Dunn, Siddle, Fagan, Donoghue, Franks,Leask (Barmby), Thompson, Hewitt.
Wigan: Reeves, Morris, Sutherland, Taylor,Jackson, Gillibrand, Clements, Oats (McCunnell), Rogers, King, Worswick. Ref: H Hackney

1974 MORECAMBE 2 (Richmond, Sutton) DARTFORD 1 (Cunningham) Att: 19,000
Morecambe: Coates, Pearson, Bennett, Sutton, Street, Baldwin, Done, Webber,Roberts (Galley), Kershaw, Richmond.
Dartford: Morton, Read, Payne, Carr, Burns,Binks, Light, Glozier, Robinson (Hearne), Cunningham, Halleday. Ref: B Homewood

1975 MATLOCK TOWN 4 (Oxley, Dawson, T Fenoughty, N Fenoughy) SCARBOROUGH 0 Att: 21,000
Matlock: Fell, McKay, Smith, Stuart, Dawson, Swan, Oxley, N Fenoughy, Scott, T Fenoughty, M Fenoughty.
Scarborough: Williams, Hewitt, Rettitt, Dunn, Marshall, Todd, Houghton, Woodall, Davidson, Barnby, Aveyard. Ref: K Styles

1976 SCARBOROUGH 3 (Woodall, Abbey, Marshall(p)) STAFFORD R. 2 (Jones 2) aet Att: 21,000
Scarborough: Barnard, Jackson, Marshall, H Dunn, Ayre (Donoghue), HA Dunn, Dale,Barmby, Woodall, Abbey, Hilley.
Stafford: Arnold, Ritchie, Richards, Sargeant,Seddon, Morris, Chapman, Lowe, Jones, Hutchinson, Chadwick. Ref: R Challis

1977 SCARBOROUGH 2 (Dunn(p), Abbey) DAGENHAM 1 (Harris) Att: 21,500
Scarborough: Chapman, Smith, Marshall (Barmby), Dunn, Ayre, Deere, Aveyard,Donoghue, Woodall, Abbey, Dunn.
Dagenham: Hutley, Wellman, P Currie, Dunwell,Moore, W Currie, Harkins, Saul, Fox, Harris, Holder. Ref: G Courtney

1978 ALTRINCHAM 3 (King, Johnson, Rogers) LEATHERHEAD 1 (Cook) Att: 20,000
Altrincham: Eales, Allan, Crossley, Bailey, Owens, King, Morris, Heathcote,Johnson, Rogers, Davidson (Flaherty).
Leatherhead: Swannell, Cooper, Eaton, Davies,Reid, Malley, Cook, Salkeld, Baker, Boyle (Bailey). Ref: A Grey

1979 STAFFORD RANGERS 2 (A Wood 2) KETTERING TOWN 0 Att: 32,000
Stafford: Arnold, F Wood, Willis, Sargeant, Seddon, Ritchie, Secker, Chapman, AWood, Cullerton, Chadwick (Jones).
Kettering: Lane, Ashby, Lee, Eastell, Dixey,Suddards, Flannagan, Kellock, Phipps, Clayton, Evans (Hughes). Ref: D Richardson

1980 DAGENHAM 2 (Duck, Maycock) MOSSLEY 1 (Smith) Att : 26,000
Dagenham: Huttley, Wellman, Scales, Dunwell, Mooore, Durrell, Maycock, Horan,Duck, Kidd, Jones (Holder).
Mossley: Fitton, Brown, Vaughan, Gorman, Salter,Polliot, Smith, Moore, Skeete, O'Connor, Keelan (Wilson). Ref: K Baker

1981 BISHOP'S STORTFORD 1 (Sullivan) SUTTON UNITED 0 Att:22,578
Bishop's Stortford: Moore, Blackman, Brame, Smith (Worrell), Bradford, Abery, Sullivan,Knapman, Radford, Simmonds, Mitchell.
Sutton Utd.: Collyer, Rogers, Green, J Rains,T Rains, Stephens (Sunnucks), Waldon, Pritchard, Cornwell, Parsons. Ref: J Worrall

1982 ENFIELD 1 (Taylor) ALTRINCHAM 0 Att:18.678
Enfield: Jacobs, Barrett, Tone, Jennings, Waite, Ironton, Ashford, Taylor,Holmes, Oliver (Flint), King. Ref: B Stevens
Altrincham: Connaughton, Crossley, Davison, Bailey,Cuddy, King (Whitbread), Allan, Heathcote, Johnson, Rogers, Howard.

1983 TELFORD UTD 2 (Mather 2) NORTHWICH VICTORIA 1 (Bennett) Att: 22,071
Telford: Charlton, Lewis, Turner, Mayman (Joseph), Walker, Easton, Barnett,Williams, Mather, Hogan, Alcock.
Northwich: Ryan, Fretwell, Murphy, Jones,Forshaw, Ward, Anderson, Abel (Bennett), Reid, Chesters, Wilson. Ref: B Hill

1984 NORTHWICH VICTORIA 1 (Chester) BANGOR CITY 1 (Whelan) Att: 14,200
Replay NORTHWICH 2 (Chesters(p), Anderson) BANGOR 1 (Lunn) Att: 5,805 (at Stoke)
Northwich: Ryan, Fretwell, Dean, Jones, Forshaw (Power 65), Bennett, Anderson,Abel, Reid, Chesters, Wilson. Ref: J Martin
Bangor: Letheren, Cavanagh, Gray, Whelan, Banks,Lunn, Urqhart, Morris, Carter, Howat, Sutcliffe (Westwood 105) . Same in replay.

1985 WEALDSTONE 2 (Graham, Holmes) BOSTON UNITED 1 (Cook) Att: 20,775
Wealdstone: Iles, Perkins, Bowgett, Byatt, Davies, Greenaway, Holmes, Wainwright,Donnellan, Graham (N Cordice 89), A Cordice.
Boston: Blackwell, Casey, Ladd,Creane, O'Brien, Thommson, Laverick (Mallender 78), Simpsom, Gilbert, Lee, Cook. Ref: J Bray

1986 ALTRINCHAM 1 (Farrelly) RUNCORN 0 Att: 15,700
Altrincham: Wealands, Gardner, Densmore, Johnson, Farrelly, Conning, Cuddy,Davison, Reid, Ellis, Anderson. Sub: Newton.
Runcorn: McBride, Lee, Roberts,Jones, Fraser, Smith, S Crompton (A Crompton), Imrie, Carter, Mather, Carrodus. Ref: A Ward

1987 KIDDERMINSTER HARRIER S 0 BURTON ALBION 0 Att: 23,617
Replay KIDDERMINSTER 2 (Davies 2) BURTON 1 (Groves) Att: 15,685 (at West Brom)
Kidderminster: Arnold, Barton, Boxall, Brazier (sub Hazlewood in rep), Collins (subPearson 90 at Wembley), Woodall, McKenzie, O'Dowd, Tuohy, Casey, Davies. sub:Jones.
Burton: New, Essex, Kamara, Vaughan, Simms, Groves, Bancroft, Land, Dorsett, Redfern, (sub Wood in replay), Gauden. Sub: Patterson.
Ref: D Shaw

1988 ENFIELD 0 TELFORD UNITED 0 Att: 20,161, Ref: L Dilkes
Replay ENFIELD 3 (Furlong 2, Howell) TELFORD 2 (Biggins, Norris(p)) Att: 6,912 (at W Brom)
Enfield: Pape, Cottington, Howell, Keen (sub Edmonds in rep), Sparrow (subHayzleden at Wembley), Lewis (sub Edmonds at Wembley), Harding, Cooper, King,Furlong, Francis.
Telford: Charlton, McGinty, Storton, Nelson, Wiggins, Mayman (sub Cunningham inrep (sub Hancock)), Sankey, Joseph, Stringer (sub Griffiths at Wembley,Griffiths in rep), Biggins, Norris.

1989 TELFORD UNITED 1 (Crawley) MACCLESFIELD TOWN 0 Att: 18,102
Telford: Charlton, Lee, Brindley, Hancock, Wiggins, Mayman, Grainger, Joseph,Nelson, Lloyd, Stringer. Subs: Crawley, Griffiths.
Macclesfield: Zelem, Roberts, Tobin, Edwards, Hardman, Askey, Lake, Hanton,Imrie, Burr, Timmons. Subs: Devomshire, Kendall.
Ref: T Holbrook

1990 BARROW 3 (Gordon 2, Cowperthwaite) LEEK TOWN 0 Att: 19,011
Barrow: McDonnell, Higgins, Chilton, Skivington, Gordon, Proctor, Doherty(Burgess), Farrell (Gilmore), Cowperthwaite, Lowe, Ferris.
Leek: Simpson, Elsby (Smith), Pearce, McMullen, Clowes, Coleman (Russell),Mellor, Somerville, Sutton, Millington Ref: T Simpson

1991 WYCOMBE W. 2 (Scott, West) KIDDERMINSTER H. 1 (Hadley) Att: 34,842
Wycombe: Granville, Crossley, Cash, Kerr, Creaser, Carroll, Ryan, Stapleton,West, Scott, Guppy (Hutchinson). Ref: J Watson
Kidderminster: Jones, Kurila, McGrath, Weir, Barnett, Forsyth, Joseph (Wilcox), Howell (Whitehouse), Hadley, Lilwall, Humphries

1992 COLCHESTER UTD 3 (Masters, Smith, McGavin) WITTON ALBION 1 (Lutkevitch) Att: 27,806
Colchester: Barrett, Donald, Roberts, Knsella, English, Martin, Cook, Masters,McDonough (Bennett 65), McGavin, Smith. Ref: K P Barratt
Witton: Mason, Halliday, Coathup, McNeilis, JimConnor, Anderson, Thomas, Rose,Alford, Grimshaw (Joe Connor), Lutkevitch (McCluskie)

1993 WYCOMBE W. 4 (Cousins, Kerr, Thompson, Carroll) RUNCORN 1 (Shaughnessy) Att: 32,968
Wycombe: Hyde, Cousins, Cooper, Kerr, Crossley, Thompson (Hayrettin 65),Carroll, Ryan, Hutchinson, Scott, Guppy. Sub: Casey.
Runcorn: Williams, Bates, Robertson, Hill, Harold (Connor 62), Anderson, Brady(Parker 72), Brown, Shaughnessy, McKenna, Brabin
Ref: I J Borritt

1994 WOKING 2 (D Brown, Hay) RUNCORN 1 (Shaw (pen)) Att: 15,818
Woking: Batty, Tucker, L Wye, Berry, Brown, Clement, Brown (Rattray 32), Fielder, Steele, Hay (Puckett 46), Walker. Ref: Paul Durkin
Runcorn: Williams, Bates, Robertson, Shaw, Lee, Anderson, Thomas, Connor, Mclnerney (Hill 71), McKenna, Brabin. Sub: Parker

1995 WOKING 2 (Steele, Fielder) KIDDERMINSTER H. 1 aet (Davies) Att: 17,815
Woking: Batty, Tucker, L Wye, Fielder, Brown, Crumplin (Rattray 42), S Wye, Ellis, Steele, Hay (Newberry 112), Walker. Sub: Read(gk)
Kidderminster: Rose, Hodson, Bancroft, Webb, Brindley (Cartwright 94), Forsyth, Deakin, Yates, Humphreys (Hughes 105), Davies, Purdie. Sub: Dearlove (gk) Ref: D J Gallagher

1996 MACCLESFIELD TOWN 3 (Payne, OG, Hemmings) NORTHWICH VICTORIA 1 (Williams) Att: 8,672
Macclesfield: Price, Edey, Gardiner, Payne, Howarth(C), Sorvel, Lyons, Wood (Hulme 83), Coates, Power, Hemmings (Cavell 88).
Northwich: Greygoose, Ward, Duffy, Burgess (Simpson 87), Abel (Steele), Walters, Williams, Butler (C), Cooke, Humphries, Vicary. Ref: M Reed

1997 DAGENHAM & REDBRIDGE 0 WOKING 1 (Hay 112) Att: 24,376
Dagenham: Gothard, Culverhouse, Connor, Creaser, Jacques (sub Double 75), Davidon, Pratt (Naylor 81), Parratt, Broom, Rogers, Stimson (John 65).
Woking: Batty, Brown, Howard, Foster, Taylor, S Wye, Thompson (sub Jones 115), Ellis, Steele (L Wye 108), Walker, Jackson (Hay 77). Ref: J Winter

1998 CHELTENHAM TOWN 1 (Eaton 74) SOUTHPORT 0 Att: 26,387
Cheltenham: Book, Duff, Freeman, Banks, Victory, Knight (Smith 78), Howells, Bloomer, Walker (sub Milton 78), Eaton, Watkins. Sub: Wright.
Southport: Stewart, Horner, Futcher, Ryan, Farley, Kielty, Butler, Gamble, Formby (sub Whittaker 80), Thompson (sub Bollard 88), Ross. Sub: Mitten. Ref: G S Willard

1999 FOREST GREEN ROVERS 0 KINGSTONIAN 1 (Mustafa 49) Att: 20,037
Forest Green Rovers: Shuttlewood, Hedges, Forbes, Bailey (Smart 76), Kilgour, Wigg (Cook 58), Honor (Winter 58), Drysdale, McGregor, Mehew, Sykes. Subs (not used): Perrin, Coupe
Kingstonian: Farrelly, Mustafa, Luckett, Crossley, Stewart, Harris, Patterson, Pitcher, Rattray, Leworthy (Francis 87), Akuamoah. Subs (not used): John, Corbett, Brown, Tranter Ref: A B Wilkie

2000 FOREST GREEN ROVERS 0 CANVEY ISLAND 1 at Villa Park Att: 10,007
Forest Green Rovers: Perrin, Cousins, Lockwood, Foster, Clark, Burns, Daley, Drysdale (Bennett 46), Foster (Hunt 75), Meecham, Slater. Subs (not used): Hedges, Prince, Ghent
Canvey Island: Harrison, Duffy, Chenery, Bodley, Ward, Tilson, Stimson (Tanner 83), Gregory, Vaughan (Jones 76), Parmenter. Subs (not used): Bennett, Miller, Thompson. Ref: A G Wiley

FINAL

CANVEY ISLAND (1)1 v 0 (0) FOREST GREEN ROVERS

Chenery 16

Att: 10,007

Canvey Island

Ashley Harrison
John Kennedy
Chris Duffy
Ben Chenery
Mick Bodley
Steve Ward
Steve Tilson
Mark Stimson
(sub Adam Tanner 83 mins)
Neil Gregory
Wayne Vaughan
(sub Andy Jones 76 mins)
Steve Parmenter

Subs not used:
Micky Bennett
Adam Miller
Ian Thompson

Forest Green Rovers

Steve Perrin
Rob Cousins
Adam Lockwood
Martin Foster
Billy Clark
Chris Burns
Tony Daley
Jason Drysdale
(sub Frankie Bennett 46 mins)
Adrian Foster
(sub Paul Hunt 75 mins)
Alex Meecham
Stuart Slater

Subs not used:
Ian Hedges
Luk Prince
Matthew Ghent

Referee: Mr A G Wiley (Staffordshire)

Trophy joy for Ben Chenery, the scorer of the winning goal for Canvey Island
Photo: Darren C Thomas

Top:
Canvey Island's Andy Jones has the ball pinched by Forest Green's keeper Stephen Perrin.
Photo:
Neil Thaler

Centre:
Forest Green Rovers' Adam Lockwood and Canvey Island's Andy Jones battle for the ball.
Photo:
Neil Thaler

Bottom:
Ben Chenery (left) heads the goal that wins Canvey Island the FA Trophy.
Photo:
Bill Wheatcroft

Ben Chenery's match winning goal. Photo: Darren C Thomas

Canvey Island celebrate their Trophy success. Photo: Darren C Thomas

FA TROPHY OVERALL RECORDS

The table is a record of the performance of the top 56 teams that have played in the Trophy since its inception in 1970. During that time we have seen many teams enjoying successful periods in the competition and this is an attempt to reward teams for their consistency during the various rounds as well as whether they actually win the Trophy or not. The points are calculated as follows: Last 64 = 1point; Last 32 = 2 points; Last 16 = 3 points; Last 8 = 4 points; Last 4 = 5 points; Finalists = 6 points; Winners = 7 points. *John Anderson*

1999	*2000*	*2001*		*S*	*P*	*W*	*L*	*%*	*Pts*	*Best*
2	1	1	Telford United	32	95	66	29	69.47	88	Winners x 3
1	2	2	Altrincham	32	94	64	30	68.09	81	W x 2
3	3	3	Runcorn	32	96	64	32	66.67	77	Finalist x 3
4	4	4	Enfield	27	82	57	25	69.51	70	Winners x 2
5	5	5	Northwich Victoria	32	83	52	31	62.65	70	Winners 1984
6	6	6	Kidderminster Harriers	31	75	45	30	60.00	66	Winners 1987
7	7	7	Stafford Rangers	32	78	48	30	61.54	65	Winners x 2
8	8	8	Macclesfield Town	28	74	48	26	64.86	62	Winners x 2
13	9	9	Kettering Town	32	71	39	32	54.93	62	Finalist x 2
14	12	70	Yeovil Town	32	70	38	32	54.29	61	SF x 2
12	10	11	Scarborough	20	60	43	17	71.67	60	Winners x 3
9	11	12	Boston United	32	75	43	32	57.33	60	Finalist 1985
10	13	13	Cheltenham Town	29	85	57	28	67.06	57	Winners 1998
11	14	14	Dagenham	18	67	50	17	74.63	55	Winners 1980
17	18	15	Morecambe	32	81	50	31	61.73	54	Winners 1974
18	19	16	Burton Albion	32	82	50	32	60.98	54	Finalist 1987
19	16	17	Woking	27	74	50	24	67.57	52	Winners x 3
16	15	18	Dartford	28	67	39	28	58.21	52	Finalist 1974
15	17	19	Wycombe Wanderers	19	52	35	17	67.31	51	Winners x 2
21	21	20	Weymouth	32	69	37	32	53.62	50	last 8 x 2

20	20	21	Bangor City	22	53	31	22	58.49	47	Finalist 1984
23	23	22	Bromsgrove Rovers	32	72	40	32	55.56	47	last 8 x 2
28	24	23	Bishop Auckland	27	71	44	27	61.97	46	last 8 x 3
22	22	24	Barrow	29	63	35	28	55.56	46	Winners 1990
24	25	25	Merthyr Tydfil	32	71	39	32	54.93	45	last 8 - 1976
27	26	26	Worcester City	31	68	37	31	54.41	45	last 8 x 4
30	28	27	Marine	27	62	35	27	56.45	44	SF x 2
25	27	28	Bath City	32	73	41	32	56.16	44	last 8 - 1990
34	29	29	Sutton United	27	59	32	27	54.24	42	Finalist 1981
26	30	30	Slough Town	27	58	31	27	53.46	42	SF x 2
35	32	31	Dover Athletic	32	64	32	32	50.00	41	SF 1998
29	31	32	Witton Albion	32	82	50	32	60.98	40	Finalist 1992
32	33	33	Hyde United	32	81	49	32	60.49	40	SF x 3
38	39	34	Blyth Spartans	27	58	31	27	53.45	39	last 8 x 2
31	34	35	Nuneaton Borough	32	63	31	32	49.21	38	last 8 x 3
33	35	36	Barnet	22	52	30	22	57.69	37	Finalist 1972
39	36	37	Bedford Town	15	42	27	15	64.29	36	SF 1975
40	40	38	Matlock Town	32	78	47	31	60.26	36	Winners 1975
36	37	39	Chorley	32	69	37	32	53.62	36	SF 1996
37	38	40	Gateshead	31	64	33	31	51.56	36	last 8 x 3
41	41	41	Grantham	32	69	37	32	53.62	33	last 8 x 2
52	46	42	Southport	23	58	35	23	60.34	32	Finalist 1998
42	42	43	Welling United	19	40	21	19	52.50	32	last 8 - 1989
43	43	44	Chelmsford City	32	65	33	32	50.77	30	SF 1970
65	49	45	Kingstonian	27	67	42	25	62.69	29	Winners x 2
44	44	46	Maidstone United	17	43	26	17	60.47	29	last 8 x 2
45	45	47	Mossley	26	59	33	26	55.93	29	Finalist 1980
46	48	48	Dagenham & Redbridge	12	32	20	12	62.50	28	Finalist 1997
47	47	49	Wigan Athletic	9	27	18	9	66.67	27	Finalist 1973
48	50	50	Wealdstone	26	59	34	25	57.63	27	Winners 1985
53	51	51	Spennymoor United	27	53	26	27	49.06	26	SF 1978
59	60	52	Stevenage Borough	12	38	26	12	68.42	25	SF 1997
49	52	53	Hillingdon Borough	16	40	24	16	60.00	25	Finalist 1971
50	53	54	Aylesbury United	23	50	27	23	54.00	25	last 8 - 1981
56	56	55	Stalybridge Celtic	32	69	37	32	53.62	25	last 16 - 1992
51	54	56	Bishops Stortford	27	55	29	26	52.73	25	Winners 1981

F.A. CARLSBERG VASE

450 clubs

2000-2001 REVIEW

This season's FA Vase top scorer John Fowler of Croydon Athletic is presented with his award by FA Chief Executive Adam Crozier and Carlsberg's Jonathon Gibson. Photo: Darren Thomas

FIRST QUALIFYING ROUND

1	Dunston Fed Brewery	3	v	0	Denaby United	116
2	Willington	0	v	3	Hallam	84
3	Evenwood Town	2	v	5	Ramsbottom United	38
4	Squires Gate	5	v	0	Bacup Borough	60
5	Chadderton	1	v	3	Rossendale United	110
6	Guisborough Town	0	v	1	Prescot Cables	106
7	West Allotment Celtic	0	v	1	Northallerton Town	42
8	Thornaby-on-Tees	1	v	1	Blackpool Mechanics	25
R	Blackpool Mechanics	2	v	3	Thornaby-on-Tees	
9	Worsbro Bridge MW	2	v	1	Maltby Main	99
10	Darwen	3	v	2	Louth United	55
11	Morpeth Town	2	v	3*	Brandon United	51
12	Prudhoe Town	1	v	5	Glasshoughton Welf.	31
13	Hatfield Main	1	v	0	Harrogate Railway	56
14	Fleetwood Freeport	2	v	1	Washington I. H.	192
15	Bill'ham Synthonia	3	v	1	Peterlee Newtown	79
16	Borrowash Victoria	3	v	2	Marconi	57
17	Ludlow Town	3	v	1	Selston	61
18	St Andrews	1	v	0	Wolverhampton Cas.	28
19	Blackstone	5	v	4*	Highgate United	60
20	Cheslyn Hay	2	v	4	Shifnal Town	42
21	Highfield Rangers	1	v	1*	Studley BKL	34
R	Studley BKL	0	v	1	Highfield Rangers	41
22	Boldmere St M	4	v	0	Downes Sports	90
23	Staveley MW	3	v	1	Holwell Sports	97
24	Meir KA	2	v	0	Stafford Town	
25	Arnold Town	2	v	1*	Kirby Muxloe	152
26	Witham Town	2	v	4	Brackley Town	77
27	Swaffham Town	1	v	1*	Bedford United	66
R	Bedford United	3	v	2	Swaffham Town	75
28	Sawbridgeworth T	1	v	2	Haverhill Rovers	47
29	Hoddesdon Town	2	v	0*	Burnham Ramblers	70
30	AFC Wallingford	3	v	2	Ipswich Wanderers	125
31	Brentwood	1	v	2	Brache Sparta	46
32	Tiptree United	3	v	1	Royston Town	72
33	Long Buckby	1	v	6	Dereham Town	60
34	Warboys Town	3	v	0	Thetford Town	64
35	Hadleigh United	2	v	1	Southend Manor	100
36	St Margaretsbury	2	v	2*	Dunstable Town	60
R	Dunstable Town	4	v	1	St Margaretsbury	58
37	Bicester Town	1	v	0	Edgware Town	47
38	Potton United	2	v	3	Holmer Green	35
39	Harwich & Parkeston	4	v	0	Brook House	60
40	Southall	5	v	3	Chalfont St Peter	45
41	Downham Town	2	v	1	Harpenden Town	72
42	Langford	1	v	2*	Kempston Rovers	56
43	Ware	2	v	0	Leverstock Green	
44	N'mpton Spencer	3	v	3*	Haringey Borough	47
R	Haringey Borough	1	v	1*	N'mpton Spencer	44
	Haringey Borough won 3-2 after penalties					
45	Wellingborough Tn	1	v	0*	Desborough Town	48
46	Wokingham Town	1	v	0	Whitehawk	114
47	Wick	5	v	0	Lancing	105
48	Blackfield & Langley	1	v	1*	Whitstable Town	160
R	Whitstable Town	3	v	0	Blackfield & Langley	126
49	Southwick	3	v	2	Crowborough Ath	83
	Tie awarded to Crowborough, Southwick removed for fielding an ineligible player					
50	Camberley Town	0	v	3	Bracknell Town	106
51	Reading Town	3	v	2	Three Bridges	53
52	Horsham	4	v	0	Pagham	266
53	Hailsham Town	1	v	2*	Carterton Town	120
54	Portsmouth R N	0	v	1	Moneyfields	63
55	VCD Athletic	2	v	1*	Tunbridge Wells	55
56	Windsor & Eton	3	v	2	Ash United	98
57	Whitchurch United	1	v	0	Peacehaven & Tels	58
58	Gosport Borough	0	v	4	Ashford Tn (Middx)	102
59	Brockenhurst	3	v	1	Chatham Town	106
60	Brislington	3	v	2	Odd Down	70
61	Frome Town	1	v	0	Westbury United	172
62	Bemerton Hth Hqns	2	v	0	Almondsbury Town	71
63	Wellington Town	1	v	2	Hallen	
64	Fairford Town	1	v	3*	Keynsham Town	62
65	Devizes Town	1	v	2	Backwell United	101
66	Bridport	2	v	2*	Christchurch	136
R	Christchurch	2	v	5	Bridport	58

FIRST QUALIFYING ROUND STATISTICS

Home Victories 42
Away Victories 24
Replays 7

Best Attendance 266
Horsham v Pagham

Average Attendance 79

Best Home Victory
Squire Gate 5 v 0 Bacup Borough
Wick 5 v 0 Lancing

Best Away Victory
Long Buckby 1 v 6 Dereham Town

FA Vase First Qualifying Round

Witham Town's No 6 (yellow) stops another Brackley attack

Photo: Neil Thaler

Borrowash Victoria 3 Marconi 2 Vics forward Andy Beckford scores his side's second goal in a 3-2 thriller

Photo: Martin Wray

Lee Bradley fires home a dramatic injury time winner for Bedford United deep in injury time (after Swaffham had equalised 'shallow' in injury time!)

Photo: Gordon Whittington

SECOND QUALIFYING ROUND

1	Garforth Town	1 v 3	Jarrow Rfg Boldon CA	
2	Easington Colliery	1 v 0	Shotton Comrades	37
3	Maine Road	3 v 4	N'castle Benfield Snts	48
4	Hatfield Main	1 v 2	Atherton LR	42
5	Newcastle Blue Star	1 v 1*	Castleton Gabriels	88
R	Castleton Gabriels	1 v 1*	Newcastle Blue Star	86
	Castleton Gabriels won 4-2 after penalties			
6	Squires Gate	4 v 1	Tadcaster Albion	
7	Poulton Victoria	1 v 2	Cheadle Town	128
8	Northallerton Town	0 v 2	Holker Old Boys	40
9	Selby Town	2 v 0	Atherton Collieries	50
10	Woodley Sports	2 v 3	Dunston Fed Brewery	71
11	Hebburn	1 v 4	Glasshoughton Welf.	55
12	Bridlington Town	1 v 2	Goole	255
13	Durham City	1 v 2	West Auckland Tn	120
14	Brandon United	4 v 0	Horden CW	85
15	Sheffield	2 v 0	Pontefract Collieries	81
16	Kennek Ryhope CA	1 v 2	Hall Road Rangers	45
17	Curzon Ashton	4 v 1	Darwen	103
18	Ramsbottom United	4 v 3*	Thackley	178
19	Billingham Synthonia	3 v 0	Salford City	114
20	Rossington Main	0 v 2	Marske United	70
21	Rossendale United	1 v 0	Parkgate	130
22	Yorkshire Amateur	3 v 6	St Helens Town	35
23	Ashington	1 v 3	Billingham Town	109
24	Oldham Town	1 v 2*	Thornaby-on-Tees	45
25	Great Harwood Tn	3 v 2	Armthorpe Welfare	62
26	Chester-le-Street T	2 v 0	Hallam	64
27	South Shields	2 v 1	Penrith	83
28	Esh Winning	0 v 2	Prescot Cables	
29	Worsbro Bridge MW	1 v 3*	Fleetwood Freeport	101
30	Winterton Rangers	5 v 2	Shildon	60
31	Liversedge	4 v 2	Nelson	104
32	Brodsworth	0 v 4	Pickering Town	61
33	Abbey Hey	2 v 1	Whickham	110
34	Barwell	2 v 0	Staveley MW	108
35	Shirebrook Town	2 v 1	Pelsall Villa	105
36	Dudley Town	3 v 0	Rainworth MW	38
37	Buxton	3 v 2	Boston Town	161
38	Lye Town	2 v 0	Southam United	
39	Westfields	1 v 0	Sandwell Borough	41
40	Barrow Town	5 v 2	Blackstone	52
41	Bolehall Swifts	1 v 0	Anstey Nomads	42
42	Cradley Town	1 v 3	Pegasus Juniors	39
43	Handrahan Timbers	2 v 0	Dunkirk	64
44	Heath Hayes	3 v 0	Bourne Town	62
45	Arnold Town	1 v 0	Malvern Town	181
46	West Mids Police	1 v 6	Halesowen Harriers	70
47	Gornal Athletic	0 v 4	Bridgnorth Town	73
48	Causeway United	3 v 0	Meir KA	100
49	Boldmere St Michaels	1 v 0	Bloxwich Town	95
50	Nettleham	0 v 5	Kidsgrove Athletic	56
51	Highfield Rangers	7 v 0	Birstall United	42
52	Knypersley Victoria	0 v 4	Holbeach United	81
53	Stapenhill	1 v 1*	St Andrews	73
R	St Andrews	3 v 1*	Stapenhill	80
54	Long Eaton United	1 v 1*	Alvechurch	
R	Alvechurch	1 v 2*	Long Eaton United	40
55	Gedling Town	3 v 1	Ludlow Town	71
56	Shifnal Town	0 v 2	Ibstock Welfare	106
57	Tividale	4 v 4*	Kington Town	52
R	Kington Town	2 v 1*	Tividale	82
58	Stourport Swifts	8 v 1	Kings Heath	59
59	Wednesfield	0 v 4	Borrowash Victoria	53
60	Quorn	2 v 1	Kimberley Town	102
61	Leek CSOB	3 v 0	Friar Lane OB	91
62	Sutton Town	1 v 1*	Star	25
R	Star	0 v 3	Sutton Town	30
63	Rushall Olympic	9 v 0	Sandiacre Town	111
64	Glapwell	1 v 1*	Willenhall Town	67
R	Willenhall Town	2 v 1	Glapwell	57
65	Tring Town	1 v 4	Arlesey Town	65
66	Holmer Green	1 v 5	Somersett Am. V&E	48
67	Lowestoft Town	10 v 1	Leyton	208
68	Waltham Abbey	2 v 1	Hoddesdon Town	70
69	Cheshunt	3 v 2	Yaxley	35
70	Kempston Rovers	1 v 1*	Wootton Blue Cross	91
R	Wootton Blue Cross	4 v 3*	Kempston Rovers	200
71	Milton Keynes City	4 v 1	Kingsbury Town	69
72	Marlow	1 v 0	Clacton Town	152
73	Great Yarmouth Tn	1 v 0	Cockfosters	99
74	Beaconsfield SYCOB	0 v 2	Bicester Town	31
75	Haverhill Rovers	1 v 1*	Hornchurch	91
R	Hornchurch	2 v 0	Haverhill Rovers	57
76	Cornard United	0 v 7	Leighton Town	70
77	St Neots Town	1 v 1*	Flackwell Heath	84
R	Flackwell Heath	6 v 0	St Neots Town	62
78	Southall	1 v 2	AFC Wallingford	27
79	Clapton	2 v 4	Brache Sparta	20
80	Eynesbury Rovers	0 v 1	Haringey Borough	55
81	Dereham Town	0 v 1	Halstead Town	
82	Welwyn Garden City	2 v 0	Somersham Town	63
83	Harefield United	1 v 2	Stowmarket Town	62
84	Barking	3 v 0	Wingate & Finchley	99
85	March Town United	1 v 2	Concord Rangers	42
86	Stewarts & Lloyds	5 v 2	Ely City	25
87	Ilford	0 v 1	Aveley	87
88	Basildon United	v	Maldon Town	
	w/o for Maldon Town, Basildon Utd. withdrawn			
89	Saffron Walden Tn	5 v 2	East Ham United	99
	at Bishop's Stortford			

90	Tiptree United	3	v	0	Hadleigh United	83
91	Bedford United	3	v	2	Newmarket Town	80
92	Warboys Town	2	v	5	Potters Bar Town	66
93	Soham Town Rngrs	1	v	3	Gorleston	111
94	Needham Market	2	v	0	Brightlingsea United	72
95	Felixstowe/Walton U	1	v	2*	Wivenhoe Town	125
96	Buckingham Town	3	v	1	Stanway Rovers	92
97	Wellingborough Tn	0	v	1	Dunstable Town	45
98	Downham Town	7	v	1	Norwich United	83
99	Bury Town	2	v	3	Bowers United	121
100	Ruislip Manor	0	v	5	East Thurrock Utd	82
101	Ware	3	v	4	Chatteris Town	
102	Bugbrooke St M	1	v	2	Hullbridge Sports	56
103	Biggleswade Town	2	v	0	Hertford Town	51
104	Brackley Town	0	v	4	AFC Sudbury	113
105	Stansted	1	v	6*	Hanwell Town	40
	Hanwell Town removed for playing a suspended player - Stansted re-instated					
106	Whitton United	0	v	2	Mildenhall Town	56
107	Harwich & P'ston	2	v	1	Brimsdown Rovers	57
108	Dorking	2	v	3	Erith Town	101
109	Croydon Athletic	5	v	2	Ringmer	63
110	Godalming & G'ford	1	v	3	Herne Bay	77
111	Ashford Tn (Middx)	2	v	1	Beckenham Town	76
112	Hillingdon Borough	2	v	0	Chipstead	42
113	Crowborough Ath	0	v	2	Sheppey United	79
114	Merstham	0	v	1	Cobham	40
115	Horsham	3	v	1	Egham Town	199
116	North Leigh	0	v	2	BAT Sports	74
117	Viking Greenford	0	v	4	Wokingham Town	39
118	Eastleigh	4	v	1	Whitchurch United	60
119	Chessington Utd	0	v	0*	East Preston	58
R	East Preston	3	v	1*	Chessington United	83
120	Cray Wanderers	2	v	3	Sidley United	102
121	Windsor & Eton	0	v	1	Epsom & Ewell	98
122	Oakwood	0	v	2	Lordswood	31
123	Fareham Town	1	v	3	Eastbourne United	113
124	Cove	4	v	2*	VCD Athletic	
125	Whitstable Town	2	v	0	Shoreham	146
126	Abingdon Town	1	v	4	Molesey	69
127	Milton United	2	v	4	Greenwich Borough	40
128	Bracknell Town	1	v	2	Hythe United	
129	Walton Casuals	5	v	3	Selsey	69
130	Arundel	8	v	5*	Chess'ton & Hook U	60
131	Hungerford Town	0	v	2	Carterton Town	80
132	Eastbourne Town	5	v	1	Andover	
133	Corinthian Casuals	1	v	2	Wick	66
134	Sandhurst Town	0	v	4	Lewes	68
135	Didcot Town	3	v	0*	Reading Town	90
136	Moneyfields	1	v	2	Brockenhurst	78
137	Thatcham Town	1	v	2*	Redhill	95
138	Farnham Town	0	v	4	Hassocks	42
139	Chichester City U	2	v	0	Littlehampton Town	130
140	Abingdon United	1	v	0	Slade Green	95
141	Westfield	3	v	1	Wantage Town	51
142	Melksham Town	3	v	0	Keynsham Town	85
143	Shepton Mallet	0	v	2	Pershore Town	140
144	Bishop Sutton	0	v	6	St Blazey	114
145	Elmore	4	v	1*	Dawlish Town	105
146	Swindon S'marine	4	v	1	Ross Town	60
147	Bemerton H Hqns	0	v	2	Falmouth Town	125
148	Downton	2	v	5	Cirencester Academy	45
149	Harrow Hill	3	v	0	Barnstaple Town	60
150	Backwell United	0	v	1	Warminster Town	37
151	Willand Rovers	1	v	0	Welton Rovers	150
152	Bournemouth	1	v	1*	Calne Town	81
R	Calne Town	1	v	1*	Bournemouth	83
	Bournemouth won 6-5 after penalties					
153	Brislington	3	v	2*	Frome Town	62
154	Bridgwater Town	1	v	0	Bridport	202
155	Clevedon United	4	v	1	Bristol Manor Farm	349
156	Bideford	3	v	0	Cullompton Rangers	80
157	Chard Town	1	v	2	Street	49
158	Hallen	1	v	0	Shortwood United	56
159	Minehead Town	1	v	2	Torrington	60
160	Ilfracombe Town	0	v	3	Tuffley Rovers	85

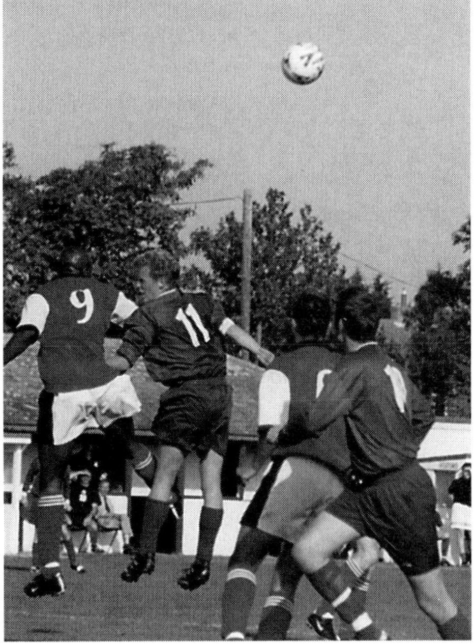

Whitstable's Ray Aboagye heads clear from Shoreham's Kane Anderson (11). Photo: Alan Coomes

SECOND QUALIFYING ROUND STATISTICS

Home Victories 83 **Away Victories** 77

Replays 11

Best Attendance

349 - Clevedon United v Bristol Manor Farm

Average Attendance 81

Best Home Victory

Rushall Olympic 9 v 0 Sandiacre Town

Lowestoft Town 10 v 1 Leyton

Best Away Victory

Cornard United 0-7 Leighton Town

Left: Action from National Park as home side Curzon Ashton in stripes won through 4-1 over N.W. Counties colleagues Darwen. Photo: Colin Stevens

Below: Richard Hughes, Eastbourne Town (left) tussles with Andrew Forbes, Andover. Photo: Roger Turner

FIRST ROUND

No.	Home		v		Away	Att.
1	Winterton Rangers	2	v	3*	St Helens Town	65
2	Castleton Gabriels	0	v	1	Tow Law Town	152
3	Dunston FB	2	v	1	Liversedge	112
4	Glasshoughton Welf.	1	v	0*	Goole AFC	220
5	Seaham Red Star	5	v	3*	Hall Road Rangers	65
6	Ramsbottom United	1	v	3	Easington Colliery	210
7	South Shields	1	v	2	Jarrow Rfng Bldn CA	135
8	Squires Gate	4	v	0	Flixton	60
9	Thornaby	0	v	3*	Whitley Bay	90
10	Abbey Hey	0	v	4	Warrington Town	86
11	Marske United	6	v	1	Atherton LR	164
12	Billingham Synthonia	0	v	3	West Auckland Tn	103
13	Fleetwood Freeport	2	v	0	Cheadle Town	132
14	Great Harwood Tn	1	v	1*	Brigg Town	84
R	Brigg Town	3	v	2	Great Harwood Tn	150
15	Selby Town	0	v	0*	Rossendale United	110
R	Rossendale United	2	v	0	Selby Town	82
16	Chester-Le-Street T	0	v	1	Pickering Town	64
17	Prescot Cables	3	v	2	Brandon United	120
18	Clitheroe	2	v	0	Holker Old Boys	169
19	N'castle Benfield Sts	3	v	2	Sheffield	85
20	Curzon Ashton	2	v	3*	Billingham Town	102
21	Holbeach United	4	v	2	Bolehall Swifts	122
22	St Andrews	0	v	3	Rushall Olympic	73
23	Kidsgrove Athletic	1	v	2	Shirebrook Town	127
24	Ibstock Welfare	3	v	4	Bridgnorth Town	120
25	Handrahan Timbers	1	v	0	Westfields	63
26	Stratford Town	0	v	0*	Stourbridge	152
R	Stourbridge	0	v	2	Stratford Town	82
27	Sutton Town	0	v	3	Arnold Town	73
28	Pegasus Juniors	2	v	1	Dudley Town	51
29	Kington Town	0	v	1	Boldmere St Michaels	72
30	Willenhall Town	0	v	2	Borrowash Victoria	87
31	Quorn	0	v	2	Gedling Town	159
32	Heath Hayes	3	v	3*	Barrow Town	102
R	Barrow Town	3	v	2*	Heath Hayes	100
33	Halesowen Harriers	0	v	3	Oadby Town	115
34	Nantwich Town	2	v	0	Long Eaton United	61
35	Oldbury United	1	v	2	Stourport Swifts	83
36	Highfield Rangers	4	v	3*	Lye Town	37
37	Leek CSOB	1	v	1*	Causeway United	90
R	Causeway United	1	v	2	Leek CSOB	100
38	Barwell	1	v	0	Buxton	148
39	Stotfold	5	v	1	Brache Sparta	45
40	Bowers United	4	v	2	Cogenhoe United	
41	Biggleswade Town	4	v	2*	Great Yarmouth Tn	62
42	Hornchurch	2	v	0	Bicester Town	
43	AFC Sudbury	5	v	2	Wootton Blue Cross	302
44	Maldon Town	2	v	1	Somersett Am. V&E	79
45	Chatteris Town	0	v	2	Diss Town	104
46	Stansted	1	v	3	Bedford United	90
47	East Thurrock Utd	3	v	0	Wivenhoe Town	122
48	Marlow	5	v	1	Flackwell Heath	222
49	Harwich & Parkeston	3	v	4	Dunstable Town	110
50	Mildenhall Town	3	v	2	Saffron Walden Tn	167
51	Lowestoft Town	2	v	1	Potters Bar Town	263
52	Stewarts & Lloyds	2	v	3	Welwyn Garden City	45
53	Barking	3	v	1	Concord Rangers	84
54	Fakenham Town	1	v	3	Aveley	147
55	Stowmarket Town	4	v	0	Haringey Borough	96
56	Ford Sports Dav.	1	v	0	Needham Market	85
57	Waltham Abbey	4	v	3	Raunds Town	84

(at Raunds Town)

Waltham Abbey removed for playing suspended player under another name

No.	Home		v		Away	Att.
58	Arlesey Town	4	v	0	Leyton Pennant	159
59	Hullbridge Sports	1	v	4	Wembley	70
60	Hemel Hempstead T	2	v	0	Wallingford	124
61	Leighton Town	7	v	2	Downham Town	93
62	Cheshunt	2	v	1	Tiptree United	57
63	Gorleston	5	v	1	Halstead Town	150
64	Milton Keynes City	2	v	1	Buckingham Town	87
65	Tooting & Mitcham U	5	v	2*	Bedfont	108
66	Hythe United	1	v	0	Eastbourne Town	86
67	Chichester City Utd	5	v	2	Eastbourne United	65
68	Redhill	1	v	3	Greenwich Borough	116
69	Sheppey United	0	v	3	Herne Bay	101
70	Croydon Athletic	4	v	1	BAT Sports	80
71	Fleet Town	1	v	2	Epsom & Ewell	96
72	Chertsey Town	2	v	2*	Banstead Athletic	128
R	Banstead Athletic	2	v	0	Chertsey Town	61
73	Cobham	0	v	1	Thamesmead Town	40
74	Abingdon United	1	v	0	East Preston	95
75	Erith Town	1	v	2	Whitstable Town	61
76	Arundel	2	v	3	Molesey	83
77	Ashford Tn (Middx)	1	v	0	Hillingdon Borough	85
78	Walton Casuals	2	v	2*	Cove	73
R	Cove	2	v	0	Walton Casuals	
79	Hassocks	2	v	2*	Horsham	306
R	Horsham	2	v	1*	Hassocks	241
80	Wokingham Town	3	v	2	Lordswood	61
81	Lewes	2	v	1	Wick	153
82	Westfield	1	v	0	Sidley United	78
83	Melksham Town	3	v	0	Eastleigh	89
84	Highworth Town	1	v	2	Brislington	109
85	Warminster Town	4	v	1*	Elmore	98
86	Carterton Town	2	v	0	Cirencester Academy	28
87	Brockenhurst	4	v	3*	Didcot Town	110
88	Clevedon United	3	v	1	Torrington	153
89	Hallen	4	v	1	Harrow Hill	48
90	Street	3	v	1	Pershore Town	113
91	Tuffley Rovers	0	v	2	Lymington & New M	60
92	Wimborne Town	2	v	0	AFC Newbury	153
93	Swindon S'marine	0	v	3	Yate Town	61
94	Falmouth Tn AFC	4	v	1	Willand Rovers	210
95	Bideford	1	v	3	Bridgwater Town	146
96	St Blazey	4	v	1	Bournemouth	181

FIRST ROUND STATISTICS

Home Victories 61
Away Victories 35
Replays 8

Best Attendance 306
Hassocks v Horsham
Average Attendance 110

Best Home Victory
Marske United 6 v 1 Atherton L R
Leighton Town 7 v 2 Downham Town
Best Away Victory
Abbey Hey 0 v 4 Warrington Town

Raunds Town defend with Richard Bunting, Fazel Koriya, James Mariner, Jamie Kearns and Steve Salisman. Partly hidden, Waltham Abbey goal ace Ricky Burbridge.

Photo: Peter Barnes

Wimborne Tn 2 AFC Newbury 0

Magpies keeper Steve Staples makes an excellent reflex save to push the ball over the bar following an AFC Newbury attack in the first half.

Photo: Martin Wray

Benfield keeper David Hodgson tips the ball away from a Sheffield corner

Photo: Graham Brown

SECOND ROUND

	Home				Away	Att
1	Squires Gate	3	v	2	Glossop North End	65
2	Glasshoughton Welf.	0	v	2	Billingham Town	80
3	Ossett Albion	3	v	4	Bedlington Terriers	289
4	Crook Town	0	v	3	Rossendale Utd	126
5	Prescot Cables	5	p	2*	Seaham Red Star	100
6	Skelmersdale United	1	v	2*	St Helens Town	135
7	Mossley	2	v	3*	Consett	260
8	Easington Colliery	0	v	1	Clitheroe	73
9	Brigg Town	2	v	1	Jarrow Rfng Bldn CA	188
10	West Auckland Tn	1	v	4	Dunston Fed. Brewery	85
11	Warrington Town	0	v	3	Fleetwood Freeport	131
12	Eccleshill United	3	v	1	N'castle Benfield Sts	55
13	Tow Law Town	1	v	0	Whitley Bay	216
14	Marske United	2	v	1	Pickering Town	167
15	Barrow Town	1	v	2	Barwell	160
16	Shirebrook Town	0	v	1	Newcastle Town	210
17	Handrahan Timbers	2	v	3*	Bridgnorth Town	81
18	Holbeach United	1	v	2*	Heanor Town	86
19	Oadby Town	2	v	1	Boldmere St M	120
20	Highfield Rangers	1	v	3*	Rushall Olympic	66
21	Alfreton Town	3	v	4	Arnold Town	195
22	Stourport Swifts	3	v	2	Chasetown	56
23	Gedling Town	2	v	2*	Leek CSOB	81
R	Leek CSOB	0	v	1	Gedling Town	65
	(at Gedling Town FC - reversed tie)					
24	Pegasus Juniors	2	v	2*	Nantwich Town	75
R	Nantwich Town	4		2	Pegasus Juniors	56
25	Stratford Town	1	v	2	Mickleover Sports	127
26	Borrowash Victoria	4	v	1	Milton Keynes City	71
27	Biggleswade Town	4	v	2	Gorleston	89
28	Arlesey Town	2	v	0	Aveley	188
29	Hornchurch	1	v	0	Letchworth	80
30	Mildenhall Town	3	v	3*	Stowmarket Town	173
R	Stowmarket Town	0	v	1	Mildenhall Town	157
31	Woodbridge Town	2	v	2*	Barking	138
R	Barking	3	v	0	Woodbridge Town	114
32	Stotfold	3	v	2	Great Wakering Rvrs	85
33	Welwyn Garden C	1	v	3*	Dunstable Town	73
34	Raunds Town	3	v	2*	AFC Sudbury	168
35	Bowers Utd	3	v	0	Wroxham	74
36	Cheshunt	0	v	4	Maldon Town	77
37	Wembley	1	v	2	London Colney	75
38	Hemel Hempstead T	1	v	1	Tilbury	113
	abandoned after 90 mins - waterlogged pitch					
R	Tilbury	1	v	2*	Hemel Hempstead T	91
39	Ford Sports Dav'try	0	v	3	East Thurrock Utd	50
40	Leighton Town	2	v	5	Berkhamsted Town	62
41	Bedford United	0	v	1	Diss Town	95
42	Marlow	1	v	0	Lowestoft Town	181
43	Whitstable Town	0	v	1	Hythe United	140
44	Epsom & Ewell	2	v	1	Banstead Ath.	114
45	AFC Totton	4	v	0	Molesey	81
46	Cowes Sports	4	v	0	Horsham YMCA	75
47	Lewes	0	v	1	Westfield	97
48	Greenwich Borough	3	v	3*	Cove	36
R	Cove	2	v	1	Greenwich Borough	
49	Saltdean United	4	v	1	Chichester City Utd	66
50	Metropolitan Police	1	v	2	Croydon Athletic	102
51	Ramsgate	0	v	2	Ashford Tn (Middx)	133
52	Horsham	5	v	2	Herne Bay	189
53	Abingdon United	0	v	0*	Burgess Hill Town	111
	Burgess Hill Town	2	v	1	Abingdon United	149
54	Deal Town	0	v	2	Tooting & Mitcham U	232
55	Wokingham Town	0	v	4	Thamesmead Town	59
56	Lymington & New M	2	v	0	Bridgwater Town	106
57	Brockenhurst	3	v	2	Paulton Rovers	112
58	Clevedon United	0	v	2	Hallen	
59	Melksham Town	1	v	2	Porthleven	151
60	Warminster Town	1	v	3	Falmouth Town	135
61	Brislington	1	v	2	Wimborne Town	90
62	St Blazey	4	v	4*	Carterton Town	189
R	Carterton Town	3	v	1	St Blazey	78
63	Taunton Town	9	v	0	Street	431
64	Chippenham Town	2	v	0	Yate Town	481

SECOND ROUND STATISTICS

Home Victories 30

Away Victories 34

Replays 8

Best Attendance 481
Chippenham Town v Yate Town

Average Attendance 127

Best Home Victory
Taunton Town 9 v 0 Street

Best Away Victory
Cheshunt 0 v 4 Maldon Town
Wokingham Town 0 v 4 Thamesmead Town

Top: Desperate moments in the Shirebrook defence as Newcastle Town try and get in another strike on goal.
Photo: Martin Wray

Centre: Cove's Bruce Tydeman (yellow) fires through the Greenwich Borough wall to open the scoring in the FA Vase Second Round.
Photo: Alan Coomes

Bottom: Jamie Kearns (Raunds Town) and Terry Rayner (AFC Sudbury) tussle near the touchline in the second half at Nene Park.
Photo: Peter Barnes

THIRD ROUND

1	Fleetwood Freeport	2	v	3*	Clitheroe	327
2	Stourport Swifts	1	v	0*	Dunston Fed. Brewery	74
3	Prescot Cables	1	v	1*	Oadby Town	119
R	Oadby Town	3	v	1	Prescot Cables	204
4	Mickleover Sports	3	v	1	Newcastle Town	192
5	Borrowash Victoria	3	v	3	Eccleshill United	74
6	Billingham Town	2	v	1	Tow Law Town	86
7	Squires Gate	0	v	3	St Helens Town	121
8	Arnold Town	3	v	1	Gedling Town	271
9	Bridgnorth Town	0	v	3	Rushall Olympic	89
10	Rossendale United	2	v	3	Brigg Town	270
11	Consett	3	v	0	Heanor Town	126
12	Bedlington Terriers	0	v	0*	Nantwich Town	381
R	Nantwich Town	0	v	1	Bedlington Terriers	159
13	Barwell	1	v	2*	Marske United	143
14	Berkhamsted Town	2	v	0	Hythe United	98
15	Cove	6	v	1	London Colney	
16	Mildenhall Town	0	v	0*	Porthleven	270
R	Porthleven	2	v	1*	Mildenhall Town	200
17	Maldon Town	1	v	2	Hallen	100
18	Biggleswade Town	2	v	5	Brockenhurst	101
19	Thamesmead Town	2	v	1	Raunds Town	32
20	Ashford Tn (Middx)	2	v	0	Saltdean United	97
21	Westfield	3	v	0	Bowers United	77
22	Lymington & New M	3	v	4	Stotfold	185
23	Hemel Hempstead T	1	v	2	Croydon Athletic	117
24	Wimborne Town	3	v	2*	East Thurrock Utd	163

25	Diss Town	2	v	3*	Taunton Town	504
26	Barking	1	v	2	Chippenham Town	228
27	AFC Totton	3	v	1	Horsham	117
28	Epsom & Ewell	1	v	1*	Marlow	76
R	Marlow	2	v	1	Epsom & Ewell	87
29	Tooting & Mitcham U	1	p	0	Dunstable Town	155
30	Arlesey Town	4	v	1	Burgess Hill Town	243
31	Cowes Sports	0	v	1	Hornchurch	93
32	Falmouth Town	3	v	0	Carterton Town	200

THIRD ROUND STATISTICS

Home Victories 19

Away Victories 13

Replays 4

Best Attendance 504
Diss Town v Taunton Town

Average Attendance 164

Best Home Victory
Cove 6 v 1 London Colney

Best Away Victory
Squires Gate 0 v 3 St Helens Town
Bridgnorth Town 0 v 3 Rushall Olympic
Biggleswade Town 2 v 5 Brockenhurst

FA Carlsberg Vase Third Round: Berkhampstead Town v Hythe United 2-0

FOURTH ROUND

1	Hallen	2	v	1	Borrowash Victoria	124
2	Consett	0	v	1	St Helens Town	236
3	Stourport Swifts	5	v	2	Mickleover Sports	230
4	Arnold Town	0	v	3	Tooting & Mitcham U	627
5	Berkhamsted Town	1	v	1*	Hornchurch	288
R	Hornchurch	1	v	2	Berkhamsted Town	140
6	Ashford Tn (Middx)	0	v	1	Oadby Town	160
7	Brigg Town	3	v	2	Billingham Town	301
8	AFC Totton	0	v	2	Chippenham Town	511
9	Thamesmead Town	0	v	0	Rushall Olympic	155
	abandoned after 90 mins					
R	Rushall Olympic	1		0	Thamesmead Town	131
10	Marske United	2	v	1*	Porthleven	619
11	Wimborne Town	2	v	4*	Clitheroe	502
12	Marlow	1	v	0	Stotfold	288
13	Brockenhurst	1	v	4	Taunton Town	450
14	Cove	5	v	1	Croydon Athletic	
15	Arlesey Town	6	v	0	Westfield	336
16	Bedlington Terriers	4	v	1*	Falmouth Town	782

FOURTH ROUND STATISTICS

Home Victories 9

Away Victories 7

Replays 2

Best Attendance 782
Bedlington Terriers v Falmouth Town

Average Attendance 345

Best Home Victory
Arlesey Town 6 v 0 Westfield

Best Away Victory
Arnold Town 0 v 3 Tooting & Mitcham United
Brockenhurst 1 v 4 Taunton Town

FA Carlsberg Vase Fourth Round: Rushall Olympic v Thamesmead Town
Henry Wright of Rushall waits to pounce but Thamesmead's Dave King makes no mistake. Photo: Steve Ayre

First half action from Testwood Park as Chippenham forward Simon Charity lobs theball into the goal to open the scoring for his side in this FA Vase Fourth Round match against AFC Totton. Photo: Martin Wray

Falmouth keeper Steve Taylor makes one of many fine saves against Bedlington Terriers. Photo: Graham Brown

FIFTH ROUND

	Home				Away	Att
1	Marlow	0	v	1	Marske United	399
					Middleton 90	
2	Cove	2	v	3	Chippenham Town	500
	Mancey 2, Willes 16				*Tweddle 75, Woods 80, Rawlins 82*	
3	Clitheroe	3	v	1	Rushall Olympic	461
	Sculpher 18, Greenwood 76 Stewart 87 (p)				*Moseley 3*	
4	Taunton Town	2	v	1	Arlesey Town	1074
	Hawkings 8, Laight 90				*Kitson 48*	
5	Berkhamsted Town	3	v	1	St Helens Town	291
	Smith 3 (19, 33, 80)				*Bell 5*	
6	Oadby Town	2	v	4	Bedlington Terriers	652
	Tiday 62, 85				*Chapman 41, Milner 48, Moat 61, Graham 68*	
7	Tooting & Mitcham U	4	v	1	Stourport Swifts	362
	O'Brien 14 ***Webb 3 (16, 44, 73)***				*Booth 48*	
8	Brigg Town	6	v	5*	Hallen	260
	Buckley 32, C Stead 34 Carter 79, N Stead 90(p), 104 Stones 94				*Sweenilsy 20, Dale 25 Cook 39, Green 41 Pritchard 119*	

FIFTH ROUND STATISTICS

Home Victories 5

Away Victories 3

Best Attendance 1074
Taunton Town v Arlesey Town

Average Attendance 500

Best Home Victory
Tooting & Mitcham United 4 v 1 Stourport Swifts

Best Away Victory
Oadby Town 2 v 4 Bedlington Terriers

Hat Tricks
3 Smith (Berkhamsted Town)
3 Webb (Tooting & Mitcham United)

Shall we dance? Berkhamsted's Terry Nightingale and Ged Hennigan (St Helens) step out during their FA Carlsberg Vase Fifth Round clash.
Photo: Francis Short

Stewart Willes of Cove (hidden by far goal post) slots home his side's second goal inside the opening 20 minutes leaving Chippenham keeper Ian Jones stranded. Photo: Martin Wray

Marske United's Benn Thompson attempts to turn and shoot closely watched by Sam Shepherd and goalkeeper Lee Curroll of Marlow. Photo: Arthur Evans

SIXTH ROUND

Brigg Town	**1**	**v**	**2**	**Berkhamstead Town**
Lytollis 31		Att: 531		*OG (Carter), Lowe 71*
Chippenham Town	**0**	**v**	**2**	**Clitheroe**
		Att: 1755		*Spencer 33, Jones 47*
Marske United	**1**	**v**	**1***	**Bedlington Terriers**
Kasonali 11		Att: 1359		*Cockburn 90*
Bedlington Terriers	**1**	**v**	**4**	**Marske United**
Taunton Town	**3**	**v**	**0**	**Tooting & Mitcham United**
Lynch 6, 69, Laight 89		Att: 1270		

Chippenham's Matt Rawlins prepares to swing a cross over against Clitheroe. Photo: Steve Ayre

Rob Gawthorpe and fellow defenders see another Berkhamsted attempt go narrowly wide in the visitors' 2-1 victory at Brigg in the Quarter Finals of the FA Vase. Photo: Arthur Evans

SEMI-FINALS

1st LEG

Taunton Town 5 v 0 **Clitheroe**

Fields 10, Kelly 18, 24, Bastow 29, Lynch 41 Att: 1563

Taunton Town: Draper, Down, Chapman, West, Hawkings, Kelly, Fields, Laight, Cann, Bastow, Lynch. Subs: Parker, Hapgood, Tallon, Groves, Ayres.
Clitheroe: Richens, Gardner, Hart, Stewart, Sculpher, Reynolds, Aspinwell, Cowking, Cryer, Spencer, Jones. Subs: Greenwood, Jackson, Whittingham, Anderton, Senior.

2nd LEG

Clitheroe 4 v 3 **Taunton Town**

Spencer 2, Stewart 14, Aspinall 19, 50 Att: 652 West 40, Fields 45, Parker 84

Clitheroe: Richens, Gardner, Hart, Stewart, Sculpher, Reynolds, Aspinwall, Greenwood, Cryer, Spencer, Cowking. Subs: Anderton, Whittingham, Jackson, Jones, Senior.
Taunton Town: Draper, Down, Chapman, West, Hawkings, Kelly, Fields, Laight, Cann, Bastow, Parker. Subs: Hapgood, Groves, Tallon, Abrams, Ayres.

Derek Fields, Taunton Town, glances towards goal in the First Leg of the Vase Semi Final against Clitheroe at Wordsworth Drive.

SEMI-FINALS

1st LEG

Bedlington Terriers	0 v 3	Berkhamsted Town
	Att: 1032	Lowe 23 (p), 87, Richardson 35

Bedlington Terriers: Sams, Harmison, Hildreth, Rowe, Melrose, Teasdale, Cross, Chapman, Moat, Milner, Cockburn. Subs: Hogg, Gibb, Graham, Boon, Bond.
Berkhamsted Town: O'Connor, Mullins, Lowe, Aldridge, Coleman, Brockett, Yates, Adebowale, Richardson, Smith, Nightingale. Subs: Franklin, Knight, Rinshell, Heron, Hall.

2nd LEG

Berkhamsted Town	2 v 1	Bedlington Terriers
Smith 12, Richardson 37	Att: 1542	Milner 39

Berkhamsted Town: O'Connor, Mullins, Lowe, Aldridge, Coleman, Brockett, Yates, Adebowale, Richardson, Smith, Nightingale. Subs: Hall, Knight, Ringsell, Heron, Franklin.
Bedlington Terriers: Sams, Harmison, Hildreth, Rowe, Melrose, Teasdale, Cross, Chapman, Moat, Milner, Cockburn. Subs: Hogg, Gibb, Graham, Bond, Boon

Paul Aldridge (Berkhamsted Town) and John Milner (Bedlington Terriers). Photo: Eric Marsh

Darren Coleman (Berkhamsted Town) and Willie Moat (Bedlington Terriers). Photo: Eric Marsh

Ellis Laight (Taunton Town striker) pictured against Clitheroe in the First Leg of the Vase Semi-Final at Taunton. Photo courtesy of the Somerset County Gazette

Sean O'Connor (Berkhamsted Town) and Dean Gibb (Bedlington Terriers) airborne in the second half
Photo: Eric Marsh

Top:
Berkhamsted's penalty.
Photo: Neil Thaler

Centre:
Taunton's Derek Fields rounds Sean O'Connor for goal number one.
Photo: Steve Ayre

Bottom:
Berkhamsted's John Richardson is close yet again but it was not his day.
Photo: Steve Ayre

FINAL

Taunton Town	2	v	1	**Berkhamsted Town**
Fields 41, Laight 45				*Lowe 71*

Att: 8,439
At Villa Park

Taunton Town: Ryan Draper, Ian Down, Alan Chapman, Paul West, Darren Hawkings, Tom Kelly, Derek Fields (sub Lee Groves 64 minutes), Ellis Laight (Man of the Match), Darren Cann (sub Darren Tallon 88 minutes), Ian Bastow, Antony Lynch (sub Leon Hapgood 86 minutes). Subs not used: Lee Ayres, Martin Parker

Berkhamsted Town: Sean O'Connor, Andy Mullins, Paul Lowe, Paul Aldridge, Darren Coleman, Luke Brockett, Neil Yates, Andy Adebowale, John Richardson, Ben Smith, Terry Nightingale. Subs not used: Craig Ringsell, Graham Hall, Mark Knight, Kevin Franklin, Mark Osborne.

Above left: Ryan Baker stops another Berkhamsted attack. Photo: Neil Thaler

Above right: Berkhamsted's Ben Smith battles with Taunton's defence. Photo: Neil Thaler

Bottom left: Ellis Laight shoots and scores Taunton's econd. Photo: Neil Thaler

F.A. CARLSBERG VASE FINAL

Taunton Town 2 v 1 Berkhamsted Town

Until a booking in the 22nd minute there was nothing to record in the Taunton column of match jottings, unless you wished to comment on their incredible fortune in keeping a clean sheet. Berkhamsted were completely dominant and not just through physical strength but with some praiseworthy passing and interplay. An amazing opening saw Ben Smith miss a half chance, an Andy Mullins shot smack against the post, Ryan Draper force Smith wide when through on goal and then save a volley from the same player. Amazingly, this was all in the first eight minutes!

Racing through on the edge of the area John Richardson appeared to be dragged down by Darren Hawkings but Mr Wolstenholme judged otherwise. Despite Taunton fans often voicing an opposing view, the official contributed appropriately to the flow of the game by dealing with indiscretions in a quiet manner, as the game proceeded. That is until that booking for Paul West, the Taunton skipper.

Taunton suddenly burst into life. Ellis Laight took the ball to the Holte End for the first time and nearly scored. Then, in the 30th minute a beautifully worked move saw Laight flick on for Derek Fields to close in on Sean O'Connor. The keeper blocked the first attempt but Fields was able to tap home the return. The Peacocks were on their way to a first victory in 18 finals, including their previous Vase Final appearance.

Richardson then hit Draper with a shot and his header shortly after was held by Draper, but Taunton were no longer overwhelmed. Laight's persistence made a second chance for Fields, whose shot was gathered by O'Connor, before, on the stroke of half time, Laight, playing in a stadium where he had supported his home city's Villa, took advantage of a slip by Darren Coleman to race on and shoot past O'Connor. That, to many, was game set and match.

However, after the break the Ryman side attempted a brave revival. Despite three weeks of constant games - one every 36 hours on average - which had left several players only just climbing off the treatment table, they still caused some Somerset flutters. West had to head over his own bar. Draper dropped a Richardson cross but Terry Nightingale could only drag it wide of the post. Man of the match Laight then hit the cross bar from 25 yards as the entertainment continued.

Twice Draper's fingertips just did sufficient to make Richardson and Nightingale head over. Smith, a shadow of his usual sharp self, made a shooting chance for Richardson which Draper was able to fall on. At O'Connor's end, Antony Lynch, another player not fully fit, forced a corner from which a goal line clearance was necessary. Then came a lifeline for Berko. Paul West handled an Aldridge shot in the area. Skipper Paul Lowe coolly placed the ball well wide of Draper's left hand to set up a tense last 15 minutes.

Taunton were not to be denied. Although Draper had to race out to beat Richardson to a long ball and Mullins hit a post not knowing he was offside, Taunton kept the Hertfordshire defence busy. Laight chipped just over the angle, he and Hapgood needed thwarting by O'Connor and Hapgood was only just stopped in the act of shooting by Aldridge's plunge. All too soon for Berkhamsted the final whistle sounded, although both teams can take credit for 90 pulsating minutes.

Graciously, Taunton manager Russell Musker declared that the better side had lost. On scoring opportunities, Berkhamsted were on top. But we all know the cliché 'it's goals that count' is proved true by the record books.

Arthur Evans

Berkhamsted Town: Sean O'Connor, Andy Mullins, Paul Lowe (scored 71mins), Paul Aldridge, Darren Coleman, Luke Brockett, Neil Yates, Andy Adebowale, John Richardson, Ben Smith, Terry Nightingale
Subs not used: Craig Ringsell (g/k), Graham Hall, Mark Knight, Kevin Franklin and Mark Osborne

Taunton Town: Ryan Draper, Ian Down, Alan Chapman, Paul West, Darren Hawkings, Tom Kelly. Derek Fields (scored 41 mins, subbed Lee Groves 64 mins), Ellis Laight (scored 45mins, MoM), Darren Cann (sub Darren Tallon 88 mins), Ian Bastow, Antony Lynch (sub Leon Hapgood 86 mins)
Subs not used: Lee Ayres (g/k) and Martin Parker

Referee: Mr E K Wolstenholme (Lancashire FA) assisted by Mr G Salisbury (Lancashire FA) and Mr B D Baker (Hampshire FA)

Top:
Taunton Town, FA Carlsberg Vase Winners.
Photo: Neil Thaler

Centre:
Ellis Laight, Russel Musher and Derek Fields, Taunton Town goalscorers and manager.
Photo: Neil Thaler

Bottom:
Tom Kelly and Russell Musker celebrate Taunton Town's FA Vase win.
Photo: Colin Stevens

FA CARLSBERG VASE AT A GLANCE

THIRD ROUND

Diss Town 2
Taunton Town 3

Biggleswade Town 2
Brockenhurst 5

Arlesey Town 4
Burgess Hill Town 1

Westfield 3
Bowers United 0

Arnold Town 3
Gedling Town 1

Tooting & Mitcham 1
Dunstable Town 0

Stourport Swifts 1
Dunston Fed Brew. 0

Mickleover Sports 3
Newcastle Town 1

Cove 6
London Colney 1

Hemel Hempstead 1
Croydon Athletic 2

AFC Totton 3
Horsham 1

Barking 1
Chippenham Town 2

Wimborne Town 3
East Thurrock Utd 2

Fleetwood Freeport 2
Clitheroe 3

Thamesmead Town 2
Raunds Town 1

Bridgnorth Town 0
Rushall Olympic 3

Ashford Town (Mx) 2
Saltdean Utd 0

Prescot Cables 1, 1
Oadby Town 1, 3

Bedlington Terr. 0, 1
Nantwich Town 0, 0

Falmouth Town 3
Carterton Town 0

Epsom & Ewell 1, 1
Marlow 1, 2

Lymington & NM 3
Stotfold 4

Barwell 1
Marske United 2

Mildenhall Town 0, 1
Porthleven 0, 2

Rossendale Utd 2
Brigg Town 3

Billingham Town 2
Tow Law Town 1

Maldon Town 1
Hallen 2

Borrowash Victoria 3
Eccleshill Utd 3

Consett 3
Heanor Town 0

Squires Gate 0
St Helens Town 3

Cowes Sports 0
Hornchurch 1

Berkhamsted Town 2
Hythe United 0

FOURTH ROUND

Brockenhurst 1
Taunton Town 4

Arlesey Town 6
Westfield 0

Arnold Town 0
Tooting & Mitcham 3

Stourport Swifts 5
Mickleover Sports 2

Cove 5
Croydon Athletic 1

AFC Totton 0
Chippenham Town 2

Wimborne Town 2
Clitheroe 4

Thamesmead T 0, 0
Rushall Olympic 0, 1

Ashford Town (Mx) 0
Oadby Town 1

Bedlington Terriers 4
Falmouth Town 1

Marlow 1
Stotfold 0

Marske United 2
Porthleven 1

Brigg Town 3
Billingham Town 2

Hallen 2
Borrowash Victoria 1

Consett 0
St Helens Town 1

Berkhamsted T 1, 2
Hornchurch 1, 1

FIFTH ROUND

Taunton Town 2
Arlesey Town 1

Tooting & Mitcham 4
Stourport Swifts 1

Cove 2
Chippenham Town 3

Clitheroe 3
Rushall Olympic 1

Oadby Town 2
Bedlington Terriers 4

Marlow 0
Marske United 1

Brigg Town 6
Hallen 5

Berkhamsted T 3
St Helens Town 1

SIXTH ROUND

Taunton Town 3
Tooting & Mitcham 0

Chippenham Town 0
Clitheroe 2

Bedlington Terriers 1 1
Marske United 1 4

Brigg Town 1
Berkhamsted T 2

SEMI FINALS

Taunton Town 5, 3
Clitheroe 0, 4

Bedlington Terriers 0, 1
Berkhamsted Town 3, 2

FINAL

Taunton Town 2
Berkhamsted Town 1

TOP GOALSCORING CLUBS

Taunton Town	31
Cove	26
Arlesey Town	21
Berkhamsted Town	21
Rushall Olympic	20
Stourport Swifts	20
Bedlington Terriers	19
Brigg Town	19
Clitheroe	19
Brockenhurst	18
Hallen	18
Horsham	17
Borrowash Victoria	16
Leighton Town	16
Marske United	16
Squires Gate	16
St Helens Town	16
St Blazey	15
Tooting & Mitcham Utd	15
Croydon Athletic	14
Dunstable Town	14
Arnold Town	13
Carterton Town	13
East Thurrock Utd	13
Prescot Cables	13
Barking	12
Barrow Town	12
Biggleswade Town	12
Billingham Town	12
Dunston Fed Brewery	12
Falmouth Town	12
Fleetwood Freeport	12
Lowestoft Town	12
Oadby Town	12
Stotfold	12
AFC Sudbury	11
Ashford Town (Middx)	11
Downham Town	11
Greenwich Borough	11
Marlow	11
Rossendale United	11
Arundel	10
Bedford United	10
Bowers United	10
Glasshoughton Welfare	10
Gorleston	10
Mildenhall Town	10
Ramsbottom United	10

TOP GOALSCORERS

J Fowler	Croydon Athletic	10
I Mancey	Cove	9
N Webb	Tooting & Mitcham	9
I Dunn	Holbeach Utd	8
M Phillips	Stotfold	8
E Laight	Taunton Town	8
A Lynch	Taunton Town	8
D Kitson	Arlesey Town	7
P Rowntree	Billingham Town	7
P Stone	Brockenhurst	7
B Devereux	AFC Sudbury	6
G Briscoe	Borrowash Victoria	6
B Thompson	Brockenhurst	6
T Fearns	St Helens Town	6
L Booth	Stourport Swifts	6
T Simpson	Arnold Town	5
S Todd	Ashford Town (Mx)	5
B Smith	Berkhamsted Town	5
L Cooke	Cove	5
A Fletcher	Dunston Fed Brewery	5
D Band	Falmouth Town	5
D Brierley	Heath Hayes	5
S Flain	Horsham	5
J Pritchard	Marlow	5
R Walker	Oadby Town	5
C Sargeson	Rossendale United	5
D Miles	Saffron Walden Town	5
S Longworth	Squires Gate	5
D Fields	Taunton Town	5
G Blake	Wokingham Town	5
T Fontenelle	Arlesey Town	4
J Milner	Bedlington Terriers	4
N Stead	Brigg Town	4
S Tweddle	Chippenham Town	4
L Cryer	Clitheroe	4
N Spencer	Clitheroe	4
A Cook	Hallen	4
D Dale	Hallen	4
S Kasonali	Marske United	4
M Ayres	Rushall Olympic	4
H Wright	Rushall Olympic	4

HAT-TRICK SCORERS

Bold indicates scored 4

B Devereux	AFC Sudbury	2Q
B Devereux	AFC Sudbury	1P
D Kitson	Arlesey Town	4P
S Todd	Ashford Town (Mx)	1Q
B Smith	Berkhamsted T	5P
C Henson	Borrowash Vic	2Q
D Osgood	Bracknell Town	1Q
P Stone	Brockenhurst	1P
S Taylor	Carterton Town	2P
J Laidlaw	Chichester City U	1P
D Godley	Cirencester Acad.	2Q
L Cooke	**Cove**	**3P**
I Mancey	Cove	4P
J Fowler	Croydon Athletic	2Q
J Fowler	Croydon Athletic	1P
K Dickerson	**Dereham Town**	**1Q**
S Frohawk	Downham Town	2Q
J Rose	Downham Town	2Q
N Woon	Elmore	2Q
B Wheeler	Falmouth Town	2P
J Charles	Flackwell Heath	2QR
G Ingram	Gorleston	2Q
A Jones	Halesowen Harr.	2Q
D Dale	Hallen	1P
K Rowlands	**Hanwell Town**	**2Q**
I Dunn	**Holbeach Utd**	**2Q**
I Dunn	Holbeach United	1P
S Flain	Horsham	2Q
G Geddes	Horsham	1Q
A Kinsey	Kidsgrove Athletic	2Q
C Morrisey	Leighton Town	2Q
P Thompson	Lowestoft Town	2Q
M Barkas	Newcastle Ben. S	2Q
D Miles	**Saffron Walden**	**2Q**
L Adamson	Seaham Red Star	1P
T Fearns	St Helens Town	2Q
M Phillips	Stotfold	1P
M Phillips	**Stotfold**	**3P**
S Marsh	Stourport Swifts	2Q
M Saye	Swindon S'marine	2Q
E Laight	Taunton Town	2P
N Webb	**Tooting & Mitch.**	**1P**
N Webb	Tooting & Mitcham	5P
R Burbridge	**Waltham Abbey**	**1P**
N Holden	Warrington Town	1P

PAST F.A. VASE FINALS

1975 HODDESDON TOWN 2 — EPSOM & EWELL 1 — Att: 9,500
Sedgwick 2 — Wales — Ref: Mr R Toseland
Hoddesdon: Galvin, Green, Hickey, Maybury, Stevenson, Wilson, Bishop, Picking, Sedgwick, Nathan, Schofield
Epsom & Ewell: Page, Bennett, Webb, Wales, Worby, Jones, O'Connell, Walker, Tuite, Eales, Lee

1976 BILLERICAY TOWN 1 — STAMFORD 0 (aet) — Att: 11,848
Aslett — Ref: Mr A Robinson
Billericay: Griffiths, Payne, Foreman, Pullin, Bone, Coughlan, Geddes, Aslett, Clayden, Scott, Smith
Stamford: Johnson, Kwiatowski, Marchant, Crawford, Downs, Hird, Barnes, Walpole, Smith, Russell, Broadbent

1977 BILLERICAY TOWN 1 — SHEFFIELD 1 (aet) — Att: 14,000
Clayden — Coughlan og — Ref: Mr J Worrall
Billericay: Griffiths, Payne, Bone, Coughlan, Pullin, Scott, Wakefield, Aslett, Clayden,Woodhouse, McQueen. Sub: Whettell
Sheffield: Wing, Gilbody, Lodge, Hardisty, Watts, Skelton, Kay, Travis, Pugh, Thornhill,Haynes. Sub: Strutt
Replay BILLERICAY TOWN 2 — SHEFFIELD 1 — Att: 3,482
Aslett, Woodhouse — Thornhill — at Nottingham Forest
Billericay: Griffiths, Payne, Pullin, Whettell, Bone, McQueen, Woodhouse, Aslett, Clayden, Scott, Wakefield
Sheffield: Wing, Gilbody, Lodge, Strutt, Watts, Skelton, Kay, Travis, Pugh, Thornhill, Haynes

1978 NEWCASTLE BLUE STAR 2 — BARTON ROVERS 1 — Att: 16,858
Dunn, Crumplin — Smith — Ref: Mr T Morris
Newcastle: Halbert, Feenan, Thompson, Davidson, S Dixon, Beynon, Storey, P Dixon, Crumplin, Callaghan, Dunn. Sub: Diamond
Barton Rovers: Blackwell, Stephens, Crossley, Evans, Harris, Dollimore, Dunn, Harnaman, Fossey, Turner, Smith. Sub: Cox

1979 BILLERICAY TOWN 4 — ALMONDSBURY GREENWAY 1 — Att: 17,500
Young 3, Clayden — Price — Ref: Mr C Steel
Billericay: Norris, Blackaller, Bingham, Whettell, Bone, Reeves, Pullin, Scott, Clayden,Young, Groom. Sub: Carrigan
Almondsbury: Hamilton, Bowers, Scarrett, Sulllivan, Tudor, Wookey, Bowers, Shehean, Kerr,Butt, Price. Sub: Kilbaine

1980 STAMFORD 2 — GUISBOROUGH TOWN 0 — Att: 11,500
Alexander, McGowan — Ref: Neil Midgeley
Stamford: Johnson, Kwiatkowski, Ladd, McGowan, Bliszczak I, Mackin, Broadhurst, Hall,Czarnecki, Potter, Alexander. Sub: Bliszczak S
Guisborough: Cutter, Scott, Thornton, Angus, Maltby, Percy, Skelton, Coleman, McElvaney,Sills, Dilworth. Sub: Harrison

1981 WHICKHAM 3 — WILLENHALL 2 (aet) — Att: 12,000
Scott, Williamson, Peck og — Smith, Stringer — Ref: Mr R Lewis
Whickham: Thompson, Scott, Knox, Williamson, Cook, Ward, Carroll, Diamond, Cawthra,Robertson, Turnbull. Sub: Alton
Willenhall: Newton, White, Darris, Woodall, Heath, Fox, Peck, Price, Matthews, Smith,Stringer. Sub: Trevor

1982 FOREST GREEN ROVERS 3 — RAINWORTH M.W 0 — Att: 12,500
Leitch 2, Norman — Ref: Mr K Walmsey
Forest Green: Moss, Norman, Day, Turner, Higgins, Jenkins, Guest, Burns, Millard, Leitch, Doughty. Sub: Dangerfield
Rainworth M.W: Watson, Hallam, Hodgson, Slater, Sterland, Oliver, Knowles, Raine, Radzi, Reah, Comerford. Sub: Robinson

1983 V.S. RUGBY 1 — HALESOWEN TOWN 0 — Att: 13,700
Crawley — Ref: Mr B Daniels
VS Rugby: Burton, McGinty, Harrison, Preston, Knox, Evans, ingram, Setchell, Owen,Beecham, Crawley. Sub: Haskins
Halesowen Town: Coldicott, Penn, Edmonds, Lacey, Randall, Shilvock, Hazelwood, Moss, Woodhouse,P Joinson, L Joinson. Sub: Smith

1984 STANSTED 3 — STAMFORD 2 — Att: 8,125
Holt, Gillard, Reading — Waddicore, Allen — Ref: Mr T Bune
Stanstead: Coe, Williams, Hilton, Simpson, Cooper, Reading, Callanan, Holt, Reevs,Doyle, Gillard. Sub: Williams
Stamford: Parslow, Smitheringate, Blades, McIlwain, Lyon, Mackin, Genovese, Waddicore,Allen, Robson, Beech. Sub: Chapman

1985 HALESOWEN TOWN 3 — FLEETWOOD TOWN 1 — Att: 16,715
L Joinson 2, Moss — Moran — Ref: Mr C Downey
Halesowen: Coldicott, Penn, Sherwood, Warner, Randle, Heath, Hazlewood, Moss (Smith),Woodhouse, P Joinson, L Joinson
Fleetwood Town: Dobson, Moran, Hadgraft, Strachan, Robinson, Milligan, Hall, Trainor, Taylor(Whitehouse), Cain, Kennerley

1986 HALESOWEN TOWN 3 — SOUTHALL 0 — Att: 18,340
Moss 2, L Joinson — Ref: Mr D Scott
Halesowen: Pemberton, Moore, Lacey, Randle (Rhodes), Sherwood, Heath, Penn, Woodhouse, PJoinson, L Joinson, Moss
Southall: Mackenzie, James, McGovern, Croad, Holland, Powell (Richmond), Pierre,Richardson, Sweales, Ferdinand, Rowe

1987 ST. HELENS 3 — WARRINGTON TOWN 2 — Att: 4,254
Layhe 2, Rigby — Reid, Cook — Ref: Mr T Mills
St Helens: Johnson, Benson, Lowe, Bendon, Wilson, McComb, Collins (Gledhill), O'Neill,Cummins, Lay, Rigby. Sub: Deakin
Warrington: O'Brien. Copeland, Hunter, Gratton, Whalley, Reid, Brownville (Woodyer), Cook,Kinsey, Looker (Hill), Hughes

1988 COLNE DYNAMOES 1 — EMLEY 0 — Att: 15,000
Anderson — Ref: Mr A Seville
Colne Dynamoes: Mason, McFafyen, Westwell, Bentley, Dunn, Roscoe, Rodaway, Whitehead (Burke),Diamond, Anderson, Wood (Coates)
Emley: Dennis, Fielding, Mellor, Codd, Hirst (Burrows), Gartland (Cook), Carmody,Green, Bramald, Devine, Francis

1989 TAMWORTH 1 — SUDBURY TOWN 1 aet — Att: 26,487
Devaney — Hubbick — Ref: Mr C Downey
Tamworth: Bedford, Lockett, Atkins, Cartwright, McCormack, Myers, Finn, Devaney, Moores,Gordon, Stanton. Subs: Rathbone, Heaton
Sudbury Town: Garnham, Henry, G Barker, Boyland, Thorpe, Klug, D Barker, Barton, Oldfield,Smith, Hubbick. Subs: Money, Hunt
REPLAY TAMWORTH 3 — SUDBURY TOWN 0 — Att: 11,201
Stanton 2, Moores — at Peterborough
Tamworth: Bedford, Lockett, Atkins, Cartwright, Finn, Myers, George, Devaney, Moores,Gordon, Stanton. Sub: Heaton
Sudbury Town: Garnham, Henry, G Barker, Boyland, Thorpe, Klug, D Barker, Barton, Oldfield,Smith, Hubbick. Subs: Money, Hunt

1990 YEADING 0 — BRIDLINGTON TOWN 0 aet — Att: 7,932
Ref: Mr R Groves
Yeading: Mackenzie, Wickens, Turner, Whiskey (McCarthy), Croad, Denton, Matthews, James(Charles), Sweates, Impey, Cordery
Bridlington: Taylor, Pugh, Freeman, McNeill, Warburton, Brentano, Wilkes (Hall), Noteman,Gauden, Whiteman, Brattan (Brown)

Replay YEADING 1 — BRIDLINGTON TOWN 0 — Att: 5,000
Sweales — at Leeds Utd FC
Yeading: Mackenzie, Wickens, Turner, Whiskey, Croad (McCarthy), Schwartz, Matthews,James, Sweates, Impey (Welsh), Cordery
Bridlington: Taylor, Pugh, Freeman, McNeill, Warburton, Brentano, Wilkes (Brown), Noteman,Gauden (Downing), Whiteman, Brattan

1991 GRESLEY ROVERS 4 — GUISELEY 4 aet — Att: 11,314
Rathbone, Smith 2, Stokes — Tennison 2, Walling, A Roberts — Ref: Mr C Trussell
Gresley: Aston, Barry, Elliott (Adcock), Denby, Land, Astley, Stokes, K Smith, Acklam,Rathbone, Lovell (Weston)
Guiseley: Maxted, Bottomley, Hogarth, Tetley, Morgan, McKenzie, Atkinson (Annan),Tennison, Walling, A Roberts, B Roberts

Replay GUISELEY 3 — GRESLEY ROVERS 1 — Att: 7,585
Tennison, Walling, Atkinson — Astley — at Bramall Lane
Guiseley: Maxted, Annan, Hogarth, Tetley, Morgan, McKenzie (Bottomley), Atkinson,Tennison (Noteman), Walling, A Roberts, B Roberts
Gresley: Aston, Barry, Elliott, Denby, Land, Astley, Stokes (Weston), K Smith, Acklam, Rathbone, Lovell (Adcock)

1992 WIMBORNE TOWN 5 — GUISELEY 3 — Att: 10,772
Richardson, Sturgess 2, Killick 2 — Noteman 2, Colville — Ref: Mr M J Bodenham
Wimborne: Leonard, Langdown, Wilkins, Beacham, Allan, Taplin, Ames, Richardson, Bridle,Killick, Sturgess (Lovell), Lynn
Guiseley: Maxted, Atkinson, Hogarth, Tetley (Wilson), Morgan, Brockie, A Roberts,Tennison, Noteman (Colville), Annan, W Roberts

1993 BRIDLINGTON TOWN 1 — TIVERTON TOWN 0 — Att: 9,061
Radford — Ref: Mr R A Hart
Bridlington: Taylor, Brentano, McKenzie, Harvey, Bottomley, Woodcock, Grocock, A Roberts, Jones, Radford (Tyrell), Parkinson. Sub: Swailes
Tiverton Town: Nott, J Smith, N Saunders, M Saunders, Short (Scott), Steele, Annunziata, KSmith, Everett, Daly, Hynds (Rogers)

1994 DISS TOWN 2 — TAUNTON TOWN 1 — Att: 13,450
Gibbs (p), Mendham — Fowler — Ref: Mr K. Morton
Diss Town: Woodcock, Carter, Wolsey (Musgrave), Casey (Bugg), Hartle, Smith, Barth, Mendham, Miles, Warne, Gibbs
Taunton Town: Maloy, Morris, Walsh, Ewens, Graddon, Palfrey, West (Hendry), Fowler, Durham, Perrett (Ward), Jarvis

1995 ARLESEY TOWN 2 — OXFORD CITY 1 — Att: 13,670
Palma, Gyalog — S Fontaine — Ref: Mr G S Willard
Arlesey: Young, Cardines, Bambrick, Palma (Ward), Hull, Gonsalves, Gyalog, Cox, Kane,O'Keefe, Marshall (Nicholls). Sub: Dodwell
Oxford: Fleet, Brown (Fisher), Hume, Shepherd, Muttock, Hamilton (Kemp), Thomas, Spittle, Sherwood, S Fontaine, C Fontaine. Sub: Torres

1996 BRIGG TOWN 3 — CLITHEROE 0 — Att: 7,340
Stead 2, Roach — Ref: Mr S J Lodge
Brigg: Gawthorpe, Thompson, Rogers, Greaves (Clay), Buckley (Mail), Elston, C Stead, McLean, N Stead (McNally), Flounders, Roach
Clitheroe: Nash, Lampkin, Rowbotham (Otley), Baron, Westwell, Rovine, Butcher, Taylor (Smith), Grimshaw, Darbyshire, Hill (Dunn)

1997 NORTH FERRIBY UTD. 0 — WHITBY TOWN 3 — Att: 11,098
Williams, Logan, Toman — Ref: Graham Poll
North Ferriby: Sharp, Deacey, Smith, Brentano, Walmsley, M Smith, Harrison (Horne), Phillips (Milner), France (Newman), Flounders, Tennison
Whitby Town: Campbell, Williams, Logan, Goodchild, Pearson, Cook, Goodrick (Borthwick), Hodgson, Robinson, Toman (Pyle), Pitman (Hall)

1998 TIVERTON TOWN 1 — TOW LAW TOWN 0 — Att: 13,139
Varley — Ref: M A Riley
Tiverton: Edwards, Felton, Saunders, Tatterton, Smith J, Conning, Nancekivell (Rogers), Smith K (Varley), Everett, Daly, Leonard (Waters)
Tow Law: Dawson, Pickering, Darwent, Bailey, Hague, Moan, Johnson, Nelson, Suddick, Laidler (Bennett), Robinson.

1999 BEDLINGTON TERRIERS 0 — TIVERTON TOWN 1 — Att: 13, 878
Rogers 88 — Ref: W. C. Burns
Bedlington Terriers: O'Connor, Bowes, Pike, Boon (Renforth), Melrose, Teasdale, Cross, Middleton (Ludlow), Gibb, Milner, Bond. Subs: Pearson, Cameron, Gowans
Tiverton Town: Edwards, Fallon, Saunders, Tatterton, Tallon, Conning (Rogers), Nancekivell (Pears), Varley, Everett, Daly, Leonard. Subs: Tucker, Hynds, Grimshaw

2000 TAUNTON TOWN 2 — BERKHAMPSTED TOWN 1 — (at Villa Park) Att: 8,439
Fields 41, Laight 45 — Lowe 71 — Ref: E. K. Wolstenholme
Taunton Town: Draper, Down, Chapman, West, Hawkings, Kelly, Fields (Groves), Laight, Cann (Tallon), Bastow, Lynch (Hapgood). Subs: Ayres, Parker
Berkhampsted Town: O'Connor, Mullins, Lowe, Aldridge, Coleman, Brockett, Yates, Adebowale, Richardson, Smith, Nightingale. Subs: Ringsell, Hall, Knight, Franklin, Osborne

All Finals at Wembley unless otherwise shown

F.A. CARLSBERG VASE CLUB RECORDS

The table is a record of the performance of the top 50 teams that have played in the Vase since its inception in 1975, a period of 26 years. During that time we have seen many teams enjoying successful periods in the competition and this is an attempt to reward teams for their consistency during the various rounds as well as whether they actually win the Vase or not. The various columns of the table represent the following:

1	2000	the position of the team in the table at the end of the 2000 season.
2	2001	the position of the team in the table at the end of the 2001 season.
3.	S	the number of seasons that the team has played in the competition
4.	P	number of rounds the team has played in, ie, if a team had to replay it is counted as one match
5.	W	the number of matches the team has won in the Vase
6.	L	number of matches the team lost, usually one per season unless the team won the Competition
7.	%	the percentage success rate of the team calculated by dividing wins by matches played x 100
8.	Pts	points are calculated as follows: 1st Rnd - 1 point, 2nd Rnd - 2 points, 3rd Rnd - 3 points, 4th Rnd - 4 points, 5th Rnd - 5 points, 6th Rnd - 6 points, Semis - 7 points, Final - 8 points, Winner - 9 points.
9.	Best	best performance in the competition by that team and the year. 'x' a number means that they reached that stage more than once, ie, 3rd x 3 means they reached the Third Round 3 times

Although I have tried my best to ensure that the information is as accurate as possible it is inevitable that an error or two (or three!) will be present. I would be very grateful if anyone who spots a mistake would contact me via the Team Talk address so that I can correct the table.

John Anderson

Positions									
2000	*2001*		*S*	*P*	*W*	*L*	*%*	*Pts*	*Best*
1	1	Hungerford Town	27	79	52	27	65.82	78	SF x 3
2	2	Stamford	24	69	46	23	66.67	73	W 1980
3	3	Buckingham Town	23	59	36	23	61.02	67	6th x 2
6	4	North Ferriby United	26	75	49	26	65.33	66	F 97
4	5	Guiseley	17	63	47	16	74.60	64	W 1991
5	6	Barton Rovers	20	63	43	20	68.25	64	F 1978
14	7	Brigg Town	27	71	45	26	63.38	64	W 1996
7	8	Burnham	17	47	30	17	63.83	60	SF 1983
8	9	Tiverton Town	18	65	49	16	75.38	59	W x 2
9	10	Irthingborough Diamonds	15	53	38	15	71.70	58	SF x 2
10	11	Hinckley Athletic	23	60	37	23	61.67	58	5th x 2
11	12	Newcastle Blue Star	17	51	35	16	68.63	57	W 1978
12	13	Whickham	21	58	38	20	65.52	57	W 1981
25	14	Clitheroe	25	64	39	25	60.94	57	F 1996
18	15	Warrington Town	21	59	38	21	64.41	56	F 1987
21	16	Banstead Athletic	27	65	38	27	58.46	55	SF 1997
53	17	Taunton Town	9	47	39	8	82.98	54	W 2001
13	18	Wisbech Town	16	48	32	16	66.67	54	SF x 2
15	19	Sudbury Town	11	46	35	11	76.09	53	F 1989
17	20	Friar Lane Old Boys	27	66	39	27	59.09	53	SF x 2
16	21	Billericay Town	9	44	38	6	86.36	52	W x 3
60	22	Chippenham Town	25	68	43	25	63.24	52	F 2000
29	23	Paulton Rovers	21	56	35	21	62.50	51	5th 1990
24	24	Bridgnorth Town	25	62	37	25	59.68	51	5th x 2
19	25	Lincoln United	21	50	29	21	58.00	51	6th 1975
22	26	Harefield United	26	56	30	26	53.57	51	6th 1990
20	27	Halesowen Town	12	45	35	10	77.78	50	W x 2
32	28	Diss Town	24	60	37	23	61.67	50	W 1994
30	29	Arlesey Town	27	63	37	26	58.73	50	W 1995
23	30	Hucknall Town	17	53	36	17	67.92	49	6th 1986
28	31	Molesey	17	49	32	17	65.31	49	6th 1982
45	32	Burgess Hill Town	24	61	37	24	60.66	48	5th 1998
76	33	Bedlington Terriers	15	55	40	15	72.73	47	F 1999
40	34	Wimborne Town	19	54	36	18	66.67	47	W 1992
25	35	Newport IOW	18	48	28	18	60.87	47	5th x 2
27	36	Gresley Rovers	19	53	34	19	64.15	46	F 1991
31	37	Eastleigh	26	68	42	26	61.76	46	4th x 3
36	38	Guisborough Town	15	39	24	15	61.54	45	F 1980
39	39	Windsor & Eton	16	50	34	16	68.00	44	SF 1981
65	40	Falmouth Town	15	45	30	15	66.67	44	6th 1987
47	41	Great Yarmouth Town	21	50	29	21	58.00	44	SF 1983
33	42	Almondsbury Town	25	59	34	25	57.63	44	F 1979
34	43	Tunbridge Wells	27	61	34	27	55.74	44	4th x 5
35	44	Newbury Town	20	45	25	20	55.56	44	6th 1994
38	45	Abingdon Town	20	43	23	20	53.49	44	5th x 3
63	46	Ossett Albion	25	50	25	25	50.00	44	4th x 3
41	47	Thackley	23	62	39	23	62.90	43	5th 1981
43	48	Sheffield	27	62	35	27	56.45	43	F 1977
37	49	Rainworth MW	22	49	27	22	55.10	43	F 1982
58	50	Cheshunt	21	58	37	21	63.79	42	6th 1982

ENGLAND SEMI-PROFESSIONAL REPRESENTATIVE FOOTBALL

REVIEW OF THE SEASON

The best news to come out of a very lively new look Football Association is that under the guidance of Steve Parkin, their new National League Manager, Greg Fee is negotiating with the four home countries to set up a four nations end of season tournament in which our England non-League international side can compete.

We have played the Welsh in 'friendly' internationals in recent seasons, and last February a tight 0-0 draw was fought out at Nene Park, Rushden.

The Southern Irish have sent a team over to England on a couple of occasions, and we have toured the republic twice. Our first trip in 1990 included names such as Paul Furlong, Paul Rogers, Phil Gridelet, David Howell, Mark Carter and Andy Pape who all went on to play in the Football League . This trip was special for me as I was asked by the F.A. to act as tour administration manager alongside Tony Jennings the head coach. We won both games and it was a very happy experience.

The second trip didn't bring such a good result as we lost 0-2 to a very good Irish side in Dublin in 1997.

The Scottish side may be the most difficult to enthuse about the tournament as they haven't a national team that naturally fits the title of a Non-League International squad.

Back Row: Steve Avory (Assistant Coach), Paul Beesley, Ken Charlery, Scott Guyett, Scott Cooksey, Stuart Drummond, Kevin McIntyre, Gary Patterson, Tim Ryan, Steve Feldman (Doctor), John Owens (Chief Coach)
Front Row: Warren Patmore, Carl Ruffer, Nick Roddis, Tarkan Mustafa, Geoff Pitcher, Wayne Brown and Steve Jones.
Photo: Andrew Chitty

Ken Charlery scores a simple tap in but it's not only his first for England but England's 100th goal at this level.
Photo: Andrew Chitty

Their `junior' football in Glasgow and Edinburgh is strong with a number of experienced ex-senior professionals and promising youngsters, while many of the Highland League's best clubs are moving into the Scottish League and the East of Scotland League is not considered as strong as the other areas.

However, it is hoped that the Scottish F.A. will grasp the nettle and set up the criteria for selection of a truly representative Scotland Semi-Professional International squad to take its place in what should be a very competitive and strong Four Nations Home International Tournament in May.

England could still play Holland and Italy, in mid season, as friendly games to enable John Owens to build his squad.

Last season's draw with Wales was followed by a comprehensive 3-0 victory in Holland. But John's squad will now be missing all the Rushden & Diamonds players, Tarkan Mustafa, Paul Underwood, Justin Jackson and Warren Patmore with ex-England skipper Gary Butterworth and Simon Wormull who won two caps in 1999-2000 also taken out of the reckoning.

Some discussions have taken place concerning an age limit for the England squad. This is to discourage older ex-Football Premier League players filling places that would be more beneficial for up and coming youngsters to gain experience.

I'm sure John Owens is well aware of this situation, and there will only occasionally be instances of senior players being capped, such as Peter Taylor and Ken Charlery. But an actual rule would take out the chances of caps for good honest part time professionals, with jobs that prevent them going full time, who have given wonderful service to the game and perhaps reach their peak in their late twenties or early thirties.

Last season's Internationals were fine for rewarding our best players, but as a spectacle they were both disappointing as they were treated as inconsequential friendlies by the media, the crowd and probably, if truth be known, even by the organising F.A. themselves.

So hopefully the negotiations of the 'new F.A.' will bear fruits and we will be able to report on an exciting new tournament in next year's Directory.

T.W.

ENGLAND SEMI-PROFESSIONAL GOALSCORERS 1979-2001

Carter	*13	Cordice	2	Charles	1	Roddis	1
Ashford	6	Hayles	2	Davies	1	Rogers	1
Davison	5	Hill	2	Furlong	1	Sellars	1
Williams, C	5	Howell	2	Hines	1	Smith, I	1
Culpin	4	Mutrie	2	Humphreys	1	Smith, O	1
Johnson	4	Patmore	2	Kimmins	1	Stephens	1
Adamson	3	Watson, J	2	Leworthy	1	Stott	1
Grayson	3	Whitbread	2	McDougald	1	Webb	1
OG	3	Agana	1	Mayes	1	Wilcox	1
Watkins	3	Bradshaw	1	O'Keefe	1	Taylor, S	1
Alford	2	Browne	1	Pitcher	1	Bolton	1
Barrett	2	Cavell	1	Robbins	1	Venables	1
Casey	2	Charlery	1	Robinson	1		

** in 11 + 1 sub appearances*

ENGLAND SEMI-PROFESSIONAL INTERNATIONAL MANAGERS 1979-2001

		P	*W*	*D*	*L*	*F*	*A*
1979	Howard Wilkinson	2	2	0	0	6	1
1980 - 1984	Keith Wright	17	9	5	3	30	16
1985 - 1988	Kevin Verity	12	7	2	3	23	15
1989 - 1996	Tony Jennings	19	10	4	5	27	18
1997	Ron Reid	2	0	1	1	0	2
1998 to date	John Owens	9	5	4	0	15	6
	Total Record	**61**	**33**	**16**	**12**	**101**	**58**

John Owens and 'The Doc' Steve Feldman look relaxed on the way to Nene Park for the Welsh International.
Photo: Peter Barnes

FA XI 4 v 0 UNIBOND LEAGUE

Brodie 2, Campbell, Arnold

(at Lancaster City)

FAXI SQUAD: Wayne Brown (Chester), Simon Marples (Doncaster), Kevin McIntyre (Doncaster), Scott Guyett (Southport), Paul Beesley (Chester), Tim Ryan (Doncaster Rovers), Paul Carden (Chester), Chris Blackburn (Chester), Neil Campbell (Doncaster), Steve Brodie (Scarborough), Steve Hawes (Altrincham). **SUBSTITUTES:** Barry Miller (Doncaster), Andy Woods (Scarborough), Matt Doughty (Chester), Steve Jones (Leigh RMI), Ian Arnold (Southport)

UNIBOND SQUAD: David McCarthy (Hucknall), Gary Scott (Altrincham), Michael Clandon (Burscough), Wayne Bullimore (Boston United), Kenny Mayers (Lancaster), Paul Davis (Emley), Nicky Peverill (Barrow), Chris Waddle (Worksop), Kirk Jackson (Worksop), Steve Howshan (Barrow), Stuart Locke (Stalybridge). **SUBSTITUTES:** Chris Clarke (Marine), Gary Williams (Accrington Stanley), Dave Gamble (Marine), Chris Ward (Lancaster), Robert Tonks (Emley).

FA XI 3 v 1 RYMAN LEAGUE

Charlery, Stevens, Burns — *Bolt (pen)*

(at Boreham Wood)

FAXI SQUAD: Paul Bostock (Boston Utd), Tarkan Mustafa (Rushden & Diamonds), Lee Flynn (Hayes), Colin Hoyle (Boston United), Steve West (Woking), Lee Matthews (Dagenham & Redbridge), Matt Fisher (Kettering Town), Rob Cousins (Forest Green Rovers) (Captain), Ken Charlery (Boston United), Dale Watkins (Kettering), Stuart Slater (Forest Green Rovers), Dave Stevens (Hayes), Chris Burns (Forest Green Rovers). Substitutes at half time: Dave Stevens (Hayes) for Dale Watkins, Chris Burns (Forest Green Rovers) for Rob Cousins.

RYMAN SQUAD: Richard Hurst, Mark Rooney (St Albans City), Mark Stimpson (Canvey Island), Paul Harford (Sutton United), Gary Waters (Heybridge Swifts), Richard Horner (Sutton United), John Keeling (Purfleet), James Bunn (Enfield), Joe Baker (Billericay Town), Steve Watson (Farnborough Town), Danny Bolt (Sutton United), Gary Wraight (St Albans City), Nicky Haydon (Heybridge Swifts), Gary Ansell, Dean Parrott, Ryan Moran (St Albans City).

FA XI 3 v 2 BRITISH UNIVERSITIES

Martindale, Davis, Barnard — *Brent, Sedgemore*

(at Burton Albion)

FAXI SQUAD: Chris McKenzie (Nuneaton Borough), (Ryan Young (Nuneaton Borough)), Mark Bailey (Nuneaton Borough), Mark Barnard (Northwich), Terry Angus (Nuneaton Borough), Gavin Smith (Worksop Town), Neil Moore (Telford United), (Mark Haran (Hednesford Town)), Ian Brunskill (Droylsden), (Shaun Wray (Nuneaton Borough)), Simeon Bambrook (Emley), Gary Martindale (Telford United), Neil Davis (Hednesford Town), (Delton Francis (Nuneaton Borough)), Steve Palmer Telford United (Steve Nicholson (Emley)).

UNIVERSITIES SQUAD: (Clubs where known) James Robinson (Hitchin Town), Simon Travis (Telford United), Stuart Langraish, Andy Hylton, Matt Daly, Andy Murfin (Kettering Town), Matt Hayfield (Woking), Nick Roddis (Woking), James Bent (Yeovil Town), Peter Smith (Marine), Steve Perkins (Woking), Dan Worthington, Andy Quy (Halesowen Town), Jake Sedgemore, Martin Sullivan (Dorchester Town), Max Rooke, Tom Rutter, Ryan Spencer (Hayes), Tim Harwood.

FA XI 6 v 1 COMBINED SERVICES

Roddis, Braithwaite, Perkins — *Wall*
Moore, Collins, Shearer (pen)

FAXI SQUAD: Paul Hyde (Dover Athletic), Tim Cole (Dagenham & Redbridge), Ashley Vickers (Dagenham & Redbridge), Nick Roddis (Woking), Lee Shearer (Dover Athletic), Steve Ward (Canvey Island), Jamie Pitman (Woking), Steve Perkins (Woking), Joff Vansittart (Dover Athletic), Neil Gregory (Canvey Island), Mark Bentley (Aldershot), Leon Braithwaite (Margate), Vince Matassa (Woking), Phil Collins (Margate), Barry Moore (Hayes). **SUBSTITUTES:** Barry Moore for Mark Bentley, Vince Matassa for Paul Hyde, Phil Collins for Joff Vansittart, Leon Braithewaite for Neil Gregory.

COMBINED SERVICES SQUAD: SSgt D May APTC (ASPT Aldershot), LCpl J Collins R Signals (21 Sig Regt (AS), Colerne, Sgt P Alford R Signals (6Bn REME) Tidworth, POPT S Riley RN (HMS Nelson) Portsmouth, Cpl B Kyall RAF (RAF Rudloe Manor) Wilts, Fg Offr A Pluckrose RAF (RAF Cosford) Wolverhampton, LPTP S O'Neil (HMS Glasgow), Sgt D Boughen R Signals (642 Sig TP) BFPO 52, Cfn C Wall REME (3(UK) Div Sig Regt) Bulford, Cpl G Seddon RAF (RAF Cosford) Wolverhampton, D Preston, Cpl M Preston RAF (RAF Odiham) Hook, Cpl S Cooper RAF (RAF Coltishall) Norfolk, WO1 A Higgins.

HIGHLAND LEAGUE 0 v 3 FAXI

Ryan, Pitcher, Jones

(at Clachnacuddin)

HIGHLAND SQUAD: Roe (Buckie Thistle), McDonald (Forres Mechanics), McBride (Fraserburgh), Anderson (Buckie Thistle), Milne (Fraserburgh), Still (Keith), Hart (Brora), Baxter (Cove), Dolan (Deveronvale), Brown (Forres Mechanics), Robertson (Keith).

SUBSTITUTES: Sanderson (Forres Mechanics) for Dolan 69, Cadger for Robertson 77, Coutts (Cove) for Brown 77, Sinclair (Nairn) for Hart 80.

FAXI SQUAD: Bastock (Boston), Moore (Telford), Goodliffe (Hayes), Ryan (Doncaster), Travis (Telford), Pitcher (Kingstonian), Drummond (Morecambe), Patterson (Kingstonian), Jones (Leigh RMI), Charlery (Boston), Brodie (Scarborough).

SUBSTITUTES: Brown (Chester) for Bastock 46, Roddis (Woking) for Brodie 54, McDougald (Dagenham & Redbridge) for Charlery 63.

TRAINING IN THE RAIN

Top: A defensive wall with two attackers blocking their view: Wayne Brown (it's not often a keeper is in the wall!), Paul Berkley, Junior McDougald, Ken Charlery and Mark Rafter with Warren Patmore and Geoff Pitcher in the way.

Centre: Low clouds threaten to envelope the squad but instead coach Steve Avory leads the warm up.

Bottom: Scott Guyett and Wayne Brown in the centre of the action as corner kicks are practised.

Photos: Andrew Chitty

ENGLAND 0 v 0 WALES

(at Rushden & Diamonds)

as first reported in Team Talk magazine

ENGLAND SQUAD: Brown (Chester) (Cooksey (Hereford) 88), Skiverton (Yeovil) (West (Woking) 89), Goodliffe (Hayes), Ryan (Doncaster) (Ellender (Scarborough) 78), Mustafa (Rushden & Diamonds), Drummond (Morecambe), Pitcher (Kingstonian), Patterson (Kingstonian), Underwood (Rushden & Diamonds) (McIntyre (Doncaster) 83), Jackson (Rushden & Diamonds), Patmore (Yeovil) (McGregor (Nuneaton) 78).

WELSH SQUAD: Pennock (Yeovil) (Roberts (Dagenham & Redbridge) 71), O'Brien (Carmarthen), Barnhouse (Carmarthen), York (Barry), Evans (Barry) (Shepherd (Newport) 65), Flynn (Barry) (Hughes (Aberystwyth) 76), Needs (Merthyr), Jenkins (Barry), Lloyd (Barry), G Williams (Hereford) (M Williams (Newport) 90), Evans (Caersws). Sub: Peters (Rushden & Diamonds).

Full Marks For Effort - But No Goals

The rain soaked grounds of the East Midlands prevented the England squad from enjoying a relaxed and thorough preparation for the visit of Wales to Rushden & Diamonds' Nene Park.

A few set pieces were prepared on a Kettering all weather pitch but sadly, coaches John Owens and Steve Avory couldn't give the lads the build up that has prepared previous squads so well for their internationals.

It was good to see Jim Conway, the Kidderminster Harriers Physiotherapist back with the lads, but regular squad Doctor, Steve Feldman was bravely battling against a virus, and was a good advert for the general fitness of the group! (His terrier tackling was also missed from the training ground).

It was F.A. Administrator Fiona Daly's first International and she kept her unbeaten representative match record intact following the four F.A. XI victories earlier in the season.

Team Talk photographers Gordon Whittington and Peter Barnes joined the party at the Marriott Hotel, Northampton and for the first time since the eighties we set up an official squad photo at the hotel.

Set pieces were planned in hot sunshine on an all weather surface and after lunch the lads had a restful afternoon before a short team talk and the drive to Nene Park, where a perfect surface was a terrific compliment to the acting grounds manager Paul Knowles.

The Welsh manager Tommi Morgan knows John Owens and his squad very well after their recent annual meetings and right from the first whistle a really well organised Welsh rear-guard smothered everything the English could throw at them.

Playing as usual with three centre backs, Tim Ryan, an ever present for Owens, Jason Goodliffe who had recently returned from injury and new cap, Terry Skivington, who proved to be one of the evening's successes, John Owens had the Rushden `players' , Paul Underwood (with a new streamlined haircut) and Tarkan Mustafa on the flanks.

Mustafa certainly tore forward at every opportunity, but with the Kingstonian mid field duo of Gary Pattison and Geoff Pitcher not quite on their usual dynamic form and Warren Patmore coming deep to link with mid field, as Justin Jackson made his probing diagonal runs to the wings, crosses were finding their way to the far post with no one on hand to finish.

The giant centre half, Neil O'Brien followed Patmore around and the whole Welsh side closed down and chased every loose ball with great effect. As usual the dangerous left foot of Gary Lloyd brilliantly exploited all set pieces and the volatile Adrian Needs was constantly ready to upset England captain Gary Pattison.

The intensity of the battle was fascinating to those who knew the `history' of the game between the two old rivals, although there were not that many chances created.

Tony Pennock saved brilliantly from Geoff Pitcher while Chester City's, Wayne Brown looked polished in everything he did in his first international.

Stuart Drummond flashed in and out of the game as the mid field battle swung back and forth, but to be honest, a draw was a fair reward for the Welsh although England had most of the possession.

Back Row (l-r): Stuart Drummond, Warren Patmore, Steve West, Scott Cooksey, Wayne Brown, Jason Goodliffe and Paul Ellender. Middle Row: Jim Conway, Terry Skiverton, Paul Underwood, Tarkan Mustafa, Kevin McIntyre, Marc McGregor, Steve Feldman (Doctor). Front Row: Justin Jackson, Gary Patterson, John Owens, Steve Avory, Geoff Pitcher and Tim Ryan. Photo: Peter Barnes

First caps were won by Paul Ellender and Steve West as substitutes with Scott Cooksey, back after a Football League spell with Shrewsbury Town, Kevin McIntyre and Marc McGregor also adding to their totals with substitute appearances in the second half.

Two players had to pull out of the original squad; Steve Brodie the little Scarborough striker who was injured and Southport's Mike Marsh who had just started a new job and couldn't take the three days off, this disappointed John Owens who phoned Mike to see if he could help in any way, but the ex-Liverpool player explained the timing was wrong as he would love to play for England, but having just started a new career he hoped he would be good enough to be considered next season.

England's next squad will be travelling on Tuesday 20th March to Holland for their match in Weert at the Wilmelmina FC on Thursday 22nd March at 19.20pm.

It would be good to see plenty of England supporters over in Holland to cheer on our lads and there are some very reasonably priced flights from Easi Jet at Luton Airport (Tel: 0870 6000000). *TONY WILLIAMS*

HOLLAND 0 v 3 ENGLAND

Roddis, Charlery, McDougald

(at Weert)

ENGLAND SQUAD (4.3.3.): Scott Cooksey (Hereford United); Tarkan Mustafa (Rushden & Diamonds), Scott Guyett (Southport), Tim Ryan (Doncaster Rovers), Kevin McIntyre (Doncaster Rovers); Nick Roddis (Woking), Gary Patterson (Kingstonian), Stuart Drummond (Morecambe); Geoff Pitcher (Kingstonian), Warren Patmore (Yeovil Town) and Steve Jones (Leigh RMI). Subs: Junior McDouglad for Jones, Ken Charlery for Patmore, Paul Beesley for Guyett, Carl Ruffer for McIntyre.

John Owens could be forgiven if he came to the conclusion that his players might find synchronised swimming easier to cope with in the torrential rain and on the flooded pitches that he and his party have experienced during just about every training session, plus the important internationals at Crawley, Hayes, Padova, Genemuiden and now Weert.

Luckily after difficult training conditions the playing pitch at `Wilhelmina O8' FC was better than expected, but the build up hadn't been easy for Fiona Daly, the F.A.'s administrator in charge of a non-League squad tour for the first time.

She was let down by the coach connection on the way to the airport and anyone, who has seen the amount of kit taken on these trips, will realise how difficult it is to move twenty people with football baggage.

A two hour delay at the airport following the problem of seven withdrawals all tested the character of the party, but when the hotel was finally reached they saw a wonderful spread of pitches and training facilities within walking distance.

But no, these were not available for the England squad, who travelled the twelve kilometres to Weert, where they managed some light training at the ground to be used on Thursday.

Whatever the problems were, no one was heard to complain; indeed it was quite obvious that every single member involved, from the chairman of the F.A.'s representative committee, Group Captain Peter Hilton, to the driver (on loan!) was quite obviously pleased to be involved and was ready with a smile and a bit of `mickey taking' whenever possible.

Potential new caps were obviously thrilled to be there. So Scott Guyett, Nick Roddis, Steve Jones, Carl Ruffer, Paul Beesley, Ken Charlery and Junior McDougald (who joined the party on Wednesday) were all keen to know the starting eleven, as Wednesday's training in the pouring rain took on a more personal aspect as defensive and attacking formations were prepared.

John Owens' selection was 4.3.3 - Scott Cooksey (Hereford United); Tarkan Mustafa (Rushden & Diamonds), Scott Guyett (Southport), Tim Ryan (Doncaster Rovers), Kevin McIntyre (Doncaster Rovers); Nick Roddis (Woking), Gary Patterson (Kingstonian), Stuart Drummond (Morecambe); Geoff Pitcher (Kingstonian), Warren Patmore (Yeovil Town) and Steve Jones (Leigh RMI). The manager decided not to use three centre backs for the first time:

"Holland coaches have seen how we have played in the recent years and we must do a little extra to create more chances and force a victory. The last time we won in Holland was in 1985 and, although we have never lost to the Dutch, our recent 0-0 draw with Wales also underlined the fact that we must increase our attacking options.

With this selection I hope Steve Jones can use his speed and direct style down the left, while I have given Geoff Pitcher more freedom, although he will start on the right. If he moves in there will be plenty of room for Tarkan Mustafa to storm forward.

In cold and wet conditions it is extremely difficult to plan tactics, while keeping everyone involved and moving about!"

So a trip to PSV Eindhoven and a swim in the pool livened up the afternoon and a look at the Wales match video in the evening also brought out a few home truths and one or two laughs - how many touches, Geoff Pitcher?

On match day there was another trip to Weert for some practice on set pieces, which at last avoided the rain, and it was back for a rest before John's ninth international - could he keep his unbeaten record and indeed increase the goals ratio?

"When you lose players of the quality of Jason Goodliffe (Hayes), Paul Underwood and Justin Jackson (Rushden & Diamonds), Steve Brodie (Scarborough), Mike Marsh (Southport), Steve West (Woking) and Terry Skivington (Yeovil Town) you wonder just how the side will perform, but all our players are quality performers and the new lads are extra keen to impress.

Once again Steve Avory and I have been impressed with the completely dedicated application from all the party. Our medical team of Jim Conway (Physio) and Steve Feldman (Doctor) have had a couple of dodgy stomachs to sooth, but everyone desperately wants to be involved."

Photographer Andrew Chitty had admitted he had developed a passion for trains in recent months and consequently he disappeared `up line' from time to time attempting to photograph The Flying Dutchman over a `pretty bridge'!

This was just what we needed! Although he did manage to record the tour as you can see, there is a warning to magazine readers: if you see him covering a match in your area, try to avoid him unless you are willing to discuss trains, cycling or possibly Third Lanark FC.

Supporters from many clubs including Dagenham & Redbridge, Yeovil Town, Dulwich Hamlet and Morecambe welcomed Gary Patterson as he led his England side on to a surprisingly firm surface.

Early attacking down the left brought a knock to Steve Jones who was already uncomfortable as he was recovering from a disturbed stomach. John Owens was worried that, with Pilcher also wondering away from the right, it was imperative that Mustafa used the open spaces on that flank.

With Warren Patmore leading the line well and holding up the ball to bring his mid-field into play England certainly looked more likely to score.

Unfortunately, Jones had to come off after twelve minutes, but his replacement Junior McDougald was obviously in good form and before half time Patmore had missed with two chances and a couple of free kicks had flashed just wide. Holland also just failed to score from two breakaways.

At half time the England `keepers swapped over as planned and Wayne Brown immediately had to save a rasping drive before he had `settled in'.

Following this save an attack down the left finished with McIntyre firing over a high cross, which sailed over the leaping (Wassah!) Patmore to debutant Nick (don't call me stupid!) Roddis. He coolly slotted home and put a couple of minutes on his planned `assembly' at his school next Monday morning!

What a wonderful experience it was for the captain of British Universities, who had also played for the FAXI against Combined Services this season having moved from Hayes to Woking last summer. I must admit it was a special moment for me to witness just how much his first cap had meant to him - and now he had a goal to celebrate!

This was a signal for England to take complete control and it wasn't long before the manager could safely introduce the three remaining members of the squad - Carl Ruffer and Paul Beesley (Chester City) and Ken Charlery (Boston United) for Pitcher, Guyett and Patmore.

The final stage of the game brought some quality football with England playing a revised 4.4.2 formation and it was Ken Charlery, on the bench for England at Kidderminster in 1989 when he didn't come on against Wales, who scored England's 100th goal by tapping in following another McIntyre cross and won his treasured cap after a twelve year wait.

A final `coup de grace' came from Daggers' McDougald, who picked up a good through ball from Paul Beesley beating three players and coolly sliding home a beautiful third which gave the manager a splendid victory and kept his record intact.

The home club's hospitality was impressive and the visitors' spirit overflowed as all the underwater training and freezing set pieces seemed worthwhile.

Messrs Owens, Avory, Conway and Feldman had done it again, while Fiona `Admin' Daly also had an unbeaten representative match record this season and the Group Captain heard that the R.A.F. had beaten the Navy 3-0 to win the Inter-Services Championship - what a double!

A quiet wind down in Eindhoven was enjoyed by management and some players while the Chester lads and others with Friday matches stayed in the hotel to enjoy the winning feeling before an early night - very impressive and maybe our senior international example is working at our level as well!

An early start the next morning took everyone back to the airport with a very satisfied feeling and a squad, who should justifiably feel proud of how they represented their country on and off the field. *TW*

England Internationals receive their caps from Jimmy Greaves at Villa Park.
Back Row (l-r): David Miller and Keith Bryan (the manager's scouting assistants), Steve Avory (Assistant Manager/Coach), Carl Ruffer, Ken Charlery, Kevin McIntyre, Wayne Brown, Stuart Drummond, Tim Ryan, Junior McDougald, John Owens (Chief Manager/Coach), Roland Maughan (F.A. Official). Front Row: Jason Goodliffe, Marc McGregor, Jimmy Greaves, Geoff Pitcher and Neil Roddis. Photo: Ian Morsman

ENGLAND SEMI-PRO CAPS 1979-2001

KEY TO COUNTRY CODES:
E - Eire; I - Italy; F - Finland;
G - Gibraltar; H - Holland; N - Norway;
S - Scotland; W - Wales.

Players capped for the first time during season 2000-01 are shown in bold.

Gary Abbott (Welling) 87 I(s), S(s), 92 W(s) 3

David Adamson (Boston Utd) 79 SH, 80 ISH 5

Tony Agana (Weymouth) 86 E 1

Carl Alford (Kettering T. & Rushden & Ds) 96 EH 2

Ian Arnold (Kettering Town) 95 W(s)H 2

Jim Arnold (Stafford Rangers) 79 SH 2

Nick Ashby (Kettering & Rushden & Ds)
94 FN, 95 G 96 EH 5

Noel Ashford (Enfield & Redbridge For.)
82 GHS, 83 IHS, 84 WHSI, 85 WI(s), 86 EE,
87 W(s), IHS, 90 WE, 91 I(s) 21

John Askey (Macclesfield) 90 W 1

Paul Bancroft (Kidderminster H.)
89 IW, 90 IWE, 91 W 6

Chris Banks (Cheltenham T.) 98 H, 99 W 2

Keith Barrett (Enfield) 81 HSI, 82 GIHS, 83 IHS,
84 W(s)HS, 85 IHS 16

Laurence Batty (Woking) 93 F(s), 95 WHG 4

Mark Beeney (Maidstone) 89 I(s) 1

Paul Beesley (Chester C.) 01 H(s) 1

Dean Bennett (Kidderminster H) 00 W(s) 1

Graham Benstead (Kettering) 94 WFN(s) 3

Kevin Betsy (Woking) 98 H(s) 1

Marcus Bignot (Kidderminster H) 97 H 1

Jimmy Bolton (Kingstonian) 95 G 1

Steve Book (Cheltenham Town) 99 IHW 3

Gary Brabin (Runcorn) 94 WFN 3

Mark Bradshaw (Halifax T.) 98 H 1

Colin Brazier (Kidderminster) 87 W 1

Stewart Brighton (Bromsgrove) 94 W 1

Steve Brooks (Cheltenham) 88 W(s), 90 WE 3

Derek Brown (Woking) 94 F(s)N 2

Kevan Brown (Woking) 95 WHG 96 H 97 E 5

Wayne Brown (Chester C.) 01 WH(s) 2

Corey Browne (Dover) 94 F(s)N(s), 95 H(s) 3

David Buchanan (Blyth) 86 E(s)E 2

Brian Butler (Northwich) 93 F 1

Steve Butler (Maidstone) 88 W, 89 IW 3

Gary Butterworth (Rushden & Diamonds)
97 EH, 98 H, 99 IHW, 00 I 7

Chris Byrne (Macclesfield T.) 97 H 1

Mark Carter (Runcorn & Barnet)
87 WIHS, 88 W, 89 IW, 90 IE, 91 IW(s) 11

Kim Casey (Kidderminster) 86 WEE(s), 87 WI 5

Paul Cavell (Redbridge) 92 W, 93 F 2

Lee Charles (Hayes) 99 I(s) H(s) W(s) 3

Kevin Charlton (Telford) 85 WI 2

Ken Charlery (Boston U.) 01 H(s) 1

Andrew Clarke (Barnet) 90 EE 2

David Clarke (Blyth Spartans) 80 IS(s)H, 81 HSI,
82 IHS, 83 HS, 84 HSI 14

Gary Clayton (Burton) 86 E 1

Robert Codner (Barnet) 88 W 1

John Coleman (Morecambe) 93 F(s) 1

Darren Collins (Enfield) 93 F(s), 94 WFN 4

Andy Comyn (Hednesford T.
98 H(s), 99 I(s)H(s)W(s) 4

Steve Conner (Dartford, Redbridge & Dagenham & R)
90 I, 91 IW, 92 W, 93 F 5

David Constantine (Altrincham) 85 IHS, 86 W 4

Robbie Cooke (Kettering) 89 W(s), 90 I 2

Scott Cooksey (Hednesford T.) 97 E, 98 H(s), 01 W(s)H
4

Alan Cordice (Wealdstone)
83 IHS, 84 WS(s), I(s), 85 IHS 9

Rob Cousins (Yeovil Town) 00 I(s)HW 3

Ken Cramman (Gateshead & Rushden & Diamonds)
96 E 97 EH 3

Paul Cuddy (Altrincham) 87 IHS 3

Paul Culpin (Nuneaton B) 84 W, 85 W(s) IHS 5

Michael Danzey (Woking) 99 IH 2

Paul Davies (Kidderminster H.)
86 W, 87 WIS, 88 W, 89 W 6

John Davison (Altrincham)
79 SH, 80 IS, 81 HSI, 82 GIHS, 83 IHS,
84 WHIS, 85 IHS, 86 WEE 24

John Denham (Northwich Victoria) 80 H 1

Peter Densmore (Runcorn) 88 W, 89 I 2

Phil Derbyshire (Mossley) 83 H(s)S(s) 2

Mick Doherty (Weymouth) 86 W(s) 1

Neil Doherty (Kidderminster H.) 97 E 1

Stuart Drummond (Morecambe) 00 I(s)HW, 01 WH 5

Paul Ellender (Scarborough) 01 W(s) 1

Lee Endersby (Harrow Bor.) 96 H 1

Mick Farrelly (Altrincham) 87 IHS 3

Steve Farrelly (Macclesfield & Kingstonian)
95 H(s)G(s), 00 IHW(s) 5

Trevor Finnegan (Weymouth) 81 HS 2

Murray Fishlock (Yeovil Town) 99 H(s) 1

Richard Forsyth (Kidderminster) 95 WHG 3

Ian Foster (Kidderminster H) 00 W(s) 1

Paul Furlong (Enfield) 90 IEE, 91 IW 5

Mark Gardiner (Macclesfield T.) 97 E 1

Jerry Gill (Yeovil T.) 97 E 1

John Glover (Maidstone Utd) 85 WIHS 4

Mark Golley (Sutton Utd.)
87 H(s)S, 88 W, 89 IW, 92 W 6

Jason Goodliffe (Hayes) 00 IHW, 01 W 4

Paul Gothard (Dagenham & Redb.)
97 E(s), 99 I(s)W(s) 3

Neil Grayson (Cheltenham T.) 98, H 99 IHW 4

Phil Gridelet (Hendon & Barnet) 89 IW, 90 WEE 5

Steve Guppy (Wycombe W.) 93 W 1

Scott Guyett (Southport) 01 H 1

Steve Hanlon (Macclesfield) 90 W 1

David Harlow (Farnborough T.) 97 E(s)H 2

Barry Hayles (Stevenage Bor.) 96 EH 2

Brian Healy (Morecambe) 98 H 1

Tony Hemmings (Northwich) 93 F 1

Andy Hessenthaler (Dartford) 90 I 1

Kenny Hill (Maidstone Utd) 80 ISH 3

Mark Hine (Gateshead) 95 W(s)H 2

Simeon Hodson (Kidderminster) 94 WFN 3

Colin Hogarth (Guiseley) 95 WH 2

Steven Holden (Kettering) 94 WFN(s), 95 HG 5

Mark Hone (Welling) 90 I, 93 F, 94 W(s)F(s)N 5

Gary Hooley (Frickley) 85 W 1

Dean Hooper (Kingstonian) 98 H 1

Keith Houghton (Blyth Spartans) 79 S 1

Barry Howard (Altrincham) 81 HSI, 82 GIHS 7

Neil Howarth (Macclesfield) 95 H(s) 97 E 2

David Howell (Enfield) 85 H(s)S(s), 86 WE, 87 WIHS,
88 W, 89 IW, 90 IEE 14

Lee Howells (Cheltenham T.) 98, H 99 W 1

Lee Hughes (Kidderminster) 96 EH 97 EH 4

Delwyn Humphreys (Kidderminster H.)
91 W(s), 92 W, 94 WFN, 95 WH 7

Steve Humphries (Barnet) 87 H(s) 1

Nicky Ironton (Enfield) 83 H(s), 84 W 2

Justin Jackson (Morecambe & Rushden & Diamonds)
00 W 01 W 2

Tony Jennings (Enfield)
79 SH, 80 ISH, 81 HSI, 82 GIHS 12

Jeff Johnson (Altrincham) 81 SI, 82 GIHS, 83 IHS,
84 HSI, 84 IHS, 86 W(s)EE 18

Steve Jones (Leigh RMI) 01 H 1

Tom Jones (Weymouth) 87 W 1

Anton Joseph (Telford Utd. & Kidderminster H.) 84 S(s),
85 WIHS, 86 W(s), 87 WI(s)H, 88 W, 89 IW, 90 IEE 14

Andy Kerr (Wycombe) 93 W 1

Ged Kimmins (Hyde Utd.) 96 E(s)H(s) 97 E(s) 3

Mike Lake (Macclesfield) 89 I 1

Andy Lee (Telford U. & Witton A.) 89 I(s), 91 IW 3

David Leworthy (Farnborough & Rushden & Diamonds)
93 W, 94 W 97 EH 4

Kenny Lowe (Barnet) 91 IW 2

Martin McDonald (Macclesfield) 95 G(s) 1

**Junior McDougald (Dagenham & Redbridge)
01 H(s) 1**

Mark McGregor (Forest Green Rovers & Nuneaton
Borough)
00 I(s)H(s) 01 W(s) 3

Kevin McIntyre (Doncaster Rovers) 00 H(s)W, 01 W(s)H
4

John McKenna (Boston Utd)
88 W(s), 90 IEE, 91 IW, 92 W 7

John Margerrison (Barnet) 87 W 1

Simon Marples (Doncaster Rovers) 00 IH 2

Leroy May (Stafford R.) 95 G(s) 1

Bobby Mayes (Redbridge) 92 W 1

Paul Mayman (Northwich Vic) 80 IS 2

Stewart Mell (Burton) 85 W 1

Neil Merrick (Weymouth) 80 I(s)S 2

Russell Milton (Dover) 94 FN 2

Trevor Morley (Nuneaton) 84 WHSI, 85 WS(s) 6

Tarkan Mustafa (Rushden & Diamonds) 01 WH 2

Les Mutrie (Blyth Spartans) 79 SH, 80 ISH 5

Mark Newson (Maidstone U) 84 WHSI, 85 W 5

Doug Newton (Burton) 85 WHS 3

Paul Nicol (Kettering T) 91 IW, 92 W 3

Steve Norris (Telford) 88 W(s) 1

Joe O'Connor (Hednesford T.) 97 EH(s) 2

Eamon O'Keefe (Mossley) 79 SH 2

Frank Ovard (Maidstone) 81 H(s)S(s)I(s) 3

Andy Pape (Harrow Bor. & Enfield) 85 W(s)HS,
86 W(s)E, 87 WIHS, 88 W, 89 IW, 90 IWE 15

Brian Parker (Yeovil Town) 80 S 1

Warren Patmore (Yeovil Town) 99 IHW, 00 IH, 01 WH 7

Gary Patterson (Kingstonian) 99 IH, 00 IHW, 01 WH 7

Steve Payne (Macclesfield T.) 97 H 1

Trevor Peake (Nuneaton Bor) 79 SH 2

"OLD BOYS" CORNER

Brian Thompson

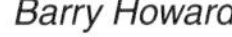

Barry Howard

Colin Williams

Mickey Stephens

David Pearce (Harrow Bor) 84 I(s) 1

Brendan Phillips (Nuneaton Bor. & Kettering T.) 79 SH, 80 S(s)H 4

Gary Philips (Barnet) 82 G 1

Owen Pickard (Yeovil T.) 98 H(s) 1

Geoff Pitcher (Kingstonian) 99W, 00 IHW, 01 WH 6

Phil Power (Macclesfield T.) 96 E(s)H(s) 2

Ryan Price (Stafford R. & Macclesfield) 92 W(s) 93 WF 96 EH 97 H 6

Steve Prindiville 98 H(s) 1

Simon Read (Farnborough) 92 W(s) 1

Andy Reid (Altrincham) 95 W 1

Carl Richards (Enfield) 86 E 1

Derek Richardson (Maidstone U) 83 I, 84 W, 86 E 4

Ian Richardson (Dagenham & Red) 95 G 1

Kevin Richardson (Bromsgrove) 94 WFN 3

Paul Richardson (Redbridge) 92 W, 93 WF 3

Terry Robbins (Welling) 92 W, 93 WF, 94 WFN 6

Peter Robinson (Blyth S) 83 IHS, 84 WI, 85 W 6

Nick Roddis (Woking) 01 H 1

John Rogers (Altrincham) 81 HSI, 82 I(s)S 5

Paul Rogers (Sutton) 89 W, 90 IE(2), 91 IW 6

Colin Rose (Witton Alb.) 96 E(s)H 2

Kevin Rose (Kidderminster) 94 F(s)N 2

Brian Ross (Marine) 93 W(s)F(s), 94 W(s) 95 WH 5

Carl Ruffer (Chester City) 01 H(s) 1

Tim Ryan (Southport & Doncaster Rovers) 98 H, 99 IHW, 00 IHW, 01 WH 9

Neil Sellars (Scarboro) 81 HSI, 82 GH(s)S, 83 IHS 9

Mark Shail (Yeovil T.) 93 W 1

Simon Shaw (Doncaster Rovers) 99 IH 2

Peter Shearer (Cheltenham) 89 I(s) 1

Paul Shirtliff (Frickley A. & Boston U.) 86 EE, 87 WIH, 88 W, 89 IW, 90 IWEE, 92 W, 93 WF 15

Paul Showler (Altrincham) 91 I(s)W 2

Gordon Simmonite (Boston Utd.) 79 S(s)H(s), 80 ISH 5

Gary Simpson (Stafford R.) 86 EE, 87 IHS, 90 IWEE 9

Wayne Simpson (Stafford) 94 FN(s) 2

Terry Skiverton (Yeovil Town) 01 W 1

Glenn Skivington (Barrow) 90 IWE, 91 IW 5

Adrian Smith (Kidderminster H) 00 I(s)H(s)W 3

Alan Smith (Alvechurch) 82 GIS 3

Ian Smith (Mossley) 80 ISH(s) 3

Mark Smith (Stevenage Bor.) 96 EH 98 H, 99 IHW, 00 IHW(s) 9

Ossie Smith (Runcorn) 84 W 1

Tim Smithers (Nuneaton), 85 W(s)I, 86 W 3

Adam Sollitt (Kettering Town) 00 I(s)H(s)W 3

Simon Stapleton (Wycombe) 93 W 1

Mickey Stephens (Sutton), 82 GS(s), 86 WEE(s) 5

Billy Stewart (Southport) 98 H 1

Bob Stockley (Nuneaton Bor) 80 H 1

Steve Stott (Kettering T., Rushden & Ds & Yeovil T.) 95 WH(s)G, 96 EH, 99 HW(s) 7

Peter Taylor (Maidstone) 84 HSI 3

Steve Taylor (Bromsgrove R.) 95 G 1

Shaun Teale (Weymouth) 88 W 1

Stuart Terry (Altrincham) W 1

Brian Thompson (Yeovil & Maidstone) 79 SH, 81 HSI, 82 IHS, 83 IHS, 84 WHSI 15

Neil Thompson (Scarborough) 87 WIHS 4

Steve Thompson (Wycombe) 93 W 1

Kevin Todd (Berwick Rangers) 91 W 1

Mark Tucker (Woking) 96 E 1

Tony Turner (Telford) 85 W 1

Paul Underwood (Rushden & Diamonds) 99 IH, 00 I, 01 W 4

David Venables (Stevenage Bor.) 94 W(s), 95 HG 96 EH(s) 5

Jamie Victory (Cheltenham T.) 98 H(s) 1

David Waite (Enfield) 82 G 1

Paul Walker (Blyth) 86 WEE(s), 87 S(s) 4

Steve Walters (Northwich Victoria) 97 H 1

Mark Ward (Northwich Victoria) 83 S(s) 1

Dale Watkins (Cheltenham T.) 98 H, 99 I(s), 00 IHW 5

John Watson (Wealdstone, Scarborough & Maidstone) 79 S(s)H, 80 ISH, 81 HSI, 82 IHS, 83 IHS, 84 W(s)HSI 18

Liam Watson (Marine) 95 WH(s) 2

Paul Watts (Redbridge Forest) 89 W, 90 IEE, 91 I, 92 W, 93 WF 8

Paul Webb (Bromsgrove R & Kidderminster H) 93 F, 94 WFN(s) 95 WHG 96 EH 97 EH 11

Mark West (Wycombe W) 91 W 1

Steve West (Woking) 01 W(s) 1

Barry Whitbread (Runcorn & Altrincham) 79 SH, 80 ISH, 81 I 6

Russ Wilcox (Frickley) 86 WE 2

Barry Williams (Nuneaton Borough) 99 H(s)W 2

Colin Williams (Scarborough & Telford Utd. 81 HS, 82 IHS 5

Roger Willis (Barnet) 91 I(s) 1

Paul Wilson (Frickley) 86 W 1

Simon Wormull (Dover Athletic) 99 I(s)W 2

Mark Yates (Cheltenham Town) 99 IW 2

THE NATIONWIDE CONFERENCE

Founded 1979

President: J C Thompson MBIM, Minst.M, FID

Chairman: W J King **Chief Executive:** J A Moules

Secretary: M A Annett, The Nationwide Conference,
Collingwood House, Schooner Court, Crossways,
Dartford, Kent DA2 6QQ
Tel: 01322 303120 Fax: 01322 303121

The Conference season was dominated by the enthralling race for the championship between Yeovil Town and Rushden & Diamonds.

Yeovil's youngsters surprised everyone, including their manager David Webb, as they raced off to a good start and when Webb joined his old friend, the chairman of Southend, one felt this was a very strange move so early after taking over at Yeovil, but at least it was painless for the club he was leaving in second position.

Yeovil's chairman John Fry's emphatic decision to appoint Colin Addison was welcomed at Yeovil, who promptly beat the Diamonds at Nene Park and steadily moved away at the top of the league.

Conference clubs then impressively supplied all five non-League clubs in the Third Round where they all applied themselves with immense credit.

Dagenham & Redbridge gaining most plaudits for appearing to be at least the equal of Premier Division Charlton Athletic, while Geoff Chapple's quite uncanny knack of regularly producing knock-out heroes season after season, gave Kingstonian victories over Brentford and Southend United.

Yeovil played their normal F.A. Cup role to perfection, but Rushden & Diamonds enjoyed a live Sky cup tie at Luton, but lost and one thought their recent experiences perhaps limited their desire to get caught up in too many F.A. Cup or Trophy battles.

Conference clubs were invited in to the LDV Vans Trophy for the first time, but strangely these games proved a bit of an anti-climax and nuisance compared with Conference points or F.A. Cup or Trophy tries. No doubt if the later rounds had been reached a different viewpoint would have been taken, but that equally applies to League clubs'. The F.A. Umbro Trophy saw the big names all disappear before the Quarter Final, but the chances of a good crowd for a Chester City v Hereford United Villa Park meeting was discussed and considered a promising final!

Forest Green Rovers and Canvey Island painfully and emphatically put paid to that however, and the Rovers completed an amazingly disciplined and determined end to the season by moving away from the relegation zone with a squad of trophy tied players and also reaching Villa Park with practically another squad who were also able to play in the knock-out tournament.

Canvey Island proved to be a severe thorn in the Conference side however, and eliminated Stevenage Borough, Telford United and Chester City before winning the Trophy. This was the first time a club outside the Conference had lifted the silverware since Bishops Stortford beat Sutton United in an all Isthmian final in 1981.

Throughout the season it appeared, through press reports, that the Football League really was prepared to accept a two up and two down arrangement between the Division Three and The Conference.

So a staggering 71-1 vote against, with only Wycombe Wanderers loyal to their `roots', was very depressing for all who were looking forward to new incentives with the Conference.

Of course with two up a play off system involving the clubs finishing in second to fifth position would have created a tremendous run-in to the season with practically all matches important as clubs battled for play-off places or avoidance of the relegation zone.

But with one up it just wasn't the same and so in a knee jerk reaction a play-off scheme was voted in and it was possibly not the most sensible decision for the club chairmen to have taken.

Yes, they all thought their clubs had a better chance of finishing in the top five rather than as champions and yes, it would bring more gate revenue in, but in no way could these financial benefits make it right to prevent the champions from gaining automatic, and deserved, promotion to the Football League.

In the situation it wasn't surprising that the F.A. vetoed the Conference play-off plan underlying the most important aim on the Conference agenda should be to persuade the F.A. and The Football League to find a way in which two up and two down can be acceptable to all.

The play-off would then be a great success and hopefully this is the way forward at a time when we could alternatively see the Conference disappearing into the Football League and presumably a new linking competition similar to the Conference taking its place between the Football League and the Non-League pyramid. We shall see!

TW

FINAL LEAGUE TABLE 2000-01

		P	W	D	L	F	A	W	D	L	F	A	Pts	GD
1	**Rushden & Diamonds**	**42**	**14**	**6**	**1**	**41**	**13**	**11**	**5**	**5**	**37**	**23**	**86**	**42**
2	Yeovil Town	42	14	3	4	41	17	10	5	6	32	33	80	23
3	Dagenham & Redbridge	42	13	4	4	39	19	10	4	7	32	35	77	17
4	Southport	42	9	5	7	33	24	11	4	6	25	22	69	12
5	Leigh RMI	42	11	5	5	38	24	8	6	7	25	33	68	6
6	Telford United	42	13	1	7	33	23	6	7	8	18	28	65	0
7	Stevenage Borough	42	8	7	6	36	33	7	11	3	35	28	63	10
8	Chester City	42	9	8	4	29	19	7	6	8	20	24	62	6
9	Doncaster Rovers	42	11	5	5	28	17	4	8	9	19	26	58	4
10	Scarborough	42	7	9	5	29	25	7	7	7	27	29	58	2
11	Hereford United	42	6	12	3	27	19	8	3	10	33	27	57	14
12	Boston United	42	10	7	4	43	28	3	10	8	31	35	56	11
13	Nuneaton Borough	42	9	5	7	35	26	4	10	7	25	34	54	0
14	Woking	42	5	10	6	30	30	8	5	8	22	27	54	-5
15	Dover Athletic	42	9	6	6	32	22	5	5	11	22	34	53	-2
16	Forest Green Rovers	42	6	9	6	28	28	5	6	10	15	26	48	-11
17	Northwich Victoria	42	8	7	6	31	24	3	6	12	18	43	46	-18
18	Hayes	42	5	6	10	22	31	7	4	10	22	40	46	-27
19	Morecambe	42	8	5	8	35	29	3	7	11	29	37	45	-2
20	Kettering Town	42	5	5	11	23	31	6	5	10	23	31	43	-16
21	Kingstonian	42	3	5	13	19	40	5	5	11	28	33	34	-26
22	Hednesford Town	42	2	6	13	24	38	3	7	11	22	48	28	-40

LEADING GOALSCORERS 2000-01

Total		League	FAC	FAT
27	Duane Darby (Rushden & Dia.)	24	0	3
21	Warren Patmore (Yeovil Town)	18	3	0
20	Justin Jackson (Rushden & Dia.)	18	1	1
20	Steve Jones (Leigh RMI)	19	1	0
18	Alex Meecham (Forest Green Rvrs)	13	0	5
	Rob Elmes (Hereford United)	14	0	4
17	Ken Charlery (Boston United)	13	3	1
16	Darren Hay (Stevenage Borough)	15	0	1

Total		League	FAC	FAT
15	Ian Arnold (Southport)	13	1	1
	Mark Beesley (Chester City)	11	2	2
	Tony Black (Leigh RMI)	11	3	1
	Jake Edwards (Telford United)	10	2	3
	Neil Illman (Stevenage Borough)	11	0	4
	John Norman (Morecambe)	10	1	4
	Geoff Pitcher (Kingstonian)	7	5	3
14	Marc McGregor (Nuneaton Borough)	13	1	0
	Steve Whitehall (Chester City)	7	4	3

ATTENDANCES 2000-01

Highest

Boston United	v Doncaster Rovers	**3,155**
Chester City	v Southport	**2.861**
Dagenham & Redbridge	v Yeovil Town	**2,136**
Doncaster Rovers	v Nuneaton Borough	**3,648**
Dover Athletic	v Doncaster Rovers	**1,604**
Forest Green Rovers	v Yeovil Town	**1,756**
Hayes	v Rushden & Diamonds	**1,844**
Hednesford Town	v Rushden & Diamonds	**1,516**
Hereford United	v Yeovil Town	**3,393**
Kettering Town	v Boston United	**2,092**
Kingstonian	v Woking	**1,717**
Leigh RMI	v Rushden & Diamonds	**1,405**
Morecambe	v Scarborough	**2,023**
Nothwich Victoria	v Chester City	**2,651**
Nuneaton Borough	v Rushden & Diamonds	**2,614**
Rushden & Diamonds	v Dover Athletic	**5,482**
Scarborough	v Doncaster Rovers	**2,381**
Southport	v Rushden & Diamonds	**2,255**
Stevenage Borough	v Rushden & Diamonds	**2,171**
Telford United	v Dagenham & Redbridge	**2,317**
Woking	v Kingstonian	**2,246**
Yeovil Town	v Rushden & Diamonds	**8,868**

Lowest

Boston United	v Yeovil Town	**1,303**
Chester City	v Kingstonian	**834**
Dagenham & Redbridge	v Scarborough	**877**
Doncaster Rovers	v Forest Green Rovers	**1,8716**
Dover Athletic	v Kingstonian	**632**
Forest Green Rovers	v Leigh RMI	**407**
Hayes	v Leigh RMI	**415**
Hednesford Town	v Dover Athletic	**693**
Hereford United	v Kingstonian	**867**
Kettering Town	v Forest Green Rovers	**1,068**
Kingstonian	v Hednesford Town	**651**
Leigh RMI	v Kettering Town	**351**
Morecambe	v Doncaster Rovers	**638**
Nothwich Victoria	v Kingstonian	**788**
Nuneaton Borough	v Morecambe	**1,031**
Rushden & Diamonds	v Northwich Victoria	**1,141**
Scarborough	v Telford United	**723**
Southport	v Boston United	**1,003**
Stevenage Borough	v Hednesford Town	**1,450**
Telford United	v Leigh RMI	**281**
Woking	v Hayes	**1,139**
Yeovil Town	v Hednesford Town	**2,280**

RESULTS CHART 2000-01

plus attendance chart

Home Team / *Away Team*	Boston United	Chester City	Dagenham & Redb	Doncaster Rovers	Dover Athletic	Forest Green Rov.	Hayes	Hednesford Town	Hereford United	Kettering Town	Kingstonian	Leigh RMI	Morecambe	Northwich Victoria	Nuneaton Bor.	Rushden & D.	Scarborough	Southport	Stevenage Bor.	Telford United	Woking	Yeovil Town
Boston United		0-0 2078	5-1 1386	3-1 3155	1-2 1804	0-0 2368	0-1 1667	3-4 1730	5-3 1836	4-3 3108	2-1 2145	0-1 1580	2-1 1832	1-1 1556	4-1 1573	1-1 3434	2-2 1752	1-0 1621	3-3 2199	2-1 1756	0-0 1767	4-1 1303
Chester City	2-2 1087		1-1 1202	3-0 2316	1-0 2273	0-1 1292	0-0 1658	0-1 1451	2-1 2224	2-1 2102	0-0 634	1-1 1858	1-0 1717	1-1 1717	4-0 1708	1-2 4040	3-2 805	0-1 2861	1-1 1708	1-0 1362	3-3 1694	2-1 2265
Dagenham & Redbridge	2-1 1037	1-1 1241		2-1 1206	1-1 1359	3-1 1256	2-0 1145	6-1 952	2-1 1410	5-1 1219	1-2 1252	2-1 1231	3-2 1063	1-0 1256	1-1 1361	0-2 1686	1-0 877	0-1 1183	3-0 958	0-0 1001	1-2 1359	2-0 2136
Doncaster Rovers	4-2 2296	1-0 2553	1-0 2232		1-1 1640	3-0 1871	0-0 1769	3-1 2033	2-1 2380	0-0 1884	0-2 1787	4-0 1532	1-0 1924	0-2 2794	1-1 3648	3-2 3538	0-2 3024	1-0 1877	0-0 2545	1-2 2026	0-1 2437	2-0 2111
Dover Athletic	0-0 764	1-1 1112	3-1 1461	1-1 1604		1-2 750	4-1 1026	4-0 929	1-0 1072	1-0 976	1-3 632	1-2 929	2-2 847	3-0 688	2-1 815	4-1 1407	0-2 933	0-1 954	1-0 1503	1-3 1161	0-0 1027	1-1 1293
Forest Green Rovers	0-3 872	1-1 943	4-4 902	2-2 952	2-1 702		1-2 804	0-2 871	1-1 1076	3-2 758	3-1 547	3-0 407	0-0 756	1-0 723	0-0 781	0-0 1144	2-3 542	2-0 951	2-3 1043	1-1 775	0-0 804	0-1 1756
Hayes	1-1 929	1-3 784	4-1 981	0-3 750	3-2 677	1-0 634		1-1 586	0-2 701	2-1 548	1-1 738	1-2 415	1-1 686	2-2 620	0-0 732	0-3 1844	0-1 562	1-0 615	0-1 853	0-1 586	1-2 1001	2-3 707
Hednesford Town	2-4 646	0-0 1435	0-2 836	2-4 930	0-0 693	1-1 654	1-3 925		0-3 1043	1-2 838	3-2 881	1-2 804	0-0 942	7-1 800	0-3 1105	2-3 1516	0-1 754	0-1 965	1-1 802	1-1 1046	1-2 805	1-2 1044
Hereford United	1-1 2056	2-0 2321	0-1 1561	0-1 1755	4-2 1903	3-1 2168	3-2 1368	1-1 2557		0-0 1561	0-0 867	1-1 1918	2-2 1437	0-0 2461	1-1 1743	3-1 2005	1-1 1304	0-0 2438	1-1 2251	2-0 2431	0-1 1280	2-2 3393
Kettering Town	2-2 2092	4-0 1216	0-0 1070	0-0 1106	0-2 1479	1-3 1068	0-2 1560	2-0 1498	0-2 1406		3-1 1203	0-1 1087	1-5 1217	2-3 1102	1-2 1791	0-2 4750	1-1 1159	1-1 1145	1-2 1755	0-1 1405	2-0 2479	2-1 2115
Kingstonian	0-0 842	1-3 1125	2-3 809	1-1 1321	0-0 723	0-1 774	0-1 902	1-0 651	0-3 833	0-1 707		0-2 929	1-6 885	1-0 942	2-2 788	2-4 1363	2-2 694	3-1 904	0-2 990	0-1 867	0-3 1717	3-4 1613
Leigh RMI	2-2 1124	0-1 501	1-2 451	0-1 811	2-1 485	1-1 451	4-0 414	2-2 475	2-1 503	1-0 351	2-1 402		1-0 834	3-0 501	6-2 501	1-0 1405	2-0 836	2-2 835	1-4 403	1-1 552	2-0 455	2-3 565
Morecambe	2-0 1009	0-2 1557	2-3 742	2-1 638	1-2 1006	0-2 1017	4-0 1272	0-0 1275	1-1 1125	2-0 1164	3-2 1060	1-2 1106		4-0 886	4-2 1485	2-1 1816	4-4 2023	1-3 1937	1-2 1021	0-0 1013	3-0 942	0-0 1439
Northwich Victoria	0-3 1035	1-1 2651	3-0 1060	1-1 1115	2-0 907	0-0 833	3-4 808	2-2 953	1-0 1104	1-2 1011	2-1 788	1-1 1208	1-0 1008		2-2 902	0-0 2016	3-0 942	0-2 1074	3-2 909	0-1 812	4-0 957	1-2 1015
Nuneaton Borough	3-1 2001	1-2 1363	2-0 1302	1-0 1337	1-2 1414	2-0 1172	1-1 1510	5-1 1223	1-2 1362	1-1 1865	2-1 1423	2-1 1145	5-1 1031	3-1 802		1-1 2614	1-2 1247	1-2 1275	0-3 1402	1-1 1531	1-1 1357	0-2 1426
Rushden & Diamonds	0-0 4570	2-0 3966	2-1 3069	0-0 4036	2-1 5482	0-0 3352	4-0 2568	5-1 2906	1-0 4188	1-1 4627	2-1 3842	1-1 3882	4-1 3778	2-1 1141	2-1 4080		1-0 3553	4-0 3574	2-2 4048	3-0 4107	2-0 3667	1-2 5283
Scarborough	2-2 1279	0-2 1193	0-1 1202	3-1 2381	2-0 1082	1-0 838	2-0 814	0-0 943	2-4 891	0-1 1082	1-0 1275	1-1 1087	2-2 1536	4-0 845	0-0 1089	0-3 1107		1-1 1125	2-2 789	1-1 723	3-2 1156	2-2 972
Southport	3-1 1003	1-0 1279	0-1 1264	1-0 1629	2-1 1635	1-1 1421	2-0 1252	2-0 1006	1-1 1367	2-3 1258	2-2 1153	1-2 1589	1-2 2117	1-1 1643	1-2 1192	1-3 2255	3-1 1269		2-2 1506	3-0 1354	0-1 1377	3-0 1310
Stevenage Borough	3-2 2129	1-2 1748	0-2 2055	0-0 2425	1-1 1505	3-1 1654	3-3 2171	4-1 1450	2-1 1265	2-0 1845	2-5 2007	3-0 1479	1-1 1317	3-1 1622	1-1 1471	0-2 3327	1-1 2032	1-3 1366		5-3 1446	0-3 2022	0-0 1755
Telford United	3-2 1109	3-0 1058	0-1 2317	1-0 1267	0-2 415	1-0 709	2-0 542	2-1 1141	1-0 1848	2-1 386	0-1 860	2-1 281	2-0 753	2-3 1019	2-1 1362	1-2 1510	1-0 395	2-3 1373	2-2 648		3-1 1249	1-2 1821
Woking	1-1 1661	1-0 2264	4-4 2319	1-1 1948	4-1 1574	2-0 1779	1-2 1139	1-1 1384	0-3 2062	1-1 1840	0-0 2246	1-1 1421	3-1 1309	1-1 1544	0-2 1696	1-4 2101	1-1 1625	1-2 1586	1-1 1780	3-0 1506		2-3 2216
Yeovil Town	2-1 3585	2-1 2862	1-3 4025	2-0 2605	4-0 2306	2-0 4361	3-0 3206	4-2 2280	2-3 4639	2-0 2302	3-1 2902	6-1 3401	3-2 2550	1-0 2891	0-0 2774	0-0 8868	0-1 2823	0-1 4705	1-1 3073	2-0 3106	1-0 2462	

2000-01 VARIETY CLUB TROPHY

FIRST ROUND

	Home				Away	Att
	Boston United	1	v	5	**Nuneaton Borough**	527
	Elding 1				McGregor 17[p] 41, Francis 47 88, Sykes 90	
	Dagenham & Redbridge	1	v	2	**Stevenage Borough**	318
	Goodwin 67				Armstrong 71, Illman 79	
	Kettering Town	3	v	0	**Forest Green Rovers**	221
	Fisher 2, Brown 48, Shutt 81					
	Hayes	3	v	5	**Woking**	164
	Moore 27, 34, Preston 70				Steele 18 56, Druce 33 81, Pitman 85	
	Hednesford Town	1	v	0	**Telford United**	349
	Norbury 11					
	Northwich Victoria	3	v	3	**Leigh RMI**	309
	Holdcroft 12, Fletcher 23 90				Ridings 34, Kielty 69, 86	
R	**Leigh RMI**	1	v	0	**Northwich Victoria**	169
	Jones 77					

SECOND ROUND

	Home				Away	Att
	Southport	1	v	0	**Doncaster Rovers**	443
	Maamria 44					
	Chester City	2	v	2	**Hednesford Town**	584
	Blackburn 37, M Beesley 53				Lake 59, Davis 77	
R	**Hednesford Town**	1	v	3	**Chester City**	147
	Russell 48				Ruffer 75, Woods 98, Carden 117	
	Dover Athletic	0	v	1	**Kingstonian**	312
					Luckett 84	
	Rushden & Diamonds	2	v	1	**Stevenage Borough**	412
	Sigerre 25, McElhatton 68				Illman 48	
	Nuneaton Borough	2	v	0	**Scarborough**	614
	Sykes 35 76					
	Morecambe	5	v	2	**Leigh RMI**	395
	Eastwood 61, Talbot 75 101 103 113				German 33, Black 55(p)	
	Woking	0	v	1	**Yeovil Town**	445
					Patmore 63	
	Hereford United	0	v	1	**Kettering Town**	604
					Adams	

QUARTER FINALS

Home				Away	Att
Southport	0	v	3	**Chester City**	685
				M Beesley 7 64, Carden 32	
Kingstonian	1	v	0	**Rushden & Diamonds**	190
Akuamoah 11					
Nuneaton Borough	2	v	0	**Morecambe**	602
Weaver 58, Wray 72					
Yeovil Town	2	v	0	**Kettering Town**	709
Way 33, Poole 73					

SEMI-FINALS

Home				Away	Att
Chester City	2	v	1	**Nuneaton Borough**	602
Blackburn 4, Wright 113				Angus 45	
Yeovil Town	0	v	5	**Kingstonian**	295
				Pitcher 8, Luckett 13, Winston 17[p] 22, Saunders 75	

FINAL

Home				Away	Att
Kingstonian	0	v	0	**Chester City**	495

Chester won 4-2 after kicks from the penalty spot.

MANAGER OF THE YEAR 2000-01

BRIAN TALBOT
Rushden & Diamonds
Photo: Peter Barnes

The Conference championship race wasn't decided until the last week of the season and here we see the eventual champions' manager Brian Talbot (Rushden & Diamonds) on the left, talking to his great rival Colin Addison (Yeovil Town). The sporting way in which both managers conducted themselves throughout the pressure of the chase was a credit to non-league football. Both managers are awarded Merit Awards and of course Brian was elected 'The Conference Manager of the Year'.

GOALKEEPER OF THE YEAR 2000-01

WAYNE BROWN
Chester City and England
Photo: Andrew Chitty

WING BACKS OF THE YEAR 1999-2000

(Right)

LEFT BACK

PAUL UNDERWOOD
Rushden & Diamonds
and
England

Photo: Peter Barnes

(Left)

RIGHT BACK

TARKAN MUSTAFA
Rushden & Diamonds
and
England

Photo: Peter Barnes

CENTRE BACK 2000-01

TERRY SKIVERTON
Yeovil Town and England
Photo: Garry Letts

CENTRE BACK 2000-01

SCOTT GUYETT
Southport and England
Photo: Peter Barnes

MIDFIELD 2000-01

NICK CRITTENDEN
Yeovil Town
Photo: Garry Letts

MIDFIELD 2000-01

GEOFF PITCHER
Kingstonian and England
Photo: Andrew Chitty

MIDFIELD 2000-01

DARREN WAY
Yeovil Town
Photo: Garry Letts

MIDFIELD 2000-01

STEVE JONES
Leigh RMI and England
Photo: Andrew Chitty

STRIKERS 2000-01

(Left)

DUANE DARBY
Rushden & Diamonds

Photo: Peter Barnes

Also
Conference
Player of the Year

(Right)

JUSTIN JACKSON
Rushden & Diamonds
and
England

Photo: Peter Barnes

BARNET

Barnet, like colleagues Scarborough, had known the joy of qualifying to leave the non-League ranks in 1991 and now they have followed their northern rivals back to the Conference after nine seasons in which they reached Division Two for one season in 1993-94.

Manager John Still had a great career in the non-League game and featured in the last ever F.A. Amateur Cup Final at Wembley in 1974 when he was in the Bishop Stortford side that beat Ilford 4-1. And his experiences as a manager and player throughout the Conference Division Three zone will surely be a great help to the club as they attempt to steady themselves and push back to challenge for a speedy return to The Football League.

Last season's disasters have been well documented with a managerial change which sadly didn't work and the most thrilling of climaxes as the Bees entertained Torquay United to settle the relegation issue on the last day of the season.

To the neutral who followed proceedings through television the overwhelming image of the day will be the sportsmanship and goodwill shown by both sets of supporters who made up the impressive 5,523 crowd.

Both clubs showed a few more glamourous clubs the spirit in which such a match should be contested, and on a very sad occasion at least great credit went to everyone involved.

Barnet were a famous amateur club before turning part time professional. The Barry Fry era became folk law within the game and the club has the goodwill of a great many fans up and down the country.

The enthusiasm of their own local supporters used to rival those of Enfield and Wycombe Wanderers for buying the Directory when orders of sixty per club were normal. It will be interesting to see whether that hard core is still there, ready to cheer their beloved Barnet back up the pyramid with the same enthusiasm.

T.W.

Back row, left to right: Gordon Ogbourne (kit man), Frank Murphy, Richard Nugent, Roger Willis, Hakan Hayrettin, Mick Bodley, Gary Phillips, Nicky Evans, Mark Flashman, Geoff Cooper, Gary Blackford, Gary Poole, David Tomlinson, Paul Wilson, Andy McDade (physio). **Front row:** Mark Carter, Wayne Turner, Paul Richardson, David Howell, Edwin Stein, Stan Flashman, Barry Fry, Tony Lynch, Kenny Lowe, Gary Bull, Duncan Horton, Kevin Durham

BARNET

GROUND DETAILS

Underhill Stadium.
Barnet Lane,
Hertfordshire EN5 2BE

TEL: 020 8441 6932
Fax: 020 8447 0655

Match Tickets: From £8 - £15. (£10/£12 for away fans)

Directions:
Take junction 23 off the M25, follow signs for Barnet (A100), the ground is located at the foot of Barnet Hill.

Capacity: 4,057

Founded: 1888

Nickname: The Bees

Sponsors: Maximuscle

Colours: Black & amber shirts, amber shorts & socks

Change colours: Navy with yellow trim

Midweek matchday: Tuesday 7.45

Newsline: 09068 12 15 44 (calls charged at premium rate)

Reserve League:

CLUB OFFICIALS

Chairman: Tony Kleanthous

Chief Executive: Andrew Adie

Football Secretary: D Stanley

Press Officer: Dennis Signy OBE

Commercial Manager: Ben Keogh

MATCHDAY PROGRAMME

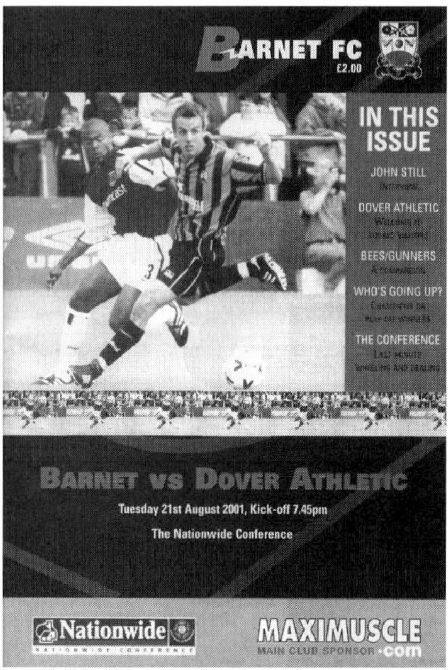

Pages: 48 Price: £2.00
Editor: Kevin Mullen
Tel Nos: 020 84416932 (H)
07774132066 (M)

FOOTBALL MANAGEMENT TEAM

MANAGER	**JOHN STILL**
Date of Appointment	16th March 2001
Date of Birth:	24th April 1950
Place of Birth:	West Ham
PREVIOUS CLUBS	
As manager	Barnet 06.97-11.00
As asst. manager/coach	Lincoln City
As player	Leyton Orient
HONOURS	
As manager	None
As player	None

Asst Manager: Ian Culverhouse
Physiotherapist: John Stannard

Season	League	Div.	Pos.	Home P	W	D	L	F	A	Away W	D	L	F	A	Pts	Manager
00-01	Football Lge	3	24	46	9	8	6	44	29	3	1	19	23	52	45	John Still/Tony Cottee/John Still
99-00	Football Lge	3	6	46	12	6	5	36	24	9	6	8	23	29	75	John Still
98-99	Football Lge	3	16	46	10	5	8	30	31	4	8	11	24	40	55	John Still
97-98	Football Lge	3	7	46	10	8	5	35	22	9	5	9	26	29	70	John Still
96-97	Football Lge	3	15	46	9	9	5	32	23	5	7	11	14	28	58	Terry Bullivant
95-96	Football Lge	3	8	46	13	6	4	40	19	5	10	8	25	26	70	Ray Clemence
94-95	Football Lge	3	12	42	8	7	6	37	27	7	4	10	19	36	56	Ray Clemence
93-94	Football Lge	2	24	46	4	6	13	22	32	1	7	15	19	54	28	Gary Phillips
92-93	Football Lge	3	3	42	16	4	1	45	19	7	6	8	21	29	79	Edwin Stein
91-92	Football Lge	4	7	42	16	1	4	48	23	5	5	11	33	38	69	Barry Fry/Edwin Stein

HONOURS

FA Amateur Cup 1945-46. Runners-up 1947-48, 1958-59.
FA Trophy runners-up 1971-72.
Athenian League x 5. Athenian Premier Div. x 2.
Southern League Div.1 1965-66. Div. 1 South 1976-77.
Southern League Cup 1976-77.
London League 1897, 1906, 1907.
London Senior Cup x 3. London Charity Cup x 2.
Middlesex Senior Cup x 2. Middlesex Charity Cup x 2.
Herts Senior Cup x 12. Herts Charity Cup x 25.
Wendy Fair Capital League 1988-89.
Clubcall Cup 1988-89.
Football Conference Winners 1990-91.
Football Conference runners-up 1986-87, 1987-88, 1989-90.

PREVIOUS

Leagues: Olympian League, London League, Athenian League, Southern League, Alliance Premier, Gola League, Vauxhall Conference, Football League.

Names: Barnet Alston.

Grounds: Queens Road, Totteridge Lane.

Past Players who progressed to the Football League

Colin Powell (Charlton Ath), Gary Borthwick (AFC Bournemouth), Graham Pearce (Brighton & H.A), Russell Townsend (Northampton Tn), Colin Barnes (Torquay Utd), Gary Phillips (Brentford), Keith Alexander (Grimsby Town), Nicky Bissett (Brighton & H.A.), Robert Codner (Brighton & H.A.), Lee Payne (Newcastle Utd), Phil Gridelet (Barnsley), david Regis & Paul Harding (Notts County).

CLUB RECORDS

Attendance: 11,026
v Wycombe W., FA Amateur Cup 4th Rnd, 1951-52.

Career Goalscorer: Arthur Morris, 400, 1927-34.

Career Appearances: Les Eason, 648, 1965-74, 1977-78.

Transfer Fee Paid: £130,000
to Peterborough Utd for Greg Heald.

Transfer Fee Received: £800,000
from Crystal Palace for Dougie Freedman.

BEST SEASON

FA Cup: 3rd Round
1964-65, 1970-71, 1972-73, 1981-82, 1990-91, 1991-92, 1993-94.

FA Trophy: Finalists 1971-72.

League: Conference Champions 1990-91.

LAST SEASON

F.A. Cup: 2nd Round
F.A. Trophy: -
League: 24th in Nationwide Division 3
Top Goalscorer: Tony Cottee, Darren Currie & Tony Richards - 10

BARNET

Match Facts 2000-01

	Date	Comp.	H/A	Opponents	Att.	Result		Goalscorers	Lge Pos.
1	12.08	FL	H	Shrewsbury Town	2090	W	3-0	McGleish, Currie, Purser	
2	19.08	FL	H	Mansfield Town	1732	D	3-3	Arber, Stockley, McGleish	4
3	26.08	FL	H	Cardiff City	2264	D	2-2	McGleish, Charlery	6
4	28.08	FL	A	York City	1981	L	0-1		8
5	02.09	FL	A	Chesterfield	4340	W	2-1	Sawyers, Charlery	7
6	09.09	FL	H	Kidderminster Harriers	2110	D	0-0		7
7	12.09	FL	H	Exeter City	1322	D	1-1	Charlery	
8	16.09	FL	A	Darlington	3929	L	0-1		10
9	23.09	FL	H	Hull City	2109	D	1-1	Strevens	11
10	30.09	FL	A	Plymouth Argyle	3421	W	3-2	Richards 2, Arber	10
11	08.10	FL	H	Macclesfield Town	1841	L	0-2		12
12	14.10	FL	A	Carlisle United	2487	W	2-0	Niven, McGleish	9
13	17.10	FL	A	Southend United	4124	L	0-2		
14	21.10	FL	H	Halifax Town	1580	W	1-0	Doolan (pen)	9
15	24.10	FL	A	Leyton Orient	4707	L	1-3	Riza	
16	28.10	FL	H	Lincoln City	1642	W	4-3	Niven, Goodhind, Riza, Richards	9
17	04.11	FL	A	Rochdale	3667	D	0-0		10
18	11.11	FL	H	Blackpool	2583	W	7-0	Cottee, Richards 2, Currie 3, Arber	8
19	25.11	FL	A	Torquay United	1735	L	1-2	Richards	9
20	02.12	FL	A	Cheltenham Town	3594	L	3-4	Currie, Cottee, Riza	11
21	16.12	FL	H	Scunthorpe United	2086	W	4-2	Cottee 3, Riza	9
22	23.12	FL	A	Hartlepool United	3133	L	1-6	Richards	12
23	26.12	FL	H	Brighton & Hove Albion	3908	L	0-1		13
24	01.01	FL	A	Shrewsbury Town	2991	L	2-3	Arber, McGleish	13
25	13.01	FL	H	York City	2731	W	2-0	Richards, Cottee	11
26	27.01	FL	H	Hartlepool United	2565	L	1-3	Cottee	12
27	03.02	FL	H	Chesterfield	2372	D	1-1	Arber	13
28	10.02	FL	A	Kidderminster Harriers	2566	L	1-2	Cottee	16
29	17.02	FL	H	Darlington	1818	W	3-0	Cottee, Currie, Arber	15
30	20.02	FL	A	Exeter City	3572	L	0-1		
31	24.02	FL	A	Hull City	3268	L	1-2	Gower	16
32	27.02	FL	A	Mansfield Town	1623	L	1-4	Strevens	
33	03.03	FL	H	Plymouth Argyle	2979	D	1-1	Currie	16
34	06.03	FL	H	Carlisle United	1480	L	0-1		
35	11.03	FL	A	Macclesfield Town	2060	L	0-3		17
36	14.03	FL	A	Brighton & Hove Albion	5587	L	1-4	Doolan (pen)	
37	17.03	FL	H	Southend United	2654	W	2-1	Strevens, Currie	16
38	24.03	FL	A	Halifax Town	1639	L	0-3		18
39	31.03	FL	A	Scunthorpe United	2963	L	1-2	Heald	20
40	04.04	FL	A	Cardiff City	6209	L	0-1		
41	07.04	FL	H	Cheltenham Town	1977	D	2-2	Currie (pen), Strevens	20
42	14.04	FL	H	Leyton Orient	3759	L	1-2	Currie (pen)	21
43	16.04	FL	A	Lincoln City	3391	L	1-2	Doolan	22
44	21.04	FL	H	Rochdale	2381	W	3-0	Heald 2, Arber	21
45	28.04	FL	A	Blackpool	5289	L	2-3	Purser, Parkinson (og)	24
46	05.05	FL	H	Torquay United	5527	L	2-3	Green (og), Purser	24

CUP COMPETITIONS

Worthington Cup

Round	H/A	Opponents	Result		Goalscorers
1st Round 1st leg	H	Wycombe Wanderers	W	2-1	Doolan, McGleish
1st Round 2nd leg	A	Wycombe Wanderers	L	1-3	Richards

FA Cup

Round	H/A	Opponents	Result		Goalscorers
First Round	H	Hampton & Richmond Borough	W	2-1	Cottee, Currie
Second Round	A	Walsall	L	1-2	Richards

Harrison	Stockley	Sawyers	Bowling	Heald	Arber	Currie	Doolan	McGleish	Richards	Brown	Darcy	Purser	Toms	Charlery	Strevens	Nowlan	Bell	Naisbitt	Goodhind	Niven	Riza	Cottee	Gledhill	Flynn	Gower	Pluck	Dawson	Collin	Midgley	
1	2	3	4	5	6	7	8	9	10	11	S	S	S																	1
1	2		4	5	6	7	8	10		3		S	11	9	S															2
1	2	3		5	6	7	8	10		11	S			S	9	4														3
1	2	3		5	6	7	8	10		S	S		11	9	S	4														4
1	2	3	4	5	6	7	8	10		11				9																5
1	2	3	4	5	6	7	8	10	S				11	9	S	S														6
1	2	3	4	5	6	7	8	10	S				11	9		S														7
1	2	3	4	5	6	7	8	10		S			11	9	S		S													8
1	2			5	6	7		9	10	3			11		S		4	S	3											9
	2			5	6	7	8	9	10				11		S		4	1	3	S										10
	2			5	6	7	8	S	9			S	11		10		4	1	3											11
	2	3		5	6	7	8	9	10	11							S	1		4										12
	2	3		5	6	7		9	10	8			11		S			1		4										13
	2	3		5	6	7	8	S	9				11		S			1		4	10									14
	2	3		5	6	7	8	9				S	11					1		4	10									15
	2	3			6	7	8		9				11					1	5	4	10									16
	2			5	6	7	8	S	9				11					1	3	4	10									17
	2	3		5	6	7	8	S	9	S			11					1		4	S	10								18
	2	3		5	6	7	8		9	S		S	11					1		4		10								19
	2	3			6	7	8					S	11					1	5	4	10	9	S							20
	2	3		5		7	8			S			11					1	6	4	10	9								21
	2	3		5	6	7			9	11		S	S					1	6	4	10		S							22
1	2	3		5	6	7		9	S				11						8	4	S	10	S							23
1	2	3		5	6	7		S					11				9		8	4	S	10								24
1	2	S	4	5	6	7			9	11							8	S	3			10		11		S				25
1	2		4	5	6	7			9				S				8		3			10		11	S					26
1	2			5	6	S			9	11									4	3		10		3	7					27
1	2			5	6	S			9	11					S		8		4			10		3	7					28
1	2				6	7			9	11					S				5	4		10	S	3	8					29
1	2				6	7			9	11					S				5	4		10		3	8					30
1	2				6	7			9	11					S				5	4		10		3	8					31
1	2	S		5	6	7			9	11		S			10		S			4				3	8					32
1				5	6	7			S	11					9				3	4		10	2		8					33
1	2			5	6	7				11		S	S		9		S		3	4		10			8					34
1	2	S		5	6		8								9				S			10		3	7		4	11		35
1	2	3		5	6	7	8		9			S			10				4								11	S		36
1	2	3			6	7	8		9				S		10				5					11	S		4			37
1	2	3			6	7	8		9						10				5					11			4		S	38
1	2	3		5	6	7	8			11		S			9				4	S				11	10					39
1	2	3		5	6	7	8		S			10			9				4								11			40
1	2	3		5	6	7	8			11		S			9				4	S									10	41
1	2			5	6	7	8		S	11		S			10				4					3					9	42
	2			5	6	7	8		9	11		S			11			1	4					3	S				10	43
	2			5	6	7	8		9	11		10	S		S			1	4	S				3						44
	2	S		5	6	7	8		9	10		10			S			1	4					3						45
1	2			5	6	7	8		9	11		10	S					S	4					3	S					46

PLAYING SQUAD

BARNET

Player	*Birthplace*	*D.O.B.*	*Previous Clubs*
GOALKEEPERS			
Lee Harrison	Billericay	12.09.71	Fulham, Charlton
Danny Naisbitt	Bishop Auckland	25.11.78	Walsall
DEFENDERS			
Greg Heald ES	Enfield	26.09.71	Peterborough Utd, Enfield
Lee Flynn	London	04.09.73	Hayes, Hendon, Boreham Wood, Romford
Mark Arber	Johannesburg	08.10.77	Tottenham
Robert Sawyers	Dudley	20.11.78	Wolves
Warren Goodhind	Johannesburg	16.08.77	From Trainee
MIDFIELD			
Austin Berkley	Dartford	28.01.73	Shrewsbury, Swindon, Gillingham
Fraser Toms	Ealing	13.09.79	Charlton
John Doolan	Liverpool	07.05.74	Mansfield, Everton
Lee Gledhill	Bury	07.11.80	From Trainee
Lee Pluck	London		From Trainee
Leon Bell	Hitchin	19.12.80	From Trainee
Mark Gower ES, EY	Edmonton	05.10.78	Tottenham (£32,500)
Steve Searle	Lambeth	07.03.77	Sittingbourne
FORWARDS			
Ben Strevens	Edgware	24.05.80	Wingate & Finchley
Neil Midgley	Cambridge	21.10.78	Kidderminster Harriers, Ipswich
Stuart Niven	Glasgow	24.12.78	Ipswich
Wayne Purser	Basildon	13.04.80	QPR

BOSTON UNITED

Boston United finished in twelfth place with what can be described as an even campaign, went down in the Fourth Qualifying Round of the F.A. Cup in a replay at Burton Albion and survived the Third Round of the Trophy well at Tamworth 3-0 before bowing out at Tiverton 2-1 in Round Four.

Clearly, for a club with its potential Boston can do better and a place in the Nationwide League should be a minimum target, whilst anything less than an appearance in the First Round Proper of the F.A. Cup and the last eight of the Trophy can be deemed to be an under-achievement.

The league programme started badly and the team had sunk to 22nd place in the league after seven matches, which had yielded four points from draws, but three consecutive wins in September and a total run of five victories in seven matches halted the slide and the ultimate mid-table position was reached early in October with some good results in December and January bringing the heady height of seventh place, but this was a false winter dawn and with no wins in February and only one success in March by a single goal at home to Southport normal service was resumed, which meant that a final unbeaten flourish at the end of the season - five wins and two draws - could not make any serious difference to matters although a 5-1 home win against Dagenham & Redbridge suggested that things could have been better.

The fact that 74 league goals were scored against 63 conceded suggests that the attack was at least adequate with Charlery a constant menace to opposing defences and Rawle, Costello and Raynor earning good marks.

Will the new season bring some tangible successes such as promotion?

W.M

BOSTON UNITED FC 2001-02

Back row: (left to right) Daryl Clare, Andy Lodge, Nick Conroy, Paul Bastock, Simon Weatherstone, James Gould. **Middle row:** Dan Wormham, Mark Clifford, Peter Costello, Ross Weatherstone, Jamie Cook, Mickey Brown, Anthony Elding, Mark Monington, Gez Murphy, Paul Taylor. **Front row:** Gerry Evans (youth team manager), Simon Rusk, David Town, Steve Evans (manager), Michael Sneddon, Mark Angel, Alan Lewer (assistant manager)
Missing from picture: Mike Marsh (captain), Ken Charlery, Mark Freeman, Paul Ellender.

BOSTON UNITED

GROUND DETAILS

York Street, Boston, Lincs. PE21 6HN

TELEPHONE: 01205 364406 office, 01205 365524/5 matchday no., Fax: 01205 354063 Website: www.bostonunited.co.uk

Directions:
A1 to A17 Sleaford-Boston, over rail crossing, bear right at Eagle pub to lights over Haven Bridge,thro the lights opposite New Store,then rightinto York Street Ground just off town centre.Ten minutes walk to **station** Little **Parking** at ground.use streets and local car parks

Capacity: 6,200
Cover: 6,200
Seats: 1,826

Clubhouse: (01205 362967) Open every day except Tuesday. Live entertainmen tSaturday, pool, darts, dominoes, Sunday football teams. Bar for visitors and VP lounge

Club Shop: At club office (as secretary's address). A new shop is next to the Board Room and is open every home match.Mail orders accepted

March Tickets:
Adults: £8.50 - £9.50 concessions £7.50 - £8.50
Season ickets: Adults £140-£150 Conc's £120-£130

MATCHDAY PROGRAMME

Price: £2.00
Editor: Tel: 01205 364406 (office)

Founded: 1934

Nickname: The Pilgrims

Sponsors: "Finn Forest"

Colours: Black & amber striped shirts, black shorts with amber stripes

Change colours: White with amber and black trim

Midweek matchday: Wednesday

Newsline: 0898 121 539

Reserve League: Central Conference

CLUB OFFICIALS

Chairman: P Malkinson

President: Mr A E Bell

Vice-Chairman: A.Malkinson

Directors: P Malkinson, S J Malkinson, A Malkinson, T Ruck, R Hackford, R Carrington, C Woodcock

General Manager / Secretary / / Comm. Manager: John Blackwell, 14-16 Spain Place, Boston, Lincs PE26 6HN Tel: 01205 364406 (office)

Chief Executive: Kevan Mucleston

FOOTBALL MANAGEMENT TEAM

MANAGER **STEVE EVANS**

Date of Appointment: October 1998
Date of Birth: 30th October 1962
Place of Birth: Glasgow

PREVIOUS CLUBS
As manager: Holbeach Utd., Stamford AFC
As asst. manager/coach: -
As player: St. Johnstone, Ayr United, Bolton Wanderers

HONOURS
As manager: United Counties 97-98 (Stamford) Southern Lge. Prem. Div. 99-00
As player: -

Asst Manager: Alan Lewer
Physiotherapist: Kevin Sullivan

Season	League	Div.	Pos.	Home P	Home W	Home D	Home L	Home F	Home A	Away W	Away D	Away L	Away F	Away A	Pts	Manager
00-01	Conference	-	12	42	10	7	4	43	28	3	10	8	31	35	56	Steve Evans
99-00	Southern	Premier	1	42	18	2	1	64	15	9	9	3	38	24	92	Steve Evans
98-99	Southern	Premier	2	42	12	5	4	42	21	5	11	5	27	30	67	Steve Evans
97-98	N.P.L.	Premier	2	42	11	6	4	29	23	11	6	4	26	17	78	Greg Fee
96-97	N.P.L.	Premier	6	44	12	7	3	43	25	10	6	6	31	22	79	Greg Fee

Season	League	Div.	Pos.	P	W	D	L	F	A	Pts	Manager
95-96	N.P.L.	Premier	2	42	23	6	13	86	59	75	Mel Sterland
94-95	N.P.L.	Premier	5	42	20	11	11	80	43	71	Mel Sterland
93-94	N.P.L.	Premier	3	42	23	9	10	90	43	78	Peter Morris
92-93	Conference	-	22	42	9	13	20	50	69	40	Peter Morris
91-92	Conference	-	8	42	18	9	15	71	66	63	Dave Cusack

HONOURS

Southern Lge. Premier Div. 99-00; R-up 98-99.
Northern Premier Lge 72-73 73-74 76-77 77-78
(R-up 71-72 95-96)
Lge Cup 73-74 75-76(R-up 77-78),
Challenge Shield 73-74 74-75 76-77 77-78;
Lincs Senior Cup (12);
East Anglian Cup 60-61;
Central Alliance 61-62 (Lg Cup 61-62);
Utd Counties Lge 65-66 (Lg Cup 65-66);
West Midlands (Reg) Lg 66-67 67-68,
Eastern Professional F'loodlit Cup 71-72 (R-up 76-77);
Midland Lg R-up 55-56.
Non-League Champion of Champions Cup
72-73 73-74 76-77 77-78
Lincolnshire Lge 99-00 (Res.)

PREVIOUS

Leagues: Midland 21-58 62-64; Southern League 58-61 98-00; Central Alliance 61-62; United Counties 65-66; West Midlands (Regional) 66-68; Northern Premier 68-79, 93-98; Alliance Premier (Conference) 79-93

Names: Boston Town; Boston Swifts
Grounds: None

Past Players who progressed to the Football League

Jim Smith (Colchester), Steve Thompson(Lincoln), Brendon Phillips (Mansfield), Gordon Simmonite (Blackpool), Simon Garner (Blackburn), John Froggatt & Bobby Svarc (Colchester), David Gilbert, Neil Grayson, Jamie Pascoe, Robbie Curtis, Dean Trott (Northampton), Tim Dalton(Bradford C.), Gary Jones (Southend) David Norris (Bolton W.) Mark Rawle (Southend United)

CLUB RECORDS

Attendance: 10,086
v Corby Tn, floodlit inauguration 1955

Goalscorer: Chris Cook (181)

Appearances: Billy Howells, 500+

Win: 12-0
v Spilsby Tn, Grace Swan Cup, 92-93

Fee Paid: £14,000
for Micky Nuttell (Wycombe Wanderers)

Fee Received: £50,000
for David Norris to Bolton W. (2000)

BEST SEASON

FA Trophy: Runners-up 84-85

FA Cup: Third Round replay 73-74, 1-6 V Derby County (H), after 0-0
also 3rd Rd. 55-56, 0-4 v Tottenham H. (A)
71-72, 0-1 v Portsmouth (H)
League clubs defeated: Derby 55-56, Southport 70-71,Hartlepool 71-72, Crewe 82-83

League: 3rd Conference 1988-89

LAST SEASON

F.A. Cup: 4th Qualifying Round
F.A. Trophy: Fourth Round
Conference: 12th
Top Goalscorer: **Ken Charlery**
Player of the Year: **Jody Cowshall**
Captain: **Lee Howarth**

BOSTON UNITED

Match Facts 2000-01

	Date	Comp.	Opponents	Gate	Score	Goalscorers
1	19/08	Conf	FOREST GREEN ROVERS	2368	0 - 0	
2	22/08	Conf	Nuneaton Borough	2001	1 - 3	Minett 70
3	26/08	Conf	Woking	1661	1 - 1	Howarth 50
4	30/08	Conf	CHESTER CITY	2078	0 - 0	
5	02/09	Conf	DOVER ATHLETIC	1804	1 - 2	De Souza 75
6	05/09	Conf	Dagenham & Redbridge	1037	1 - 2	Costello 78[p]
7	09/09	Conf	Leigh RMI	1124	2 - 2	Fewings 32, Costello 47
8	13/09	Conf	YEOVIL TOWN	1303	4 - 1	Wilson 44[p] 74[p], Rawle 87, Steele 90[og]
9	16/09	Conf	MORECAMBE	1832	2 - 1	Stanhope 29, Dick 51
10	23/09	Conf	Northwich Victoria	1035	3 - 0	Charlery 4, Fewings 7, Wilson 50[p]
11	26/09	Conf	Southport	1003	1 - 3	Wilson 71[p]
12	30/09	Conf	DONCASTER ROVERS	3155	3 - 1	Fewings 6, Hoyle 24, Charlery 49
13	04/10	Conf	TELFORD UNITED	1756	2 - 1	Charlery 54, Rawle 90
14	08/10	Conf	Rushden & Diamonds	4570	0 - 0	
15	14/10	Conf	Stevenage Borough	2129	2 - 3	Raynor 33, Charlery 67
16	21/10	Conf	HEDNESFORD TOWN	1730	3 - 4	Rawle 28 53, Charlery 38
17	04/11	Conf	Kingstonian	842	0 - 0	
18	11/11	Conf	SCARBOROUGH	1752	2 - 2	Fewings 24, Wilson 61
19	18/11	Conf	Dover Athletic	764	0 - 0	
20	25/11	Conf	Hereford United	2056	1 - 1	Howarth 58
21	02/12	Conf	HAYES	1667	0 - 1	
22	16/12	Conf	NUNEATON BOROUGH	1573	4 - 1	Wray 1[og], Rawle 62 65, Bacon 75[og]
23	26/12	Conf	Kettering Town	2092	2 - 2	Rawle 12, Norris 85
24	30/12	Conf	Forest Green Rovers	872	3 - 0	Raynor 60, Norris 79 82
25	01/01	Conf	KETTERING TOWN	3108	4 - 3	Raynor 33, Rawle 38, Norris 43, Wilson 75
26	06/01	Conf	STEVENAGE BOROUGH	2199	3 - 3	Wilson 34, Rawle 36, Charlery 41
27	20/01	Conf	WOKING	1767	0 - 0	
28	10/02	Conf	LEIGH RMI	1580	0 - 1	
29	17/02	Conf	Yeovil Town	3585	1 - 2	Rawle 89
30	24/02	Conf	NORTHWICH VICTORIA	1556	1 - 1	Diaf 63
31	27/02	Conf	Chester City	1087	2 - 2	S Weatherstone 58, Charlery 78[p]
32	03/03	Conf	Morecambe	1009	0 - 2	
33	10/03	Conf	RUSHDEN & DIAMONDS	3434	1 - 1	Charlery 87
34	17/03	Conf	Doncaster Rovers	2296	2 - 4	S Weatherstone 39, Charlery 55[p]
35	25/03	Conf	SOUTHPORT	1621	1 - 0	Rusk 35
36	31/03	Conf	Telford United	1109	2 - 3	S Weatherstone 29, Charlery 90
37	11/04	Conf	DAGENHAM & REDBRIDGE	1386	5 - 1	Costello 24 49, Charlery 42[p], Town 79, S Weatherstone 85
38	16/04	Conf	Scarborough	1279	2 - 2	Costello 73 82
39	21/04	Conf	KINGSTONIAN	2145	2 - 1	Town 37, Stanhope 59
40	23/04	Conf	Hednesford Town	646	4 - 2	S Weatherstone 56, Costello 63[p], Town 72, Haran 90[og]
41	28/04	Conf	Hayes	929	1 - 1	Charlery 5
42	05/05	Conf	HEREFORD UNITED	1836	5 - 3	Cook 16 63, Charlery 34, Howarth 72, Rusk 83

OTHER COMPETITIONS

Date	Comp.	Opponents	Gate	Score	Goalscorers
26/07	Lincs SC QF	SCUNTHORPE UNITED	619	1 - 0	Rawle 90
12/08	DML Shield	BURTON ALBION	835	0 - 4	
20/09	Variety CT 1	NUNEATON BOROUGH	527	1 - 5	Elding 1
28/10	FA Cup Q4	BURTON ALBION	2144	1 - 1	Charlery 8
31/10	FA Cup Q4 R	Burton Albion	2299	2 - 3	Charlery 17, Stanhope 87
28/11	Lincs SC SF	Grantham Town	453	1 - 0	Rawle 80
13/01	FA Trophy 3	Tamworth	846	3 - 0	Norris 15 20 27
31/01	Lincs SC F	STAMFORD	465	1 - 2	Rawle 56
03/02	FA Trophy 4	Tiverton Town	1436	1 - 2	Charlery 70[p]

1	2	3	4	5	6	7	8	9	10	11	Substitutes Used
Bastock	Wooding	Hoyle	Rennie	Howarth	Lucas	Raynor	Costello	Minett	Rawle	Nuttell	Fewings (8); Livett (9); De Souza (11)
Bastock	Wooding	Lucas	Gowshall	Howarth	Rennie	Stanhope	Cramman	Raynor	De Souza	Nuttell	Livett (7); Minett (8); Rawle (10)
Bastock	Gowshall	Lucas	Hoyle	Howarth	Lodge	Stanhope	Dick	Nuttell	Fewings	Raynor	De Souza (7); Rawle (10); Livett (8)
Bastock	Gowshall	Lucas	Hoyle	Howarth	Lodge	Stanhope	Livett	Raynor	De Souza	Rawle	Fewings (6)
Bastock	Gowshall	Lucas	Hoyle	Howarth	Lodge	Stanhope	De Souza	Rawle	Livett	Raynor	Costello (10); Fewings (3)
Bastock	Gowshall	Lucas	Hoyle	Howarth	Lodge	Stanhope	Costello	Raynor	De Souza	Nuttell	Rawle (6); Minett (9); Fewings (10)
Bastock	Gowshall	Lucas	Rennie	Wooding	Howarth	Dick	Costello	Wilson	Fewings	De Souza	Lodge (4); Hoyle (6); Rawle (11)
Bastock	Wooding	Lucas	Hoyle	Gowshall	Wilson	Stanhope	Raynor	Dick	Fewings	De Souza	Livett (8); Minett (10); Rawle (11)
Bastock	Woodling	Hoyle	Gowshall	Lucas	Stanhope	Wilson	Raynor	Dick	Fewings	De Souza	Elding (10); Rawle (11)
Bastock	Wooding	Hoyle	Gowshall	Lucas	Stanhope	Wilson	Dick	Raynor	Charlery	Fewings	Rawle (11)
Bastock	Wooding	Hoyle	Gowshall	Lucas	Stanhope	Dick	Wilson	Raynor	Charlery	Fewings	Minett (6)
Bastock	Wooding	Gowshall	Hoyle	Lucas	Minett	Wilson	Raynor	Dick	Fewings	Charlery	Stanhope (6) sub Elding
Bastock	Wooding	Lucas	Curtis	Gowshall	Wilson	Minett	Raynor	Dick	Fewings	Charlery	Rawle (4); French (7)
Bastock	Wooding	Lucas	Hoyle	Gowshall	Wilson	Stanhope	Raynor	Dick	Fewings	Charlery	French (8); Rawle (10)
Bastock	Wooding	Lucas	Hoyle	Curtis	Wilson	French	Charlery	Raynor	Rawle	Dick	Nuttell (10); Stanhope (7)
Bastock	Wooding	Hoyle	Gowshall	Lucas	French	Wilson	Raynor	Dick	Charlery	Rawle	Nuttell (5); Fewings (11)
Bastock	Gowshall	Lucas	Hoyle	Howarth	Wilson	Stanhope	Raynor	Dick	Charlery	Fewings	Rawle (10); French (7)
Bastock	Gowshall	Hoyle	Howarth	Lucas	Mills	Wilson	Raynor	Turner	Fewings	Charlery	French (8); Rawle (10)
Bastock	Gowshall	Curtis	Howarth	Lucas	Mills	Minett	Raynor	Turner	Charlery	Fewings	Rawle (11)
Bastock	Gowshall	Howarth	Hoyle	Curtis	Mills	Raynor	Dick	Turner	Charlery	Fewings	Lucas (5); Rawle (11); Minett (8)
Bastock	Gowshall	Hoyle	Howarth	Lodge	Stanhope	Mills	Raynor	Turner	Charlery	Fewings	Lucas (5); Rawle (11)
Bastock	Gowshall	Hoyle	Howarth	Lodge	Mills	Wilson	Dick	Raynor	Charlery	Rawle	Costello (7); Nuttell (10); Fewings (11)
Bastock	Gowshall	Lodge	Hoyle	Howarth	Wilson	Raynor	Dick	Norris	Rawle	Charlery	Costello (6); Fewings (7)
Bastock	Gowshall	Lodge	Hoyle	Howarth	Wilson	Raynor	Dick	Norris	Rawle	Charlery	Fewings (10); Mills (2); Nuttell (11)
Bastock	Gowshall	Lodge	Hoyle	Howarth	Wilson	Raynor	Dick	Norris	Rawle	Charlery	Fewings (6); Costello (7); Mills (11)
Bastock	Gowshall	Hoyle	Howarth	Lodge	Norris	Wilson	Dick	Raynor	Charlery	Rawle	Mills (2); Costello (7); Fewings (9)
Bastock	Howarth	Lodge	Hoyle	Costello	Wilson	Stanhope	Dick	Fewings	Rawle	Charley	Lucas (9); Elding (10); Nuttell (11)
Bastock	Gowshall	Hoyle	Howarth	Lodge	Clifford	Costello	Raynor	Dick	Charlery	Rawle	Nuttell (10)
Bastock	Gowshall	Howarth	S W'rstone	Lodge	Norris	Clifford	Costello	Raynor	Nuttell	Rawle	Diaf (4); R W'rstone (9)
Bastock	Clifford	R W'rstone	Howarth	Lucas	Costello	Diaf	S W'rstone	Raynor	Nuttell	Cooke	Gowshall (3); Charlery (7)
Bastock	Howarth	Lucas	R W'rstone	Clifford	Diaf	Raynor	Charlery	Nuttell	Cook	S W'rstone	Gowshall (4); Hoyle (7)
Bastock	Clifford	Lucas	R W'rstone	Howarth	Diaf	S W'rstone	Charlery	Raynor	Cook	Elding	Costello (6); Dick (3)
Bastock	Clifford	Gowshall	R W'rstone	Lucas	Cook	S W'rstone	Dick	Raynor	Charlery	Nuttell	Lodge (9); Elding (11)
Bastock	Clifford	Lodge	R W'rstone	Gowshall	Dick	Rusk	Charlery	Nuttell	S W'rstone	Cook	Hoyle (4); Raynor (6); Fewings (9)
Bastock	Hoyle	Lodge	R W'rstone	Gowshall	Clifford	Rusk	Dick	S W'rstone	Charlery	Nuttell	Lucas (3); Costello (4); Cook (9)
Bastock	Gowshall	Lucas	Hoyle	Howarth	S W'rstone	Rusk	Charlery	Nuttell	Costello	Dick	Stanhope (3); Town (9); Cook (10)
Bastock	Howarth	Lucas	Gowshall	Rusk	Costello	Dick	Charlery	Town	Cook	S W'rstone	Stanhope (6); Nuttell (8); Elding (9)
Bastock	Howarth	Gowshall	Lucas	Rusk	Costello	Dick	Charlery	Town	Cook	S W'rstone	Elding (9); Lodge (10); Stanhope (5)
Bastock	Stanhope	Gowshall	Howarth	Lucas	S W'rstone	Costello	Dick	Cook	Charlery	Town	Rusk (6); Lodge (9); Elding (11)
Bastock	Howarth	Lodge	Gowshall	Clifford	Costello	Stanhope	S W'rstone	Nuttell	Town	Cook	Elding (8); Lucas (9); Conroy (11)
Bastock	Clifford	Lucas	Gowshall	Howarth	Costello	Stanhope	Charlery	Town	S W'rstone	Cook	Lodge (4); Rusk (10)
Bastock	Howarth	Lucas	Lodge	Clifford	Rusk	Stanhope	Costello	Town	Charlery	Cook	Elding (9); Conroy (1)

PLAYING SQUAD

BOSTON UNITED

Player	*Birthplace*	*D.O.B.*	*Previous Clubs*
GOALKEEPERS			
Paul Bastock	Leamington	19.05.70	Coventry, Cambridge U, Kettering T
Nick Conroy	Peterborough		Yaxley, Stamford, Yaxley, Kettering T
DEFENDERS			
Andy Lodge Stamford	Whittlesey		Whittlesey U, Bury T, Spalding U, Stamford, Wisbech T,
Mark Freeman NC	Walsall	27.01.70	Cheltenham T (£15,000), Gloucester C, Hednesford T, Willenhall T, Bilston T, Wolves
Mark Monington	Mansfield	21.10.70	Rochdale, Rotherham, Burnley
Ross Weatherstone	Reading	16.05.81	Oxford Utd
MIDFIELD			
Peter Costello DMP	Halifax	31.10.69	Bradford C, Rochdale, Peterborough, Lincoln, Dover Ath. Nuneaton B, Kettering T, South Africa
Simon Livett	Plaistow	08.01.69	West Ham, Leyton O, Camb.U, Billericay T, Southend, Enfield
Jimmy Dick	Scotland		Airdrie
Mike Marsh	Liverpool	21.07.69	Southport (£15,000), Kidderminster H, Southport, Barrow, Southend, Galatasaray, Coventry, West Ham, Liverpool, Kirkby T
NC			
Jamie Cook	Oxford	02.08.79	Oxford Utd
James Gould		15.01.82	Northampton
Mark Angel	Newcastle	23.08.75	Darlington, WBA, Oxford U., Sunderland, Walker Central
Paul Wilson	Forest Gate	26.09.64	Barnet, Barking, Billericay T, West Ham
NC			
Simon Rusk	Peterborough		Peterborough
FORWARDS			
Paul Fewings	Hull	18.02.78	Hull C, Hereford U
David Town	Bournemouth	09.12.76	Rushden & Diamonds, Bournemouth
Gez Murphy	Leicester		Telford Utd, Gresley R, Atherstone Utd, Solihull B, VS Rugby, Leicester (Trainee)
Darryl Clare Eire u-21	Jersey	01.08.78	Grimsby
Ken Charlery NC, ESP	Stepney	28.11.64	Barnet (£25,000), Stockport, Peterborough, Birmingham, Peterborough, Watford, Peterborough, Maidstone Utd, Fisher Ath., Basildon Utd, Beckton Utd
Simon Weatherstone	Reading	26.01.80	Oxford Utd
Mickey Brown	Birmingham	08.02.68	Shrewsbury, Preston, Shrewsbury, Bolton, Shrewsbury

CHESTER CITY

After the shock of their unlucky departure from the Nationwide League the previous season it was probably too much to expect that Chester City would bounce back immediately and they did not with a final eighth place in the Conference suggesting a period of consolidation rather than anything else.

It was perhaps significant that their first match in new circumstances was at Rushden & Diamonds (a 2-0 defeat) and thereafter league form was patchy with third place being reached for a brief period early in October 2000. In fact, from 12th September until 16th December (a single goal defeat at Doncaster) no league matches were actually lost and 13th January to 10th March was another unbeaten period with only two draws to mar their record, but there were no signs that the supremacy of Rushden & Diamonds or Yeovil Town would be threatened, so the final run in of sixteen matches caused by fixture congestion produced only three successes and a final disappointing position.

The cups did produce ample consolation and omens for a better future. In the F.A. Cup Fourth Qualifying Round Easington Colliery were beaten 2-0 on their own ground and better followed with Plymouth Argyle failing to improve on a First Round 1-1 draw in Cheshire by losing the home replay 2-1. Oxford United then came to Chester and lost a thriller 3-2 and a Third Round visit to Blackburn Rovers brought an honourable defeat 2-0.

The F.A. Trophy promised great things with a Third Round home win 2-0 against Doncaster Rovers, followed by more home successes against St. Albans City 3-2, Blyth Spartans 4-2 and Southport 1-0, which led to a two-legged Semi-Final against Canvey Island and two disappointing 2-0 scorelines. A penalty shoot-out at Kingsmeadow against the Kingstonian team after a scoreless draw brought at least one piece of silverware - the Nationwide Conference Variety Club Trophy.

A glance at the table will quickly shown one of the main problems - a weak attack with ten of the final sixteen matches seeing Chester scoreless. So a sound defence was not enough and new manager Gordon Hill will have some head scratching to do. Sadly it may be politics not football that prevents the club recovering fully.

W.M.

Back Row: Neil Fisher, David Kerr, Martyn Lancaster, Dean Greygoose, Mattie Woods, Wayne Brown, Paul Beesley, Paul Carden, Neil Fitzhenry. **Middle:** Gordon Hill (Youth Coach), Mark Beesley, Andy Shelton, Dean Spink, Scott Ruscoe, Nick Richardson, Darren Moss, Chrsi Blackburn, Craig Gaunt, Graham Vile (Centre of Excellence Director). **Front:** Darren Wright, Paul Berry, Terry Smith (Chairman), Graham Barrow (Manager), Joe Hinnegan (Physio), Matt Doughty, Steve Finney

CHESTER CITY

GROUND DETAILS

Deva Stadium,BumpersLane, Chester CH1 4LT

Tel: 01244 371376 or 371809
Admin. Office Fax: 01244 390265
Commercial Office Fax: 01244 390243
email: chesterfc@The Deva.FSBusiness.co.uk
Web site: http://www.chesterfc.co.uk

SIMPLE DIRECTIONS:
Follow signs to Chester , into Town Centre, then follow signs to Queensferry (A548) to Sealand Road. Turn into Bumpers Lane, signed Chester City F.C.Two miles to Town centre and British Rail, Chester (01244 340170). Car Parking at ground

MATCH TICKETS: Adults £10-£12 concessions £7-£9

CAPACITY: Normally 6,000 but 3,000 for first five games

SEATED: 3,094

COVERED TERRACING: 2,640

Refreshments: Six tea bars
Clubhouse: Open matchdays & for private bookings
Contact: The club office on 01244 371376
Function/Banqueting facilities: Yes
Limited guests on match day at #1,50 each
CLUB SHOP: Yes

MATCHDAY PROGRAMME

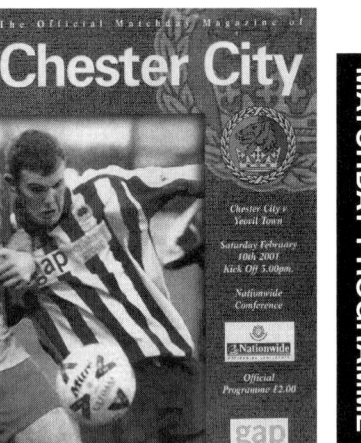

Pages: 36 Price: £2.00

Editor: Norman Spencer
chesterfc@The Deva.FSBusiness.co.uk

Local Press: Chester Chronicle, Evening Leader
Local Radio: Radio Merseyside, Marcher Sound

Founded: 1884

Nickname: The Blues

Club Sponsors: Red Square

Club colours: Sky & navy blue striped shirts, blue shorts, navy blue socks

Change colours: Gold & black/black/black

Midweek home matchday: Tuesday

Reserves' League: Lancashire Division One.

Clubcall 0906 8121633

CLUB OFFICIALS

President

Honory Vice Presidents J Kane, L Lloyd, M Swallow

Chairman Terry Smith

Directors G Smith, M Smith, M Fair

Secretary Michael Fair

Commercial Manager Michael Beech

FOOTBALL MANAGEMENT TEAM

MANAGER GORDON HILL

Date of Appointment: July 2001
Date of Birth: 01.04.52
Place of Birth: Staines

PREVIOUS CLUBS
As manager
As player Manchester United,Derby County Q.P.R., Millwall

HONOURS
As manager
As player Seven Full England Caps F.A.Cup winners & Runners Up

Assistant Manager:

Physiotherapist: Chris Malkin

Community Officer: Brian Croft

Season

Season	League	Div.	Pos.	Home P	Home W	Home D	Home L	Home F	Home A	Away W	Away D	Away L	Away F	Away A	Pts	Manager
00-01	Conference	-	8	42	9	8	4	29	19	7	6	8	20	24	62	Graham Barrow
99-00	Football Lge	3	24	46	5	5	13	20	36	5	4	14	24	43	39	Kevin Ratcliffe/Terry Smith/Ian Atkins
98-99	Football Lge	3	14	46	6	12	5	28	30	7	6	10	29	36	57	Kevin Ratcliffe
97-98	Football Lge	3	14	46	12	7	4	34	15	5	3	15	26	46	61	Kevin Ratcliffe
96-97	Football Lge	3	6	46	11	8	4	30	16	7	8	8	25	27	70	Kevin Ratcliffe
95-96	Football Lge	3	8	46	11	9	3	45	22	7	7	9	27	31	70	Kevin Ratcliffe
94-95	Football Lge	2	23	46	5	6	12	23	42	1	5	17	14	42	29	Mike Pejic/Derek Mann*/Kevin Ratcliffe*
93-94	Football Lge	3	2	42	13	5	3	35	18	8	6	7	34	28	74	Graham Barrow
92-93	Football Lge	2	24	46	6	2	15	30	47	2	3	18	19	55	29	Harry McNally/Graham Barrow
	Premiership formed, Div. 2 became Div. 1 etc.															
91-92	Football Lge	3	18	46	10	6	7	34	29	4	8	11	22	30	56	Harry McNally

HONOURS

League Division 3N Cup 35-36 36-37; R-up 45-46
Debenhams Cup 77
Welsh Cup Winners 07-08 32-33 46-47
R-up 08-09 09-10 34-35 35-36
52-53 53-54 54-55 57-58 65-66 69-70
Combination 1908-09 R-up 1903-1908 (5 times)
Cheshire County Lge 21-22 25-26 26-27 R-up 30-31
Cheshire Senior Cup 1894-95 96-97 1903-04
07-08 08-09 30-31 31-32
R-up 1887-88 92-93 93-94 1904-05 10-11 28-29

PREVIOUS

Leagues: The Combination 1890-1899, 1901-1910
Lancashire Combination 1910-1914
Cheshire County League 1919-1931
Football League 1931-2000

Grounds: Faulkner St. 1885-98; Old Showground 1898-99
Whipcord Lane 1901-06; Sealand Road. 1906-1990
Moss Rose, Macclesfield (ground share) 90-92

Names: Chester F.C. until 1983

Past Players who progressed to the Football League

not yet applicable

CLUB RECORDS

Attendance: 5,638
v Preston N.E., Div. 3, 2.4.1994
(Sealand Rd.) 20,500 v Chelsea, FAC 16.1.52

Record win: 12-0
v York City, Div. 3N, 1.2.1936

Record defeat: 2-11
v Oldham Ath. (A), Div. 3N, 19.1.1952

Career goalscorer: Stuart Rimmer 135 (84-88 & 91-98)

Career appearances: Ray Gill 406 League Apps. 51-62

Transfer fee paid: £94,000
for Stuart Rimmer, to Barnsley, Aug. 1991

Transfer fee received: £300,000
for Ian Rush from Liverpool, May 1980

BEST SEASON

FA Trophy: Semi Finalists, 2000-01

FA Cup: 5th Round
1890-91, 1976-77, 79-80

As Conference club: 3rd Rd, 2000-01

Conference 8th

Nationwide Trophy (Lg Cup) Winners 2000-01

LAST SEASON

F.A. Cup: Third Round
FA Trophy: Semi-Final
League: 8th
Top Goalscorer: Mark Beesley
Player of the Year: Paul Beesley
Captain: Andy Porter

CHESTER CITY

Match Facts 2000-01

	Date	Comp.	Opponents	Gate	Score	Goalscorers
1	19/08	Conf	Rushden & Diamonds	3966	0 - 2	
2	22/08	Conf	DONCASTER ROVERS	2616	3 - 0	M Beesley 1 60, Carden 81
3	26/08	Conf	DOVER ATHLETIC	2273	1 - 0	Wright 86[p]
4	30/08	Conf	Boston United	2078	0 - 0	
5	02/09	Conf	SOUTHPORT	2861	0 - 1	
6	05/09	Conf	Morecambe	1557	2 - 0	Blackburn 37, Woods 67
7	09/09	Conf	Yeovil Town	2862	1 - 2	Bent 88[og]
8	12/09	Conf	NORTHWICH VICTORIA	1717	1 - 1	Blackburn 77
9	23/09	Conf	Kingstonian	1125	3 - 1	Whitehall 14 74[p], Evans 84
10	26/09	Conf	NUNEATON BOROUGH	1708	4 - 0	Crowley 37[og], M Beesley 50 65, Evans 84
11	30/09	Conf	Hednesford Town	1435	0 - 0	
12	03/10	Conf	Scarborough	1193	2 - 0	Whitehall 42, M Beesley 48
13	08/10	Conf	KETTERING TOWN	2102	2 - 1	Whitehall 61 66
14	14/10	Conf	Forest Green Rovers	943	1 - 1	Fisher 57
15	21/10	Conf	LEIGH RMI	1858	1 - 1	Wright 90
16	04/11	Conf	Dagenham & Redbridge	1244	1 - 1	Porter 87
17	11/11	Conf	STEVENAGE BOROUGH	1708	1 - 1	M Beesley 46
18	02/12	Conf	WOKING	1694	3 - 3	Fisher 7, Whitehall 35, Porter 65[p]
19	16/12	Conf	Doncaster Rovers	2553	0 - 1	
20	23/12	Conf	HAYES	1658	0 - 0	
21	26/12	Conf	HEREFORD UNITED	2224	2 - 1	M Beesley 26, Whitehall 85
22	01/01	Conf	Hereford United	2321	0 - 2	
23	27/01	Conf	MORECAMBE	1717	1 - 0	Lancaster 13
24	10/02	Conf	YEOVIL TOWN	2265	2 - 1	Ruscoe 17, M Beesley 32
25	17/02	Conf	Northwich Victoria	2651	1 - 1	Haarhoff 33
26	20/02	Conf	TELFORD UNITED	1362	1 - 0	Woods 8
27	27/02	Conf	BOSTON UNITED	1087	2 - 2	Woods 49, Doughty 84
28	03/03	Conf	Hayes	784	3 - 1	M Beesley 38 63[p], Woods 79[p]
29	13/03	Conf	Southport	1279	0 - 1	
30	17/03	Conf	HEDNESFORD TOWN	1491	0 - 1	
31	23/03	Conf	Nuneaton Borough	1363	2 - 1	M Beesley 13, Whitehall 29
32	27/03	Conf	Telford United	1058	0 - 3	
33	03/04	Conf	Dover Athletic	1112	1 - 1	Whitehall 48
34	14/04	Conf	FOREST GREEN ROVERS	1292	0 - 1	
35	16/04	Conf	Stevenage Borough	1748	2 - 1	Fisher 4, Wright 44
36	18/04	Conf	Leigh RMI	501	1 - 0	Wright 25
37	21/04	Conf	DAGENHAM & REDBRIDGE	1202	1 - 1	Woods 86
38	24/04	Conf	Kettering Town	1216	0 - 4	
39	26/04	Conf	KINGSTONIAN	834	0 - 0	
40	28/04	Conf	Woking	2264	0 - 1	
41	01/05	Conf	SCARBOROUGH	805	3 - 2	Fisher 45, M Beesley 52, Piercewright 75[og]
42	05/05	Conf	RUSHDEN & DIAMONDS	4040	1 - 2	Gaunt 58

OTHER COMPETITIONS

Date	Comp.	Opponents	Gate	Score	Goalscorers
17/10	Variety CT 2	HEDNESFORD TOWN	584	2 - 2	Blackburn 37, M Beesley 53
28/10	FA Cup Q4	Easington Colliery	478	2 - 0	Whitehall 7, M Beasley 83
18/11	FA Cup 1	PLYMOUTH ARGYLE	2393	1 - 1	Wright 78
28/11	FA Cup 1 rep	Plymouth Argyle	3264	2 - 1	Whitehall 42, Ruscoe 107
05/12	LDV Vans 1N	HULL CITY	770	1 - 0	Carden 52
09/12	FA Cup 2	OXFORD UNITED	2798	3 - 2	P Beesley 35, Whitehall 54 60
18/12	Variety CT 2 R	Hednesford Town	147	3 - 1	Ruffer 75, Woods 98, Carden 117
06/01	FA Cup 3	Blackburn Rovers	15223	0 - 2	
13/01	FA Trophy 3	DONCASTER ROVERS	1479	2 - 0	Whitehall 29 35
30/01	LDV Vans 2N	Port Vale	2507	0 - 2	
03/02	FA Trophy 4	ST ALBANS CITY	1442	3 - 2	Ruffer 13, Ruscoe 55, Blackburn 77
06/02	Variety CT QF	Southport	685	3 - 0	M Beesley 7 64, Carden 32
24/02	FA Trophy 5	BLYTH SPARTANS	1831	4 - 2	Haarhoff 6, M Beesley 23, P Beesley 81, Whitehall 90
10/03	FA Trophy QF	SOUTHPORT	3204	1 - 0	Woods 88
31/03	FA Trophy SF(1)	Canvey Island	1221	0 - 2	
07/04	FA Trophy SF(2)	CANVEY ISLAND	2647	0 - 2	
03/05	Variety CT SF	NUNEATON BOROUGH	602	2 - 1	Blackburn 4, Wright 113
07/05	Variety CT F	Kingstonian	495	0 - 0	Won 4-2 after kicks from the penalty spot.

1	2	3	4	5	6	7	8	9	10	11	Substitutes Used
Greygoose	Lancaster	Gaunt	P Beesley	Woods	Doughty	Carden	Blackburn	Kerr	Finney	Wright	M Beesley (2), Richardson (8), Ruffer (9)
Greygoose	Woods	P Beesley	Lancaster	Doughty	Gaunt	Carden	Blackburn	Finney	M Beesley	Ruffer	A Shelton (10), Wright (9)
Greygoose	Lancaster	Doughty	Gaunt	P Beesley	Woods	Carden	Blackburn	Finney	M Beesley	Ruffer	Shelton (2), Evans (9)
Brown	P Beesley	Woods	Ruffer	Lancaster	Doughty	Gaunt	Blackburn	Evans	Carden	M Beesley	Finney (11), Kerr (4)
Brown	Lancaster	Doughty	Gaunt	P Beesley	Woods	Carden	Blackburn	Evans	M Beesley	Ruffer	Shelton (2), Finney (6), Richardson (8)
Brown	Woods	P Beesley	Kerr	Doughty	Gaunt	Carden	Blackburn	Evans	M Beesley	Wright	Lancaster (4), Richardson (10), Fisher(11)
Brown	Kerr	Doughty	Gaunt	P Beesley	Woods	Carden	Blackburn	Evans	M Beesley	Wright	Fisher (2), Finney (9), Richardson (11)
Brown	Woods	P Beesley	Evans	Doughty	Gaunt	Carden	Blackburn	Moss	M Beesley	Finney	Fisher (2), Ruffer (4)
Brown	Moss	Doughty	Woods	Lancaster	Fisher	Carden	Blackburn	M Beesley	Whitehall	Richardson	Evans(9), Kerr (11), Finney (10)
Brown	P Beesley	Woods	Lancaster	Doughty	Blackburn	Carden	Fisher	M Beesley	Whitehall	Moss	Evans (9), Woodyatt (11)
Brown	Woods	Gaunt	P Beesley	Moss	Carden	Blackburn	Fisher	Doughty	M Beesley	Whitehall	Lancaster (3), Kerr (5), Finney (10)
Brown	Woods	P Beesley	Fisher	Doughty	Lancaster	Carden	Blackburn	Moss	Whitehall	M Beesley	
Brown	Woods	P Beesley	Fisher	Doughty	Lancaster	Carden	Blackburn	Moss	Whitehall	M Beesley	Wright (9), Ruffer (11)
Brown	Moss	Woods	Lancaster	Doughty	P Beesley	Carden	Blackburn	Fisher	M Beesley	Whitehall	Wright (2)
Brown	Carden	Doughty	Woods	Lancaster	P Beesley	Porter	Blackburn	M Beesley	Whitehall	Fisher	Roscoe (3), Ruffer (4), Wright (11)
Brown	Lancaster	Doughty	Woods	Ruffer	P Beesley	Carden	Blackburn	M Beesley	Whitehall	Porter	Fisher (2), Ruscoe (8), Wright (9)
Brown	Fisher	Doughty	Woods	P Beesley	Ruffer	Carden	Blackburn	Porter	M Beesley	Wright	Ruscoe (2)
Brown	Fisher	Doughty	Woods	Lancaster	Ruffer	Carden	Blackburn	M Beesley	Whitehall	Porter	Gaunt (5), Wright (8), Ruscoe (9)
Brown	Fisher	Doughty	Gaunt	Lancaster	P Beesley	Ruffer	Porter	M Beesley	Whitehall	Blackburn	Ruscoe (11), Wright (4)
Brown	Fisher	Doughty	Gaunt	Ruffer	Lancaster	Carden	Porter	M Beesley	Whitehall	Blackburn	Ruscoe (4) sub Wright
Brown	P Beesley	Ruffer	Fisher	Doughty	Lancaster	Carden	Blackburn	Ruscoe	Whitehall	M Beesley	Wright (9)
Brown	P Beesley	Ruffer	Fisher	Doughty	Lancaster	Carden	Blackburn	Ruscoe	Whitehall	M Beesley	Wright (9), Moss (11)
Brown	Fisher	Doughty	Woods	Lancaster	P Beesley	Carden	Blackburn	M Beesley	Whitehall	Ruscoe	Wright (10), Haarhoff (11)
Brown	Fisher	Doughty	Lancaster	Ruffer	P Beesley	Haarhoff	Blackburn	Woods	M Beesley	Ruscoe	Woodyatt (3), Wright (8)
Brown	Fisher	Lancaster	Ruffer	P Beesley	Doughty	Carden	Haarhoff	Ruscoe	Woods	M Beesley	Gaunt (6)
Brown	Gaunt	P Beesley	Woods	Fisher	Doughty	Lancaster	Haarhoff	Carden	Ruscoe	M Beesley	Moss (8)
Priestley	Woods	P Beesley	Gaunt	Lancaster	Fisher	Carden	Haarhoff	Ruscoe	M Beesley	Moss	Doughty (4), Whitehall (10)
Priestley	Moss	Lancaster	Gaunt	P Beesley	Doughty	Carden	Fisher	Ruscoe	Woods	M Beesley	Wright (9), Berry (11)
Brown	Ruffer	Gaunt	Woods	Lancaster	Doughty	Carden	Ruscoe	Fisher	M Beesley	Whitehall	Porter (3), Moss (6), Haarhoff (11)
Brown	Fisher	Doughty	Lancaster	Ruffer	P Beesley	Carden	Porter	M Beesley	Whitehall	Ruscoe	Wright (8), Woods (10), Haarhoff (11)
Brown	P Beesley	Ruffer	Ruscoe	Doughty	Lancaster	Carden	Fisher	Moss	M Beesley	Whitehall	Priestley (5), Woodyatt (10), Haarhoff (11)
Brown	Woods	P Beesley	Fisher	Ruscoe	Lancaster	Carden	Moss	Woodyatt	Whitehall	Wright	Gaunt (9), Haarhoff (7)
Priestley	P Beesley	Woods	Haarhoff	Ruscoe	Lancaster	Blackburn	Porter	Moss	Whitehall	Wright	Berry (4), Woodyatt (8)
Brown	Moss	Doughty	Lancaster	Woods	P Beesley	Carden	Blackburn	M Beesley	Whitehall	Ruscoe	Fisher (3), Wright (9)
Brown	Gaunt	P Beesley	Woods	Lancaster	Fisher	Carden	Blackburn	Ruscoe	Whitehall	Wright	Doughty (9), M Beesley (11)
Brown	Woods	Lancaster	Doughty	Ruscoe	Fisher	Carden	Blackburn	Woodyatt	Whitehall	Wright	M Beesley (11), Gaunt (4)
Brown	Lancaster	P Beesley	Woods	Gaunt	Fisher	Carden	Blackburn	Wright	Whitehall	Ruscoe	M Beesley (8), Woodyatt (10), Doughty (11)
Brown	Woods	Gaunt	Ruscoe	Lancaster	Fisher	Carden	Blackburn	Woodyatt	M Beesley	Wright	Moss (7), Doughty (2)
Brown	Gaunt	Blackburn	Doughty	Lancaster	Fisher	Carden	Woodyatt	Wright	Whitehall	M Beesley	Priestley (1), Ruscoe (4), Haarhoff (11)
Priestley	Gaunt	Blackburn	Doughty	Lancaster	Fisher	Woodyatt	Wright	Whitehall	M Beesley	Moss	Ruscoe(3), Kerr (9)
Priestley	Woods	Ruscoe	Lancaster	Blackburn	Fisher	Wright	Moss	M Beesley	Whitehall	Woodyatt	Porter (7), Kerr (8), Doughty (2)
Brown	Ruscoe	Gaunt	Doughty	Lancaster	Fisher	Kerr	Porter	Moss	M Beesley	Woodyatt	Haarhoff (2), Wright (7) sub Whitehall

PLAYING SQUAD

CHESTER CITY

Bold print denotes England semi-professional international.

GOALKEEPERS

Wayne Brown ESP	Southampton	14.01.77	Weston-Super-Mare, Bristol C

DEFENDERS

Martin Lancaster	Wigan	10.11.80	From Trainee
Phil Robinson	Manchester	28.09.80	Blackpool
Neil Fitzhenry	Billinge	24.09.78	Wigan
Michael Rose	Salford	28.07.82	Manchester Utd
Stephen Rose	Salford	23.11.80	Bristol R, Manchester Utd

MIDFIELD

Chris Blackburn	Chester		From Trainee
David Kerr	Dumfries	06.09.74	Manchester C, Mansfield
Andy Shelton	Sutton Coldfield	19.06.80	From Trainee
Andy Porter	Holmes Chapel	17.09.68	Wigan, Port Vale
Simon Vickers	Scotland		Clyde
Scott Ruscoe	Stoke	01.06.76	Newtown, Port Vale, Stoke

FORWARDS

Darren Wright	Warrington	07.09.79	From Trainee
Chris Malkin	Hoylake	04.06.67	Telford Utd, Blackpool, Millwall, Overpool, Stork
Jimmy Haarhoff	Lusaka	27.05.81	Birmingham
Paul Berry	Liverpool		Warrington T
Steve Whitehall	Bromborough	08.12.66	Oldham, Mansfield, Rochdale, Southport

DAGENHAM & REDBRIDGE

Promoted Dagenham & Redbridge set themselves a target for the season of consolidation in the Conference and fair runs in Cup competitions. What followed was far beyond anything the club and its supporters could have ever dreamt.

Their first game back in the Nationwide Conference, after an absence of four seasons, saw them travel to Unibond League champions Leigh RMI and come away with a 2-1 victory. Three days later they came back down to earth with a bang when a 20-month unbeaten home record was ended having lost 1-2 to Kingstonian. Only two defeats, both against eventual champions Rushden & Diamonds, were suffered in their next ten league matches as the club made steady progress up the table.

In the F.A. Cup Fourth Qualifying Round, the Daggers defeated Hendon 3-1 after five postponements and four days later saw off the challenge of Hayes 3-1 to progress through to the Second Round. League defeats against Southport and Northwich were not the best way to go into an F.A. Cup tie away to Lincoln City, but the Daggers finally achieved their first victory over a Football League side. Having outplayed the Imps for the majority of the game it seemed a replay would be the outcome until Mark Janney tapped the ball under goalkeeper Matthew Ghents body in the final minute to put the Daggers into the Third Round for the first time ever.

Two league victories over Kingstonian and Leigh RMI and a defeat at Dover Athletic on New Years day took them up to the most important match in their history at the Valley, home of Premier League Charlton Athletic.

The Daggers were quoted as huge outsiders to get a draw against Charlton, but they had the audacity to take a fully deserved lead just before half time through Junior McDougald. Time ticked on and only a deflected equaliser four minutes from time denied them one of the F.A. Cups greatest upsets of all time. Instead they had earned a draw and they turned down the chance of financial rewards by deciding to play the game at Victoria Road and give themselves every chance of a victory. Garry Hill was rewarded with the League Managers Association performance of the week, the first time the award has ever gone outside the Football League. In the run-up to the replay, the media hit Dagenham like never before, but the constant attention had a disastrous effect when the club lost in the Third Round of the F.A. Trophy by a 90th minute goal from visiting Weymouth.

Due to an icy pitch, the F.A. Cup replay was postponed and was eventually played on the day of the Fourth Round. With a home tie against Tottenham Hotspur awaiting the victors, the Daggers again took the game to their more illustrious opponents in front of their record attendance of 5,394. They were finally defeated when Shaun Newton scored in the first minute of extra time with Tim Cole having an equaliser ruled out for pushing. At the end of the game they had deservedly earned the standing ovation they received from both sets of spectators.

The first Saturday of February saw the Daggers defeated at Nuneaton Borough and many thought the Daggers had reached their peak and would now drop down the table. Instead they went on a nine game winning run which also saw them knock Yeovil Town off the top of the table with a 3-1 victory at Huish Park. This superb run finally came to an end at Hayes, one game short of equalling the Conference record, but had seen the club rise to third place. Manager Garry Hill was named as joint manager of the month for February, but won the honour outright in March.

Coming into the final week of the season, the Daggers were still in third place, and a 3-2 win at Morecambe confirmed their joint highest ever position. They finished the season as they began with a victory in Lancashire, this time over fourth place Southport to round off the most successful season in their history.

During the season they did add some silverware when they won the Ryman One-2-One Charity Shield defeating Farnborough Town 2-0. Prior to the start of the new season they will face F.A. Trophy winners Canvey Island in the Essex Senior Cup Final, held over due to their opponents fixture congestion.

DAVE SIMPSON

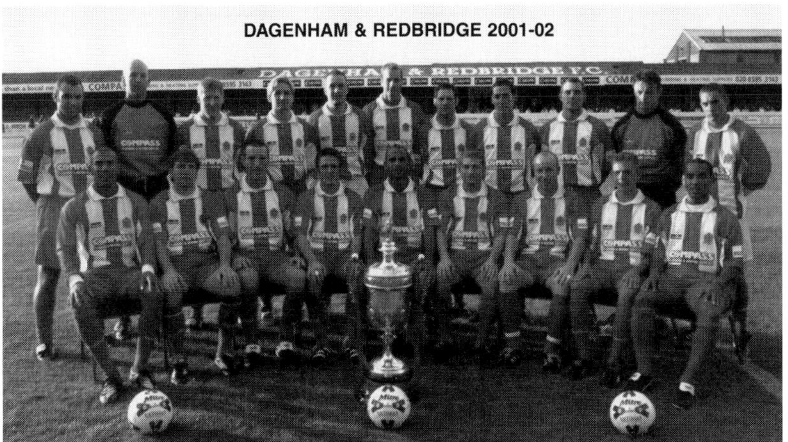
DAGENHAM & REDBRIDGE 2001-02

Back row (L to R): Danny Shipp, Paul Gothard, Steve McGavin, Jason Broom, Tim Cole, Ashley Vickers, Danny Hill, Mark Rooney, Tony Lock, Tony Roberts, Dave Bastion
Front row: Junior McDougald, Mark Brennan, Lee Goodwin, Danny Hayzelden, Matt Jones, Mark Janney, Paul Terry, Steve Vaughan, Mark Stein

DAGENHAM & REDBRIDGE

GROUND DETAILS

Victoria Road,
Dagenham
RM10 7XL

Tel: 0208 592 1549
Fax: 0181593 7227
email: info@daggers.co.uk
web site: http://www.daggers.co.uk

DIRECTIONS: On A112 between A12 & A13. Buses 103 & 174, Dagenham East tube station, turn left and after approximately 500 yards take 5th turning left into Victoria Road.

CAPACITY: 6,000
SEATS: 1,014
COVERED: 3,000

CLUBHOUSE: Open 7 days 11am-11pm. Hot & cold food available.
For Functions: Tony Manhood 0208 592 7194
Shop Contact: SteveThompson 0208 5927194

CLUB SHOP: Open on matchdays for enquiries on other days contact Steve, above.

MATCHDAY PROGRAMME

Pages: 48 **Price:** £2.00
Editor: Dave Simpson Tel: 07860 119430

Other Club Publications: None

Local Press: Dagenham Post, Ilford Courier,Yellow Advertiser, Walthamstow Guardian, Barking & Dagenham Recorder

Local Radio: BBC Radio Essex, Capital Gold, GLR London Live

Formed: 1992
Nickname: Daggers
Colours: Red and white shirts, red shorts, red socks
Change strip: Blue & white stripes,black shorts and socks.
Midweek matchday: Tuesday
Reserves Lge: No Reserves this season
Sponsors Main: Compass Plumbing Supplies
Kit: Vandanell
Programme: Recorder Group Newspapers
Match Reports: 0930 555840

CLUB OFFICIALS

Chairman: Dave Andrews

Joint Presidents: John & Brian East

Vice Chairman: David Ward

Secretary: Derek Almond, 149 Kings Head Hill, Chingford, London E4 7JG Tel: 0181 524 2689

Commercial Manager: Steve Thompson c/o Club

Press Officer: Dave Simpson Tel: 07860 119430

FOOTBALL MANAGEMENT TEAM

MANAGER: GARRY HILL

Date of appointment: 7th May 1999
Date of Birth: 15th October 1959
Place of Birth: Essex

PREVIOUS CLUBS
As manager: St. Albans, Heybridge Swifts
As player: None

HONOURS
As manager: Isthmian Prem. League 99-00
As player: N.A.

Asst Manager: Terry Harris
Chief Scout: Mick Loughton
Safety Officer: Bill Doig
Physio: Richard Harper

Season	League	Div.	Pos.	Home P	W	D	L	F	A	Away W	D	L	F	A	Pts	Manager
00-01	Conference	-	3	42	13	4	4	39	19	10	4	7	32	35	77	Garry Hill
99-00	Isthmian	Prem.	1	42	20	1	0	58	13	12	4	5	39	22	101	Garry Hill
98-99	Isthmian	Prem.	3	42	10	8	3	40	15	10	5	6	31	29	73	Ted Hardy
97-98	Isthmian	Prem.	4	42	11	6	4	43	25	10	4	7	30	25	73	Ted Hardy
96-97	Isthmian	Prem.	4	42	11	3	7	32	21	7	8	6	25	22	65	Ted Hardy

Season	League	Div.	Pos.	P	W	D	L	F	A	Pts	Manager
95-96	Conference	-	21	42	7	12	23	43	73	33	Graham Carr
94-95	Conference	-	15	42	13	13	16	56	69	52	Dave Cusack
93-94	Conference	-	6	42	15	14	13	62	54	59	John Still
92-93	Conference	-	3	42	19	11	12	75	47	67	John Still
91-92	*Conference*	*-*	*7*	*42*	*18*	*9*	*15*	*69*	*56*	*63*	*John Still* as Redbridge Forest

HONOURS

(Ryman) Isthmian League Prem. Div. 99-00

(Ryman) Isthmian one2one Charity Shield 2000-01

F.A. Trophy Runners-up 96-97

Essex Senior 97-98

PREVIOUS

Names:
Ilford FC (1881) & Leytonstone (1886) merged in 1979 to form Leytonstone-Ilford.
They & Walthamstow Avenue (1900) merged in 1988 to form Redbridge Forest
who in turn merged with Dagenham (1949) in 1992 to form Dagenham & Redbridge.

Grounds: None

Leagues: GMV Conference 92-96; Isthmian Lge 96-2000

Past Players who progressed to the Football League

Warren Barton (via Maidstone Utd '89 to Wimbledon '90)
Andy Hessenthaler (Watford '91)
Juan Mequel DeSouza (Birmingham C. '94)
Ian Richardson (Birmingham City '95)

CLUB RECORDS

Attendance: 5,500 v Leyton Orient - FA Cup 1st Rnd - 14.11.92
5,492 v Charlton A - F.A.Cup 3rd Rd Replay- 27.01.01

Career goalscorer (all competitions): Paul Cobb 84 (97-01)
Danny Shipp 81 (95-01)

Career appearances (all competitions): Jason Broom - 304
(Steve Corner - 257. Paul Watts - 174)

Win: 8-1 v Woking (A)
GMV Conference 19/4/94
7-0 v Oxford (H) Isthmian Lge1/11/97

Defeat: 0-5
v Stalybridge Celtic (A) GMV Conference 31/4/94
v Northwich Victoria, GMV Conference 3/9/94
v Hyde Utd (H) FA Trophy 2nd Rd.
v Croydon ,Isthmian Lg.Cup(A) 99/00

Transfer fee paid as Dagenham & Redbridge F.C. £15,000
to Purfleet for Paul Cobb in August 1997

Transfer fee received as Dagenham & Redbridge F.C. #65.00
from Birmingham City for Ian Richardson in May 1995

BEST SEASON

FA Cup: Third Round Proper Replay 00-01
0-1 aet v Charlton Ath.(Premier League) (H), after 1-1 (A)

League clubs defeated: Lincoln City 00-01

FA Trophy: Runners-up 96-97

League: 3rd Conference 92-93, 00-01

LAST SEASON

F.A. Cup: 3rd Round Proper

F.A. Trophy: 3rd Round

Conference: 3rd

Top Goalscorer: Danny Shipp 12

Player of the Year: Lee Mathews

Captain: Mark Brennan

DAGENHAM & REDBRIDGE

Match Facts 2000-01

	Date	Comp.	Opponents	Gate	Score	Goalscorers
1	19/08	Conf	Leigh RMI	451	2 - 1	Keane 22, Matthews 79
2	22/08	Conf	KINGSTONIAN	1252	1 - 2	Brennan 65
3	26/08	Conf	RUSHDEN & DIAMONDS	1686	0 - 2	
4	28/08	Conf	Stevenage Borough	2055	2 - 0	Keen 13, Terry 68
5	02/09	Conf	Scarborough	1202	1 - 0	McDougald 47[p]
6	05/09	Conf	BOSTON UNITED	1037	2 - 1	Cobb 32, Terry 40
7	09/09	Conf	NUNEATON BOROUGH	1361	1 - 1	Browne 65
8	12/09	Conf	Kettering Town	1070	0 - 0	
9	16/09	Conf	Forest Green Rovers	902	4 - 4	Matthews 50, Jones 67, Keen 73, Hatswell 88[og]
10	23/09	Conf	HEDNESFORD TOWN	952	6 - 1	Brennan 42, McDougald 53 90, Broughton 56 61, Cobb 87
11	26/09	Conf	Rushden & Diamonds	3069	1 - 2	Cole 16
12	30/09	Conf	HEREFORD UNITED	1410	2 - 1	Terry 44, Cole 73
13	03/10	Conf	HAYES	1145	2 - 0	Broughton 28 45
14	06/10	Conf	Doncaster Rovers	2232	0 - 1	
15	14/10	Conf	WOKING	1359	1 - 2	McDougald 22
16	21/10	Conf	Telford United	2317	1 - 0	Broughton 36[p]
17	04/11	Conf	CHESTER CITY	1244	1 - 1	Shipp 72
18	25/11	Conf	SOUTHPORT	1183	0 - 1	
19	02/12	Conf	Northwich Victoria	1060	0 - 3	
20	16/12	Conf	Kingstonian	809	3 - 2	Janney 20, McDougald 41 88
21	26/12	Conf	DOVER ATHLETIC	1359	1 - 1	McDougald 58
22	30/12	Conf	LEIGH RMI	1231	2 - 1	McDougald 16, Jones 18
23	01/01	Conf	Dover Athletic	1461	1 - 3	Haworth 53
24	10/02	Conf	Nuneaton Borough	1302	0 - 2	
25	17/02	Conf	KETTERING TOWN	1219	5 - 1	Goodwin 12 14, Broom 44, McDougald 45[p], Opara 90
26	20/02	Conf	Yeovil Town	4025	3 - 1	Matthews 20, Shipp 37 49
27	24/02	Conf	Hednesford Town	836	2 - 0	Janney 59, Opara 90
28	03/03	Conf	FOREST GREEN ROVERS	1256	3 - 1	Broom 4 89, Shipp 37
29	06/03	Conf	SCARBOROUGH	877	1 - 0	Goodwin 8
30	17/03	Conf	Hereford United	1561	1 - 0	Terry 56
31	20/03	Conf	STEVENAGE BOROUGH	958	3 - 0	Shipp 23 70, Heffer 45
32	25/03	Conf	MORECAMBE	1063	3 - 2	Cole 65, Cobb 81[p] 90
33	27/03	Conf	DONCASTER ROVERS	1206	2 - 1	Cobb 48, Goodwin 67
34	31/03	Conf	Hayes	981	1 - 4	Gallagher 57
35	07/04	Conf	TELFORD UNITED	1011	0 - 0	
36	11/04	Conf	Boston United	1386	1 - 5	Shipp 2
37	14/04	Conf	Woking	2319	4 - 4	Lock 40, Hayzelden 56, Cobb 64, Goodwin 85
38	16/04	Conf	YEOVIL TOWN	2136	2 - 0	Goodwin 25, Lock 56
39	21/04	Conf	Chester City	1202	1 - 1	Goodwin 53
40	28/04	Conf	NORTHWICH VICTORIA	1256	1 - 0	Cobb 71
41	03/05	Conf	Morecambe	742	3 - 2	Hayzelden 1, Shipp 24 54
42	05/05	Conf	Southport	1264	1 - 0	Cole 7

OTHER COMPETITIONS

Date	Comp.	Opponents	Gate	Score	Goalscorers
19/09	Variety CT 1	STEVENAGE BOROUGH	318	1 - 2	Goodwin 67
13/11	FA Cup Q4	Hendon	519	3 - 1	Broughton 30, Matthews 66, Terry 69
18/11	FA Cup 1	HAYES	1150	3 - 1	Keen 16, Watts 61[og], Jones 72
20/11	Ryman Shield	Farnborough Town	251	2 - 0	Cobb 45, Shipp 47
09/12	FA Cup 2	Lincoln City	2823	1 - 0	Janney 90
19/12	Essex SC 3	HARLOW TOWN	270	4 - 1	Rust 14, Cobb 38, Haworth 80 88
06/01	FA Cup 3	Charlton Athletic	19059	1 - 1	McDougald 42
13/01	FA Trophy 3	WEYMOUTH	1784	0 - 1	
27/01	FA Cup 3 rep	CHARLTON ATHLETIC	5394	0 - 1	
01/02	Essex SC 4	EAST THURROCK UNITED	n/k	3 - 2	
13/02	Essex SC QF	MALDON TOWN	328	4 - 0	Terry 9, Janney 76, Broom 78 84
13/03	Essex SC SF	HEYBRIDGE SWIFTS	412	2 - 1	Vickers 57, Jones 69
04/08	Essex SC F	CANVEY ISLAND	1095	2 - 2	Shipp 69, Goodwin 117 Won 5-4 after pens.

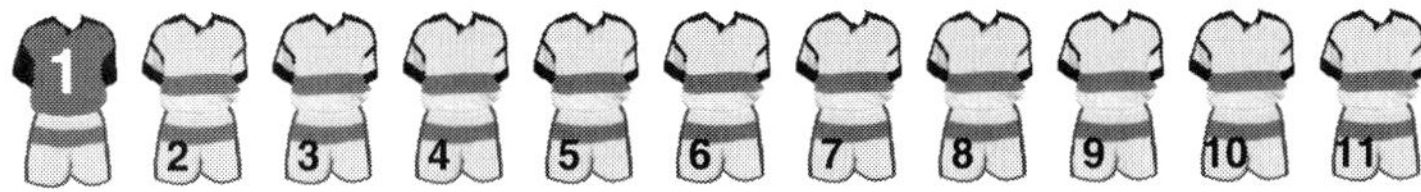

1	2	3	4	5	6	7	8	9	10	11	Substitutes Used
Roberts	Keane	Payne	Vickers	Forbes	Brennan	Cole	Matthews	Shipp	McDougald	Jones	Terry (3), Cobb (10), Howard (9)
Roberts	Cole	Naylor	Vickers	Matthews	Brennan	Janney	Cobb	Forbes	McDougald	Jones	Terry (3), Shipp (8), Haworth (9)
Roberts	Cole	Vickers	Matthews	Broome	Janney	Brennan	Forbes	Jones	Cobb	McDougald	Shipp (5), Terry (8), Keen (10)
Roberts	Terry	Cole	Keen	Matthews	Jones	Payne	Vickers	Brennan	McDougald	Howarth	Forbes (4), Shipp (11), Janney (10)
Honey	Cole	Vickers	Goodwin	Matthews	Brennan	Janney	Terry	Heffer	McDougald	Jones	Shipp (10)
Honey	Cole	Jones	Goodwin	Matthews	Janney	Vickers	Cobb	Brennan	McDougald	Terry	Shipp (8), Heffer (11)
Roberts	Goodwin	Cole	Matthews	Vickers	Janney	Terry	Brennan	Jones	Cobb	McDougald	Heffer (9), Browne (10)
Roberts	Cole	Jones	Goodwin	Matthews	Janney	Vickers	Heffer	Brennan	Terry	McDougald	Keen (3), Browne (11)
Roberts	Cole	Goodwin	Matthews	Vickers	Brennan	Janney	Terry	Jones	Heffer	McDougald	Keen (2), Haworth (4), Browne (8)
Roberts	Cole	Broom	Goodwin	Matthews	Brennan	Janney	Heffer	Broughton	McDougald	Jones	Cobb (3), Payne (6)
Roberts	Cole	Janney	Jones	Matthews	Heffer	Brennan	Broom	Terry	Broughton	McDougald	Keen (4), Cobb (11)
Roberts	Cole	Broom	Terry	Matthews	Brennan	Janney	Heffer	Broughton	McDougald	Jones	Payne (7), Keen (9), Cobb (10)
Roberts	Cole	Janney	Jones	Matthews	Heffer	Brennan	Broom	Terry	Broughton	McDougald	Payne (7)
Roberts	Keen	Broom	Terry	Matthews	Brennan	Janney	Heffer	Broughton	McDougald	Jones	Cobb (3), Payne (4)
Roberts	Cole	Broome	Terry	Matthews	Brennan	Janney	Heffer	Broughton	McDougald	Jones	Cobb (6), Keen (10), Vickers (11)
Roberts	Cole	Vickers	Keen	Matthews	Broome	Janney	Terry	Broughton	Heffer	Jones	Goodwin (4), Shipp (9), Cobb (11)
Roberts	Cole	Broom	Goodwin	Matthews	Terry	Janney	Cobb	Shipp	Heffer	Jones	McDougald (8), Keen (9)
Roberts	Heffer	Vickers	Keen	Matthews	Terry	Janney	Cobb	Broome	Forbes	Broughton	Jones (5), Haworth (8), Shipp (11)
Roberts	Goodwin	Cole	Keen	Vickers	Terry	Forbes	Heffer	Jones	Haworth	McDougald	Janney (4), Broughton (10), Shipp (2)
Roberts	Cole	Vickers	Hamsher	Matthews	Terry	Janney	Heffer	Broom	Shipp	McDougald	Jones (6)
Roberts	Cole	Vickers	Goodwin	Matthews	Terry	Hamsher	Heffer	Broom	McDougald	Shipp	Jones (6)
Roberts	Janney	Vickers	Goodwin	Matthews	Hamsher	Broom	Heffer	Jones	Shipp	McDougald	Haworth (9)
Roberts	Cole	Vickers	Goodwin	Keen	Forbes	Hamsher	Heffer	Jones	Cobb	Haworth	Shipp (5)
Roberts	Terry	Broom	Ayres	Matthews	Hayzelden	Jones	Forbes	Brennan	Shipp	McDougald	Keen (4), Opara (6), Cobb (9)
Roberts	Goodwin	Cole	Matthews	Vickers	Janney	Terry	Heffer	Broom	Opara	McDougald	Forbes (8), Hayzelden (9), Cobb (11)
Roberts	Vickers	Broom	Goodwin	Matthews	Terry	Janney	Heffer	Shipp	McDougald	Hayzelden	Opara (9), Cobb (10)
Roberts	Vickers	Goodwin	Matthews	Broom	Terru	Janney	Heffer	Hayzelden	Shipp	McDougald	Opara (9)
Roberts	Cole	Vickers	Goodwin	Matthews	Terry	Janney	Heffer	Shipp	McDougald	Broom	Wignall (5)
Roberts	Cole	Vickers	Goodwin	Matthews	Terry	Janney	Heffer	Broom	McDougald	Shipp	Brennan (6), Jones (7), Opara (10)
Roberts	Goodwin	Cole	Matthews	Vickers	Jones	Terry	Heffer	Broom	Shipp	McDougald	Brennan (8), Gallagher(9), Keen (10)
Roberts	Cole	Vickers	Goodwin	Matthews	Terry	Gallagher	Heffer	Jones	McDougald	Shipp	Wignall (4), Brennan (8), Cobb (10)
Roberts	Cole	Vickers	Goodwin	Matthews	Terry	Lock	Heffer	Jones	McDougald	Shipp	Brennan (7), Janney (8), Cobb (10)
Roberts	Cole	Vickers	Goodwin	Matthews	Terry	Lock	Heffer	Jones	Cobb	Shipp	Brennan (4), Janney (7), Broom (9)
Roberts	Cole	Vickers	Goodwin	Broom	Terry	Janney	Cobb	Shipp	Heffer	Jones	Keen (7), Gallagher (11), Wignall (3)
Roberts	Rooney	Broom	Wignall	Matthews	Terry	Gallagher	Heffer	Shipp	Lock	Jones	Brennan (7), Cobb (8), McDougald (10)
Roberts	Cole	Vickers	Goodwin	Wignall	Brennan	Broom	Heffer	Jones	McDougald	Shipp	Keen (2), Gallagher (7), Lock (11)
Roberts	Cole	Vickers	Goodwin	Rooney	Terry	Janney	Heffer	Lock	McDougald	Hayzelden	Cobb (7), Shipp (10), Jones (11)
Roberts	Cole	Rooney	Goodwin	Lock	Terry	Janney	Heffer	Jones	McDougald	Shipp	Hayzelden (5), Cobb (10), Keen (11)
Roberts	Cole	Lock	Goodwin	Rooney	Terry	Janney	Heffer	Shipp	McDougald	Jones	Brennan (8), Cobb (3)
Roberts	Goodwin	Matthews	Cole	Broom	Janney	Heffer	Jones	Terry	McDougald	Shipp	Cobb (5), Hayzelden (6), Keen (10)
Roberts	Cole	Rooney	Goodwin	Matthews	Broom	Terry	Heffer	Shipp	McDougald	Hayzelden	Forbes (4), Cobb (9), Keen (11)
Roberts	Cole	Rooney	Matthews	Forbes	Terry	Gallagher	Heffer	Jones	Hayzelden	Cobb	Broom (5), Janney (7), McDougald (9)

PLAYING SQUAD

DAGENHAM & REDBRIDGE

Player / *Honours*	*Birthplace*	*D.O.B.*	*Previous Clubs*
GOALKEEPERS			
Tony Roberts Wales Int.	Holyhead	04.08.69	QPR, Millwall, St.Albans C
Paul Gothard ESP	Essex	24.06.74	Hayes, Dagenham & Red, Grays Ath., Chelmsford C, Colchester
DEFENDERS			
Lee Matthews RP	Southend		Southend, Purfleet, £3,000 to Dag & Red
Ashley Vickers RP	Sheffield	14.06.72	Sheffield U, Worcester C, Malvern T, 61 Club, Heybridge S
Lee Goodwin RP	Stepney	05.09.78	West Ham
Tim Cole RP	London		Walthamstow Pennant, Leyton Pennant
Mark Rooney	Lambeth	19.05.78	St.Albans C, Aylesbury Utd, Watford
MIDFIELD			
Jason Broom RP, FA XI	Essex	15.10.69	Eton Manor, Billericay T, £3,000 to Dag & Red
Mark Brennan EY, u-21 Int	Rossendale	04.10.65	Ipswich, Middlesbrough, Manchester C, Oldham, Australia
Mark Janney RP	Romford	02.12.77	Spurs
Matt Jones ES, RP	Chiswick	09.10.70	Arsenal, Souhend, Chelmsford C, Heybridge S, St.Albans C
Steve Heffer RP	London	11.01.73	West Ham, Southend, Swindon, Grays A., Hendon, Boreham Wood
Kieran Gallagher	London		Aylesbury Utd, Barnet, Chelsea (Junior)
Steve Forbes	Hackney	24.12.75	Stevenage B, Colchester, Millwall, Sittingbourne
Danny Hazelden	Essex		Grays Ath., Hornchurch, Aveley, Wimbledon (Junior)
FORWARDS			
Junior McDougald ESP, RP	Big Spring	12.01.75	Spurs, Brighton, Rotherham, FC Toulon, Camb.C., Millwall, Camb.C., Leyton O
Paul Terry RP	London		Charlton, Bromley
Danny Shipp RP	Romford	25.09.76	West Ham, Coleraine
Mark Stein EY	Cape Town	29.01.66	Luton, Bournemouth, Chelsea, Stoke, Oxford Utd, QPR, Luton
Steve McGavin NC, FAT	North Walsham	24.01.69	Colchester, Southend, Wycombe, Birmingham, Colchester, Sudbury T
Tony Lock	Harlow	03.09.76	Colchester, Kettering T, Colchester

DONCASTER ROVERS

Doncaster Rovers had, what can only be described as, a moderate season in the Conference, which was not improved by early exits from both knock-out competitions, but perhaps it might have been worse.

By the end of September a dozen matches had been played with only four victories, so a realistic promotion challenge was out of the question, although the period up to the end of the year did produce an improvement with ten matches producing six victories, including a fine home success against eventual champions Rushden & Diamonds.

However, the early months of 2001 were followed with only three successes being gained until the end of March with four draws and five losses and the run in of seven matches was no more encouraging with only two wins to record.

The defence conceded 43 goals during the Conference campaign, but the attack only managed 47 by contrast, so manager Steve Wignall has a few problems to solve for the coming season and the club may not start as one of the favourites for promotion and a return to Nationwide League status.

The knock-out competitions were a big disappointment with F.A. Cup action ending in the Fourth Qualifying Round after a visit to Southport and a single goal defeat, the first match at Belle Vue having seen four goals shared.

The Trophy challenge was always going to be tough as the Third Round draw meant a visit to Chester City - and a two goal defeat.

Things can only improve at Belle Vue - or can they? Season 2001-02 may provide some answers.

W.M.

DONCASTER ROVERS 2001-02

Back row, l to r: Barry Miller, Robert Gill, Neil Campbell, Barry Richardson, Andy Warrington, Mark Sale, Francis Tierney, Paul Barnes. Middle row from l to r: Paul Carden, Andy Watson, Tim Ryan, Kevin Sandwith, Colin Hawkins, Jamie Price, Kevin McIntyre, Gareth Owen. **Front row:** Jimmy Kelly, Mattie Caudwell, Tristram Whitman, Steve Wignall (manager), Dave Penney (assistant manager), Paul Green, Simon Marples, Dean Barrick, Jamie Paterson.

DONCASTER ROVERS

GROUND DETAILS

Belle Vue Ground, Bawtry Road, Doncaster, S. Yorks. DN4 5HT

TELEPHONE 01302 539441
Fax 01302 539679

Website: www.doncasterroversfc.co.uk
email: info@doncasterroversfc.co.uk

SIMPLE DIRECTIONS:
From north & west: Into Doncaster town centre and follow sign to Bawtry (A638) and after 1.2 miles take 3rd exit at roundabout into Bawtry Road.
From east: M18, then A630, A18 and A638 (Bawtry Road)
From south: M18 junct 3, A6182, then A18 and A638

MATCH TICKETS: Adults:£9-£11, OAPs £6-£7 concessions £3-£6
CAR PARK: Large park at ground (£3)

CAPACITY: 7,219
SEATED: 1,252
COVERED TERRACING: 4,753

SOCIAL FACILITIES: Possible clubhouse in near future. Four tea bars.Food outlets on ground on matchdays

CLUB SHOP: Open daily 10-4pm and on matchdays.

MATCHDAY PROGRAMME

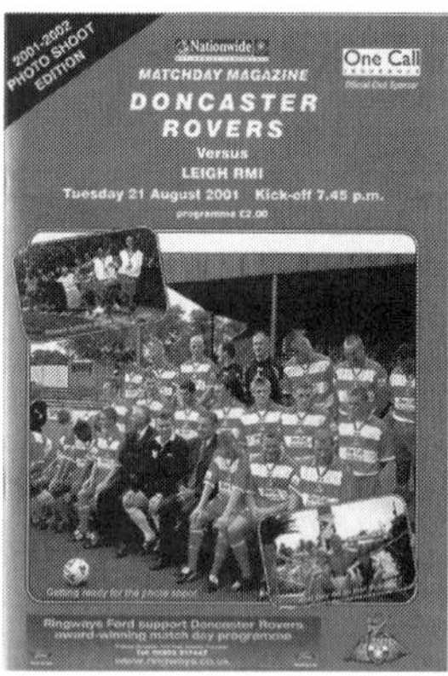

Pages: 40 **Price:** £2.00
Editor: Peter Tuffrey, c/o the club
'Conference Programme of the Year 2000-01'
Other club publications:
Supporters' Club Handbook and Two fanzines
Local Press: Doncaster Star; Yorkshire Post
Local Radio: Radio Hallam; Radio Sheffield, Trax FM

Founded: 1879

Nickname: The Rovers

Sponsors: One Call Insurance

Club Colours: Red & white hoops, red shorts, red socks.

Change Colours: Green & white.

Midweek matchday: Tuesday

Reserve Team's League: Avon Insurance 1st Division

CLUB OFFICIALS

President Vacant

Chairman John Ryan

Vice Chairman Peter Wetzel

Chief Executive Joe Higgins

Club Secretary Mrs K Joan Odale
c/o the club
Tel: 01302 539441 Fax: 01302 539679

Commercial Executives: Miles Cartwright/Alick Jeffrey
c/o the club
Tel: 01302 539441 Fax: 01302 539679

FOOTBALL MANAGEMENT TEAM

MANAGER **STEVE WIGNALL**
Date of Appointment 3rd May 2000
Date of Birth: 17th September 1954
Place of Birth: Liverpool

PREVIOUS CLUBS
As manager Aldershot, Colchester Utd., Stevenage Borough
As asst. manager/coach Aldershot
As player Doncaster Rovers, Colchester Utd., Brentford, Aldershot

HONOURS
As manager Football Lge - AutoWindscreen R-up, 2 playoffs -1 promotion
Isthmian Lge - 2 promotions
As player AutoWindscreen R-up

* * *

First Team Coach: Dave Penney
Reserve / Youth team Manager: Micky Walker
Physio: Jon Bowden

Season	League	Div.	Pos.	P	Home W	Home D	Home L	Home F	Home A	Away W	Away D	Away L	Away F	Away A	Pts	Manager
00-01	Conference	-	9	42	11	5	5	28	17	4	8	9	19	26	58	Steve Wignall
99-00	Conference	-	12	42	7	5	9	19	21	8	4	9	27	27	54	Ian Snodin / Steve Wignall
98-99	Conference	-	16	42	7	5	9	26	26	5	7	9	25	29	48	Ian Snodin

Season	League	Div.	Pos.	P	W	D	L	F	A	Pts	Manager
97-98	F. League	3	24	46	4	8	34	30	113	20	Kerry Dixon
96-97	F. League	3	19	46	14	10	22	52	66	52	Ian Atkins
95-96	F. League	3	13	46	16	11	19	49	60	59	Sammy Chung
94-95	F. League	3	9	42	17	10	15	58	64	58	Sammy Chung
93-94	F. League	3	15	42	14	10	18	44	57	52	Steve Beaglehole
92-93	F. League	3	16	42	11	14	17	42	57	47	Steve Beaglehole
91-92	F. League	4	21	42	9	8	25	40	65	35	Billy Bremner

HONOURS

Division 3 N 1934-35, 46-47, 49-50;
Division 4 1965-66, 68-69;
Sheffield County Cup 1890-91, 1911-12,
35-36, 37-38, 55-56, 67-68, 75-76, 85-86;
Yorkshire Electricity Cup 1995-96;
Midland Counties League 1896-97, 98-99;
Northern Intermediate Lge Cup 1984-95, 86-87
Nationwide McMillan Trophy (Conf. Lge Cup) 98-99, 99-00

PREVIOUS

Leagues: Midland Alliance Lge 1890-91; Midland League 1891-1901, 03-04 & 05-15,20-23; Football League 1901-3, 04-05, 23-Sept 39, 42-44, 45-98; Midland Comb. 1915-16; E Midlands War Lge Oct 1939-40; War Lge North 1940-42, 44-45

Names: None

Ground: 1880-1916 Intake Ground; 1920-22 Benetthorpe Ground; 1922 > Belle Vue (formerly known as Low Pasture)

Past Players

who progressed to the Football League

CLUB RECORDS

Attendance: 37,149 v Hull City, Div. 3N, 2.10.1948

Career Goalscorer: Tom Keetley, 180, 1923-29

Career Appearances: Fred Emery, 417, 1925-36

Win: 10-0 v Darlington (H), Div. 4, 25.01.64

Defeat: 0-12 v Small Heath (A), Division 2, 11.04.03

Transfer Fee Paid: £62,500 to Torquay United for Darren Moore, July 1995

Transfer Fee Received: £350,000 from Bradford City for Darren Moore, 1997

BEST SEASON

FA Trophy: 4th Rd 99-00 (2nd season)

FA Cup: 5th Rd 1951-52, 53-54, 54-55 & 55-56

League Cup: 5th Round 1975-76

League: 7th , League Div. 2, 1901-02

LAST SEASON

FA Trophy: Third Round

FA Cup: Fourth Qualifying Round

League: 9th

Leading Goalscorer Neil Campbell

Players' Player of the Year Barry Miller

Captain Barry Miller

Club Captain Barry Miller

DONCASTER ROVERS

Match Facts 2000-01

	Date	Comp.	Opponents	Gate	Score	Goalscorers
1	19/08	Conf	NUNEATON BOROUGH	3648	1 - 1	Paterson 26
2	22/08	Conf	Chester City	2616	0 - 3	
3	26/08	Conf	Forest Green Rovers	952	2 - 2	Barnard 51 66
4	28/08	Conf	WOKING	2437	0 - 1	
5	02/09	Conf	MORECAMBE	1924	1 - 0	Barnard 62
6	05/09	Conf	Northwich Victoria	1115	1 - 1	Campbell 77
7	09/09	Conf	Kingstonian	1321	1 - 1	Cauldwell 24
8	12/09	Conf	SOUTHPORT	1877	1 - 0	Shaw 62
9	16/09	Conf	HEREFORD UNITED	2380	2 - 1	Campbell 18 62
10	23/09	Conf	Yeovil Town	2605	0 - 2	
11	26/09	Conf	HEDNESFORD TOWN	2033	3 - 1	Paterson 19 85, Campbell 63
12	30/09	Conf	Boston United	3155	1 - 3	Paterson 85[p]
13	03/10	Conf	Kettering Town	1106	0 - 0	
14	06/10	Conf	DAGENHAM & REDBRIDGE	2232	1 - 0	Campbell 4
15	14/10	Conf	Hayes	750	3 - 0	Pick 5[og], Alford 54[p], Turner 61
16	20/10	Conf	NORTHWICH VICTORIA	2794	0 - 2	
17	04/11	Conf	Leigh RMI	811	1 - 0	Paterson 19[p]
18	11/11	Conf	RUSHDEN & DIAMONDS	3538	3 - 2	Paterson 16[p], Whitman 32, Penney 45
19	28/11	Conf	Southport	1629	0 - 1	
20	02/12	Conf	STEVENAGE BOROUGH	2545	0 - 0	
21	09/12	Conf	Hereford United	1755	1 - 0	Turner 76
22	16/12	Conf	CHESTER CITY	2553	1 - 0	McIntyre 2
23	26/12	Conf	Scarborough	2381	1 - 3	Whitman 44
24	01/01	Conf	SCARBOROUGH	3024	0 - 2	
25	06/01	Conf	Woking	1948	1 - 1	Whitman 79
26	20/01	Conf	FOREST GREEN ROVERS	1871	3 - 0	Campbell 2, Penney 65, Whitman 74
27	27/01	Conf	Dover Athletic	1604	1 - 1	Turner 63
28	03/02	Conf	Nuneaton Borough	1377	0 - 1	
29	06/02	Conf	Telford United	1287	0 - 1	
30	10/02	Conf	KINGSTONIAN	1787	0 - 2	
31	17/02	Conf	DOVER ATHLETIC	1640	1 - 1	Cauldwell 59
32	17/03	Conf	BOSTON UNITED	2296	4 - 2	Whitman 5, Atkins 48, Paterson 89[p] 90
33	24/03	Conf	Hednesford Town	930	4 - 2	Cauldwell 22 90, Barrick 40, Campbell 90
34	27/03	Conf	Dagenham & Redbridge	1206	1 - 2	Hawkins 46
35	31/03	Conf	KETTERING TOWN	1884	0 - 0	
36	10/04	Conf	YEOVIL TOWN	2111	2 - 0	Turner 16, Tierney 21
37	14/04	Conf	HAYES	1769	0 - 0	
38	16/04	Conf	Rushden & Diamonds	4036	0 - 0	
39	18/04	Conf	Morecambe	638	1 - 2	Paterson 27[p]
40	21/04	Conf	LEIGH RMI	1532	4 - 0	Paterson 43[p] 48, Kelly 55, Tierney 58
41	28/04	Conf	Stevenage Borough	2425	0 - 0	
42	05/05	Conf	TELFORD UNITED	2026	1 - 2	Kelly 46

OTHER COMPETITIONS

Date	Comp.	Opponents	Gate	Score	Goalscorers
17/10	Variety CT 2	Southport	443	0 - 1	
28/10	FA Cup Q4	SOUTHPORT	1886	2 - 2	Marples 50, Paterson 88
31/10	FA Cup Q4 R	Southport	1354	0 - 1	
25/11	Sheff SC 1	Sheffield	145	4 - 1	Campbell 6 89, Sherwood 32, Walling 42
05/12	LDV Vans 1N	ROCHDALE	1453	3 - 2	Turner 39 92, Penney 39
07/12	Sheff SC 2	Yorkshire Main	250	14 - 0	Duerden (6), Gill (2), Watson (2), Campbell, Walling, Green(2) (at Brodsworth Miners Welfare)
09/01	LDV Vans 2N	Hartlepool United	2466	1 - 3	Campbell 49
13/01	FA Trophy 3	Chester City	1479	0 - 2	
06/03	Sheff SC QF	ECCLESFIELD RED ROSE	716	7 - 0	Watson(2), Campbell(3), Turner, Whitman
26/04	Sheff SC SF	WORKSOP TOWN	1397	2 - 1	Turner 11, Alford 40
09/05	Sheff SC F	Emley	1930	2 - 1	Whitman 68, Turner 86 (at Sheffield Wednesday)

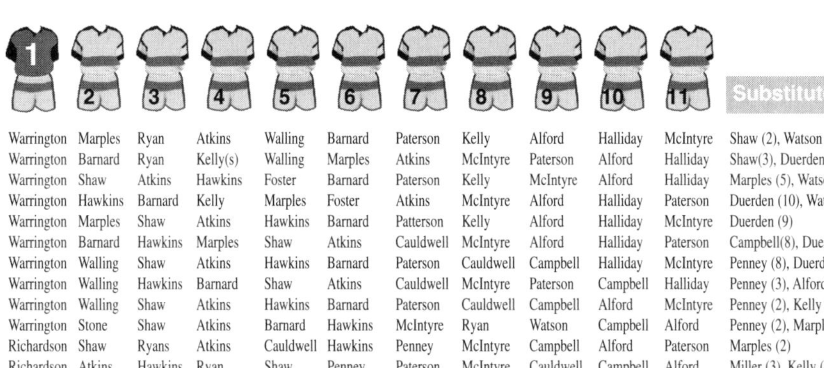

1	2	3	4	5	6	7	8	9	10	11	Substitutes Used
Warrington	Marples	Ryan	Atkins	Walling	Barnard	Paterson	Kelly	Alford	Halliday	McIntyre	Shaw (2), Watson (8)
Warrington	Barnard	Ryan	Kelly(s)	Walling	Marples	Atkins	McIntyre	Paterson	Alford	Halliday	Shaw(3), Duerden (11)
Warrington	Shaw	Atkins	Hawkins	Foster	Barnard	Paterson	Kelly	McIntyre	Alford	Halliday	Marples (5), Watson (11)
Warrington	Hawkins	Barnard	Kelly	Marples	Foster	Atkins	McIntyre	Alford	Halliday	Paterson	Duerden (10), Watson (11), Cauldwell (6)
Warrington	Marples	Shaw	Atkins	Hawkins	Barnard	Patterson	Kelly	Alford	Halliday	McIntyre	Duerden (9)
Warrington	Barnard	Hawkins	Marples	Shaw	Atkins	Cauldwell	McIntyre	Alford	Halliday	Paterson	Campbell(8), Duerden (11)
Warrington	Walling	Shaw	Atkins	Hawkins	Barnard	Paterson	Cauldwell	Campbell	Halliday	McIntyre	Penney (8), Duerden (10)
Warrington	Walling	Hawkins	Barnard	Shaw	Atkins	Cauldwell	McIntyre	Paterson	Campbell	Halliday	Penney (3), Alford (11)
Warrington	Walling	Shaw	Atkins	Hawkins	Barnard	Paterson	Cauldwell	Campbell	Alford	McIntyre	Penney (2), Kelly (8), Halliday (10)
Warrington	Stone	Shaw	Atkins	Barnard	Hawkins	McIntyre	Ryan	Watson	Campbell	Alford	Penney (2), Marples (3), Halliday (9)
Richardson	Shaw	Ryans	Atkins	Cauldwell	Hawkins	Penney	McIntyre	Campbell	Alford	Paterson	Marples (2)
Richardson	Atkins	Hawkins	Ryan	Shaw	Penney	Paterson	McIntyre	Cauldwell	Campbell	Alford	Miller (3), Kelly (9), Watson (10)
Richardson	Marples	Barnard	Atkins	Miller	Kelly	Penney	McIntyre	Paterson	Campbell	Alford	Watson (6), Duerden (10)
Richardson	Marples	Kelly	Atkins	Miller	Barnard	Paterson	Penney	Campbell	Turner	McIntyre	Cauldwell (8), Halliday (10)
Richardson	Marples	Atkins	Miller	Barnard	Kelly	Paterson	Penney	McIntyre	Campbell	Turner	Cauldwell (8), Alford (10), Halliday (11)
Richardson	Marples	Barnard	Atkins	Miller	Kelly	Penney	McIntyre	Paterson	Campbell	Turner	Watson (9), Alford (10), Cauldwell (7)
Richardson	Marples	Shaw	Watson	Miller	Ryan	Paterson	Penney	Alford	Whitman	McIntyre	Cauldwell (4)
Richardson	Marples	Shaw	Watson	Miller	Ryan	Paterson	Penney	Turner	Whitman	Kelly	Cauldwell (4), Alford (9), Duerden(10)
Richardson	Marples	Miller	Ryan	Shaw	Kelly	Penney	McIntyre	Patterson	Whitman	Turner	Watson (6), Atkins (9)
Richardson	Marples	Shaw	Watson	Miller	Ryan	Patterson	Penney	Turner	Whitman	McIntyre	Cauldwell(4), Campbell (9)
Richardson	Stone	Miller	Ryan	Shaw	Cauldwell	Kelly	Penney	McIntyre	Turner	Whitman	Hawkins (2)
Richardson	Marples	Hawkins	Kelly	Miller	Ryan	Cauldwell	Atkins	Turner	Whitman	McIntyre	Campbell (9)
Richardson	Marples	Atkins	Ryan	Miller	Hawkins	Kelly	Cauldwell	McIntyre	Turner	Whitman	Shaw (6), Watson (7), Campbell (10)
Richardson	Marples	Shaw	Ryan	Miller	Cauldwell	Penney	McIntyre	Patterson	Turner	Whitman	Campbell (10)
Richardson	Marples	Shaw	Hawkins	Miller	Ryan	Cauldwell	Penney	Campbell	Whitman	McIntyre	Kelly(2), Alford (4), Paterson (7)
Richardson	Marples	Shaw	Miller	Hawkins	Williams	Penney	McIntyre	Campbell	Whitman	Patterson	Watson (2), Turner (9)
Richardson	Marples	Miller	Williams	Shaw	Campbell	Penney	Hawkins	McIntyre	Turner	Whitman	Watson (6)
Richardson	Marples	Shaw	Hawkins	Miller	Williams	Watson	Penney	Turner	Campbell	McIntyre	Whitman (7), Paterson(9)
Richardson	Marples	Shaw	Miller	Hawkins	Williams	Penney	McIntyre	Turner	Campbell	Paterson	Atkins (3), Kelly (11), Whitman (9)
Richardson	Marples	Shaw	Hawkins	Ryan	Williams	Paterson	Penney	Campbell	Whitman	McIntyre	Turner(3), Kelly (7), Watson (10)
Richardson	Marples	Cauldwell	Hawkins	Miller	Ryan	Williams	Atkins	Campbell	Smith	McIntyre	Watson (7), Turner (9)
Richardson	Marples	Barwick	Atkins	Miller	Ryan	Watson	Penney	Campbell	Whitman	Cauldwell	Paterson (11), Kelly(7), Turner (9)
Richardson	Shaw	Barrick	Ryan	Miller	Hawkins	Kelly	Penney	Cauldwell	Campbell	Whitman	
Richardson	Shaw	Barrick	Ryan	Miller	Hawkins	Kelly	Penney	Cauldwell	Campbell	Whitman	Tierney (7), Paterson(9), Turner (11)
Richardson	Shaw	Barrick	Hawkins	Miller	Ryan	Kelly	Penney	Campbell	Whitman	Cauldwell	McIntyre (4), Tierney (7), Paterson (11)
Richardson	Marples	Barrick	Ryan	Miller	Kelly	Tierney	McIntyre	Campbell	Turner	Paterson	Hawkins (2), Watson (7), Whitman (10)
Warrington	Marples	Barrick	Kelly	Miller	Ryan	Tierney	McIntyre	Campbell	Turner	Paterson	Whitman (10)
Richardson	Marples	Barrick	Ryan	Miller	Kelly	Tierney	McIntyre	Campbell	Turner	Paterson	Watson (7), Hawkins (6), Cauldwell (11)
Richardson	Marples	Barrick	Ryan	Miller	Penney	Tierney	McIntyre	Campbell	Turner	Paterson	Hawkins (6), Watson (7), Whitman (11)
Warrington	Marples	Barrick	Kelly	Miller	Ryan	Tierney	McIntyre	Campbell	Whitman	Paterson	Hawkins(2), Watson (6), Alford (9)
Richardson	Shaw	Barrick	Ryan	Miller	Kelly	Tierney	McIntyre	Campbell	Whitman	Paterson	Turner (9)
Richardson	Shaw	Barrick	Kelly	Miller	Tierney	Ryan	McIntye	Campbell	Whitman	Paterson	Turner (9), Cauldwell (10)

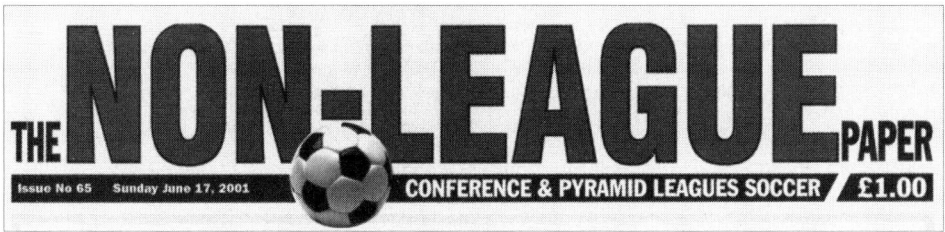

PLAYING SQUAD

DONCASTER ROVERS

Bold print denotes England semi-professional international.

Player *Honours*	*Birthplace*	*D.O.B.*	*Previous Clubs*
GOALKEEPERS			
Barry Richardson	Wallsend	05.08.69	Sunderland, Scarborough, Northampton, Preston, Lincoln
Andy Warrington	Sheffield	10.0676	York City
DEFENDERS			
Simon Marples ESP	Sheffield		Sheffield Wed., Rotherham, Stocksbridge Park Steels, £12,000 to Doncaster
Tim Ryan ESP	Stockport	10.12.74	Doncaster R, Buxton, Scunthorpe, Southport
Colin Hawkins	Galway	17.08.77	St.Patrick's Ath., Coventry
Barry Miller	Ealing	29.03.76	Gillingham (£10,000), Farnborough T, Wokingham T
Dean Barrick	Hemsworth	30.09.69	Bury, Preston, Cambridge Utd, Rotherham, Sheff.Wed
Kevin Sandwith	Workington	30.04.78	Telford Utd, Barrow, Carlisle
MIDFIELD			
David Penney	Wakefield	17.08.64	Pontefract Coll., Derby, Oxford U, Swansea, Cardiff
Andy Watson	Leeds	13.11.78	Garforth Town
Jimmy Kelly	Liverpool	14.02.73	Wrexham, Wolves, Hednesford T, £15,000 to Doncaster R
Matty Cauldwell	Chesterfield	16.01.78	Hallam
Kevin McIntyre ESP	Liverpool	23.12.77	Tranmere
Gareth Owen Wales u-21	Chester	21.10.71	Wrexham
Jamie Paterson	Dumfries	26.04.73	Halifax, Scunthorpe, Falkirk, Halifax
Paul Carden	Liverpool	29.03.79	Chester C (£10,000), Rochdale, Blackpool
Scott Willis	Liverpool	20.02.82	Carlisle, Mansfield, Wigan
FORWARDS			
Neil Campbell	Middlesbrough	26.01.77	York, Scarborough, Southend, £10,000 to Doncaster R
Tristam Whitman	Nottingham		Arnold T, £10,000 to Doncaster R
Francis Tierney	Liverpool	09.10.75	Witton Alb., Exeter, Witton Alb., Notts Co, Crewe
Mark Sale	Burton	27.02.72	Rushden & Diamonds, Colchester, Mansfield, Preston, Torquay, Birmingham, Cambridge Utd, Stoke
Paul Barnes	Leeds	16.11.67	Bury, Huddersfield, Burnley, Birmingham, York, Stoke C., Notts Co

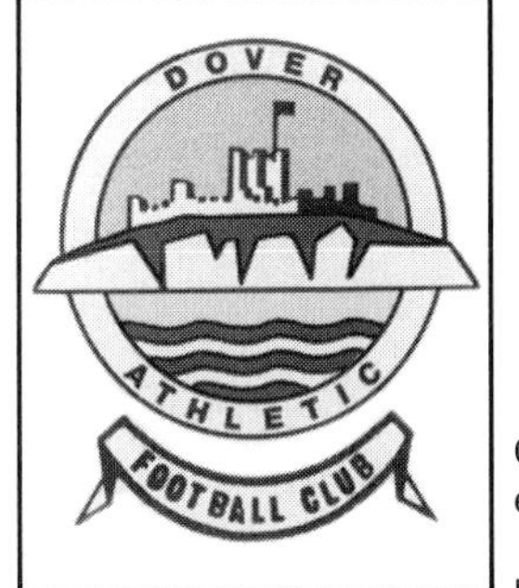

DOVER ATHLETIC

The main Dover Athletic achievement of season 2000-01 was that Conference status was preserved but there were no knock-out successes to inspire confidence for the future.

There was no period of the season when it can be said that they had a good run, although three wins in their opening five matches meant a brief top half position in the table. Thereafter, it was a struggle for survival in reality with an opening day 4-0 victory at home to Hednesford Town the season's best result, while it must be said in their favour that a defeat of a similar size at Yeovil Town on 3rd October was the nearest they came to being routed.

The attack by scoring 54 Conference goals passed muster, but a defence, which conceded 56 in return must need strengthening and manager Bill Williams will need to address that problem urgently.

The knock-out competitions were sad with a visit to Aldershot Town in the F.A. Cup Fourth Qualifying Round bringing an end to dreams by a single goal debacle.

The F.A. Trophy produced a really tough Third Round draw - a visit to Hereford United and a two-goal defeat.

Dover Athletic, if successful, has a good potential to draw good crowds but they need to win a cup or two to achieve that aim, which is easier said than done, but the Garden of England is not over-crowded with top football clubs, so the opportunities do exist for something special.

W.M

DOVER ATHLETIC 2001-02

Back row, (L-R): Danny Hockton, Colin Vowden, Keith Scott, Lee Shearer, James Campbell and Matt Carruthers
Middle Row: Robin Hastie (Kit Manager), Chris Dorrian, Jake Leberl,Kevin Hudson, John McGuire (Physio), Paul Hyde, Jimmy Strouts, Jamie Day and David Chapman- Jones (Physio)
Front Row: Niall Inman, John Elliott, Lee McRobert, Steve Norman, Gary Bellamy (Manager), Clive Walker (Asst Manager) ,Tom Hickman and Michael Lane,

DOVER ATHLETIC

GROUND DETAILS

Crabble Athletic Ground
Lewisham Road
River, Dover,
Kent. CT17 0JB

Telephone No : 01304 822373 Fax: 01304 821383

Simple Directions: Follow the A2 from Canterbury until you pass the Forte Posthouse on your left and approach a r-about with McDonalds & petrol station on your left. Turn right signed 'Town Centre' & follow down the hill.

Capacity: 6,500
Seated: 1,000
Terracing - **Covered:** 4,900 **Uncovered:** None

SOCIAL FACILITIES:
Social Club open 7 days a week. Meals available.
Steward: Gavin Hughes 01304 822306.

CLUB SHOP:
At the ground. Open matchdays for general souvenirs.
Contact 01304 822373

Founded: 1983

Nickname: The 'Whites'

Club Sponsors: Jenkins & Pain

Club colours: White shirts
Black shorts, white socks

Change colours: Yellow shirts
yellow shorts, yellow socks

Reserve team's league: Kent League Div. 1

Midweek home matchday: Tuesday

CLUB OFFICIALS

Chairman Jim Gleeson
Directors J.Spencer and C Harman

Secretary D.Hmmon
c/o club
01304 822373

Commercial Manager & Press Officer **Dave Scoggins**
Tel: 01304 240041

MATCHDAY PROGRAMME

Pages: 40 Price: £2.00

Editor: Dave Scoggins 01304 822373
or 07775 763245
email: dover.athletic@virgin.net

Local Press: Dover Express; Dover Mercury
Local Radio: Radio Kent; Invicta FM
Neptune Radio

FOOTBALL MANAGEMENT TEAM

MANAGER: **GARY BELLAMY**
Date of Appointment 11.06.01
Date of Birth: 04.07.62
Place of Birth: Worksop

PREVIOUS CLUBS
As manager Chelmsford City
As coach
As player Chesterfield, Wolvfes, Cardiff C
Leyton Orient

HONOURS
As manager Two Dr.Martens promotions
As player Div 4 x 2, Div 3 x1.Sherpa Van Trophy and We;lsh F.A.Cup

Assistant Manager Clive Walker

Reserve Team Manager Steve Nolan

Youth Team Managers Jim Gleeson, Richard Langley
Bill Friend, Dave Scoggins, John Spencer, Paul Tillman
Gary Waller, Rob Cowan, Tom Smyth and Dave Mortley

Physiotherapist Shaun Roper
Club Doctor Dr. S F Hodnett MBBCH BAO

Season	League	Div.	Pos.	Home P	W	D	L	F	A	Away W	D	L	F	A	Pts	Manager
00-01	Conference	-	15	42	9	6	6	32	22	5	5	11	22	34	53	Bill Williams
99-00	Conference	-	6	42	10	7	4	43	26	8	5	8	22	30	66	Bill Williams
98-99	Conference	-	11	42	7	9	5	27	21	8	4	9	27	27	58	Bill Williams
97-98	Conference	-	13	42	10	4	7	34	29	5	6	10	26	41	55	Bill Williams
96-97	Conference	-	17	42	7	9	5	32	30	5	5	11	25	38	50	Joe O'Sullivan/ Bill Williams

Season	League	Div.	Pos.	P	W	D	L	F	A	Pts	Manager
95-96	Conference	-	20	42	11	7	24	51	74	40	Peter Taylor
94-95	Conference	-	16	42	11	16	15	48	55	49	Chris Kinnear
93-94	Conference	-	8	42	17	7	18	48	49	58	Chris Kinnear
92-93	Southern Lge	Prem.	1	40	25	11	4	65	23	86	Chris Kinnear
91-92	Southern Lge	Prem.	2	42	23	15	4	66	30	84	Chris Kinnear

HONOURS

Southern League — Premier Division 89-90, 92-93
Southern Division 87-88
Championship Match 1990, 1993
Premier Inter League Cup 90-91
Challenge Cup 91-92

Kent Senior Cup 90-91, R-up 93-94, 96-97

PREVIOUS

Leagues: Kent League, Southern League

Grounds: None

Names: Dover FC

Past Players who progressed to the Football League

Ricky Reina (Brentford) 1997

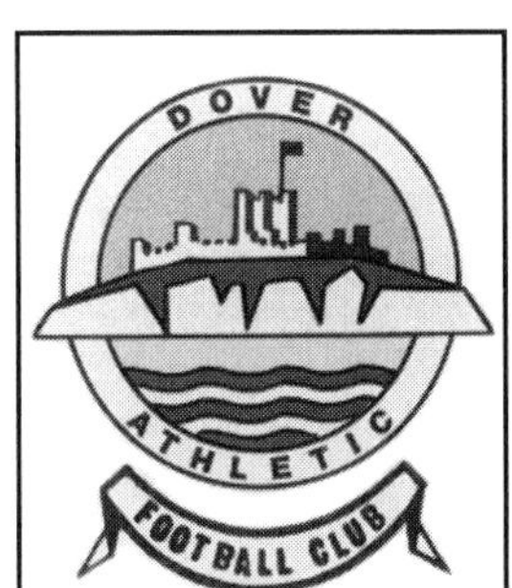

CLUB RECORDS

Attendance: 4,035 v Bromsgrove Rovers Southern League April 92

Win: 7-0 v Weymouth 03.04.1990

Defeat: 1-7 v Poole Town

Career Goalscorer: Lennie Lee 160

Career Appearances: Jason Bartlett 539

Transfer Fees Paid: £50,000 for David Leworthy (Farnborough Town) Aug. 93

Received: £50,000 for Ricky Reina (Brentford) '97

BEST SEASON

FA Cup: Fourth Qualifying Round x 8

(as Dover FC)
2nd Round 75-76 1-4 v Southend Utd. (A)
League club defeated Colchester Utd.

FA Trophy: Semi-Final 97-98

FA Amateur Cup: Did not compete

League: 6th Conference 99-00

LAST SEASON

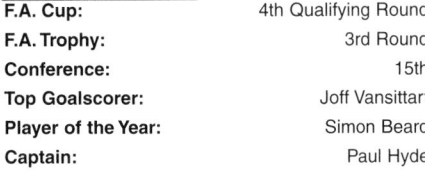

F.A. Cup: 4th Qualifying Round
F.A. Trophy: 3rd Round
Conference: 15th
Top Goalscorer: Joff Vansittart
Player of the Year: Simon Beard
Captain: Paul Hyde

DOVER ATHLETIC

Match Facts 2000-01

	Date	Comp.	Opponents	Gate	Score	Goalscorers
1	19/08	Conf	HEDNESFORD TOWN	929	4 - 0	McRobert 33, Pinnock 52 71, Shearer 84
2	22/08	Conf	Hayes	677	2 - 3	Carruthers 68, McRobert 80
3	26/08	Conf	Chester City	2273	0 - 1	
4	28/08	Conf	KETTERING TOWN	976	1 - 0	Vansittart 15
5	02/09	Conf	Boston United	1804	2 - 1	Vansittart 42, Hoyle 59[og]
6	05/09	Conf	FOREST GREEN ROVERS	750	1 - 2	Le Bihan 3
7	09/09	Conf	WOKING	1027	0 - 0	
8	11/09	Conf	Stevenage Borough	1505	1 - 1	Shearer 69[p]
9	16/09	Conf	Telford United	415	2 - 0	Carruthers 32, Strouts 76 (at Worcester City)
10	23/09	Conf	SCARBOROUGH	933	0 - 2	
11	26/09	Conf	KINGSTONIAN	632	1 - 3	Farrelly 11[og]
12	30/09	Conf	Leigh RMI	485	1 - 2	Vansittart 20
13	03/10	Conf	Yeovil Town	2306	0 - 4	
14	08/10	Conf	NORTHWICH VICTORIA	688	3 - 0	Shearer 78, Vansittart 84, McRobert 86
15	14/10	Conf	MORECAMBE	847	2 - 2	Beard 35, Vansittart 63
16	21/10	Conf	Hereford United	1903	2 - 4	Le Bihan 6 8
17	04/11	Conf	NUNEATON BOROUGH	815	2 - 1	Shearer 74, Gittens 83[og]
18	11/11	Conf	Southport	1635	1 - 2	Vansittart 74
19	18/11	Conf	BOSTON UNITED	764	0 - 0	
20	25/11	Conf	Forest Green Rovers	702	1 - 2	Brown 41
21	02/12	Conf	RUSHDEN & DIAMONDS	1407	4 - 1	Strouts 29, Hockton 45 87, Shearer 82
22	16/12	Conf	HAYES	1026	4 - 1	Hockton 22, Vansittart 45 90, Brown 78[p]
23	26/12	Conf	Dagenham & Redbridge	1359	1 - 1	Hockton 90
24	01/01	Conf	DAGENHAM & REDBRIDGE	1461	3 - 1	Strouts 43, Shearer 66[p], Hockton 78
25	06/01	Conf	Kettering Town	1479	2 - 0	Vansittart 50 59
26	27/01	Conf	DONCASTER ROVERS	1604	1 - 1	Hockton 19
27	10/02	Conf	Woking	1574	1 - 4	Hockton 67[p]
28	17/02	Conf	Doncaster Rovers	1640	1 - 1	Strouts 44
29	24/02	Conf	Scarborough	1082	0 - 2	
30	03/03	Conf	TELFORD UNITED	1161	1 - 3	Hockton 84[p]
31	10/03	Conf	Northwich Victoria	907	0 - 2	
32	17/03	Conf	LEIGH RMI	929	1 - 2	Beard 9
33	26/03	Conf	Hednesford Town	693	0 - 0	
34	31/03	Conf	YEOVIL TOWN	1293	1 - 1	Brown 28
35	03/04	Conf	CHESTER CITY	1112	1 - 1	Shearer 44
36	10/04	Conf	HEREFORD UNITED	1072	1 - 0	Carruthers 40
37	14/04	Conf	Morecambe	1006	2 - 1	Vansittart 46, Brown 88
38	16/04	Conf	SOUTHPORT	954	0 - 1	
39	21/04	Conf	Nuneaton Borough	1414	2 - 1	Carruthers 12, Vansittart 62
40	24/04	Conf	Kingstonian	723	0 - 0	
41	28/04	Conf	Rushden & Diamonds	5482	1 - 2	Vansittart 31
42	05/05	Conf	STEVENAGE BOROUGH	1503	1 - 0	Hockton 42[p]

OTHER COMPETITIONS

Date	Comp.	Opponents	Gate	Score	Goalscorers
10/10	Variety CT 2	KINGSTONIAN	312	0 - 1	
31/10	FA Cup Q4	Aldershot Town	2873	0 - 1	
05/12	LDV Vans 1S	AFC Bournemouth	2171	1 - 1	Hockton 29 Lost 2-4 after penalties)
13/01	FA Trophy 3	Hereford United	1294	0 - 1	
13/02	Kent SC QF	MARGATE	741	2 - 1	Norman 73, Carruthers 112
19/04	Kent SC SF	BROMLEY	264	7 - 0	Hockton 28 31, Strouts 43 71, Vansittart 46, McRobert 53 81
07/05	Kent SC F	GRAVESEND & NORTHFLEET	1002	0 - 4	

1	2	3	4	5	6	7	8	9	10	11	Substitutes Used
Hyde	Munday	Shearer	Leberl	Norman	Carruthers	Strouts	Le Bihan	McRobert	Vansittart	Brown	Pinnock (11), Hogg (10)
Hyde	Munday	Norman	Leberl	Shearer	Strouts	Le Bihan	Pinnock	Vansittart	Carruthers	McRobert	T Browne (8)
Hyde	Munday	Norman	Leberl	Shearer	Strouts	Carruthers	Le Bihan	Vansittart	Pinnock	Beard	Hogg (8), Browne (10), McRobert (11)
Hyde	Munday	Norman	Leberl	Shearer	Strouts	Hogg	Carruthers	Vansittart	Beard	McRobert	Moore (4), T Browne (11)
Hyde	Browne	Norman	Leberl	Shearer	Strouts	Carruthers	Le Bihan	Vansittart	Beard	McRobert	Moore (9)
Hyde	Munday	Norman	Leberl	Shearer	Le Bihan	Strouts	Pinnock	Vansittart	Carruthers	McRobert	Beard (7), Hogg (2)
Hyde	Shearer	Munday	Beard	Browne	Strouts	Leberl	Le Bihan	Norman	Carruthers	Vansittart	Pinnock (10)
Hyde	Munday	Norman	Leberl	Shearer	T Browne	Pinnock	Le Bihan	Strouts	Beard	Vansittart	McRobert (2), Carruthers (7)
Hyde	Browne	Norman	Leberl	Shearer	Strouts	Carruthers	Le Bihan	Pinnocks	Briggs	Beard	Hogg (10)
Hyde	Shearer	Leberl	Beard	Browne	Pinnock	Strouts	Le Bihan	Norman	Carruthers	Vansittart	Briggs (6), Brown (7), McRobert(10)
Hyde	T Browne	Munday	Leberl	Shearer	Strouts	Le Bihan	Beard	Vansittart	S Brown	Carruthers	Pinnock (6), McRobert (10)
Hyde	Munday	Norman	Leberl	Shearer	Beard	Carruthers	Le Bihan	Pinnock	Brown	McRobert	Hogg (6), Vansittart (7), Strouts (10)
Hyde	Munday	Shearer	Leberl	Norman	Strouts	Le Bihan	Beard	McRobert	Vansittart	Brown	Browne (4), Carruthers (9), Pinnock (10)
Hyde	Munday	Norman	Browne	Shearer	Le Bihan	Strouts	Vansittart	Brown	Beard	Darcy	Carruthers (4), Pinnock (9)
Hyde	Shearer	Munday	Beard	Browne	Darcy	Hogg	Norman	Vansittart	Brown	McRobert	Pinnock (4), Strouts (7), Carruthers (10)
Hyde	Browne	Shearer	Beard	Norman	Hogg	Strouts	Darcy	Le Bihan	Vansittart	Carruthers	McRobert (6), Moore (7), Godden(10)
Hyde	Shearer	Munday	Beard	Browne	Chapman	Darcy	Norman	Brown	Vansittart	McRobert	Carruthers (4)
Hyde	Browne	Shearer	Beard	Norman	Darcy	Strouts	Chapman	Le Bihan	Vansittart	Brown	Carruthers (11), Hogg (10), McRobert (2)
Hyde	Shearer	Munday	Beard	Browne	Chapman	Le Bihan	Norman	McRobert	Vansittart	Brown	Carruthers (10)
Hyde	Munday	Norman	Browne	Shearer	Beard	Chapman	Le Bihan	McRobert	Carruthers	Brown	Moore (4), Hogg (9)
Hyde	Shearer	Pluck	Beard	Carruthers	Strouts	Chapman	Le Bihan	Norman	Vansittart	Hockton	Clarke (10)
Hyde	White	Munday	Pluck	Carruthers	Chapman	Strouts	Beard	Norman	Vansittart	Hockton	Brown (11)
Hyde	Munday	Norman	Shearer	Chapman	Strouts	Le Bihan	Beard	Vansittart	Hockton	Carruthers	White (8), McRobert 99)
Hyde	Munday	Norman	Pluck	Shearer	White	Strouts	Le Bihan	Beard	Vansittaty	Hockton	McRobert (4), S Brown (6)
Hyde	Munday	Shearer	Beard	Norman	Carruthers	Chapman	Strouts	Le Bihan	Vansittart	Hockton	McRobert (6)
Hyde	Shearer	Pluck	Beard	Munday	Chapman	Strouts	Le Bihan	Norman	Vansittart	Hockton	Brown (5), Carruthers (7)
Hyde	Pluck	Norman	Chapman	Shearer	Beard	Carruthers	Strouts	Vansittart	Hockton	Le Bihan	McRobert (6), Leberl (8), Brown (10)
Hyde	Leberl	Norman	Chapman	Shearer	Beard	Carruthers	Strouts	Beall	Brown	Le Bihan	
Hyde	Leberl	Norman	Chapman	Shearer	Beard	Carruthers	Beall	Vansittart	Hockton	Le Bihan	Brown (4), Stokes (9), Pluck (10)
Hyde	Shearer	Leberl	Pluck	Carruthers	Beall	Strouts	Le Bihan	Norman	Vansittart	Brown	Hockton (11), McRobert (4)
Hyde	Munday	Leberl	Shearer	Norman	Carruthers	Chapman	Strouts	McRobert	Vansittart	Hockton	Beall (2), Beard (3), Brown (11)
Hyde	Munday	Beard	Shearer	Norman	Carruthers	Chapman	Leberl	McRobert	Vansittart	Brown	Pluck (6), Hockton (10)
Hyde	Munday	Norman	Shearer	Leberl	Beard	Hockton	Chapman	Vansittart	S Brown	Carruthers	
Hyde	Shearer	Beard	Leberl	Munday	Strouts	Chapman	Norman	Carruthers	Vansittart	Brown	McRobert (3), Hockton (11)
Hyde	Munday	Norman	Leberl	Shearer	Beard	Strouts	Chapman	Vansittart	S Brown	Carruthers	Hockton (10), McRobert (11)
Hyde	Munday	Norman	Leberl	Shearer	Strouts	Chapman	Le Bihan	Vansittart	Carruthers	McRobert	Pluck (2), Brown (8)
Hyde	Norman	Brown	Leberl	Shearer	Pluck	Carruthers	Strouts	Vansittart	Chapman	Okator	Brown(6), McRobert (10)
Hyde	T Browne	Norman	Leberl	Shearer	Pluck	Strouts	Chapman	Okafar	Hockton	Brown	Le Bihan (2), McRobert (6), Vansittart (10)
Hyde	Munday	Norman	Leberl	Shearer	Chapman	Carruthers	Strouts	Vansittart	McRobert	Le Bihan	Browne (10), Okafor (11)
Hyde	Munday	Norman	Shearer	Browne	Chapman	Strouts	Le Bihan	Okafar	Vansittart	Carruthers	McRobert (9)
Hyde	Munday	Norman	Browne	Shearer	Beard	Strouts	Chapman	Le Bihan	Carruthers	Vansittart	Pluck (6), McRobert (9)
Hyde	Munday	Norman	Browne	Shearer	Beard	Strouts	Chapman	Le Bihan	Carruthers	Hockton	Brown (11)

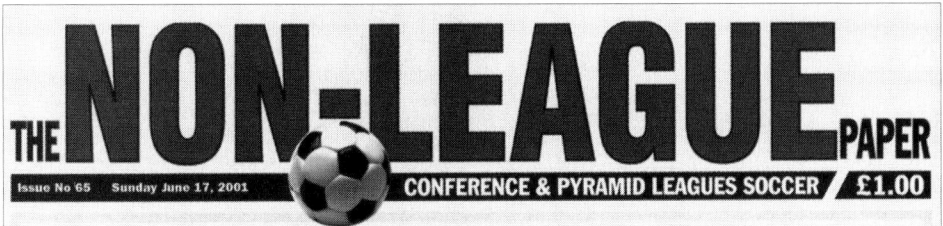

PLAYING SQUAD

DOVER ATHLETIC

Player / *Honours*	*Birthplace*	*D.O.B.*	*Previous Clubs*
GOALKEEPERS			
Paul Hyde FAT, GMVC	Hayes	07.04.63	Hayes, Hillingdon, Wycombe, Leicester, Leyton O
Kevin Hudson	Kent		Folkestone Invicta, Margate, Folkestone T, Canterbury C, Dover Ath.
DEFENDERS			
Lee Shearer	Rochford	23.10.77	Leyton O
Jake Leberl	Manchester		Crewe
Colin Vowden	Newmarket	13.09.71	Kettering T, Cambridge Utd, Cambridge C, Newmarket T
Jason Moore	London	16.02.79	Ramsgate, Dover Ath., Folkestone Invicta, Dover Ath., West Ham
MIDFIELD			
Neil Le Bihan British Univ.	Croydon	14.03.76	Spurs, Peterborough
James Strouts Combined Services	Kent		Harrogate RA, Frickley Ath., Harrogate T, Sittingbourne, Dover Ath., Stevenage B
Steve Norman	Harold Wood	30.01.79	Gillingham, St.Leonards
Craig Etherington	Basildon	16.09.79	West Ham
Jamie Day	Sidcup	13.09.79	Bournemouth, Arsenal
John Elliot SY ES	Scotland	04.07.80	Airdrie, Dundee
FORWARDS			
Matt Carruthers	Dover	22.07.76	Dover Ath., Ashford T, Folkestone Invicta
Lee McRobert	Bromley	04.10.72	Ashford T, Sittingbourne, Millwall, Hastings T, Ashford T
Danny Hockton	Barking	07.02.79	Stevenage B (£7,500), Millwall
Niall Inman Eire Y & u-21	Wakefield	06.02.78	Peterborough
Keith Scott NC, FAT	London	09.06.67	Colchester, Reading, Wycombe, Norwich, Stoke, Swindon, Wycombe, Lincoln, Leicester Utd

FARNBOROUGH TOWN

With the words of their ultra confident manager/chairman Graham Westley proving to be true - the high ideals and aims of Farnborough Town appeared to successfully take shape as the well supported, well publicised Aldershot seemed to lose their way and the Canvey Island challenge was muted by two successful cup runs.

None of the successful promoted clubs in the Conference enjoyed good cup runs and even Rushden & Diamonds disappointed their fans in the F.A. Cup and Trophy.

Farnborough could hardly have done worse! Scraping through a Second Qualifying round tie with Oxford City after a replay before losing to Aylesbury United at home in the F.A. Cup and then losing at the firstl hurdle, 0-2 at Billericay Town in the F.A. Trophy.

Town were never out of the top four however and once they had taken over in top spot at the beginning of January, they never looked back.

An outstanding defence was supplemented by a free scoring attack and a goal ratio of 44-9 during a run of sixteen consecutive league victories put the title out of reach of even Canvey Island.

The Essex club's heroic cup exploits had left them with too much of a fixture backlog although they did win at Farnborough as a last defiant fling late in the season.

Graham Westley was the only chairman to vote against the play off scheme that the F.A. also denounced and he is in the middle of a battle to secure a ground that will meet all the required criteria in the future.

Politics apart, there have been some superb signings, which included Gary Pattison England's captain and Steve Farrelly the giant England goalkeeper plus the impressive Joff Vansittart and Rockie Baptiste up front.

Last season's leading goalscorers Lenny Piper and Gary Crawshaw will also be available and the whole squad looks capable of building a challenge as the season develops.

The confidence is there, so too are a charismatic leader and a high powered squad - but what about the ground?

T.W.

FARNBOROUGH TOWN FC 2001-02

Back Row L-R: Eseyas Yemane, Tony Taggart, Miguel De Souza, Steve Farrelly, Graham Benstead (G/K Coach), Darren Bonfield, Keith Dublin, Steve Darlington, Scott Bennetts. **Middle row:** Stuart Gallagher (fitness), Jom Brown (Physio), Rocky Baptiste, Barry Laker, Gary Patterson, Mark Harper, Graham Pearce (Coach), Nathan Bunce, Danny Hodges, Lee Riddell, Lenny Piper, Ron Berry (kit). **Front row:** Justin Gregory, Danny Jones, Gary Crawshaw, Steve Watson, Graham Westley (Chairman-Manager), Michael Warner, Darren Annon, Chris Piper, Tim O'Shea **Photo:** Eric Marsh

FARNBOROUGH TOWN

GROUND DETAILS

The Aimita Stadium,
Cherrywood Road,
Farnborough,
Hampshire GU14 8UD

Telephone: 01252 541469
Fax: 01252 372640

Directions: From M3 exit 4, take A325 towards Farnborough, right into Prospect Ave. (club signposted), 2nd right into Cherrywood Rd, ground on right.
20-30 min walk from Farnborough Main, Farnborough North and Frimley BR stations.
Whippet mini-bus 19 No 12 Bus passes ground.

Capacity: 4,163
Seated: 627
Covered Terracing: 1,350

Clubhouse:
Open matchdays. Crisps etc.

Club Shop:
Boro' Leisurewear shop - all types of club leisurewear and matchballs (contact Gaye Hoyle 01252 691129)
Supporters Club shop:
Old programmes, scarves, badges etc (contact Paul Doe).

MATCHDAY PROGRAMME

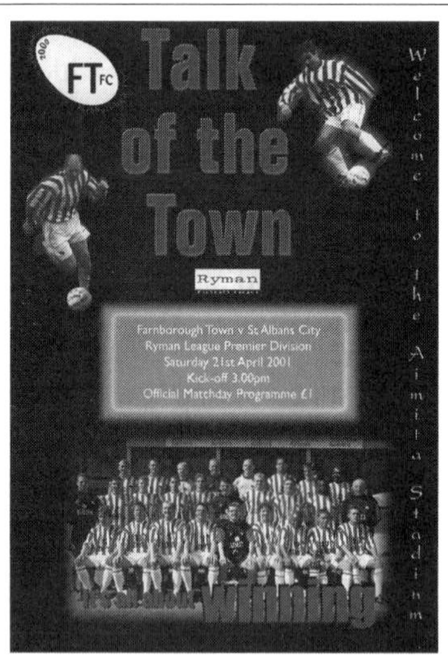

Pages: 40 Price: £2
Editor: Jane White

Local Press: Farnborough News
Local Radio: BBC Southern Counties
County Sound

Founded:	1967
Nickname:	The "Boro"
Club Sponsor:	AMITA Corporation
Club Colours:	Red & white shirts,
Change colours:	All Navy blue
Midweek matchday:	Tuesday
Reserves' League:	Capital League
Club Website:	www.fttc.co.uk

CLUB OFFICIALS

President: **Charles Mortimer**
Chairman: **Graham Westley**
Non Executive Directors: **Matthew Mills, Ron Berry, Tony McAleese & John Thridgould**
Football Secretary: **Vince Williams** Tel: 01252 541469
Commercial Consultant: **Michael Warner** Tel: 07855 407211
Press Officer: **Vince Williams**

FOOTBALL MANAGEMENT TEAM

MANAGER: **GRAHAM WESTLEY**
Date of Appointment: 1st August 1999
Date of Birth: 4th March 1968
Place of Birth: Isleworth

PREVIOUS CLUBS
As manager: Enfield, Kingstonian
As player: QPR, Gillingham, Walton & Hersham

HONOURS
As manager: Ryman Lge Champs. 2000-01; Ryman Lge Cup 99-00

* * *

Asst. Manager/Coach: Graham Pearce
Reserve Team Manager:
Youth Team Manager: Koo Dumbuy
Physio: Jim Brown

Season	League	Div.	Pos.	Home P	W	D	L	F	A	Away W	D	L	F	A	Pts	Manager
00-01	Isthmian	P	1	42	14	5	2	43	13	17	1	3	43	14	99	Graham Westley
99-00	Isthmian	P	12	42	8	5	8	25	19	6	6	9	27	36	53	Graham Westley
98-99	Conference	-	22	42	6	5	10	29	48	1	6	14	12	41	32	Alan Taylor
97-98	Conference	-	18	42	10	3	8	37	27	2	5	14	19	43	44	Alan Taylor
96-97	Conference	-	7	42	9	6	6	35	29	7	7	7	23	24	61	Alan Taylor
95-96	Conference	-	10	42	8	6	7	29	23	7	8	6	34	35	59	Alan Taylor
94-95	Conference	-	14	42	8	5	8	23	31	7	5	9	22	33	55	Alan Taylor
93-94	Southern	P	1	42	15	4	2	43	18	10	3	8	31	26	82	Alan Taylor
92-93	Conference	-	21	42	8	5	8	34	36	4	6	11	34	51	47	Ted Pearce
91-92	Conference	-	5	42	8	7	6	36	27	10	5	6	32	26	66	Ted Pearce

HONOURS

Southern League — Prem. Div. 90-91 93-94,

Isthmian League — Prem. Div. 00-01, R-up 88-89, Div 1 84-85, Div 2 78-79, Lge Cup 99-00,

Athenian Lg — Div 2 78-79,

Spartan Lge — 72-73 73-74 74-75 (Lg Cup 74-75),

London Spartan Lge — 75-76 (Lg Cup 75-76),

Hants Senior Cup — 74-75 81-82 83-84 85-86 90-91 (R-up 93-94)

PREVIOUS

Leagues: Surrey Senior 68-72; Spartan 72-76; Athenian 76-77; Isthmian 77-89 99-01; Alliance Premier (Conference) 89-90 91-93 94-99; Southern 90-91 93-94.

Grounds: Queens Road, Farnborough (1969-1976)

Past Players who progressed to the Football League

Dennis Bailey (Crystal Palace),
Paul Mortimer (Charlton Athletic),
Tommy Jones (Aberdeen),
Allan Cockram (Brentford),
Paul Holsgrove (Millwall),
Maik Taylor (Barnet),
Martin Rowlands (Brentford)

CLUB RECORDS

Attendance: 3,581 v Brentford 22/11/95 (FA Cup)

Win: 11-0 v Chertsey Town (H), Spartan League 72-73

Defeat: 2-10 v Worplesdon (H), Surrey Senior Lge Div. 1 68-69

Career Goalscorer: Simon Read 209, 1986-1994

Career Appearances: Brian Broome 529, 1980-1994

Season Goalscorer: Simon Read 53, 1988-89

Transfer Fee Paid: Undisclosed

Transfer Fee Received: £50,000 from Dover Athletic for David Leworthy, August1993

BEST SEASON

FA Cup: 3rd Rd Proper replay 91-92, 0-1 v West Ham U. (A) after 1-1

League clubs defeated: Torquay Utd 91-92

FA Trophy: Quarter Final 92-93

FA Vase: Semi-Final 75-76 76-77

League: 5th Conference 91-92

LAST SEASON

F.A. Cup: Third Qualifying Round
F.A. Trophy: First Round
League: Champions Isthmian League
Top Goalscorer: Lennie Piper 25
Player of the Year: Barry Laker
Captain: Steve Watson

FARNBOROUGH TOWN

Match Facts 2000-01

	Date	Comp.	Opponents	Gate	Score	Goalscorers
1	19/08	Rym P	Canvey Island	643	1 - 0	Darlington 49
2	22/08	Rym P	GRAVESEND & NORTHFLEET	452	1 - 0	Piper 34
3	26/08	Rym P	CARSHALTON ATHLETIC	521	3 - 0	Crawshaw 48, Baird 71, Dublin 81
4	28/08	Rym P	Grays Athletic	284	3 - 0	Baird 50, Laker 75, Piper 83
5	02/09	Rym P	Purfleet	301	2 - 0	Watson 29, Crawshaw 68
6	05/09	Rym P	BASINGSTOKE TOWN	764	1 - 1	Dack 30
7	09/09	Rym P	Maidenhead United	459	1 - 0	Piper 45
8	16/09	Rym P	ENFIELD	725	1 - 1	Crawshaw 48
9	19/09	Rym P	HEYBRIDGE SWIFTS	367	0 - 1	
10	23/09	Rym P	Chesham United	511	4 - 1	Crawshaw 13 63, Watson 33, Corbett 88
11	07/10	Rym P	Croydon	175	1 - 0	Watson 31
12	11/11	Rym P	Sutton United	644	0 - 1	
13	18/11	Rym P	HITCHIN TOWN	488	3 - 0	Piper 6 71, De Souza 90
14	25/11	Rym P	St Albans City	708	4 - 2	Laker 25, Piper 28[p] 72, Crawshaw 36
15	09/12	Rym P	Hampton & Richmond Borough	609	0 - 1	
16	16/12	Rym P	PURFLEET	502	3 - 2	Crawshaw 76, Darlington 77, Taggart 88
17	23/12	Rym P	Slough Town	582	2 - 0	Piper 27, Watson 67
18	26/12	Rym P	ALDERSHOT TOWN	3478	1 - 0	Laker 66
19	30/12	Rym P	Gravesend & Northfleet	681	1 - 2	Crawshaw 21
20	06/01	Rym P	SUTTON UNITED	781	2 - 1	Piper 24 71
21	13/01	Rym P	Carshalton Athletic	440	5 - 0	Harper 24, De Souza 46, Darlington 59, Taggart 82, Corbett 85
22	27/01	Rym P	Basingstoke Town	946	1 - 0	Warner 57
23	30/01	Rym P	BILLERICAY TOWN	497	3 - 0	Warner 25 76, Darlington 60
24	03/02	Rym P	GRAYS ATHLETIC	736	3 - 0	Crawshaw 45, Baird 71, C Piper 80
25	10/02	Rym P	Enfield	313	3 - 0	Crawshaw 25, L Piper 39, Baird 88
26	17/02	Rym P	MAIDENHEAD UNITED	685	4 - 1	Gregory 46, Corbett 53, L Piper 68, Baird 89
27	20/02	Rym P	HARROW BOROUGH	534	3 - 1	Crawshaw 37, Laker 80, Watson 88
28	24/02	Rym P	Dulwich Hamlet	517	2 - 0	Laker 20 49
29	03/03	Rym P	CROYDON	700	3 - 1	Laker 30, Darlington 58, Crawshaw 70
30	06/03	Rym P	DULWICH HAMLET	502	3 - 0	Corbett 64, Baird 85, Watson 90
31	10/03	Rym P	Heybridge Swifts	457	3 - 2	Baird 32, Warner 40, Watson 74
32	24/03	Rym P	Harrow Borough	376	3 - 2	L Piper 14, Annon 69, Crawshaw 80
33	31/03	Rym P	HENDON	684	2 - 0	L Piper 65, Laker 77
34	07/04	Rym P	Hitchin Town	391	2 - 1	L Piper 15[p], Dack 83
35	09/04	Rym P	Hendon	303	2 - 0	Crawshaw 42, L Piper 48
36	14/04	Rym P	SLOUGH TOWN	688	1 - 1	Crawshaw 75
37	16/04	Rym P	Aldershot Town	3197	1 - 1	Corbett 80
38	19/04	Rym P	CHESHAM UNITED	517	0 - 0	
39	21/04	Rym P	ST ALBANS CITY	677	4 - 0	Mendonca 31, L Piper 48 52, Gregory 90
40	28/04	Rym P	Billericay Town	726	2 - 1	L Piper 36, Corbett 75
41	01/05	Rym P	CANVEY ISLAND	1124	1 - 2	C Piper 27
42	05/05	Rym P	HAMPTON & RICHMOND BOROUGH	1097	1 - 1	Taggart 13

OTHER COMPETITIONS

Date	Comp.	Opponents	Gate	Score	Goalscorers
12/09	Lge Cup 1	ENFIELD	260	2 - 1	B Mendonce 97[p], Yeoman 110
30/09	FA Cup Q2	OXFORD CITY	539	3 - 3	Crawshaw 48, Piper 61, Hooper 90
03/10	FA Cup Q2 R	Oxford City	347	2 - 1	Piper 40, Baird 53
14/10	FA Cup Q3	AYLESBURY UNITED	699	0 - 2	
24/10	FMC 1	Walton & Hersham	129	0 - 1	
29/10	Hants SC 2	Brockenhurst	175	4 - 1	Piper 10 60, Hodges 18, Teggart 89
04/11	FA Trophy 1	Billericay Town	453	0 - 2	
20/11	Ryman Shield	DAGENHAM & REDBRIDGE	251	0 - 2	
28/11	Lge Cup 2	HEMEL HEMPSTEAD TOWN	152	5 - 1	Piper 85 110, De Souza 96, Warner 97, Taggert 111
18/12	Hants SC 3	BLACKFIELD & LANGLEY	75	0 - 0	(3-2p)
16/01	Lge Cup 3	BASINGSTOKE TOWN	282	1 - 3	Crawshaw 25
18/02	Hants SC QF	Havant & Waterlooville	252	0 - 3	

Farnborough's new signings, missing from the team photo, Joff Vansittart and Rocky Baptiste.

PLAYING SQUAD

FARNBOROUGH TOWN

Player	*Birthplace*	*D.O.B.*	*Previous Clubs*
GOALKEEPERS			
Darren Bonfield	London		Boreham Wood, Hitchin T, Wealdstone, Kingsbury T
Steve Farrelly ESP, FAT	Liverpool	27.03.65	Kingstonian, Barrow, Rotherham, Macclesfield, Chester
DEFENDERS			
Keith Dublin EY, RL	Brent	29.01.66	Canvey Island, Southend, Watford, Brighton, Chelsea
Barry Laker RL	London		Sutton Utd, Banstead Ath., Wimbledon (Junior)
Danny Hodges EY, RL	Greenwich	14.09.76	Sutton Utd, Wimbledon
Darren Deegan	London		Staines T, Millwall
Jim Gardner RL	Beckenham	26.10.78	Exeter, Wimbledon
Justin Gregory RL	Sussex		Dulwich Hamlet, Crawley T, Hastings T, Crawley T, Hastings T, Worthing, Shoreham
Michael Warner RL	Harrogate	17.01.74	Northampton, Tamworth, Redditch Utd
Tim O'Shea Eire Y, RL	Pimlico	12.11.66	Instant Dict (HK), Eastern (HK), Gillingham, Leyton Orient, Tottenham
Tony Taggert RL	London	Brentford	
MIDFIELD			
Darron Annon RL	London	17.02.72	Enfield, Kingstonian, Brentford, Carshalton Ath
Gary Patterson ESP, FAT	Newcastle	27.11.72	Kingstonian, Wycombe, Shrewsbury, Notts Co
Lennie Piper EY, RL	London	08.08.77	St.Albans C, Welling Utd, Gillingham, Wimbledon
Scott Corbett RL	London		Kingstonian, Hampton
Steve Watson RL	London		Sutton Utd, Croydon, Whyteleafe, Crystal Palace (Junior)
FORWARDS			
Chris Piper RL	London		St.Albans C, Charlton
Danny Jones	London		Enfield
Gary Crawshaw NC, RL (2)	Reading	04.02.71	Aylesbury Utd, Stevenage B, Hendon, Staines T, Wycombe W., Luton T.
Joff Vansittart	Sussex	12.09.74	Dover Ath, Sutton Utd, Crawley T, Brighton
Miguel De Souza	Newham	11.02.70	Boston Utd, Rushden & Diamonds, Peterborough, Wycombe, Birmingham, Dagenham & Red, Dorchester T, Yeovil T, Bristol C, Charlton
Rocky Baptiste	London		Luton, Hayes, Wealdstone, Willesden Hawkeye, Chelsea (Junior)
Steve Darlington RL	London		Enfield, Kingstonian, Wokingham T, Staines T, Windsor & Eton, Chalfont St.Peter, Hounslow

FOREST GREEN ROVERS

A tough season, grappling for every valuable point in the Conference certainly produced the icing on the seasonal cake at the end of the campaign when a second Trophy Final appearance in three years brought everyone at the club another special occasion to remember.

With David Norton and Nigel Spink sharing managerial duties after the departure of Frank Gregan, the club's most successful manager, a number of loan signings and a concentrated effort throughout the club brought an undefeated run throughout the last nine Conference matches and a final respectable place of sixteenth.

A three week spell in which an F.A. Trophy success against Rushden & Diamonds followed Conference draws at Rushden and Southport probably proved the turning point when the squad realised all was not lost.

The F.A. Cup hadn't brought much relief as a Frankie Bennett hat trick at Bath City brought a place in the First Round only to disappointingly lose at home to Morecambe.

Bennett proved a vital scorer of knock-out goals again in the successful Trophy semi-final at Hereford, but the club's Villa Park appearance which was a special joy to the two `ex-Villans' in charge was a little disappointing.

Nigel Spink has been given sole control for season 2001-2002 and it will be interesting to see if that tremendous battling spirit can be retained as he works to improve the quality of the squad.

An outstanding signing is Simon Travis from Telford United who is on the verge of England Semi-Professional squad and hopefully the experienced Carl Heggs will prove a regular scorer while Jamie Impey and Simon Futcher could be new names to make their mark in the Conference this season.

T.W.

FOREST GREEN ROVERS 2001-02

Back Row, l-r: Mark Shaw, Jamie Impey, Carl Heggs, Nathan Lightbody, Steve Jenkins, Luke Middleton, Daniel Allen. **Middle row:** Bob Baird (physio), Rob Cousins, Ian Hedges, Ellis Glassup, Steve Perrin, Mark Cooper, Simon Futcher, Dave Tyrell (kit manager). **Front row:** Martin Foster, Tony Daley (fitness), Darren Perrin (youth academy), Nigel Spink (manager), Paul Birch (1st team coach), Alex Meecham, Ade Adams.

FOREST GREEN ROVERS

GROUND DETAILS

`The Lawn',
Nympsfield Road,
Forest Green,
Nailsworth,
Glos. GL6 0ET

TELEPHONE NUMBERS:

01453 834860
(Matchday & Club AdministrationCentre)
Fax: 01453 835291
Lawnside Fitness Suite: 01453 832268
Social Club: 01453 833295

SIMPLE DIRECTIONS:
About 4 miles south of Stroud on the A46 towards Bath. InNailsworth turn into Spring Hill from the mini roundabout and the ground is approx. half a mile up the hill on the left. The nearest BR station is Stroud

CAPACITY: 5,141
COVERED TERRACING: 2500
SEATED: 526

SOCIAL FACILITIES: Clubhouse open every evening. Bar and lounge. Open before and after Saturday matches.

CLUB SHOP: Open only on matchdays selling souvenirs and programmes. Contact Andy Whiting.

MATCHDAY PROGRAMME

Welcome to the Lawn
Official Match Day Programme 2000/01

Pages: 52 Price: £1.50

Editor: Clive White Tel: 01453 834860

Other club publications: None

Local Press: Stroud News & Journal
Gloucester Citizen

Local Radio: Severn Sound
BBC Radio Gloucestershire

Founded: 1890
Nickname: Rovers
Sponsors: Sheffield Insulations
Club Colours: Black & white striped shirts, black shorts, red socks.
Change Colours: All Yellow.
Midweek matchday: Wednesday
Reserves' League: College Academy
Youth League: Glos. CountyYouth Lge

CLUB OFFICIALS

President E G Smith
Chairman Trevor Horsley
Secretary David Honeybill

c/o The lawn, Nympsfield Road,
Forest Green, Nailsworth, Glos. GL6 0ET
Tel: 01453 834860 Fax: 01453 835291

Press Officer Heather Cook
Tel: 01453 823281 Mobile 07775 603287

Managing Director Colin Peake

FOOTBALL MANAGEMENT TEAM

MANAGER: NIGEL SPINK

Date of Appointment June 2001
Date of Birth: 8th August 1958
Place of Birth: Chelmsford

PREVIOUS CLUBS
As manager
As Asst. Man/Coach
As player Chelmsford City, Aston Villa, West Bromwich Albion, Millwall

HONOURS
As manager FA Trophy R-up (jt)
As player E: 1. B: 2; Eur. Cup; Eur. Super Cup

Coach: Paul Birch
Physio: Bob Baird
Fitness Coach: Tony Daley
Youth Academy: **darren Perrin**

Season	League	Div.	Pos.	P	Home W	Home D	Home L	Home F	Home A	Away W	Away D	Away L	Away F	Away A	Pts	Manager
00-01	Conference	-	16	42	6	9	6	28	28	5	6	10	15	26	48	F Gregan/ N. Spink & D. Norton
99-00	Conference	-	19	42	11	2	8	35	23	2	6	13	19	40	47	Frank Gregan
98-99	Conference	-	12	42	9	5	7	28	22	6	8	7	27	28	58	Frank Gregan
97-98	Southern	Prem	1	42	16	3	2	51	20	11	5	5	42	35	89	Frank Gregan

Season	League	Div.	Pos.	P	W	D	L	F	A	Pts	Manager
96-97	Southern	Southern	1	42	27	10	5	87	40	91	Frank Gregan
95-96	Southern	Southern	8	42	22	8	12	85	55	74	Frank Gregan
94-95	Southern	Midland	18	42	11	13	18	56	76	46	Frank Gregan
93-94	Southern	Midland	15	42	12	12	18	61	84	48	Pat Casey / Frank Gregan
92-93	Southern	Midland	19	42	12	6	24	61	97	42	Geoff Medcroft
91-92	Southern	Midland	19	42	14	4	24	66	88	46	Bobby Jones

HONOURS

FA Trophy R-up 98-99,
FA Vase 81-82,
Southern League - Premier Div . 97-98,
Southern Div . 96-97;
Hellenic Lg 81-82,
Gloucs Nthn Sen Lg 37-38 49-50 50-51,
Gloucs Sen Cup 84-85 85-86 86-87,
Gloucs Sen Amat Cup (N) 26-27 45-46 71-72 75-76 77-78,
Gloucs Sen Prof Cup 84-85 85-86 86-87.

PREVIOUS

Leagues: Stroud & Dist. 1890-1921, Glos Northern Snr 22-67, Glos Co. 67-73, Hellenic 73-82, Southern League 82-98, Conference 98-.

Name: Stroud FC, 1989-92

Ground: None

Past Players who progressed to the Football League

G Rogers (Newport Co. 85)
K Gill (Newport Co. 85),
M England (Bristol Rov 85).
Wayne Hartswell (Oxford Utd. 00)

CLUB RECORDS

Attendance: 3,002
v St. Albans City, FA Umbro Trophy 18.04.99

Win: 8-0
v Fareham Town Southern Lge. Southern Div. 96-97

Defeat: 0-7
v Moor Green, Southern Lge. Midland Div. 85-86.

Career Goalscorer: Karl Bayliss

Career Appearances: Tommy Callinan

Transfer Fee paid: £20,000
for Adrian Randall from Salisbury City

Transfer Fee Received: £35,000
for Marc McGregor to Nuneaton Borough (July 2000)
for Wayne Hatswell to Oxford United (Dec. 2000)

BEST SEASON

FA Cup: 2nd Round 99-00
0-3 v Torquay Utd. (H)

FA Trophy: Runners-up 98-99, 00-01

FA Vase: Winners 81-82.

League: 12th Conference 98-99

LAST SEASON

F.A. Cup: First Round
F.A. Trophy: Runners up
Conference: 16th
Top Goalscorer: Alex Meecham
Player of the Year:
Captain:

FOREST GREEN ROVERS

Match Facts 2000-01

	Date	Comp.	Opponents	Gate	Score	Goalscorers
1	19/08	Conf	Boston United	2368	0 - 0	
2	23/08	Conf	STEVENAGE BOROUGH	1043	2 - 3	Meechan 40, Sullivan 66
3	26/08	Conf	DONCASTER ROVERS	952	2 - 2	Hatswell 48, Meechan 55
4	28/08	Conf	Telford United	709	0 - 1	(at Worcester City)
5	02/09	Conf	HAYES	804	1 - 2	Foster 23
6	05/09	Conf	Dover Athletic	750	2 - 1	Norton 38, Clark 50
7	09/09	Conf	Rushden & Diamonds	3352	0 - 0	
8	13/09	Conf	KINGSTONIAN	547	3 - 1	Foster 1, Clark 26, Meechan 33
9	16/09	Conf	DAGENHAM & REDBRIDGE	902	4 - 4	Meechan 5 39, Foster 44, Hatswell 80
10	23/09	Conf	Leigh RMI	451	1 - 1	Foster 23
11	27/09	Conf	SCARBOROUGH	542	2 - 3	Daley 54[p], Foster 71
12	30/09	Conf	Kettering Town	1068	3 - 1	Meechan 16 71, Hatswell 28
13	03/10	Conf	Nuneaton Borough	1172	0 - 2	
14	08/10	Conf	HEDNESFORD TOWN	871	0 - 2	
15	14/10	Conf	CHESTER CITY	943	1 - 1	Foster 48
16	21/10	Conf	Woking	1779	0 - 2	
17	31/10	Conf	Northwich Victoria	843	0 - 0	
18	04/11	Conf	MORECAMBE	756	0 - 0	
19	11/11	Conf	Hereford United	2168	1 - 3	Bennett 78
20	25/11	Conf	DOVER ATHLETIC	702	2 - 1	Hatswell 4 53
21	16/12	Conf	Stevenage Borough	1654	1 - 3	Daley 45
22	26/12	Conf	YEOVIL TOWN	1756	0 - 1	
23	30/12	Conf	BOSTON UNITED	872	0 - 3	
24	01/01	Conf	Yeovil Town	4361	0 - 2	
25	06/01	Conf	TELFORD UNITED	775	1 - 1	Clark 14
26	20/01	Conf	Doncaster Rovers	1871	0 - 3	
27	27/01	Conf	NORTHWICH VICTORIA	723	1 - 0	Meechan 18[p]
28	10/02	Conf	RUSHDEN & DIAMONDS	1144	0 - 0	
29	17/02	Conf	Southport	1421	1 - 1	Lightbody 41
30	03/03	Conf	Dagenham & Redbridge	1256	1 - 3	Meechan 62
31	13/03	Conf	Hayes	634	0 - 1	
32	17/03	Conf	KETTERING TOWN	758	3 - 2	Cooper 14, Eaton 76, Meechan 87
33	25/03	Conf	Scarborough	838	0 - 1	
34	28/03	Conf	LEIGH RMI	407	3 - 1	Meechan 56 90, A Foster 58
35	14/04	Conf	Chester City	1292	1 - 0	Doughty 68[og]
36	16/04	Conf	HEREFORD UNITED	1076	1 - 1	M Foster 45
37	19/04	Conf	Hednesford Town	654	1 - 1	A Foster 74
38	21/04	Conf	Morecambe	1017	2 - 0	Sykes 58, Meechan 90
39	25/04	Conf	WOKING	804	0 - 0	
40	28/04	Conf	SOUTHPORT	951	2 - 0	Sykes 78, Lockwood 83
41	01/05	Conf	NUNEATON BOROUGH	781	0 - 0	
42	05/05	Conf	Kingstonian	774	1 - 0	Eaton 55

OTHER COMPETITIONS

Date	Comp.	Opponents	Gate	Score	Goalscorers
19/09	Variety CT 1	Kettering Town	221	0 - 3	
28/10	FA Cup Q4	BATH CITY	977	3 - 1	Bennett 28 48 88
18/11	FA Cup 1	MORECAMBE	1023	0 - 3	
14/01	FA Trophy 3	BARTON ROVERS	654	6 - 1	Hedges 14, Clark 37, Campbell 60, Meechan 74 85[p], Cousins 90
03/02	FA Trophy 4	Matlock Town	802	2 - 2	Foster 6, Meechan 60
14/02	FA Trophy 4 R	MATLOCK TOWN	425	3 - 1	Drysdale 21, Slater 60, Lightbody 90
24/02	FA Trophy 5	RUSHDEN & DIAMONDS	1018	2 - 0	Lightbody 25, M Foster 33
07/03	Glos SC 1	CINDERFORD TOWN	169	0 - 2	
10/03	FA Trophy QF	WORKSOP TOWN	1448	2 - 1	Clark 11, Lightbody 48
31/03	FA Trophy SF(1)	HEREFORD UNITED	2711	2 - 2	Bennett 62, Meechan 80[p]
07/04	FA Trophy SF(2)	Hereford United	4175	4 - 1	Bennett 14, Meechan 28, Burns 59, A Foster 81
13/05	FA Trophy Final	CANVEY ISLAND	10,007	0 - 1	(at Aston Villa)

1	2	3	4	5	6	7	8	9	10	11	Substitutes Used
Spink	Cousins	Hatswell	Clark	Drysdale	Daley	Norton	Burns	Sullivan	Bailey	Meechan	Hedges (5), Campbell (7), Lightbody (10)
Spink	Cousins	Hatswell	Clark	Hedges	Burns	Daley	Norton	Bailey	Meechan	Sullivan	Campbell (8)
Spink	Cousins	Hatswell	Norton	Clark	Burns	Daley	Drysdale	Sullivan	Bailey	Meechan	Lightbody (7), Hedges (8)
Spink	Cousins	Hatswell	Clark	Drysdale	Burns	Daley	Norton	Bailey	Meechan	Bennett	Sullivan (2), Lightbody (5)
Spink	Cousins	Norman	Clark	Hatswell	Burns	Daley	Drysdale	Bennett	Foster	Meechan	Lightbody (8), Bailey (9)
Spink	Cousins	Hatswell	Clark	Drysdale	Burns	Daley	Norton	Foster	Meechan	Da Bailey	Bailey (9) Hedges (11)
Spink	Cousins	Hatswell	Norton	Clark	Burns	Daley	Drysdale	Foster	Meechan	Da Bailey	Bailey (9)
Spink	Cousins	Hatswell	Clark	Drysdale	Burns	Daley	Norton	Da Bailey	Meechan	Foster	Hedges (2), Thomas (7), Bailey (11)
Spink	Cousins	Norton	Clark	Hatswell	Burns(s)	Daley	Drysdale	Da Bailey	Foster	Meechan	Thomas (7), Hedges (8), Bennett (10)
Spink	Cousins	Hatswell	Clark	Norton	Burns	Da Bailey	Daley	Drysdale	Foster	Meechan	Thomas (10)
Spink	Cousins	Hatswell	Clark	Drysdale	Burns	Daley	Norton	Da Bailey	Meechan	Foster	Bailey (2), Bennet (9)
Spink	Cousins	Clark	Hedges	Hatswell	Daley	Norton	Meechan	Thomas	Drysdale	Foster	Da Bailey (6), De Bailey (11), Birkby (8)
Spink	Cousins	Hatswell	Drysdale	Clark	Hedges	Norton	Daley	Thomas	Foster	Meechan	Birkby (8), Bennett (2), De Bailey (11)
Spink	Cousins	Hatswell	Drysdale	Clark	Hedges	Norton	Daley	Foster	Meechan	Bennett	De Bailey (6), Campbell (8), Thomas (11)
Perrin	Cousins	Norton	Clark	Hatswell	Burns	Bennett	Drysdale	Hedges	Foster	Meechan	De Bailey (7), Kilgour (9)
Perrin	Cousins	Norton	Clark	Hatswell	Burns	Bennett	Drysdale	Daley	Bailey	Slater	Thomas (2), Campbell (9)
Perrin	Cousins	Hatswell	Drysdale	Clark	Hedges	Norton	Burns	Slater	De Bailey	Bennett	Daley (11)
Perrin	Cousins	Norton	Clark	Hatswell	Burns	Hedges	Drysdale	Slater	De Bailey	Bennett	Campbell (7), Daley (11)
Perrin	Cousins	Hedges	Kilgour	Drysdale	Campbell	Burns	Norton	Daley	De Bailey	Slalter	Thomas (7), Bennett (10), Lightbody (5)
Perrin	Cousins	Hatswell	Norton	Clark	Burns	Daley	Drysdale	Slater	Foster	Bailey	Hedges (4), Birkby (10), Lightbody (11)
Perrin	Cousins	Cort	Norton	Clark	Hedges	Daley	Drysdale	Foster	Lightbody	Slater	Thomas (7), Bailey (9)
Perrin	Cousins	Clark	Drysdale	Norton	Burns	Daley	Cort	Slater	Lightbody	Foster	De Bailey (6)
Perrin	Cousins	Clark	Drysdale	Norton	Burns	Cort	Slater	Foster	Lightbody	Bennett	Dobson (4), Daley (10), De Bailey (11)
Perrin	Cousins	Drysdale	Clark	Cort	Norton	Burns	Daley	Slater	Foster	Meechan	Hedges (7), Bennet (8)
Perrin	Cousins	Norton	Clark	Cort	Burns	Hedges	Drysdale	Slater	Eaton	Meechan	Daley (9)
Perrin	Cousins	Clark	Hedges	Drysdale	Burns	Daley	Cort	Slater	Meechan	Waton	Dobson (6), Lightbody (7)
Perrin	Cousins	M Foster	Clark	Cort	Burns	Lightbody	Nicholson	Drysdale	Meechan	Eaton	A Foster (7), Prince (9)
Perrin	Cousins	M Foster	Clark	Cort	Burns	Lightbody	Hedges	Slater	Eaton	Meechan	A Foster (11)
Perrin	Hedges	Clark	Cort	Drysdale	Cousins	M Foster	Lightbody	Slater	Meechan	Eaton	Daley (8), Prince (2)
Perrin	Hedges	Cort	M Foster	Clark	Burns	Lightbody	Drysdale	Eaton	Meechan	Slater	Daley (7), A Foster (9), Cousins (2)
Perrin	Cousins	Cort	Clark	Drysdale	Burns	M Foster	Slater	Eaton	Meechan	Lightbody	Prince (5), A Foster (11)
Perrin	Cousins	M Foster	Clark	Cort	Prince	Cooper	A Foster	Slater	Eaton	Meechan	
Perrin	Cousins	Lockwood	M Foster	S Clarke	Prince	Cooper	Slater	Eaton	Meechan	A Foster	Daley (8)
Perrin	Cousins	Lockwood	Clark	Drysdale	Sykes	Cooper	M Foster	A Foster	Meechan	Middleton	
Perrin	Cousins	Lockwood	Clark	M Foster	Cooper	Middleton	Slater	A Foster	Meechan	Sykes	Olney (9), Shaw (11)
Perrin	Cousins	Lockwood	Clark	M Foster	Burns	Cooper	Bennett	A Foster	Meechan	Shaw	Sykes (6), Middleton (8), Olney (9)
Ghent	Cousins	Lockwood	M Foster	S Clarke	Cooper	Slater	Sykes	A Foster	Meechan	Shaw	Bennett (11)
Perrin	Cousins	Lockwood	M Foster	Burns	Cooper	Middleton	Daley	A Foster	Meechan	Sykes	Bennett (7)
Perrin	Cousins	Lockwood	M Foster	Burns	Cooper	Daley	Bennett	A Foster	Meechan	Sykes	Middleton (7), Lightbody (10), Slater 911)
Perrin	Cousins	M Foster	Burns	Lockwood	Cooper	Shaw	Slater	Sykes	A Foster	Lightbody	Eaton (8), Middleton (11)
Ghent	Lockwood	Clark	Prince	Cooper	Burns	Shaw	Middleton	A Foster	Eaton	Sykes	Hedges (2), M Foster (8), Hunt (9)
Perrin	Cousins	Lockwood	Clark	M Foster	Cooper	Burns	Prince	A Foster	Eaton	Shaw	Hedges (7), Hunt (9)

PLAYING SQUAD

FOREST GREEN ROVERS

(Bold print indicates an England Semi-Professional International)

Player *Honours*	*Birthplace*	*D.O.B.*	*Previous Clubs*
GOALKEEPERS			
Steve Perrin	Wiltshire		Melksham T, Trowbridge T
Ellis Glassup	Cornwall		St.Austell
DEFENDERS			
Rob Cousins ESP, RL	Bristol	09.01.71	Bristol C, Bath C, Yeovil T
Ian Hedges	Bristol	05.02.69	Bath C, Bournemouth, Gloucester C, Bristol Manor Farm
Jamie Impey	Bournemouth		Dorchester T
Peter Smith	Gloucester		From Youth team
Simon Travis	Preston	22.03.77	Telford Utd, Stockport, Holywell T, Torquay
British Univ.			
MIDFIELD			
Graeme Little	Gloucester		From Reserves
Lee McMullen	Gloucester		From Reserves
Luke Middleton	Gloucester		Swansea, Southampton, Topsham T
Luke Prince	Aston Villa		
Mark Cooper	Wakefield	18.12.68	Hednesford T, Rushden & Diamonds, Leyton Orient, Hartlepool, Exeter, Wycombe, Fulham, Birmingham, Exeter, Bristol C
Mark Shaw	Nottingham		Matlock T, Eastwood T, Matlock T
Martin Foster	Rotherham	29.10.77	Doncaster R, Greenock Morton, Leeds
FORWARDS			
Tony Daley England Int.	Birmingham	18.11.67	Aston Villa, Wolves, Watford, Walsall
Paul Hunt DMP	Swindon	08.10.70	Swindon, Charlton, Cardiff, Bristol R, Brann Bergen, Cirencester T
Alex Meechan	Plymouth	29.01.80	Bristol C, Swindon
Carl Heggs	Leicester	11.10.70	Carlisle, Rushden & Diamonds, Northampton, Swansea, WBA, Paget R, Doncaster R, Leicester Utd
Jason Eaton	Bristol	29.01.69	Newport Co., Yeovil T, Cheltenham T, Gloucester C, Bristol C, Bristol R, Trowbridge T
Nathan Golightly	Bristol		From Youth team
Simon Futcher	Swindon		Swindon Supermarine

HAYES

Being situated in the heart of the West London suburbs, it is difficult for Hayes Football Club to create a real identity of its own, although it has invested well from huge fees received from Jason Roberts and Les Ferdinand and the ground is very smart. Long serving manager Terry Brown, himself an experienced non-League player with West of London clubs has manfully kept his squad out of the relegation places, but every year the battle becomes harder to survive.

After four victories in the first six matches and an impressive sixth position, the lively Rocky Baptiste was whisked away by Luton Town following his hat trick against Northwich Victoria and a run of twelve Conference matches from October to the new year produced only three goals and the club sunk to seventeenth position.

From then on it was a constant battle for survival with Baptiste and Jimmy Quinn being brought in on loan to provide vital goals. Just like their rivals Forest Green Rovers they saved themselves in the run in, with one defeat in nine games and a vital last match victory of 3-1 at Hednesford saw Rocky Baptiste emerge the hero with two goals and the Middlesex club finished in a respectable eighteenth position!

The F.A. Cup, with victory over old friends and fellow strugglers Dulwich Hamlet was followed by defeat at another ex-Isthmian Premier club Dagenham & Redbridge but Rushden & Diamonds were not the sort of opponents to draw in the F.A. Trophy when a confidence boost was needed!

No doubt Hayes will be amongst the early season's favourites for relegation, and once again it will be a long hard season for the loyal band of club officials who have manfully kept their club amongst the non-League elite for so long.

T.W.

Back Row: Ben Hodson, Alvin Watts, Dominic Sterling, Paul Gothard, Matt Hodson, Dean Coppard, Jason Tucker, Rocky Baptiste.
Middle Row: Mark Molesley, Barry Moore, Ryan Spencer, Mark Preston, Brendon Gallen, Danny Tilbury.
Front Row: Dave Killick (Chief Scout), Steve Barnes, Steve McKimm, Jason Goodliffe (Captain), Derek Goodall (Chairman), Lee Flynn, Dave Stevens, Errol Telemaque, Terry Brown (Manager)

HAYES

GROUND DETAILS

Townfield House
Church Road
Hayes
Middx. UB3 2LE

Telephone Number: 0208 573 2075

Simple Directions: M25, M4, A312 (Hayes By-Pass), A4020 (Uxbridge Road) and Church Rd. is on the left.

Capacity: 6,500
Seated: 450
Terracing - **Covered:** 2,000
Uncovered: 4,050

SOCIAL FACILITIES:
Clubhouse open Sat 12 - 11pm. Sun 12 - 3pm, 7 - 11pm. Midweek 6.30 - 11pm. Hot and cold snacks are available.

CLUB SHOP:
Wide range of programmes & souvenirs. Contact Lee Hermitage, c/o the club.

MATCHDAY PROGRAMME

Hayes
Official Matchday Programme £1.50
Conference Programme of the Year 1998/99 & 1999/2000 - Wirral Programme Club
TAYLOR WOODROW
IN TODAY'S ISSUE
- Goth interview
- Boardroom news
- Hereford in detail
- Hayes openers
- Basingstoke photos

Nationwide
NATIONWIDE CONFERENCE
versus Hereford United Saturday 26th August 2000 Kick-off 3.00

Pages: 32 Price: £1.50
Editor: Ken Green
Other club publications: None
Local Press: Hayes Gazette
Local Radio: Capital Radio

Founded: 1909
Nickname: The Missioners
Club Sponsors: Taylor Woodrow

Club colours: Red & white shirts black shorts, black socks

Change colours: Blue shirts blue shorts, blue socks

Reserve team's league: Suburban Premier
Midweek home matchday: Tuesday
Local Newspapers: Hayes Gazette
Local Radio: Capital Radio

CLUB OFFICIALS

President Les Lovering

Chairman Derek Goodall

Vice Chairman Trevor Griffith

Financial Director Charles Mackintosh

Directors D Goodall, C Porter, E Stevens, T Griffith, C Mackintosh, A Bond, J Bond, N Griffith, T Gorman.

Football Secretary John Bond Jnr.

Press Officer Trevor Griffith
c/o the club Tel: 0208 573 2075

FOOTBALL MANAGEMENT TEAM

MANAGER: **TERRY BROWN**
Date of Appointment: November 1993
Date of Birth: 5th August 1952
Place of Birth: Hillingdon

PREVIOUS CLUBS
As manager: None
As coach: Wokingham Town
As player: Hayes, Slough Town, Hayes, Wokingham Town

HONOURS
as manager: Isthmian League Championship 95-96
As player: None

* * *

Assistant Manager Willy Wordsworth

Coach Dave Killick

Physio Carl Ballard

Season	League	Div.	Pos.	Home P	Home W	Home D	Home L	Home F	Home A	Away W	Away D	Away L	Away F	Away A	Pts	Manager
00-01	Conference	-	18	42	5	6	10	22	31	7	4	10	22	40	46	Terry Brown
99-00	Conference	-	11	42	7	3	11	24	28	9	5	7	33	30	56	Terry Brown
98-99	Conference	-	3	42	12	3	6	34	25	10	5	6	29	25	74	Terry Brown
97-98	Conference	-	12	42	10	4	7	36	25	6	6	9	26	27	58	Terry Brown
96-97	Conference	-	15	42	7	7	7	27	21	5	7	9	27	34	50	Terry Brown

Season	League	Div.	Pos.	P	W	D	L	F	A	Pts	Manager
95-96	Isthmian	Prem	1	42	24	14	4	76	32	86	Terry Brown
94-95	Isthmian	Prem	3	42	20	14	8	66	47	74	Terry Brown
93-94	Isthmain	Prem	13	42	15	8	19	63	72	53	Clive Griffiths
92-93	Isthmian	Prem	10	42	16	13	13	64	59	61	Clive Griffiths
91-92	Isthmian	Prem	19	42	10	14	18	52	63	44	Harry Manoe

HONOURS

Isthmian League 95-96
Athenian League 56-57
Spartan League 27-28
Great Western Suburban League 1920-24 (4 times)
Middlesex Senior Cup 19-20, 20-21, 25-26, 30-31, 35-36, 39-40, 49-50, 81-82, 95-96, 99-00
London Senior Cup 31-32, 80-81
Middlesex Charity Cup - 15 Times
London Charity Cup 60-61

PREVIOUS

Leagues: Local leagues 1909-14; Gt. Western Suburban 19-22; London 22-24; Spartan 24-30; Athenian 30-71; Isthmian 71-96.

Names: Bokwell Mission

Ground: Botwell Common

Past Players who progressed to the Football League

Cyril Bacon (Orient 46), Phil Nolan (Watford 47), Dave Groombridge (Orient 51), Jimmy Bloomfield (Brentford 52), Derek Neate & Les Champleover(Brighton 56 & 57), Gordon Phillips (Brentford 63), Robin Friday (Reading 74), Les Smith (A Villa), Cyrille Regis (WBA 1977), Les Ferdinand (QPR 87),Derek Payne (Barnet 88), Paul Hyde (Wycombe 91), Dean Hooper (Swindon95), Jason Roberts (Wolverhampton W. 97)

CLUB RECORDS

Attendance: 15,370 v Bromley FA Amateur Cup, 10.2.51

Win: Unknown
Defeat: Unknown
Career Goalscorer: Unknown

Career Appearances: Reg Leather 701

Transfer Fees
Paid: £6,000 for Gary Keen (Hendon) 1990 Joe Francis (Enfield) 1996

Received: £30,000 for Les Ferdinand (Q.P.R.) 1987

BEST SEASON

FA Cup: 2nd Round (replay)
72-73: 0-1 v Reading (H) after 0-0
99-00: 2-3 aet v Hull City (A) after 2-2
also 2nd Round 90-91 & 91-92
League clubs defeated:
Bristol Rov.72-73, Cardiff C.90-91, Fulham 91-92

FA Trophy: Quarter Final
78-79, 1-2 v Runcorn (A)
97-98, 0-1 v Cheltenham Town (A)

FA Amateur Cup: Runners Up 1930-31

League: 3rd Conference 98-99

LAST SEASON

F.A. Cup: First Round
F.A. Trophy: Third Round
Conference: 18th
Top Goalscorer: Rocky Baptiste
Player of the Year:
Captain: Jason Goodliffe

HAYES

Match Facts 2000-01

	Date	Comp.	Opponents	Gate	Score	Goalscorers
1	19/08	Conf	Telford United	542	0 - 2	(at Worcester City)
2	22/08	Conf	DOVER ATHLETIC	677	3 - 2	Moore 2, Stevens 54, B Hodson 89
3	26/08	Conf	HEREFORD UNITED	701	0 - 2	
4	28/08	Conf	Kingstonian	902	1 - 0	Baptiste 52
5	02/09	Conf	Forest Green Rovers	804	2 - 1	Baptiste 47, Coppard 81
6	05/09	Conf	KETTERING TOWN	548	2 - 1	McKimm 54, Barnes 60
7	09/09	Conf	SCARBOROUGH	562	0 - 1	
8	12/09	Conf	Woking	1139	2 - 1	Stevens 21, Moore 73
9	23/09	Conf	NUNEATON BOROUGH	732	0 - 0	
10	26/09	Conf	YEOVIL TOWN	707	2 - 3	Baptiste 14, Stevens 44
11	30/09	Conf	Northwich Victoria	808	4 - 3	Baptiste 41 44 45, Moore 78
12	03/10	Conf	Dagenham & Redbridge	1145	0 - 2	
13	07/10	Conf	LEIGH RMI	415	1 - 2	Stevens 23
14	14/10	Conf	DONCASTER ROVERS	750	0 - 3	
15	21/10	Conf	Southport	1252	0 - 2	
16	31/10	Conf	Rushden & Diamonds	2568	0 - 4	
17	04/11	Conf	TELFORD UNITED	584	0 - 1	
18	11/11	Conf	Morecambe	1272	0 - 4	
19	02/12	Conf	Boston United	1667	1 - 0	Stevens 59
20	09/12	Conf	RUSHDEN & DIAMONDS	1044	0 - 3	
21	16/12	Conf	Dover Athletic	1026	1 - 4	Boylan 84
22	23/12	Conf	Chester City	1658	0 - 0	
23	26/12	Conf	STEVENAGE BOROUGH	853	0 - 1	
24	01/01	Conf	Stevenage Borough	2171	3 - 3	Preston 56, Boylan 80, Watts 85
25	06/01	Conf	HEDNESFORD TOWN	586	1 - 1	Boylan 77
26	20/01	Conf	Hereford United	1368	2 - 3	Moore 35, Gallen 90
27	27/01	Conf	Kettering Town	1650	2 - 0	Hodson 21, Town 89
28	10/02	Conf	Scarborough	814	0 - 2	
29	17/02	Conf	WOKING	1001	1 - 2	Hodson 78
30	24/02	Conf	Nuneaton Borough	1510	1 - 1	Hodson 44
31	27/02	Conf	KINGSTONIAN	738	1 - 1	Quinn 62
32	03/03	Conf	CHESTER CITY	784	1 - 3	Quinn 61
33	10/03	Conf	Leigh RMI	414	0 - 4	
34	13/03	Conf	FOREST GREEN ROVERS	634	1 - 0	Molesley 81
35	17/03	Conf	NORTHWICH VICTORIA	620	2 - 2	Quinn 47, Coppard 82
36	24/03	Conf	Yeovil Town	3206	0 - 3	
37	31/03	Conf	DAGENHAM & REDBRIDGE	981	4 - 1	Quinn 30 47, Baptiste 39, Everitt 80
38	07/04	Conf	SOUTHPORT	615	1 - 0	Baptiste 44
39	14/04	Conf	Doncaster Rovers	1769	0 - 0	
40	16/04	Conf	MORECAMBE	686	1 - 1	Baptiste 89
41	28/04	Conf	BOSTON UNITED	929	1 - 1	Quinn 61
42	05/05	Conf	Hednesford Town	925	3 - 1	Bunce 4, Baptiste 59 81

OTHER COMPETITIONS

Date	Comp.	Opponents	Gate	Score	Goalscorers
14/08	Middx Super Cup	ASHFORD TOWN (MIDDX)	200	4 - 0	McKimm 44, Spencer 45, Preston 53, Barnes 63
19/09	Variety CT 1	WOKING	164	3 - 5	Moore 27 34, Preston 70
28/10	FA Cup Q4	DULWICH HAMLET	464	4 - 2	Preston 24 65, Boylan 86, Telemaque 90
18/11	FA Cup 1	Dagenham & Redbridge	1150	1 - 3	Boylan 45
13/01	FA Trophy 3	RUSHDEN & DIAMONDS	842	0 - 1	
06/03	Middx SC 2	Bedfont	n/k	4 - 1	
20/03	Middx SC QF	Edgware Town	n/k	2 - 0	
27/03	Middx SC SF	HARROW BOROUGH	n/k	1 - 2	B Hodson 42

1	2	3	4	5	6	7	8	9	10	11	Substitutes Used
Gothard	Goodliffe	Flynn	Sterling	Coppard	Spencer	McKimm	Moore	Stevens	Tucker	Barnes	Baptiste (2), Preston (10), Moseley (7)
Gothard	Sterling	Flynn	Coppard	Spencer	Baptiste	McKimm	Moore	Stevens	Preston	Barnes	B Hodson (6), Watts (10)
Gothard	Spencer	Coppoard	Sterling	Flynn	Preston	Moore	McKimm	Barnes	Baptiste	Stevens	B Hodson 96), Tucker (7)
Gothard	Coppard	Flynn	Sterling	Spencer	Baptiste	McKimm	Moore	Stevens	Barnes	Preston	B Hodson (9), Bryson (11)
Gothard	Spencer	Coppard	Sterling	Flynn	Baptiste	McKimm	White	Barnes	Stevens	Moore	Bezhadi(8), B Hodson (9)
Gothard	Sterling	Flynn	Coppard	Spencer	Baptiste	McKimm	Bryson	Moore	Stevens	Barnes	Tucker (9), White (11)
Gothard	Spencer	Coppard	Sterling	Flynn	Molesey	McKimm	Tucker	Barnes	Stevens	Baptiste	White (5), Telemarque (6), Moore (8)
Gothard	Coppard	Flynn	Sterling	Spencer	Moseley	McKimm	Moore	Baptiste	Stevens	Barnes	White (11)
Hodson	Spencer	Flynn	Coppard	Sterling	Baptiste	McKimm	Molesey	Stevens	Moore	White	Barnes (2), Preston (6), Telemaque (9)
Hodson	Sterling	Flynn	Coppard	Spencer	White	McKimm	Baptiste	Moore	Stevens	Barnes	Preston (5)
Hodson	Spencer	Coppard	Sterling	Flynn	McKimm	Baptiste	White	Barnes	Stevens	Moore	Gallen (8), Preston (10)
Hodson	Sterling	Flynn	Coppard	Spencer	Gallen	McKimm	Baptiste	Moore	Stevens	Barnes	Molesey(6), White (8), Preston (11)
Hodson	Spencer	Coppard	Sterling	White	Flynn	Moore	McKimm	Barnes	Stevens	Baptiste	Gallen (5), Preston (11)
Hodson	Spencer	Coppard	Pluck	Watts	Flynn	Molesey	McKimm	Moore	Stevens	Baptiste	Barnes (7), Telemaque (11)
Hodson	Spencer	Watts	Sterling	Flynn	Pluck	McKimm	Moore	Molesey	B Hodson	Stevens	Bezhadi (2), Barnes (9), Telemaque (11)
M Hodson	Sterling	Flynn	Spencer	Watts	Molesey	McKimm	Moore	Stevens	Preston	Barnes	B Hodson (10), Bezhadi (4), Telemarque (9)
M Hodson	Spencer	Watts	Sterling	Pluck	Flynn	McKimm	Moore	Barnes	B Hodson	Boylan	Molesey (2), Coppard (3) Telemaque (9)
M Hodson	Preston	Flynn	Watts	Sterling	Pluck	McKimm	Moore	Molesey	Boylan	Barnes	Coppard (2), B Hodson (4), Telemaque (6)
Bossu	Bezhadi	Watts	Sterling	Hannigan	Flynn	McKimm	Newton	Moore	Stevens	Boylan	Coppard (2), Telemarque (11)
Hodson	Bezhadi	Watts	Sterling	Hannigan	Flynn	Moore	Newton	McKimm	Stevens	Boylan	Barnes (5), Preston (2)
Hodson	Watts	Sterling	Hannigan	Bezhadi	Newton	Moore	McKimm	Flynn	Stevens	Boylan	Telemaque (5), Gallen (8)
Gothard	Spencer	Flynn	Watts	Sterling	Goodliffe	Preston	Newton	Stevens	Moore	Boylan	Coppard (2), Telemarque (7)
Gothard	Boylan	Flynn	Watts	Sterling	Goodliffe	Spencer	Newton	Moore	Stevens	Preston	Coppard (7), McKimm (8)
Gothard	Goodliffe	Flynn	Watts	Sterling	Spencer	McKimm	Newton	Moore	Stevens	Preston	Telemaque (10), Boylan (8)
Gothard	Spencer	Coppard	Sterling	Goodliffe	Flynn	McKimm	Moore	Preston	Telemaque	Boylan	Stevens(10)
Gothard	Sterling	Boylan	Dyer	Coppard	Spencer	Gallen	Moore	McKimm	Stevens	B Hodson	Molesey (4), Bezhadi (6), Telemarque (10)
Gothard	Spencer	Watts	Sterling	Gallen	McKimm	Coppard	Moore	Boylan	Town	Hodson	Nyamah(9)
Gothard	Spencer	Nyamah	Watts	Sterling	Goodliffe	McKimm	Hodson	Town	Moore	Preston	Coppard (4), Boylan (8)
Gothard	Spencer	Watts	Sterling	Goodliffe	Nyamah	McKimm	Moore	Preston	Stevens	Town	Hodson (11)
Gothard	Bezhadi	Gallen	Watts	Sterling	Goodliffe	McKimm	Preston	Hodson	Nyamah	Molesey	Town (3)
Gothard	Bezhadi	Nyamah	Watts	Sterling	Goodliffe	McKimm	Moore	Quinn	B Hodson	Preston	Molesey (2), Stevens (9), Coppard (11)
Gothard	Molesey	Watts	Sterling	Goodliffe	Nyamah	Moore	McKimm	Preston	Quinn	B Hodson	M Hodson(11), Coppard (3), Telemarque (5)
Gothard	Bezhadi	Nyamah	Watts	Sterling	Molesey	McKimm	Stevens	Moore	Quinn	Preston	Hodson (2), Gallen (3), Coppard (4)
Gothard	Bezhadi	Coppard	Watts	Sterling	Gallen	McKimm	Moore	B Hodson	Stevens	Preston	Molesley (2), Telemarque (10)
M Hodson	Moore	Coppard	Watts	Sterling	Gallen	Preston	McKimm	Everitt	B Hodson	Quinn	Bezhadi (5), Telemarque (10)
Gothard	Watts	Goodliffe	Herbert	Bezhadi	Coppard	Moore	McKimm	Everitt	Quinn	Baptiste	B Hodson (4), Molesley (5), Preston (9)
Gothard	Molesley	Gallen	Coppard	Bunce	Goodliffe	McKimm	Moore	Quinn	Baptiste	Everitt	
Gothard	Molesely	Gallen	Coppard	Bunce	Goodliffe	McKimm	Moore	Quinn	Baptiste	Everitt	
Gothard	Molesley	Gallen	Coppard	Bunce	Goodliffe	McKimm	Moore	Quinn	Baptiste	Everitt	B Hodson (9), Sterling (11), M Hodson (1)
M Hodson	Bunce	Goodliffe	Coppard	Molesley	Gallen	McKimm	Moore	Quinn	Baptiste	Everitt	Sterling (4), Stevens (5), Preston (6)
M Hodson	Molesley	Gallen	Sterling	Bunce	Goodliffe	McKimm	Moore	Quinn	Baptiste	Everitt	Coppard (2), Preston (3), Stevens (10)
M Hodson	Bunce	Goodliffe	Molesley	Sterling	Gallen	McKimm	Moore	Quinn	Baptiste	Everitt	

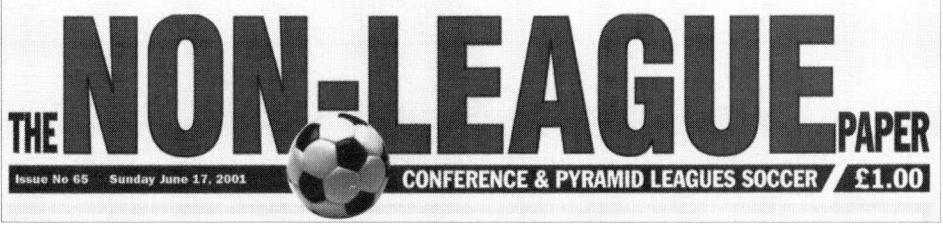

PLAYING SQUAD

HAYES

(Bold print indicates an England Semi-Professional International)

Player *Honours*	*Birthplace*	*D.O.B.*	*Previous Clubs*
GOALKEEPERS			
Bertrand Bossu	Calais	14.10.80	Barnet
DEFENDERS			
Ryan Spencer British Univ.	London	03.01.79	Tottenham H, Ruislip Manor
Dominic Sterling	London		Wimbledon, Wealdstone
Matt Coppard			From Youth team
Brendan Gallen	London		From Youth team
James Spencer	London		From Youth team
Jon Ashton	Plymouth	04.08.79	Exeter, Plymouth
MIDFIELD			
Dave Everitt	London		Staines T, Banstead A., Chesham U., Walton & H. Chesham U, Sutton U, Leyton Orient, Walton & Hersham
Ben Hodson	Nottingham	25.01.76	Forest Green R, Wycombe
Bobby Bezhadi	London		Stevenage B
Danny Tilbury	London		From Youth team
Dean Clark	Hillingsdon	31.03.80	Uxbridge, Brentford
Mark Molesey	London		From Youth team
FORWARDS			
Alvin Watts	London	17.06.79	Yeading
Dave Stevens	Ashford	29.04.79	Crystal Palace, Bromley, Dulwich Hamlet, £35,000 to Hayes
Ian Hodge	Cornwall		St.Ives, Porthleven
Kevin Warner	London		Brook House, Uxbridge, Yeading
Lee Johnston	London		From Youth team

HEREFORD UNITED

Eleventh place in the Conference represented another disappointing season for Hereford United. It meant that a return to the Nationwide League status they crave was as far off as ever and the knock-out competitions in the end not only did not provide any consolation, but - worse still - raised hopes which were then cruelly dashed.

That was the picture when the Trophy challenge came to an astonishing end. Victories were achieved over Dover Athletic (1-0 at home), away to Leigh RMI in a replay 2-1 after a goalless draw at home, and then after another replay against Morecambe on penalties after an away goalless draw and 1-1 equality at home. Burton Albion were then defeated by a single goal in the last eight at Edgar Street.

This meant a two-legged semi-final against struggling Forest Green Rovers and a very hard earned draw in the away leg should have brought a success in the return match at home and a lucrative final. Instead, the visitors played out of their skins in a dramatic first half and took the match 4-1 and with it a visit to Villa Park.

A Fourth Qualifying Cup visit to Woking saw an early exit from the F.A. Cup by a single goal, while the Conference effort has already been mentioned.

Here a goodish start meant fourth place going into the end of season programme, but by now fixture congestion, effects of Foot & Mouth and other factors - you name it and it happened - brought only two wins in the final thirteen Conference matches and five defeats.

A favourable goal difference (60 to 46) would suggest that Chairman-Manager Graham Turner probably has the right blend of players at his disposal with striker Elmes a big asset, so perhaps all they need is a change of luck. So, was the opening match success against relegated Barnet an omen?

W.M.

HEREFORD UNITED 2001-02

Back Row L-R: Matthew Clarke, Mark Williams, Scott Voice, Matthew Baker, Rob Elmes, Paul Pally, Tony James.
Middle Row: John Shirley, Scott Goodwin, Steve Piearce, John Snape, Gavin Williams, James Quiggin.
Front Row: Ian Rodgerson (Physio), Tony Ford (Fitness Coach), Ian Wright (Capt), Graham Turner (Chairman/Director of Football), Phil Robinson (Coach).

HEREFORD UNITED

GROUND DETAILS

Edgar Street,
Hereford.
HR4 9JU

Telephone Tel: 01432 276666
Fax 01432 341359
Club Call 09068 121645

E-mail HUFCbulls@hotmail.com
Website: http://www.herefordunited.co.uk

SIMPLE DIRECTIONS: From Hereford city centre follow signs to Leominster (A49) into Edgar Street. Car parking for 1000 (approx.) available near the ground. Nearest railway station Hereford

CAPACITY: 8,843
SEATED: 2,761
COVERED TERRACING: 6,082

SOCIAL FACILITIES: Clubhouse open on matchdays

CLUB SHOP: Yes

MATCHDAY PROGRAMME

Pages: 32 Price: £1.50

Editor: Lee Symonds

Other club publications: None

Local Press: Hereford Journal; Hereford Times; Worcester Evening News

Local Radio: BBC Hereford & Worcester

Founded: 1924

Nickname: The Bulls

Sponsors: Sun Valley

Club Colours: White & black shirts, black shorts, white trim; white socks.

Change Colours: Red shirts; red shorts; red socks

Midweek matchday: Tuesday

Reserve League: Central Conference

CLUB OFFICIALS

Chairman/Director of Football Graham Turner

Company Secretary Joan Fennessy

Directors George Hyde Ron Jukes, Grenville Smith, Hugh Brookes, Aidon Mcgiven.

Club Secretary Joan Fennessy
c/o the club
Tel: 01432 276666 Fax: 01432 341359

FOOTBALL MANAGEMENT TEAM

MANAGER: **GRAHAM TURNER**

Date of Appointment August 1995
Date of Birth: 5th October 1947
Place of Birth: Ellesmere Port

PREVIOUS CLUBS
As manager Shrewsbury T., Aston Villa, Wolverhampton W.
As player Wrexham, Chester City, Shrewsbury T.
HONOURS
As manager League: Div.3 78-79 (Shrewsbury), Div.4 87-88, Div.3 88-89; S.V.T. 87-88 (Wolves)
As player England - Youth cap.

* * *

Coaches: Tony Ford & Phil Robinson (player-coach)

Chief Scout: Ron Jukes

Physio: Ian Rodgerson

Season	League	Div.	Pos.	P	Home W	Home D	Home L	Home F	Home A	Away W	Away D	Away L	Away F	Away A	Pts	Manager
00-01	Conference	-	11	42	6	12	3	27	19	8	3	10	33	27	57	Graham Turner
99-00	Conference	-	8	42	9	6	6	43	31	6	8	7	18	21	59	Graham Turner
98-99	Conference	-	13	42	9	5	7	25	17	6	5	10	24	29	55	Graham Turner
97-98	Conference	-	6	42	11	7	3	30	19	7	6	8	26	30	67	Graham Turner

Season	League	Div.	Pos.	P	W	D	L	F	A	Pts	Manager
96-97	F. League	3	24	46	11	14	21	50	65	47	Graham Turner
95-96	F. League	3	6	46	20	14	12	65	47	74	Graham Turner
94-95	F. League	3	16	42	12	13	17	45	62	49	Graham Turner
93-94	F. League	3	20	42	12	6	24	60	79	42	Greg Downs & John Layton
92-93	F. League	3	17	42	10	15	17	47	60	45	Greg Downs & John Layton
91-92	F. League	4	17	42	12	8	22	44	57	44	John Sillett

HONOURS

Football League Div. 3 75-76, Div. 4 R-up 72-73;

Southern League R-up 45-46 50-51 71-72
NW Championship 58-59
Div. 1 58-59,
Cup Winners 52 57 59

Welsh Cup Winners 89-90,
R-up 3 times;

PREVIOUS

Leagues: Birmingham League; Birmingham Combination; Southern League 39-72; Football League 72-97

Names: None

Ground: None

CLUB RECORDS

Attendance: 18,114
v Sheffield Wed., FA Cup 3rd Rd, 4.1.58

Career Goalscorer: Unknown
Career Appearances: unknown

Win: 6-0 v Burnley (A), Div. 4 24.1.87

Defeat: 0-6 v Rotherham Utd (A), Div. 4 29.4.89

Transfer Fee Paid: £75,000
to Walsall for Dean Smith, 7.94

Transfer Fee Received: £250,000
for Darren Peacock from Q.P.R., 3.91
+ a further £240,000
when he moved to Newcastle Utd. 3.91

BEST SEASON

FA Trophy: Semi-Finals 00-01

FA Cup: 4th Rd 71-72 (as Southern League side), 76-77, 81-82, 89-90, 91-92

League: 22nd Football League Div. 2

LAST SEASON

F.A. Cup: Fourth Qualfying Round
F.A. Trophy: Semi Final
Conference: 11th
Top Goalscorer: Rob Elmes (18)
Player of the Year: Matthew Clarke
Captain: Ian Wright

Past Players who progressed to the Football League

Since joining the Conference: Gavin Mahon (Brentford)

HEREFORD UNITED

Match Facts 2000-01

	Date	Comp.	Opponents	Gate	Score	Goalscorers
1	19/08	Conf	SOUTHPORT	2438	0 - 0	
2	22/08	Conf	Kettering Town	1406	2 - 0	Lane 34, Giddings 89
3	26/08	Conf	Hayes	701	2 - 0	Williams 43, Elmes 63
4	28/08	Conf	NORTHWICH VICTORIA	2461	0 - 0	
5	02/09	Conf	Woking	2062	3 - 0	Williams 15, Lane 59[p], Rodgerson 66
6	05/09	Conf	TELFORD UNITED	2431	2 - 0	Robinson 45, Snape 47
7	09/09	Conf	HEDNESFORD TOWN	2557	1 - 1	Wright 70
8	12/09	Conf	Nuneaton Borough	1362	2 - 1	Rodgerson 13, Giddings 18
9	16/09	Conf	Doncaster Rovers	2380	1 - 2	Giddings 53
10	23/09	Conf	STEVENAGE BOROUGH	2251	1 - 1	Lane 77[p]
11	26/09	Conf	LEIGH RMI	1918	1 - 1	Hanson 4
12	30/09	Conf	Dagenham & Redbridge	1410	1 - 2	Williams 12
13	03/10	Conf	Kingstonian	833	3 - 0	McIndoe 18, Elmes 26, Williams 79
14	08/10	Conf	YEOVIL TOWN	3393	2 - 2	Gardiner 2, Williams 68
15	14/10	Conf	Rushden & Diamonds	4188	0 - 1	
16	21/10	Conf	DOVER ATHLETIC	1903	4 - 2	Clarke 46, Wright 53, Elmes 55 63
17	04/11	Conf	Scarborough	891	4 - 2	Elmes 4, Williams 24 61, McIndoe 65
18	11/11	Conf	FOREST GREEN ROVERS	2168	3 - 1	Williams 30, Elmes 64, Hedges 90[og]
19	25/11	Conf	BOSTON UNITED	2056	1 - 1	Clarke 71
20	02/12	Conf	Morecambe	1125	1 - 1	Piearce 74
21	09/12	Conf	DONCASTER ROVERS	1755	0 - 1	
22	16/12	Conf	KETTERING TOWN	1561	0 - 0	
23	26/12	Conf	Chester City	2224	1 - 2	Lane 79[p]
24	01/01	Conf	CHESTER CITY	2321	2 - 0	Lane 54[p], Elmes 56
25	06/01	Conf	Northwich Victoria	1104	0 - 1	
26	20/01	Conf	HAYES	1368	3 - 2	Giddings 67 70, Elmes 78
27	27/01	Conf	Telford United	1848	0 - 1	
28	10/02	Conf	Hednesford Town	1043	3 - 0	Robinson 1, Elmes 60, Quiggin 85
29	17/02	Conf	NUNEATON BOROUGH	1743	1 - 1	Bull 90
30	12/03	Conf	Stevenage Borough	1265	1 - 2	Clarke 2
31	17/03	Conf	DAGENHAM & REDBRIDGE	1561	0 - 1	
32	23/03	Conf	Leigh RMI	503	1 - 2	Elmes 54
33	27/03	Conf	Southport	1367	1 - 1	Wright 90
34	03/04	Conf	WOKING	1280	0 - 1	
35	10/04	Conf	Dover Athletic	1072	0 - 1	
36	14/04	Conf	RUSHDEN & DIAMONDS	2005	3 - 1	Warburton 6[og], Elmes 33 38
37	16/04	Conf	Forest Green Rovers	1076	1 - 1	Burns 13[og]
38	18/04	Conf	KINGSTONIAN	867	0 - 0	
39	21/04	Conf	SCARBOROUGH	1304	1 - 1	Rodgerson 33
40	28/04	Conf	MORECAMBE	1437	2 - 2	Rodgerson 22, Bull 85
41	01/05	Conf	Yeovil Town	4639	3 - 2	Elmes 14, Snape 51, Rodgerson 90
42	05/05	Conf	Boston United	1836	3 - 5	Parry 2, Elmes 57, Piearce 90[p]

OTHER COMPETITIONS

Date	Comp.	Opponents	Gate	Score	Goalscorers
28/10	FA Cup Q4	Woking	2076	0 - 1	
19/12	LDV Vans 1S	YEOVIL TOWN	853	4 - 0	Williams 40, Snape 42, Clarke 49, Quiggin 87
09/01	LDV Vans 2S	READING	1693	1 - 2	Williams 70
13/01	FA Trophy 3	DOVER ATHLETIC	1294	1 - 0	Williams 33
03/02	FA Trophy 4	LEIGH RMI	1491	0 - 0	
19/02	FA Trophy 4 R	Leigh RMI	441	2 - 1	Williams 41, Elmes 79
24/02	FA Trophy 5	Morecambe	1109	0 - 0	
27/02	FA Trophy 5 R	MORECAMBE	1372	1 - 1	Williams 45[p](3-1p)
10/03	FA Trophy QF	BURTON ALBION	3238	1 - 0	Elmes 8
31/03	FA Trophy SF(1)	Forest Green Rovers	2711	2 - 2	Elmes 27 78
07/04	FA Trophy SF(2)	FOREST GREEN ROVERS	4175	1 - 4	Wright 62

1	2	3	4	5	6	7	8	9	10	11	Substitutes Used
Cooksey	Lane	Wright	James	Clarke	Rodgerson	Snape	Robinson	McIndoe	Elmes	Williams	Piearce (11)
Cooksey	Lane	Clarke	Robinson	Wright	James	Rodgerson	Snape	McIndoe	Elmes	Williams	Giddings (10)
Cooksey	Lane	Robinson	Wright	Clarke	James	Rodgerson	Snape	McIndoe	Elmes	Williams	Giddins (10)
Cooksey	Wright	James	Clarke	Lane	Robinson	Snape	McIndoe	Rodgerson	Williams	Elmes	Parry (9), Giddings (11)
Cooksey	Lane	James	Wright	Clarke	Rodgerson	Robinson	Snape	McIndoe	Giddings	Williams	Gardiner (3), Parry (7), Elmes (10)
Cooksey	Lane	Clarke	James	Wright	Robinson	Rodgerson	Snape	McIndoe	Giddings	Williams	Elmes (10)
Cooksey	Lane	Wright	James	Clarke	Rodgerson	Robinson	Snape	McIndoe	Giddings	Williams	Gardiner (3), Parry (6), Elmes (10)
Cooksey	Lane	Clarke	James	Wright	Robinson	Rodgerson	Snape	McIndoe	Giddings	Williams	Parry (7), Elmes (10)
Cooksey	Lane	Clarke	Robinson	Wright	James	Parry	Snape	Giddings	Williams	McIndoe	Elmes (11), Gardiner (3)
Cooksey	Lane	Wright	James	Clarke	Parry	Robinson	Snape	McIndoe	Giddings	Williams	Hanson (6), Elmes (8)
Cooksey	Lane	Clarke	James	Wright	Robinson	Snape	McIndoe	Hanson	Giddings	Williams	Moran (9), Elmes (10)
Cooksey	Lane	Clarke	Robinson	Wright	James	Rodgerson	Snape	Elmes	Williams	McIndoe	Hanson (4), Piearce (7)
Cooksey	Lane	Clarke	James	Wright	Robinson	Rodgerson	Snape	McIndoe	Elmes	Williams	Gardiner (5)
Cooksey	Lane	Clarke	James	Gardiner	Robinson	Snape	McIndoe	Hanson	Elmes	Williams	Giddings (9)
Cooksey	Lane	Wright	James	Clarke	Robinson	Parry	Snape	McIndoe	Williams	Quinn	Quiggin (7)
Cooksey	Wright	Gardiner	Clarke	Rodgerson	Snape	Robinson	McIndoe	Quinn	Williams	Lane	James (3), Elmes (9)
Cooksey	Lane	Clarke	Robinson	Wright	James	Rodgerson	Snape	Elmes	Williams	McIndoe	Giddings (9)
Cooksey	Lane	Wright	James	Sturgess	Rodgerson	Robinson	Snape	McIndoe	Williams	Elmes	
Cooksey	Lane	Wright	Wall	Sturgess	Rodgerson	Robinson	Snape	McIndoe	Williams	Elmes	Clarke (6), Piearce (10)
Cooksey	Lane	Sturgess	Robinson	Wright	James	Clarke	Snape	Elmes	Williams	McIndoe	Gardiner (6), Piearce (10)
Cooksey	Lane	Wright	Gardiner	Sturgess	Clarke	Snape	Robinson	McIndoe	Elmes	Williams	
Cooksey	Lane	Wright	Gardiner	Sturgess	Clarke	Robinson	Snape	McIndoe	Elmes	Williams	Piearce (6)
Cooksey	Lane	Sturgess	Clarke	Wright	Gardiner	Robinson	Rodgerson	McIndoe	Giddins	Williams	Wall (5), Elmes (10)
Cooksey	Lane	Sturgess	Clarke	Wright	Wall	Robinson	Snape	McIndoe	Williams	Elmes	
Cooksey	Clarke	Wright	Wall	Sturgess	Rodgerson	Robinson	Snape	McIndoe	Elmes	Williams	Bull (9) sub Giddings
Cooksey	Clarke	Sturgess	Wall	Wright	Robinson	Rodgerson	Snape	McIndoe	Elmes	Williams	Gardiner (5), Giddings (11)
Cooksey	Clarke	Sturgess	Robinson	Quiggin	Wall	Rodgerson	Snape	Elmes	Williams	Giddings	
Cooksey	Rodgerson	Gardiner	Wall	Clarke	Quiggin	Snape	Robinson	McIndoe	Elmes	Williams	Giddings (11)
Cooksey	Clarke	Gardiner	Wall	Sturgess	Rodgerson	Robinson	Snape	Quiggin	Elmes	Williams	Bull (9), James (3)
Cooksey	Clarke	Sturgess	James	Wright	Robinson	Quiggin	Snape	Rodgerson	Elmes	Williams	Bull (8), Giddings (9), Parry (11)
Cooksey	Clarke	James	Wright	Wall	Quiggin	Snape	Robinson	Parry	Elmes	Giddings	Hanson (6), Bull (11)
Cooksey	Wright	Sturgess	James	Shirley	Robinson	Quiggin	Crowe	Rodgerson(s)		Elmes	ParrySnape (8)
Baker	Clarke	Wright	James	Shirley	Quiggin	Crowe	Snape	Rodgerson	Giddings	Parry	Hanson (9), Bull (10)
Baker	Wall	Sturgess	James	Shirley	Robinson	Rodgerson	Crowe	Giddings	Parry	Williams	Snape (6), Clarke (9), Bull (11)
Cooksey	Clarke	Sturgess	James	Wright	Robinson	Quiggin	Snape	Crowe	Elmes	Williams	Parry (7), Shirley (9)
Cooksey	Wright	Clarke	James	Sturgess	Quiggin	Snape	Robinson	Shirley	Elmes	Williams	
Cooksey	Clarke	Sturgess	James	Wright	Robinson	Quiggin	Snape	Shirley	Elmes	Williams	Rodgerson (6), Giddings (7)
Cooksey	Clarke	Sturgess	James	Wright	Rodgerson	Quiggin	Snape	Shirley	Elmes	Williams	Plotnik (3), Parry (7)
Cooksey	Shirley	James	Wright	Sturgess	Rodgerson	Snape	Robinson	Quiggin	Williams	Parry	Giddings (9), Piearce (11)
Cooksey	James	Sturgess	Shirley	Rodgerson	Robinson	Quiggin	Snape	Elmes	Williams	Parry	Bull (7) sub Piearce, Giddings (10)
Cooksey	Sturgess	Clarke	James	Shirley	Robinson	Rodgerson	Snape	Parry	Elmes	Williams	
Cooksey	Clarke	Sturgess	James	Rodgerson	Robinson	Shirley	Snape	Elmes	Williams	Parry	Piearce (3), Quiggin (11)

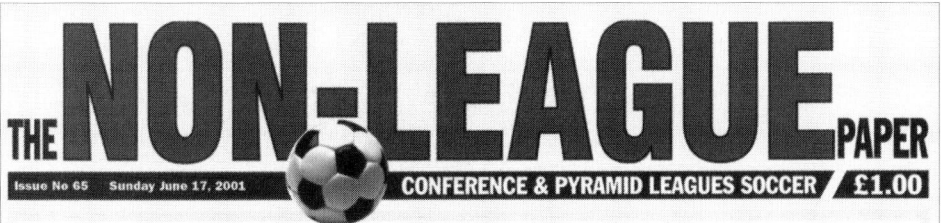

PLAYING SQUAD (Bold print indicates an England Semi-Professional International) HEREFORD UNITED

Player *Honours*	*Birthplace*	*D.O.B.*	*Previous Clubs*
GOALKEEPERS			
Scott Cooksey ESP	Birmingham	24.06.72	Derby, Shrewsbury, Bromsgrove R, Peterborough U., Hednesford T, Shrewsbury T.
DEFENDERS			
Tony James	Birmingham		WBA
Ian Wright	Lichfield	10.03.72	Stoke, Bristol R, Stoke
Matthew Clarke British Univ.	Cardiff		Cradley T, Halesowen H, Halesowen T, Kidderminster H
Paul Parry	Hereford		Youth team
Mark Williams	Liverpool	10.11.78	Rotherham, Rochdale
MIDFIELD			
Chris Lane	Liverpool	24.05.79	Everton
Gavin Williams	Hereford		Youth team
John Snape	Birmingham		WBA, Bromsgrove R, Northfield T, Stourbridge, Halesowen T
Ian Rodgerson	Hereford	09.04.66	Pegasus Jun., Hereford U., Cardiff C., Birmingham C., Sunderland, Cardiff C.
Phil Robinson	Stratford	06.01.67	Aston Villa, Wolves, Notts Co., Huddersfield, Chesterfield, Notts Co., Stoke
Scott Goodwin	Hull	13.09.78	Hednesford T, Grantham T, Shepshed Dynamo, Coventry
FORWARDS			
Steve Piearce	Sutton Coldfield	29.09.76	Wolves, Doncaster R, Halesowen T
Rob Elmes	Birmingham		Boldmere St.Michaels, Bromsgrove R, Halesowen T
Craig Hanson	Derby		Derby Co.
Scott Voice	Birmingham	12.08.74	Bilston T, Stourbridge, Bilston T, Stourbridge, Wolves
Steve Bull Eng.Int	Tipton	28.03.65	Wolves, WBA, Tipton T
Danny Davidson			Leek T, Rocester, Burton Alb

LEIGH R.M.I.

One of the pleasant features of the game has been the continued success of the likes of Leigh RMI, whose fifth place in the Conference was a splendid effort built on a consistent series of results during the season, which saw the team as high as third after four matches, briefly as low as fourteenth after ten games and then hovering above half-way until a final flourish of a double against Morecambe and home win over relegated Kingstonian 2-1 produced the excellent final placing.

The knock-out competitions produced nothing great although a thrilling Fourth Qualifying F.A. Cup success over Scarborough 4-3 brought a visit to high-flying Millwall in the First Round and no disgrace in a 3-0 defeat.

In the F.A. Trophy Hucknall Town came and went 1-0 in the Third Round, but the next outing was disappointing as a goalless draw at Hereford United created hopes of a good run, which were ended in the home replay by a narrow 2-1 defeat.

The 63-57 goals difference suggests that Leigh were better in attack than defence with Black, Jones, Monk and Ridings regularly on the score sheet, so in 2001-02 Manager Steve Waywell will be looking to reduce the goals against column whilst seeking more from the front men, who will miss the flying winger, James

If he succeeds who knows what successes the new campaign will bring?

W.M.

Leigh on the attack against Woking at Hilton Park last season

LEIGH R.M.I.

GROUND DETAILS

Hilton Park,
Kirkhall Lane,
Leigh WN7 1RN
Tel: 01942 743743 (Office)
Fax: 01942 768856
Web site: http://www.leigh-rmi.co.uk

DIRECTIONS:
From M61 junction 5, follow the Westhoughton sign to r'about, then follow signs to Leigh. Keep on main road to the traffic lights, left into Leigh Road, carry on about 3 miles to the traffic lights. Turn left and first right to the next set of lights. Right onto Atherleigh Way, A579 at the first set of traffic lights, turn left (B & Q on right), at the next set of lights turn right into Kirkhall Lane (Leigh town centre), at the 2nd opening on right turn into Prescott St., carry on to top, turn right, ground on left.

CAPACITY: 8000
COVER: 4,000
SEATS: 2,000

CLUBHOUSE: Open matchdays with food available. Pre-match meals can be arranged.
2 separate function facilities for 200 and 100.

CLUB SHOP: At the ground & open most days. Contact club.

MATCHDAY PROGRAMME

Pages: 32 Price: £1.50

Editor: Secretary

Local Press: Bolton Evening News

Local Radio: Radio Lancs, Red Rose Radio, G.M.R.

Formed: 1896

Nickname: Railwaymen

Sponsors: Standish Print

Colours: Red & white striped shirts black shorts and white socks

Change colours: All Yellow

Midweek home matchday: Tuesday

Reserve Team Lancashire League

CLUB OFFICIALS

Chairman: Chris Healey

Vice Chairman: Alan Leach

Directors: A Kirkman, L Berry, K Freer, W Taylor, T Leece, A Blakeley, G Culshaw

President: G H Fisher

Secretary: Alan Robinson
55 Janice Drive, Fulwood, Preston, Lancs. PR2 9TY.
Tel: 01772 719266 (H)
01942 743743 (Club)

Press Officer: Secretary

FOOTBALL MANAGEMENT TEAM

MANAGER: STEVE WAYWELL

Date of Appointment: Aug/Sept 1995
Date of Birth: 4th June 1954
Place of Birth: Bury

PREVIOUS CLUBS
As manager: Curzon Ashton
As asst. manager: Ashton United
As player: Burnley, Stalybridge C., Chorley, Hyde U., Stalybridge C.

HONOURS
As manager: N.P.L. - Prem. Div. 99-00; Div. 1 R-up 96-97
As asst. manager: None
As player: F.A.Youth CupWinners medal with Burnley

Asst Manager: Dave Miller
First Team Coach: Gerry Luczka
Physiotherapist: Dave Pover
Chief Scout: TBA

Season	League	Div.	Pos.	Home P	W	D	L	F	A	Away W	D	L	F	A	Pts	Manager
00-01	Conference	-	5	42	11	5	5	38	24	8	6	7	25	33	68	Steve Waywell
99-00	N.P.L.	Premier	1	44	15	3	4	42	17	13	5	4	49	28	92	Steve Waywell
98-99	N.P.L.	Premier	8	42	6	10	5	30	26	10	5	6	33	28	63	Steve Waywell
97-98	N.P.L.	Premier	3	42	12	6	3	32	15	9	7	5	31	26	76	Steve Waywell

Season	League	Div.	Pos.	P	W	D	L	F	A	Pts	Manager
96-97	N.P.L.	One	2	42	24	11	7	65	33	83	Steve Waywell
95-96	N.P.L.	One	14	40	14	7	19	53	59	49	Steve Waywell
94-95	N.P.L.	Premier	22	42	9	4	29	49	94	31	Mick Holgate
93-94	N.P.L.	Premier	20	42	8	12	22	50	75	*35	Mick Holgate
92-93	N.P.L.	Premier	13	42	14	10	18	72	79	52	Ken Wright
91-92	N.P.L.	Premier	13	42	13	14	15	44	52	53	Ken Wright

HONOURS

Northern Premier League Champions 1999-2000
NPL League Cup 99-00, Division 1 R-up 96-97;
Premier Inter League (GMAC) Cup 87-88;
Cheshire County Lg 78-79,
Challenge Shield 78-79;
Lancs Combination 57-58
R-up 29-30 55-56 66-67,
Lg Cup 28-29 53-54 56-57 65-66,
Div 2 R-up 48-49 50-51;
West Lancs League 10-11 11-12;
Lancs Junior Cup 24-25 29-30 (R-up x 4);
Lancs Floodlit Trophy 84-85 (R-up 83-84);
Lancs FA Cup 84-85

PREVIOUS

Leagues: Lancashire Alliance 1891-97;
Lancashire League 1897-1900;
Lancashire Combination 17-18, 19-39, 46-68;
Cheshire County League 68-82;
North West Counties League 82-83;
Northern Premier League 83-2000

Name: Horwich R.M.I. until 1995

Ground: Grundy Hill, Horwich until 1994

PastPlayers who progressed to the Football League

Harold Lea (Stockport 58),
David Holland (Stockport 59),
Jim Cunliffe (Stockport 60),
Frank Wignall (Everton 58),
Gary Cooper (Rochdale73),
Tony Caldwell (Bolton 83),
Raymond Redshaw (Wigan 84),
Tony Ellis (Oldham 86),
Paul Jones (Oldham , Nov. 99),
SteveJones (Crewe Alex 01).

CLUB RECORDS

Attendance:
(at Horwich) 8,500 v Wigan Ath Lancs Jnr Cup 54
(at Leigh) 7,125 v Fulham, FAC 98-99

Win: Unknown

Career Appearances: Neil McLachlan

Career Goalscorer: Neil McLachlan

Defeat: 2-9 v Brandon Utd (H) FA Cup 1998-99

Transfer fee paid: £6,000 to Vauxhall Motors for Peter Cumiskey 99-00

Transfer fee received: £75,000 from Crewe A. for Steve Jones 2001

BEST SEASON

FA Trophy: Quarter Final 90-91

FA Cup: First Round
28-29, 1-2 v Scarborough (H),
82-83, 0-3 v Blackpool (A)
98-99 (replay), 0-2 v Fulham (H) after 1-1,
00-01, 0-3 v Millwall (H - played away)

FA Vase: N/A

League: 00-01 5th Conference

LAST SEASON

F.A. Cup: First Round
F.A. Trophy: Fourth Round replay
Conference: 5th
Top Goalscorer: Steve Jones
Player of the Year: Dave Ridings
Captain: Andy Farrell

LEIGH RMI

Match Facts 2000-01

	Date	Comp.	Opponents	Gate	Score	Goalscorers
1	19/08	Conf	DAGENHAM & REDBRIDGE	451	1 - 2	Black 60
2	22/08	Conf	Southport	1589	2 - 1	Black 14, Cumiskey 34
3	26/08	Conf	Kettering Town	1087	1 - 0	Black 30
4	28/08	Conf	SCARBOROUGH	836	2 - 0	Ridings 4, Harris 46
5	02/09	Conf	Stevenage Borough	1479	0 - 3	
6	05/09	Conf	HEDNESFORD TOWN	475	2 - 2	Jones 17 36
7	09/09	Conf	BOSTON UNITED	1124	2 - 2	Harris 16, Mason 75
8	12/09	Conf	Telford United	281	1 - 2	Mason 72 (at Worcester City)
9	16/09	Conf	Nuneaton Borough	1145	1 - 2	Black 83
10	23/09	Conf	FOREST GREEN ROVERS	451	1 - 1	Matthews 42
11	26/09	Conf	Hereford United	1918	1 - 1	Matthews 10
12	30/09	Conf	DOVER ATHLETIC	485	2 - 1	Black 27[p], Jones 58
13	03/10	Conf	RUSHDEN & DIAMONDS	1405	1 - 0	Jones 69
14	07/10	Conf	Hayes	415	2 - 1	Ridings 42, Black 47
15	14/10	Conf	TELFORD UNITED	552	1 - 1	Black 88[p]
16	21/10	Conf	Chester City	1858	1 - 1	Black 79[p]
17	04/11	Conf	DONCASTER ROVERS	811	0 - 1	
18	11/11	Conf	Woking	1421	1 - 1	Black 68[p]
19	02/12	Conf	Kingstonian	929	2 - 0	Jones 47, Black 81
20	16/12	Conf	SOUTHPORT	835	2 - 2	Jones 16[p], Ridings 27
21	26/12	Conf	Northwich Victoria	1208	1 - 1	Jones 36
22	30/12	Conf	Dagenham & Redbridge	1231	1 - 2	Ridings 39
23	01/01	Conf	NORTHWICH VICTORIA	501	3 - 0	Ridings 13 67, Kielty 76
24	06/01	Conf	Scarborough	1087	1 - 1	Monk 86
25	27/01	Conf	Hednesford Town	804	2 - 1	Kielty 69, Jones 87
26	10/02	Conf	Boston United	1580	1 - 0	Hoyle 67[og]
27	03/03	Conf	NUNEATON BOROUGH	501	6 - 2	Monk 4, Kielty 18, Ridings 24, Jones 38 87 90
28	10/03	Conf	HAYES	414	4 - 0	Jones 20 82, Swan 54, Kielty 81
29	17/03	Conf	Dover Athletic	929	2 - 1	Ridings 15, Jones 72
30	23/03	Conf	HEREFORD UNITED	503	2 - 1	Monk 21, Ridings 90
31	28/03	Conf	Forest Green Rovers	407	1 - 3	Ridings 45
32	31/03	Conf	Rushden & Diamonds	3882	1 - 1	Black 47
33	03/04	Conf	KETTERING TOWN	351	1 - 0	Black 72
34	10/04	Conf	STEVENAGE BOROUGH	403	1 - 4	Monk 19
35	14/04	Conf	Yeovil Town	3401	1 - 6	Jones 44[og]
36	16/04	Conf	WOKING	455	2 - 0	Jones 63 75
37	18/04	Conf	CHESTER CITY	501	0 - 1	
38	21/04	Conf	Doncaster Rovers	1532	0 - 4	
39	24/04	Conf	YEOVIL TOWN	565	2 - 3	Ridings 24, Jones 69
40	26/04	Conf	MORECAMBE	467	1 - 0	Kielty 81
41	28/04	Conf	KINGSTONIAN	402	2 - 1	Hayder 10, Jones 26
42	05/05	Conf	Morecambe	1106	2 - 1	Ridings 75, Jones 77[p]

OTHER COMPETITIONS

Date	Comp.	Opponents	Gate	Score	Goalscorers
11/08	NPL Shield	LANCASTER CITY	251	2 - 1	Mason 8, Kilbane 49[og]
17/10	Variety CT 1	Northwich Victoria	309	3 - 3	Ridings 34, Kielty 69 86
28/10	FA Cup Q4	Scarborough	858	4 - 3	Black 4 5 54, Jones 43
19/11	FA Cup 1	Millwall	6907	0 - 3	
09/01	Lancs MT 2	ROSSENDALE UNITED	n/k	1 - 0	Jones
13/01	FA Trophy 3	HUCKNALL TOWN	235	1 - 0	Spooner 90
23/01	Variety CT 1 R	NORTHWICH VICTORIA	169	1 - 0	Jones 77
30/01	Lancs MT QF	Lancaster City	155	1 - 1	Black 2, Murphy 113
03/02	FA Trophy 4	Hereford United	1491	0 - 0	
15/02	Variety CT 2	Morecambe	395	2 - 5	German 33, Black 55[p]
19/02	FA Trophy 4 R	HEREFORD UNITED	441	1 - 2	Black 87
06/03	Lancs MT QF R	LANCASTER CITY	131	0 - 3	

1	2	3	4	5	6	7	8	9	10	11	Substitutes Used
Felgate	Monk	Harris	Blackmore	Scott	Jones	Udall	Kielty	Farrell	Black	Swan	Cumiskey (2), Mason (8)
Dootson	Harris	Scott	Udall	Jones	Kielty	Swan	Ridings	Black	Cumiskey	Farrell	Mason (9)
Dootson	Scott	Farrell	Udall	Swan	Harris	Kielty	Ridings	Cumiskey	Black	Jones	Mason(9)
Dootson	Harris	Scott	Jones	Udall	Kielty	Farrell	Ridings	Cumiskey	Black	Swan	Reid(6)
Dootson	Scott	Farrell	Udall	Swan	Harris	Kielty	Ridings	Cumiskey	Black	Jones	Durkin (5), Mason (9)
Dootson	Harris	Scott	Jones	Udall	Kielty	Farrell	Ridings	Cumiskey	Black	Swan	Mason (10)
Dootson	Scott	Udall	Swan	Farrell	Kielty	Harris	Ridings	Cumiskey	Black	Jones	Mason (7), German (9)
Dootson	Scott	Farrell	Udall	Kielty	Harris	Ridings	Jones	Cumiskey	Black	Swan	German (2), Mason (9), Durkin (11)
Dootson	Scott	German	Udall	Farrell	Harris	Kielty	Ridings	Mason	Black	Jones	Durkin (2), Matthews (6), Cumiskey (9)
Dootson	Scott	Devenney	Udall	Farrell	Swan	Kielty	Ridings	Matthews	Black	Jones	German (3), Walker (6), Mason (9)
Dootson	Scott	German	Udall	Farrell	Kielty	Ridings	Jones	Matthews	Black	Swan	Felgate (1)
Felgate	Scott	German	Farrell	Devenney	Swan	Kielty	Ridings	Jones	Matthews	Black	Mason (10), Harris (5)
Felgate	Scott	German	Udall	Farrell	Kielty	Ridings	Harris	Jones	Black	Swan	
Felgate	Scott	Udall	Farrell	German	Swan	Kielty	Ridings	Jones	Monk	Black	Matthews (10), Devenney (11)
Felgate	Scott	German	Udall	Farrell	Swan	Kielty	Ridings	Monk	Black	Jones	Matthews (4), Harris (9)
Felgate	Scott	Devenney	Udall	Farrell	Swan	Monk	German	Harris	Black	Jones	Critchley (7), Dootson (10)
Felgate	Trees	German	Durkin	Farrell	Swan	Kielty	Ridings	Harris	Black	Jones	Matthews (4), Morrell (9), Monk (11)
Felgate	Trees	German	Swann	Farrell	Harris	Kielty	Ridings	Monk	Black	Jones	Durkin (6), Morrell (10)
Felgate	Spooner	German	Durkin	Farrell	Swan	Trees	Ridings	Kielty	Black	Jones	Monk (9)
Felgate	Spooner	German	Durkin	Farrell	Swan	Monk	Ridings	Morrell	Trees	Jones	Matthews (9)
Felgate	Spooner	German	Trees	Farrell	Swan	Durkin	Ridings	Jones	Morrell	Monk	Matthews (10), Kielty (4)
Felgate	Spooner	German	Swan	Farrell	Durkin	Ridings	Kielty	Jones	Monk	Morrell	Critchley (3), Matthews (8), Harris (11)
Felgate	Spooner	German	Swan	Farrell	Durkin	Ridings	Kielty	Jones	Monk	Morrell	Critchley (2), Harris (7), Matthews (11)
Felgate	Spooner	German	Durkin	Farrell	Swan	Monk	Ridings	Morrell	Kielty	Jones	Matthews (9), Trees (2)
Felgate	Spooner	Swan	Farrell	German	Monk	Ridings	Durkin	Kielty	Black	Jones	Harris (5), Trees (3)
Felgate	Spooner	Durkin	Farrell	Trees	Monk	Kielty	Ridings	Harris	Black	Jones	German (2)
Felgate	Spooner	Trees	Durkin	Farrell	Swan	Monk	Ridings	Kielty	Black	Jones	Murphy (6)
Felgate	Spooner	Trees	Durkin	Farrell	Swan	Monk	Ridings	Kielty	Black	Jones	German (8)
Farrell	Spooner	Farrell	Swan	Trees	Durkin	Kielty	Ridings	Monk	Black	Jones	
Dootson	Spooner	Trees	Farrell	Durkin	Swan	Ridings	Kielty	Monk	Black	Gardner	German (3), Jones (9)
Dootson	Spooner	Trees	Farrell	Durkin	Swan	Ridings	Kielty	Jones	Black	Monk	German(3), Gardner (8), Hayder (10)
Dootson	Spooner	German	Durkin	Farrell	Swan	Monk	Ridings	Kielty	Black	Jones	
Dootson	Spooner	German	Farrell	Durkin	Swan	Ridings	Kielty	Jones	Black	Monk	Trees (2)
Dootson	Spooner	German	Farrell	German	Swan	Ridings	Kielty	Jones	Black	Monk	Trees (6), Hayder (8), Gardner (11)
Dootson	Spooner	Durkin	German	Farrell	Trees	Monk	Ridings	Kielty	Black	Jones	
Dootson	Spooner	Trees	Farrell	Durkin	Swan	Ridings	Kielty	Jones	Black	Monk	Gardner(2), German (7), Hayder (10)
Dootson	Trees	German	Farrell	Durkin	Swan	Ridings	Kielty	Jones	Black	Monk	Spooner (5), Hayder (11)
Dootson	Trees	German	Spooner	Farrell	Swan	Monk	Ridings	Kielty	Black	Jones	Mason (2)
Felgate	Spooner	German	Farrell	Murphy	Swan	Ridings	Kielty	Jones	Black	Monk	Trees (5), Hayder (10)
Felgate	Spooner	German	Trees	Farrell	Swan	Ridings	Kielty	Jones	Black	Monk	Harris (2), Hayder (10)
Felgate	Trees	German	Farrell	Harris(s)	Swan	Ridings	Jones	Kielty	Hayder	Monk	Black (8)
Felgate	Trees	German	Farrell	Kielty	Swan	Ridings	Jones	Hayder	Black	Monk	

PLAYING SQUAD

LEIGH R.M.I.

(Bold print indicates an England Semi-Professional International)

Player *Honours*	*Birthplace*	*D.O.B.*	*Previous Clubs*
GOALKEEPERS			
David Felgate Wales Int., UP	Blaenau Ffestiniog	04.03.60	Blaenau Ffestiniog, Bolton, Lincoln, Grimsby, Bolton, Bury, Chester C, Wigan
Craig Dootson	Preston		Preston, Morecambe, Bamber Bridge, £4,000 to Leigh
DEFENDERS			
David German UP	Sheffield	16.10.73	Sheffield U, Halifax, Macclesfield, Winsford U
Iain Swan	Glasgow	04.07.80	Oldham, Partick Thistle
Richard Harris UP	Manchester	12.07.67	Ashton U, Altrincham, Hyde U, Runcorn, Hyde U, Altrincham
Andy Farrell	Colchester	07.10.65	Colchester, Burnley, Wigan, Rochdale, Morecambe
Jamie Udall	Blackpool		Morecambe, Lancaster C
Neil Durkin	Blackburn		Darwen
Nicky Spooner EY	Manchester	05.06.71	Charleston Battery (USA), Bolton, Manchester Utd
Paul Robertson	Manchester	05.02.72	Hyde Utd, Droylsden, Altrincham, Barrow, Accrington S. Witton Alb., Doncaster R, Runcorn, Bury, Stockport, York
MIDFIELD			
Tony Black UP	Barrow	15.07.69	Burnley U, Bamber Bridge, Wigan, Accrington Stanley, Chorley
Dave Ridings UP	Farnworth	27.02.70	Bury, Curzon Ashton, Halifax, Lincoln, Ashton U, Crewe
Ged Kielty UP	Manchester	01.09.76	Manchester C, Cobh Ramblers, Southport, Barrow, Altrincham
Neil Critchley	Crewe	18.10.78	Crewe
Neil Fisher	St.Helens	07.11.70	Chester C, Connah's Quay, Chester C, Bolton
Steve Thompson	Oldham	02.11.64	Halifax, Rotherham, Burnley, Leicester, Luton, Bolton
FORWARDS			
Ian Monk GMVC, UP	Burnley	30.06.68	Clitheroe, Ashton U, Macclesfield, Morecambe
Marcus Hallows	Bolton	07.07.75	St.Patricks Ath., Sligo R, Stockport, Leigh RMI
Michael Reynolds	Huddersfield	19.06.74	Ayr Utd, Emley
Troy Hayder	Manchester		Winsford Utd, Flixton, Chorley, Rhyl, Curzon Ashton

MARGATE

Experienced managers in the three feeder leagues below the Conference knew if their squad is to be successful then their players too must be experienced at this level.

Margate's Chris Kinnear is a shrewd campaigner and a look at the lads who brought him success will underline the fact that they knew their way around to great effect!

Early season favourites Burton Albion were steadily overhauled, with a philosophy of not giving anything away on their trips away from Hartsdown Park and using the strength and finishing power of Phil Collins and Leon Braithwaite.

An average start saw Margate in twelfth position at the beginning of September and their move towards a challenging position was steady, but not spectacular.

A home defeat to Banstead Athletic in the F.A. Cup cannot have improved confidence, but five wins in the next six league games put that right and Collins had scored two hat tricks before Christmas and he was `buzzing'.

A good Trophy victory at Woking took them on to Stevenage Borough, but this test proved too tough and Kinnear's squad were able to settle down to a serious league challenge with only Burton Albion to overhaul.

A short spell at the top was enjoyed in the new year, but it wasn't until an amazing eleven league game sequence saw just one goal conceded and four points dropped in two draws, that first place was gained and secured with an obvious degree of confidence.

Burton Albion were wavering and the consistency provided by Margate's no nonsense defence and strikers who were always dangerous despite their side often defending in depth saw the championship clinched before the vital game with Albion in Burton.

Phil Collins scored six and Leon Braithwaite three in a five days spell of three vital games and 2,366 turned up to see the vital point secured at home to Newport in a tense 0-0 draw.

Margate will be difficult to beat, they may not be pretty to watch, but I suspect the will consolidate and be ready to set their sights higher at the end of the season.

T.W.

MARGATE FC 2001-02

Back Row, l-r: Steve Hafner, Paul Lamb, Lee Williams, Dean Yorath, Paul Sykes, Mark Munday, Lee Turner, Charlie Mitten, Simon Beard, Graham Porter (captain), Jay Saunders, Paul Lewis, Leon Braithwaite, Tommy Tyne (now Dover Ath.).

Front row: Bill Edwards, Simon Ullathorne, Mo Takalogabhashi, Gary Blackford, Chris Kinnear (manager), Kevin Raine (assistant manager), Phil Collins, John Keister, Mike Azzopardi, Robert Codner.

MARGATE

GROUND DETAILS

Hartsdown Park,
Hartsdown Road,
Margate CT9 5QZ

Telelpone: 01843 221769
Fax: 01843 221769
Email: office@margatefc.com
Web site: www.margatefc.com

Directions:
A28 into Margate, turn right opposite Dog & Duck P.H. into Hartsdown Road, proceed over crossroads and ground is on left.
Ten mins walk from Margate (BR)

Capacity: 4,800
Cover: 4,250
Seats: 550

Clubhouse:
Flexible hours, private functions, matchday facilities.

Club Shop:
Contacts: Dave and Debra Canham (01843 2217691)

MATCHDAY PROGRAMME

Pages: 44 Price: £2.00
Editor:Steve Parmenter(Tel No:227 833525)

Local Press:
Isle of Thanet Gazette, Thanet Times, Thanet Extra
Local Radio:
Radio Kent, Invicta Radio, TLR

Formed: 1896

Nickname: The Gate

Sponsors: A Gomez Ltd.

Newsline: 0891 800 665

Colours: Royal Blue shirts & shorts, white socks

Change colours: Lime Green shirts & shorts, black socks

Midweek matchday: Tuesday

Reserves' League: Bass Kent Lg. Div 1

CLUB OFFICIALS

Chairman: Keith Piper

President: Gordon Wallis

Vice Chairman: Jim Parmenter

Directors: K Piper & J Parmenter

Secretary: Ken Tomlinson
65 Nash Road, Margate , Kent CT9 4BT
Tel & Fax: 01843 291040 (M) 07710033566

Commercial Manager: Mrs Joscelyn Dodds
Tel: 01843 221769

Press Officer: Jim Parmenter
01227832121

FOOTBALL MANAGEMENT TEAM

MANAGER **CHRIS KINNEAR**
Date of Appointment: August 1996
Date of Birth: 10th July 1954
Place of Birth: Dagenham

PREVIOUS CLUBS
As manager: Dover Athletic
As player: West Ham, Leyton Orient, Wealdstone, Maidstone U., Barnet, Dagenham, Dover A.

HONOURS
As manager: Southern Lge: Prem Div. x 3, R-up x1; Southern Div. x1, R-up x1; Lge. Cup x2, R-up x1
Kent Senior Cup: x 2, R-up x 1

* * *

Asst. Manager: Kevin Raine
Physio: John Griffin
Chief Scout: Kevin Raine
Reserve Manager: Mark Harrop

Season	League	Div.	Pos.	Home P	Home W	Home D	Home L	Home F	Home A	Away W	Away D	Away L	Away F	Away A	Pts	Manager
00-01	Southern	P	1	42	17	2	2	47	14	11	5	5	28	13	91	Chris Kinnear
99-00	Southern	P	3	42	13	4	4	33	16	10	4	7	31	27	77	Chris Kinnear
98-99	Southern	S	2	42	13	5	3	44	16	14	3	4	40	17	89	Chris Kinnear
97-98	Southern	S	6	42	14	3	4	37	16	9	5	7	34	26	77	Chris Kinnear
96-97	Southern	S	5	42	11	2	8	36	29	10	7	4	34	18	72	Chris Kinnear
95-96	Southern	S	11	42	11	5	5	36	22	7	0	14	32	40	59	Karl Elsey
94-95	Southern	S	13	42	9	2	10	36	37	6	5	10	24	35	52	Mark Weatherley & Andy Woolford
93-94	Southern	S	9	42	13	2	6	44	25	7	6	8	32	33	68	Mark Weatherley & Andy Woolford
92-93	Southern	S	10	42	9	4	8	30	30	10	3	5	35	28	64	Lee Smelt
91-92	Southern	S	14	42	6	10	5	28	24	7	6	8	21	32	55	Tommy Taylor

HONOURS

HONOURS

Southern Lge 35-36, 00-01
Lge Cp 67-68,97-98, R-up 61-62 74-75,
Div 1 62-63, R-up 66-67, Div 1 Sth 77-78,
East Div R-up 33-34,
Southern Div. R-up: 98-99
Merit Cup 66-67 77-78, Midweek Sect. 36-37,
Kent Lge (4), R-up (5), Div 2 (4), Lge Cp 5),
Kent Senior Cup (5),
Kent Senior Shield (8),
Kent F'lit Cp 62-63 66-67 75-76

PREVIOUS

Leagues: Kent 11-23 24-28 29-33 37-38 46-59; Southern 33-37, 59-2001

Grounds: Margate College; Dreamland, Northdown Rd; Garlinge

Name: Thanet Utd 1981-89

Past Players who progressed to the Football League

Over 40 including

J Yeomanson (West Ham 47),
D Bing & G Wright (West Ham 51), T Bing (Spurs 56),
S Foster (C Palace 61), J Fraser (Watford 62),
R Walker (Bournemouth 65), K Bracewell (Bury 66),
T Jenkins & R Flannigan (Reading 69-70),
M Blyth (Millwall 78), M Buglione (St Johnstone 92)

CLUB RECORDS

Attendance: 14,500
v Spurs, FA Cup 3rd Rd 73

Goalscorer: Dennis Randall 66 (season 66-67)

CareerAppearances: Bob Harrop

Win: 8-0
v Tunbridge Wells (H) 66-67,
& v Chatham Town (H) 87-88

Defeat: 11-0
v AFC Bournemouth (A), FAC 1st Rd. 20.11.71

Fee paid: £5,000
for Steve Cuggy (Dover Ath93)

Fee received: Undisclosed
for Martin Buglione (St Johnstone 92-93)

BEST SEASON

FA Trophy: Third Round replay 78-79

FA Cup: Third Round
72-73 0-6 v Spurs (),
36-37 1-3 v Blackpool (A)

League clubs defeated: Gillingham 29-30,
Q. P.R., Crystal Palace 35-36,
Bournemouth & Boscombe Ath. 61-62, Swansea 72-73

FA Amateur Cup: Never entered

LAST SEASON

F.A. Cup: 2nd Qual. Round

F.A. Trophy: Fourth Round

Southern League: Champions

Top Goalscorer: Phil Collins (34)

Player of the Year: Jay Saunders

Captain: Graham Porter

MARGATE

Match Facts 2000-01

	Date	Comp.	Opponents	Gate	Score	Goalscorers
1	19/08	DM P	MOOR GREEN	460	0 - 1	
2	22/08	DM P	Welling United	619	0 - 1	
3	26/08	DM P	Halesowen Town	363	0 - 0	
4	28/08	DM P	FISHER ATHLETIC	366	5 - 0	Munday 35[p] 58[p] 85[p], Collins 65 90
5	02/09	DM P	Stafford Rangers	950	2 - 0	Collins 43, Braithwaite 63
6	05/09	DM P	CAMBRIDGE CITY	428	2 - 1	Collins 17 40
7	09/09	DM P	BURTON ALBION	629	1 - 3	Takalogabashi 80
8	16/09	DM P	Havant & Waterlooville	578	3 - 2	Collins 8, Martin 82 90
9	19/09	DM P	WELLING UNITED	509	5 - 0	Porter 3, Saunders 12, O'Connell 20, Munday 85, Takalogabashi 71
10	23/09	DM P	Bath City	679	1 - 1	Martin 26
11	07/10	DM P	WEYMOUTH	197	3 - 0	O'Connell 30, Saunders 34, Takalogabashi 54
12	21/10	DM P	HAVANT & WATERLOOVILLE	336	1 - 0	Williams 80
13	24/10	DM P	Fisher Athletic	131	0 - 1	
14	04/11	DM P	KING'S LYNN	406	3 - 1	Munday 25, Porter 50, Collins 68
15	18/11	DM P	MERTHYR TYDFIL	395	3 - 2	Collins 10 14 80
16	25/11	DM P	STAFFORD RANGERS	405	3 - 1	Munday 10 40, Martin 89[p]
17	09/12	DM P	Tamworth	422	0 - 1	
18	16/12	DM P	King's Lynn	784	4 - 1	Collins 6 40 83, Munday 30
19	23/12	DM P	CLEVEDON TOWN	525	2 - 0	Braithwaite 31, Munday 51
20	26/12	DM P	Crawley Town	978	0 - 0	
21	01/01	DM P	FOLKESTONE INVICTA	950	3 - 2	O'Connell 25 64, Williams 90
22	06/01	DM P	Worcester City	1207	1 - 0	Tucker 4[og]
23	27/01	DM P	Merthyr Tydfil	500	2 - 0	Collins 14, Braithwaite 65
24	10/02	DM P	Salisbury City	623	1 - 0	Collins 28
25	20/02	DM P	Ilkeston Town	483	3 - 0	Collins 7 43, Keister 68
26	24/02	DM P	TAMWORTH	861	1 - 0	Collins 85
27	03/03	DM P	HALESOWEN TOWN	689	1 - 0	Keister 45
28	10/03	DM P	Dorchester Town	623	1 - 0	Saunders 28
29	17/03	DM P	SALISBURY CITY	925	1 - 1	Keister 20
30	20/03	DM P	Moor Green	234	4 - 0	Munday 45, Martin 71, Collins 80, Saunders 90
31	24/03	DM P	BATH CITY	706	2 - 0	Saunders 3, Collins 55
32	31/03	DM P	Newport County	747	0 - 0	
33	07/04	DM P	ILKESTON TOWN	755	2 - 0	Blackford 53, Lamb 77
34	10/04	DM P	Weymouth	1267	0 - 1	
35	14/04	DM P	Folkestone Invicta	765	2 - 2	Munday 26 85
36	16/04	DM P	CRAWLEY TOWN	1138	3 - 0	Braithwaite 6, Collins 87 89
37	21/04	DM P	Clevedon Town	297	2 - 1	Saunders 27, Martin 70
38	24/04	DM P	DORCHESTER TOWN	1006	3 - 2	Collins 15 20, Braithwaite 29
39	26/04	DM P	Cambridge City	401	2 - 0	Collins 18 63
40	28/04	DM P	WORCESTER CITY	1385	3 - 0	Collins 45[p] 46[p], Munday 88
41	01/05	DM P	NEWPORT COUNTY	2366	0 - 0	
42	05/05	DM P	Burton Albion	1464	0 - 2	

OTHER COMPETITIONS

Date	Comp.	Opponents	Gate	Score	Goalscorers
30/09	FA Cup Q2	BANSTEAD ATHLETIC	300	0 - 1	
31/10	Kent SC 1	SITTINGBOURNE	148	6 - 0	Takogholobashi(2), Munday, Braithwaite, Collins, O'Connell 80
14/11	Lge Cup 1	TONBRIDGE ANGELS	160	4 - 0	Collins 45 85, Saunders 75, Martin 80
02/12	FA Trophy 2	CLEVEDON TOWN	340	2 - 1	Porter 53, Munday 85
13/01	FA Trophy 3	Woking	1542	2 - 1	Collins 20, Braithwaite 31
23/01	Lge Cup 2	Baldock Town	142	0 - 1	
03/02	FA Trophy 4	Stevenage Borough	1515	1 - 2	O'Connell 81
13/02	Kent SC QF	Dover Athletic	741	1 - 2	Collins 75

PLAYING SQUAD

MARGATE

Player	*Birthplace*	*D.O.B.*	*Previous Clubs*
GOALKEEPERS			
Lee Turner DMP	London	04.03.65	Gravesend, Bury T, Corinthian, Sittingbourne, Corinthian, Leyton Orient
Charlie Mitten	Woolwich	09.10.74	Gillingham, Dover Ath., Thamesmead T
DEFENDERS			
Billy Edwards DMP	12.05.75		Sutton Utd, Tooting & Mitcham, Sutton Utd, Fisher Ath
Gary Blackford DMP	Redhill	25.09.68	Dagenham & Red, Brsibane Strikers (Aust), Slough T, Enfield, Dagenham & Red, Barnet, Fisher Ath., Croydon,
			Whyteleafe
Graham Porter DMP	29.10.74		Ashford T, Erith & Belvedere, Horsham, Maidstone Utd
Iain O'Connell DMP	Southend	09.10.70	Dover Ath (£3,000), Southend
Jay Saunders DMP	Kent	15.01.79	Gravesend, Gillingham
Lee Williams Michael Azzopardi	Kent London		Gillingham (Trainee) Dulwich Hamlet, Tooting & Mitcham
Paul Lamb DMP	Kent	19.04.73	Gravesend, Ramsgate, Margate, Dartford, Ramsgate
Tony Dixon DMP	Kent	17.03.61	Dover Ath., Gravesend, Erith & Belvedere
MIDFIELD			
Adrian Webster DMP	Australia		Ashford T, Folkestone Invicta, Ashford T, Charlton
Dean Yorath DMP	Kent	18.12.79	From Youth team
Denver Birmingham DMP	07.02.77		Harrow B, Chesham Utd, Crawley T, Erith & Belvedere
John Keister Sierra Leone Int., DMP	Manchester	11.11.70	Stevenage B, Shrewsbury, Chester C, Tigres
Mo Takaloboghasi DMP	Kent	15.10.79	From Local football
Paul O'Brien DMO	Kent	10.02.75	Ashford T (£4,000), Dover Ath
Simon Beard	Bromley	08.09.72	Dover Ath, Hastings T, Sittingbourne, West Ham
FORWARDS			
Phil Collins DMP	Kent	03.07.72	Dartford, Cray W, Sheppey Utd
Leon Braithwaite DMP	London	17.12.72	Welling Utd, St.Patricks Ath., Charlton Ath., Exeter C., Bishop's Stortford
Paul Sykes DMP	Kent	08.11.76	Welling Utd, Gillingham (Trainee)
Tommy Tyne	Lambeth	02.03.81	Millwall

MORECAMBE

After the high finish of the previous season and the club record purchase of Steve Walters from Northwich Victoria for £25,000 (later to be sold to Stevenage Boro) and a number of other high quality captures, hopes were high of a successful league campaign. That was not to be as at the end of the season the Shrimps were in the lowest ever Conference position, and only two points above the relegation mark.

The campaign, however, was memorable for Morecambe's F.A. Cup exploits. Reaching the Third Round proper for only the second time in the club's history (39 years to the day from the previous occasion), 6,000 fans crammed into Christie Park to see the Shrimps tackle the Tractor Boys of Ipswich. A 0-3 defeat didn't tell the full picture. The day will live long in the memory of all Shrimp devotees.

The other Cup competitions brought little success. A defeat at Lincoln City, a little unluckily 2-3 in our first incursion into the LDV Vans Trophy, was followed by an early exit from the McMilan Trophy (League Cup) 0-2 at Nuneaton after a 5-2 extra time victory over Leigh RMI. The semi-final of the Lancashire Trophy was reached, but local rivals Southport put paid to any hopes of glory with a 3-1 victory at Christie Park, the F.A. Umbro Trophy saw the Shrimps progress to the Fifth Round after replay victories against Evesham and Burscough, but a penalty shoot out while defeat at Hereford United ended our hopes of glory.

Some kudos was gained at the season's end with the Reserves, managed by Jeff Udall, completing a Lancashire League Cup and League double, with a great many of the players having graduated from the academy ranks.

MORECAMBE FC 2001-02

Back row, left to right: Ryan Zico-Black, Andy Gouck, Andy Lyons, Wayne Curtis, Mark Smith, Kevin Baldwin, Craig Mawson, Mark Quayle, Lee Colkin, Neil Uberschar, Russ McKenna, Alex Porter.
Middle row: Dave Edge (physio), Ian Dalziel (assistant Manager), Robbie Talbot, Gary Thompson, Jamie Murphy, Paul McGuire, Chris Lightfoot, Stewart Drummond, Adriano Rigoglioso, Michael Stringfellow, Carl Stamford, John Hardiker, Craig Blinkhorn, Jeff Udall (reserve team manager), Richard Danson (youth team manager).
Front row: Les Dewhurst (kit man), Claudia Manfredi (physio), Andy Fensome, Michael Knowles, Dave McKearney, Jim Harvey (manager), John Norman, Ian Arnold, David Perkins, Dave Stewart (youth team manager), Tom Sawyer (kit man).

MORECAMBE

GROUND DETAILS

Christie Park,
Lancaster Road,
Morecambe,
Lancashire LA4 5TJ

TELEPHONE 01524 411797
Fax: 01524 411797

email: neil@morecambefc.com
Web site: http://www.morecambefc.com

DIRECTIONS:
From south leave M6 motorway at junction 34. Follow signs for Morecambe through Lancaster, on A589, go straight across the first 2roundabouts, and at the third (with the Shrimp pub on your left), follow thesigns for Town Centre - Christie Park is approx. 600 metres on your left

CAPACITY: 6,300
SEATED: 1,200
COVERED TERRACING: 4,300

CLUB SHOP: On ground and open on matchdays. Also commercial office open Monday to Friday 9.00 - 5.00 selling the same goods

SOCIAL FACILITIES: J B's open normal licensing hours

MATCHDAY PROGRAMME

Pages: 48 Price: £1.50
Editor: Sean O'Connor
Other club publications: "Gazetta de la Shrimpa"

Local Press: Morecambe Visitor; Morecambe Guardian; Lancashire Evening Post; The Citizen

Local Radio: Radio Lancashire; Red Rose Radio; Bay Radio

Founded: 1920

Nickname: The Shrimps

Club sponsor: Newton Engineering

Club colours: Red shirts, black shorts, black & white socks

Change colours: White shirts, black shorts and white socks.

Midweek home matchday: Tuesdays, 7.45pm kick-off

Reserve Team's League: Lancashire Lge Div. A & North West All. Yth Div.

CLUB OFFICIALS

Honorary President Jim Bowen

Chairman Peter McGuigan

Vice Chairman Graham Hodgson

Directors Peter Cross, Stuart Forrest, Mark Hallam, Stuart Redman, Rod Taylor

Company & Club Secretary Neil Marsdin

Commercial Manager Peter Howard

FOOTBALL MANAGEMENT TEAM

MANAGER JIM HARVEY

Date of Appointment June 1994
Date of Birth: 2nd May 1958
Place of Birth: Lurgan, Northern Ireland

PREVIOUS CLUBS
As manager None
As asst. manager Morecambe (Jan - June 1994)
As player Glenavon, Arsenal, Hereford Utd., Bristol C., Tranmere Rov., Crewe Alex.

HONOURS
As manager Spalding Cup 97-98; NPL R-up 94-95
As player N. Ireland - u23.,
Leyland Daf Cup, Mercantile Trophy
Promotion from Division 4 & Division 3

* * *

Assistant Manager Ian Dalziel
Second Team Manager Jeff Udall
2nd Team Asst. Manager Tony Gribbins
Football in the Community Derek Quinn
Sports Therapist David Edge

Season

Season	League	Div.	Pos.	P	Home W	Home D	Home L	Home F	Home A	Away W	Away D	Away L	Away F	Away A	Pts	Manager
00-01	Conference	-	19	42	8	5	8	35	29	3	7	11	29	37	45	Jim Harvey
99-00	Conference	-	3	42	10	7	4	46	29	8	9	4	24	19	70	Jim Harvey
98-99	Conference	-	14	42	9	5	7	31	29	6	3	12	29	47	53	Jim Harvey
97-98	Conference	-	5	42	11	4	6	35	30	10	6	5	42	34	73	Jim Harvey
96-97	Conference	-	4	42	10	5	6	34	23	9	4	8	35	33	66	Jim Harvey

Season	League	Div.	Pos.	P	W	D	L	F	A	Pts	Manager
95-96	Conferece	-	9	42	17	8	17	78	72	59	Jim Harvey
94-95	N.P.L.	Premier	2	42	28	10	4	99	34	94	Jim Harvey
93-94	N.P.L.	Premier	7	42	20	7	15	90	56	67	Bryan Griffiths
92-93	N.P.L.	Premier	3	42	25	11	6	93	51	86	Bryan Griffiths
91-92	N.P.L.	Premier	2	42	23	9	10	64	32	78	Bryan Griffiths

HONOURS

F.A. Trophy 73-74,
Spalding Cup 97-98,
Northern Premier Lge R-up 91-92 94-95,
Presidents Cup 91-92,
Lancs Combination 24-25 61-62 62-63 66-67 67-68
R-up 1923-24, 25-26,
Lg Cup 26-27 45-46 64-65 66-68;
Lancashire Junior Cup (now ATS Trophy) x8
25-27 61-63 68-69 85-87 92-93, 95-96;
Lancashire Senior Cup 67-68,

PREVIOUS

Leagues: Lancs Combination 1920-68, Northern Premier 1968-1995

Grounds: Woodhill Lane 1920-25, shared with cricket club who still play there

Past Players who progressed to the Football League

Fred Blondel (Bury 1946),
Herbert Harrison (Accrington 1947),
Gordon Milne (Preston 1956),
Ray Charnley (Blackpool 1957),
Geoff Slack (Stockport 1958),
Ron Mitchell (Leeds 1958), Derek Armstrong (Carlisle 1961),
Alan Taylor(Rochdale 1973),
John Coates (Southport via Burscough & Skelmersdale 1975),
Keith Galley (Southport 1975),
Brian Thompson (West Ham 1977),
Malcolm Darling (Bury 1978)
David Eyres (Blackpool), Kenny Lowe (Barnet via Barrow),
Steve Gardner (Bradford City), Dave Lancaster (Chesterfield)

CLUB RECORDS

Attendance: 9,324 v Weymouth FA Cup 4.1.62

Win: 14-0 v Rossendale Utd, Lancs Combination Sept 1967 (Arnold Timmins scored 8)

Defeat: 0-14 v Chorley(A), 19th April 1946

Transfer fee paid: £25,000 to Northwich V. for Steve Walters, July 2000

Transfer fee received: £175,000 from Rushden & Diamonds for Justin Jackson, July 2000

Career Goalscorer: Keith Borrowdale 289 1956-68, 78-79 Lancashire Combination
John Coleman 130 1990-1995 (Northern Premier League)

Career Appearances: Steve Done 523 + 7 sub 1968-78

BEST SEASON

FA Cup: 3rd Round 1961-62, 2000-01
League clubs defeated: Chester City, Cambridge Utd.

FA Trophy: Winners 73-74, Q-final 72-73, 77-78, 93-94

League: 3rd Conference 1999-2000

LAST SEASON

F.A. Cup: 3rd Round

F.A. Trophy: 5th Round

Conference: 19th

Top Goalscorer: John Norman

Player of the Year: Andy Fensome

Captain: Dave McKearney

Semi-Professional Capped Players

John Coleman, Mike Bignall, Brian Healy, Stewart Drummond, Justin Jackson

MORECAMBE

Match Facts 2000-01

	Date	Comp.	Opponents	Gate	Score	Goalscorers
1	19/08	Conf	WOKING	1504	3 - 0	Eastwood 11 29, Heald 88
2	22/08	Conf	Scarborough	1536	2 - 2	Eastwood 45, Norman 87
3	26/08	Conf	Northwich Victoria	1008	0 - 1	
4	28/08	Conf	NUNEATON BOROUGH	1485	4 - 2	Walters 15, Norman 32, Drummond 73, Black 85
5	02/09	Conf	Doncaster Rovers	1924	0 - 1	
6	05/09	Conf	CHESTER CITY	1557	0 - 2	
7	09/09	Conf	KETTERING TOWN	1164	0 - 2	
8	11/09	Conf	Hednesford Town	942	0 - 0	
9	16/09	Conf	Boston United	1832	1 - 2	Heald 77
10	23/09	Conf	TELFORD UNITED	1013	0 - 0	
11	30/09	Conf	Yeovil Town	2550	2 - 3	Drummond 37, Eastwood 41
12	08/10	Conf	KINGSTONIAN	1060	3 - 2	Lyons 40, Eastwood 50, Drummond 87[p]
13	14/10	Conf	Dover Athletic	847	2 - 2	Black 20, Thompson 82
14	21/10	Conf	RUSHDEN & DIAMONDS	1816	2 - 1	Eastwood 27, Black 38
15	04/11	Conf	Forest Green Rovers	756	0 - 0	
16	11/11	Conf	HAYES	1272	4 - 0	Sterling 9[og], Thompson 38, Norman 51 77
17	02/12	Conf	HEREFORD UNITED	1125	1 - 1	Quayle 78
18	16/12	Conf	SCARBOROUGH	2023	4 - 4	Thompson 4, Quayle 6 23 62
19	26/12	Conf	Southport	2117	2 - 1	Drummond 53, Thompson 67
20	01/01	Conf	SOUTHPORT	1937	1 - 3	Eastwood 69
21	27/01	Conf	Chester City	1717	0 - 1	
22	10/02	Conf	Kettering Town	1217	5 - 1	Hunter 29, Quayle 42, Norman 55 70 80
23	17/02	Conf	HEDNESFORD TOWN	1275	0 - 0	
24	03/03	Conf	BOSTON UNITED	1009	2 - 0	McKearney 45, Quayle 67
25	06/03	Conf	NORTHWICH VICTORIA	886	4 - 0	Norman 22, McKearney 25 81[p], Black 74
26	10/03	Conf	Kingstonian	885	6 - 1	Norman 4, Quayle 18, Murphy 45, Drummond 65, McKearney 80p, Talbot 84
27	13/03	Conf	Woking	1309	1 - 3	Black 80
28	17/03	Conf	YEOVIL TOWN	1438	0 - 0	
29	25/03	Conf	Dagenham & Redbridge	1063	2 - 3	Talbot 63 71
30	31/03	Conf	STEVENAGE BOROUGH	1021	1 - 2	Drummond 67
31	07/04	Conf	Rushden & Diamonds	3778	1 - 4	Norman 58
32	12/04	Conf	Nuneaton Borough	1031	1 - 5	Quayle 57
33	14/04	Conf	DOVER ATHLETIC	1006	1 - 2	Rigoglioso 51
34	16/04	Conf	Hayes	686	1 - 1	Eastwood 51
35	18/04	Conf	DONCASTER ROVERS	638	2 - 1	Talbot 11, Rigoglioso 42
36	21/04	Conf	FOREST GREEN ROVERS	1017	0 - 2	
37	23/04	Conf	Stevenage Borough	1317	1 - 1	Eastwood 88[p]
38	26/04	Conf	Leigh RMI	467	0 - 1	
39	28/04	Conf	Hereford United	1437	2 - 2	Drummond 33, Talbot 53
40	01/05	Conf	Telford United	753	0 - 2	
41	03/05	Conf	DAGENHAM & REDBRIDGE	742	2 - 3	Eastwood 42[p], Talbot 67
42	05/05	Conf	LEIGH RMI	1106	1 - 2	Talbot 36

OTHER COMPETITIONS

Date	Comp.	Opponents	Gate	Score	Goalscorers	
28/10	FA Cup Q4	Bedlington Terriers	912	3 - 1	Hardiker 30, Thompson 41, Black 89	
18/11	FA Cup 1	Forest Green Rovers	1023	3 - 0	Hatswell 40[og], Norman 65, Thompson 81	
28/11	LDV Vans 1N	Lincoln City	1194	2 - 3	Walters 59, Dowe 53	
09/12	FA Cup 2	CAMBRIDGE UNITED	3427	2 - 1	Hardiker 7, Quayle 74	
06/01	FA Cup 3	IPSWICH TOWN	5923	0 - 3		
09/01	Lancs MT 1	Radcliffe Borough	210	1 - 1	Wright 84	
13/01	FA Trophy 3	Burscough	582	3 - 3	Black 13, Hardiker 29, Quayle 51	
16/01	Lancs MT 1 R	RADCLIFFE BOROUGH	n/a	(w/o)		
22/01	FA Trophy 3 R	BURSCOUGH	585	3 - 0	Walters 29, Black 33, Norman 48	
24/01	Lancs MT 2	Nelson	229	6 - 0	Eastwood(3), Shelley, Thompson, Heald	
30/01	Lancs MT QF	SQUIRES GATE	397	4 - 1	Norman 12 66, Quayle 62, Lee 86	
03/02	FA Trophy 4	Evesham United	738	0 - 0		
06/02	FA Trophy 4 R	EVESHAM UNITED	634	4 - 1	Norman 50 57 90, Lee 83	
15/02	Variety CT 2	LEIGH RMI	395	5 - 2	Eastwood 61, Talbot 75 101 103 113	
24/02	FA Trophy 5	HEREFORD UNITED	1109	0 - 0		
27/02	FA Trophy 5 R	Hereford United	1372	1 - 1	Drummond 71	Lost 1-3 after penalties
20/03	Lancs MT SF	SOUTHPORT	n/k	1 - 3	Thompson	
03/04	Variety CT QF	Nuneaton Borough	602	0 - 2		

1	2	3	4	5	6	7	8	9	10	11	Substitutes Used
Smith	Fensome	McKearney	Hardiker	Wright	Rogoglioso	Drummond	Walters	Takano	Eastwood	Norman	McGuire (5), Price (9), Heald (10)
Smith	Fensome	Wright	McKearney	Hardiker	Walters	Rigoglioso	Drummond	Takano	Norman	Eastwood	Murphy (3), McGuire(7), Heald (9)
Smith	Fensome	McKearney	Murphy	Hardiker	Rigoglioso	Drummond	L Smith	Norman	Takano	Eastwood	Black (6), Heald (8), Walters (10)
Smith	Fensome	Hardiker	McKearney	Murphy	Walters	Drummond	Takano	Eastwood	Norman	Thompson	McGuire (2), Rigoglioso (8), Black(11)
Smith	Fensome	Brown	McKearney	Murphy	Walters	Thompson	Drummond	Eastwood	Norman	Takano	Rigoglioso (9), Black (11), (Banks (1)
Smith	Fensome	Brown	McKearney	Murphy	Walters	Drummond	Thompson	Eastwood	Norman	Lyons	Takano (3), Black (8), Wright (9)
Smith	Fensome	Brown	McKearney	Murphy	Walters	Thompson	Drummond	Eastwood	Norman	Lyons	Takano (3), Black (7), Wright (9)
Smith	Fensome	Murphy	McKearney	Lyons	Price	Potts	Drummond	Rigoglioso	Norman	Heald	Black (7), Takano (11)
Smith	Fensome	McKearney	Murphy	Wright	Rigoglioso	Price	Drummond	Lyons	Norman	Keeling	McGuire (2), Heald (5), Eastwood (11)
Smith	McGuire	Hardiker	McKearney	Murphy	Walters	Rigoglioso	Drummond	Dowe	Norman	Lyons	Eastwood (9), Black (10), Heald (11)
Smith	Fensome	Hardiker	McKearney	Lyons	Black	Drummond	Walters	Eastwood	Rigoglioso	Dowe	Norman (6), McGuire (11)
Smith	Fensome	Hardiker	McKearney	Lyons	Walters	Drummond	Dowe	Rigoglioso	Black	Eastwood	Murphy(5), Thompson (8), Hunter (11)
Smith	Fensome	McKearney	Hardiker	Lyons	Black	Drummond	Walters	Eastwood	Rigoglioso	Dowe	Thompson (9), Norman (10), Hunter (11)
Smith	Fensome	Lyons	McKearney	Hardiker	Walters	Black	Drummond	Dowe	Rigoglioso	Eastwood	Murphy (5), Thompson (7), Norman (9)
Smith	Fensome	McKearney	Hardiker	Lyons	Walters	Black	Drummond	Eastwood	Thompson	Norman	Knowles (7), Heald (9), Rigoglioso (10)
Smith	Fensome	Lyons	McKearney	Hardiker	Walters	Thompson	Drummond	Dowe	Norman	Eastwood	Knowles (6), Rigoglioso (7), Black (11)
Smith	Fensome	Perkins	McKearney	Hardiker	Walters	Thompson	Drummond	Dowe	Norman	Black	Quayle (9), Rigoglioso (10), Knowles (11)
Smith	Fensome	Perkins	McKearney	Hardiker	Thompson	Walters	Drummond	Black	Quayle	Norman	McGuire (5), Stringfellow (7), Eastwood (10)
Smith	Fensome	Murphy	McKearney	Hardiker	Knowles	Takano	Drummond	Walters	Quayle	Norman	McGuire (5), Thompson (6), Eastwood (7)
Smith	Fensome	Hardiker	McKearney	Murphy	Walters	Drummond	Rigoglioso	Takano	Thompson	Quayle	Eastwood (3), Heald (8), McGuire (9)
Smith	Fensome	Brown	McKearney	Hardiker	Walters	Lee	Drummond	Quayle	Lyons	Thompson	Norman (6), Eastwood (9), Black(11)
Smith	Fensome	McKearney	Murphy	Lyons	Lee	Drummond	Walters	Hunter	Quayle	Norman	Rigoglioso (4), Eastwood (10), Swanwick (11)
Smith	Fensome	Lyons	McKearney	Hardiker	Walters	Lee	Drummond	Quayle	Norman	Hunter	Talbot (9), Murphy (10), Eastwood (11)
Smith	Fensome	Lyons	McKearney	Hardiker	Murphy	Lee	Drummond	Quayle	Norman	Black	Talbot (9), Walters (10)
Smith	Fensome	Murphy	McKearney	Hardiker	Lyons	Lee	Drummond	Quayle	Norman	Black	Talbot (9), Rigoglioso (10)
Smith	Fensome	Lyons	McKearney	Hardiker	Murphy	Lee	Drummond	Quayle	Norman	Black	Thompson (7), Rigoglioso (9), Talbot (10)
Smith	Fensome	Murphy	McKearney	Hardiker	Lyons	Lee	Drummond	Quayle	Norman	Black	Talbot ((9), Hunter (10), Rigoglioso (11)
Smith	Fensome	McKearney	Murphy	Hardiker	Black	Lyons	Drummond	Lee	Norman	Quayle	Thompson (10, Takano (6), Talbot (11)
Smith	Fensome	Murphy	McKearney	Hardiker	Lyons	Lee	Drummond	Quayle	Norman	Black	Baldwin (3), Talbot (9), Thompson (11)
Smith	Fensome	Lyons	McKerney	Hardiker	Murphy	Lee	Drummond	Talbot	Norman	Thompson	Takano (3), Black (7), Quayle (10)
Smith	Fensome	Brown	McKearney	Hardiker	Murphy	Lee	Drummond	Quayle	Norman	Black	Hunter (7), Talbot (9), McGuire (10)
Banks	Fensome	Brown	McKearney	Hardiker	Murphy	Lee	Drummond	Quayle	Norman	Black	Eastwood (7), Talbot (9), Stringfellow (10)
Smith	Fensome	Lyons	McKearney	Stringfellow	Murphy	Rigoglioso	Drummond	Talbot	Black	Hunter	Brown (3), Quayle(9), Eastwood (11)
Smith	Fensome	Hardiker	McKearney	McGuire	Stringfellow	Rigoglioso	Drummond	Talbot	Lyons	Quayle	Murphy (7), Eastwood (11), Heald (9)
Smith	Fensome	Hardiker	McKearney	McGuire	Stringfellow	Rigoglioso	Drummond	Talbot	Perkins	Eastwood	Black (9), Lyons (10), Norman (11)
Banks	Fensome	Lyons	McKearney	Hardiker	Stringfellow	Rigoglioso	Drummond	Talbot	Eastwood	McGuire	Black (6), Norman (7), Takano (9)
Banks	Swanwick	Brown	McKearney	Takano	L Smith	Black	Heald	Norman	Hunter	Uberschar	Talbot (8), Eastwood (10), Alty (11)
Banks	Fensome	Brown	McKearney	Hardiker	L Smith	Drummond	Talbot	Rigoglioso	Eastwood	Black	Norman 96), Hunter (10), Lyons (11)
Smith	Fensome	Hardiker	McKearney	Lyons	Stringfellow	Drummond	Talbot	Rigoglioso	Norman	Hunter	Brown (8), Swanwick (3)
Smith	Fensome	Murphy	McKearney	Lyons	L Smith	Drummond	Talbot	Takano	Rigoglioso	Hunter	Black (6), Stringfellow (9), Brown (11)
Banks	Uberschar	Swanwick	McKearney	Perkins	L Smith	Stringfellow	Talbot	Takano	Eastwood	Black	Alty (2), Hunter (6), Rigoglioso (7)
Banks	Fensome	McKearney	Swanwick	Lyons	Drummond	Talboy	Rigoglioso	Eastwood	Norman	Black	Takano (7), Uberschar (10), Hunter (11)

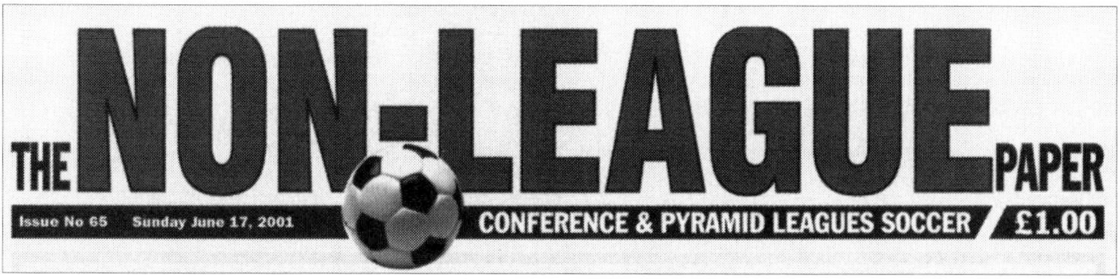

PLAYING SQUAD

MORECAMBE

(Bold print indicates an England Semi-Professional International)

Player *Honours*	*Birthplace*	*D.O.B.*	*Previous Clubs*
GOALKEEPERS			
Mark Smith	Birmingham	02.01.73	Nottingham F, Crewe, Walsall, Rushden & D, Bedford T
DEFENDERS			
Greg Brown	Wythenshawe	31.07.78	Chester C, Macclesfield
Andy Fensome	Northampton	18.02.68	Norwich, Camb.U, Preston, Rochdale, Barrow
Mark Wright Scot.S & Y	Manchester	29.01.70	Everton, Huddersfield, Wigan, Chorley
John Hardiker	Preston	07.07.82	Youth Team
David McKearney	Liverpool	20.06.68	Prescot Cables, Bolton, Northwich V, Crewe, Wigan, Chorley
Paul Maguire	Manchester	17.11.79	Youth team
David Perkins	Blackpool		From Youth team
Jamie Murphy	Manchester	25.02.73	Halifax, Cambridge Utd, Doncaster R, Blackpool
Nick Coyle ES	Morecambe		From Youth team
MIDFIELD			
Stuart Drummond ESP	Preston	11.12.75	Youth team
Andy Gouck	Blackpool	08.06.72	Southport, Rochdale, Blackpool
Andy Heald	Manchester		From Youth team
Michael Knowles	Morecambe	03.03.74	From Youth team
Ryan-Zico Black NI Y	Manchester		From Youth team
FORWARDS			
Gary Thompson	Kendal	24.11.80	Youth team
Adriano Rigoglioso	Liverpool	28.05.79	Liverpool, Marine
John Norman	Birkenhead	26.06.71	Tranmere, Mold Alex., Morecambe, Hednesford T
Phil Eastwood	Whalley	06.04.78	Burnley
Wayne Curtis	Barrow	06.03.80	Holker OB
Ian Arnold ESP	Durham	04.07.72	Southport, Kidderminster H, Stalybridge C, Kettering T, Carlisle, Middlesbrough
Mark Quayle	Liverpool	02.10.78	Altrincham, Ilkeston T, Leigh RMI, Halifax, Notts Co., Everton
Robbie Talbot	Liverpool		Burscough (£10,000), Marine, Rochdale

NORTHWICH VICTORIA

Written off before the season began, Vics again confounded the "experts" by consolidating Conference status for a 22nd time. The newer kids on the block had bigger grounds, bigger squads, bigger wage structures and - supposedly - bigger ambitions, so a long, hard season lay in prospect before a ball had even been kicked in anger.

Manager Mark Gardiner did his best to instil a fighting spirit in his squad, but with financial restrictions and the pressures of a proposed ground move bringing to bear, supporters harboured suspicions that one or other of Gardiner and his chairman, Rod Stitch, would not survive the season. In the end, a stormy September spelt the end for the manager while the hard-working chairman finally reached breaking point in March.

After the first third of the campaign brought just two wins, it seemed the the prophets of doom would be right. The nadir came at Keys Park on the first Saturday in September when Hednesford turned a 1-0 half-time deficit into a 7-1 victory and Vics' heaviest Conference defeat.

A month later, following four consecutive defeats, the directors decide to part company with Gardiner. The Greens needed an inspirational appointment - and they got it. Keith Alexander proved to be the slice of fortune the club desperately needed. Vics' first full-time manager, Alexander brought a highly professional approach that impressed everybody at the club.

The impact was immediate with just one defeat in 10 matches - and that was a 2-1 reversal for a "fringe" side against Hyde United in the Cheshire Senior Cup.

The FA Cup might have been a distraction from Keith's brief of keeping the club in the Conference, but double headers with Bury - who became Vics' first Football League scalp since 1984 - and Leyton Orient brought the Greens national recognition and much-needed finances to swell the club's coffers. The cup run also raised expectations that the team had enough about it to pick up sufficient points to beat the drop.

As the run-in began in earnest, vital wins over Kingstonian and Telford, together with valuable draws at Hayes and Southport put safety within touching distance of safety. In the end, Vics finished in seventeenth spot.

Alexander left for Lincoln in July 2001, but the appointment of ex-Northern Ireland international Jimmy Quinn has Vics fans believing they will be able to prove their doubters owing once again - and start a new era at their new Wincham ground as a Conference club.

William Hughes

NORTHWICH VICTORIA FC 2001-02

Back row (l-r): Gary Talbot, Andrew Brownrigg, Gary Burke, Paul Gibson, Richard Norris, Adie Mike, Mark Barnard. **Middle row:** Phil Lea (physio), Mark Devlin, Marcus Jones, Jimmy Quinn (manager), Gregg Blundell, Peter Holcroft, Steve Davis (assistant manager). **Front row:** Richard Mitchell, Mark Bailey, Darren Knowles, Steve Garvey, Steve Walsh.

NORTHWICH VICTORIA

GROUND DETAILS

The Drill Field,
Drill Field Road,
Northwich,
Cheshire. CW9 5HN

TELEPHONE: 01606 41450
Fax: 01606 330577.
Club Newsline: 0900802 2713
Web site: www.nvfc.co.uk

SIMPLE DIRECTIONS: Leave M6 at Junc.19 and follow A556 towards Chester. At second roundabout (approx. 6 miles), turn right onto A533. Ground on right behind Volunteer Public House

CAPACITY: 6,000
SEATED: 660
COVERED TERRACING: 3,500

CLUB SHOP: Located inside ground. Open match days. Manager: Andy Dakin
SOCIAL FACILITIES:
Large social club with members lounge and separate functionroom - both available for hire Tel: 01606 43120. Food available on matchdayswith prior notice. Bass beers, Pool, Darts, TV. New suite now available offering matchday & midweek catering

MATCHDAY PROGRAMME

Pages: 48 Price: £1.50

Editor: William Hughes & James Wood

Other club publications: 'Distant Vics'
(a bi-monthly magazine for exiled Vics' fans)

Local Press: Northwich Guardian (Wed.); Northwich Chronicle (Wed.); Daily Post; Manchester Evening News Pink (Sat.)
Local Radio: GMR (BBC Manchester); Piccadilly Radio; Signal Radio

Founded: 1874

Nickname: The Vics, Greens, Trickies

Club Sponsors: Bridgnorth Publishing

Club colours: Green shirts, white shorts and black socks

Change colours: Sky Blue shirts / navy blue shorts

Midweek home matchday: Tuesday

Reserve Team's league: Lancashire League

CLUB OFFICIALS

Chairman T.B.A.
Acting Chairman Dave Stone

Company Secretary Graham Cookson
Chief Executive John Stitch
Directors Dave Price, Jim Rafferty

Associate Directors
Graham Cookson, Dave Edgeley, Ted Carthy, Dave Bush, Dave Thomas.

President & Football Secretary Derek Nuttall
c/o the club
Tel: 01606 41450 Fax: 01606 330577

FOOTBALL MANAGEMENT TEAM

MANAGER: JIMMY QUINN
Date of Appointment 27.07.01
Date of Birth 18.12.59
Place of Birth Belfast
PREVIOUS CLUBS
As manager Reading and Swindon Town
As coach Peterborough United
As player Congleton, Oswestry, Swindon, Blackburn Rovers, Leicester City, Bradford City, West Ham United, Bournemouth & B, Reading, Peterborough United,Northwich Victoria, hererford United, Hayes, Nantwich ,Cirencester
HONOURS
As manager Division One play off final
As coach
as player N.Ireland International
2nd Div Play offWinners 86-7

Assistant Manager: Steve Davies
Physio: Phil Lea
Reserve & Youth Team Manager Ted Carthy

Season	League	Div.	Pos.	Home P	W	D	L	F	A	Away W	D	L	F	A	Pts	Manager
00-01	Conference	-	17	42	8	7	6	31	24	3	6	12	18	43	46	M Gardiner/Keith Alexander
99-00	Conference	-	18	42	10	8	3	33	25	3	4	14	20	53	51	Mark Gardiner
98-99	Conference	-	7	42	11	3	7	29	21	8	6	7	31	30	66	Phil Wilson/Mark Gardiner
97-98	Conference	-	9	42	8	9	4	34	24	7	6	8	29	35	60	Phil Wilson
96-97	Conference	-	6	42	11	5	5	31	20	6	7	8	30	34	63	Mark Hancock/ Phil Wilson

Season	League	Div.	Pos.	P	W	D	L	F	A	Pts	Manager
95-96	Conference	-	8	42	16	12	14	72	64	60	Brian Kettle
94-95	Conference	-	10	42	14	15	13	77	66	57	John Williams
93-94	Conference	-	15	42	11	19	12	44	45	52	John Williams
92-93	Conference	-	11	42	16	8	18	68	55	56	Sammy McIlroy/John Williams
91-92	Conference	-	11	42	16	6	20	63	58	54	Sammy McIlroy

HONOURS

Welsh Cup R-up 1881/82,1888-89;
FA Trophy 1983/84, R-up 1982/83 & 1995/96;
Bob Lord Trophy 1979/80, 92/93;
Northern Premier Lge R-up 1976/77;
Northern Premier Lge Cup 1972/73, R-up 1978/79;
Cheshire County Lge 1956/57, R-up 1924/25, 47/48;
Cheshire County Lge Cup 1925/35;
Manchester Lge 1902/03, R-up 1900/01, 03/04, 07/08, 08/09, 11/12; The Combination R-up 1890/91;
Cheshire Senior Cup 1880-81, 81/82, 82/83, 83/84, 84/85, 85/86,1928/29, 36/37, 49/50, 54/55, 71/72, 76/77, 78/79, 83/84, 93/94. R-up 1891/92,96/97, 1905/06, 08/09, 47/48, 50/51, 63/64, 65/66, 69/70, 70/71, 77/78, 85/86; 98/99
Staffordshire Senior Cup 1978/79, 79/80, 89/90, R-up 1986/87, 90/91;
CheshireAmateur Cup 1901/02, R-up 1898/99, 02/93,
Northwich Senior Cup 1948/49, 58/59,59/60, 63/64, 64/65, 65/66, 67/68, 68/69, 69/70, 71/72, 74/75, R-up x7;
Mid Cheshire Senior Cup 1984/85, 85/86, 87/88, 89/90, 00-01 91/92, 93/94, 94/95, 96/97,98/99; R-up 1982/83, 83/84, 90/91, 92/93;
North-West Floodlit Lge 1966/67, 75/76;
Cheshire Lge Lancs. Comb. Inter-Lge Cup 1961/62;
Guardian Charity Shield 1985/86, 86/87, 87/88

PREVIOUS

Leagues: The Combination 1890-1892, Football League Div.2 1892-94, The Combination 1894-1898, The Cheshire League 1898-1900, Manchester League 1900-12, Lancashire 1912-19, Cheshire County League 1919-68, Northern Premier League 1968-79

Grounds: None

Past Players who progressed to the Football League

Tony Hemmings (Wycombe W), Tony Bullock (Barnsley), Darren Tinson (Macclesfield T) Lee Steele (Shrewsbury Town),Paul Tait (Crewe Alex),Shaun Teale (Tranmere R & Aston Villa) , Mark Birch (Carlisle U),Mark Birch (Carlisle U) and Gary Fletcher (Leyton Orient)

CLUB RECORDS

Attendance: 11,290 v Witton Albion, Cheshire League, Good Friday 1949

Win: 17-0 v Marple Ass. 15.12.1883
Defeat: 3-10 v Port Vale 7.2.1931

Career Goalscorer: Peter Burns 160 - 1955-65
Career Appearances: 970 by Ken Jones 1969-85

Transfer Fee paid: £12,000 to Hyde United for Malcolm O'Connor - August 1988

Transfer Fee received: £75,000 from Leyton Orient for Gary Fletcher - June 2001

BEST SEASON

FA Cup: Quarter Finals 1883-84
League clubs defeated: Rochdale, Peterborough, Watford, Chester C., Crewe Alexandra, Bury

FA Trophy: Winners 83-84
R-up 82-83 95-96

League: **4th** Conference 80-81

LAST SEASON

F.A. Cup: Second Round
F.A. Trophy: Round
Conference: 17th
Top Goalscorer: Gary Fletcher
Player of the Year: Adie Mike
Captain: John Robertson

NORTHWICH VICTORIA

Match Facts 2000-01

	Date	Comp.	Opponents	Gate	Score	Goalscorers
1	19/08	Conf	Kingstonian	942	0 - 1	
2	22/08	Conf	TELFORD UNITED	812	0 - 1	
3	26/08	Conf	MORECAMBE	1008	1 - 0	Fletcher 34
4	28/08	Conf	Hereford United	2461	0 - 0	
5	02/09	Conf	Hednesford Town	800	1 - 7	Simpson 16
6	05/09	Conf	DONCASTER ROVERS	1115	1 - 1	Devlin 45
7	09/09	Conf	STEVENAGE BOROUGH	909	3 - 2	Quinn 4 38, Holcroft 53
8	12/09	Conf	Chester City	1717	1 - 1	Fletcher 17
9	16/09	Conf	Scarborough	845	0 - 4	
10	23/09	Conf	BOSTON UNITED	1035	0 - 3	
11	30/09	Conf	HAYES	808	3 - 4	Quinn 5 49, Vicary 45
12	03/10	Conf	SOUTHPORT	1074	0 - 2	
13	08/10	Conf	Dover Athletic	688	0 - 3	
14	14/10	Conf	YEOVIL TOWN	1015	1 - 2	Devlin 28
15	20/10	Conf	Doncaster Rovers	2794	2 - 0	Bailey 15, Cooke 74
16	31/10	Conf	FOREST GREEN ROVERS	843	0 - 0	
17	04/11	Conf	WOKING	957	4 - 0	Fletcher 3 34, Mike 52 69
18	11/11	Conf	Kettering Town	1102	3 - 2	Devlin 38, Fletcher 53, Mike 64
19	02/12	Conf	DAGENHAM & REDBRIDGE	1060	3 - 0	Fletcher 37 76, Norris 79
20	16/12	Conf	Yeovil Town	2891	0 - 1	
21	26/12	Conf	LEIGH RMI	1208	1 - 1	Devlin 2
22	01/01	Conf	Leigh RMI	501	0 - 3	
23	06/01	Conf	HEREFORD UNITED	1104	1 - 0	Mitchell 73
24	27/01	Conf	Forest Green Rovers	723	0 - 1	
25	03/02	Conf	HEDNESFORD TOWN	953	2 - 2	Blundell 3, Mike 9
26	10/02	Conf	Stevenage Borough	1622	1 - 3	Blundell 1
27	17/02	Conf	CHESTER CITY	2651	1 - 1	Blundell 65
28	20/02	Conf	Rushden & Diamonds	2820	1 - 2	Bailey 25
29	24/02	Conf	Boston United	1556	1 - 1	Lewis 45
30	03/03	Conf	SCARBOROUGH	942	3 - 0	Devlin 30, Fletcher 36, Barnard 63
31	06/03	Conf	Morecambe	886	0 - 4	
32	10/03	Conf	DOVER ATHLETIC	907	2 - 0	Mike 42, Devlin 72
33	17/03	Conf	Hayes	620	2 - 2	Mike 66, Bailey 87
34	25/03	Conf	RUSHDEN & DIAMONDS	2016	0 - 0	
35	31/03	Conf	Southport	1643	1 - 1	Burke 57
36	10/04	Conf	KINGSTONIAN	788	2 - 1	Mike 7, Barnard 76[p]
37	14/04	Conf	Telford United	1019	3 - 2	Blundell 77, Talbot 82, Lewis 85
38	16/04	Conf	KETTERING TOWN	1011	1 - 2	Devlin 41
39	21/04	Conf	Woking	1544	1 - 1	Devlin 69
40	24/04	Conf	Nuneaton Borough	802	1 - 3	Mike 13
41	28/04	Conf	Dagenham & Redbridge	1256	0 - 1	
42	05/05	Conf	NUNEATON BOROUGH	902	2 - 2	Mike 76, Mitchell 90

OTHER COMPETITIONS

Date	Comp.	Opponents	Gate	Score	Goalscorers
19/09	Ches. SC 1	ALTRINCHAM	412	1 - 0	Devlin 45
17/10	Variety CT 1	LEIGH RMI	309	3 - 3	Holdcroft 12, Fletcher 23 90
28/10	FA Cup Q4	Sheffield	761	5 - 1	Mike 39, Fletcher 42 80, Davis 60, Norris 84 (at Sheffield Utd)
14/11	Ches. SC QF	HYDE UNITED	283	1 - 2	Poland 23
18/11	FA Cup 1	Bury	2844	1 - 1	Fletcher 73
28/11	FA Cup 1 R	BURY	2869	1 - 0	Mike 72
09/12	FA Cup 2	LEYTON ORIENT	2703	3 - 3	Fletcher 51 62, Mike 70
20/12	FA Cup 2 R	Leyton Orient	4028	2 - 3	
13/01	FA Trophy 3	Matlock Town	784	0 - 2	
23/01	Variety CT 1 R	Leigh RMI	169	0 - 1	

1	2	3	4	5	6	7	8	9	10	11	Substitutes Used
Key	Bailey	Bates	Robertson	Burke	Devlin	Norris	Rose	Mike	Kimmins	Vicary	Fletcher (10), Laurie (11)
Key	Robertson	Bates	Bailey	Burke	Devlin	Laurie	Holcroft	Mike	Kimmins	Vicary	Ellis (4), Fletcher (7), Rose (8)
Key	Bailey	Robertson	Davis	Bates	Norris	Rose	Devlin	Vicary	Mike	Fletcher	Kimmins (9), Cooke (10), Laurie (11)
Key	Bates	Robertson	Davis	Bailey	Norris	Rose	Devlin	Vicary	Kimmins	Fletcher	Poland (9), Burke (10)
Key	Simpson	Robertson	Davis	Bates	Norris	Devlin	Rose	Vicary	Fletcher	Kimmins	Holcroft (8), Laurie (9), Poland (11)
Rigby	Robertson	Bates	Bailey	Simpson	Devlin	Norris	Rose	Quinn	Fletcher	Vicary	Burke (6), Holcroft(8), Ellis (11)
Rigby	Bailey	Robertson	Simpson	Bates	Norris	Devlin	Holcroft	Vicary	Quinn	Fletcher	Ellis (5), Laurie 99), Kimmins (11)
Rigby	Robertson	Ellis	Bailey	Simpson	Devlin	Norris	Holcroft	Quinn	Fletcher	Vicary	Laurie (10), McDermott (11)
Rigby	Bailey	Ellis	Robertson	Simpson	Devlin	Norris	Holcroft	Quinn	Fletcher	Vicary	Laurie (8), Kimmins (9), Walsh (10)
Rigby	Bailey	Robertson	Simpson	Ellis	Norris	Rose	Holdcroft	Vicary	Devlin	Fletcher	Burke (4), McDermott (8), Laurie (11)
Key	Davis	Robertson	Simpson	Burke	Norris	Rose	Devlin	Ellis	Quinn	Vicary	Poland (5), Laurie (6), Mike (7)
Rachel	Robertson	Taaffe	McDermitt	Simpson	Burke	Holcroft	Rose	Devlin	Quinn	Vicary	Mike (4), Norris (9)
Key	Davis	Ellis	Bailey	Burke	Simpson	Norris	Holcroft	Quinn	Poland	Vicary	Mike (10), Walsh (2)
Key	Davis	Robertson	Simpson	Bailey	Norris	Devlin	Holdcroft	Ellis	Mike	Vicary	Walsh (9), Cooke (10), Fletcher (11)
Key	Robertson	Walsh	Davis	Bailey	Burke	Norris	Holdcroft	Devlin	Mike	Fletcher	Bates (3), Cooke (10), Vicary (11)
Key	Robertson	Walsh	Davis	Bailey	Burke	Norris	Holdcroft	Devlin	Fletcher	Cooke	Bates (2), Rose (8), Mike(11)
Key	Robertson	Davis	Burke	Bailey	Norris	Henry	Devlin	Barnard	Mike	Fletcher	Rose (7), Cooke (10), Poland (11)
Key	Bailey	Davis	Robertson	Barnard	Norris	Henry	Burke	Davis	Fletcher	Mike	Walsh (10), Cooke(11), Poland (2)
Key	Robertson	Davis	Burke	Bailey	Norris	Simpson	Devlin	Barnard	Mike	Fletcher	Henry (7), Lewis (10), Poland (11)
Key	Bailey	Davis	Robertson	Bates	Burke	Norris	Simpson	Devlin	Fletcher	Mike	Poland (3) sub Vicary; Walsh (5)
Key	Robertson	Barnard	Ellis	Bailey	Burke	Norris	Simpson	Devlin	Mike	Poland	Walsh (7), Cooke (8)
Key	Walsh	Ellis	Davis	Robertson	Bailey	Burke	Simpson	Devlin	Poland	Mike	Cooke (7), Quigley (2), Vicary (10)
Key	Robertson	Davis	Simpson	Bailey	Robinson	Henry	Devlin	Barnard	Mitchell	Mike	Newhouse (8)
Key	Bailey	Simpson	Talbot	Barnard	Burke	Norris	Robinson	Devlin	Fletcher	Mike	Blundell (3), Holcroft (8), Mitchell (10)
Key	Talbot	Davis	Burke	Norris	Devlin	Fletcher	Bailey	Barnard	Blundell	Mike	Mitchell (7)
Key	Bailey	Bates	Davis	Talbot	Burke	Norris	Blundell	Fletcher	Mike	Devlin	Mitchell (2)
Key	Bates	Davis	Talbot	Burke	Barnard	Norris	Devlin	Fletcher	Mike	Blundell	Simpson (8), Walling(9)
Key	Bates	Barnard	Davis	Talbot	Burke	Norris	Bailey	Devlin	Mike	Mitchell	Walsh (4), Walling (8), Houghton (11)
Key	Walling	Robertson	Talbot	Bates	Norris	Bailey	Devlin	Barnard	Lewis	Mike	Burke (7)
Key	Bates	Walling	Robertson	Talbot	Barnard	Norris	Devlin	Lewis	Fletcher	Mike	Holcroft (4), Burke (9), Mitchell (10)
Key	Bates	Barnard	Walling	Talbot	Robertson	Norris	Burke	Devlin	Mike	Fletcher	Mitchell (6), Walsh (7), Bailey (3)
Key	Bates	Talbot	Robertson	Burke	Barnard	Norris	Devlin	Fletcher	Mike	Blundell	Mitchell (9), Bailey (11)
Key	Bates	Talbot	Robertson	Burke	Barnard	Norris	Walling	Devlin	Blundell	Mike	Bailey (7), Mitchell (8), Walsh (10)
Key	Bates	Barnard	Talbot	Robertson	Burke	Norris	Blundell	Devlin	Mike	Lewis	Walling (11), Bailey (3)
Key	Bates	Talbot	Burke	Barnard	Robertson	Norris	Lewis	Devlin	Blundell	Mike	Bailey (5), Chandler (8), Walling (10)
Key	Bates	Robertson	Talbot	Barnard	Burke	Norris	Devlin	Blundell	Lewis	Mike	Challender (9), Mitchell (10), Walling (11)
Key	Bates	Barnard	Talbot	Robertson	Burke	Norris	Challender	Blundell	Mike	Devlin	Mitchell (2), Lewis (5), Holcroft (8)
Key	Walling	Barnard	Talbot	Norris	Burke	Blundell	Devlin	Lewis	Mike	Mitchell	Holcroft (5), Robertson (11)
Key	Bates	Barnard	Talbot	Robertson	Burke	Norris	Lewis	Blundell	Mike	Devlin	Challender (1), Walling (10), Mitchell (8)
Rigby	Walling	Barnard	Talbot	Robertson	Bailey	Norris	Blundell	Devlin	Mitchell	Mike	Walsh (5), Challender (6), Lewis (10)
Rigby	Walling	Talbot	Robertson	Barnard	Norris	Challender	Burke	Devlin	Blundell	Mike	Bailey (4), Mitchell (6), Lewis (10)
Rigby	Walling	Barnard	Talbot	Challender	Burke	Norris	Blundell	Devlin	Mike	Lewis	Bailey (5), Holcroft (9), Mitchell (11)

PLAYING SQUAD

NORTHWICH VICTORIA

(Bold print indicates an England Semi-Professional International)

Player *Honours*	*Birthplace*	*D.O.B.*	*Previous Clubs*
GOALKEEPERS			
Paul Gibson	Sheffield	01.11.76	Notts Co., Manchester Utd
DEFENDERS			
Jamie Bates	Manchester		Maine Road, Runcorn, Stalybridge C
Garry Burke	Manchester		Woodley Sports, Runcorn
Mark Bailey	Stoke	12.08.76	Stoke, Rochdale
Andy Brownrigg	Sheffield	02.08.76	Greenock Morton, Kidderminster H, Yeovil T, Stalybridge C, Rotherham, Norwich, Hereford Utd
Darren Knowles	Sheffield	08.10.70	Hartlepool, Scarborough, Stockport, Sheffield Utd
Gary Talbot	Manchester	06.10.70	Altrincham (£2,500), Winsford Utd, Barnton, Wilmslow Alb., Rhyl
Greg Challender	Manchester	05.02.73	Chorley, Droylsden, Finn Harps, Droylsden, Barrow, Winsford Utd, Accrington Stanley, Stalybridge Celtic, Altrincham, Bath C, Southport, Preston, Mossley, Horwich RMI, Oldham
Mark Barnard	Sheffield	27.11.75	Doncaster R, Darlington
Steve Capper	Manchester		From Youth team
Steve Davis EY	Birmingham	26.07.65	Oxford Utd, Barnsley, Burnley, Crewe, Stoke
Steve Walsh	Warrington		From Local football
MIDFIELD			
Mark Devlin	Irvine	08.01.73	Stoke, Exeter
Richard Norris	Birkenhead	05.01.78	Marine, Crewe
John Knapper	Nottingham		Ilkeston T, Eastwood T, Belper T
Marcus Jones	Stone		Yeovil T, Cheltenham, Scarborough, Telford Utd, VS Rugby, Hinckley Ath., Willenhall T, Bolehall Swifts, Chasetown, Stoke
Neil Ellis	Liverpool	30.06.69	Leek T, Worcester C, Corby T, Kettering T, Maidstone U, Bangor C, Oswestry T, Stalybridge C, Ashton Utd, Chorley, Chester C, Tranmere R
FORWARDS			
Adie Mike ES, EY	Manchester	16.11.73	Manchester C, Stockport, Bury, Hartlepool, Doncaster R, Leek T, Hednesford T, Southport
Gregg Blundell	Liverpool		Vauxhall Motors (£8,500), Tranmere, Kendal Utd
Jimmy Quinn NI Int.	Belfast	18.11.59	Hayes, Highworth T, Hereford Utd, Northwich V, Swindon, Peterborough, Reading, Bournemouth, West Ham, Bradford C, Leicester C, Swindon, Blackburn, Swindon, Oswestry T
Richard Mitchell	Stoke	14.09.73	Nuneaton B, Stafford R, Droylsden, Macclesfield, Southport, Port Vale
Steve Garvey	Stalybridge	22.11.73	Blackpool, Crewe

NUNEATON BOROUGH

For Nuneaton Borough the highlight of an average season came in the F.A. Cup with - in effect- four fine performances.

First, in the Fourth Qualifying Round Stevenage Borough visited Manor Park and must have been pleased with a 1-1 draw, but in the replay the Hertfordshire side was shocked by a 2-1 reverse, which meant a visit to Stoke City in the First Round Proper and a brave goalless draw followed by a further blank 90 minutes in the replay in Nuneaton before McGregor in injury time netted the superb giant-killing goal in front of 4,487 fans.

It was too good to last and the Second Round outing took the club to Bournemouth and a 3-0 defeat, which was followed early in January in the Trophy by a short trip to Bilston, where the team lost by the odd goal in five. A semi-final place in the Nationwide Conference Variety Trophy at Chester City and a narrow 2-1 defeat was scant consolation for this debacle.

Survival in the Conference was now the priority and a final run in of two wins and three draws from six matches brought an ultimate position of thirteenth - not bad but not good but comfortably clear of the relegation zone.

A 60-60 for and against final statistic would suggest that the attack needs little in the way of improvement as 5-0 and 5-1 victories over Hednesford Town and Morecambe will testify, but a 6-2 drubbing at Leigh RMI sends a message that the defence can be improved, although Stoke City might not agree.

The late season goal scoring efforts of on loan guest Barnes were more commendable and manager Steve Burr who will be looking to 2001-02 with quiet confidence if Marc McGregor regains full fitness.

W.M.

NUNEATON BOROUGH FC 2001-02

Back row, left to right: Roy Dunckley, Carl Bacon, Warren Peyton, Richard Lavery and Andy Thackeray
Middle Row: Andy Fern (Scout), Richie Norman, Shaun Wray, Barry Williams, Ryan Young, Chris Mackenzie, Simon Weaver, Adam Cooper, Michael Anderson, Paul Egan (Physio) and Rod Brown (Kit Manager).
Front Row: Jason Peake,Terry Angus, Steve Burr (Manager), Marc McGregor, Nicky Kennerdale, Jamie Williams and Richard Leadbeater. **Photo:** Nuneaton Telegraph

NUNEATON BOROUGH

GROUND DETAILS

Manor Park,
Beaumont Road,
Nuneaton,
Warks. CV11 5HD

Tel.: 02476 385738
Fax: 02476 342690

Simple Directions:
A444 to Nuneaton from M6 junction 3, 2nd exit at 1st round-about, 2nd exit at 2nd r'about, left at 3rd r'bout, 2nd right into Greenmoor Rd, turn right at the end, grd on left. Ground 1 mile from Nuneaton Trent Valley (BR)

Capacity: 6,500
Seated: 520
Terracing - **Covered:** 3,000
Uncovered: 3,500

SOCIAL FACILITIES: Clubhouse open every evening, weekend lunchtimes & matchdays.

CLUB SHOP: Sells souvenirs, programmes & replica kits
Contact Commercial department

MATCHDAY PROGRAMME

Pages: 48 **Price:** £1.50

Editorial Team:
Rod Grubb, John Moore, Andy Pace
Steve Packer, Martin Renshaw & Scott Renshaw

Other club publications: None

Local Press:
Nuneaton Telegraph & Weekly Tribune
Local Radio: Mercia Sound, BBC CWR

Formed: 1937

Nickname: The Boro

Club colours: Blue & white stripes,white shorts

Change colours: Orange shirts with black shorts

Reserve team's league: Central Conference

Midweek home matchday: Tuesday 7.45pm

Club Sponsors:
Website: www.nuneatonborough.co.uk

CLUB OFFICIALS

Chairman: Phil Clayton

Executive Directors:
Gordon Chislett, Phil Clayton, Graham Cooper, Howard Kerry, David Lee, Ralph Nollett, Dave Radburn, Roger Stanford, Trevor Wooley

Secretary: Paul Lewis
7 Garfitt Road, Kirby Muxloe,
Leicestershire
Tel: 0116 239 4981 (H) 07711 410642 (M)

Commercial Director: Phil Clayton
c/o the club

Press Officers: Phil Clayton
c/o the club

FOOTBALL MANAGEMENT TEAM

MANAGER: **STEVE BURR**
Date of Appointment: October 2000
Date of Birth: 12th January 1961
Place of Birth: Aberdeen

PREVIOUS CLUBS
As manager: None
As Asst. Man./Coach
Nuneaton Borough 1998
As player: Stafford R,Macclesfield, Hednesford T

HONOURS
As manager: None
As player: Conference, F.A. Trophy x 2
NPL Champions. F.A.XIs

1st Team Coach: Andy Thackeray
Physio: Julie Hayter
Reserve Team Manager: Ron Bradbury
Youth Team Manager: Mick Denis
Scouts: Andy Fern & Mark O'Kane

Season	League	Div.	Pos.	Home P	W	D	L	F	A	Away W	D	L	F	A	Pts	Manager
00-01	Conference	-	13	42	9	5	7	35	26	4	10	7	25	34	54	B Phillips/
99-00	Conference	-	15	42	7	6	8	28	25	5	9	7	21	28	51	Brendal Phillips
98-99	Southern	Premier	1	42	16	3	2	52	15	11	6	4	39	18	90	Brendan Phillips
97-98	Southern	Premier	12	42	12	3	6	39	22	5	3	13	29	39	57	Brendan Phillips
96-97	Southern	Premier	7	42	15	2	4	44	20	4	7	10	17	32	65	Brendan Phillips

Season	League	Div.	Pos.	P	W	D	L	F	A	Pts	Manager
95-96	Southern	Midland	1	42	30	5	7	82	35	95	Brendan Phillips
94-95	Southern	Midland	7	42	19	11	12	76	55	68	Elwyn Roberts
93-94	Southern	Premier	22	42	11	8	23	42	66	41	John Barton
92-93	Southern	Midland	1	42	29	5	8	102	45	92	George Rooney/John Barton
91-92	Southern	Midland	6	42	17	11	14	68	53	62	Les Green

HONOURS

Alliance Prem Lge R-up (2) 83-85
Southern Lg Premier Div. 98-99, R-up 66-67 74-75
League Cup Win 95-96
Midland Div 81-82 92-93, Champ 95-96
Lg Cup R-up 62-63, Merit Cup 92-93 (jt)
Birmingham Lg 55-56 (Nth Div 54-55)
Birmingham Comb. R-up 3
Birmingham Snr Cup 6, R-up 3

PREVIOUS

Leagues: Central Amateur 37-38; B'ham Comb 38-52; West Mids (B'ham) 52-58;Southern 58-79 81-82 88-99. GM Conference (Alliance Premier & Gola) 79-81 82-8

Names: None

Ground: None

Past Players who progressed to the Football League

A Morton (Fulham 70), R Edwards (Port Vale 72), K Stephens (Luton 78), T Peake (Lincoln C. 79), P Sugrue (Man City 80), M Shotton & T Smithers (Oxford U. 80), D Thomas (Wimbledon 81), P Richardson (Derby C. 84), P Culpin (Coventry 85), R Hill/T Morley/E McGoldrick/A Harris (Northampton 85/86), D Bullock (Huddersfield 93) M Christie (Derby Co. 98) A Ducros (Kidderminster Harriers) 2000

CLUB RECORDS

Attendance: 22,114 v Rotherham, FA Cup 3rd Rd 1967

Defeat: 1-8 (55-56 & 68-69)

Win: 11-1 (45-46 & 55-56)

Goalscorer: Paul Culpin 201 (Career)
55 (Season - 92/93)

Career Appearances: Alan Jones 545 (62-74)

Transfer Fee Paid: £35,000
for Marc McGregor from Forest Green R. 2000

Transfer Fee Received: £80,000
for Andy Ducros to Kidderminster H. 2000

BEST SEASON

FA Cup: Third Round replay 66-67
1st Rd 19 times

FA Trophy: Quarter final- 76-77(rep), 79-80, 86-87

League: Runners-up Conference 83-84, 84-85

LAST SEASON

F.A. Cup: Second Round
F.A. Trophy: Third Round
Conference: 13th
Top Goalscorer: Marc McGregor 16
Player of the Year: Chris McKenzie
Captain: Wayne Simpson

NUNEATON BOROUGH

Match Facts 2000-01

	Date	Comp.	Opponents	Gate	Score	Goalscorers
1	19/08	Conf	Doncaster Rovers	3648	1 - 1	Warrington 29[og]
2	22/08	Conf	BOSTON UNITED	2001	3 - 1	Charles 6, McGregor 47 51
3	26/08	Conf	TELFORD UNITED	1531	1 - 1	Angus 22
4	28/08	Conf	Morecambe	1485	2 - 4	Sykes 71, King 87
5	02/09	Conf	YEOVIL TOWN	1426	0 - 2	
6	05/09	Conf	Kingstonian	788	2 - 2	Francis 45, McGregor 61
7	09/09	Conf	Dagenham & Redbridge	1361	1 - 1	McGregor 55
8	12/09	Conf	HEREFORD UNITED	1362	1 - 2	McGregor 47
9	16/09	Conf	LEIGH RMI	1145	2 - 1	McGregor 51 81
10	23/09	Conf	Hayes	732	0 - 0	
11	26/09	Conf	Chester City	1708	0 - 4	
12	30/09	Conf	SOUTHPORT	1275	1 - 2	Francis 78
13	03/10	Conf	FOREST GREEN ROVERS	1172	2 - 0	Williams 49, Francis 85
14	06/10	Conf	Woking	1696	2 - 0	McGregor 83 89
15	14/10	Conf	Scarborough	1089	0 - 0	
16	21/10	Conf	STEVENAGE BOROUGH	1402	0 - 3	
17	04/11	Conf	Dover Athletic	815	1 - 2	McGregor 30
18	11/11	Conf	HEDNESFORD TOWN	1223	5 - 1	McGregor 39 65[p], Francis 80 87, Sykes 82
19	02/12	Conf	Kettering Town	1791	2 - 1	Norman 3[og], King 32
20	16/12	Conf	Boston United	1573	1 - 4	King 17[p]
21	26/12	Conf	RUSHDEN & DIAMONDS	2614	1 - 1	Charles 88
22	01/01	Conf	Rushden & Diamonds	4080	1 - 2	Sykes 50
23	20/01	Conf	Telford United	1382	1 - 2	Charles 34
24	27/01	Conf	WOKING	1357	1 - 1	B Williams 5
25	03/02	Conf	DONCASTER ROVERS	1377	1 - 0	King 63
26	10/02	Conf	DAGENHAM & REDBRIDGE	1302	2 - 0	Charles 4, McGregor 28
27	17/02	Conf	Hereford United	1743	1 - 1	B Williams 38
28	24/02	Conf	HAYES	1510	1 - 1	Peake 61
29	03/03	Conf	Leigh RMI	501	2 - 6	J Williams 71 90
30	13/03	Conf	Yeovil Town	2774	0 - 0	
31	17/03	Conf	Southport	1192	2 - 1	Angus 82, Thackeray 84
32	23/03	Conf	CHESTER CITY	1363	1 - 2	Wray 4
33	31/03	Conf	KINGSTONIAN	1423	2 - 1	Barnes 24 45
34	07/04	Conf	Stevenage Borough	1471	1 - 1	Barnes 58
35	12/04	Conf	MORECAMBE	1031	5 - 1	Wray 4, Barnes 22 85, Peake 31, Thackeray 74
36	14/04	Conf	SCARBOROUGH	1247	1 - 2	Angus 48
37	16/04	Conf	Hednesford Town	1105	3 - 0	Barnes 36 79, Charles 85
38	21/04	Conf	DOVER ATHLETIC	1414	1 - 2	Barnes 1
39	24/04	Conf	NORTHWICH VICTORIA	802	3 - 1	Angus 15, Peake 25, Barnes 90
40	28/04	Conf	KETTERING TOWN	1865	1 - 1	Barnes 56
41	01/05	Conf	Forest Green Rovers	781	0 - 0	
42	05/05	Conf	Northwich Victoria	902	2 - 2	Wray 6, Peake 80

OTHER COMPETITIONS

Date	Comp.	Opponents	Gate	Score	Goalscorers
20/09	Variety CT 1	Boston United	527	5 - 1	McGregor 17[p] 41, Francis 47 88, Sykes 90
10/10	Variety CT 2	SCARBOROUGH	614	2 - 0	Sykes 35 76
28/10	FA Cup Q4	STEVENAGE BOROUGH	1554	1 - 1	Francis 73
31/10	FA Cup Q4 R	Stevenage Borough	1219	2 - 1	Smith 58[og], Sykes 79
14/11	Birm. SC 2	SUTTON COLDFIELD TOWN	291	2 - 1	Mitchell 42 82
18/11	FA Cup 1	Stoke City	8437	0 - 0	
21/11	FA Cup 1 rep	STOKE CITY	4477	1 - 0	McGregor 90
09/12	FA Cup 2	AFC Bournemouth	5835	0 - 3	
13/01	FA Trophy 3	Bilston Town	806	2 - 3	B Williams 15, Charles 27
30/01	Birm. SC 3	GORNAL ATHLETIC	235	6 - 1	Peake, Wray, Charles, King, Williams, A N Other
20/02	Birm. SC QF	BIRMINGHAM CITY	468	2 - 4	Peake 39, Williams 60
03/04	Variety CT QF	MORECAMBE	602	2 - 0	Weaver 58, Wray 72
03/05	Variety CT SF	Chester City	602	1 - 2	Angus 45

1	2	3	4	5	6	7	8	9	10	11	Substitutes Used
Young	Thackeray	Love	Crowley	Gittens	Angus	Taylor	Charles	McGregor	King	Williams	Brennan(10)
Young	Angus	Love	Simpson	Williams	Crowley	Taylor	Brennan	Thackeray	Charles	McGregor	Mitchell (10)
Young	Crowley	Gittens	Angus	Thackeray	Taylor	Brennan	Williams	Love	Charles	McGregor	Sykes (8)
Young	Angus	Love	Williams	Gittens	Thackeray	Crowley	Brennan	Taylor	Charles	McGregor	King (4), Simpson (6), Sykes(8)
Young	Simpson	Gittens	Angus	Williams	Taylor	Sykes	Love	Crowley	Charles	McGregor	Francis (3), Mitchell (10), Brennan (11)
Young	Angus	Love	Simpson	Weaver	Thackeray	Taylor	Crowley	Charles	McGregor	Francis	Williams (9), Brennan (10)
McKenzie	Thackeray	Simpson	Weaver	Angus	Love	Taylor	Crowley	Charles	McGregor	Francis	Sykes (2), Gittens (4), Brennan (7)
McKenzie	Williams	Simpson	Weaver	Angus	Love	Crowley	Brennan	Charles	McGregor	Francis	White (2), Kotylo(5), Sykes (9)
McKenzie	Simpson	Gittens	Angus	Love	Crowley	Taylor	Sykes	Charles	McGregor	Brennan	Kotylo (6), Francis (9)
Young	Simpson	Love	Taylor	Gittens	Crowley	Brennan	Charles	McGregor	Kotylo	Sykes	Williams (4), Francis (9)
McKenzie	Simpson	Love	Gittens	Taylor	Crowley	Brennan	Kotylo	McGregor	Charles	Sykes	Francis (5), Angus (6) Williams (7)
McKenzie	Williams	Crowley	Gittens	Angus	Love	Brennan	Taylor	Kotylo	Charles	McGregor	Sykes (7), Simpson (9), Francis (10)
McKenzie	Williams	Love	Simpson	Weaver	Angus	Thackeray	Taylor	Crowley	McGregor	Francis	Sykes (8), Charles (10)
McKenzie	Thackeray	Simpson	Weaver	Angus	Love	Crowley	Taylor	McGregor	Williams	Francis	King(2), Gittens (4), Charles (11)
McKenzie	Bacon	Love	Simpson	Gittens	Angus	Sykes	Taylor	McGregor	Williams	Francis	Charles (11)
McKenzie	Simpson	Gittens	Angus	Bacon	Williams	Taylor	Sykes	Love	McGregor	Charles	Wray(5), Francis (7), Crowley(8)
McKenzie	Bacon	Angus	Gittens	Wray	Love	Crowley	King	Charles	Francis	McGregor	B Williams (7), J Williams (10), Weaver (3)
McKenzie	Bacon	Weaver	Angus	Love	Wray	Crowley	King	Charles	McGregor	Francis	Sykes (2), Simpson (7)
McKenzie	Sykes	Weaver	Angus	Love	Wray	Crowley	Taylor	King	McGregor	Francis	Thackeray (3), J Williams (8), B Williams (11)
McKenzie	Crowley	Weaver	Angus	Sykes	Wray	B Williams	King	Love	Mitchell	Francis	J Williams (8), Bacon (5), Charles (10)
McKenzie	Weaver	Angus	Love	J Williams	Taylor	Wray	King	Peake	Charles	Francis	Mitchell (2), Sykes (5), B Williams (8)
McKenziE	Angus	Love	J Williams	Weaver	Taylor	Crowley	Peake	Wray	Charles	Sykes	Simpson (3), Young (6), Francis (7)
Young	Bacon	Love	Simpson	B Williams	Angus	J Williams	Peake	King	McGregor	Charles	Crowley (2), Sykes (7)
McKenzie	Bacon	Angus	Simpson	Love	B Williams	King	Peake	J Williams	Charles	McGregor	Sykes (9), Kennerdale (11)
McKenzie	Bacon	Simpson	Weaver	Love	B Williams	King	Peake	J Williams	Charles	McGregor	Sykes(9), Kennerdale (11)
McKenzie	Bacon	Love	Simpson	Weaver	B Williams	King	Peake	Charles	McGregor	J Williams	Sykes (7), Crowley (6)
McKenzie	Bacon	Weaver	Simpson	Love	King	Peake	B Williams	J Williams	McGregor	Charles	Crowley (11)
McKenzie	Bacon	Love	Simpson	Weaver	King	B Williams	Peake	J Williams	McGregor	Charles	Sykes (10), Kennerdale (11)
McKenzie	Bacon	Love	Simpson	B Williams	Angus	King	Sykes	Francis	Peake	J Williams	Crowley (8), White (3), Thackeray (2)
McKenzie	J Williams	Simpson	Weaver	Angus	B Williams	Thackeray	Peake	Crowley	Charles	Francis	King (11)
McKenzie	Thackeray	Simpson	Weaver	Angus	Peake	Crowley	B Williams	J Williams	Francis	Wray	Harvey (8), Sykes (9), King (10)
McKenzie	B Williams	Angus	Simpson	Weaver	Love	Thackeray	Peake	Crowley	Wray	Charles	J Williams (6), King (2), Sykes (10)
McKenzie	Thackeray	Angus	Simpson	King	Weaver	Crowley	Barnes	Wray	Peake	J Williams	B Williams (5), Charles (9), Love (11)
McKenzie	Thackeray	Angus	Simpson	Crowley	Weaver	Wray	Charles	Barnes	Peake	J Williams	Love (8)
McKenzie	Weaver	Angus	Simpson	J Williams	Wray	Peake	Crowley	Thackeray	Charles	Barnes	
McKenzie	Thackeray	Angus	Simpson	Weaver	Wray	Crowley	Peake	J Williams	Barnes	Charles	Hanney (5), Love (3), King (11)
McKenzie	Weaver	Angus	Simpson	J Williams	Crowley	Wray	Peake	Thackeray	Charles	Barnes	Love (5), Francis (2)
McKenzie	Thackeray	Weaver	Angus	Love	Wray	Crowler	Peake	Williams	Barnes	Charles	Hanney (7), King (9), Francis (11)
McKenzie	Angus	Simpson	Weaver	Love	Thackeray	Crowley	Peake	Wray	Barnes	Charles	King (9)
McKenzie	Weaver	Angus	Simpson	Love	Wray	Peake	Crowley	Thackeray	Barnes	Charles	
Young	J Williams	Prindiville	Love	Bacon	Weaver	Thackeray	Taylor	King	Charles	Francis	Simpson (8), Peake (10)
McKenzie	J Williams	Angus	Love	Simpson	Weaver	Thackeray	Peake	Wray	Charles	Barnes	Francis (10), White (2)

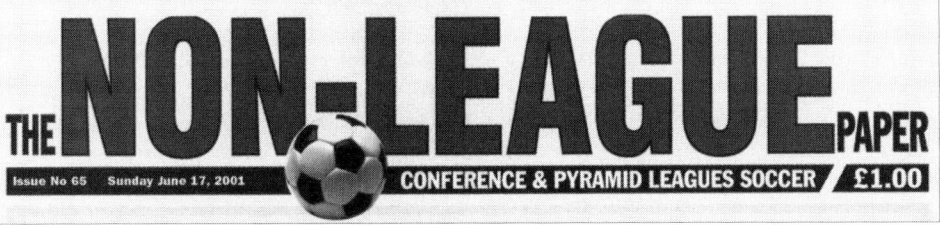

PLAYING SQUAD

NUNEATON BOROUGH

(Bold print indicates an England Semi-Professional International)

Player *Honours*	*Birthplace*	*D.O.B.*	*Previous Clubs*
GOALKEEPERS			
Chris Mackenzie	Northampton	14.05.72	Corby T, Hereford U, Leyton O
Ryan Young	Birmingham		Plymouth, Chasetown
DEFENDERS			
Terry Angus DMP	Coventry	14.01.66	VS Rugby, Northampton, Fulham, Slough T
Mickey Love	Stockport	27.11.73	Bedworth U, Hinckley T, Hinckley Ath., Wigan, Wycombe, Hinckley Ath., Tamworth,Northampton, Stevenage B
Barry Williams ESP, DMP	Birmingham	06.05.73	Alvechurch, Ely C, Redditch U
Andy Thackeray Rochdale,	Huddersfield	13.02.68	Manchester C, Huddersfield, Newport Co., Wrexham, Halifax T.
Simon Weaver	Doncaster	20.12.77	Sheffield Wed., Ilkeston T
MIDFIELD			
Alex Sykes British Univ.	Newcastle-u-Lyme	02.04.74	Westfields, Mansfield, Cheltenham, Endsleigh, Forest Green R
Dave Crowley DMP	Coventry	07.09.68	Coventry, Bedworth U, Stafford R
Jamie Williams	Coventry		Hinckley Utd, Coventry
Jason Peake ES, EY	Leicester	29.09.71	Plymouth, Rochdale, Bury, Brighton, Rochdale, Halifax
Richard Lavery	Coventry	28.05.77	Hinckley Utd, Tamworth, Atherstone Utd, Sutton Coldfield T, Massey Ferguson, Stratford T, Nuneaton B, Hinckley Ath., Bedworth Utd
FORWARDS			
Lee Charles ESP	Hillingdon	20.08.71	Chertsey T, QPR, Hayes
Marc McGregor ESP	Southend	30.04.78	Oxford U, Endsleigh, Forest Green R, £35,000 to Nuneaton B
Nick Kennerdale	Nottingham		Eastwood T, Shepshed Dynamo, Leicester Utd, Armitage, Doncaster R
Warren Peyton			Bury, Rochdale

SCARBOROUGH

Scarborough, like many other teams, now know - if they did not already realise the fact - that it is easier to be demoted to the Conference than to rise out of it and by any standards 2000-01 was a disappointing season, since tenth place would certainly not satisfy supporters of such an ambitious club.

The chance of higher honours became unlikely after the first six matches produced only a win and a draw and four consecutive successes in September still failed to make any impression on the front runners.

Thereafter, it was a `stop-go' situation with enough wins to make disaster improbable, although a final total of sixteen draws would indicate a need to score that extra goal, which could make a big difference between success and mediocrity. A 56-54 goals situation, in fact, would suggest that an improvement in attack could pay big dividends, although the likes of Ellender, Pounder, Williams and Diallo had their moments.

The knock-out challenges lasted for a total of three matches starting with defeat at home to RMI in the F.A. Cup Fourth Qualifying Round by a thrilling 4-3 scoreline, while in the F.A. Trophy a brilliant Round Three victory at Runcorn by four clear goals was followed by the sight of visiting Burton Albion scoring the only goal of the game in Round Four.

The team is being run by Manager Neil Thompson and no-one will be envious of the task he faces, as funds are low and the squad needs strengthening.

W.M.

SCARBOROUGH FC 2001-02

Back Row L-R: Mitch Cook, Danny Brunton, John Keegan, Paul Ellender (no longer at the Club), Romain Faure, Paul Newton, Andy Woods, Darryn Stamp, Shaun Rennison, Paul Atkinson, David Pounder, Mick Tarmey
Front Row: Steve Brodie, Adam Jewell, Gareth Stoker, Ray McHale, Neil Thompson, Ian Kerr, Jamie Burt, Denny Ingram, Jason Blunt

SCARBOROUGH

Founded:	1879
Nickname:	The Seadogs
Club Sponsors:	OCM Ltd
Colours	Red shirts, red shorts, red socks
Change colours:	White shirts, black shorts, white socks
Midweek Matchday:	Tuesday
Youth League	Youth Aliance

GROUND DETAILS

McCain Stadium
Seamer Road
Scarborough
N. Yorkshire YO12 4HF

TELEPHONE
Tel: 01723 375094
Fax: 01723 366211
Newsline: 0891 121650

SIMPLE DIRECTIONS The ground is situated on the main Scarborough to York road (A64), about half a mile beyond B&Q on the left as you go into Scarborough. Scarborough central (BR) about 2 miles. Car Parking: Ample in streets around the ground.

CAPACITY	5,900
SEATING	3,500
COVERED TERRACING	1,000

CLUB SHOP: Monday to Friday 09.00-17.00 and matchdays

SOCIAL FACILITIES: Clubhouse - open matchdays only

MATCHDAY PROGRAMME

Pages: 44 Price: £1.50
Editor: James Hunter

Other club publications: None

Local Press:
Scarborough Evening News; The Mercury

Local Radio: Radio York; Y.C.R. Radio

CLUB OFFICIALS

Owner Darrell Littlewood & Michael Taylor

Chairman Darrell Littlewood

President John R Birley

Vice Chairman Michael Taylor

Chief Executive Ian Davison

Directors Darrell Littlewood, Michael Taylor, Andy Borrie, Patrick Waterhouse, Ian Davison.

Secretary Jade Sprintall

Admin. Manager Karola Powell

FOOTBALL MANAGEMENT TEAM

MANAGER: NEIL THOMPSON

Date of Appointment	August 2000
Date of Birth	2nd October 1963
Place of Birth	Beverley

PREVIOUS CLUBS

As manager	York City
As coach	York City
As player	Nottm. Forest , Hull City, Scarborough, Ipswich Town Barnsley, Oldham (Loan), York City

Assistant Manager	Ray McHale
Physiotherapist	Mick Tarmey
Community Officer	Mitch Cook
Youth Team Coach	Ian Kerr
Groundsman	Paul Barnett

Season	League	Div.	Pos.	Home P	W	D	L	F	A	Away W	D	L	F	A	Pts	Manager
00-01	Conference	-	10	42	7	9	5	29	25	7	7	7	27	29	58	C. Addison/ Neil Thompson
99-00	Conference	-	4	42	10	6	5	36	14	9	6	6	24	21	69	Colin Addison
98-99	F. League	3	24	46	8	3	12	30	39	6	3	14	20	38	48	Mike Wadsworth

Season	League	Div.	Pos.	P	W	D	L	F	A	Pts	Manager
97-98	F. League	3	6	46	19	15	12	67	58	72	Mike Wadsworth
96-97	F. League	3	12	46	16	15	15	65	68	63	Mike Wadsworth
95-96	F. League	3	23	46	8	16	22	39	69	40	Ray McHale
94-95	F. League	3	21	42	8	10	24	49	70	34	Philip Chambers
93-94	F. League	3	14	42	15	8	19	55	61	53	Philip Chambers
92-93	F. League	3	13	42	15	9	18	66	71	54	Ray McHale
91-92	F. League	4	12	42	15	12	15	64	68	57	Ray McHale

HONOURS

FA Trophy 72-73 75-76 76-77
Vauxhall Conference 86-87
Bob Lord Trophy 83-84
NPL Lge Cup 76-77
North Eastern Cos Lge 62-63, Lge Cup 62-63
Midland Lge 29-30
Scarborough & Dist. Lge 45-46
E. Riding Cup x 8; N. Riding Sen. Cup x 17

PREVIOUS

Leagues: Northern 1898-1910 14-26
Yorkshire Combination 10-14; Yorkshire 26-27;
Midland 27-40 46-60 63-68
Scarborough & Dist. 45-46
Northern Counties 60-62; North Eastern 62-63;
Northern Premier 68-79
Alliance Premier 79-87 99-
Football League 87-99

Name: None

Past Players who progressed to the Football League

Not yet applicable

CLUB RECORDS

Attendance: 11,162
v Luton Town, FAC 3rd Rd, 1938

Victory: 6-0 v Rhyl Athletic, FA Cup 29.11.30

Defeat: 0-8 v Mansfield Town (H), FA Cup 22.11.52

Career Goalscorer: Unknown

Career Appearances: 196 Steve Richards 87-91

Transfer Fee Paid: £100,000
for Martin Russell to Leicester C., Feb. 87

Transfer Fee Received: £350,000
for Craig Short from Notts Co. (£150K 7/89 + £250K9/92)

BEST SEASON

FA Cup: 3rd Round 30-31 37-38 75-76 77-78

FA Trophy: Winners 72-73 75-76 76-77

Football League: 5th in Division 4, 88-89

League Cup: 4th Round 92-93

LAST SEASON

F.A. Cup: Fourth Qualifying Round
F.A. Trophy: Fourth Round
Conference: 10th
Top Goalscorer: Steve Brodie
Player of the Year: Paul Ellender
Captain: Denny Ingram
Highest League Attendance: 2,381

SCARBOROUGH

Match Facts 2000-01

	Date	Comp.	Opponents	Gate	Score	Goalscorers
1	19/08	Conf	Stevenage Borough	2032	1 - 1	Brodie 80
2	22/08	Conf	MORECAMBE	1536	2 - 2	Ellender 27, Betts 75
3	26/08	Conf	KINGSTONIAN	1275	1 - 0	Williams 12
4	28/08	Conf	Leigh RMI	836	0 - 2	
5	02/09	Conf	DAGENHAM & REDBRIDGE	1202	0 - 1	
6	05/09	Conf	Southport	1269	1 - 3	Tate 2
7	09/09	Conf	Hayes	562	1 - 0	Brodie 8
8	12/09	Conf	RUSHDEN & DIAMONDS	1107	0 - 3	
9	16/09	Conf	NORTHWICH VICTORIA	845	4 - 0	Pounder 12 57, Brodie 24 71
10	23/09	Conf	Dover Athletic	933	2 - 0	Williams 49 80
11	27/09	Conf	Forest Green Rovers	542	3 - 2	Brodie 16, Betts 52, Williams 64
12	30/09	Conf	WOKING	1156	3 - 2	Williams 3, Rennison 23, West 29[og]
13	03/10	Conf	CHESTER CITY	1193	0 - 2	
14	06/10	Conf	Telford United	395	0 - 1	(at Worcester City)
15	14/10	Conf	NUNEATON BOROUGH	1089	0 - 0	
16	21/10	Conf	Kettering Town	1159	1 - 1	Brodie 28
17	04/11	Conf	HEREFORD UNITED	891	2 - 4	Diallo 18, Pounder 44
18	11/11	Conf	Boston United	1752	2 - 2	Diallo 53, Brodie 59
19	18/11	Conf	STEVENAGE BOROUGH	789	2 - 2	Pounder 2, Betts 87[p]
20	25/11	Conf	YEOVIL TOWN	972	2 - 2	Diallo 49, Betts 87[p]
21	02/12	Conf	Hednesford Town	754	1 - 0	Ellender 35
22	16/12	Conf	Morecambe	2023	4 - 4	Brodie 22 60 85, Diallo 52
23	26/12	Conf	DONCASTER ROVERS	2381	3 - 1	Thompson 28, Diallo 43, Ingram 45
24	01/01	Conf	Doncaster Rovers	3024	2 - 0	Ellender 44, Pounder 78
25	06/01	Conf	LEIGH RMI	1087	1 - 1	Rennison 30
26	27/01	Conf	SOUTHPORT	1125	1 - 1	Diallo 42
27	10/02	Conf	HAYES	814	2 - 0	Stoker 30, Pounder 83
28	17/02	Conf	Rushden & Diamonds	3553	0 - 1	
29	24/02	Conf	DOVER ATHLETIC	1082	2 - 0	Ellender 13, Pounder 16
30	03/03	Conf	Northwich Victoria	942	0 - 3	
31	06/03	Conf	Dagenham & Redbridge	877	0 - 1	
32	17/03	Conf	Woking	1625	1 - 1	Diallo 33
33	25/03	Conf	FOREST GREEN ROVERS	838	1 - 0	Diallo 78
34	03/04	Conf	Kingstonian	694	2 - 2	Ellender 3, Jordan 35
35	07/04	Conf	KETTERING TOWN	1082	0 - 1	
36	10/04	Conf	TELFORD UNITED	723	1 - 1	Pounder 77
37	14/04	Conf	Nuneaton Borough	1247	2 - 1	Williams 51 56
38	16/04	Conf	BOSTON UNITED	1279	2 - 2	Burt 11, Pounder 18
39	21/04	Conf	Hereford United	1304	1 - 1	Ellender 24
40	28/04	Conf	HEDNESFORD TOWN	943	0 - 0	
41	01/05	Conf	Chester City	805	2 - 3	Jordan 41, Burt 51
42	05/05	Conf	Yeovil Town	2823	1 - 0	Thompson 6[p]

OTHER COMPETITIONS

Date	Comp.	Opponents	Gate	Score	Goalscorers
21/07	N Riding SF	MIDDLESBROUGH	1200	1 - 1	Williams 20 (5-4p)
09/08	N Riding F	YORK CITY	n/k	0 - 1	
10/10	Variety CT 2	Nuneaton Borough	614	0 - 2	
28/10	FA Cup Q4	LEIGH RMI	858	3 - 4	Diallo 52, Betts 73[p], Rennison 80
06/12	LDV Vans 1N	Stoke City	2336	1 - 3	Brunton 89
13/01	FA Trophy 3	Runcorn	420	4 - 0	Stoker 53, Pounder 70, Ingram 74, Russell 77
03/02	FA Trophy 4	BURTON ALBION	1462	0 - 1	

1	2	3	4	5	6	7	8	9	10	11	Substitutes Used
Woods	Russell	Betts	Ingram	Ellender	Rennison	Williams	Stoker	Jones	Brodie	Pounder	Windass (2)
Woods	Rennison	Ingram	Ellender	Betts	Stoker	Jones	Russell	Brodie	Pounder	Williams	S Morris (5)
Woods	Russell	Betts	Ingram	Ellender	Rennison	Williams	Stoker	Jones	Brodie	Pounder	Tate (11)
Woods	Rennison	Betts	Ingram	Ellender	Russell	Stoker	Jones	Williams	Tate	Brodie	S Morris (6), Pounder (9)
Woods	Ingram	Betts	Thompson	Ellender	Rennison	Williams	Stoker	Jones	Brodie	Pounder	Tate (3), Russell (4)
Woods	Betts	Ingram	Ellender	Brunton	Jones	Stoker	Williams	Pounder	Tate	Brodie	S Morris (9)
Woods	Russell	Ingram	Ellender	Brunton	Jones	Williams	Stoker	Betts	Tate	Brodie	
Woods	Ellender	Brunton	Ingram	Betts	Jones	Stoker	Russell	Tate	Brodie	Williams	Rennison (6), Pounder (9)
Woods	Russell	Brunton	Ingram	Ellender	Faure	Williams	Betts	Tate	Brodie	Pounder	Stoker (9)
Woods	Faure	Ingram	Ellender	Russell	Betts	Williams	Jones	Brunton	Pounder	Brodie	Rennison (5), Morris (7), Gildea (10)
Woods	Ellender	Brunton	Ingram	Betts	Faure	Russell	Jones	Williams	Brodie	Pounder	Stoker (11)
Woods	Russell	Brunton	Ingram	Ellender	Jones	Williams	Betts	Rennison	Brodie	Pounder	Stoker (11)
Woods	Betts	Brunton	Ingram	Ellender	Rennison	Russell	Savic	Jones	Brodie	Williams	Pounder (10), Stoker (2)
Woods	Russell	Brunton	Ingram	Ellender	Jones	Williams	Betts	Savic	Tate	Pounder	Stoker (8), Diallo (9)
Woods	Russell	Shuttleworth	Ingram	Rennison	Thompson	Betts	Stoker	Tate	Diallo	Jones	Morris (10)
Woods	Ellender	Thompson	Rennison	Russell	Ingram	Betts	Shuttleworth	Tate	Williams	Brodie	Jones (6), Stoker (7), Pounder (9)
Woods	Betts	Brunton	Ingram	Ellender	Faure	Jones	Stoker	Diallo	Brodie	Pounder	Gildea (3), Williams (7)
Woods	Betts	Ellender	Rennison	Thompson	Williams	Faure	Stoker	Pounder	Diallo	Brodie	
Woods	Betts	Thompson	Rennison	Ellender	Faure	Williams	Stoker	Diallo	Brodie	Pounder	Windross (4)
Priestley	Betts	Thompson	Rennison	Ellender	Ingram	Williams	Stoker	Diallo	Brodie	Pounder	Toone (7)
Priestley	Betts	Rennison	Ellender	Thompson	Williams	Ingram	Stoker	Pounder	Brodie	Diallo	Faure (7)
Priestley	Russell	Thompson	Rennison	Ellender	Pounder	Ingram	Williams	Stoker	Diallo	Brodie	Lyth (10)
Priestley	Brunton	Thompson	Ellender	Rennison	Ingram	Russell	Diallo	Williams	Brodie	Pounder	
Priestley	Ingram	Thompson	Brunton	Ellender	Russell	Stoker	Williams	Windross	Brodie	Pounder	S Morris (9)
Priestley	Thompson	Brunton	Rennison	Ellender	Ingram	Williams	Stoker	Diallo	Brodie	Pounder	Windross (9), Faure (2), Morris (10)
Woods	Russell	Brunton	Rennison	Ellender	Thompson	Williams	Stoker	Diallo	Brodie	Pounder	Morris (2), Faure (6), Atkinson (10)
Woods	Atkinson	Brunton	Rennison	Lyth	Ingram	Williams	Stoker	Robinson	Faure	Pounder	Dawson (2), Di Lella (10), Burt (11)
Woods	Atkinson	Ingram	Lyth	Rennison	Brunton	Williams	Stoker	Di Lella	Pounder	Robinson	Morris (9), Burt (11)
Woods	Atkinson	Brunton	Rennison	Ellender	Lyth	Williams	Stoker	Robinson	Burt	Pounder	Faure (7)
Woods	Atkinson	Rennison	Ellender	Lyth	Brunton	Faure	Stoker	Di Lella	Robinson	Pounder	Brodie (6), S Morris (10)
Woods	P Atkinson	Brunton	Rennison	Ellender	Thompson	Stoker	Di Lella	S Morris	Brodie	Pounder	Dawson (6), Faure (8), Robinson (10)
Woods	Atkinson	Brunton	Rennison	Ellender	Lyth	Blunt	Stoker	Diallo	Brodie	Burt	D Pounder (10)
Woods	Atkinson	Brunton	Rennison	Ellender	Faure	Blunt	Stoker	Burt	Diallo	Pounder	Jordan (8)
Woods	Brunton	Rennison	P Atkinson	Ellender	Thompson	Blunt	Stoker	Jordan	Diallo	Stamp	Piercewright (10), Burt (11)
Woods	Dawson	Brunton	Rennison	Ellender	Thompson	Blunt	Stoker	Diallo	Burt	Jordan	Pounder (3), Piercewright (5)
Woods	Atkinson	Brunton	Rennison	Ellender	Faure	Blunt	Jordan	Burt	Diallo	Pounder	Stoker (8), Williams (9), Morris (10)
Woods	Atkinson	Brunton	Ellender	Rennison	Faure	Blunt	Stoker	Burt	Williams	Pounder	
Woods	Atkinson	Brunton	Rennison	Ellender	Faure	Blunt	Stoker	Burt	Williams	Pounder	Piercewright (6), Jordan (9)
Woods	Atkinson	Reed	Thompson	Ellender	Brunton	Stoker	Blunt	Pounder	Williams	Burt	Jordan (2), Diallo (11)
Woods	P Atkinson	Brunton	Rennison	Reed	Thompson	Jordan	Stoker	Burt	Williams	Pounder	Dawson (5), Diallo (8), Brodie (9)
Woods	Atkinson	Brunton	Rennison	Keegan	Piercewright	Jordan	Blunt	Pounder	Brodie	Williams	Dawson (2), Diallo (10), Burt (11)
Woods	Atkinson	Rennison	Thompson	Keegan	Brunton	Blunt	Jewell	Burt	Pounder	Brodie	Dawson (8), Diallo (9), Windross (11)

PLAYING SQUAD

SCARBOROUGH

Bold print denotes England semi-professional international.

Player *Honours*	*Birthplace*	*D.O.B.*	*Previous Clubs*
GOALKEEPERS			
Andy Woods	Colchester	15.01.76	Halifax, Doncaster R
Paul Newton	York		From Trainee
DEFENDERS			
Lee Sinnott EY, Eu-21	Pelsall	12.07.65	Walsall, Watford, Bradford, Crystal P, Huddersfield, Oldham
Paul Ellender	Yorkshire	21.10.74	Scunthorpe, Gainsborough T, Altrincham, £50,000 Scarborough
Denny Ingram	Sunderland	27.06.76	Hartlepool
Neil Thompson GMVC	Beverley	02.10.63	Nottingham F, Hull, Scarborough, Ipswich, Barnsley, York
Shaun Rennison	Northallerton	23.11.80	From Trainee
Andy Dawson	York	08.12.79	Carlisle, York
Barry Shuttleworth	Accrington	09.07.77	Harrogate T, Scarborough, Blackpool, Rotherham, Bury
Martin Reed	Scarborough	10.01.78	York
Paul Atkinson	York		From Trainee
MIDFIELD			
Gareth Stoker	Bishop Auckland	22.02.73	Leeds, Hull, Hereford U, Cardiff, Rochdale
Steve Brodie	Sunderland	14.01.73	Sunderland
Jason Blunt	Penzance	16.08.77	Blackpool, Leeds
Scott Jordan	Newcastle	19.07.75	York
FORWARDS			
Stewart Morris	Newcastle	21.09.80	From Trainee
Cherif Diallo	Senegal		Brighton, Draguignan (France)
Romain Faure	France		AS Cannes (France)
Darryn Stamp	Beverley	21.09.78	Scunthorpe
Jamie Burt	Newcastle		Bridlington T, FC Aberdeen, Whitby T, Carlisle, Newcastle

SOUTHPORT

Fourth place in the Conference, albeit a few points short of a challenge to the teams above them, would suggest that Southport had a good season and this is undoubtedly the case, although the fans might well feel that they are a `nearly' team which needs that vital something extra to lift them back to where they belong - the Nationwide League.

So what is missing? A goals difference of 58-46 would suggest that another ten or twelve goals would make a big difference, although the regular scoring contributions of the likes of Marsh, Guyett, Parke and Arnold were praiseworthy. Of these only Parke remains.

After a slowish start Southport were always doing enough to ensure a high place in the table with October and January the best months and December virtually washed out by bad weather.

The knock-out efforts were adequate with F.A. Cup action bringing a Fourth Qualifying Cup elimination of Doncaster Rovers (2-2 away and 1-0 in the home replay). A visit to Hayes in Round One Proper brought a 2-1 success, but Kingstonian scored the odd goal in three in Round Two at Haig Avenue to end the challenge.

In the F.A. Trophy results in Round Three and Four were encouraging - a 3-0 home success over Hednesford Town and superb single goal triumph at holders Kingstonian. Then a journey to Weymouth was also successful 2-1, but Chester City away in the last eight was just too much - a single goal defeat.

Having lost Mark Wright as Manager the club immediately signed up Stalybridge Celtic's successful leader, Phil Wilson, but he will need time to settle in.

W.M.

SOUTHPORT 2001-02

SOUTHPORT

GROUND DETAILS

Haig Avenue,
Southport,
Merseyside. PR8 6JZ

TELEPHONE: Ground: 01704 533422
Ticket Office: 01704 533422
Fax: 01704 533422

SIMPLE DIRECTIONS:
From M6 - M58 through Ormskirk (A570) to Southport.
Straight on at Tesco/McDonalds roundabout.
Right at the mini roundabout and the ground is on the right

CAPACITY:	6,008
SEATED:	1,660
COVERED TERRACING:	1,100

SOCIAL FACILITIES:
Clubhouse open 6.00-11.00 every night and match days.
Tel: 01704 530182

CLUB SHOP: New shop opened 1999.
Scarves, replica kits and large range of souvenirs for sale.
Contact D Hitchcock, c/o Southport F.C or
e-mail: derek@hitchcock98.freeserve.co.uk

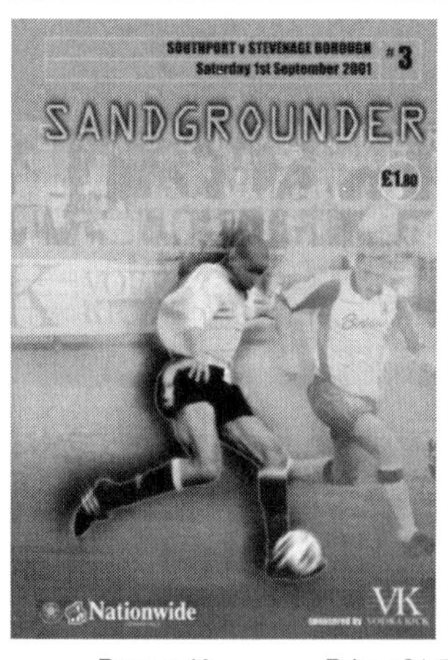

MATCHDAY PROGRAMME

Pages: 40 Price: £1.50

Editor: Derek Hitchcock (07976 555782)

Other club publications: None

Local Press: Southport Visiter; The Champion
Local Radio: Dune F.M.; Radio Merseyside; Red Rose, Radio City; Radio Lancashire

Founded:	1881
Nickname:	The Sandgrounders
Club Sponsors:	Apollo Leisure
Club colours:	Old Gold & black
Change colours:	tbc
Midweek home matchday:	Tuesday
Reserves' League:	Lancashire League

CLUB OFFICIALS

President Jack Carr

Chairman Charles Clapham
Directors C Clapham, B J Hedley, A Pope, P Abrams, T Medcroft, J Carr, S Porter, S Shrouder.

Football Secretary Ken Hilton
34 Mill Lane, Burscough, Ormskirk, Lancs. L40 5TS
Tel: 01704 894504 (H) 01704 840775 (B)

Sales & Marketing Manager Derek Hitchcock
Tel: 07976 555782
e-mail: derek@hitchcock98.freeserve.co.uk
Press Officer Derek Hitchcock

FOOTBALL MANAGEMENT TEAM

MANAGER: PHIL WILSON
Date of Appointment: June 2001
Date of Birth: 6th December 1950
Place of Birth: Wallasey

PREVIOUS CLUBS
As manager: Caernarfon T., Stalybridge Celtic, Leek T. Northwich Vics., Stalybridge C.
As player: New Brighton, Runcorn, Mossley, Altrincham, Northwich Victoria.

HONOURS
As manager: N.P.L. Championship 91-92, 00-01
As player: Conference Championship, N.P.L. Championship x 2; F.A. Trophy Winner, R-up x 2

* * *

Assistant Manager:	Ted McMinn
Reserve Team Coach:	Mike Vaughan
Physiotherapist:	Chris Goodson
Youth development:	tbc

Season	League	Div.	Pos.	Home P	W	D	L	F	A	Away W	D	L	F	A	Pts	Manager
00-01	Conference	-	4	42	9	5	7	33	24	11	4	6	25	22	69	Mark Wright
99-00	Conference	-	9	42	10	5	6	31	21	5	8	8	24	35	58	Paul Futcher / Mark Wright
98-99	Conference	-	18	42	6	9	6	29	28	4	6	11	18	31	45	Paul Futcher
97-98	Conference	-	16	42	9	5	7	32	26	4	6	11	24	32	50	Paul Futcher
96-97	Conference	-	11	42	8	5	8	27	28	7	5	9	24	33	55	Steve Joel / Ronnie Moore

Season	League	Div.	Pos.	P	W	D	L	F	A	Pts	Manager
95-96	Conference	-	6	42	18	12	12	77	64	66	Billy Ayre
94-95	Conference	-	3	42	21	9	12	68	50	72	Brian Kettle/Billy Ayre
93-94	Conference	-	4	42	18	12	12	57	51	66	Brian Kettle
92-93	N.P.L.	Premier	1	42	29	9	4	103	31	96	Brian Kettle
91-92	N.P.L.	Premier	7	42	16	17	9	57	48	65	Brian Kettle

HONOURS

FA Trophy R-up 97-98;

Football League Division Four Champions 1972/73 Runners-up 1966/67;

Third Division North Section Cup 1937/38;

Northern Premier League 1992/93 League Cup 1990/91, League Shield 1993/94;

Liverpool Senior Cup 1930/31, 1931/32, 1943/44, 1957/58 (shared), 1963/64 (shared), 1974/75, 1990/91, 1992/93, 1998/99;

Lancashire Senior Cup 1904/05; Lancashire Junior Cup 1919/20, 1992/93, 1996-97, 1997-98

PREVIOUS

Leagues: Northern Premier League, Football League, Lancashire Combination

Grounds: Ash Lane

Names: Southport Central; Southport Vulcan

Past Players who progressed to the Football League

Shaun Teale,
Andy Mutch,
Steve Whitehall,
Tony Rodwell

CLUB RECORDS

Attendance: 20,010 v Newcastle United FA Cup - 1932

Record win: 8-1 v Nelson - 01.01.31

Record defeat: 0-11 v Oldham - 26.12.62

Career goalscorer: Alan Spence 98

Career appearances: Arthur Peat 401 - 1962-72

Transfer fee paid: £20,000 for Martin McDonald from Macclesfield Town - 1995

Transfer fee received: £25,000 from Rochdale for Steve Whitehall - 1991

BEST SEASON

FA Cup: Quarter Final, 1931-32. Lost to Newcastle Utd (The first Division 3 North team to reach the Quarter Finals)

FA Trophy: Runners-up 97-98, 0-1 v Cheltenham Town

League: Football League Div. 3 23rd 73-74

LAST SEASON

F.A. Cup: Second Round

F.A. Trophy: Sixth Round

Conference: 4th

Top Goalscorer: Ian Arnold

Player of the Year:

Captain: Andy Gouck

SOUTHPORT

Match Facts 2000-01

	Date	Comp.	Opponents	Gate	Score	Goalscorers
1	19/08	Conf	Hereford United	2438	0 - 0	
2	22/08	Conf	LEIGH RMI	1589	1 - 2	Parke 87
3	26/08	Conf	YEOVIL TOWN	1310	3 - 0	Furlong 49, Parke 65 73
4	28/08	Conf	Rushden & Diamonds	3574	0 - 4	
5	02/09	Conf	Chester City	2861	1 - 0	Arnold 23[p]
6	05/09	Conf	SCARBOROUGH	1269	3 - 1	Whittaker 7, Arnold 22[p], Parke 69
7	09/09	Conf	TELFORD UNITED	1354	3 - 0	Maamria 80, Arnold 82 85
8	12/09	Conf	Doncaster Rovers	1877	0 - 1	
9	16/09	Conf	Kettering Town	1145	1 - 1	Marsh 90[p]
10	23/09	Conf	WOKING	1377	0 - 1	
11	26/09	Conf	BOSTON UNITED	1003	3 - 1	Whittaker 7, Arnold 20, Stuart 26
12	30/09	Conf	Nuneaton Borough	1275	2 - 1	Parke 45, Maamria 74
13	03/10	Conf	Northwich Victoria	1074	2 - 0	Guyett 21, Gouck 65
14	14/10	Conf	Kingstonian	904	1 - 3	Parke 28
15	21/10	Conf	HAYES	1252	2 - 0	Parke 45, Whittaker 50
16	04/11	Conf	Hednesford Town	965	1 - 0	Marsh 51[p]
17	11/11	Conf	DOVER ATHLETIC	1635	2 - 1	Arnold 40 82
18	25/11	Conf	Dagenham & Redbridge	1183	1 - 0	Whittaker 39
19	28/11	Conf	DONCASTER ROVERS	1629	1 - 0	Marsh 75[p]
20	16/12	Conf	Leigh RMI	835	2 - 2	Whittaker 14, Arnold 46
21	22/12	Conf	STEVENAGE BOROUGH	1506	2 - 2	Clark 19, Parke 72
22	26/12	Conf	MORECAMBE	2117	1 - 2	Arnold 57
23	01/01	Conf	Morecambe	1937	3 - 1	Jones 39, Parke 43, Maamria 51
24	06/01	Conf	RUSHDEN & DIAMONDS	2255	1 - 3	Lane 16
25	20/01	Conf	Yeovil Town	4705	1 - 0	Lane 79
26	27/01	Conf	Scarborough	1125	1 - 1	Guyett 74
27	10/02	Conf	Telford United	1373	3 - 2	Elam 15, Clark 18, Arnold 22
28	17/02	Conf	FOREST GREEN ROVERS	1421	1 - 1	Marsh 34
29	03/03	Conf	KETTERING TOWN	1258	2 - 3	Marsh 28, Arnold 85
30	13/03	Conf	CHESTER CITY	1279	1 - 0	Parke 28
31	17/03	Conf	NUNEATON BOROUGH	1192	1 - 2	Marsh 76[p]
32	25/03	Conf	Boston United	1621	0 - 1	
33	27/03	Conf	HEREFORD UNITED	1367	1 - 1	Grayston 63
34	31/03	Conf	NORTHWICH VICTORIA	1643	1 - 1	Marsh 90[p]
35	07/04	Conf	Hayes	615	0 - 1	
36	10/04	Conf	Woking	1586	2 - 1	Linighan 4, Arnold 70
37	14/04	Conf	KINGSTONIAN	1153	2 - 2	Stuart 77, Obong 90
38	16/04	Conf	Dover Athletic	954	1 - 0	Linighan 52
39	21/04	Conf	HEDNESFORD TOWN	1006	2 - 0	Arnold 8, Parke 79
40	28/04	Conf	Forest Green Rovers	951	0 - 2	
41	30/04	Conf	Stevenage Borough	1366	3 - 1	Parke 10 61, Obong 26
42	05/05	Conf	DAGENHAM & REDBRIDGE	1264	0 - 1	

OTHER COMPETITIONS

Date	Comp.	Opponents	Gate	Score	Goalscorers
17/10	Variety CT 2	DONCASTER ROVERS	443	1 - 0	Maamria 44
28/10	FA Cup Q4	Doncaster Rovers	1886	2 - 2	Marsh 55[p], Elam 73
31/10	FA Cup Q4 R	DONCASTER ROVERS	1354	1 - 0	Marsh 38[p]
14/11	Lancs MT 1	DARWEN	309	3 - 0	
18/11	FA Cup 1	Havant & Waterlooville	1118	2 - 1	Stuart 44, Arnold 74
09/12	FA Cup 2	KINGSTONIAN	3659	1 - 2	Maamria 39
09/01	Lancs MT 2	Barrow	493	5 - 3	Parke 25, Linighan 31, Elam 37, Maamria 43 68
13/01	FA Trophy 3	HEDNESFORD TOWN	1091	3 - 0	Arnold 57, Lane 65, Marsh 90[p]
23/01	L'pool SC QF	ST HELENS TOWN	277	4 - 1	
03/02	FA Trophy 4	Kingstonian	1245	1 - 0	Gouck 52
06/02	Variety CT QF	CHESTER CITY	685	0 - 3	
20/02	Lancs MT QF	MARINE	403	5 - 0	O'Brien 1, Bolland 20, Parke 33, Maamria 73 85
24/02	FA Trophy 5	Weymouth	1839	2 - 1	Guyett 2, Marsh 35[p]
10/03	FA Trophy QF	Chester City	3204	0 - 1	
20/03	Lancs MT SF	Morecambe	n/k	3 - 1	
24/04	Lancs MT F	LANCASTER CITY	779	1 - 0	Mayers 90[og]Chorley

1	2	3	4	5	6	7	8	9	10	11	Substitutes Used
Dickinson	Teale	Guyett	Bolland	Clark	Stuart	Grayston	Marsh	Gouck	Furlong	Parke	
Dickinson	Teale	Bolland	Guyett	Clark	Marsh	Gouck	Grayston	Furlong	Parke	Elam	Pell (4), Whittaker (9), Stuart (11)
Dickinson	Teale	Guyett	Bolland	Marsh	Gouck	Grayston	Whittaker	Furlong	Arnold	Parke	
Dickinson	Clark	Guyett	Teale	Stuart	Bolland	Grayston	Gouck	Marsh	Furlong	Parke	Whittaker (5), Arnold (10), Elam (11)
Dickinson	McCauley	Stewart	Linnighan	Guyett	Clark	Marsh	Gouck	Arnold	Furlong	Grayston	Teale (9), Maamria (10), Elam (2)
Dickinson	Linighan	Guyett	Bolland	McCauley	Marsh	Gouck	Whittaker	Grayston	Arnold	Parke	Stuart (8), Maamria (11)
Dickinson	Linighan	Guyett	Bolland	McCauley	Marsh	Gouck	Grayston	Whittaker	Arnold	Maamria	Teale (9)
Dickinson	McCauley	Stuart	Linighan	Guyett	Bolland	Grayston	Gouck	Marsh	Arnold	Maamria	Whittaker (3), Teale (4), Furlong (10)
Dickinson	Linighan	Guyett	Bolland	McCauley	Grayston	Marsh	Gouck	Parke	Whittaker	Maamria	Furlong (5), Elam (10)
Dickinson	Guyett	Bolland	Teale	Clark	Marsh	Gouck	Grayston	Whittaker	Maamria	Parke	Elam (5), Arnold (9), Furlong (11)
Dickinson	Guyett	Bolland	Teale	Stuart	Marsh	Grayston	Whittaker	Furlong	Arnold	Parke	Clark (9), Maamria (11)
Dickinson	Grayston	Teale	Clark	Bolland	Stuart	Parke	Marsh	Whittaker	Arnold	Gouck	Maamria (7), Furlong (9)
Dickinson	Clark	Stuart	Teale	Guyett	Bolland	Grayston	Gouck	Marsh	Arnold	Parke	Furlong (3)
Dickinson	Clark	Grayston	Teale	Guyett	Bolland	Marsh	Gouck	Arnold	Parke	Furlong	Linighan (9)
Dickinson	Guyett	Bolland	Teale	Clark	Marsh	Gouck	Grayston	Arnold	Parke	Furlong	Elam (5), Maamria (9), Whittaker (11)
Dickinson	Teale	Clark	Bolland	Furlong	Marsh	Gouck	Grayston	Stuart	Arnold	Maamria	Linighan (5)
Dickinson	Guyett	Bolland	Teale	Marsh	Clark	Gouck	Grayston	Furlong	Arnold	Parke	Pell (11) sub Stuart
Dickinson	Teale	Guyett	Bolland	McCauley	Clark	Grayston	Gouck	Whittaker	Arnold	Parke	Elam (9), Linighan (11)
Dickinson	Linighan	Bolland	Teale	Clark	McCauley	Gouck	Marsh	Bradshaw	Arnold	Parke	Whittaker (6), Maamria (10)
Dickinson	McCauley	Stuart	Teale	Guyett	Bolland	Marsh	Grayston	Arnold	Parke	Whittaker	Clark (3), Elam (9), Maamria (11)
Dickinson	Guyett	Bolland	Teale	Clark	Bagshaw	Grayston	Marsh	Arnold	Parke	Maamria	Elam (6), Pell (10)
Dickinson	McCauley	Guyett	Teale	Clark	Marsh	Grayston	Jones	Whittaker	Arnold	Parke	Maamria (8), Burke (9), Linighan (11)
Dickinson	Clark	Linighan	Teale	Guyett	Jones	Marsh	Grayston	Arnold	Parke	Maamria	Burke (6), Elam (10)
Dickinson	Clark	Guyett	Bolland	Stuart	Lane	Marsh	Gouck	Grayston	Arnold	Maamria	Elam (5), Whittaker (9), Parke (10)
Dickinson	Guyett	Teale	Clark	Lane	Gouck	Marsh	O'Brien	Elam	Arnold	Maamria	Grayston (8), Whittaker 99), Parke (10)
Dickinson	Lane	Elam	Teale	Guyett	Clark	Marsh	Gouck	Maamria	Parke	O'Brien	Grayston (2), Arnold (9), Whittaker (11)
Dickinson	Lane	Clark	Teale	Guyett	Bolland	Marsh	Gouck	Arnold	Grayston	Elam	
Dickinson	Lane	Bolland	Teale	Clark	Marsh	Gouck	Grayston	Elam	Arnold	Parke	Furlong (2), Whittaker (9), Maamria (11)
Dickinson	Teale	Lane	Grayston	Marsh	Gouck	Whittaker	Arnold	Maamria	Guyett	Bolland	Elam (3), O'Brien (4), Furlong (7)
Dickinson	Clark	Guyett	Bolland	Lane	Grayston	Marsh	Gouck	Elam	Arnold	Parke	Whittaker (9), Teale (10)
Dickinson	Clark	Guyett	Bolland	Lane	Marsh	Gouck	Grayston	Elam	Arnold	Parke	Teale (4), Whittaker (9), Maamria (11)
Dickinson	Guyett	Lane	Stuart	Clark	Linighan	Marsh	Grayston	Maamria	Arnold	Parke	Elam (4), Bolland (9)
Dickinson	Linighan	Guyett	Clark	Lane	Stuart	Grayston	Marsh	Arnold	Parke	Maamria	Teale (3), Elam (9), Furlong (10)
Dickinson	Clarke	Guyett	Linighan	Lane	Marsh	Grayston	Elam	Stuart	Furlong	Maamria	Whittaker (5), Obong (10)
Dickinson	Clark	Stuart	Linighan	Guyett	Bolland	Marsh	Grayston	Arnold	Maamria	Elam	Furlong (3), Teale (5), Parke (9)
Dickinson	Lane	Stuart	Teale	Linighan	Bolland	Clark	Grayston	Arnold	Furlong	Elam	Parke (9), McCauley (10)
Dickinson	Clark	Bolland	Linighan	Lane	Marsh	Grayston	Stuart	Elam	Arnold	Parke	Whittaker (9) Obong (10), Furlong (11)
Dickinson	Lane	Stuart	Linighan	Guyett	Bolland	Clark	Grayston	Arnold	Furlong	Elam	
Dickinson	Linighan	Guyett	Bolland	Lane	Stuart	Clark	Grayston	Elam	Arnold	Parke	Whittaker (9), Obong 911)
Dickinson	Lane	Underwood	Guyett	McCauley	Clark	Grayston	Stuart	Elam	Arnold	McAuley	Parke (2), Whittaker (3)
Dickinson	Lane	McCauley	Teale	Guyett	Bolland	Clark	Grayston	Whittaker	Obong	Parke	
Dickinson	Lane	McCauley	Guyett	Teale	Bolland	Clark	Grayston	Whittaker	Obong	Parke	Stuart (3), Elam (9), Furlong (10)

PLAYING SQUAD

SOUTHPORT

(Bold print indicates an England Semi-Professional International)

Player *Honours*	*Birthplace*	*D.O.B.*	*Previous Clubs*
GOALKEEPERS			
Steve Dickinson	Bradford		Bradford C, Guiseley
DEFENDERS			
Martin Clark	Accrington	12..09.70	Preston, Lancaster C, Accrington Stanley, Crewe
Neil Grayston	Keighley	25.11.75	Bradford C, Bradford PA
Shaun Teale ESP	Southport	10.03.64	Southport, Northwich V, Weymouth, Bournemouth, Aston Villa, Tranmere, Happy Valley, Motherwell, Carlisle
Carl Macauley Barrow,	Liverpool		Manchester C, Witton Alb., Vauxhall GM, Prescot Cables,
			Telford U
Barry Jones	Prescot	20.06.70	York, Wrexham, Liverpool, Prescot Cables
Gary Bauress UL	Liverpool	19.01.71	Stalybridge C, Barrow, Leek T, Stalybridge C, Ashton Utd, Stalybridge C, Tranmere, Everton
James Connelly	Preston		Preston
John Robertson	Liverpool	08.01.74	Northwich V, Lincoln, Wigan
MIDFIELD			
Lee Elam	Bradford		Guiseley
Brian McGorry	Liverpool	16.04.70	Telford Utd, Torquay, Hereford Utd, Cardiff, Wycombe, Peterborough, Bournemouth, Weymouth
Chris Lane	Liverpool	24.05.79	Hereford Utd, Everton
Steve Jones UL	Stoke		Stalybridge C, Leek T, Eastwood Hanley, Stafford R, Stoke
FORWARDS			
Simon Parke	Bradford		Bradford PA, Guiseley
Tony Sullivan UL	Liverpool		Stalybridge C, Prescot Cables
Ian Cooke UL	Liverpool	01.11.73	Stalybridge C, Northwich V, Cammell Laird
Stuart Whittaker	Liverpool	02.01.75	Macclesfield, Wigan, Bolton, Liverpool (Junior)
Kevin Leadbeater	Liverpool		Skelmersdale Utd

STALYBRIDGE CELTIC

The Unibond League could hardly have stage managed a better championship challenge. The race was contested until the last week when Celtic beat near rivals Emley 3-2 away despite finishing with ten men. A superb crowd of 3,708 watched this battle and over 2,000 turned up at Droylsden to see a last minute penalty gain another away victory, and then 1,432 welcomed the champions home in an anti-climax which was lost 0-2!

Stalybridge had secured their return to the Conference, but the celebrations were somewhat marred by the news that manager Phil Wilson was off to take the vacant Southport job.

Only a point separated the top two clubs who between them secured 203! But third placed Bishop Auckland were another sixteen points away so there was a big gulf of quality between the leaders and the chasing pack.

Celtic's average attendance rose by 230 over the year and their 96 goals were shared out impressively between Parr, Jones, Sullivan and McNeil.

Apart from the League the club won the Cheshire Senior Cup with an impressive 5-1 victory over Stockport County and the President's Cup on penalties against Blyth Spartans after a 3-3 draw. Once again the goals flowed!

Looking back over the season, early exits from the F.A. Cup (Third Qualifying Round at Billingham Town) and the F.A. Trophy (0-2 at Marine in the Third Round) probably kept the season clear for their successful league run in which saw Celtic only lose three league games in the second half of the season. The coming campaign will depend a lot on the new manager and his new team settling quickly, but it won't be easy and the new found support of last season will be needed to help consolidation.

T.W

Stalybridge celebrate after their final game of the season having won the Unibond Championship, the President's Cup and the Cheshire Senior Cup. Photo: Colin Stevens

STALYBRIDGE CELTIC

GROUND DETAILS

Bower Fold,
Mottram Road,
Stalybridge,
Cheshire SK15 2RT

Telephone:	0161 338 2828
Fax:	0161 338 8256.
Club Website:	www.stalybridgeceltic.co.uk

Directions:
M6 to A556 to M63 to M67; end of Motorway through roundabout to traffic lights, left; left at end into Mottram Road, up hill, down hill into Stalybridge, ground on left next to Hare & Hounds pub.

Capacity:	6,150
Seats:	1,300
Cover:	1,300

Clubhouse:
Open matchdays and evenings during the week. Food available on matchdays.

Club Shop: Contact John Hall (H) 01457 869262

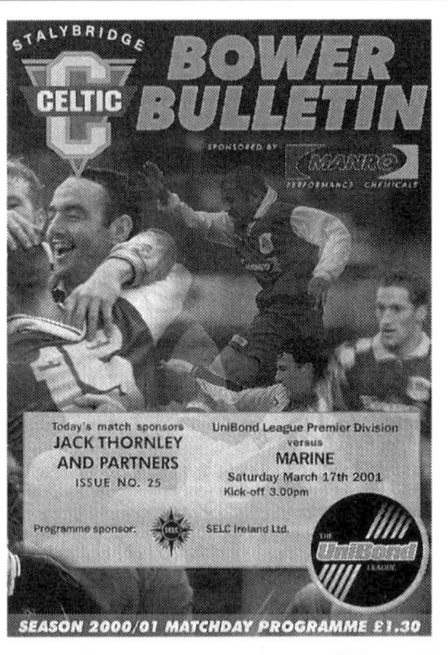

MATCHDAY PROGRAMME

Pages: 40 Price: £1.30

Editor: Nick Shaw Tel: 0161 633 1117

Other club publications:

Local Press: Manchester Evening News, Manchester Evening News Pink (Sat.eve.), Aston Reporter, Ashton Advertiser

Local Radio:
G.M.R. (BBC Manchester), Piccadilly Radio

Sponsors:	Manro Performance Chemicals
Formed:	1909
Nickname:	Celtic
Club colours:	Blue & white shirts blue shorts, blue socks
Change colours:	Old gold hooped shirts green shorts, green socks
Midweek matchday:	Tuesday
Reserves' League:	None

CLUB OFFICIALS

President:	Roy Oldham
Chairman:	Peter Dennerley
Vice Chairman:	Dorothy Norton
Directors:	B McCallum, G Crossley, G Greenwood, E Stafford, J Dillon
Football Secretary:	Martyn Torr c/o the club. Tel: 0161 628 3387 (H) 0161 338 2828 (B) 0161 338 8256 (Fax)
Commercial Manager:	John Hall Tel: 01457 869262
Press Officer:	Keith Trudgeon Tel: 0161205 7631 (B) 0161 304 8934 (H)

FOOTBALL MANAGEMENT TEAM

MANAGER	**PAUL FUTCHER**
Date of Appointment	July 2001
Date of Birth:	25th September 1956
Place of Birth:	Chester

PREVIOUS CLUBS

As manager	Darlington, Gresley Rovers, Southport
As player	Chester C., Luton T., Manchester C., Oldham A., Derby Co., Barnsley, Halifax T., Grimsby

HONOURS

As manager	Southern Lge Prem. 1996-97, Derbys. Sen. Cup (x2) (Gresley R.) FA Trophy R-up 97-98; Lancs ATS Trophy 97-98; Liverpool Sen. Cup 98-99
As player	England: u21 (11)

Assistant Manager:
Physio:
Chief Scout:
Youth Development:

Season	League	Div.	Pos.	P	Home W	Home D	Home L	Home F	Home A	Away W	Away D	Away L	Away F	Away A	Pts	Manager
00-01	N.P.L.	P	1	44	19	1	2	57	15	12	8	2	39	17	102	Phil Wilson
99-00	N.P.L.	P	7	44	13	5	4	42	27	5	7	10	22	27	66	Phil Wilson
98-99	N.P.L.	P	10	42	13	5	3	43	23	3	6	12	28	40	59	Brian Kettle
97-98	Conference	-	22	42	6	5	10	33	38	1	3	17	15	55	29	Brian Kettle
96-97	Conference	-	13	42	9	5	7	35	29	5	5	11	18	29	52	P Wragg/D Frain/B Kettle
95-96	Conference	-	14	42	9	3	9	29	37	7	4	10	30	31	55	Peter Wragg
94-95	Conference	-	18	42	9	5	6	29	27	2	8	11	23	45	47	Peter Wragg
93-94	Conference	-	14	42	6	6	9	27	28	8	6	7	27	27	54	Phil Wilson/Peter Wragg
92-93	Conference	-	12	42	7	10	4	25	26	6	7	8	23	29	56	Phil Wilson
91-92	N.P.L.	P	1	42	15	5	1	48	14	11	9	1	36	19	92	Phil Wilson

HONOURS

Northern Premier League Prem Div 91-92, 00-01, R-up 90-91; Div.1 R-up 87-88; Cheshire County Lg 79-80, R-up 77-78, Lg Cup 21-22 R-up 46-47,81-82; Challenge Shield 77-78, R-up 79-80, Res Div R-up 81-82; N.W. Cos Lg 83-84, 86-87, Lge Cup R-up 83-84, Champions v Cup Winners Trophy 83-84; Lancs Comb Div 2 11-12; Cheshire Snr Cup 52-53, R-up 54-55, 80-81; Manchester Snr Cup 22-23, Intermediate Cup 57-58, 68-69, R-up 56-57, 67-68, 69-70; Challenge Shield 54-55, (Junior Cup 62-63); Lancs Floodlit Cup 88-89, R-up 89-90; Reporter Cup R-up 74-75; Edward Case Cup 77-78.

PREVIOUS

Leagues: Lancashire Combination 1911-12, Central League 1912-21, Football League 1921-23, Cheshire County Lge 1923-1982, North West Counties 1982-87, Northern Premier 1987-92, 98-01 Conference 92-98.

Grounds: None
Names: None

Past Players who progressed to the Football League

Too numerous to list. but includes recently Eamoon O'Keefe, John Anderson, Lee Trundle

CLUB RECORDS

Attendance: 9,753 v WBA, FA Cup replay, 22-23

Win: 16-2; v Manchester NE 1.5.26; v Nantwich 22/10/32

Defeat: 0-6 v Northwich Victoria

Career appearances: Kevin Booth 354
Career goalscorer: Unknown
Goalscorer (season): Chris Camden 45, 91-92

Fee paid: £15,000 to Kettering Town for Ian Arnold 95

Fee received: £16,000 for Lee Trundle from Southport

BEST SEASON

FA Cup: Second Round 93-94, 1-3 v Carlisle Utd.(A); 99-00 1-2 v Chester City (H).
League clubs defeated: None

FA Trophy: Third Round 1991-92, 0-1 v Witton Albion (A).

League: 12th Conference 92-93

LAST SEASON

F.A. Cup: 3rd Qual. Round
F.A. Trophy: Third Round
League: N.P.L. Champions
Top Goalscorer: Steve Jones (25)
Player of the Year: Kevin Parr
Captain: Gary Bauress

STALYBRIDGE CELTIC

Match Facts 2000-01

	Date	Comp.	Opponents	Gate	Score	Goalscorers
1	19/08	Unib P	SPENNYMOOR UNITED	314	3 - 2	Parr 6 40, S Jones 82
2	26/08	Unib P	Marine	304	3 - 0	Sullivan 10 74, Jones 50
3	28/08	Unib P	WHITBY TOWN	456	1 - 1	Sullivan 27
4	02/09	Unib P	Gateshead	268	2 - 2	McNeil 6, Parr 71
5	05/09	Unib P	DROYLSDEN	545	4 - 1	Evans 48, Sullivan 49 86, McNeil 66
6	09/09	Unib P	BISHOP AUCKLAND	509	2 - 0	McNeil 53, Bauress 79
7	12/09	Unib P	Gainsborough Trinity	291	0 - 0	
8	23/09	Unib P	Accrington Stanley	935	4 - 1	Sullivan 7 11 60, Bauress 56[p]
9	26/09	Unib P	Hucknall Town	361	2 - 2	Crookes 56, Jones 75
10	03/10	Unib P	Altrincham	823	0 - 0	
11	06/10	Unib P	LANCASTER CITY	530	5 - 0	Bauress 2[p], Parr 13 44, McNeil 59 67
12	21/10	Unib P	GAINSBOROUGH TRINITY	498	7 - 1	McNeil 10, Parr 17 82, Evans 37 53, Crookes 56, Sullivan 68
13	24/10	Unib P	WORKSOP TOWN	641	1 - 0	Parr 45
14	11/11	Unib P	BAMBER BRIDGE	483	3 - 0	Jones 44, McNeil 79, Scott 82
15	18/11	Unib P	Leek Town	303	2 - 0	Jones 66, Parr 67
16	25/11	Unib P	EMLEY	1006	4 - 2	McNeil 3 55, Jones 49, Crookes 65
17	09/12	Unib P	Lancaster City	304	2 - 3	Pickford 16, Jones 68
18	16/12	Unib P	Whitby Town	315	1 - 0	Jones 75
19	23/12	Unib P	FRICKLEY ATHLETIC	612	3 - 0	Sullivan 26, Jones 44, McNeil 79
20	26/12	Unib P	Hyde United	1009	2 - 1	Pickford 59 66
21	06/01	Unib P	BARROW	718	1 - 0	Sullivan 10
22	09/01	Unib P	RUNCORN	427	3 - 1	Ward 48, McNeil 63, Sullivan 76
23	27/01	Unib P	GATESHEAD	609	2 - 1	Crookes 38, Jones 72
24	03/02	Unib P	ACCRINGTON STANLEY	675	4 - 0	Parr 11 53, Filson 68 82
25	13/02	Unib P	HYDE UNITED	1078	3 - 1	Parr 4, Crookes 42, Jones 47
26	20/02	Unib P	Burscough	276	1 - 1	Williamson 38
27	24/02	Unib P	ALTRINCHAM	1025	1 - 0	Crookes 74
28	27/02	Unib P	Barrow	864	0 - 0	
29	06/03	Unib P	HUCKNALL TOWN	477	1 - 0	Evans 78
30	10/03	Unib P	Frickley Athletic	402	0 - 0	
31	13/03	Unib P	Worksop Town	602	1 - 1	Jones 22
32	17/03	Unib P	MARINE	663	2 - 1	Pickford 3, Parr 42
33	20/03	Unib P	Colwyn Bay	239	7 - 1	McNeil 10 90, Jones 12 65, Sullivan 15, Locke 39[p], Parr 60
34	23/03	Unib P	Bamber Bridge	416	2 - 0	Sullivan 54[p], Crookes 74
35	27/03	Unib P	LEEK TOWN	593	1 - 2	Parr 36
36	31/03	Unib P	Spennymoor United	129	1 - 0	Vicary 26
37	10/04	Unib P	Blyth Spartans	309	2 - 1	McNeil 29, Filson 60
38	14/04	Unib P	COLWYN BAY	626	4 - 0	Pickford 15, Sullivan 26, Jones 43, McNeil 82
39	16/04	Unib P	Runcorn	407	1 - 2	Parr 56
40	18/04	Unib P	BLYTH SPARTANS	362	2 - 0	Cook 18, Crookes 67
41	21/04	Unib P	Bishop Auckland	238	2 - 0	Filson 19, Jones 42
42	28/04	Unib P	Emley	3708	3 - 2	Filson 50, Jones 60, Cooke 90
43	01/05	Unib P	Droylsden	2040	1 - 0	Lock 90[p]
44	05/05	Unib P	BURSCOUGH	1432	0 - 2	

OTHER COMPETITIONS

Date	Comp.	Opponents	Gate	Score	Goalscorers	
22/08	Ches. SC P	Vauxhall	n/k	2 - 0	McNeil, Sullivan	
19/09	Ches. SC 1	Winsford United	69	1 - 0	Bauress 16[p]	
30/09	FA Cup Q2	BLYTH SPARTANS	523	2 - 0	McNeil 27, Evans 88	
14/10	FA Cup Q3	BILLINGHAM TOWN	479	1 - 1	Pickford 58	
17/10	FA Cup Q3 R	Billingham Town	188	0 - 3		
09/11	FA Trophy 1	BEDWORTH UNITED	196	4 - 1	Jones 8, McNeil 12, Parr 58, Sullivan 70	
21/11	Ches. SC QF	Witton Albion	213	2 - 1	Parr 37, Pickford 66	
02/12	FA Trophy 2	WITTON ALBION	552	2 - 0	McNeil 6, Parr 80	
12/12	Lge Cup 7	DROYLSDEN	178	2 - 3	Evans 55, Bauress 60	
03/01	Lge Cup 7	CHORLEY	167	4 - 2	Sullivan 7, Green 9, Evans 51 59	
13/01	FA Trophy 3	Marine	441	0 - 2		
22/01	Ches. SC SF	Hyde United	642	4 - 1	Sullivan 2, Jones 21 33 58	
30/01	Lge Cup 7	Radcliffe Borough	140	2 - 0	Kelly 65[og], Cooke 75	
06/02	Lge Cup 7	Congleton Town	109	3 - 1	Pickford 5, Green 43, Jones 70	
03/03	Pres. Cup QF	Ashton United	559	2 - 1	Sullivan 57, McNeil 59	
02/04	Ches. SC F	STOCKPORT COUNTY	855	5 - 1	Parr 10 15 24, Jones 18 33	(at Hyde United)
04/04	Pres. Cup SF	VAUXHALL	243	2 - 1	Crossland 7, Jones 95	
24/04	Pres. Cup F	Blyth Spartans	560	3 - 3	Cooke 14, Sullivan 33, Williamson 59	Won 3-2 after pens.

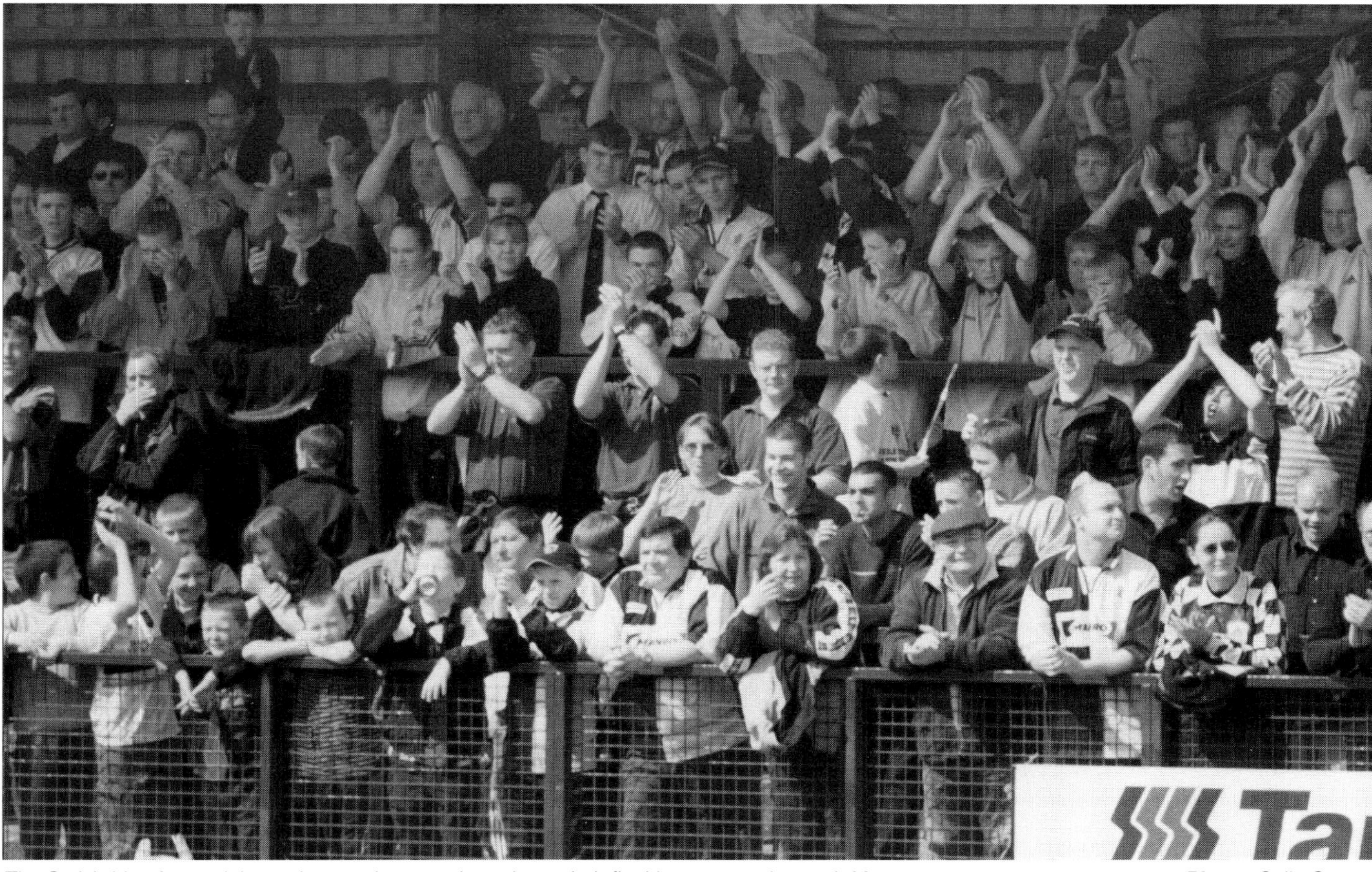

The Stalybridge fans celebrate the team's promotion prior to their final league match on 5th May.

Photo: Colin Stevens

PLAYING SQUAD

STALYBRIDGE CELTIC

Player	*Birthplace*	*D.O.B.*	*Previous Clubs*
GOALKEEPERS			
Gary Ingham UL	Rotherham	09.10.74	Leek T, Stocksbridge PS, Stalybridge C, Doncaster R, Gainsborough T, Maltby MW, Bridlington T, Goole T, Shepshed Chart., Gainsborough T, Rotherham
David Fish	Manchester		Woodley Sports, Stockport (Trainee)
DEFENDERS			
Derek Ward UL	Birkenhead	17.05.72	Northwich V, Southport, Bury
Dominic Crookes UL	Nottingham	07.12.74	Northwich V, Dagenham & Red., Telford Utd, Mansfield
Ged Murphy	Manchester	19.12.78	Leigh RMI, Nuneaton B, Stafford R, Barrow, Oldham
Matt Williamson UL	Manchester		Glossop NE
Matt Woods	Gosport	09.09.76	Chester C, Everton
Stuart Locke NC, UL	Manchester		Leigh RMI, Leek T, Macclesfield, Stalybridge C, Northwich V, Manchester C
MIDFIELD			
Winfield Steele UL	Basildon	28.02.77	Chorley, Winsford Utd, Bury
Ged Courtney	Liverpool		Marine, Kendal T, Accrington Stanley, Southport
Kevin Parr UL	Manchester		Glossop NE
Richard Morris UL	Crewe		Crewe
Richard Peacock	Sheffield	29.10.72	Lincoln, Hull, Sheffield Utd
Steve Heaton UL	Manchester		Glossop NE
Steve Pickford UL	Manchester		Glossop NE, Leigh RMI, Glossop NE
Steve Wood NC, FAT	Oldham	23.06.63	Macclesfield, Stalybridge C, Droyldsen, Mossley, Chadderton
FORWARDS			
Andy Evans	Aberystwyth	25.11.75	Barnsley, Aberystwyth T
Matthew McNeil UL	Manchester		Woking, Stalybridge Celtic, Woodley Sports, Altrincham, Curzon Ashton
Paul Higginbotham	Manchester		Salford C, Winsford Utd, Chorley, Conwy Utd, Leek T, Bangor C, Stalybridge C, Altrincham, Stalybridge C, Barrow, Witton Alb., Manchester C (Trainee)

STEVENAGE BOROUGH

An ambitious outfit like Stevenage Borough will never be happy with seventh place in the Conference, particularly when there was no knock-out joy to sugar the pill.

In the latter competition the club made an immediate exit from the F.A. Cup against Nuneaton Borough in the Fourth Qualifying Round, when a 2-1 home defeat in a replay after a 1-1 draw away was most unwelcome news, while in the F.A.. Trophy a 5-1 crushing of Aldershot Town in Hampshire in Round Three and 2-1 victory over Margate raised hopes of a good run, which were destroyed cruelly in the last sixteen when a blank game at Canvey Island and 1-1 draw in the replay was followed by a penalty shoot-out for the Essex club, the ultimate winners of the competition.

Actual Conference form was notable for a 71-61 goals difference, which clearly indicated a good attack and plenty of contributors such as Hay, Illman, Martin, Clarke and Armstrong, but a strengthening of the defence is necessary to avoid another `nearly' tag.

Manager Paul Fairclough is a fine analyst of the game and will have noted these problems so if he can counter them a realistic challenge for greater things can be expected.

W.M.

STEVENAGE BOROUGH 2001-02

Back Row L-R**:** Paul Armstrong, Adrian Clarke, Martin Williams, Paul Abbott, John Hamsher, Leon Smith, Neil Illman. **Middle Row:** Matt Fisher, Darran Hay, Jason Goodliffe, Robin Trott, Paul Wilkerson, John Dreyer, Sam Sodje, Paul Sturgess, Roy Squire (Kit manager). **Front Row:** Kevin Hales (Asst. Manager), DJ Campell, Steve Walters, Paul Fairclough (Manager), Sam McMahon, John Morgan, Keith Allinson (Physio).

STEVENAGE BOROUGH

GROUND DETAILS

Stevenage Stadium,
Broadhall Way,
Stevenage,
Herts SG2 8RH

Tel: 01438 223223
Fax: 01438 743666
email:
Web site: http://www.stevenageborofc.com

SIMPLE DIRECTIONS:
Stevenage South exit off A1(M) - ground on right at second roundabout.Spectators are however advised to go straight on at this roundabout and park inthe Showground opposite the stadium. The stadium is one mile from Stevenage BRstation. Buses SB4 and SB5

CAPACITY: 6,546

SEATED: 2,002

COVERED TERRACING: 2,000

Groundsman: Colin Payne

CLUB SHOP: Mon - Sat 9-5.30. Broadhall Way, Stevenage. 01438 218061. Sells a complete range of club merchandise including a customising service. Mail Order, credit cards accepted, contact Emma Doherty (01438 218061)

SOCIAL FACILITIES:
Tel.: 01438 218079. Clubhouse at ground open Monday to Friday 7 - 11pm,Saturday noon - 2.00 & 4.30 - 11pm, Sunday: All day from noon. Contact: Jenny Cairns

FOOTBALL MANAGEMENT TEAM

MANAGER:	PAUL FAIRCLOUGH
Date of Appointment	2000
Date of Birth	31st January 1950
Place of Birth	Liverpool
PREVIOUS CLUBS	
As manager	Hertford Town, Stevenage Bor. (90-99)
As coach	Hemel Hempstead, Finchley
As player	Harlow Town, St Albans City, Hertford Town
HONOURS	
As manager	GMVC 95-96, Isthmian Prem 93-94, Div. 1 91-92
As player	None

Assistant Manager	Kevin Hales
1st Team Coach	Kevin Hales
Reserve Team Manager	Neil Trebble
Physiotherapist	Keith Allinson
Chief Scout	Alan Carrington
Scouts	Steve Williams, Derek Mardle, Frank Radcliffe

Nickname:	Boro'
Club Sponsors:	Sun Banking Corporation
Club colours:	White & red shirts, black & white trim shorts and white with red trim socks
Change colours:	Yellow shirts, yellow shorts, yellow socks
Midweek home matchday:	Monday
Reserve Team's League:	Capital League

CLUB OFFICIALS

Chairman	Phillip Wallace
Club Administrator (Including Press work)	Roger Austin 01438 218072
Commercial Manager	Clive Abrey 01438 218073

PROGRAMME
Pages: 36 Price: £1.80
Editor: Steve Watkins Tel: 01438 318891

Other club publications: The Borough Yearbook

Local Press: Stevenage Gazette; Comet; Stevenage Mercury; Herald
Local Radio: Chiltern Radio; BBC Three Counties Radio

Season	League	Div.	Pos.	Home P	W	D	L	F	A	Away W	D	L	F	A	Pts	Manager
00-01	Conference	-	7	42	8	7	6	36	33	7	11	3	35	28	63	Paul Fairclough
99-00	Conference	-	10	42	8	5	8	26	20	8	4	9	34	34	57	R./ Steve Wignall /P Fairclough
98-99	Conference	-	6	42	9	9	3	37	23	8	8	5	25	22	68	Paul Fairclough / Richard Hill
97-98	Conference	-	15	42	8	8	5	35	27	5	4	12	24	36	51	Paul Fairclough
96-97	Conference	-	3	42	15	4	2	53	23	9	6	6	34	30	82	Paul Fairclough
				P	W	D	L	F	A						Pts	
95-96	Conference	-	1	42	27	10	5	101	44						91	Paul Fairclough
94-95	Conference	-	5	42	20	7	15	68	49						67	Paul Fairclough
93-94	Isthmian	Prem.	1	42	31	4	7	88	39						97	Paul Fairclough
92-93	Isthmian	Prem.	7	42	18	8	16	62	60						62	Paul Fairclough
91-92	Isthmian	One	1	40	24	10	6	83	34						82	Paul Fairclough

HONOURS

GM Vauxhall Conference 95-96,
Isthmian Lge Prem 93-94,
Div 1 91-92, Div 2 (North) 85-86 90-91;
Utd Counties Lg Div 1 80-81 (Div 1 Cup 80-81),
Herts SnrCup R-up 85-86, 93/94;
Herts Charity Cup R-up 93-94,
Herts Charity Shield R-up83-84,
Televised Sports Snr Floodlit Cup 89-90,
Eastern Professional F'lit Cup Group winner
81-82 85-86 86-87 88-89 90-91 91-92,
South Co's Comb. Cup 91-92;
Essex & Herts Border Comb.(Reserves) 94/95
Essex & Herts (Western Div) 95-96

PREVIOUS

Leagues: Chiltern Youth 76-79; Wallspan South Combination 79-80; United Counties 80-84; Isthmian 84-94

Grounds: King George V Playing Field 1976-80

Past Players who progressed to the Football League

Richard Wilmot & NeilTrebble (Scunthorpe Utd) 1993,
Simon Clark (Peterborough United) 1994,
Leo Fortune West (Gillingham) 1995,
Phil Simpson (Barnet) 1995,
Barry Hayles (Bristol C.) 1997)

CLUB RECORDS

Attendance: 6,489 v Kidderminster H., GM Vauxhall Conference 25.1.97

Win: 11-1 v British Timken Athletic (H), United Counties League Div.1, 1980-81

Defeat: 0-7 v Southwick (H), Isthmian League Div. 1, 1987-88

Career goalscorer: Barry Hayles

Career appearances: Martin Gittings

Transfer fee paid: £20,000 for Richard Leadbetter to Hereford United 1999

Transfer fee received: £300,000 for Barry Hayles (Bristol R.) July 97

BEST SEASON

FA Cup: Fourth Round replay 97-98. 1-2 v Newcastle Utd. (A) after 1-1 also 3rd Round 1996-97. 0-2 v Birmingham City (A)

League clubs defeated: Leyton Orient 96-97; Cambridge Utd., Swindon Town 97-98

FA Trophy: Semi Final 96-97. 1-2 v Woking in Replay at Watford

League: Conference Champions 95-96

LAST SEASON

F.A. Cup: Fourth Qualifying Round
F.A. Trophy: Fifth Round
Conference: 7th
Top Goalscorer: Neil Illman
Player of the Year: Mark Smith
Captain: Mark Smith
Highest League Attendance: 3,327

STEVENAGE BOROUGH

Match Facts 2000-01

	Date	Comp.	Opponents	Gate	Score	Goalscorers
1	19/08	Conf	SCARBOROUGH	2032	1 - 1	Hay 14
2	23/08	Conf	Forest Green Rovers	1043	3 - 2	Illman 75 90, Clarke 81
3	26/08	Conf	Hednesford Town	802	1 - 1	Illman 19
4	28/08	Conf	DAGENHAM & REDBRIDGE	2055	0 - 2	
5	02/09	Conf	LEIGH RMI	1479	3 - 0	Wraight 16, Trott 26, Graham 66
6	05/09	Conf	Rushden & Diamonds	4048	2 - 2	Hay 19, Warburton 90[og]
7	09/09	Conf	Northwich Victoria	909	2 - 3	Hay 67 87
8	11/09	Conf	DOVER ATHLETIC	1505	1 - 1	Clarke 39[p]
9	16/09	Conf	YEOVIL TOWN	1755	0 - 0	
10	23/09	Conf	Hereford United	2251	1 - 1	Armstrong 21
11	26/09	Conf	Woking	1780	1 - 1	Roddis 75[og]
12	30/09	Conf	TELFORD UNITED	1446	5 - 3	Leadbeater 34 40, Pearson 59 76, Martin 61
13	14/10	Conf	BOSTON UNITED	2129	3 - 2	Clarke 75, Hay 82 90
14	21/10	Conf	Nuneaton Borough	1402	3 - 0	Hay 1, Clarke 42, Armstrong 80
15	04/11	Conf	KETTERING TOWN	1845	2 - 0	Hay 65, Armstrong 90
16	11/11	Conf	Chester City	1708	1 - 1	Armstrong 72
17	18/11	Conf	Scarborough	789	2 - 2	Kirby 27, Hay 33
18	25/11	Conf	KINGSTONIAN	2007	2 - 5	Martin 8, Bunce 50
19	02/12	Conf	Doncaster Rovers	2545	0 - 0	
20	16/12	Conf	FOREST GREEN ROVERS	1654	3 - 1	Broughton 72 86, Illman 90
21	22/12	Conf	Southport	1506	2 - 2	Clarke 68[p] 73[p]
22	26/12	Conf	Hayes	853	1 - 0	Clarke 38
23	01/01	Conf	HAYES	2171	3 - 3	Hay 17, Illman 48, Phillips 53
24	06/01	Conf	Boston United	2199	3 - 3	Broughton 43, Illman 71, Morgan 73
25	27/01	Conf	RUSHDEN & DIAMONDS	3327	0 - 2	
26	10/02	Conf	NORTHWICH VICTORIA	1622	3 - 1	Hay 6 55, Armstrong 84
27	17/02	Conf	Kingstonian	990	2 - 0	Hay 24, Illman 28
28	03/03	Conf	Yeovil Town	3073	1 - 1	Trott 78
29	12/03	Conf	HEREFORD UNITED	1265	2 - 1	Hay 43, Armstrong 82
30	20/03	Conf	Dagenham & Redbridge	958	0 - 3	
31	26/03	Conf	WOKING	2022	0 - 3	
32	31/03	Conf	Morecambe	1021	2 - 1	Hay 10, Sodje 63
33	02/04	Conf	HEDNESFORD TOWN	1450	4 - 1	Walters 37, Morgan 42, Armstrong 49, Hamsher 60[p]
34	07/04	Conf	NUNEATON BOROUGH	1471	1 - 1	McMahon 40
35	10/04	Conf	Leigh RMI	403	4 - 1	Illman 26 40 52, Clarke 65
36	16/04	Conf	CHESTER CITY	1748	1 - 2	Martin 26
37	18/04	Conf	Telford United	648	2 - 2	Walters 16, Armstrong 87
38	21/04	Conf	Kettering Town	1755	2 - 1	Illman 4, Clarke 29
39	23/04	Conf	MORECAMBE	1317	1 - 1	McMahon 8
40	28/04	Conf	DONCASTER ROVERS	2425	0 - 0	
41	30/04	Conf	SOUTHPORT	1366	1 - 3	Martin 58
42	05/05	Conf	Dover Athletic	1503	0 - 1	

OTHER COMPETITIONS

Date	Comp.	Opponents	Gate	Score	Goalscorers
04/08	Herts CC 1	St Albans City	n/k	3 - 1	
19/09	Variety CT 1	Dagenham & Redbridge	318	2 - 1	Armstrong 71, Illman 79
24/10	Variety CT 2	Rushden & Diamonds	412	1 - 2	Illman 48
28/10	FA Cup Q4	Nuneaton Borough	1554	1 - 1	Leadbeater 29
31/10	FA Cup Q4 R	NUNEATON BOROUGH	1219	1 - 2	Trott 41
14/11	Herts CC QF	Cheshunt	n/k	7 - 1	Okpala 1, Illman 16 40[p], Bridge 28, Briggs 60[p] 85, Douglas 70[p]
19/12	Herts SC 2	BERKHAMSTED TOWN	n/k	1 - 0	Illman 6
09/01	Herts SC QF	Hitchin Town	405	2 - 1	Abbott 30, Leadbeater 51
13/01	FA Trophy 3	Aldershot Town	2965	5 - 1	Clarke 17, Hay 59, Phillips 62, Illman 66 68
03/02	FA Trophy 4	MARGATE	1515	2 - 1	Illman 45, Phillips 77
24/02	FA Trophy 5	Canvey Island	1010	1 - 1	Illman 20
26/02	FA Trophy 5 R	CANVEY ISLAND	1148	0 - 0	Lost 2-4 after penalties
06/03	Herts SC SF	Ware	n/k	1 - 3	Brissett 10
01/05	Herts CC SF	Hitchin Town	102	1 - 6	Nwokej 20

1	2	3	4	5	6	7	8	9	10	11	Substitutes Used
Wilkerson	Kirby	Nyamah	Smith	Bunce	Graham	Wraight	McMahon	Clarke	Hay	Illman	Armstrong (8), Browne (9), Hockton (10)
Wilkerson	Kirby	Trott	Smith	Bunce	Wraight	Nyamah	Graham	Clarke	Armstrong	Illman	Miller (7)
Wilkerson	Kirby	Smith	Bunce	Miller	Graham	Nyamah	Clarke	Wraight	Armstrong	Illman	
Wilkerson	Miller	Trott	Smith	Bunce	Wraight	Nyamah	Graham	Clarke	Armstrong	Illman	Metcalfe (3), Hay (6)
Taylor	Kirby	Trott	Smith	Bunce	Graham	Wraight	Worrall	Clarke	Armstrong	Hay	
Taylor	Kirby	Trott	Smith	Bunce	Wraight	Graham	Searle	Clarke	Armstrong	Hay	Nyamah (6), Illman (10), Miller (8)
Taylor	Trott	Smith	Bunce	Kirby	Graham	Wraight	Dyer	Armstrong	Clarke	Hay	Miller (6), Illman (9), Nyamah (10)
Taylor	Kirby	Trott	Smith	Bunce	Miller	Graham	Clarke	Illman	Armstrong	Hay	Pearson (9), Nyamah (7)
Taylor	Kirby	Trott	Smith	Bunce	Graham	Miller	Searle	Clarke	Armstrong	Hay	Pearson (6), Nyamah (9), Wraight (10)
Taylor	Kirby	Trott	Bunce	Miller	Wraight	Searle	Clarke	Illman	Armstrong	Hay	Dyer (7), Pearson 99), Martin (10)
Taylor	Kirby	Trott	Smith	Bunce	Miller	Martin	Searle	Clarke	Illman	Hay	Dyer (8), Armstrong (10)
Taylor	Kirby	Nyamah	Ayres	Bunce	Martin	Miller	Searle	Dyer	Armstrong	Leadbeater	Graham (9), Pearson (11)
Wilkerson	Miller	Trott	Smith	Ayres	Metcalfe	Illman	McMahon	Clarke	Armstrong	Leadbeater	Kirby (8), Hay (11)
Wilkerson	Miller	Trott	Smith	Bunce	Metcalfe	Martin	McMahon	Clarke	Hay	Leadbeater	Kirby (8), Armstrong (11)
Wilkerson	Kirby	Trott	Smith	Bunce	Metcalfe	Martin	McMahon	Clarke	Hay	Armstrong	
Wilkerson	Kirby	Trott	Smith	Bunce	Metcalfe	Martin	McMahon	Armstrong	Clarke	Hay	Miller (6), Illman (9), Leadbeater (11)
Wilkerson	Miller	Trott	Smith	Bunce	Kirby	Martin	McMahon	Clarke	Hay	Armstrong	Illman (11)
Wilkerson	Miller	Trott	Smith	Bunce	Kirby	Martin	McMahon	Clarke	Hay	Armstrong	Illman (2), Morgan (6), Phillips (9)
Wilkerson	Miller	Trott	Smith	Bunce	Phillips	Morgan	McMahon	Metcalfe	Hay	Armstrong	Clarke (7), Kirby (10), Martin (11)
Wilkerson	Miller	Trott	Smith	Bunce	Phillips	Martin	Morgan	Clarke	Broughton	Armstrong	Illman (2)
Wilkerson	Miller	Smith	Bunce	Trott	Phillips	Martin	McMahon	Clarke	Hay	Broughton	Illman (10)
Wilkerson	Kirby	Trott	Smith	Bunce	Phillips	Martin	McMahon	Clarke	Hay	Broughton	Armstrong (11)
Wilkerson	Kirby	Trott	Smith	Bunce	Phillips	Martin	McMahon	Clarke	Hay	Armstrong	Illman (11)
Wilkerson	Kirby	Smith	Bunce	Miller	Martin	Phillips	Morgan	Broughton	Clarke	Illman	Hay (9), Metcalfe (11)
Taylor	Hamsher	Miller	Smith	Bunce	Phillips	Martin	McMahon	Leadbeater	Illman	Brissett	Hay (5), Armstrong (11)
Wilkerson	Hamsher	Trott	Smith	Bradshaw	D Phillips	Martin	Metcalfe	Hay	Illman	Leadbeater	Armstrong (11)
Wilkerson	Hamsher	Trott	Smith	Bradshaw	D Phillips	Martin	McMahon	Clarke	Hay	Illman	Miller (5), Armstrong (11)
Wilkerson	Hamsher	Smith	Bradshaw	Trott	Martin	McMahon	D Phillips	Clarke	Illman	Hay	Brissett (9), Armstrong (10)
Wilkerson	Hamsher	Miller	Smith	Bradshaw	D Phillips	Martin	McMahon	Hay	Armstrong	Clarke	Kirby (7), Morgan (11)
Wilkerson	Hamsher	Miller	Smith	Bradshaw	D Phillips	Martin	McMahon	Hay	Armstrong	Clarke)	Bunce (4), Morgan (7), Illman (11)
Taylor	Hamsher	Miller	Trott	Bradshaw	D Phillips	McMahon	Morgan	Hay	Illman	Walters	Armstrong (6)
Taylor	Hamsher	Trott	Smith	Cort	Phillips	Walters	Martin	Morgan	Hay	Illman	Clarke (9), Sodje (10) sub Armstrong
Taylor	Hamsher	Trott	Smith	Cort	Martin	Walters	McMahon	Morgan	Armstrong	Illman	Miller (3), Abbot (8), Bridge (11)
Taylor	Hamsher	Miller	Smith	Bradshaw	Martin	Walters	McMahon	Morgan	Armstrong	Illman	Bridge (5)
Taylor	Hamsher	Miller	Sodge	Cort	Martin	McMahon	Morgan	Clarke	Illman	Abbot	Duckett (8), Armstrong (10)
Taylor	Hamsher	Trott	Sodge	Cort	Martin	Abbott	McMahon	Morgan	Clarke	Illman	Miller (3), Armstrong (5)
Wilkerson	Hamsher	Sodje	Cort	Miller	Martin	D Phillips	McMahon	Walters	Clarke	Armstrong	Abbott (5), Morgan (7)
Wilkerson	Hamsher	Sodje	Smith	Miller	Martin	McMahon	Illman	Clarke	Walters	Armstrong	Cort (8), Morgan (11)
Wilkerson	Miller	Hamsher	Sodje	Cort	Morgan	McMahon	Walters	Illman	Clarke	Boylan	D Phillips (8), Armstrong (11)
Wilkerson	Hamsher	Sodje	Smith	Cort	Morgan	McMahon	Phillips	Martin	Clarke	Illman	Trott (6), Armstrong (11)
Wilkerson	Hamsher	Sodje	Smith	Cort	McMahon	D Phillips	Martin	Illman	Clarke	Armstrong	Miller (2), Morgan (3)
Wilkerson	Hamsher	Sodje	Smith	Trott	Martin	McMahon	D Phillips	Morgan	Clarke	Illman	Armstrong (2), Abbott (9), Bridge (11)

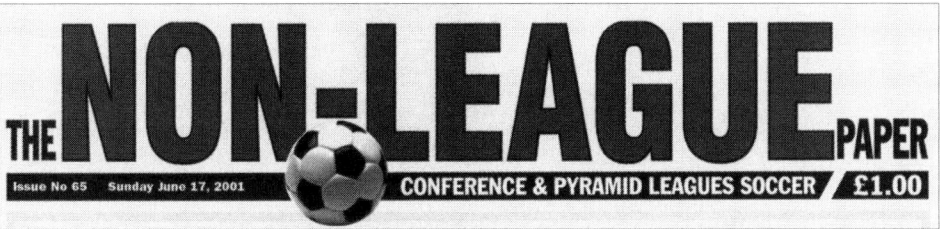

PLAYING SQUAD

STEVENAGE BOROUGH

Bold print indicates England Semi-Professional Internationals

Player *Honours*	*Birthplace*	*D.O.B.*	*Previous Clubs*
GOALKEEPERS			
Paul Wilkerson	Hertford	11.12.74	Watford, Slough T, Welling U
DEFENDERS			
Robin Trott	Orpington	17.08.74	Gillingham, Welling U, £8,000 to Stevenage B
Jason Goodliffe ESP	Hillingdon	07.03.74	Hayes, Brentford
John Hamsher	Lambeth	14.01.78	Rushden & Diamonds, Fulham
Paul Sturgess	Dartford	04.08.75	Hereford Utd, Brighton, Millwall, Charlton
Ryan Crossley	Halifax	23.07.80	Bury, Huddersfield
MIDFIELD			
Sam McMahon	Newark	10.02.76	Leicester, Camb.U
Dean Martin	Islington	31.08.74	KA Akureyri (Finland), Stevenage B, Hereford Utd, Brentford, Kettering T, West Ham, Fisher Ath
John Morgan	London		Enfield (£7,500)
Leon Smith	Bolton	18.02.80	Morecambe
Matt Fisher	Mansfield		Kettering T, Gedling T, Ashfield Utd, Army
Steve Walters EY, ESP	Plymouth	09.01.72	Morecambe (£17,000), Northwich V, Crewe
FORWARDS			
Chris Pearson	Leicester	05.01.76	Hinckley T, Notts Co., Hinckley T, Kettering T, £14,000 to Stevenage B
Darren Hay FAT	Hitchin	17.12.69	Biggleswade T, Camb.U, Woking
Paul Armstrong	Herts		From Academy
Adrian Clarke ES	Cambridge	28.09.74	Arsenal, Southend
Martin Williams	Luton	12.07.73	Reading, Luton, Leicester
DJ Campbell	London		Chesham Utd, Aston Villa (Trainee)

TELFORD UNITED

Telford United have struggled in recent seasons, but a sixth place in the Conference in 2000-01 might suggest that this is now at an end and the good people of Shropshire will welcome it.

The main problem - as a 51-51 goals difference statistic will show - is an adequate defence and only moderate attack, which Manager Jake King must urgently address.

At no stage of the season, in which poor weather did the club no favours as the new stadium developed, was there any apparent danger of relegation, but the first three months of 2001 were a productive period with nine of their victories coming during that time and four successes in the last half dozen outings ensured respectability.

The knock-out competitions were also respectable if not brilliant with Hinckley United removed from the F.A. Cup at the Fourth Qualifying Round stage (1-1 away and 4-1 in the replay), but Blackpool came to the Bucks Head Ground and a 3-1 scoreline saw Telford's demise.

The Trophy was better with a 2-1 Third Round success at King's Lynn followed by another away victory (2-1 at Billericay Town), but yet another away match was too much as the club fell to a single goal defeat at eventual winners Canvey Island.

Wembley triumphs remain a slightly distant memory, but hope springs eternal.

W.M.

TELFORD UNITED FC 2001-02

Back row L-R: Andrew Rose (Physio), Gary Fitzpatrick, Steve Palmer, Kevin Davies, Richard Scott, Ryan Price, Jim Bentley, Jake Edwards, Nick Porter, Jordan King, Charlie Walker (Chief Scout)

Front row: Mark Albrighton, Gary Martindale, Neil Moore, Kevin Jobling (Assistant Manager), Jake King (Manager), Roger Preece (Coach), Peter Smith, Lee Fowler, Gareth Hamner

TELFORD UNITED

GROUND DETAILS

New Bucks Head Ground
The Bucks Way,
Telford,
Shropshire TF12NJ

Tel: 01952 640064
Fax: 01952 640021
email: dawnbird@lineone.net
web site: www.telford.united@ lineone.net

SIMPLE DIRECTIONS:

Signposted from M54 Junction 6.

Due to contruction of a new stadium on the same site the following details apply for season 2001-02

CAPACITY:	4,268
SEATED:	Nil
COVERED TERRACING:	2,960

SOCIAL FACILITIES:
During 2001-02 season - nil

CLUB SHOP:
Telephone 01952 640064for details

MATCHDAY PROGRAMME

Pages: 32 Price: £1.60

Editor: Dawn Bird (General Manager)

Other club publications: None

Local Press: Shropshire Star; Telford Journal
Local Radio: BBC Radio Shropshire;
Beacon Radio; Telford FM; WABC

Founded:	1876
Nickname:	The Bucks
Club Sponsors:	GKN Wheels
Club colours:	Red.Blue.Red
Change colours:	White,black,black
Midweek home matchday:	Tuesday
Reserves' League:	Central Conference

CLUB OFFICIALS

President	Gerald Smith
Chairman	Andy Shaw
Football Secretary	Mike Ferriday c/o the club 01543 273516
Commercial Manager	T.B.A.
Press Officer	Robert Cave 0771 0227337

FOOTBALL MANAGEMENT TEAM

MANAGER: **JAKE KING**
Date of appointment: March 2000
Date of Birth: 29th January 1955
Place of Birth: Glasgow

PREVIOUS CLUBS
as manager Telford Utd (11.96-5.97), Shrewsbury Town (97-2000)
as player Shrewsbury T., Cardiff C., Wrexham

HONOURS
as manager None
as player Football League 3rd Div. Championship; 4th Div. Runners-up

* * *

Assistant Manager:	Kevin Jobling
Coach:	Roger Preece
Chief Scout:	Charlie Walker
Physio:	Andy Rose
Youth development:	Charlie Walker

Season

	League	Div.	Pos.	Home P	W	D	L	F	A	Away W	D	L	F	A	Pts	Manager
00-01	Conference	-	6	42	13	1	7	33	23	6	7	8	18	28	65	Jake King
99-00	Conference	-	16	42	12	4	5	34	21	2	5	14	22	45	51	Alan Lewer / Jake King
98-99	Conference	-	17	42	7	8	6	24	24	3	8	10	20	36	46	Jimmy Mullen / Alan Lewer
97-98	Conference	-	20	42	6	7	8	25	31	4	5	12	28	45	42	Steve Daly / Jimmy Mullen
96-97	Conference	-	9	42	6	7	8	21	30	10	3	8	25	26	58	Wayne Clarke

	League	Div.	Pos.	P	W	D	L	F	A	Pts	Manager
95-96	Conference	-	13	42	15	10	17	51	56	55	Wayne Clarke
94-95	Conference	-	19	42	10	16	16	53	62	46	Gerry Daly / George Foster
93-94	Conference	-	17	42	13	12	17	41	49	51	Gerry Daly
92-93	Conference	-	15	42	14	10	18	55	60	52	Gerry Daly
91-92	Conference	-	6	42	19	7	16	62	66	64	Gerry Daly

HONOURS

FA Trophy Winners 71-72, 82-83, 88-89.
R-up 69-70, 87-88;
Birmingham League1920-21, 1934-35, 1935-36;
Cheshire League 1945-46, 1946-47, 1951-52;
Edward Case Cup 1952-53, 1954-55;
Welsh Cup 1901-02, 1905-06, 1939-40;
BirminghamSenior Cup 1946-47;
Walsall Senior Cup 1946-47;
Birmingham League Challenge Cup 1946-47;
Shropshire Senior Cup (30);
Southern League Cup 1970-71;
Midland Floodlit Cup 1970-71, 1982-83, 1988-89,
Runners-up 1969-70, 1987-88

PREVIOUS

Leagues: Southern League, Cheshire League, Birmingham League

Name: Wellington Town (prior to 1969)

Grounds: None

Past Players who progressed to the Football League

A.Walker (Lincoln City),G.French (Luton Town),
K.McKenna (Tranmere Rovers), S.Norris (Scarborough),
David Pritchard (Bristol Rovers) 1994,
Sean Parrish (Doncaster Rovers) 1994,
Steve Foster (Bristol R.);
Peter Wilding, Roger Preece, Mark Williams & Martyn Naylor - all to Shrewsbury 1997

CLUB RECORDS

Attendance: 13,000 v Shrewsbury Town, Birmingham League - 1936

Win: **Unknown**
Defeat: **Unknown**

Career appearances: **Unknown**
Career goalscorer: Jack Bentley

Transfer fee paid: £20,000 to Wrexham for Jake Edwards

Transfer fee received: £50,000 from Scarborough for Stephen Norris

BEST SEASON

FA Cup: 5th Round 84-85, 0-3 v Everton (A), 47,402.
Also 4th Rd. 83-84, 3rd Rd.86-87, 2nd Rd. 82-83, 85-86, 91-92

League clubs defeated: Wigan, Rochdale, Stockport C., Darlington, Stoke C.,Lincoln C., Bradford C

FA Trophy: Winners 70-71, 82-83, 88-89. R-up 69-70, 87-88

League: 3rd Conference 81-82

LAST SEASON

F.A. Cup: First Round
F.A. Trophy: Sixth Round
Conference: 6th
Top Goalscorer: Jake Edwards
Player of the Year: Neil Moore
(Club) Captain: Neil Moore
Highest League Attendance: 2,317

TELFORD UNITED

Match Facts 2000-01

	Date	Comp.	Opponents	Gate	Score	Goalscorers	
1	19/08	Conf	HAYES	542	2 - 0	Jobling 19, Martindale 73	(at Worcester City)
2	22/08	Conf	Northwich Victoria	812	1 - 0	Malkin 6	
3	26/08	Conf	Nuneaton Borough	1531	1 - 1	Murphy 80	
4	28/08	Conf	FOREST GREEN ROVERS	709	1 - 0	Murphy 54	(at Worcester City)
5	02/09	Conf	RUSHDEN & DIAMONDS	1510	1 - 2	Palmer 29	(at Worcester City)
6	05/09	Conf	Hereford United	2431	0 - 2		
7	09/09	Conf	Southport	1354	0 - 3		
8	12/09	Conf	LEIGH RMI	281	2 - 1	Palmer 29, Edwards 35	(at Worcester City)
9	16/09	Conf	DOVER ATHLETIC	415	0 - 2		(at Worcester City)
10	23/09	Conf	Morecambe	1013	0 - 0		
11	26/09	Conf	KETTERING TOWN	386	2 - 1	Murphy 45, J Edwards 48	(at Worcester City)
12	30/09	Conf	Stevenage Borough	1446	3 - 5	Edwards 3 36, Jobling 80	
13	04/10	Conf	Boston United	1756	1 - 2	Martindale 42	
14	06/10	Conf	SCARBOROUGH	395	1 - 0	Travis 47	(at Worcester City)
15	14/10	Conf	Leigh RMI	552	1 - 1	Farrell 55[og]	
16	21/10	Conf	DAGENHAM & REDBRIDGE	2317	0 - 1		
17	04/11	Conf	Hayes	584	1 - 0	Edwards 62	
18	02/12	Conf	Yeovil Town	3106	0 - 2		
19	16/12	Conf	WOKING	1249	3 - 1	Martindale 50, Jobling 56, Preece 72	
20	26/12	Conf	Hednesford Town	1046	1 - 1	Jobling 71	
21	06/01	Conf	Forest Green Rovers	775	1 - 1	Martindale 44[p]	
22	20/01	Conf	NUNEATON BOROUGH	1382	2 - 1	Moore 46, J Edwards 90	
23	27/01	Conf	HEREFORD UNITED	1848	1 - 0	Malkin 85	
24	06/02	Conf	DONCASTER ROVERS	1287	1 - 0	Martindale 11	
25	10/02	Conf	SOUTHPORT	1373	2 - 3	Bentley 30, Martindale 41	
26	13/02	Conf	HEDNESFORD TOWN	1141	2 - 1	Albrighton 65, Malkin 74	
27	20/02	Conf	Chester City	1362	0 - 1		
28	27/02	Conf	Woking	1106	0 - 3		
29	03/03	Conf	Dover Athletic	1161	3 - 1	Davies 3, Albrighton 40, Murphy 90	
30	13/03	Conf	KINGSTONIAN	860	0 - 1		
31	23/03	Conf	Kettering Town	1405	1 - 0	Murphy 79	
32	27/03	Conf	CHESTER CITY	1058	3 - 0	Malkin 14, Palmer 39, Murphy 68	
33	31/03	Conf	BOSTON UNITED	1109	3 - 2	Murphy 11, Palmer 72, Huckerby 86	
34	07/04	Conf	Dagenham & Redbridge	1011	0 - 0		
35	10/04	Conf	Scarborough	723	1 - 1	Moore 68	
36	14/04	Conf	NORTHWICH VICTORIA	1019	2 - 3	Moore 18, Huckerby 71	
37	16/04	Conf	Kingstonian	867	1 - 0	Palmer 12	
38	18/04	Conf	STEVENAGE BOROUGH	648	2 - 2	Edwards 36, Martindale 47[p]	
39	24/04	Conf	Rushden & Diamonds	4107	0 - 3		
40	28/04	Conf	YEOVIL TOWN	1821	1 - 2	Bentley 42	
41	01/05	Conf	MORECAMBE	753	2 - 0	Edwards 37, Travis 82	
42	05/05	Conf	Doncaster Rovers	2026	2 - 1	Edwards 56 80	

OTHER COMPETITIONS

Date	Comp.	Opponents	Gate	Score	Goalscorers	
24/07	Shrops SC 1	Bridgnorth Town	400	2 - 0	Edwards 35 40	
26/07	Shrops SC SF	Shifnal Town	500	4 - 0	Palmer(2), Moore, Edwards	
01/08	Shrops SC F	WOLVERHAMPTON WANDERERS	750	0 - 2		(at Shrewsbury Town)
18/09	Variety CT 1	Hednesford Town	349	0 - 1		
28/10	FA Cup Q4	Hinckley United	675	1 - 1	Gale 48	
13/11	FA Cup Q4 R	HINCKLEY UNITED	1254	4 - 1	Moore 39, Edwards 54 63, Palmer 75	
18/11	FA Cup 1	Blackpool	2780	1 - 3	Martindale 65	
13/01	FA Trophy 3	Trafford	435	1 - 1	Sandwith 56	
16/01	FA Trophy 3 R	TRAFFORD	788	7 - 1	Edwards 5 71, Moore 19, Martindale 46 67, Palmer 57, Huckerby 70	
03/02	FA Trophy 4	King's Lynn	1357	2 - 1	Robinson 8[og], Jobling 60	
24/02	FA Trophy 5	Billericay Town	709	3 - 2	Palmer 10, Martindale 43, Edwards 51	
10/03	FA Trophy QF	Canvey Island	807	0 - 1		

1	2	3	4	5	6	7	8	9	10	11	Substitutes Used
Price	Fowler	Davies	Moore	Bentley	McGorry	Jobling	Painter	Travis	Martindale	Malkin	Preece(8)
Price	Fowler	Davies	Moore	Gayle	McGorry	Jobling	Palmer	Travis	Martindale(	Malkin(s)	Preece (8), Murphy (10)
Price	Travis	Davies	Moore	Gayle	Fowler	McGorry	Jobling	Martindale	Malkin	Palmer	Murphy (10), Preece (11)
Price	Fowler	Davies	Moore	Gayle	McGorry	Jobling	Palmer	Travis	Martindale	Murphy	Preece (8)
Price	Travis	Davies	Albrighton	Gayle	Fowler	McGorry	Jobling	Martindale	Murphy	Palmer	Edwards (10)
Price	Albrighton	Davies	Fowler	Preece	McGorry	Jobling	Palmer	Travis	Martindale	Murphy	Sandwith (4), Cartwright (5)
Price	Albrighton	Gayle	Moore	Travis	Palmer	McGorry	Jobling	Davies	Martindale	Murphy	Edwards (5)
Williams	Albrighton	Davies	Moore	Gayle	McGorry	Jobling	Palmer	Travis	Martindale	Edwards	Murphy (11)
Williams	Travis	Davies	Moore	Gayle	Albrighton	McGorry	Jobling	Martindale	Edwards	Palmer	Cartwright (2), Murphy (10)
Williams	Jobling	Davies	Moore	Gayle	Albrighton	McGorry	Cartwright	Martindale	Murphy	Palmer	Bridgewater (8), Edwards (10), S Edwards (9)
Williams	Albrighton	Davies	Moore	Gayle	McGorry	Jobling	Palmer	Travis	J Edwards	Murphy	Cartwright (9)
Williams	Travis	Davies	Moore	Gayle	Albrighton	McGorry	Jobling	Edwards	Murphy	Palmer	Cartwright (3), Martindale (10)
Price	Albrighton	Davies	Moore	Gayle	McGorry(s)	Jobling	Palmer	Travis	Martindale	Murphy	
Price	Travis	Davies	Moore	Gayle	Albrighton	McGorry	Jobling	Martindale	Murphy	Palmer	J Edwards (10)
Price	Travis	Davies	Bentley	Gayle	Albrighton	Cartwright	Jobling	Palmer	Martindale	Murphy	Bridgewater (7), Edwards (10)
Price	Travis	Davies	Albrighton	Gayle	Moore	Cartwright	Jobling	Edwards	Murphy	Palmer	Bridgewater (7)
Price	Travis	Moore	Gayle	Davies	Albrighton	Preece	Jobling	Palmer	Edwards	Martindale	Sandwith (7), Malkin (10), Murphy (11)
Price	Jobling	Moore	Gayle	Bentley	Sandwith	Preece	McGorry	Palmer	Malkin	J Edwards	Murphy (10)
Price	Jobling	Sandwith	Moore	Bentley	Fowler	Preece	McGorry	Martindale	Edwards	Palmer	Murphy (9), Travis (11)
Price	Bentley	Fowler	Moore	Sandwith	Preece	McGorry	Jobling	Travis	Martindale	J Edwards	Murphy (10), Malkin (11)
Price	Travis	Moore	Bentley	Sandwith	Fowler	Preece	McGorry	Jobling	Martindale	Edwards	Williams (1)
Williams	Gayle	Albrighton	Moore	Sandwith	McGorry	Jobling	Palmer	Travis	Martindale	J Edwards	Huckerby (7)
Williams	Travis	Sandwith	Moore	Bentley	Albrighton	McGorry	Jobling	Martindale	Edwards	Palmer	Malkin (9), Huckerby (11)
Williams	Bentley	Albrighton	Moore	Sandwith	McGorry	Jobling	Palmer	Travis	Martindale	Edwards	Fitzpatrick (2), Huckerby (11), Malkin (8)
Williams	Travis	Sandwith	Moore	Bentley	Albrighton	Bridgwater	Fitzpatrick	Martindale	Edwards	Palmer	Davies (3), Huckerby (7), Malkin (10)
Williams	Albrighton	Davies	Moore	Bentley	McGorry	Jobling	Palmer	Travis	Martindale	Edwards	Malkin (10), Murphy (11)
Williams	Bently	Albrighton	Moore	Sandwith	McGorry	Jobling	Palmer	Travis	Martindale	Malkin	Fitzpatrick (8), Edwards (10)
Williams	Albrighton	Davies	Moore	Bentley	McGorry	Jobling	Palmer	Travis	Martindale	Malkin	Huckerby (8), Murphy (10)
Williams	Bentley	Albrighton	Moore	Travis	Jobling	McGorry	Palmer	Davies	Edwards	Malkin	Murphy (10), Fitzpatrick (2)
Williams	Fowler	Davies	Gayle	Albrighton	Fitzpatrick	Jobling	Palmer	Travis	Martindale	J Edwards	Murphy (4), Sandwith (5), Preece (9)
Williams	Bentley	Davies	Fowler	Jobling	Sandwith	Preece	Fitzpatrick	Palmer	Murphy	Malkin	Martindale (10), Huckerby (11)
Price	Bentley	Fowler	Moore	Jobling	Sandwith	McGorry	Fitzpatrick	Palmer	Murphy	Malkin	Huckerby (10)
Price	Jobling	Sandwith	Moore	Bentley	Fowler	McGorry	Fitzpatrick	Murphy	Malkin	Palmer	Huckerby (10)
Price	Jobling	Davies	Moore	Bentley	Fowler	Preece	McGorry	Murphy	Malkin	Sandwith	Huckerby (9), Edwards (11)
Price	Albrighton	Davies	Moore	Bentley	Fowler	Preece	Jobling	Murphy	Malkin	Huckerby	Travis (6), Edwards (9), Martindale (11)
Price	Travis	Davies	Moore	Bentley	Fowler	McGorry	Jobling	Murphy	Malkin	Palmer	Albrighton (2), Edwards (9), Huckerby (10)
Williams	Fowler	Davies	Moore	Albrighton	McGorry	Jobling	Palmer	Travis	Martindale	Edwards	
Williams	Fowler	Davies	Moore	Albrighton	McGorry	Palmer	Jobling	Travis	Martindale	Edwards	Huckerby (5)
Williams	Fowler	Davies	Moore	Bentley	McGorry	Jobling	Palmer	Travis	Martindale	Malkin	Huckerby (10), Edwards (11)
Williams	Bentley	Davies	Moore	Palmer	McGorry	Jobling	Travis	Malkin	Edwards	Huckerby	Fitzpatrick (5), Martindale (9)
Williams	Fowler	Davies	Moore	Bentley	McGorry	Jobling	Palmer	Travis	Huckerby	Edwards	
Williams	Fowler	Davies	Moore	Bentley	McGorry	Jobling	Palmer	Travis	Huckerby	Edwards	Fitzpatrick (10)

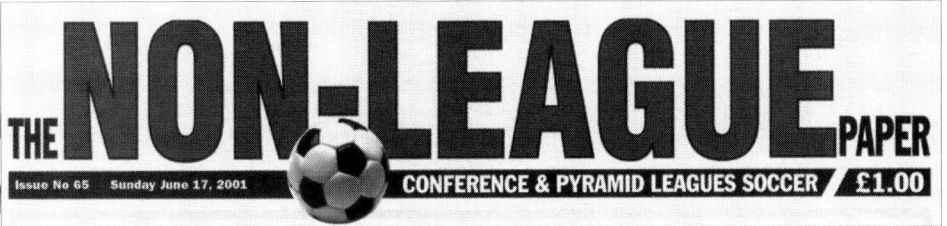

PLAYING SQUAD

TELFORD UNITED

(Bold print indicates an England Semi-Professional International)

Player *Honours*	*Birthplace*	*D.O.B.*	*Previous Clubs*
GOALKEEPERS			
Ryan Price ESP, GMVC	Wolverhampton	13.03.70	Bolton, Stafford R, Birmingham, Macclesfield, £10,000 to Telford U
Dean Williams	Lichfield	05.01.72	Tamworth, Brentford, Doncaster R, Gateshead
DEFENDERS			
Mark Allbrighton	Coventry		Nuneaton B, Atherstone U, £15,000 to Telford U
Jim Bentley	Liverpool	11.06.76	Manchester CM
Martin Naylor	Walsall	02.08.77	Hereford U, Telford U, Shrewsbury
Brian Gayle	Kingston	03.06.65	Wimbledon, Manchester C, Ipswich, Sheffield U, Exeter, Rotherham, Bristol R, Shrewsbury
Neil Moore	Liverpool	21.09.72	Everton, Norwich, Burnley, Macclesfield
Gareth Hanmer	Shrewsbury	12.01.73	Shrewsbury, WBA, Newtown
Kevin Davies	Sheffield	15.11.78	Sheffield Utd
Lee Fowler	Eastwood	21.06.69	Halifax, Doncaster R, Preston, Stoke
MIDFIELD			
Roger Preece	Much Wenlock	09.06.69	Coventry, Wrexham, Chester, Telford U, Shrewsbury
Steve Palmer	Birmingham		Wednesfield
Gary Fitzpatrick Eire Y	Birmingham	05.08.71	Leicester C, VS Rugby, Moor Green, Hednesford T, £15,000 to Telford U
Kevin Jobling	Sunderland	01.01.68	Leicester, Grimsby, Shrewsbury
Richard Scott	Dudley	29.09.74	Peterborough, Shrewsbury, Birmingham
FORWARDS			
Gary Martindale	Liverpool	24.06.71	Burscough, Bolton, Peterborough, Notts Co., Rotherham
Jake Edwards	Manchester	11.05.76	Wrexham, £20,000 to Telford U
Ben Henshaw	Wolverhampton		Oxford U
Peter Smith	Rhuddlan	15.09.78	Crewe

WOKING

Those of us, who have seen some of Woking's finest hours at Wembley and, of course, the Hawthorns, will be disappointed to see them as `also rans' in the higher levels of the Non-League game as fourteenth place in the latest Conference campaign will confirm. Add to that early departures from the knock-out competitions and you see a very mediocre situation.

In the latest season the bread and butter matches at the beginning of the campaign suggested impending disaster with only one victory - a single goal at Doncaster - achieved by the end of September, but three victories in October and a single goal Fourth Qualifying Round F.A. Cup win at home to Hereford United provided some relief.

November was notable for poor weather and no victories, while the F.A. Cup venture ended in a long trip to Carlisle, where Woking's share of six goals was a late effort by West.

Thereafter, it was a struggle with intermittent victories bringing a total of thirteen by the end of the season, which meant an eleven point cushion between them and relegated Kettering with three victories and a draw in early Spring ensuring safety. A52-57 goal difference statistic suggests a modest attacking effort allied to an unreliable defence, although - Carlisle apart - there were no disastrous routs to report.

Woking's name was once synonymous with Trophy success, so a Third Round single goal defeat at home to Margate was not actually a very nice pill to swallow and Manager Colin Lippiatt has a few headaches to face.

W.M.

WOKING 2001-02

Back Row L-R: Paul Steele, Charlie Griffin, Steve West, Michael Fowler, Rob Hollingdale. **Middle Row:** Ian Burns (Youth team Manager), Steve Jenner (Asst Youth team Man.), David Piper, Junior Kadi, Anthony Tucker, Stuart Baverstock, Vince Matassa, Gavin McFlynn, Phil Ruggles, Ron Rawlings (Kitman), Barry Kimber (Physio). **Front Row:** Jamie Pitman, Scott Smith, Stuart Reekes, Scott Steele, Colin Lippiatt (Manager), Kevan Brown (Asst. Manager), Warren Haughton, Barry Moore, Scott Huckerby, Martin Randall.

WOKING

GROUND DETAILS

Kingfield Stadium,
Kingfield,
Woking,
Surrey. GU22 9AA.

Tel: 01483 772470
Fax: 01483 888423

Web site: http://www.wokingfc.co.uk

Simple Directions:
M25 J10 or 11, signposted from outskirts of Town. Ground 1 mile. Woking B.R. Station & buses from Woking.

Capacity:		6,000
Seated:		2,500
Terracing -	**Covered:**	1,400
	Uncovered:	2,100

SOCIAL FACILITIES:
Clubhouse open on matchdays. Food available.

CLUB SHOP: Phone 01483 772470 for details.

WOKING
tele people.com
Nationwide
Fox
WOKING -v- YEOVIL TOWN
Nationwide Conference
Tuesday 22nd August 2000 - Kick Off - 7.45pm
Vol 9 No.1

MATCHDAY PROGRAMME

Pages: 48 **Price:** £2.00
Editor: Paul Beard 01344 482018

Other club publications:
"Winning isn't Everything" (fanzine)

Local Press: Woking News & Mail; Woking Herald; Surrey Advertiser
Local Radio: BBC Surrey Sussex; County Sound; BBC Southern Counties

Founded:	1889
Nickname:	The Cards
Club colours:	Red & white halved shirts & black shorts
Change colours:	Yellow and navy
Midweek home matchday:	Tuesday 7.45pm.
Club Sponsors:	Tele People.com
Newsline	09066 555070

CLUB OFFICIALS

Chairman Terry Molloy

Vice Chairman John Buchanan

Football Secretary Phil J Ledger
19 Ainsdale Way, Woking, Surrey. GU21 3PP.
Tel: 01483 725295 (H), 07831 271369 (M)

Commercial Director John Dukes

Press Officer Terry Molloy
01483 767417

Club Administrator Sue Day

Commercial Manager Philip Shorter

FOOTBALL MANAGEMENT TEAM

MANAGER: **COLIN LIPPIATT**

Date of Appointment: March 2000
Date of Birth: 1st January 1942
Place of Birth: Hayes

PREVIOUS CLUBS
As manager: Yeovil Town 2.98-10.99
As asst. man./coach: Windsor & Eton, Farnbrough Town, Woking, Kingstonian; Kingstonian
As player: Hayes, Wokingham & Maidenhead

HONOURS
As asst. man./coach: (Woking) FA Trophy 94, 95, 97, Conf R-up 95, 96; (Windsor & Eton) Athenian Lge (2); FA Vase S-F & Q-F

* * *

Assistant Manager:	Kevan Brown
Player / Coach:	Scott Steele
Youth Team Manager:	Ian Burns
Physio:	Barry Kimber

Season	League	Div.	Pos.	P	Home W	Home D	Home L	Home F	Home A	Away W	Away D	Away L	Away F	Away A	Pts	Manager
00-01	Conference	-	14	42	5	10	6	30	30	8	5	8	22	27	54	Colin Lippiatt
99-00	Conference	-	14	42	5	6	10	17	27	8	7	6	28	26	52	Brian McDermott/Colin Lippiatt
98-99	Conference	-	9	42	9	5	7	27	20	9	4	8	24	25	63	John McGovern/Brian McDermott
97-98	Conference	-	3	42	14	3	4	47	22	8	5	8	25	24	74	John McGovern
96-97	Conference	-	5	42	10	5	6	41	29	8	5	8	30	34	64	Geoff Chapple

Season	League	Div.	Pos.	P	W	D	L	F	A	Pts	Manager
95-96	Conference	-	2	42	25	8	9	83	54	83	Geoff Chapple
94-95	Conference	-	2	42	21	12	9	76	54	75	Geoff Chapple
93-94	Conference	-	3	42	18	13	11	58	58	67	Geoff Chapple
92-93	Conference	-	8	42	17	8	17	58	62	59	Geoff Chapple
91-92	Isthmian	Prem.	1	42	30	7	5	96	25	97	Geoff Chapple

HONOURS

FA Trophy 93-94, 94-95, 96-97
FA Amateur Cup 57-58
GM VauxhallConference R-up 94-95, 95-96
Isthmian League: 91-92, R-up 56-57
Div.2 South 86-87
Isthmian Lge Cup: 90-91, R-up 89-90
Surrey Senior Cup: 12-13, 26-27, 55-56, 56-57, 71-72, 90-91, 93-94, 95-96, 99-00;
London Senior Cup R-up 82-83
Isthmian League Charity Shield 91-92, 92-93
Vauxhall Championship Shield 94-95, R-up 95-96.

PREVIOUS

Leagues: Isthmian 1911-92

Grounds: Wheatsheaf, Ivy Lane (pre 1923)

Past Players who progressed to the Football League

Ray Elliott (M'wall 46), Charlie Mortimore (A'shot 49), Robert Edwards (Chelsea 51), Ron Newman (Portsmouth 55), Mervyn Gill (Southampton 56),John Mortimore (Chelsea 51), Reg Stratton (Fulham 59), George Harris (Newport Co. 61), Norman Cashmore (A'shot 63), Alan Morton (C. Palace 67), William Holmes (Millwall 70), Richard Forbes (Exeter 79), Kevin Rattray (Gillingham 95), Steve Foster (Bristol Rov. 97), Justin Jackson (Notts Co. 98), Kevin Betsy (Fulham 98).

CLUB RECORDS

Attendance: 6,000
v Swansea, FA Cup - 1978/79
v Coventry C., FA Cup - 1996-97

Win: 17-4 v Farnham, 1912-13

Defeat: 0-16 v New Crusaders, 1905-06

Career Goalscorer: C Mortimore 331, 1953-65

Career Appearances: B Finn 564, 1962-74

Transfer Fees
Paid: £30,000 for Justin Jackson (Morecambe) - 1996

Received: £150,000 for Steve Foster (Bristol Rovers) - May 1997
£125,000 for Kevin Betsy (Fulham)

BEST SEASON

FA Cup: 4th Round 90-91, 0-1 v Everton (H)
League clubs defeated: West Brom. Alb., Cambridge U., Millwall (96-97)

FA Trophy: Winners 93-94, 94-95, 96-97.

FA Amateur Cup: Winners 75-58

League Conference Runners-up 94-95, 95-96

LAST SEASON

F.A. Cup: First Round
F.A. Trophy: Third Round
Conference: 14th
Top Goalscorer: Charlie Griffin
Player of the Year: Vince Matassa
Captain: Steve West
Highest League Attendance: 2,246

WOKING

Match Facts 2000-01

	Date	Comp.	Opponents	Gate	Score	Goalscorers
1	19/08	Conf	Morecambe	1504	0 - 3	
2	22/08	Conf	YEOVIL TOWN	2216	2 - 3	West 4, Watson 11
3	26/08	Conf	BOSTON UNITED	1661	1 - 1	Steele 30[p]
4	28/08	Conf	Doncaster Rovers	2437	1 - 0	Steele 66[p]
5	02/09	Conf	HEREFORD UNITED	2062	0 - 3	
6	05/09	Conf	Yeovil Town	2462	0 - 1	
7	09/09	Conf	Dover Athletic	1027	0 - 0	
8	12/09	Conf	HAYES	1139	1 - 2	Hayfield 80[p]
9	16/09	Conf	RUSHDEN & DIAMONDS	2101	1 - 4	West 77
10	23/09	Conf	Southport	1377	1 - 0	Steele 42
11	26/09	Conf	STEVENAGE BOROUGH	1780	1 - 1	Steele 69
12	30/09	Conf	Scarborough	1156	2 - 3	Randall 51, Steele 77[p]
13	02/10	Conf	Hednesford Town	805	2 - 1	Randall 15, Pitman 72
14	06/10	Conf	NUNEATON BOROUGH	1696	0 - 2	
15	14/10	Conf	Dagenham & Redbridge	1359	2 - 1	Alighieri 23[p], Griffin 45
16	21/10	Conf	FOREST GREEN ROVERS	1779	2 - 0	Randall 52, Griffin 74
17	04/11	Conf	Northwich Victoria	957	0 - 4	
18	11/11	Conf	LEIGH RMI	1421	1 - 1	Griffin 90[p]
19	02/12	Conf	Chester City	1694	3 - 3	Randall 23, Steele 32 41[p]
20	09/12	Conf	HEDNESFORD TOWN	1384	1 - 1	Randall 53
21	16/12	Conf	Telford United	1249	1 - 3	Randall 86
22	26/12	Conf	KINGSTONIAN	2246	0 - 0	
23	01/01	Conf	Kingstonian	1717	3 - 0	Kadi 9, Griffin 14 73
24	06/01	Conf	DONCASTER ROVERS	1948	1 - 1	Griffin 16
25	20/01	Conf	Boston United	1767	0 - 0	
26	27/01	Conf	Nuneaton Borough	1357	1 - 1	Sharpling 81
27	10/02	Conf	DOVER ATHLETIC	1574	4 - 1	Sharpling 28 47, Griffin 39, S Steele 45
28	17/02	Conf	Hayes	1001	2 - 1	Sharpling 12, P Steele 40
29	24/02	Conf	KETTERING TOWN	1840	1 - 1	Griffin 60
30	27/02	Conf	TELFORD UNITED	1106	3 - 0	McGorry 24[og], Sharpling 59 68
31	03/03	Conf	Rushden & Diamonds	3667	0 - 2	
32	13/03	Conf	MORECAMBE	1309	3 - 1	McKearney 15[og], Kadi 69, Griffin 83
33	17/03	Conf	SCARBOROUGH	1625	1 - 1	Griffin 63
34	26/03	Conf	Stevenage Borough	2022	3 - 0	Perkins 1, Sharpling 44 88
35	03/04	Conf	Hereford United	1280	1 - 0	Perkins 71
36	10/04	Conf	SOUTHPORT	1586	1 - 2	Randall 90
37	14/04	Conf	DAGENHAM & REDBRIDGE	2319	4 - 4	Hayfield 34, Griffin 36 90, Sharpling 38
38	16/04	Conf	Leigh RMI	455	0 - 2	
39	21/04	Conf	NORTHWICH VICTORIA	1544	1 - 1	West 82
40	25/04	Conf	Forest Green Rovers	804	0 - 0	
41	28/04	Conf	CHESTER CITY	2264	1 - 0	Griffin 88
42	05/05	Conf	Kettering Town	2479	0 - 2	

OTHER COMPETITIONS

Date	Comp.	Opponents	Gate	Score	Goalscorers
19/09	Variety CT 1	Hayes	164	5 - 3	Steele 18 56, Druce 33 81, Pitman 85
10/10	Variety CT 2	YEOVIL TOWN	445	0 - 1	
28/10	FA Cup Q4	HEREFORD UNITED	2076	1 - 0	Pitman 30
18/11	FA Cup 1	Carlisle United	2647	1 - 5	West 72
13/01	FA Trophy 3	MARGATE	1542	1 - 2	Perkins 46
20/02	Surrey SC 1	Godalming & Guildford	462	3 - 1	Ruggles, Da Costa(2)
20/03	Surrey SC QF	Carshalton Athletic	103	4 - 1	
31/03	Surrey SC SF	CRYSTAL PALACE	n/k	0 - 3	

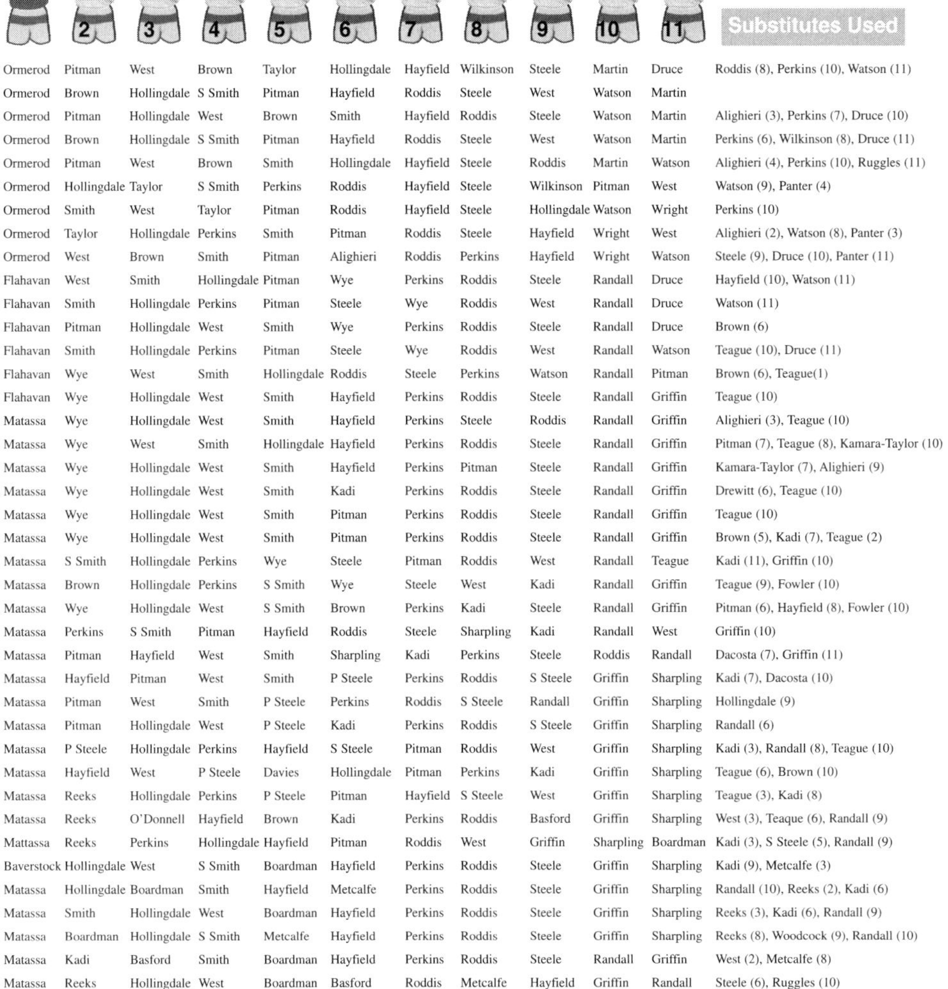

1	2	3	4	5	6	7	8	9	10	11	Substitutes Used
Ormerod	Pitman	West	Brown	Taylor	Hollingdale	Hayfield	Wilkinson	Steele	Martin	Druce	Roddis (8), Perkins (10), Watson (11)
Ormerod	Brown	Hollingdale	S Smith	Pitman	Hayfield	Roddis	Steele	West	Watson	Martin	
Ormerod	Pitman	Hollingdale	West	Brown	Smith	Hayfield	Roddis	Steele	Watson	Martin	Alighieri (3), Perkins (7), Druce (10)
Ormerod	Brown	Hollingdale	S Smith	Pitman	Hayfield	Roddis	Steele	West	Watson	Martin	Perkins (6), Wilkinson (8), Druce (11)
Ormerod	Pitman	West	Brown	Smith	Hollingdale	Hayfield	Steele	Roddis	Martin	Watson	Alighieri (4), Perkins (10), Ruggles (11)
Ormerod	Hollingdale	Taylor	S Smith	Perkins	Roddis	Hayfield	Steele	Wilkinson	Pitman	West	Watson (9), Panter (4)
Ormerod	Smith	West	Taylor	Pitman	Roddis	Hayfield	Steele	Hollingdale	Watson	Wright	Perkins (10)
Ormerod	Taylor	Hollingdale	Perkins	Smith	Pitman	Roddis	Steele	Hayfield	Wright	West	Alighieri (2), Watson (8), Panter (3)
Ormerod	West	Brown	Smith	Pitman	Alighieri	Roddis	Perkins	Hayfield	Wright	Watson	Steele (9), Druce (10), Panter (11)
Flahavan	West	Smith	Hollingdale	Pitman	Wye	Perkins	Roddis	Steele	Randall	Druce	Hayfield (10), Watson (11)
Flahavan	Smith	Hollingdale	Perkins	Pitman	Steele	Wye	Roddis	West	Randall	Druce	Watson (11)
Flahavan	Pitman	Hollingdale	West	Smith	Wye	Perkins	Roddis	Steele	Randall	Druce	Brown (6)
Flahavan	Smith	Hollingdale	Perkins	Pitman	Steele	Wye	Roddis	West	Randall	Watson	Teague (10), Druce (11)
Flahavan	Wye	West	Smith	Hollingdale	Roddis	Steele	Perkins	Watson	Randall	Pitman	Brown (6), Teague(1)
Flahavan	Wye	Hollingdale	West	Smith	Hayfield	Perkins	Roddis	Steele	Randall	Griffin	Teague (10)
Matassa	Wye	Hollingdale	West	Smith	Hayfield	Perkins	Steele	Roddis	Randall	Griffin	Alighieri (3), Teague (10)
Matassa	Wye	West	Smith	Hollingdale	Hayfield	Perkins	Roddis	Steele	Randall	Griffin	Pitman (7), Teague (8), Kamara-Taylor (10)
Matassa	Wye	Hollingdale	West	Smith	Hayfield	Perkins	Pitman	Steele	Randall	Griffin	Kamara-Taylor (7), Alighieri (9)
Matassa	Wye	Hollingdale	West	Smith	Kadi	Perkins	Roddis	Steele	Randall	Griffin	Drewitt (6), Teague (10)
Matassa	Wye	Hollingdale	West	Smith	Pitman	Perkins	Roddis	Steele	Randall	Griffin	Teague (10)
Matassa	Wye	Hollingdale	West	Smith	Pitman	Perkins	Roddis	Steele	Randall	Griffin	Brown (5), Kadi (7), Teague (2)
Matassa	S Smith	Hollingdale	Perkins	Wye	Steele	Pitman	Roddis	West	Randall	Teague	Kadi (11), Griffin (10)
Matassa	Brown	Hollingdale	Perkins	S Smith	Wye	Steele	West	Kadi	Randall	Griffin	Teague (9), Fowler (10)
Matassa	Wye	Hollingdale	West	S Smith	Brown	Perkins	Kadi	Steele	Randall	Griffin	Pitman (6), Hayfield (8), Fowler (10)
Matassa	Perkins	S Smith	Pitman	Hayfield	Roddis	Steele	Sharpling	Kadi	Randall	West	Griffin (10)
Matassa	Pitman	Hayfield	West	Smith	Sharpling	Kadi	Perkins	Steele	Roddis	Randall	Dacosta (7), Griffin (11)
Matassa	Hayfield	Pitman	West	Smith	P Steele	Perkins	Roddis	S Steele	Griffin	Sharpling	Kadi (7), Dacosta (10)
Matassa	Pitman	West	Smith	P Steele	Perkins	Roddis	S Steele	Randall	Griffin	Sharpling	Hollingdale (9)
Matassa	Pitman	Hollingdale	West	P Steele	Kadi	Perkins	Roddis	S Steele	Griffin	Sharpling	Randall (6)
Matassa	P Steele	Hollingdale	Perkins	Hayfield	S Steele	Pitman	Roddis	West	Griffin	Sharpling	Kadi (3), Randall (8), Teague (10)
Matassa	Hayfield	West	P Steele	Davies	Hollingdale	Pitman	Perkins	Kadi	Griffin	Sharpling	Teague (6), Brown (10)
Matassa	Reeks	Hollingdale	Perkins	P Steele	Pitman	Hayfield	S Steele	West	Griffin	Sharpling	Teague (3), Kadi (8)
Matassa	Reeks	O'Donnell	Hayfield	Brown	Kadi	Perkins	Roddis	Basford	Griffin	Sharpling	West (3), Teaque (6), Randall (9)
Mattassa	Reeks	Perkins	Hollingdale	Hayfield	Pitman	Roddis	West	Griffin	Sharpling	Boardman	Kadi (3), S Steele (5), Randall (9)
Baverstock	Hollingdale	West	S Smith	Boardman	Hayfield	Perkins	Roddis	Steele	Griffin	Sharpling	Kadi (9), Metcalfe (3)
Matassa	Hollingdale	Boardman	Smith	Hayfield	Metcalfe	Perkins	Roddis	Steele	Griffin	Sharpling	Randall (10), Reeks (2), Kadi (6)
Matassa	Smith	Hollingdale	West	Boardman	Hayfield	Perkins	Roddis	Steele	Griffin	Sharpling	Reeks (3), Kadi (6), Randall (9)
Matassa	Boardman	Hollingdale	S Smith	Metcalfe	Hayfield	Perkins	Roddis	Steele	Griffin	Sharpling	Reeks (8), Woodcock (9), Randall (10)
Matassa	Kadi	Basford	Smith	Boardman	Hayfield	Perkins	Roddis	Steele	Randall	Griffin	West (2), Metcalfe (8)
Matassa	Reeks	Hollingdale	West	Boardman	Basford	Roddis	Metcalfe	Hayfield	Griffin	Randall	Steele (6), Ruggles (10)
Matassa	Reeks	Hollingdale	West	Boardman	Metcalfe	Perkins	Roddis	Steele	Griffin	Randall	Hayfield (7), Kadi (9), Edghill (11)
Matassa	S Smith	Hollingdale	West	Boardman	Metcalfe	Perkins	Roddis	Edghill	Griffin	Randall	Kadi (6), Hayfield (8), Steele (11)

PLAYING SQUAD

WOKING

(Bold print indicates an England Semi-Professional International)

Player *Honours*	*Birthplace*	*D.O.B.*	*Previous Clubs*
GOALKEEPERS			
Anthony Tucker	London		Fulham
Vince Matassa Australia u-21	Australia		Basingstoke T
DEFENDERS			
Scott Smith New Zealand Int.	Christchurch	06.03.75	Rotherham, Kettering T
Michael Danzey ESP	Widnes	08.02.71	Nottingham F, Peterborough, St.Albans C, Camb.U, Aylesbury U, £15,000 to Woking
Jamie Pitman	Trowbridge	06.01.76	Swindon, Hereford U, Yeovil T
Kevan Brown ESP, FAT, Div.3	Andover	25.06.68	Southampton, Brighton, Aldershot, Woking, Yeovil T
David Piper	Bournemouth	31.10.77	Yeovil T, Southampton
Dean Chandler	London	05.06.76	Slough T, Yeovil T, Lincoln, Torquay, Charlton
Paul Steele	Wiltshire		Yeovil T, Chippenham T
MIDFIELD			
Scott Steele FAT, SS	Motherwell	19.09.71	Airdrie
Barry Moore	London	04.02.77	Hayes, Hampton
Junior Kadi	London	16.08.79	Kingstonian, Whyteleafe, Coventry
Rob Hollingdale	London		Boreham Wood (£15,000), Wembley
Terry McFlynn	Magherafelt	27.03.81	QPR, Manchester Utd
FORWARDS			
Steve West	Essex	15.11.72	Arsenal, Purfleet, Tilbury, Aveley, E.Thurrock U, Concord R, Enfield, £35,000 to Woking
Charlie Griffin	Bath	25.06.79	Swindon (£25,000), Chippenham T
Scott Huckerby	Nottingham		Telford Utd, Ilkeston T, Lincoln
Warren Haughton	Birmingham		Tamworth, Sutton Coldfield T, VS Rugby, Stafford R, Stourbridge, Leicester C.

YEOVIL TOWN

Yeovil Town enjoyed their best ever season in the Conference. The fact that this was difficult to detect as the campaign finished in disappointment was sad for all concerned as the Glovers' real mistake was to take too large a lead too early.

After a wonderful cup run, defeating Colchester United (Div. 2) 5-1, Blackpool (promoted from Div. 3) 1-0 away and just losing in injury time to Bolton Wanderers (promoted to the Premier), and a lead at the top of the Conference they were everyone's target.

Rushden & Diamonds learning from the same experience in two previous years were happy to tuck in behind them and let Yeovil take the strain. The Somerset youngsters did find it tough and then when two quality loan signings Howard Forinton and Martin Barlow were injured without completing ninety minutes between them, the omens were very much with `The Diamonds'.

One thing is certain in football and that was Colin Addison, one of the most popular, experienced and knowledgeable managers in England would have ensured his young squad built on last year's wonderful season and with a little strengthening and tightening up they would surely have come back stronger and better equipped to gain that elusive promotion - just as Rushden & Diamonds had done over the past year.

But sadly a quite disastrous sequence of events saw Addison forced out and Yeovil will be starting afresh again this season.

T.W

Back Row, left to right: Chris Weale, Chris Giles, Colin Pluck, Jon Sheffield, Anthony Tonkin, Roy O'Brien, Stephen Collis.
Middle Row: Stuart Housley (Youth Team Manager), James Bent, Andy Turner, Terry Skiverton, Carl Alford, Glenn Poole, Nick Crittendon, Maurice O'Donnell (Reserve Team Manager)
Front Row: Steve Thompson (First Team Player- Coach), Andy Lindegaard, Lee Johnson, Darren Way, Gary Johnson (Manager), Michael McIndoe, Barrington Belgrave, Richard Parkinson, Tony Farmer (Physio).
Squad members not in photo: Tom White and Faisil Mali

YEOVIL TOWN

GROUND DETAILS

Huish Park,
Lufton Way,
Yeovil
Somerset, BA22 8YF

TELEPHONE 01935 423662
Fax 01935 473956
Web site: http://www.ytfc.net

SIMPLE DIRECTIONS:
Leave A303 at Cartgate roundabou, take A3088 towards Yeovil. First exit at next roundabout, then first exit at next roundabout into Lufton Way.
Railway station - Yeovil Pen Mill (Bristol/Westbury to Weymouth) 2.5 miles from ground.
Bus service from station on Saturday

CAPACITY:	9,607
SEATED:	5,253
COVERED TERRACING:	3,508

SOCIAL FACILITIES: Matchdays hot + cold food available. Meals can be ordered provided advance notice is given. All weather astro turf pitch available for bookings 9am-10pm

CLUB SHOP: Open matchdays & 10-4 weekdays, selling a full range of souvenirs, match programmes, scarves, hats, replica kits and badges

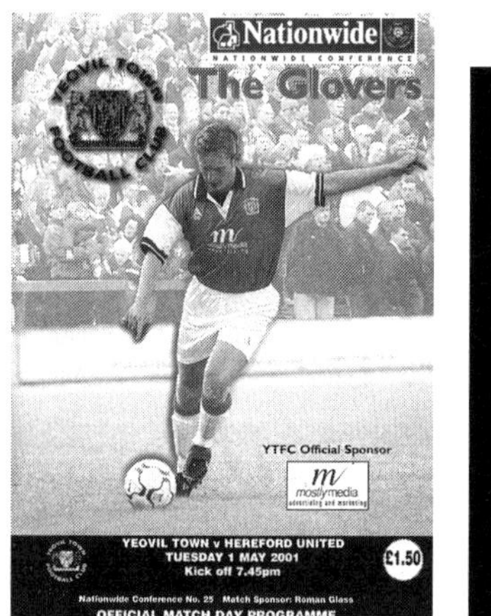

MATCHDAY PROGRAMME

Pages: 48 Price: £1.50

Editor: Shaun Small

Other club publications: "100 Huish Heroes" £3; Centenary Book £14.99 (Both available from the club)

Local Press: Western Gazette; Western Daily Press; Bristol Evening Post; Sunday Independent; Yeovil Express & Clarion
Local Radio: Radio Bristol; Somerset Sound; Orchard FM

Nickname:	Glovers
Sponsors:	Bradfords Building Supplies
Club Colours:	Green & white shirts white shorts & green socks
Change Colours:	All Blue
Midweek matchday:	Tuesday
Reserve League:	Screwfix Direct Western League Prem. Div

CLUB OFFICIALS

Chairman	John Fry
President	S N Burfield M.B.E.
Company Secretary	G R Smith
Club Secretary	Jean Cotton c/o the club
Commercial Sales Manager	Alan Skirton

FOOTBALL MANAGEMENT TEAM

MANAGER: **GARY JOHNSON**

Date of Appointment	June 2001
Date of Birth:	28th September 1955
Place of Birth:	London

PREVIOUS CLUBS

As manager	Newmarket Town, Cambridge Utd., Kettering Town, Latvia
Youth Academy Director	Watford
As coach	Cambridge Utd.
As player	Watford, Malmo, Newmarket Town

* * *

Coach:	Steve Thompson
Reserve team manager:	Maurice O'Donnell
Youth development:	Stuart Housley
Chief Scout:	Frank Leworthy
Physio:	Tony Farmer

Season	League	Div.	Pos.	Home P	W	D	L	F	A	Away W	D	L	F	A	Pts	Manager
00-01	Conference	-	2	42	14	3	4	41	17	10	5	6	32	33	80	D Webb/ Colin Addison
99-00	Conference	-	7	42	11	4	6	37	28	7	6	8	23	35	64	C.Lippiatt/Steve Thompson/Dave Webb
98-99	Conference	-	5	42	8	4	9	35	32	12	7	2	33	22	71	Colin Lippiatt
97-98	Conference	-	11	42	14	3	4	45	24	3	5	13	28	39	59	Graham Roberts/Colin Lippiatt
96-97	Isthmian	Prem.	1	42	17	3	1	49	17	14	5	2	34	17	101	Graham Roberts

Season	League	Div.	Pos.	P	W	D	L	F	A	Pts	Manager
95-96	Isthmian	Prem.	4	42	23	11	8	83	51	80	Graham Roberts
94-95	Conference	-	22	42	8	14	20	50	71	*37	Brian Hall/Graham Roberts
93-94	Conference	-	19	42	14	9	19	49	62	51	Steve Rutter/Brian Hall
92-93	Conference	-	4	42	18	12	12	59	49	66	Steve Rutter
91-92	Conference	-	15	42	11	14	17	40	49	47	Steve Rutter

HONOURS

Southern Lge 54-55, 63-64, 70-71
R-up 23-24, 31-32, 34-35, 69-70, 72-73
Southern Lge Cup 48-49, 54-55, 60-61, 65-66
Vauxhall-Opel Lge (Isthmian) 87-88, R-up 85-86, 86-87
ICIS Prem. (Isthmian) 96-97;
AC Delco Cup 87-88.
Bob Lord Trophy 89-90
R-up 93-94

PREVIOUS

Leagues: Western League, London Combination, Southern League, Alliance Premier79-85, Isthmian85-88, GMV Conference 88-95, Isthmian 95-97

Names: Yeovil & Petters Utd

Ground: Pen Mill ground 1895-1921, Huish 1921-1990

Past Players who progressed to the Football League

Over 40 players & 18 managers including, since 1985,

Nigel Jarvis (Torquay), Ian Davies (Bristol Rovers),

Alan Pardew Crystal Palace), Paul Miller (Wimbledon)

Guy Whittingham (Portsmouth),

Mark Shail (Bristol City), Malcom McPherson (WestHam),

Howard Forinton & Jerry Gill (Birmingham City)

CLUB RECORDS

Attendance: 8,612
v Arsenal 3rd Rd FA Cup 02/1/93

Career Goalscorer: Dave Taylor 285 1960-69

Career Appearances: Len Harris, 691, 1958-72

Win: 10-0
v Kidderminster Harriers (H), Southern Lge. 27.12.1955
v Bedford Town (H), Southern Lge. 4.3.61

Defeat: 0-8
v Manchester Utd., FA Cup 5th Rd.
12.2.49 at Maine Rd. (81,565)

Transfer Fee Paid: £17,500
to Oxford City for Howard Forinton 1.97

Transfer Fee Received: £75,000
for Mark Shail from Bristol City

BEST SEASON

FA Cup: 5th Rd 1948-49
League clubs defeated: 20

FA Trophy: Semi-Final
70-71 71-72

League: 2nd Conference 00-01

LAST SEASON

F.A. Cup: 3rd Round

F.A. Trophy: 5th Round

Conference: 2nd

Top Goalscorer: Warren Patmore

Captain: Terry Skiverton

Player of the Year: TBA

YEOVIL TOWN

Match Facts 2000-01

	Date	Comp.	Opponents	Gate	Score	Goalscorers
1	19/08	Conf	KETTERING TOWN	2302	2 - 0	Bent 20, Belgrave 61
2	22/08	Conf	Woking	2216	3 - 2	Belgrave 21, Tonkin 49, Smith 65
3	26/08	Conf	Southport	1310	0 - 3	
4	28/08	Conf	HEDNESFORD TOWN	2280	4 - 2	Crittenden 5, Bent 40, Steele 43, Belgrave 75
5	02/09	Conf	Nuneaton Borough	1426	2 - 0	Way 17[p], Patmore 37
6	05/09	Conf	WOKING	2462	1 - 0	Steele 80
7	09/09	Conf	CHESTER CITY	2862	2 - 1	Patmore 43, Crittenden 72
8	13/09	Conf	Boston United	1303	1 - 4	Patmore 18
9	16/09	Conf	Stevenage Borough	1755	0 - 0	
10	23/09	Conf	DONCASTER ROVERS	2605	2 - 0	Campbell 14[og], Way 70[p]
11	26/09	Conf	Hayes	707	3 - 2	Belgrave 7, Patmore 36 61
12	30/09	Conf	MORECAMBE	2550	3 - 2	Crittenden 9, Way 76, Patmore 77
13	03/10	Conf	DOVER ATHLETIC	2306	4 - 0	Smith 25, Patmore 34 53, Way 42
14	08/10	Conf	Hereford United	3393	2 - 2	Belgrave 4, Patmore 22
15	14/10	Conf	Northwich Victoria	1015	2 - 1	Smith 55, Way 81[p]
16	21/10	Conf	KINGSTONIAN	2902	3 - 1	Patmore 49, Belgrave 72 75
17	04/11	Conf	Rushden & Diamonds	5283	2 - 1	Patmore 43, Way 84[p]
18	25/11	Conf	Scarborough	972	2 - 2	Smith 41, Way 56
19	02/12	Conf	TELFORD UNITED	3106	2 - 0	Moore 4[og], White 27
20	16/12	Conf	NORTHWICH VICTORIA	2891	1 - 0	Patmore 37
21	26/12	Conf	Forest Green Rovers	1756	1 - 0	Belgrave 73
22	01/01	Conf	FOREST GREEN ROVERS	4361	2 - 0	Patmore 24 37
23	20/01	Conf	SOUTHPORT	4705	0 - 1	
24	29/01	Conf	Hednesford Town	1044	2 - 1	Crittenden 21, Patmore 82
25	10/02	Conf	Chester City	2265	1 - 2	Bent 85
26	17/02	Conf	BOSTON UNITED	3585	2 - 1	McIndoe 43, Betts 73[p]
27	20/02	Conf	DAGENHAM & REDBRIDGE	4025	1 - 3	Way 8
28	03/03	Conf	STEVENAGE BOROUGH	3073	1 - 1	Patmore 75
29	10/03	Conf	Kettering Town	2115	1 - 2	Skiverton 41
30	13/03	Conf	NUNEATON BOROUGH	2774	0 - 0	
31	17/03	Conf	Morecambe	1438	0 - 0	
32	24/03	Conf	HAYES	3206	3 - 0	Goodliffe 29[og], Steele 45, Belgrave 50
33	31/03	Conf	Dover Athletic	1293	1 - 1	Way 68[p]
34	07/04	Conf	Kingstonian	1613	4 - 3	Forinton 51, Patmore 70 90, Akuamoah 82[og]
35	10/04	Conf	Doncaster Rovers	2111	0 - 2	
36	14/04	Conf	LEIGH RMI	3401	6 - 1	Bent 7 50, Skiverton 53 78, Crittenden 60, Tonkin 85
37	16/04	Conf	Dagenham & Redbridge	2136	0 - 2	
38	21/04	Conf	RUSHDEN & DIAMONDS	8868	0 - 0	
39	24/04	Conf	Leigh RMI	565	3 - 2	O'Brien 60, Bent 66, McIndoe 73
40	28/04	Conf	Telford United	1821	2 - 1	McIndoe 38, Steele 51
41	01/05	Conf	HEREFORD UNITED	4639	2 - 3	Crittenden 12, Piper 58
42	05/05	Conf	SCARBOROUGH	2823	0 - 1	

OTHER COMPETITIONS

Date	Comp.	Opponents	Gate	Score	Goalscorers
10/10	Variety CT 2	Woking	445	1 - 0	Patmore 63
18/10	Som. PC 1	Wellington	175	2 - 0	Risbridger 59, Giles 66
31/10	FA Cup Q4	HORSHAM	1966	1 - 1	Kirby 69[og]
08/11	FA Cup Q4 R	Horsham	1907	2 - 0	Piper 58 87[p]
18/11	FA Cup 1	COLCHESTER UNITED	4552	5 - 1	Patmore 50 85, Belgrave 53, Skiverton 57, Way 80[p]
22/11	Som. PC 2	Taunton Town	266	0 - 2	
10/12	FA Cup 2	Blackpool	3757	1 - 0	Crittenden 45
19/12	LDV Vans 1S	Hereford United	853	0 - 4	
06/01	FA Cup 3	Bolton Wanderers	11161	1 - 2	Patmore 25
09/01	Variety CT QF	KETTERING TOWN	709	2 - 0	Way 33, Poole 73
13/01	FA Trophy 3	BATH CITY	3507	2 - 1	Way 71, Bent 74
03/02	FA Trophy 4	Emley	1754	4 - 2	Nicholson 3[og], Poole 23, Betts 36, Smith 90
24/02	FA Trophy 5	Burton Albion	2469	1 - 2	Lindegaard 90
30/04	Variety CT SF	KINGSTONIAN	295	0 - 5	

1	2	3	4	5	6	7	8	9	10	11	Substitutes Used
Pennock	Piper	Skiverton	White	Tonkin	O'Brien	Belgrave	Smith	Crittenden	Patmore	Bent	Way(3), Thompson(11)
Pennock	Piper	Tonkin	Skiverton	Steele	Way	Smith	Crittenden	Belgrave	Patmore	Bent	Foster (11)
Pennock	Piper	Skiverton	Steele	Tonkin	Way	Smith	Crittenden	Belgrave	Patmore	Bent	Foster (10), O'Brien (11)
Pennock	Piper	Skiverton	Steele	Tonkin	Way	O'Brien	Crittenden	Belgrave	Patmore	Bent	White (4), Lindegaard (10)
Pennock	Piper	Tonkin	Skiverton	Steele	Way	Belgrave	Smith	Patmore	Crittenden	Bent	White (11)
Pennock	Piper	Skiverton	Steele	Tonkin	Way	Crittenden	Smith	Belgrave	Patmore	Bent	Lindegaard(11)
Pennock	Piper	Skiverton	Steele	Tonkin	Way	Smith	Crittenden	Belgrave	Patmore	Bent	Lindegaard (11)
Pennock	Piper	Tonkin	Skiverton	Steele	Way	Smith	Crittenden	Belgrave	Patmore	Bent	Lindegaard (8), O'Brien (11)
Pennock	Piper	Tonkin	Skiverton	White	Way	Belgrave	Smith	Patmore	Crittenden	Bent	Lindegaard (11)
Pennock	Piper	Tonkin	Skiverton	White	Smith	Way	Crittenden	Belgrave	Patmore	Lindegaard	Peters (11)
Pennock	Piper	Tonkin	Skiverton	White	Way	Smith	Crittenden	Peters	Belgrave	Patmore	O'Brien (9)
Pennock	Piper	Skiverton	White	Tonkin	Peters	Way	Smith	Crittenden	Belgrave	Patmore	Lindegaard (6)
Pennock	Piper	Skiverton	White	Tonkin	Way	Lindegaard	Smith	Crittenden	Patmore	Belgrave	Poole (9), Bent (11)
Pennock	Piper	Tonkin	Skiverton	White	Way	Smith	Crittenden	Lindegaard	Belgrave	Patmore	Bent (8)Peters (9)
Pennock	Piper	Skiverton	White	Tonkin	Crittenden	Way	Smith	Peters	Belgrave	Patmore	
Pennock	Piper	Skiverton	White	Tonkin	Peters	Way	Smith	Patmore	Belgrave	Crittenden	Lindegaard (6), O'Brien (7)
Pennock	Piper	Tonkin	Skiverton	White	Way	Belgrave	Smith	Patmore	Crittenden	Lindegaard	O'Brien (11)
Pennock	Piper	Tonkin	Skiverton	White	Way	Belgrave	Smith	Bent	Crittenden	Lindegaard	Steele (9), O'Brien (11)
Pennock	Piper	Skiverton	White	Tonkin	Lindegaard	Way	Smith	Crittenden	Belgrave	Patmore	O'Brien (6), Bent (11)
Pennock	Piper	Skiverton	White	Tonkin	Lindegaard	Way	Smith	Crittenden	Patmore	Belgrave	O'Brien (6), Meechan (11)
Pennock	Piper	Tonkin	Skiverton	White	Way	O'Brien	Crittenden	Lindegaard	Belgrave	Patmore	Risbridger (6)
Pennock	Piper	White	Skiverton	Tonkin	Way	Smith	Crittenden	Lindegaard	Belgrave	Patmore	Bent (9), Betts (10)
Pennock	Piper	Skiverton	White	Betts	Way	Lindegaard	Smith	Crittenden	Belgrave	Patmore	Poole (5), Bent (7)
Pennock	Piper	Betts	Skiverton	Way	O'Brien	Smith	Crittenden	Lindegaard	Patmore	Belgrave	Poole (9)
Pennock	Piper	Betts	Skiverton	White	Way	Belgrave	Smith	Patmore	Crittenden	Poole	Lindegaard (2), Bent (7), Thompson (8)
Weale	Piper	Skiverton	White	Betts	Crittenden	O'Brien	Smith	McIndoe	Belgrave	Patmore	Jones (9), Bent (11)
Pennock	Piper	Betts	Skiverton	White	Way	Belgrave	Smith	Patmore	Crittenden	McIndoe	Lindegaard (2), Jones (7), Bent (8)
Pennock	Betts	Skiverton	White	Tonkin	Crittenden	Way	Smith	McIndoe	Patmore	Gritton	Lindegaard (11), O'Brien (4)
Pennock	Betts	Tonkin	Skiverton	O'Brien	Way	Gritton	Smith	Patmore	Crittenden	McIndoe	Belgrave (7)
Pennock	Betts	Skiverton	Way	Tonkin	O'Brien	Gritton	Smith	Patmore	Crittenden	McIndoe	Bent (7), Poole (8), Belgrave (11)
Pennock	Betts	Tonkin	Jones	O'Brien	Way	Steele	Smith	Patmore	Crittenden	McIndoe	Belgrave (11)
Pennock	Steele	Tonkins	Jones	Way	O'Brien	Betts	Crittenden	Patmore	Belgrave	Lindegaard	Gritton (9), McIndoe (11)
Pennock	Betts	Skiverton	O'Brien	Tonkin	Lindegaard	Way	Jones	Crittenden	Belgrave	Patmore	Weale (1), Barlow (6), Forinton (11)
Weale	Betts	Tonkin	Skiverton	O'Brien	Way	Belgrave	Forinton	Patmore	Crittenden	Jones	Piper (2), Steele (5), McIndoe (8)
Pennock	Piper	Tonkin	Skiverton	White	Way	Jones	Poole	Crittenden	Patmore	Belgrave	McIndoe (2), Lindegaard (8), Steele (10)
Pennock	Piper	Skiverton	White	Tonkin	Crittenden	Way	Jones	McIndoe	Belgrave	Bent	O'Brien (6), Smith (8), Lindegaard (10)
Pennock	Piper	Tonkin	Skiverton	White	Way	Jones	McIndoe	Crittenden	Bent	Belgrave	Steele (11), Smith (7)
Pennock	Piper	Skiverton	White	Tonkin	Crittenden	Way	Jones	McIndoe	Belgrave	Patmore	Betts (9), Bent (11) sub O'Brien
Pennock	Piper	Tonkin	Jones	White	Way	Skiverton	O'Brien	Crittenden	McIndoe	Bent	Steele (9), Lindegaard (11)
Pennock	Piper	Tonkin	Jones	White	Way	Skiverton	O'Brien	Crittenden	McIndoe	Bent	Betts (4), Lindegaard (9), Steele (11)
Pennock	Piper	Tonkin	Skiverton	White	Way	Betts	Crittenden	McIndoe	O'Brien	Begrave	Patmore (10)
Pennock	Piper	Betts	White	Tonkin	Way	O'Brien	Crittenden	McIndoe	Belgrave	Bent	Weale (1), Giles (4), Smith (5)

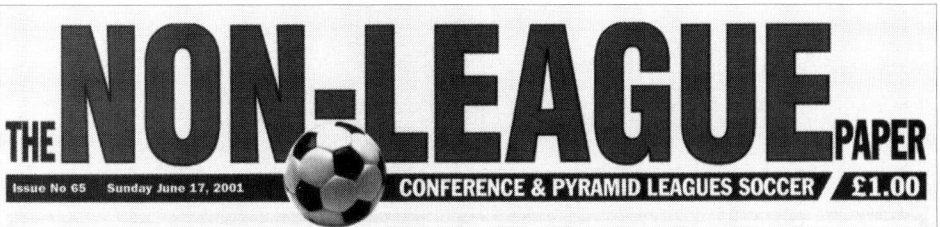

PLAYING SQUAD

YEOVIL TOWN

(Bold print indicates an England Semi-Professional International)

GOALKEEPERS

Player *Honours*	*Birthplace*	*D.O.B.*	*Previous Clubs*
Chris Weale	Yeovil		From Youth team
Jon Sheffield	Bedworth	01.02.69	Plymouth, Peterborough, Cambridge Utd, Norwich

DEFENDERS

Player *Honours*	*Birthplace*	*D.O.B.*	*Previous Clubs*
Murray Fishlock ESP	Marlborough	23.09.73	Swindon, Gloucester C, Trowbridge T, Hereford U
Anthony Tonkin			Falmouth T., Plymouth Arg.
British Univ.			
Terry Skiverton ESP	Mile End	26.06.75	Welling Utd, Wycombe, Chelsea
Colin Pluck	London	06.09.78	Dover Ath., Hayes, Stevenage B, Morton, Watford
Tom White	Bristol	26.01.76	Bristol R

MIDFIELD

Player *Honours*	*Birthplace*	*D.O.B.*	*Previous Clubs*
Glenn Poole			Tottenham H. (YTS), Witham Town, Ford United
Nick Crittenden	Ascot	11.11.78	Chelsea
Steve Thompson ESP, FAT, GMVC, RP	Plymouth	12.01.63	Bristol C, Torquay, Saltash U, Slough T, Wycombe, Woking £5,000 to Yeovil T
Andy Lindegard	Dorset		Westlands Sports
Roy O'Brien	Cork	27.11.74	Arsenal, Wigan, Bournemouth, Dorchester T
Rep.of Ire S & Y			
Darren Way ES	Plymouth	21.11.79	Norwich
Jamie Willmott	Bristol	Bristol R	
Lee Johnson	Newmarket	07.06.81	Watford
Michael McIndoe	Edinburgh	02.12.79	Hereford Utd (£25,000), Luton

FORWARDS

Player *Honours*	*Birthplace*	*D.O.B.*	*Previous Clubs*
Barrington Belgrave	Plymouth		Plymouth
James Bent	Yeovil		From Youth team
Andy Turner ES, Eire u-21	Woolwich	23.03.75	Rotherham, Wolves, Crystal Palace, Portsmouth, Tottenham
Carl Alford ESP	Denton	11.02.72	Doncaster R, Stevenage B, Rushden & Diamonds, Kettering T, Macclesfield, Witton Alb., Burnley, Stockport, Rochdale

NORTHERN PREMIER LEAGUE

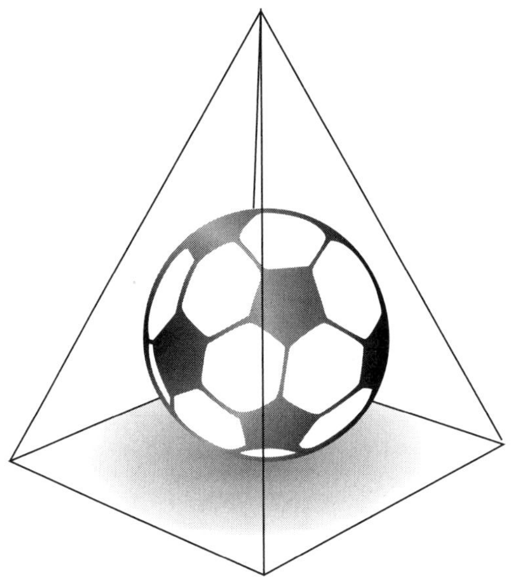

PYRAMID SECTION

UniBond NORTHERN PREMIER

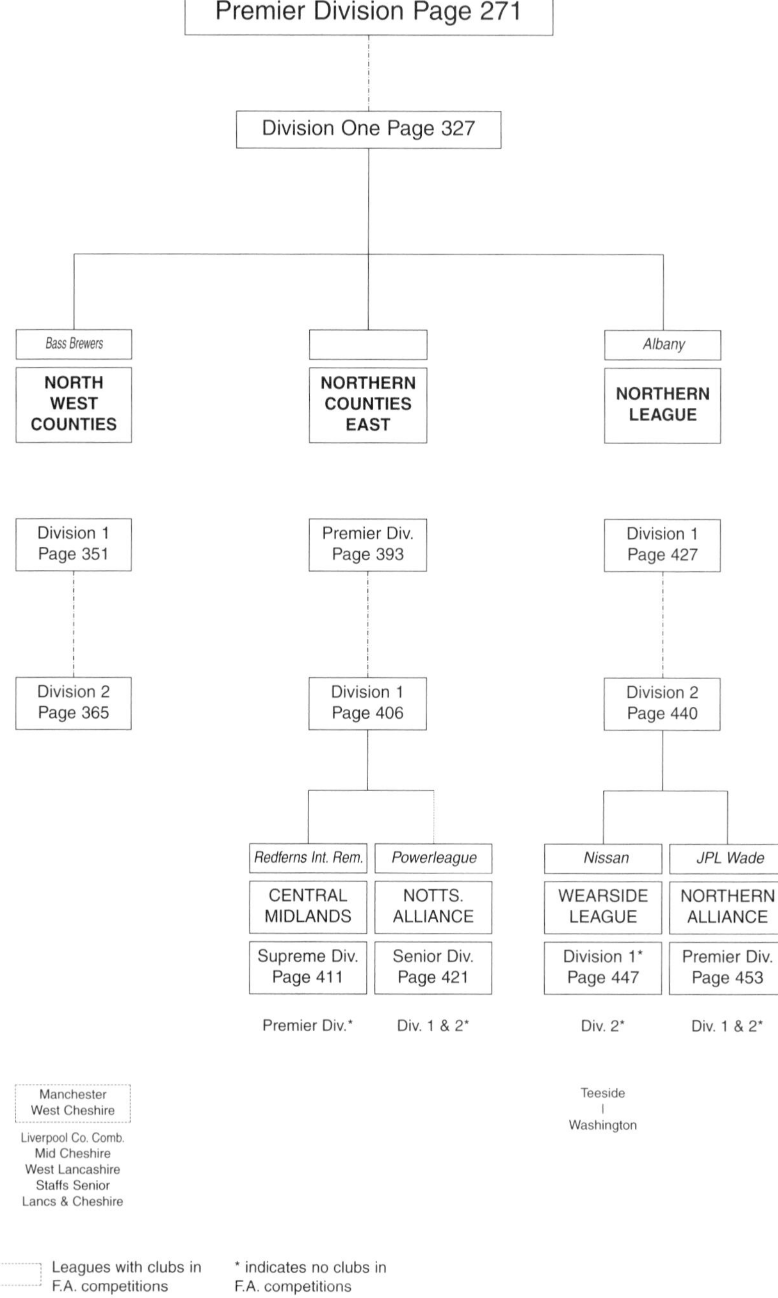

Leagues with clubs in F.A. competitions

* indicates no clubs in F.A. competitions

UniBond League

President: N White F.S.C.A.

SecretaryTreasurer: R D Bayley

22 Woburn Drive, Hale, Altrincham, Cheshire WA15 8LZ

Tel: 0161 980 7007 Fax: 0161 904 8850

Press Officer: P Bradley

7 Guest Road, Prestwich, Manchester M25 7DJ

Tel: 0161 773 4959 (H) 0161 798 5198 (B) Fax: 0161 773 0930

The first full season of the Millennium proved to be the most interesting for several years with intriguing battles at the top and bottom of both Divisions going into the final week of the campaign.

Indeed, such was the situation at the top of the Premier Division that more than 7,000 fans watched Stalybridge Celtic's final three fixtures with over 3,700 attending their clash at fellow promotion contenders Emley on the penultimate Saturday, whilst more than 2,000 turned out three days later at arch local rivals Droylsden to witness Celtic clinch the title with the only goal of the game coming from the penalty spot in something like the eighth minute of added time. Finally, over 1,500 welcomed the new champions back to their Bower Fold home on the final day, where in a carnival atmosphere lowly Burscough spoiled the party and denied the Celts a new record by inflicting a 2-0 defeat. Stalybridge's final tally of 102 points only equalled Colne Dynamo's 1989-90 total, which the ill fated Lancashire club achieved in two matches less than Celtic.

Runners up Emley, however, became the only UniBond League club, and possibly the only semi-professional club, ever to register over a century of points and fail to take the title.

At the opposite end of the table cash strapped Spennymoor United were dead and buried a long time before the finishing line, but the matter of who accompanied them was not settled until the final day of the season. During the early part of the campaign Frickley Athletic had looked odds on certainties to be relegated especially after suffering a12-0 reverse at Worksop Town, which set a record score for the UniBond League. About the same time as Athletic's embarrassing defeat Colwyn Bay were riding high in fifth place but failed to win another game for five months, and they too had spells when they appeared doomed. But both enjoyed fine end of season runs, whilst Leek Town, who seemed safe with a month to go, had a disastrous April and on the final day any of the three could have gone down with the "Moors". The Welsh outfit beat Barrow 2-0 and Frickley won 1-0 at Lancaster City, leaving Leek the losers even though they beat Bishop Auckland 3-1.

The First Division title went to a famous old name in Bradford Park Avenue, who eventually cantered home by ten points, although for much of the race it was a great deal closer than the final margin suggested. Although they lost as many games as runners-up Vauxhall Motors, the telling factor was the low number of drawn games in which Avenue were involved - just five as opposed to the Motormen's ten. So Vauxhall had to be content with mere promotion as opposed to the title in their first season of UniBond action, but spare a thought for third place Ashton United, who finished only one point behind the newcomers. It was the fifth time in the nine seasons they have been members of the League that the Hurst Cross outfit have finished in third spot and surely their time must come soon.

At the bottom Congleton Town, like Spennymoor in the top flight, were doomed a long way before the conclusion of the season but any one of Gretna, Guiseley, Kendal Town, Eastwood Town or Winsford United could have joined the Bears with just two games to go. In the end it was Winsford who must count themselves unlucky, as they were relegated with a record number of points having a final tally of 44 even with six points deducted for playing ineligible players due to administrative errors. The previous highest number of points for a side relegated from the First Division was Goole Town's 40 in 1994-95.

The UniBond League Challenge Cup saw Lancaster City retain the trophy they won the previous campaign to become only the second club to be successful in successive seasons. Runcorn, who said farewell to their famous old Canal Street ground at the end of the season, are the only other club to have retained the League Cup. City, however, were made to struggle in the Final by Bishop Auckland, who took the match to a fourteen penalty shoot out!

The President's Cup Final also went to a penalty shoot out as Stalybridge Celtic added more silverware to their Championship and Cheshire Senior Cup successes, whilst the Chairman's Cup was landed by Barrow who defeated First Division Harrogate Town in yet another battle of spot kicks after 120 minutes of open play had failed to produce a result.

The League had four representatives in the First Round of the FA Cup and Gateshead claimed the scalp of Football League outfit Halifax Town with a superb 2-0 away victory. Barrow, Frickley Athletic and First Division Radcliffe Borough, however, all found full time opposition too hot to handle as did Gateshead at the next time of asking at Swindon Town.

There were three big money moves which saw UniBond League players progress into the full time game with Leicester City leading the way by taking Altrincham's Kevin Ellison straight in to the FA Premiership. The League's leading scorer, Lancaster City's Chris Ward, was signed by Birmingham City and Worksop Town landed a sizeable fee for the League's second leading scorer, Kirk Jackson.

Sadly the League were dealt a major blow at the end of year 2000 when long serving Chairman Ken Marsden suffered a serious illness and, unfortunately, is unlikely to return to the treadmill of running a major league. Ken was one of the brains behind the founding of the Northern Premier League in the late sixties as well as the formation of the forerunner of the Football Conference in 1979. His great experience gained in the game over many years will be sorely missed should he not recover his health sufficiently to carry on.

Phil Bradley, UniBond League Press Officer

PREMIER DIVISION FINAL LEAGUE TABLE 2000-01

			Home					Away					
		P	*W*	*D*	*L*	*F*	*A*	*W*	*D*	*L*	*F*	*A*	*Pts*
1	Stalybridge Celtic	44	19	1	2	57	15	12	8	2	39	17	102
2	Emley	44	16	5	1	44	19	15	3	4	43	23	101
3	Bishop Auckland	44	15	2	5	45	24	11	5	6	43	29	85
4	Lancaster City	44	15	4	3	48	27	9	5	8	36	33	81
5	Worksop Town	44	10	8	4	60	30	10	5	7	42	30	73
6	Barrow	44	14	3	5	49	26	7	6	9	34	37	72
7	Altrincham	44	13	4	5	45	24	7	6	9	35	34	70
8	Gainsborough Trinity	44	13	6	3	35	19	4	8	10	24	37	65
9	Accrington Stanley	44	12	4	6	44	34	6	6	10	28	33	64
10	Hucknall Town	44	11	4	7	34	30	6	8	8	23	33	63
11	Gateshead	44	9	7	6	39	26	7	5	10	29	35	60
12	Bamber Bridge	44	9	3	10	34	31	8	5	9	29	34	59
13	Runcorn	44	12	5	5	35	27	3	5	14	21	43	55
14	Blyth Spartans	44	10	6	6	28	17	5	3	14	33	47	54
15	Burscough	44	8	6	8	32	27	6	4	12	27	41	52
16	Hyde United	44	9	8	5	48	36	4	4	14	24	43	51
17	Whitby Town	44	4	8	10	27	35	9	3	10	33	41	50
18	Marine	44	8	7	7	30	31	4	6	12	32	47	49
19	Colwyn Bay	44	9	6	7	42	45	3	4	15	26	57	46
20	Frickley Athletic	44	6	8	8	31	34	4	7	11	19	45	45
21	Droylsden	44	7	3	12	29	40	6	3	13	21	40	45
22	Leek Town	44	8	5	9	26	30	4	3	15	19	40	44
23	Spennymoor United*	44	3	2	17	17	48	1	3	18	15	60	16

** Points deducted*

PREMIER DIVISION LEADING GOALSCORERS 2000-01

(in order of League goals)

Lge	*Cup*	*Total*		
29	14	43	Chris Ward	Lancaster C
28	12	40	Kirk Jackson	Worksop T
24	9	33	Nicky Peverill	Barrow
23	8	31	Simeon Barbrook	Emley
22	10	32	Simon Yeo	Hyde United
22	9	31	Andy Shaw	Bishop Auckland
22	7	29	Glen Robson	Blyth Spartans
22	7	29	Andy Whittaker	Bamber Bridge
22	5	27	Rod Thornley	Altrincham

PREMIER DIVISION AVERAGE ATTENDANCES 2000-01

	99-00	*00-01*
Accrington Stanley	667	613
Altrincham	-	597
Bamber Bridge	328	272
Barrow	1191	1065
Bishop Auckland	233	206
Blyth Spartans	366	328
Burscough	196	230
Colwyn Bay	226	287
Droylsden	266	311
Emley	289	536
Frickley Athletic	166	190
Gainsborough Trinity	427	393
Gateshead	282	213
Hucknall Town	275	246
Hyde United	538	427
Lancaster City	287	334
Leek Town	302	257
Marine	317	277
Runcorn	256	287
Spennymoor United	227	135
Stalybridge Celtic	416	649
Whitby Town	423	322
Worksop Town	418	495

PREMIER DIVISION RESULTS CHART 2000-01

plus Attendance Chart

		1	2	3	4	5	6	7	8	9	10	11	12	13	14	15	16	17	18	19	20	21	22	23
1	**Accrington**	**X**	**2-1**	**1-3**	**2-1**	**3-1**	**3-3**	**2-0**	**2-2**	**3-0**	**3-1**	**1-1**	**1-1**	**3-1**	**1-2**	**4-1**	**1-2**	**2-1**	**3-2**	**2-1**	**1-0**	**1-4**	**0-2**	**3-4**
		X	1006	663	406	601	504	314	542	591	718	511	535	386	319	567	666	873	451	856	602	935	509	929
2	**Altrincham**	**5-2**	**X**	**1-2**	**1-1**	**0-2**	**3-1**	**2-2**	**3-0**	**3-0**	**0-2**	**3-1**	**0-2**	**3-2**	**1-0**	**2-0**	**3-1**	**1-1**	**3-1**	**2-1**	**5-0**	**0-0**	**3-1**	**1-2**
		681	X	427	514	630	622	603	501	565	641	552	585	620	438	662	649	529	579	676	540	823	568	718
3	**Bamber Bridge**	**3-0**	**1-1**	**X**	**1-2**	**0-2**	**1-3**	**0-1**	**3-4**	**2-1**	**1-1**	**0-1**	**2-0**	**4-2**	**1-3**	**2-1**	**1-4**	**1-0**	**2-0**	**3-1**	**0-0**	**0-2**	**5-0**	**1-2**
		390	408	X	503	155	307	186	238	170	428	229	201	170	220	243	395	252	218	234	229	416	181	220
4	**Barrow**	**3-0**	**2-3**	**3-1**	**X**	**1-4**	**2-0**	**2-2**	**3-2**	**2-0**	**1-3**	**2-0**	**3-2**	**3-1**	**5-0**	**1-0**	**2-2**	**3-0**	**1-0**	**1-2**	**5-0**	**0-0**	**2-3**	**2-1**
		1456	1272	1280	X	961	954	1188	799	903	1283	1048	1024	1001	968	1216	1169	996	840	903	1001	864	1082	1216
5	**Bishop Auckland**	**2-1**	**2-0**	**5-2**	**2-2**	**X**	**1-0**	**4-0**	**5-1**	**2-1**	**1-3**	**2-0**	**3-1**	**0-1**	**2-0**	**3-1**	**1-3**	**3-1**	**1-1**	**0-2**	**2-0**	**0-2**	**2-1**	**2-1**
		236	238	185	299	X	194	206	157	165	202	147	192	328	181	130	208	122	243	145	260	238	235	223
6	**Blyth Spartans**	**1-0**	**1-1**	**0-0**	**1-1**	**1-2**	**X**	**1-0**	**5-2**	**0-1**	**2-1**	**3-0**	**1-0**	**2-1**	**1-1**	**0-0**	**0-1**	**0-0**	**4-1**	**3-0**	**0-1**	**1-2**	**0-2**	**1-0**
		372	383	401	249	399	X	297	321	295	380	243	298	484	303	388	338	290	210	365	271	309	323	295
7	**Burscough**	**0-0**	**1-1**	**3-0**	**1-2**	**2-1**	**3-1**	**X**	**1-2**	**3-1**	**0-1**	**1-2**	**1-1**	**0-1**	**2-1**	**1-0**	**2-3**	**1-0**	**1-3**	**0-0**	**4-1**	**1-1**	**2-3**	**2-2**
		310	329	347	333	180	234	X	179	175	212	112	185	181	191	281	229	165	266	166	189	276	227	287
8	**Colwyn Bay**	**2-4**	**1-2**	**1-1**	**2-0**	**3-3**	**1-0**	**4-1**	**X**	**3-2**	**0-4**	**0-0**	**3-3**	**2-2**	**0-2**	**2-1**	**1-2**	**4-1**	**2-3**	**2-2**	**3-2**	**1-7**	**2-1**	**3-2**
		213	278	214	585	231	288	222	X	244	364	305	212	285	223	312	251	318	302	334	229	239	296	361
9	**Droylsden**	**0-4**	**2-1**	**0-1**	**2-1**	**0-3**	**1-2**	**1-2**	**1-0**	**X**	**1-3**	**1-1**	**4-0**	**0-0**	**1-1**	**2-4**	**3-2**	**1-0**	**2-3**	**0-2**	**4-1**	**0-1**	**1-3**	**2-5**
		202	554	163	253	179	230	195	201	X	238	133	121	214	168	561	120	177	162	142	187	2040	207	404
10	**Emley**	**1-0**	**3-1**	**1-0**	**0-0**	**3-1**	**1-0**	**2-1**	**4-1**	**2-1**	**X**	**0-0**	**1-0**	**2-0**	**0-0**	**3-1**	**1-0**	**1-1**	**3-2**	**2-1**	**3-3**	**2-3**	**4-0**	**5-3**
		465	686	200	372	304	280	471	416	261	X	482	434	325	221	379	194	378	236	460	224	3708	517	769
11	**Frickley Athletic**	**0-2**	**3-3**	**1-2**	**3-2**	**0-1**	**4-2**	**1-0**	**6-2**	**1-1**	**1-3**	**X**	**2-2**	**1-0**	**1-2**	**1-1**	**0-0**	**1-3**	**0-1**	**1-1**	**2-0**	**0-0**	**1-1**	**1-5**
		197	223	174	225	140	170	141	90	119	328	X	162	169	139	139	140	231	159	197	173	402	152	305
12	**Gainsborough T**	**2-0**	**1-0**	**2-0**	**2-0**	**0-0**	**4-2**	**2-1**	**1-0**	**0-1**	**3-2**	**2-2**	**X**	**0-2**	**1-1**	**2-1**	**1-1**	**4-1**	**2-0**	**2-0**	**2-1**	**0-0**	**1-3**	**1-1**
		406	418	386	495	369	428	328	375	324	338	406	X	410	310	254	365	339	336	356	302	291	318	1084
13	**Gateshead**	**0-0**	**2-1**	**0-2**	**1-2**	**0-3**	**2-5**	**1-1**	**4-2**	**1-1**	**0-1**	**5-0**	**1-1**	**X**	**1-2**	**3-0**	**1-0**	**2-1**	**3-0**	**5-1**	**4-0**	**2-2**	**1-1**	**0-0**
		230	251	185	276	195	417	130	205	174	231	211	157	X	135	131	185	227	211	251	251	268	127	245
14	**Hucknall Town**	**2-0**	**1-3**	**1-0**	**1-4**	**2-5**	**4-1**	**3-2**	**1-0**	**1-2**	**0-2**	**3-1**	**1-0**	**2-2**	**X**	**1-2**	**3-1**	**2-0**	**1-1**	**1-0**	**1-0**	**2-2**	**0-1**	**1-1**
		343	290	181	347	145	215	175	218	164	270	210	222	165	X	190	246	101	207	184	181	361	174	820
15	**Hyde United**	**3-3**	**4-2**	**1-4**	**4-4**	**1-1**	**6-2**	**1-1**	**1-1**	**3-2**	**1-2**	**0-0**	**0-1**	**3-1**	**5-1**	**X**	**1-1**	**2-1**	**2-1**	**1-1**	**4-0**	**1-2**	**3-2**	**1-3**
		455	674	311	343	366	417	262	417	402	623	428	323	307	529	X	181	452	381	276	256	1109	362	624
16	**Lancaster City**	**1-1**	**4-1**	**3-2**	**1-1**	**1-0**	**1-1**	**5-2**	**1-0**	**0-2**	**3-3**	**0-1**	**2-1**	**2-0**	**4-1**	**1-4**	**X**	**3-2**	**3-1**	**3-1**	**2-0**	**3-2**	**3-1**	**2-0**
		358	382	247	737	418	267	266	235	308	318	490	240	277	220	301	X	297	381	240	305	304	331	429
17	**Leek Town**	**0-2**	**0-0**	**1-1**	**2-1**	**3-1**	**0-4**	**4-0**	**2-4**	**1-1**	**0-1**	**2-1**	**1-0**	**1-2**	**0-0**	**2-0**	**0-2**	**X**	**2-2**	**2-1**	**3-1**	**0-2**	**0-1**	**0-3**
		387	327	202	362	366	222	251	241	255	260	213	194	251	235	178	149	X	282	203	212	303	205	352
18	**Marine**	**1-1**	**0-4**	**2-1**	**1-2**	**1-3**	**1-1**	**3-5**	**2-0**	**1-0**	**0-2**	**1-0**	**2-2**	**1-1**	**1-1**	**1-1**	**1-1**	**2-0**	**X**	**4-1**	**1-0**	**0-3**	**4-1**	**0-1**
		225	451	231	329	310	202	364	212	271	268	267	220	226	271	263	254	246	X	316	242	304	274	351
19	**Runcorn**	**2-0**	**0-2**	**2-3**	**3-1**	**4-4**	**1-0**	**2-0**	**1-0**	**3-1**	**1-1**	**2-1**	**1-1**	**1-2**	**2-1**	**1-1**	**1-0**	**0-1**	**2-2**	**X**	**2-0**	**2-1**	**2-1**	**0-4**
		222	407	219	275	929	207	275	218	191	293	212	207	555	207	117	145	257	392	X	214	407	159	209
20	**Spennymoor Utd**	**1-6**	**0-4**	**1-2**	**2-3**	**0-3**	**1-2**	**0-2**	**1-1**	**0-1**	**0-2**	**0-5**	**0-3**	**1-4**	**0-1**	**3-0**	**0-3**	**2-0**	**2-2**	**2-0**	**X**	**0-1**	**1-2**	**0-1**
		160	198	90	244	171	162	77	133	146	122	119	75	164	72	139	91	58	97	87	X	129	232	169
21	**Stalybridge Celtic**	**4-0**	**1-0**	**3-0**	**1-0**	**2-0**	**2-0**	**0-2**	**4-0**	**4-1**	**4-2**	**3-0**	**7-1**	**2-1**	**1-0**	**3-1**	**5-0**	**1-2**	**2-1**	**3-1**	**3-2**	**X**	**1-1**	**1-0**
		675	1025	483	718	509	362	1432	626	545	1006	612	498	609	477	1078	530	593	663	427	314	X	456	641
22	**Whitby Town**	**0-0**	**2-2**	**1-1**	**0-2**	**1-1**	**1-0**	**0-2**	**5-1**	**0-1**	**0-1**	**2-2**	**0-1**	**0-1**	**2-2**	**1-3**	**1-5**	**1-2**	**3-2**	**3-1**	**3-3**	**0-1**	**X**	**1-1**
		451	542	237	228	268	431	389	322	361	363	232	251	193	280	257	316	229	269	333	296	315	X	522
23	**Worksop Town**	**0-2**	**1-2**	**1-1**	**4-2**	**1-2**	**4-3**	**1-0**	**1-1**	**5-0**	**1-2**	**12-0**	**1-1**	**2-2**	**1-1**	**4-1**	**4-2**	**3-1**	**3-3**	**1-1**	**6-0**	**1-1**	**3-2**	**X**
		428	665	430	667	272	396	388	317	354	763	618	737	464	324	394	610	461	464	553	335	602	658	X

UNIBOND LEAGUE CUP COMPETITIONS

GROUP STAGE TABLES

GROUP 1

Bishop Auckland	4	3	0	1	11	8	9
Blyth Spartans	4	2	1	1	7	7	7
Gateshead	4	1	2	1	6	4	5
Whitby Town	4	0	3	1	4	6	3
Spennymoor United	4	0	2	2	4	7	2

GROUP 2

Lancaster City	4	4	0	0	9	2	12
Workington	4	3	0	1	9	4	9
Barrow	4	2	0	2	6	6	6
Gretna	4	0	1	3	5	10	1
Kendal Town	4	0	1	3	2	9	1

GROUP 3

Farsley Celtic	4	2	1	1	5	3	7
Harrogate Town	4	1	2	0	5	4	6
Emley	4	2	0	2	5	5	6
Bradford Park Ave.	4	1	2	1	7	8	5
Frickley Athletic	4	0	2	2	5	7	2

GROUP 4

Hyde United	4	3	1	0	15	7	10
Ashton United	4	2	1	1	12	8	7
Altrincham	4	1	2	1	8	6	5
Stocksbridge Park Steels	4	1	1	2	10	14	4
Ossett Town	4	0	1	3	6	16	1

GROUP 5

Bamber Bridge	4	4	0	0	9	2	12
Accrington Stanley	4	2	1	1	12	6	7
Runcorn	4	2	1	1	9	4	7
Trafford	4	1	0	3	7	15	3
Winsford United	4	0	0	4	3	13	0

GROUP 6

Marine	4	3	0	1	9	6	9
Vauxhall Motors	4	3	0	1	6	3	9
Burscough	4	2	1	1	9	6	7
Witton Albion	4	1	1	2	5	8	4
Colwyn Bay	4	0	0	4	3	9	0

GROUP 7

Droylsden	4	3	1	0	9	6	10
Stalybridge Celtic	4	3	0	1	11	6	9
Chorley	4	2	0	2	11	9	6
Radcliffe Borough	4	1	1	2	5	7	4
Congleton Town	4	0	0	4	3	11	0

GROUP 8

Gainsborough Trinity	4	4	0	0	9	2	*9
Worksop Town	4	1	2	1	9	9	5
Guiseley	4	1	2	1	5	6	5
Lincoln United	4	1	1	2	5	6	4
North Ferriby United	4	0	1	3	2	7	1

GROUP 9

Belper Town	4	4	0	0	15	3	12
Hucknall Town	4	3	0	1	7	4	9
Leek Town	4	2	0	2	6	8	6
Matlock Town	4	1	0	3	5	11	3
Eastwood Town	4	0	0	4	2	9	0

GROUP WINNERS LEAGUE TABLE

Belper Town	4	4	0	0	15	3	12
Bamber Bridge	4	4	0	0	9	2	12
Lancaster City	4	4	0	0	9	2	12
Hyde United	4	3	1	0	15	7	10
Droylsden	4	3	1	0	9	6	10
Bishop Auckland	4	3	0	1	11	8	9
Gainsborough Trinity	4	4	0	0	9	2	*9
Marine	4	3	0	1	9	6	9
Farsley Celtic	4	2	1	1	5	3	7

Top 8 qualify for League Cup, Farsley Celtic for President's Cup

GROUP RUNNERS-UP LEAGUE TABLE

Stalybridge Celtic	4	3	0	1	11	6	9
Workington	4	3	0	1	9	4	9
Hucknall Town	4	3	0	1	7	4	9
Vauxhall Motors	4	3	0	1	6	3	9
Accrington Stanley	4	2	1	1	12	6	7
Ashton United	4	2	1	1	12	8	7
Blyth Spartans	4	2	1	1	7	7	7
Harrogate Town	4	1	2	0	5	4	6
Worksop Town	4	1	2	1	9	9	5

Top 7 qualify for President's Cup (+ Farsley Celtic)
Harrogate & Worksop for the Chairman's Cup

3rd PLACED TEAMS LEAGUE TABLE

Runcorn	4	2	1	1	9	4	7
Burscough	4	2	1	1	9	6	7
Chorley	4	2	0	2	11	9	6
Barrow	4	2	0	2	6	6	6
Leek Town	4	2	0	2	6	8	6
Emley	4	2	0	2	5	5	6
Altrincham	4	1	2	1	8	6	5
Gateshead	4	1	2	1	6	4	5
Guiseley	4	1	2	1	5	6	5

Top 6 qualify for Chairman's Cup (+ Harrogate & Worksop)

LEAGUE CHALLENGE CUP

	Belper Town	1	v	0	Droylsden
	Hyde United	0	v	2	Bishop Auckland
	Lancaster City	1	v	0	Bamber Bridge
	Marine	2	v	1	Gainsborough Trinity
	Lancaster City	6	v	1	Belper Town
	Marine	0	v	3	Bishop Auckland
Final	Lancaster City	2	v	2*	Bishop Auckland

Lancaster City won 4-3 after penalties

PRESIDENT'S CUP

	Ashton United	1	v	2	Stalybridge Celtic
	Blyth Spartans	1	v	0*	Workington
	Farsley Celtic	0	v	3	Accrington Stanley
	Hucknall Town	2	v	4*	Vauxhall Motors
	Blyth Spartans	2	v	1	Accrington Stanley
	Stalybridge Celtic	2	v	1	Vauxhall
Final	Blyth Spartans	3	v	3*	Stalybridge Celtic

Stalybridge Celtic won 3-2 after penalties

CHAIRMAN'S CUP

	Barrow	4	v	2	Emley
	Burscough	0	v	1	Worksop Town
	Chorley	2	v	0	Leek Town
	Harrogate Town	1	v	0	Runcorn
	Chorley	0	v	2	Barrow
	Harrogate Town	1	v	0	Worksop Town
Final	Harrogate Town	1	v	1*	Barrow

Barrow won 3-0 after penalties

* after extra time

NORTHERN PREMIER LEAGUE - PREMIER DIVISION - THE LAST TEN YEARS

	91-92	92-93	93-94	94-95	95-96	96-97	97-98	98-99	99-00	00-01
Accrington Stanley	8	6	16	15	7	11	20	22r	-	9
Alfreton Town	-	-	-	-	-	21	22r	-	-	-
Altrincham	-	-	-	-	-	-	8	**1**p	-	7
Bamber Bridge	-	-	-	-	**1**	20	19	4	17	12
Bangor City	20	-	-	-	-	-	-	-	-	-
Barrow	-	8	8	11	4	5	**1**p	-	13	6
Bishop Auckland	11	10	4	9	11	2	10	20	8	3
Blyth Spartans	-	-	-	-	6	7	18	14	14	14
Boston United	-	-	3	5	2	6	2	to Southern Lge		-
Bridlington Town	-	-	21	-	-	-	-	-	-	-
Burscough	-	-	-	-	-	-	-	-	-	15
Buxton	5	14	15	7	20	23r	-	-	-	-
Chorley	21	18	10	18	14	13	15	21r	-	-
Colwyn Bay	-	12	6	12	18	16	13	15	20	19
Droylsden	15	20	17	20	21r	-	-	-	15	21
Emley	6	16	13	13	8	4	6	13	5	2
Fleetwood Town	10	19	22	-	-	-	-	-	-	-
Frickley Athletic	14	7	5	19	19	18	16	16	16	20
Gainsborough Trinity	18	11	12	8	5	10	5	6	11	8
Gateshead	-	-	-	-	-	-	-	5	3	11
Goole Town	12	22	-	-	-	-	-	-	-	-
Guiseley	-	-	-	3	10	9	9	3	22r	-
Horwich RMI	13	13	20	22	-	-	-	-	-	-
Hucknall Town	-	-	-	-	-	-	-	-	18	10
Hyde United	9	9	9	4	3	3	12	9	2	16
Knowsley United	-	-	18	16	15	15	-	-	-	-
Lancaster City	-	-	-	-	-	17	19	19	6	4
Leek Town	4	5	2	to Southern	17	**1**p	-	-	19	22r
Leigh RMI	-	-	-	-	-	-	3	8	**1**p	-
Marine	2	4	**1**	**1**	12	8	11	17	4	18
Matlock Town	19	15	14	14	22r	-	-	-	-	-
Morecambe	3	3	7	2p	-	-	-	-	-	-
Mossley	16	21	-	-	-	-	-	-	-	-
Radcliffe Borough	-	-	-	-	-	-	21r	-	-	-
Runcorn	-	-	-	-	-	12	4	12	9	13
Shepshed Albion	22	-	-	-	-	-	-	-	-	-
Southport	7	**1**p	-	-	-	-	-	-	-	-
Spennymoor United	-	-	-	6	9	19	14	18	21	23r
Stalybridge Celtic	**1**p	-	-	-	-	-	-	10	7	**1**p
Witton Albion	-	-	-	10	13	22r	-	-	-	-
Whitby Town	-	-	-	-	-	-	-	7	12	17
Whitley Bay	17	17	11	21	-	-	-	-	-	-
Winsford United	-	2	19	17	16	14	7	11	23r	-
Worksop Town	-	-	-	-	-	-	-	2	10	5

ACCRINGTON STANLEY

CLUB OFFICIALS

Chairman: **Eric Whalley**
President: **J C Prescott/J Hudson**
Secretary: **Philip Terry**
8 Princess Street, Colne, Lancs BB8 9AN.
Tel: 01286 866768 (H), 01282 864000 (B).
Commercial Director: **John de Maine**

FOOTBALL MANAGEMENT TEAM

Manager: John Coleman
Asst Manager: Jimmy Bell
Osteopath: Martin Dixon D.O.
Physio: Paul Jones

FACT FILE

Formed: 1968
Nickname: Reds
Sponsors: Red Rose Assurance
Newsline: 09068 543 121
Colours: Red/red/red
Change colours: All White
Midweek home matchday: Wednesday
Youth Lge: Lancs Youth Floodlit League.

2000-2001

Player of the Year: Paul Mullin 20
Players P.o.Y.: Steve Carragher
Young P.o.Y.: Robbie Williams
Captain: Jay Flannery
Top Scorer: Paul Mullin

Programme - Pages: 32 Price: £1
Editor: P Terry/D Ellis. (01282 866768)
Local Press: Accrington Observer, Lancashire Evening Telegraph. Local Radio: Radio Lancashire, Red Rose Radio.

GROUND Crown Ground, off Livingstone Road, Accrington.Tel: 01254383235.
Unofficial Website: www.accrington stanley.co.uk **EMail Address:** info@accystan.co.uk
Directions: Arriving on A680 from Clayton-le-Moors Livingstone Rd is on left 50 yds past Crown Hotel. From M62/M66, through town centre on A680 -Livingstone Rd 500 yds on right after Victoria Hospital. 1 1/2 miles from Accrington(BR).
Capacity: 4,000 Cover: 1,650 Seats: 700
Clubhouse: Open five nights and matchdays. Private functions. Well stocked tea-bar in ground.
Club Shop: Sells replica kits, sweaters, t-shirts, videos, photos etc. Contact: Liz Rackstraw

PREVIOUS Leagues: Lancs Combination 70-78; Cheshire County 78-82; North West Counties 82-87.
Names: None. Grounds: None.

CLUB RECORDS **Attendance**: 2,465 v Farsley Celtic 06.05.01 Unibond Division One.
(10,081 v Crewe Alexandra, F.A. Cup Second Round Proper 5/12/92 - played at Ewood Park,Blackburn).
Career Goalscorer: David Hargreaves 328. **Career Appearances:** Chris Grimshaw 362.
Win: 10-0 v Lincoln United 99-00, 9-0 v Ashton Town 75-76
Fee Paid : £15,000 Paul Mullin from Radcliffe Borough 00-01**Fee Received**: £60,000 for Gary Williams from Doncaster R

BEST SEASON **FA Trophy**: 2ndt Rd 99-00 **F.A.Cup:** 2nd Rd 92-93 1-6 v Crewe Alexandra (H) League clubs defeated: None.

HONOURS N West Counties Lg R-up 86-87; Cheshire County Lg Div 2 80-81 (R-up 79-80);Lancs Comb 73-74 77-78 (R-up 71-72 75-76), Lg Cup 71-72 72-73 73-74 76-77;George Watson Trophy 71-72 73-74 ; John Duckworth Trophy 85-86; Lancs Junior Cup (now ATS Trophy) R-up 83-84 96-97; Lancs U18 Cup 89-90;N.W.All Div Cup 94-95; Anglo-Barbados Cup 95.

Players Progressing: David Hargreaves (Blackburn R. 77), Ian Blackstone (York C.), Gus Wilson (Crewe), Glen Johnstone (Preston), DarrenLyons (Bury), Martin Clark (Crewe 92-93), Mark Wright (Wigan 93-94), Paul Collings (Bury 93-94), Brett Ormerod (Blackpool 96-97), Harvey Cunningham (Doncaster R.).

L-R Back Row: John Coleman (manager), Mark Brennan, Duncan Robertshaw, Mark Ceraolo, Paul Mullin, jamie Speare, Robbie Williams, Steve Hollis, jonathon Smith,Jimmy Bell (asst. manager). Front Row: Russell Payne, Gary Williams, Steve Carragher, jay Flannery (capt.), Paul Burns, Simon Carden, Brett Baxter. Photo: T R Slinger.

Date	Comp.	Opponents	Att.	Score	Goalscorers
19.08	Unib P	Leek Town	387	2 - 0	Watson 35[p] 44
22.08	Unib P	ALTRINCHAM	1006	2 - 1	Ceraolo 3, Shirley 7
26.08	Unib P	EMLEY	718	3 - 1	Mullin 75 82, Burns 87[p]
28.08	Unib P	Barrow	1456	0 - 3	
02.09	Unib P	Whitby Town	451	0 - 0	
05.09	Unib P	RUNCORN	856	2 - 1	Watson 20, Burns 29[p]
09.09	Unib P	WORKSOP TOWN	929	3 - 4	Carragher 42, Ceraolo 53 76
12.09	Unib P	Lancaster City	358	1 - 1	Hollis 32
16.09	Unib P	Hucknall Town	343	0 - 2	
19.09	Unib P	BISHOP AUCKLAND	601	3 - 1	Carragher 17, Burns 49[p], Maddock 56
23.09	Unib P	STALYBRIDGE CELTIC	935	1 - 4	Ceraolo 81
26.09	Unib P	Burscough	310	0 - 0	
30.09	FA Cup Q2	Durham City	299	2 - 2	Ceraolo 69, Brennan 80
03.10	FA Cup Q2 R	DURHAM CITY	597	4 - 2	Mullin 3 48 87, Ceraolo 46
08.10	Unib P	LEEK TOWN	873	2 - 1	Burns 1, Mullin 22
10.10	Unib P	Spennymoor United	160	6 - 1	Mullin 11, Burns 34, Ceraolo 44 56, Payne 65, Williams 89
14.10	FA Cup Q3	Bedlington Terriers	515	2 - 5	Mullin 2, Flannery 89
21.10	Unib P	Frickley Athletic	197	2 - 0	Williams 59 85
24.10	Unib P	LANCASTER CITY	666	1 - 2	Burns 28
28.10	Unib P	SPENNYMOOR UNITED	602	1 - 0	Burns 13
04.11	FA Trophy 1	Chorley	377	1 - 1	Williams 48
07.11	FA Trophy 1 R	CHORLEY	443	2 - 1	Mullin 29, Patterson 75
11.11	Unib P	Blyth Spartans	372	0 - 1	
18.11	Unib P	DROYLSDEN	591	3 - 0	Mullin 11 69 83
25.11	Unib P	Runcorn	222	0 - 2	
02.12	FA Trophy 2	Radcliffe Borough	407	3 - 0	Williams 36, Payne 72 86
05.12	Lge Cup 5	TRAFFORD	252	4 - 3	Ceraolo 11 52[p], Wilson 55 84
09.12	Unib P	COLWYN BAY	542	2 - 2	Wilson 62[p] 88
12.12	Lge Cup 5	RUNCORN	180	1 - 1	Carden 70
16.12	Unib P	Hyde United	455	3 - 3	Hollis 51, Mullin 54 80
23.12	Unib P	Emley	465	0 - 1	
26.12	Unib P	BAMBER BRIDGE	663	1 - 3	Flannery 74
03.01	Lge Cup 5	WINSFORD UNITED	217	6 - 0	Brennan 4, Carden 20, Hollis 27, Williams 32, Mullin 73, Payne 81
06.01	Unib P	Bishop Auckland	236	1 - 2	Carden 38
09.01	Lancs MT 2	Lancaster City	161	0 - 5	
13.01	FA Trophy 3	Emley	494	0 - 3	
20.01	Unib P	GAINSBOROUGH TRINITY	575	1 - 1	Carragher 17
23.01	Lge Cup 5	Bamber Bridge	201	1 - 2	Carden 61
03.02	Unib P	Stalybridge Celtic	675	0 - 4	
06.02	Unib P	GATESHEAD	386	3 - 1	Ceraolo 13[p], Payne 29, G Williams 79
10.02	Unib P	FRICKLEY ATHLETIC	511	1 - 1	Ceraolo 77
17.02	Unib P	HYDE UNITED	567	4 - 1	Flannery 47, Ceraolo 74, Brennan 84 90
20.02	Unib P	Colwyn Bay	213	4 - 2	Burns 26, Ceraolo 33, Mullin 70, Williams 73
24.02	Unib P	Gainsborough Trinity	406	0 - 2	
10.03	Unib P	Gateshead	230	0 - 0	
13.03	Pres. Cup QF	Farsley Celtic	104	3 - 0	Mullin 5, Turner 75, Carden 83
17.03	Unib P	WHITBY TOWN	509	0 - 2	
20.03	Unib P	Marine	225	1 - 1	Bell 84
25.03	Unib P	Altrincham	681	2 - 5	Carden 69[p], Coleman 85
27.03	Unib P	HUCKNALL TOWN	319	1 - 2	Carden 77
03.04	Pres. Cup SF	Blyth Spartans	318	1 - 2	Brennan 9
14.04	Unib P	MARINE	451	3 - 2	Ceraolo 15 Carden 26 59
16.04	Unib P	Bamber Bridge	390	0 - 3	
21.04	Unib P	Droylsden	202	4 - 0	Mullin 3 39, Coleman 21, Payne 26
24.04	Unib P	BARROW	406	2 - 1	Baxter 24, Ceraolo 90
28.04	Unib P	BLYTH SPARTANS	504	3 - 3	Coleman 9 49, Baxter 30
02.05	Unib P	BURSCOUGH	314	2 - 0	Carden 1, Williams 37
05.05	Unib P	Worksop Town	428	2 - 0	Baxter 66, Carragher 75

PLAYING SQUAD

GOALKEEPERS: James Speare (Sligo R), Bobby Harris (Padiham)

DEFENDERS: Peter Cavanagh (Liverpool), Steve Hollis (Ashton Utd), Robbie Williams (St.Domincs), Jonathan Smith (Great Harwood), Steve Caswell (Droylsden), Paul Howarth (Shrewsbury), Paul Burns (Morecambe)

MIDFIELDERS: Brett Baxter (Ashton Utd), Duncan Robertshaw (Burnley), Steve Flitcroft (Blackburn), John Doolan (Ashton Utd), Mark Shirley (Morecambe), Mark Brennan (Ashton Utd), Simon Carden (Radcliffe B)

FORWARDS: Russell Payne (Ashton U.), Lutel James (Bury), Mark Ceraolo (Ashton U.), John Coleman (Ashton U.), Gary Williams (Doncaster), Tom Beech (Bromley), Paul Mullin (Radcliffe B)

ALTRINCHAM

CLUB OFFICIALS

Chairman: Mark Harris
President: Noel White
Deputy Chairman: Anthony Taylor
Vice President: Bill King
Secretary: Graham Heathcote
Press Officer: John Pollit
Match Secretary: George Heslop

FOOTBALL MANAGEMENT TEAM

Manager: Bernard Taylor
Coach/Asst Manager: Graham Heathcote
Physiotherapist: Gary Thompson
Kit Manager: Keith Mairs

FACT FILE

Formed: 1903
Nickname: The Robins
Sponsor: Hillcrest Homes
Colours: Red & white striped/black/white
Change colours: Yellow/green/green
Midweek matchday: Tuesday
Reserves' League: Lancashire League
Youth League: Altrincham Youth

Season 00-01

Top Scorers :Kevin Ellison & Danny Murphy 10
Captain & P.o.Y.: Steven Hawse

GROUND: Moss Lane, Altrincham, Cheshire WA15 8AP
Tel: 0161 928 1045 Fax: 0161 926 9934

Directions: M6 junction 19; A556/M56 (Manchester Airport) to junction 7; signs Hale and Altrincham; through 1st traffic lights then 3rd right into Westminster Road and continue into Moss Lane. Ground on right.

CAPACITY: 6,085 **COVER:** Yes **SEATS:** 1,154

Clubhouse: Bar under the stand open on match days only. Two snack bars on ground for pies, crisps, soft drinks etc **Club Shop:** Yes

Programme
Pages: 36 Price: £1.20
Editor: Graham Rowley, Tel: 0161 928 1045
Local Press: Sale & Altrincham Messenger; Sale & Altrincham Express; Manchester Evening News
Local Radio: GMR (BBC); Signal Radio; Piccadilly Radio

PREVIOUS **Leagues:** Manchester 03-11, Lancashire Comb. 11-19, Cheshire County 19-68, Northern Premier 68-79, 97-99; Conference 79-97 99-00 **Grounds:** Pollitts Field -1903-1910 **Names:** None

RECORDS **Attendance:**10,275 Altrincham Boys v Sunderland Boys,English Schools Shield 3rd Round 28.02.25
Goalscorer: Jack Swindells 252 - 1965-71 **Appearances:** JohnDavison 677 - 1971-86
Win: 9-2 v Merthyr Tydfil,Vauxhall Conference, Feb 1991 **Defeat:** Unknown
Fee Paid: £15,000 to Blackpool for Keith Russell
Fee Received: From Scarborough for Paul Ellender 2000

BEST SEASON **FA Trophy:** Winners 77-78, 85-86 **League:** Conference Champions 1979-80, 80-81
FA Cup: 85-86 4th Round, 0-2 v York City (A) League clubs defeated:10

HONOURS FA Trophy 77-78, 85- 86; Alliance Premier League 79-80, 80-81; Bob Lord Trophy 80-81; Northern Prem. Lge: Champions 98-99; Lge.Cup 69-70 97-98; N.P.L. Shield 79-80; Cheshire County League: Champions 65-66, 66-67; Lge Cup 50-51, 52-53, 63-64; Cheshire Senior Cup 04-05, 33-34, 66-67,81-82; Manchester League 04-05; Cheshire Amateur Cup 03-04.

Players Progressing: Several, most recent being G Barrow (Wigan Ath. 81), J Rogers(Wigan Ath., 82), P Conning (Rochdale, 86), E Bishop (Tranmere R. 88), P Edwards (Crewe, 88), A Kilner (Stockport C. 90), P Showler (Barnet, 91), S Johnson & A Reid (Bury 92), C Freeman (Doncaster R. 93), T Carke (Shrewsbury T. 93),Nicky Daws (Bury), Kevin Ellison (Leicester City), Danny Adams (Macclesfield Town)

Alrincham 'keeper Stuart Coburn (partly hidden) clears the danger during the match against champions Stalybridge.
Photo: Colin Stevens

Date	Comp.	Opponents	Att.	Score	Goalscorers
19.08	Unib P	GATESHEAD	620	3 - 2	Ellison 12, Quayle 14, Ward 90[p]
22.08	Unib P	Accrington Stanley	1006	1 - 2	Ellison 14
26.08	Unib P	Whitby Town	542	2 - 2	Hawse 14, Landon 74
28.08	Unib P	LANCASTER CITY	649	3 - 1	Landon 15, Quayle 22, Power 70
05.09	Unib P	Marine	451	4 - 0	Talbot 17, Hawes 63, Ellison 66, Power 90
09.09	Unib P	EMLEY	641	0 - 2	
12.09	Unib P	COLWYN BAY	501	3 - 0	Furlong 67, Ellison 88, Landon 88
16.09	Unib P	Worksop Town	665	2 - 1	Furlong 47, Ellison 77
19.09	Ches. SC 1	Northwich Victoria	412	0 - 1	
23.09	Unib P	Spennymoor United	198	4 - 0	Ellison 33, Furlong 36, Hawes 49, Landon 85
26.09	Unib P	Runcorn	407	2 - 0	Chambers 17, Ellison 90
30.09	FA Cup Q2	MOSSLEY	727	0 - 3	
03.10	Unib P	STALYBRIDGE CELTIC	823	0 - 0	
08.10	Unib P	Droylsden	554	1 - 2	Hawes 68
10.10	Unib P	LEEK TOWN	529	1 - 1	Murphy 55
14.10	Unib P	SPENNYMOOR UNITED	540	5 - 0	Furlong 11 14, Crane 44, Schueber 48, Hay 68
16.10	Unib P	Hyde United	674	2 - 4	Scott 40 57
21.10	Unib P	BLYTH SPARTANS	622	3 - 1	Murphy 44, Hay 82, Gallagher 89
24.10	Unib P	Barrow	1272	3 - 2	Landon 22, Hay 73 81
04.11	FA Trophy 1	Ilkeston Town	597	1 - 1	Thomas 82
07.11	FA Trophy 1 R	ILKESTON TOWN	322	4 - 3	Hay 22, Landon 24 92[p], Talbot 98
11.11	Unib P	GAINSBOROUGH TRINITY	585	0 - 2	
18.11	Unib P	Bishop Auckland	238	0 - 2	
22.11	Lge Cup 4	HYDE UNITED	211	1 - 1	Glendenning 89
25.11	Unib P	Bamber Bridge	408	1 - 1	Hay 15
02.12	FA Trophy 2	BISHOP AUCKLAND	437	2 - 2	Murphy 1, Ward 60
06.12	FA Trophy 2 R	Bishop Auckland	235	1 - 3	Maddox 74
09.12	Unib P	MARINE	579	3 - 1	Hay 8 15, Hawes 51
16.12	Unib P	Leek Town	327	0 - 0	
23.12	Unib P	WHITBY TOWN	568	3 - 1	Finney 5 29 70
01.01	Unib P	FRICKLEY ATHLETIC	552	3 - 1	Ellison 20, Murphy 72, Gallagher 84
06.01	Unib P	BURSCOUGH	603	2 - 2	Finney 3, Murphy 85
09.01	Lge Cup 4	ASHTON UNITED	193	1 - 1	Ellison 2
13.01	Unib P	Gateshead	251	1 - 2	Ellison 69
16.01	Lge Cup 4	Ossett Town	165	5 - 1	Murphy 3 36, Scheuber 23, Finney 35, Haws 63
20.01	Unib P	Blyth Spartans	383	1 - 1	Gallagher 74
27.01	Unib P	WORKSOP TOWN	718	1 - 2	Murphy 80
06.02	Lge Cup 4	STOCKSBRIDGE PARK STEELS	176	1 - 3	Finney 90[p]
10.02	Unib P	Lancaster City	382	1 - 4	Murphy 7
13.02	Unib P	Frickley Athletic	223	3 - 3	Craney 18, Finney 28[p], Scheuber 84
17.02	Unib P	BISHOP AUCKLAND	630	0 - 2	
20.02	Unib P	HUCKNALL TOWN	438	1 - 0	Hawse 89
24.02	Unib P	Stalybridge Celtic	1025	0 - 1	
06.03	Unib P	BAMBER BRIDGE	427	1 - 2	Finney 12
17.03	Unib P	DROYLSDEN	565	3 - 0	Craney 15, Murphy 44, Thornley 59
25.03	Unib P	ACCRINGTON STANLEY	681	5 - 2	Thornley 1 45 90[p], Finney 13, Farley 90
27.03	Unib P	BARROW	514	1 - 1	Finney 35
31.03	Unib P	Gainsborough Trinity	418	0 - 1	
03.04	Unib P	Colwyn Bay	278	2 - 1	Finney 4, Landon 72[p]
07.04	Unib P	Emley	686	1 - 3	Thornley 61
14.04	Unib P	RUNCORN	676	2 - 1	Thornley 19, Bowker 82
16.04	Unib P	Burscough	329	1 - 1	Thornley 80
28.04	Unib P	HYDE UNITED	662	2 - 0	Murphy 25, Thorley 51
05.05	Unib P	Hucknall Town	290	3 - 1	Craney 12 70, Thornley 60

PLAYING SQUAD

GOALKEEPERS: Stuart Coburn (Trafford)

DEFENDERS: Jason Gallagher (Hyde U.), Mark Sertori (Cheltenham), Gary Scott (Leigh RMI), Mark Maddox (Barrow), Chris Adams (Ashton U.), Steve Hawes (Hull), Paul Taylor (Hyde U.), David Swannick (Morecambe)

MIDFIELDERS: Ian Craney (Youth), Kevin Hulme (York), Jerry Illingworth (Ashton Utd), Stuart Quinn (Leigh RMI), Danny Murphy (Mossley)

FORWARDS: Rod Thornley (Congleton), Lee Poland (Northwich), Carl Furlong (TNS), Phil Power (Macclesfield)

BAMBER BRIDGE

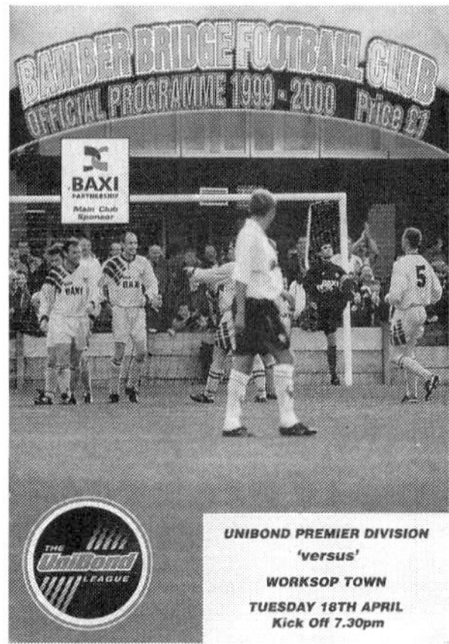

CLUB OFFICIALS

President: **Arthur Jackson**
Chairman: **D Allan**
Vice Chairman: **Dave Spencer**
Secretary : **David Spencer**
c/o B.B.F.C.
Commercial Manager: **Keith Brindle**

FOOTBALL MANAGEMENT TEAM

Manager: **Tony Greenwood**
Asst Manager: **Phil Entwistle**
Physio: **Shaun Riley**

FACT FILE

Founded: 1952
Nickname: Brig
Sponsors: Baxi Partnership
Colours: White/black/black
Change Colours: All yellow
Midweek Matches: Tuesday
Reserves' League: Lancashire Legue
Website: www.bamberbridge-fc,co.uk

PROGRAMME

Pages: 36 Price: £1
Editor: Dave Rowland (01772 465659)

GROUND

Irongate, Brownedge Road, Bamber Bridge, Preston, Lancs.PR5 6UX
Tel Nos: Club Office 01772-909690; Social Club 01772-909695; Fax No. 01772-909691
Directions: M6 Junct 29, A6 (Bamber Bridge Bypass) towards Walton-le-Dale, to r'bout, A6 London Road to next r'bout, 3rd exit signed Bamber Bridge (Brownedge Road) and first right. Ground 100 yds at end of road on left. Just over a mile from Bamber Bridge (BR).
Capacity: 3,000 Seats: 1008 Cover: 800
Clubhouse: On ground. Open all day Saturday matchdays, every evening and Sunday lunch. Refreshment cabin on ground serves hot & cold drinks & snacks etc during matches.
Club Shop: Sells various club souvenirs etc plus large selection of programmes. Contact Russ Rigby (01772 909690)

PREVIOUS
Leagues: Preston & District 52-90; North West Counties 90-93.
Grounds: King George V Ground, Higher Walton 1952-86. **Names:** None

CLUB RECORDS
Attendance: 2,300 v Czech Republic, Pre-Euro 96 Friendly.
Win: 8-0 v Curzon Ashton N.W.Co. 94-95. **Defeat:** Unknown
Fee Paid: £10,000 to Horwich R.M.I.for Mark Edwards.
Fee Received: £15,000 from Wigan Athletic for Tony Back, 1995.

BEST SEASON
FA Vase: Semi Final 91-92 (lost 0-2 on agg to Wimborne Tn).
FA Cup: 2nd Round Proper, 99-00, v Cambridge United (A) Lost 0-1

HONOURS
Nth West Co's Lge R-up 92-93 (Div 2 91-92, F'lit Cup R-up 91-92); Preston &Dist Lge(4) (R-up (3); Guildhall Cup 78-79 80-81 84-85 89-90, R-up 77-78 79-80 87-88; Lancs Amtr Shield 81-82, R-up 80-81 89-90; Lancastrian Brigade Cup 76-77 89-90 90-91; A.T.S.Lancs Trophy 94-95, R-Up 95-96, NPL Chall Cup 94-95; NPL 1st Div R-Up 94-95; NPL Prem Div Champ 95-96.

Date	Comp.	Opponents	Att.	Score	Goalscorers
19.08	Unib P	Frickley Athletic	174	2 - 1	Whittaker 45, Jones 53
22.08	Unib P	BARROW	503	1 - 2	Burton 1
26.08	Unib P	COLWYN BAY	238	3 - 4	Whittaker 28 40, Greenwood 78
28.08	Unib P	Burscough	347	0 - 3	
02.09	Unib P	Emley	200	0 - 1	
05.09	Unib P	LANCASTER CITY	395	1 - 4	Whittaker 50
09.09	Unib P	GAINSBOROUGH TRINITY	201	2 - 0	Pates 45, Whittaker 76
12.09	Unib P	Runcorn	219	3 - 2	Whittaker 12 89, Jones 82
26.09	Unib P	Lancaster City	247	2 - 3	Burton 31 48
30.09	FA Cup Q2	MARSKE UNITED	229	1 - 1	Aspinall 35[p]
03.10	FA Cup Q2 R	Marske United	238	2 - 0	Whittaker 27 28
06.10	Unib P	Barrow	1280	1 - 3	Burton 90
14.10	FA Cup Q3	GATESHEAD	255	1 - 1	Pates 29
18.10	FA Cup Q3 R	Gateshead	231	1 - 3	Willoughby 85
21.10	Unib P	LEEK TOWN	252	1 - 0	Jones 6
24.10	Unib P	DROYLSDEN	170	2 - 1	Smith 73, Burton 83
28.10	Unib P	Whitby Town	237	1 - 1	Connell 37[og]
04.11	FA Trophy 1	ATHERSTONE UNITED	211	1 - 3	Carey 72
11.11	Unib P	Stalybridge Celtic	483	0 - 3	
18.11	Unib P	MARINE	218	2 - 0	Pates 7, Whittaker 61
21.11	Lge Cup 5	RUNCORN	147	2 - 0	Whittaker 18, Keeling 90
25.11	Unib P	ALTRINCHAM	408	1 - 1	Burton 79
02.12	Unib P	Colwyn Bay	214	1 - 1	Smith 75
05.12	Lge Cup 5	WINSFORD UNITED	151	2 - 1	Smith 38, Whittaker 73
09.12	Unib P	Gainsborough Trinity	386	0 - 2	
16.12	Unib P	HUCKNALL TOWN	220	1 - 3	Greenwood 88
23.12	Unib P	Bishop Auckland	185	2 - 5	Farley 34, Burton 90
26.12	Unib P	Accrington Stanley	663	3 - 1	Ryan 45, Aspinall 52, Burton 59
06.01	Unib P	Gateshead	185	2 - 0	Carroll 31, Greenwood 75
13.01	Unib P	FRICKLEY ATHLETIC	229	0 - 1	
23.01	Lge Cup 5	ACCRINGTON STANLEY	201	2 - 1	Ryan 12, Pates 42
27.01	Unib P	Blyth Spartans	400	0 - 0	
30.01	Lge Cup 5	Trafford	73	3 - 0	Burton 51, Whittaker 60 75
03.02	Unib P	Leek Town	202	1 - 1	Whittaker 8
10.02	Unib P	WHITBY TOWN	181	5 - 0	Cooper 5, Whittaker 41 82, Burton 80, Ryan 90
13.02	Lancs MT 2	Skelmersdale United	92	3 - 1	Robinson 8 23[p], Whittaker 39
17.02	Unib P	EMLEY	428	1 - 1	Crompton 64
20.02	Lancs MT	QF	Clitheroe	227	1 - 0 Greenwood 90
24.02	Unib P	Hucknall Town	181	0 - 1	
27.02	Unib P	HYDE UNITED	243	2 - 1	Band 7[og], Greenwood 20
03.03	Lge Cup QF	Lancaster City	269	0 - 1	
06.03	Unib P	Altrincham	427	2 - 1	Robinson 16[p], McCann 57
10.03	Unib P	Spennymoor United	90	2 - 1	Whittaker 28 56
17.03	Unib P	BLYTH SPARTANS	307	1 - 3	Whittaker 42
20.03	Lancs MT SF	LANCASTER CITY	365	0 - 1	
23.03	Unib P	STALYBRIDGE CELTIC	416	0 - 2	
27.03	Unib P	BISHOP AUCKLAND	155	0 - 2	
31.03	Unib P	Worksop Town	430	1 - 1	Robinson 27
03.04	Unib P	GATESHEAD	170	4 - 2	Burton 28 50, Tasdemir 39 80
10.04	Unib P	Marine	231	1 - 2	Ryan 10
14.04	Unib P	Droylsden	163	1 - 0	Stewart 87
16.04	Unib P	ACCRINGTON STANLEY	390	3 - 0	Whittaker 65 77, Robinson 81
21.04	Unib P	Hyde United	311	4 - 1	Whittaker 55 77 80, Ryan 67
24.04	Unib P	BURSCOUGH	186	0 - 1	
28.04	Unib P	RUNCORN	234	3 - 1	Whittaker 23 52, Westwood 88
03.05	Unib P	WORKSOP TOWN	220	1 - 2	Whittaker 11
05.05	Unib P	SPENNYMOOR UNITED	229	0 - 0	

PLAYING SQUAD

GOALKEEPERS: Billy Stewart (Hednesford)

DEFENDERS: Andy Farley (Southport), Paul Lin (Preston), Karl Gleave (Bury), Steve Aspinall (Chorley), Phil Robinson (Blackpool)

MIDFIELDERS: John Turner (Preston), David Leaver (Accrington Stanley), Paul Crompton (Lancaster), Peter Smith (Exeter), Servet Tasdemir (Great Harwood)

FORWARDS: Simon Burton (Atherton LR), Karl Robinson (Marine), Mike Moran (Local)

BARROW

CLUB OFFICIALS

Match Secretary; Neil McDonald
Birchfield, 6A Salthouse Rd., Barrow-in-Furness, Cumbria Tel: 01229 828227 (H) 07703 499482 (M)

Press Officer: Phil Yelland
83 Camus Drive, Edinburgh EH10 6QY
Tel: 0131 445 1010 (H) & Fax
0131 476 8131 (B)

Manager: Kenny Lowe
Assistant Manager: Tony Chilton

FACT FILE

Founded: 1901
Nickname: Bluebirds
Sponsors: Chas Kendall - Bookmakers
Club Colours: All white with blue trim
Change Colours: Yellow/blue/blue
Midweek matchday: Tuesday
Barrow Soccer Hotline: 09066 555820
Local Press: North West Evening Mail, Barrow & West Cumberland Advertiser
Local Radio: BBC Radio Furness, BBC Radio Cumbria, Red Rose Radio, Bay Radio

Pages: 44 Price: £1.40
Editorial Team:
Darren Gardner, Phil Yelland, & Russell Dodd

GROUND: Holker Street Stadium, Wilkie Road, Barrow-in-Furness, CumbriaLA14 5UW Tel: 01229 820346

Directions: M6 to junction 36, A590 to Barrow, enter Barrow on Park Road and after about 2 miles turn left into Wilkie Rd - ground on right. B.R.1/4 mile

Capacity: 4,500 **Seated:** 1000 **Covered Terracing:** 1,200

Clubhouse: Barrow Sports & Leisure centre next to groun Open matchdays and Functions only. Snack bars on ground **Club Shop:** Situated on the ground.

2000-2001: Captain: Neil Doherty P.o.Y.: Simon Bishop Top Scorer: Nicky Peverell 33

PREVIOUS **Leagues:** Lancs Comb 01-21; Football League 21-72; Northern Premier 72-79, 83-84,86-89, 92-98; 99- GM Vauxhall Conference 79-83, 84-86, 89-92, 98-99 **Grounds:** The Strawberry & Little Park, Roose **Names:**None

RECORDS **Attendance:** 16,854 v Swansea Town, FA Cup 3rd Rd. 1954
Career Appearances: Colin Cowperthwaite 704 **Career Goalscorer:** Colin Cowperthwaite 282 (Dec '77-Dec '92).
Defeat: 1-10 v Hartlepool Utd, Football Lge Div 4, 1959 **Win:** 12-0 v Cleator, FA Cup 1920.
Transfer Fee Paid: £9,000 for Andy Whittaker (Ashton Utd, July 94).
Transfer Fee Received: £40,000 for Kenny Lowe (Barnet, Jan 91)

BEST SEASON **FA Trophy:** Winners 1989-90, Semi-Final 87-88
FA Cup: Third Round Proper 9 times including once as a non-League club 90-91, 0-1 v Bolton Wanderers (A)

HONOURS F.A. Trophy Winners 89-90, Northern Premier League 97-98, 88-89, 83-84; Lge Cup R-up 87-88, Lge Shield 84-85 R-up 89-90 98-99; Bob Lord Trophy R-up 90-91, Cumbrian Cup 82-8383-84 (R-up 84-85), Lancs Floodlit Cup R-up 86-87, Lancs Sen Cup 54-55 (R-up 51-52 65-66 66-67 69-70), Lancs Challenge Trophy 80-81 (R-up 81-82 84-85), Lancs Comb 20-21, R-up 13-14, Div 2 R-up 04-05 10-11. Unibond Chairman's Cup (00-01)

Players progressing: I McDonald, N McDonald, J Laisby, B Diamond, F Gamble, B Knowles, G Skivington, P Byron, L Edwards, K Lowe, M Dobie, T Rigby, N Doherty.

Barrow celebrate winning the Unibond Chairman's Cup. **Left to right, back row**: Wayne Bullimore,Lee Ellison, Lee Warren, Mark Hume, Simon Bishop, Lee Rogers, Anthony Hall and Grant Holt. **Front Row**: Jason Ainsley, Nicky Peverell, Neil Doherty (Captain) Steve Housham and Graham Anthony. Missing from photo: Scott Maxfield and Gareth Jones

Date	Comp.	Opponents	Att.	Score	Goalscorers
08.08	C.K. Trophy(1)	Workington	n.k	1 - 0	Tucker
15.08	C.K.Trophy(2)	WORKINGTON	n.k	2 - 2	Housham 15, Ellison 55
19.08	Unib P	EMLEY	1283	1 - 3	Housham 85
22.08	Unib P	Bamber Bridge	503	2 - 1	Peverill 2, Whittle 76
26.08	Unib P	Spennymoor United	244	3 - 2	Doherty 43, Peverill 76, Housham 86
28.08	Unib P	ACCRINGTON STANLEY	1456	3 - 0	Bullimore 17, Ellison 27, Peverill 59
02.09	Unib P	Leek Town	362	1 - 2	Housham 64
05.09	Unib P	BURSCOUGH	1188	2 - 2	Ellison 37, Anthony 51
09.09	Unib P	HYDE UNITED	1216	1 - 0	Peverell 38[p]
20.09	Friendly	CARLISLE UNITED	247	2 - 1	Peverell, Peel
23.09	Unib P	Worksop Town	667	2 - 4	Peverill 68, Doherty 75
27.09	Unib P	Gateshead	276	2 - 1	Housham 21, Peverill 49
30.09	FA Cup Q2	DROYLSDEN	1153	3 - 0	Doherty 37, Housham 42, Peel 74
06.10	Unib P	BAMBER BRIDGE	1280	3 - 1	Housham 13, Peverill 44, Ellison 77
14.10	FA Cup Q3	Emley	586	2 - 1	Hume 31, Peverill 74
21.10	Unib P	Hucknall Town	347	4 - 1	Peverill 1 54, Housham 20, Bullimore 81
24.10	Unib P	ALTRINCHAM	1272	2 - 3	Housham 67, Ellison 74
28.10	FA Cup Q4	WHITLEY BAY	1714	6 - 1	Housham 14, Maxfield 32, Ellison 44, Peverill 55 67, Peel 76
04.11	FA Trophy 1	RUNCORN	1327	0 - 1	
11.11	Unib P	WHITBY TOWN	1082	2 - 3	Hume 81, Housham 83
14.11	Lge Cup 2	Kendal Town	237	3 - 1	Roberts 5, Ainsley 65, Peverill 76
18.11	FA Cup 1	LEYTON ORIENT	3608	0 - 2	
25.11	Unib P	Gainsborough Trinity	495	0 - 2	
02.12	Unib P	DROYLSDEN	903	2 - 0	Ellison 64, Peverill 73
09.12	Unib P	Emley	372	0 - 0	
16.12	Unib P	BISHOP AUCKLAND	961	1 - 4	Roberts 19
23.12	Unib P	Burscough	333	2 - 1	Peverill 63 88
26.12	Unib P	Lancaster City	737	1 - 1	Roberts 76
01.01	Unib P	LANCASTER CITY	1169	2 - 2	McKechnie 4, Bullimore 69
06.01	Unib P	Stalybridge Celtic	718	0 - 1	
09.01	Lancs MT 2	SOUTHPORT	493	3 - 5	Housham 27, Bullimore 62, Peverill 81[p]
13.01	Unib P	Droylsden	253	1 - 2	Peverill 33
20.01	Unib P	RUNCORN	903	1 - 2	Hume 44
23.01	Lge Cup 2	Lancaster City	174	0 - 1	
27.01	Unib P	MARINE	840	1 - 0	Housham 14
30.01	Lge Cup 2	WORKINGTON	274	0 - 2	
03.02	Unib P	Bishop Auckland	299	2 - 2	Peverill 34, Roberts 43
06.02	Lge Cup 2	GRETNA	201	3 - 2	Hill 31, Jones 37, Peverill 63
13.02	Unib P	Blyth Spartans	188	1 - 1	Peverill 63
17.02	Unib P	BLYTH SPARTANS	954	2 - 0	Peverill 36 39[p]
19.02	Unib P	Hyde United	343	4 - 4	Jenkinson 4, Doherty 21, Peverill 73 79
24.02	Unib P	Runcorn	275	1 - 3	Bullimore 81
27.02	Unib P	STALYBRIDGE CELTIC	864	0 - 0	
03.03	Chairman QF	EMLEY	752	4 - 2	Anthony 35, Peverill 51, Holt 53, Roberts 77
10.03	Unib P	LEEK TOWN	996	3 - 0	Peverill 21 44
13.03	Unib P	COLWYN BAY	799	3 - 2	Holt 48, Peverill 70[p] 84
17.03	Unib P	HUCKNALL TOWN	968	5 - 0	Anthony 22, Hume 26 28, Ellison 88, Roberts 90
27.03	Unib P	Altrincham	514	1 - 1	Holt 83
31.03	Unib P	FRICKLEY ATHLETIC	1048	2 - 0	Peverill 55, Hume 76
03.04	Chairman SF	Chorley	395	2 - 0	Peverill 45, Hume 80
10.04	Unib P	Whitby Town	228	2 - 0	Holt 1, Ellison 80
12.04	Unib P	GATESHEAD	1001	3 - 1	Bullimore 35[p], Holt 60, Jones 90
14.04	Unib P	SPENNYMOOR UNITED	1001	5 - 0	Roberts 25, Ellison 45 52, Hill 67, Holt 69
16.04	Unib P	Marine	329	2 - 1	Ellison 26[p], Bullimore 81
19.04	Chairman F	Harrogate Town	903	1 - 1	Holt 65 (3-0)
21.04	Unib P	GAINSBOROUGH TRINITY	1024	3 - 2	Hume 31, Roberts 61 67
24.04	Unib P	Accrington Stanley	406	1 - 2	Holt 26
28.04	Unib P	WORKSOP TOWN	1216	2 - 1	Housham 30, Anthony 88
01.05	Unib P	Frickley Athletic	225	2 - 3	Holt 73, Lowe 81
05.05	Unib P	Colwyn Bay	585	0 - 2	

PLAYING SQUAD

GOALKEEPERS: Simon Bishop (Dunston Fed)

DEFENDERS: Lee Turnbull (Halifax), Mark Hume (Doncaster), Simon Shaw (Doncaster), Lee Warren (Doncaster), Lee Rogers (Grantham), Anthony Hall (Gateshead), Andy Hill (Vickers SC)

MIDFIELDERS: Steve Housham (Scunthorpe), Steve Gaughan (Halifax), Wayne Bullimore (Grantham), Graham Anthony (Carlisle), Mike McKechnie (Barrow Rangers)

FORWARDS: Neil Doherty (Kidderminster), Grant Holt (Halifax), Gareth Jones (Dalton Utd), Nicky Peverell (Blyth), Ian Duerdan (Kingstonian), Steve Gill (Barrow Rangers)

BISHOP AUCKLAND

CLUB OFFICIALS

Chairman: **Tony Duffy**
Vice-Chairman: T.B.A.
Secretary/Press Off.: **Tony Duffy,**
90 Escomb Road, Bishop Auckland,
Co. Durham, DL14 6TZ
Commercial Manager: T.B.A.

FOOTBALL MANAGEMENT TEAM

Manager: Tony Lee
Asst Mgr: Tony Boylan
Physio: Dave Nesbitt

FACT FILE

Formed: 1886
Nickname: Bishops
Sponsors:Helios Properties PLC
Colours: Sky & Navy blue
Change colours: Red & white.
Midweek home matchday: Wednesday.
Reserve Team: None.

2000-01

Captain: Mark Salmon
Top scorer & P.o.Y.: Andrew Shaw 34

Pages: 28 Price: £1.
Editor: Bobby Wake (01388 609428)
Local Press: Northern Echo, Evening Gazette, N'castle Journal. Local Radio: Radio Cleveland, Radio Metro, Radio Newcastle. Century Radio

GROUND Kingsway, Bishop Auckland, County Durham Tel. 01388 603686
Club Email: john.cowey@compaqnet.co.uk

Directions: A1 to Scotch Corner (Turn off A68 from A1) or M6 Junc A38 (A685 to Brough), then follow signs to Bishop Auckland. Ground in town centre, rear off Newgate St. Half mile from station.

Capacity: 3,500 Cover: 2,000 Seats: 600

Clubhouse: Open every day noon-4 & 7-11pm, plus Saturday matchdays all day. Large bar, pool, juke box. Also snack bar within grounds sells hot & cold pies & drinks.

Club Shop: Yes Metal Badges: £3.00.

PREVIOUS Leagues: N East Counties 1889-90/ Northern Alliance 1890-91/ Northern 1893-1988.

CLUB RECORDS **Attendance:** 17,000 v Coventry, FA Cup 2nd Rd 6/12/52. **Appearances:** Bob Hardisty.
Win: 12-3 v Kingstonian, Amateur Cup 55. **Defeat:** 0-7 v Halifax Tn FA Cup 2nd Rd66-67.
Fee Paid: £2,000. Fee Received: £9,000 for David Laws from Weymouth.

BEST SEASON **FA Amateur Cup:** Winners 10 times **FA Trophy:** Quarter Finals 78-79, 88-89, 96-97, 99-00
FA Cup: 4th Rd 54-55, 1-3 v York City (H). League clubs defeated: Crystal Palace, Ipswich 54-55, Tranmere 56-57.

HONOURS FA Amateur Cup 1895-96, 1899-1900 13-14 20-22 34-35 38-39 54-56 57-58 (R-up(8)01-02 05-06 10-11 14-15 45-46 49-51 53-54); Northern Lg(19) 1898-99 1900-02 08-10 11-12 20-21 30-31 38-39 46-47 49-52 53-5666-67 84-86, R-up (17) 78-79 86-87 96-97, Lg Cup(7) 49-51 53-55 59-60 66-67 75-76); D'ham Chall Cup 1891-92 98-99 1930-31 38-39 51-52 55-56 61-62 66-67 84-8585-86 87-88 96-97, 98-99 HFS Loans Lg Div 1 R-up 88-89. Plus tournaments in Isle of Man, Spain, Portugal etc

Players Progressing: B Paisley (Liverpool), F Richardson & S O'Connell (Chelsea 46 & 54), R Hardisty & K Williamson (Darlimgton 46 & 52), WShergold (Newport 47), N Smith (Fulham 48), R Steel & K Murray (Darlington 50),A Adey (Doncaster 50), F Palmer & A Stalker (Gateshead 51 & 58), A Sewell(Bradford City 54), G Barker (Southend 54), J Major (Hull 55), H Sharratt(Oldham 56), F McKenna (Leeds 56), J Barnwell (Arsenal 56), D Lewis (Accrington Stanley 57), C Cresswell (Carlisle 58), W Bradley (Man Utd), L Brown(Northampton), P Baker (Southampton), M Gooding (Rotherham), K Nobbs & A Toman(Hartlepool), P Hinds (Dundee Utd), Jeff Smith (Bolton W.) 2001.

A jubilant Bishop Auckland after their victory over Brandon United in the final of the Durham County Cup.

Date	Comp.	Opponents	Att.	Score	Goalscorers
19.08	Unib P	Colwyn Bay	231	3 - 3	Mellanby 3, Howarth 36, Brunskill 38
22.08	Unib P	Blyth Spartans	399	2 - 1	Melson 39, Brunskill 70
28.08	Unib P	Frickley Athletic	140	1 - 0	Dunwell 19
02.09	Unib P	MARINE	243	1 - 1	Brunskill 58
06.09	Unib P	EMLEY	202	1 - 3	Bayles 38
09.09	Unib P	Stalybridge Celtic	509	0 - 2	
13.09	Unib P	FRICKLEY ATHLETIC	147	2 - 0	Shaw 3 57
16.09	Unib P	GAINSBOROUGH TRINITY	192	3 - 1	Bayles 27, Mellamby 41, Shaw 48[p]
19.09	Unib P	Accrington Stanley	601	1 - 3	Shaw 20[p]
23.09	Unib P	Hyde United	366	1 - 1	Mellanby 37
27.09	Unib P	BLYTH SPARTANS	194	1 - 0	Dunwell 90
30.09	FA Cup Q2	Gateshead	255	1 - 2	Dunwell 85
04.10	Unib P	GATESHEAD	328	0 - 1	
06.10	Unib P	WHITBY TOWN	235	2 - 1	Dunwell 43 60
18.10	Unib P	WORKSOP TOWN	223	2 - 1	Bell 31, Dunwell 59
21.10	Unib P	Burscough	180	1 - 2	Smith 90
25.10	Durham CC 1	SOUTH SHIELDS HARTON & WESTOE	54	8 - 0	Lee 38, Shaw 42 67 70 86 89, Dunwell 74 79
28.10	Unib P	LEEK TOWN	122	3 - 1	Nelson 16, Mellanby 35 40
04.11	FA Trophy 1	WHITBY TOWN	175	1 - 1	Rennison 64[og]
11.11	Unib P	Droylsden	179	3 - 0	Morley 7[og], Bell 38 83
14.11	FA Trophy 1 R	Whitby Town	324	2 - 2	Mellanby 44 68 (5-4p)
18.11	Unib P	ALTRINCHAM	238	2 - 0	Shaw 10, Lee 79[p]
21.11	Durham CC 2	HORDEN COLLIERY WELFARE	56	2 - 0	Dunwell 5, Lee 25[p]
25.11	Unib P	Marine	310	3 - 1	Shaw 9 86, Bayles 83
29.11	Lge Cup 1	WHITBY TOWN	79	4 - 2	Mellanby 2, Dunwell 6, Nelson 33, Bell 85
02.12	FA Trophy 2	Altrincham	437	2 - 2	Gallagher 45, Lee 50
06.12	FA Trophy 2 R	ALTRINCHAM	235	3 - 1	Shaw 9, Mellanby 64, Milroy 70
13.12	Lge Cup 1	BLYTH SPARTANS	77	4 - 1	Shaw 36 41, Brunskill 45, Bayles 47[p]
16.12	Unib P	Barrow	961	4 - 1	Smith 25 44, Shaw 26, Brunskill 29
20.12	Lge Cup 1	Gateshead	93	0 - 3	
23.12	Unib P	BAMBER BRIDGE	185	5 - 2	Shaw 57 82, Linn 69[og], Mellanby 70 89
03.01	Durham CC QF	Washington Nissan	64	3 - 0	Dunwell 45, Mellanby 52, Lee 55
06.01	Unib P	ACCRINGTON STANLEY	236	2 - 1	Salmon 48, Mellanby 80
13.01	FA Trophy 3	Burton Albion	1173	0 - 2	
27.01	Unib P	BURSCOUGH	206	4 - 0	Gallagher 9, Shaw 21[p] 39[p], Mellanby 23
30.01	Lge Cup 1	Spennymoor United	99	3 - 2	Brunskill 39 70, Foster 44
03.02	Unib P	BARROW	299	2 - 2	Hutt 89, Mellanby 90
14.02	Durham CC SF	TOW LAW TOWN	155	5 - 1	Shaw 1 33[p] 79, Bayles 38, Brunskill 70
17.02	Unib P	Altrincham	630	2 - 0	Brunskill 22, Smith 42
21.02	Unib P	LANCASTER CITY	208	1 - 3	Mellanby 14
24.02	Unib P	DROYLSDEN	165	2 - 1	Shaw 40 55
03.03	Lge Cup QF	Hyde United	275	2 - 0	Mellanby 50, Bell 90
06.03	Unib P	Emley	304	1 - 3	Bell 73
10.03	Unib P	Runcorn	929	4 - 4	Brunskill 61, Bell 78, Shaw 89, Downey 90 (at Widnes RLFC)
14.03	Unib P	Gateshead	195	3 - 0	Bayles 17, Mellanby 27, Brunskill 68
17.03	Unib P	SPENNYMOOR UNITED	260	2 - 0	Brunskill 59, Gallagher 63
21.03	Unib P	RUNCORN	145	0 - 2	
23.03	Unib P	Lancaster City	418	0 - 1	
27.03	Unib P	Bamber Bridge	155	2 - 0	Shaw 61[p] 68
31.03	Unib P	COLWYN BAY	157	5 - 1	Mellanby 22, Brunskill 45 58, Shaw 87[p] 90[p]
03.04	Lge Cup SF	Marine	182	3 - 0	Mellanby 15 78 90
10.04	Unib P	Hucknall Town	145	5 - 2	Lee 22 43, Mellanby 56 75, Brunskill 73
12.04	Unib P	Spennymoor United	171	3 - 0	Shaw 28[p] 68, Mellanby 48
14.04	Unib P	HUCKNALL TOWN	181	2 - 0	Shaw 71[p], Milroy 90
16.04	Unib P	Whitby Town	268	1 - 1	Brunskill 9
18.04	Unib P	HYDE UNITED	130	3 - 1	Salmon 16, Gallagher 54, Bell 90
21.04	Unib P	STALYBRIDGE CELTIC	238	0 - 2	
24.04	Unib P	Worksop Town	272	2 - 1	Mellanby 38 67
28.04	Unib P	Gainsborough Trinity	369	0 - 0	
01.05	Lge. Cup F	Lancaster City	530	2 - 2	Brunskill 7 78 Lost 3-4 after penalties
05.05	Unib P	Leek Town	366	1 - 3	Mellanby 10
07.05	Durham CC F	BRANDON UNITED	n.k	2 - 0	(at Durham City)

PLAYING SQUAD

GOALKEEPERS: Martin Hall (West Auckland), Steve Jones (Gateshead), David Campbell (Whitby)

DEFENDERS: Steve West (West Auckland), Thomas Dunn (Middlesbrough), Mark Salmon (Acklam Steelworks), David Kitchen (Gateshead), Steve Hutt (Harlepool), Tony Lee (North Shields)

MIDFIELDERS: David Gallagher (Guisborough), Steve Bell (Guisborough), Jason Ainsley (Barrow), David Bayles (Shildon), Dion Riatt (Tow Law), Brian Rowe (Bedlington Terriers)

FORWARDS: Danny Brunskill (North Shields), Paul Dalton (Dunston Fed), Jonathan Milroy (West Auckland), Carl Chillingsworth (Whitby), Andy Shaw (Spennymoor)

BLYTH SPARTANS

CLUB OFFICIALS

Chairman:**Tommy Hedley**
Secretary: **Joe Hobin,** 23 Princes Gdns, Malvins Close, Blyth, Northumberland, NE24 2HJ. Tel: 01670 360820.
Press Officer: **Ken Teasdale**

FOOTBALL MANAGEMENT TEAM

Manager: John Charlton
Assistant Manager: Graeme Clarke

FACT FILE

Formed: 1899 Nickname: Spartans
Sponsors: Federation Brewery.
Colours:Green & white stripes/black
Change colours: Orange
Midweek Matches: Tuesday
Reserves' League: Northern Alliance
Local Press:Newcastle Journal & Evening Chronicle.

2000-01

Leading goalscorer: Glen Robson 29
Captain: Ian Dixon
P.o.Y.: Richard Forster

Pages: 64 Price: £1
Editor: Brian Grey Tel: 0191 2650119

GROUND: Croft Park, Blyth, Northumberland. Tel: 01670 354818 FAX: 01670 545592
Website: www.spartans.freeserve.co.uk

Directions: Through Tyne tunnel heading north on A19, take Cramlington turn A1061, follow signs for Newsham/Blyth. Right fork at railway gates in Newsham, down Plessey Rd, ground can be seen on left. Buses X24, X25, X26, X1 from Newcastle.

Capacity: 6,000 Seats: 300 Cover: 1,000

Clubhouse: Open every night plus Saturday & Sunday lunch & matchdays. Available for wedding functions. Pies & sandwiches available.

Souvenir Shop: Large selection. Contact: Bob Bell (01670 545592)

PREVIOUS Leagues: Northumberland 01-07; Northern Alliance 07-13, 46-47; North Eastern13-14 19-39 47-58 62-64; Northern Combination 45-46; Midland 58-60; Northern Counties 60-62; Northern 62-94. Names: None Grounds: None

CLUB RECORDS Fee Received: £30,000 for Les Mutrie (Hull City) 1979. Fee Paid:

BEST SEASON **FA Trophy:** Quarter-Final replay 79-80 82-83. **FA Amateur Cup:** Semi-Final 71-72.
FA Cup: 5th Rd replay 77-78 (lost to Wrexham). 1st Round on 47 occasions. League Clubs defeated: Ashington, Gillingham 22-23, Crewe Alexandra,Stockport County 71-72, Chesterfield, Stoke City 77-78, Bury 95-96.

HONOURS Nth Lg(10) 72-73 74-76 79-84 86-88 94-95, (R-up 71-72 73-74 77-78 84-85 94-95),Lg Cup(5) 72-73 77-79 81-82 91-92 94-95, Presidents Cup 96-97; Nth Eastern Lg35-36 (R-up 22-23, Lg Cup 49-50 54-55); Northumberland Lg 03-04; Northern All.08-09 12-13 (R-up 46-47); Northumberland Snr Cup (19); Shields Gazette Cup 95-96.

Players Progressing: William McGlen (Manchester Utd 46), Joe Roddom (Chesterfield 48), Henry Mills (Huddersfield 48), John Allison (Reading 49), James Kelly (Watford 49), Robert Millard (Reading 49), Jim Kerr (Lincoln 52), James Milner (Burnley 52), John Hogg (Portsmouth 54), John Allison(Chesterfield 55), John Inglis (Gateshead 57), John Longland (Hartlepool 58),Alan Shoulder (Newcastle 79), Les Mutrie (Hull City 79), Steve Carney(Newcastle 80), Craig Liddle (Middlesbrough 94), Paul O'Connor (Hartlepool 95). Gustavo Di Lella (Hartlepool 98)

Blyth's Ian Dixon wins this midfield challenge during the game at Hucknall. Photo: Graham Brown

Date	Comp.	Opponents	Att.	Score	Goalscorers
19.08	Unib P	GAINSBOROUGH TRINITY	298	1 - 0	Little 21
22.08	Unib P	BISHOP AUCKLAND	399	1 - 2	Rowe 80
26.08	Unib P	Hyde United	417	2 - 6	Robson 24 57
28.08	Unib P	GATESHEAD	484	2 - 1	Robson 24, Rowe 90
02.09	Unib P	Burscough	234	1 - 3	Robson 54
05.09	Unib P	Whitby Town	431	0 - 1	
09.09	Unib P	LEEK TOWN	290	0 - 0	
12.09	Unib P	Spennymoor United	162	2 - 1	Chandler 4, Robson 85
16.09	Unib P	WHITBY TOWN	323	0 - 2	
23.09	Unib P	Colwyn Bay	288	0 - 1	
27.09	Unib P	Bishop Auckland	194	0 - 1	
30.09	FA Cup Q2	Stalybridge Celtic	523	0 - 2	
03.10	Unib P	SPENNYMOOR UNITED	271	0 - 1	
08.10	Unib P	HUCKNALL TOWN	303	1 - 1	Perry 30
14.10	Unib P	DROYLSDEN	295	0 - 1	
16.10	Unib P	Emley	280	0 - 1	
21.10	Unib P	Altrincham	622	1 - 3	Hay 62
25.10	N'humbs SC 1	West Allotment Celtic	n.k	1 - 2	
28.10	Unib P	Droylsden	230	2 - 1	Robson 12, Little 70
31.10	Lge Cup 1	GATESHEAD	313	2 - 1	Innes 22, Perry 25
04.11	FA Trophy 1	HINCKLEY UNITED	330	2 - 0	Forster 81[p], Pepper 88
11.11	Unib P	ACCRINGTON STANLEY	372	1 - 0	Hay 80
18.11	Unib P	Lancaster City	267	1 - 1	Little 9
25.11	Unib P	Worksop Town	396	3 - 4	Brookes 34[og], Pepper 38, Keegan 90
02.12	FA Trophy 2	STAFFORD RANGERS	480	3 - 0	Innes 11, Robson 14 20
13.12	Lge Cup 1	Bishop Auckland	77	1 - 4	Williams 63
16.12	Unib P	Runcorn	207	0 - 1	
19.12	Lge Cup 1	SPENNYMOOR UNITED	154	3 - 1	Dixon 38, Robson 51, Evans 79
23.12	Unib P	RUNCORN	365	3 - 0	Perry 9, Radigan 25, Chandler 57
26.12	Unib P	Gateshead	417	5 - 2	Chandler 4, Radigan 6 37, Robson 70, Innes 72
06.01	Unib P	Leek Town	222	4 - 0	Perry 58, Robson 74 90, Dixon 90
13.01	FA Trophy 3	Hyde United	556	0 - 0	
16.01	FA Trophy 3 R	HYDE UNITED	561	2 - 1	Pepper 27, Innes 61
20.01	Unib P	ALTRINCHAM	383	1 - 1	Forster 85
27.01	Unib P	BAMBER BRIDGE	400	0 - 0	
03.02	FA Trophy 4	MAIDENHEAD UNITED	902	2 - 1	Stewart 32, Hay 83
13.02	Unib P	BARROW	188	1 - 1	Robson 37
15.02	Lge Cup 1	Whitby Town	118	1 - 1	Forster 6
17.02	Unib P	Barrow	954	0 - 2	
24.02	FA Trophy 5	Chester City	1831	2 - 4	Perry 64, Robson 67
27.02	Unib P	Frickley Athletic	170	2 - 4	Perry 66, Wrightson 89
10.03	Unib P	COLWYN BAY	321	5 - 2	Robson 23 72, Dixon 24, Pepper 60 86
13.03	Pres. Cup QF	WORKINGTON	250	1 - 0	Pepper 108
17.03	Unib P	Bamber Bridge	307	3 - 1	Stewart 7, Robson 71 75[p]
20.03	Unib P	FRICKLEY ATHLETIC	243	3 - 0	Perry 17 74, Radigan 81
25.03	Unib P	Hucknall Town	215	1 - 4	Robson 16[p]
27.03	Unib P	WORKSOP TOWN	295	1 - 0	Little 60
31.03	Unib P	LANCASTER CITY	338	0 - 1	
03.04	Pres. Cup SF	ACCRINGTON STANLEY	318	2 - 1	Robson 28, Radigan 58
10.04	Unib P	STALYBRIDGE CELTIC	309	1 - 2	Radigan 40
14.04	Unib P	EMLEY	380	2 - 1	Perry 79 80
16.04	Unib P	Gainsborough Trinity	428	2 - 4	Robson 68[p], Perry 88
18.04	Unib P	Stalybridge Celtic	362	0 - 2	
21.04	Unib P	BURSCOUGH	297	1 - 0	Robson 3
24.04	Pres. Cup F	STALYBRIDGE CELTIC	560	3 - 3	Stewart 48, Robson 62 87 Lost 2-3 after penalties
26.04	Unib P	MARINE	210	4 - 1	Pepper 10, Innes 58, Robson 85 90
28.04	Unib P	Accrington Stanley	504	3 - 3	Robson 41 55, Perry 81
01.05	Unib P	Marine	202	1 - 1	Robson 24
05.05	Unib P	HYDE UNITED	388	0 - 0	

PLAYING SQUAD

GOALKEEPERS: Paul Gimore (Seaham Red Star)

DEFENDERS: Carl Pepper (Darlington), Richard Forster (Hartlepool), Graham Pepper (Gateshead), Craig Skelton (Darlington), Andy Martin (Queen of the South), Colin Morton (Hibernian)

MIDFIELDERS: John Hutton (Sheffield Wed), Neil Radigan (Whitby), Justin Keegan (Darlington), Lee Scroggins (Darlington), Gary Innes (Seaham Red Star)

FORWARDS: Glenn Robson (Harrogate T), Craig Perry (Billingham T), Steve Stewart (Chester-le-Street)

BRADFORD PARK AVENUE

CLUB OFFICIALS

Chairman: **Frank Thornton**
President: **Charlie Atkinson**
Secretary: **Steven Burnett**
6 Holburn Court, Low Moor,Bradford, W Yorks. BD12 0DD (01274 678854)
Press Officer: **Tim Clapham**
Commercial Manager: **Chris Higgins**

FOOTBALL MANAGEMENT TEAM

Manager: Trevor Storton
Asst Manager: Ian Thompson
Physio: Ray Killick

FACT FILE

Formed: 1907
Reformed: 1988
Nickname: Avenue
Club Sponsor: Ham Construction
Colours: White & Green/white/ white
Change colours W:hite/black/black
Midweek Matches: Wednesday
Reserves' league: N/A

GROUND

Horsfall Stadium, Cemetery Road, Bradford, West Yorks BD6 2NG (01274 604578)

Directions: M62 Jct 26. Along M606 to the end. At roundabout takeA6036 (signed Halifax) and pass Odsal Stadium on left hand side. At next roundabout take 3rd exit A6036 (Halifax), in approx. 1 mile turn left into Cemetery Rd (by Kings Head Pub). Ground 150 yards on left
Capacity: 5,000 Cover: 2,000 Seats: 1,247
Club Shop: Yes - contact Russell Foulds (c/o Ground) or 01924 440901 **Clubhouse:** Yes

Programme
Pages: 36 Price: £1.20
Editor: Martin Worthy 01924 384477

Local Press: Telegraph & Argus
Local Radio: Radio Leeds

PREVIOUS
Leagues: Southern 07-08; Football League 08-70; Northern Premier 70-74; West Riding County Amtr 88-89; Central Mids 89-90; N. W. Counties 90-95
Grounds: Park Avenue 07-73; Valley Parade 73-74; Manningham Mills 88-89; Bramley R.L.F.C.,McLaren Field 89-93; Batley 93-96

CLUB RECORDS
Attendance: 1,007 v Bradford City 97 (Centenary Chall). 32,810 v Blackpool, War Cup 1944
Win: 11-0 v Denby Dale FAC 1908 **Defeat:** 0-7 v Barnsley 1911
Scorer: Len Shackleton 171 1940-46 **Appearances:** Tommy Farr 542 1934-50
Fee Received: £34,000 for K Hector (Derby County 1966)
Fee Paid: £24,500 for L Leuty (Derby County 1950)

BEST SEASON
FA Vase: 2nd Rd Prop 94-95
FA Trophy: 3rd Rd 98-99
FA Cup: Qtr finals 12-13, 19-20, 45-46

HONOURS Football Lge Div 2 R-up 1914; 3rd Div N 28; Yorkshire Lge 21, 23;Midland Lge 32; West Riding Snr Cup 11,13,25,27,32,36,51,53,63, County Cup 29,90-91, N.W.C. Lg Champions 94-95, N.W.C. Carling Challenge Trophy 94-95

Back Row, left to right: T. Storton (Manager), F. Thornton (Chairman), P. Lindley, J. Maxwell, N. Lacey, N. Bagshaw, P. Marquis, M. Thompson, G. Kelly, I. Thompson (Assistant Manager) and R. Robinson (Vice Chairman).
Front Row: M. James, W. Benn, K. O'Brien, M. Hancock,(captain), A. Quinn, D. Calcutt, A. Hayward, D. Simpson (Kit Man)

Date	Comp.	Opponents	Att.	Score	Goalscorers
19.08	Unib 1	CHORLEY	272	1 - 1	Thompson 30
22.08	Unib 1	Harrogate Town	325	2 - 1	Calcutt 9, Thompson 65
26.08	Unib 1	Gretna	92	1 - 0	Bagshaw 81
28.08	Unib 1	WORKINGTON	253	1 - 0	Maxwell 30
02.09	FA Cup P	BRANDON UNITED	256	1 - 0	Thompson 28
09.09	Unib 1	Vauxhall	134	0 - 2	
16.09	FA Cup Q1	SALFORD CITY	209	0 - 1	
23.09	Unib 1	Trafford	183	3 - 1	Hayward 36 60, Hancock 90
27.09	Unib 1	EASTWOOD TOWN	158	4 - 1	Quinn 27, Thompson 77, Marquis 84, Hancock 87
30.09	Unib 1	North Ferriby United	215	1 - 2	Maxwell 78
06.10	Unib 1	LINCOLN UNITED	205	2 - 0	Hancock 40, Maxwell 43
10.10	Unib 1	Ossett Town	192	1 - 1	James 32
14.10	Unib 1	GUISELEY	340	3 - 0	Brown 29[og], Stratford 41, Marquis 80
21.10	Unib 1	Congleton Town	410	2 - 0	Hayward 25 50
23.10	Unib 1	Ashton United	212	2 - 0	Hayward 4, Marquis 66
28.10	Unib 1	MATLOCK TOWN	218	0 - 2	
04.11	FA Trophy 1	Gainsborough Trinity	392	2 - 3	Quinn 74, Maxwell 46
11.11	Unib 1	KENDAL TOWN	183	4 - 0	Hancock 37, Burrow 46[og], Hayward 78, Garrity 90[og]
18.11	Unib 1	Eastwood Town	170	1 - 0	Hayward 73
21.11	Lge Cup 3	Harrogate Town	139	1 - 1	Benn 57
25.11	Unib 1	ASHTON UNITED	274	1 - 2	Hancock 89[p]
29.11	Lge Cup 3	EMLEY	157	3 - 2	Maxwell 24, Benn 48[p], Hayward 76
02.12	Unib 1	Kendal Town	122	1 - 0	James 57
09.12	Unib 1	WINSFORD UNITED	188	4 - 0	Hayward 67 90, Maxwell 74, Benn 78
11.12	W Rid SC 2	Yorkshire Amateur	0	2 - 1	Maxwell 36, Thompson 55
16.12	Unib 1	Witton Albion	376	2 - 5	Denney 6, Hancock 35[p]
19.12	Lge Cup 3	Frickley Athletic	133	3 - 3	Hayward 5 78, Maxwell 64
23.12	Unib 1	TRAFFORD	277	1 - 0	Hayward 43
06.01	Unib 1	VAUXHALL	405	0 - 1	
13.01	Unib 1	Chorley	312	1 - 2	Denney 43
24.01	Lge Cup 3	FARSLEY CELTIC	112	0 - 2	
27.01	Unib 1	CONGLETON TOWN	233	1 - 2	Maxwell 21
31.01	Unib 1	HARROGATE TOWN	189	4 - 2	Hayward 24, Maxwell 25 53, Hancock 30
03.02	Unib 1	Belper Town	216	2 - 0	Hayward 4 80
13.02	W Rid SC QF	Glasshoughton Welfare	0	2 - 0	Thompson 25 65
17.02	Unib 1	Workington	323	5 - 2	Thompson 5, Benn 16, Maxwell 55 70, Calcutt 60
24.02	Unib 1	Matlock Town	300	4 - 1	Maxwell 9 23 64, Thompson 67
10.03	Unib 1	Stocksbridge Park Steels	291	3 - 0	Maxwell 63, Quinn 84, Hancock 86
14.03	W Rid SC SF	OSSETT TOWN	177	0 - 2	
17.03	Unib 1	FARSLEY CELTIC	339	3 - 0	Hayward 25 47, Hancock 54[p]
24.03	Unib 1	OSSETT TOWN	286	3 - 2	Maxwell 36 57, James 85
28.03	Unib 1	BELPER TOWN	175	2 - 1	Lacey 8, Hayward 46
31.03	Unib 1	Lincoln United	213	2 - 2	Hayward 45, Calcutt 72
04.04	Unib 1	RADCLIFFE BOROUGH	197	0 - 1	
07.04	Unib 1	STOCKSBRIDGE PARK STEELS	275	1 - 0	Maxwell 48
14.04	Unib 1	NORTH FERRIBY UNITED	338	2 - 1	Lacey 45, Hayward 90
16.04	Unib 1	Farsley Celtic	264	3 - 0	O'Brien 3, Hayward 85 90
21.04	Unib 1	Winsford United	215	2 - 1	Hayward 65, Simpson 73[p]
25.04	Unib 1	WITTON ALBION	386	4 - 1	Thompson 36 86, Lindley 75, Hayward 86
28.04	Unib 1	GRETNA	320	2 - 2	Bagshaw 8, Hancock 24
01.05	Unib 1	Guiseley	367	0 - 0	
05.05	Unib 1	Radcliffe Borough	269	2 - 1	Maxwell 2 47

PLAYING SQUAD

GOALKEEPERS: Gavin Kelly (Whitby)

DEFENDERS: Martin James (Winsford Utd), Neil Bagshaw (Rotherham), Mike Thompson (Frickley), Neil Lacey (Emley), Kieron O'Brien (Harrogate RA), Mark Hancock (Frickley)

MIDFIELDERS: Paul Wharton (Farsley Celtic), Andy Quinn (Gainsborough), Phil Lindley (Local), Dean Calcutt (Emley), Wayne Benn (Halifax), Ian Richards (Halifax), Michael Quigley (Northwich)

FORWARDS: Jason Maxwell (Gainsborough), Michael Nunn (Army), Andy Hayward (Frickley), Ian Brigg (Thackley)

BURSCOUGH

CLUB OFFICIALS

Chairman: **Frank Parr**
Vice Chairman: **Stuart Heaps**
President: **Rod Cottam**
Secretary/Press Off. **Stan Strickland**
109 Redgate, Ormskirk, Lancs L39 3NW
H 01695574722 B 01695 574722
M 07970 030588
Email sstrick@109redgate.freeserve.co.uk

FOOTBALL MANAGEMENT TEAM

Manager: John Davison
Asst Manager: Peter King
Physio: Tom Spencer

FACT FILE

Founded: 1946
Nickname: Linnets
Sponsors: Seyfert Ltd.
Colours: Green/white/green
Change colours: Red/black/red
Midweek Matches: Tuesday
Reserves: Lancashire League

2000-01

Captain: Andy McMullen
Top Scorer: Robbie Talbot 21
P.o.Y.: Andy McMullen

Pages:44 Price £1.00
Editor: Stan Strickland
(01695 574722)

Local Radio: Radio Lancs,Red Rose.

GROUND: Victoria Park, Bobby Langton Way, Mart Lane, Burscough, Ormskirk, Lancs L40 0SD Tel: 01704 893237 Website: www.burscough-fc.co.uk
Directions: M6 Jct 27, follow signs thru Parbold A5209, right into Junction Lane (signed Burscough & Martin Mere) to lights, right onto A59 to Burscough Village, 2nd left over canal bridge into Mart Lane to ground. 200 yards from Burscough Bridge BR station (Wigan-Southport line). Half mile from Burscough Junction (Ormskirk Preston line)
Capacity: 2,500 Seats: 270 Cover: 1,000
Clubhouse: `Barons Club' (privately owned, access outside grd). Mon-Thurs 7-11pm, Fri 4-11pm, Sat 1-11pm, Sun noon-3 & 7-10.30pm. No food **Club Shop:** Yes

PREVIOUS **Leagues:** Liverpool Co Comb. 46-53, Lancs Comb. 53-70, Cheshire Co.70-82, North West Cos 82-98, Unibond NPL98-01

CLUB RECORDS **Attendance:** 4,798 v Wigan Athletic,F.A.Cup 3rd Qual.Rd.1950-51
Goalscorer: Johnny Vincent 60 53-54. Most Goals in Game: Louis Bimpson 7. In Career: Wes Bridge 188
Win: 10-0 v Cromptons Recreation 1947 & v Nelson 1948-49, both Lancs. Comb.
Defeat: 0-9 v Earlstown,Liverpool County Comb.1948-49 **Fee paid:** £2,500 Stuart Rudd (Skelmersdale Utd 00-01)
Fee Received: £12,000 for Michael Yates (Dundee) 99-00

BEST SEASON **FA Cup:** 1st Rd 59-60 77-78 79-80 80-81
FA Trophy: 1982-83 99-00 **FA Vase:** 1994-95 (Last 16)

HONOURS Liverpool Challenge Cup 47-48 50-51,54-55; George Mahon Cup 47-48; Liverpool County Comb Div 1, 49-50 (Div 2 53-54, 67-68); Lancs Comb.Div 2 53-54; Lancs Comb Div 1 55-56 69-70; Lord Wavertree Cup 67-68; Cheshire County Lge R-up 70- 71, League Cup 74-75 (R-up 73-74); Lancs Jnr Cup 47-4849-50 66-67; Liverpool Non-Lg Snr Cup 55/56, 71-72; North West Counties Lge 82-83, Lge Cup 92-93 95-96(R-up 91-92), Challenge Shield 82-83, 95-96; Liverpool Senior Cup R-up 92-93,95-96, 99-00.

Players progressing: L Bimpson, B Parker (Liverpool 53), B Pilson (Stoke 53-54), A Green (Huddersfield), K Waterhouse (Preston), F Gamble (Derby 80), Tony Rigby (Bury), S Teale (Aston Villa), L Watson (Preston), K Formby A Russell (Rochdale 94) G Martindale (Bolton 94), S Perkins (Plymouth A. 97), M.Yates (Dundee 99), L. Trundle (Wrexham, R. Lowe (Shrewsbury T.)

Right:
Ged Nolan and Andy McMullen get up well despite the best efforts of Stalybridge Celtic's Martin Filson.
Photo: Colin Stevens

Date	Comp.	Opponents	Att.	Score	Goalscorers
19.08	Unib P	HYDE UNITED	281	1 - 0	Bowen 8
22.08	Unib P	Lancaster City	266	2 - 5	Knowles 86, Talbot 90
26.08	Unib P	Gainsborough Trinity	328	1 - 2	Rudd 51
28.08	Unib P	BAMBER BRIDGE	347	3 - 0	Knowles 19, Talbot 45, McEvilly 87
02.09	Unib P	BLYTH SPARTANS	234	3 - 1	Knowles 64, Birch 79, Talbot 89
05.09	Unib P	Barrow	1188	2 - 2	McEvilly 81 90
09.09	Unib P	Frickley Athletic	141	0 - 1	
12.09	Unib P	MARINE	266	1 - 3	Wilde 90
16.09	Unib P	SPENNYMOOR UNITED	189	4 - 1	Wilde 23, Nolan 53, Lawless 86, Talbot 90
19.09	Unib P	Colwyn Bay	222	1 - 4	Lawless 89[p]
23.09	Unib P	Whitby Town	389	2 - 0	Talbot 79, Lawless 81
26.09	Unib P	ACCRINGTON STANLEY	310	0 - 0	
30.09	FA Cup Q2	RUNCORN	346	2 - 1	McEvilly 69, Talbot 90
07.10	Unib P	Marine	364	5 - 3	McEvilly 43 90, Knowles 58, Talbot 69 73
14.10	FA Cup Q3	Witton Albion	335	0 - 0	
17.10	FA Cup Q3 R	WITTON ALBION	253	6 - 1	McEvilly 4, Talbot 28 70, McMullen 50, Stanton 65
21.10	Unib P	BISHOP AUCKLAND	180	2 - 1	Talbot 34, Knowles 86
24.10	Lge Cup 6	WITTON ALBION	128	1 - 1	Lawless 75
28.10	FA Cup Q4	RADCLIFFE BOROUGH	459	1 - 1	Leahy 37
04.11	FA Trophy 1	Shepshed Dynamo	142	3 - 2	Talbot 15, Wilde 85 89
11.11	FA Cup Q4 R	Radcliffe Borough	789	1 - 2	Talbot 29
18.11	Unib P	WORKSOP TOWN	287	2 - 2	McEvilly 26, Wilde 28
21.11	L'pool SC 1	SKELMERSDALE UNITED	126	5 - 1	Howard 14 23, Talbot 60[p] 77, Rudd 65
25.11	Unib P	Spennymoor United	77	2 - 0	Farrell 1, Talbot 88
28.11	Lancs MT 1	ATHERTON LR	70	2 - 1	Rudd 33, Talbot 88
02.12	FA Trophy 2	GAINSBOROUGH TRINITY	229	1 - 0	Clandon 64
09.12	Unib P	LEEK TOWN	165	1 - 0	Dodd 13[og]
12.12	Lge Cup 6	MARINE	124	5 - 3	Lawless 2, Talbot 5, Wilde 10, Clandon 51, Rudd 90
23.12	Unib P	BARROW	333	1 - 2	McEvilly 12
26.12	Unib P	Runcorn	275	0 - 2	
02.01	Lge Cup 6	Colwyn Bay	109	3 - 1	Lawless 11 26, Wilde 66
06.01	Unib P	Altrincham	603	2 - 2	Lawless 18[p] 75
09.01	L'pool SC QF	WARRINGTON TOWN	77	5 - 1	Wilde 62 70 85, McMullen 67, Talbot 90
13.01	FA Trophy 3	MORECAMBE	582	3 - 3	Talbot 8, Farrell 56, Wilde 77
22.01	FA Trophy 3 R	Morecambe	585	0 - 3	
27.01	Unib P	Bishop Auckland	206	0 - 4	
30.01	Lancs MT 2	Marine	183	0 - 1	
03.02	Unib P	HUCKNALL TOWN	191	2 - 1	McEvilly 40, Howard 90
10.02	Unib P	GAINSBOROUGH TRINITY	185	1 - 1	Howard 78
13.02	Lge Cup 6	Vauxhall	83	0 - 1	
17.02	Unib P	Hucknall Town	175	2 - 3	McEvilly 34 47
20.02	Unib P	STALYBRIDGE CELTIC	276	1 - 1	McMullen 67
24.02	Unib P	WHITBY TOWN	227	2 - 3	Nolan 67, Rudd 90
03.03	Chairman QF	WORKSOP TOWN	199	0 - 1	
06.03	L'pool SC SF	MARINE	182	2 - 2	Lawless 31[p], McEvilly 75 (5-4p)
10.03	Unib P	Droylsden	195	2 - 1	Lawless 45[p], Rudd 51
13.03	Unib P	EMLEY	212	0 - 1	
17.03	Unib P	GATESHEAD	181	0 - 1	
20.03	Unib P	Worksop Town	388	0 - 1	
24.03	Unib P	RUNCORN	166	0 - 0	
28.03	Unib P	Gateshead	130	1 - 1	McEvilly 47
31.03	Unib P	Leek Town	251	0 - 4	
02.04	Unib P	Emley	471	1 - 2	Leahy 90[p]
14.04	Unib P	LANCASTER CITY	229	2 - 3	McEvilly 11, Wilde 44
16.04	Unib P	ALTRINCHAM	329	1 - 1	Wilde 26
18.04	Unib P	FRICKLEY ATHLETIC	112	1 - 2	Birch 25
21.04	Unib P	Blyth Spartans	297	0 - 1	
24.04	Unib P	Bamber Bridge	186	1 - 0	Leahy 17[p]
26.04	Unib P	COLWYN BAY	179	1 - 2	McMullen 26
28.04	Unib P	DROYLSDEN	175	3 - 1	Dugdale 58 77, Nolan 62
30.04	Unib P	Hyde United	262	1 - 1	Lawless 45
02.05	Unib P	Accrington Stanley	314	0 - 2	
05.05	Unib P	Stalybridge Celtic	1432	2 - 0	McEvilly 28, Lawless 49
31.07	L'pool SC F	SOUTHPORT	n.k	1 - 0	McEvilly 37

PLAYING SQUAD

GOALKEEPERS: John Bagnall (Winsford Utd), Matthew Taylor (Preston)

DEFENDERS: Ged Nolan (St.Helens), Carl Flood (Youth), Neil Hanson (Bootle), Chris Stanton (Prescot Cables), Andy McMullen (Prescot Cables), Marvin Molyneux (Youth), Ryan Bowen (Youth), Gary Parr (Bootle), Tommy Molloy (Youth), Karl Clark (Youth)

MIDFIELDERS: Jamie Cassidy (Northwich), Billy Knowles (St.Helens), Ged Hennigan (Droylsden), Ray Birch (Congleton), Steve Leahey (Youth), Gareth Evans (Droylsden), Steve Alty (Altrincham)

FORWARDS: Lee Furlong (Southport), Stuart Rudd (Skelmersdale), Carl Howarth (Nelson), John Lawless (Youth), Lee McElvilly (Bootle), Dave Dugdale (Youth)

BURTON ALBION

Pages: 48 Price: £1
Editor: David Twigg (01283 562013)

Local Press: Burton Daily Mail (01283 43311)
Local Radio: Radio Derby,Centra F.M.

CLUB OFFICIALS

Chairman: **C B Robinson** 01283 37272(W)
Vice Chairman:
Secretary: **Tony A Kirkland**, 40 Hurst Drive, Stretton, Burton-on-Trent DE13 0ED
07774 102485 (Mobile)
Commercial Man: **Fleur Robinson**
Press Officer: **David Twigg** (01283 562013)

FACT FILE

Formed: 1950 Nickname: Brewers
Sponsors: B.I. Industries
Colours: Yellow with black trim
Change colours: Blue
Midweek matchday: Tuesday
Club Websites:
www.burtonalbionfc.co.uk
www.brewerstreet.com

FOOTBALL MANAGEMENT TEAM

Manager: Nigel Clough
Assistant Manager: Gary Crosby
Physio: Matt Brown

2000-01

Captain: Darren Stride
Top Goalscorer: Darren Stride 19
P.O.Y. Darren Wassell

GROUND Eton Park, Princess Way, Burton-on-Trent DE14 2RU Tel: 01283 565938
Directions: From south M42 - A38 (Lichfield), follow signs forBurton, take 2nd turn for Burton (A5121), right at island - ground on left: From M6 north - jct 15 and follow A50 for Stoke and Uttoxeter, follow A50 signsto Burton, continue under bypass, left into Shakespeare Rd after canal bridge (opp. Navigation Inn), ground at end. From M6 North, leave at Jct 15 .Follow A50 Stoke & Uttoxeter. Leave for A38 South to Burton & Lichfield at Toyota Factory.Leave Burton North A5121 past Pirelli Factory to Island .Turn right ground is on left.
Capacity: 4,500 Cover: 2,500 Seats: 464 Floodlights: Yes
Clubhouse: `The Football Tavern' - open normal pub hours. Full hot & cold menu.
Steward: T.B.A. Club Shop: Yes

PREVIOUS **Leagues:** West Midlands 1950-58; Southern 58-79; Northern Premier 79-80, Southern (Dr.Martens) 1980-20001
Ground: Wellington Street 50-57

CLUB RECORDS **Attendance:** 5,860 v Weymouth, Southern Lg Cup Final 2nd leg, 1964
(22,500 v Leicester City, F.A. Cup 3rd Rd 1984 - played at Derby County F.C.)
Goalscorer: Ritchie Barker, 157. **Appearances:** Phil Annable, 567
Fee Paid: £21,000 to for R Jones and J Pearson (Kidderminster)
Fee Received: £60,000 for Darren Carr (C Palace 89)

BEST SEASON **FA Trophy:** R-up 86-87 (SF 74-75) **FA Cup:** 3rd Rd Prop 55-56, 84-85. 1st Rd 9 times

HONOURS Sth Lg Cup 63-64 96-97, 99-00 (R-up 88-89), Div 1 (Nth) R-up 71-72 73-74; Nth Prem Lg Chall Cup 82-83 (R-up 86-87), Presidents Cup R-up 85-86 (SF 86-87); BirminghamSnr Cup 53-54 70-71 (R-up 86-87); FA Trophy R-up 86-87; GMAC Cup SF 86-87; Bass Charity Vase 81-82 85-86, Challenge Cup 84-85; Wt Mids Lg R-up 53-54; Staffs Sen Cup 55-56

Players progressing: L Green & T Parry & S Aston (Hartlepool65/66), G Hunter (Lincoln 65), D Jones (Newport 68), R Barker & J Bourne & TBailey (Derby 67/69/70), M Pollock & S Buckley (Luton 74), P Ward (Brighton75), Tony Moore (Sheffield Utd 79), C Swan & G Clayton (Doncaster 80 & 86), RJobson (Watford 82), P Haycock (Rotherham 86), A Kamara (Scarborough 87), PGroves (Leicester City 88), S Cotterill & J Gayle (Wimbledon 89), D Carr(Crystal Pal. 89), D Smith & D Roberts (Wolves 90 & 92)

Date	Comp.	Opponents	Att.	Score	Goalscorers
27.07	Bass Vase	NOTTINGHAM FOREST	n.k	2 - 3	Webster, Moore[p]
31.07	Bass Vase	STOKE CITY	n.k	3 - 0	Webster 48, Stride 51, Starbuck 88
12.08	DML Shield	Boston United	835	4 - 0	Webster 44[p], Thomas 60, Holmes 72, Anderson 84
19.08	DM Prem	Newport County	961	1 - 1	Robinson 82[og]
22.08	DM Prem	KING'S LYNN	1089	1 - 1	Webster 86[p]
26.08	DM Prem	FISHER ATHLETIC	875	3 - 0	Webster 2, Blount 55, Anderson 64
28.08	DM Prem	Tamworth	1245	3 - 2	Stride 49, Anderson 76, Glasser 90[p]
02.09	DM Prem	MERTHYR TYDFIL	1097	1 - 0	Anderson 86
05.09	DM Prem	Halesowen Town	669	2 - 1	Stride 54, Kavanagh 85
09.09	DM Prem	Margate	629	3 - 1	Anderson 18, Kavanagh 32, Clough 75
16.09	DM Prem	WELLING UNITED	1461	1 - 1	Clough 49
19.09	DM Prem	King's Lynn	613	1 - 1	Stride 39
23.09	DM Prem	DORCHESTER TOWN	1030	1 - 1	Kavanagh 20
30.09	FA Cup Q2	Halesowen Town	668	2 - 0	Kavanagh 27, Stride 51
06.10	DM Prem	Cambridge City	826	1 - 1	Webster 83
14.10	FA Cup Q3	Tamworth	1456	1 - 1	Rennie 43
17.10	FA Cup Q3 R	TAMWORTH	1579	3 - 1	Anderson 45, Stride 49, Webster 58
21.10	DM Prem	SALISBURY CITY	1085	5 - 0	Webster 26[p], Stride 78, Starbuck 65 86, Anderson 82
24.10	DM Prem	TAMWORTH	1102	3 - 1	Starbuck 9 28, Stride 15
28.10	FA Cup Q4	Boston United	2144	1 - 1	Glasser 22
31.10	FA Cup Q4 R	BOSTON UNITED	2299	3 - 2	Starbuck 58[p] 70, Anderson 78
04.11	DM Prem	Bath City	1051	1 - 3	Blount 52
11.11	DM Prem	CLEVEDON TOWN	1021	1 - 0	Stride 90
14.11	Lge Cup 1	Tamworth	411	1 - 2	Anderson 47
18.11	FA Cup 1	Kidderminster Harriers	3384	0 - 0	
22.11	Birm. SC 2	Gornal Athletic	187	1 - 3	
28.11	FA Cup 1 R	KIDDERMINSTER HARRIERS	3760	2 - 4	Blount 71, Wassall 84
02.12	FA Trophy 2	YEADING	784	4 - 1	Moore 52 74 87, Lyons 72
09.12	DM Prem	WORCESTER CITY	1284	1 - 0	Starbuck 32
16.12	DM Prem	Moor Green	859	2 - 1	Blount 42, Moore 56[p]
23.12	DM Prem	Merthyr Tydfil	581	5 - 1	Stride 11 25, Moore 50[p] 70, Anderson 83
26.12	DM Prem	STAFFORD RANGERS	2501	0 - 0	
01.01	DM Prem	Ilkeston Town	1516	1 - 2	Clough 33
06.01	DM Prem	NEWPORT COUNTY	1266	2 - 1	Moore 50[p], Stride 81
09.01	DM Prem	Fisher Athletic	186	4 - 0	Blount 12, Lyons 29, Stride 33, Webster 73[p]
13.01	FA Trophy 3	BISHOP AUCKLAND	1173	2 - 0	Moore 28, Stride 45
20.01	DM Prem	Weymouth	1005	1 - 1	Anderson 9
23.01	DM Prem	CAMBRIDGE CITY	946	2 - 2	Wassell 22, Holden 28[og]
27.01	DM Prem	BATH CITY	1376	2 - 2	Moore 58 66
03.02	FA Trophy 4	Scarborough	1462	1 - 0	Stride 54
10.02	DM Prem	Clevedon Town	519	2 - 1	Stride 70, Ryan 80
13.02	DM Prem	HALESOWEN TOWN	1006	1 - 0	Stride 32
17.02	DM Prem	Welling United	732	2 - 1	Webster 26, Stride 58
20.02	DM Prem	FOLKESTONE INVICTA	921	0 - 2	
24.02	FA Trophy 5	YEOVIL TOWN	2469	2 - 1	Moore 64[p], Anderson 87
03.03	DM Prem	Worcester City	1727	1 - 1	Moore 4
06.03	DM Prem	MOOR GREEN	1039	2 - 1	Anderson 73, Stride 86
10.03	FA Trophy QF	Hereford United	3238	0 - 1	
24.03	DM Prem	Folkestone Invicta	395	2 - 0	Webster 15, Webster 39
31.03	DM Prem	CRAWLEY TOWN	1320	2 - 1	Pullan 36[og], Moore 90
07.04	DM Prem	Salisbury City	559	0 - 1	
12.04	DM Prem	Havant & Waterlooville	416	1 - 1	Hoyle 82
14.04	DM Prem	ILKESTON TOWN	1606	1 - 0	Sugden 51
16.04	DM Prem	Stafford Rangers	1674	2 - 0	Starbuck 5, Sugden 80
21.04	DM Prem	HAVANT & WATERLOOVILLE	1066	4 - 0	Anderson 38, Sugden 45[p] 72, Moore 46
24.04	DM Prem	WEYMOUTH	1155	1 - 0	Moore 47
28.04	DM Prem	Dorchester Town	605	3 - 1	Moore 9, Kavanagh 64, Stride 64
01.05	DM Prem	Crawley Town	485	2 - 2	Sugden 5[p] 54[p]
05.05	DM Prem	MARGATE	1464	2 - 0	Moore 45, Sugden 60

PLAYING SQUAD

GOALKEEPERS: Matthew Duke (Sheffield Utd), Dan Robinson (Blackpool)

DEFENDERS: Mark Blount (Gresley R), Darren Wassall (Birmingham), Terry Henshaw (Notts Co), Colin Hoyle (Boston Utd), Jason Kavanagh (Cambridge Utd)

MIDFIELDERS: Nigel Clough (Manchester C), Pat Lyons (WBA), Steve Evans (Aston Villa), Paul Wraith (Youth), Neil Glasser (Grantham), Darren Stride (Youth), Liam Walshe (Gresley R)

FORWARDS: Christian Moore (Ilkeston), Aaron Webster (Youth), Sean Farrell (Notts Co), Andy Garner (Gresley R), Dale Anderson (Bromsgrove R)

COLWYN BAY

CLUB OFFICIALS

Chairman: T.B.A.

Secretary / Press Officer: **Mike Roberts,**
18 Belgrave Road,Colwyn Bay, N.Wales
Tel Nos:01492 534724(H)
07887 782565 (M)

FOOTBALL MANAGEMENT TEAM
Manager: Colin Caton
Assistant Manager: Dean Martin
Physio: Colin Edwards

FACT FILE

Formed: 1885
Nickname: `Bay' or `Seagulls'
Sponsors: Bay View Centre
Colours: Sky Blue.
Change colours: Tangerine
Reserve Team:
Midweek home matchday: Tuesday

2000-01 Captain: Graham Roberts
P.o.Y.: James McIlvogue
Top scorer: Deiniol GRaham 25

Pages: 28 Price: £1
Editor: Neil Brampton (01492 533341)
Local Press: North Wales Weekly News, North Wales Pioneer.
Club Website: www.cbfc.skynow.co.uk

GROUNDLlanelian Road, Old Colwyn, N.Wales. Tel: 01492 514581
Email Address:mikerobs@cbfc.freeserve.co.uk
Directions: M55 North Wales Coast - approaching Colwyn Bay take 1st exit signposted Old Colwyn, left at bottom slip road, straight over r'bout into Llanelian Rd - ground half mile on right. 2 miles from Colwyn Bar BR station.
Capacity: 2,500 Seats: 250 Cover: 700
Clubhouse: Open matchdays only.
Club Shop: Yes - contact: A Holden 01492 534287 Metal Badges: Yes

PREVIOUS Leagues: Nth Wales Coast 01-21 33-35; Welsh National 21-30; Nth Wales Comb. 30-31; Welsh Lg (Nth) 45-84; North West Counties 84-91
Grounds: Eiras Park 1930-82; Llanelian Road 82-92; Northwich Victoria FC 92-93; Ellesmere Port Stadium94-95 (2 years in exile thro' dispute with FAW re League of Wales).

CLUB RECORDS **Attendance:** 5,000 (at Eiras Park) v Borough United, 1964.
Goalscorer: Peter Donnelly **Appearances:** Bryn A Jones

BEST SEASON **FA Trophy:** Quarter Finals 96-97. **F.A Cup:** Second Round Proper 95-96. League clubs defeated: Wrexham(Welsh Cup)

HONOURS Northern Premier Lg Div 1 91-92 (Div 1 Cup 91-92); North West Counties Lg R-up90-91 (Div 3 R-up 83-84, Lg Cup 88-89, Floodlit Cup 90-91; Welsh Cup SF 91-92;Welsh National Lg R-up 27-28 29-30; Nth Wales Comb. 30-31; Welsh Lg Nth 64-6582-83 83-84 (R-up 35-36 45-46 63-64), Lg Cup 27-28; Alves Cup 63-64; Cookson Cup 73-74 79-80 80-81 81-82 83-84; Barritt Cup 79-80 81-82 83-84; Nth Wales Coast Chal. Cup 30-31 31-32 81-82 82-83 83-84 95-96 97-98; Nth Wales Coast Jnr Cup 1898-99. North Wst Coast Cup 99-00.

Players progressing: Peter Suddaby (Blackpool), Gareth Davies (Wrexham).

Back Row: Glen Graham, Colin Caton (player/manager), James McIlvogue, Alun Evans, Graham Roberts, Richie Roberts, Jamie Jardine. Paul Jones, Owain Roberts, Craig Lawton.
Front Row: Mark Woods, Dean Williams, Marc Lambert, Jon Cross.

Date	Comp.	Opponents	Att.	Score	Goalscorers
19.08	Unib P	BISHOP AUCKLAND	231	3 - 3	Cross 22, Hutt 42[og], Evans 44
22.08	Unib P	Droylsden	201	0 - 1	
26.08	Unib P	Bamber Bridge	238	4 - 3	Evans 14 26 67, Graham 59
28.08	Unib P	RUNCORN	334	2 - 2	Caton 63, Graham 71
02.09	Unib P	Spennymoor United	133	1 - 1	Lambert 80
05.09	Unib P	HYDE UNITED	312	2 - 1	McIlvogue 50, Limbert 67
09.09	Unib P	GATESHEAD	285	2 - 2	McIlvogue 28, Limbert 34
12.09	Unib P	Altrincham	501	0 - 3	
19.09	Unib P	BURSCOUGH	222	4 - 1	Graham 6 50 84, Roberts 43
23.09	Unib P	BLYTH SPARTANS	288	1 - 0	Evans 73
25.09	Unib P	Hyde United	417	1 - 1	Cross 4
30.09	FA Cup Q2	Marine	366	3 - 4	Gibbons 59, Graham 62 88
03.10	Unib P	DROYLSDEN	244	3 - 2	Graham 53[p], McIlvogue 82, Limbert 86
14.10	Unib P	WORKSOP TOWN	361	3 - 2	Graham 11[p] 37, Evans 54
31.10	Lge Cup 6	Marine	138	0 - 1	
04.11	FA Trophy 1	TAMWORTH	321	3 - 3	D Graham 58 79, G Graham 62
07.11	FA Trophy 1 R	Tamworth	362	1 - 2	Cross 63
11.11	Unib P	Runcorn	218	0 - 1	
18.11	Unib P	HUCKNALL TOWN	223	0 - 2	
25.11	Unib P	Frickley Athletic	90	2 - 6	Lennon 37, Graham 58
28.11	Lge Cup 6	Vauxhall	104	0 - 2	
02.12	Unib P	BAMBER BRIDGE	214	1 - 1	Evans 84
09.12	Unib P	Accrington Stanley	542	2 - 2	McIlvogue 20, Evans 69
23.12	Unib P	Hucknall Town	218	0 - 1	
26.12	Unib P	MARINE	302	2 - 3	Lawton 84, Evans 85
02.01	Lge Cup 6	BURSCOUGH	109	1 - 3	
06.01	Unib P	Gainsborough Trinity	375	0 - 1	
09.01	Lge Cup 6	WITTON ALBION	116	2 - 3	Barber 69, Kendrick 89
13.01	Unib P	Whitby Town	322	1 - 5	Lennon 2
27.01	Unib P	EMLEY	364	0 - 4	
03.02	Unib P	Gateshead	205	2 - 4	Graham 17 38
20.02	Unib P	ACCRINGTON STANLEY	213	2 - 4	Graham 35, Flannery 89[og]
24.02	Unib P	Emley	416	1 - 4	Lennon 54
03.03	Unib P	FRICKLEY ATHLETIC	305	0 - 0	
10.03	Unib P	Blyth Spartans	321	2 - 5	Evans 18, Davies 90
13.03	Unib P	Barrow	799	2 - 3	Davis 47, McIlvogue 90
17.03	Unib P	LANCASTER CITY	251	1 - 2	Williams 70
20.03	Unib P	STALYBRIDGE CELTIC	239	1 - 7	Lawton 70
24.03	Unib P	Marine	212	0 - 2	
27.03	Unib P	SPENNYMOOR UNITED	229	3 - 2	Evans 14[p], O Roberts 35, G Roberts 86
31.03	Unib P	Bishop Auckland	157	1 - 5	Caton 48
03.04	Unib P	ALTRINCHAM	278	1 - 2	Graham 34[p]
07.04	Unib P	GAINSBOROUGH TRINITY	212	3 - 3	McIlvogue 53 58, Graham 89[p]
10.04	Unib P	Lancaster City	235	0 - 1	
14.04	Unib P	Stalybridge Celtic	626	0 - 4	
16.04	Unib P	Leek Town	241	4 - 2	McIlvogue 11, Graham 17 74, Roberts 19
21.04	Unib P	WHITBY TOWN	296	2 - 1	D Graham 35, K Graham 44[og]
26.04	Unib P	Burscough	179	2 - 1	D Graham 7, Limbert 63
28.04	Unib P	LEEK TOWN	318	4 - 1	Limbert 13, Evans 21 89, McIlvogue 61
01.05	Unib P	Worksop Town	317	1 - 1	McIlvogue 81
05.05	Unib P	BARROW	585	2 - 0	McIlvogue 1 6

PLAYING SQUAD

GOALKEEPERS: Paul Smith (TNS)

DEFENDERS: Colin Caton (Witton Alb), Craig Hogg (Everton), Jamie Jardine (Bangor C), Dean Williams (Malvern), Paul Jones (Connah's Quay), Mark Price (Connah's Quay)

MIDFIELDERS: Craig Lawton (Port Vale), Jonathan Cross (Chester), Jason Jones (Oswestry), Owain Roberts (Ruthin), Simon Richards (Flexsys Cefn Druids), Glen Graham (Flint), Marc Limbert (Altrincham), Stuart Scheuber (Altrincham)

FORWARDS: Graham Roberts (Macclesfield), Deniol Graham (Cwmbran), John Fisher-Cooke (Rhyl), James McIlvogue (Conwy Utd), Alun Evans (Ebbw Vale)

DROYLSDEN

CLUB OFFICIALS

Chairman: **David Pace**

Secretary: **Alan Slater**
83 King Edward Rd.,Hyde,
Cheshire SK14 5JJ
Tel & Fax: 0161 368 3687

FOOTBALL MANAGEMENT TEAM

Manager: David Pace
Asst Manager: Aeon Lattie
Physio Alan Cross

FACT FILE

Formed: 1892 Nickname: The Bloods
Sponsors:Alpha Court Windows ,Federation Brewery & Hastings Taxis
Colours: Red /black/black
Change colours: All Blue
Midweek matchday: Tuesday

2000-01

Captain & Top Scorer: Carl Holmes (11)
P.o.Y.: Paul Phillips

Pages: 24 Price: £1.00
Editor: T.B.A.Local Press: Droylsden Reporter, Advertiser
Local Radio: BBC Manchester
Club Website: www,winters 29.fsnet.co,uk

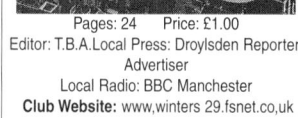

GROUND The Butchers Arms Ground, Market Street, Droylsden, Manchester M43 7AY Tel: 0161 370 1426/8341 FAX: 0161 370 8341

Directions: The ground lies 4 miles east of Manchester via the A662 Ashton New Road, behind Butchers Arms Hotel.From M60 Jct 23 (opening August 2000) Follow A662 to Doylsden. Right at lights in town centre through mini roundabout and ground on left.

Capacity: 3,500 Cover: 2,000 Seats:500

Clubhouse: Pub hours except matchdays. Pool and darts **Shop:** Yes Metal Badges

PREVIOUS **Leagues:** Manchester; Lancs Com 36-39, 50-68; Cheshire County 39-50, 68-82; NW Counties 82-87

CLUB RECORDS **Attendance:** 4,250 v Grimsby, **FA Cup** 1st rd 1976
Scorer: E Gillibrand 78 (1931-32) **Win:** 13-2 v Lucas Sports Club
Fee Received: £11,000 for Tony Naylor (Crewe)

BEST SEASON **FA Cup:** 2nd Rd 78-79. League clubs defeated: Rochdale 78-79
FA Vase: **FA Trophy:**

HONOURS Unibond Division 1 Champions 98-99 Northern Prem Lge Div 1 R-up 89-90 Div 1 Cup 87-88; R-U 88-9,98-9 NPL President's Cup Winners 98-99 NW Counties Lge Div 2 86-87 ; Cheshire County Lge R-up 39-40 45-46 , Lge Cup 77-78 (R-up 76-77);Lancs Comb Div 2 R-up 55-56 58-59 62-63; Manchester Lge 30-31 32-33 (Lge Cup 23-24 33-34); Manchester Prem Cup 80-81 (R-up 83-84 90-91 93-94); Man Sen Cup 72-73 75-76 78-79 (R-up 72-73 75-76 78-79); Manchester Interm Cup 59-6064-65 69-70; Manchester Chall Shield 46-47

Players progressing: Albert Butterworth & F Letchford (Blackpool 1931), William Davies & Maurice Randall (Crewe 1947), William Mellor (Accrington 1950), Geoff Tonge (Bury 1960), David Campbell (WBA 1962), Kevin Randall (Bury 1965), Peter Litchfield (Preston 1979), Tony Naylor (Crewe 1990)

L-R Back Row: Neil Whalley, Dave Ashton, Kevin Lampkin, Paul Phillips, Carl Holmes, Dominic Morley, Stuart Corms, Alan Cross (physio). Front Row: John Stannard, Wes Kimmey, lee Prior, Danny Warner. Photo: Alan Slater.

Date	Comp.	Opponents	Att.	Score	Goalscorers
19.08	Unib P	WHITBY TOWN	207	1 - 3	Kinney 45
22.08	Unib P	COLWYN BAY	201	1 - 0	Kinney 15
26.08	Unib P	Worksop Town	354	0 - 5	
28.08	Unib P	HYDE UNITED	561	2 - 4	Corns 3, Green 17
02.09	Unib P	Gainsborough Trinity	324	1 - 0	Corns 40
05.09	Unib P	Stalybridge Celtic	545	1 - 4	Warner 89
09.09	Unib P	SPENNYMOOR UNITED	187	4 - 1	Green 11 44 48, Holmes 54
23.09	Unib P	Lancaster City	308	2 - 0	Corns 66, Lampkin 82
26.09	Unib P	GAINSBOROUGH TRINITY	121	4 - 0	Prior 8 65, Holmes 38, Warner 82
30.09	FA Cup Q2	Barrow	1153	0 - 3	
03.10	Unib P	Colwyn Bay	244	2 - 3	Corns 40 75
08.10	Unib P	ALTRINCHAM	554	2 - 1	Holmes 29 80
14.10	Unib P	Blyth Spartans	295	1 - 0	Holmes 75
21.10	Unib P	Emley	261	1 - 2	Kinney 80
24.10	Unib P	Bamber Bridge	170	1 - 2	Holmes 85[p]
28.10	Unib P	BLYTH SPARTANS	230	1 - 2	Stannard 47
04.11	FA Trophy 1	BROMSGROVE ROVERS	199	0 - 0	
07.11	FA Trophy 1 R	Bromsgrove Rovers	185	0 - 1	
11.11	Unib P	BISHOP AUCKLAND	179	0 - 3	
18.11	Unib P	Accrington Stanley	591	0 - 3	
21.11	Lge Cup 7	CONGLETON TOWN	45	1 - 0	Warner 18
28.11	Lge Cup 7	Chorley	122	3 - 2	Stannard 3, Lattie 63, Corns 73
02.12	Unib P	Barrow	903	0 - 2	
05.12	Lge Cup 7	RADCLIFFE BOROUGH	102	2 - 2	Ashton 45 90
12.12	Lge Cup 7	Stalybridge Celtic	178	3 - 2	Holmes 68 78[p] 90[p]
16.12	Unib P	Frickley Athletic	119	1 - 1	Landon 61
23.12	Unib P	GATESHEAD	214	0 - 0	
26.12	Unib P	Whitby Town	361	1 - 0	Peel 13
06.01	Unib P	Marine	271	0 - 1	
13.01	Unib P	BARROW	253	2 - 1	Holmes 48, Young 80
27.01	Unib P	Spennymoor United	146	1 - 0	Landon 36
30.01	Manc. PC QF	Curzon Ashton	171	1 - 0	Landon 83
03.02	Unib P	Runcorn	191	1 - 3	Callaghan 90
06.02	Unib P	FRICKLEY ATHLETIC	133	1 - 1	Jones 27
10.02	Unib P	HUCKNALL TOWN	168	1 - 1	Pell 45
17.02	Unib P	WORKSOP TOWN	404	2 - 5	Pell 78[p], Ashton 80
19.02	Manc. PC SF	Salford City	160	1 - 1	Young 11 (4-3p)
24.02	Unib P	Bishop Auckland	165	1 - 2	Pell 33
06.03	Unib P	RUNCORN	142	0 - 2	
10.03	Unib P	BURSCOUGH	195	1 - 2	Pell 30
13.03	Lge Cup QF	Belper Town	135	0 - 1	
17.03	Unib P	Altrincham	565	0 - 3	
25.03	Unib P	LEEK TOWN	177	1 - 0	Pell 52
27.03	Unib P	LANCASTER CITY	120	3 - 2	Pell 37 45 87
31.03	Unib P	Gateshead	174	1 - 1	Pell 27
03.04	Unib P	Hucknall Town	164	2 - 1	Young 45, Warner 35
12.04	Unib P	MARINE	162	2 - 3	Nolan 39, Cunningham 89
14.04	Unib P	BAMBER BRIDGE	163	0 - 1	
16.04	Unib P	Hyde United	402	2 - 3	Holmes 7, Warner 22
18.04	Manc. PC F	Ashton United	n.k	0 - 4	(at Oldham Athletic)
21.04	Unib P	ACCRINGTON STANLEY	202	0 - 4	
28.04	Unib P	Burscough	175	1 - 3	Young 82
01.05	Unib P	STALYBRIDGE CELTIC	2040	0 - 1	
03.05	Unib P	Leek Town	255	1 - 1	Green 65
05.05	Unib P	EMLEY	238	1 - 3	Young 55

PLAYING SQUAD

GOALKEEPERS: Paul Phillips (Curzon Ashton), Thomas Giesler (TSV Bobingen)

DEFENDERS: Danny Warner (Curzon Ashton), Dave Ashton (Curzon Ashton), James Glendenning (Altrincham), Steve Shiel (Winsford Utd), Mark Bradshaw (Halifax), Aeon Lattie (Flixton)

MIDFIELDERS: Carl Holmes (Buxton), Dominic Morley (Southport), Lloyd Richardson (Salford C), Gary Thomas (Mossley), Dave Nolan (Runcorn)

FORWARDS: Andy Green (Barrow), Frank Gibbons (Oswestry), Robert Pell (Southport), Michael Moore (Ashton Utd), Robert Trees (Leigh RMI), Chris Young (Curzon Ashton), Rico Richards (Manchester C)

EMLEY

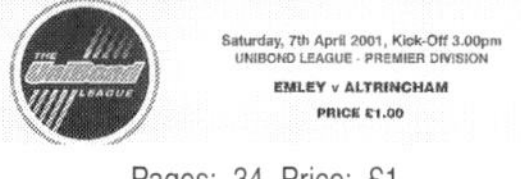

Pages: 34 Price: £1
Editor: Alan Blackman (01924 403959)
Local Press: Hudd'field Examiner, Hudd'field & Dist't Chronicle.,Wakefield Express
Local Radio: Radio Leeds, Radio Sheffield, Pulse FM, Huddersfield FM.,Ridings F.M.

CLUB OFFICIALS

Chairman: **Peter Matthews.**
President: **Peter Maude**

Secretary/Press Officer: **Richard Poulain**
17, Smithy Lane, Skelmanthorpe,
Huddersfield HD89DF.
Tel:01484 860323 H,07711 620726 M&B

FOOTBALL MANAGEMENT TEAM

Manager: Ronnie Glavin.
First Team Coach: John Peachey
Asst Manager: Jimmy Martin
Physio: Daryl Brook.

FACT FILE

Formed: 1903
Nickname: 'The Pewits
Sponsors: Eurotrail
Colours: Maroonblue/white/maroon
Change Colours. White/navy/navy
Mid week matchday: Monday.
Reserves' Lge: N. Co's E
Web: http:// www.emlyyafc.free-online.co.uk
E.Mail: rpemleyfc@talk21.com

Season 2000-01
Captain: Steve Nicholson
Top Scorer: Simeon Bambrook
P.o.Y.: Paul David

GROUND Wakefield Wildcats RLFC., Belle Vue Stadium, Doncaster Rd., Wakefield Tel. No: 01924 211611

Directions: Jct 39 M1 ,follow A636 to Wakefield, then A638 Doncaster Road 1 mile from town centre.

Capacity: 11,000 Cover: 5,000 Seats: 1,050

Clubhouse: (01924 848398). Members' social club open seven nights a week and Saturday & Sunday. Bingo, discos, occasional cabaret.

Club Shop: Yes Contact Mrs Linda Sykes

HONOURS FA Vase Runners-up 87-88; Northern Premier Lge Div 1 R-up 90-91; Northern Counties E Lge 87-88, 88-89 (R-up 85-86); Yorkshire Lg 75-76 77-78 79-80 81-82(R-up(5) 72-74 76-77 78-79 80-81, Lg Cup 69-70 78-79 81-82, Div 2 R-up 69-0; Sheffield & Hallamshire Senior Cup 75-76 79-80 80-81 83-84 88-89 90-91 91-9297-98; Huddersfield Challenge Cup 82-83 83-84 85-86; Huddersfield Lg(4) 65-69.

PREVIOUS **Leagues:** Huddersfield; Yorkshire 69-82; Northern Counties East 82-89.
Names: None **Grounds:** None.

CLUB RECORDS **Attendance:** 5,134 v Barking, Amateur Cup 3rd Proper 1/2/69.
18,629 v West Ham Utd, at Upton Pk, 3rd Rd Proper 3/1/99.
Win: 12-0 v Ecclesfield Red Rose9-6-97
Defeat: 7-1 v Altrincham 25-4-98.
Goalscorer: Mick Pamment 305. **Appearances:** Ray Dennis 762.
Fee Received: £60,000 for Michael Reynolds (Ayr Utd 98)

BEST SEASON **FA Amateur Cup:** Third Round replay 69-70.
FA Vase: Runners-up 87-88 (Semi-Final86-87).
FA Trophy: Quarter Final 98-99
FA Cup: Third Round Proper 97-98 (1-2 v West Ham Utd)

Players progressing: A Sweeney (Hartlepool Utd 79), G Cooper(Huddersfield Tn 84), J Francis (Sheffield Utd 88), S Smith (Crewe Alexandra1992), C Alcide (Lincoln City 95), C Hurst (Huddersfield Tn 97), G Hurst (Ayr Utd 98), M.Reynolds (Ayr United 1998)

Emley's Gary Hatto (white shorts) does just enough to hold off Gary Innes of Blyth during their league match at Croft Park last season. **Photo:** Graham Brown.

Date	Comp.	Opponents	Att.	Score	Goalscorers
19.08	Unib P	Barrow	1283	3 - 1	David 47, Bambrook 62 70
26.08	Unib P	Accrington Stanley	718	1 - 3	Day 90
28.08	Unib P	SPENNYMOOR UNITED	224	3 - 3	Bambrook 60, Day 70, Gregory 85
02.09	Unib P	BAMBER BRIDGE	200	1 - 0	Gregory 53
06.09	Unib P	Bishop Auckland	202	3 - 1	Thorpe 62, Bambrook 73 87
09.09	Unib P	Altrincham	641	2 - 0	Day 25, Bambrook 90
11.09	Unib P	HUCKNALL TOWN	221	0 - 0	
16.09	Unib P	LANCASTER CITY	194	1 - 0	Wilson 81
19.09	Unib P	Gainsborough Trinity	338	2 - 3	Robshaw 65, David 86
23.09	Unib P	Leek Town	260	1 - 0	Bambrook 40
25.09	Unib P	MARINE	236	3 - 2	Tonks 17 32, Bradshaw 45
30.09	FA Cup Q2	SALFORD CITY	261	3 - 1	Tonks 73, Nicholson 88, Bambrook 90
03.10	Unib P	Whitby Town	363	1 - 0	Nicholson 84
06.10	Unib P	WORKSOP TOWN	769	5 - 3	Wilson 48, Bambrook 59 80[p], Nazha 85 90
14.10	FA Cup Q3	BARROW	586	1 - 2	Nazha 49
16.10	Unib P	BLYTH SPARTANS	280	1 - 0	Nicholson 57
21.10	Unib P	DROYLSDEN	261	2 - 1	Tonks 46, Wilson 69
25.10	Unib P	Gateshead	231	1 - 0	Nazha 42
30.10	Lge Cup 3	FRICKLEY ATHLETIC	236	1 - 0	Bambrook 65
04.11	Unib P	GATESHEAD	325	2 - 0	Wood 11, Hatto 86
18.11	Unib P	Spennymoor United	122	2 - 0	Nazha 4, Daly 14
18.11	Sheff SC 1	Athersley Recreation	98	3 - 1	Prendergast 16 32, Gregory 19
25.11	Unib P	Stalybridge Celtic	1006	2 - 4	Braybrook 7, Daly 25
29.11	Lge Cup 3	Bradford Park Avenue	157	2 - 3	Bambrook 45[p], Bradshaw 47
02.12	FA Trophy 2	VAUXHALL	256	5 - 3	Hatto 28, Bambrook 44 59, Nazha 68 75
04.12	Sheff SC 2	STOCKSBRIDGE PARK STEELS	184	5 - 1	Bambrook 30 61[p], Nazha 24, Wilson 42, Burton 89
09.12	Unib P	BARROW	372	0 - 0	
11.12	Lge Cup 3	HARROGATE TOWN	174	0 - 1	
16.12	Unib P	Marine	268	2 - 0	Day 33, Bambrook 61
23.12	Unib P	ACCRINGTON STANLEY	465	1 - 0	Wilson 31
26.12	Unib P	Frickley Athletic	328	3 - 1	Bambrook 39[p] 66, Nicholson 53
01.01	Unib P	GAINSBOROUGH TRINITY	434	1 - 0	Bambrook 24
06.01	Unib P	Lancaster City	318	3 - 3	Day 49 76, Bambrook 66[p]
13.01	FA Trophy 3	ACCRINGTON STANLEY	494	3 - 0	Hatto 5, Thorpe 22, Day 75
16.01	Lge Cup 3	Farsley Celtic	94	2 - 1	Henderson 32[og], Tonks 67
20.01	Unib P	WHITBY TOWN	517	4 - 0	Day 11, Thorpe 51 60, Nicholson 89
27.01	Unib P	Colwyn Bay	364	4 - 0	Prendergast 25, Nazha 37, Jones 59[og], Wilson 90
03.02	FA Trophy 4	YEOVIL TOWN	1754	2 - 4	Day 25, Bambrook 64[p]
06.02	Unib P	Hucknall Town	270	2 - 0	Day 60, Bambrook 89
10.02	Unib P	LEEK TOWN	378	1 - 1	Nazha 60
17.02	Unib P	Bamber Bridge	428	1 - 1	Day 86
24.02	Unib P	COLWYN BAY	416	4 - 1	Nazha 21 68 90, Tonks 43
03.03	Chairman QF	Barrow	752	2 - 4	Wilson 13, Day 85
06.03	Unib P	BISHOP AUCKLAND	304	3 - 1	Nazha 6, Day 32, Wilson 36
10.03	Sheff SC QF	THE WETHERBY	190	6 - 1	Burton 3, Bradshaw 7, Wilson 12 17 86, Nazha 20
13.03	Unib P	Burscough	212	1 - 0	Day 83
17.03	Unib P	HYDE UNITED	379	3 - 1	Hatto 29[p], Bambrook 76, Day 87
23.03	Unib P	Worksop Town	763	2 - 1	Day 30 67
30.03	Unib P	Hyde United	623	2 - 1	Bambrook 84 90
02.04	Unib P	BURSCOUGH	471	2 - 1	Bambrook 50[p], Day 82
07.04	Unib P	ALTRINCHAM	686	3 - 1	Day 6 31, Wilson 77
10.04	Sheff SC SF	Frickley Athletic	177	3 - 0	Crossley 31, Nazha 35, Wilson 43
14.04	Unib P	Blyth Spartans	380	1 - 2	Bambrook 35
16.04	Unib P	FRICKLEY ATHLETIC	482	0 - 0	
21.04	Unib P	Runcorn	293	1 - 1	Bambrook 12
24.04	Unib P	RUNCORN	460	2 - 1	Day 63, Prendergast 72
28.04	Unib P	STALYBRIDGE CELTIC	3708	2 - 3	David 8, Tonks 88
05.05	Unib P	Droylsden	238	3 - 1	Wilson 9 80, Nazha 75
09.05	Sheff SC F	DONCASTER ROVERS	1930	1 - 2	Prendergast 17 (at Sheffield Wednesday)

PLAYING SQUAD

GOALKEEPERS: Paul Cuss (Huddersfield), Leigh Walker (Barnsley)

DEFENDERS: Steve Nicholson (Farsley Celtic), Ryan Crossley (Bury), Rory Prendergast (Nuneaton), Nicky Wood (Huddersfield), Andy Wilson (Ossett Alb)

MIDFIELDERS: Simeon Bambrook (Garforth), Paul David (Bradley R), Gary Hatto (Frickley), Mark Wilson (Ossett T), Jamie Robshaw (Denaby)

FORWARDS: Mike Norbury (Hednesford), Danny Day (Ossett Alb), Wael Nazha (AO Kavala), Charlie Bradshaw (Droylsden), Chris Prasher (Youth)

FRICKLEY ATHLETIC

FRICKLEY
A F C
PRICE £1.00
THE OFFICIAL MATCHDAY PROGRAMME OF
THE UniBond LEAGUE
FRICKLEY ATHLETIC F.C.
SEASON 2000/01
FRICKLEY ATHLETIC
V
RUNCORN
Main Club Sponsors NEXT Distributions Ltd.

Pages: 40 Price: £1
Editor: S Pennock Tel: 01302 835956
Local Press: South Yorks Times, Hemsworth & South Elmsall Express. Local Radio: Radio Sheffield, Radio Hallam, Radio Leeds.

CLUB OFFICIALS

Chairman: **Mike Twiby**
Tel: 01977 648070
Financial Secretary: **J.Handley**
Tel: 01977 643420
Secretary : Ruth Simpson,67 Brooksfield Court, South Kirby, Pontefract,.WF9 3DL
Tel No: 01977 641116

FOOTBALL MANAGEMENT TEAM

Manager: Steve Richards
(01482 651382)

FACT FILE

Formed: 1910 Nickname: The Blues
Sponsors: Next Distributions
Colours: All blue with white stripe on shirt
Change colours: Yellow & black.
Midweek home matchday: Tuesday
Reserves' League: Doncaster Senior
Website: www.frickleyafc.co.uk

2000-01

Captain: Steve Price P.o.Y.: Chris Hurst
Top Goalscorer: Chris Hurst

GROUNDWestfield Lane, South Elmsall, Pontefract Tel/Fax: 01977 642460
Email Address: steve@ frickleyafc.co.uk
Directions: Follow signs for South Elmsall from A1 and A638. Left at Superdrug warehouse, right at T junction and immediately left up Westfield Lane. Left into Oxford Road (opposite Westfield Hotel) - ground at bottom on right. Two miles from South Elmsall (BR).
Capacity: 6,000 Cover: 2,500 Seats: 800
Clubhouse: On ground open matchdays, food available.
Club Shop: Yes

PREVIOUS Leagues: Sheffield; Yorkshire 22-24; Midland Counties 24-33 34-60 70-76;Cheshire County 60-70; Northern Premier 76-80; GMV Conference (Alliance Premier) 80-87. Name: Frickley Colliery

CLUB RECORDS **Attendance:** 6,500 v Rotherham United, FA Cup First Round 1971.
Goalscorer: K Whiteley. **Defeat:** 0-12 v Worksop 2000-01 Unibond Premier **Fee Paid:** £1,800.
Fee Received: £12,500 for Paul Shirtliff (Boston Utd) & £12,500 for Russ Wilcox (Northampton)

BEST SEASON **FA Cup:** 3rd Rd 1985-86 (1-3 v Rotherham H).2nd Rd 84-85 (0-1 at Darlington). 1st Rd 36-37 57-58 63-64 71-72 73-74 83-84 86-87 88-89 00-01. League clubs defeated: Hartlepool United 85-86. **FA Trophy:** Quarter-Finals 84-85.

HONOURS Alliance Premier Lg R-up 85-86, Midland Counties Lg R-up 72-73 (Lg Cup 75-76),Yorkshire Lg R-up 23-24, Sheffield & Hallamshire Senior Cup 27-28 56-57 60-6162-63 66-67 78-79 85-86 87-88 89-90 99-00, Sheffield Assoc. Lg 20-21 (R-up 11-12).
Players Progressing: Dennis Smith & Jack Brownsword (Hull1946), Stan Scrimshaw (Halifax 1947), William Callaghan (Aldershot 1949), Leo Dickens 1950), John Ashley & Graham Caulfield (York 1950 & 67), Ron Barritt(Leeds 1951), John Pickup (Bradford PA 1955), Tom Hymers & Arthur Ashmore &Stewart Gray (Doncaster 1958 & 66 & 78), Colin Roberts (Bradford City 1959),Derek Downing (Middlesbrough 1965), Graham Reed & Russell Wilcox (Northampton1985 & 86), Will Foley (Swansea 1986), Gary Brook (Newport 1987), Wayne Scargill (Bradford City 94-95), Andy Hayward (Rotherham Utd.).

Back Row,left to right: Grahan Ramshaw, Steve Richards (Manager), Brendan West, Dean Jones, Chris Hurst, Matthew Wilkinson, Rob Hanby, Mark Lafferty, Steve Price, Gary Marrow (Assistant Manager), Scott Collins and Mick Geohegan (Physio). **Front Row:** Chris Hilton, Ian Edge, Stewart Morris, Mark Wilkinson, Gary Duffty, Martin Fox, Paul Burton and Tommy Brookes.

Date	Comp.	Opponents	Att.	Score	Goalscorers
19.08	Unib P	BAMBER BRIDGE	174	1 - 2	Watson 81
22.08	Unib P	Gainsborough Trinity	406	2 - 2	Hayward 46, Duffty 58
26.08	Unib P	Hucknall Town	210	1 - 3	Duffty 88
28.08	Unib P	BISHOP AUCKLAND	140	0 - 1	
02.09	Unib P	Runcorn	212	1 - 2	Cranson 66
09.09	Unib P	BURSCOUGH	141	1 - 0	Hayward 73[p]
13.09	Unib P	Bishop Auckland	147	0 - 2	
16.09	Unib P	Hyde United	428	0 - 0	
19.09	Unib P	WORKSOP TOWN	305	1 - 5	Wilson 7
23.09	Unib P	MARINE	159	0 - 1	
26.09	Unib P	Worksop Town	618	0 - 12	
30.09	FA Cup Q2	STOCKSBRIDGE PARK STEELS	167	1 - 0	Beckett 80
03.10	Unib P	HUCKNALL TOWN	139	1 - 2	Hilton 4
07.10	Unib P	Gateshead	211	0 - 5	
10.10	Unib P	GAINSBOROUGH TRINITY	162	2 - 2	Goodyear 16, Brookes 22
14.10	FA Cup Q3	Mossley	373	1 - 1	McAreavey 62
17.10	FA Cup Q3 R	MOSSLEY	286	3 - 0	Hanby 97, McAreavey 105 109
21.10	Unib P	ACCRINGTON STANLEY	197	0 - 2	
28.10	FA Cup Q4	HYDE UNITED	330	1 - 0	Hanby 39
30.10	Lge Cup 3	Emley	236	0 - 1	
04.11	FA Trophy 1	Spennymoor United	125	1 - 3	Hurst 44[p]
18.11	FA Cup 1	Northampton Town	3896	0 - 4	
25.11	Unib P	COLWYN BAY	90	6 - 2	Duffty 17, Clarke 27 89 90, Jones 66, Edge 74
28.11	Lge Cup 3	FARSLEY CELTIC	101	0 - 1	
02.12	Sheff SC 1	Wombwell Main	90	3 - 0	McAreavey 44, Duffty 68 90
09.12	Sheff SC 2	DINNINGTON TOWN	58	3 - 2	Jones 45, Hurst 63 91
16.12	Unib P	DROYLSDEN	119	1 - 1	Price 62
19.12	Lge Cup 3	BRADFORD PARK AVENUE	133	3 - 3	Duffty 35, West 45, Jones 56
23.12	Unib P	Stalybridge Celtic	612	0 - 3	
26.12	Unib P	EMLEY	328	1 - 3	Duffty 10
01.01	Unib P	Altrincham	552	1 - 3	Duffty 5
06.01	Unib P	HYDE UNITED	139	1 - 1	Lewis 44
09.01	Lge Cup 3	Harrogate Town	135	2 - 2	Lewis 62 63
13.01	Unib P	Bamber Bridge	229	1 - 0	Lewis 43
27.01	Unib P	RUNCORN	197	1 - 1	Chambers 8
03.02	Unib P	SPENNYMOOR UNITED	173	2 - 0	Lewis 57, Jones 90
06.02	Unib P	Droylsden	133	1 - 1	Hirst 83[p]
10.02	Unib P	Accrington Stanley	511	1 - 1	Lewis 31
13.02	Unib P	ALTRINCHAM	223	3 - 3	Chambers 1 24, Hirst 13[p]
17.02	Unib P	LEEK TOWN	231	1 - 3	Gregory 18
20.02	Unib P	Spennymoor United	119	5 - 0	Gregory 18, Lewis 42, Duffty 70 90, Chambers 83
24.02	Unib P	Marine	267	0 - 1	
27.02	Unib P	BLYTH SPARTANS	170	4 - 2	Chambers 8 17 64, Beckett 88
03.03	Unib P	Colwyn Bay	305	0 - 0	
06.03	Sheff SC QF	Parkgate	n.k	1 - 0	McAreavey 90
10.03	Unib P	STALYBRIDGE CELTIC	402	0 - 0	
13.03	Unib P	Whitby Town	232	2 - 2	Hurst 50, Jones 64
17.03	Unib P	Leek Town	213	1 - 2	Hurst 76
20.03	Unib P	Blyth Spartans	243	0 - 3	
24.03	Unib P	GATESHEAD	169	1 - 0	Hurst 49
31.03	Unib P	Barrow	1048	0 - 2	
10.04	Sheff SC SF	EMLEY	177	0 - 3	
14.04	Unib P	WHITBY TOWN	152	1 - 1	Marsh 23
16.04	Unib P	Emley	482	0 - 0	
18.04	Unib P	Burscough	112	2 - 1	Price 81[p], Beckett 90
21.04	Unib P	LANCASTER CITY	140	0 - 0	
01.05	Unib P	BARROW	225	3 - 2	Duffty 55, Hurst 77[p], Hilton 83
05.05	Unib P	Lancaster City	490	1 - 0	Hurst 47

PLAYING SQUAD

GOALKEEPERS: Mark Wilkinson (Sheffield), Mark Samways (Matlock)

DEFENDERS: Rob Hanby (Gainsborough), Dean Jones (Ilkeston), Matthew Wilkinson (Selby), Mark Ogley (Stalybridge), Chris Gowen (York), Nicky Limber (Gainsborough), Paul Foot (Bridlington)

MIDFIELDERS: Ian Edge (Sheffield), Richard Bashforth (Youth), Steve Price (Gainsborough), Matthew Russell (Scarborough), Simon Collins (Macclesfield), Andy Gregory (Emley)

FORWARDS: Gary Duffty (Matlock), Craig Marsh (Matlock), Carl Fothergill (Kettering), Graham Lewis (Northwich)

GAINSBOROUGH TRINITY

CLUB OFFICIALS

Chairman: **Pat Lobley**
President: **Ken Marsden.**
Secretary/Press Officer: **Frank Nicholson**
9 North Street, Morton,
Gainsborough, Lincs DN213AS.
Tel. 01427 615239, Fax 01427 615239.
Commercial Director: **Tim Hanson.**

FOOTBALL MANAGEMENT TEAM

Manager: Phil Tingay
Asst Manager: Phil Tingay
Physio: Mick Gilbert

FACT FILE

Formed: 1873
Nickname: The Blues
Sponsors: Eastern Generation.
Colours: All Blue
Change colours: Green/black/green
Midweek home matchday: Tuesday
Reserve Team's League:

GROUND
The Northolme, Gainsborough, Lincs DN21 2QW
Tel: 01427 - 613295 (office) 615625 (club) 613295 (Fax)
Directions: The Northolme is situated opposite the Texaco and Fina petrol stations on the A159 Gainsborough to Scunthorpe road. Two miles from Lea Road (BR)
Capacity: 4,000 Cover: 2,500 Seats: 1,015
Clubhouse: Executive `Club on the Park' (01427 615625) open Saturday matchday lunchtimes. Restaurant facilities.
Club Shop: Yes, contact Wendy Godley (01427 611612)

PROGRAMME
Pages: 44 Price: £1
Editor: Basil Godley Tel: 01427 611612

Local Press: Gainsborough News, Lincolnshire Echo.
Local Radio: BBC Radio Lincs, Lincs FM

PREVIOUS **Leagues:** Midland Counties 1889-96, 12-60, 61-68, Football Lge 1896-1912, Central Alliance 60-61.
Names: None Grounds: None

CLUB RECORDS **Attendance:** 9,760 v Scunthorpe Utd. Midland Lge. 1948.
Fee Paid: £3,000 for Stuart Lowe (Buxton 89-90). **Fee Received:** £30,000 for Tony James (Lincoln 1988).
Win: 7-0 v Fleetwood Town and Great Harwood Town. **Defeat:** 2-7 v Hyde Utd.

BEST SEASON **FA Cup:** 3rd Rd 1886-87, 1st Rd on 33 occasions. **FA Trophy:** 2nd Rd, 2nd replay86-87.

HONOURS Northern Premier Lge Cup 81-82 96-97 (R-up 71-72); Midland Co's Lge 1890-91,1927-28, 48-49, 66-67 (R-up 1891-92, 1895-96, 13-14, 28-29); Lincs Senior Cup 1889-90, 92-93, 94-95, 97-98, 1903-05, 06-07, 10-11, 46-49, 50-51, 57-59, 63-64

Players Progressing: Since 1980 - Stewart Evans (Sheffield Utd 80), Tony James, Ian Bowling & John Schofield (Lincoln 88), Dave Redfern(Stockport 91), Richard Logan (Huddersfield 93), Glenn Humphries (Hull City).

Back Row: Andy Sharpe, Chris James, Paul Watts, Steve Price, Steve Curry, Neil Allison, Steve Williams, Alex Allen, Kevin Noteman.
FrontRow: Nick Limber, Ian Gore, Simon Drayton, Chris Newton, John Reed, Ian McLean, Colin Hunter. Missing: Steve Circuit

Date	Comp.	Opponents	Att.	Score	Goalscorers
04.08	Lincs SC QF	GRANTHAM TOWN	n.k	0 - 2	
19.08	Unib P	Blyth Spartans	298	0 - 1	
22.08	Unib P	FRICKLEY ATHLETIC	406	2 - 2	Circuit 17, Allison 79
26.08	Unib P	BURSCOUGH	328	2 - 1	Hunter 36, Watts 75
28.08	Unib P	Worksop Town	737	1 - 1	Price 47[p]
02.09	Unib P	DROYLSDEN	324	0 - 1	
05.09	Unib P	Hucknall Town	222	0 - 1	
09.09	Unib P	Bamber Bridge	201	0 - 2	
12.09	Unib P	STALYBRIDGE CELTIC	291	0 - 0	
16.09	Unib P	Bishop Auckland	192	1 - 3	Watts 80
19.09	Unib P	EMLEY	338	3 - 2	Reed 38, Jones 45[p], Newton 81
23.09	Unib P	GATESHEAD	410	0 - 2	
26.09	Unib P	Droylsden	121	0 - 4	
30.09	FA Cup Q2	Horden Colliery Welfare	135	3 - 1	Watts 15, Allison 44, Limber 71
10.10	Unib P	Frickley Athletic	162	2 - 2	S Pickering 62, Gore 89
14.10	FA Cup Q3	WHITLEY BAY	371	0 - 0	
17.10	FA Cup Q3 R	Whitley Bay	339	0 - 2	
21.10	Unib P	Stalybridge Celtic	498	1 - 7	Watts 45
24.10	Unib P	HYDE UNITED	254	2 - 1	Watts 43 73
28.10	Unib P	MARINE	336	2 - 0	Ellington 44, Linighan 45
31.10	Lge Cup 8	Worksop Town	455	3 - 2	Newton 6, Charles 27, Drayton 49
04.11	FA Trophy 1	BRADFORD PARK AVENUE	392	3 - 2	Linighan 50, Ellington 21 53
11.11	Unib P	Altrincham	585	2 - 0	Ellington 1, Talbot 10[og]
14.11	Lge Cup 8	LINCOLN UNITED	305	1 - 0	Collinson 84
18.11	Unib P	RUNCORN	356	2 - 0	Ellington 63, Watts 74
25.11	Unib P	BARROW	495	2 - 0	Pickering 34, Holmes 76
28.11	Lge Cup 8	North Ferriby United	179	3 - 0	Bassinder 3, Newton 51, Ellington 88
02.12	FA Trophy 2	Burscough	229	0 - 1	
09.12	Unib P	BAMBER BRIDGE	386	2 - 0	Bassinder 5 77
12.12	Lge Cup 8	GUISELEY	223	2 - 0	Holmes 70, Drayton 89
23.12	Unib P	Lancaster City	240	1 - 2	Newton 89
26.12	Unib P	WORKSOP TOWN	1084	1 - 1	Newton 61
01.01	Unib P	Emley	434	0 - 1	
06.01	Unib P	COLWYN BAY	375	1 - 0	Gore 13
13.01	Unib P	Leek Town	194	0 - 1	
20.01	Unib P	Accrington Stanley	575	1 - 1	Charles 81
27.01	Unib P	WHITBY TOWN	318	1 - 3	Bassinder 17
03.02	Unib P	LANCASTER CITY	365	1 - 1	Linighan 90
10.02	Unib P	Burscough	185	1 - 1	Ellington 72
17.02	Unib P	Runcorn	207	1 - 1	Linighan 58
24.02	Unib P	ACCRINGTON STANLEY	406	2 - 0	Circuit 42, Newton 90
03.03	Lge Cup QF	Marine	142	1 - 2	Bassinder 4
06.03	Unib P	SPENNYMOOR UNITED	302	2 - 1	Bassinder 11, Allison 25
10.03	Unib P	Hyde United	323	1 - 0	Bassinder 68
13.03	Unib P	HUCKNALL TOWN	310	1 - 1	Ellington 90
20.03	Unib P	Spennymoor United	75	3 - 0	Newton 17, Bassinder 28, Ellington 36
23.03	Unib P	Whitby Town	251	1 - 0	Circuit 42
31.03	Unib P	ALTRINCHAM	418	1 - 0	Watts 43
07.04	Unib P	Colwyn Bay	212	3 - 3	Ellington 9 75, Watts 61
10.04	Unib P	LEEK TOWN	339	4 - 1	Donnelly 2, Watt 63, Reed 73, Drayton 84
14.04	Unib P	Gateshead	157	1 - 1	Watts 35
16.04	Unib P	BLYTH SPARTANS	428	4 - 2	Watts 5 7 62, Newton 42
21.04	Unib P	Barrow	1024	2 - 3	Gore 24, Newton 48
28.04	Unib P	BISHOP AUCKLAND	369	0 - 0	
05.05	Unib P	Marine	220	2 - 2	Watts 80, Reed 86

PLAYING SQUAD

GOALKEEPERS: Kevin Martin (Whitby)

DEFENDERS: Ian Gore (Boreham Wood), Joby Gowshall (Boston Utd), Brian Linighan (Hallam), Neil Allison (Geyling Utd), Wayne Hall (York), Alex Allen (Brodsworth), Danny Brown (Hull)

MIDFIELDERS: John Reed (Ethnikos Perez), Steve Circuit (Leek), Phil Brown (Kettering), Gavin Bassinder (Mansfield), Darren Holmes (Hallam), Chris Hurst (Frickley)

FORWARDS: Paul Watts (Boston Utd), Andy Stanhope (Boston Utd), Rick Ranshaw (Grantham), Lee Ellington (Exeter)

GATESHEAD

CLUB OFFICIALS

President: **J C Thomas**

Chairman: **John Gibson**

Vice Chairman: **Mark Donnelly**

General Manager: **Mark Donnelly**

Secretary: & Press Officer: **Mike Coulson**

FOOTBALL MANAGEMENT TEAM

Managers : Paul Proudlock& Gary Gill

Physio: Bev Dougherty

FACT FILE

Founded: 1930
Nickname: The Tynesiders
Sponsors: Cameron Hall Developments Ltd
Colours: White with black trim/ black/ white
Change colours: All red
Midweek home matchday: Wednesday
Reserves League: Vaux Wearside League
Supporters' Unofficial Website:
www.heedarmy.co.uk

Season 2000-01

Captain: Sam Kitchen
Top Scorer: Wayne Edgcumbe 21
P.o.Y.: Wayne Edgcumbe (Supporters)
Richie Watson (Players)

Pages: 24 Price: £1.00
Editor: Tony Miller, 07949 126198

Local Press: Gateshead Post, Newcastle Chronicle & Echo, Sunderland Echo, Sunday Sun. Local Radio: BBC Radio Newcastle, Metro FM, Century Radio.

GROUND International Stadium, Neilson Road, Gateshead, NE10 0EF. Tel: 0191 478 3883 Fax : 0191 477 1315.

Directions: From the South follow A1(M) to Granada services (Birtley),take right hand fork marked A194(M) (Tyne Tunnel, South Shields) follow A194 to first roundabout, turn left onto A184 - then 3 miles to stadium. Turn right at traffic lights into Neilson Road. BY RAIL to Newcastle Central Station,transfer to the Metro System and then to Gateshead Stadium.

Capacity: 11,795 Seats: 11,795 Cover: 3,300

Clubhouse: Bar inside Tyne & Wear stand open before, during and after matches

Club Shop: Sells full range of souvenirs, badges, programmes & fanzines. Contact: Mike Coulson (0191 478 3883)

PREVIOUS **Leagues:** Football League - Div. 3 N. 30-58, Div.4 58-60, Northern Counties League 60-62, North Regional League 1962-1968, Northern Premier 68-70, 73-83,85-86, 87-90; Wearside 70-71; Midland Lge 71-72; Alliance Premier (Conference)83-85, 86-87, 90-98. **Grounds:** Redheugh Park - 1930-1971

CLUB RECORDS **Attendance:** 11,750 v Newcastle United (Pre-Season Friendly. 7th August 95)
Win: 8-0 v Netherfield, Northern Premier League. **Defeat:** 0-9 v Sutton United, 22.09.90, GMVC.
Career goalscorer: Bob Topping **Career appearances:** Simon Smith, 450, 85-94
Fee paid: £9,000 for Paul Cavell (Dagenham &Redbridge). **Fee received:** For Kenny Cramman from Rushden & D.

BEST SEASON **FA Cup:** Quarter Final, 1952-53. **FA Trophy:** Quarter Final, 0-1 v Wycombe W. (A) 13.3.93

HONOURS Football League Div. 3 North R-up 31-32, 49-50; Northern Premier - Champions82-83, 85-86; Runners-up 89-90; Northern Premier League Cup R-up 89-90;Multipart Shield 85-86.

Players Progressing: Osher Williams(Southampton, Stockport, Port Vale, Preston), John McGinley (Sunderland,Lincoln), Billy Askew (Hull City, Newcastle United), Lawrie Pearson (Hull City,Port Vale), Ian Johnson (Northampton Town), Ken Davies (Stockport), Kenny Lowe(Birmingham C., Barnet, Darlington, Stoke C.)

Date	Comp.	Opponents	Att.	Score	Goalscorers
19.08	Unib P	Altrincham	620	2 - 3	Dalton 36, Edgcumbe 57
26.08	Unib P	Lancaster City	277	0 - 2	
28.08	Unib P	Blyth Spartans	484	1 - 2	Thompson 40
02.09	Unib P	STALYBRIDGE CELTIC	268	2 - 2	Bowey 1, Thompson 90
06.09	Unib P	SPENNYMOOR UNITED	251	4 - 0	Pitt 11, Edgcumbe 23 81, Ross 45
09.09	Unib P	Colwyn Bay	285	2 - 2	Thompson 3, Proudlock 45
16.09	Unib P	RUNCORN	251	5 - 1	Edgcumbe 2, Dalton 34, Lynch 70, Bowey 76, Milbourne 85
19.09	Unib P	Spennymoor United	164	4 - 1	Bowey 18, Thompson 21, Edgcumbe 57, Milbourne 72
23.09	Unib P	Gainsborough Trinity	410	2 - 0	Edgcumbe 4, Bowey 85
27.09	Unib P	BARROW	276	1 - 2	Ross 62
30.09	FA Cup Q2	BISHOP AUCKLAND	255	2 - 1	Bowey 31, Thompson 90
04.10	Unib P	Bishop Auckland	328	1 - 0	Thompson 81
07.10	Unib P	FRICKLEY ATHLETIC	211	5 - 0	Dalton 27, Edgcumbe 35 39 62, McAlindon 88
14.10	FA Cup Q3	Bamber Bridge	255	1 - 1	Thompson 33
18.10	FA Cup Q3 R	BAMBER BRIDGE	231	3 - 1	Dalton 58, Bowey 68, Ross 81
21.10	Unib P	Marine	226	1 - 1	Edgecumbe 90
25.10	Unib P	EMLEY	231	0 - 1	
28.10	FA Cup Q4	BILLINGHAM TOWN	381	4 - 2	Preen 2 83, Bowey 41, Ross 63
31.10	Lge Cup 1	Blyth Spartans	313	1 - 2	Dalton 87
04.11	Unib P	Emley	325	0 - 2	
11.11	Unib P	LEEK TOWN	227	2 - 1	Proudlock 27, Preen 88
15.11	Lge Cup 1	SPENNYMOOR UNITED	146	1 - 1	Tremble 29
18.11	FA Cup 1	Halifax Town	1902	2 - 0	Hall 45, Dalton 84
02.12	FA Trophy 2	Marine	209	1 - 2	Edgcumbe 34
09.12	FA Cup 2	Swindon Town	3907	0 - 5	
20.12	Lge Cup 1	BISHOP AUCKLAND	93	3 - 0	Dalton 5 60, Preen 11
23.12	Unib P	Droylsden	214	0 - 0	F
26.12	Unib P	BLYTH SPARTANS	417	2 - 5	Dalton 23, Preen 36
06.01	Unib P	BAMBER BRIDGE	185	0 - 2	
09.01	Lge Cup 1	Whitby Town	193	1 - 1	Tracey 60
13.01	Unib P	ALTRINCHAM	251	2 - 1	Ross 48, Tracey 89
27.01	Unib P	Stalybridge Celtic	609	1 - 2	Preen 29
03.02	Unib P	COLWYN BAY	205	4 - 2	Edgecumbe 21 25 51, Preen 64
06.02	Unib P	Accrington Stanley	386	1 - 3	Preen 76
10.02	Unib P	Hyde United	307	1 - 3	Kitchen 10
17.02	Unib P	MARINE	211	3 - 0	Alderson 25, Edgcumbe 47, McAlindon 73
24.02	Unib P	Leek Town	251	2 - 1	McAlindon 28, Ross 70
06.03	Unib P	Worksop Town	464	2 - 2	Edgcumbe 25 38
10.03	Unib P	ACCRINGTON STANLEY	230	0 - 0	
14.03	Unib P	BISHOP AUCKLAND	195	0 - 3	
17.03	Unib P	Burscough	181	1 - 0	McAlindon 12
21.03	Unib P	WHITBY TOWN	127	1 - 1	Alderson 86
24.03	Unib P	Frickley Athletic	169	0 - 1	
28.03	Unib P	BURSCOUGH	130	1 - 1	Bowman 68
31.03	Unib P	DROYLSDEN	174	1 - 1	Edgcumbe 37
03.04	Unib P	Bamber Bridge	170	2 - 4	Alderson 58, Preen 61
12.04	Unib P	Barrow	1001	1 - 3	Edgcumbe 63
14.04	Unib P	GAINSBOROUGH TRINITY	157	1 - 1	McAlindon 61
16.04	Unib P	Hucknall Town	165	2 - 2	Edgcumbe 73, Thompson 76
21.04	Unib P	WORKSOP TOWN	245	0 - 0	
24.04	Unib P	Whitby Town	193	1 - 0	McAlindon 18
26.04	Unib P	HYDE UNITED	131	3 - 0	Thompson 3, Preen 50, McAlindon 82
28.04	Unib P	LANCASTER CITY	185	1 - 0	Preen 16
02.05	Unib P	HUCKNALL TOWN	135	1 - 2	Alderson 32
05.05	Unib P	Runcorn	555	2 - 1	Edgcumbe 74, Preen 77

PLAYING SQUAD

GOALKEEPERS: Adrian Swan (Spenymoor), John Mohan (Marske Utd)

DEFENDERS: Richie Watson (Spennymoor), Paul Talbot (York), Rob Jones (Spennymoor), Chris Lynch (Bishop Auckland), Martin Reed (York), Rob Bowman (Bohemians)

MIDFIELDERS: Steve Agnew (York), Paul Proudlock (Carlisle), Paul Thompson (Stevenage), Steve Bowey (Forest Green R), Phil Ross (Bishop Auckland)

FORWARDS: Richie Alderson (Durham), Lee Ellison (Barrow), Robbie Painter (Halifax), Gareth McAlinden (Scarborough), David Connor (Billingham Syn), Steve Preen (Queen of the South), Wayne Edgcumbe (Tow Law)

HUCKNALL TOWN

Pages: 92 Price: £1.20
Editor/Press Officer: Secretary
Local Press : Hucknall & Bulwell Dispatch; Nottm Evening Post; Nottm Football Post
Club Website: www.hucknalltownfc.co.uk
EMAIL address: swmatters &virgin.net

CLUB OFFICIALS

Chairman: Vice-Chairman: **Glen Lathell**
President: **Andy Stewart**

Secretary: **Simon Matters,** 199 Nottingham Road, Hucknall, Nottingham, NG15 7QB
Tel No: 0115 9525338

FOOTBALL MANAGEMENT TEAM

Manager: John Ramshaw
Assistant Manager: Billy Millar
Physio: Ken Burton

FACT FILE

Founded: 1987
Nickname: The Town
Sponsors: Doff-Portland
Colours: Yellow/black/yellow
Change colours: All red
Midweek matches: Tuesday
Reserves' League: Mid Reg Alliance Prem

2000-01
Captain: Dave McCarthy
P.o.Y.: Dave McCarthy
Top Scorers: Simon Martin (31)

GROUND Watnall Road, Hucknall, Notts NG15 7LP Tel: 0115 956 1253

Directions: M1 jct 27, A608 to lights, right onto A611 to Hucknall, right at r'bout (new by-pass), over next r'bout, right at next r'bout into Watnall Rd -grd on right. From M1 jct 26 follow Nottm signs to lights on island, left onto A610, right at Three Ponds Pub onto B600 towards Watnall, 200 yds past Queens Head turn right signed Hucknall, follow over m'way and past Rolls Royce -ground on left. Nearest station Hucknall

Capacity: 5,000 Seats: 270 Cover: 2,200 Floodlights: Yes

Clubhouse: Every night and weekend lunchtimes **Club Shop:** Yes, contact Sec.

PREVIOUS

Leagues: Bulwell & Dist. 46-59 60-65; Central All. 59-60; Notts Spartan 65-70; Notts All. 70-89; Central Midlands 89-92 Northern Counties East 92-97, Unibond 97-

Ground: Wigwam Park 46-54 Name: Hucknall Colliery Welfare (until pit closure 1988)

CLUB RECORDS

Attendance: 1,436 v Ilkeston Town, FA Cup 4th Qual 28/10/00 **Appearances:** Dave McCarthy 282

Goals: Maurice Palethorpe approx 400 (80s & (0s)

BEST SEASON

FA Cup: 4th Q Rd v Ilkeston Town 00-01 lost 0-1

FA Vase: Quarter Final 85-86 **FA Trophy:** 3rd Rd v Redditch 98-99 , Leigh RMI 00-01

HONOURS

Northern Counties (East) Lg Div 1 R-up 92-93 (Lg Cup 93-94 96-97 97-98) Presidents Cup 96-97; Central Mids Lg x2 89-91 R-up 91-92, Lg Cup x3 89-92; Notts All.Sen (4) 76-78 87-89, Div 1 Div 1 72-73 80-81 86-87 Div 2 70-71; Intermediate Cup 72-73 78-81 84-84; Lge Cup 78-79; Notts Snr Cup 84-85 90-91 97-98 99-00, R-up 83-84 85-86 87-88 89-90 98-99 00-01 Unibond Lg.: Div 1 R-Up 98-99

Dale Wright (no. 7, dark shorts) gets his head to this corner during Town's match against Hyde United at Watnall Road. Photo: Brian Pickering.

Date	Comp.	Opponents	Att.	Score	Goalscorers
19.08	Unib P	Marine	271	1 - 1	Tomlinson 83
22.08	Unib P	WORKSOP TOWN	820	1 - 1	Martin 60
26.08	Unib P	FRICKLEY ATHLETIC	210	3 - 1	Soar 3, Wright 31, Martin 86
28.08	Unib P	Leek Town	235	0 - 0	
02.09	Unib P	Hyde United	529	1 - 5	Taylor 6[p]
05.09	Unib P	GAINSBOROUGH TRINITY	222	1 - 0	Martin 44
09.09	Unib P	LANCASTER CITY	246	3 - 1	Roberts 7, Martin 15, Tomlinson 90
11.09	Unib P	Emley	221	0 - 0	
16.09	Unib P	ACCRINGTON STANLEY	343	2 - 0	Tomlinson 12, Orton 46
23.09	Unib P	Runcorn	207	1 - 2	Begley 84
26.09	Unib P	STALYBRIDGE CELTIC	361	2 - 2	Cooke 51, Brown 87
30.09	FA Cup Q2	CONGLETON TOWN	211	4 - 0	Hayman 15, Cooke 44, Roberts 57[p], Morris 67
03.10	Unib P	Frickley Athletic	139	2 - 1	Cooke 37, Wright 41
08.10	Unib P	Blyth Spartans	303	1 - 1	Morris 18
14.10	FA Cup Q3	MAIDENHEAD UNITED	380	3 - 2	Martin 5, Taylor 29, Morris 42
21.10	Unib P	BARROW	347	1 - 4	Ludlam 77
24.10	Unib P	WHITBY TOWN	174	0 - 1	
28.10	FA Cup Q4	ILKESTON TOWN	1436	0 - 1	
04.11	FA Trophy 1	Moor Green	246	1 - 0	Cooke 25
14.11	Lge Cup 9	BELPER TOWN	132	0 - 2	
18.11	Unib P	Colwyn Bay	223	2 - 0	Martin 47, Cooke 54
28.11	Lge Cup 9	Eastwood Town	148	2 - 1	Martin 50, Morris 52
02.12	FA Trophy 2	REDDITCH UNITED	231	1 - 0	Wright 17
09.12	Unib P	SPENNYMOOR UNITED	181	1 - 0	Rankin 21
12.12	Lge Cup 9	Matlock Town	180	2 - 1	Martin 33, Morris 51
16.12	Unib P	Bamber Bridge	220	3 - 1	Soar 36, Wright 39 90
23.12	Unib P	COLWYN BAY	218	1 - 0	Martin 29
06.01	Notts SC 3	Hucknall Rolls Royce	300	4 - 0	Martin 26 35, Regis 65, Wright 68
13.01	FA Trophy 3	Leigh RMI	235	0 - 1	
23.01	Lge Cup 9	LEEK TOWN	81	3 - 0	Martin 1 75, Regus 90
27.01	Unib P	HYDE UNITED	190	1 - 2	Brown 44
03.02	Unib P	Burscough	191	1 - 2	Wright 1
06.02	Unib P	EMLEY	270	0 - 2	
10.02	Unib P	Droylsden	168	1 - 1	Morris 90
13.02	Notts SC QF	EASTWOOD TOWN	215	8 - 0	Morris 10, Taylor 15 40, Martin 26, Cooke 50 85, Roebuck 60, Bignall 80
17.02	Unib P	BURSCOUGH	175	3 - 2	Brown 20, Cooke 35, Wright 74
20.02	Unib P	Altrincham	438	0 - 1	
24.02	Unib P	BAMBER BRIDGE	181	1 - 0	Morris 62
27.02	Unib P	LEEK TOWN	101	2 - 0	Morris 35, Martin 65
03.03	Pres. Cup QF	VAUXHALL	153	2 - 4	Ricketts 21, Roberts 76
06.03	Unib P	Stalybridge Celtic	477	0 - 1	
10.03	Unib P	MARINE	207	1 - 1	Soar 85
13.03	Unib P	Gainsborough Trinity	310	1 - 1	Roebuck 9
17.03	Unib P	Barrow	968	0 - 5	
20.03	Notts SC SF	WELBECK COLLIERY WELFARE	168	5 - 2	Bignall 16 70 76, Martin 26, Wright 89
25.03	Unib P	BLYTH SPARTANS	215	4 - 1	Wright 40 50 66, Rankin 63
27.03	Unib P	Accrington Stanley	319	2 - 1	Martin 8, Taylor 90
31.03	Unib P	RUNCORN	184	1 - 0	Rankin 48
03.04	Unib P	DROYLSDEN	164	1 - 2	Martin 18
10.04	Unib P	BISHOP AUCKLAND	145	2 - 5	Martin 55, Wright 61
12.04	Unib P	Lancaster City	220	1 - 4	Morris 78
14.04	Unib P	Bishop Auckland	181	0 - 2	
16.04	Unib P	GATESHEAD	165	2 - 2	Martin 42 65[p]
18.04	Unib P	Worksop Town	324	1 - 1	Cooke 24
21.04	Unib P	Spennymoor United	72	1 - 0	Wright 29
28.04	Unib P	Whitby Town	280	2 - 2	Martin 57[p] 70[p]
02.05	Unib P	Gateshead	135	2 - 1	Morris 43, Martin 73
05.05	Unib P	ALTRINCHAM	290	1 - 3	Cooke 36
10.05	Notts SC F	GEDLING TOWN	660	1 - 0	Wright 67 (at Notts County)

PLAYING SQUAD

GOALKEEPERS: Dave McCarthy (Oakham Utd)

DEFENDERS: Mark Place (Matlock), Greg Fee (Gainsborough), Stuart Clarke (Sheffield Utd), Paul Cox (Ilkeston), Kieran Begley (Local), Simon Brown (Notts Co), Nathan Hollingworth (Teversal), Tommy Gallagher (Hinckley Utd), Jermaine Bailey (Ilkeston)

MIDFIELDERS: Darryl Rankin (Alfreton), Dale Wright (Ilkeston), Paul Sherlock (Bedford), Mike McLarnon (Shepshed), Phil Bignall (Youth)

FORWARDS: Leroy Chambers (Altrincham), Lee McGlinchey (Shepshed), Gary Ricketts (Hinckley Utd)

HYDE UNITED

CLUB OFFICIALS

Chairman: S C Hartley

Secretary: Tony Beard,
30 Fishermans Close,Winterley, Sandbach,
Cheshire. CW11 4SW
Tel & Fax: 01270 212473
07778 792502 (M) See email below.

Commercial Manager: Amanda Goodall
Tel No: 0161 368 1031

FOOTBALL MANAGEMENT TEAM

Manager: Mike McKenzie
Coach: Osher Williams / IanLamb
Physio: Jerry Clowes

FACT FILE

Formed: 1919
Nickname: The Tigers
Club Sponsors: T.M.I.Metals
Colours: Red/white/red
Change White/red/whitew
Midweek home matchday: Monday
Website: www.hydeunitedfc.com

2000-01

Captain: John Foster
P.o.Y. : Matthew Taylor
Top Scorer: Simon Yeo 32

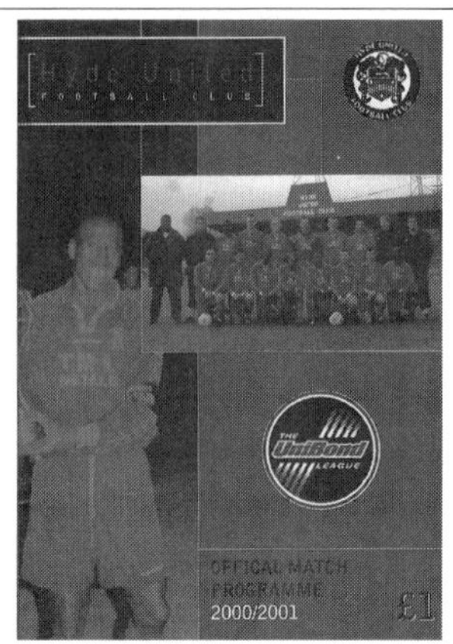

Pages: 32 Price: £1.
Editor: M Dring

Local Press: Tameside Advertiser
& Hyde Reporter.
Local Radio: GMR, Key 103

GROUND
Tameside Stadium, Ewen Fields, Walker Lane, Hyde SK14 5PL (0161 368 1031).
Directions: On entering Hyde follow signs for Tameside Leisure Park - in Walker Lane take 2nd car park entrance nr Leisure Pool, follow road around to the stadium. Quarter of a mile from Newton (BR). Train from Manchester (15 minutes)
Capacity: 4,130 Cover: 2,000 Seats: 660
Clubhouse: (0161 368 1621). Open most nights, 150 seats. +Sponsors Lounge for 70
Club Shop: Replica shirts, scarves, sports shirts, baseball caps, bronx hats,badges. Contact Tony Beard (0161 3631031 or Email: beard@fishermans.fslife.co.uk

PREVIOUS **Leagues:** Lancs & Cheshire 19-21; Manchester 21-30; Cheshire County 30-68, 70-82; Northern Prem. 68-70

CLUB RECORDS **Attendance:** 9,500 v Nelson, FA Cup 1952. **Scorer:** P O'Brien 247. **Appearances:** S Johnson 623.
Defeat: (as Hyde F.C.) 0-26 v Preston North End, F.A. Cup.
Fee Paid: £8,000 for Jim McCluskie (Mossley, 1989). **Fee Received:** £50.000 for Colin Little (Crewe Alexandra) 1995.

BEST SEASON **FA Cup:** 1st Rd 54-55 (v Workington), 83-84 (v Burnley),94-95 v Darlington.
FA Trophy: Semi Final 88-89 94-95 95-96

HONOURS Prem Inter-Lge Cup R-up(2) 88-90; NPL R-up(2) 87-89, 99-00 (Lg Cup 85-86 88-89 95-96(R-up 83-84 94-95), Chal. Shield 96-97, (R-up 86-87 90-91); Cheshire Co. Lg(3)54-56 81-82 (Lg Cup 33-34 52-53 54-55 72-73 81-82, Lg Chal. Shield(2) 80-82; Manchester Lg(5) 20-23 28-29 29-30 (Lg (Gilgryst) Cup(4) 27-29 49-50 70-71);Cheshire Snr Cup 45-46 62-63 69-70 80-81 89-90 96-97; Manchester Prem. Cup 93-94, 94-95, 95-96, 98-99,Snr Cup 74-75, Int Cup 55-56 56-57(jt), Jnr Cup 21-22 68-69;Lancs & Cheshire F'lit Cup(2) 54-56; Ashton Chal. Cup(6) 30-34 39-40 47-48;Hyde Chal Cup(2) 27-29; Reporter Cup(3) 72-74 75-76; Gavin Nicholson Mem Trophy79-80; Lancs F'lit Trophy(2) 86-88; Edward Case Cup(4), Unifilla Cup Winners: 99-00.

Players P rogressing: C McClelland & J Webber & P Barry (B'burn 1946 & 47 & 48),L Battrick (Manc. City 1968), J Hilton (Wrexham 1950), D Teece (Hull 1952), R Calderbank & William Bell & Neil Colbourne (R'dale 1953 & 74 & 80), Jeff Johnson (Stockport 1976), David Constantine & Donald Graham (Bury 1979), George Oghani (Bolton 1983), Kevin Glendon (Burnley 1983), Peter Coyne (Swindon 1984),Colin Little (Crewe Alex. 1995),Lutel James (Bury)

Back Row: Mike McKenzie (manager), Brendan Aspinall, Gavin Salmon, Peter Band, Paul Taylor, Graham Bennett, Karl Marginson, Ally Pickering, Stuart Lamb, Ian Lamb (Coach). **Front:** John Foster, Steve Tobin, Neil Hall, Paul Robertson, Matty Taylor, Lloyd Richardson, Simon Yeo, Gus Wilson (Captain). **Photo:** Don Goodwin

Date	Comp.	Opponents	Att.	Score	Goalscorers
17.08	Testimonial	MANCHESTER CITY	n.k	2 - 3	Tobin, Salmon for Mike McKenzie
19.08	Unib P	Burscough	281	0 - 1	
21.08	Unib P	LEEK TOWN	452	2 - 1	Yeo 8 44
26.08	Unib P	BLYTH SPARTANS	417	6 - 2	Aspinall 10, Yeo 39 43, Band 46 75, Hanson 64
28.08	Unib P	Droylsden	561	4 - 2	Taylor 53[p], Banim 73 87, Yeo 83
02.09	Unib P	HUCKNALL TOWN	529	5 - 1	Yeo 5 41 62[p] 84, Hanson 52
05.09	Unib P	Colwyn Bay	312	1 - 2	Banim 55
09.09	Unib P	Barrow	1216	0 - 1	
11.09	Unib P	WORKSOP TOWN	624	1 - 3	Banim 14
16.09	Unib P	FRICKLEY ATHLETIC	428	0 - 0	
18.09	Ches. SC 1	CHEADLE TOWN	244	6 - 1	Hanson 10 70, Banim 43 87, Yeo 48 80
23.09	Unib P	BISHOP AUCKLAND	366	1 - 1	Hall 90
25.09	Unib P	COLWYN BAY	417	1 - 1	Yeo 57
30.09	FA Cup Q2	Clitheroe	408	2 - 1	Yeo 44, Taylor 48[p]
10.10	Unib P	Marine	263	1 - 1	Beeston 18
14.10	FA Cup Q3	BRIGG TOWN	422	2 - 1	Taylor 38, Yeo 78
16.10	Unib P	ALTRINCHAM	674	4 - 2	Yeo 49 80, Banim 65, Salmon 90
21.10	Unib P	Spennymoor United	139	0 - 3	
24.10	Unib P	Gainsborough Trinity	254	1 - 2	Yeo 20
28.10	FA Cup Q4	Frickley Athletic	330	0 - 1	
04.11	Unib P	MARINE	381	2 - 1	Hall 15, Richardson 90
14.11	Ches. SC QF	Northwich Victoria	283	2 - 1	Banim 57, Tobin 90
18.11	Unib P	WHITBY TOWN	362	3 - 2	Beeston 5, Band 60, Hanson 71
22.11	Lge Cup 4	Altrincham	211	1 - 1	Richardson 44
27.11	Lge Cup 4	Ashton United	216	4 - 3	Yeo 29 67, Hanson 64, Wilkinson 75
02.12	FA Trophy 2	SPALDING UNITED	339	1 - 0	Yeo 75
16.12	Unib P	ACCRINGTON STANLEY	455	3 - 3	Hanson 38 56, Beeston 85
26.12	Unib P	STALYBRIDGE CELTIC	1009	1 - 2	Yeo 45
06.01	Unib P	Frickley Athletic	139	1 - 1	Band 32
08.01	Lge Cup 4	STOCKSBRIDGE PARK STEELS	223	5 - 2	Yeo 4 54 78, Beirne 19, Longden 49[og]
13.01	FA Trophy 3	BLYTH SPARTANS	556	0 - 0	
16.01	FA Trophy 3 R	Blyth Spartans	561	1 - 2	Banim 90
22.01	Ches. SC SF	STALYBRIDGE CELTIC	642	1 - 4	Banim 83
27.01	Unib P	Hucknall Town	190	2 - 1	Banim 42, Trainer 71
29.01	Lge Cup 4	OSSETT TOWN	212	5 - 1	Beirne 6, Banim 23 32, Tobin 28, Laurie 67
10.02	Unib P	GATESHEAD	307	3 - 1	Yeo 25, Rimmer 30, Banim 69
13.02	Unib P	Stalybridge Celtic	1078	1 - 3	Band 88
17.02	Unib P	Accrington Stanley	567	1 - 4	Banim 64
19.02	Unib P	BARROW	343	4 - 4	Charles 23 36, Yeo 50, Banim 67
24.02	Unib P	Lancaster City	301	4 - 1	Yeo 62 66 86, Tobin 88
27.02	Unib P	Bamber Bridge	243	1 - 2	Yeo 31
03.03	Lge Cup QF	BISHOP AUCKLAND	275	0 - 2	
06.03	Unib P	Leek Town	178	0 - 2	
10.03	Unib P	GAINSBOROUGH TRINITY	323	0 - 1	
17.03	Unib P	Emley	379	1 - 3	Taylor 44
24.03	Unib P	SPENNYMOOR UNITED	256	4 - 0	Band 30 51 53, Grant 90
25.03	Unib P	Whitby Town	257	3 - 1	Beeston 22, Hall 63, Yeo 90
28.03	Unib P	Runcorn	117	1 - 1	Grant 50
30.03	Unib P	EMLEY	623	1 - 2	Grant 45
12.04	Unib P	RUNCORN	276	1 - 1	Yeo 33
14.04	Unib P	Worksop Town	394	1 - 4	Yeo 50
16.04	Unib P	DROYLSDEN	402	3 - 2	Salmon 3 42, Band 56
18.04	Unib P	Bishop Auckland	130	1 - 3	Salmon 76
21.04	Unib P	BAMBER BRIDGE	311	1 - 4	Salmon 44
26.04	Unib P	Gateshead	131	0 - 3	
28.04	Unib P	Altrincham	662	0 - 2	
30.04	Unib P	BURSCOUGH	262	1 - 1	Grant 8
03.05	Unib P	LANCASTER CITY	181	1 - 1	Salmon 86
05.05	Unib P	Blyth Spartans	388	0 - 0	

PLAYING SQUAD

GOALKEEPERS: Richard Acton (Runcorn)

DEFENDERS: John Foster (Bury), Stuart Taylor (New Zealand), Paul Ashwell (Local), Adam Critchley (Chorley), Clive Brown (Bangor C), Bradley Sandeman (Leek)

MIDFIELDERS: Matty Taylor (Cheadle T), Darren McConnell (Stockport), Nehru McKenzie (Youth), Colin Hall (Oldham), Neil Hall (Droylsden), Peter Band (Bollington), Lee Matthews (Curzon Ashton)

FORWARDS: Simon Yeo (Coleraine), Gavin Salmon (Atherton LR), Gareth Rowe (Alsager), Josh Howard (Stalybridge), Martin Doherty (Leek)

LANCASTER CITY

CLUB OFFICIALS

Chairman: **Ian Sharp** Pres: **M Woodhouse**

Chief Executive: **M.Parkinson**

Secretary: **Barry Newsham**
13 Kingsdale Road, Lancaster LA1 5NE
Tel No: 01524 64024

Match Secretary: **Mike Sparks**
Email : mike@sparks13.freeserve.co,uk

Commercial Man.: **Bill Byrne**

FOOTBALL MANAGEMENT TEAM

Manager: Tony Hesketh
Coach: Barry Stimpson
Physio: G.Hardy, D Hughes

FACT FILE

Formed: 1902
Nickname: Dolly Blues
Sponsors: Reebok
Colours: Blue/white/blue
Change colours: All white
Midweek matchday: Tuesday
Reserve League: Lancashire League

Club Website:
www.lancastercityfc.freeserve.co.uk

2000-01
Captain: P. Horner/K. Mayers
Top Scorer: C. Ward 43
P.o.Y: Paul Sparrow

LANCASTER CITY F.C.
OFFICIAL PROGRAMME 2000/2001 SEASON
PRICE £1
Reebok
Main Club Sponsor
Premier Division
v
FRICKLEY ATHLETIC
Saturday 5th May
3.00 p.m. Kick off

Pages: 32 Price: £1
Editor: Bill Byrne

Local Press: Lancaster Guardian, Morecambe Visitor, Lancashire Evening Post, Lancaster Citizen.
Local Radio:
Red Rose, Radio Lancashire, Bay Radio

GROUND Giant Axe, West Road, Lancaster LA1 5PE Tel: 01524 382238 (Office).
Capacity: 3153 Cover: 900 Seats: 513
Directions: M6 junc 33, follow into city, left at lights immediately after Waterstones bookshop, 2nd right, pass railway station on right, follow road down hill, ground 1st right. 5 mins walk from both bus & rail stations
Clubhouse: "The Dolly Blue Tavern" just outside the ground. Also a new tea bar inside ground serving food and drinks. **Club Shop:** Inside ground, selling metal badges, pennants, programmes and other souvenirs etc. Contact Dave Crawford at club.

PREVIOUS **Leagues:** Lancs Combination 05-70; Northern Premier 70-82; North West Counties82-87.
Name: Lancaster Town. **Ground:** Quay Meadow 05-06 (club's 1st 2 games only!)

CLUB RECORDS **Attendance:** 7,500 v Carlisle, FA Cup 1936.
Goalscorer: David Barnes 130 League & cup. **Appearances:** Edgar J Parkinson, 591 league & cup.
Win: 8-0 v Leyland Motors (A), 83-84. **Defeat:** 0-10 v Matlock T, NPL Division One, 73-74

BEST SEASON **FA Vase:** Second Rd 86-87 90-91. **FA Cup:** 2nd Rd 46-47 (1-4 v Gateshead) 72-73 (1-2 v Notts County)
FA Trophy: Third Rd 74-75 75-76. League Clubs defeated: Barrow, Stockport County 21-22

HONOURS Northern Prem. Lg Cup R-up 79-80 (Div 1 Cup R-up 90-91), Lancs Combination 21-22 29-30 34-35 35-36 (R-up 19-20 22-23 27-28 51-52, Lg Cup 21-22, Div 2 R-up14-15), Lancs Jun. Cup (ATS Challenge Trophy) 27-28 28-29 30-31 33-34 51-52 74-75 (R-up 06-07 08-09 19-20 26-27,00-01), Lancs Yth (u18) Cup 87-88 88-89 (R-up 86-87 89-90), President's Cup 1994-95 Unibond Div 1 95-96, Div 1 Lge Cup 95-96., Lg.Challenge Cup 99-00

Players Progressing: J McNamee (Workington 75), B O'Callaghan (Stoke C.), I Stevens (Stockport Co. 86), G Johnstone (P.N.E. 93), M Clark & W Collins (Crewe Alex.), G Wilson (Crewe Alex.). P.Thomson (NAC Breda 99) Chris Ward (Birmingham City)

L-R Back Row: Dave Hughes (physio), Farrell Kilblane, Kevin Barnes (now Fleetwood), Mark Cheal, Chris Ward (now Birmingham C.), Cyril Sharrock, Paul Horridge, Kenny Mayers, Phil Horner (now Blackpool), Paul Sparrow, Dean Martin, Graham Byram (reserve manager).

Front Row: Gavin Hardy (physio), Ian Dickinson (now Chorley), Lee Clitheroe, Paul Haddow, Tony Hesketh (manager), Ian Sharp (chairman), Barry Stimpson (asst. man.), Jimmy Graham, Brian Welch, Stewart Clitheroe, Hughie Sharkey (trainer).

Insets (clockwise from top left): Colin Potts, Phil Brown, Mark Thornley, Brian Welch.

Photo: Lancaster & Morecambe Newspapers Ltd.

Date	Comp.	Opponents	Att.	Score	Goalscorers
11.08	NPL Shield	Leigh RMI	251	1 - 2	Ward 20
22.08	Unib P	BURSCOUGH	266	5 - 2	Kilbane 42, Martin 46, L Clitheroe 62, Ward 72 76[p]
26.08	Unib P	GATESHEAD	277	2 - 0	Mayers 54 84
28.08	Unib P	Altrincham	649	1 - 3	Ward 25
02.09	Unib P	WORKSOP TOWN	429	2 - 0	Ward 63[p], Kilbane 70
05.09	Unib P	Bamber Bridge	395	4 - 1	Martin 8, Welch 12 33, Fowler 88
09.09	Unib P	Hucknall Town	246	1 - 3	Kilbane 89
12.09	Unib P	ACCRINGTON STANLEY	358	1 - 1	Barnes 28
16.09	Unib P	Emley	194	0 - 1	
19.09	Unib P	Marine	254	1 - 1	Ward 85
23.09	Unib P	DROYLSDEN	308	0 - 2	
26.09	Unib P	BAMBER BRIDGE	247	3 - 2	Welch 7, Clitheroe 34, Butler 35
30.09	FA Cup Q2	Brigg Town	189	2 - 2	Barnes 90, Kilbane 90
03.10	FA Cup Q2 R	BRIGG TOWN	185	3 - 4	Ward 31 93, Haddow 90
06.10	Unib P	Stalybridge Celtic	530	0 - 5	
14.10	Unib P	RUNCORN	240	3 - 1	Ward 6, Mayers 51, Clitheroe 69
17.10	Unib P	MARINE	381	3 - 1	Ward 33 83, L Clitheroe 73
21.10	Unib P	Worksop Town	610	2 - 4	Welch 77, Kilbane 89
24.10	Unib P	Accrington Stanley	666	2 - 1	Ward 43[p] 53
14.11	FA Trophy 1	Racing Club Warwick	91	4 - 0	Graham 30, Haddow 33, Welch 54 83
18.11	Unib P	BLYTH SPARTANS	267	1 - 1	Haddow 90
22.11	Lancs MT 1	BLACKPOOL MECHANICS	120	2 - 1	Simpson 20[og], Ward 52
02.12	FA Trophy 2	BROMSGROVE ROVERS	161	0 - 1	
09.12	Unib P	STALYBRIDGE CELTIC	304	3 - 2	Haddow 41 79, Ward 88[p]
19.12	Lge Cup 2	KENDAL TOWN	77	3 - 0	Welch 4 77, Butler 31
23.12	Unib P	GAINSBOROUGH TRINITY	240	2 - 1	Brown 53, Wood 85
26.12	Unib P	BARROW	737	1 - 1	Ward 84[p]
01.01	Unib P	Barrow	1169	2 - 2	Clitheroe 15, Ward 18[p]
03.01	Lge Cup 2	Gretna	94	2 - 1	Morton 23, Ward 82
06.01	Unib P	EMLEY	318	3 - 3	Brown 16, Wood 23[og], Mayers 70
09.01	Lancs MT 2	ACCRINGTON STANLEY	161	5 - 0	Martin 21, Brown 41, Ward 55, Potts 84 89
13.01	Unib P	SPENNYMOOR UNITED	305	2 - 0	Ward 28[p] 58
23.01	Lge Cup 2	BARROW	174	1 - 0	Ward 25
27.01	Unib P	LEEK TOWN	297	3 - 2	Mayers 4, Welch 19, Ward 30
30.01	Lancs MT QF	LEIGH RMI	155	1 - 1	Welch 75, Martin 102
03.02	Unib P	Gainsborough Trinity	365	1 - 1	Linighan 24[og]
06.02	Lge Cup 2	Workington	214	3 - 1	Ward 5 10 90
10.02	Unib P	ALTRINCHAM	382	4 - 1	Welch 27, Potts 49, Ward 55 79
17.02	Unib P	Whitby Town	316	5 - 1	Ward 30 42, Mayers 68[p], Welch 74, Potts 90
21.02	Unib P	Bishop Auckland	208	3 - 1	Welch 35, Ward 70, Mayers 82
24.02	Unib P	HYDE UNITED	301	1 - 4	Welch 52
03.03	Lge Cup QF	BAMBER BRIDGE	269	1 - 0	Potts 29
06.03	Lancs MT QF R	Leigh RMI	131	3 - 0	Potts 36, Ward 65[p], Brown 76
10.03	Unib P	WHITBY TOWN	331	3 - 1	Martin 33, Ward 39, Potts 45
13.03	Unib P	Spennymoor United	91	3 - 0	Martin 30, Ward 47 57[p]
17.03	Unib P	Colwyn Bay	251	2 - 1	Potts 53, Welch 61
20.03	Lancs MT SF	Bamber Bridge	365	1 - 0	Haddow 49
23.03	Unib P	BISHOP AUCKLAND	418	1 - 0	Haddow 82
27.03	Unib P	Droylsden	120	2 - 3	Ward 10, Brown 55
31.03	Unib P	Blyth Spartans	338	1 - 0	Ward 33
03.04	Lge Cup SF	BELPER TOWN	204	6 - 1	Haddow 30 35, Ward 63 65 88, Mayers 84
10.04	Unib P	COLWYN BAY	235	1 - 0	Welch 82
12.04	Unib P	HUCKNALL TOWN	220	4 - 1	Mayers 15, Brown 21, Welch 77, Haddow 80
14.04	Unib P	Burscough	229	3 - 2	Ward 23[p] 43, Welch 68
18.04	Unib P	Leek Town	149	2 - 0	Mayers 37[p], Potts 88
21.04	Unib P	Frickley Athletic	140	0 - 0	
24.04	Lancs MT F	Southport	779	0 - 1	(at Chorley)
26.04	Unib P	Runcorn	145	0 - 1	
28.04	Unib P	Gateshead	185	0 - 1	
01.05	Lge. Cup F	BISHOP AUCKLAND	530	2 - 2	Haddow 12 51 (4-3p)
03.05	Unib P	Hyde United	181	1 - 1	Brown 90
05.05	Unib P	FRICKLEY ATHLETIC	490	0 - 1	

PLAYING SQUAD

GOALKEEPERS: Mark Thornley (Barrow), Andy Banks (Morecambe)

DEFENDERS: Paul Sparrow (Rochdale), Jimmy Graham (Guiseley), Farrell Kilbane (Stafford R), Stewart Clitheroe (Port Vale), Paul Rigby (Kendal)

MIDFIELDERS: Brian Butler (Leigh RMI), Dean Martin (Stalybridge), Paul Haddow (Barrow), Kenny Mayers (Morecambe), Lee Clitheroe (Oldham), Colin Potts (Bamber Bridge)

FORWARDS: Andy Whittaker (Bamber Bridge), Neil Morton (Morecambe), Mark Cheal (Youth), Brian Welch (Clitheroe), Phil Brown (Kendal)

MARINE

CLUB OFFICIALS

Chairman: **Tom Culshaw**
President: **Dennis Hargreaves**
Secretary: **John Wildman**
4 Ashbourne Avenue, Blundellsands,
Liverpool L23 8TX Tel: 0151 924 5248
Press Officer: **David Wotherspoon**

FOOTBALL MANAGEMENT TEAM

Manager: Roly Howard
Asst Mgr/Coach: Roger Patience
Physio: John Bradshaw

FACT FILE

Formed: 1894
Nickname: The Mariners
Sponsors: Johnsons the Cleaners
Colours: White/black/black
Change colours: Yellow & Green
Midweek matchday: Tuesday
Reserves' League: Lancs. League Div. One

GROUND Rossett Park, College Road, Crosby, Liverpool(Tel: 0151 924 1743)
Directions: College Road is off main Liverpool-Southport road (A565) in Crosby. Ground ten minutes walk from Crosby & Blundellsands (Mersey Rail). Bus No. 92
Capacity: 2,800 Cover: 1,400 Seats: 400

Clubhouse: Open daily. Concert Hall (250 seats), Members Lounge (100 seats).
Club Shop: Sells replica kit and range of souvenirs.Metal Badges in home and away colours. Contact Dave Rannard 0151474 9848

PROGRAMME
Pages: 24 Price: 80p
Editor: David Wotherspoon
Local Press: Crosby Herald, Liverpool Echo, Daily Post Local Radio: BBC Radio Merseyside, Radio City

PREVIOUS
Leagues: Liverpool Zingari; Liverpool Co. Comb.; Lancs Combination 35-39, 46-69; Cheshire County 69-79.
Name: Waterloo Melville **Ground:** Waterloo Park1894-1903

CLUB RECORDS
Attendance: 4,000 v Nigeria, Friendly 1949
Goalscorer: Paul Meachin 200 **Win:** 14-2 v Rossendale Utd (A), Cheshire County Lge 25/2/78
Appearances: Peter Smith 952 **Defeat:** 2-11 v Shrewsbury Town F.A.Cup 1st Rd 1995
Fee Paid: £6,000 for Jon Penman (Southport Oct. 1995) **Fee Received:** £20,000 for Richard Norris (Crewe 96)

BEST SEASON
FA Trophy: Semi Final 83-84, 91-92 **FA Amateur Cup:** Runners up 31-32 (SF 46-47)
FA Cup: 3rd Rd 92-93, 1-3 v Crewe Alex. (A) League clubs defeated: Barnsley 75-76, Halifax T. 92-93

HONOURS
FA Amateur Cup R-up 31-32; Northern Prem Lg 94-95, R-up 85-86 91-92, Lg Cup 84-85 91-92 (R-up 80-81 85-86); Presidents Cup R-up 83-84 86-87; Cheshire Co. Lg73-74 75-76 77-78 (R-up 72-73); Lancs Comb. R-up 46-47 (Lg Cup 46-47 63-64 68-69); Liverpool Comb. 27-28 30-31 33-34 34-35 (Lg Cup 30-31); Lancs Tphy 87-88 90-91; Lancs Jnr Cup 78-79; Lancs Amtr Cup (5); Liverpool Snr Cup 78-79 84-8587-88 89-90 94-95 99-00; Liverpool Non-Lge Cup 68-69 75-76 76-77; Liverpool Chal. Cup 42-43 44-45 71-72.

Players Progressing: A Sharrock, S Brooks (Southport 73 &77), A Jones (Leeds 60), G Williams (Preston 72), J Lacy (Fulham), P Beesly (Sheffield Utd), M Kearney (Everton 81), A Finlay (Shrewsbury 81), P Cook (Norwich), P Edwards (Crewe), I Nolan (Tranmere), J McAteer(Bolton W.), R Norris (Crewe 96).

The Millenium Stand at Marine erupts as Mark Schofield sees his header go into the net for an injury time winner in their 4-3 FA Cup match against Colwyn Bay.
Photo: Anne Hood

Date	Comp.	Opponents	Att.	Score	Goalscorers
19.08	Unib P	HUCKNALL TOWN	271	1 - 1	Robinson 60
22.08	Unib P	Runcorn	392	2 - 2	Morgan 51, Baines 90
26.08	Unib P	STALYBRIDGE CELTIC	304	0 - 3	
02.09	Unib P	Bishop Auckland	243	1 - 1	Morgan 64
05.09	Unib P	ALTRINCHAM	451	0 - 4	
09.09	Unib P	WHITBY TOWN	274	4 - 1	Randles 8, Robinson 14, Gautrey 28, Morgan 72
12.09	Unib P	Burscough	266	3 - 1	Gamble 32[p] 52[p], Bainbridge 81
16.09	Unib P	Leek Town	282	2 - 2	Bainbridge 20, McHale 72
19.09	Unib P	LANCASTER CITY	254	1 - 1	Morgan 27
23.09	Unib P	Frickley Athletic	159	1 - 0	Randles 4
25.09	Unib P	Emley	236	2 - 3	Bainbridge 48, Gamble 68
30.09	FA Cup Q2	COLWYN BAY	366	4 - 3	Bainbridge 10, Robinson 25 60, Schofield 90
07.10	Unib P	BURSCOUGH	364	3 - 5	Courtney 35, Gamble 45, Gautrey 61
10.10	Unib P	HYDE UNITED	263	1 - 1	Gamble 66[p]
14.10	FA Cup Q3	RADCLIFFE BOROUGH	325	0 - 2	
17.10	Unib P	Lancaster City	381	1 - 3	Robinson 8
21.10	Unib P	GATESHEAD	226	1 - 1	Gautrey 38
24.10	Unib P	RUNCORN	316	4 - 1	Robinson 14, Rimmer 41, Douglas 45, Gamble 55
28.10	Unib P	Gainsborough Trinity	336	0 - 2	
31.10	Lge Cup 6	COLWYN BAY	138	1 - 0	Robinson 32
04.11	Unib P	Hyde United	381	1 - 2	Douglas 29
11.11	Unib P	SPENNYMOOR UNITED	242	1 - 0	Hughes 90
14.11	Lge Cup 6	VAUXHALL	215	3 - 0	Rimmer 9, Black 29, Gamble 32
18.11	Unib P	Bamber Bridge	218	0 - 2	
25.11	Unib P	BISHOP AUCKLAND	310	1 - 3	Gamble 81
02.12	FA Trophy 2	GATESHEAD	209	2 - 1	Courtney 52, Thompson 63
09.12	Unib P	Altrincham	579	1 - 3	Courtney 58
12.12	Lge Cup 6	Burscough	124	3 - 5	Bainbridge 45, Courtney 67, Gamble 84
16.12	Unib P	EMLEY	268	0 - 2	
23.12	Unib P	WORKSOP TOWN	351	0 - 1	
26.12	Unib P	Colwyn Bay	302	3 - 2	Courtney 15 57, Burns 65
06.01	Unib P	DROYLSDEN	271	1 - 0	Gamble 28
09.01	L'pool SC QF	EVERTON	297	3 - 2	Courtney 58 77, Randles 62
13.01	FA Trophy 3	STALYBRIDGE CELTIC	441	2 - 0	Gamble 57, Randles 84
27.01	Unib P	Barrow	840	0 - 1	
30.01	Lancs MT 2	BURSCOUGH	183	1 - 0	Courtney 21
03.02	FA Trophy 4	RUSHDEN & DIAMONDS	965	0 - 6	
10.02	Unib P	Worksop Town	464	3 - 3	Lally 5, Black 43, Courtney 74
15.02	Lge Cup 6	Witton Albion	114	2 - 1	Bainbridge 34, Randles 86
17.02	Unib P	Gateshead	211	0 - 3	
20.02	Lancs MT QF	Southport	403	0 - 5	
24.02	Unib P	FRICKLEY ATHLETIC	267	1 - 0	Courtney 68
03.03	Lge Cup QF	GAINSBOROUGH TRINITY	142	2 - 1	Bainbridge 81, Gamble 98
06.03	L'pool SC SF	Burscough	182	2 - 2	Courtney 55, Bainbridge 90 (4-5p)
10.03	Unib P	Hucknall Town	207	1 - 1	Black 67
17.03	Unib P	Stalybridge Celtic	663	1 - 2	Courtney 33
20.03	Unib P	ACCRINGTON STANLEY	225	1 - 1	Black 90
24.03	Unib P	COLWYN BAY	212	2 - 0	Courtney 2, Gamble 33
31.03	Unib P	Whitby Town	269	2 - 3	Black 19, Lally 81
03.04	Lge Cup SF	BISHOP AUCKLAND	182	0 - 3	
10.04	Unib P	BAMBER BRIDGE	231	2 - 1	Bainbridge 12 30
12.04	Unib P	Droylsden	162	3 - 2	McDaid 28, Courtney 44, Bainbridge 81
14.04	Unib P	Accrington Stanley	451	2 - 3	Gamble 45, Black 90
16.04	Unib P	BARROW	329	1 - 2	Douglas 4
21.04	Unib P	LEEK TOWN	246	2 - 0	Lally 3, Courtney 38
26.04	Unib P	Blyth Spartans	210	1 - 4	Black 21
28.04	Unib P	Spennymoor United	97	2 - 2	Hussin 67, Bainbridge 74
01.05	Unib P	BLYTH SPARTANS	202	1 - 1	Townsend 17
05.05	Unib P	GAINSBOROUGH TRINITY	220	2 - 2	Bainbridge 61 71

PLAYING SQUAD

GOALKEEPERS: Chris Clarke (Chorley)

DEFENDERS: Kevin Formby (Southport), Mark Nulty (Youth), Jon Gautrey (Southport), John Wareing (Youth)

MIDFIELDERS: Eddie Hussin (Winsford Utd), Anthony Lally (Kendal), Phil McDiarmid (Southport), Stuart Gelling (Colwyn Bay), Ricky Bainbridge (Buxton)

FORWARDS: David Thompson (Southport), John Morgan (Southport), Nel Black (Tranmere), Richie Townsend (Cwmbran)

RUNCORN F.C. HALTON

CLUB OFFICIALS

Chairman: **Dr David Robertson**

Vice Chairman: **Tony Bamber**

Secretary: **Debbie Quayle,** 57 The Moorings, Lydiate,Liverpool L31 2PR
Tel No: 0151 531 1296 (H)
0161 200 4925 (W)

FACT FILE

Formed: 1918
Nickname: The Linnets
Midweek matchday: Tuesday
Colours: Yellow/&green/yellow
Change colours: All red
Reserve's league: Lancashire
Youth's league: Northwest Alliance
Website: www.runcornfc.co.uk

FOOTBALL MANAGEMENT TEAM

Manager: Liam Watson
Assistant Manager: Neil Whalley

GROUND Autoquest Stadium, Lowerhouse Lane, Widnes, Cheshire. WA8 7DZ
Tel No: Matchdays only 0151 5106000 Fax matchdays only 0151 510 6001
Directions: From M62 take junction 7 and follow signs to Widnes and Autoquest Stadium. Follow Widnes by -pass and then turn right onto Ashley Way. At roundabout take second exit and go straight onto the next roundabout where the Stadium ia on the right.
Capacity: Cover: Seats:
Clubhouse: Open on matchdays. Light snacks available.
Club Shop: Phone club.

PROGRAMME
Pages: 36 Price: £1.30
Editor: Alex Keenan Tel. 01928 590425

Local Press: Runcorn Weekly News, Liverpool Echo, Runcorn World, Manchester Evening News.
Radio: Radio Merseyside, GMR.Wire F.M

PREVIOUS **Leagues:** Lancs Combination; Cheshire Co. Lg; Northern Prem. Lge. 68 -81; Alliance Premier (Conference) 81-96.
Names: Runcorn **Grounds:** None

CLUB RECORDS **Attendance:** 10,111 v Preston - FA Cup 1938-39.
Goalscorer: Alan Ryan (66 goals in 64 appearances 67-68).
Win: 11-1 v Congleton Town 64-65. **Defeat:** 0-9 v Wellington 46-47.
Fee Paid: £17,000 for Simon Rudge, Hyde Utd, 1989. **Fee Received:** £80,000 for Ian Woan, Nottm Forest, 1990.

BEST SEASON **FA Trophy:** Runners-up 85-86, 92-93, 93-94. **FA Cup:** Second Round Replay 85-86,0-4 v Wigan Ath. (A), after 1-1. Second Round also 47-48, 67-68, 77-78, 86-87,87-88, 88-89. League clubs defeated: Scunthorpe Utd., Notts. Co., Chester City,Wrexham.

HONOURS Lancs Jnr Cup 1918-19; Cheshire Lg 1919-20, 36-37, 38-39, 39-40, 62-63;Cheshire Snr Cup 24-25, 35-36, 61-62, 64-65, 67-68, 73-74, 74-75, 84-89 (5times), R-up 93-94; Cheshire Co. Bowl 37-38; Northern Premier Lg 75-76, 80-81(R-up 74-75); NPL Chall Cup 74-75, 79-80, 80-81; NPL Challenge Shield 80-81,81-82; Alliance Premier Lg 81-82, Gola Lg Championship Shield 82-83, 85-86; Bob Lord Trophy 82-83, 84-85, R-up 91-92. FA Trophy R-up 85-86, 92-93, 93-94.NPL Pres.Cup 98-99

Players Progressing: Mark McCarrick, Eddie Bishop, Jim Cumbes, Graham Abel,Barry Knowles, Mark Jones, Don Page, David Pugh, Ian Woan, Gary Brabin, Paul Robertson, Mike Smith,Mark Carter

Date	Comp.	Opponents	Att.	Score	Goalscorers
19.08	Unib P	Worksop Town	553	1 - 1	Moseley 12
22.08	Unib P	MARINE	392	2 - 2	Nolan 63[p], Moseley 87
26.08	Unib P	LEEK TOWN	257	0 - 1	
28.08	Unib P	Colwyn Bay	334	2 - 2	McAllister 38, Rigby 45
02.09	Unib P	FRICKLEY ATHLETIC	212	2 - 1	Robinson 27, Nolan 58
05.09	Unib P	Accrington Stanley	856	1 - 2	Speare 45[og]
12.09	Unib P	BAMBER BRIDGE	219	2 - 3	McNally 4, Watson 42
16.09	Unib P	Gateshead	251	1 - 5	Rigby 59
20.09	Ches. SC 1	STOCKPORT COUNTY	134	1 - 4	Nolan 45[p]
23.09	Unib P	HUCKNALL TOWN	207	2 - 1	Watson 12, Nolan 30
26.09	Unib P	ALTRINCHAM	407	0 - 2	
30.09	FA Cup Q2	Burscough	346	1 - 2	Brunskill 18
14.10	Unib P	Lancaster City	240	1 - 3	McNally 74
16.10	Friendly	LIVERPOOL	2500	1 - 4	
21.10	Unib P	Whitby Town	333	1 - 3	McAllister 35
24.10	Unib P	Marine	316	1 - 4	Price 84
04.11	FA Trophy 1	Barrow	1327	1 - 0	McAllister 60
11.11	Unib P	COLWYN BAY	218	1 - 0	McAllister 59
18.11	Unib P	Gainsborough Trinity	356	0 - 2	
21.11	Lge Cup 5	Bamber Bridge	147	0 - 2	
25.11	Unib P	ACCRINGTON STANLEY	222	2 - 0	Nolan 26, Robinson 56
02.12	FA Trophy 2	GUISELEY	302	2 - 1	Price 16, Robinson 88
12.12	Lge Cup 5	Accrington Stanley	180	1 - 1	McNally 24
16.12	Unib P	BLYTH SPARTANS	207	1 - 0	Tomlinson 80
19.12	Lge Cup 5	Winsford United	48	2 - 0	Price 32, Watson 62
23.12	Unib P	Blyth Spartans	365	0 - 3	
26.12	Unib P	BURSCOUGH	275	2 - 0	Ness 9, Watson 82
03.01	Lge Cup 5	TRAFFORD	121	6 - 1	Watson 22 62, McNally 42 87, Price 49, Benson 84
06.01	Unib P	SPENNYMOOR UNITED	214	2 - 0	Watson 37 52
09.01	Unib P	Stalybridge Celtic	427	1 - 3	McNally 28
13.01	FA Trophy 3	SCARBOROUGH	420	0 - 4	
20.01	Unib P	Barrow	903	2 - 1	Watson 52 71
27.01	Unib P	Frickley Athletic	197	1 - 1	Ness 6
03.02	Unib P	DROYLSDEN	191	3 - 1	Lunt 23, Watson 57[p], McAllister 71
17.02	Unib P	GAINSBOROUGH TRINITY	207	1 - 1	Price 7
20.02	Unib P	Leek Town	203	1 - 2	Lunt 78
21.02	Friendly	EVERTON	700	0 - 1	
24.02	Unib P	BARROW	275	3 - 1	McAllister 23, McNally 66, Watson 75
06.03	Unib P	Droylsden	142	2 - 0	Price 19, Watson 35
10.03	Unib P	BISHOP AUCKLAND	929	4 - 4	McAllister 9, Watson 19, McNally 43, Lunt 44 (at Widnes RLFC)
13.03	Chairman QF	Harrogate Town	240	0 - 1	
16.03	Unib P	WORKSOP TOWN	209	0 - 4	
21.03	Unib P	Bishop Auckland	145	2 - 0	Chantler 27, Robinson 77
24.03	Unib P	Burscough	166	0 - 0	
28.03	Unib P	HYDE UNITED	117	1 - 1	McNally 80
31.03	Unib P	Hucknall Town	184	0 - 1	
07.04	Unib P	WHITBY TOWN	159	2 - 1	McAllister 41, Lunt 62
12.04	Unib P	Hyde United	276	1 - 1	Cowley 74
14.04	Unib P	Altrincham	676	1 - 2	McAlister 30
16.04	Unib P	STALYBRIDGE CELTIC	407	2 - 1	Lunt 59 82
21.04	Unib P	EMLEY	293	1 - 1	McAllister 13
24.04	Unib P	Emley	460	1 - 2	McNally 27
26.04	Unib P	LANCASTER CITY	145	1 - 0	Watson 90[p]
28.04	Unib P	Bamber Bridge	234	1 - 3	Lunt 79
01.05	Unib P	Spennymoor United	87	0 - 2	
05.05	Unib P	GATESHEAD	555	1 - 2	Watson 44

PLAYING SQUAD

GOALKEEPERS: Mark Winstanley (Bootle)

DEFENDERS: Tony Ward (Chorley), Steve Carragher (Accrington Stanley), Chris Price (Morecambe), Peter Ellis (Knowsley), John Benson (Marine), David Ness (Youth)

MIDFIELDERS: David Robinson (Ashton Utd), Gary Lunt (Crewe), Dave Gamble (Marine), Steve Latham (Youth), Neil Whalley (Droylsden), Mike Tomlinson (Warrington), Paul McNally (Marine)

FORWARDS: Mike Moseley (Youth), John McAllister (Prescot Cables), Liam Watson (Accrington Stanley), Alan Cowley (Local)

VAUXHALL MOTORS F.C.

CLUB OFFICIALS

President: F G Ward
Chairman: Tony Woodley
Vice Chairman: Len Jones
Treasurer: Steven McInerney
Secretary: Mrs Carole Paisey
26 South Rd., West Kirby, Wirral CH48 3HQ
FAX/Tel:0151 625 6936

FOOTBALL MANAGEMENT TEAM

Manager: Alvin McDonald
Asst. Manager: Peter carroll

FACT FILE

Formed: 1987
Re-formed 1995
Nickname: Motormen
Club Sponsors: Vauxhall
Colours: White/royal blue/white
Midweek Matchday: Tuesday
Reserves' Lge: Wset Cheshire Lge.
Club Website: www.vauxhall.co.uk

2000-01

Captain: Phil Brazier
P.o.Y.: Kevin Lynch
Top Scorer: Nicky Young (29)

GROUND Vauxhall Sports Ground, Rivacre Road, Hooton, Ellesmere Port, South Wirrall.
Tel: 0151 328 1114 (Ground) 0151 327 2294 (Club) Email: admin@vauxhallfc.co.uk

Directions: M 53 junction 5, take the A41 to Chester. At the first set of lights (at Chimneys pub) turn left into Hooton Green. Follow to end and turn left at T-junction, to the end & right at the T-junction into Rivacre Rd, ground is 250 yards on right.
Floodlights: Yes
Clubhouse: Yes **Club Shop:** Yes

HONOURS West Cheshire Lge 86, 95, R-up 84, W. Ches. Lge Bowl 68, Pyke Cup 2000, R-up 73, N.W.C. Lge. 2nd Div 88-89 95-96; Raab Karcher Chall Cup 90-91;.NWC Challenge Cup 98-99, Division 1 99-00, Floodlit Trophy Winners 99-00. Cheshire Amateur Cup R-up 87 94
Wirral Senior Cup 87, R-up 83, 84, 95, 00; Wirrall Amateur Cup 86 R-up 87; Wirral Junior Cup 83

PREVIOUS **Leagues:** Ellesmer Port Lge., Wirral Combination, West Cheshire League 66-87, 92-95; North West Counties Lg 87-92, 95-00,
Names: Vauxhall Motors 63- 87, Vauxhall GM 88-92, 95-99

BEST SEASON **FA Vase:** S-Final 99-00 v ChippenhamTown 0-1 aet (2 legs) **FA Cup:**

RECORDS **Attendance:** 1,500 v English F.A. XI, 1987

VAUXHALL MOTORS
having just received the Runners-up Trophy for season 2000-01 in Unibond Division One.

Date	Comp.	Opponents	Att.	Score	Goalscorers
19.08	Unib 1	Matlock Town	251	3 - 0	Young 17, Blundell 42, Lynch 65
22.08	Ches. SC P	STALYBRIDGE CELTIC	n.k	0 - 2	
26.08	Unib 1	TRAFFORD	85	4 - 2	Nesbitt 45, Young 50, Lacy 58, Welton 90
28.08	Unib 1	Lincoln United	114	4 - 4	Nesbitt 15, Young 20 79, Brady 71
09.09	Unib 1	BRADFORD PARK AVENUE	134	2 - 0	Young 59, Blundell 74
12.09	Unib 1	Witton Albion	262	4 - 1	Lacy 3, Young 44, Lawton 56, Nesbitt 77
16.09	Unib 1	Ossett Town	85	3 - 1	Blundell 20 35, Young 61
19.09	Unib 1	CHORLEY	98	5 - 0	Blundell 24 28 41, Lynch 44, Welton 89
23.09	Unib 1	GUISELEY	156	3 - 0	Nesbitt 16, Blundell 58, Welton 90
26.09	Unib 1	Winsford United	102	2 - 2	Blundell 13, Welton 84
30.09	Unib 1	Workington	339	2 - 0	Young 28, Lawton 40
07.10	Unib 1	OSSETT TOWN	110	2 - 2	Nesbitt 22, Blundell 52
14.10	Unib 1	MATLOCK TOWN	128	3 - 2	Welton 2 87, Young 85
21.10	Unib 1	Stocksbridge Park Steels	176	0 - 1	
24.10	Unib 1	Kendal Town	101	1 - 3	Cumiskey 54[p]
28.10	Unib 1	HARROGATE TOWN	121	8 - 1	Nesbitt 8, Blundell 24 44 78 87, Lynch 38, Young 43, Lawton 52
04.11	FA Trophy 1	LINCOLN UNITED	183	4 - 0	Blundell 6 19 68, Young 71
11.11	Unib 1	Farsley Celtic	156	2 - 1	Blundell 25 45
14.11	Lge Cup 6	Marine	215	0 - 3	
28.11	Lge Cup 6	COLWYN BAY	104	2 - 0	Cumiskey 35, Hart 57
02.12	FA Trophy 2	Emley	256	3 - 5	Wright 23, Cumiskey 36, Rigby 42
09.12	Unib 1	STOCKSBRIDGE PARK STEELS	130	1 - 2	Wright 46
16.12	Unib 1	Gretna	61	2 - 1	Young 44 87
23.12	Unib 1	FARSLEY CELTIC	100	4 - 0	Lynch 24, Young 30, Wright 60, Blundell 85
26.12	Unib 1	North Ferriby United	221	2 - 3	Blundell 32, Nesbitt 68[p]
06.01	Unib 1	Bradford Park Avenue	405	1 - 0	Lacy 90
13.01	Unib 1	BELPER TOWN	140	3 - 1	Young 15, Cumiskey 17, Nesbitt 75
27.01	Unib 1	EASTWOOD TOWN	104	1 - 1	Cumiskey 17
30.01	Lge Cup 6	Witton Albion	156	3 - 0	Davies 64 90, Young 90
03.02	Unib 1	GRETNA	112	3 - 2	Cumiskey 4, Young 24, Rigby 88
13.02	Lge Cup 6	BURSCOUGH	83	1 - 0	Young 29
17.02	Unib 1	WINSFORD UNITED	110	2 - 0	Nesbitt 17[p], Young 51
24.02	Unib 1	Trafford	137	1 - 2	Lynch 66
03.03	Pres. Cup QF	Hucknall Town	153	4 - 2	Riley 69, Nesbitt 80, Young 91, Lynch 120
10.03	Unib 1	Radcliffe Borough	222	0 - 1	
13.03	Unib 1	ASHTON UNITED	204	0 - 2	
17.03	Unib 1	NORTH FERRIBY UNITED	92	0 - 1	
20.03	Unib 1	Chorley	147	5 - 5	Lynch 17, Young 40 56 74, Hart 90
24.03	Unib 1	Congleton Town	275	2 - 0	Lynch 40, Young 58
27.03	Unib 1	WITTON ALBION	168	1 - 1	Lynch 15
31.03	Unib 1	KENDAL TOWN	96	1 - 0	Haddrell 52
04.04	Pres. Cup SF	Stalybridge Celtic	243	1 - 2	Lacey 59
10.04	Unib 1	WORKINGTON	209	4 - 0	Haddrell 5, Young 17, Lawton 34, Nesbitt 69[p]
12.04	Unib 1	Harrogate Town	293	2 - 1	Young 3 50
14.04	Unib 1	Belper Town	179	1 - 1	Nesbitt 60
16.04	Unib 1	LINCOLN UNITED	215	2 - 2	Cumiskey 7, Haddrell 50
21.04	Unib 1	Guiseley	217	1 - 1	Haddrell 36
24.04	Unib 1	CONGLETON TOWN	217	3 - 0	Cumiskey 24 48, Wright 75
28.04	Unib 1	RADCLIFFE BOROUGH	301	1 - 1	Wright 44
01.05	Unib 1	Eastwood Town	124	4 - 0	Lawton 13, Cumiskey 60, Young 76, Lynch 82
05.05	Unib 1	Ashton United	172	0 - 2	

PLAYING SQUAD

GOALKEEPERS: Chris Holmes (Newcastle T), Steve Hilton (Marine)

DEFENDERS: Phil Brazier (Rochdale), Kevin Thompson (Heswall), Neil Rigby (Trafford), Kevin Lynch (Prescot Cables), Wayne McDermott (Leek), Liam Croxton (Radcliffe B), Ian Horrigan (Rhyl), Matt Haddrell (Newcastle T)

MIDFIELDERS: Jon Stahope (Connah's Quay), Robbie Lawton (Marine), Stuart Wright (Heswall), Carl Spellman (Curzon Ashton), Carl Nesbitt (Poulton Vics)

FORWARDS: Terry Fearns (St.Helens), Nicky Young (Bromborough Pool), Paul Hart (Altrincham), Darren Vicary (Stalybridge)

WHITBY TOWN

CLUB OFFICIALS

Chairman: **Graham Manser.**

President: **Brooks Mileson**

Secretary: **Charlie Woodward**
6 Westlands Ave, Whitby,
North Yorks YO21 3DZ Tel: 01947 602312

Press Officer: Secretary

FOOTBALL MANAGEMENT TEAM

Manager: Harry Dunn
Asst Manager: David Logan
Physio: A.Gallavant

FACT FILE

Formed: 1926
Nickname: Seasiders
Sponsors: Sports Net.
Colours: All Royal Blue
Change Colours: All white.
Midweek matchday: Tuesday
Reserve League: Teeside League

2000-2001

Captain: David Logan
P.o.Ys.: G.Rennison & D Goodchild
Top scorer: Lee Ludlow 24

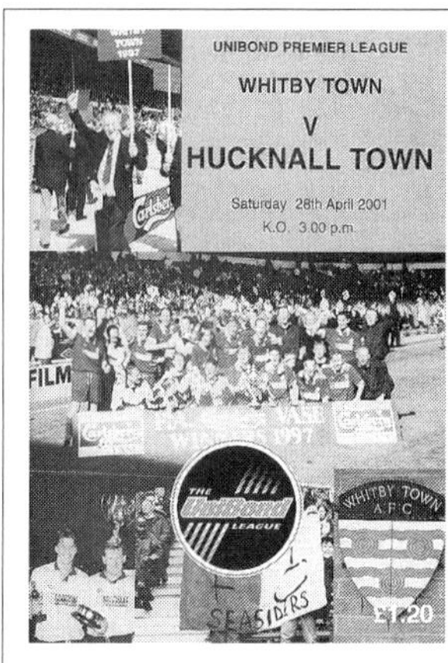

Pages: 40 Price: £1.20
Editor: C Woodward (01947 602312)

Local Press: Whitby Gazette, Northern Echo.
Local Radio: Yorkshire Coast Radio

GROUND Turnbull Ground, Upgang Lane, Whitby, North Yorks
Fax: 01947 603779 Tel: 01947 604847

Directions: Take the A174 road from town centre.
Ground on offside travelling towards Sandsend.

Capacity: 3,200 Cover: 500 Seats: 300

Clubhouse: Mon-Fri 7-11pm, Sat 12-11pm, Sun 12-2 & 7-10.30.
Club Shop: Yes

PREVIOUS **Leagues:** Northern League 1926-97. **Name:** Whitby United (pre 1950). **Grounds:** None

CLUB RECORDS **Attendance:** 4,000 v Scarborough, N Riding Senior Cup 18.4.65
Career Goalscorer: Paul Pitman (375) **Career Appearances:** Paul Pitman (468)
Win: 11-2 v Cargo Fleet Works 1950 **Fee Paid:** £2,500 for John Grady (Newcastle Blue Star 90)
Defeat: 3-13 v Willington 24.3.28 **Fee Received:** £5,000for Graham Robinson (Gateshead 97)

BEST SEASON **FA Vase:** Winners 97. **FA Amateur Cup:** Runner-up 1964-65
FA Trophy: QuarterFinals 1983-84 **FA Cup:** 2nd Round 83-84

HONOURS FA Amateur Cup Runners-up 64-65; FA Vase Winners 96-97; NPL Div 1 97-98;Northern Lge 92-93 96-97 (R-up 27-28 63-64 67-68 81-82 82-83), Lg Cup 28-29 63-64 69-70 76-77 84-85 95-96; Rothmans National Cup 75-76 77-78; Nth Riding SnrCup 64-65 67-68 82-83 89-90, 98-99; N Riding Bene Cup 92-93; J R Cleator Cup 84-85 92-93 95-96 96-97; Mickey Skinner Trophy [5], Unibond Presidents Cup Finalists 99-00

Players Progressing: Malcolm Poskett (Hartlepool), Sammy Kemp (Huddersfield), Jimmy Mulvaney (Hartlepool, Barrow, Stockport), Bobby Veart (Hartlepool), Derek Hampton & Trevor Smith & John Linacre & Phil Linacre(Hartlepool), Mark Hine (Grimsby). David Logan (Mansfield)

Left - Right
Back Row:
M. Taylor,
M. Pitts
I. Williams
D.Campbell
D.Goodchild,
G Robinson
G.Rennison

Front Row:
C.Skelton
D.Key
Mascot
D Logan
(captain)
B.Dixon

Date	Comp.	Opponents	Att.	Score	Goalscorers
19.08	Unib P	Droylsden	207	3 - 1	Chillingworth 38[p], Ure 81, Rennison 90
22.08	Unib P	Spennymoor United	232	2 - 1	Ludlow 57 68
26.08	Unib P	ALTRINCHAM	542	2 - 2	Dixon 26, Radigan 33
28.08	Unib P	Stalybridge Celtic	456	1 - 1	Ludlow 80
02.09	Unib P	ACCRINGTON STANLEY	451	0 - 0	
05.09	Unib P	BLYTH SPARTANS	431	1 - 0	Ludlow 36
09.09	Unib P	Marine	274	1 - 4	Chillingworth 51
16.09	Unib P	Blyth Spartans	323	2 - 0	Key 50, Radigan 87
23.09	Unib P	BURSCOUGH	389	0 - 2	
26.09	Unib P	SPENNYMOOR UNITED	296	3 - 3	Ludlow 16 81, Chillingsworth 51
30.09	FA Cup Q2	Chorley	269	2 - 0	Ludlow 77, Ure 87
03.10	Unib P	EMLEY	363	0 - 1	
06.10	Unib P	Bishop Auckland	235	1 - 2	Jones 76[og]
10.10	Unib P	Worksop Town	658	2 - 3	Messer 47, Goodchild 65
14.10	FA Cup Q3	Easington Colliery	192	0 - 1	
21.10	Unib P	RUNCORN	333	3 - 1	Taylor 38, Ure 43, Connell 70
24.10	Unib P	Hucknall Town	174	1 - 0	Connell 70
28.10	Unib P	BAMBER BRIDGE	237	1 - 1	Goodchild 14
04.11	FA Trophy 1	Bishop Auckland	175	1 - 1	Chillingworth 28
11.11	Unib P	Barrow	1082	3 - 2	Robinson 53, Messer 72, Ludlow 86
14.11	FA Trophy 1 R	BISHOP AUCKLAND	324	2 - 2	Logan 30, G Robinson 48 (4-5p)
18.11	Unib P	Hyde United	362	2 - 3	Ludlow 7, Messer 88
21.11	Lge Cup 1	Spennymoor United	101	0 - 0	
25.11	Unib P	LEEK TOWN	229	1 - 2	Hawtin 19[og]
29.11	Lge Cup 1	Bishop Auckland	79	2 - 4	Skelton 49, Walker 54
02.12	Unib P	Leek Town	205	1 - 0	Chillingsworth 29
16.12	Unib P	STALYBRIDGE CELTIC	315	0 - 1	
23.12	Unib P	Altrincham	568	1 - 3	Ludlow 83
26.12	Unib P	DROYLSDEN	361	0 - 1	
06.01	Unib P	WORKSOP TOWN	522	1 - 1	Ludlow 16
09.01	Lge Cup 1	GATESHEAD	193	1 - 1	Goodchild 2
13.01	Unib P	COLWYN BAY	322	5 - 1	Ludlow 20 34 45 72[p]
20.01	Unib P	Emley	517	0 - 4	
27.01	Unib P	Gainsborough Trinity	318	3 - 1	Ludlow 39, Marsh 69, Robinson 70
10.02	Unib P	Bamber Bridge	181	0 - 5	
15.02	Lge Cup 1	BLYTH SPARTANS	118	1 - 1	Kay 67
17.02	Unib P	LANCASTER CITY	316	1 - 5	Ludlow 11
20.02	N Rid SC Q1	Guisborough Town	170	3 - 1	Ludlow 20 75, Own-Goal 52
24.02	Unib P	Burscough	227	3 - 2	Rennison 21, Ludlow 45, Skelton 50
10.03	Unib P	Lancaster City	331	1 - 3	March 11
13.03	Unib P	FRICKLEY ATHLETIC	232	2 - 2	Logan 45, Robinson 59
17.03	Unib P	Accrington Stanley	509	2 - 0	McAuley 52, Ludlow 63
21.03	Unib P	Gateshead	127	1 - 1	Robinson 32
23.03	Unib P	GAINSBOROUGH TRINITY	251	0 - 1	
25.03	Unib P	HYDE UNITED	257	1 - 3	Goodchild 50
31.03	Unib P	MARINE	269	3 - 2	Rennison 35, Robinson 63, Goodchild 83
07.04	Unib P	Runcorn	159	1 - 2	Ellis 90[og]
10.04	Unib P	BARROW	228	0 - 2	
14.04	Unib P	Frickley Athletic	152	1 - 1	Ludlow 2
16.04	Unib P	BISHOP AUCKLAND	268	1 - 1	Skelton 74
21.04	Unib P	Colwyn Bay	296	1 - 2	Robinson 67
24.04	Unib P	GATESHEAD	193	0 - 1	
26.04	N Rid SC Q2	NORTHALLERTON TOWN	104	3 - 1	Skelton 29 63, Robinson 43
28.04	Unib P	HUCKNALL TOWN	280	2 - 2	Rennison 7, Ludlow 12

PLAYING SQUAD

GOALKEEPERS: Terry Burke (Blyth)

DEFENDERS: Ian Williams (Gretna), Ben Dixon (Woodlands Wellington), David Logan (Bishop Auckland), Matthew Pitts (Workington), David Goodchild (North Ormesby), Graeme Williams (Guisborough), Graham Rennison (York)

MIDFIELDERS: Alex Gildea (Scarborough), Craig Veart (Spennymoor), Gus Di Lella (Durham), Richard Booth (Northallerton), Andy Howarth (Spennymoor), Kenny Cramman (Gateshead), Andy Hirst (Newcastle Blue Star)

FORWARDS: Lee Ure (Norton), Darren Sankey (Marske Utd), Neil Burns (Crook), Graeme Robinson (Gateshead)

WORKSOP TOWN

CLUB OFFICIALS

Chairman: **John Shuker**
Club Secretary: **Keith Illett,** 2 Mount Ave., Worksop, Notts (01909 487934)
General Manager**: Danny Hague**
Company Secretary: **L.Hood**
Press Officer: **Mel Bradley**
Commercial Manager: **Ray Lucas**

FOOTBALL MANAGEMENT TEAM

Team Manager: Paul Mitchell
Coach: Peter Rinkcavage
Physio: Graham Bacon

FACT FILE

Formed: 1861 Nickname:The Tigers
Sponsors: D.T.H. Engineers/Eyres of Worksop/Norwood Fisheries/Erriccsons

Colours: Amber & black/white/white
Change colours: Yellow/white/yellow
Midweek home matchday: Tuesday.
Reserves' League: County Sen.B.I.R. U19s: F.A.Northern Academy
Youth Teams' Lge: U21's Central Mid U18s Notts Imp.

00-01 Captain: Linden Whitehead
P.o.Y.: Gavin Smith
Leading Scorer: Kirk Jackson 41

Welcome to Sandy Lane • 2000/2001 Season
WORKSOP TOWN F.C.
Tigers
v Accrington Stanley
Saturday 5th May 2001
3.00pm
(UniBond League Premier Division)
Programme produced by Guardian Newspapers
Official Match Day Programme £1

Pages: 28-32 Price: £1
Editor: Mel Bradley (01909 500491/500500)
Local Press: Worksop Guardian, Worksop Star, Nottingham Football Post.
Local Radio: Radio Sheffield, Radio Hallam, Radio Lincoln.,Trax FM

GROUND

Babbage Way, off Sandy Lane, Worksop, Notts S80 1UJ (01909 501911).
Directions: M1 jct 31 (from north) jct 30 (from south), follow Worksop signs,join A57 and follow signs for Sandy Lane Industrial Estate - ground on left. 5mins walk from station.
Capacity: 3,000 Cover: 1,000 Seats: 900
Clubhouse: Tigers Club. Normal licensing hours. Pool, quiz nights, disco etc.
Club Shop: `The Tigershop' 30 page catalogue from Steve Jarvis, 10 Wood End Drive, Ravenshead, Notts NG15 9EJ.

PREVIOUS **Leagues:** Midland (Counties)1896-98 1900-30 49-60 61-68 69-74, Sheffield Assoc. 1898-99 1931-33, Central Comb. 33-35, Yorkshire 35-39, Central All. 47-49 60-61, Northern Premier 68-69,74-
Grounds: Netherton Road, Bridge Meadow, Central Ave. (pre 1989), The Northolme (Gainsborough Trin. - shared) 89-92.

CLUB RECORDS **Attendance:** 2,100 v Chris Waddle XI Linden Whitehead's testimonial 0 7.05.01
Goalscorer: Kenny Clark, 287 **Appearances:** Kenny Clark 347
Win: 20-0 v Staveley, 1/9/1894 **Defeat:** 1-11 v Hull City Res., 55-56.
Fee Received: £47,000 for Jon Kennedy, Sunderland May 2000 **Paid:** £5,000 for Kirk Jackson to Grantham Town, 98-99

BEST SEASON **FA Cup:** 3rd Rd: 07-08 v Chelsea (A) 1-9, 21-22 v Southend (H) 1-2, 22-23 v Spurs (A) 0-0, 0-9, 55-56 v Swindon (A) 0-1. 2nd Rd: 25-26, 1st Rd: 20-21, 26-27, 61-62, 78-79. **League Clubs defeated:** Rotherham T. 1894-95, Grimsby T. 94-95, Nelson 1921-22, Chesterfield 22-23, Coventry C. 25-26, Bradford C. 55-56. **FA Trophy**: Q,Final 1-2 v Forest Green 00-01

HONOURS N.P.L. Presidents Cup 85-86 95-96, Unibond Div One Runners-up 97-98, Unibond Premier Div. Runners-up 98-99 Sheffield Assoc. Lg 1898-99, Sheffield & Hallamshire Snr Cup 23-24 52-53 54-55 65-66 69-70 72-73 81-82 84-85 96-97, Mansfield Charity Cup 22-23; Midland Cos Lg 21-22 65-66 72-73 (R-up 62-6366-67 73-74).

Players P rogressing: J Brown (Sheff Wed), G Dale (Chesterfield 48), A Daley (Doncaster 50), K Wood (Grimsby 51), H Jarvis (Notts Co. 51), B Taylor (Leeds 51), S Rhodes 51, D Gratton 52, A Hodgkinson 53, J Harrison 67 (Sheffield Utd), S Lloyd & P Marshall (Scunthorpe 54), A Rhodes (QPR 54), R Moore (Rotherham 55), H Mosby (Crewe 56), L Moore (Derby 57), H Bowery (Nottm Forest 75), T Moore (Rochdale 84), S Adams (Scarborough 87), D Moss (Doncaster 93), Jon Kennedy (Sunderland 00), K Jackson (Darlington 01).

L-R Back Row: Chris Waddle, Phil Stafford, Gavin Smith, Steve Johnson, Jamie Holmshaw, Darren Brookes, Ian Ironside, Gary Townsend, Kenny Clark, Mickey Goddard, Kirk Jackson, John Hibbins, Graham Bacon (physio). Front Row: Scott Oxley, Carl Smith, Adam Nixon, lindon Whitehead, Richard Mason, Ryan Davis, Ryan Ludlam.

Date	Comp.	Opponents	Att.	Score	Goalscorers
19.08	Unib P	RUNCORN	553	1 - 1	Jackson 18
22.08	Unib P	Hucknall Town	820	1 - 1	Jackson 90
26.08	Unib P	DROYLSDEN	354	5 - 0	Jackson 7 31 42, Hibbins 26, Brooks 37
28.08	Unib P	GAINSBOROUGH TRINITY	737	1 - 1	Ludlam 53
02.09	Unib P	Lancaster City	429	0 - 2	
05.09	Unib P	LEEK TOWN	461	3 - 1	Jackson 45 89, Clark 60
09.09	Unib P	Accrington Stanley	929	4 - 3	Jackson 56 74, Whitehead 59, Clark 61
11.09	Unib P	Hyde United	624	3 - 1	Johnson 37, Jackson 43, Whitehead 50
16.09	Unib P	ALTRINCHAM	665	1 - 2	Clark 25
19.09	Unib P	Frickley Athletic	305	5 - 1	Johnson 10, Whitehead 32 53 75, Jackson 73
23.09	Unib P	BARROW	667	4 - 2	Townsend 25, Jackson 48 90, Whitehead 50
26.09	Unib P	FRICKLEY ATHLETIC	618	12 - 0	Davies 6, Whitehead (3), **Jackson (6**) 22p 44 75 77 79 82, Waddle 41,Clark 86
30.09	FA Cup Q2	Whitley Bay	620	1 - 2	Johnson 67
06.10	Unib P	Emley	769	3 - 5	Johnson 10, Townsend 25, Waddle 51
10.10	Unib P	WHITBY TOWN	658	3 - 2	C Smith 23, Whitehead 25, Johnson 59
14.10	Unib P	Colwyn Bay	361	2 - 3	Jackson 2 75
18.10	Unib P	Bishop Auckland	223	1 - 2	Johnson 6
21.10	Unib P	LANCASTER CITY	610	4 - 2	Smith 51, Whitehead 63, Jackson 64, Johnson 86
24.10	Unib P	Stalybridge Celtic	641	0 - 1	
31.10	Lge Cup 8	GAINSBOROUGH TRINITY	455	2 - 3	Smith 14, Brookes 34
04.11	FA Trophy 1	Paget Rangers	249	2 - 1	Jackson 20, Bettney 65
07.11	Lge Cup 8	Lincoln United	123	4 - 3	Jackson 6 33 80, Townsend 28
11.11	Sheff SC 1	OUGHTIBRIDGE WAR MEMORIAL SC	297	6 - 0	OG 22, Ludlam 28, Marsh 31, Brooks 53, Johnson 64, Townsend 70
14.11	Lge Cup 8	NORTH FERRIBY UNITED	311	1 - 1	G Smith 83
18.11	Unib P	Burscough	287	2 - 2	Whitehead 27, Jackson 51
25.11	Unib P	BLYTH SPARTANS	396	4 - 3	Whitehead 25, Jackson 30 65, Ludlam 36
28.11	Lge Cup 8	Guiseley	171	2 - 2	Townsend 57, Jackson 58
02.12	FA Trophy 2	ATHERSTONE UNITED	329	4 - 2	Jackson 12 25, Johnson 45, Whitehead 75
16.12	Sheff SC 2	FRECHEVILLE CA	292	5 - 1	McCormick 19[og], Jackson 22, Ludland 52[p], Whitehead 72,Gray 89
23.12	Unib P	Marine	351	1 - 0	Townsend 81
26.12	Unib P	Gainsborough Trinity	1084	1 - 1	Ludlam 82[p]
06.01	Unib P	Whitby Town	522	1 - 1	Gray 4
13.01	FA Trophy 3	BROMSGROVE ROVERS	586	3 - 2	Townsend 37, Ludlam 49[p]. Jackson 90
27.01	Unib P	Altrincham	718	2 - 1	Whitehead 60, Townsend 75[p]
03.02	FA Trophy 4	CONGLETON TOWN	724	6 - 2	Jackson 7 66, Whitehead 17, Johnson 24, Townsend 27[p], Smith 41
10.02	Unib P	MARINE	464	3 - 3	Jackson 7, Johnson 15, Gray 65
17.02	Unib P	Droylsden	404	5 - 2	Jackson 14 88, Whitehead 23, Ludlam 73, Smith 77
24.02	FA Trophy 5	Tiverton Town	1937	2 - 1	Jackson 4, Townsend 35
03.03	Chairman QF	Burscough	199	1 - 0	Pearce 42
06.03	Unib P	GATESHEAD	464	2 - 2	Whitehead 48, Johnson 69
10.03	FA Trophy QF	Forest Green Rovers	1448	1 - 2	Davies 89
13.03	Unib P	STALYBRIDGE CELTIC	602	1 - 1	Johnson 43
16.03	Unib P	Runcorn	209	4 - 0	Johnson 35, Townsend 71[p] 75 78
17.03	Sheff SC QF	Hemsworth Miners Welfare	402	2 - 1	Townsend 49[p], Muller 83
20.03	Unib P	BURSCOUGH	388	1 - 0	Townsend 90[p]
23.03	Unib P	EMLEY	763	1 - 2	Smith 60
27.03	Unib P	Blyth Spartans	295	0 - 1	
31.03	Unib P	BAMBER BRIDGE	430	1 - 1	Muller 16
03.04	Chairman SF	Harrogate Town	623	0 - 1	
10.04	Unib P	SPENNYMOOR UNITED	335	6 - 0	Stafford 21, Muller 47 85 86, Johnson 54, Varley 64
12.04	Unib P	Leek Town	352	3 - 0	Townsend 48 53 83
14.04	Unib P	HYDE UNITED	394	4 - 1	Townsend 21, Stafford 25, Hutchinson 39[og], Muller 81
16.04	Unib P	Spennymoor United	169	1 - 0	Stafford 65
18.04	Unib P	HUCKNALL TOWN	324	1 - 1	Townsend 36
21.04	Unib P	Gateshead	245	0 - 0	
24.04	Unib P	BISHOP AUCKLAND	272	1 - 2	Whitehead 21
26.04	Sheff SC SF	Doncaster Rovers	1397	1 - 2	
28.04	Unib P	Barrow	1216	1 - 2	Gray 20
01.05	Unib P	COLWYN BAY	317	1 - 1	Gray 26
03.05	Unib P	Bamber Bridge	220	2 - 1	Smith 19, Townsend 88
05.05	Unib P	ACCRINGTON STANLEY	428	0 - 2	

PLAYING SQUAD

GOALKEEPERS: Jamie Holmshaw (Gainsborough)

DEFENDERS: Darren Bradshaw (Stevenage), Ryan Ludlam (Sheffield Wed), Gavin Smith (Sheffield Wed), Darren Brookes (Alfreton), Richard Mason (Boston Utd)

MIDFIELDERS: Chris Waddle (Torquay), Mick Goddard (Hallam), Carl Smith (Burnley), Steve Jonhson (Buxton), Martin Diggle (Hallam), Linden Whitehead (Alfreton), Ryan Davis (Luton)

FORWARDS: Gary Townsend (Youth), Andy Womble (Belper), Andy Gray (Grantham), Kristof Kotylo (Nuneaton), Paul Eshelby (Northwich)

LEEK TOWN — Match Facts 2000-01

Date	Comp.	Opponents	Att.	Score	Goalscorers
19.08	Unib P	ACCRINGTON STANLEY	387	0 - 2	
21.08	Unib P	Hyde United	452	1 - 2	Callan 56
26.08	Unib P	Runcorn	257	1 - 0	Twigg 30
28.08	Unib P	HUCKNALL TOWN	235	0 - 0	
02.09	Unib P	BARROW	362	2 - 1	Lovatt 30, Diskin 80
05.09	Unib P	Worksop Town	461	1 - 3	Sandeman 71
09.09	Unib P	Blyth Spartans	290	0 - 0	
16.09	Unib P	MARINE	282	2 - 2	Twigg 15, Sandeman 60
23.09	Unib P	EMLEY	260	0 - 1	
30.09	FA Cup Q2	Newcastle Town	402	1 - 1	Marrow 54
03.10	FA Cup Q2 R	NEWCASTLE TOWN	397	3 - 2	Marrow 29, Callan 45, Sandeman 95
08.10	Unib P	Accrington Stanley	873	1 - 2	Whittaker 42
10.10	Unib P	Altrincham	529	1 - 1	Marrow 4
14.10	FA Cup Q3	Sudbury	425	1 - 1	Twigg 56[p]
17.10	FA Cup Q3 R	SUDBURY	281	1 - 2	Sandeman 65
21.10	Unib P	Bamber Bridge	252	0 - 1	
24.10	Staffs SC 1	Newcastle Town	102	2 - 0	Gardner 10[p], Sutton 22
28.10	Unib P	Bishop Auckland	122	1 - 3	Dunn 70[og]
04.11	FA Trophy 1	RADCLIFFE BOROUGH	217	2 - 2	Marrow 32, Houghton 38
11.11	Unib P	Gateshead	227	1 - 2	Hawtin 57
18.11	Unib P	STALYBRIDGE CELTIC	303	0 - 2	
21.11	FA Trophy 1 R	Radcliffe Borough	178	1 - 2	Marrow 5
23.11	Staffs SC 2	Shifnal Town	0	0 - 3	
25.11	Unib P	Whitby Town	229	2 - 1	Mason 30, Twigg 70
28.11	Lge Cup 9	Belper Town	131	1 - 5	Mason 40
02.12	Unib P	WHITBY TOWN	205	0 - 1	
09.12	Unib P	Burscough	165	0 - 1	
16.12	Unib P	ALTRINCHAM	327	0 - 0	
23.12	Unib P	SPENNYMOOR UNITED	212	3 - 1	Twigg 64[p] 74, Callan 65
06.01	Unib P	BLYTH SPARTANS	222	0 - 4	
13.01	Unib P	GAINSBOROUGH TRINITY	194	1 - 0	Sandeman 85
23.01	Lge Cup 9	Hucknall Town	81	0 - 3	
27.01	Unib P	Lancaster City	297	2 - 3	Woodray 3, Callan 45
30.01	Lge Cup 9	MATLOCK TOWN	107	3 - 0	Callan 14 18, Marrow 79
03.02	Unib P	BAMBER BRIDGE	202	1 - 1	Sandeman 57[p]
10.02	Unib P	Emley	378	1 - 1	Williams 2
15.02	Lge Cup 9	Eastwood Town	0	2 - 0	Callan 58, Bott 80
17.02	Unib P	Frickley Athletic	231	3 - 1	Doherty 40, Hobby 47, Poland 88
20.02	Unib P	RUNCORN	203	2 - 1	Hobby 60 80
24.02	Unib P	GATESHEAD	251	1 - 2	Hobby 14
27.02	Unib P	Hucknall Town	101	0 - 2	
03.03	Chairman QF	Chorley	207	0 - 2	
06.03	Unib P	HYDE UNITED	178	2 - 0	Callan 31 52
10.03	Unib P	Barrow	996	0 - 3	Jones 85
17.03	Unib P	FRICKLEY ATHLETIC	213	2 - 1	Whittaker 62, Davidson 82
25.03	Unib P	Droylsden	177	0 - 1	
27.03	Unib P	Stalybridge Celtic	593	2 - 1	Whittaker 8, Poland 69
31.03	Unib P	BURSCOUGH	251	4 - 0	Whittaker 3 29, Poland 70, McPherson 82
10.04	Unib P	Gainsborough Trinity	339	1 - 4	Whittaker 77
12.04	Unib P	WORKSOP TOWN	352	0 - 3	
16.04	Unib P	COLWYN BAY	241	2 - 4	Poland 2, Whittaker 35
18.04	Unib P	LANCASTER CITY	149	0 - 2	
21.04	Unib P	Marine	246	0 - 2	
26.04	Unib P	Spennymoor United	88	0 - 2	
28.04	Unib P	Colwyn Bay	318	1 - 4	Poland 90
03.05	Unib P	DROYLSDEN	255	1 - 1	Davidson 90
05.05	Unib P	BISHOP AUCKLAND	366	3 - 1	Whittaker 36, Hawtin 39, Hobby 66

SPENNYMOOR UNITED Match Facts 2000-01

Date	Comp.	Opponents	Att.	Score	Goalscorers
19.08	Unib P	Stalybridge Celtic	314	2 - 3	R Jones 67, Bowes 70
22.08	Unib P	WHITBY TOWN	232	1 - 2	Sowden 47
26.08	Unib P	BARROW	244	2 - 3	Jones 48, Forgham 71
28.08	Unib P	Emley	224	3 - 3	Bowes 1, Zand 8, Foreman 37
02.09	Unib P	COLWYN BAY	133	1 - 1	Veart 59
06.09	Unib P	Gateshead	251	0 - 4	
09.09	Unib P	Droylsden	187	1 - 4	Leonard 38
12.09	Unib P	BLYTH SPARTANS	162	1 - 2	Bellamy 1
16.09	Unib P	Burscough	189	1 - 4	Foreman 64
19.09	Unib P	GATESHEAD	164	1 - 4	Jones 40
23.09	Unib P	ALTRINCHAM	198	0 - 4	
26.09	Unib P	Whitby Town	296	3 - 3	Toman 76, Veart 82, Osborne 90
30.09	FA Cup Q2	BEDLINGTON TERRIERS	248	0 - 3	
03.10	Unib P	Blyth Spartans	271	1 - 0	Leonard
10.10	Unib P	ACCRINGTON STANLEY	160	1 - 6	Osbourne 82
14.10	Unib P	Altrincham	540	0 - 5	
21.10	Unib P	HYDE UNITED	139	3 - 0	Jones 18, Leonard 33, Zand 63
24.10	Durham CC 1	South Shields	n.k	0 - 2	
28.10	Unib P	Accrington Stanley	602	0 - 1	
04.11	FA Trophy 1	FRICKLEY ATHLETIC	125	3 - 1	Veart 8 11, Shalwell 42
11.11	Unib P	Marine	242	0 - 1	
15.11	Lge Cup 1	Gateshead	146	1 - 1	Foreman 69
18.11	Unib P	EMLEY	122	0 - 2	
21.11	Lge Cup 1	WHITBY TOWN	101	0 - 0	
25.11	Unib P	BURSCOUGH	77	0 - 2	
02.12	FA Trophy 2	Trafford	104	0 - 2	
09.12	Unib P	Hucknall Town	181	0 - 1	
19.12	Lge Cup 1	Blyth Spartans	154	1 - 3	Barton 81
23.12	Unib P	Leek Town	212	1 - 3	Harris 5
06.01	Unib P	Runcorn	214	0 - 2	
13.01	Unib P	Lancaster City	305	0 - 2	
27.01	Unib P	DROYLSDEN	146	0 - 1	
30.01	Lge Cup 1	BISHOP AUCKLAND	99	2 - 3	Williamson 61 80
03.02	Unib P	Frickley Athletic	173	0 - 2	
20.02	Unib P	FRICKLEY ATHLETIC	119	0 - 5	
06.03	Unib P	Gainsborough Trinity	302	1 - 2	Veart 52
10.03	Unib P	BAMBER BRIDGE	90	1 - 2	Williamson 21
13.03	Unib P	LANCASTER CITY	91	0 - 3	
17.03	Unib P	Bishop Auckland	260	0 - 2	
20.03	Unib P	GAINSBOROUGH TRINITY	75	0 - 3	
24.03	Unib P	Hyde United	256	0 - 4	
27.03	Unib P	Colwyn Bay	229	2 - 3	Veart 4[p], Jones 22
31.03	Unib P	STALYBRIDGE CELTIC	129	0 - 1	
10.04	Unib P	Worksop Town	335	0 - 6	
12.04	Unib P	BISHOP AUCKLAND	171	0 - 3	
14.04	Unib P	Barrow	1001	0 - 5	
16.04	Unib P	WORKSOP TOWN	169	0 - 1	
21.04	Unib P	HUCKNALL TOWN	72	0 - 1	
26.04	Unib P	LEEK TOWN	88	2 - 0	Jones 18, Swalwell 90[p]
28.04	Unib P	MARINE	97	2 - 2	Howarth 5, Bromley 58
01.05	Unib P	RUNCORN	87	2 - 0	Swalwell 31, Bromley 87
05.05	Unib P	Bamber Bridge	229	0 - 0	

DIVISION ONE FINAL LEAGUE TABLE 2000-01

		P	*W*	*D*	*L*	*F*	*A*	*W*	*D*	*L*	*F*	*A*	*Pts*
1	Bradford Park Avenue	42	14	2	5	43	19	14	3	4	40	21	89
2	Vauxhall Motors	42	13	5	3	53	20	10	5	6	42	30	79
3	Ashton United	42	12	6	3	53	22	11	3	7	38	27	78
4	Stocksbridge Park Steels	42	10	6	5	47	35	9	7	5	33	25	70
5	Trafford*	42	12	5	4	36	25	8	4	9	34	37	68
6	Belper Town	42	8	7	6	37	32	10	4	7	34	30	65
7	Witton Albion	42	10	7	4	29	20	5	9	7	22	30	61
8	Ossett Town	42	10	6	5	34	27	6	6	9	32	31	60
9	Radcliffe Borough	42	10	4	7	38	27	7	4	10	34	44	59
10	Chorley	42	7	9	5	40	34	8	5	8	31	36	59
11	Harrogate Town	42	9	6	6	39	30	6	4	11	21	40	55
12	Matlock Town	42	8	5	8	40	42	6	5	10	30	32	52
13	North Ferriby United	42	10	2	9	33	37	4	8	9	31	36	52
14	Workington	42	8	5	8	26	27	5	7	9	27	33	51
15	Lincoln United	42	11	5	5	35	25	2	7	12	25	50	51
16	Gretna	42	8	5	8	42	33	4	7	10	30	49	48
17	Guiseley	42	6	8	7	19	22	5	7	9	18	28	48
18	Kendal Town*	42	9	7	5	35	24	3	5	13	25	45	47
19	Farsley Celtic	42	7	3	11	26	31	5	8	8	27	40	47
20	Eastwood Town	42	7	5	9	21	29	6	3	12	19	34	47
21	Winsford United	42	6	8	7	35	33	7	3	11	26	37	44
22	Congleton Town	42	6	2	13	24	44	2	4	15	19	50	30

DIVISION ONE LEADING GOALSCORERS 2000-01

Lge	*Cup*	*Total*		
28	3	31	Mark Dobie	Gretna
25	4	29	Nicky Young	Vauxhall Motors
24	3	27	Andy Haward	Bradford P A
22	8	30	Steve Taylor	Matlock Town
22	6	28	Gary Hurlstone	Stocksbridge
22	4	26	Danny Mills	Chorley
21	1	22	Danny Worthington	Winsford Utd

DIVISION ONE RESULTS CHART 2000-01

		1	2	3	4	5	6	7	8	9	10	11	12	13	14	15	16	17	18	19	20	21	22
1	Ashton U	X	3-4	0-2	7-2	4-1	0-2	1-0	9-2	0-0	4-1	8-1	3-1	2-2	0-0	1-1	3-0	3-2	0-0	2-0	1-0	0-0	2-1
2	Belper T	0-4	X	0-2	1-1	3-1	4-0	2-2	0-0	1-1	1-1	3-2	3-1	3-1	2-2	0-1	4-6	1-2	0-2	1-1	4-1	2-1	2-0
3	Bradford	1-2	2-1	X	1-1	1-2	4-1	3-0	2-2	3-0	4-2	4-0	2-0	0-2	2-1	3-2	0-1	1-0	1-0	0-1	4-0	4-1	1-0
4	Chorley	2-1	1-1	2-1	X	1-1	3-1	1-4	2-2	1-1	1-0	2-2	8-1	1-1	3-2	1-1	3-3	0-1	0-3	5-5	2-0	0-1	1-2
5	Congleton	0-1	1-4	0-2	2-4	X	2-0	1-3	2-1	3-1	1-3	2-0	0-0	2-1	1-4	2-1	0-1	0-3	2-6	0-2	1-2	2-2	0-3
6	Eastwood	2-1	0-0	0-1	0-2	1-0	X	1-1	4-1	0-1	0-2	2-0	0-0	0-4	3-1	0-2	2-1	0-2	2-2	0-4	1-0	1-2	2-2
7	Farsley C	0-3	2-3	0-3	0-1	1-0	0-0	X	2-0	0-1	1-1	1-2	3-1	1-2	1-1	3-2	1-3	1-2	1-0	1-2	2-3	3-0	2-1
8	Gretna	1-1	1-2	0-1	0-2	5-1	0-1	3-3	X	1-1	2-0	4-3	2-3	2-0	5-4	1-0	3-2	1-1	7-1	1-2	1-1	1-2	1-2
9	Guiseley	1-2	1-1	0-0	0-1	0-1	0-2	1-1	0-0	X	1-0	0-0	3-2	0-4	1-1	0-3	4-1	1-1	0-1	1-1	3-0	1-0	1-0
10	Harrogate	3-2	3-1	1-2	3-0	5-1	3-0	0-3	2-2	1-1	X	0-3	5-0	2-1	1-0	0-4	2-2	1-1	4-1	1-2	2-2	0-2	0-0
11	Kendal T	4-3	2-2	0-1	3-0	4-0	1-1	0-2	0-1	1-1	0-0	X	1-0	2-0	2-2	2-2	1-0	3-2	1-2	3-1	1-2	2-2	2-0
12	Lincoln U	1-2	1-0	2-2	1-4	2-1	1-0	2-0	3-1	3-1	0-1	1-0	X	0-1	2-1	1-0	2-0	1-2	2-2	4-4	1-1	3-0	2-2
13	Matlock T	0-1	3-2	1-4	0-3	4-2	0-4	2-2	7-0	2-0	3-1	3-3	2-1	X	2-2	1-0	3-2	1-2	1-4	0-3	1-2	2-2	2-2
14	N Ferriby	1-3	1-2	2-1	0-3	2-1	2-0	2-1	2-6	1-0	4-1	2-2	3-1	2-1	X	2-0	1-2	2-2	1-3	3-2	0-3	0-2	0-1
15	Ossett T	0-3	3-0	1-1	3-3	1-1	2-0	2-0	0-0	2-1	1-2	2-1	1-2	1-0	0-3	X	5-2	1-1	3-1	1-3	3-2	0-0	2-1
16	Radcliffe	2-3	1-2	1-2	3-2	3-1	1-0	0-1	2-1	0-1	3-0	1-0	2-2	1-1	4-0	5-6	X	1-1	2-0	1-0	1-2	0-0	4-2
17	St'bridge	2-2	0-4	0-3	2-2	3-1	4-1	6-0	4-1	4-2	0-0	2-1	3-3	3-2	0-2	3-3	1-2	X	1-2	1-0	2-1	5-2	1-1
18	Trafford	3-1	1-0	1-3	1-0	2-0	0-1	2-2	1-0	1-1	4-1	2-2	1-0	1-2	1-1	2-1	2-2	3-1	X	2-1	3-1	2-1	1-4
19	Vauxhall	0-2	3-1	2-0	5-0	3-0	1-1	4-0	3-2	1-6	8-1	1-0	2-2	3-2	0-1	2-2	1-1	1-2	4-2	X	2-0	1-1	4-0
20	Winsford U	1-0	1-2	1-2	2-0	2-2	2-3	5-0	3-3	0-3	2-0	1-3	2-2	4-1	1-1	0-0	1-2	0-3	3-2	2-2	X	0-0	2-2
21	Witton Alb	1-1	0-1	5-2	0-0	0-0	3-1	0-0	1-4	1-0	0-1	2-0	2-1	2-2	1-0	2-0	3-1	1-1	2-0	1-4	1-0	X	1-1
22	Workington	2-0	0-1	2-5	2-0	3-2	1-0	2-2	0-1	0-1	0-3	2-0	2-2	0-0	4-2	0-1	2-0	2-1	0-0	0-2	1-3	1-1	X

ASHTON UNITED

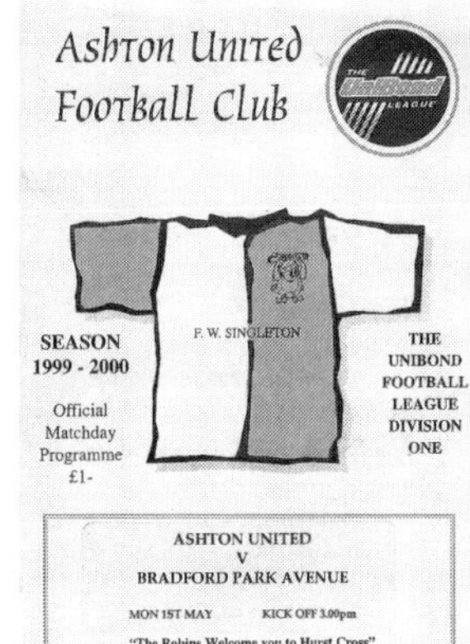

CLUB OFFICIALS

Chairman: Terry Styring
President: R.Thomasson
Vice Chairman: J Milne
Secretary:Stuart Jones
217 Rose Hill Road,Ashton-under-Lyne,Lancs. OL6 8HT. H/Fax: 01613441170
Mobile; 07788 613608
Press Officer: S.Howe

FOOTBALL MANAGEMENT TEAM

Manager: Gerry Quinn
Physio: Chris Moseley

FACT FILE

Formed: 1878
Club Sponsors: T.B.A.
Nickname: Robins
Colours: Red & white halves/black/red
Change colours: All yellow
Midweek matchday: Tuesday
Website: www.aufc4.freeserve.co.uk

PROGRAMME
Pages: 22 Price: £1
Editor:Ken & Steve Lee
Local Press: Ashton Reporter, Ashton Advertiser Local Radio: GMR

GROUND Surrey Street, Hurst Cross, Ashton-u-Lyne OL6 8DY. Tel; 0161339 4158. (office) 01613 301511 (Social Club). Fax 0161 339 4158

Directions: M62 jct 20, A627(M) to Oldham, keep in right hand 2 lanes, leave at Ashton sign after 2 miles passing Belgrade Hotel, take A627 at next island,keep in left lane and take slip road signed Ashton-under-Lyme, at island follow Stalybridge/Park Road sign, go straight ahead for 3 miles to ground at Hurst Cross. BR to Charles Street (Ashton), or Stalybridge. Buses 331, 332, 337, 408(Ashton-Stalybridge) all pass ground

Capacity: 4,500 Seats: 250 Cover: 750

Clubhouse: Open 11am-11pm. Refreshment bar open matchdays

Club Shop: Yes - contact Ken or Steve Lee (0161 330 9800)

PREVIOUS **Leagues:** Manchester; Lancs Comb 12-23, 48-64, 66-68; Midland 64-66; Cheshire Co. 23-48, 68-82; Nth West Count 82-92.
Name: Hurst 1878-1947. Ground: Rose Hill 1878-1912

CLUB RECORDS **Attendance:** 11,000 v Halifax Town, FA Cup First Round 1952.
Scorer: Mark Edwards, 37 **Appearances:** Micky Boyle, 462.
Win: 11-3 v Staylbridge Manchester Interm Cup 55 **Defeat:** 11-1 v Wellington Town Cheshire Lge 46-47.
Fee Paid: £9,000 for Andy Whittaker (Netherfield, 1994) **Fee Received:** £15,000 for Karl Marginson (Rotherham, Mar. 1993)

BEST SEASON **FA Trophy**: Qtr Final v Dagenham (0-1) (A0 96-97
FA Cup: 1st Rd replay 52-53, 1-2 v Halifax T (A), after 1-1. Also 1st Rd 55-56, 1-6 v Southport (A)

HONOURS Northern Prem Lge Div 1 Cup 94-95; Manchester Sen Cup 1884-85 13-14 75-76 77-78; Manchester Lge 11-12; Lancs Comb. Div 2 60-61 (Lge Cup 62-63);Manchester Prem. Cup 79-80 82-83 92-93; North West Counties Lge 91-92;Challenge Cup 91-92, Div 2 87-88; Floodlit League 90-91; Challenge Shield 92-93; Manchester Chall Shield 35-36 38-39 49-50 53-54 (R-up 34-35 39-40), Manchester Interm Cup 58-59 62-63 65-66, R-up 60-61 64-65; Manchester Jnr Cup 1894-95 10-12 32-33; Unifilla Div 1 Cup 96-97,98-99

Players progressing: A Ball (Blackpool), J Mahoney (Stoke C.), B Daniels(Manchester C.), R Jones (Rotherham U.), A Arrowsmith (Liverpool), N Stiffle(Crystal Palace), K Marginson (Rotherham U), P Wilson (Plymouth Argyle)

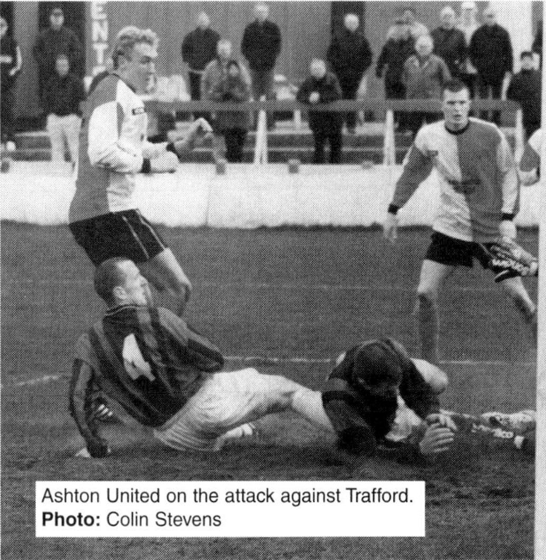

Ashton United on the attack against Trafford.
Photo: Colin Stevens

BELPER TOWN

CLUB OFFICIALS

Chairman: **Phil Varney**
President: **Alan Benfield**
Secretary: **Bryan Rudkin**
121 Marsh Lane, Belper, Derbys, DE56 1GU. Tel: 01773 827091 Mobile: 07710 444195
Press Officer: **Nigel Oldrini**

FOOTBALL MANAGEMENT TEAM

Manager: Martin Rowe
Asst Manager/ Coach: Graham Reiter

FACT FILE

Formed: 1883
Nickname: Nailers
Colours: Yellow/black/black & yellow
Change colours: All white
Midweek home matchday: Tuesday
Reserves' League: Midlands Reg All

2000-2001

Captain:Craig Weston
P.o.Y.: Sean Gummer
Top scorer: Carl Cunningham 22

Pages: 36 Price £1.00
Editor:Mark Allington 01773 826057
Local Press: Belper News, Derby Evening Telegraph, Belper Express
Local Radio: BBC Radio Derby

GROUND

Address: Christchurch Meadow, Bridge Street, Belper DE56 1BA (01773825549).
Directions: From M1 North, Jnct 28 onto A38 towards Derby, turn off at A610 (Ripley/Nottingham), then 4 exit at roundabout towards Ambergate. At junction with A6 (Hurt Arms Hotel) left to Belper. Ground on right past traffic lights. 400 yards from Belper (BR)
Capacity: 2,640 Cover: 1,000 Seats: 200
Clubhouse: Open matchdays and for functions with bar and hot and cold food available.

PREVIOUS
Leagues: Central Alliance 57-61; Midland Co's 61-82, Northern Counies East 1982-87
Grounds: Acorn Ground prior to 1951
Names: None

CLUB RECORDS
Attendance: 3,200 v Ilkeston Town, 1955
Goalscorer: Mick Lakin 231
Appearances: Gil Rhodes
Fee Received: #2,000 for Craig Smith from Hinckley United
Fee Paid: Nil.
Victory: 15-2 v Nottingham Forest 'A'1956
Defeat: 0-12 v Goole Town 1965

BEST SEASON
FA Vase: Semi-final 94-95**FA Amateur Cup:** Not entered
FA Trophy: 3rd Qual Rd 97-98
FA Cup: 1st Rd Prop 1887-88 (4th Qual. Rnd 1964-65,00-01)

HONOURS
Northern Counties East Lge 84-85, Midland Counties Lg 79-80; Central Alliance Lge 58-59; Derbys Snr Cup 58-59 60-61 62-63 79-80

Players progressing: None

Back row, left to right: N.Broadhurs, C.Payne, A. Quy. D.Smith. R.Mayes, M.Lawson, M.Wood, and S.Kennedy. C.Wilson,
Front Row: D.Turner, C.Cunningham, L.Handbury, C.Weston, B.Morgan,and R.Butler

CHORLEY

CLUB OFFICIALS

Chairman: Jack Kirkland

Commercial Manager: T.B.A.

Secretary / Press Officer:
Mick Wearmouth
6 Avondale Rd, Chorley, Lancs. PR7 2ED
Tel: 01257 271395

FOOTBALL MANAGEMENT TEAM

Manager: Ken Wright

FACT FILE

Formed: 1883
Nickname: The Magpies
Sponsors: Coloroll.
Colours:
White & black stripes/black/black & white
Change colours: All yellow
Midweek matchday: Tuesday
Reserve League: Alliance League

2000-01
Leading goalscorer: Danny Mills 26
Captain: Paul Fleming
P.o.Y.: Danny Mills

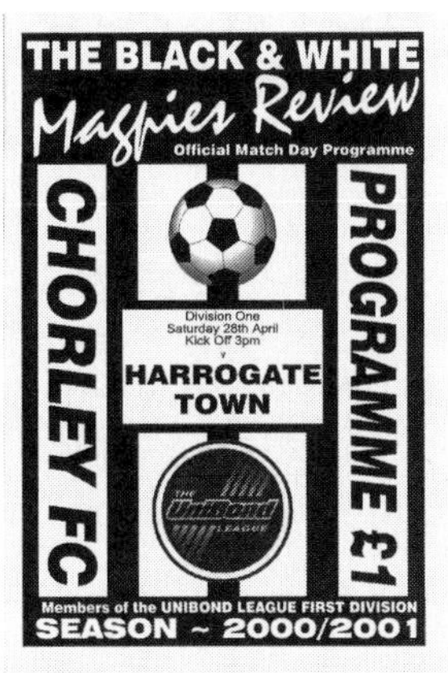

THE BLACK & WHITE
Magpies Review
Official Match Day Programme
CHORLEY FC
PROGRAMME £1
Division One
Saturday 28th April
Kick Off 3pm
v
HARROGATE TOWN
Members of the UNIBOND LEAGUE FIRST DIVISION
SEASON ~ 2000/2001

Pages: 32 Price: £1.
Editor: Mike Neild
Local Press: Lancs Evening Post, Chorley Guardian.
Local Radio: Radio Lancs.

GROUND Victory Park, Duke Street, Chorley, Lancs
Tel: 01257 263406

Directions: M61 jct 6, A6 to Chorley, going past Yarrow Bridge Hotel on Bolton Rd turn left at 1st lights into Pilling Lane, 1st right into Ashley St..,ground 2nd left. From M6; jct 27, follow signs to Chorley, left at lights,continue for 2 1/2 miles on A49, right onto B5251, on entering Chorley turn right into Duke Street 200yds after Plough Hotel. 1/4 mile from Chorley (BR).

Capacity: 4,100 Cover: 2,800 Seats: 900

Clubhouse: 01257 275662. Open every evening. Weekend entertainment, Snacks available

Club Shop: Yes.

PREVIOUS Leagues: Lancs Alliance 1890-94; Lancs 94-1903; Lancs Comb. 03-68, 69-70;Northern Premier 68-69, 70-72, 82-88; Cheshire County 72-82; GMV Conference 88-90.
Grounds: Dole Lane 1883-1901; Rangletts Park 01-05; St George's Park 05-20. Name: None

CLUB RECORDS **Attendance:** 9,679 v Darwen, 1931-32. **Goalscorer:** Peter Watson.
Fee Paid: Undisclosed to Marine for Brian Ross 1995. **Fee Received:** £22,500 for Paul Mariner (Plymouth, 1973).

BEST SEASON **FA Cup:** 2nd Rd 86-87 (lost in replay at Preston), 90-91 (lost at Shrewsbury). **FA Trophy:** Semi-Final 1995-96.

HONOURS Northern Premier Lg 87-88, Cheshire Co. Lg 75-76 76-77 81-82, Lancs Comb. 19-2022-23 27-28 28-29 32-33 33-34 45-46 59-60 60-61 63-64 (R-up 21-22 26-27 48-4962-63 64-65 65-66, Lg Cup 24-25 58-59 62-63), Lancs Lg 1896-97 98-99, Lancs Alliance 1892-93 (R-up 94-95), Lancs Jnr Cup 1894-95 1908-09 23-24 39-40 45-4657-58 58-59 60-61 63-64 64-65 75-76 79-80 81-82 82-83.

Players Progressing: Charles Ashcroft (Liverpool 1946),William Healey (Arsenal 49), Stan Howard (Huddersfield 52), Derek Hogg (Leicester 52), William Norcross (Southport 59), Micky Walsh (Blackpool 71),Paul Mariner (Plymouth 73), Graham Barrow (Wigan 76), Steve Galliers (Wimbledon77), Kevin Tully (Bury 80), Geoff Twentyman (Preston 83), Gary Buckley (Bury84), Chris Hunter (Preston 84).

Chorley on the attack against Ashton United.
Photo: Colin Stevens.

EASTWOOD TOWN

CLUB OFFICIALS

Chairman: **George Belshaw**
Vice Chairman: **Roy Cheatle**
President:
Secretary / Press Officer: **Paddy Farrell**
7 Primrose Rise, Newthorpe,
Notts.NG16 2BB Tel/Fax: 01773 786186

FOOTBALL MANAGEMENT TEAM
Manager: Bryan Chambers
Ass.Manager: Coach:
Physio: Paul Smith

FACT FILE
Formed: 1953
Nickname: The Badgers
Sponsors: Hayley Conference Centres
Colours: Black & white stripes/black/black
Change Colours: Yellow/blue/yellow
Midweek matchday: Tuesday
Club's EMAIL : patriciafarrell@barbox.net

2000-2001
Captain & P.o.Y.: Paul Gould
Top Goalscorer: Mark Smith 12

EASTWOOD TOWN FOOTBALL CLUB
MAIN SPONSOR
HAYLEY
CONFERENCE CENTRES
UNIBOND DIVISION ONE
HAYLEY
CONFERENCE CENTRES
EASTWOOD TOWN
v
CONGLETON TOWN
Saturday 31st March, 2001
Kick-off 3pm
OFFICIAL PROGRAMME
Price £1

Pages: 50 Price: £1.00
Editor: Paddy Farrell 01773786186

Local Press: Eastwood Advertiser
Nottingham Evening Post, Derby Telegraph
Local Radio: Radio Nottingham, Radio Trent

GROUND Coronation Park, Eastwood, Notts. Tel: 01773 715823

Directions: From North - M1 jct 27, follow Heanor signs via Brinsley to lights in Eastwood. Turn left then first right after Fire Station - ground entrance on Chewton Street. From South - M1 jct 26, A610 to Ripley, leave at 1st exit(B6010), follow to Eastwood, left at lights, first left at `Man in Space' -ground entrance on Chewton Street. Nearest station - Langley Mill. Buses every10 mins (R11, R12 or R13) from Victoria Centre, Nottingham - approx 40 mins

Capacity: 5,500 Cover: 1,150 Seats: 650

Clubhouse: Social club open normal licensing hours (Sat 11am-11pm, midweek matches 6.30-11pm). Hot & cold food available. Steward; Richard James (01773715823)

Club Shop: Sells programmes, mugs, scarves, badges etc. Contact R K Storer - 0115 9199596

PREVIOUS **Leagues:** Notts Alliance 53-61; Central Alliance 61-67; East Midlands 67-71; Midland Counties 71-82; N.C.E. 82-87.
Names: None -predecessors Eastwood Collieries disbanded in 1953
Ground: Coronation Park 1953-65 - previous pitch now town bowling green

CLUB RECORDS **Attendance:** 2,723 v Enfield, FA Amateur Cup, February 1965.
Goalscorer: Martin Wright. Appearances: Arthur Rowley, over 800 1st team games, but not a single booking, 1955-76
Win: 21-0 v Rufford Colliery 26/10/54 & Ilkeston Town 10/5/69 **Defeat:** 0-8 v Hucknall Town (a) 13/02/01
Fee Paid: £500 for Jamie Kay, Gainsborough Trin.90-91 **Fee Received:** £72,500 for Richard Liburd, Middlesbrough 92-93

BEST SEASON **FA Amateur Cup:** Third Round replay 1967-68. **FA Trophy:** First Round1978-79
FA Cup: 1st Round Proper 99-00, v Exeter City (A)

HONOURS Northern Counties (East) Lg R-up 82-83 84-85; Midland Counties Lg 75-76(R-up 74-75 77-78), Lg Cup 77-78 79-80; Central Alliance 63-64 (R-up 64-65);Notts Alliance 56-57 (R-up 53-54 54-55 55-56 57-58 58-59 59-60), Lg Cup 55-56;East Midlands Lg R-up 68-69; Notts Senior Cup (winners 9 and R-up 5);Evans Halshaw Floodlit Cup 94-95R-up 89-90 97-98; Notts Intermediate Cup 86-87;98-99.99-00 Ripley Hospital Charity Cup(6)76-81.Mid Regional All (Prem) 99-00 R-up 97-8,98-9

Players progressing: J Butler (Notts Co 57), A Woodcock A Buckley Andrew Todd (Nottm F), P Richardson (Derby), S Buckley (Luton), R Liburd (Middlesbrough 92-93), Martin Bullock (Barnsley 94-95), Neil Illman (Plymouth 95-96), Lee Marshall (Scunthorpe 97), Glenn Kirkwood(Donc"ter

L-R back Row: Richard Smith, Jay Bonser, Dwayne Soar, Kevin Mabon, Martyn Chadbourne, Gary Breach, James Dooley, Chris Bradshaw. Front Row: Gary Castledine, Nick Kennerdale, Gary Sucharewyck, Paul Gould (capt.), Danny Bryant, Mark Smith, Gavin Worboys.

FARSLEY CELTIC

CLUB OFFICIALS

Chairman: **John E. Palmer**
Vice Chairman:
Secretary: **Mrs. Margaret Lobley**
29 Spring Bank Road, Farsley, Leeds, West Yorks LS28 5LS
Tel: 01132 575675

FOOTBALL MANAGEMENT TEAM

Manager: Martin Haresign
Assistant Manager: Steve Learoyd
Coach: John Deacy

FACT FILE

Formed: 1908
Nickname: Villagers
Colours: Sky & navy/navy/navy
Change colours: All white
Midweek home matchday: Wednesday
Reserves' League: N.C.E.Res. Div

2000-01

Captain: Paul Stevenson
Top scorers :Ian Blackstone & Robbie Whellans both 21
P.o.Y.: Lee Connor

Follow the Celts
Official Programme £1.20
Farsley Celtic A.F.C.
Throstle Nest
V
Winsford United
10th March 2001

Pages: 32 Price £1
Editor: Howard Stevenson

Local Press: Yorkshire Evening Post, Telegraph & Argus, Pudsey Times
Local Radio: Radio Leeds, Radio Aire, Radio Pennine

GROUND: Throstle Nest, Newlands, Farsley, Pudsey, Leeds LS28 5BE
Club Email: phil@yorkshirefolk.fsnet.co.uk Tel: 01532 561517
Directions: From North East: A1 south to Wetherby, A58 to Leeds, at 1st island (approx 8 miles) take 3rd exit (A6120 ring-rd), follow Bradford signs to 12th r'bout (approx 12 miles) - 1st exit (B6157 Stanningley). From M62 jct 26, M606 (Bradford) to r'bout, 4th exit (A6177) passing McDonalds on left, continue on Rooley Lane - Sticker Lane passing Morrisons store on left to lights (approx 3 miles) - right onto A647 (Leeds) to 2nd r'bout, 2nd exit (B6157 Stanningley). Continue 800yds passing Police & Fire Stations on left.Turn left down New Street at Tradex warehouse before turning right into Newlands. Ground at bottom of road. One mile from New Pudsey (BR)
Capacity: 4,000 Cover: 1,000 Seats: 430
Clubhouse: Lounge, games room and committee room Open every evening and Friday and weekend lunchtimes. New multi-purpose Leisure Centre available evenings and afternoons
Club Shop: League & non-League progs & magazines. Club badges, scarves,ties, sweaters, training suits, polo & T-shirts. Various souvenirs & photos. Contact: Brian Falkingham, 27 Rycroft Ct., Leeds LS13 4PE. 0113 255 0749 e-mail: clubshop@breathemail.net

PREVIOUS **Leagues:** West Riding County Amateur; Leeds Red Triangle; Yorkshire 49-82; Northern Counties East 82-87
Grounds: Red Lane, Farsley; Calverley Lane, Farsley (prior to 1948)

CLUB RECORDS **Attendance:** 11,000 (at Elland Road) v Tranmere Rovers, FA Cup 1st Rd 1974

BEST SEASON **FA Amateur Cup:** Third Round, 34-35
FA Cup: 1st Rd 74-75 (see above). Lost 0-2. **FA Vase:** Quarter Final 87-88

HONOURS West Riding County Cup 57-58 59-60 66-67 70-71 83-84 87-88 95-96 96-97 00-01; Yorkshire League 59-60 68-69 (R-up 57-58 58-59 70-71 71-72); Div 2 51-52;League Cup 62-63 63-64 66-67 96-97

Players progressing: Barry Smith (Leeds 1951), Paul Madeley (Leeds 1962),William Roberts (Rochdale 1988), Stuart McCall (Bradford City)

Back Row,left to right: Steve Learoyd (Assistant Manager), Lee Connors, Andy Shields, Andy Cygan, Martin Regan, Liam Sutclliffe, Ian Blackstone, Paul Stevenson,Wayne Noteman, John Palmer (Chairman), Martin Haresign, Ian McCreedy (Physio)
Front Row: Damien Place, Wes Freeman, Phil Turner, Robbie Wellans, Steve Perrin , Richard Hepworth and John Deacy (coach)

GRETNA

CLUB OFFICIALS

Chairman: **Brian Fulton**

President: **Thomas Kerr**

Secretary: **Ron MacGregor**
Brackenhurst, Lochmaben, Lockerbie, Scotland DG111QA (01387 811820)

FOOTBALL MANAGEMENT TEAM

Manager: Rowan Alexander
Ass.Manager: Derek Frye
Physio: William Bentley

FACT FILE

Formed: 1946
Nickname: Black & whites
Club colours:
Black & white hoops/black/black & white
Change colours: All maroon (b & w trim)
Midweek matchday: Tuesday
Reserves' league: Carlisle & District

2000-2001

Captain: Mark Dobie
Po.Y & Top Scorer : Mark Dobie (31)

Pages: 28 Price: 80p
Editor: R MacGregorTel: 01387 811820

Local Press : Cumberland News
Evening News & Star ,Dumfries & Galloway Standard Local Radio: C.F.M.; Radio Cumbria,West Sound Radio,BBC Solway

GROUND Raydale Park, Dominion Rd., Gretna, Dumfriesshire
Tel: 01461 337602

Directions: 8 miles north of Carlisle on A74. Take slip road to Gretna over border bridge, left at Crossways Inn for Township along Annan Rd for quarter of a mile, left into Dominion Rd, ground on right. Buses leave Carlisle on the half hour. Also trains from Carlisle

Capacity: 2,200 Cover: 800 Seats: 385

Clubhouse: Bar in ground-visitors most welcome.

Club Shop: Yes, contact Alan Watson 01387 251550, matchdays & postal sales

PREVIOUS **Leagues:** Dumfriesshire Amateur 46-47; Carlisle & District 47-51;Cumberland 51-52; Northern 83-92

CLUB RECORDS **Attendance:** 2,307 v Rochdale, F.A. Cup First Round Proper,16/11/91.
Scorer: Denis Smith **Appearances:** William Cross
Win: 20-0 v Silloth 62-63 **Defeat:** 2-9 v Ashton United Div. 1 2000-01
Fee Received: £10,000 from Queen of the South for Derek Townsley 96

BEST SEASON **FA Trophy:** 2nd Rd 84-85 88-89 90-91 93-94
FA Cup: 1st Rd Prop 91-92 (lost 1-3 in replay at Rochdale) & 93-94 (lost 2-3 to Bolton Wanderers)
FA Vase: 2nd Rd 80-81 83-84

HONOURS Northern Lg 90-91 91-92 (Lg Cup 90-91); Cumberland Senior Cup (9); JR Cleator Cup 89-90 90-91 91-92; Craven Cup 91-92; Carlisle & Dist. Lg (28)(Charity Shield (25), Lg Cup (20); Benevolent Cup (15)

Players progressing: John Hamilton (Hartlepool Utd) 1982, Russell Black &Don Peattie (Sheffield Utd) 1984, Mark Dobie (Cambridge Utd) derek Townsley (Queen of South,Motherwell),Craig Potts (Queen of South)

L-R Back Row: Billy Bentley (physio), Derek Frye (asst. manager), Kane Young, Micky Waller, Mark Dobie, Henry Smith, Phil Coxall, Richard Close, David Mawson, Rowan Alexander (manager). Front Row: jimmy Brown, Ryan Errington, Stephen Skinner, Craig Irving, Matty Lea, Lee Armstrong, Rodney Patterson. Photo: Alan Watson.

GUISELEY

CLUB OFFICIALS

Chairman: **Philip Rogerson**

Secretary: **Bruce Speller**
71 Oxford Avenue, Guiseley,
Leeds LS20 9BY
Tel: 01943 874534
Email: bruce.speller@virgin.net
Club Website: www.guiseleyafc.co.uk

Press Officer: **John Martin**
Tel: 01943 879473
Directors: P. Rogerson, S.Allen

FACT FILE

Formed: 1909 Sponsors: OHS Ltd.
Cols:White/navy/white Change:Yellow/Navy
Midweek home matchday: Monday
Reserves' League: Lancashire League

2000-01

Leading goalscorer: Andrew Shuttleworth 8
Captain: Andy Williams
P.o.Y.: Andy Williams

FOOTBALL MANAGEMENT TEAM

Manager: Neil Parsley
Assistant Manager: Phil Sharpe
Physio: John Rhodes

GROUND: Nethermoor, Otley Road, Guiseley, Leeds LS20 8BT
Tel: 0943 873223

Directions: Via M1 to M62 jct 28, follow Airport signs to junction of A65 at Horsforth. R-about turn left onto A65 through Rawdon to Guiseley centre. Ground 1/4 mile past traffic lights, on the right,entrance on A65 opposite Silver Cross factory. Further car parking available,frst right after ground, off Ings Crescent. 5 mins walk from Guiseley (BR/Metro) station.

Capacity: 3,000 Cover: 1,040 Seats: 427

Clubhouse: Open before and after all games (closes 11pm). Tel: 01943 872872
Snack bar within ground open before and during matches.

Club Shop: Sells programmes, various items of clothing, key rings, badges, mugs etc.
Phone Jennifer Rogerson 01943 879236

Programme
Pages: 40 Price: £1
Editor: T.B.A.

Local Press: Yorkshire Evening Post, Bradford Telegraph & Argus, Airedale &Wharfedale Observer, Wharfe Valley Times.

PREVIOUS **Leagues:** West Riding Co. Amtr; West Yorks; Yorkshire 68-82; Northern Co's East82-91.

CLUB RECORDS **Attendance:** 2,486 v Bridlington Town, FA Vase Semi Final 1st Leg 89-90.

BEST SEASON **FA Cup:** First Round Proper 1994-95, 1-4 v Carlisle Utd. (at Valley Parade); 99-00, v Forest Green Rov. (A)
FA Vase: Winners 1990-91 (R-up 91-92, S.F. 94-95).
FA Trophy: Semi-Final 1994-95.

HONOURS FA Vase 90-91 (R-up 91-92), Northern Premier Lg Div 1 94-95 (Presidents Cup 94-95, Div 1 Cup 92-93), Northern Counties (East) Lg 90-91 (Lg Cup 90-91), West Riding County Cup(5 inc 94-95), Yorkshire Lg R-up 79-80 81-82 (Lg Cup 79-80).

Players Progressing: Keith Walwyn (York City), Frank Harrison (Halifax Town),Dean Walling (Carlisle United), Richard Annan (Crewe Alexandra). Dave Hanson (Halifax Town), Geoff Horsfield (Birmingham City)

Back Row Left - Right: Ryan Senior, Dave Henry, Peter Myers, Simon Trevitt, Tom Morgan, Gary Strodder (Capt.), James Nettleton, Benn Gallagher, Matt Daly, Colin Hogarth, Andrew Shuttleworth.
Front: Jermaine Manners, David Cooke, Simon Phillips, Neil Parsley (Player/Manager), Danny Walsh, Kevin Newhouse, Phil Sharpe (Assistant Manager). Photo: Darren Thomas

HARROGATE TOWN

CLUB OFFICIALS
Chairman: Bill Fotherby
President: Leslie Silver
Club/Company Secretary
Brian Russell 24 Hall Lane, Harrogate, HG13DK Tel/Fax: 01423 525341
General Secretary: Roy Dalby
123a Dene Park, Harrogate, HG14JX
Managing Director: Nigel Pleasants
Director of Football: Michael Hennigan

FOOTBALL MANAGEMENT TEAM
Team Manager: **John Reed**
Player/Coach: Neil Aspin

FACT FILE
Formed: 1919
Nickname: Town
Colours: Yellow/black/yellow
Change colours:Blue/white/blue
Midweek home matchday: Tuesday

2000-01
Leading goalscorer: Craig Elliott 17
Captain: Scott Bairstow
Supporter's P.O.Y: Chris Hudson
Players' P.O.Y: Chris Hill

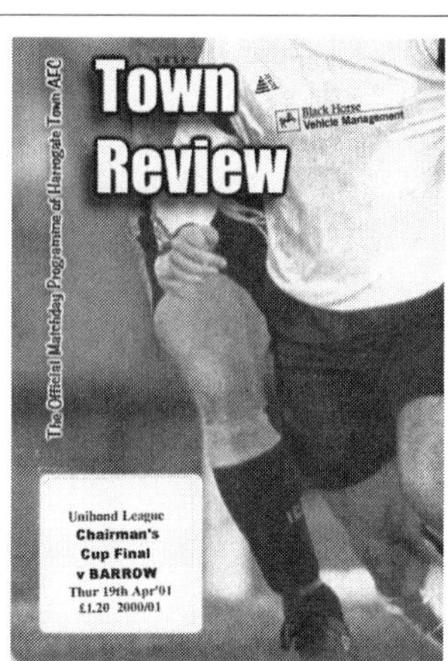

Pages: 32 Price: £1.20
Editor: Bob Head
01423 549153 - 07799 834918M
Local Press: Yorkshire Post Group
Harrogate Advertiser Series
Local Radio: Radio Leeds, Radio York
Stray FM.

GROUND: Wetherby Road, Harrogate.Tel:01423 883671 Clubhse, 01423 880675 Office&Fax Sec.& Admin.Tel. & Fax: 01423 525341 Website:www.harrogatetownafc.co.uk

Directions: From Leeds turn right at traffic lights (Appleyard's) into Hookstone Road, continue to Woodlands Hotel (traffic lights) turn left into Wetherby Road, ground on the right. From Harrogate (BR), turn left and left again, cross road (Odeon Cinema), proceed for about 400yds to main road, crossover to The Stray (open land) using footpath which leads to Wetherby Rd, ground 200yds on left.
From the West on A59 straight on to Wetherby Rd from Empress roundabout. ground on left.
From North: A59 exit from M1 then southern bypass to Wetherby Rd
Capacity: 3,800 Cover: 900 Seats: 450
Clubhouse: On ground, open every match day and for functions & special events.
Club Shop: Variety of souvenirs (Phil Harrison- 01423 525211)

PREVIOUS **Names:** Harrogate FC1919-32, Harrogate Hotspurs 35-48 **Ground:** Starbeck Lane 1919-20
Leagues: West Riding 1919-20 Yorkshire 20-21, 22-31, 57-82; Midland 21-22; Northern 31-32; Harrogate & District 35-37 West Yorkshire 46-57; Northern Counties East 82-87

CLUB RECORDS **Attendance:** 4,280 v Railway Athletic, Whitworth Cup final 1950.
Win: 13-0 v Mackllefield **Defeat:** 1-10 v Methley United 1956

BEST SEASON **FA Vase:** 4th Round 89-90 **FA Cup:** 3rd Qual. Rd Replay 87-88 (0-2 at Bishop Auckland after 1-1 draw)
F.A.Trophy: 3rd Rd Replay v Spennymoor United 99-00

HONOURS Northern Premier Lge Div 1 Cup 89-90; Northern Counties (East) Div 1(Nth) R-up 84-85 plus 3rd 85-86 & promoted (Reserve Div 85-86, Reserve Div Cup 86-87); Yorkshire League Div 1 26-27 R-up 62-63 Div 2 81-82, Div 3 R-up 71-72 80-81; West Riding County Cup 62-6372-73 85-86; West Riding Challenge Cup 24-25 26-27

Players progressing: Tony Ingham (Leeds 47), Stewart Ferebee (York C. 79),Tim Hotte (Halifax T. 85), Andy Watson (Halifax T. 88), Ian Blackstone(York C. 95) , Eric Stephenson (Leeds United1932)

Back Row: Rob Hunter (Asst. Manager), Eamonn Elliott, Gary Shaw, Chris Hubson, Chris Hill, Gavin Kelly, Paul Allen, Dave Merris, Lee Poole, Lee Beeton, Richard Scarth (Physio), Peter Gunby (Coach). **Front:** Andy Toman, Steve Osborne, Nigel Smith, Scott Bairstow (capt), Dave Fell (Manager), Bill Fotherby (Chairman), Danny Spence, Iain Dunn, Jason Ryan, Peter Atkinson.

KENDAL TOWN

CLUB OFFICIALS

Chairman: **David Willan**
President: **M Macklin**
Secretary: **Dale Brotherton**
Lime House, Holme Hill, Dalston, Carlisle.
CA5 7DH (Mobile 07977 759903)
Secretary: **Craig Campbell**
34 High Sparrowmire, Kendal Cumbria LA9 5PD
01539 725557 (H)
Press Officer: **Peter Savage** (01539 726488)

FOOTBALL MANAGEMENT TEAM

Manager:Mick Hoyle
Asst Manager: Keith Galley
Physio: Stan Casey

FACT FILE

F ormed: 1920
Nickname: The Field
Colours:
Black & white stripes/black/black
Change colours:
Yellow/blue/yellow
Midweek home matchday: Tuesday

GROUND Parkside Road, Kendal, Cumbria Tel: 01539 727472

Directions: M6 junction 36, follow signs for Kendal (South), right at lights,left at r-bout to `K' Village - Parkside Rd on right opposite factory main offices - ground 400 yds. A mile & a half from Oxenholme (BR) station - bus service to `K' village, No 41 or 41A
Capacity: 2,490 Cover: 1,000 Seats: 250
Clubhouse: The Park, open all matchdays. Pies & pasties available **Club Shop:** No

Programme
Pages: 32 Price: £1.00
Editor: John Wharton (01539734209)
Local Press: Westmorland Gazette
Lancaster Evening Post
Local Radio: Radio Cumbria, The Bay.

PREVIOUS **Leagues:** Westmorland; North Lancs; Lancs Combination 45-68; Northern Premier 68-83; North West Counties 83-87

CLUB RECORDS **Attendance:** 5,184 v Grimsby Town, FA Cup 1st Rd 1955
Goalscorer: Tom Brownlee. **Win:** 11-0 v Great Harwood 22/3/47. **Defeat:** 0-10 v Stalybridge Celtic 1/9/84
Fee Paid: Undisclosed for Tom Brownlee (Bradford C., 66). **Fee Received:** £10,250 for Andy Milner (Man. City 95)

BEST SEASON **FA Vase:** 3rd Rd 89-90 **FA Trophy:** 2nd Rd 80-81.
FA Cup: 2nd Rd replay 63-64, 1-4 v Chesterfield(A) after 1-1. 2nd Rd 49-50, 1st Rd 45-4648-49 52-53 54-55 55-56 64-65

HONOURS Lancs Comb. 48-49 64-65 (R-up 45-46 53-54 61-62 63-64, Lg Cup 55-56 60-61), Westmorland Snr Cup(12) 24-25 31-33 35-36 46-48 63-64 65-66 71-72 86-8789-89 90-91

Players progressing: John Laidlaw (Carlisle 1946), Louis Cardwell (Crewe 1947),Herbert Keen (Barrow 1953), Alec Aston (Preston 1955), Horace Langstreth(Torquay 1956), John Simpson (Lincoln 1957), Dennis Rogers (Accrington 1959),Tom Brownlee (Bradford City 1965), Peter McDonnell (Bury 1973), Keith Silken(Workington 1973), Roger Wicks (Darlington 1981), Andy Milner (Man City)

Kendal's Craig Allardyce getting in an excellent sliding tackle on Guiseley striker Phil Denney.
Photo: Darren C Thomas

LEEK TOWN

CLUB OFFICIALS

President: **Godfrey Heath**
Acting Chairman: **Paul Burston**
Vice Chairman: **Mike Cope**
Directors: **Robin Halton, Carl France, Warren France, Tony Pickford**
Secretary: **Christine Osmond:** 10 Corporation Street,Stoke on Trent Staffs. ST44AU (01782 847936 (H)
Commercial Manager: **Ken Warburton**
Press Officer: **Mike Cope**

FOOTBALL MANAGEMENT TEAM

Manager: Karl Wilcox & Mark Bromley
Coiach: Matt Booth Physio: K Birch-Martin

FACT FILE

Founded: 1946
Nickname: The Blues
Club Sponsors: Kerrygold
Colours: White with blue trim/white/white
Change colours: All yellow
Reserve team league: Manchester League
Midweek home matchday: Tuesday
Newsline: 0930 55 54 53

THE LAST TEN YEARS

Season	League	Div.	Position
91-92	N.P.L.	P	4
92-93	N.P.L.	P	5
93-94	N.P.L.	P	2
94-95	S.L.	P	7
95-96	N.P.L.	P	17
96-97	N.P.L.	P	1
97-98	Conf.	-	19
98-99	Conf.	-	21
99-00	N.P.L.	P	19
00-01	N.P.L.	P	22

GROUND Harrison Park, Macclesfield Road, Leek ST13 8LD
Tel: 01538 399278 Fax: 01538 399826

Directions: Opposite Courtaults chemical works on A523 Macclesfield to Buxton road half a mile out of Leek heading towards Macclesfield.

Capacity: 3,600 Seated: 625 Covered Terracing: 2,675

Club Shop: Contact club on 01538 399278.

Clubhouse: `Blues' Bar open nightly & weekend lunchtimes. 01538 383734

Programme
Pages: 40 Price: £1.50
Editor: M.Cope
Local Newspapers: Leek Post & Times, Evening Sentinel
Local Radio: Radio Stoke, Signal Radio

PREVIOUS **Leagues:** Staffs County, Manchester 51-54 57-73, West Mids (B'ham) 54-56,Cheshire County 73-82, North West Counties 82-87, Northern Premier 87-94 95-97,Southern League 94-95, Conference 97-99
Names: Abbey Green Rovers/ Leek Lowe Hamil. **Grounds:** None

CLUB RECORDS **Attendance:** 5,312 v Macclesfield Town, F.A. Cup Second Qualifying Round 73-74 **Win:** Unknown **Defeat:** Unknown
Transfer fee paid: £2,000 for Simon Snow (Sutton Town) **Transfer fee received:** £30,000 for Tony Bullock (Barnsley)
Career goalscorer: Dave Suttons 144 **Career appearances:** Gary Pearce 447.

BEST SEASON **FA Cup:** 2nd Rd 90-91, 0-4 v Chester (A) after 1-1 League clubs defeated: Scarborough 90-91.
FA Trophy: Runners-up 89-90, Q-F 85-86.

HONOURS FA Trophy R-up 89-90; Northern Premier Lg 96-97, R-up 93-94 (Div 1 89-90, Div 1Cup R-up 88-89, Presidents Cup R-up 93-94, Lg Shield 90-91); North West Co's LgCup 84-85 (Charity Shield 84-85); Cheshire County Lg 74-75 (Challenge Shield74-75); Manchester Lg 51-52 71-72 72-73 (Lg Cup 72-73); Staffs Snr Cup 95-96,R-up 54-55 81-82 95-96, Jnr Cup 51-52 70-71 (R-up 47-48 48-49 49-50)); StaffsCo. Lg 50-51 69-70 70-71 73-74 (R-up 47-48 49-50, Lg Cup 70-71 73-74); LeekPost Charity Shield 46-47; Leek Cup 47-48 52-53 70-71 71-72 (R-up 46-47); MayBank Cup 47-48 50-51 71-72; Hanley Cup 48-49 70-71 (R-up 49-5); Mid Cheshire LgDiv 2 87-88 (Div 2 Cup 87-88); Evans Halshaw Floodlit Cup Winners 93-94 94-95; Southern Lge Cup R-up 94-95; Unibond Lge Chall Cup R-up 95-96

Players progressing: Geoff Crosby (Stockport 52), Bill Summerscales (70), Mark Bright (81) & Martyn Smith (84) allto Port Vale, Paul Edwards (Crewe 89), Tony Bullock (Barnsley 97)

LINCOLN UNITED

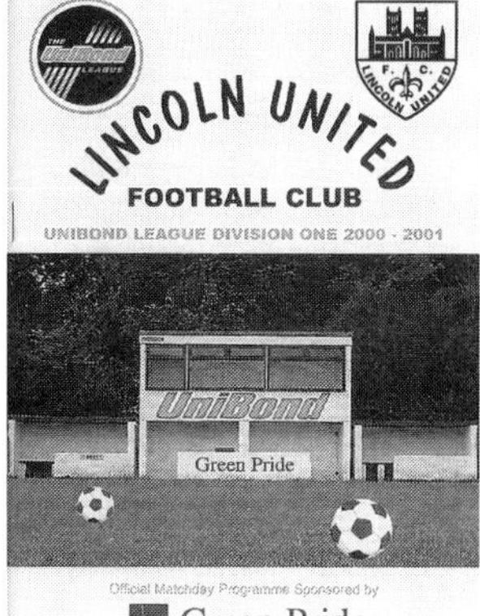

CLUB OFFICIALS

Chairman: **Peter Doyle**
President: **Phil Morley**
Vice Chairman: **W.White**
Commercial Manager: **Roy Parnham**

Secretary/Press Officer: **Tom Hill,**
4,Westwood Drive, Swanpool, Lincoln LN6 0HJTel Nos: 01522 683630 (H) 07885 020797 (M)

FOOTBALL MANAGEMENT TEAM

Managers: Allen Crombie
Physio: Anthony Adams

FACT FILE

Formed: 1938
Nickname: United
Colours: White/red/white
Change Colours: All Yellow
Midweek home matchday: Wednesday
Reserves ' League: Lincolnshire

2000-2001

Captain: Andy Moore
Top Goalscorer: Ian Williams 11
P.o.Y.: Ben Brown

GROUND Ashby Avenue, Hartsholme, Lincoln Tel: 01522 690674
Directions: From Newark A46 onto Lincoln relief road (A446), right at 2nd r'bout for Birchwood (Skellingthorpe Rd), go for 1 mile passing lake and Country Park, 1st right 10yds after 30mph sign into Ashby Ave., ground entrance200 yds, opposite Old Peoples home. From north follow A57 via Saxilby until reaching A46 Lincoln Relief Road - continue on this and turn left at r'bout signed Birchwood then as above. 3 miles from Loncoln Central (BR)
Capacity: 2,714 Seats: 400 Covered: 1,084
Clubhouse: Open daily normal licensing hours. Matchday snack bar -hot &cold food & drinks
Club Shop: Yes. Contact: Julie Portas (01522 885484)

Programme
Pages: 40 Price:#1.00
Editor:Roy Parnham TelNo: 01522 687543

Local Press: Lincolnshire Echo
Lincoln Standard

PREVIOUS **Leagues:** Lincs 45-48 60-67; Lincoln 48-60; Yorks 67-82; Northern Co'sEast 82-86, 92-95; Central Mids 82-92
Grounds: Skew Bridge (40s); Co-op Sports Ground (to mid 60s); Hartsholme Cricket Ground (to 82)
Name: Lincoln Amateurs (until an ex-pro signed in 1954)

CLUB RECORDS **Attendance:** 2,000 v Crook Town, FA Amateur Cup 1st Rd Proper, 1968
Scorer: Tony Simmons 215 **Appearances:** Steve Carter 447
Win: 12-0 v Pontefract Colls 95. **Defeat:** 0-7 v Huddersfield Town FA Cup 1st Round Proper16-11-91
Fee Paid: £1000 for Paul Tomlinson (Hucknall Town ,Dec 2000)
Fee Received: £3,000 for Dean Dye (Charlton Ath., 7.91)

BEST SEASON **FA Cup:** First Round Proper 91-92 (0-7 at Huddersfield Town), 97-98 v Walsall (0-2 Away)
FA Trophy: 3rd 3Rd **F.A.Vase:**

HONOURS Northern Counties East - Prem Div. 94-95, Div 1 92-93, Div 1 Sth 82-83,Div 2 85-86, Presidents Cup 94-95; Yorks Lg 70-71 73-74 (Lg Cup 70-71); Lincs Lg 63-64; Lincs Snr `A' Cup 72-73 85-86 95-96, R-up 91-92 94-95, `B' Cup 63-6470-71; Central Mids Lg 91-92 (Wakefield Cup 90-91); Evans Halshaw Floodlit Cup R-up 92-93; Lincs I'mediate Cup(7) 67-73 80-81; Blankney Hunt Inter Lge 95-96,Cup 95-96 Lincs Sen Cup: R-up 97-98 Unifla Div 1 Cup R-up 97-98

Back Row, left to right: Tom Hill (Secretary), Robin Taylor (Director), Paul Titcombe (Asst. Manager), Paul Burton, Kev Riley, Adam Gilbert, Paul Ward, Steve Curry, Simon Daniels, Ben Brown, James Drinkall, Lee Soar, Tony Adams (Trainer), Kev Hilton (Match Secretary) and Phil Morley (President). **Front Row:** Chris Hudson, Dave Frecklington, Paul Tomlinson, Richard Taylor, Jason Sedland, Pete Doyle (Chairman), Chris White, Allen Crombie (Manager),Gary Walters, Danny Hargreaves, Dominic Revill and Chris Ellis (Committee)

MATLOCK TOWN

CLUB OFFICIALS

Chairman: **Donald Carr**
Vice Chairman: **Michael Tomlinson**
Secretary: **Keith Brown**
`Barncroft', 1 Malvern Gardens
Matlock, Derbyshire DE4 3JH
01629 584231 (H) 01335 390301 (B)
Press Officer: **Ian Richardson**
Commercial Manager: **Tom Wright**

FOOTBALL MANAGEMENT TEAM

Manager: Tommy Spencer
Physio: Michael Cunningham

FACT FILE

Formed: 1885
Nickname: The Gladiators
Sponsors: Westons of Wirksworth/ Panasonic/ Tarmac & Peak 107 F.M.
Colours: Royal Blue/white/blue
Change colours: All yellow
Midweek home matchday: Tuesday
Reserves' League: Beauvale Mid All
Local Press: Matlock Mercury
Derbyshire Times, Derby Evening Telegraph, Chesterfield Express
Local Radio: Radio Derby, Peak 107 F.M.

PROGRAMME
Pages 40 Price £1.00
Editor: Mike Tomlinson (01629 583866)
Website: www.databasix.net/matlock town

GROUND Causeway Lane, Matlock, Derbyshire
Tel: 01629 583866 (& Fax)

Directions: On A615, 500 yds from town centre and Matlock (BR)
Capacity: 7,500 Cover: 2,000 Seats: 240
Clubhouse: Gladiators Social Club, on ground, open matchdays only
Club Shop: Yes. Contact: Sue Tomlinson (01629 583866)

PREVIOUS **Ground:** Hall Leys (last century). **Leagues:** Midland Counties 1894-96; Matlock & District; Derbys Senior; Central Alliance 24-25 47-61; Central Combination 34-35; Chesterfield & District 46-47; Midland Counties 1961-69

CLUB RECORDS **Attendance:** 5,123 v Burton Albion, FA Trophy 1975
Win: 10 v 0 Lancaster (A) **74** **Defeat:** 1-8 v Chorley (A) 71
Career **Goalscorer:** Peter Scott. **Career** **Appearances:** Mick Fenoughty
Fee Paid: £2,000 for Kenny Clarke1996 **Fee Received:** £10,000 for Ian Helliwell (York)

BEST SEASON **FA Trophy:** 74-74
FA Cup: 3rd Rd 76-77. 1st Rd 1885-86 86-87 86-8787-88 1959-60 74-75 75-76 89-90
League clubs defeated: Mansfield Town 76-77

HONOURS Northern Prem Lge R-up 83-84, Lge Cup 77-78, Shield 78-79; Midland Counties Lge 61-62 68-69; Central All (North) 59-60
60-61, R-up 61-62 62-63,Div 1 Cup R-up 61-62, Div 2 59-60, Div 2 Cup 59-60 60-61; Derbyshire Sen Cup74-75 76-
77 77- 78 80-81 83-84 84-85 91-92, R-up 60-61 72-73 73-74 75-76 80-8181-82 82-83 89-90 93-94 97-98;
Derbyshire Div Cup (North) 61-62 R-up 62-63;Evans Halshaw Floodlit Cup 88-89 91-92; Anglo-Italian Non-League Cup 79

Players progressing: Keith Haines (Leeds 1959), Wayne Biggins (Burnley 1984),Darren Bradshaw (Chesterfield 1987), Les McJannet (Scarborough 1987), Ian Helliwell (York 1987)

NORTH FERRIBY UNITED

CLUB OFFICIALS

President: Brian Thacker
Chairman: Les Hare
Vice Chairman: John Greenly
Press Officer: Les Hare
Secretary: Stephen Tather
16 Peasholme, Heads Lane, Hessle,
E Yorks HU13 0NY
Tel: 01482 642046 (H) Fax 01482 647244;
01482 351903 (B)

FOOTBALL MANAGEMENT TEAM

Manager: Brian France
Asst Mgr: Paul Olsson
Physio: Martin Woodmansey

FACT FILE

Founded: 1934
Nickname: United
Sponsors: Dransfield Developments
Colours: All white
Change colours: All yellow
Midweek matches: Tuesday
Reserves League: Humber Premier

2000-01
Captain: Mike Trotter
P.o.Y.: Paul Farley
Top Scorer: Mike Blythe 15

North Ferriby United AFC
v
Ashton United F.C.

UNIBOND LEAGUE DIVISION 1 SEASON 2000/2001
OFFICIAL MATCHDAY PROGRAMME
Thursday 3rd May 2001 7.45pm
DRANSFIELD PROPERTIES LIMITED

GROUND: Grange Lane, Church Road, North Ferriby HU14 3AA Tel: 01482 634601
Directions: Main Leeds-Hull road A63 or M62, North Ferriby is 8 miles west of Hull. Into North Ferriby, thru village passed the Duke of Cumberland Hotel, right down Church Rd, ground half mile on left. One mile from North Ferriby (BR)

Capacity: 3,000 Seats: 250 Cover: 1,000 Floodlights: Yes

Clubhouse: Bar, lounge, TV, pool open every night **Club Shop:** Yes

Programme
Pages: 40 Price: £1.20
Editor: Tony Brown

Local Press: Hull Daily Mail

HONOURS FA Vase Finalist 96-97; Yorkshire Lg R-up 75-76, Lg Cup 74-75, Div 2 70-71; N.C.E. Prem Div : Champions 99-00 R-up 97-98, Div 1 85-86 (Lg Cup R-up) 90-91 97-98, Presidents Cup 90-91, 98-99, 99-00 Div 1 (North), R-up 82-83, Res. Div R-up 90-91; E. Riding Snr Cup (9), E. Riding Church Lg 37-38

PREVIOUS L eagues: East Riding Church; East Riding Amateur; Yorks 69-82

BEST SEASON **FA Cup:** 3rd Q 97-98,98-99 **FA Vase:** R-up 96-97, SF 88-89, QF 89-90

RECORDS **Attendance:** 1,800 v Tamworth, FA Vase Semi-Final, 1989
Goalscorer: Andy Flounders 50, 98-99 **Appearances:** Richard Woomble, 74-94
Win: 9-0 v Hatfield Main, N.C.E. Lge Prem 97-98. **Defeat:** 1-7 v North Shields,N.C.E. Lge Prem 91.
Fee received: £6,000 for Dean Windass (Hull City,1988)

Players progressing: T Hotte (Hull) 88, I Ironside (Halifax) 88, D France, D Windass & M Matthews (Hull) 91.

OSSETT ALBION

CLUB OFFICIALS

President: Miss Helen Worth
Chairman: Neville A Wigglesworth
Vice-Chairman: S B Garside
Commercial Manager: D Riley
01924 240247
Press Officer: Neville Wigglesworth
01924 275630
Secretary: David Chambers, 109 South Parade, Ossett, Wakefield, WF5 0BE.
Tel:01924 276004 (H)

FOOTBALL MANAGEMENT TEAM

Manager: Eric Gilchrist
Physio: Nicky Davies
Coach: Tony Passmore

FACT FILE

Founded: 1944
Nickname: Albion
Sponsors: Arco
Colours: Old gold & black/black/gold
Change colours: All white
Midweek matches: Wednesday
Reserves' Lge: NCEL Res Div
Website: www.pyke42.freeserve.co.uk

2000-01

Captain: C. Shaw
P.o.Y.: M. Carter
Top Scorer: M. Carter 16

MATCH DAY PROGRAMME
OSSETT ALBION
F C
Premier Division
Main Sponsors
TASCA TANKERS
HARROGATE RA
£1

44 pages £1
Editor: N Wigglesworth (01924 275630)

Local Press: Wakefield Express
Local Radio: Ridings FM

GROUND: Dimple Wells, Ossett (01924 273618-club, 01924 280450-grd)
Directions: M1 jct 40. Take Wakefield road, right at Post House Hotel down Queens Drive. At end right then second left down Southdale Rd. At end right,then first left down Dimple Wells (cars only). Coaches take second left following the road for 200yds bearing left twice. Four miles from both Wakefield and Dewsbury BR stations. Buses 116 and 117
Capacity: 3,000 Seats: 200 Cover: 500 Floodlights: Yes
Clubhouse: 3 bars + function room, open 7 days per week - catering available
Club Shop: Selling various souvenirs & programmes. Contact chairman

PREVIOUS
Leagues: Heavy Woollen Area 44-49; West Riding Co. Amtr 49-50; West Yorks 50-57; Yorks 57-82.
Ground: Fearn House

RECORDS
Attendance: 1,200 v Leeds Utd, floodlight opening 1986
Win: 12-0 v British Ropes(H), Yorks. Lge Div. 2 6/5/59
Defeat: 2-11 v Swillington (A), W. Yorks. Lge Div. 1 25/4/56
Goalscorer: John Balmer **Appearances:** Peter Eaton, 800+ (22 yrs)
Fee Received: **Fee Paid:**

BEST SEASON
FA Cup: **FA Vase:**

HONOURS
Yorks Lg 74-75 R-up 59-60 61-62, Lg Cup 75-76, 76-77, Div 2 78-79, 80-81 R-up 58-59;
N.C.E. Prem. Div. R-up 00-01 Div 1 86-87 Lg Cup 83-84; West Yorks Lg 53-54 55-56 Div 2 52-53, Lg Cup 52-53;
W. Riding County Cup 64-65 65-66 67-68; Wheatley Cup 56-57 58-59

Players progressing: Gary Brook (Newport, Scarborough, Blackpool) 1987, Ian Ironside (Barnsley, Middlesbrough, Scarborough) 1980.

OSSETT TOWN

CLUB OFFICIALS

President: Paul Jervis
Chairman: Graham Firth
Football Chairman: Peter Wilkinson
Commercial Manager: Graham Willis
Secretary: Trevor Green,
2 Eliots Close, Castleford, W.Yorks. WF10 3TT
Tel Nos: 01977 550922(H) 07901 754553 (M)
EMAIL: Trevor@Churm.greatXscape.uk

FOOTBALL MANAGEMENT TEAM

Manager: Gary Brook
Asst Manager: B. Crawther
Coach: Mick Polli

FACT FILE

Founded: 1936
Sponsors:: Builders Supply(Wakefield) Ltd
Colours: All red
Change colours: All sky
Midweek matches: Tuesday
Reserves' League: Lancashire League

Website: www.ossetttown.freeserve.co.uk

2000-2001

Captain:Craig Boardman
P.o.Y.: Ryan Gray
Top Goalscorer: Michael Midwood 17

Pages: 56 Price: £1.00
Editor: Secretary Tel: 01924 277652

Local Press:
Dewsbury Reporter,
Wakefield Express

GROUND: Ingfield, Prospect Road, Ossett, Wakefield WF5 8AN Tel: 01924 272960
Directions: M1 jct 40, B6129 to Ossett, left into Dale Street, left again at lights opposite bus station on ring road, ground on left. Nearest stations Dewsbury or Wakefield Westgate - both three miles from. Buses 116, 117, 126 and127 from Wakefield, buses 116, 126 and 127 from Dewsbury, buses 117, 118 or 216 from Leeds
Capacity: 4,000 Seats: 360 Cover: 650 Floodlights: Yes
Clubhouse: Open Fri & Sun lunchtimes, all day Sat and every evening. Pie & peas, chips, soup from tea bar **Club Shop:** Yes

PREVIOUS **Leagues:** Leeds 36-39; Yorkshire 45-82; N.C.E. 83-99 **Ground:** Fern House (pre-1958)

RECORDS
Attendance: 2,600 v Manchester Utd, friendly 1988
Win: 10-1 v Harrogate RA (H), N.C.E. Lge Prem. Div. 27/4/93
Defeat: 0-7 v Easington Colliery, FA Vase 8/10/83
Fee received: £1,350 for Derek Blackburn (Swansea 1957)
Appearances: Steve Worsfold **Goalscorer:** Dave Leadbeater

HONOURS Northern Counties East - Lg Cup 89-90, Div 2 88-89, Res. Div 88-89, Res.Cup 87-88 88-89; West Riding County Cup 58-59 81-82.

Players progressing: Arnold Kendall (Bradford C.) 1949, Ron Liversidge(Bradford C.) 56, Derek Blackburn (Swansea) 57, Simon Lowe (Barnsley) 83, Gary Chapman (Bradford C.) 88, Mick Norbury (Scarborough) 1989, Mike Williams(Sheffield W.) 90, Dean Trott (Northampton) 98, Paul Cuss (Huddersfield Town) 98.

LEFT:
Matt Smithard in action against Chorley.

RIGHT:
Star striker Scott Jackson breaking through against Matlock Town.
Scott netted nine goals in just five games before a ligament injury ended his season.

RADCLIFFE BOROUGH

CLUB OFFICIALS

Chairman: Bernard Manning (Junior)

President: Bernard Manning (Senior)

Vice Chairman: J. Ryan

Company Secretary: Graham E Fielding
Football Secretary: Ian Hannay
Both c/o Radcliffe Borough

FOOTBALL MANAGEMENT TEAM

Manager: Kevin Glendon
Coach:Mike Farrelly
Physio: Roy Davies

FACT FILE

Formed: 1949
Sponsors: Martin Darlington Transport
Nickname: Boro'
Colours: All blue
Change colours: All orange
Midweek home matchday: Tuesday
Reserve Team:No

2000-01

Captain: Mark Dempsey
P.o.Y.: Danny Hurst
Top scorer:Niell Hardy 22

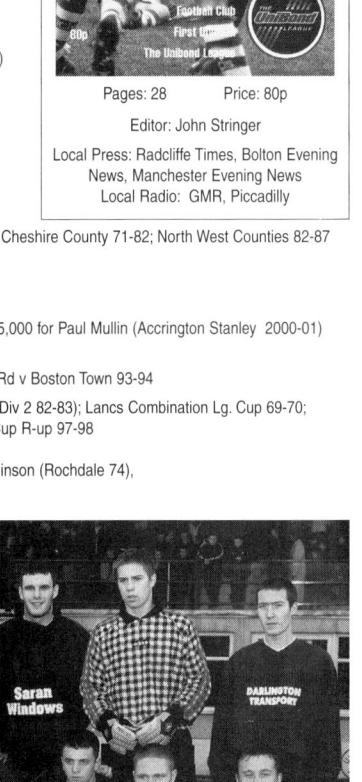

Pages: 28 Price: 80p

Editor: John Stringer

Local Press: Radcliffe Times, Bolton Evening News, Manchester Evening News
Local Radio: GMR, Piccadilly

GROUND: Stainton Park, Pilkington Road, Radcliffe, Lancs., M26 3PE 0161 724 5937 (club) 0161 724 8346 (Office) 0161 723 3178(Fax) Website: www.radcliffeborough.co.uk
Directions: M62 junction 17 - follow signs for Whitefield and Bury . Take A665 to Radcliffe. Thro' town centre, turn right into Unsworth St. (opposite Turf Hotel). Ground on left half mile Colshaw Close East. 1/2 mile from Radcliffe(BR)
Capacity: 3,000 Cover: 1,000 Seats: 350
Clubhouse: (0161 724 5937) `The Boro' - public house on ground. Food available
Club Shop: No

PREVIOUS **Leagues:** South East Lancs; Manchester 53-63; Lancs Comb. 63-71; Cheshire County 71-82; North West Counties 82-87
Ground: Bright Street 1949-70.

CLUB RECORDS **Attendance:** 2,495 v York City (F.A.C 1st Round 2000-01)
Goalscorer: Ian Lunt **Appearances:** Chris Lilley.
Fee Paid: £5,000 for Gary Walker(Buxton, 1991). **Fee Received:** £15,000 for Paul Mullin (Accrington Stanley 2000-01)

BEST SEASON **FA Trophy:** 3rd Rd v Gateshead 1995-96
FA Cup: 1st Round Proper, 00-01 v York City 1-4) **FA Vase:** 4th Rd v Boston Town 93-94

HONOURS Unibond Lge Div One Champ 96-97; North West Counties Lg 84-85 (Div 2 82-83); Lancs Combination Lg. Cup 69-70; Manchester Lg R-up 55-56 (Lg Cup 58-59 joint); Manchester Prem. Cup R-up 97-98

Players progressing: Jim Hayman (Bury 50), Ian Wood (Oldham Athletic 65), Robert Hutchinson (Rochdale 74), Gary Haworth (Rochdale 84), Kevin Hulme (Bury 89)

Back Row,left to right: Mike Farrelly (Assistant Manager),Ian Senior, Simon Kelly, David Bean, Niell Hardy, Ian Callaghan, Danny Hurst and Simon Carden (now Accrington Stanley) **Front Row:** Scott Wilson, Eamonn Kelly, Ian Lunt, Mark Dempsey (Captain), Levi Edwards, David Collins, Richard Battersby, Tony Whealing and James Price.

ROSSENDALE UNITED

CLUB OFFICIALS

Chairman: A Connelly **V Chair:** LeeBrierley
President: David White
Press Offcer: Kevin Procter
Secretary: Kevin Proctor,5 Booth Street, Waterfoot, Rossendale, Lancs BB4 9AL
Tel No: 01706 223405
Email Address: rossendaleunited@zen.co.uk

FOOTBALL MANAGEMENT TEAM

Manager: James McCluskie
Ass. Man. Andy Grimshaw Coach: David White.Physios: Billy Howarth&Chris Connelly

FACT FILE

Founded: 1898 Nickname: The Stags
Sponsors: Hurstwood Developments
Colours: Blue & white stripes/blue/blue
Change cols: Red&yellow stroipes/red/red
Midweek matchday: Tuesday
Reserves ' League: Lancashire
Website: www.nip.to@zen.co.uk

2000-01

Captain: Gary Rishton
P.o.Y.: Jason Heffernan`
Top Scorer: Craig Sargeson 39

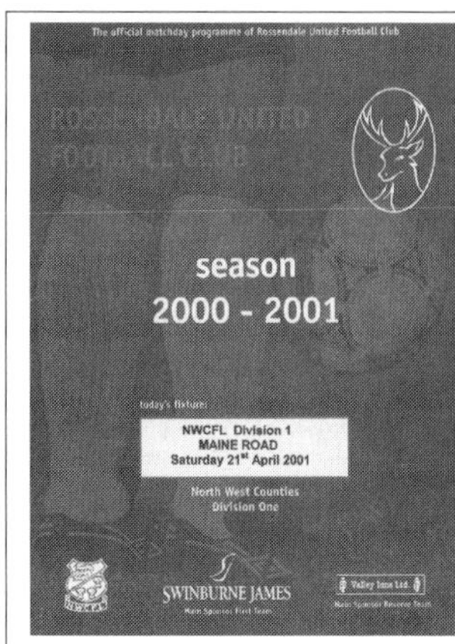

Programme: 28 pages-£1.00
Editor: David Hawarth

Local Radio: Red Rose, Radio Lancashire.
Local Press: Lancs Evening Telegraph, Rossendale Free Press

GROUND Dark Lane, Staghills Rd, Newchurch, Rossendale, Lancs BB4 7UA
Tel: 01706 215119 (Ground); 01706 213296 (Club)
Directions: M60 Junc 18, M66 north following signs for Burnley, then A682 to Rawstenstall, take 2nd exit sign Burnley A682, at 1st lights turn right into Newchurch Rd, 1.5 miles turn right into Staghills Rd, grd 800 yards right
Capacity: 2,500 Cover: Yes Seats: 500 Floodlights: Yes
Clubhouse: Evenings & matchdays. Hot snacks. Pool, satellite TV, concert room
Club Shop: Yes

PREVIOUS **Leagues:** N.E. Lancs Comb.; Lancs Comb. 1898-99 1901-70; Central Lancs 1899-1901; Cheshire County 70-82; NWC 82-89 93-01; N.P.L. 89-93. **Grounds:** None

RECORDS **Attendance:** 12,000 v Bolton Wanderers FA Cup 2nd Rd 71
Appearances: Johnny Clarke 770, 1947-65 **Goalscorer:** Bob Scott
Fee Paid: £3,000 for Jimmy Clarke (Buxton, 1992)
Fee Received: £1,500 for Dave O'Neill (Huddersfield Town, 1974)
Win: 17-0v Ashton Town, Lancs Comb.1911-12
Defeat: 0-14 v Morecambe, Lancs Comb. 67-68

BEST SEASON **FA Cup:** 2nd Rd 71-72, 1-4 v Bolton W. at Bury FC. Also 1st Rd 75-76 Also 1st Rd 75-76, 0-1 v Shrewsbury T. (H)
FA Trophy : 2nd Rd 81-82 **FA Vase:** 5th Rd 86-87,88-89

HONOURS N.W.C. Lg Div 1 88-89 00-01(R-up 87-88 93-94), Div 2 R-up 85-86, Chall Cup 93-94

Players progressing: T Lawton, G Smith (Bradford C 52), E Hartley & W O'Loughton (Oldham 56/60), C Blunt (Burnley 64), F Eyre (Bradford PA 69), D O'Neill (Huddersfield), C Parker (Rochdale 92).

Rossendale celebrate winning the North West Counties Championship.

SPENNYMOOR UNITED

Chairman & Press Off: Barrie Hindmarch
Vice Chairman: P. Fletcher
Football Match Secretary
Brian Boughen,141 Durham Rd, Spennymoor, Co.Durham. DL16 6JU Tel No: 01388 81187
Com Man: Des Beamson
Gen Sec: Tom Metcalfe (01388 811561)

FOOTBALL MANAGEMENT TEAM
Caretaker Managers: Craig Veart & Stuart Dawson
Physio: Peter Carey
Coach: Managerial team

FACT FILE
Founded: 1904
Nickname: The Moors
Sponsors: T.B.A.
Club colours: Black & white stripes/black/white.
Change colours: All red
Midweek home matches: Tuesday
Reserve Team: None
2000-01
Captain:Craig Veart
P.o.Y.: Rob Jones
Top scorers: Ross Foreman,Rrob Jones 4

SPENNYMOOR UNITED A.F.C.
OFFICIAL PROGRAMME SEASON 2000-01

Pages: 44 Price: £1
Editor: Gary Nunn

Local Press: Northern Echo; The Journal

GROUND Brewery Field, Durham Road, Spennymoor, County Durham DL16 6JN Tel: 01388 811934 Directions: From South; A1(M), A167, A688, straight on at mini-r'bout, 3rd exit at next large r'bout (St Andrews church opposite), pass Asda on left, straight on at junction, pass Salvin Arms (Durham Rd), ground 200 yds on left. From A167North - leave at Croxdale (N.E.S.S. factory), right at cemetery on left - this is Durham Rd - ground half mile on right. Nearest rail station is Durham -buses from there.
Capacity: 7,500 Seats: 300 Cover: 2,000
Clubhouse: (01388 814100) Open eves. 7-11pm, Sat 12-11pm (matchdays only), Sun12-2 & 7-10.30pm. Bar snacks. Private functions. Tea bar in ground. **Club Shop:** Sells replica kit, memorabilia, programmes etc. Contact Peter Fletcher (01388 814100).

PREVIOUS **Leagues:** Northern 05-08 60-90; North Eastern 08-37 38-58; Wearside 37-38;Midland Counties 58-60; Northern Counties East 90-93. **Ground:** Wood Vue 1901-1904. **Names:** None.

CLUB RECORDS **Attendance:** 7,202 v Bishop Auckland, Durham County Challenge Cup 30/3/57.
Win: 19-0 v Eden Colliery, North Eastern Lge 6/2/37. **Defeat:** 0-16 v Sunderland`A', Durham Snr Cup 4.1.02 (H.T.: 0-10)
Goalscorer: Dougie Humble 200+. **Appearances:** Ken Banks 600+.
Fee Paid: £3,500 for Don Prattie (Gretna) Fee Received: £20,000 for Michael Heathcote (Sunderland, 88).

BEST SEASON **FA Trophy:** Semi Final 77-78
FA Cup: 3rd Rd 36-37, 1-7 v West Bromwich Albion(A). League clubs defeated : Hartlepool 27-28, Southport 75-76.

HONOURS Northern Premier Lg Cup 93-94 (Div 1 R-up 93-94); Northern Lg(6) 67-68 71-7273-74 76-79 (R-up(3) 74-75 79-81), Lg Cup(5) 65-66 67-68 79-81 86-87; Turney Wylde Cup 80-81; J R Cleator Cup 80-81 86-87; Northern Counties (East) Lg 92-93(Lg Cup 92-93); Durham Challenge Cup 29-30 44-45 45-46 53-54 62-63 67-68 72-7373-74 74-75 75-76 78-79 82-83 93-94 94-95 95-96 97-98; Durham Benevolent Bowl26-27 29-30 31-32 47-48 58-59 60-61; North Eastern Lg(4) 09-10 44-46 56-57 (Lg Cup 28-29).

Players Progressing: Over fifty, including: H. Hubbick (Burnley, 3.25), T .Dawson (Charlton, 3.39), T. Flockett (Charlton, 4.49), J. Smallwood(Chesterfield, 12.49), J. Oakes (Aldershot, 5.54), J. Adams (Luton Town, 53),Alan Moore (Chesterfield), Michael Heathcote (Sunderland, 5.87), Jason Ainsley(Hartlepool, 94), Richie Alderson (York City 97), Graeme Paxton (Newcastle Utd 97)

00-01 Player of the Year and Joint Top Goalscorer, Rob Jones (inset) seen below in a defensive role as he heads clear this Hyde United corner.

STOCKSBRIDGE PARK STEELS

STEELS REVIEW
Club Sponsor:
JOHN CRAWSHAW QUALITY BUTCHERS
SHEFFIELD SENIOR CUP - SEASON 2000/2001
STOCKSBRIDGE PARK STEELS
v
DENABY UNITED
Tuesday 14th November 2000 - K.O. 7.45pm
Official Matchday Programme 80p

Pages: 28 Price:1.00
Editor: Edwin O'Sullivan
Tel: 0114 288 4218

Local Press:
Sheffield Trader, Green'un, The Star

CLUB OFFICIALS

President: **J.Newton**
Chairman: **A Bethel**
Vice-Chairman: **M Grimmer**
Secretary: **Michael Grimmer**
48 Hole House Lane, Stocksbridge
Sheffield S36 1BT Tel: 0114 288 6470
Press Officer: **Edwin O'Sullivan**
Commercial Manager: Andrew Horsley
Tel: 0114 288 3867

FOOTBALL MANAGEMENT TEAM

Manager: Mick Horne
Asst Manager: Trevor Gough
Physio: Sean Hird

FACT FILE

Formed: 1986
Nickname: Steels
Sponsors:Weatherglaze
Colours: Yellow/blue/yellow
Change colours: All blue
Midweek matches: Tuesday
Reserves' League: Beefeater County Senior

2000-01
Captain: Jon Brown
P.o.Y.: Lee Wainwright
Top Scorer: Gary Hurlestone (28)

GROUND Bracken Moor Lane, Stocksbridge, Sheffield. Tel: 0114 288 2045
Fax: 0114 288 8305 Club Website: http://members.aol.com/spsfc/

Directions: M1 jct 35a (from S), 36 (from N), A616 to Stocksbridge.
On arrival in Stocksbridge turn left into Nanny Hill under the Clock Tower and continue up the hill for about 500 yds - ground on left

Capacity: 3,500 Cover: 1,000 Seats: 450

Clubhouse: Open 7 days (lunchtime & evenings). No food. Separate foodbar for matches

Club Shop:(H.O'Sullivan 0114 2884218) badges, mugs, shirts, progs,watches and scarves .

PREVIOUS **Ground:** Stonemoor 49-51 52-53 **Names:** Stocksbridge Works, Oxley Park;clubs merged in 1986
Leagues: Sheffield Amateur/ Sheffield Association/Yorkshire 49-82

CLUB RECORDS **Attendance:** 2,000 v Sheffield Wed., Floodlight opening Oct '91
Fee Received: £15,000 for Lee Mills (Wolves, 1992) **Fee Paid:** Nil
Win: 5-0 v Warrington Town NPL 96-97 **Defeat:** 1-6 v Harrogate NPL 99-00
Scorer: Trevor Jones (145) **Appearances:** Not known

BEST SEASON **FA Cup:** 4th Q 50-1, 56-7 **FA Trophy:** 3rd Q 96-97 **FA Vase:** 4th Rd 95-96.

HONOURS Northern Co's East Prem Div 93-94, R-up 95-96, Div 1 91-92, Lg Cup 94-95; Sheffield Snr Cup 92-93 95-96,98-99. Oxley Park F C: County Sen Div 1 85-86:Stocksbridge Works FC: Yorkshire Lge Div 1 51-52 54-55 55-56 56-57 57-58 61-62 62-63, Div 2 50-51 64-65, Div 3 70-71 74-75, Lge Cup 61-62 Sheffield Snr Cup 51-52

Players progressing: Peter Eustace (Sheffield Wednesday) 1960 (from Stocksbridge Works) , Lee Mills (Wolverhampton W.) 1992

L-R Back Row: Biggins, Fearon, Dunphy (now Hallam), Flynn, Turner, Brown, Longden, Wainwright, Askey. Front Row: Robinson, Fidler, Rowan, Newton (President), Gough (asst. manager), John Crawshaw (main sponsor), Horne (manager), Fothergill (now Kettering), Hurlstone, Ashton.

TRAFFORD

CLUB OFFICIALS

Chairman: **David Brown**

President: **David Roberts**

Secretary: **Graham Foxall**
90 Grosvenor Road, Urmston M41 5AQ
Tel: 0161 747 4502

FOOTBALL MANAGEMENT TEAM

Manager: Mark Molyneaux
Asst Manager: Wayne Goodison
Coach: T.B.A.

FACT FILE

Formed: 1990
Nickname: The North
Sponsors: Caffro Construction Ltd
Colours: All White
Change colours: Azure & black,black,black
Midweek Matchday: Tuesday
Reserve League: Mid Cheshire Div 1

2000-01
Captain: Darren Emmett
P.o.Y.: Bobby Jones
Top Scorer: Darren Emmett 26

Pages: 44 Price: £1
Editor: David Murray (0161 775 7509)

Local Press: Stretford & Urmston Messenger, Manchester Evening News
Local Radio: GMR Talk, Piccadilly Radio, Century 105

GROUND:
Shawe View, Pennybridge Lane, Flixton, Urmston, Manchester M41 5DL Tel: 0161 7471727
Website: www.traffordfc.freeserve.co.uk Email: dave-murray@traffordfc.freeserve.co.uk
Directions: M60 jct 9, B5158 towards Urmston, at 1st r/about take 1st exit, 1st lights turn right into Moorside Road, at nextr/about 2nd exit into Bowfell Rd, at next lights turn sharp left, then immediately right into Pennybridge Lane next to Bird-in-Hand Pub parking on left 100yds
Capacity: 2,500 Cover: 740 Seats: 292
Clubhouse: Yes **Club Shop:** Yes

PREVIOUS **Leagues:** Mid Cheshire 90-92; North West Counties 92-97. Name: NorthTrafford 90-94.

CLUB RECORDS **Attendance:** 803 v Flixton (NPL Div 1 27/12/97)
Goalscorer: Garry Vaughan 88 **Appearances:** Garry Vaughan293
Win: 10-0 v Haslingden St Mary's (LancsAmt Shield 91) **Defeat:** 0-6 v Oldham Town (NWCL Div 2 93)
Fee Paid: Undisclosed for Jock Russell (Radcliffe Borough) **Fee Received:** Undisclosed for Mike Turner (Witton A.)

BEST SEASON **FA Vase:** 5th Rd 95-96 **FA Trophy:** 3rd Round 2000-01
FACup: 2nd Rd Qual 95-96,99-00

HONOURS Lamont Pils Trophy 93-94; NWCL Div 1 96-97, Div 2 R-up 93-94, Lge ChallCup R-up 96-97; Res Div 93-94; Carling Chall Cup R-up 94-95; Manchester PremCup R-up 94-95, R-up 96-97, Res Div Champ 96-97, Cup 96-97; Manchester Amt Cup 96-97. Unifilla 1st Div Cup 97-98 Unibond Presidents Cup 99-00 Mid Cheshire Div 2 99-00

Players progressing: Anthony Vaughan (Ipswich, Manchester City & Nott'm Forest)

Back row, left to right: Wayne Goodison (Assistant Manager), Dave Norman, Frank Glover, Paul Dowle, Chris Patterson, Peter Mellor, Lee Southwood, Mark Molyneux (Player Manager), Bobby Jones, Richard Bibby, Billy McCartney, Alan Pannett,and David Brown (Chairman). **Front Row:** Chris Houghton, George Turner, Craig Doyle, Darren Emmett, Darrell Bates, Leon Diaczuk, Anthony Hogan, Mark Henshaw and Stacy Lewis Photo: Dave Murray

WITTON ALBION

CLUB OFFICIALS

President: **T Stelfox**

Chairman: **M Worthington**

Secretary: **Phil Chadwick**
29 Jack Lane, Davenham, Northwich,
Cheshire CW9 8LF Tel: 01606 44845

FOOTBALL MANAGEMENT TEAM

Manager: Eddie Bishop
Physio: Steve Crompton

FACT FILE

Formed: 1887 Nickname: The Albion
Colours: Red & white stripes
Change colours: All yellow
Midweek matchday: Tuesday
Reserve League: Altrincham U21

2000-01

Captain: Charlie Bond
P.o.Y.: Brian Pritchard
Top Scorer: David Anane

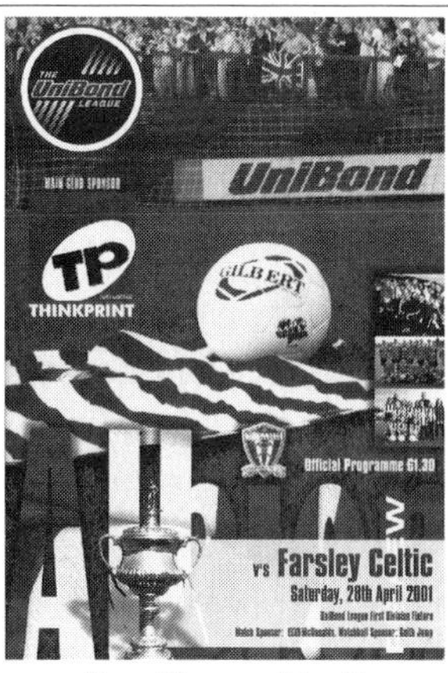

Pages: 32 Price: £1
Editor: Brian Pritchard (01606 43008)

Local Press: Northwich Guardian, Northwich Chronicle
Local Radio: BBC GMR, BBC Radio Stoke

GROUND Bargain Booze Stadium, Wincham Park, Chapel St, Wincham, Northwich. Tel/Fax: 01606 43008 Email: bp-uh-2000@aol.com
Website~: www.wittonalbion.co.uk
Directions: M6 junc 19. A556 towards Northwich, after 3 miles turn onto A559 at beginning of dual carriageway, after 3/4 mile turn left opposite Black Greyhound Inn, grd 1/2 mile on left immediately after crossing Canal Bridge
Capacity: 4,500 Seated: 650 Cover: 2,300
Clubhouse: Concert room and Vice-Presidents room open matchdays, Tuesday,Thursday, Friday evenings. Food available for private functions **Club Shop:** Yes

PREVIOUS **Leagues:** Lancs Comb.; Cheshire County -79; Northern Premier 79-91, GMV Conference 91-94
Grounds: Central Ground, Witton Street, Northwich

CLUB RECORDS **Attendance:** 3,940 v Kidderminster Harriers - FA Trophy Semi-Final 13.4.91 (Wincham Road)
9,500 v Northwich Victoria - Cheshire League 7.4.50 (Cenral Ground)
Win: 13-0 v Middlewich (H) NS Cup .**Defeat:** 0-9 v Macclesfield Town (a) 18.9.65
Fee Paid: £12,500 to Hyde Utd for Jim McCluskie 91 **Fee Received:** £11,500 for Peter Henderson from Chester City.
Goalscorer: Frank Fidler 175 (1947-1950) **Appearances:** Alf Ashley 556 (1946-1958)

BEST SEASON **FA Trophy:** Runners-up 91-92, Semi-Finals 90-91, 92-93
FA Cup: 91-92 Second Round 91-92, 1-5 v Preston North End (A). League clubs defeated: Halifax Town91-92

HONOURS Northern Prem Lge 90-91; Cheshire County Lge 48-49 49-50 53-54 (R-up 50-51),Lge Cup 53-54 75-76; Cheshire County Sen Cup (7); FA Trophy R-up 91-92 (SF 90-91 92-93)

Players progressing: P Henderson (Chester C.), Chris Nicholl (Burnley - ex-Southampton manager), Phil Power (Crewe), Neil Parsley & Mike Whitlow (Leeds), Geoff Horsfield (Halifax Town ,Fulham), Robert Trees (Bristol Rovers).

Left toRight

Back Row: Mark Simms, Mike Turner*, Gareth West*, Paul Hennin, Brian Pritchard.
Middle Row: Matt Staley, Martin Faulkner, Danny Graystone, Alan Minshall, Lee Anderson, David Heywood Andy Hough*
Front Row: Dave Anane, Gary Coley*, Eddie Bishop*, Charlie Bould, (Captain), Nigel Gleghorn, Lee Cox Steve Haw

* indicates player who has left the club

WORKINGTON

CLUB OFFICIALS

Chairma: Dale Brotherton
President: Minnie Thexton
Vice Chairman: Humphrey Dobie
Match Sec.: Steve Durham (01946 61380)
Secretary: Dale Brotherton
Lime House, Holm Hill, Dalston, Carlisle
CA5 7BX Tel: 07977 759903
Football Consultant: Dave McParland

FOOTBALL MANAGEMENT TEAM

Manager: Peter Hampton
Asst. Man: Keith Mason
Physio: Les Sharkey

FACT FILE

Formed: 1884 (reformed 1921)
Nickname: Reds
Sponsors: AXA Homesearch Direct
Colours: All red
Change colours: yellow & black/black/yellow
Midweek matchday: Tuesday
Reserves' League: West Cumberland

20001
Captain Alan Grayr
P.o.Y.: Alan Gray
Top Scorer: Barry Irving 8

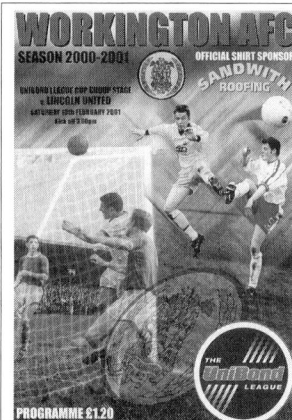

Pages: 36 Price: £1
Press Off/ Ed: Steve Durham (01946 61380)

Local Press: Evening News & Star, Times & Star
Local Radio: BBC Radio Cumbria, C.F.M

GROUND: Borough Park, Workington, Cumbria CA14 2DT Tel: 01900 602871
Website: www.workingtonredsafc.co.uk

Directions: A66 into town, right at `T' junction, follow A596 for 3/4 mile - ground is then visible and signposted. Ground is north of town centre 1/4 mile from Workington (BR) station &1/2 mile from bus station

Capacity: 2,500 Cover: 800 Seats: 300 Floodlights: Yes

Clubhouse: Open matchdays and for private functions. Food on matchdays restricted menu

Club Shop: Sells programmes, badges, magazines, pennants, photographs, replica kit, T-shirts. etc. Contact Keith Lister (01900 812867)

HONOURS Football League: 5th in Div 3 65-66, 3rd Div 4 63-64, Cumberland County Cup 1886-91(x5) 95-00(x5) 1906-08(x2) 09-10 24-25 34-35 36-38(x2) 49-50 53-54 67-68 85-86 95-96, 99-00 (R-up 1885-86 91-92 1899-1901(x2) 02-03 08-09 11-12 23-24 26-27 29-30, 46-47 68-69 78-79) Football League Cup QF 63-64 64-65; N.P.L. Presidents Cup 83-84; North Eastern Lge R-up 38-39, Lge Cup 34-35 36-37 R-up 37-38; N.W. Trains Lg Div 1 98-99

PREVIOUS **Leagues:** Cumberland Assoc. 1890-94; Cumberland Sen. Lge 94-1901, 03-04; Lancashire Lge 1901-03; Lancashire Comb. 04-10; North Eastern 10-11, 21-51; Football League 51-77
Grounds: Various 1884-1921, Lonsdale Park 21-37

BEST SEASON **FA Cup:** 4th Rd 33-34. 1st Rd - 53 occasions.
FA Trophy: Q. Final 99-00 **FA Vase:** 6th Rd, 98-99 (1st season)

RECORDS **Attendance:** 21,000 v Manchester Utd, FA Cup 3rd Rd 4/1/58
Goalscorer: Billy Charlton 193 **Win:** 17-1 v Cockermouth Crusaders, Cumb-erland Sen. Lge 19/1/01
Appearances: Bobby Brown 419 **Defeat:** 0-9 v Chorley (A), NPL Prem. Div., 10/11/87
Fee Paid: £6,000 for Ken Chisholm (Sunderland,'56) **Fee Received:** £33,000 for Ian McDonald (Liverpool, '74)

Players progressing: Numerous, the best known being John Burridge.

Back Row, left to right: Graeme Carr, Barry Irving, Gary Milne, Stuart Williamson, Kevin Wolfe, Wayne Johnson, Alan Gray, Keith Mason and Ted Sharkey. **Front Row:** Ricky Graham, Chris Kelleher, Graham Goulding, Peter Hampton (Manager), Marc Green, Nigel Nichol and Glenn Murray

JOHN DAVISON (Altrincham)
England's record Semi-Pro cap holder with 24.

Robins' Remembered

Five England Semi-Pro Internationals from Cheltenham Town's glorious championship winning year - Back row (left to right) Lee Howells, Jamie Victory & Steve Book and in front Dale Watkins & Neil Grayson

NORTH WEST COUNTIES FOOTBALL LEAGUE

President: W J King

Chairman: S Tomlinson

Secretary: Geoff Wilkinson

46 Oaklands Drive, Penwortham, Preston PR1 0YY Tel: 01772 746312

The season of 2000-01 will be remembered mainly as one disrupted by the weather, the petrol crisis and the foot and mouth epidemic, but it also marked the renaissance of Rossendale United, who claimed the North West Counties League First Division title with a superb run in, which clinches a return to the UniBond League for the ambitious Lancashire club.

The Stags did not have it all their own way in a very competitive year, as the lead changed hands many times during the season, Clitheroe, Prescot Cables, St Helens Town and Salford City all topping the table for considerable spells. It was Rossendale, though, under the astute management of Jim McCluskie, who kept their nerve to take pole position with games running out, Clitheroe ending the season as worthy runners up with Ramsbottom United finishing in a best ever third position.

Clitheroe also flew the NWCFL flag in the FA Carlsberg Vase where they reached the Semi-Final stage after a great run, and despite a rousing second leg display, the Blues could not claw back a large first leg deficit, but became the first team to inflict defeat on the eventual Vase winning side. St Helens Town also performed well, rekindling memories of their Vase win in 1987, before bowing out to eventual finalists Berkhamsted in the quarter finals.

With St Helens Town, Fleetwood Freeport, Kidsgrove Athletic, Salford City and Prescot Cables all proving worthy contenders throughout a fascinating season at the top, the coming season bodes well for the League.

Newcastle Town and Mossley will be disappointed by seasons dogged by inconsistency, whilst Skelmersdale United, many people's tip for the title this year, only found their true form late on after the successes of 1999-2000.

A clutch of Manchester sides occupied the mid-table positions with Curzon Ashton and Woodley Sports both ending in comfortable positions following promotion last term, with Abbey Hey and Maine Road also finishing well clear of the relegation places.

Nantwich Town and Atherton Collieries also garnered enough points from steady campaigns to avoid the bottom two places, but Glossop North End found themselves nervously looking over their shoulders towards the end of the season as their league form dipped dramatically.

Great Harwood Town, after occupying a bottom two place for much of the season and seeing their ground closed due to a foot and mouth outbreak, found their shooting boots at the end to climb clear, whilst the fight for the other safety position went down to the final match of the season where Flixton drew at Leek CSOB to send the Staffordshire side down, joining Cheadle Town who had earlier been relegated.

Warrington Town emulated Rossendale in their Second Division campaign which saw them stalk the leaders for the first half of the season before marching to the top thanks to consistency, and an iron nerve in key top of the table clashes. The Yellows now return to the top flight eager to find further success.

To complete a good season for the town of Warrington, Tetley Walker finished in second place after an excellent campaign which saw them stave off strong challenges from Nelson, Squires Gate and Blackpool Mechanics, but off the field problems left the club without a home for the coming season, and Tetley have subsequently resigned from the League.

Taking their place in the First Division are Atherton LR, who staged the biggest comeback since Lazarus to finish third after languishing in sixteenth place as recently as December, the arrival of Alan Lord from neighbours Atherton Collieries proving the catalyst for success.

For the second consecutive year, Nelson narrowly missed out despite playing some great football, whilst for Squires Gate and Blackpool Mechanics a fall away in form late on was to prove costly for the Fylde neighbours.

Alsager enjoyed a good season, particularly on their travels to Lancashire, Padiham claimed a top half spot in their first season back in the NWCFL, and Daisy Hill finsihed in a best ever league position in a morale boosting season for the Westhoughton club.

Chadderton, Darwen and Formby ended in mid-table spots just above Stone Dominoes, whose debut season promised much early on before a dramatic loss of form, and Bacup Borough's gradual improvement continued with another solid season.

Holker Old Boys, Bootle, Castleton Gabriels and Ashton Town all found the going mixed, with Colne and Oldham Town occupying the bottom two places at the conclusion of the season.

The Worthington Challenge Trophy saw the form book turned upside down with shocks coming thick and fast. Second Division Formby claimed the silverware after defeating Curzon Ashton on penalties after a 1-1 draw at Gigg Lane in a game they dominated for large spells, the Squirrels having already accounted for Salford City, Cheadle Town, Fleetwood Freeport and Kidsgrove Athletic en route to the Final. The League would like to thank Bass Brewers for sponsoring this season's Challenge Cup competition.

In the Second Division Trophy, Squires Gate made up for their league disappointment by defeating Bacup Borough 1-0 at Skelmersdale's White Moss Park to claim the first silverware for the Fylde side since they joined the NWCFL.

Only one county cup came to the NWCFL with Glossop North End boss Syd White weaving his county cup magic once again to win the Derbyshire Senior Cup with a penalties victory over Glapwell, White having led the Hillmen to back-to-back Manchester Premier Cup wins in the 1990s.

Leek CSOB reached the Staffordshire Senior Cup Semi-Final, with Salford City and Curzon Ashton reaching the same stage of the Manchester Premier Cup.

Finally, Salford City and Woodley Sports won the Northern and Southern sections of the reserve competition, with Salford also claiming the Reserve Division Cup to clinch a memorable double.

Scott White

HONOURS LIST 2000-01

FIRST DIVISION

Champions	Rossendale United
Runners Up	Clitheroe

SECOND DIVISION

Champions	Warrington Town
Runners Up	Tetley Walker

RESERVE DIVISION NORTH

Champions	Salford City
Runners Up	Clitheroe

RESERVE DIVISION SOUTH

Champions	Woodley Sports
Runners Up	Glossop North End

WORTHINGTON CHALLENGE TROPHY

Winners	Formby
Finalists	Curzon Ashton

SECOND DIVISION TROPHY

Winners	Squires Gate
Finalists	Bacup Borough

RESERVE DIVISION CUP

Winners	Salford City
Finalists	Colne

MONTHLY AWARD WINNERS 2000-01

FIRST DIVISION

	Manager of the Month	*Player of the Month*	*ICIS "Safe Hands" Award*
September	Benny Phillips (Mossley)	Mickey Bierne (Flixton)	Tommy Allen (Mossley)
October	Tommy Lawson (Prescot C)	Gary Jensen (Prescot C)	Mark Andrews (Rossendale)
November	Jim McCluskie (Rossendale)	Mike Norton (Woodley Spts)	Phil Wood (St Helens Town)
December	Mick Hoyle (Fleetwood Fprt)	Russ Brierley (Ramsbottom)	Steve Morris (Woodley Spts)
January	Ray Walker (Newcastle Town)	Paul Clarke (St Helens Town)	Simon Pay (Kidsgrove Ath)
February	Jimmy Wallace (Kidsgrove)	Gary Jensen (Prescot C)	Tim Mullock (Newcastle T)
March	Peter Hennerty (Formby)	Russ Brierley (Ramsbottom)	Steve Morris (Woodley Spts)
April	Russ Perkins (Skelmersdale)	Ross Clegg (Mossley)	Robbie Holcroft (Sk'sdale)

SECOND DIVISION

	Manager of the Month	*Player of the Month*	*ICIS "Safe Hands" Award*
September	Alan Aspinall (Tetley Walker)	Barry Massay (Atherton LR)	Stuart Barton (Blackpool M)
October	Graham Howarth (Padiham)	Rob Park (Blackpool M)	Neil McCormack (Warrington)
November	Gordon Fell (Squires Gate)	Mike Heverton (Warrington)	Gareth Gray (Squires Gate)
December	Alan Blair (Warrington)	Mark Wilson (Formby)	Darryl Sloane (Bacup Boro)
January	B Wilson/S Parker (B Mech)	Gavin Salmon (Atherton LR)	Thomas Baldwin (Black.l M)
February	Alan Aspinall (Tetley Walker)	Neal Smith (Tetley Walker)	Neil Canning (Nelson)
March	Jim McCluskie (Rossendale)	Carl Waters (Holker OB)	Adam Potts (Bacup Boro)
April	Alan Lord (Atherton LR)	Barry Massay (Atherton LR)	Ian Hartley (Padiham)

FINAL LEAGUE TABLES 2000-01

FIRST DIVISION

	P	W	D	L	F	A	Pts	GD
Rossendale Utd	42	29	5	8	114	44	92	70
Clitheroe	42	27	8	7	105	47	89	58
Ramsbottom Utd	42	28	4	10	85	44	88	41
St Helens Town	42	26	9	7	98	40	87	58
Fleetwood Freeport	42	26	4	12	90	50	82	40
Kidsgrove Athletic	42	24	10	8	81	46	82	35
Salford City	42	23	10	9	87	41	79	46
Prescot Cables	42	24	5	13	94	54	77	40
Newcastle Town	42	20	7	15	69	45	67	24
Mossley	42	19	7	16	73	56	64	17
Curzon Ashton	42	18	9	15	67	66	63	1
Skelmersdale Utd	42	17	8	17	69	69	59	0
Woodley Sports	42	16	9	17	69	69	57	0
Abbey Hey	42	15	6	21	76	92	51	-16
Maine Road	42	15	3	24	75	102	48	-27
Nantwich Town	42	10	9	23	46	79	39	-33
Atherton Collieries	42	11	6	25	43	88	39	-45
Glossop North End	42	9	4	29	41	111	31	-70
Great Harwood Tn	42	7	9	26	44	93	30	-49
Flixton	42	5	13	24	47	100	28	-53
Leek CSOB	42	5	12	25	39	89	27	-50
Cheadle Town	42	5	9	28	42	129	24	-87

SECOND DIVISION

	P	W	D	L	F	A	Pts	GD
Warrington Town	38	24	7	7	90	31	79	59
Tetley Walker	38	24	5	9	83	41	77	42
Atherton LR	38	24	3	11	88	50	75	38
Nelson	38	21	11	6	89	44	74	45
Squires Gate	38	21	7	10	75	47	70	28
Blackpool Mechanics	38	21	6	11	85	47	69	38
Alsager	38	19	8	11	48	42	65	6
Padiham	38	20	4	14	83	71	64	12
Daisy Hill	38	18	6	14	78	80	60	-2
Chadderton	38	17	7	14	68	58	58	10
Darwen	38	16	7	15	72	66	55	6
Formby	38	15	8	15	65	56	53	9
Stone Dominoes	38	15	6	17	62	63	51	-1
Bacup Borough	38	13	9	16	59	60	48	-1
Holker Old Boys	38	14	5	19	67	79	47	-12
Bootle	38	11	8	19	70	76	41	-6
Castleton Gabriels	38	10	7	21	52	90	37	-38
Ashton Town	38	8	3	27	46	98	27	-52
Colne	38	4	4	30	37	107	16	-70
Oldham Town	38	3	3	32	38	149	12	-111

RESERVE DIVISION NORTH

	P	W	D	L	F	A	Pts	GD
Salford City	20	17	0	3	47	15	51	32
Clitheroe	20	13	2	5	60	28	41	32
Maine Road	20	11	3	6	41	29	36	12
Rossendale Utd	20	10	1	9	40	43	31	-3
Fleetwood Freeport	20	8	3	9	57	49	27	8
Colne	20	8	2	10	39	40	26	-1
Nelson	20	7	5	8	34	39	26	-5
Padiham	20	8	2	10	43	51	26	-8
Chadderton	20	7	4	9	41	48	25	-7
Squires Gate	20	5	7	8	36	43	22	-7
Bacup Borough	20	1	1	18	20	73	4	-53

RESERVE DIVISION SOUTH

	P	W	D	L	F	A	Pts	GD
Woodley Sports	20	13	2	5	56	26	41	30
Glossop North End	20	11	5	4	38	28	38	10
Newcastle Town	20	10	7	3	40	23	37	17
Abbey Hey	20	9	6	5	41	32	33	9
Curzon Ashton	20	10	2	8	45	31	32	14
Ashton Town	20	8	4	8	31	28	28	3
Atherton LR	20	8	3	9	38	38	27	0
Daisy Hill	20	8	2	10	31	39	26	-8
Flixton	20	5	7	8	28	39	22	-11
Cheadle Town	20	4	4	12	25	46	16	-21
Atherton Collieries	20	2	2	16	19	62	8	-43

LEADING GOALSCORERS 2000-01

FIRST DIVISION

		L	C	T
Craig Sargeson	Rossendale Utd	34	5	39
Terry Fearns	St Helens Town	32	6	38
Jock Russell	Maine Road	35	2	37
Gary Jensen	Prescot Cables	30	5	35
Russ Brierley	Ramsbottom Utd	28	7	35
Mike Norton	Woodley Sports	25	4	29
Lee Cryer	Clitheroe	18	11	29
Lee Cooper	St Helens Town	24	4	28
Neil Spencer	Clitheroe	21	7	28
Steve O'Neill	Prescot Cables	23	3	26
Kevin Barnes	Fleetwood F'port	21	3	24
Tony Carroll	Salford City	21	3	24
Kevin Leadbetter	Skelmersdale Utd	20	4	24
Darren Twigg	Kidsgrove Athletic	22	1	23
David Gray	Rossendale Utd	17	6	23
Peter Smith	Fleetwood F'port	14	9	23

SECOND DIVISION

		L	C	T
Paul Baker	Darwen	30	4	34
Carl Waters	Holker Old Boys	31	2	33
Lee Chambers	Padiham	29	4	33
Barry Massay	Atherton LR	22	5	27
Scott Sugden	Squires Gate	21	5	26
Rob Park	Blackpool Mechanics	22	1	23
Paul Ryder	Bootle	19	4	23
Mark Wilson	Formby	17	6	23
Keith Johnstone	Blackpool Mechanics	17	5	22
Steve Longworth	Squires Gate	14	7	21
Jonathon Irvine	Nelson	20	0	20
Ryan Cain	Daisy Hill	18	2	20
Kiko Rodrigues	Nelson	18	2	20
Mike Heveren	Warrington Town	17	3	20

FIRST DIVISION RESULTS CHART 2000-01

		1	2	3	4	5	6	7	8	9	10	11	12	13	14	15	16	17	18	19	20	21	22
1	Abbey Hey	X	1-0	7-0	0-0	0-1	1-5	4-0	4-0	1-1	0-1	2-2	5-1	1-2	2-2	3-1	1-3	2-1	1-2	0-4	1-3	0-4	2-3
2	Atherton C	2-5	X	3-2	0-2	0-4	0-6	1-2	1-1	2-0	0-1	3-1	3-2	0-1	0-0	3-2	3-2	0-2	0-3	1-0	3-1	1-0	0-4
3	Cheadle	1-1	2-1	X	1-4	0-0	3-4	2-0	3-0	1-1	0-5	0-0	0-2	0-1	3-2	2-4	0-4	0-3	1-6	1-3	1-1	1-3	2-2
4	Clitheroe	3-5	4-2	13-0	X	2-2	1-0	2-4	4-0	6-1	1-0	4-1	3-0	1-1	3-0	0-1	2-1	2-1	1-2	0-0	1-0	3-1	5-1
5	Curzon	0-4	5-2	2-2	0-1	X	1-2	1-0	4-1	3-0	0-2	3-1	2-3	1-0	3-1	3-2	0-2	0-3	0-0	1-3	0-0	4-0	1-0
6	Fleetwood	4-2	2-1	2-0	4-0	1-1	X	2-2	3-0	1-0	1-3	1-0	4-3	3-1	1-0	2-0	3-2	4-1	0-1	1-2	1-0	2-1	1-1
7	Flixton	1-2	3-0	1-1	1-2	2-4	1-4	X	1-5	0-0	0-2	1-1	3-1	1-6	3-2	2-2	2-2	1-5	0-4	4-4	1-2	0-1	0-0
8	Glossop NE	2-3	0-3	1-0	0-3	0-0	1-5	2-2	X	2-0	1-2	3-1	1-4	0-4	2-3	1-2	1-2	0-1	1-2	0-3	1-2	0-2	0-3
9	Gt Harwood	2-1	1-0	6-1	1-2	1-3	0-3	2-2	5-0	X	2-3	0-1	1-6	2-2	0-2	0-2	0-1	2-3	2-3	0-1	1-1	0-2	2-1
10	Kidsgrove	3-4	4-0	1-1	1-1	1-0	1-1	3-1	0-1	3-3	X	5-0	2-1	1-4	2-1	1-0	0-3	1-1	2-2	0-0	0-2	5-2	0-1
11	Leek CSOB	1-1	0-1	4-0	1-3	0-1	1-4	1-1	1-2	4-0	1-1	X	1-2	0-2	1-1	1-0	0-5	2-5	0-4	0-0	0-4	1-1	2-4
12	Maine Road	5-2	3-3	3-2	3-3	3-2	3-4	3-0	2-3	3-2	1-3	4-1	X	0-0	4-2	0-1	2-4	0-3	0-1	1-2	0-3	1-8	2-0
13	Mossley	1-2	2-0	3-2	1-1	3-0	1-2	2-0	2-2	3-0	0-2	3-0	2-1	X	0-1	1-3	2-0	1-2	0-3	1-2	5-4	2-1	1-1
14	Nantwich	2-1	1-1	1-0	0-5	3-1	0-1	0-0	0-1	2-0	1-2	1-3	3-1	1-5	X	0-0	0-1	1-2	2-3	0-4	1-2	3-2	1-2
15	Newcastle	4-1	6-0	2-0	0-3	2-3	1-0	2-0	2-1	0-0	1-1	2-0	6-0	0-1	2-0	X	0-1	4-0	0-1	1-0	1-2	2-2	3-0
16	Prescot	4-1	2-1	6-1	3-1	6-0	2-1	2-2	5-0	0-2	1-1	7-1	0-2	4-3	5-0	0-2	X	1-0	0-2	0-2	1-1	0-1	2-1
17	Ramsbottom	1-0	1-0	1-2	0-1	1-1	3-2	2-1	3-0	1-1	0-3	1-1	6-1	4-1	2-0	3-0	2-0	X	3-0	2-4	1-0	3-0	3-0
18	Rossendale	3-0	5-1	9-1	1-3	4-1	2-1	6-1	8-0	7-1	4-2	1-1	2-0	2-0	1-2	2-1	1-1	0-1	X	1-2	2-2	7-1	3-1
19	St Helens	10-2	2-0	3-1	1-2	5-2	2-0	5-0	9-2	4-0	0-2	0-0	2-0	1-1	1-1	2-1	3-1	1-2	3-0	X	1-1	2-1	1-2
20	Salford C	5-0	2-0	7-0	1-4	2-2	1-0	2-0	3-0	4-0	0-2	2-1	3-0	1-0	4-0	1-2	0-1	3-0	3-1	1-1	X	4-0	4-2
21	Skelmersdale	2-0	0-0	2-0	2-2	1-2	2-1	1-0	3-1	0-2	2-3	1-0	1-2	3-2	1-1	1-1	4-3	0-1	2-1	2-3	3-3	X	3-0
22	Woodley	0-1	1-1	5-2	3-1	0-3	2-1	5-1	1-2	6-0	1-4	3-1	3-0	1-0	2-2	1-1	3-4	1-5	0-2	2-0	0-0	0-0	X

SECOND DIVISION RESULTS CHART 2000-01

		1	2	3	4	5	6	7	8	9	10	11	12	13	14	15	16	17	18	19	20
1	Alsager	X	2-1	1-0	1-0	1-1	0-1	0-0	2-1	1-2	2-4	1-0	3-2	2-1	0-1	5-0	1-4	0-2	2-2	0-2	0-0
2	Ashton T	0-2	X	1-2	2-0	0-3	1-1	2-1	1-0	1-2	3-2	1-3	0-4	3-5	1-4	1-0	0-2	1-0	2-5	1-2	1-2
3	Atherton LR	1-3	2-1	X	4-1	3-0	2-0	1-2	4-0	3-0	2-0	2-1	2-3	1-0	1-3	4-3	3-1	0-2	2-0	1-1	0-3
4	Bacup Boro	1-2	4-3	0-2	X	0-1	0-0	5-2	1-2	3-4	1-3	0-0	2-1	3-0	0-1	4-2	1-3	4-1	3-1	2-0	0-4
5	Blackpool M	0-0	2-0	1-4	3-2	X	4-0	4-1	2-5	2-2	3-1	0-1	0-3	2-2	0-0	5-1	4-1	1-1	2-1	2-1	0-4
6	Bootle	3-1	2-2	1-6	1-2	0-4	X	3-0	1-2	2-1	2-2	4-2	2-0	2-1	1-1	12-0	0-3	0-1	0-2	4-4	1-3
7	Castleton G	0-0	2-2	2-4	0-1	1-6	2-2	X	0-2	3-1	0-3	1-1	2-0	3-1	3-3	3-2	5-1	1-3	2-1	2-5	0-4
8	Chadderton	2-0	8-1	0-3	2-1	0-3	0-2	2-0	X	3-2	5-2	0-1	1-1	3-0	2-2	2-0	2-0	2-1	1-1	0-4	0-3
9	Colne	0-3	2-1	0-5	0-2	0-3	1-2	0-3	2-2	X	0-2	1-3	2-4	0-1	1-5	2-2	2-3	0-5	1-1	0-5	0-5
10	Daisy Hill	0-1	3-1	1-4	2-2	0-7	2-1	5-1	3-1	3-2	X	0-0	5-3	4-1	1-1	3-0	2-1	4-4	3-2	2-1	1-1
11	Darwen	0-4	5-1	3-4	2-2	0-1	5-4	1-1	2-1	1-0	1-4	X	3-1	7-3	1-1	3-2	1-2	4-1	1-0	1-3	1-0
12	Formby	0-0	5-2	1-0	0-1	2-1	2-1	3-1	1-1	2-1	2-1	2-1	X	2-2	1-2	6-0	3-0	2-1	0-1	0-2	1-2
13	Holker OB	6-0	4-0	1-0	0-0	0-6	3-3	2-0	2-3	2-1	1-3	3-5	2-1	X	3-2	5-0	2-2	2-0	2-0	2-3	3-1
14	Nelson	0-2	3-2	2-2	3-2	2-1	4-1	3-0	2-1	4-0	6-0	2-1	0-0	1-0	X	5-0	6-1	3-3	0-2	0-1	3-4
15	Oldham T	0-1	0-2	1-4	1-4	0-6	1-6	1-4	1-0	5-2	2-3	1-5	3-3	3-1	2-2	X	0-6	0-2	0-1	0-2	1-9
16	Padiham	3-0	3-2	4-1	1-1	0-2	3-2	4-0	5-2	2-1	6-1	4-1	0-0	1-2	0-6	8-1	X	1-0	4-2	1-4	0-2
17	Squires Gate	0-1	5-0	3-5	1-1	0-2	2-1	3-1	0-0	2-1	1-0	2-1	2-1	2-1	0-0	4-1	5-1	X	4-1	3-1	2-0
18	Stone Dom	1-2	1-2	1-2	4-2	1-0	3-1	2-3	0-5	3-1	1-0	3-3	2-2	4-0	1-3	2-0	3-0	1-4	X	1-2	1-1
19	Tetley Wlkr	1-2	3-0	1-0	1-1	1-0	2-1	3-0	1-1	4-0	3-1	1-0	3-1	4-1	2-3	7-2	0-0	1-2	1-3	X	0-1
20	Warrington	0-0	2-1	2-2	0-0	6-1	2-0	4-0	1-4	4-0	5-2	3-1	2-0	2-0	1-0	5-0	1-2	1-1	0-1	0-1	X

LEADING GOALSCORERS 2000-01

FIRST DIVISION		L	C	T
Craig Sargeson	Rossendale United	34	5	39
Terry Fearns	St Helens Town	32	6	38
Jock Russell	Maine Road	35	2	37
Gary Jensen	Prescot Cables	30	5	35
Russ Brierley	Ramsbottom United	28	7	35
Mike Norton	Woodley Sports	25	4	29
Lee Cryer	Clitheroe	18	11	29
Lee Cooper	St Helens Town	24	4	28
Neil Spencer	Clitheroe	21	7	28
Steve O'Neill	Prescot Cables	23	3	26
Kevin Barnes	Fleetwood Freeport	21	3	24
Tony Carroll	Salford City	21	3	24
Kevin Leadbetter	Skelmersdale Utd	20	4	24

SECOND DIVISION		L	C	T
Paul Baker	Darwen	30	4	34
Carl Waters	Holker Old Boys	31	2	33
Lee Chambers	Padiham	29	4	33
Barry Massay	Atherton LR	22	5	27
Scott Sugden	Squires Gate	21	5	26
Rob Park	Blackpool Mechanics	22	1	23
Paul Ryder	Bootle	19	4	23
Mark Wilson	Formby	17	6	23
Keith Johnstone	Blackpool Mechanics	17	5	22
Steve Longworth	Squires Gate	14	7	21
Jonathon Irvine	Nelson	20	0	20
Ryan Cain	Daisy Hill	18	2	20
Kiko Rodrigues	Nelson	18	2	20
Mike Heveren	Warrington Town	17	3	20

ABBEY HEY

Secretary: Gordon Lester, 6 Newhaven Avenue, Hr.Openshaw, Manchestewr M11 1HU
Tel Nos: 0161 370 0270 (H) 0161 200 4630 (W)

Ground: Abbey Stadium, Goredale Avenue, Gorton, Manchester 18
Tel: 0161 231 7147 (Club) Fax: 01823 490281

Directions: A57 towards Hyde, right into Woodland Avenue approx one & a half miles past Belle Vue junction, right again into Ryder Brow Rd, 1st left after bridge into Goredale Ave. **Nearest Railway Station:** Ryder Brow
Capacity: 1000 Seats: 100 Cover: 300 Floodlights: Yes

Honours Manchester Amat. Lge 65-66: S.E. Lancs Lge 66-67, 68-69 R-up 67-68; Div.2 68-69; Lge Shield 65-66: Manc. Co. Amat. Cup 64-65, 67-68, 68-69, R-up 63-64: Manchester Lge Prem. Div. 81-82, 88-89, 90-91, 93-94, 94-95; Div. 1 70-71; Div.2 88-89, 92-93, 93-94; Gilcryst Cup 76-77, 88-89, R-up 97-88; Open Tphy 78-79,79-80, 92-93: Manchester Chall. Tphy 82-83, 95-96, 96-97. N.W. Trains Div 2 R-up 98-99

Previous Leagues: Manchester Amateur; South East Lancs; Manchester Lge.

Record Attendance: 400 v Manchester City XI oct 99

FACT FILE

Formed: 1902
Colours:Red& black/black/black
Midweek matchday: Tuesday

CLUB PERSONNEL

Chairman: James Whittaker
0161 445 0036

Emergency Contact; G.Lester
0161 370 0270 or 0161 236 3311 ext 2800

ATHERTON COLLIERIES

Secretary: Emil Anderson, 109 Douglas St, Atherton M46 9EB Tel Nos: 01942 879209 (H) 0161 288 6355 (W) 0792 937461 (M) Email: geocities.com/ath-c-g-c

Ground: Atherton Colls Football Ground,Alder St., Atherton, Gt ManchesterTel:01942884649.

Directions: M61 Jct 5, follow sign for Westhoughton, left onto A6, right ontoA579 (Newbrook Rd/Bolton Rd) into Atherton. At first set of lights turn leftinto High Street, 2nd left into Alder St. to ground. Quarter mile from AthertonCentral (BR).
Seats: 300 Cover: 1,000 Capacity: 2,500 Floodlights: Yes

Clubhouse: Open Mon-Fri 7-11pm, Sat 11am-11pm, Sun noon-3 & 7-10.30pm. Hot &cold food on matchdays. **Club Shop:** No, but programmes & badges are available

PREVIOUS Leagues: Bolton Combination 20-50, 52-71; Lancs Combination 50-52, 71-78; Cheshire County 78-82.

HONOURS: BNWCFL 3rd Div Champ 86/87; Bridge Shield 85/86; Lancs County FA Shield19/20, 22/23, 41/42, 45/46. 56/57, 64/65; Tennents F/lit Trophy Finalist 94/95; NWCFL Div 2 R/up 95/96

RECORDS **Attendance:** 3,300 in Lancs Combination, 1920's

Players Progressing: J Parkinson (Wigan), Russell Beardsmore(Manchester Utd).

FACT FILE

Founded: 1916
Nickname: Colls
Club Sponsors: Kensite
Colours: Black & white stripes/white/white..
Change colours: Yellow/blue/yellow
Reserves' Lge: NWTL Res Div
Midweek Matches: Tuesday
Programme: 40 pages, 70p
Editor: Secretary
2000-01 Captain: Paul Griffin
Top Scorer: Ian Gibson
Club Website:
geocities@frank35.freeserve.co.uk

CLUB PERSONNEL

Chairman: Steve Payne
Vice Chairman:
President: J Fielding
Managers: Denis Haslam & Tommy Feste
Physio: Chris Roberts

ATHERTON L.R.

Secretary: Steve Hartle, 32 Greensmith Way, Westhoughton,Bolton BL5 3DR (01942840906-H)

Ground: Crilly Park, Spa Road, Atherton, Greater Manchester (01942 883950).

Directions: M61 to Jct 5, follow signs for Westhoughton, left onto A6, right onto A579 (Newbrook Rd/Bolton Rd) over the railway bridge, right into Upton Rd passing Atherton Central Station, left into Springfield Rd and left again into Hillside Rd into Spa Rd and ground.
Capacity: 3,000 Seats: 250 Cover: 3 sections Floodlights: Yes

Clubhouse: Open normal licensing hours. **Club Shop:** No

PREVIOUS **Name:** Laburnum Rovers 56-80 **Grounds:** Laburnum Road 56-58 Hagfold 58-66
Leagues: Bolton Comb.; Cheshire County 80-82; NWCL 82-94; NPL 94-97.

RECORDS **Attendance:** 1,856 v Aldershot Town, FA Vase Quarter-Final replay 5/3/94.
Appearances: Jimmy Evans **Fee Paid:** £500 for Joey Dunn from Warrington T.
Scorer: Shaun Parker **Fee Received:** £1,500 for Stuart Humphries to Barrow

BEST SEASON **FA Cup:** 3rd Qual Rd 96-97, 0-2 v Bamber Bridge
FA Vase: Semi-Final rep. 94-95, 1-2 v Diss Town **FA Trophy:** 1st Qual Rd 96-97

HONOURS: North West Co Lge 92-93 93-94, Champs Trophy 92-93 93-94, F/Lit Trophy 93-94; N.P.L.Div.1 Cup R-up 95-96,Goldline Trophy 98-99, Bolton Hosp Cup: 84-85; W.Houghton Ch C 81-82

Players progressing to Football League: Barry Butler (Chester), Lee Unsworth(Crewe).

FACT FILE

Formed: 1956
Nickname: The Panthers
Sponsors: Bolton Evening News
Colours: Yellow & Navy
Change colours: Green & White
Midweek Matches: Tuesday
Reserves' League: North West Co Res Div
Programme: 48 pages 70p (Best in league)
Editor: Tim Lees
Local Radio: GMR

CLUB PERSONNEL

Chairman:Alan Grundy
Financial Director: Terry Poole
Manager: Alan Lord Ass Manr: Jason Holroyd
Coach: Danny Johnson

CLITHEROE

Secretary: Colin Wilson, 4 Moss Street, Clitheroe, Lancs BB7 1DP
Tel/Fax: 01200 424370 Mobile: 07714 382232

Ground: Shawbridge, Clitheroe, Lancs (01200 423344).
Directions: M6 jct 31, A59 to Clitheroe (17 miles), at 5th r'bout continue for half a mile and turn left at Pendle Road. Ground one mile, behind Bridge Inn' on the right. 11 miles from Blackburn BR station: Clitheroe
Capacity: 2,000 Seats: 300 Cover: 1200 Floodlights: Yes
Clubhouse: Open during matches. Snacks available **Club Shop:** Yes.

HONOURS FA Vase Runners-up 95-96; Lancs Comb. 79-80, Lg Cup 34-35; Lancs Challenge Tphy 84-85; NW C Lge 85-86, Div 2 84-85, Div 3 83-84; East Lancs Floodlit Trophy 94-95.N.W.Trains Floodlit Cup: 98-99

PREVIOUS Leagues: Blackburn & Dist.; Lancs Comb. 03-04 05-10 25-82.

BEST SEASON FA Cup: FA Vase: Runners-up 95-96

RECORDS Attendance: 2,000 v Mangotsfield, FA Vase Semi/F 95-96.
Goalscorer: Don Francis Appearances: Lindsey Wallace.

Players progressing Ray Woods (Leeds 1950), Chris Sims (Blackburn 1960), Lee Rogerson (Wigan Ath), Carlo Nash (Crystal Palace).

FACT FILE

Formed: 1877.
Nickname: The Blues
Colours: Blue & white /blue/blue
Change colours: All yellow
Midweek matchday: Tuesday
Reserves' Lge: N.W.C.L

Chairman: S Rush

CONGLETON TOWN

Secretary and Press Officer: David Wilcock, 4,Maxwell Rd., Congleton, Cheshire CW12 3HY.
Tel: 01260 276347 (H) 01260 270275 (B) Email address: Accessed from website

GROUND Booth Street Ground, Crescent Road, Congleton, Cheshire Tel: 02602 74460
Directions: On approach to Congleton via Clayton bypass take second right after fire station, into Booth Street. Two miles from Congleton (BR)
Capacity: 5,000 Cover: 1,200 Seats: 250
Clubhouse: Open match days only **Club Shop:** Yes. Contact:Gerry Brocklehurst
PREVIOUS **Leagues:** Crewe & Dist; North Staffs; Macclesfield; Cheshire 20-39, 46-65, 78-82; Mid Cheshire 68-78; Nth West Co 82-87, N.P.L. 87-01
Name: Congleton Hornets (prior to current club's formation in 1901)
CLUB RECORDS **Attendance:** 7,000 v Macclesfield, League 53-54 **Fee Paid:** None.
Goalscorer: Mick Biddle 150+ **Fee Received:** £5,000 for D Frost (Leeds)
Appearances: Ray Clack 600+ & Graham Harrison 600+
BEST SEASON **FA Trophy:** 3rd Qual. Rd 89-90 90-91. **FA Vase:** 4th Rd 76-77 80-81
FA Cup: 1st Rd 89-90, 0-2 v Crewe A. (A) League clubs defeated: None
HONOURS North West Counties League R-up 85-86; Cheshire County League R-up 20-2121-22 (Div 2 81-82); Mid Cheshire League 73-74 75-76 77-78 (R-up 69-70 71-72 76-77, League Cup 71-72; Cheshire Senior Cup 20-21 37-38
Players progressing: Ron Broad (Crewe 55), Jack Mycock (Shrewsbury 58),Steve Davies (Port Vale 87), L Hamlet (Leeds), Jimmy Quinn (West Ham), Ian Brightwell (Man City)

FACT FILE
Formed: 1901 Nickname: Bears
Colours:White &blacktrim/black/black & white
Change colours:Red & White
Midweek home matchday: Tuesday
Website:http://members.aol.com/beartown
Programme: Pages: 48 Price: £1.00
Editor: Ken Mead c/oClub
Local Radio: Radio Stoke, Signal.

2000-01
Captain: Steve Callear
P.o.Y.: Lyndon Beardmore
Top Scorer: Rod Thornley 18

CLUB PERSONNEL
Chairman: Peter Evans
Vice Chairman: Steve Burgess
Manager:Sean Connor
Assistant Manager: Darren Washington
Coach: John Brown
Physio: Paul Kelly

CURZON ASHTON

Secretary: Robert Hurst, 36 Russell Road, Partington, Manachester M31 4DZ
Tel: 0161 775 3883 Fax 0161 775 8787 Mob 0771 325 2310 Email:curzonashton@byford.co.uk
Ground: National Park, Katherine Street, Ashton-under-Lyne OL7 6DA (0161 330 6033)
Directions: M60 Jct 23 to Ashton- u -Lyme on Manchester Rd (A635) then turn into Williams Street.Ground at bottom of road.One and a half miles from Ashton-under-Lyne (BR)
Capacity: 5,000 Cover: 450 Seats: 350 Floodlights: Yes
Clubhouse: Every night. Food on matchdays. **Club Shop:** Contact Roy Howe, 0161 220 8345

PREVIOUS **Leagues:** Manchester Amat.; Manchester (-1978); Cheshire Co. 78-82; N.W C. 82-86 Northern Prem. Lge. 87-97, N.C.E. 97-98, N.W.C. 98-01

BEST SEASON **FA Cup:** 3rd Qual. Rd replay 89-90, 1-3 v Mossley (A) after 1-1
FA Vase: Semi-Final 79-80 **FA Trophy:** 2nd Qual. Rd 82-83, 84-85

HONOURS **NWC Lge Div.2 r-up 99-00;** Cheshire Co. Lge Div 2 R-up 78-79: Manchester Lge 77-78, R-up 74-75 75-76; Lge Cup 77-78, R-up 74-75 75-76; Murray Shield R-up 75-76: Manchester Amat. Lge 63-64 65-66, R-up 64-65: Manchester Prem. Cup x 5

RECORDS **Attendance:** 1,826 v Stamford, FA Vase SF 1980
Goalscorer: Alan Sykes **Appearances:** Alan Sykes 620
Win: 7-0 v Ashton United **Defeat:** 0-8 v Bamber Bridge

FACT FILE
Formed: 1963Nickname: The Blues
Colours: All Blue Change colours: All Red
Midweek matches: Tuesday
Programme: 40pages £1.00
Editor: Robert Hurst (0161 775 3883)
2000-01 Capt: M Wearden P.o.Y.: P Wearden
Top Scorer: Josh Mittan
Website: www.curzon-ashton.co.uk
CLUB PERSONNEL
Chairman: Harry Galloway
Vice Chairman: R.onnie Capstick
Chief Executive: Harry Twamley
President: Peter Mayo
Press Officer:Graham Shuttleworth
Treasurer: Sam Shuttleworth
Manager: Gary Lowe
Assistant Manager: Derek Hall
Physio: Martin Rothwell

FLEETWOOD FREEPORT

Secretary: Kevin Pennington, 1 Carlisle Avenue, Fleetwood, Lancs. FY7 8LP.
Tel: 01253 771602 (H); 01253 822626 (B) 07967 192843 (M)
Email Address: fleetwoodfreeportfc@btinternet .com
or:kevin@fffcfreeserve.co.uk

Ground: Highbury Stadium, Park Avenue, Fleetwood, Lancs (01253 770702)

Directions: From M55, junction 3, follow signs (A585) to Fleetwood. At Nautical College campus (onleft) traffic island take first left, at second island take 6th exit. Stadium is 3/4 mile on left.

Floodlights: Yes

PREVIOUS **Leagues:** None **Names:** Fleetwood Wanderers (97-98)

RECORD **Attendance:** 6,150 v Rochdale F.A.Cup 1st Round 65-66

HONOURS NWCFL v 2 Champions: 98-99 Div 2 trophy Winners: 98-99

FACT FILE

Founded: 1997

(amalgamation of Fleetwood F.C. and Fleetwood Town who had disbanded at the end of season 1995-96)

Colours: Red & white/black/red

Midweek Matchday: Tuesday

Club Website: www.fleetwoodfreeportfc.co.uk

CLUB PERSONNEL

Chairman: Jim Betmead

31 St. Peters Place, Fleetwood, Lancs. FY7 6EB.

Tel: 01253 771550 (H); 0966 414750 (B)

2000-01

Captain & P.O.Y.: Steve Hartley

Top Goalscorer:Kevin Barnes 26

FLIXTON

Secretary: Terry Langford, 56 Garstang Ave, Bolton, BL2 6JN Tel: 07939 557261 (M)
Ground: Valley Road, Flixton, Manchester M41 8RQ Tel: 0161 748 2903
Directions: Leave M60 take B5214 signed Urmston. At 2nd R'about take 3rd exit. Take right only lane on the exit into Davyhulme Rd. Follow road to Valley Rd, just after a left hand bend after 1.5 miles. Ground is at the other end of the road. Coaches as above and carry on to the next R'about take 4th exit (Woodbridge Rd). The ground is at the bottom of this road.
Capacity: 2,000 Cover: 650 Seats: 250
Clubhouse: Open daily 1.00pm-11pm. Sandwiches available most eves **Club Shop:** No
PREVIOUS **Leagues:** South Manchester & Wythenshawe 60-63; Lancs & Cheshire 63-73; Manchester 73-86; North West Counties 86-96; Northern Premier 97-00
CLUB RECORDS **Attendance:** 1:1,543 v Brigg Town FA Vase Semi-Final 95-96
Goalscorer: John Mitchell **Appearances:** John Mitchell & Stan Matthews
Win: 10-2 Irlam 94-95 **Defeat:** 1-10 v Knowsley Utd 90-91
BEST SEASON **FA Cup:** 1st Qual. Rd replay 91-92, 1-2 v Mossley (A) after 1-1
FA Vase: Semi-final 95-96 v Brigg Town
HONOURS N.W.Co Div I 95-96, Div 2 94-95 Lg.Cup 94-95 95-96 (R-up 87-88), Div 3 R-up 86-87; Manc. Lg R-up 78-79 81-82 85-86, Div 1 77-78, Open Tphy 80-81; Lancs Amtr Cup 79-80 (R-up 80-81); Manc. Chal. Tphy 83-84 (R-up x2 84-86); Manc. Prem. Cup R-up 86-87 91-92; Manc. Amtr Cup R-up 88-89

FACT FILE

Formed: 1960
Nickname: Valley Roaders
Colours: Blue & white stripes/blue/blue
Change Colours: Gold/black/black
Midweek home matchday: Tuesday
Reserves' League: North West Alliance
Programme - Pages: 36 Price: £1.00
Editor: T.B.A.

CLUB PERSONNEL

Chairman: John Mitchell
President: F H Eadie
Manager: Alan McGreevy
Club Email: footytel@cwcom.net
Matchday Tel: - As Secretary

GLOSSOP NORTH END

Secretary: Peter Hammond, 15 Longmoor Road, Simmondley, Glossop, Derbys SK139NH
Tel: 01457 863852(H) 01457 854411(B)

Ground: Surrey Street, Glossop, Derbys (01457 855469).
Directions: A57 to Glossop.Left at traffic lights (near Tresco sign) into Glossopbrook Road then Follow road to top of hill and ground is on right. Buses 236 and 237 from Manchesterpass ground. Railway Station: Glossop Central.
Capacity: 2,374 Seats: 209 Cover: 509 Floodlights: Yes
Clubhouse: Licensed bar. Hot & cold drinks and pies etc on matchdays. **Club Shop:** Yes

HONOURS NWC Lge Lamot Pils Tphy 90-91; Manchester Lg 27-28(Gilgryst Cup 22-23 29-30 34-35 74-75); FA Amateur Cup QF 08-09. Manchester Premier Cup 1997 and 1998. Derbyshire Senior Cup 2000-01.
PREVIOUS **Leagues:** Midland 1896-98; Football Lge 1898-1915; Manchester Lge 15-56 66-78; Lancs Combination 56-66; Cheshire County 78-82.
Names: Glossop North End 1886-1898; Glossop FC 1898-1992.
BEST SEASON **FA Cup:** Quarter Final 1909 **FA Vase:**
RECORDS **Attendance:** 10,736 v Preston North End, FA Cup 1913/14
Fee paid: £3,000 for Andy Gorton (Lincoln City, 1989).
Fee received: £3,000 for Andy Gorton (Oldham Athletic, 1990).
Players progressing: Jimmy Rollands (Rochdale), Ray Redshaw (Wigan Athletic).

FACT FILE

Founded: 1886 Re-formed 1992
Nickname: Hillmen
Sponsor: T.B.A.
Colours: All royal Blue
Change colours: All gold.
Midweek Matches: Tuesday
Reserves' League: N.W.Co Res Lg
Programme: 32 pages, 50p
Editor: John Hamilton (01457 866216)

CLUB PERSONNEL

Chairman: Syd White
President: C T Boak
Press Officer: Secretary
Manager: Micky Boyle
Asst Manager: Ian Boyle
Physio:Mick Parr

Curzon Ashton line up before their Worthington Challenge Trophy Final at Bury FC's ground. The Division One side were beaten by Second Division Formby FC on penalties after drawing 1-1 after extra time. Photo: Colin Stevens

Daisy Hill

Fleetwood Freeport FC

GREAT HARWOOD TOWN

Secretary: Mark Jones, 15 Elm Close, Rishton, Blackburn, BB1 4HN Tel: 01254 876822(H)
Ground: The Sportsmans, Wood Street, Great Harwood, Lancs Tel: 01254 883913
Directions: M66 from Manchester to Haslingden exit, A680 through Baxenden, Accrington to Clayton-le-Moors, left at the Hyndburn Bridge Hotel into Hyndburn Road and right into Wood Street to ground. Or M6 jct 31,Clitheroe/Skipton road to Trafalgar Hotel, A677 to Blackburn, left at Moat House Hotel and follow ring-road to M65 junction, A678 to Rishton, left at lights (B6536) to Gt Harwood, right at Town Gate into Queen Str., follow signs for Lomax Square, left into Park Rd, right into Balfour Street to ground. 3miles from Rishton (BR), 6 miles from Blackburn (BR). Various buses from Heyes Lane & Park Road to Blackburn & Accrington
Capacity: 2,500 Cover: 700 Seats: 200
Clubhouse: The Sportsman just outside ground. Normal licensing hours. Full bar facilities. Squash courts and gym. Hot & cold snacks & drinks on matchdays from tea bar in ground
Club Shop: Sells programmes, badges, key rings, shirts. Contact: J McKay (c/o club)

HONOURS North West Counties League R-up 91-92 (Div 2 90-91, Lamot Pils Tphy 89-90 (R-up 90-91), Tennents Floodlit Trophy 91-92), Lancs ATS Challenge Trophy 91-92 (R-up 90-91)

PREVIOUS Leagues: West Lancashire; Lancs Comb. 79-82; N.W.C. 82-92; N.P.L. 92-99

CLUB RECORDS **Attendance:** 5,397 v Manchester Utd, 1980.
BEST SEASON **FA Cup:** 1st Qual. Round replay 92-93, 1-2 v Atherton LR (H), after 1-1
FA Vase: Quarter Finals 90-91, 1-2 v Littlehampton Town (A)

FACT FILE

Formed: 1965
Nickname: Robins
Club Sponsors: None
Colours: All red
Change colours: All blue
Midweek Matches: Monday
Reserves' league: West Lancs Lge
Programme: Pages: 20 Price: 20p
Editor: D Bennet

CLUB PERSONNEL

Chairman: William Holden
Press Officer: K Lambert
Commercial Manager: Mark Smith
Manager: M Crabbe
Asst Manager: Dave Sargent

KIDSGROVE ATHLETIC

Secretary: Alan Thompson, 7 Sandown Road, Crewe, Cheshire CW1 3TE
Tel: 01270 256588 (H) 07712 956400 (M)

Ground: Clough Hall, Hollinswood Road, Kidsgrove, Stoke-on-Trent, Staffs
Tel: 01782 782412

Directions: M6 Jct 16, A500 towards Stoke, 2nd jctn onto A34 towards Manchester, turn right at 1st lights down hill,rt at lights into Cedar Rd , 2nd right into Lower Ash Rd, 3rd left into Hollinwood Rd to ground. BR Kidsgrove (5mins)
Capacity: 4,500 Seats: 400 Cover: 600 Floodlights: Yes

Clubhouse: Yes

HONOURS NWC Div. 1 97-97; NWC Chall. Cup 97-98; Mid Cheshire Lg 70-71 78-79 86-87 87-88, R-up 68-69 85-86; Lg Cup 67-68 69-70 85-86, R-up 84-85 86-87; Staffs County Lge; Burslem & Tunstall Lge. Floodlit Trophy R-up: 1999

PREVIOUS **Leagues:** Staffordshire County, Mid Cheshire Lge.

BEST SEASON **FA Cup:** **FA Vase:** Semi-Final 1997-98

RECORDS **Attendance:** 1,903 v Tiverton Town, FA Vase S-F 1998.

FACT FILE

Formed: 1952
Colours: Royal blue & white/royal blue & white/blue
Change Colours: All yellow
Midweek Matches: Wewdnesday

CLUB PERSONNEL

Chairman: Terry Hillman
Vice Chairmen: Arthur Duckworth & Alan Hall
President: Ernie Langford
Manager:Dave Sutton Coach: Russell Batho
Physio: Graham Plant

2000-01

Captain: John Diskin
Player of The Year: Darren Twigg
Top Goalscorer: Darren Twigg 23

MAINE ROAD

Secretary: Derek Barber, Flat 4, Maple Court, 259 Wellington Rd., Heaton Moor, Stockport SK4 5BS (0161 431 8243) **Ground:** Manchester County FA Ground, Brantingham Rd., Chorlton-cum-Hardy, Manchester M21 0TT (0161 861 0344) **Directions:** M60 Jct 7, A56 towards City Centre, right onto A5145 Chorlton/Stockport, thro' lights, left at next lights into Wilbraham Rd (A6010) to Chorlton, thro' lights for approx 1 mile. Left into Withington Rd, first left into Brantingham Rd, ground 300 yds on left. 2 miles from Stretford (Metrolink (tram)), 3 miles from Piccadilly & Victoria , Virgin & First North Western trains. Buses16 16A 85 87 87A 168 188 275.
Clubhouse: Matchdays (Snacks on ground) **Shop:** No.
Capacity: 2,000 Seats: 200 Cover: 700 Floodlights: Yes.

HONOURS Manc. Prem. Lg(4) 82-86, Cup 82-83 83-84;98-98 Man.Co Prem. Cup 87-8 Chal. Cup(4) 82-83 84-87; NW Co's Lg Div 2 89-90 (R-up 88-89).

PREVIOUS **Leagues:** Rusholme Sunday 55-66; Manchester Amtr Sunday 66-72; Manchester 72-87 **Name:** City Supporters Rusholme
Grounds: Hough End PF 55-73; Ward Street O.B. 73-75; Tootal Spts Ground 75-79; Leesfield 79-80

BEST SEASON **FA Cup:** 2nd Qual. 2nd replay 92-93 **FA Vase:** 4th Rd 94-95

RECORDS **Attendance:** 875 v Altrincham, FA Cup 2nd Qual. Rd 29/9/90
Goalscorer: John Wright 140 **Appearances:** Gordon Wood 465
Win: 15-0 v Little Hulton 2/9/86 **Defeat:** 0-7 v Newcastle Town

FACT FILE

Founded: 1955
Nickname: Blues
Sponsors:Parry's Jewellers
Colours: Blue/blue/yellow
Change Colours: Yellow, Green,Yellow
Midweek matchday: Tuesday
Reserves ' League: NW Co's Lge Res. Div.
Programme: 48 pages ,50p
Editor: Mr P,Ramsden (0161 448 1659)

CLUB PERSONNEL

Chairman: R Meredith
President: F G Thompson
Press Officer: P Ramsden
Manager: Chris Simms
Physio: E Jenkinson

2000-01 Leading goalscorer: Jock Russell 37
Captain: Jock Russell
P.o.Y.: Jock Russell

MOSSLEY

Secretary: David Buckley, 18 Chellow Dene, Mossley, Ashton-under-Lyne, Lancs. OL5 0NB.
Tel: 01457 835989 Email:bobbuckley@mossleyafc.fsnet.co.uk
Ground: Seel Park, Market Street, Mossley, Lancs. (Grd 01457 832369), (Club 01457 836104)
Directions: From north; M60 J.23, then A635 to Ashton-U-Lyne, A670 Mossley to town centre Grd behind market place. From south; M6 Junc 19, A556, M56 to Junc 3, A5103 to M'chester, then Mancunian Way (A57M) to A635. Follow Ashton signs 5m, the Mossley signs via A670 to town centre. Rail: Mossley BR. Buses 153 from Manchester, 343 from Oldham, 350 from Ashton
Capacity: 4,500 Cover: 1,500 Seats: 200 Floodlights: Yes
Clubhouse: Open nights and matchdays **Club Shop**: Yes

HONOURS FA Trophy Runners-up 79-80; Northern Premier League 78-79 79-80 (R-up 80-81 81-82 82-83, Chall Cup 78-79; NWC Floodlit Trophy R-up 95-96 NWTL Div 1 R-up 98-99

BEST SEASON **FA Cup:** 2nd Rd replay 49-50, also 2nd Rd 80-81 & 1st Rd 6 times.
FA Trophy: Runners-up 79-80 **FA Vase:** 6th Rd 96-97, 99-00

PREVIOUS **Leagues:** Ashton; South East Lancs; Lancs Comb. 18-19; Cheshire County 19-72; Northen Prem. **Names:** Park Villa 03-04; Mossley Juniors 04-09.

RECORDS **Attendance:** 7,000 v Stalybridge 1950 **Fee Paid:** £2,300
Fee Received: £25,000 for Eamon O'Keefe (Everton, 1979)

FACT FILE
Formed: 1903 Nickname: Lilywhites
Colours:All white Change: Yellow/blue/blue
Midweek matchday: Tuesday
Programme: 28 Pages £1.00
Editor: John A. Cawthorne
Local Press : Oldham Evening Chronicle/ Mossley & Saddleworth Reporter/Manchester Evening News/Tameside Advertiser/Pink Final
Local Radio: BBC GMR/Key 103/ 96.2 Revolution

CLUB PERSONNEL
Chair: Sam Rigby Pres.: J Wharmby
Manager: Benny Phillips
Website: www.welcometo/mossleyafc
www.mossley.20m.com
Email: mossleyafc@hotmail.com

2000-01
Leading goalscorer: Pedro Brennan 20
Captain: Paul Taylor
P.o.Y.: Paul Taylor

NANTWICH TOWN

Secretary: Bernard Lycett, 'Rivington", Clay lane, Haslington, Crewe CW11 5SE
Tel: 01270 584066 (H) 07876320280 Email Address: blycett@aol
Ground: Jackson Avenue, off London Road, Nantwich, Cheshire. Tel: 01270 624098
Directions: M6 Jct 16, A500 for Nantwich (about 8 miles), continue on A52 over railway crossing (London Rd), second right after railway crossing into Jackson Ave.
From Chester, use the A51.
Three miles from Crewe (BR).
Capacity: 1,500 Seats: 150 Cover: 555 Floodlights: Yes

Clubhouse: Every night except Sunday 8pm-11pm. Hot pies available **Club Shop:** Yes

HONOURS Cheshire Co. Lg 80-81; Ches. Snr Cup 75-76; N.W. Co.Lg.Cup 94-95

PREVIOUS **Leagues:** Shropshire & Dist.; The Combination 1892-94; Lancs Comb. 12-15; Cheshire Combination 19-38; Manchester; Mid-Cheshire; Cheshire County 68-82.
Name: Nantwich FC (pre 1973)

RECORDS **Attendance:** 2,750 v Altrincham, Cheshire Senior Cup 66-67
Fee r eceived: £4,000 from Stafford Rangers for D.Dawson
Record Goalscorer in Season: Gerry Duffy, 42 in 61-62

2000-01 **Captain:** Christian Morris **P.o.Y.:** Stuart Heeps **Top Scorer:** Jon Dawson (11)

FACT FILE

Founded: 1884
Nickname: Dabbers
Club Sponsors: Jim Barrie Plant Hire
Colours: Black & white/black/black
Change colours: All green
Midweek matchday: TuesdayReserves' League:Springbank Midland
Programme: 18 pages, 65
Editor: Che Kerrin (01270 624098)

Club Website: www.nantwichtownfc.co.uk

CLUB PERSONNEL

Chairman: Clive Jackson
6 Spencer Close, Crewe CW2 8DT
01270 664469 (H) 07970 546238 (B)

Manager: David Cooke
Physio: Ivan Robertson

NEWCASTLE TOWN

Secretary: John F Cotton, 293 Weston Rd., Weston Coyney, Stoke-on-Trent, Staffs. St3 6HA
Tel: 01782 333445 e-mail: bagshotboy@madasafish.com
Ground: Lyme Valley Parkway Stadium, Lilleshall Rd, Clayton, Newcastle-under-Lyne, Staffs (01782 662351) (Club 01782 662350 also a fax)
Directions: M6 jct 15, A500 for Stoke, left at r'bout A519 for Newcastle, rightat 2nd r'bout into Stafford Ave., 1st left into Tittensor Road to ground. 3miles from Stoke-on-Trent (BR).
Seats: 300 Cover: 1,000 Capacity: 4,000 Floodlights: Yes **Club Shop:** Yes
Clubhouse: Saturday matchdays 12-7.30pm, midweek 5-11pm. Hot & cold food available.

HONOURS: Nth West Co's Lg Div 1 R-up 95-96 96-97,99-00 Div 2 R-up 91-92, Challenge Cup 96-97, R-up 99-00 F/Lit Trophy R-up 96-97; Lamot Pils Tphy 91-92; Mid Cheshire Lg Div1 85-86, R-up 86-78, Div 2 82-83, 90-91, Lge Cup 84-85; Walsall Snr Cup 93-94 94-95 R-up 95-96; Sentinel Cup 94-95; Tennents Floodlit Trophy 92-93 95-96; Staffs Snr Cup R-up 95-96; Staffs M/W F/Light Lge 94-95 R-up 95-96; Umbro Over 35 Chall Cup 94-95.
RECORDS - **Attendance:** 3,948 v Notts County FA Cup Nov 96 **Win:** 8-1 v Holker Old Boys **Defeat:** 0-5 v Eastwood Hanley (A) **Appearances:** Neil Pesteridge 355 (Lg only) **Goalscorer:** Shaun Wade 105 (NWCL only) **F.A.Vase:** S-Final 99-00
PREVIOUS - **Leagues:** Hanley & Dist. Sunday; North Staffs Sunday; Potteries & Dist.Sunday; Res Refuge Ass Mid; Newcastle & Dist/ Staffs Co.; Mid Cheshire. **Names:** Parkway Hanley (founded 1964, later Clayton Park, ParkwayClayton); Newcastle Town (founded 1980) - clubs merged in 1986.

FACT FILE
Founded: 1964 Nickname: Castle.
Sponsors: Premaster Mechanical Services Ltd
Colours: All Royal Blue/blue/white
Change colours: All yellow
Midweek Matches: Tuesday
Reserve Team: SpringbankVending.Midland
Programme: 40 pages, #1.00
Editor: Kim Beckett 01782 659449 (H)
Website: www.nitvision.net/newcastletownfc

2000-01
Captain: Dean Gillick P.o.Y.: Ian Banks
Top Scorer: Dean Wilson 15

CLUB PERSONNEL
Chairman: J W Walker
Vice-Chairman: K G Walshaw
Press Officer: Ray Tatton (01782 644916)
Manager: Jimmy Wallace
Asst Manager: Michael Bates
Physio: Harry Wilshaw

Curzon Ashton

Daisy Hill

Clitheroe

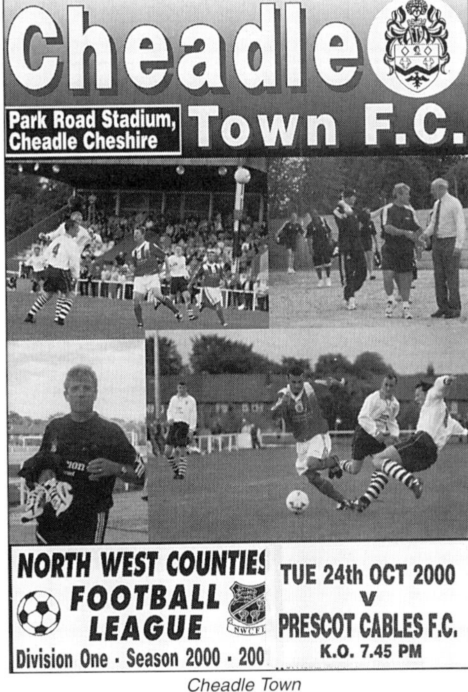

Cheadle Town

PRESCOT CABLES

Secretary: Doug Lace,20 Cable Road, Prescott,Merseyside L35 5AW
Ground: Valerie Park, Hope Street, Prescot. L34 6HD (Tel No: 0151 430 0507)
EMail: kenderbyshire@blueyonder.co.uk
Ground:Directions: M62 Jct 7. A57 to Prescot. Take 3rd exit at roundabout after two and a half miles. Turn right after another 1/2 mile. Right at Hope & Anchor pub, into Hope Street..
Capacity: 4,400 Seats: 200 Cover: 550 Floodlights: Yes

Clubhouse: Refreshment bar, open matchdays/evenings for hot & cold refreshments
Club Shop: No but ties & metal badges available.

HONOURS Lancs Comb. 56-57 (Lg Cup 47-48); Ches. Lg Div 2 76-77; Mid Ches. Lg 76-77; L'pool Non-League Cup(4) 51-53 58-59 60-61; L'pool Chal. Cup(5) 28-30 48-4961-62 77-78; George Mahon Cup 36-37.

PREVIOUS **Leagues:** Liverpool Co. Comb.; Lancs Comb. 1897-98 18-20 27-33 36-67; Ches. Co. 33-36 78-82; Mid Cheshire 67-78.
Names: Prescot Athletic; Prescot Cables 46-65 80-90; Prescot Town 65-80.

BEST SEASON **FA Cup:** 2nd Rd 57-58 59-60 **FA Vase:** 2nd Rd 1998-99

RECORDS **Attendance:** 8,122 v Ashton National, 1932

FACT FILE
Founded: 1886
Nickname: Tigers
Colours: Gold/black/gold
Change colours: All blue
Midweek Matches: Tuesday
Programme: 30 pages,70p
Editor: Ken Derbyshire

CLUB PERSONNEL
President: Mr B F Taylor
Chairman: Ted Mercer
Vice Chairman: G.Hayward
Commercial Manager: Arthur McCumiskey
Manager:Tommy Lawson
Asst Manager: Andy Gray

2000-01
Leading goalscorer: Gary Jensen 35
Captain: Simon Hughes
P.o.Y: Gary Jensen

RAMSBOTTOM UNITED

Secretary: John Maher, 75 Ramsbottom Road, Hawkshaw, Bury BL8 4JS. Tel: 01204852742

Ground: Riverside Ground, Acre Bottom, Ramsbottom. Tel: 01706 822799(Cricket Club)
Answe Phone: 01204 852742 (for match details) **Floodlights**: Yes
Email Sddress: final.inspection@madison filter.com
Directions: M66(North) to junction 1, take A56 towards Ramsbottom. After one mile turn left into Bury New Road. Turn left after the Danisco Paper Mill along the road running parallel with the East Lancs Railway. From North: M65- A56 Follow signs ro Ramsbottominto town centre.

HONOURS: Bolton Comb. Div. One Champs 72-73; Bolton Comb. Prem Div. 76-77, 86-87; Manchester Lge Div. One Champs 90-91; Manchester Lge Div. 1 Cup Winners 90-91; Gilgryst Cup Winners 94-95; NWCFL Div 2 Champ 96-97, Trophy 95-96

RECORDS **Attendance:** 829 v Southport F.A.C. 3Q 98-99 NWCFL Div 2 29/3/97

PREVIOUS **Leagues:** Bury Amateur League, Bolton Combination, Manchester Lge.
BEST SEASON: F.A. Cup: 3rd Q 1998-99 **F.A. Vase:** 2nd Round 98-99, 99-00

FACT FILE

Formed: 1966
Colours: Blue with white trim/blue/white
Midweek Matchday: Tuesday
Club website: fittp..//members,xoom

CLUB PERSONNEL

Chairman: H Williams (01706 822799)

2000-01

Captain : Warren Brierley
P.o.Y.: Mike Smith
Top Goalscorer: Russell Brierley 37

SALFORD CITY

Secretary: Frank McCauley, 22 Beverley Road, Pendlebury, Salford M27 4HY
Tel: 0161 288 0603. mccauley@yahoo.co.uk (E-mail).
Ground: Moor Lane, Kersal, Salford, Manchester. Tel: 0161 792 6287
Directions: M62 jct 17, A56 Bury New Road to Manchester, continue thro' 4 sets of lights, right into Moor Lane, ground 500 yds left. 4 miles from Manchester Victoria (BR). Buses 96, 139, 94, 95 to Moor Lane
Capacity: 8,000 Seats: 260 Cover: 600 Floodlights: Yes
Clubhouse: Open matchdays only. Hot snacks

HONOURS Lancashire Amateur Cup 72-73 74-75 76-77; Manchester Senior Cup, Manchester Challenge Cup, Manchester Lg 74-75 75-76 76-77 78-79. Reserve Division North 2000-01. Reserve Division North Cup 2000-01.

PREVIOUS **Leagues:** Manchester 63-80; Cheshire Co. 80-82.
Names: Salford Central 40-63; Salford Amateurs 1963 until merger with Anson Villa; Salford FC.
Ground: Crescent, Salford

BEST SEASON **FA Cup:** **FA Vase:**

RECORDS **Attendance:** 3,000 v Whickham FA Vase 1981

FACT FILE

Founded: 1940
Nickname: Ammies
Colours: White with blue trim/blue/blue
Change colours: All blue
Midweek Matches: Tuesday
Reserves' League: NWC Res. Div. S.
Programme: 24 pages, 50p
Editor: Scott White

CLUB PERSONNEL

Chairman: DavidTaylor
Managers: Tom Foster & Matt Wardrop
Press Officer: Scott White
Commercial Manager: Stevie Plant

SKELMERSDALE UNITED

Secretary: Bryn Jones, 34 Bromilow Road, Skelmersdale, Lancs. WN8 8TU
Ground: White Moss Park, White Moss Road, Skelmersdale, Lancs Tel: 01695 722723

Directions: M58 Jct 3, at 2nd r'bout take 3rd exit towards Skelmersdale, continue for approx 1 mile, ground on the right. 4 miles from Ormskirk (BR)
Capacity: 10,000 Seats: 250 Cover: 1,000 Floodlights: Yes
Clubhouse: None. Matchday food bar sells hot drinks, soup, pies & pasties etc
Club Shop: No, but badges available in two colours.

HONOURS FA Amateur Cup 70-71 R-up 66-67; Ches. Co. Lg 68-69 69-70, Jubilee Cup 69-70; Lancs F'lit Cup 69-70; Lancs Jnr Cup 69-70 70-71; Ashworth Cup 70-71; Barassi Anglo-Italian Cup 70-71; Lancs Non-Lge Cup 73-74 74-75; North West Co's Lg Cup: 99-00 R-up 82-83.N.W.Co Div 2 R-Up: 97-98

PREVIOUS **Leagues:** Liverpool County Comb., Lancashire Comb. 1891-93, 03-07, 21-24 55-68, 76-78, Cheshire County 68-71 78-82, Northern Premier 71-76.

BEST SEASON **FA Cup:** 1st Rd 67-68, 0-2 v Scunthorpe(A), 68-69, 0-2 v Chesterfield(A), 71-72, 0-4 v Tranmere R. (A) **FA Amateur Cup:** Winners 70-71

RECORDS **Attendance:** 7,000 v Slough, FA Amat Cup Q-F '67

FACT FILE
Founded: 1882
Nickname: Skem
Sponsors:Matalan
Colours: Blue & white stripes/blue/blue
Change colours: Red & white stripes/red/red
Midweek Matches: Tuesday
Reserves play North West Counties Res. Div.
Programme: 32 pages, £1
Editor: M.Ratcliffe

CLUB PERSONNEL
President: D.Tomlinson
Chairman: A,Gore - Vice Chairman: T Garner
Press Officer: Secretary
Manager: Russ Perkins
Asst Manager: Peter McDermott
Coach: Paul Gallagher - Physio: Billy Leigh

2000-01
Leading goalscorer: Kevin Leadbetter 24
Captain: David Chadwick
P.o.Y.: David Chadwick

ST HELENS TOWN

Secretary: W J Noctor, 95 Sutton Park Drive, Marshalls Cross, St H .WA9 3TR (01744 816182)
Ground: St Helens R.L.F.C. , Knowsley Road, St Helens **Directions: From South:** M62 Jct 7-5th exit (St Helens) 3rd r'about (Sherdley), follow Town Centre signs. Left at r'about to L'pool & Prescot.Rt at lights then left at Black Bull after 1 mile. Ground on right. **From North:** M6.Jct 23 take A580 to L'pool.7 mile left to A570 and 1st Rt into Bleak Hilll Road.Left at sharp right hand bend after 1 mile into Mill Brow. At T jct left at Black Bull, turn right -ground on left.
Capacity: 19,100 **Seats:** 2,362 **Cover:** 12,408 **Floodlights:** Yes

Clubhouse: Weekdays 8-11pm, Saturday matchdays 2-6.30pm. **Club Shop:** Yes

HONOURS: FA Vase 86-87; George Mahon Cup 49-50; Lancs Comb. 71-72, Div 2 50-51, Lg Cup R-up 70-71;Liverpool Snr Non Lge Cup R-up 76-77; Lancs Jnr Cup R-up 66-67; Bass Charrington Cup 73-74; Carling Chall Cup r-up 93-94; N.W.C. Floodlit Trophy r-up 97-98.

PREVIOUS **Leagues:** Lancs Comb. 03-14 49-75; Liverpool County Comb. 49-74; Cheshire County 74-82. **Grounds:** Park Road 01-52; City Road 52-53.

BEST SEASON **FA Cup:** 4th Q Rd 85-86 **FA Vase:** Winners 86-87

RECORDS **Gate:** 4,000 v Manchester City, Bert Trautmann transfer match,April 1950.
Goalscorer: S Pennington **W in:** 10-4 v Everton `B' 1952
Appearances: Alan Wellens **Defeat** : 1-8 v Liverpool Res., L'pool Snr Cup 1950

FACT FILE
Founded: 1946
Nickname: `Town'
Colours: Red & white/white/red
Change colours: Royal blue & white/white/royal blue
Midweek Matches: Wednesday
Programme: 24 pages, 50p
Editor: John McKiernan (01744 600612)
Local Press: Reporter, Star, Echo.

CLUB PERSONNEL
Chairman/Press Officer: J Barrett
Public Liaison Officer: John McKiernan
01744 635826 (H) 01744 24348 (W)
Manager: James McBride
Asst Manager: G Walker
Coach: John Neary

2000-01
Leading goalscorer: Terry Fearns 38
Captain: Chris Quirk
P.o.Y.: Terry Nestor

WARRINGTON TOWN

Secretary: Harry Boden, 10 Landseer Ave, Warrington Tel: 01925 659796 (H) 0589 512675(M)

Ground: Cantilever Park, Common Lane, Latchford, Warrington WA4 2RS
Tel:01925 631932 (Club), 01925-653044 (FAX).
Directions: M6 junction 20, then A50 towards Warrington. After 2 miles turn left immediately after swing bridge into Station Road, ground 600yds on left. From town centre travel 1 mile south on A49, left at lights into Loushers Lane, ground quarter mile on right. 2miles from Warrington Bank Quay (BR)
Capacity: 2,000 Cover: 650 Seats: 350 Floodlights: Yes **Club Shop:** Yes
Clubhouse: Weekdays 1-11pm, Sat. 12-11pm, Sun. 12-3 & 7-10.30pm. Bar food on matchdays
PREVIOUS **Leagues:** Warrington & Dist. 49-52; Mid-Cheshire 52-78; Cheshire Co. 78-82; N.W.C. 82-90; N.P.L 90-97. **Name:** Stockton Heath 1949-62.
RECORDS **Attendance:** 2,600 v Halesowen T., FA Vase S-F 1st leg 85-86.
Goalscorer: Steve Hughes 167
Fee Received: £60,000 for Liam Watson (Preston N. E.) 92-93
BEST SEASON **FA Cup:** 4th Qual. Rd 94-95 replay with Hyde Utd..
FA Vase: Runners-up 86-87 **FA Trophy:** Quarter-Finalists 92-93
HONOURS: FA Vase R-up 86-87; N.W.C. Lge 89-90 (Lg Cup 85-86 87-88 88-89 (R-up 89-90), Div 2 R-up 86-87, Div 3 R-up 82-83; Mid-Cheshire Lg 60-61 R-up 57-58, Lg Cup 54-55 55-56 11-12 72-73, Altrincham Amat. Cup 54-55,
Players progressing recently: M Leonard (Everton), N Whalley & L Watson (P.N.E.) 92-93.

FACT FILE
Formed: 1948
Nickname: The Town
Colours: Blue & yellow/blue/blue
Change colours:Blue & yellow squares/blue
Midweek matchday: Tuesday
Reserves' League: Mid-Cheshire
Programme 24 Pages £1.00
Editor:Rob Wood (01925 480207)

CLUB PERSONNEL
Chairman: Harry Boden
Vice Chairman: D.J.Hughes
Press Officer: Colin Serjent
Manager: Alan Lord
Asst Manager: Dave Hughes
Coach: Paul Knights
Physio: T.B.A.

WINSFORD UNITED

Secretary: Peter Warburton, 3 Massey Avenue, Winsford, Cheshire CW7 3DU (01606554295)

Ground Address: Barton Stadium, Wharton, Winsford, Cheshire CW7 3EU (01606 593021).
Directions: From north; M6 junction 19, A556 towards Northwich to Davenham,then A5018 to Winsford. From south; M6 junction 18, A54 through Middlewich to Winsford. Ground quarter mile off main road in Wharton area of town. 1 mile from Winsford (BR).
Capacity: 6,000 Cover: 5,000 Seats: 250
Clubhouse: Mon-Sat 8-11pm, Sun 8-10.30pm **Club Shop:** Yes, contact Kay Lomas
PREVIOUS **Name:** Over Wanderers (pre 1914). **Leagues:** The Combination 02-04; Cheshire Co. 19-40, 47-82; N.W.C. 82-87, N.P.L 87-01.
CLUB RECORDS **Attendance:** 7,000 v Witton Albion 1947.
Goalscorer: Graham Smith 66. **Appearances:** Edward Harrop 400.
Fee Paid: Nil. **Fee Received:** £6,000 for Neville Southall from Bury.
BEST SEASON **F.A. Cup:** 2nd Rd 1887-88. 1st Rd 1975-76 1991-92
F.A. Trophy: Qtr Finals 77-78. League clubs defeated: None.
HONOURS N.P.L. R-up 92-93, Div 1 R-up 91-92, Lg Cup 92-93, Presidents Cup 92-93; Cheshire Co. Lg 20-21 76-77 (R-up 74-75 79-80),Lg Cup x 7 R-up x 3; Cheshire Snr Cup 58-59 79-80 92-93; Mid-Cheshire Snr Cup 90-91 92-93 (R-up 88-89); Cheshire Amateur Cup 00-01 02-03; Lancs Comb/Cheshire County Inter-Lg Cup 62-63.
Players P rogressing recently: Mark Came (Bolton W. 84), Dave Bamber (Blackpool), Bob Sutton (West Ham U.), J Richardson (Sheff. U.), Stanley Wood (W.B.A.), R Pearce (Luton T.).

FACT FILE
Founded: 1883
Nickname: Blues
Colours: Royal blue & White/white/blue
Change colours: Maroon/white/white.
Midweek matchday: Tuesday
Programme: Pages: 24 Price: 80p
Editor: R. Astles Tel: 01270 661623
Local Press: Winsford Chronicle, Winsford Guardian.
Local Radio: Signal, Piccadilly.

CLUB PERSONNEL
Chairman: M Morgan
President: A Bayliss
Vice Chairman: D Cotterill
Player/Manager: Steve Shaughnessy
Asst Manager: John Imrie

WOODLEY SPORTS

Secretary: Ian Woodhouse, 4 Firethorn Drive, Godley, Hyde SK14 3SN
Tel: 0161 3511631 (H), 0161 330 6837 (B) 07775 688277 (M)

Ground: Lambeth Grove Stadium, Lambeth Grove, Woodley, Stockport.
Tel: 0161 494 6429

Directions: M60 Jct 25, follow signs (A560) Bredbury, take left filter at lights which brings you onto A560 Stockport Road for approx 1 mile, turn left at pub, Lowes Arms into Mill Street which goes into Mill Lane. Over bridge take 2nd right into Woodlands Avenue, then 1st left into Lambeth Grove.
Ground 200 yards ahead.
Floodlights: Yes

HONOURS NWC Div 2 99-00

RECORD **Attendance:** 1,500 v Stockport County

PREVIOUS **Leagues:** Lancashire & Cheshire, Manchester League.

BEST SEASON **FA Cup:** 99-00 **FA Vase:** 1st Round 1998-99

FACT FILE
Founded: 1970
Colours: Red & royal blue/royal/white
Midweek Matchday: Tuesday

CLUB PERSONNEL
Chairman: Ian Campbell
14 Gloucester Rd., Gee Cross, Hyde.
Tel: 0161 368 4060(H)

2000-01
Captain: David Blow
P.o.Y. & Top Scorer: Mike Norton 30

Action from Curzon Ashton's 3-1 victory over Nantwich Town. Nantwich keeper Steven Heeps punches clear despite the efforts of a flying Phil Ainscough. Photo: Colin Stevens

DIVISION TWO

ALSAGER

Secretary: Pauline Matthews, 43 Ellgrave Street, Dalehall, Stoke -0n-Trent, St6 4DJ
Tel No: 01782 834296

Ground: The Town Ground, Wood Park, Alsager. Tel: 01270 882336

Directions: M6, Junction 16, A500 towards Stoke. Leave A500 at 2nd exit (A34 to Congleton), at 2nd set of lights turn left for Alsager. Turn right opposite Caradon/Twyfords (500 yds), into Moorhouse Ave., Woodlaid Court 1/2 mile on right.
Nearest Railway station: Alsager

Floodlights: Yes

HONOURS Jt R-up Mid Cheshire Div. 2, R-up Springbank Vending Lge.

PREVIOUS **Leagues:** Mid Cheshire Div. 2; Springbank Vending Lge.

RECORD **Attendance:** 110 v Formby Sept 99, League 200 v Port Vale (friendly)

FACT FILE

Founded: 1968
Colours: Black & white/black/black
Change colours: Yellow & sky blue/yellow/yellow
Midweek Matches: Wednesday

CLUB PERSONNEL

Chairman: Clive Smart
Tel: 01270 872917H
1st Team Sec.: Pauline Matthews
Tel: 01782 834296H

2000-01 Leading goalscorer: Gareth Rowe
Captain: Kenny Lawton
P.o.Y.: Chris Dick

ASHTON TOWN

Secretary: Stephen Barrett, 11 Clement Avenue, Atherton M46 0PT
Tel Nos: 01942 889492 (H) 01942 529312 (W)

Ground: Edge Green Street, Ashton-in-Makerfield, Wigan WN4 8SY (01942 510677)

Directions: M6 Jct 23, A49 to Ashton-in-M. Right at lights onto A58 towards Bolton. After 3/4 mile turn right at `Rams Head' P.H. into Golbourne Rd. After 200 yds right into Edge Green Str. Ground at end.

Floodlights: No

HONOURS Warrington Lg Guardian Cup.

PREVIOUS **Leagues:** Warrington, Lancs Comb. 03-11 71-78, Ches. Co. 78-82.

BEST SEASON **FA Vase:** Prelim. Rd 84-85

RECORD **Gate:** 600 v Accrington Stanley 76-77

FACT FILE

Founded: 1962
Colours: Red with white trim/red/red
Change colours: All sky blue
Midweek Matches: Tuesday

CLUB PERSONNEL

President: W Pomfrett
Chairman: Len Riley
Manager: Norman Hickson

BACUP BOROUGH

Secretary: Frank Manning, 38 Acre Avenue, Stacksteads, Bacup OL13 0HN
Tel: 01706 877460 (H)

Ground: West View, Cowtoot Lane, Blackthorn, Bacup, Lancashire (01706 878655).

Directions: From M62, M66 onto A681 through Rawtenstall to Bacup centre, leftonto A671 towards Burnley, after approx 300 yds right (immed. before the IrwellInn) climbing Cooper Street, right into Blackthorn Lane then first left intoCowtoot Lane to ground.

Capacity: 3,000 Seats: 500 Cover: 1,000 Floodlights: Yes

Clubhouse: Open matchdays and private functions (for which buffets can beprovided). Pies and sandwiches on matchdays. **Club Shop**: Not yet

HONOURS Lancs Jnr Cup 10-11 (R-up 22-23 74-75); Lancs Comb. 46-47 (Lg Cup R-up46-47 80-81; NW Co's Lg Div 2 R-up 89-90.

PREVIOUS **League:** Lancs Comb. 03-82Name: Bacup FC.Grounds: None

BEST SEASON **FA Cup:** **FA Vase:**

RECORD **Gate:** 4,980 v Nelson 1947 **Scorer:** Jimmy Clarke

FACT FILE

Founded: 1875
Nickname: The Boro
Club Sponsors:B&EBoys Ltd
Colours:White with black trim,black,black
Change colours:Yellow,Blue,Blue
Midweek Matches: Tuesday.
Programme: 22Pages 50p
Editor: D Whatmough (0706 875041)

CLUB PERSONNEL

President: W.Shufflebottom
Chairman: Ken Peters
Vice Chairman: D.Whatmough
Manager: Brent Peters
Assistant Manager: Simon Holding

BLACKPOOL MECHANICS

Secretary: William Singleton, c/o Club. Tel: 01253 312113(H) 01253 761721(B)

Ground: Jepson Way, Common Edge Rd, Blackpool, Lancs FY4 5DY (01253 761721).

Directions: M6 to M55, follow Airport signs. Left at r'bout along A583 (Preston New Rd) to lights, right into Whitehill Rd, becomes School Rd, to lights.Straight over main road & follow signs for Blackpool Mechanics F.C. to ground.Rail to Blackpool North - then bus 11c from Talbot Rd bus station (next to rail station) to Shovels Hotel, Common Edge Rd.

Capacity: 2,000 Seats: 250 Cover: 1,700 Floodlights: Yes

Clubhouse: Match days, training nights. Dancehall. Matchday, hot food.

Club Shop: Manager Andrew Sneddon (01253 729962). Ties, sweaters, old programmes, badges.

HONOURS Lancs Comb Bridge Shield 72-73; NW Co's. Lg Div 3 85-86; W Lancs Lg 60-61 62-63; Lancs County FA Shield 57-58 60-61:

PREVIOUS **Leagues:** Blackpool & Fylde Comb., West Lancs, Lancs Comb. 62-68.
Grounds: Stanley Pk 47-49

RECORD **Gate:** 1,200 v Morecambe, Lancs Comb, August 1968

2000-01 **Captain:** John Oliver **P.o.Y.:** Keith Johnstone **Top Scorer:** Rob Park 23

FACT FILE

Founded: 1947 Nickname: Mechs
Sponsors: Bloomfield Bakery Blackpool.
Club colours: Tangerine/white/tangerine
Change colours: All blue
Midweek matchday: Wednesday
Programme: 10 pages, 50p
Editor: David Gore

CLUB PERSONNEL

Chairman: Henry Baldwin
Vice Chairman: John Sanderson
President: Gregory Gregorio
Commercial Manager: John Sanderson
Manager: Brian Wilson
Asst Man.: Stuart Parker
Coach: William Singleton.

BOOTLE

Secretary: William Jones, 36 Rydecroft, Woolton, Liverpool L25 7UT
Tel Nos: 0151 428 2203(H) 0793 912893 (W)
Ground: Bucks Park, Northern Perimeter Rd, Netherton, Bootle. L307PT (0151 526 1850)
Directions: End of M57 & M58 follow signs to Bootle and Docks A5063.
Turn right at next lights by Police station. Entrance 100 yds on right.
Old Roan station 300yds. Bus 55 (150yds from grd), 302 341 345 350 (350yds).
Capacity: 5,000 Seats: 400 Cover: 1,400 Floodlights: Yes
Clubhouse: Normal pub hours. Darts & pool **Club Shop:** Yes
HONOURS N.W.C. Lge Div 2 R-up 92-93 (F'lit Trophy 93-94), Liverpool Chall. Cup 64-65 75-76 78-79, Liverpool Amtr Cup 65-66 67-68 73-74, Lancs Amtr Cup 69-70, Liverpool Co. Comb. (x9) 64--66 67-74, George Mahon Cup (x6) 66--68 68-70 72--74, Lancs Comb. 75-76 76-77, Lge Cup 75-76, Cheshire County Lge Div 2 78-79.
PREVIOUS Leagues: Liverpool Shipping, Liverpool Co Comb., Lancs Comb. 74-78, Cheshire Lge 78-82. **Name:** Langton 1953-73 **Grounds:** Edinburgh Park 1953-73, Orrell Mount Park 73-8

FACT FILE
Founded: 1954
Nickname: Bucks
Sponsors: Taximex
Colours: All royal blue with amber trim
Change colours: Yellow/black/black
Midweek matchday: Tuesday
Reserves' League: Liverpool Co. Combination
Programme: 32 pages, 50p
Editor: Secretary

CLUB PERSONNEL
Chairman: Frank Doran
Manager: T.B.A.

CASTLETON GABRIELS

Secretary: David Lord, 34 Fairway, Castleton, Rochdale OL11 3BU Tel: 01706 522719
Ground: Butterworth Park, Chadwick Lane, off Heywood Rd., Castleton, Rochdale. Tel: 01706 527103) **Directions:** M62 Jct 20, A6272M to r'bout. Left towards Castleton (A664Edinburgh Way) to next r'bout, keeping Tesco Superstore to the left, take 1st exit to next r'bout, take 2nd exit into Manchester Rd (A664), after just under mile turn right at `Top House' P.H. into Heywood Rd., to end & ground on right
Capacity: 1,500 Seats: 400 Cover: 650 Floodlights: Yes
Clubhouse: Open seven nights a night and all day Saturday. Pie & peas and sandwiches available matchdays (pie & peas only at Reserve matches) **Club Shop:** No
HONOURS Manchester Lge 86-87, Murray Shield 86-87; Res Div Cup 95-96.
PREVIOUS **Leagues:** Rochdale Alliance 24-84; Manchester 84-89.
Name: St Gabriels (pre-1960s) **Ground:** Park pitches; Springfield Pk 60-81.
RECORDS **Gate:** 640 v Rochdale, pre-season friendly 1991 **Win:** 8-0 v Squires Gate N.W.Co.Div 2 94 **Defeat:** 1-10 v Blackpool Mechanics N.W.Co.Div 2 95

FACT FILE
Founded: 1924 Nickname: Gabs
Club Sponsors: Kick Off
Colours: Royal blue with red trim/blue/blue
Change colours: All red
Midweek matchday: Tuesday
Reserves ' League: N.W.C. Res. Div.
Programme: 28 pages, 50p
Editor: David Jones (01942 730220 -W)

CLUB PERSONNEL
Chairman: T E Butterworth
Vice Chairman: R Butterworth
Press Officer: Secretary
Manager/Coach:David Jones
Assistant Manager:Roy Grundy
Coach: Neil Mills

CHADDERTON

Secretary: Ronald Manton,77 Denton Lane, Chadderton, Oldham OL9 9AC
Ground: Andrew Street, Chadderton, Oldham, Lancs (0161 624 9733) **Capacity:** 2,500
Directions: M62 Jct 20, A627(M) to M'chester.. M'way becomes dual carriageway. Left at 1st major traffic lights A669 Middleton Rd, then first left into Butterworth Street. Andrew Street is 2nd right. Oldham Werneth (BR) 1 m or Mills Hill (BR) I m.Buses 24,181 & 182 to Middleton Rd from Manchester (Piccadilly Gardens). Seats: 200 Cover: 600 Floodlights: Yes
Clubhouse: Matchdays only. Hot & cold snack during & after games **Club Shop:** No
HONOURS M'chester Am Lg 62-63, North Div 55-56, M. Prem Cup R-up 82-83, Chall Tphy 71-72, R-up 72-73, M. Lg Div 1 66-67, Div 2 64-65, Gilgryst Cup 69-70, Murray Shield 65-66, Lancs Comb. Cup R-up 81-82, Alf Pettit & Hulme Celtic Cup 61-62, NWC F/lit Tphy R-up 92-93 Manchester Umbro International Cup Winners 2000
PREVIOUS Leagues: Oldham Amat., Manchester Amat., Manchester 64-80, Lancs Comb. 80-82
RECORD Gate: 1,500 v Guinness Ex'ts 1969 **Appearances:** Billy Elwell 750+ (64-90)
Players progressing: (include) David Platt (Crewe), John Pemberton (Crewe)

FACT FILE
Founded: 1947 Nickname: Chaddy
Sponsors: ASDA
Nationwide Building Society and Asda
Colours: All red
Change colours: All Yellow
Midweek Matches: Tuesday
Reserves' Lge: NWC Res. Div.
Programme: 28-32 pages Editor: David Greaves

2000-01
Top Scorer & P.o.Y.: Chris Barlow
Captain: Tony Lucas

CLUB PERSONNEL
Chairman: Harry Mayall
President: Derek Glynn
Press Officer: John Fitton
Manager: Martin Farrell

CHEADLE TOWN

Secretary: David Busby, 9 Tatton Road, Handforth, Wilmslow, Cheshire Sk9 3QZ
Tel Nos: 01625 524116 ((H) o7932 634630 (M)
Ground: Park Road Stadium, Park Road, Cheadle, Cheshire SK8 2AN (0161 4282510).
Directions: M60 Jct 2, follow signs towards Cheadle (A560), first left after lights into Park Road, ground at end. 1 mile from Gatley (BR), buses from Stockport.
Capacity: 2,500 Seats: 300 Cover: 300 Floodlights Yes
Clubhouse: Open every night. Food available **Club Shop**: No
HONOURS Manchester Lg Div 1 79-80 (R-up 80-81 81-82); Manchester Amtr Cup 79-80;Lamot Pils R-up 90-91; NWCFL Div 2 Trophy R-up 95-96:
PREVIOUS **Leagues**: Manchester (pre 1987)
RECORD **Attendance :** 1,700 v Stockport County, August 1994.
Scorer: Peter Tilley **Appearances:** John McArdle
Players progressing: Ashley Ward (Crewe), Steve Bushell (York), Dean Crowe(Stoke).
2000-01- Captain: Ian Henderson **Top Scorer:** Tony Coyne 120

FACT FILE
Founded: 1961
Colours: White/black/black
Change colours: All blue.
Midweek Matches: Tuesday
Reserves' Lge: NW Counties Lge
Programme: 24 pages,80p.
Editor: Stuart Crawford

CLUB PERSONNEL
President: Freddie Pye
Chairman: Chris Davies
Vice-Chairman: Clive Williams
Press Officer: Chris Davies (0161 428 2510).
Manager: Martin Wardle
Physio: Paul Wardle

Daniel Wrigley (Oldham Town) clears the ball from Eddie Bishop (Witton Albion). Photo: Keith Clayton

FA Cup Second Qualifying Round. Emley v Salford City 3-1. Home keeper Paul Cuss spreads himself and saves Salford forward Tom Murphy's shot. Photo: Bill Wheatcroft

Formby FC line up before the Worthington Challenge Trophy Final at Bury FC. The North West Counties Division Two side beat Division One side Curzon Ashton 5-3 on penalties after a 1-1 draw after extra time. Photo: Colin Stevens

COLNE F C

Secretary: Mrs Adele Cutts, 22 Snellgrove, Colne. BB8 0QS (01282 862947)

Ground: Holt House Stadium, Holt House, Colne. (Tel: 01282 862545)
Directions: Enter Colne from M65 to roundabout, keep left follow signs for Keighley. At next roundabout turn left, continue on Harrison Drive over mini roundabout & follow road to ground. Nearest Railway station - Colne.
Capacity: 1,800 Seats: 100 Cover: 1000 Floodlights: Yes

Clubhouse: Yes, Small Lounge Bar open on matchdays **Club Shop:** No
HONOURS BEP Cup Winners 96-97
BEST SEASON **FA Cup:** **FA Vase:**
RECORDS **Attendance:** 240 v Nelson 97-98
Scorer: Geoff Payton **Appearances:** Nick Roscoe
PREVIOUS **Leagues:** East Lancashire League

FACT FILE

Formed: 1996
Colours: All red
Change colours: All yellow
Midweek Matchday: Thursday
Programme: Yes Editor: Ray Moore

CLUB PERSONNEL

Chairman: D Blacklock (01282 696340)
Press Officer: Ray Moore(01282 868857)
Manager:Denzil Hart

DAISY HILL

Secretary: Bob Naylor, 8 Bailey Fold, Westhoughton, Bolton, Lancs BL5 3HH 01942 813720
Ground: New Sirs, St James Street, Westhoughton, Bolton, Lancs. 01942 818544
Directions: M61 Jct 5, A58 (Snydale Way/Park Road) for 1.5 miles, left into Leigh Road (B5235) for 1 mile, right into village then left between Church and School into St James Street. Ground 250 yds on the left. Half mile from Daisy Hill (BR)
Capacity: 2,000 Seats: 200 Cover: 250 Floodlights: No Club Shop: No
Clubhouse: Open normal licensing hours during any football activity. Snacks on matchdays
HONOURS Bolton Comb Prem Div 62-63 72-73 75-76 77-78, Lg Cup 59-60 61-62 71-72 72-73; Lancs Shield 61-62 71-72 86-87:
PREVIOUS **Leagues:** Westhoughton; Bolton Comb.; Lancs Combination. 78-82.
Name: Westhoughton Town **Record Goals & Apps:** Alan Roscoe 300-450
BEST SEASON **FA Cup:** **FA Vase:**
RECORD **Attendance:** 2,000 v Horwich RMI,Westhoughton Charity Cup Final 79-80
PLAYERS PROGRESSING: Barry Butler (Chester C)+ Phil Priestley (Rochdale)via AthertonLR

FACT FILE

Founded: 1894(first known records)
Reformed: 1952
Colours: All royal blue Change: All amber
Midweek Matches: Tuesday
Reserves' Lge NWCL Res Div
Programme: 40 pages 80p
Editor: Ian Templeman

CLUB PERSONNEL

Chairman: Steve Mahon
Manager:Alan Aspinall
Coach: Tommy Berry

2000-01

Leading Scorers: Ryan Cain & Dominic Shinks 19
Captain: Paul Prescott
P.o.Y.: Ross McNair

DARWEN

Secretary: Lynn Atkinson, 58 Harwood St.., Darwen, Lancs BB3 1PD (01254761755)
Ground: Anchor Ground, Anchor Road, Darwen, Lancs BB3 0BB, (01254 705627)
Directions: A666 Blackburn / Bolton road, 1 mile north of Darwen town centre,turn right at Anchor Hotel, ground 200 yds on left. One and a half miles from Darwen (BR), bus 51 to Anchor Hotel.From M65 Jct 4 signs to Darwen.Left at A666,1/2 mile left at anchor Hotel. ground 200 yds on left Capacity: 4,000 Seats: 250 Cover: 2,000 Floodlights: Yes
Clubhouse: Matchday only **Club Shop:** No
HONOURS Lancs Comb 31 32 73 75: Comb Cup 30 31 75; Lancs Jun Cup 73; Geo Watson Trophy 73; LFA Yth Cup 75; NWC Cup 83; Lancs F/Lit Trophy 90; NWC Res Div Cup 94; Blackburn & Dist Yth Lge 94 95 97, Cup 94 95 97; NW All Chall Cup 96.
PREVIOUS **Leagues:** Football Alliance 1889-91, Football Lg 1891-99, Lancs Lg 99-03,Lancs Comb. 03-75, Ches. Co. 75-82. **Ground:** Barley Bank
RECORD **Gate:** (Anchor Ground) 10,000 v Fleetwood Lancs Jun Cup 1920
BEST SEASON **FA Cup**: Semi Finals 1881

FACT FILE

Founded: 1875
Sponsors: Prince Moran
Colours: Red & white/red/red
Change colours: All blue
Midweek Matches: Tuesday
Reserves' League: NWC Res. Div.
Programme: 20 pages, £1.00 Editor: S.Hart
Local papers:Darwen Advertiser,Lancs Eve.Tel

CLUB PERSONNEL

President: E Devlin
Chairwoman: Mrs K Marah
Manager: S Wilkes
Asst Manager: M Atkinson
Physio: Mick Sharples

FORMBY

Secretary: Dave Dickinson,2 Seafield,Formby,Merseyside L374EL Tel : 01704 870944
Ground: Brows Lane, Formby,Merseyside (01704 8335050) **Directions:** A565 Liverpool - Southport turn left at lights oppositeTesco into Altcar Rd, left at T junction to r'bout (opposite Cross House Inn) take 2nd exit then sharp left into Duke Street, 1st right into Elbow Lane, ground 50yds on left. Formby (BR) 1/2m, buses from Formby &Southport stations
Capacity: 2,000 Seats: 200 Cover: 500 Floodlights: No
Clubhouse: None. Matchday refreshment bar stocks hot food & drinks
Club Shop: Sells programmes, badges & souvenirs. **HONOURS** Liverpool Co. Comb. 48-49, R-up 64-65; Liverpool Senior Cup 77-78, R-up 84-85; Challenge Cup 52-53 63-64 67-68, R-up 64-65; Amtr Cup 29-30 47-48 48-49;Lamot Pils Trophy 94-95; George Mahon Cup 64-65, R-up 55-56 56-57; Lancs Co FA Amt Cup 34-35, Woirthingtobn Trophy 00-01
PREVIOUS Leagues: Liverpool Co. Comb. 19-68/ Lancs Comb. 68-71, Ches. Co. 71-82.
BEST SEASON **FA Cup:** 1st Rd 73-74, 0-2 v Oldham Ath. (H) **FA Trophy:** 1st Rd 73-74, lost to Stalybridge Celtic **FA Vase:** 2nd Rd 96-97, lost to Tetley Walker

Founded: 1919 Nickname: Squirrels
Club Sponsors: DKS Packaging
Colours: Yellow/blue/yellow
Change:Green/black/black
Midweek Matches: Tuesday
Reserves : Liverpool Co.unty Comb
Prog: 36 pages, £1.00 Ed:Dave Cookson (01772 311681) Website: www.formbfc.co.uk

CLUB PERSONNEL

Chairman: Chris Welsh
Comm. Man.: Dave Dickinson (01704 70944)
Managers: Peter Hennerty & Mike Scott
Physio: Barry O'Connor

2000-01

Capt. & P.o.Y.: Howard Rubbery
Top scorer: Mark Wilson

HOLKER OLD BOYS

Secretary: Allan Wilson, 56 Fairfield Lane, Barrow-in-Furness, Cumbria. LA13 9HL
Tel: 01229 822751 (W) 01229 822983 (H)

Ground: Rakesmoor Lane, Hawcoat, Barrow-in-Furness, Cumbria (01229 828176)

Directions: M6 Jct 36, A590 to Barrow-in-Furness, on entering Barrow, continue across r'bout, 2nd right (Dalton Lane) to top of road, right into Rakesmoor Lane, ground on right.

Capacity: 2,500 Seats: 220 Cover: 500 Floodlights: Yes

Clubhouse: Mon-Fri 8-11pm, Sat noon-11pm, Sun normal licensing. Pies & peas on matchdays

Club Shop: No

HONOURS W Lancs Lg 86-87, R-up 85-86; Lancs Junior Shield 88-89 90-91.

PREVIOUS **Leagues:** North Western; Furness Premier; West Lancs 70-91.

RECORDS **Attendance:** 1240 v Barrow ATS Trophy 95-96 **Win:** 12-0
Defeat: 1-8 v Newcastle T. (H) 91-92 **Scorer:** Dave Conlin

2000-01 **Captain:** Mike Brown **P.O.Y.:**Gary Waters **Top Scorer:** Carl Waters 34

FACT FILE
Founded: 1936 Nickname: Cobs
Club Sponsors: Kitchen Design Studio
Colours: Green & white stripes/green/green
Change colours: Blue/red
Midweek Matches: Tuesday
Programme: 8 pages, 30p

CLUB PERSONNEL
President: R Brady
Chairman: Ron Moffatt
Vice Chairman: Ray Sharp
Press Officer: John Taylor
Manager: Dereck Birrell
Asst Manager: Jim Capstick
Coach: Jim Ballantyne
Physio: Mark Hetherington

LEEK C.S.O.B.

Secretary: Stan Lockett, 5 Fitzherbert Close, Swynnerton, Stone, Staffs ST150PQ,
Tel: 01782 796062 (H) 0944 493106 (M)

Ground: Harrison Park, Macclesfield Road, Leek, Staffs, Tel: 01538 383734
Club Email: stan@slockett.freeserve.co.uk

Directions: M6 south Junc 17, A534 to Congleton - follow signs for Leek (A54), carry on to junction with A523, right onto A523, this road is direct to Leek, ground 8 miles on right just into Leek.

Capacity: 3,600 Seating: 625 Covered Terracing: 2,675 Floodlights: Yes

PREVIOUS **Leagues:** Leek & Moorland Lge, Staffs County North, Refuge Midland Lge.

RECORDS **Attendance:** 293 v Tamworth F.A.Cup 1998-99

BEST SEASON **FA Cup:** 3rd Q 98-99 **FA Vase:**

HONOURS Refuge Midland Lge 95-96. Lge Cup 94-95 95-96; Leek Cup 94-95 95-96; Midland Ref Charity Shield 95-96; Sportsline Chall Cup 95-96.
NWCL Div. 1 winners - Programme of the Year 2000/01

FACT FILE
Founded: 1945
Colours: Red& Black/Black/Black
Change colours: All Yellow
Midweek Matchday:Tuesday
Programme: Yes Editor: Stan Lockett

CLUB PERSONNEL
Chairman: K J Hill, 11 Springfield Drive, Leek, Staffs ST13 Tel: 01538 371859
Manager: Chris McMullen
Asst Man: Andrew Walters
Physio: Noel Carroll

2000-01
Leading goalscorer: Neil Robinson 16
Captain: Tim Tweats P.o.Y.: Marc Hubbard

NELSON

Secretary: Cyril King, 1 Grange Ave, Barrowford, Nelson, Lancashire BB9 8AN(01282 695578)

Ground: Victoria Park, Lomeshaye Way, Nelson, Lancs (01282 613820)

Directions: M65 jct 13, 1st left (A6068 Fence), 2nd left (B6249 for Nelson),2nd right sign Lomeshaye Village to grd

Capacity: 1500 Seats:150Cover: 200 Floodlights: Yes

Clubhouse: Bar open matchdays **Club Shop:** Yes

HONOURS Lancs Lge 54-55; Lancs Comb. 1949-50 51-52; Lg Cup 49-50 50-51 59-60; Bridge Shield 75-76 81-82; Lancs Jnr Cup 54-55; N.W.C. Div 2 Cup 96-97.

BEST SEASON **FA Cup:** 2nd Rd Proper 30-31(replay) **FA Vase:**

PREVIOUS **Leagues:** Lancashire 1889-98 1900-01; Football League 1898-1900; Lancashire Comb. 01-16 46-82; N.W.C. 82-88; West Lancashire 88-92.

FACT FILE

Founded: 1881
Nickname: Blues
Colours: Blue & white stripes/black/blue
Change colours: White/red
Midweek matchday: Wednesday
Reserve League: N.W.C. Res. Div.

CLUB PERSONNEL

Chairman: A.T.Barnes
Vice-Chairman: A Barnes
Manager: John Bailey
Assistant Manager:Andy Wych

NORTON UNITED

Secretary: Dennis Vicker, 86 Ford Green Road, Smallthorne, Stoke-on-Trent ST6 1NX
Tel: 01782 822727 (H) 01785 354200 (B)

Ground: Norton CC & MWI, Community Drive, Smallthorne, Stoke-on-Trent
Tel: 01782 838290

Directions: M6 J16, A500 to BUrslem/Tunstall, turn off, bear right at traffic island to Burslem, through lights to Smallthorne, take 3rd exit on mini roundabout, turn right by pedestrian crossing into Community Drive, ground 200 metres on left.
Nearest Station: Stoke-on-Trent (mainline) Longport (local)

PREVIOUS **League:** Midland League to 2001

RECORDS **Attendance:** 147 v Milton United, 1991

HONOURS Midland League - Champions 00-01 98-99 96-97, League Cup 00-01 96-97 91-92; Staffs FA Senior Vase 98-99

FACT FILE
Founded: 1989
Colours: Black & white stripes/black/black
Change Cols.: Red & black stripes/white/white
Midweek Matchday: Wednesday
Programme:

CLUB PERSONNEL
Chairman
Stephen Beaumont
8 Maitland Grove, Trentham, Stoke-on-Trent.
Tel: 01782 642321 (H)

OLDHAM TOWN

Secretary: Billy O'Niel,WhitebankStadium, Whitebank Road,Oldham.OL8 3JH (0161 624 2689)
Ground: Whitebank Stadium, Whitebank Rd, Hollins, Oldham, Lancs OL8 3JH(0161 624 2689)
Directions: M62 jct 18, M66 to Heaton Pk, right on to A576, left at 2nd lights on to A6104, follow Victoria Ave. on to Hollinwood Ave. under bridge to roundabout take 2nd exit onto Hollins Road, follow Hollins Rd for one & a half miles to Fire Station, left on through gate leading onto Elm Rd and follow to next left, Whitebank Rd on left.
Capacity: 1,000 Seats: 101 Cover: Yes Floodlights: Yes
Clubhouse: Open evenings and matchdays
HONOURS NWC: Div 2 97-98, R-up 94-95; Div 3 R-up 85--86; Lg.Champions 97-98
Res Div R-up 94-95, Cup 94/95:

PREVIOUS **Leagues:** Manchester Amateur; Lancashire Comb. 81-82.

BEST SEASON **FA Cup:** **FA Vase:**

RECORD **Attendance:** 495 v Halifax Town, '96.

FACT FILE

Founded: 1964
Colours: Blue,white,blue
Change Colours:
Midweek Matches: Tuesday
Programme: 16 pages, 50p
Editor: Secretary

CLUB PERSONNEL

Chairman: Ken Hughes
Manager: Len Cantello

PADIHAM

Secretary: Tony Brooks, 10 Newton Street, Burnley BB12 0LG Tel: 01282 709782 (H)
Ground: Arbories Memorial Sports Ground, Well Street, Padiham, Lancs. BB12 8LE
Tel: 01282 773742 e-mail: brooks@household60.freeserve.co.uk
Directions: M65, J8, then follow A6068 (signed Clitheroe & Padiham). At lights at bottom of hill, turn right into Dean Range/Blackburn Road towards Padiham. At the next junction turn into Holland street opposite church, then into Well Street at the side of the Hare & Hounds pub to the ground. Nearest rail station: Burnley
Floodlights: Yes
Honours: Lancs Amateur Cup R-up 66, Lancs Amateur Shield R-up 97, Burnley, Pendle & Rossendale Hosp. Cup 96, R-up 91; Lancs Comb. Trophy 81, R-up 82; NWC Div. 3 R-up 83-84; W. Lancs Div.1 99-00, Div.2 71-72 76-77 R-up 96-97, Pres. Cup R-up 79 94 97; E. Lancs Amat Lge R-up 06-07 **Best Season:** FA Cup: Third Rd., 1883-84
Previous Leagues: Lancashire Comb.; NW Counties; West Lancs.; N.E. Lancs;
NE Lancs Combination; East Lancs Amateur Lge.

FACT FILE

Formed: 1964
Colours: Royal blue & white/white/red
Change: Red & black/black/black
Midweek Matchday: Tuesday

Chairman: Mick Muldoon
Brook Foot Farm Barn, Grove Lane,
Padiham, Lancs.
Tel: 01282 778831

SQUIRES GATE

Secretary: Jeff Webster, 168 Highcross Road, Poulton-Le-Fylde, FY6 8DA.
Tel/Fax: 01253 890846. Mobile 077406 44335
Ground: School Road, Marton, Blackpool, Lancs. Tel: 01253 798584
Directions: M6 to M55 jct 4, left onto A583, right at 1st lights (Whitehall Rd) follow signs for airport. Ground approx 1.5 miles on right. Nearest station Blackpool South.
Capacity: 1000 Seats: 2 new stands (100 seats) Cover: One side Floodlights: Yes
Clubhouse: Yes

HONOURS West Lancs Lg: Div 2 80-81, Richardson Cup 86-87, N.W.C.L 2nd Div Trophy winners 2000/01
PREVIOUS **Leagues:** W. Lancs (pre-1991)
RECORD **Attendance:** 600 v Everton 95
2000-01 Leading goalscorer: Scott Sugden 26
Captain: Alex RawsonP.o.Y.: Brian Manchester

FACT FILE
Formed: 1948
Colours: Royal/black/royal
Midweek Matches: Tuesday
Programme: 20 pages

CLUB PERSONNEL
Chairman: P Mack (01772 339955)
Life Vice President: Wilf Carr
ManagerGordon Fell
Assistant Manager: Joe Dewhurst
Reserves Manager: Dean Whitehead

STAND ATHLETIC

Secretary: Thomas H Edwards, 3 Burndale Drive, Unsworth, Bury BL9 8EN
Tel: 0161 766 3432
Football & Fixture Secretary: Alan C Davis, 86 Polefield Rd., Prestwich, Manchester M25 2QW
0161 773 9196 (H) 0161 773 9191 (F) 07957 638332 (M)

Ground: Ewood Bridge, Manchester Road, Haslingden, Lancs. BB4 6JY
Tel: 01706 217814
Directions: M66 northbound, exit at Blackburn/Clitheroe turn-off. keep in left hand lane to roundabout, turn left passing Haslingden Cricket Club on rhs, follow road to bottom of hill, around a sharp left-hand bend. Ground is 100 yards on right.
Capacity: Floodlights: Yes
PREVIOUS **Leagues:** Bury Amateur, South East Lancs., Lancs & Cheshire, Manchester to 01.
HONOURS Manchester League Prem Div. 98-99 99-00 00-01, Div.1 94-95
Manchester Chall. Trophy 94-95; Manchester County Cup R-up 95-96;
Lancs. Amateur Shield R-up 00-01

FACT FILE
Founded: 1964
Colours: Blue & yellow/blue/blue
Change cols: Red & black stripes/black/black
Midweek Matchday: Tuesday
Programme:

CLUB PERSONNEL
Chairman: John Barrington
Manager:
Asst. Man.:

STONE DOMINOES

Secretary: Gordon Chadwick, 52 High Lane, Brown Edge, Stoke-on-Trent, Staffs ST6 8RU
Tel: 01782 505342 (H) 01785 815551 (B)

Ground: Springbank Park, Yarnfield Lane, Yarnfield, nr Stone, Staffs. Tel: 01785 761891

Directions: M6 South , J15, take A500 to A34, take south route to Stone (5 miles), through traffic lights to Walton Hotel (still on A34), turn right to Yarnfield Lane, approx. 2 miles over M6, ground on left before entering village
Nearest rail station: Stoke/Stone Floodlights: Yes

Honours: Midland League Div. 1 99-00, Div. 2 R-up 96-97,
Div.1 Cup 98-99, Div. 2 Cup 96-97, Charity Shield 00

Previous League: Midland League

Record Attendance: 124 v Audley, Staffs. Vase Nov. 99

FACT FILE

Formed: 1987
Colours: Red/black/black
Midweek Matchday: Wednesday

Chairman: Bob Bowers
Springbank House, Station Road,
Barlaston, Staffs.
Tel: 01782 373298 (H) 01785 815551 (B)

Action from Curzon Ashton v Ramsbottom United. Photo: Colin Stevens

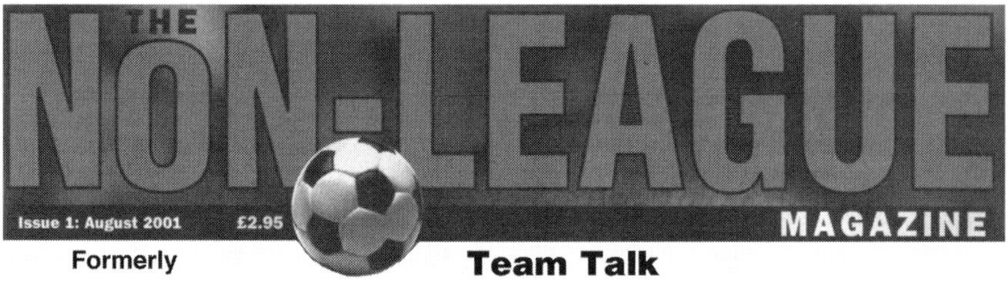

Curzon Ashton frontman Phil Ainscough watches as Nantiwich Town clear his team's attack. Curzon went on to win 3-1. Photo: Colin Stevens

Curzon Ashton's first game in their climb back to the Unibond pitted them against neighbours Mossley. Goalscorer Nigel Evans is seen here challenged by Mossley's Mark Paver. Photo: Colin Stevens

LIVERPOOL COUNTY FOOTBALL COMBINATION

Secretary: J F Deal

Press Officer: Jim Stanway, 10 Olive Vale, Liverpool L15 4PQ   Tel: 0151 281 5704

The County Combination came quite close to a clean sweep of all the competitions in which the clubs entered - a measure of its dominance on the amateur level on Merseyside. It is obvious that the respective playing strength remains as relatively high as ever and congratulations go to all clubs who flew the Combination flag home and away.

Pride of place must inevitably go to Yorkshire Copper Tube who deservedly won the league title for the second time in their history with a delightfully attacking brand of football. It was just reward for their manager, Billy Roberts, who over the last four years - two at Plessey and two at YCT - has built a squad rivalled by very few in its depth and variety. In fact, Billy's team lost only three vital games all season and justified their position as favourites by cruising through five rounds of the Lancashire Amateur Cup, their only difficult tie being a one goal win against fellow County Combination side, Mossley Hill.

The champions were pushed virtually all the way by the previous champions, Waterloo Dock, but defeat in both league fixtures between the two rivals did the Dock no favours, although they inflicted defeats on YCT in two cup competitions at the semi final stage. In both, the Dock went on to annex the cups, defeating fellow County Combination side, Lucas Sports, in the final of the LCFA Challenge Cup, and Speke in the final of the Peter Coyne League Cup.

On the down side, the league lost a club for the second season running when Edinburgh Park-based club, Ayone, could not carry on soon after Christmas and resigned from the League in February. It was particularly sad for the club as they had struggled for several years, continually losing their best players to local rivals, despite the return of 'Rocky' Strahan a couple of seasons ago. The club were one of the longest-serving clubs in the League and during the 1980s and early 1990s were one of the strongest sides on Merseyside.

FINAL LEAGUE TABLE 2000-01

			Home						Away					
		P	*W*	*D*	*L*	*F*	*A*	*W*	*D*	*L*	*F*	*A*	*Pts*
1	Yorkshire Copper Tube	32	13	1	2	60	22	14	2	0	60	12	84
2	Waterloo Dock*	32	12	1	3	63	19	13	1	2	47	13	74
3	Royal Seaforth	32	10	4	2	44	23	10	2	4	40	27	66
4	St Dominics	32	12	1	3	55	22	8	4	4	36	30	65
5	Crawfords	32	8	2	6	25	25	11	1	4	37	20	60
6	Ford Motors	32	8	4	4	36	30	9	1	6	39	41	56
7	Mossley Hill*	32	7	5	4	41	29	8	3	5	36	27	46
8	Speke	32	6	3	7	35	30	4	8	4	32	25	41
9	South Liverpool	32	3	8	5	20	22	7	1	8	32	39	39
10	Lucas Sports	32	6	2	8	33	34	4	5	7	26	27	37
11	Prescot Leisure*	32	6	2	8	45	33	5	2	9	27	41	33
12	Halewood Town	32	2	3	11	22	51	6	2	8	34	41	29
13	Marconi	32	3	2	11	37	56	5	3	8	41	69	29
14	St Aloysius*	32	5	4	7	27	44	3	5	8	25	31	27
15	Dunningsbridge Park*	32	3	4	9	29	44	3	4	9	21	49	23
16	Birchfield	32	4	1	11	20	41	1	2	13	20	62	18
17	Cheshire Lines	32	1	2	13	15	57	3	3	10	29	53	17

** Points deducted. Ayone resigned - record expunged*

RESULTS CHART 2000-01

		1	**2**	**3**	**4**	**5**	**6**	**7**	**8**	**9**	**10**	**11**	**12**	**13**	**14**	**15**	**16**	**17**
1	Birchfield	X	3-2	2-3	0-1	1-2	0-3	2-1	2-4	0-5	1-4	1-2	2-0	0-1	2-1	3-3	0-2	1-7
2	Cheshire Lines	4-3	X	1-3	1-1	1-5	0-1	1-6	0-4	1-4	0-1	1-2	0-6	0-2	3-4	1-1	1-3	0-11
3	Crawfords	2-1	3-0	X	4-1	2-1	2-1	2-2	0-2	0-2	3-2	0-3	3-1	1-3	2-0	1-1	0-1	0-4
4	Dunningsbridge P	3-1	1-4	1-4	X	5-1	3-3	0-1	3-3	0-3	1-1	2-4	5-1	3-5	0-2	2-2	0-6	0-3
5	Ford Motors	2-2	5-2	1-0	3-0	X	2-1	3-2	5-2	2-2	3-0	1-1	2-2	3-5	3-1	0-2	0-3	1-5
6	Halewood Town	2-1	2-6	0-0	2-2	2-4	X	0-1	2-4	2-4	4-3	1-3	1-1	0-4	1-6	1-3	1-4	1-5
7	Lucas Sports	3-0	1-1	1-2	3-1	1-5	1-2	X	3-0	3-1	2-5	3-4	2-1	6-1	1-3	1-1	1-4	1-3
8	Marconi	7-1	5-2	1-7	0-2	4-5	1-6	1-1	X	2-2	2-4	3-2	2-4	2-3	1-4	4-5	2-5	0-3
9	Mossley Hill	3-2	3-2	0-1	3-3	6-1	8-2	2-1	6-2	X	1-1	2-2	2-2	0-2	2-3	0-0	3-2	0-3
10	Prescot Leisure	0-2	1-2	3-5	15-1	3-1	6-0	2-2	1-4	3-5	X	1-5	2-0	1-1	5-1	1-0	0-1	1-3
11	Royal Seaforth	7-2	3-2	2-1	3-2	4-4	1-0	3-1	4-0	1-1	2-0	X	4-1	5-2	2-3	2-2	1-1	0-1
12	St Aloysius	1-1	3-3	0-2	2-1	1-3	2-4	1-3	4-3	0-3	3-1	1-5	X	2-1	3-3	2-1	0-8	2-2
13	St Dominics	9-0	3-1	1-3	3-2	4-0	5-2	4-2	3-2	5-2	9-1	1-0	2-2	X	2-0	3-1	0-2	1-2
14	South Liverpool	2-0	1-1	0-3	1-1	2-3	1-1	1-1	3-3	0-1	3-0	2-3	0-0	1-1	X	2-1	0-2	1-1
15	Speke	5-2	4-1	1-2	0-1	1-2	4-3	1-1	5-5	3-1	2-0	1-2	1-3	1-1	4-0	X	1-2	1-4
16	Waterloo Dock	6-2	5-0	2-0	6-2	0-2	1-4	2-1	18-1	4-0	2-0	4-0	2-1	2-1	5-0	2-2	X	2-3
17	Yorkshire C T	6-0	10-0	4-1	3-0	4-0	4-1	2-0	10-2	1-0	3-4	3-2	1-0	3-3	3-1	0-7	3-1	X

FIRST DIVISION CLUBS

CRAWFORDS
Secretary: Dennis Bakstad, 26 Oxford Drive, Halewood, Liverpool L26 0TW
Tel: 0151 487 5657 (H)
Ground: Cheshire Lines, Southmead Road, Liverpool 19 Tel: 0151 427 7176
Colours: Yellow/Blue/Blue

MOSSLEY HILL
Secretary: Mick Ware, 9 Harefield Road, Speke, Liverpool L24 0SA Tel: 0151 486 0071
Ground: Mossley Hill Athletic Sports Ground, Mossley Hill Road, Liverpool L18 8DX
Tel: 0151 724 4377
Colours: Claret & Amber/Claret/Amber

FORD MOTORS
Secretary: Terry Doyle, 17 Brackendale, Halton Brook, Runcorn, Cheshire WA7 2EF
Tel: 01928 568329 (H) 0151 431 5011 (B)
Ground: Ford Sports & Social Club, Cronton Lane, Widnes Tel: 0151 424 7078
Colours: Sky & Navy/Navy/Navy

ST ALOYSIUS
Secretary: Gary Walsh, 14 Waverley Drive, Prescot, Merseyside L34 1PU
Tel: 0151 449 1131
Ground: Edinburgh Pk, Townsend Lane, Liverpool 6
Colours: Red/White/Red

HALEWOOD TOWN
Secretary: Steve Jones, 14 Fir Avenue, Halewood, Liverpool L26 0UB Tel: 0151 486 4557
Ground: Hollies Road, Halewood, Liverpool 26
Tel: 0151 487 7418
Colours: Black & White stripes/Black/Black

ST DOMINICS
Secretary: Mick Donohue, 20 Grant Close, Liverpool L14 0LJ Tel: 0151 283 1351
Ground: St Dominics School Playing Ground, Cordens Road, Huyton, Liverpool 36
Colours: Green/Green/Green

LUCAS SPORTS
Secretary: Tony Brodrick, 5 Broadheath Terrace, Widnes WA8 7PU Tel: 0151 423 4615
Ground: Arncliffe Leisure Centre, Mackets Lane, Liverpool 25
Colours: Yellow/Blue/Yellow

SOUTH LIVERPOOL
Secretary: Jim Stanway, 10 Olive Vale, Wavertree, Liverpool L15 8JH
Tel: 0151 281 5704 (H) 0151 801 8220 (B)
Ground: Girls Field, Jericho Lane, Otterspool, Liverpool 17
Colours: White/Black/Red

PRESCOT LEISURE
Secretary: Dave Hughes, 33 Clover Hey, St Helens, Merseyside WA11 9NN
Tel: 01744 737047
Ground: Wood Lane, Prescot, Merseyside
Colours: Yellow & Green/Green/Yellow

SPEKE
Secretary: Bill Locke, 30 All Saints Road, Speke, Liverpool L24 3TF Tel: 0151 486 1954
Ground: Dunlops Sports Ground, Speke Hall Avenue, Speke, Liverpool 24
Tel: 0151 486 1588
Colours: Black & Amber/Black/Black & Amber

ROYAL SEAFORTH
Secretary: Tony Stanton, 203 Hilary Avenue, Huyton, Liverpool L14 6UR Tel: 0151 489 9980
Ground: Edinburgh Park, Townsend Lane, Liverpool L6 0BB Tel: 0151 263 5267
Colours: Black & White stripes/Black/Black

WATERLOO DOCK
Secretary: Jim Davies, 19 Scorton Street, Liverpool L6 4AS Tel: 0151 264 8179
Ground: Edinburgh Park, Townsend Lane, Liverpool 4 Tel: 0151 263 5267
Colours: Sky & Navy/Navy/Navy

MARCONI
Secretary: Dave Jones, 6 Ashwood Close, Kirkby, Liverpool L33 1ZB Tel: 0151 549 0663
Ground: Whitefield, Marconi Sports Club, Roby Road, Liverpool 36 Tel: 0151 489 1031
Colours: Blue & White/Black/Black

YORKSHIRE COPPER TUBE
Secretary: Jim Murray, 58 Penley Crescent, Westvale, Kirkby L32 0RS Tel: 0151 548 3547
Ground: YCT Factory, East Lancashire Road, Kirkby Tel: 0151 548 1775
Colours: Blue/Blue/Blue

CARLSBERG WEST CHESHIRE A.F.L.

President: Ken Halsall
Chairman: Ray Prescott
General Secretary: John Marshall Tel: 01244 376844

As with the rest of the country, the season was played out against a very watery back cloth with the final games being completed in mid May. However Cammell Laird had wrapped up the Division One championship long before then, having been proclaimed champions with a quarter of their games remaining. Lairds also became the tenth successive West Cheshire League side to lift the Cheshire Amateur Cup with a single goal success over fellow league side Vauxhalls. Finishing as Division One runners up were the much improved Christleton, who also maintained their stranglehold on the Chester Senior Cup. Previous champions, Poulton Victoria had to settle for third place but had considerable consolation in collecting the Pyke Cup, with Vauxhalls again finishing as beaten finalists, and they also collected the Wirral Senior Cup following their final victory over Mersey Royal.

Completing a hat trick of Runcorn District successes were Helsby who, as representatives of the Cheshire FA, also came back from Westmorland as Northern County champions following their last stage success at Milnthorpe Corinthians. The introduction of a two up two down rule between Divisions One and Two created increased interest and a frantic battle ensued as teams scrambled to avoid the Division One relegation trap door. Blacon YC fought hard but unsuccessfully to climb clear of the bottom slot they had occupied all season while defeat in their last game saw Capenhurst Villa also make the drop.

Replacing Blacon and Capenhurst in the top flight are Liverpool outfits Aintree Villa and MANWEB. An unbeaten home record was the strong base for Villa's title win while, following an exciting battle with Upton AA and Pavilions, there was a second consecutive promotion for runners up MANWEB as they reached Division One status after just two seasons in the league. Cammell Laird Reserves threatened to spoil someone's party by finishing in the top two but fell away towards the end although they came out on top in the West Cheshire Bowl final when defeating Castrol Social. Another side tasting cup success was Chester Challenge Cup winners, Christleton Reserves.

The season's most impressive playing record belonged to Mallaby who went through their Third Division campaign unbeaten and for good measure picked up two other trophies. The West Cheshire Shield final win saw them defeat new boys FC Pensby and this came after they had defeated three Second Division outfits on their way to securing the Wirral Amateur Cup. During Mallaby's second season in our league they suffered only one defeat and that was against First Division opposition in the Cheshire Amateur Cup. Joining them in Division Two in August will be runners up Manor Athletic while making the reverse journey are Shell Reserves and the Capenhurst Reserves outfit who make the drop due to their senior side's demotion.

The annual representative game against the Mid Cheshire League was a victim of the weather while Vauxhall Motors won the early season charity competition, the Bill Weight Memorial Trophy, and Maghull picked up the 36 gallons of beer for winning the Carlsberg shoot out competition. The league sponsors "Player of the Year" award went to Merseyside Police veteran Steve Griffiths, while the Carlsberg club of the year (for on and off the field discipline) went to Manor Athletic. The one change to the constitution for season 2001-02 sees South Wirral League champions Grange Athletic replace Castrol Social Reserves who have resigned their membership. As the area's top supply league for match officials, the Carlsberg West Cheshire AFL is delighted to congratulate two ex-panel members, Mike Dean and Dave Pugh, on being in the first batch of full time professional referees as appointed by the FA.

FINAL LEAGUE TABLES 2000-01

DIVISION ONE

	P	W	D	L	F	A	Pts
Cammell Laird	30	24	5	1	82	27	77
Christleton	30	17	5	8	61	33	56
Poulton Victoria	30	15	6	9	73	59	51
Maghull	30	13	8	9	41	37	47
Mersey Royal	30	12	9	9	53	39	45
Helsby	30	13	5	12	59	61	44
Vauxhall Motors	30	10	11	9	57	41	41
Heswall	30	11	7	12	45	46	40
General Chemicals	30	10	6	14	45	50	36
Ashville	30	9	9	12	40	52	36
Shell	30	10	5	15	46	56	35
Stork	30	9	8	13	44	58	35
Newton	30	10	4	16	42	75	34
Mond Rangers	30	9	6	15	39	57	33
Capenhurst Villa	30	8	8	14	47	61	32
Blacon Youth Club	30	6	6	18	48	70	24

DIVISION TWO

	P	W	D	L	F	A	Pts
Aintree Villa	30	20	7	3	75	28	67
Manweb	30	19	6	5	55	30	63
Cammell Laird Res	30	17	4	9	58	38	55
Upton Athletic Assoc.	30	14	9	7	72	49	51
Pavilions	30	16	3	11	67	58	51
Poulton Victoria Res	30	14	3	13	65	63	45
New Brighton	30	13	5	12	56	43	44
Mersey Royal Res	30	13	6	11	56	59	42
Heswall Reserves	30	11	7	12	53	53	40
Christleton Res	30	11	4	15	53	52	37
Castrol Social	30	10	5	15	47	62	35
Merseyside Police	30	10	3	17	53	71	33
Ashville Reserves	30	9	5	16	47	68	32
Capenhurst Villa Res	30	9	3	18	45	76	30
West Kirby	30	7	8	15	44	68	29
Shell Reserves	30	7	2	21	43	71	23

DIVISION ONE RESULTS CHART 2000-01

		1	2	3	4	5	6	7	8	9	10	11	12	13	14	15	16
1	Ashville	X	1-1	1-2	0-3	2-3	1-1	0-4	1-1	0-1	2-2	2-1	4-2	3-3	0-3	1-2	1-1
2	Blacon Youth Club	0-4	X	1-2	6-1	0-4	4-2	3-4	2-7	1-3	1-1	3-1	2-4	4-1	1-0	0-2	1-1
3	Cammell Laird	5-1	2-1	X	2-2	3-1	3-0	2-1	3-0	4-1	3-1	2-1	3-1	4-1	1-1	3-0	2-1
4	Capenhurst	1-1	4-2	0-3	X	1-2	1-3	3-3	4-3	2-0	1-4	2-3	2-2	1-2	2-0	2-0	4-2
5	Christleton	0-1	1-0	1-2	1-1	X	1-3	3-1	0-0	1-1	2-0	3-1	8-0	1-1	1-3	5-2	1-0
6	General Chemicals	1-2	1-0	1-3	0-0	0-3	X	2-0	2-0	3-1	0-1	1-1	2-3	4-1	1-1	1-2	1-1
7	Helsby	4-1	3-3	0-4	2-1	0-2	2-1	X	1-2	0-1	3-2	2-0	3-2	0-2	1-2	4-3	1-1
8	Heswall	1-2	0-0	0-3	4-1	1-2	2-0	0-4	X	0-0	1-3	3-0	3-0	1-2	0-3	1-1	1-0
9	Maghull	4-1	2-1	5-3	3-1	0-2	1-0	1-1	1-1	X	1-3	0-1	1-0	0-0	2-0	1-0	2-1
10	Mersey Royal	2-1	0-0	1-1	2-0	0-0	2-3	5-0	1-2	1-0	X	6-0	2-4	3-2	1-1	2-4	0-0
11	Mond Rangers	0-2	5-2	0-2	0-0	2-1	0-2	1-3	0-2	2-2	0-0	X	0-4	2-5	3-0	7-2	1-0
12	Newton	0-2	1-0	0-7	1-0	0-4	3-2	2-5	0-0	2-2	1-0	0-3	X	1-5	3-0	1-3	0-4
13	Poulton Victoria	1-1	4-3	1-3	2-1	1-2	7-2	5-0	3-5	3-4	1-3	1-1	3-3	X	2-0	1-0	5-2
14	Shell	2-0	4-1	1-3	0-1	2-4	2-1	3-4	3-1	1-0	1-2	1-1	3-1	1-2	X	2-2	2-5
15	Stork	1-1	0-4	1-1	4-4	1-0	1-4	3-3	1-3	1-0	2-1	0-1	0-1	1-2	4-1	X	0-0
16	Vauxhall Motors	0-1	5-1	1-1	4-1	4-2	1-1	1-0	3-0	1-1	2-2	4-1	2-0	3-4	6-3	1-1	X

PYKE CHALLENGE CUP 2000-01

FIRST ROUND

Ashville	v	Capenhurst Villa	1-4	Stork	v	Mersey Royal	1-2
Helsby	v	Vauxhalls	2-6	Gen Chemicals	v	Cammell Laird	2-1
Christleton	v	Heswall	2-0	Blacon YC	v	Maghull	3-3, 5*3
Shell	v	Mond Rangers	6-0	Newton	v	Poulton Vics	0-7

SECOND ROUND

Capenhurst Villa	v	Mersey Royal	2-0	Vauxhalls	v	Gen Chemicals	3-1
Christleton	v	Blacon YC	6-1	Shell	v	Poulton Vics	1-5

SEMI-FINALS

Capenhurst Villa	v	Vauxhalls	1-1, 1*3	Christleton	v	Poulton Victoria	1-2

FINAL

Poulton Victoria v Vauxhalls 3-1

DIVISION TWO WEST CHESHIRE BOWL 2000-01

SEMI-FINALS

Castrol Social	v	Mersey Royal Res	2-1	Cammell Laird Res	v	Poulton Vics Rs	2-2, 4*2

FINAL

Cammell Laird Res v Castrol Social 3-2

DIVISION THREE WEST CHESHIRE SHIELD 2000-01

SEMI-FINALS

Mallaby	v	Manor Athletic	6-0	FC Pensby	v	Aintree Villa Rs	1-1, 3*1

FINAL

FC Pensby v Mallaby 1-3

CARLSBERG MANAGER OF THE MONTH AWARDS

August	John Power	Cammell Laird Reserves
September	Dave Tills	Christleton
October/November	Chris Camden/Micky Dunn	Poulton Victoria
December	Reg McGuire/Damian Standing	Mersey Royal
January	Chris Camden/Micky Dunn	Poulton Victoria
February	John McClennan	New Brighton
March	John Brett	Mallaby
April	Dave Merrick	Manor Athletic
May	Dave Jennions	Manweb

AINTREE VILLA

Chairman: John Gregson Formed: 1954
Secretary: Alf Shepherd, 154 Altway, Aintree, Liverpool L10 6LG
Tel: 0151 526 9287 (H)
Ground: Aintree racecourse.
Colours: Tangerine/white/white
Sponsors: Woolton Carpets/Aintree Conservative Club

ASHVILLE

Chairman: Eddie Parker **Club Formed:** 1949
Secretary: Dave Walton, 15 Wellesley Road, Wallasey, Wirral, Merseyside, L445UR Tel: 0151 639 9196
Ground: Villa Park, Cross Lane, Wallasey Village, Wallasey, Tel: 0151 638 2127 **Colours:** White & black/black/black
Sponsors: Kelly Sports & West Wallasey Van Hire.

CAMMELL LAIRD

Chairman: Steve McGlasson
Secretary: Ray Steele. Tel Nos: 0151 650 0372 & (M) 07966 298673 c/o Lairds Sports Club, St Peters Road,Rock ferry, Wirral CH42 1PY
Ground: Kirklands, St Peters Road, Rock Ferry, Birkenhead
Tel: 0151 645 5991 **Colours:** All blue **Formed:** 1900
Sponsors: Met Arc. & Advantage Mortgage Services

CHRISTLETON

Chairman: Ron Mayers
Secretary: Ken Price, 35 Canadian Ave, Hoole, Chester CH2 3HQ Tel: 01244 313513
Ground: Little Heath, Christleton Tel: 01244 332153
Colours: Red/black/red **Formed** 1897 Re-Formed: 1966
Sponsors: Allans Skip Hire

GENERAL CHEMICALS

Chairman: Dave Robinson
Secretary: Tony Riley 171 Cotton Lane, Runcorn, Cheshire WA7 5JB
Tel: 01928 565390
Ground: Picow Farm Road, Runcorn
Colours: Blue & white/blue/blue & white **Formed:** 1958
Sponsors: Maltacourt Ltd

HELSBY

Chairman: John Close
Secretary: John Evans, 35 Hill View Ave., Helsby, Ches. WA6 0ES Tel: 01928 724817 (H)
Ground: Helsby Sports & Social Club Tel: 01928 722267
Colours: White/green/green **Formed:** 1895
Sponsors: Brand - Rex EVC. & Helsby Sports & Social Club

HESWALL

Chairman: Brian Flanagan
Secretary: Jake Horan ,13 Reedville Rd, Bebington, Wirral L63 2HS
Tel: 0151 644 0459
Ground: Gayton Pk,Brimstage Rd, Heswall, Wirral Tel:01513428172
Colours: Yellow/royal blue/yellow **Formed:** 1891
Sponsors: Pyramids Shopping Centre

MAGHULL

Chairman: Les Jacques **Secretary:** Danny Sherlock, 14 Alexander Drive, Lydiate, Merseyside L31 2NJ Tel: 0151 526 2306
Ground: Old Hall Field, Hall Lane, Maghull, Merseyside (0151 526 7320) **Directions:** M57 or M58 to end (Switch Island), A59 towards Preston (Northway)to lights at Hall Lane, right following signs for Maghull BR. then 200 yds on the left.1/2 m from Maghull (Merseyrail)
Colours: Blue & red stripes/blue/blue **Sponsors:** Soldier of Fortune

MANWEB

Chairman: James Parry Formed: 1932
John Shimmin, 54 Gonville Rd., Bootle, Merseyside L20 9LR
tel: 0151 933 5763 (H)
Ground: Manweb Sports & Social Club, Thingwall Rd., Liverpool L15 7LB Tel: 0151 281 5364 Colours: White/navy/white
Sponsors: Comasec yate Ltd

MERSEY ROYAL

Chairman: Tony Nelson **Secretary:** Dave Lawson 7 Mount Park, Higher Bebington, Wirral L63 5RD Tel: 0151 608 2261
Ground: Bromborough Pool Village, The Green, South View Rd., Bromborough Pool. Tel: 0151 645 3476
Colours: Navy & light blue striped shirts **Formed:** 1946
Sponsor: E.Casey

MOND RANGERS

Chairman: David Holland
Secretary: Steve Kinsella, 3 Bramble Way, Beechwood, Runcorn, Cheshire WA7 3HN Tel Nos: 01928 715178 (H) 07867 972919 (W)
Ground: Pavilions Club, Sandy Lane, Weston Point, Runcorn WA7 5EX
Tel: 01928 590508 **Colours:** Blue & black stripes **Formed:**1967
Sponsors: Rocksavage Power Co. & Domestic Boiler Services

NEWTON

Chairman: John Murray
Secretary: Alan Dabner, 79A Eleanor Road, Bidston, Wirral CH43 7RW. Tel NOs: 0151 653 2151 (H) 0151 993 2151 (B)
Ground: Millcroft, Frankby Road, Greasby, Wirral Tel: 0151 677 8382
Colours: Yellow/green/yellow **Formed:** 1933
Sponsors: Cory Brothers Shipping Ltd.

POULTON VICTORIA

Chairman: Thonas Quinn
Secretary: George Cooper,1 Foxhey Road, Wallasey, Wirral CH44 2ES. Tel Nos: 0151 201 2072 (H) 0151 638 9112 (W)
Ground: Victoria Park, Rankin Street, Wallasey Tel: 0151 638 3559
Colours: All Royal Blue **Formed:** 1935
Sponsors: Carlsberg & Bass

SHELL F.C.

Chairman: Gerry Fraser
Secretary: Steven Foden, 23 Hornbeam Avenue, Great Sutton, South Wirral Ch65 7AQ. Tel Nos: 0151 356 8837 (H) 07941 187632 (M)
Ground: Chester Road, Whitby, Ellesmere Port, South Wirral
Tel: 0151 200 7080 **Colours:** Yellow /navy/navy **Formed:** 1924
Sponsors: Abba Security Systems Ltd.

STORK

Chairman: Brian Favengen
Secretary: Steve Carter
7 Elm Road, Bebington, Wirral L63 8PF Tel: 0151 645 6697
Ground: Unilever Sports Ground, Bromborough
Colours: All green **Formed:** 1920
Sponsors: The Village Leisure Hotel

VAUXHALL MOTORS RESERVES

Chairman: Tony Woodley
Secretary: Carole Paisey, 26 South Road, West Kirby, Wirral L48 3HQ (0151 6256 936)
Ground: Vauxhall Sports Ground, Rivacre Road, Hooton, Ellesmere Port (0151 3281114)
Colours: White/royal blue/white **Formed:** 1963

BLACON YOUTH CLUB
Chairman: Peter Barnes
Secretary: Colin Lawson,54 Adelaide Rd., Blacon, Chester CH1 5SZ Tel: 01244 375508 (H)
Ground: Cairns Crescent Playing Fields, Cairns Crescent, Blacon, Chester. **Colours:** Black & white stripes/black/black **Formed:** 1964
Sponsors: George Starkey Painter & Decorator & McDonalds

CAPENHURST VILLA Formed: 1952
Chairman: Brian Heyes
Secretary: Martin Williams, 157 Hope Farm Road, Great Sutton, South Wirral L662TJ Tel: 0151 339 8935
Ground: Capenhurst Sports Ground, Capenhurst Lane, Capenhurst Tel: 0151 339 4101 **Colours:** All maroon
Sponsors: Handbridge Decorators & Commercial Properties

CASTROL SOCIAL FC Formed: 1954
Secretary: Mike Caulfield, 2 Weaver Road, Whitby, Ellesmere Port CH66 2JJ. Tel: 0151 355 5966 (H)
Ground: Castrol Sports & Social Club, Chester Road, Whitby, Ellesmere Port(0151 355 1730)
Colours: Royal & emerald/royal/white

MALLABY FC Formed: 1965
Chairman: G M Langan
Secretary: Tommy Kenny, 11 Seeley Ave., Claughton, Birkenhead CH41 0BX Tel: 0151 653 5925 (H)
Ground: Balaclava, Birkenhead Park.
Colours: Red & black stripes/black/red

MANOR ATHLETIC Formed: 1968
Chairman: Tony Bell
Secretary: Stewart Galtress, 3 Centurion Close, Meols, Wirrall CH47 7BZ Tel: 0151 632 3211 email: s-galtress@hotmail.com
Ground: Unilever Sports Ground, Bromborough
Colours: All royal blue

MERSEYSIDE POLICE Formed: 1885
Secretary: Gary Dinsmore, 3 Chaffinch Close, West Derby, Liverpool L12 0NX Tel: 0151 220 0285 (H)
Ground: Police Club, Fairfield, Prescot Road, Liverpool L7 0JD Tel: 0151 228 2352
Colours: All navy b lue with red trim.

NEW BRIGHTON Formed: 1993
Secretary: Carl Gidman. 64 Ford Road, Upton, Wirrall CH49 0TG Tel: 0151 678 1858 (H/B)
Ground: Harrison Drive, Wallasey Village, Wallasey
Colours: Red & white/white/red & white

PAVILIONS Formed: 1998
Secretary: Beverley Crilly, 26 Perrin Ave., Weston Point, Runcorn WA7 4BJ Tel: 01928 575938 (H)
Ground: Pavilions Complex, Sandy Lane, Weston Point, Runcorn Tel: 01928 590508
Colours: Blue & white stripes/blue/blue

UPTON ATHLETIC ASSOC. Formed: 1964
Secretary: Barry Gaulton, 24 St Marks Crescent, Whitby, Ellesmere Port L66 2XD (0151 339 1504)
Ground: Cheshire County Council Sports & Social Club, Plas Newton Lane, Chester (01244 318367)
Colours: All blue

WEST KIRBY Formed: 1895
Secretary: Roy Williamson, 85 Wood Lane, Greasby, Wirrall CH49 2PX Tel: 0151 677 4860 (H)
Ground: Johnston Recreation Ground, Neston Road, Willaston, South Wirrall.
Colours: White/black/black

plus
Ashville Reserves; Cammell Laird Reserves; Christleton Reserves; Heswall Reserves; Mersey Royal Reserves; Poulton Victoria Reserves.

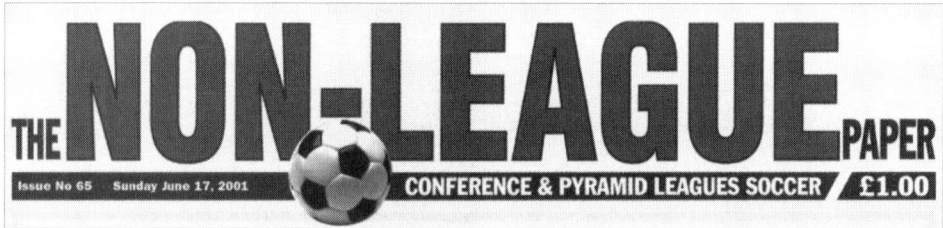

THE BASS/WPRC
MID CHESHIRE ASSOCIATION FOOTBALL LEAGUE

Founded 1948

President: R Atherton **Chairman:** J Walton
Hon. Secretary: G Edgeley, 61 Harris Rd, Lostock Gralam, Northwich, Cheshire CW9 7PE
Tel & Fax: 01606 352799 01606 79411 (B) Email: ledgegem@aol.com

FINAL LEAGUE TABLES 2000-01

DIVISION ONE

	P	W	D	L	F	A	Pts
Barnton	30	23	2	5	82	28	71
Poynton	30	17	8	5	77	45	59
Middlewich Town	30	18	3	9	50	33	57
Pilkington	30	18	3	9	65	48	57
Knutsford	30	15	10	5	52	29	55
Cheadle HN	30	14	7	9	51	38	49
Linotype	30	13	7	10	58	40	46
Grove United	30	14	4	12	63	59	46
Rylands	30	11	8	11	44	51	41
Padgate St Oswalds	30	8	11	11	42	63	35
Garswood United	30	11	1	18	48	64	34
Trafford Reserves	30	8	5	17	40	68	29
Crewe FC	30	8	4	18	36	55	28
Chorlton Town	30	8	3	19	48	87	27
Bollington Athletic	30	7	5	18	54	64	26
Whitchurch Alport	30	4	5	21	39	77	17

DIVISION TWO

	P	W	D	L	F	A	Pts
Broadheath Central	26	21	3	2	75	27	66
Styal	26	20	3	3	74	26	63
Golborne Sports	26	15	5	6	85	41	50
Warrington Borough	26	11	7	8	44	34	40
Chester Nomads	26	11	6	9	47	42	39
Rylands Reserves	26	11	5	10	44	42	38
Lostock Gralam	26	10	6	10	57	59	36
Cheadle HN Reserves	26	10	6	10	54	64	36
Malpas	26	8	10	8	60	45	34
Linotype Reserves	26	9	3	14	47	55	30
Pilkington Reserves	26	7	5	14	58	63	26
Poynton Reserves	26	5	9	12	46	56	24
Garswood Reserves	26	7	3	16	43	82	24
Littlemoor	26	0	3	23	31	129	3

HONOURS BOARD

DIVISION ONE

	League Champions	Runners Up	League Cup Winners	Runners Up
2000-01	Barnton	Poynton	Rylands	Poynton
1999-00	Barnton	Middlewich Town	Knutsford	Rylands
1998-99	Barnton	Linotype	Barnton	Beeches
1997-98	Barnton	Knutsford	Barnton	Knutsford
1996-97	Barnton	Linotype	Barnton	Bramhall

DIVISION TWO

	League Champions	Runners Up	League Cup Winners	Runners Up
2000-01	Broadheath Central	Styal	Styal	Pilkington Reserves
1999-00	Trafford Reserves	Crewe FC	Crewe FC	Trafford Reserves
1998-99	Padgate St Oswalds	Grove United	Padgate St Oswalds	Broadheath Central
1997-98	Garswood United Res	Pilkington	Padgate St Oswalds	Garswood United Res
1996-97	Lostock Gralam	Beeches	Beeches	Pilkington

BILL GRAY TROPHY - CLUB OF THE SEASON

2000-01	Lostock Gralam FC
1999-00	Bollington Athletic FC
1998-99	Malpas FC
1997-98	Pilkington FC
1996-97	Barnton FC

PLAYER OF THE SEASON

2000-01	Chris Leigh (Knutsford FC)
	Lee Webber (Pilkington FC)
	Simon Heaton (Cheadle HN FC)
1999-00	Stephen Nugent (Garswood Utd FC)
1998-99	Christopher McCabe (Styal FC)

DIVISION ONE CLUBS

BARNTON AFC

Chairman: William Perrin **Manager:** Mark Emmerson
Secretary: Michael Webster, 92 Church Road, Barnton CW8 4JE (01606 782960)
Ground: Townfield, Townfield Lane, Barnton
Colours: Black & White Stripes/Black
Change Colours: Blue & yellow /blue

BROADHEATH CENTRAL FC

Chairman: Ian Beresford **Manager:** Peter Cavanagh
Secretary: David Murphy,113 Downs Drive,Timperley, Altrincham Wa14 5QU (0161 718 0523)
Ground: Viaduct Road, Broadheath, Altrincham
Colours: Black & Red Stripes/Black
Change Colours: Blue & White Stripes/White

CHEADLE HEATH NOMADS

Chairman: Roy Welsh **Manager:** Peter Blundell
Secretary: George Gibbons, 20A Gillbent Road,Cheadle Hulme,SK8 6NB Tel No: 0161 440 9951
Ground: The Heath, Norbreck Ave, Cheadle, Stockport
Colours: Maroon & Sky blue,Maroom/maroon
Change Colours: Yelow & Green/Green/Green

CHORLTON TOWN

Chairman: Peter Grogan **Manager:** Sandy Slater
Secretary: Jim Calderbank, 21 South Meade, Timperley, Altrincham, Cheshire WA15 6QL
Ground: Parkway Ground, Rylstone Avenue,Chorlton
Colours: Red & Black/White/white
Change Colours: Yellow or Blue/Blue/Red

CREWE FC

Chairman: Patrick Slack **Manager:** Ian O'Reilly
Secretary: Mrs M Vickers, 59 Hall-o-Shaw St, Crewe (01270 581578)
Ground: Cumberland Sprts Grnd, Thomas St, Crewe
Colours: Sky Blue/Marooon/White
Change Colours: Yellow/Black/Blue

GARSWOOD UNITED FC

Chairman: Barry Mavers **Manager:** Alan Clarke
Secretary: Tony McKeown,44 Dunsdale Drive, Ashton, Wigan WN4 8PT Tel No: 01942 724259
Ground: The Wooders, Simms Lane End, Garswood
Colours: Blue & White Halves/Blue/Blue
Change Colours: All Yellow

GROVE UNITED FC

Chairman: Mark Boothby **Manager:** John Whiteley
Secretary: Mark Boothby,68 DenesideCrescent,Hazel Grove SK7 4NU Tel NO: 0161 285 1211
Ground: Half Moon Lane, Offerton, Stockport
Colours: Green & Yellow/green/white
Change Colours: All Blue

KNUTSFORD FC

Chairman: Ken Harrison **Manager:** Srewart Dow
Secretary: Kevin Deeley, 28 East Street, Guide Bridge, Manchester, M34 5DX (0161 320 9650)
Ground: Manchester Road, Knutsford
Colours: Red /Black/Black
Change Colours: Black & White stripes/White/White

LINOTYPE FC

Chairman: James Barry **Manager:** Glyn Williams
Secretary: Brian McGuiness, 36 Barrington Road, Altrincham, Cheshire (0161 929 0021)
Ground: British Airways Club, Clay Lane, Timperley
Colours: White/Black
Change Colours: Red & Black/White/red

MIDDLEWICH TOWN FC

Chairman: Steven Morris **Manager:** David Twite
Secretary: Philip Hassell,1 Whitegate `Close,Middlewich,Cheshire CW10 0RF Tel Nos: 01606 832185 (H) 01606832734 (W)
Ground: Seddon Street, Middlewich (01606 835842)
Colours: Red/Black/Red
Change Colours: White/black

PADGATE ST OSWALDS FC

Chairman: Graham Millins **Manager:** Nick Armitage
Secretary: Brian Hughes, 13 Jubilee Ave, Padgate, Warrington WA1 3JY (01925 490924)
Ground: Bennets Rec. Ground, Station Rd, Padgate
Colours: White /Black/White
Change Colours: Yellow/Green/Yellow

PILKINGTON AFC

Chairman: Barry Meadows **Manager:** David Burrows
Secretary: Kevin Guy,22 Ennerdale Avenue,Ashton -in-Makerfield WN4 5BA Tel No: 01942 723693
Ground: Ruskin Drive, St Helens
Colours: Sky blue 7navy,navy/navy
Change Colours: Red & black/red/red

POYNTON

Chairman: David Corcoran **Manager:** Charlie Jones
Secretary: Mark Warburton, 27 Alderley Close, Hazel Grove, Stockport SK7 6BS (01625 873872)
Ground: London Road North, Poynton
Colours: Red & Black/Black/Red
Change Colours: Blue & White/Blue/Blue

RYLANDS FC

Chairman: Alan Jackson **Manager:** Terry Selby
Secretary: Ian Finchett, 31 Elizabeth Drive, Padgate, Warrington WA1 4JQ (01925 816911)
Ground: Rylands Rec. Club, Gorsey Lane, Warrington
Colours: Blue & Black/Black/Black
Change Colours: Red & Black/Black/Red

STYAL FC

Chairman: Barry Green **Manager:** Jim Vince
Secretary: Alan Jones, 1 Oak Brow Cottages, Altrincham Rd, Styal, Wilmslow SK9 4JE (01625 530270)
Ground: Altrincham Road, Styal
Colours: Yellow/Black/Black
Change Colours: Blue/White/White

TRAFFORD FC RESERVES

Chairman: David Brown **Manager:** Dave Norman
Secretary: Graham Foxhall, 62 Grosvenor Rd, Urmston, Manchester M41 5AQ (0161 746 9726)
Ground: Shawe View, Pennybridge Lane, Urmston
Colours: All White
Change Colours: SkyBlue/ Black/Blackk

DIVISION TWO CLUBS

BOLLINGTON ATHLETIC FC

Chairman: Albert Hall **Manager:** Michael Quigley
Secretary: Anthony Holmes, 1 Princess Drive, Bollington, Macclesfield SK10 5ES (01625 574913)
Ground: Recreation Ground, Bollington
Colours: Green & Black/Green
Change Colours: Maroon/Sky/Sky

CHESTER NOMADS FC

Chairman: Phil Darlington **Manager:** Bob Delgado
Secretary: Ritz Ritzema, 22 Cross Green Upton, Chester CH2 1QR (01244 379791)
Ground: Garrison Ground, Eaton Rd, Handbridge
Colours: Amber/Black
Change Colours: Grey/Red

CROSSFIELDS FC

Chairman: Michael Hickey **Manager:** Derek Evans
Secretary: Frank Whitehouse, 153 Birdwell Drive, Gt. Sankey, Warrington Tel: 01925 728710 (H) 01925 625750 (B)
Ground: Hood Lane Rec., Gt. Sankey, Warrington
Colours: Primrose & blue
Change Colours: Orange & black

DATEN FC

Chairman: Trevor Farrington
Manager: Robert Jones
Secretary: Michael Henshall, 21 Upwood Rd., Lowton, Warrington WA3 2RL Tel: 01942 724471 01772 321800 (B)
Ground: Culcheth Sports Club, Charnock Rd., Culcheth Tel: 01925 763096
Colours: Sky & royal blue
Change Colours: Blue & white stipes/navy

LOSTOCK GRALAM FC

Chairman: D Washburn **Manager:** Andy Hough
Secretary: Andy Hough, 31 Beechwood Drive, Wincham, Northwich CW9 6EY (01565 733383)
Ground: Slow & Easy Hotel, Manchester Road, Lostock Gralam.
Colours: All Blue
Change Colours: Green & Yellow Halves/Black

GOLBORNE SPORTS FC

Chairman: Bill Hiltyon **Manager:** Andrew Smallman
Secretary: Stephen Whittle, 20 West Ave., Golborne, Warrington WA3 3EA Tel: 01942 715570 (H) 07979 550732 (M)
Ground: Simpson Playing Fields, Stone Cross Lane, Lowton WA3 2SL Tel: 01942 510161
Colours: All Yellow
Change Colours: All blue

MALPAS FC

Chairman: Robert Leslie **Manager:** Martin Holden
Secretary: Bernard Lloyd, 15 Springfield Ave, Malpas, Cheshire SY14 8QD (01948 860812)
Ground: Malpas & Dt SC, Oxheys, Wrexham Rd, Malpas
Colours: Blue/Blue/Yellow
Change Colours: Green & White Hoops/White/White

WARRINGTON BOROUGH FC

Chairman: Harry Buden **Manager:** Derek Holden
Secretary: John Kent, 126 Cumberland ST, Warrington, WA4 1EX (01925 482970)
Ground: Cantilever Park (01925 724421)
Colours: Blue & Yellow Halves/Blue/Blue
Change Colours: All Red

WHITCHURCH ALPORT

Chairman: Peter Wainwright **Manager:** A.Allmark
Secretary: Matthew Huxley, 36 Wrexham Road, Whitchurch,Shrops. SY13 1ER Tel No: 01948 664578
Ground: Yockings Park, Blackpark Rd, **Colours:** Green /Black/Green

Plus
Cheadle H N Reserves; Linotype Reserves, Pilkington Reserves, Poynton Reserves, Garswood Reserves & Middlewitch Town Reserves.

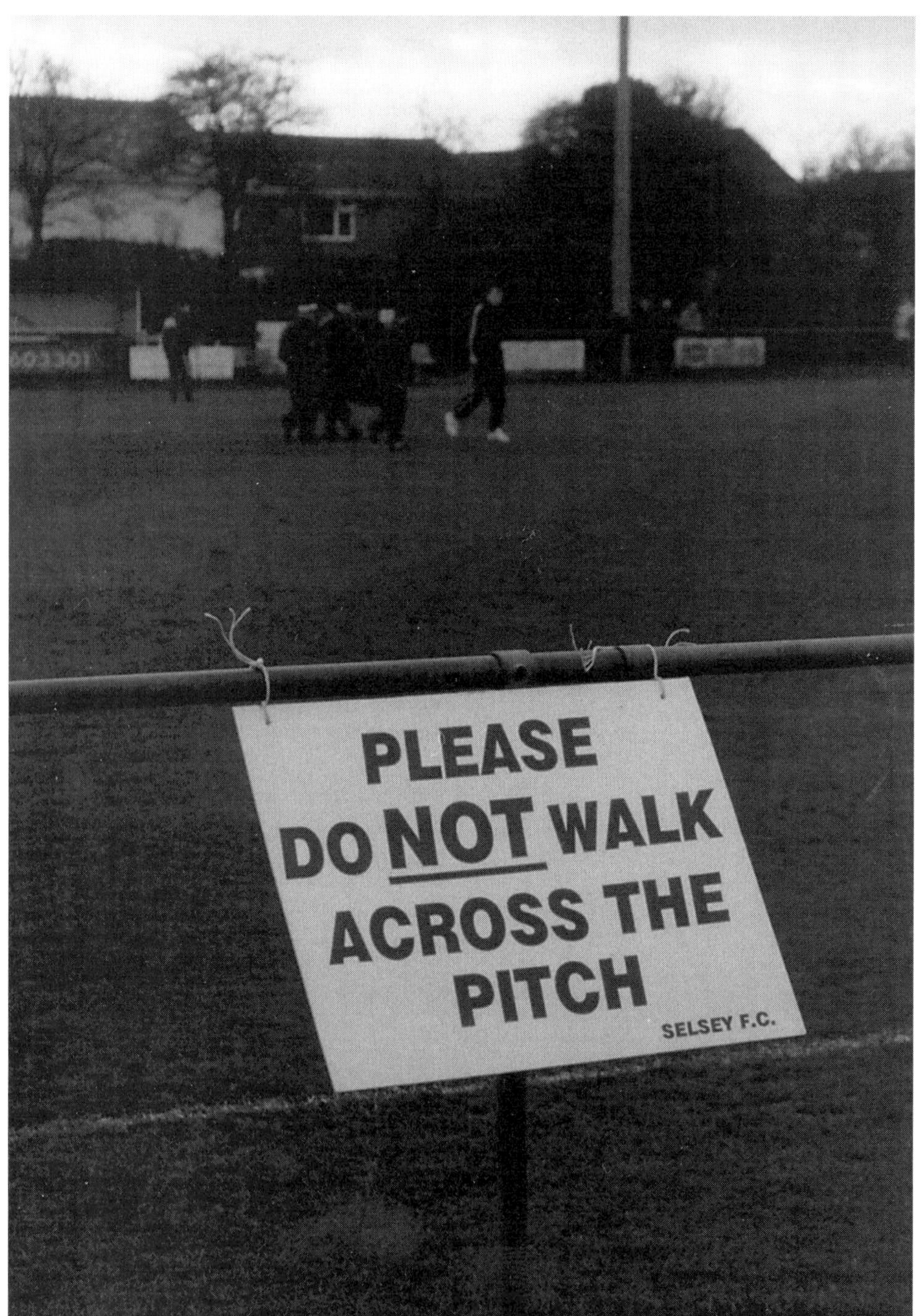

Photo: Graham Cotterill

THE ASDA LOGIC WEST LANCASHIRE FOOTBALL LEAGUE

President: D Procter Esq.

Chairman & General Secretary: W Carr Esq.

60 Selby Avenue, Blackpool FY4 2LZ

Kirkham & Wesham followed up on their Cup and League Double of the previous season by repeating their success, and adding the Lancashire Challenge Shield to their trophy cabinet. This is only the third time the "Treble" has been achieved since the league was formed in 1904. They also came close to completing the season unbeaten but lost their last game of the season to Blackrod Town. Dalton United were again runners-up in the Premier Division, the Lancashire Shield denied them by Kirkham & Wesham in the final on the County Ground Leyland.

As a result of the resignation of Lansil early in the season and Leyland Motors at the completion, there were no relegations from the Premier Division. Blackpool Wren Rovers and Tempest United from Bolton were promoted from Division One. BAC Preston and Thornton Cleveleys have been relegated to Division Two, while Crooklands Casuals in their first season, and Millom, both clubs from Cumbria, won promotion to the First Division. Three new clubs, Mill Hill St Peters, Stoneclough and Tottington, have all been accepted into Division Two.

For the Season 2001-02 the Premier Division retains its complement of sixteen teams and the two lower divisions will operate with fourteen teams in each, while the two Reserve Divisions for member clubs will have fifteen teams each, making a total membership of 44 clubs with a total of 74 teams.

The League is especially sad to lose two of its oldest established clubs, Chorley Motors (formerly Leyland Motors Chorley) and Leyland Motors Athletic. Both clubs have long connections with the league going back to 1919. They are not only a loss to ourselves but a loss to football.

FINAL LEAGUE TABLES 2000-01

PREMIER DIVISION

	P	W	D	L	F	A	Pts	GD
Kirkham/Wesham	28	22	5	1	90	24	71	66
Dalton United	28	20	2	6	79	34	62	45
Blackrod Town	28	18	5	5	72	38	59	34
Fulwood Amat.	28	14	8	6	62	36	50	26
Norcross/Warbreck	28	13	5	10	70	62	44	8
Springfields	28	13	5	10	56	48	44	8
Charnock Richard	28	11	8	9	44	50	41	-6
Garstang	28	11	5	12	43	59	38	-16
Leyland Motors Ath	28	9	5	14	41	53	32	-12
Freckleton	28	8	6	14	34	53	30	-19
Barnoldswick Utd	28	7	7	14	44	60	28	-16
Vickers Sports C	28	6	9	13	39	69	27	-30
Eagley	28	7	4	17	45	58	25	-13
Wyre Villa	28	6	5	17	41	65	23	-24
Burnley United	28	4	3	21	43	94	15	-51

DIVISION ONE

	P	W	D	L	F	A	Pts	GD
Blackpool Wren R	30	22	3	5	77	45	69	32
Tempest United	30	19	7	4	87	33	64	54
Milnthorpe Corinth.	30	17	5	8	80	51	56	29
Poulton Town	30	15	5	10	61	41	50	20
Feniscowles	30	15	4	11	47	45	49	2
Carnforth Rngrs	30	14	6	10	50	44	48	6
Hesketh Bank	30	13	4	13	69	59	43	10
Lancs Constab	30	11	6	13	69	79	39	-10
Fleetwood Hesk.	30	11	5	14	47	54	38	-7
Wigan SMR	30	10	6	14	54	67	36	-13
Whinney Hill	30	10	6	14	48	62	36	-14
Burnley Belvedere	30	9	8	13	54	63	35	-9
Haslingden St M	30	9	8	13	52	66	35	-14
Turton	30	9	5	16	57	65	32	-8
Thornton Cleveleys	30	7	5	18	53	88	26	-35
Bac/Ee Preston	30	4	7	19	40	83	19	-43

HONOURS LIST 2000-01

Richardson Cup	Winners: Kirkham & Wesham	Runners up: Vickers Sports Club
President's Cup	Winners: Blackpool Wren Rovers	Runners up: Fleetwood Hesketh
Tavern Cup	Winners: Crooklands Casuals	Runners up: Lytham St Annes
Lancashire Challenge Shield	Winners: Kirkham & Wesham	Runners up: Dalton United

Wilmslow Albion, winners of the Murray Shield 2000-01

Wythenshawe Amateurs, winners of the Gilgryst Cup 2000-01

AIR MILES MANCHESTER FOOTBALL LEAGUE

Honorary President: Norman Noder

League Secretary: Joe Hall, 31 Sunhill Close, Rochdale, Lancashire OL16 4RU.
Tel. 01706 719829 Fax. 01706 719828 Email – jj.hall@zoom.co.uk

The League's congratulations go to Stand Athletic, who successfully negotiated a frenetic end of season programme to clinch a third successive league title, following in the footsteps of the great Maine Road side of the 1980's, the Whitefield based side are now set for a first season in the North West Counties Football League after attaining all the qualifications requirements necessary.

Wythenshawe Amateurs finished as runners-up despite losing only three league matches all season, and they will be very pleased with a great season which saw them claim some consolation when they defeated Stand Athletic 1-0 in the Gilgryst Cup Final thanks to a late Andy Walker strike. Atherton Town faded a little towards the end of an exhausting campaign to finish third by eight points, and also inflicted a 1-0 defeat on Champions Stand to end their season on a high. In fourth place were classy Eccles based outfit Mitchell Shackleton, who once again proved to be a very durable and skilful outfit under the watchful eyes of Dave Rowan. Just behind them were East Manchester whose season never really got going after a phenomenal start to the season with Mike Norton in freescoring form, but they did reach the semi-finals of the Manchester Challenge Trophy and Gilgryst Cup. Sixth place went to Failsworth Town who recovered superbly to climb above half the Division in a great end of season run-in, dropping only two points from the last 33 available, and the Long Lane side could emerge as a real force next season.Willows too were a side to watch, enjoying their best season ever to finish seventh largely thanks to the goalscoring form of Jamie Shepley who ended the Premier Division leading marksman with 25 goals.

Dukinfield Town endured a roller-coaster season with goals at a premium, though they did reach the Fourth Round of the Cheshire Amateur Cup.

Likewise, Prestwich Heys started well with their crop of talented youngsters, but their form dipped at the end of the campaign when a top half finish looked likely. Sacred Heart, after looking likely top four material early on in the season, dropped off sharply finish in tenth position, taking only five out the last 27 points, but this was still a solid start to Premier Division life for the Rochdale side. Monton Amateurs flickered into life at the end of a difficult season to claim three straight wins, whilst Elton Fold and Springhead drew far too many games to make inroads up the table but finished well clear of the bottom two positions. Stockport Georgians again struggled, but showed a mean streak on occasions to perhaps indicate better times are around the corner whilst Pennington finished bottom of the pile after a campaign collecting only three league wins.

Congratulations also go to League newboys Leigh Athletic who romped to the First Division title after a great season which saw them lose only one league game after the 26th August. The free-scoring form of Danny and Rick Wilson played a crucial part in their success, with a handful of players also getting into double figures.

The runners-up spot went to New Mills after a nervous end of season in which they had to win five of their last six matches go second, and to add to a great campaign at Church Lane, the Millers also collected the Derbyshire Divisional Cup and were beaten finalists in the Murray Shield.

It is hard not to feel sympathy for Breightmet United who had a superb campaign, but finished in third place despite garnering 67 points, ten points clear of fourth placed Hindsford. United were the only side to defeat Leigh after August in a league fixture to underline the quality at the club. Hindsford looked on course for a top two place, but a dramatic fall off in form and goalscoring left them looking to next season. Similarly, Whitworth Valley, who were many people's favourite for promotion, saw vital games slip away from them towards the end of the season. Wythenshawe Town boasted the League's leading goalscorer in Darren Mee, but conceded too many to get amongst the front-runners but look a good bet for a more sustained challenge next season. Belden staged a remarkable second half recovery to rise from the basement to eighth, as well as picking up the Manchester Challenge trophy. Whalley Range were the season's most improved side and were unlucky not to finish in the top half, whilst Wilmslow Albion gained some consolation for their inconsistent league form in claiming the Murray Shield by beating New Mills 2-1.

Tintwistle Villa could not get going inn a stop-start campaign, but showed plenty of quality, and Hollinwood finished in a creditable tenth position in a season blighted by postponements. Ashton Athletic showed some good defensive qualities during a solid season, but Avro will be disappointed not have built on last term's success this time around. Manchester Royal put aside off field problems to finish outside the bottom two, where Old Alts and Milton ended the campaign, but both sporadically burst into life with some good wins.

Wythenshawe Amateurs won the Second Division title from Springhead in a close contest, whilst Wilmslow Albion ran away with the Third Division title, Willows claiming the runners-up spot in a close run battle with Sacred Heart. Leigh Athletic added to the First Division title with an Open Trophy victory over East Manchester in a nail-biting encounter which Leigh won 3-2.

FINAL LEAGUE TABLES 2000-01

PREMIER DIVISION

	P	W	D	L	F	A	Pts	GD
Stand Athletic	28	21	0	7	91	25	63	+66
Wythenshawe Am	28	17	8	3	57	32	59	+25
Atherton Town	28	16	6	6	46	27	54	+19
Mitchell Shackleton	28	13	7	8	56	37	46	+19
East Manchester	28	13	6	9	58	48	45	+10
Failsworth Town	28	14	2	12	51	44	44	+7
Willows	28	11	8	9	57	63	41	-6
Dukinfield Town	28	12	4	12	39	40	40	-1
Prestwich Heys	28	10	8	10	56	57	38	-1
Sacred Heart	28	10	7	11	44	46	37	-2
Monton Amateurs	28	9	5	14	51	61	32	-10
Elton Fold	28	7	10	11	32	43	31	-11
Springhead	28	5	12	11	46	57	27	-11
Stockport G'gians	28	4	4	20	38	77	16	-39
Pennington	28	3	3	22	29	94	12	-65

Urmston - Record expunged

FIRST DIVISION

	P	W	D	L	F	A	Pts	GD
Leigh Athletic	30	23	4	3	93	41	73*	+52
New Mills	30	22	3	5	99	35	69	+64
Breightmet United	30	21	4	5	106	30	67	+76
Hindsford	30	17	6	7	71	48	57	+23
Whitworth Valley	30	18	1	11	73	63	55	+10
Wythenshawe Tn	30	13	9	8	87	67	48	+20
Belden	30	12	6	12	70	68	42	+2
Whalley Range	30	12	5	13	56	77	41	-21
Wilmslow Albion	30	11	5	14	86	79	38	+7
Tintwistle Villa	30	9	8	13	60	66	35	-6
Hollinwood	30	9	4	17	56	100	31	-44
Ashton Athletic	30	8	6	16	44	68	30	-24
Avro	30	7	8	15	58	81	29	-23
Manchester Royal	30	7	2	21	39	92	23	-53
Old Alts	30	6	4	20	51	85	22	-34
Milton	30	5	5	20	44	93	20	-49

GILGRYST CUP 2000-01

SEMI-FINALS

Stand Athletic v East Manchester 2*1

Wythenshawe Ams v Prestwich Heys 4-2

FINAL

Wythenshawe Ams v Stand Athletic 1-0 at Stockport Georgians FC

MURRAY SHIELD 2000-01

SEMI-FINALS

Hindsford v Wilmslow Albion 3*4

Leigh Athletic v New Mills 4*6

FINAL

Wilmslow Albion v New Mills 2-1 at Stockport Georgians FC

OPEN TROPHY 2000-01

SEMI-FINALS

Prestwich Heys Res v Leigh Athletic Res 2*3

Willows Res v East Manchester R 1-2

FINAL

Leigh Athletic Res v East Manchester Res 3-2 at New Mills FC

LEADING GOALSCORERS 2000-01

PREMIER DIVISION

	Lge	Cup	Total
Jamie Shepley (Willows)	22	3	25
Phil Hornby (Atherton Town)	19	2	21
Martyn Stewart (East Manchester)	15	6	21
Micky Bartholomew (Stand Athletic)	14	6	20
Chris Denham (Stand Athletic)	17	2	19
John Robinson (Mitchell Shackleton)	16	2	18
Mark Wilson (Stand Athletic)	13	5	18
Brandon Jolly (Prestwich Heys)	13	4	17
Mike McNamara (Springhead)	12	3	15
Mark Denham (Stand Athletic)	11	4	15
Neil Allen (Stockport Georgians)	14	0	14
Baz Kabani (Wythenshawe Ams)	11	3	14
Alex Ritchie (Prestwich Heys)	11	3	14
Andy Walker (Wythenshawe Ams)	11	3	14
Darren Schofield (Springhead)	10	3	13
Danny Self (Springhead)	4	7	11
Mike Norton (East Manchester)	10	0	10
Anthony Pauls (Sacred Heart)	10	0	10
Ray Beer (Wythenshawe Ams)	9	1	10
Graham Bragg (Monton Amateurs)	9	1	10
Mark Crossland (Dukinfield Town)	8	2	10
Steve Holt (Sacred Heart)	8	2	10
Bob Fulham (Springhead)	4	6	10

ATHERTON TOWN

Secretary: G Butler, 43 Hope Fold Ave., Atherton, Lancs M29 0BW Tel: 01942 870326
Ground: Howe Bridge Spts Centre, Howe Bridge, Atherton Tel: 01942 884882
Directions: A579 Atherton to Leigh road - Sports Centre 800 yds on left
Colours: Royal/white/royal

DUKINFIELD TOWN

Secretary: Paul Bishop, 21 Church Walk, Stalybridge, Cheshire Tel: 0161 303 0398
Ground: Blocksages Playing Fields, Birch Lane, Dukinfield.
Directions: From Ashton centre follow Kings St, turn left into Chapel St. thenright turn into Foundry St/Birch Lane. Ground 880 yds on right, behind publicbaths.
Colours: All yellow

EAST MANCHESTER

Secretary: D Wilkinson, 76 Sandy Lane, Dukinfield, Cheshire SK16 5NL Tel: 0161 330 4450
Ground: Wright Robinson College, Abbey Hey, Gorton. or possibly Droylsden FC
Directions: Leave Manchester via Ashton Old Road (A635). Turn into Abbey Hey Lane and Wright Robinson College is just over half a mile down road on your left as road bends to right.
Colours: All royal blue

ELTON FOLD

Secretary: Guy Mallinson, 14 Lonsdale St, Bury BL8 2QD Tel: 0161 797 7090
Ground: Bolton Rd Sports Club, Bolton Rd, Bury
Directions: A58 from Bury to Bolton. 1 mile from Bury pass Wellington Pub onright 200 yards turn left into Connaught St. Halfway down turn right in betweenhouses into car park
Colours: Blue & black/black/black

FAILSWORTH TOWN

Secretary: David Walton, 45 Woodend Street, Oldham, Lancs Tel: 0161 627 5480
Ground: GMT White House, Heaton Park, Manchester
Directions: M66 junc 5 towards Manchester, ground approx 1mile on right behindWhite House GMT Club.
Colours: Black & white/white/white

LEIGH ATHLETIC

Formed: 1959
Secretary: Alan Marsh Tel: 01942 678500
Ground: Madley Park, Charles St., Leigh
Directions: Exit A580 at junction with A574 onto Warrington Road and follow into Leigh town centre. Turn right into King Street and turn right into Church Street (Boars Head Public House). Take sixth left into Charles Street and ground straight ahead.
Colours: Yellow/ Blue/ Blue

MITCHELL SHACKLETON

Secretary: Ian Street, 11 Senior Road, Peel Green, Eccles, M30 7PZ Tel: 0161 789 7061
Ground: Salteye Park, Peel Green, Eccles Tel: 0161 788 8373
Directions: Leave M63 at Peel Green r'bout (jct 2), take A57 Liverpool Roadtowards Irlam, ground entrance half mile on left behind Kara Cafew opposite Barton airport. Or, follow A57 from Manchester via Salford & Eccles, then follow Irlam signs.
Colours: Green & white/black/black

MONTON AMATEURS

Secretary: T Lee, 28 Wheatley Rd, Swinton, Manchester M27 3RW Tel: 0161 793 8033
Ground: Granary Lane, Worsley
Directions: From Eccles Centre turn right into Worsley Rd at Patricroft Bridge.Ground approx 1 mile on left, entrance just before Bridgewater Hotel
Colours: All royal

NEW MILLS

Secretary: Barry Land, 165 Lowleighton Road, New Mills, High Peak SK22 4LR Tel: 01663 746174
Ground: Church Lane, New Mills (01663 747435).
Directions: From A6 (Buxton Road), turn into Albion Road (A6015) at New Mills Newtown Train Station. Follow to junction of Church Road/Church Lane and ground on left.
Colours: Amber/black/black

PENNINGTON

Secretary: Joanne Hindley, 30 Sycamore Road, Atherton, Manchester (01942897273)
Ground: Jubilee Park, Leigh Rd, Atherton (01942 894703).
Directions: The entrance to the pathway to the ground is approx. 1 mile from Leigh Centre on the left hand side of the B5215 Atherton Road, the entrance is directly opposite the GMT depot.
Colours: White/blue/blue

PRESTWICH HEYS

Secretary: Stephen Howard, 28 Brandram Road, Prestwich, Manchester M25 1HJ Tel: 0161 773 4408
Ground: Sandgate Rd, Prestwich Tel: 0161 773 8888
Directions: Follow Old Bury Rd (A665) from Manchester to Prestwich, right intoHeywood Rd, 3rd left into Mount Rd/Sandgate Rd - ground on right.
Colours: Red & white/red/red

ROCHDALE SACRED HEART

Secretary: Joe Devlin, 61 Buersil Ave., Rochdale, Lancs. OL16 4TR
Tel: 01706 712602
Ground: Fox Park, Belfield Mill Lane, Rochdale
Directions: From Rochdale town centre follow the A640 to Milnrow, at Kingsway junction turn left into Albert Royds Street and turn right again into Bellfield Mill Lane.
Colours: All red

SPRINGHEAD

Secretary: K Gibson, 1 Little Oak Close, Lees, Oldham OL4 3LW Tel: 0161 627 3760
Ground: St John St, Lees, Oldham (0161 627 0260).
Directions: From Oldham (Mumps r'bout) follow A669 towards Lees for approx onemile, left into St John St, ground 500yds on right.
Colours: Black & red/black/black

STOCKPORT GEORGIANS

Secretary: Ged Newcombe, 7 Chiltern Close, Hazel Grove, Stockport SK7 5BQ Tel: 0161483 0004
Ground: Cromley Rd, Stockport, Tel: 0161 483 6581
Directions: Follow A6 from Stockport centre, turn right at Cemetery intoBranhall Lane. After 1 mile turn left at r/about into Woodsmoor Lane. Take 1st right Flowery Fields then right into Cromley Road
Colours: Purple/white/black

WILLOWS

Secretary: Frank Miller, 11 Edmund Street, Salford, Manchester (0161 737 2411)
Ground: Salteye Park, Peel Green, Eccles
Directions: From Eccles town centre take A57 and pass under M63 at Peel Green Roundabout, after approx. 400 yds turn left into a lay-by, the changing rooms are just behind Kara Cafe. For matchday contacts telephone Willows Club 0161 736 1451
Colours: All red

WYTHENSHAWE AMATEURS

Secretary: John Sobierajsh, 5 Wensley Drive, Withington, Manchester Tel: 0161 445 3415
Ground: Longley Lane, Northenden Tel: 0161 998 7268
Directions: Princess Parkway from Manchester to Post House hotel, via PalatineRd & Moor End Rd to Longley Lane - ground entrance opposite Overwood Rd.
Colours: Blue & white stripes/blue/blue

DIVISION ONE CLUBS

ASHTON ATHLETIC

Secretary: Steve Halliwell, 20 Kings Road, Golborne, Warrington Tel Nos: 01942 517728 (H) 0374 180165 (M)
Ground: Brocstedes Park, Farm Road , N Ashton, Wigan Tel: 01942 716360.
Colours: Yellow & Black stripes/ Black/ Black

AVRO

Secretary: Karen Birch, 27 Brooks Drive, Failsworth, Manchester M35 0L5 Tel: 0161 682 6731
Ground: Lancaster Club, Broadway, Failsworth
Colours: Red & Black/red/red

BELDEN (previously (B.I.C.C.)

Secretary: L. Stone, 51 Coppleridge Drive, Crumpsall, Manchester M8 4PB Tel: 0161 740 6621
Ground: Belden Works, Blackley New Road, Blackley. Tel: 0161 740 9151
Directions: Follow Rochdale Rd A664 from Manchester. Turn left at Brackley intoOld Market St, then fork right into Blackley New Rd, ground 300yards on left.(0161 740 9151)
Colours: Blue & white/blue/blue

BREIGHTMET UNITED

Secretary: Raymond Walsh, 94 Hatherleigh Walk, Breightmet, Bolton (01204435197)
Ground: Moss Park, Back Bury Rd, Breightmet, Bolton (01204 33930).
Colours: Black & white stripes/black/red

HINDSFORD

Secretary: Samantha Evans, 17 Belmont Avenue, Atherton M46 9RR RTel Nos: 01942 895869 (H) 07767 492411 (M)
Ground: Squires Lane, Tyldesley
Colours: Red /blue/red & blue

HOLLINWOOD

Secretary: Ken Evans, 20 Meadow Rise, High Crompton, Shaw, Oldham OL2 7QG (01706840987).
Ground: Lime Lane, Hollinwood (0161 681 3385).
Colours: Yellow & Navy/ Navy / Navy

MANCHESTER ROYAL

Secretary: N Kinvig, 3 Cranleigh Drive, Cheadle (0161 491 0824)
Ground: Barnes Hospital, Cheadle.
Colours: Red & black/black/black

MILTON

Secretary: Andrew Cole, 21 Whittle Drive, Shaw, Oldham OL2 8TJ Tel Nos: 01706 291973 (H) 0771 8331262 (M)
Ground: Athletic Stadium, Springfield Pk, Rochdale.
Colours: Green& Black,Black/Black

OLD ALTRINCHAMIANS

Secretary: Phil Lewis, 10 Woodfield Grove, Sale, M33 6JW (0161 973 7082)
Ground: Crossford Bridge Playing Fields, Meadows Rd, Sale.
Colours: Black & white stripes/black/black

ROYSTON TOWN

Secretary: Phil Dean (0161 287 8436)
Ground: Crompton Cricket Club, Shaw
Colours: Yellow and Black

TINTWISTLE VILLA

Secretary: William Higginbottom, 61 West Drive, Tintwistle, Glossop (01457852467)
Ground: West Drive, Tintwistle
Colours: Black & white stripes/black/black

UNSWORTH

Secretary: Suzanne Angle (0161 766 4073)
Ground: Hillock Playing Fields, Whitefield
Colours: Blue and Yellow

WARTH FOLD

Chairman: Denzil Hart (0161 723 1977)
Ground: The Elms, Whitefield
Colours: Not known
Year joined League - 2001 (first season in open age football)

WHALLEY RANGE

Secretary: Ronnie Lapsley, 16 Mosswood Park , Didsbury, Manchester M20 5QW (0161 613 5467).
Ground: Kings Rd, Chorlton (0161 881 2618).
Colours: Red & black stripes/black/black

WHITWORTH VALLEY

Secretary: Alan Riley, 31 John Street, Whitworth, Rochdale OL12 8BT Tel Nos: 01706 852619 (H) 07930 543924 (M)
Ground: Rawstron Str, Whitworth (01706 853030).
Colours: Black & white/black/red

WILMSLOW ALBION

Secretary: Norma Winn, 236 Derbyshire Lane, Stretford, Manchester (0161 2869520)
Ground: Oakwood Farm, Styal Road, Wilmslow
Colours: Green & White/ Green/ Green

WYTHENSHAWE TOWN

Secretary: Ray Pattison, 68 Westgatel Gardens, Royal Oak Est. Baguley M23 1BA (0161 374 3086)
Ground: Ericstan Park, Timpson Rd, Baguley, Manchester (0161 998 5076).
Colours: All royal Blue

NORTH WESTERN FINAL LEAGUE TABLES 2000-01

LIVERPOOL C.M.S. LEAGUE

PREMIER DIV.	*P*	*W*	*D*	*L*	*F*	*A*	*Pts*
Tapes for Industry	16	13	1	2	82	18	40
Marlow	16	12	2	2	58	26	38
Shillingsworth	16	12	1	3	61	27	37
Red Rum	16	12	1	3	58	31	37
Dee News	16	7	2	7	45	42	23
Maggies	16	5	1	10	40	52	16
The Farm	16	5	0	11	41	61	15
Vertex	16	2	0	14	9	121	6
Queen Victoria	16	0	0	16	3	19	0

SOUTHPORT & DISTRICT AMATEUR LEAGUE

DIVISION ONE	*P*	*W*	*D*	*L*	*F*	*A*	*Pts*
Garth	21	8	2	1	102	37	56
Inter Group Comms.	21	15	3	3	86	38	48
Formby Dons	21	8	6	7	52	48	30
St Paul's	21	7	5	9	47	75	26
The Dales	21	7	2	12	52	67	23
Southport YMCA	21	6	3	12	33	62	21
El Two	21	4	5	12	37	54	17
Formby JSCOB	21	5	2	14	39	67	17

ST HELENS & DISTRICT COMBINATION

PREMIER DIV	*P*	*W*	*D*	*L*	*Pts*
College St Helens	24	19	4	1	61
Billinge	24	16	5	3	53
Shoe FC	24	16	4	4	52
Gerard Arms	24	13	6	5	45
Penlake Juniors	24	13	5	6	44
Eccleston United	24	9	5	10	32
Nutgrove	24	10	1	13	31
Rainford North End	24	7	4	13	25
Carr Mill	24	5	9	10	24
Sidac Social	24	6	6	12	24
Old Congs	24	6	5	13	23
Junction	24	4	3	17	15
East Sutton Labour	24	3	1	20	10

I-ZINGARI LEAGUE

PREMIER DIVISION	*P*	*W*	*D*	*L*	*F*	*A*	*Pts*
Mills	26	19	2	5	74	25	59
Aigburth PH*	26	17	2	7	64	36	56
Quarry Bank OB	26	16	5	5	73	40	53
REMYCA United	26	16	2	8	66	43	50
NELTC	25	13	6	6	51	38	45
Old Xaverians	26	12	5	9	55	49	41
East Villa*	26	12	3	11	62	62	36
Hill Athletic*	26	10	2	14	47	47	31
Stoneycroft	26	8	5	13	48	59	29
ROMA	26	8	4	14	37	50	28
Edge Hill BCOB*	26	7	5	14	31	52	28
St Philomena's	26	7	5	14	48	69	26
St Marys College OB	26	5	5	16	38	65	20
Sacre Coeur FP	25	2	7	16	31	90	13

PRESTON & DISTRICT LEAGUE

PREMIER DIVISION	*P*	*W*	*D*	*L*	*Pts*
Samlesbury Brew	16	14	2	0	44
Burscough Richmond	15	11	1	3	34
Euxton Villa	16	11	1	4	34
Southport Trinity	16	8	0	8	24
Croston Sports Club	16	7	0	9	21
Skelmersdale Utd Res	16	6	1	9	19
Lostock St Gerards	16	4	1	11	13
Longridge Town	15	3	1	11	10
Appley Bridge	14	1	3	10	6

Below: Curzon Ashton's Matty Wearden and Leon Hymas of Formby in action during the Worthington Challenge Trophy final at Bury. Photo: Colin Stevens

LANCASHIRE EVENING POST SUNDAY LEAGUE

PREMIER DIVISION	*P*	*W*	*D*	*L*	*Pts*
Arkwrights CCA	22	21	1	0	64
Ingol Rangers	22	18	1	3	55
Victoria Hotel	22	14	2	6	44
Hesketh Gamull	22	13	0	9	39
Charnock Celtic	22	11	2	9	35
BAC Continental	22	10	3	9	33
Anderton Arms	22	10	1	11	31
AFC Sumners	22	9	1	12	28
Bradley Wanderers	22	6	5	11	23
Forest Arms	22	5	4	13	19
Bonds of Longridge	22	1	5	16	8
Brindle	22	1	1	20	4

CROSBY & DISTRICT SUNDAY LEAGUE

DIVISION ONE	*P*	*W*	*D*	*L*	*F*	*A*	*Pts*
Osset Sound	20	16	3	1	53	13	51
Saltbox	20	15	2	3	55	24	47
Eden Vale	20	14	2	4	60	24	44
Woodpecker	20	11	3	6	66	33	36
St William of York	20	11	0	9	48	60	33
Lighthouse	20	8	4	8	38	35	28
Advance Clutch	20	8	1	11	40	28	25
Nags Head	20	6	4	10	39	42	22
Whitehouse	20	7	1	12	45	66	22
Wynstay	20	2	1	17	19	70	7
Phoenix	20	1	1	18	20	88	4

Freehouse resigned - record expunged

ORMSKIRK & DISTRICT SUNDAY LEAGUE

DIVISION ONE	*P*	*W*	*D*	*L*	*F*	*A*	*Pts*
RNA Kirkby	22	17	5	0	71	20	56
Altway Valentine	22	17	1	4	78	29	52
Plan It	22	14	5	3	56	30	47
Coach & Horses	22	10	4	8	53	36	34
Alt Park United	22	9	4	9	37	50	31
Melling Victoria	22	10	3	9	38	39	*30
Memorial	22	7	4	11	41	63	25
Weld Blundell	22	6	6	10	37	64	24
Toby Celtic	22	7	2	13	47	51	23
Croftmere Sefton Arms	22	6	2	14	39	59	20
RAOB Kirkby	22	5	3	14	33	54	18
Nac	22	1	7	14	32	67	10

** points adjustment*

WHARFEDALE TRIANGLE SUNDAY LEAGUE

PREMIER DIVISION	*P*	*W*	*D*	*L*	*F*	*A*	*Pts*
Park Rangers	18	14	3	1	69	26	45
Horsforth Fairweather	18	14	3	1	66	24	45
Horsforth Rangers	18	11	3	4	64	35	36
Rawdon	18	9	1	8	38	49	28
Keighley Athletic	18	8	1	9	55	60	25
Thackley Commercial	18	8	0	10	71	60	24
Station Wanderers	18	6	5	7	28	26	23
Westfield	18	4	4	10	43	63	16
Crown Celtic	18	3	1	14	34	77	10
Shipley Town	18	2	1	15	33	81	7

Above: Action from the Worthington Challenge Trophy Cup final at Bury FC. Formby clear a Curzon Ashton attack as they go on their way to victory after a penalty shoot out.
Photo: Colin Stevens

Tow Law Town's keeper watches the ball go wide during his club's visit to Castleton Gabriels. Photo: Colin Stevens

Curzon Ashton's Mark Philips wins an aerial challenge during his side's 4-1 victory-over Darwen. Photo: Colin Stevens

Castleton Gabriel's keeper punches clear during his side's FA Vase tie against Tow Law Town. The visitors from the North East won 1-0. Photo: Colin Stevens

Matty Weardon in action for his team, Curzon Ashton during his side's 4-1 home victory over Darwen.
Photo: Colin Stevens

Curzon Ashton Number 5 Matt Wearden puts himself into a challenge against Nantwich Town and helps his team on their way to a 3-1 victory. Photo: Colin Stevens

NORTHERN COUNTIES EAST FOOTBALL LEAGUE

FEEDER TO: NORTHERN PREMIER LEAGUE

President: H F Catt **Chairman:** C Morris

Secretary/Treasurer: B Wood, 6 Restmore Avenue, Guiseley, Leeds LS20 9DG
Tel: 01943 874558

With almost 290 fixtures postponed during the season, the majority for the incessant wet weather, the fixture lists for many teams towards the end of the campaign became an endurance test for players, club and match officials alike and all came through with flying colours.

Premier Division

Since winning the championship two seasons ago and failing to make the Unibond grade, which meant that local rivals Ossett Town were promoted instead, Ossett Albion have been keen to make amends. By recruiting former Liversedge manager Eric Gilchrist, plus quite a few players from the same club, they confirmed their intentions in early season by taking over at the top of the Division from mid-October onwards. However, Brigg Town always produce a strong team though strangely they have never actually won the championship.

It would be too simple to say that it became a 'two horse race' for the championship as Arnold, Goole and Alfreton Town were waiting for any slip-ups by the two leading clubs. However, by early March a gap was beginning to open up between Albion and Town with perhaps the crucial fixture being on Easter Monday when Brigg won 2-1 away at Albion's Dimple Wells ground. That took Town five points clear of Albion and they held on to their lead to take the Championship by an eventual ten points difference. However, whilst there was success on the field and even though there were sterling efforts by Brigg club officials to make ground improvements on time, the honour of Unibond promotion goes to Ossett Albion and the League wishes them well. It's very likely Brigg Town will be challenging for that honour at the end of next season.

As both bottom clubs in the Unibond League are Cheshire based, it seems unlikely that the NCE will receive a demoted club which means an escape for Armthorpe Welfare, who were next to bottom in the Division. The axe falls on Staveley MW, though, who will move to Division One.

Division One

If anyone had told Borrowash Victoria at the start of the season that they would have to play fourteen League (plus two Cup) games from 10 April to 10 May to finish their campaign, they would have been dismissed as crazy. However, that's what the Derbyshire club had to do to win the Division One Championship and it actually went to their very last match when a win was required to move the club ahead of their closest rivals Pickering Town. With such an unbalanced match list because of so many postponements, it was hard to judge whether Vics and Town would hang on to the end - their main rivals being Mickleover Sports, Bridlington Town, newcomers Gedling Town and Hall Road Rangers. The closure of Tadcaster's ground for a long period due to the effects of flooding also added to the Division's fixture problems.

Promotion to the Premier Division is expected for Borrowash (subject to some work on their floodlights) and for Pickering. Re-election looms for Rossington Main and Tadcaster Albion, whilst the Division should see new club Lincoln Moorlands promoted from the CML.

Reserve Division

Eugene Lacy, manager of Farsley Celtic Reserves, certainly has the 'golden touch', with his team losing just three League matches (and only two the season before) to take the Reserve Division Championship for the second consecutive season. Liversedge Reserves and Eccleshill United Reserves were the two other teams who pressured them to the end, though in a championship marred by the number of points deductions having to be made for ineligible players. Ossett Town Reserves have decided not to compete next season, whilst it is expected Pontefract Colliery Reserves will be the new team.

NCE Cup Competitions

The first of the League's finals was the two-legged President's Cup with Selby Town defeating Ossett Albion 3-2 on aggregate. The other two-legged final was for the Wilkinson Sword when away goals were the deciding factor after Pickering Town and Bridlington Town had fought out two draws - the 'Pikes' took the Sword on the strength of two away goals at Town's Queensgate Stadium. Ossett Town were the eventual 2-1 extra time winners at Glasshoughton in the Reserve Division Cup.

HONOURS LIST 2000-01

Premier Division	Winners	Brigg Town	Runners Up	Ossett Albion
Division One	Winners	Borrowash Victoria	Runners Up	Pickering Town
Reserve Division	Winners	Farsley Celtic Reserves	Runners Up	Liversedge Reserves
League Cup	Winners	Sheffield	Runners Up	Gedling Town
President's Cup	Winners	Selby Town	Runners Up	Ossett Albion
Wilkinson Sword Trophy	Winners	Pickering Town	Runners Up	Bridlington Town
Reserve Division Cup	Winners	Ossett Town Reserves	Runners Up	Thackley Reserves
Derbyshire Senior Cup			Runners Up	Glapwell
Lincs Senior 'A' Cup			Runners Up	Louth United
Nottinghamshire Senior Cup			Runners Up	Gedling Town

FINAL LEAGUE TABLES 2000-01

PREMIER DIVISION

	P	W	D	L	F	A	Pts
Brigg Town	38	29	5	4	87	36	92
Ossett Albion	38	25	7	6	84	33	82
Alfreton Town	38	23	4	11	71	44	73
Goole	38	19	9	10	65	46	66
Hallam	38	19	7	12	61	51	64
Arnold Town	38	16	14	8	67	46	62
Sheffield	38	15	15	8	59	38	60
Thackley	38	16	9	13	59	57	57
Selby Town	38	16	7	15	71	71	55
Glapwell	38	13	11	14	62	58	50
Denaby United	38	15	4	19	54	63	49
Buxton	38	12	9	17	38	57	45
Harrogate Railway	38	11	9	18	59	65	42
Eccleshill United	38	9	13	16	48	58	40
Liversedge	38	9	13	16	50	63	40
Glasshoughton Welfare	38	9	11	18	57	64	38
Garforth Town	38	9	10	19	56	75	37
Brodsworth MW	38	11	7	20	41	86	*37
Armthorpe Welfare	38	9	7	22	53	81	34
Staveley MW	38	6	7	25	42	92	25

DIVISION ONE

	P	W	D	L	F	A	Pts
Borrowash Victoria	30	22	4	4	74	28	70
Pickering Town	30	21	6	3	67	24	69
Mickleover Sports	30	18	5	7	65	39	59
Bridlington Town	30	15	7	8	48	41	52
Gedling Town	30	14	7	9	47	37	49
Hall Road Rangers	30	14	6	10	43	37	48
Parkgate	30	13	6	11	60	52	45
Hatfield Main	30	13	4	13	54	49	43
Maltby Main	30	11	6	13	36	48	39
Yorkshire Amateur	30	9	5	16	33	53	32
Worsbrough Bridge MW	30	9	4	17	31	54	31
Louth United	30	8	6	16	48	58	30
Pontefract Colls	30	6	9	15	37	56	27
Winterton Rangers	30	8	6	16	30	53	*27
Rossington Main	30	7	5	18	39	54	26
Tadcaster Albion	30	6	6	18	29	58	24

* Points adjustment

PREMIER DIVISION RESULTS CHART 2000-01

		1	2	3	4	5	6	7	8	9	10	11	12	13	14	15	16	17	18	19	20
1	Alfreton Town	X	1-0	1-0	2-3	3-1	1-2	0-3	1-1	5-1	1-0	0-2	1-0	2-1	1-2	3-0	1-0	4-1	4-1	3-1	3-1
2	Armthorpe Welf.	3-1	X	4-1	1-3	1-2	1-2	2-3	2-1	3-0	2-6	2-1	2-4	1-2	1-1	1-1	0-2	0-0	1-3	1-2	0-2
3	Arnold Town	1-0	1-2	X	0-2	1-0	3-0	3-1	1-1	1-0	1-1	1-1	1-1	1-1	4-3	5-3	0-1	4-1	1-2	5-1	4-0
4	Brigg Town	3-0	3-1	0-2	X	6-1	1-0	4-3	3-1	1-0	2-1	3-2	2-1	5-1	2-0	6-2	2-2	2-1	1-1	3-0	5-1
5	Brodsworth MW	1-5	0-7	0-2	0-2	X	1-0	2-1	1-1	2-1	1-1	3-1	1-1	0-0	2-1	1-1	0-4	2-4	1-0	2-0	1-1
6	Buxton	0-1	2-1	1-1	0-0	1-0	X	2-1	1-0	1-3	0-2	1-0	1-1	2-1	0-0	0-4	1-1	1-2	0-4	2-2	1-4
7	Denaby Utd	2-4	3-0	0-1	0-3	1-0	0-0	X	1-0	0-3	2-1	2-2	1-2	0-2	0-1	1-0	1-3	2-0	1-2	3-0	3-2
8	Eccleshill Utd	0-0	2-2	1-1	0-1	1-3	3-0	4-0	X	1-1	1-1	1-1	3-0	0-3	1-0	0-0	0-4	2-3	1-1	1-1	0-3
9	Garforth Town	1-1	4-0	3-3	0-2	2-3	1-1	0-4	2-7	X	2-0	3-2	3-2	1-2	3-1	1-2	2-0	2-2	0-0	1-1	1-2
10	Glapwell	1-2	1-2	1-1	1-1	4-3	1-3	0-0	0-2	4-1	X	2-1	3-1	0-1	7-1	1-1	1-1	1-0	0-3	2-2	3-1
11	Glasshoughton W	3-1	7-1	1-3	2-3	0-0	1-1	1-2	2-3	1-1	4-1	X	1-2	0-1	0-0	1-0	2-1	0-2	0-0	3-0	4-2
12	Goole	1-3	3-0	0-0	1-2	3-1	2-1	2-1	2-0	0-2	4-1	0-0	X	2-0	3-2	1-0	3-3	2-0	1-1	4-0	2-1
13	Hallam	1-2	4-1	0-1	0-1	3-0	3-0	3-2	3-0	2-2	1-1	2-1	1-2	X	2-1	1-0	0-3	4-1	2-1	3-2	1-1
14	Harrogate Rlwy	0-2	0-1	2-1	2-1	9-1	0-1	1-2	0-1	2-2	2-2	2-2	3-1	4-0	X	2-2	2-4	3-0	0-2	1-0	2-1
15	Liversedge	0-2	3-3	1-1	0-3	4-0	1-0	2-1	1-4	1-0	0-1	1-3	2-4	3-3	2-0	X	2-2	2-3	3-3	1-0	1-1
16	Ossett Albion	3-0	4-1	0-0	1-2	4-1	4-2	4-0	3-0	3-1	3-2	4-0	2-1	2-0	0-2	1-0	X	5-1	1-0	3-1	1-0
17	Selby Town	1-1	3-1	5-5	2-0	4-0	1-2	0-1	1-1	5-3	4-2	6-1	1-4	3-1	2-2	1-1	0-2	X	2-0	3-1	2-1
18	Sheffield	3-1	0-0	2-0	1-1	3-1	4-1	1-1	5-1	3-1	0-1	2-1	0-0	0-1	4-1	1-1	1-1	2-1	X	1-3	0-0
19	Staveley MW	0-4	1-1	0-3	0-2	0-1	0-5	3-4	1-0	3-1	1-4	4-2	0-2	2-4	2-2	0-2	0-2	4-2	2-2	X	0-4
20	Thackley	0-4	2-1	3-3	3-1	3-2	1-0	3-1	3-2	2-1	0-1	1-1	0-0	1-1	3-2	2-0	1-0	0-1	0-0	3-2	X

LEAGUE CUP 2000-01

FIRST ROUND

Borrowash Victoria	v	Pontefract Colls	4-3	Maltby Main	v	Mickleover Sports	2-1
Parkgate	v	Hatfield Main	1-4	Winterton Rangers	v	Yorkshire Amat	3-1

SECOND ROUND

Alfreton Town	v	Glapwell	2-3	Borrowash Victoria	v	Selby Town	2-0
Brodsworth MW	v	Arnold Town	0-4	Garforth Town	v	Pickering Town	4-2
Gedling Town	v	Eccleshill United	3-1	Hall Road Rangers	v	Denaby United	2-3
Hallam	v	Glasshoughton Welf.	3-1	Harrogate Railway	v	Tadcaster Albion	5-2
Liversedge	v	Bridlington Town	2-1	Louth United	v	Winterton Rngrs	0-0, 6-1
Maltby Main	v	Hatfield Main	1-3	Ossett Albion	v	Buxton	1-0
Rossington Main	v	Brigg Town	0-3	Sheffield	v	Goole	2-0
Staveley MW	v	Armthorpe Welfare	4-1	Worsbrough Bridge	v	Thackley	0-2

THIRD ROUND

Arnold Town	v	Brigg Town	4-3	Borrowash Victoria	v	Liversedge	2-0
Denaby United	v	Ossett Albion	2-4	Gedling Town	v	Glapwell	2-1
Harrogate Railway	v	Garforth Town	2-1	Louth United	v	Hatfield Main	1-2
Staveley MW	v	Sheffield	2-3	Thackley	v	Hallam	2-1

Denaby re-instated

FOURTH ROUND

Arnold Town	v	Denaby United	3-0	Gedling Town	v	Borrowash Vic	3-3, 3-2
Sheffield	v	Harrogate Railway	1-0	Thackley	v	Hatfield Main	4-0

SEMI-FINALS

Gedling Town	v	Arnold Town	1-0	Thackley	v	Sheffield	1-1, 0-1

FINAL

Sheffield	v	Gedling Town	2-1	at Alfreton Town

PRESIDENT'S CUP 2000-01

FIRST ROUND

Borrowash Victoria	v	Bridlington Town	2-0	Brigg Town	v	Glasshoughton Welf	1-3
Brodsworth MW	v	Glapwell	1-2	Goole	v	Alfreton Town	2-3
Liversedge	v	Winterton Rangers	1-0	Ossett Albion	v	Mickleover Sports	6-1
Selby Town	v	Arnold Town	4-2	Yorkshire Amat	v	Hall Road Rangers	1-4

Yorkshire Amateur re-instated

SECOND ROUND

Alfreton Town	v	Liversedge	1-3	Borrowash Victoria	v	Glapwell	2-1
Glasshoughton Welf	v	Ossett Albion	1-2	Selby Town	v	Yorkshire Amateur	1-0

SEMI-FINALS

Borrowash Victoria	v	Ossett Albion	1-2	Liversedge	v	Selby Town	1-2

FINAL 1st Leg

Ossett Albion	v	Selby Town	0-2

FINAL 2nd Leg

Selby Town	v	Ossett Albion	1-2	Selby Town won 3-2 on aggregate

WILKINSON SWORD TROPHY 2000-01

FIRST ROUND

Borrowash Victoria	v	Mickleover Sports	1-0	Hall Road Rangers	v	Bridlington Town	2-3
Louth United	v	Maltby Main	3-0	Parkgate	v	Rossington Main	4-2
Tadcaster Albion	v	Pickering Town (at PT)	1-4	Pontefract Colls	v	Hatfield Main	4-2
Winterton Rangers	v	Worsbro Bridge MW	0-2	Yorkshire Amateur	v	Gedling Town	0-2

SECOND ROUND

Bridlington Town	v	Borrowash Victoria	4-2	Gedling Town	v	Parkgate	2-0
Pickering Town	v	Louth United	2-1	Pontefract Colls	v	Worsbrough Bridge	1-2

Parkgate re-instated

SEMI-FINALS

Parkgate	v	Bridlington Town	0-3	Pickering Town	v	Worsbrough Bridge	3-2

FINAL 1st Leg

Bridlington Town v Pickering Town 2-2

FINAL 2nd Leg

Pickering Town v Bridlington Town 1-1

Aggregate: 3-3. Pickering Town won on away goals

LEADING GOALSCORERS 2000-01

PREMIER DIVISION

Caine Cheetham	Alfreton Town	26
Peter Collier	Selby Town	25
Jonathan Pickess	Sheffield	23
Simon Roach	Brigg Town	21
Michael Godber	Sheffield	20
Lee Morris	Hallam	19
Brendan Yates	Glapwell	19
Graham Marchant	Garforth Town	17
Matthew Flynn	Harrogate Railway	16
Christian Shaw	Ossett Albion	16
Michael Carter	Ossett Albion	15
Michael Gadsby	Arnold Town	15

DIVISION ONE

Simon Bailey	Louth United	20
Gareth Collinson	Rossington Main	20
Brian Cusworth	Parkgate	20
Matthew Edeson	Bridlington Town	18
Paul Palmer	Hall Road Rangers	17
Gary Briscoe	Borrowash Victoria	16
Gary Jones	Louth United	16
Adam Walsh	Pickering Town	16
Stefan Zoll	Yorkshire Amat/Pickering T	15

RESERVE DIVISION

Peter Lytollis	Brigg Town Reserves	36
James Nestor	Farsley Celtic Reserves	29
David Bell	Pickering Town Reserves	15
Sam Polli	Ossett Town Reserves	15
Steve Smith	Emley Reserves	15
Andrew Markham	Brigg Town Reserves	13
Guy Sandland	Emley Reserves	12

ALFRETON TOWN

Secretary: Roger Taylor, 9 Priory Rd, Alfreton, Derbys. DE55 7JT Tel: 01773 835121
Ground: Town Grnd, North St., Alfreton, Derbys Tel: 01773 830277 Newsline: 521734 Admin.
Directions: M1 junction 28 and follow A38 towards Derby for 1 mile,left onto B600, right at main road to town centre and after half a mile turn left down North Street - ground on right. Half mile from Alfreton (BR) station.Buses 242 & 243 from both Derby and Mansfield

Capacity: 5,000 Cover: 1,000 Seats: 350 Floodlights: Yes

Clubhouse: H &C food & drinks on ground. Supporters Club bar outside ground open every day.
Club Shop: Programmes & club souvenirs. Contact Brian Thorpe Tel: 01773 836251
Club Website: alfretontownfc.com

HONOURS: N.C.E. Lg 84-85 (Lg Cup 84-85); Midland Co. Lg 69-70 73-74 76-77 (R-up 71-72 80-81 81-82), Lg Cup 71-72 72-73 73-74; Derbyshire Sen Cup 60-61 69-70 72-73 73-74 81-82 94-95 (R-up 62-63 64-65 77-78 79-80 84-85 87-88 92-93) Div Cup (N) 64-65; Evans Halshaw Floodlit Cup 87-88 95-96; Cent All Lg.R-Up 63-64; NPL Div 1 R-Up 95-96

PREVIOUS **Leagues:** Central All.(pre-reformation 21-25) 59-61; Midland (Counties) 25-27 61-82; N.C.E. 82-87; Northern Premier 87-99

BEST SEASON **FA Trophy:** 1st Rd Proper 94-95. **FA Vase:** 5th Round 99-00
FA Cup: 1st Rd 3rd replay 69-70. Also 1st Rd 73-74. - League clubs defeated: Lincoln 24-25

RECORDS **Attendance:** 5,023 v Matlock Tn, Central All 60.
Scorer: J Harrison 303 **Win:** 15-0 v Loughborough, Midland Lge. 69-70
Appearances: J Harrison 560 **Defeat:** 1-9 v Solihull FAT 97, 0-8 v Bridlington 92.

FACT FILE
Formed: 1959 Nickname: The Reds
Sponsors: Coldseal Windows
Colours: all Red Change colours: all White
Midweek home matchday: Tuesday
Res League: Mid Regional Alliance + Under 18s, 16s, 15s, 13s, & 12s
Programme: Pages: 32 Price: £1
Editor: Chris Tacey (01302 722415)

CLUB PERSONNEL
Chairman: Wayne Bradley
Vice Chairman: Dave Gregory
Dev. Manager: Glen Waudby
Manager: Jason Maybury
Assistant Manager: David Lloyd
Physio: Mick Jenkins

2000-01
Leading Goalscorer: Caine Cheetham 29
Captain: Darren Schofield
P.o.Y. - Manager's: Darren Schofield
Players' Gary Thorpe Supp. Steve Heath

ARMTHORPE WELFARE

Secretary: Maureen Cottam, The Orchards, Whiphill Lane, Armthorpe, Doncaster DN3 3JP. Tel: 01302 832514 (H)
Ground: Welfare Ground, Church St, Armthorpe, Doncaster DN3 3AG.Tel:(M)07771 853899-(match days only)
Directions: M18 junc 4, A630, left at r'bout then proceed to next r'bout and turn right. Ground 400yds on left behind Plough Inn. Doncaster (BR) 2 1/2 miles. Buses A2, A3 & 181 pass ground
Capacity: 2,500 Seats: 200 Cover: 400 Floodlights: Yes Club Shop: No

Clubhouse: No. Refreshments on ground. Wheatsheaf Hotel used after matches

HONOURS Northern Co's East Lg R-up 87-88 (Lg Cup R-up 91-92, Div 1 R-up 83-84, East Central Div 1 84-85); Doncaster & Dist. Lg 82-83 (Div 1 81-82, Div 2 79-80, Div 3 78-79; Lg Cup 79-80 80-81 81-82 82-83; Challenge Cup 82-83); West Riding Chall. Cup 81-82 82-83; Goole & Thorne Dist. Cup 82-83
PREVIOUS **League:** Doncaster Senior
RECORD **Attendance** : 2,000 v Doncaster R., Charity match 85-86
Appearances: Gary Leighton **Scorer:** Martin Johnson
Win: 7-0 **Defeat:** 1-7

FACT FILE
Founded: 1926
(Disbanded 1974, re-formed 1976)
Nickname: Wellie
Club Sponsors: Houston Transport
Colours: Green & white hoops,green green.
Change colours: Navy/white/navy
Midweek matches: Tuesday
Programme: 24 pages
Editor: John Morgan, 01302 834475 (H)
Local paper: Doncaster Evening Star

CLUB PERSONNEL
Chairman: Gaey McCue Tel: 07668 555256
Vice Chairman: James Houston
Comm. Manager: Peter Camm
Press Officer: Sharon Morgan
Manager: Carl Leighton
Asst Manager: John McKeown
Coach: Steve Taylor
Physio: Joey Johnson

ARNOLD TOWN

Secretary: Tony Beale, 6 Elms Gardens, Ruddington, Nottm NG11 6DZ (0115 9211451)
Ground: King George V Recreation Ground, Gedling Rd, Arnold, Notts (0115 9263660)
Directions: From M1 jct 26, take A610 to B6004 (Stockhill Lane) 3 miles to A60. Right at A60, immediate left (St Albans Rd), thru lights by Wilkinsons left onto Hallams Lane. Ground on right opposite market. From A1(M)/A614/A60 to lights (Harvester on right), left thru lights to, St. Albans Rd then as above. Nottingham Midland (BR) 4 miles. Buses 55,57.58, 59 pass ground. From A6514 left onto A60 for 1/4 m then rt onto Nottingham Rd to town centre by Wilkinsons.
Capacity: 3,400 Seats: 150 Cover: 950 Floodlights: Yes
Clubhouse: Licensed bar open matchdays & training night. Also tea-bar on matchdays
Club Shop: Sells progs, scarves, badges, mugs etc, contact Philip Steele (0115 9281323

HONOURS (Arnold & Arnold Town): Central Mids Lg 92-93 (R-up 88-89, Lg Cup 87-88 (R-up 90-91), F/lit Cup 89-90); NCE Lg 85-86, R-up 83-84, 94-95; Div 1 94-95; Presidents Cup 94-95; Central All 62-63; Notts Snr Cup x9, r-up x 5; Midland Co's Lg R-up 70-71 75-76, Lg Cup 74-75 (R-up 68-69 70-71 80-81). **PREVIOUS Leagues:** Central Mids 89-93. Arnold FC: Bulwell & Dist, Notts Spartan, Notts Comb (pre 55), Central All. 55-63/ Midland 63-82/ NCE 82-86/ Central Mids 86-89. Kingswell: Notts Yth/ Notts Amat./Notts Spartan/ E. Mids Reg.(pre'76)/Midland 76-82/ NCE 82-86/ Central Mids 86-89. **Names:** Arnold FC (founded 1928 as Arnold St Marys) merged with Arnold Kingswell(founded 1962) 1989
BEST SEASON FA Cup:1st Rd replay 77-78 **FA Vase.**:4th Rd **FA Trophy:** 2nd Replay 71-2

FACT FILE
Founded: 1989 Nickname: Eagles
Sponsors: Mapperley Sports/Neartone Printers
Colours: Yellow (blue trim)/blue/yellow
Change Colours:All red
Midweek matches: Tuesday
Reserves' Lge:
Programme: 48-52 pages £1
Editor: Melvyn Draycott 0115 9442654
2000-01 Captain: Paul Mitchell
Top Scorer : Tony Simpson 18
P.o.Y :. Paul Mitchell

CLUB PERSONNEL
President: Alan Croome Chairman: David Law
Vice-Chairman: Roy Francis
General Manager: Ray O'Brien
Comm. Manager: Len Robinson
Team Man: Iain McCulloch
Asst Man: Bill Brindley Physio: Norman Collins
Press Officer: Brian Howes (0115 9856986)
Website: www.arnoldfc.com
Email: mail@arnoldfc.com

BORROWASH VICTORIA

Secretary.: Ian Collins, 30 Margreave Road, Chaddesden, Derby DE21 6JD
Tel: 01332 739437

Ground: Robinson Construction Bowl, Borrowash Road, Spondon, Derby
Tel: 01332 669688.

Directions: M1 jct 25, A52 towards Derby, 3rd left off by-pass into Borrowash Rd, ground 400 yds on left. 2 miles from Spondon (BR). Nottingham to Derby buses pass nearby.

Capacity: 5,000 Seats: Yes Covered: 500 Floodlights: Yes

Clubhouse: Normal pub hours. Hot & cold food. **Club Shop:** No

PREVIOUS **Leagues:** Derby Sun. School & Welf. 52-57; Derby Comb.; Midland 79-82; N.C.E.; Cen Mid Lg. **Ground:** Dean Drive 1911-84

RECORDS **Attendance:** 2,000 v Nottim Forest,(floodlight opening 22/10/85)
Win: 11-1 **Defeat**: 3-8 **Goalscorer:** Paul Acklam **Appearances:** Neil Kellogg

BEST SEASON **FA Cup** 3rd Qual. Rd 91-92. **FA Vase:** 4th Rd 90-91,00-01

HONOURS N.C.E. Lg Div 1 00-01,Div 1 Sth 83-84 (R-up 84-85, Div 2 Sth R-up 82-83), Derby Comb. 77-78 (R-up(10) 65-66 68-74 75-77 78-79, Lg Cup 68-69 75-76 (R-up 63-64 66-67), Midland Co's Lg Div 80-81 (Div 1 Cup 80-81), Derbys Snr Cup R-up 90-91, Derbys Div. Cup 73-74 (R-up 70-71 72-73), Cen. Midl Lg B E Webbe Cup R-up 88-89 (Res. Cup 94-95)

FACT FILE
Founded: 1911
(Reformed 1963)
Nickname: Vics
Club Sponsors: Robinson Construction
Colours: Red & white stripes/black/black
Change Colours: Navy blue/sky/sky
Mid matches: Tues Prog: 16 pages, 50p
Editor: Ian Collins (01332 739437)

CLUB PERSONNEL
Chairman: Ian Anderson
Press Officer: Secretary

Manager/Coach:Mick Rodgers
Asst Man:Gary Adul Physio:Geoff.Woolley

2000-01
Top Scorer: Gary Briscoe 16 Capt:LeeThomas

BRIGG TOWN

Secretary: Robert B Taylor, `Highfield House', Barton Rd, Wrawby, Brigg, Lincs DN20 8SH
Tel: 01652 652284 (H) 01724 402749 (W) **Email Address:** taylors@highfield98.fsnet.com

Ground: The Hawthorns, Hawthorn Avenue, Brigg (01652 652767) Office: 01652 651605

Directions: From M180 Junc 4 Scunthorpe East, A18 through Brigg leaving on Wrawby Rd, left into recreation ground and follow road into BTFC.
Capacity: 4,000 Seats: 250 Cover: 2 Stands Floodlights: Yes

Clubhouse: Licensed club open matchdays

HONOURS F.A. Challenge Vase 95-96; Northern Co's East Lg Presidents Cup R-up 91-92 92-93, R-up 95-96; Lincs Lg 49-50 53-54 73-74 75-76 (Div 1 68-69 69-70 70-71 71-72, Lg Cup 49-50 65-66 68-69 69-70 72-73); Mids Co's Lg 77-78 (Lg Cup 77-78); Lincs `A' Snr Cup 75-76 76-77 94-95 99-00; Lincs `B' Snr Cup (5), NCE (Premier) 00-01

PREVIOUS **Leagues:** Lindsey; Lincs 48-76; Midland Counties 76-82
Grounds: Manor House Convent, Station Rd (pre 1939); Brocklesby Ox 1939-59

BEST SEASON **FA Vase:** Winners 95-96 **FA Cup:** 4th Rd Q

RECORD Attendance: 2,000 v Boston U. 1953 (at Brocklesby Ox)

FACT FILE
Formed: 1864Nickname: Zebras
Colours: Black & white stripes/black/red
Change colours: Yellow/Blue
Midweek Matchday: Wednesday
Programme: 24 pages
Editor: Match Secretary
Club Website: zebras@briggtown.co.uk

CLUB PERSONNEL
President: M.Harness
Chairman: David Crowder, Tel: 01724 864742 (H)
Match Sec: John Martin. Tel: 01652 654526 (H)
Manager: Ralph Clayton
Coach:Dave McLean

2000-01
P.o.Y. & Top Scorer: Simon Roach
Captain: Phil Rowland

BRODSWORTH WELFARE

Secretary: Nigel Hyde, 33Grosven or Crescent,Arksey, Doncaste DN5 0SX
Tel Nos: 01302 820738 (H) 01302 818536 (FAX) 07713 140632 (M)

Match Sec: Mark Bell ,55 Doncaster Lane< Doncaster DN6 .Tel: 0797 779 4893

Ground: Welfare Ground, Woodlands, Nr. Doncaster (01302 728380).

Directions: From A1 take A638 to Doncaster, take left after Woodlands Pub into Welfare Road, ground 50yds on left.
Regular bus service from North Bridge Bus Station, Doncaster.
Capacity: 3,000 Seats: 228 Cover: 400 Floodlights: Yes

Clubhouse: Yes, Matchday drinks and snacks **Club Shop:** No

HONOURS Yorks Lg 24-25, Donc. & Dist. Lg 84-85 (Lg Cup 85-86, Div 2 78-79, Div 2Cup 78-79), Sheffield Jnr Cup 83-84, Mexborough Montagu Cup 91-92 92-93.R-up N.C.E. Div 1 98-99

PREVIOUS **Leagues:** Doncaster Snr; Sheffield; Yorkshire.
Name: Brodsworth Main

BEST SEASON **FA Cup:** **FA Vase:** 3rd Rd 97-98

RECORD **Fee received:** £2,550 (+ Payments for apps) forDanny Schofield fromHuddersfield Town, Jan 99

FACT FILE
Founded: 1912
Nickname: Broddy
Colours:Navy & Light Blue/Navy /Navy
Change colours: Yellow & Black
Midweek home matchday: Wednesday
Programme: 50 pages
Editor: Mark Bell

CLUB PERSONNEL
Chairman: Gordon Jennings Tel: 01302 781121
Press Officer Mark Bell (0797 779 4893)
Tel: 01302 817173 (H) 07720 832147 (M)
Manager: AlanRradford
Physio: Eric Beaumont

2000-01
Captain: Mark Almunshi
Top Goalscorer: Jamie Norbury 12

Top:
Arnold Town FC
Back Row (l-r): Charlie Bannister, Matt Irons, Andy Elliott, Paul Robinson, Brett Williams, Mark Gadsby.
Middle Row: Giorgio Vitale, Darren Bogan, Craig Maddison, Jon Boulter, James Baker, Ben Simpson, Paul Mitchell.
Front Row: Bill Brindley (Asst Mngr), Peter Davey, Iain McCulloch (Mngr), Bryn Gunn, Kris Maddison.
Photo: BP Photography

Centre:
Glapwell FC in away kit.
Back Row (l-r): N Etheridge, C Taylor, P Morgan, S Poxon, C Jeffery, P Dolby, J Purdy, S Wall, D Welch, M Cooper.
Front Row: A Froggatt, D Scott, J Morgan, R Pownall, J Redfern, B Yates, L Whelton.

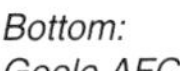

Bottom:
Goole AFC

BUXTON

Secretary / Press Officer: Julie Miszke, 21 Errwood avenue, Buxton. Sk17 9BD
Tel No & Fax : 01335 346211 (office hours) (H) 01298 70545

Ground : The Silverlands, Buxton, Derbyshire (01298 24733)

Directions: 200 yards of Buxton Market Place, opp. County Police HQ. Buxton (BR) 1/2 mile.
Capacity: 4,000 **Cover:** 2,500 **Seats:** 490 **Floodlights:** Yes
Club Shop: Yes, Pete Scott (01298 79582)
Clubhouse: (01298 23197). Open nightly + Sunday lunchtimes. licensed, no hot food

HONOURS N.P.L Lg Cup 90-91, Presidents Cup 81-82; Cheshire County 72-73(R-up 46-47 62-63, Lg Cup 56-57 57-58 68-69); Manchester Lg 31-32 (R-up 04-05 28-29 29-30 30-31, Lg Cup 25-26 26-27); Derbys. Sen. Cup 38-39 44-45 45-46 56-57 59-60 71-72 80-81 85-86 86-87.

PREVIOUS **Leagues:** The Combination 1891-99; North Derbyshire; E Cheshire; Manchester 07-32; Cheshire County 32-73; NLP 73-98.]

BEST SEASON **FA Trophy:** Qtr Finals 70-71 71-72. **FA Vase:** 98-99
FA Cup: 3rd Rd 51-52. 2nd Rd 58-59, 1st Rd 62-63League clubs defeated: Aldershot 51-52

RECORDS **Attendance:** 6,000 v Barrow, FA Cup 1st rd 51-52
Goalscorer: Dave Herbert **Fee Paid:** £5,000 for Gary Walker (Hyde Utd)
Appearances: Mick Davis **Fee Received:** £23,500 for Ally Pickering (Rotherham 89)

FACT FILE

Formed: 1877
Nickname: The Bucks
Sponsors: Triangles, Snooker Hall
Colours: Royal blue & white halves/royal/royal
Change colours: All yellow with blue trim
Midweek matchday: Tuesday
Programme: 36 pages £1.00
Editor: Tony Tomlinson
Local Press: Buxton Adverftiser and Matlock Mercury. Local Radio: Radio Derby

CLUB PERSONNEL

Chairman: Barry Goodwin
Manager: Tony Hodkinson
Asst Manager/Coach: David Bainbridge
Reserve Team Manager: Mike Dodd

DENABY UNITED

Secretary: Barrie Dalby, 6 Park Lane court,Thrybergh, Rotherham, S.Yorks. S654ET
Tel: 01709 851283 (H) 01709 860764 (B)
Ground: Tickhill Square, Denaby Main, Doncaster. Tel: 01709 864042 **Directions:** From Conisbrough take first left in Denaby along Wadworth St. From Mexborough take first right after Milestone Public House, left on to Bolton St. then left on to Wheatley Street. Rail to Conisbrough
Capacity: 6,000 Seats: 250 Cover: 350 Floodlights: Yes
Clubhouse: None **Club Shop:** No
HONOURS Yorks Lg R-up 67-68, Div 2 R-up 66-67, Div 3 R-up 81-82, Lg Cup 71-72; N.C.E. Prem Div. 96-97, Cup Winners 98-99Div 1 South R-up 83-84; Midland Lg R-up 07-08; Sheffield & Hallamshire Snr Cup 1905-06,09-10, 32-33 35-36 86-87; Thorn EMI Floodlight Comp. R-up 83-84; Sheffield Assoc. Lg 40-41; Mexborough Montague Cup (6)
PREVIOUS **Leagues:** Sheffield Ass 1900-02 13-18 19-20 40-45; Midland 02-13 20-40 45-60 61-65; Doncaster & Dist. 18-19; Central Alliance 60-61; Yorks 65-82.
Ground: Denaby Recreation Ground 1895-1912.
BEST SEASON **FA Vase:** 4th Rd 83-84 **FA Cup:** 1st Rd x 3 **FA Trophy:** 2nd Rd 71-72
RECORDS Attendance: 5,200 v Southport, FA Cup 1st Rd 1927 **Win:** 20-0 v Shirebrook M.W. (H), Cen. All. 60-61 **Fee paid:** £300 for Kevin Deakin, Mossley 1984 **Fee received:** £3,000 for Jonathan Brown (Exeter, 1990)
Players progressing: S Cowan (Doncaster 23), R Attwell (W.H.U. 38), W Ardron (Rotherham 43), J Barker (Derby 28), K Burkinshaw (Liverpool 53), A Barnsley (Rotherham 85), C Beaumont (Rochdale 88), J Brown (Exeter 90)

FACT FILE

Founded: 1895
Nickname: Reds
Colours: Red & white/red/red
Change colours: Blue & Yellow/ blue/blue
Reserves' League: B.I.R. County Sen. Lg.
Midweek matches: Tuesday
Programme:20 pages £1.00
Editor: Adrian Gillott (01302 856304)
Local press : South Yorks Times, Doncaster Free Press, Dearne Valley Weekender

CLUB PERSONNEL

Chairman: Jim Dainty
Vice Chairman:Jim Reeve
Match Sec.: Derek Mower (01709 329338 H)
President: Caroline Flint M.P.
Manager:Glynn Kenny
Physio: Jack Bramhall

ECCLESHILL UNITED

Secretary: lPamela Waite, 27 Cotswold Avenue, Wrose, Bradford BD18 1LS (01274 583008)
Ground: Plumpton Park, Kingsway, Wrose, Bradford BD2 1PN (01274 615739)

Directions: M62 jct 26 onto M606, right on Bradford Ring Road A6177, left on to A650 for Bradford at 2nd r'bout. A650 Bradford Inner Ring Road onto Canal Rd,branch right at Staples (Dixons Car showrooms on right), fork left after 30mph sign to junction with Wrose Rd, across junction - continuation of Kings Rd, 1st left onto Kingsway - ground 200 yds on right. 2 miles from Bradford (BR). Buses 624 or 627 for Wrose
Capacity: 2,225 Seats: 225 Cover: 415 Floodlights: Yes
Clubhouse: Open normal licensing hours. Bar, lounge, games room, hot &cold snacks
Club Shop: Sells range of souvenirs. Contact Roy Maule Snr, 01274662428

HONOURS N.C.E.Div 1 Winners 96-97Div 2 R-up 86-87, Res Div 86-87 89-90, R-up 87-88 94-95)); Bradford Amtr Lg Cup 61-62; Bradford & Dist. Snr Cup 84-85;Bradford & Dist. FA Snr Cup 85-86; W. Riding County Amat. Lg 76-77 West Riding Cup Finalists 99-00
PREVIOUS **Leagues:** Bradford Amat; W Riding Co Amat **Name:** Eccleshill FC
Ground: Myers Lane
BEST SEASON **FA Vase:** 99-00, 5thRd
RECORDS Attendance: 715 v Bradford C 96-97 **Win:** 10-1 v Blackpool Mechs (H), F.A.C /!Q
Defeat: 0-6 v Rossington Main (A), N.C.E. Lge Cup 2nd Rd 92-93, & v Gt. Harwood T. (A), FA Cup Prel. Rd 91-92

FACT FILE
Founded: 1948
Nickname: Eagles
Colours: Blue & white stripes/blue/blue
Change colours: All yellow
Midweek matches: Tuesday
Reserves' Lge: NCE Res. Div
Programme: 24-28 pages, 50p
Editor: Secretary
Local Press: Bradford Telegraph & Argus, Bradford Star Free Press

CLUB PERSONNEL

Chairman: Keith Firth Tel: 01274 787057 (H)
Press Officer: Bill Rawlings (01274 635753)
Manager: Raymond Price
Physio: Gordon McGlynn

Player to Progress:Terry Dolan (Hudd'sfied U)

GARFORTH TOWN

Secretary: Paul Bracewell, 24 Coupland Rd, Garforth, Leeds LS25 1AD
Tel: 0113 286 3314 (H) 0113 214 1800 (B) 07931 900260 (M)

Ground: Wheatley ParkStadium, Cedar Ridge, Brierlands Lane, Garforth, Leeds LS25 2AA
Tel: 0113 286 4083 Website: www.garforth.town.freeserve.co.uk

Directions: M1 junction 47. Take turning signed 'Garforth' (A642). Approx 200 yards turn left into housing estate opposite White Ho. (Cedar Ridge). Stadium at end of lane.
Capacity: 3,000 Seats: 278 Cover: 200 Floodlights: Yes
Clubhouse: Full Licensing Hours **Club Shop:** Yes

HONOURS N.C.E. Lg Div 1 97-98, R-up 96-97, Div 2 R-up 85-86, Lge Cup 99-00; Yorks Lg Div 3 R-up 79-80; Barkston Ash Snr Cup 80-81 84-85 85-86 86-87 92-93 94-95; Wilkinson Sword Trophy 96-97; West Riding County FA Cup 97-98 99-00
PREVIOUS **Leagues:** Leeds Sunday Comb 64-72; West Yorks 72-78; Yorks 78-82.
Names: Miners Arms 64-78, Garforth Miners 78-79
BEST SEASON **FA Vase:** Q-F 85-86
RECORDS **Attendance:** 1,014 Brendan Ormsby Testimonial v Comb. Leeds/A. Villa XI
Goalscorer: Vinnie Archer **Appearances:** Philip Matthews (82-93)
Record Fee Received: £25k for Andy Watson to Doncaster Rovers 1999
Win: 11-0 v Blidworth Welf, N.C.E.Div. 1 97-98 **Defeat:** 1-7 v Lincoln Utd (A), N.C.E. Div. 1 92-93

FACT FILE
Founded: 1964 Nickname: The Miners
Sponsors: Mansfield Breweries
Colours: Yellow/Blue/Yellow
Change colours: Red/black/red
Midweek matches: Wednesday
Reserves' League: NCE Res. Div.
Programme: 32 pages, 50p
Editor: Chris Mather 0113 286 3453 (H)

CLUB PERSONNEL
President: Norman Hebbron
Chairman: Stephen Hayle
Press Officer: Ian Coultard 0113 286 8827
Manager/Coach: Dave Harrison
Asst Manager: Phil Hutchinson
Physio: Paul Cavell
Coach: Brendon Ormsby

GLAPWELL

Secretary: Ellen Caton, 111 The Hill, Glapwell, Chesterfield. S44 5LU.
Tel: 01246 854648 (H & Fax) 07976 838423 (M)
Email: ellen@decaton.fsnet.co.uk

Ground: Hall Corner, Glapwell, Chesterfield, Derbyshire Tel: 01623 812213

Directions: M1 Junc. 29 A617 towards Mansfield, after Young Vanish Inn take filter lane left onto Bolsover Road, ground facing, use rear entrance next to garden centre
Floodlights: Yes

HONOURS Central Midlands Lg 93-94, Floodlit Cup 93-94, Evans Halshaw Floodlit Cup 96-97, Derbyshire Senior Cup 97-98 NCE Lg. Cup Finalists 99-00. R-u 00-01 (lost on penalities)

BEST SEASON **FA Vase:** 2nd Rd 96-97 **FA Cup:**

FACT FILE
Founded: 1985
Colours: Black & white stripes/white/white
Change colours: All yellow
Midweek matches: Tuesday
Programme: 48 pages £1.00
Editor: Jason Harrison
01623 842588 (H) 07966 500521 (M)
Web site: www.glapwellfc.co.uk

CLUB PERSONNEL
Chairman: Roger Caton
Manager: Graham Gladwin

2000-01
Leading goalscorer:Brendan Yates 23
Captain: Jamie Morgan
P.o.Y.: Brendan Yates

GLASSHOUGHTON WELFARE

Secretary: Eric Jones, `Marrica', Westfields Ave, Cutsyke, Castleford WF10 5JJ.
Tel: 01977 556257 (H) 01977 514157(B)

Ground: Glasshoughton Welfare, Leeds Rd, Glasshoughton, Castleford (01977518981)

Directions: From M62 use either Junct. 31 or 32 towards Castleford. From Junction 32 the road comes into Glasshoughton. From Junct. 31 turn right at 2nd roundabout at Whitwood Tech. College. The ground is on the left in Leeds Road. Car park on ground. Castleford (BR) 1 mile.
Capacity: 2,000 Seats: None Covered: 250 Floodlights: Yes

Clubhouse: Bar & refreshment facilities **Club Shop:** No

HONOURS West Riding County Cup 93-94

PREVIOUS **League:** West Yorkshire Name: Anson Sports 1964-76
Ground: Saville Park 1964-76

RECORD **Attendance:** 300 v Bradford C, 90

FACT FILE
Founded: 1964
Club colours: Blue and white shirts/blue/blue
Change colours: All yellow
Midweek Matchday: Tuesday
Reserves' Lge: N.C.E. Res. Div.
Programme: 20 pages, 20p
Prog. Editor: Nigel Lee (0113 247 6186)-W

CLUB PERSONNEL
President: R Rooker
Chairman: Gordon Day
Tel: 01977 514178 (H)
Match Sec: Barry Bennett
Tel: 01977 682593 (H)
Manager: Wayne Day
Asst Manager/Coach: M Ripley

GOOLE AFC

Secretary: Malcolm Robinson, 55 Clifton Gardens, Gools, E.Yorks. DN14 6AR
Tel: 01405 761078 (H) 07801 092952 (M)

Match Secretary: Graeme Wilson, 12 Thorntree Close, Goole, E. Yorks DN14 6LN
Tel: 01405 763316 (H)

Ground: Victoria Pleasure Grounds, Marcus St, Goole DN14 6AR
Tel: 01405 762794 Email Address: malrob@lineone.net

Directions: M62 to Junc 36, then follow signs for town centre.
Turn right at 2nd lights into Boothferry Rd, then after 300 yards turn right again into Carter St, and the ground is at the end of road.

Capacity: 3000 Seats: 200 Cover: 800 Floodlights: Yes

Club Shop: Yes **Clubhouse:** Matchdays only

HONOURS NCE Div. 1 Champions 1999-2000, Div. 1 Trophy 99-00

FACT FILE
Founded: 1997
Colours: Red/ white/ black.
Change Colours: Gold/black/gold & black
Midweek Matchday: Tuesday
Programme Editor: Adrian
Website: website.lineone.net \ ~~ darone.net

CLUB PERSONNEL
Chairman: Geoffrey Bruines
49A Pinfold Street, Howden, nr Goole, East Yorks. DN14 7DE
Tel: 01430 430048 (H) 07790 952790 (M)
Manager:Peter Daniel

2000-01
Top Goalscorer: Andy Neville 13
Captain : Sean Lanaghan

HALLAM

Secretary: Mrs Susan Muzyczka, 24 Meadow Bank Avenue, Sheffield, S7 1PB.
Tel: 0114 255 3173(H) Club Email: hallamfc@supanet.co.uk

Ground: Sandygate, **(The oldest club ground in the world 1860)** Sandygate Road, Crosspool, Sheffield S10.Tel: 0114 230 9484. Website:www.sportsworldwide.co.uk
Two new stands and full access & facilities for wheelchair users.

Directions: A57 Sheffield to Glossop Rd, left at Crosspool shopping area signed`Lodge Moor' on to Sandygate Rd. Ground half mile on left opposite Plough Inn. 51 bus from Crucible Theatre

Capacity: 1,000 Seats: 250 Cover: 400 Floodlights: Yes **Club Shop:** Yes
Clubhouse: No, use Plough Inn opposite. Hot & cold snacks on ground for matches

HONOURS: Northern Counties (East) Lg Div 1 R-up 90-91 94-95, Yorkshire Lg Div 2 60-61 (R-up 56-57), Sheffield & Hallamshire Snr Cup 50-51 61-62 64-65 67-68.

BEST SEASON **FA Vase:** 5th Rd 80-81**FA Cup:** 3 Rd Q Rd 1957 **Previous Lg: Yorks 52-82**

CLUB RECORDS **Attendance:** 2,000 v Hendon, FA Amtr Cup 3rd Rd 59
13,855 v Dulwich at Hillsborough, FA Amtr Cup 55)
Goalscorer: A Stainrod 46 **Appearances:** P Ellis 500+
Win: 7-0 v Hatfield Main (H) 92-93, & v Kiveton Park(H) 69-70
Defeat: 0-7 v Hatfield Main (A) 88-89

Players progressing: Sean Connelly (Stockport C), Howard Wilkinson (Sheff. Wed) -The F.A.'s Technical Director, L Moore (Derby C.)

FACT FILE
Formed: 1860 Nickname: Countrymen
Sponsors: Hallamshire Holdings Ltd.
Colours: Blue/white/blue
Change colours: Red/black/black
Midweek Matches: Wednesday
Programme: Yes 50p
Editor: Mark Radford (Press Off.)
Local Press: Star, Green'Un, Sheffield Telegraph, Yorkshire Post

CLUB PERSONNEL
Chairman: Tony Scanlan - 01246 415471H
Vice Chairman: P Fuller
President: A Cooper
Press Officer: Mark Radford
Tel: 0114 249 7287 (H)
Manager: K Johnson
Physio:J.Beachall
2000-01 Leading goalscorer: Lee Morris 19
Captain: Mark Highfield
P.o.Y.: Brett Storey

HARROGATE RAILWAY ATHLETIC

Secretary: W Douglas Oldfield, 80 Stonefall Ave., Harrogate, Nth Yorks HG2 7NP
Tel: 01423 540786

Ground: Station View, Starbeck, Harrogate. Tel: 01423 885539

Directions: A59 Harrogate to Knaresborough road. After approx 1.5 miles turn left just before railway level crossing. Ground is 150 yds up the lane
Adjacent to Starbeck (BR).
Served by any Harrogate to Knaresborough bus.

Capacity: 3,000 Seats: 300 Cover: 600 Floodlights: Yes

Clubhouse: Games, TV room, lounge. Open normal pub hours. Hot food available.
Club Shop: Yes

HONOURS Northern Co's (East) Lg Cup 86-87 N.C.E. Div 1 Champions 98-99
PREVIOUS **Leagues:** West Yorkshire; Harrogate District; Yorkshire 55-73 80-82.
RECORD **Attendance:** 1,400; 1962 FA Amateur Cup
2000-01 **Captain & P.o.Y.:** Danny Ames **Top Goalscorer:** Matty Flynn 16

FACT FILE
Founded: 1935 Nickname: The Rail
Sponsors: Calvert Carpets
Colours: Red & green/green/red
Change: All white
Midweek matchday: Monday
Programme Editor: Gordon Ward
Tel: 01423 880423 (H)
Local Press: Yorkshire Post, Harrogate Herald & Advertiser, York Press

CLUB PERSONNEL
President: J Robinson
Chairman: Dennis Bentley
Comm. Man: T.B.A.
Press Officer/Prog. Editor: Gordon Ward
Tel: 01423 880423 (H)
Manager: P.Marshall
Assistant.Man.: M.Margis
Physio: P.Jones

LIVERSEDGE

Secretary: Michael Balmforth, 7 Reform St., Gomersal, Cleckheaton BD19 4JX (01274 862123)

Ground: Clayborn Ground, Quaker Lane, Hightown Rd, Cleckheaton, W. Yorks (01274 862108)
Directions: M62 jct 26, A638 into Cleckheaton, right at lights on corner of Memorial Park, through next lights & under railway bridge, 1st left (Hightown Rd) and Quaker Lane is approx 1/4 mile on left and leads to ground. From M1jct 40, A638 thru Dewsbury and Heckmondwike to Cleckheaton, left at Memorial Park lights then as above. Buses 218 & 220 (Leeds-Huddersfield) pass top of Quaker Lane

Capacity: 2,000 Seats: 250 Cover: 750 Floodlights: Yes
Clubhouse: Matchdays, Tues, Thursday. Pool, TV. Snacks **Club Shop:** No

HONOURS West Riding Co. Chal. Cup 48-49 51-52 69-70; West Riding County Cup 89-90; North Counties East Lg Div 1 R-up 89-90 (Div 2 R-up 88-89); West Riding Co.Amtr Lg(6) 23-24 25-27 64-66 68-69 (Lg Cup 57-58 64-65).

PREVIOUS **Leagues:** Spen Valley; West Riding County Amateur 22-72; Yorkshire 72-82.
Ground: Primrose Lane, Hightown. **Name:** None

BEST SEASON **FA Cup:** **FA Vase:**
Players progressing: Garry Briggs (Oxford), Martin Hirst (Bristol City) Leigh Bromby (Sheffield Wed)

FACT FILE

Nickname: Sedge Founded: 1910
Colours: All blue Change: Gold & Black
Midweek Matches: Wednesday
Reserves League: NCEL Res. Div.
Programme: 28 pages, 50p
Editor: Secretary
Local Press: Yorkshire Evening Post, Telegraph & Argus, Spenbrough Guardian

CLUB PERSONNEL
Chairman: Robert Gawthorpe
Press Officer: Secretary
Manager: Wayne Bruce
Asst Mgr: Karl Milner

2000-01
Top Goalscorer: Craig Lawford 11
Captain: James Stansfield
P.o.Y.: Steve West

PICKERING TOWN

Secretary: David Chapman, 29 The Avenue, Norton Malton, N. Yorks, YO17 9EF.
Tel: 01653 693486(H)

Ground: Recreation Club, Mill Lane (off Malton Rd), Pickering, North Yorkshire
Tel: 01751 473317

Directions: A169 from Malton. On entering Pickering take 1st left past Police Station and B.P. garage into Mill Lane, ground 200 yards on right
Capacity: 2,000 Seats: 200 Cover: 500 Floodlights: Yes

Clubhouse: Open 1.30pm for Saturday games, 6pm for midweek games.
Food available from Football Club Kitchen at half-time and after games.
Club Shop: No

PREVIOUS **Leagues:** Beckett; York & District; Scarborough & District; Yorkshire72-82.
RECORD **Attendance:** 1,412 v Notts County, friendly, August 1991
HONOURS Northern Co's East Lg R-up 92-93 Div 2 87-88, Div 1 R-up 91-92, 00-01, Yorks Lg Div 3 73-74, Div 2 R-up 74-75 North Riding Snr Cup R-up 93-94 94-95, N. Riding Co. Cup 90-91, Wilkinson Sword Trophy 2000-01.

Players progressing: Chris Short (Stoke City), Craig Short (Everton) both via Scarborough

FACT FILE
Founded: 1888
Nickname: Pikes
Club Sponsors: Flamingoland
Colours: Royal/white/royal
Change colours: All Red
Midweek matches: Tuesday
Reserves' League: N.C.E. Res. Div.
Programme: 48 pages, 80p
Editor: Gerry Gregory (01751 473818)

CLUB PERSONNEL
Chairman: Anthony Dunning (01751 473697)
President: J.P.Jennison
Manager: Jimmy Reid
Assist. Manager: Gary Chapman
Physio: Clive Reynolds
Coach: Steve Brown

2000-01
Leading goalscorer: Adam Wast 17
P.o.Y: Andrew Thornton
Captain: Simon Sturdy

SELBY TOWN

Secretary: Thomas William Ardley,176 Abbots Rd,Selby, N.Yorks.O8 8AZ Tel: 01757 700356 H) 07974691437(M) Email Address: toonarkley@hotmail.com
Ground: Flaxley Rd Ground, Richard St, Scott Rd, Selby, N YorksYO8 0BS.Tel: 01757 210900
Directions: From Leeds, left at main traffic lights in Selby down Scott Rd.then 1st left into Richard St. From Doncaster go straight across main traffic lights into Scott Road then 1st left. From York right at main traffic lights into Scott Rd, and 1st left. 1 mile from Selby (BR)
Capacity: 5,000 Seats: 220 Cover: 350 Floodlights: Yes

Clubhouse: Bar at ground open first and second team matchdays **Club Shop:** Yes

HONOURS Yorkshire Lg 32-33 34-35 35-36 52-53 53-54 (R-up 24-25 25-26 27-28 28-29 30-31 31-32 50-51 55-56, Div 3 R-up 74-75, Lg Cup 37-38 53-54 54-55 62-63); N.C.E. Div 1 95-96, Div 2 R-up 89-90; W. Riding Snr Cup 37-38; W. Riding Co Cup 27-28 48-49; W. Riding Chall. Cup 34-35 35-36 Presidents Cup 00-01

PREVIOUS **League:** Yorkshire (1920-82) Ground: Bowling Green, James St. 1920-51

BEST SEASON **FA Cup:** Second Round Proper 54-55 **FA Vase:** Prel Round 89-90

RECORD **Attendance:** 7,000 v Bradford Park Avenue (FA Cup 1st Rnd 1953-54)
Players progressing: Numerous

FACT FILE

Founded: 1919
Nickname: The Robins
Sponsors: A>D>D> Computers
Colours: All red
Change colours: Amber/black/amber
Midweek Matches: Tuesday
Reserves' League: N.C.E. Res. Div.
Programme: 30 pages, 50p
Editor: Mark Fairweather, 01757 705376 (H)
Local Newspaper: Selby Times

CLUB PERSONNEL

Chairman: Ralf Pearse, Tel: 0836 336481(M)
President: A Carter
Match Sec: T.B.A.
Manager: B Lyon
Asst Manager/Coach: G.Cygan

2000-01
Catain: Matthew Potter
P.o.Y.: & Top Scorer: Peter Collier 25

SHEFFIELD

Secretary: Stephen Hall, 23 Regent Court, Bradfield Rd, Hillsborough, Sheffield S6 2BT
Tel: 0114 233 4441 (H), 01246 258918 (B)

Ground: Coach & Horses Ground, Sheffield Road, Dronfield. Sheffield

Directions: ((2) C&H - M!, J 29, A617 into Chesterfield. At traffic island turn right onto dual carriageway A61 (Sheffield). Follow over two islands and at third island follow sign 'Dronfield/Gosforth Valley'. At entrance to Dronfield, The Coach & Horses ground is at bottom of hill on the right.

Capacity: 2,000 Seats: 250 Floodlights: Yes

Clubhouse: Licensed Bar **Club Shop:** No

HONOURS FA Amateur Cup 02-03; FA Challenge Vase Runners-up 76-77; Northern Co's East Lg Cup 94-95 ,Div 1 88-89 90-91; Yorkshire Lg Div 2 76-77

PREVIOUS **League:** Yorks 49-82 **Grounds:** Abbeydale Park, Dore (1956-1989);Sheffield Amateur Sports Club, Hillsborough Park 1989-91; Sheffield International (Don Valley) Stadium 1991-94; Sheffield Sports Stadium Don Valley94-97.

BEST SEASON **FA Cup:** 4th Q Rd 00-01 **FA Vase:** R-up 76-77

RECORD **Attendance:** 2,000 v Barton Rovers, FA Vase SF 76-77

Player progressing: Richard Peacock, Hull 94-95,

FACT FILE

Founded: 1857
Nickname: The Club
Sponsors: Bumford Heating
Colours: Red & black halves/black/black
Change: All blue
Midweek matchday: Tuesday
Programme: 16 pages, 50p
Editor: David Dean (0114 232 5901)

CLUB PERSONNEL

Chairman: Richard Tims
Tel: 0114 2728888 (B)
President: Alan Methley

Manager: David McCarthy
Asst Manager: Lee Walshaw
Physio: Steve Naylor

THACKLEY

Secretary: Stewart Willingham, 3 Kirklands Close, Baildon, Shipley, West Yorks BD17 6HN
Tel: 01274 598589

Ground: Dennyfield, Ainsbury Avenue, Thackley, Bradford (01274 615571). **Directions:** On main Leeds/Keighley A657 road, turn off at Thackley corner which is 2 miles from Shipley traffic lights and 1 mile from Greengates lights.Ainsbury Avenue bears to the right 200yds down the hill. Ground is 200yds along Ainsbury Avenue on the right. 3 miles from Bradford Interchange (BR), one and ahalf miles from Shipley (BR). Buses to Thackley corner (400 yds)

Capacity: 3,000 Seats: 300 Cover: 600 Floodlights: Yes

Clubhouse: Tue-Sun evenings, matchdays and w/e lunchtimes. Hot & cold snacks on matchdays

Club Shop: Progs, souvenirs. Metal badges- £2.50 + s.a.e.Contact Geoff Scott (01274 611520)

HONOURS N.C.E. Lg R-up 94-95 (Lg Cup R-up 94-95), Yorks Lg Div 273-74, West Yorks Lg 66-67, W. Riding Co. Amtr Lg (x3) 57-60, W. Riding Co. Cup 73-74 74-75, W. Riding Co. Chal. Cup 63-64 66-67,(R-Up 94-95); Bradford & Dist. Snr Cup 12.

PREVIOUS **Leagues:** Bradford Amateur, W. Riding County Amateur, W. Yorks, Yorks 67-82.
Name: Thackley Wesleyians 1930-39

BEST SEASON **FA Vase:** 5th Rd 80-81 (01-2 v Whickham)

RECORD **Attendance:** 1,500 v Leeds Utd 1983

Players progressing: Tony Brown (Leeds), Ian Ormondroyd (Bradford City).

FACT FILE

Founded: 1930
Sponsors: Diamond International Shipping
Colours: Red & white/white/red
Change colours: All white
Midweek matches: Tuesday
Programme: 20 pages, 50p Editor: Secretary
Local Press: Bradford Telegraph & Argus, BradfordStar, Aire Valley Target.

CLUB PERSONNEL

Chairman: Secretary (acting)
Treasurer: Steven Paley
Manager/Coach: Andrew Taylor
Asst Manager: Warren Fletcher
Physio: JohnLaidler

2000-01

Captain: Craig Sugden P.o.Y.: Bryan Brooks
Top Scorer: Andrew Patterson 12

Liversedge

Selby Town. Back Row (l-r): Richard Tomlinson, Mark Turner, Mathew Potter, Shane Forrest, Paul Masterton, Ian Phillips, Nigel Croad, Dexter Tucker, Paul Roberts, Kristian Baxter. Front Row: Peter Collier, Domonic Moyles, Craig Pickles, Alan Clayton, Andrew Hart.

Sheffield FC. Back Row (l-r): Sam Sodje, Darren Bonnington, Mick Godber, Richard Davenport, Sam Saif, Darren Vine, Dave McCarthy, Richard Shipston, Stevie Spence, John Pearson. Front Row: Andy Slowe, Richard March, Dave Capper, Lee Vernon, David Hoole, Jon Pickess, Kevin Leatherday.

BRIDLINGTON TOWN

Secretary: Chris Bemrose, 16 North Back Lane, Bridlington, E. Yorks. YO16 7BA
Tel: 01262 604036 (H & Fax) 01262 676836 (B) e-mail Admin@bridtownafc.freeserve.co.uk
Ground Queensgate Stadium, Queensgate, Bridlington YO16 7LN Tel: 01262 606879
Capacity: 3,000 **Seats:** 742 **Executive Boxes:** 2 **Shop:** Yes ,matchdays **Floodlights:** Yes
Clubhouse: Open every evening & w/e lunchtimes.
Record Attendance: 432 for an F.A. Sunday Cup Semi-Final 3.3.2000
Directions From south on A165 - Pass golf course, straight over lights. Turn right at r'about by B&Q. Turn left at next lights & over rlwy bridge. At r'about bear left and then straight on up Quay Road. After lights turn right into Queensgate & ground is 800yds on right.
From south & west via A614 (formerly A166) - Straight on at lights (Hosp. on right). At r'about straight on to mini-r'about & bear right (2nd exit). Over the first lights, left at next lights (just after Kwikfit) into Queensgate & ground is 800yds on right.
2000-01 Capt: Lee Harper. Supporters' P..o.Y.: Paul Foot Top Scorer: Matt Edeson 20

FACT FILE
Founded: 1994
Sponsors: Barton Engineering
Colours: All Red Change Colours: All Blue
Midweek Matchday: Tuesday
Programme: 40 pages Price 70p
Prog. Editor: Jonathon Bemrose
Website: www.bridtownafc.freeserve.co.uk

CLUB PERSONNEL
Chairman: Gordon Reed
Vice Chairman: Barrie garton
Tel: 01262 673967 (H, B & Fax)
Match Sec.: Jonathon Bemrose
Tel: 01262 408224 (H)
01262 401487 (B)

GEDLING TOWN

Secretary: Tony White, 9 Bourne Street, Netherfield, Nottingham NG4 2FJ(0115 911 1961)
Ground: Riverside Ground, (rear of Ferryboat Inn), Stoke Lane, Stoke Bardolph, Nottingham NG14 5HX Tel: 0115 940 2145 Fax: 0115 967 31310 Office: 0115 967 0047
Directions: A612 Nottingham-Lowdham-Southwell road. Just before Burton Joyce turn right into Stoke Lane to Ferryboat P.H. Approx 1.5 miles. Ground at rear of pub.
Capacity: 2,000 Seats: None Cover: 500 Floodlights: Yes
Clubhouse: Matchdays only. Hot & cold food. Licensed bar. **Club Shop:** No
Honours: Central Mids Lg Prem 97-98 R-up 91-92, Div 1 90-91, (Res Prem 96-97 97-98); Wakefield Floodlit Trophy 92-93 R-up 95-96; Ken Marsland Cup (Res) 93-94; Notts Amtr Lg 89-90 (Snr Cup R-up 89-90).Res Lg & Cp Winners 98-99
Best season FA Vase: 3rd Rd 96-97
RECORDS **Attendance:** 250 v Arnold Town.
Win: 11-0 v Radford 91-92 **Defeat:** 2-5 v Staveley MW 93-94.
Goalscorer: Rob Orton 98 in 124 **Appearances:** Gary Ball 216

FACT FILE
Founded: 1986
Colours: Yellow & navy/navy/navy
Midweek Matchday: Tuesday
Prog 32 pages 50p
Editor: Paul Dobson

CLUB PERSONNEL
Chairman: Roland Ash
0115 952 0846 (H) 07976 817441(M)

Manager: Paul Elrick
Asst. Man: Junior Glave
Physio: Trevor Wells/Pete Tyers

HALL ROAD RANGERS

Secretary: Andrew Bannigan, 14 Southern Drive, Anlaby Park, Hull HU4 6TR (01482 568680)
Ground: Dene Park, Dene Close, Beverley Rd, Dunswell, Nr Hull (01482 850101).
Directions: M62 to A63, turn left before Humber Bridge onto A164 to Beverley,after approx 5 miles turn right onto A1079. In 2 miles turn left at large roundabout to ground 20 yards on right.
Capacity: 1,200 Seats: 250 Cover: 750 Floodlights: Yes
Clubhouse: Open all week for drinks and bar snacks. Snooker, pool,darts. **Club Shop:** Yes

HONOURS N.C.E. Lg Div 2 90-91, Yorks Lg Div 3 72-73 79-80, E. Riding Snr Cup 72-73 93-94.

PREVIOUS **Leagues:** East Riding; Yorks 68-82 **Ground:** Hull Co-Op (until 1968)

BEST SEASON **FA Cup:** **FA Vase:**

RECORDS **Attendance:**1,200 v Manchester City Aug 93
Scorer: G James **Appearances:** G James

Players progressing: Gerry Ingram (Blackpool, Sheff Wed). Mark Greaves (Hull City)

FACT FILE
Founded: 1959 Nickname: Rangers
Sponsor: Admiral Signs of Hull Ltd.
Colours: Blue & white hoops/ blue/ blue.
Change Colours: Red & Black Stripes,black
Midweek Matches: Wednesday
Reserves' League: East Riding Co.League
Programme: 36 pages, 50p
Editor/Press Officer: Secretary
Local Press: Hull Daily Mail

CLUB PERSONNEL
Chair 'n:Robert SmailesTel:01482821354 (H)
Player-Manager: Chris Lewis
Asst Mgr: Peter Smurthwaite
Coach: Ian Davis

HATFIELD MAIN

Secretary: Stuart Bagnall,53 Walnut Road, Thorne, Doncaster, S.Yorks. DN8 4HN (01405 740424 (H) 07788 730804(M)
Ground: Dunscroft Welfare Ground, Dunscroft, Doncaster, Sth Yorks Tel: 01302 841326
Directions: From Doncaster (A18) Scunthorpe Rd to Dunsville, left at Flarepath Hotel down Broadway. Ground half mile on right.
Stamforth & Hatfield (BR) 1/2 mile. Buses every 15 mins. from Doncaster.
Capacity: 4,000 Seats: 200 Cover: 600 Floodlights: Yes
Clubhouse: Full licensing hrs. Hot/cold drinks/snacks **Club Shop:** Yes
HONOURS Northern Counties East Prem Div 95-96, R-up 88-89, Div One 94-95; Yorks Lge Div 1 R-up 65-66; W Riding Cup 61-62 63-64.
PREVIOUS **League:** Doncaster Dist, Yorkshire 55-82 .**1998-99 P.o.Y.** Darren Phipps
RECORDS **Gate:** 1,000 v Leeds, A Jones testimonial. Competitive: 750 v Bishop Auckland,
Appearances: Lal Dutt **Fee received:** £1,000 for Mark Hall (York City)
Players progressing: Mark Atkins (Scunthorpe), Wayne Hall (York)

FACT FILE
Founded: 1936 Nickname: The Main
Sponsors: Manor Tyres, (Stainforth)
Colours: All red Change Colours: All blue
Midweek matchday: Tuesday
Reserves' League: None
Programme: 25 pages, 50p
Editor: Tony Ingram (01302 842795)

CLUB PERSONNEL
President: R Wright,Chairman: Peter Wright
Treasurer: Russel Wright
Commercial Manager: Stuart Robinson
Manager: Colin Douglas
Asst Manager:Glenn Hodgit &Stuart Dowing
Physio:Shaun McDonald, MascotRyan Bagnall

LINCOLN MOORLANDS

Secretary: Colin Edwards, 5 Lansdowne Avenue, Lincoln, LN6 7PU
Tel: 01522 520857 (H) 01472 352187 (B) 07970 954912 (M)
Ground: Moorland Sports Ground, Newark Rd, Lincoln LN5 9LY
Tel: 01522 520184 Office & Fax: 01522 874111
Directions: From north A1 to Markham Moor. Take A57 until Lincoln by-pass and then turn right onto A46. At 3rd r'about left into Doddington Rd. Continue until Newark Rd. - ground on left after 800 yards.
From Newark enter Lincoln on A1434, go past Forum Shopping Centre for approx. 3/4 mile. Ground on left signposted 'Moorlands Club'.
Capacity: Seats: 100 Cover: 200 Floodlights: Yes
Clubhouse: Yes **Club Shop:** No
HONOURS: Central Midlands Supreme 99-00, R-up 00-01, Lincolndshire Senior A 00-01
2000-01 **Leading Goalscorer:** Steve Bull 14
Captain: Darren Chapman **P.o.Y.:** Jamie Chesman

FACT FILE
Founded: 1989
Nickname: The Moors
Colours: White with blue trim/navy/white
Change colours: Orange/black/orange
Midweek Matchday: Wednesday
Programme: 2 pages price 75p
Editor: Kevin Griffin 01522 720940 (H)

CLUB PERSONNEL
Chairman: Graham Longhurst
Manager: Garry Goddard

LOUTH UNITED

Secretary: Ken Vincent, 64 Frederick St, Grimsby DN31 1XQ: Tel Nos: 01472 344411(H) 07957 870 330 (M) and 0797 440 5997 **Match day Secretary:** Albany Jordan(01507 607356)
Albany Jordan Ground: Park Avenue, Louth, Lincs Tel: 01507 607351 FAX: 01507 607351
Directions: A16 To Louth Market Place, exit via Eastgate/Eastfield Rd, to Fire Station turn right into Park Avenue. Ground at bottom of avenue of prefabricated bungalows.
Capacity: 2,500 Seats: None Cover: 400 Floodlights: Yes **Club Shop:** No
Clubhouse: Weekdays 6.30-11.45, Sat 12-11.45. Full bar facilities. Snacks available.

HONOURS Lincs Lg Prem 72-73 85-86 86-87 (Div 1 57-58 66-67 67-68; Lg Challenge Cup 73-74 86-87; Lg Charity Cup 55-56 56-57 67-68; Central Mids Lg Cup R-up 92-93; Wakefield F'lit Cup R-up 91-92; Lincs Snr `A' Cup 77-78. R-Up 00-01 Lincs Sen Cup R-up: 98-99
PREVIOUS **Leagues:** Lincs 47-75 82-88; Central Midlands 88-93.
Names: Louth Nats & Louth Town - merged **Grounds:** None
BEST SEASON **FA Cup:** 3Rd Q 0-2 v Emley **F.A Vase:** 4th Rd v Halesowen Town 85-86
RECORDS: **Goalscorers:** Peter Rawclife 39 **Appearances:** Steve Newby 510 **Att::** 2,500

FACT FILE
Founded: 1947 Nickname: The Lions
Sponsors: 'Brother'
Colours: Blue& red/blue/blue
Change:All Yellow
Midweek matches: Tuesday
Reserves League: Lincolnshire
Prog:50p ED/ PressOff: Albany Jordan
CLUB PERSONNEL
Chair: George Horton V-Chair: Albany Jordan
Ch Exec:Jim Walmsley Pres: Dave Fairburn
Commercial Manager: Simon Hewson
Man: Steve Newby Coach: Nigel Fanthorpe.
Physio: Kenny Vincent
2000-01 Capt: James Marshall P.o.Y.: & Top Scorer Simon Bailey 23

MALTBY MAIN

Secretary: Dave Morris, 2 Buckingham Way, Maltby. S66 7EA Tel No: 01709 814400
Email Address: nick.dunhill@ lambson.com
Ground: Muglet Lane, Maltby , Rotherham. Tel: 017941 057883
Directions: Exit M18 at junct 1 with A631. Two miles into Maltby, right at traffic lights at Queens Hotel corner on to B6427 Muglet Lane. Ground 3/4mile on left. Bus 101 from Rotherham stops at ground. Bus 287 from Sheffield to Queens Hotel, then follow as above
Capacity: 2,000 Seats: 150 Cover: 300 Floodlights: Yes
Clubhouse: No, Miners Welfare Club opposite **Club Shop**: No
HONOURS Sheffield & Hallamshire Snr Cup 77-78, N.C.E. Lge Presidents Cup 92-93 SF 90-91, Mexborough Montague Cup 76-77 80-81 90-91,Yorks Lg R-up 77-78, Sheffield Wharncliffe Cup 80-81.
CLUB RECORDS **Attendance:** 1,500 v Sheffield Wed., June 91-92 (friendly)
PREVIOUS **Leagues:** Sheffield County Senior; Yorkshire 73-82.
Name: Maltby Main 1916-65 (disbanded); Maltby Miners Welfare 1970-96

FACT FILE
Founded: 1916 Nickname: Miners
Sponsors:Milgat Computer Sustems
Colours: Red/white/black Change: All yellow
Midweek matchday: Wednesday
Prog: 36 pages, 70p Ed:Nick Dunhill
Tel No: 017941 057 883
CLUB PERSONNEL
Chairman: Gary Kitching
V-Chair: Jon Carratt President: H Henson
Match Sec: Dave Morris (01709 814400)
Manager:Russ Eagle Asst Man: Neil Pickering
Coach: Les Harris
2000-01 Captain: Darren Grady P.o.Y.: Simon Motyka Topo Scorer: Scott Somerville 6

MICKLEOVER SPORTS

Secretary: Tony Shaw, 80 Onslow Road, Mickleover, Derbys. DE3 5JB
Tel: 01332 512826 (H & Fax)
Club Website: www.mickleoversports.fsnet.co.uk
Ground: Mickleover Sports Ground, Station Rd, Mickleover, Derby (01332 521167).
Directions: Derby ring road A38 to A52, turn off at Markeaton Park Island.Take turn to Ashbourne A52, then 2nd left into Radbourne Lane. Take 3rd left into Station Road, ground on corner.

Capacity: 1,500 **Seats:** None **Cover:** 200

Clubhouse: Open Thursdays and Fridays (7-11 p.m) Saturdays and Sundays (11am-11pm) Snacks available only on Matchdays
Club Shop: No
2000-01 **Top Goalscorer:** Bevan Hudson 14 **Captain :** Corin Holness **P.o.Y.** Tom Priestley

FACT FILE

Founded: 1948
Colours: Red & White shirts/black/red
Change Colours: All blue
Midweek Matchday: Tuesday
Programme Editor: Stephen Pritchard
Tel: 01332 516271

CLUB PERSONNEL
Chairman Keith Jenkinson (01332 516 271-H)
Match Sec.: Cath Grant (01332 511359)
Manager: Mark Kelsey

PARKGATE

Secretary: Bruce Bickerdike, 2 Cardew Close, Rawmarsh, Rotherham S62 6LB
Tel: 01709 522305 Fax: 01709 528583.
Ground: Roundwood Sports Complex, Green Lane, Rawmarsh, Rotherham S62 6LA
Tel: 01709 826600 Website: www.parkgatefc.co.uk Email: bruce@parkgatefc.co.uk
Directions: From Rotherham A633 to Rawmarsh. From Doncaster A630 to Conisbrough, then A6023 through Swinton to Rawmarsh. Grd at Green Lane - right from Rotherham, left from Conisbrough at the Crown Inn. Grd 800yds right
Capacity: 1,000 Seats: 300 Cover: 300 Floodlights: Yes **Club Shop:** No.
Clubhouse: Licensed bar, 2 lounges. Meals available lunchtime Wed-Sat.
HONOURS S&HSC Finalists 0-3 v Emley 97-98, Wilkinson Sword Trophy R-up 98-99
PREVIOUS **Leagues:** County Senior Lge; Yorkshire 74-82
Ground: None **Names:** BSC Parkgate (until mid-eighties); RES Parkgate (pre-1994).
RECORD **Attendance:** v Worksop 1982
2000-01 Leading goalscorer: Brian Cusworth 20Captain: Kevin Eley
Joint P.O.Y: Craig Loftus & Matthew Telling

FACT FILE
Founded: 1969
Nickname: The Gate or The Steelmen
Kit Sponsors: JBB Investigations
Colours: All red Change: Blue & yellow
Midweek matches: Tuesday
Programme: 20 pages, 50p
Editor: Stuart Bisby (01709 545219)

CLUB PERSONNEL
President: Paul Cristinacce
Chairman: Albert T DudillTel: 01709 719459
Vice Chairman: Les Taylor
Press Officer: Secretary
Manager: Wilfred Race
Asst Man: Vincent Brady
Physio: David Proctor

PONTEFRACT COLLIERIES

Secretary: Frank Maclachlan, 188 Watling Road, Ferry Fryston, Castleford WF102QY
,Tel: 01977 512085 (H), 01977 601327 (B), 07710 586447 (M)Email: rod@erick.fsnet,co.uk
Ground: Skinner Lane, Pontefract, West Yorkshire (01977 600818)
Directions: M62 jct 32 towards Pontefract. Left at lights after roundabout for park entrance and retail park. Traffic thro town should follow racecouse signs thro lights to roundabout and back to lights. Monkhill (BR) 1/2 mile. Bahhill (BR) 1 mile. Tanshelf (BR) 1/2 mile .All Leeds and Castleford buses pass ground. **Capacity:** 1,200 **Seats:** 300 **Cover:** 400 **Floodlights:** Yes
Clubhouse: Fully licensed. Hot & cold snacks. Open before and after games **Club Shop:** No
HONOURS N.C.E. Lg Div 1 83-84 95-96 (Div 2 R-up 82-83); Floodlit Comp 87-88 88-89; Yorks Lg Div 3 81-82; W. Riding Co. Cup R-up 87-88 90-91;Embleton Cup 82-83 86-87 95-96; 99-00 Castleford FA Cup 82-83 86-87,94-95; Wilkinson Sword 95-96
Previous Leagues: West Yorkshire 58-79; Yorkshire 79-82 **Record Attendance:** 1,000 v Hull City, floodlight opening 1985. **Players progressing:** David Penney (Derby County, 1985), Andy Hayward (Rotherham U) and Dean Trott (Northampton Town

FACT FILE
Founded: 1958 Nickname: Colls
Sponsors: Liverno
Colours: Blue & black halves/black/black
Change All green Midweek Matches: Tuesday
Programme: 36 pages 70p
Editor:Rod Taylor(01977 602266
Local Press: Pontefract & Castleford Express
Website: www.nce-league.freeserve.co.uk

CLUB PERSONNEL
Chairman:Steve Lloyd 01977 795581(H)
Manager: Gary Batley Asst Mgr: David Vase
Physio: Mick Slater
2000-01 Capts: Andy Hardy (P.o.Y.)
& Dave Brook
Top Scorer: Ricardo Gabbiadini 10

ROSSINGTON MAIN

Secretary: Gerald Parsons, 15 Seaton Gardens, Rossington, Doncaster DN11 0XA
Tel: 01302 867542 (H)
Ground: Welfare Ground, Oxford Street, Rossington, Doncaster Tel: 01302 865524
Directions: Enter Rossington and go over the railway crossings. Pass the Welfare Club on right, Oxford Street is next right - ground is at bottom.8miles from Doncaster (BR)
Capacity: 2,000 Seats: 200 Cover: 500 Floodlights: Yes
Clubhouse: Evenings & matchdays, Sandwiches, rolls, satellite TV, pool. **Club Shop:** No

HONOURS Sen Lge 44-45, Cup 44-45, Cen. Mids. Prem Div. 84-85, Cup 83-84 84-85, DDSALShield 90-91 R-up 89-90.

PREVIOUS **Leagues:** Doncaster Sen, Yorkshire Lge, Sheffield County Sen, Cent Mids.

RECORDS **Attendance:** 864 v Leeds United 8/91.
Goalscorer: Mark Illman **Appearances:** Darren Phipps

FACT FILE
Founded: 1920 Nickname: The Colliery
Sponsor: RJB Mining
Colours: All blue
Change colours: Blue & black
Midweek matches: Tuesday
Reserves' League: Beefeater County Sen
Programme: 50p
Editor:Chairman

CLUB PERSONNEL
Chairman: Gerald Murden (01302 867542)
Joint Managers: D Ridley & L Ostle
Physio: J White

STAVELEY MINERS WELFARE

Secretary: Keith Burnard, 2Woodland Grove, Clowne, Chesterfield S43 4AT Tel: 01246 811063
Ground: Inkersall Road, Staveley, Chesterfield, Derbyshire Tel: 01246 471441
Directions: M1 jct 30, follow A619 Chesterfield - Staveley is 3 miles from jct30. Turn left at GK Garage in Staveley town centre into Inkersall Rd - ground 200yds on right at side of Speedwell Rooms. Frequent buses (47, 70, 72, 75, 77) from Chesterfield stop in Staveley town centre - 3 mins walk to ground
Capacity: 5,000 Cover: 400 Seats: 220 Floodlights: Yes
Clubhouse: The Staveley Miners Welfare, 500 yds from ground, open before and after games
Club Shop: Yes, contactRod Walker 01246 473655
HONOURS County Sen Lg Div 2 92-93, Div 3 91-92, Chesterfield & D. Amat Lg R-up89-90 90-91, Byron (Lge) Cup 89-90, R-up 90-91.NCE Div 1 R-up 97-98
PREVIOUS **Leagues:** Chesterfield & D. Amat 89-91; County Sen 91-93.
BEST SEASON **FA Cup:** **FA Vase:** 98-99, 3rd Rd at least
RECORDS **Attendance:** 280 v Stocksbridge, Sheffield Snr Cup 22/1/94
Goalscorer: Mick Godber **Appearances:** Shane Turner

FACT FILE
Founded: 1989 Nickname: The Welfare
Colours: Blue shirts/blue shorts
Change colours: All yellow
Midweek matches: Tuesday
Reserves' League: Beauvale Midlan Regional
Alliance: Premier Division
Programme: 32pages, #1.00
Editor: Tony Brown(01246 475644)

CLUB PERSONNEL
Chairman: John Edwards
Tel: 01246 475644 (H)
2000-01
Captain & P.o.Y.: Asa Ingall
Top Scorer: Ian Clarke 7

Top:
Pickering Town Wilkinson Sword Trophy Winners Back Row (l-r): Jim Reid (mgr), Ken Carr (kit), Pat Gaughan, Andy Thornton, Joe Connor, Matty Morton, Danny Farthing, Adam Wash, Jim Brown, Rich Dale, Steve Brown (coach), Stefan Zoll, Alex Willgrass, Clive Reynolds (physio), Jody Chapman. Front Row: Paul Wilson, Phil O'Reilly, Simon Sturdy (capt), Adam Mitchell, Mark Wood, Tom Reid.

Centre:
FA Vase First Qualifying Round Briscoe (Borrowash Victoria, stripes), the Division One Champions, fires in a low drive past onlooking Marconi defender Carokiu at the Robinson Construction Bowl.
Photo: Martin Wray

Bottom:
Maltby Main FC

TADCASTER ALBION

Secretary: Mrs Angela J Burnett Tel: 01937 832802 (H/Fax)
6 Beech Grove House, Ouston Lane, Tadcaster N.Yorks. LS24 8DP.

Ground: The Park, Ings Lane, Tadcaster, LS24 9AY. Tel: 01937 834119

Directions: From West Riding and South Yorks, turn right off A659 at John Smith's Brewery Clock.
From East Riding turn left off A659 after passing over river bridge and pelican crossing (New Street).
Capacity: 1,500 **Seats**: Planned this season **Cover:** 400 **Floodlights**: Yes
Clubhouse: No **Club Shop:** No

HONOURS None
RECORD **Attendance:**1,200 v Wincanton F.A.Vase 4th Rd 1996-7

FACT FILE

Founded: 1892
Colours: Navy & Red trim/navy & red/navy
Change colours: Green & Yellow halves
Midweek Matchday: Tuesday
Programme: 20 pages
Programme Editor: Mrs Angela Burnett (Sec.)

CLUB PERSONNEL

Chairman: Michael Burnett
Terl No: 01973 832802
President: Lord Edward Stourton
Match Sec: 01937 835017 (H/B)
Manager: Wayne Day

WINTERTON RANGERS

Secretary: G Spencer, 2 Dale Park Ave.,Winterton,Scun'pe,N Lincs.DN15 9UY (01724 732039)

Ground: West Street, Winterton, Scunthorpe, South Humberside (01724 732628).
Directions: From Scunthorpe take A1077 Barton-on-Humber for 5 miles. On entering Winterton take 3rd right (Eastgate), 3rd left (Northlands Rd)and 1st right (West St.). Ground 200yds on left
Capacity: 3,000 Seats: 200 Covered: 200 Floodlights: Yes **Club Shop:** No.
Clubhouse: Open matchdays & evenings Mon-Sat, hot & cold food available on matchdays

HONOURS Lincs Jnr Cup 47-48 61-62; Lincs Snr `B' Cup 69-70; Yorks Lg 71-72 76-77 78-79 (Lg Cup 80-81); N.C.E. Div 2 89-90; S'thorpe Lg & Cup many times.
PREVIOUS **Leagues:** Scunthorpe & Dist. 45-65; Lincs 65-70; Yorkshire 70-82.
BEST SEASON **FA Vase:** QF 76-77 **FA Cup:** 4th Qual Rd replay 76-77, 2-3 after 3-3
RECORD **Attendance:** 1,200 v Sheffield Utd, official floodlight opening, Oct. 78
Fee received: £5,000 for Henry Smith (Leeds United, 1979)

Players progressing Henry Smith (Leeds), Keith Walwyn (Chesterfield), Rick Greenhough(Chester)

FACT FILE

Founded: 1930 Nickname: Rangers
Colours: Blue & white/Black/Blue
Change colours: All red
Midweek matches: Wednesday
Programme: 28-36 pages, 50p
Editor: M Fowler (01724 734570)

CLUB PERSONNEL

Chairman: I.Grimshaw
Vice Chairman: A Smith
Press Officer: as Secretary
Manager: J. Wilkinson
2000-01 - Leading goalscorer: Ian Ritchie 6
Captain: Simon Green
P.o.Y: Gary Lockwood

WORSBROUGH M.W. & ATHLETIC

Secretary: Garry Wiggan, 9 Pantry Well, Worsbrough Bridge, Barnsley, S. Yorks S70 4SW
Tel: 01226 247023
Ground: Park Road, Worsbrough Bridge, Barnsley Tel: 01226 284452
Directions: On the A61 Barnsley-Sheffield road two miles south of Barnsley, 2miles from M1 jnt 36 opposite Blackburns Bridge. Two and a half miles from Barnsley (BR). Yorkshire Traction run buses every 10 mins thru Worsbrough Bridge.
Capacity: 2,000 Seats: 175 Cover: 175 Floodlights: Yes
Clubhouse: Yes **Club Shop:** No

HONOURS Northern Co's East Div 1 R-up 90-91 (Div 3 R-up 85-86); Sheffield SnrCup R-up 72-73; County Snr Lg 65-66 69-70 (R-up 62-63, Lg Cup 65-66); Barnsley Lg 52-53 58-59 59-60, Lg Cup 56-57 58-59 (R-up 53-54), Beckett Cup 57-58.
PREVIOUS **Leagues:** Barnsley 52-61; County Snr 62-70; Yorks 71-82.
RECORD **Attendance:** 1,603 v Blyth Spartans, FA Amateur Cup 1971

FACT FILE

Founded: 1923
Reformed: 1947
Colours: All red
Change colours: Yellow/blue
Midweek Matchday: Wednesday
Programme: 60 pages, 50p
Editor: Secretary

CLUB PERSONNEL

Chairman: Malcolm McCullough
Press Officer: T.B.A.

YORKSHIRE AMATEUR

Secretary: David Packham, 30 Roxholme Avenue, Leeds LS7 4JF (0113 262 0758)
Ground: The Bracken Edge, Roxholme Road, Leeds LS8 4DZ Tel: 0113 262 4093
Directions: From South M1 to Leeds, then A58 Wetherby Road to Fforde Green Hotel, left at lights and proceed to Sycamore Ave. (on right). From East A1 to Boot & Shoe Inn then to Shaftesbury Hotel, turn right into Harehills Lane, then to Sycamore Avenue. Two and a half miles from Leeds (BR). Buses 2, 3 & 20 from Briggate to Harehills Ave.
Capacity : 1,550 Seats: 200 Cover: 160 Floodlights: Yes **Club Shop:** Yes
Clubhouse: Bar, tea bar, games, lounge. Every night 8.30-11, Sat matchdays 12-11, Sun 12-3.

HONOURS FA Amtr Cup SF 31-32; West Riding Co. Cup(3); Yorks Lg 31-32, Div 2 58-59 (R-up 52-53 71-72), Div 3 77-78, Lg Cup 32-33; Leeds & Dist. Snr Cup.
PREVIOUS **League:** Yorks 20-24 30-82. **Ground:** Elland Road 1919-20
RECORD **Attendance:** 4,000 v Wimbledon, FA Amateur Cup QF 1932.
Players progressing: Gary Strodder and Stuart Naylor (W.B.A,), Peter Swan (Leeds U) Brian Deane (Doncaster R)

FACT FILE

Founded: 1918 Nickname: Ammers
Sponsors: Screeching Parrot
Colours: White/navy/red
Change colours: All red
Midweek Matches: Tuesday
Programme: 12 pages, 50p
Editor:John Turner (0113 225 2833)
Local Press: Yorkshire Post, Yorkshire Evening post and North Leeds Advertiser

CLUB PERSONNEL

Chairman: Andrew Wilkinson(0113 2650841)
President: Rayner Barker
Manager: Denis Metcalfe
Coach:Jjim McKay Physio: Terry Davies

REDFERNS REMOVERS CENTRAL MIDLANDS LEAGUE

FEEDER TO: NORTHERN COUNTIES LEAGUE

President: Mr R Holmes **Vice President:** Mr D Capenerhurst
Chairman & General Secretary: Frank Harwood
103 Vestry Road, Oakwood, Derby DE21 2BN
Tel: 01332 832372 Fax: 01332 835004 e-mail: frank.harwood@talk21.com

Despite the most difficult season the League has probably had in its history due to the unprecedented weather, it can be said again that the CMFL's considerable progress continues to expand, not just in the UK, but I now receive mail from throughout the world, no doubt helped by the presence of the internet and the two football sites which we feature, 'football news' and 'mitoo'.

The clubs that leave us continue to have considerable success in the competition we feed into, and this once again proves the tremendous standards throughout the League. It must be said also that clubs coming into the CMFL are a credit to the leagues they have played in previously and so have ensured that the standards have been maintained.

Lincoln Moorlands are the present side who leave us on the promotion trail, but the season belonged to Shirebrook Town, who deservedly won both the Travis Perkins Supreme Division and the Cox Accommodation League Cup. They might well have completed a treble but, due to the weather, the Wakefield Floodlit Cup competition was abandoned midway through.

New clubs to the League dominated the R & R Scaffolding Premier Division, so both North Notts who finished Champions and Bottesford Town who finished third are accordingly promoted to the top division, whilst Greenwood Meadows, who have been with the League for a number of seasons, finished in second place and are also promoted.

The Reserves Divisions titles went to Sneinton Reserves (Premier Division) and Holbrook Reserves (Reserve Division One) and Holbrook also won the Reserves Cup.

Six new clubs will be joining the League for season 2001-02, so this will further extend Stan's handy work at the end of next season. How fortunate we are as a league to have such a 'professional' and talented person to make us the envy of other leagues in our level of football.

Frank Harwood, League Chairman/General Secretary

FINAL LEAGUE TABLES 2000-01

TRAVIS PERKINS SUPREME DIVISION

	P	*W*	*D*	*L*	*F*	*A*	*Pts*
Shirebrook Town	38	27	8	3	96	29	89
Lincoln Moorlands	38	27	8	3	78	28	89
Sneinton	38	22	4	12	79	54	70
South Normanton Ath	38	20	8	10	95	57	68
Collingham	38	19	7	12	76	52	64
Clipstone Welfare	38	18	8	12	77	52	62
Long Eaton United	38	19	5	14	73	56	62
Graham Street Prims	38	19	4	15	77	58	61
Selston	38	17	10	11	68	59	61
Dunkirk	38	17	8	13	71	69	59
Holbrook	38	18	3	17	66	62	57
Hucknall Rolls	38	17	6	15	64	65	57
Welbeck Miners Welf.	38	12	9	17	56	66	45
Kimberley Town	38	13	4	21	65	78	43
Nettleham	38	11	9	18	58	65	42
Heanor Town	38	12	6	20	59	89	42
Sandiacre Town	38	11	4	23	72	87	37
Mickleover Royal B L	38	7	5	26	50	103	26
Blackwell Miners Welf.	38	6	6	26	55	102	24
Harworth Colliery Inst.	38	4	6	28	34	138	18

R & R SCAFFOLDING PREMIER DIVISION

	P	*W*	*D*	*L*	*F*	*A*	*Pts*
North Notts	32	22	4	6	96	33	70
Greenwood Meadows	32	21	5	6	75	31	68
Bottesford Town	32	20	5	7	89	49	65
Askern Welfare	32	19	6	7	75	39	63
Teversal	32	18	8	6	84	47	62
Dinnington Town	32	15	8	9	61	52	53
Ripley Town	32	15	5	12	90	61	50
Thorne Colliery	32	14	6	12	58	57	48
Radford	32	12	8	12	51	49	44
Shardlow St James	32	13	5	14	63	64	44
Ollerton Town	32	10	8	14	51	55	38
Forest Town	32	9	7	16	46	77	34
Blidworth Welfare	32	9	6	17	46	71	33
Kiveton Park	32	8	8	16	54	84	32
Stanton Ilkeston	32	8	6	18	46	67	30
Yorkshire Main	32	6	4	22	42	104	22
Mexborough Town Ath	32	2	3	27	31	118	9

FINAL LEAGUE TABLES 2000-01

RESERVE PREMIER DIVISION

	P	W	D	L	F	A	Pts
Sneinton	24	14	6	4	59	32	48
Worksop Town A	24	14	5	5	69	36	47
Sandiacre Town	24	13	5	6	62	38	44
Clipstone Welfare	24	13	3	8	52	46	42
Graham Street Prims	24	13	2	9	48	44	41
Long Eaton United	24	13	2	9	58	58	41
Dunkirk	24	12	3	9	50	52	39
Selston	24	10	4	10	52	38	34
Heanor Town	24	8	4	12	46	60	28
Shirebrook Town	24	7	5	12	47	55	26
Hucknall Rolls	24	8	2	14	44	56	26
Kimberley Town	24	5	3	16	47	76	18
Radford	24	2	4	18	31	74	10

TRAVIS PERKINS SUPREME DIVISION RESULTS CHART 2000-01

		1	2	3	4	5	6	7	8	9	10	11	12	13	14	15	16	17	18	19	20
1	Blackwell M W	X	4-5	0-1	2-5	3-1	2-4	1-4	1-3	1-1	2-3	0-6	4-3	0-2	0-0	2-1	0-3	1-2	0-3	0-3	1-1
2	Clipstone Welfare	4-1	X	0-3	1-3	1-3	4-0	2-2	0-1	4-2	2-0	1-2	0-0	3-0	2-1	2-1	2-2	1-1	4-2	3-1	1-0
3	Collingham	2-1	0-0	X	1-1	4-1	4-0	2-2	1-0	2-0	1-3	0-2	1-0	4-1	1-1	5-1	4-1	1-3	0-2	2-4	2-1
4	Dunkirk	3-1	0-0	1-5	X	1-2	6-1	5-1	1-5	1-3	3-1	2-0	2-1	0-1	1-1	1-6	4-0	2-1	1-3	0-2	1-1
5	Graham St Prims	2-1	1-0	5-1	3-2	X	1-1	3-1	0-1	1-0	1-2	2-3	2-3	2-0	5-0	3-2	1-4	0-1	0-1	1-2	3-1
6	Harworth Coll. Inst.	0-5	1-12	1-1	2-5	0-0	X	2-1	1-3	0-2	1-5	0-2	2-2	0-3	2-2	2-7	1-2	0-6	0-2	1-5	1-5
7	Heanor Town	0-3	0-4	1-5	2-2	0-4	0-1	X	0-3	3-0	5-2	0-1	2-0	2-1	0-3	2-1	1-1	1-4	3-4	2-6	0-0
8	Holbrook	0-1	3-0	2-1	5-0	2-1	2-1	4-1	X	2-3	0-1	1-3	1-5	2-2	2-4	4-0	1-3	1-2	1-2	1-4	1-0
9	Hucknall Rolls	4-3	2-1	0-3	1-1	2-1	5-0	1-2	2-1	X	2-1	2-3	3-1	0-2	4-2	2-3	2-3	0-0	1-0	2-1	0-0
10	Kimberley Town	5-1	2-0	4-0	0-2	1-2	2-0	0-4	2-2	1-3	X	1-2	1-5	3-2	1-5	4-0	1-2	1-3	1-2	1-1	1-2
11	Lincoln Moorlands	6-0	1-1	1-0	1-2	0-0	7-1	2-1	5-0	2-1	3-2	X	2-0	2-1	1-1	1-0	2-1	0-0	1-1	0-0	3-0
12	Long Eaton Utd	2-1	1-2	4-2	0-1	0-3	5-2	3-0	2-4	5-3	3-0	0-1	X	4-0	4-2	1-1	1-2	1-0	1-0	2-2	2-0
13	Mickleover RBL	2-2	1-8	1-1	2-2	2-4	2-1	1-3	2-0	0-4	0-2	0-1	1-4	X	1-0	2-4	0-5	2-4	1-1	3-4	1-2
14	Nettleham	3-3	1-2	0-1	1-3	5-2	1-0	1-2	0-2	3-0	1-0	0-0	1-2	5-3	X	2-1	5-0	0-0	0-3	1-0	0-2
15	Sandiacre Town	5-1	0-1	1-4	0-1	2-3	8-0	2-1	1-2	0-1	2-2	0-3	0-1	4-2	4-1	X	1-0	0-3	2-3	1-1	3-2
16	Selston	2-1	2-1	0-3	5-1	1-1	1-3	1-1	0-0	0-0	3-2	1-2	1-2	5-3	0-0	3-3	X	0-4	2-0	3-0	3-1
17	Shirebrook Town	1-0	3-0	2-1	4-0	3-2	2-2	3-2	2-3	6-2	3-0	3-0	3-0	7-0	2-1	3-1	1-1	X	2-1	2-0	4-0
18	Sneinton	5-3	1-2	0-3	2-1	1-3	6-0	2-3	3-1	5-1	2-0	0-0	1-2	2-0	3-1	5-2	3-2	0-0	X	0-5	3-0
19	Sth Nomanton Ath	2-2	3-0	2-1	2-4	2-1	9-0	0-2	3-0	1-1	3-3	2-3	3-1	4-2	4-2	6-1	0-2	2-2	2-4	X	1-0
20	Welbeck Miners W	3-1	1-1	3-3	0-0	2-7	1-0	8-2	2-0	0-1	3-4	1-4	0-0	2-1	2-1	5-1	1-1	0-4	3-1	1-3	X

R & R SCAFFOLDING PREMIER DIVISION RESULTS CHART 2000-01

		1	2	3	4	5	6	7	8	9	10	11	12	13	14	15	16	17
1	Askern Welfare	X	2-0	2-2	2-2	4-1	2-1	1-2	2-1	1-2	3-1	2-0	0-1	1-0	1-1	1-3	2-0	3-0
2	Blidworth Welfare	2-3	X	0-1	2-3	3-1	1-4	3-1	2-0	0-1	1-3	1-6	0-5	1-5	0-3	0-3	5-2	0-4
3	Bottesford Town	1-4	2-1	X	2-2	6-0	2-1	8-3	3-2	3-1	1-1	3-0	2-1	2-0	1-1	1-2	2-1	8-1
4	Dinnington Town	1-5	3-1	0-3	X	3-1	0-1	3-1	4-1	2-3	2-0	2-1	1-1	3-0	2-2	1-6	1-1	1-2
5	Forest Town	3-5	0-2	2-5	0-0	X	2-2	2-2	3-0	0-0	1-0	0-0	5-3	0-3	2-1	5-3	1-3	2-0
6	Greenwood Mdws	1-0	0-0	3-1	0-2	2-1	X	2-3	2-1	1-0	1-1	1-1	0-0	3-0	5-0	4-1	6-1	5-0
7	Kiveton Park	4-2	1-2	0-2	1-3	4-0	2-6	X	5-1	0-9	5-3	1-1	1-3	1-1	1-2	0-4	0-1	2-2
8	Mexborough Tn Ath	0-7	2-4	0-9	1-4	0-3	0-7	1-1	X	1-7	2-1	2-5	0-6	0-5	1-2	1-2	2-5	2-3
9	North Notts	4-0	2-1	4-2	2-1	5-0	2-1	2-2	6-0	X	1-0	4-1	0-2	5-1	4-2	2-2	2-0	8-0
10	Ollerton Town	1-4	2-2	3-1	3-0	2-2	1-2	3-0	2-0	1-1	X	0-2	4-3	2-3	2-1	1-2	0-1	3-1
11	Radford	1-1	1-1	1-1	2-2	0-2	2-1	4-2	0-0	2-5	5-0	X	2-1	2-1	1-0	1-2	1-3	3-0
12	Ripley Town	1-5	6-1	7-2	0-2	1-2	1-2	1-4	0-0	3-0	2-1	2-0	X	6-1	5-2	3-5	3-3	7-2
13	Shardlow St James	1-1	1-1	1-3	5-3	3-0	1-3	2-2	3-1	0-2	3-5	2-0	2-3	X	1-0	3-5	2-1	5-0
14	Stanton Ilkeston	0-2	0-3	0-3	0-2	1-1	1-2	0-2	4-2	0-4	2-2	3-1	4-3	2-4	X	2-3	3-2	1-2
15	Teversal	2-2	1-3	4-2	2-2	4-1	1-2	6-0	5-1	2-0	1-1	0-1	3-1	1-1	0-0	X	1-1	2-2
16	Thorne Colliery	0-2	2-2	0-2	1-2	4-1	0-2	0-0	5-2	1-0	0-2	4-2	5-5	2-0	3-1	1-0	X	3-2
17	Yorkshire Main	0-3	1-1	1-3	0-2	6-2	1-2	4-1	1-4	1-8	0-0	0-2	1-4	3-1	0-5	1-6	1-2	X

COX ACCOMMODATION LEAGUE CUP 2000-01

FIRST ROUND

Blidworth Welfare	v	Ollerton Town	0-1
Greenwood Meadows	v	Thorne Colliery	0-1
Nettleham	v	Holbrook	1-0
Dunkirk	v	Graham St Prims	3-2
Mexborough T Ath	v	Sth Normanton Ath	2-4
Ripley Town	v	Shardlow St James	0-3

SECOND ROUND

Blackwell Miners W	v	Lincoln Moorlands	0-3
Clipstone Welfare	v	Ollerton Town	3-1
Dunkirk	v	Heanor Town	2-4
Kiveton Park	v	Shirebrook Town	0-3
Nettleham	v	Hucknall Rolls	4-5
Sandiacre Town	v	Welbeck Miners Welf.	1-3
South Normanton Ath	v	Sneinton	3-1
Thorne Colliery	v	Forest Town	1-2
Bottesford Town	v	Shardlow St James	2-1
Collingham	v	Harworth Coll. Inst.	6-1
Kimberley Town	v	Grantham Rangers	6-0
Mickleover RBL	v	Askern Welfare	1-2
Radford	v	Long Eaton United	1-4
Selston	v	North Notts	1-0
Stanton Ilkeston	v	Dinnington Town	0-2
Yorkshire Main	v	Teversal	3-4

THIRD ROUND

Collingham	v	Kimberley Town	1-1, 3-1
Forest Town	v	Bottesford Town	0-2
Long Eaton United	v	Askern Welfare	6-0
South Normanton Ath	v	Heanor Town	8-0
Dinnington Town	v	Clipstone Welfare	1-3
Lincoln Moorlands	v	Hucknall Rolls	4-1
Selston	v	Teversal	0-1
Welbeck Miners W.	v	Shirebrook Town	2-5

FOURTH ROUND

Collingham	v	Bottesford Town	2-1
Shirebrook Town	v	Lincoln Moorlands	2-1
Long Eaton United	v	Clipstone Welfare	2*1
Teversal	v	Sth Normanton Ath	2*4

SEMI FINALS

Collingham	v	S Normanton Ath	0*0, 2p4
Long Eaton United	v	Shirebrook Town	1-3

FINAL

Collingham v Shirebrook Town 0-1 at Alfreton Town FC

READY MIXED CONCRETE RESERVE LEAGUE CUP 2000-01

SEMI FINALS

Dunkirk	v	Holbrook	0-2
Selston	v	Shirebrook Town	6*3

FINAL

Holbrook v Selston 2-0 at Long Eaton United FC

LEADING GOALSCORERS 2000-01

TRAVIS PERKINS SUPREME DIVISION

M Dickinson	Sneinton	29
S Dillon	Clipstone Welfare	28
L Widdowson	Shirebrook Town	27
L Grant	Graham Street Prims	26
D Brocklehurst	South Normanton Athletic	23
P Gretton	Graham Street Prims	19
R Wooldridge	Kimberley Town	16
G Davies	Harworth Colliery Institute	15
G Stacey	Long Eaton Utd/Heanor Town	15
D Dye	Nettleham	15
G Kelly	Sandiacre Town	15
M Eade	Collingham	14
J Newton	Holbrook	14
M Downing	Blackwell Miners Welfare	13
S Orr	Holbrook	13
P Tomlin	Kimberley Town	13
R Clarke	Welbeck Miners Welfare	13

R & R SCAFFOLDING PREMIER DIVISION

G Knight	Bottesford Town	35
K Mabon	Ripley Town	34
L Cartledge	Dinnington Town	26
D Short	North Notts	25
S Hutchinson	Teversal	24
J Slinger	Shardlow St James	23
A Woodcock	North Notts	20
R Walker	North Notts	19
D Spencer	Greenwood Meadows	18
C Booth	Ollerton Town	18
S Parker	Askern Welfare	17
G Evans	Bottesford Town	17
C Cockerill	Teversal	16
T Hattersley	Askern Welfare	15
M Clarke	Blidworth Welfare	15
S Gomm	Stanton Ilkeston	14
S Duckinfield	Yorkshire Main	12

ASKERN WELFARE

Secretary: Jon Stewart, 43 Sutton Road, Askern, Doncaster S.Yorks. DN6 0AG
Tel Nos: 01302 702502 (H) 01302 703035 (W)

Ground: Askern Welfare Sports Ground, Doncaster Road, Askern,Doncaster
Tel: 01302 700957.

Directions: A1/A639 Pontefract. Follow sign for Askern/Campsall.At T-junction turn right. Left at Anne Arms, right at Supersave, ground on right.

Colours: Black & white stripes/black/black
Change colours: All Red with white trim
Midweek Matchday: Wednesday

Manager: Paul Curtis

BOTTESFORD TOWN

Secretary: Jim Swan, 36 Cliff Drive, Burton-on-Stather, nr Scunthorpe, N. Lincs. DN15 9HW
Tel: 01724 720474 (H) 01724 858661 (B)

Ground: Birch Park, Ontario Road, Bottesford, Scunthorpe, N. Lincs.
Tel: 01724 871833

Directions: Exit M180 via M181 - Scunthorpe. At r'about right into Scotter Road. Over next r'about then 2nd left into South Park Rd., on to Sunningdale Rd. Right into Goodwood Rd, ground at end.

Colours: Blue & yellow/navy/yellow & navy
Change: Orange & Black

Manager: Alan Wilson

CLIPSTONE WELFARE

Secretary: Barry Clarke, 40 Church Road, Clipstone, Mansfield, NG21 9DG (01623640829).
Ground & Directions: Clipstone Lido Ground Clipstone Road West, Mansfield,Notts (01632 655674). B6030 from Mansfield, between Forest Town & Clipstone, on left entering Clipstone.
Capacity: 3000 **Seats:** 90 **Cover:** 200 **Floodlights:** No **Club Shop:** No
Honours: Notts Snr Cup 85-86 94-95, Notts Alliance 72-73 73-74 74-75 92-93 94-95 (Lg Cup 72-73 73-74 74-75 94-95 (R-up 92-93)), Notts I'mediate Cup 55-56. Central Midlands Premier Championship 94-95 96-97

Founded 1927
Colours: Black & white,black,black
Change Colours: Amber & navy/navy/amber
Midweek Matchday: Tuesday or Wednesday
Programme: Yes

Chairman: Gordon Costall
Manager: Peter Burns

COLLINGHAM

Secretary: Darren Goivannetti, 34 Armstrong Road, Retford, Notts DN22 6QY
Tel No: 01777 705893
Ground & Directions: Collingham FC, Station Road, Collingham, Newark, Notts. (01636 892303) Take A46 Newark to Lincoln road (Newark bypass). Turn left into Collingham on the A1133 road. In village turn right at traffic lights.Ground 100 yards on left.

Colours:Yellow & Black.
Change Colours: Blue & white/blue/blue
Midweek Matchday: Tuesday

Manager: Paul Hyde

DUNKIRK

Secretary: Steve Trossell, 24 Kingfisher Wharf, Castle Marina, Nottingham NG71GA (0115 9473903 or 07930 806891
Ground & Directions: The Ron Steel Sports Ground, Trentside Farm, Clifton Bridge, Nottingham (0115 9850803). Ring Road - Clifton Bridge (North End),Ind Estate, Lenton Lane.
Honours: FA Vase 5th Rd 93-94; Cen Mid Sup Div R-up 96-97, Prem Div R-up 95-96,KO Cup 97-98; Notts Alliance Div 1 84-85, Div 2 82-83, Lg Cup R-up 84-85; Notts I'mediate Cup 83-4
Capacity:1,500 **Seats:** No **Cover**: 200 **Floodlights**: Yes **Shop:** No **Clubhouse:** Yes
Record Attendance: 821 v Tiverton Town, F.A.Vase 5th Rd 93-94

Founded: 1946
Colours: Red/black/black
Change Colours: Black & whitestripes/white/red
Midweek Matchday: Tuesday
Programme : Yes
Chairman: Dave Howes
Manager: Andy Freeman
Assistant Manager: Kevin Marsh
Players Progressing: Roger Willis and Matthew McKemzie (Grimsby T)

GRAHAM STREET PRIMS

Secretary: Mrs E Wright, 6 Athol Close, Sinfin Moor, Derby DE24 9LZ
Tel: 01332 606837 (H) 01332 340131 x6855 (B)

Ground: Asterdale Sports Centre, Borrowash Road, Spondon, nr Derby. Tel: 01332 668656
Directions: M1 Junc 25, take A52 to Derby. 3rd left Borrowash Road - golf driving range on left, approx 400m further turn left into Asterdale Sports Centre. Ground at rear.
Capacity: 1,000 Seats: No Cover: Yes Floodlights: No Club shop: No Clubhouse: No

Formed: 1904
Colours: Red & white stripes/black/black
Change Colours: White/navy/navy
Midweek Matchday: Tuesday
Programme: Yes

Manager: Martin Spoonerr

Shirebrook Town FC. Back Row (l-r): Craig Shaw, Steve Hill, Craig Charlesworth, Gavin Saxby, Tony Starkey, Jordan Johnson, Justin Burdett. Front Row: Ady Carter, Martin Rowbottom, Simon Johnson, Graham Elgie, Craig Tansley, Lee Widdowson, Chris Darby. Photo: Bill Wheatcroft

Kimberley Town's Andy Daykin rushes in to beat the South Normanton player Richard Coleman to the ball. Photo: Bill Wheatcroft

Lincoln Moorlands. Photo: Lincolnshire Echo

GREENWOOD MEADOWS

Secretary: Brian Hall, 34 Sullivan Close, Marmion Estate, St Ann's, NottinghamNG3 2HX
Tel: 0115 958 2459

Ground: Greenwood Meadows, Lenton Lane, Clifton, Nottingham.
Tel: 0115 986 5913

Directions: M1 Junc 24 take A453Nottingham-Clifton Bridge to Lenton Ind Estate.
Left into Old Lenton Lane.Ground second on right on lane.

Colours: Green & white/green/green
Change:Red & black.black/black

Managers: Brian Cawthorn & Chris Nicholson

HEANOR TOWN

Secretary: Keith Costello, 45 Stainsby Avenue, Heanor, Derbys. DE75 7EL(01773 719446).
Ground & Directions: The Town Ground, Mayfield Avenue, Heanor (01773713742/715815). M1 (J26), take A610 onto A608, ground 200yds from Market Square
Capacity: 3,000 and new stand being built `**Cover:** 1,000+ new stand **Floodlights:** Yes
Honours: Central Midlands League Cup 94-95 (Runners-up 86-87 92-93, B E Webbe Removals Cup 88-89), West Midlands Reg. League Runners-up 72-73; Midland Co's League Runners-up 65-66 67-68; Derbys Senior Cup(9) 1892-94 1946-47 65-69 70-7178-79; FA Cup 1st Rd 58-59 63-64.Central Midlands Supreme Champions:94-5,96-7 Central All.Lg(2) R-up4

Nickname: The Lions
Colours: Black& white stripes/black/black
Midweek Matchday: Wednesday
Programme: 32pages 50p
Press Officer & Editor: Stan Wilton
(01332 880199)
Club House: On ground.Hot food (match days)
Chairman: John McCulloch
Manager: John Slater

HOLBROOK

Secretary: Stevan Broadhurst, 35 Laund Hill, Belper, Derbys. DE56 1FH Tel: 01773 821483
Ground: The Welfare Ground, Shaw Lane, Holbrook, Derbyshire Tel: 07932 930298
Directions: From A38 take B6179 for Kilburn, turn left at lights for Belper. 1mile on left at Bulls Head for Holbrook. 2 miles on turn right at Venturegarage into Shaws Lane.
Capacity: 1,000 **Seats:** None **Cover:** 250 **Floodlights:** No
Clubhouse: Holbrook Miners Welfare, Shaw Lane.(01332 880259) Shop: No
Honours: Central Midlands Premier Division 99-00

Founded: 1996
Nickname: The Brookies
Colours: Blue & white/blue/blue&white
Change: Red & white/red/red
Midweek Matchday:Wednesday
Programme: Yes / 24pages 50price

Chairman: T.B.A.
Manager: Mark Webster

HUCKNALL ROLLS

Secretary: Peter Williams, 38 Tiverton Close, Hucknall, Nottingham NG15 6JT
Tel: 0115 956 33691
Ground & Directions: Rolls Royce Sports & Social Club, Watnall Road, Hucknall Notts (0115 963 0134). M1 Junc 27. Follow sign A611 to Hucknall. Turn right onto by-pass. 2nd r/about turn right on to Watnall Road. Take 2nd left after fire station on R.R. Sports Ground.
Capacity: 1,000 **Cover:** yes **Floodlights**: No **Clubhouse:** Social Club always open with food

Colours: Yellow,Blue,Blue
Change colours: Blue,black,black
Midweek Matchday: Wednesday
Programme: yes

Chairman: Darryl Claypole
Manager: Roger Dawkins & Wayne Lear
Reserves: Peter Needham & Paul Hopkins

KIMBERLEY TOWN

General Manager: Brian Harrison **Press Officer:** Richard Jayes
Match Secretary: Alan Jennings, 8 Watchwood Grove, Calverton, Nottingham NG146HX
Tel: 0115 965 6100
Ground & Stag Ground, Nottingham Road, Kimberley Tel: 0115 938 2788.
Directions: Thro' Nuthall from M1 J 26 to Kimberley, ground entrance 150 yds after Stag Inn.
Capacity: 2,500 Seats: None Cover: 150 Floodlights: Yes
Clubhouse: Evenings (Except Sun) & matchdays. Hot & cold snacks available
Honours: Notts Amateur Lg Div 1 54-55, Central Alliance Div 2 R-up 57-58.

Nickname: Stags
Colours: All Blue
Change colours: All Yellow
Midweek Matchday: Tuesday
Programme: 40 pages 50p
Editor: George Brown
Chairman: George Giddens
Vice Chairman: Reg Izzard
President: Russell Penney
Manager: Julian Garmston

LONG EATON UNITED

Secretary: David Hampson, 4 Airedale Close, Long Eaton, Nottingham. NG10 3HW(0115-9726343. **Ground & Directions:** Grange Park, Station Road, Long Eaton, Nottingham (01159735700). M1 Junc 25, take A52 towards Nottingham, to island by `Bardills Garden Centre', left onto B6003 to t/lights. Turn right A453 and take 2nd left into Station Rd. Entrance on left opposite the Speedway Stadium
Capacity: 5,000 Seats: None Cover: 500 Floodlights: Yes Shop: No
Clubhouse: Open matchdays, snacks available Record Attendance: 2,000 1973 FA Cup
Honours: Derbys Snr Cup 64-65 75-76, Midland Co's Lg R-up 76-77, Central Alliance Div South 58-59, Northern Co's (East) Div 1 South 84-85.

Founded: 1956 Nickname: Blues
Sponsor: Beeston Suite Co
Colours: Blue & black/black/black
Change colours: Yellow/green/blue
Midweek Matchday: Tuesday
Programme: 20 pages 50p
Editor: G Whitehead
Chairman: J C Fairley
Manager: John Bartlett
Physio: John Burns

NETTLEHAM

Secretary: John Wilson, 21 Chancer Drive, Lincoln LN2 4LN (01522 884051).
Ground & Directions: Mulsanne Park, Field Close, Nettleham (01522 750007). A46approx. 3 miles north of Lincoln, right at Brown Cow Pub, proceed past Church2nd turning on right, ground at end

Honours: Central Mids Lg Premier Division Cup R-up 87-88, Village Tphy, Nursing Cup, Kelly Read Cup, Blankney Hunt Cup, Lincoln & Dist. Amtr Cup R-up, Joe Miller Tphy(2).

Colours: Lighgt blue/navy blue/b lue
Change Colours: yellow & navy blue.
Midweek Matchday: Tuesday

Manager: Ian Musson

NORTH NOTTS

Secretary: Shaun Breen, 1 Loundhouse Close, Skegby, Sutton-in-Ashfield, Notts. NG17 3LA
Tel: 01623 461166 (H)

Ground: Mansfield Hosiery Mills, Huthwaite Road, Sutton-in-Ashfield, Notts. NG17 3LA
Tel: 01623 552376
Directions: M1 Jct. 28 - A38 towards Mansfield. Take the A38 at Kings Mill Island, 1st left (Sutton sign), then 1st rt into Hosiery Mills ground.

Colours: Royal blue, yellow trim/royal blue, yellow trim/royal blue
Change: White, purple & green trim

Joint Managers:
Les McJannett & Kevin Gee

SANDIACRE TOWN

Secretary: Mel Williams, 38 Pasture Rd.,Stapleford, Nottingham NG9 8GL Tel: 0115 9174079
Ground: St Giles Park, Stanton Road, Sandiacre, Nottingham NG105EP Tel:0115 9392880.
Directions: M1 jct 25, follow signs to Sandiacre passing Post House on right, straight over crossroads into Rushy Lane and towards Stanton Rd, 1st right after 1000yds into Stanton Rd, ground at bottom after another1000yds. Web: www.homepage@Hworld.com/sandiacretownfc
Capacity: 2,000 Seats: None Cover: 250 Floodlights: Yes Shop: No
Clubhouse: Members Club 8-11pm. Sunday lunch, Saturday1.30-11pm. Snacks available
Honours: Central Mids Lg Premier Div 92-93 (Lg Cup 92-93), Midlands Regional Alliance R-up 91-92, Central Mids Lge Cup R-up 95-96.

Founded: 1978 Nickname: Saints
Cols:Red/navy/red Change: Yellow/sky/yellow
Midweek Matchday: Tuesday
Programme: 44 pages 50p
Ed.i/Press Off: Mel Williams (0115 917 4079)
Manager: Tony Roe Asst Man: Richard Daft
2000-01 Leading goalscorer: Gary Kelly 15
Captain: Danny Hale
P.o.Y.: Ross Whalin

SELSTON

Secretary: Alan Jones, 6 Derwent Drive, Selston, Nott NG16 6QU (01773 580436)

Ground: Mansfield Hosiery Mills Sports Ground, Mansfield Road, Sutton in Ashfield, Notts (01623 552376).

Directions: M1 junc 28, take A38 Mansfield, passthrough 7 sets of lights to island (Kings Mill Hospital), ground opositeMcDonalds on left

Colours:
Black & white/black & blue/black & white
Change Colours:
Yellow & green/sky/yellow & green

Manager: Wayne Bradley

SHIREBROOK TOWN

Secretary: Steve Wall, 26 Carter Lane West, Shirebrook, Mansfield, Notts NG208NA (01623 747638).
Ground & Directions: BRSA Sports Ground, Langwith Rd, Shirebrook, Mansfield(01623 742535). M1 jct 29, A617 to Mansfield, 2.5 miles, onto B6407 to Shirebrook, through town to Langwith Rd. Clubhouse with refreshments at the ground.
Capacity: 2,000 **Seata:** None **Cover:** 400 **Floodlights:** Yes **Club Shop:**No
Honours: Central Midlands Lg Res Prem Div 94-95 95-96. Floodlit Cup winners 97-98
Most Appearances for club: G.Quincey 262

Founded 1985
Colours: All Red & black
Change Colours: Blue & black/blue/blue
Midweek Matchday: Tuesday
Prog Editor: Mr Sharnworth (01623 748 375)

Chairman: Mr S.T. Brown (01623 743661)
Managers: S Greenwood, G Charlesworth

SNEINTON

Secretary: Albert Graves, 32 Shelford Road, Gedling, Nottingham NG4 4HW (01159878185)

Ground & Directions: Stoke Lane Gedling, Nottingham, A612 Nottingham to Southwell Road. Stoke Lane is situated off A612 between Gedling & Burton Joyce(signed Stoke Bardolph). Ground 200 yards on left over level crossing. BR. Nearest Station is Carlton.
Capacity: 1000 **Seats:** None **Cover:** 100 **Floodlights:** No **Club Shop:** No
Clubhouse: No but snacks at Tea Bar.

Founded: 1904
Colours: Blue & black/black/black
Change Colours: All Red
Midweek Matchday: Tuesday
Programme: Yes

Chairman: John W Stokeld
Manager: Tom Brookbanks

SOUTH NORMANTON ATHLETIC

Secretary: Lindon davison, 5 The Brockwell, Broadmeadows, South Normanton, Alfreton, Derbys. DE55 3BA Tel Nos: 01773 510380 (H) 07930 233210 (W)

Ground & Directions: South Normanton Athletic FC, Lees Lane, South Normanton,Derby (01773 581491). M1 Junc 28, B6019 towards South Normanton, right after 1mile (in South Normanton) at BP garage into Market Street, after quarter mile turn left immediately after The Clock pub into Lees Lane, ground at bottom on right. (Food available on matchdays)

Capacity: 3000 **Seats:** 150 **Cover:** 300 **Floodlights**:Yes

Clubhouse Yes - open on matchdays **Club Shop:** No

Formed: 1875
Colours: Yellow/navy/yellow
Change colours: Black & white/black/white
Programme: Yes - The Shiner
Midweek Matchday: Tuesday

Chairman: Glindon Davison
Manager: Rob Aitkin

TEVERSAL

Secretary: Kevin Newton, 8 Vere Ave., Sutton in Ashfield, Notts NG17 2ES
Tel: 01623 461145

Ground: Teversal Grange Country Inn, Carnarvon Street, Teversal, Sutton-in-Ashfield, Notts.
Tel: 01623 442021

Directions: M1, J28, A38 towards Mansfield. At r'about take A6075 Mansfield Woodhouse.
Next lights left B6014, Stanton Hill. At r'about take A6014 Tibshelf.
2nd on right Carnarvon St., ground at the top.

Colours: Red & black/red
Change: Blue & white stripes/ white/white

Managers: John Courtie

Stanton-Ilkeston Photo: Gordon Whittington

Shirebrook Town, Central Midlands League Cup Winners. Photo: Bill Wheatcroft

BARTON TOWN OLD BOYS

Secretary: Peter Mitchell, 56 Brigg Rd., Barton-on-Humber, North Lincs. DN18 5DR Tel: 01682 632382 (H) 07900 105204 (M)
Ground: Marsh Lane Football Ground, Marsh Lane, Barton-on-Humber, North Lincs. Tel: 07900 105204 (Secretary's Mobile)
Directions: Approaching from south on A15, Barton is the last exit before Humber Bridge. Follow A1077 into town. Right at mini r'about, at bottom of hill onto 'Holydyke'. 2nd left onto George St., then into King St. Marsh Lane is opp. junction of King St. & High St.
Colours: Light blue/dark blue/dark blue **Change colours:** Red & black stripes/black/black **Manager:** Leigh Palin

BENTLEY COLLIERY

Secretary: James P Tooth, 38 East St., Darfield, Barnsley, South Yorks. S73 9AE Tel: 01226 754012 (H/Fax)
Ground: Bentley Miners' Welfare, The Avenue, Bentley, Doncaster, S. Yorks. Tel: 01302 874420 **Directions:** North from Doncaster on A19: Selby Road. In Bentley turn right at mini r'about on Arksey Lane. Left at shops onto The Avenue and the ground is 60 yards on left.
Colours: White & claret/blue/blue **Change colours:** Yellow & red stripes/red/red **Manager:** Roy Butterworth

BLACKWELL MINERS WELFARE

Secretary: Steve Harris, 6 Pennine Close, Newton, Alfreton, Derbys DE55 5UD. Tel: 01773 779172(H) 01246 501561(W) 01773 779173 (F)
Email: steve-harris@bdrmg.co.uk Club Website: www.blackwellmwfc.org.uk - Club Email: manor@globalnet.co.uk
Ground: Welfare Ground, Primrose Hill, Blackwell, Derbyshire DE55 5JE. Tel: 01773 811295. **Directions:** M1 Junc 28, A38 towards Mansfield, left onto B6406, left again at Hilcote Arms, ground 1 mile on left just past Miners Welfare. Matchday Tel: 07890 198776
Colours: Red & white stripes/red/red **Change cols:** Green/white/green **Midweek Matchday:** Wednesday **Manager:** Trevor Hammond
2000-01 Leading Goalscorer: Mark Downing 14 Captain: Garron Haslam P.o.Y. : Alan Jepson

BLIDWORTH WELFARE

Secretary: Graham Jackson, 46 Westbrook Drive,Rainworth,Notts NG21 0FB tel No: 01623 554444
Ground: Welfare Ground, Mansfield Rd, Blidworth, Mansfield (01623 793361). **Directions:** On B6020, Rainworth side of Blidworth. From M1 jct 27 take A608 to Kirby at lights follow A611 to Kirby then take B6020through Ravenshead to Blidworth -thru village and up hill ground on right. From A1 follow A614 /A617 to Rainworth, left at lights then 1st right on to B6020 to Blidworth - ground on left at top of hill.
Colours: Orange/black/orange **Change colours:** Blue&red/blue/blue. **Manager:** Rudi Funk

DINNINGTON TOWN

Secretary: Jon Paul Wilson, Whitewalls Farm, Swinston Hill Road, Dinnington, Sheffield S25 2RY Tel: 01909 - 569977 (H) 500050 (B)
Ground: Laughton Road, Dinnington. Tel: 0771 3460150
Directions: M1 J31 onto A57 towards Worksop. At 1st lights turn left to Dinnington. Follow road into town centre and the ground is on the left.
Colours: Yellow/black/black **Change**: Green & Black/white/white **Manager:** Steve Toyne

FOREST TOWN

Secretary: Jan Nieloojadio, 14 Bransdale Avenue, Forest Town, Mansfield, Notts. NG19 0LZ Tel No: 01623 648588
Ground: Forest Town Welfare Sports Ground, Clipstone Rd West, Forest Town, Mansfield, Notts. Tel: 01623 624678
Directions: From Mansfield follow signs for Clipstone/Forest Town. The ground is situated at the Mansfield end of Forest Town on the right.
Colours: All red **Change Colours:** All white **Manager:** P.Craggs

G.A.D. KHALSA SPORTS

Secretary: Karnijit Singh Khatkar, 29 Cloverdale Drive, Sinfin, Derby DE24 3JP
Tel: 01332 607380 (H) 07973 640230 (B) email: gadkhalsa@hotmail.com
Ground: The Wharf, Shardlow, Derby. Tel: 01332 799135 (Matchday only) **Directions:** M1 J24 on to A6 Derby road. Into Shardlow past garage. Right at corner paper shop of wharf. Down to village hall. Ground adjacent.
Colours: Orange/black/orange **Change colours:** Gold & blue/navy/navy **Manager:** Roy Garratt

HARWORTH COLLIERY INSTITUTE

Secretary: Tom Brogan, 30 Lindsey Road, Harworth, Doncaster, Sth Yorks DN11 8QH Tel: 01302 750132.
Ground: Recreation Ground, Scrooby Rd, Bircotes, Doncaster Tel: 01302 750614.
Directions: Off A1(M) at Blyth, head towards Bawtry for approx 2 miles, 3rd left, ground in village at top of hill on left. Or, from Doncaster to Bawtry then head for A1(M) and turn left after caravan site - ground at top of hill.
Colours: Amber & black/black/amber & black **Change Cols:** Red & blue/red/red **Midweek Matchday:** Wednesday **Manager:** Alan Needham

KIVETON PARK

Secretary: Kevin Hull,3 Chapel way, Kiveton Park, Sheffield S26 6QTTel No: 01909 772152
Ground: Hard Lane, Kiveton Park, Sheffield. Tel: 0797 4247074. **Directions:** M1 Junct. 31. Take A57 Worksop road, first right to Todwick, at T junct. turn right. Follow road to Kiveton crossroads. Go over and ground is on right after approx 100m.
Colours: All red.. **Change Colours:**: Blue & black stripe/black/black **Manager:** Stuart Holmes

KIRKBY TOWN

Secretary: David Howard, 20 Park St., Kirkby-in-Ashfield, Notts NG17 8EB Tel: 01623 457623 (H) email: davejulie@talk21.com
Ground: East Kirkby Summit Centre, Low Moor Rd., Kirkby-in-Ashfield Tel: 01623 751822 **Directions:** M1 J28 towards Mansfield on A38. Through 4 sets of lights right at 5th. Right again at next lights, across 2 mini r'abouts then 2nd left into Pavillion Rd. Ground off.
Colours: White, green trim/green/green. **Change colours:** Orange & black quarters/black/orange. **Manager:** John Dawn

OLLERTON TOWN

Gen. Secretary: Colin Gibson MBE, 10 Manor Close, Boughton, nr Newark, Nottm. NG22 9JS Tel: 01623 860816
Secretary: Les Brown, 14 Holly Rise, New Ollerton, Notts. NG22 9UZ Tel: 01623 836023 (H)
Ground: Walesby Lane, New Ollerton, Notts
Directions: From Ollerton r'about om A614 take A6075 to Ollerton. At r'about first left & after 30m left into Walesby Lane
Colours: All red **Change colours:** Blue/white/white **Manager:** Alan Owen

RADFORD

Secretary: Miss Joan Smith, 63 Hilcot Drive, Aspley, Nottingham NG8 5HS Tel No: 0794 9091477
Ground: Radford FC, Berridge Rd. West, off Radford Road, Radford, Nottm (0115 943250). **Directions:** M1 Junc 26,take A610 to Nottingham, at duel carriageway turn left. Move to right lane andgo immediately right into Wilkinson St. At top turn right & right again at 2nd crossing.
Colours: Claret & sky blue/claret/claret **Change**: Black & white/black **Manager:** Colin Coultan **Midweek Matchday:** Tuesday

RETFORD UNITED

Secretary: John Hodgkinson, Richmond Ho., York St., East Markham, Notts. NG22 0QW Tel: 01777 870773 (H) 07850 975978 (B)
Ground: Cannon Park, Leverton Rd., Retford, Notts. Tel: 0794 9454694 Directions: From A1 take A620 past Ranby Prison and into Retford. At large r'about take 3rd exit. Pass Morrisons superstore to lights. Right at lights, then left at next set. Follow Leverton Rd. out of town. Cannon Park on RHS after two bridges.
Colours: Black & white stripes/black/black **Change colours:** Yellow/blue/white **Manager:** Jason Gray

RIPLEY TOWN

Secretary: Michael E Boam, 5 Valley Drive, Newthorpe, Notts. NG16 2DT. Tel: 01773 715277 (H) 0374 876794 (B)
Ground & Directions: Waingroves Brick Works, Peasehill Road, Ripley, Derbys. M1, J 28, A38 south to A610 signed Nottingham. Continue approx. 1 mile. Turn right into Steam Mill Lane, continue to Peasehill Road to brickworks.
Colours: Black & white stripes/black/black **Change:** Yellow/blue/white **Manager:** Paul MacFarland

SHARDLOW ST. JAMES

Secretary: Thomas Wake, 33 West End Drive, Shardlow, Derbys. E72 2EY Tel: 01332 792636 (H) 01332 852586 (B)
Ground & Directions: The Wharf, Shardlow, Derby. (07960 110624), M1 Junc 24, A6 Derby/Leicester, 6 miles out of Derby at Shardlow take next left after Shardlowchurch (on right), ground 100yds on left.
Colours: Blue & white/blue/blue. **Change**: Orange/black/orange **Manager:** Karn Sanghera **Midweek Matchday:** Wednesday

STANTON ILKESTON

Secretary: Alec Hall,12 Thoresby Road, Long Eaton, Mottingham NG10 3NP Tel No : 0115 9735443
Ground & Directions: Hallam Fields Sports Ground, Stanton Club, Hallam Fields,Nr Ilkeston, Derbys (0115 9323244), M1 (J26), take A52 Nottingham, then A6002for Ilkeston. Follow road through t/lights, turn right at next lights. Followroad to Rutland Windows. Turn left into Thurman St, to top turn left ground 200yds right. **Manager:** Chris Trueman **Midweek Matchday:** Mon. or Wed. **Colours:** All blue & white
Change: Yellow & Black

THORESBY COLLIERY WELFARE

Secretary: Barry Reece, 125 Henton Rd., Edwinstone, Mansfield, Notts. NG21 9LD Tel: 01623 822415 (H) 01623 491422 (B)
Ground: Thoresby Colliery Sports Ground, 4th Avenue, Edwinstone, Notts. Tel: 01623 822283 (Ground & Clubhouse)
Directions: A614 Ollerton r'about take A6075 Mansfield/Edwinstone. Turn left opposite 'Manvers Arms' onto 5th Avenue. Opposite Nursing Home turn right onto 4th Ave. Ground entrance ahead.
Colours: Blue & white/blue/blue **Change Colours:** Gold/black/black **Manager:** Mick Heron

THORNE COLLIERY

Secretary: Glyn Jones, 21 Haynes Close, Thorne,Doncaster, S Yorks DN8 5HR Tel No: 01405 741062
Ground & Directions: Miners Welfare, Grange Road, Moorends, Thorne, Doncaster.(01374 996474), M18 Junc 6, in THorne, turnat lights to Moorends, go almostthrough village, Grange Road on right.
Manager: Graham Jones**Colours:** Tangerine & Purple **Change:** Maroon & Navy.**Midweek Matchday:** Tuesday

WELBECK MINERS WELFARE

Secretary: Les Graham, 10 saville Way, Warsop, Mansfield, Notts. NG20 0DZ. Tel: 01623 844299
Ground: Elksley Road, Meden Vale, Mansfield. (01623 842611) **Directions:** 1 1/2 miles off A60 between Worksop and Mansfield. Signed Meden vale. (do NOT follow signs for Welbeck Colliery.) Turn off at Warsop Church.
HONOURS: Notts Alliance Div 2 93-94 (Intermediate Cup 93-94), Chesterfield & Dist. Lg 92-93
Colours: White & navy/navy/white **Change colours:** Black & yellow/black/black **Manager:** Kevin Gee

YORKSHIRE MAIN

Secretary: Dennis Tymon, 22 Pamela Drive, Warmsworth, Doncaster DN4 9RP Tel: 01302 852455
Ground: Yorkshire Main Welfare, Edlington Lane, Edlington, Doncaster Tel: 01709 864075
Directions: A1M junc 36. Proceed on A630 towards Rotherham. At 1st lights turn on to B6376. Ground on left after Fire Station.
Colours: Yellow/green/yellow**Change Colours:** Red/black/red **Manager:** Derek Wynne

NOTTS FOOTBALL ALLIANCE

Founded 1894

Chairman: Alan Wright

10 Faraday Road, Mansfield NG18 4ES Tel: 01623 624379

Treasurer: Godfrey Stafford

7 The Rushes, Gotham, Nottingham NG11 0HY Tel: 01509 820737

FINAL LEAGUE TABLES 2000-01

SENIOR DIVISION

		P	*W*	*D*	*L*	*F*	*A*	*Pts*	*GD*
1	Southwell City	28	17	7	4	76	46	58	30
2	Rainworth MW	28	15	7	6	61	36	52	25
3	Wollaton FC	28	15	5	8	81	45	50	36
4	Kimberley MW	28	14	8	6	72	47	50	25
5	Boots Athletic	28	14	5	9	73	50	47	23
6	Linby CW	28	12	7	9	61	43	43	18
7	IDP Newark	28	12	7	9	56	39	43	17
8	Keyworth Utd	28	13	4	11	51	51	43	0
9	Attenborough FC	28	12	5	11	31	39	41	-8
10	Notts Police	28	10	7	11	59	60	37	-1
11	Pelican FC	28	8	7	13	47	62	28	-15
12	Abacus FC	28	7	7	14	33	56	28	-23
13	Clifton FC	28	6	8	14	40	72	26	-32
14	Cotgrave FC	28	7	4	17	50	73	25	-23
15	Ruddington Utd	28	4	0	24	24	93	12	-69

FIRST DIVISION

		P	*W*	*D*	*L*	*F*	*A*	*Pts*	*GD*
1	Retford United	28	21	3	4	89	20	66	69
2	Radcliffe Olympic	28	20	4	4	79	22	64	57
3	Beeston Town	28	17	6	5	54	30	57	24
4	Kingswell FC	28	14	7	7	63	49	49	14
5	Thoresby CW	28	14	6	8	40	36	48	4
6	Matrix grade	28	14	4	10	49	50	46	-1
7	Chaffoteaux FC	28	11	7	10	40	44	40	-4
8	Bestwood MW	28	11	6	11	44	44	39	0
9	Southbank MW	28	11	2	15	45	55	35	-10
10	Calverton MW	28	9	3	15	47	61	30	-14
11	Magdala Amts	28	8	6	14	43	61	30	-18
12	Wollaton FC Res	28	6	10	12	37	46	28	-9
13	Basford United	28	6	6	16	43	62	24	-19
14	Awsworth Villa	28	6	3	19	24	61	21	-37
15	Boots Athletic Res	28	2	7	19	20	76	13	-56

HONOURS LIST 2000-01

SENIOR DIVISION			
Champions	Southwell City	**Runners Up**	Rainworth MW
FIRST DIVISION			
Champions	Retford United	**Runners Up**	Radcliffe Olympic
SECOND DIVISION			
Champions	Gedling MW	**Runners Up**	IDP Newark Res
THIRD DIVISION			
Champions	Kimberley MW	**Runners Up**	Retford Utd Res
SENIOR CUP			
Winners	Attenborough FC	**Finalists**	Wollaton FC
INTERMEDIATE CUP			
Winners	Gedling MW	**Finalists**	IDP Newark Res

MANAGERS OF THE YEAR

SENIOR DIVISION	John Campbell	Southwell City
FIRST DIVISION	Jason Grey	Retford United
SECOND DIVISION	Vic Hulme	Gedling MW
THIRD DIVISION	Gary Rowbottom	Kimberley MW

PLAYERS OF THE YEAR

SENIOR DIVISION	Paul Bingley	Abacus FC
	Jonathon Milner	Rainworth MW
FIRST DIVISION	Mark Brooks	Radcliffe Olympic
SECOND DIVISION	Ben Loomes	Bottesford FC
	Ashley Swain	Pinxton North End
THIRD DIVISION	Darren Hammans	Basford United Reserves
	Michael Conroy	Clifton FC Reserves
	Michael Clay	Cotgrave CW Reserves
	Nigel Jackson	Thoresby C W Reserves

SPORTING TEAMS OF THE YEAR

SENIOR DIVISION	Boots Athletic	11 points
FIRST DIVISION	Wollaton FC Reserves	2 points
SECOND DIVISION	Newark Town FC	0 points
THIRD DIVISION	Clifton FC Reserves	6 points

JOE WILLIAMS MEMORIAL

John Fisk — Ruddington United

NOTTS F.A. INTERMEDIATE CUP

Winners — Retford United — Finalists — Matrixgrade FC

NOTTS F.A. JUNIOR CUP

Finalists — Retford United Reserves

ATTENBOROUGH

Secretary: Terry Allen, 5 Coningsby Road,Woodthorpe, Nottingham NG54LG Tel: 0115 920 0698
Ground & Directions: The Village Green, The Strand, Attenborough, Beeston,Nottingham. Midway between Beeston & Long Eaton on A6005 - adjacent to NatureReserve (via Attenborough Lane).
Colours: All Royal Blue
Change colours: White/black/black.

BOOTS ATHLETIC

Secretary: Ian Whitehead
21 Rosthwaite Close, West Bridgford, Nottingham NG26RA
Tel: 0115 981 2830 (H) 0115 968 7535 (B)
Ground: Lady Bay, West Bridgford, Nottingham Tel: 0115 981 2392
Colours: Blue&white stripes, bue,blue.

Honours: Notts Alliance Div 1 91-92 (Lg Cup 91-92), Notts Snr Cup R-up 93-94,Notts Inter R-up 91-92.

CLIFTON

Secretary: Mrs Pat Brodie, 21 Cerne Close, Clifton, Nottingham. Tel: 0115 9215113

Ground: Green Lane, Clifton Est., Nottm Tel: 0115 984 4903

Colours: All white(Blue trim)

COTGRAVE COLLIERY WELFARE

Secretary: Kevin Whitehead, 51 Crosshill, Cotgrave, Nottinham. NG12 3NB Tel: 0115 989 4043

Ground: Woodview, Cotgrave, Nottingham
Colours: Red/blue/blue

KEYWORTH UNITED

Secretary: Stuart Douglas
29 Ashley Crescent, Keyworth, Nottm. NG12 5GF
Tel: 0115 937 5358

Ground: Platt Lane, Keyworth (0115 937 5998)

Colours: Green/black/green

KIMBERLEY MINERS WELFARE

Secretary: Stephen Hobster
35 Truman Street, Kimberley, Nottingham NG16 2HA
Tel Nos: 0115 938 4067 (H) 07866 77376 (M)

Ground: Digby Street, Kimberley, Nottingham (0115 938 2124)

Colours: Black & red/black/black & red

LINBY COLLIERY WELFARE

Secretary: J.Riley,70 Bolingey Way, Hucknall, Notts.NG15 6TQ
Tel No: 0115 953 3025

Ground: Church Lane, Linby, Nottingham (07971 023622)

Colours: Red ,black& white/red & black shorts

NEWARK FLOWERSERVE

Secretary: Kevin Presland, Appleby Lodge, Barnby Road, Newark, Nottingham NG24 2NE Tel: 01636 704606, 07771 507065

Ground: Lowfield Works, off hawton Lane, Balderton, Newark, Nottingham. Tel: 01636 702672

Colours: Orange/blue/orange

NOTTINGHAMSHIRE POLICE

Secretary: John Beeston **Club Colours:** All Red
17 Alandene Ave, Watnall, Nottingham NG16 1HH
Tel: 0115 938 2110
Ground: Calverton Recreation Centre, Hollingwood Lane, Calverton, Nottingham (0115965 4390)
Honours: Notts Snr R-up 91-92, Notts All. Div 1 & Lge Snr Cup R-up 85-86, PAANNat. K-O Comp 63-64.

PELICAN

Secretary: Dave Eastwood, 42 Chetwin Road, Bilborough, Nottingham NG8 4HN (0155 913 8345)
Ground: Brian Wakefield Sports Ground, Lenton Lane, Nottingham Tel: 0115 986 8255
Colours: All Blue
Honours: Notts Alliance Lg Cup 90-91(R-up 91-92 93-94).

RADCLIFFE OLYMPIC

Secretary: C Johnson, 2 The Firs, Holme Pierrepoint, Nottingham NG12 2LT Tel: 0115 933 3791

Ground: Wharf Lane, Radcliffe-on-Trent, Nottingham

Colours: All Black with Beige & red trim

RAINWORTH MINERS WELFARE

Secretary: Alan Wright, 10 Faraday Road, Mansfield NG18 4ES
Tel: 01623 624379 (H) 01623 553237 (B)
Ground: Kirklington Road, Rainworth, Notts
Directions: On A617 Mansfield - Newark Road
Colours: All white
Honours: Notts Alliance 77-78 78-79 79-80 80-81 81-82 82-83 (R-up 93-94, Lg Cup 81-82), Notts Snr Cup 80-81 81-82 (R-up 82-83 92-93), FA Vase R-up 82-82, ThornEMI F'lit Cup R-up 82-83 83-84 84-85

RUDDINGTON UNITED

Secretary: John Fisk, 3 Savages Rd., Ruddington, Nottm NG11 6EW
Tel: 0115 9842552
Ground & Directions: The Elms Park Ground, Loughborough Road, Ruddington (0115 984 4976) On A60 Nottm to Loughborough, 5 miles out of Nottingham.
Colours: Yellow & blue/blue/blue
Honours: Notts Comb. Lg 79-80, Lg Cup 70-71 76-77 80-81

SOUTHWELL CITY

Secretary: Pat Johnson
63 The Ropewalk, Southwell, Notts NG25 0AL
Tel: 01636 812594

Ground: War Memorial Recreation G round, Bishops Drive, Southwell, Notts. 01636 814386

Colours: Black& White stripes/black/black.

WOLLATON

Secretary: Paul King, 18 Lancaster Way, Strelley, Nottingham NG8 6PH
Ground: Wollaton Sports Association, Wollaton Village, Nottm
Tel: 0115 9133 134
Colours: **All** Sky Blue
Honours: Notts All. Div 1 R-up 92-93, Div 2 91-92,
I'mediate Cup R-up 91-92.

WOODHOUSE

Secretary: 1 Greenwood Close, Sutton-in-Ashfield, Nottm.
Tel: 01623 554466

Ground: Debdale Lane, mansfield Woodhouse, Nottm.
Tel: 01623 631747

Colours: Red & blue stripes/blue/blue & red

DIVISION ONE

ASC DAYNCOURT

Secretary: Adrian Cridge, 3 Regina Close, Radcliffe on Trent, Nottingham NG12 2EL. Tel: 0115 933 4771 (H) 07831 680687 (M)
Ground: Bingham Road Playing Fields, Radcliffe on Trent, Nottingham
Colours: Navy & white/navy/navy

AWSWORTH VILLA

Secretary: Paul Wilkinson, 15 Barlow Drive North, Awsworth, Nottingham NG16 2RQ.
Tel: 0115 930 4905 (H) 0115 932 8721 (B)
Ground: Shilo Park, off Attewell Road, Awsworth, Nottm.
Colours: Red & white/red/red.

BASFORD UNITED

Secretary: Maria Smith, 17 Snenfield Gardens, Rise Park, Nottingham NG5 5BH (0115 955 8045)
Ground: Greenwich Ave., Bagnall Rd, Basford, Nottm (0115 942 3918).
Directions: M1, J26 follow signs A610 Nottingham then B6004 Arnold into Mill St.
Colours: Yellow/black/yellow

BESTWOOD MINERS WELFARE

Secretary: Alan Fisher,5 Skipton Close, Ilkeston, Derbyshire DE7 9HX (0115 932 7717)
Ground: Bestwood Workshops, Park Rd, Bestwood
Colours: Red/navy blue/navy blue.

BOOTS ATHLETIC RESERVES

CALVERTON M.W.

Secretary: John Daniel, 13 Renals Ways, Calverton, Nottingham NG14 6PH 0115 965 4447 (H) 0771 5306032 (M)
Ground: Calverton Recreation Centre, Hollingwood Lane, Calverton, Nottingham Tel: 0115 965 4390
Colours: Sky Blue&navy/navy

CHAFFOTEAUX

Secretary: Mark Nicholls, 31 Telford Drive, Newthorpe, Nottm. NG16 3NN 01773 534169 (H) 0115 942 2400(B)
Ground: Basil Russell Playing Fields, Maple Drive, Nuthall, Nottingham 0115 938 4765
Colours: Red & black/red&black/black

GEDLING M.W.

Secretary: Norman Hay, 182 Gedling Rd., Arnold, Nottm. NG5 6NY Tel: 0115 926 5598
Ground: Plains Road, Mapperly, Nottingham. Tel: 0115 926 6300
Colours: Yellow/blue/yellow

KINGSWELL

Secretary: Phil Smith, 1 Mowbray Rise, Arnold, Nottm NG5 5DW Tel: 0115 956 9585 (H) 07977 633051 (M)
Ground: Williams Lee Memorial Ground, Park Road, Calverton, Nottingham Tel: 0115 965 3097
Colours: Red & White (home) All blue (away)

MAGDALA AMATEURS

Secretary: Alan Gilmour, 9 Adbolton Grove, West Bridgford, Nottingham NG2 5AR Tel: 0115 982 1071
Ground: Civil Service Sports Ground, Wilford Lane, W Bridgford.
Colours: Amber/Black/Tangerine

MATRIXGRADE

Secretary: Stephen Farmery (0115 910 6694 (H) 07979 238209 (M)
Ground: Carrington Sports Ground, Mansfield Rd., Nottm.
Colours: Yellow & black/black/black

MELTON MOWBRAY

Secretary: Anne Gibbon, 39 Main Street, Kirby Bellars, Melton Mowbray, Leics. LE14 2EA Tel: 01164 812675
Ground: Saxby Road, Melton Mowbray
Colours: Red/blue/blue

NEWARK FLOWERSERVE RESERVES

SOUTHBANK

Secretary: Gerry Bishop, 4 Foxearth Ave., Clifton, Nottm. NG11 8JQ Tel: 0115 984 2363
Ground: Carlton Hill, Nottingham
Colours: Red & White Stripes/White/Red

SOUTHWELL CITY RESERVES

WOLLATON RESERVES

DIVISION TWO

A.C. BULWELL
Secretary: Neil Fitch, 4 Hoefield Crescent, Bulwell, Nottingham NG6 8AY Tel: 0115 849 8652 (H) 07903 153105 (M)
Ground: River Leen School, Squires Avenue, Bulwell. Tel: 0115 927 8425

BILBOROUGH
Secretary: Duncan Costin, 12 Calstock Road, Woodthorpe, Nottingham NG5 4FH Tel: 0115 919 9371 (H)
Ground: Birchover Park, Brindley Road, Bilborough, Nottingham.

BILSTHORPE WELFARE
Secretary: Mick Gresswell, 40 Scarborough Road, Bilsthorpe, Nottingham. (01623 8700320
Ground: Eakring Road, Bilsthorpe, Notts
Colours: All royal blue

BOTTESFORD
Secretary: Miss Micci Angeloni, 129 Stamford St., Grantham, Lincs. NG31 7BF Tel: 01476 593581
Ground: Village hall Playing Fields, Belvoir Rd., Bottesford
Colours: Dark red & black stripes/black/black

CHAFFOTEAUX RESERVES

EASTLAKE ATHLETIC
Secretary: Andrew Fletcher, 62 Suthers Road, Kegworth, Derby DE74 2DF Tel: 01509 674752
Ground: Costock Road, East Leake.

KEYWORTH UTD RESERVES

KIMBERLEY M.W. RESERVES

KIRKTON BRICKWORKS
Secretary: Stuart Douglas, 29 Ashley Crescent, Keyworth, Nottingham NG12 5GF Tel: 0115 937 5358
Ground: Kirkton Brickworks, Nr. New Ollerton, Nottingham Tel: 01623 860481

NEWARK TOWN
Secretary: David Wildes, Forest Cottage, Brough, Newark, Nottingham NG23 7QZ Tel: 01636 676038
Ground: Devon Park

PEGASUS
Secretary: Mrs G Buxton, 75 Springfield Ave., Sandiacre, Nottingham NG10 5NA Tel: 0115 972 0741
Ground: Wierfields, Beeston Rylands, Nottingham

PELICAN RESERVES

PINXTON NORTH END
Secretary: phil Handley, 123 Alfreton Road, Pinxton, Nottingham NG16 6JZ Tel: 01773 784162 (H)
Ground: 'The Tops', Church Street (W), Pinxton, Nottingham

RUDDINGTON UTD RESERVES

SANDHURST
Secretary: Robert Crawford, 4 The Brambles, Walesby, Newark, Nottingham NG22 9PH Tel: 01623 862985
Ground: Walesby Sports & Social Club, Retford Road, Walesby.

STAPLEFORD BOROUGH
Secretary: Tony Iacovitti, 1 Esward Street, Stapleford, Nottingham NG9 8FH Tel: 0115 949 7598 (H) 07974 088210 (M)
Ground: STS Sports Ground, Breaston Lane, Risley.

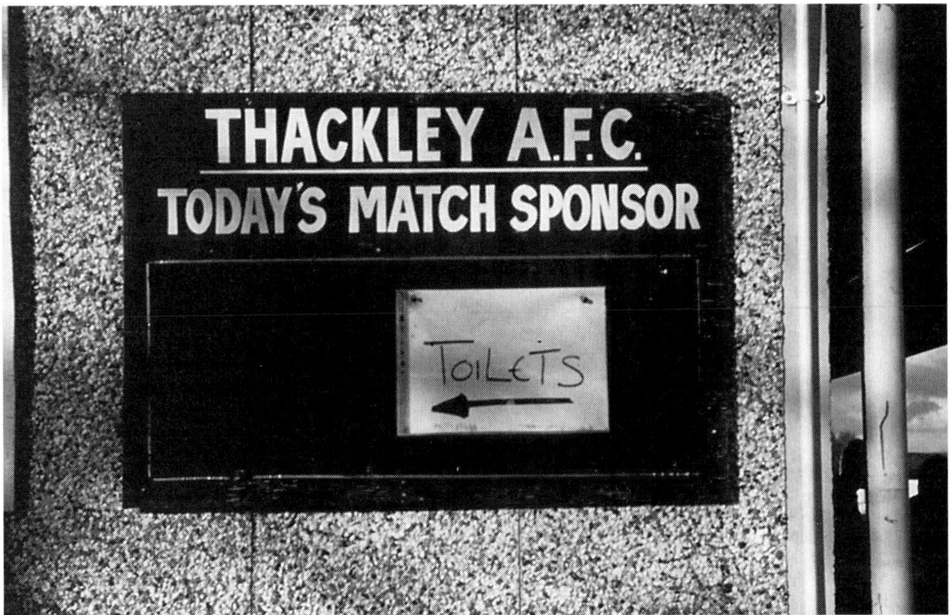

Photo: Tony Bills

THANKS TO THE PHOTOGRAPHERS

Since our first Non-League Annual in 1978 and during the life span of Team Talk we have all known that if our team of enthusiastic photographers had been paid the publications couldn't have lived more than a season.

The lads all knew and accepted this situation and I have obviously been thrilled that they have stayed to help and indeed have developed such a happy spirit amongst themselves that the little `thank yous' we have been able to organise for them, has given us all wonderful memories and many a smile.

I hope they will continue to help the Directory in the same way in future, but anyway here is a little tribute to 'the team' spaced throughout the Directory.

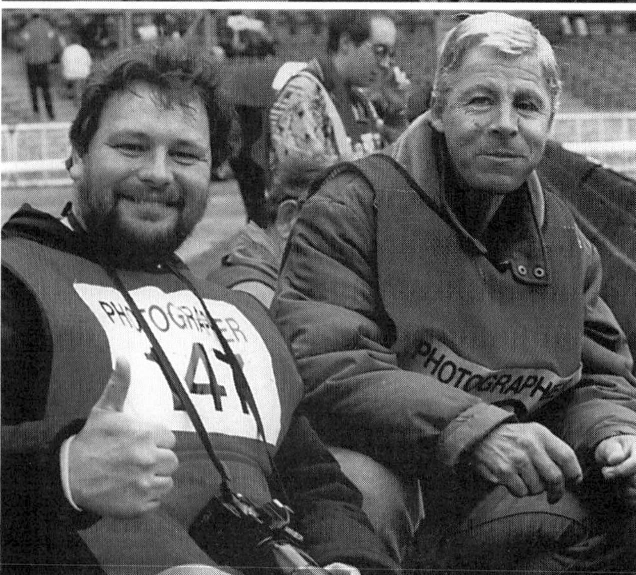

The first point that has to be accepted is:

The lads have definitely `carried' Eric Marsh (top)

Left to right back row: - Neil Thaler, Gordon Whittington, Garry Letts and Peter Barnes.
Front row - Peter Lirettoc next to brother Graham Cotterill (spelt correctly), Andrew Chitty and Roger Turner.
Photo: Neil Thaler!

Left: Two who were a great help, especially in the early days: Dave West (147) and Gordon Nicholson

Turn to page 464

NORTHERN LEAGUE

Founded 1889

President: George Courtney MBE **Chairman:** Mike Amos
Hon. Secretary & Treasurer: A Golightly, 85 Park Road North, Chester-le-Street,
Co Durham DH3 3SA Tel: 0191 388 2056 Fax: 0191 3891 1385

The sun shone for almost two hours one Saturday afternoon in March. No matter that it seemed to rain constantly throughout the rest of the season, this is the League which believes in accentuating the positive.

Season 2000-01 was, for all that, the most difficult that many can remember, a mordant theme that doubtless will be reflected throughout the Directory. It began with the problems of the fuel crisis, quickly became waterlogged and at the end was troubled - though not as greatly as some - by the foot and mouth epidemic.

When the legendary Gordon Nicholson had the first of his 24 seasons as League secretary in 1966-67, not a single game was lost to the weather. Folk talk of climate change, but there can hardly be greater contrast. Gordon is now 75, incidentally, and still working tirelessly - despite recent health problems - for Evenwood Town.

If the clouds had a silver lining, it was that so many others refused to be beaten by the extraordinary sequence of adversity. Principal among them, perhaps, were Murton - forced from their former Colliery Welfare ground when summer rain affected mining subsidence and caused a culvert to collapse beneath the pitch.

The upshot was that a huge crater opened up, so Murton - who already hadn't their troubles to seek - were obliged to ground share throughout the season and to try to find the necessary £80,000 for repair work. The national media dubbed them Britain's unluckiest football club - remember the floodlight failure on Friday the 13th? - but they were very lucky to have Tom Torrence as chairman.

Tom's resilience and indomitability earned him the Arthur Clark Memorial Award - the League's supreme off-field honour - at the annual dinner. Like many more who for many years have fought to keep football alive at this level, he deserves a medal from a higher authority, too. Murton hope to be back home early in 2001-02.

All 40 clubs and their heroic little bands of officials will have dried out by August and will continue next season. They will be joined in the Second Division by Washington Nissan, promoted by agreement from the Wearside League though formal promotion and relegation agreements between the ANL and its feeders remain suspended. The Wearside League, intent on ground upgrading, hopes to have the automatic agreement restored in 2002-03.

Once again no Albany Northern League club even gave notice of seeking promotion, should they have finished in the top two of the First Division. It is not that they lack ambition and certainly not - though the canard persists - that League officials in any way discourage them.

One or two clubs will undoubtedly seek promotion in future seasons, while others will watch the proposed National League System re-organisation with much interest. Many, however, simply feel that the cost both financially and socially of travel throughout the northern region - Manchester, Merseyside and sometimes beyond - is fiercely prohibitive. They have witnessed the struggles of others and are understandably reluctant to travel that long and dangerous road themselves. Besides, when the sun shines, it's really quite nice up here.

The comparable quality of football between the ANL and nominally higher leagues was again emphasised, when a series of stunning victories over highly placed Unibond teams saw four of our clubs in the last qualifying round. Sadly, none made the hat for the competition proper, though Easington Colliery - subsequently relegated - attracted huge media attention for their match with Chester City, in the Football League the previous season. Come to think, it poured down that day, too.

Bedlington Terriers, close to extinction just eight years previously, were again the League's dominant club - a fourth successive championship, the League Cup and a last four place in the Vase after beating ANL colleagues Marske United in the quarter-final. Marske had themselves been in the Wearside League five years before - sometimes the system works.

Ashington, long departed members of the old Third Division (North), won Second Division promotion - and the championship - after seventeen years trying. Their fans are stupendous - noisy, passionate, but not a bad word among the lot of them. They will be joined in the First Division by Washington - a first promotion since joining the Northern League in 1988-89 - and by Thornaby, for whom it is a quick return.

Penrith, members intermittently since 1948, won their first Northern League trophy by lifting the Craven Cup - for

Second Division clubs - in a memorable final against South Shields, the 100th minute winner proving the value of the new "golden goal" rule. Penrith also won the Cumberland Senior Cup for the first time in 25 years, and the League award for the best tea hut. People will go a long way for a Penrith pie, and in the Northern League they have to.

Other off-field awards went to Northallerton's Les Hood - Unsung Hero of the Year - and to Brandon, named the most hospitable club. Billingham Town veteran Paul Rowntree, 35, was named Player of the Year and also took the Golden Boot award for most League goals, while prolific Bedlington striker John Milner won the BBC Radio Newcastle Player of the Year trophy for the second successive season. Eddie Ilderton took the referees' "Silver Whistle" - silver coloured, anyhow - also for the second year running.

Chester-le-Street, Kennek Ryhope CA and Alnwick won principal honours in the Good Conduct and Fair Play awards.

The League remains enormously fortunate in its superb sponsor, the Albany Group of companies, headed by Brooks Mileson - he's the one who wrote the contract on the inside flap of a Marlboro packet, the most expensive twenty cigarettes in football history. In acknowledgement of Brooks' ever increasing generosity the League and its clubs last season raised £4200 for the Butterwick Children's Hospice in Stockton - his nominated charity - and this year have taken a mass entry in the Great North Run, to help raise money for the HC Pilgrimage Trust, another of the sponsor's favoured charities and for Marie Curie Cancer Care.

The League's 38-strong GNR contingent will be headed by 60-year-old League President George Courtney, the former FIFA referee, and by League Chairman Mike Amos - a few years younger but very much less fit. As those who know him would expect, the Chairman proposes to lead from the back.

Thanks further to Brooks Mileson's funding, the "Team of the Month" award in 2001-02 will be replaced by a "Performance of the Week" accolade, worth £100.

Another vastly successful innovation has been the Northern League Club, started in 1999-2000 as an umbrella group - a highly appropriate phrase last season - for all ANL enthusiasts. Under the inspired guidance of Martin and Denise Haworth, who also maintain and constantly update the League's superb website, the non-profit making club has continued to flourish.

A £10 annual membership, reducing to £7.50 after the first season, includes an enamel lapel badge, monthly newsletter with all fixtures, results and scorers and other statistical information, a regular copy of Northern Ventures Northern Gains - the League's acclaimed magazine - 40 page grounds guide and discounts at many club shops and tea huts.

Details of the Northern League Club are available from Martin Haworth at 17 The Turn, Morpeth, Northumberland NE61 2DU. The Northern League website is at www.northernleagueclub.co.uk

Six issues of the glossy 24 page magazine, still just 30p as it was when first published thirteen years ago, are available for £3.30 (including postage) from Peter Lax, 21 Carlton Avenue, Billingham, Cleveland. The League's 530 page millennium history is also still available for £8.99 (plus £3 postage) from Joe Burlison, 4 Carrowmore Road, Chester-le-Street, Co Durham.

So to another season, to the debate about National League re-organisation and to the worries over the radical new referee proposals which for some of our clubs could prove the financial straw that breaks the camel's back. Hasn't the meddlesome FA heard the adage, "if it ain't broke, don't fix it"?

Meteorologically, of course, we already know all about the notion that it never rains but it pours. For the moment we look on the bright side, as ever.

Mike Amos

HONOURS LIST 2000-01

LEAGUE DIVISION ONE

Champions Bedlington Terriers
Runners Up Dunston Federation Brewery

LEAGUE DIVISION TWO

Champions Ashington
Runners Up Washington I H

NORTHERN LEAGUE CHALLENGE CUP

Winners Bedlington Terriers

CRAVEN CUP

Winners Penrith

GOOD CONDUCT AWARD SCHEME

Chester le Street Town
Consett
Alnwick
Willington
Dunston Federation Brewery
Easington Colliery
Penrith
Northallerton
Hordon CW

FINAL LEAGUE TABLES 2000-01

DIVISION ONE

			Home					*Away*					
		P	*W*	*D*	*L*	*F*	*A*	*W*	*D*	*L*	*F*	*A*	*Pts*
1	Bedlington Terriers	40	16	1	3	57	13	12	4	4	51	18	89
2	Dunston Fed Brewery	40	16	2	2	57	24	10	5	5	36	25	85
3	Marske United	40	13	3	4	48	18	11	4	5	34	17	79
4	Durham City	40	13	4	3	55	20	11	2	7	40	22	78
5	Brandon United	40	14	2	4	43	24	9	6	5	43	29	77
6	Peterlee Newtown	40	13	3	4	42	27	9	6	5	33	28	75
7	Tow Law Town	40	10	4	6	50	31	10	3	7	40	33	67
8	Billingham Synthonia	40	11	6	3	51	28	7	5	8	30	30	65
9	Billingham Town	40	9	4	7	32	29	10	3	7	42	30	64
10	Consett	40	10	5	5	38	23	7	3	10	25	37	59
11	Whitley Bay	40	7	5	8	31	35	8	5	7	38	26	55
12	West Auckland Town	40	6	5	9	29	31	10	2	8	36	37	55
13	Jarrow Roofing	40	6	9	5	34	34	6	3	11	29	37	48
14	Guisborough Town	40	8	5	7	30	23	5	3	12	23	37	47
15	Chester-le-Street	40	5	4	11	29	34	8	1	11	32	30	44
16	Newcastle Blue Star	40	9	3	8	30	36	3	5	12	23	47	44
17	Seaham Red Star	40	9	0	11	32	42	5	2	13	27	69	44
18	Morpeth Town*	40	8	2	10	33	30	4	4	12	30	48	36
19	Easington Colliery	40	6	3	11	35	41	4	3	13	22	45	36
20	Hebburn Town	40	2	3	15	17	59	3	4	13	16	54	22
21	Crook Town	40	0	2	18	12	69	2	2	16	21	86	10

* Points deducted

DIVISION ONE RESULTS CHART 2000-01

		1	2	3	4	5	6	7	8	9	10	11	12	13	14	15	16	17	18	19	20	21
1	Bedlington T	X	0-2	5-0	3-1	2-0	3-0	4-0	2-1	5-0	2-0	3-0	3-0	3-0	2-0	2-0	2-3	3-0	8-2	3-2	0-1	1-1
2	B'ham Synth.	2-2	X	2-0	1-1	1-1	3-0	10-1	2-2	1-2	3-2	3-2	3-2	0-4	1-1	2-2	3-0	4-2	3-1	0-1	4-0	3-2
3	Billingham T	1-5	1-2	X	0-0	1-0	5-1	1-0	1-1	2-1	2-1	3-2	0-1	0-0	0-1	5-2	4-1	1-2	1-2	3-3	0-4	1-0
4	Brandon Utd	1-1	1-0	0-1	X	0-2	1-0	3-1	3-2	1-0	2-0	3-0	3-4	2-3	2-1	3-2	3-2	2-2	6-1	2-0	4-2	1-0
5	Chester le St	1-2	1-2	2-3	2-3	X	0-1	1-2	1-1	0-1	2-6	1-0	3-0	1-1	1-4	3-2	0-0	0-1	2-0	4-0	3-4	1-1
6	Consett	1-1	3-1	3-3	3-3	2-0	X	4-1	0-2	0-4	4-0	1-1	4-0	2-0	0-1	0-0	2-0	0-2	4-2	3-1	3-1	1-2
7	Crook Town	1-9	1-2	0-7	0-6	1-2	1-3	X	0-2	0-5	1-1	0-1	2-3	0-4	0-1	0-4	2-2	0-2	2-3	0-6	0-2	1-4
8	Dunston F B	1-0	2-1	2-1	1-3	1-0	2-1	13-0	X	2-1	3-2	3-1	0-0	3-2	4-2	3-1	2-1	2-1	7-0	0-3	2-0	4-4
9	Durham City	1-0	3-1	1-2	2-2	2-1	1-2	8-2	4-2	X	2-0	1-1	5-0	3-1	1-1	5-0	6-2	1-1	5-0	0-1	3-1	1-0
10	Easington C	0-3	4-2	1-6	1-1	4-0	1-1	6-0	2-3	2-5	X	2-0	5-1	0-3	0-1	1-2	0-0	2-3	3-2	0-3	0-1	1-4
11	Guisboro T	1-1	2-0	2-0	4-1	0-3	1-2	2-0	0-0	0-3	1-2	X	2-2	3-0	0-2	1-1	2-0	2-2	0-1	1-2	4-0	2-1
12	Hebbern T	1-5	0-3	1-1	0-1	0-3	1-0	2-4	0-1	0-5	1-1	2-4	X	2-1	0-6	2-3	2-2	1-5	0-2	1-2	1-3	0-7
13	Jarrow Rfg	4-3	2-2	0-1	2-6	3-1	1-1	3-0	1-1	1-2	1-1	2-1	0-0	X	0-3	2-2	1-1	2-0	2-4	3-3	3-1	1-1
14	Marske Utd	0-2	0-0	4-2	0-0	2-1	4-1	4-0	1-2	1-0	3-0	2-0	4-1	4-1	X	3-0	2-3	1-1	8-0	1-0	2-4	2-0
15	Morpeth T	0-3	1-2	2-2	1-2	0-6	1-3	2-0	1-0	1-0	0-2	1-1	7-0	3-1	0-2	X	3-0	3-0	4-0	1-2	1-2	1-2
16	Newcastle BS	0-1	3-2	0-5	4-0	2-1	3-1	3-1	0-5	0-0	1-0	1-2	3-2	2-1	0-2	2-1	X	0-0	2-2	2-3	2-5	0-2
17	Peterlee N	0-6	2-2	0-1	2-0	3-1	2-2	4-1	0-1	4-1	2-0	3-1	1-0	3-2	1-0	2-1	2-0	X	4-1	4-2	1-1	2-4
18	Seaham R S	0-2	3-2	1-0	0-9	4-2	2-0	3-0	3-2	0-2	1-2	1-2	4-0	0-4	1-4	2-3	3-1	1-4	X	3-2	2-0	0-2
19	Tow Law T	2-1	0-3	2-0	0-1	1-2	3-0	8-3	1-2	3-3	4-2	1-3	4-0	5-0	3-1	5-1	5-3	0-0	2-2	X	1-3	0-0
20	W Auckland	1-2	0-0	2-5	1-2	0-3	1-2	3-3	0-1	1-2	2-0	4-1	1-0	1-1	0-0	3-2	1-2	2-3	2-0	1-1	X	3-1
21	Whitley Bay	0-2	1-1	2-4	2-1	1-3	3-2	2-2	1-5	1-2	5-0	1-0	0-0	0-3	1-1	2-1	2-0	1-2	4-2	1-3	1-1	X

DIVISION ONE PAST WINNERS

	Champions	*Runners Up*
1993-1994	Durham City	Blyth Spartans
1994-1995	Tow Law Town	Billingham Synthonia
1995-1996	Billingham Synthonia	Bedlington Terriers
1996-1997	Whitby Town	Billingham Sythonia
1997-1998	Bedlington Terriers	Billingham Synthonia
1998-1999	Bedlington Terriers	Tow Law Town
1999-2000	Bedlington Terriers	Seaham Red Star
2000-2001	Bedlington Terriers	Dunston Federation Brewery

FINAL LEAGUE TABLES 2000-01

DIVISION TWO

			Home					*Away*					
		P	*W*	*D*	*L*	*F*	*A*	*W*	*D*	*L*	*F*	*A*	*Pts*
1	Ashington	36	13	1	4	54	23	12	4	2	46	18	80
2	Washington I H	36	13	5	0	45	15	10	5	3	38	20	79
3	Thornaby	36	10	4	4	39	24	13	3	2	46	26	76
4	Horden CW	36	13	2	3	36	19	7	5	6	17	16	67
5	Esh Winning	36	10	4	4	29	15	9	3	6	50	29	64
6	Northallerton Town	36	8	8	2	35	21	8	4	6	40	24	60
7	Penrith	36	10	6	2	36	18	4	6	8	24	34	54
8	Norton	36	11	5	2	28	14	5	4	9	23	37	54
9	Willington	36	7	6	5	33	25	5	6	7	19	21	48
10	Kennek Ryhope CA	36	5	6	7	18	25	7	4	7	28	28	46
11	South Shields	36	8	4	6	43	35	4	5	9	28	46	45
12	Prudhoe Town	36	6	0	12	37	43	7	5	6	32	23	44
13	Shildon	36	8	3	7	23	26	4	5	9	19	32	44
14	Alnwick Town	36	4	4	10	27	29	5	8	5	26	32	39
15	Evenwood Town	36	5	2	11	26	43	5	3	10	24	54	35
16	Sotton Comrades	36	4	6	8	28	46	4	4	10	21	39	34
17	Murton	36	4	6	8	22	46	5	2	11	31	30	32
18	Whickham	36	2	7	9	18	33	4	4	10	25	35	29
19	Eppleton CW	36	0	3	15	12	54	1	2	15	17	45	8

DIVISION TWO RESULTS CHART 2000-01

		1	**2**	**3**	**4**	**5**	**6**	**7**	**8**	**9**	**10**	**11**	**12**	**13**	**14**	**15**	**16**	**17**	**18**	**19**
1	Alnwick Town	X	0-1	3-3	2-3	1-2	1-2	4-0	3-1	0-2	3-1	1-2	2-3	0-0	4-0	2-2	0-3	1-2	0-2	0-0
2	Ashington	4-1	X	3-1	3-2	7-1	2-0	1-2	2-1	1-2	5-0	4-2	3-1	1-2	5-0	5-2	1-3	2-2	2-0	3-1
3	Eppleton C W	2-3	0-4	X	0-2	1-2	1-2	1-4	0-4	1-9	0-3	1-3	1-3	0-0	2-2	0-3	0-4	1-2	1-1	0-3
4	Esh Winning	3-0	0-1	2-1	X	4-0	0-0	1-0	1-0	1-0	1-1	0-0	1-0	4-0	2-2	2-1	2-3	0-1	5-2	0-3
5	Evenwood Town	2-2	0-1	2-1	2-4	X	1-2	2-0	0-5	1-4	0-1	0-3	0-4	0-2	1-1	7-1	2-3	0-7	3-2	3-0
6	Horden CW	0-0	3-5	4-0	2-1	4-0	X	2-0	1-0	0-5	5-2	1-0	2-0	3-1	1-0	2-0	2-2	0-2	2-1	2-0
7	Kennek Ryhope	0-1	0-0	1-0	0-4	2-2	0-0	X	2-1	1-1	2-0	2-1	1-1	1-2	3-2	0-1	1-2	1-2	0-4	1-1
8	Murton	1-1	1-12	2-1	1-4	3-1	0-5	2-2	X	1-3	2-2	1-1	0-7	2-0	0-1	2-2	1-0	3-1	1-2	0-0
9	Northallerton Town	1-1	2-2	1-2	1-1	4-4	0-0	3-0	2-2	X	1-0	3-0	3-0	3-0	1-0	2-2	2-2	1-4	4-1	1-0
10	Norton	1-2	1-1	2-1	3-1	2-0	1-0	0-2	2-0	2-1	X	1-1	3-1	1-0	1-0	4-1	3-3	1-0	0-0	0-0
11	Penrith	4-1	2-1	4-0	1-0	5-0	1-0	1-1	1-0	4-3	1-1	X	1-1	1-1	2-2	1-3	1-4	1-1	2-0	3-0
12	Prudhoe Town	5-2	0-2	3-1	1-5	1-2	3-1	0-3	0-4	1-2	2-3	6-0	X	3-1	7-0	2-3	1-2	0-3	1-5	1-4
13	Shildon	0-3	1-3	2-1	2-1	1-2	1-1	4-3	1-0	1-0	1-0	0-0	1-2	X	0-2	4-2	0-3	2-2	2-0	0-1
14	Shotton Comrades	2-2	1-2	2-1	0-8	1-5	2-0	0-1	4-3	3-3	2-2	1-5	0-3	2-2	X	1-1	2-3	2-3	1-1	2-1
15	South Shields	2-4	3-4	6-3	2-5	5-2	1-2	0-0	1-3	0-0	3-0	1-1	1-4	3-1	3-0	X	4-0	3-2	2-2	3-2
16	Thornaby	1-1	1-4	3-0	4-2	3-0	0-1	4-1	2-2	3-1	1-2	3-1	1-1	4-3	3-2	2-1	X	0-0	3-0	1-2
17	Washington I H	1-1	2-0	1-0	3-3	5-0	2-0	2-2	3-1	1-1	4-0	4-3	2-0	1-0	3-1	6-1	3-1	X	1-0	1-2
18	Whickham	1-1	0-2	0-0	1-1	1-1	0-0	1-4	0-3	1-2	1-4	4-0	0-0	1-1	1-4	3-2	2-4	1-3	X	0-0
19	Willington	2-0	1-1	4-1	1-3	4-0	0-1	0-3	5-1	2-1	3-1	1-1	1-1	2-2	0-2	1-1	0-3	1-1	5-2	X

DIVISION TWO PAST WINNERS

	Champions	*Runners Up*
1990-1991	West Auckland	Langley Park
1991-1992	Stockton	Durham City
1992-1993	Dunston Federation Brewery	Eppleton CW
1993-1994	Bedlington Terriers	Peterlee Newtown
1994-1995	Whickham	Crook Town
1995-1996	Morpeth Town	South Shields
1996-1997	Northallerton	Billingham Town
1997-1998	Chester le Street Town	West Auckland Town
1998-1999	Durham City	Shotton Comrades
1999-2000	Brandon United	Newcastle Blue Star
2000-2001	Ashington	Washington I H

ASHINGTON

Secretary: Brian Robinson, 80 Milburn Road, Ashington, N/thumberland NE63 0PG
Tel: 01670 852832 (H) 01670 521212 (B) FAX: 01670 852832

Ground: Portland Park, Ashington NE63 9XG (01670 811991 Social Club)

Directions: 200 yds north at traffic lights in centre of town

Capacity: 2,000 Seats: 350 Cover: 2,200 Floodlights: Yes

Clubhouse: Open 6-11 evening & from11am on Tuesdays (market days)
Not open Weds and Sun, darts, jukebox, snacks etc.

Club Shop No but jumpers, baseball caps etc. behind bar

PREVIOUS **Leagues:** Northern Alliance 1892-93 1902-14 69-70; Football League; North Eastern 14-21 29-58 62-64; Midland 58-60; Northern Counties 60-62; Wearside 64-65; N.P.L. 68-69.

RECORD **Attendance:** 13,199 v Rochdale, FA Cup 2nd Rd 9/12/50
Fee Received: £2,500 from W.B.A. for Tony Lowery

BEST SEASON **FA Cup:** 3rd Rd 26-27 League Clubs defeated: Halifax Town 50-51
FA Amateur Cup SF 73-74

HONOURS Northumberland Snr Cup (9) , Northumberland Chall. Bowl (6) , Midland Lg 58-59, North Eastern Lg Cup 33-34 (jt Sunderland Res.) 39-40; Northern Alliance x 4, R-up x 6; Lg Cup 47-48, Craven Cup Winners 98-99

Players progressing: Tony Lowery (W.B.A.), Les Mutrie (Colchester), R Cummins (Aberdeen), David Walton (Sheff Utd.)

FACT FILE

Formed: 1883
Nickname: The Colliers
Sponsors: Liteon
Club colours: Black & white stripes/black/white
Change colours: Blue/white
Midweek Matches: Tuesday
Programme: Yes, 50p
Editor: A Marchett (01670 854585)

CLUB PERSONNEL

Chairman: Geoff Walker
Joint Presidents:
Sir Bobby Charlton & Jackie Charlton OBE
Press Officer: Brian Bennett (01670 856606)
Manager: John Connelly
Asst.Manager: Iain Scott
Physio: Bob Robinson

BEDLINGTON TERRIERS

Secretary: Shaun Campbell,106 Wright St., Blyth. Northumberland NE24 1HG
Tel: 01670 353823 (H) 07703 529869 (M)

Ground: Welfare Park, Park Rd., Bedlington, Northumberland. Tel: 01670 825485

Directions: Into Bedlington, turn left at `Northumberland Arms' on Front St., then 2nd Right, ground on right 100 yds . Club Website: www.btfc.fsnet.co.uk

Capacity: 3,000 Seats: 300 Cover:500 Floodlights: Yes

Clubhouse: Open every evening, 7-11pm Sat. & Sun lunch. Pool, darts etc Club Shop: Yes

Record Att: 2,400 v Colchester Utd **Record Seasons Scorer:** John Milner 63 , 98-99

HONOURS Northern League Div 97-98 98-9 99-00 00-01 R-up: 85-86 9596 Div 2 94-95 (R-up 84-85), Northern Alliance 66-67 (R-up 67-68 69-70 71-72) Lg Cup 57-58 66-67 69-70 81-82, Lge Chall Cup 96-97 00-01,Northumberland Sen Cup 96-97. 97-98 Cleator Cup 97-88, 98-99, 99-00

PREVIOUS **Leagues:** Northern Alliance **Names:** Bedlington Mechanics 49-53; Colliery Welfare 53-56; Mechanics 56- 61; Bedlington United 61-65; Bedlington Colliery 65-68; Bedlington Town 68-74.

BEST SEASON **FA Cup:** 2nd Rd v Scunthorpe(a) 0-1 **FA Vase:** Final 98-9 VTiverton T 0-1

RECORDS **Attendance:** 1,013 v Blyth Spartans, Northern Lg 85-86
Win: 11-0 v West Auckland, (H) Lge 96-97 **Scorer:** John Milner 33

FACT FILE

Formed: 1949
Colours: Red & white/red&white/white
Change colours: Blue & whitw/blue&white/blue
Midweek Matches: Wednesday
Programme: 50 pages, £1.00

2000-01

Captain: Warren Teasdale
Top Scorer: John Milner (57)
P.o.Y.: John Milner

CLUB PERSONNEL

Chairman: David Perry
(0468 195350)
Vice Chairman: John Feary
Press Officer: Bill Lowery (01670 713099)
Managers: Keith Perry & Tony Lowrey
Assistant Manager: Steven Locker
Coach: Melvyn Harmison
Physio: Dave Robertson

BILLINGHAM SYNTHONIA

Secretary: Graham Craggs, 10 Embleton Grove, Wynard,Stockton on TeesTS22 5SY
Tel No: 01742 645367

Ground: The Stadium, Central Avenue, Billingham, Cleveland (Press Box 01642 532348)

Directions: Turn off A19 onto A1027 signposted Billingham, Norton (this applies from either north or south), continue straight on along Central Avenue, ground on left opposite office block. 1 mile from Billingham (BR)

Capacity: 1,970 Seats: 370 Cover: 370 Floodlights: Yes

Clubhouse: Onthe ground. Normal club hours **Club Shop:** No

HONOURS Northern Lg 56-57 88-89 89-90 95-96, R-up 49-50 50-51 51-52, Lg Cup 51-52 87-88 89-90, Div 2 86-87, Teeside Lg 36-37 (Lg Cup 34-35 38-39), Durham Chall. Cup 88-89 90-91, North Riding Snr Cup 66-67 71-72, North Riding Amat. Cup 38-39 56-57 62-63 63-64.

PREVIOUS **League:** Teeside (1923-War) **Name:** Billingham Synthonia Recreation

BEST SEASON **FA Amateur Cup** 4th Rd 48-49 **FA Vase:**
FA Trophy: Q-F replay 93-94, 1-2 v Woking after 1-1 (A)
FA Cup:1st Rd 48-49 51-52 56-57 57-58 87-88 89-90

RECORDS **Attendance:** 4,200 v Bishop Auck. 6/9/58
Scorer: Tony Hetherington **Appearances:** Andy Harbron

FACT FILE

Founded: 1923
Nickname: Synners
Sponsors: Darlington Building Society
Colours: Green & White quarters/white/white
Change colours: Blue & White
Midweek Matches: Tuesdays
Programme: 40 pages (+ads),75p
Editor: Nigel Atkinson (01642 342469)

2000-01

Captain: Dean McGee
Top Scorer: Tony Wood 18
P.o.Y.: Andrew Ripley

CLUB PERSONNEL

Chairman: Stuart Coleby
President: Frank Cook
Press Officer: Secretary
Manager: Stuart Coleby
Physio: Chris Rooney
Coach: Lenny Gunn

BILLINGHAM TOWN

Secretary: Glen Youngman,13 Blackthorne Grove, fairfield, Stockton, Cleveland TS19 7DG
Tel/Fax: 01642 655516 and Tel: 01642 862058

Ground: Bedford Terrace, Billingham, Cleveland. Tel: 01642 560043

Directions: Leave A19 on A1027 (signed Billingham). Turn left at 3rd r/bout,over bridge 1st left, 1st left again to grd

Capacity: 3,000 Seats: 176 Cover: 600 Floodlights: Yes
Clubhouse: Open matchdays. Hot & cold food **Club Shop:** No

HONOURS Durham Amateur Cup 76-77 77-78, Teesside Lg 77-78 81-82, Nth Riding Snr Cup R-up 76-77 81-82, Stockton & Dist. Lg(3)

PREVIOUS **Leagues :** Stockton & Dist. 68-74; Teesside 74-82.
Name: Billingham Social Club (pre-1982) **Ground:** Mill Lane (pre-1974)

BEST SEASON **FA Cup:** 1st Rd Proper 55-56
FA Vase: 5th Rd Proper

RECORDS **Attendance:** 1,500 v Manchester City, FA Youth Cup 1985
Scorer: Paul Rowntree 362 (1990-2001)
Appearances: Paul Rowntree 465 (including 2000-01)

Players progressing: Gary Pallister (Middlesbrough), Gerry Forrest (Southampton), Dave Robinson (Halifax), Tony Barratt (Hartlepool), Mark Hine (Grimsby), Tony Hall(Middlesbrough), Graham Hall (Arsenal).

FACT FILE
Founded: 1967 Nickname: The Social
Colours: All Blue
Change colours: Yellow/green/yellow
Midweek Matches: Tuesday
Reserves' Lge: Stockton & Dist Sunday
Programme: 28 pages, 50p
Editor:Peter Martin

2000-01
P.o.Y.: Richard Wood
Captain & Top Scorer: Paul Rowntree 56

CLUB PERSONNEL
Chairman: Tommy Donnelly
Hon. President: F Cook M.P.
President: G A Maxwell
Press Officer: Tom Donnelly
(01642 555332(H) 01642 370101(W)
Fax : 01642 651033
Manager: Alan Robinson
Asst Manager: Glen Youngman
Coaches: Tony Lye & Lee Tucker

BRANDON UNITED

Secretary: Brian Richardson, Flat 2, 30 Commercial St, Brandon, Durham DH7 8PL
Tel: 0191 378 1373

Ground: Welfare Ground, rear of Commercial St., Brandon, Durham Tel: 0191 378 2957

Directions: A690 - 3 miles west of Durham City. Buses 49 & 49A from Durham

Capacity: 3,000 Seats: 200 Cover: 300 Floodlights: Yes **Club Shop:** No
Clubhouse: Open every day, lunch & evening. Pool Entertainment at weekends

HONOURS FA Sunday Cup 75-76, Northern Lg Div 2 84-85 99-00Northern All.(2) 77-79, Lg Cup 77-78 79-80 Sunderland Shipowners Cup 81-82, Durham Co. Sunday Cup 73-74 75-76 76-77,Durham & Dist Sunday Lg(4) 73-77 (Div 2 69-70, Div 3 68-69), Staffieri Cup 75-76

PREVIOUS **Leagues:** Durham & Dist. Sunday 68-77; Northern All. 77-80; Northern Amtr 80-81; Wearside 81-83.

BEST SEASON **FA Cup:** 1st Rd replay 88-89 (lost to Doncaster). Also 1st Rd 79-80
FA Vase: QF 82-83 83-84 **FA Trophy:** 3rd Qual. Rd 87-88 89-90

RECORD **Gate:** 2,500, FA Sunday Cup SF
Record Goalscorer: Tommy Holden
Most Appearances: Derek Charlton 1977-86

Players progressing: Bryan Liddle (Hartlepool 1984) Dean Gibb (Hartlepool 1986), Paul Dalton (Manchester Utd 1988), Neil Richardson (Rotherham).

FACT FILE
Founded: 1968
Nickname: United
Sponsors: Bramble Down Landscapes
Colours: All red Change colours: All blue
Midweek Matches: Wednesday
Programme: 40 pages, 30p
Editor: Keith Nellis (0191 378 0704)

2000-01
Top Scorer: Michael Cunningham 26
Team Captain & P.o.Y: Mark Patterson

CLUB PERSONNEL
Chairman: Neil Scott
Vice Chairman: John Dickinson
President: Brian Hewitt
Press Officer: Secretary

Manager: Ken Lindoe
Physio: Keith Glendenning

CHESTER-LE-STREET TOWN

Secretary: Melvin Atkinson, 1 St Marys Close, Chester-le-Street, Co Durham DH2 3EG
Tel: 0191 288 3664
Ground: Moor Park, Chester Moor, Chester-le Street, County Durham (0191 388 3363)
Directions: Ground lies approx 2 miles south of town on A167 (C.-le-S. to Durham). Regular buses from C.-le-S. and Durham pass ground. Railway station 2 miles distant in town centre
Capacity: 3,500 Seats: 150 Cover: 1,500 Floodlights: Yes
Open Matchdays- midweek 6.30p.m.- 11.00 p.m. Saturday 12.00p.m.-7.00.Open Monday 7..30-11.00pm **Club Shop:** No, but old programmes available from editor
GROUNDS Ravensworth Welfare, Low Fell 72-73; Riverside Pk 73-78; Sacriston Welfare 78-79.
HONOURS Northern Lg Div 2 83-84 97-98; Wearside Lg 80-81 (R-up 82-83); Monkwearmouth Cup 80-81 81-82; Washington Lg; Durham Minor Cup; Washington AM Cup.

PREVIOUS **Leagues:** Newcastle City Amtr 72-75; Washington 75; Wearside 77-83
Names: Garden Farm 72-78

BEST SEASON **FA Cup: 4th Qual. Rd. 86-87, 2-3 v Caernarfon Town (H)**
FA Vase : 5th Rd v Fleetwood Town 84-85 (1-1,2-2,0-3)

RECORD **Gate:** 893 v Fleetwood FA Vase 18/2/85,
(3000 Sunderland v Newcastle,Bradford appeal match 85)
Appearances: Dean Ferry 219 (+38 subs)
Win: 9-0 v Washington N.L. 28/2/98 **Defeat:** 0-7 v Consett 6/11/96

FACT FILE
Founded: 1972 Nickname: Cestrians
Colours: Blue & white hoops/white/white
Change colours: All yellow
Midweek Matches: Tuesday
Programme: 40 pages, 50p
Editor/Press Officer:J.Thornback

2000-01
Captain & P.o.Y.: Colin Wake
Top Scorer: Martin Bowes 8

CLUB PERSONNEL
Chairman: John Tomlinson
Vice Chairman: Jack Thornback
President: John Holden
Press Off.: Jack Thornback (0191 3883554)
Manager: Paul Bryson
Asst Mgr/Coach: Stuart Sherwood
Physio: Ray Hartley

CONSETT

Secretary: Ian Hamilton, 29 Grange Street, Delves Lane, Consett, Co. Durham DH87AG
Tel: 01207 509366
Ground: Belle Vue Park, Ashdale Road, Consett, County Durham (01207 503788)
Directions: Quarter of mile north of town centre - along Medomsley Rd, left down Ashdale Rd, ground 100m yards on left. Follow signs for Sports Centre and Baths
Capacity: 4,000 Seats: 400 Cover: 1,000 Floodlights: Yes
Clubhouse: Matchdays, and evenings on request. Darts & pool **Club Shop:** No

HONOURS North Eastern Lg 39-40 (Div 2 26-27, Lg Cup 50-51(jt) 53-54), Durham Challenge 5, (R-up 2), Northern Lg R-up 76-77 (Div 2 88-89, Lg Cup 78-79 80-81), Northern Counties Lg 61-62, Sunderland Shipowners Cup 67-68, Monkwearmouth Charity Cup 67-68, Wearside Lg R-up 68-69 69-70.
PREVIOUS **Leagues:** Northern Alliance 19-26 35-37; North Eastern 26-35 37-58 62-64; Midland 58-60; Northern Counties 60-62; Wearside 64-70
Grounds: Vicarage Field (pre-1948); Leadgates Eden Colliery 48-50
BEST SEASON **FA Cup:** 1st Rd 58-59, 0-5 v Doncaster Rov. (A)
FA Trophy: 2nd Rd 78-79. **FA Vase:**
RECORD Gate: 7,000 v Sunderland Reserves, first match at Belle Vue, 1950.
Players progressing: Tommy Lumley (Charlton), Alan Ellison (Reading), Laurie Cunningham (Barnsley), Jimmy Moir (Carlisle), Jackie Boyd (West Bromwich Albion).

FACT FILE
Founded: 1899Nickname: Steelmen
Colours: Red with black & white trim/black/red
Change colours: Sky blue/dark blue/sky blue
Midweek Matches: Wednesday
Programme: 16 pages, 30p
Programme Editor: Andrew Pearson
Local Press: Journal, Northern Echo, Consett Advertiser.
2000-01
Top scorer: Tony Halliday 27
Captain & P.o.Y.: Jeff Sugden

CLUB PERSONNEL
Chairman: D.Nicholls
Vice Chairman: Stuart Moffat
President: John Hirst
Press Officer: Andrew Pearson
Tel: 01207 506194
Manager: Colin Carr
Physios: Brian Nicholson & Jim Vipond

DUNSTON FEDERATION BREWERY

Secretary: Bill Montague, 12 Dundee Close, Chapel House, Newcastle-upon-Tyne NE51JJ
Tel: 0191 2672250
Ground: Federation Park, Wellington Road, Dunston, Gateshead Tel: 0191 493 2935
Directions: Dunston/Whickham exit off A1(M), grd 400 yds north. along Dunston Rd on L. 1 mile from Dunston or Metrocentre stations. Buses from Gateshead & Metrocentre stop outside ground
Capacity: 2,000 Seats:120 Cover: 400 Floodlights: Yes
Clubhouse: Matchdays only. Hot & cold snacks, darts. **Club Shop:** No
HONOURS Northern Lge Div 1 R-up 00-01, Div 2 92-93, Challenge Cup 97-8, 98-9, 99-00; Northern Amtr Lg 77-78 R-up 2, Lg Cup 77-78 78-79 R-up 75-76, Lg Shield 78-79 79-80, Wearside Lg 88-89, 89-90. R-up 90-91, Lg Cup 90-91, N. Comb. 86-87 R-up 3, Lg Cup 83-84, 86-87 R-up 3, Sunderland Shipowners Cup 87-88, Durham Co Tphy 81-82 R-up 2, Minor Cup 79-80 R-up 78-79, Gateshead Chy Cup 77-78 80-81, Heddon Homes Cup 80-81. Cleator Cup 00-01
PREVIOUS **Ground:** Dunston public park 75-86
Names: Whickham Sports; Dunston Mechanics Sports
BEST SEASON **FA Vase:** Quarter-Finals 92-93, 0-2 v Gresley Rov. (A)
FA Cup: 3rd Qual. Rd 92-93, 0-3 v Northallerton T.
RECORDS **Attendance:** 1,550 - Sunderland Shipowners Cup Final 1/4/88
Win: 13-0 v Crook T. (H), Northern Lge Div. 1, 00-01 **Scorer:** Paul King
Defeat: 1-6 v Billingham Synthonia (A), Northern Lge Div. 1, 94-95 **Appearances:** Paul Dixon

FACT FILE
Founded: 1975 Nickname: The Fed
Sponsors: Federation Brewery
Colours: All blue with white trim
Change colours :Yellow/black
Midweek matchday: Tuesday
Reserve s' League : None
Programme: 28 pages 50p
Editor: Ian McPherson (0191 420 5583)
CLUB PERSONNEL
Chairman: Malcolm James
Vice-Chairman: Fred Fowles
President: John Smart
Press Officer: Ian McPherson (0191 420 5583)
Commercial Secretary: Malcolm James
Manager: Bobby Scaife
Asst Manager: Perry Briggs
Physio: Matt Annan
2000-01 Leading goalscorer: Andy Fletcher 36
Captain: Billy Irwin
P.o.Y.: Andy Fletcher

DURHAM CITY

Secretary: Kevin Hewitt, 21 Cerrytree Drive, Langley Park,Co Durham Dh7 9FX
Tel: 0191 3733878 (H & FAX) 0191 383 4200 (W)
Ground: New Ferens Park, Belmont Durham (0191 386 9616)
Directions
Capacity: **Seats:** **Cover:** 300 **Floodlights: Yes**
HONOURS Northern Lg 94-95 (R-up 70-71, Div 2 R-up 30-31 91-92), Durham Benevolent Bowl 55-56, Durham Challenge Cup R-up (2).Northern Div 2 Champions 98-99, Div 2 Champions 98-99 Durham Challenge Cup R-up (3)
PREVIOUS **Leagues:** Victory 18-19; N Eastern 19-21 28-38; Football Lge 21-28; Wearside 38-39 50-51. **Grounds:** Garden House Park 18-21; Holliday Park 21-38; Ferens Park 49-94. NB club disbanded in 1938
BEST SEASON **FA Cup:** 2nd Rd 25-26 57-58 (Also 1st Rd 27-28 55-56)
FA Vase: QF 87-88 **FA Amateur Cup:** 2nd Rd rep. 57-58
FA Trophy: 1st Rd 83-84
RECORD **Appearances:** Joe Raine, 552

Players progressing: Harry Houlahan (Newcastle 51), Derek Clark (Lincoln 51),Leo Dale & David Adamson (Doncaster 54/70), Stan Johnstone (Gateshead 54),Dennis Coughlan (Barnsley 57), John Wile (Sunderland 66), Brian Taylor(Coventry 68), Paul Malcolm (Rochdale 84)

FACT FILE
Reformed: 1949
Nickname: City
Sponsors: Durham City Housing Partnership
Colours: Blue & Gold Halves/Blue&yellow trimshorts and socks
Change colours:Red & White Stripes,white/white
Midweek Matches: Tuesday
Programme: 30 pages
Editor: Gordon Wright (0191 3869616)
Local Press: Northern Echo, Sunderland Echo, Evening Chronicle
CLUB PERSONNEL
Chairman: Stewart Dawson
Vice Chairman: David Asbery
President: Stewart Dawson
Commercial Manager: David Willis
Press Officer: Secretary
Manager: Brian Honour
Asst Manager/Coach: Derek Bell
Physio: Joanne Dowson

Crook Town on the occasion of Dennis Pinkney's 500th appearance for the club. He finished the season equalling Jimmy McMillan's 505 club record. Back Row (l-r): Alan Stewart (Sec), Robin Huntley, Matt Lumsdon, Elliott McCabe, Martin Blythe, Graham Curry, Martin Blight, Steve Thompson, Michael Sutcliffe, Phil Gonsalez, Robert Creek. Front Row: Gerard Wraith, Michael Dutton, Dennis Pinkney (Player-Manager), Andrew Robinson, Chris Baxter.

Marske United. Back Row (l-r): S Dowling (Asst Mngr), C Reeve, D Markham, M James, J Mohan, M Kinnair, C Gibbin Front Row: J Woods, J Middleton, G Knight, S Kasonali, Sam Woods (Mascot), N Hodgson, M Robson, S Neilson, S Murphy. Inset: C Bell (Manager)

FA Cup Third Qualifying Round - Bedlington Terriers v Accrington Stanley. Tony Chapman's goal puts the Terriers 4-1 up against the Unibond outfit. Photo: Graham Brown

GUISBOROUGH TOWN

Secretary: Keith Smeltzer,212 Woodhouse Road,Guisborough,Cleveland TS14 6LP
Tel Nos: 01642 226181 (W) 01287 201561 (H) 07811 850388 (M)
Ground: King George V Ground, Howlbeck Rd, Guisborough, Cleveland (01287636925)

Directions: From west: bear left at 2nd set of lights, left into Howlbeck Rd after quarter mile, ground at end. Buses from Middlesbrough
Capacity: 3,500 Seats: 150 Cover: 400 Floodlights: Yes Club Shop: Yes
Clubhouse: Open evenings & weekends. Hot & cold snacks & drinks from kitchen on matchdays

HONOURS FA Vase R-up 79-80; Northern Lg Cup 87-88 (Div 2 R-up 86-87), Northern Alliance 79-80 (R-up 78-79, Lg Cup 78-79); N. Riding Sen. Cup 89-90 90-91 91-92 92-93 94-95.

PREVIOUS **Leagues:** Middlesbrough & District; South Bank; Northern Alliance 77-80; Midland Counties 80-82; Northern Counties (East) 82-85.

BEST SEASON **FA Cup:** 1st Round Proper 88-89, 0-1 v Bury **F.A.Vase:** Finalists 79-80
FA Trophy: 1st Rd Proper 90-91 91-92 92-93

CLUB RECORDS **Gate:** 3,112 v Hungerford, FA Vase SF, 1980 (at Middlesbrough FC - 5,990 v Bury, FA Cup 1st Rd 1988)
Goalscorer: Mark Davis 323 **Appearances:** Mark Davis 551
Win: 6-0 v Ferryhill & v Easington **Defeat:** 0-4 v Billingham Synthonia

FACT FILE
Founded: 1973 Nickname: Priorymen
Sponsors: Hensons Windows & Conservatories
Colours: Red & white stripes/Black/Red
Change colours:Yellow Midweek day:Tuesday
Reserves ' League: Teesside Strongarm
Programme: 32pages,50p Editor: Stuart Burns
Local Press: Northern Echo, Middlesbrough Evening Gazette

2000-01
Captain: Darron Mowbray
Top Goalscorer: Michael Todd 16

CLUB PERSONNEL
Chairman:Dennis Cope
Vce Chairman: Keith Watson
President: Vacant
Press Officer: Stuart Burns
Manager: Steve Corden
Asst Manager: Steve Corden
Physio: Steve Carter

JARROW ROOFING BOLDON C.A.

Secretary/Manager: Richard McLoughlin, 8 Kitchener Terrace, Jarrow NE32 5PU
Tel: 0191 489 9825

Ground: Boldon CA Sports Ground, New Road, Boldon Colliery (0191 519 1391)

Directions: A19 to junction with A184 (Sunderland/Newcastle). Follow signs to Boldon Asda stores, then to North Road Social Club. Ground behind. East Boldon(BR) 800 yds.
Capacity: 3,500 Seats: 150 Cover: 800 Floodlights: Yes Club Shop: Yes
Clubhouse: Open eves.& w/e lunchtimes. Hotdogs, burgers etc from tea bar on matchdays

HONOURS Wearside Lg Div 2 R-up 91-92 95-96; Sunderland Shipowners Cup R-up 93-94, 94-95; Tyneside Amtr Lg R-up 90-91, Chal. Shield 90-91 (R-up 89-90); Bill Dixon Cup 90-91; Mid-Tyne Lg 87-88; Fred Giles Cup R-up 87-88; Gateshead Charity Cup SF 90-91; Monkwearmouth Cup 94-95; Craven Cup 96-97, Northern League Div One Cup R-Up 98-98

PREVIOUS **Leagues:** Mid-Tyne; Tyneside Amtr 88-91; Vaux Wearside

RECORD **Attendance:** 500 v South Shields
Appearances: Mick Haley **Goalscorer:** Paul Chow

FACT FILE
Founded: 1987Nickname: Roofing
Sponsors: Jarrow Roofing Co
Colours: Yellow with Blue trim shirts, Royal Blue & Yellow sjhorts and socks
Change colours: Yellow & Black
Midweek matchday: Wednesday
Programme: 20 pages, free with entry
Editor: Brian Marshall (0191 4217011)

2000-01
Top Goalscorer: Paul Choe: 28
Captain & P.o.Y: Scott Garrett

CLUB PERSONNEL
Chairman: Richard McLoughlin
Press Officer/Treasurer: Rose McLoughlin
Manager/ Secretary: Richard McLoughlin
Coach: John Oliver
Physio: Bob Frame

MARSKE UNITED

Secretary: Ian Rowe, 19 High Row, Loftus, Saltburn By The Sea, Cleveland. TS134SA
& Press Officer Tel: 01287 643440 (H) 01642 230546 (B) 01642 241273 (Fax)
Ground: Mount Pleasant, Mount Pleasant Ave., Marske, Redcar, Cleveland. Tel: 01642 471091
Directions: From A19 take A174 exit marked Yarm, Teesport, Redcar, Whitby and head east towards Saltburn until Quarry Lane r/about. Take 1st left (A1085) into Marske, 1st right (Meadow Rd) then 1st left (Southfield Rd),then 1st left again Mount Pleasant Ave directly into car park.
By train: Darlington to Saltburn, Marske station 300 yds from ground.
Capacity: 2,500 Seats: 169 Cover: 300 Floodlights: Yes
Clubhouse: Open every night and weekend lunchtimes. Food served after all games
Contact : Janet Pippen (01642 474985)
HONOURS N Riding Sen Cup 94-95; N Riding County Cup 80-81 85-86; Teesside Lg 80-81 84-85; Wearside Lg 95-96, R-up 93-94 94-95 96-97, Cup 92-93 94-95 95-96;M/mouth Charity Cup 93-94 95-96; Sunderland Ship. Cup 95-96 96-97.N.Lg Cup R-up: 00-01
PREVIOUS **Leagues:** Cleveland, South Bank & Dist, Teesside, Vaux Wearside.
BEST SEASON **FA Cup:** 2nd Q Rd ,00-01 **FA Vase:** Q Final replay, 00-01
RECORDS **Attendance:** 1,359 v Bedlington Terriers (F.A.Vase) **Win:** 16-0 v North Shields
Defeat: 3-9 **Goalscorer:** Chris Morgan 169 **Appearances:** John Hodgson 476
Players progressing: Peter Beagrie (Middlesbrough), Tony Butler (Blackpool), Roy Hunter (Northampton), Dave Logan (Mansfield T.)

FACT FILE
Founded: 1956Nickname: The Seasiders
Colours: Yellow/royalblue/white
Change: Royal/sky/yellow
Midweek matchday: Tuesday
Programme: 60 pages #1.00
Editor: Moss Holtby,(01642 475612)
Local Press: Sunday Sun, Middlesbrough Evening Gazette, Northern Echo

CLUB PERSONNEL
Chairman: John Hodgson
Vice Chairman: John Corner
President: Raymond Jarvis
Commercial Manager: Steve Davies
Manager: Charlie Bell
Assistant Manager: Stephen Dowling
Physios: Eric Barrett & Owen Hughes
Coaches: Charlie Bell & Stephen Dowling
Kit Manager: Colin Gilbert

Top: Newcastle Blue Star's Lee Suddes scores with a close range diving header. Photo: Alan Watson

Centre: The decisive goal of this FA Vase First Round tie as Tow Law Town (player partially hidden on right) head home the only goal of the game. Photo: Colin Stevens

Bottom: Whitley Bay FC. Back Row (l-r): Lee Picton, Neil Fairbairn, Adam Clementson, David Sproat, Marc Nash. Middle Row: Mark Cameron (Coach), Joe Jabs (Physio), Geoff Stephenson (Captain), Jamie McLeod (now at Prudhoe Town), Karl Muir, Richie Latimer, Marc Walmsley, Steve Cuggy, Denis Livermore, Jon King (now at Spenny moor United), Brian Smith, Gary Middleton, Tony Burgess (Asst Manager), Andy Gowens (Manager). Front Row: Chris Pearson, Glen Renforth (now at Totton FC), Ian Irving, Steve Walker, David Carr, Andy Bowman, Steve Pyle, Warren Dawson, Michell Boumsong

MORPETH TOWN

Secretary: Les Scott,1 Bennetts Walk, Morpeth, Northumberland NE61 1TP
Tel Nos: 01670 517390 (H) 0780 3483509 (M)
Ground: Craik Park, Morpeth Common, Morpeth, Northumberland. (01670 513785)
Directions: Morpeth is signed off the A1 onto A197. Take the B6524, right at Mitford sign, then right after about a mile into the ground, next to Morpeth Common
Capacity: 1000 Seated: 150 Cover: 150 Floodlights Yes
Clubhouse: Yes **Club Shop**: No

HONOURS Northern Alliance 83-84, 93-94 (R-up 37-38, 65-66, 73-74, 81-82, 84-85); Challenge Cup Winners 38-39, 85-86, 93-94 (R-up 36-37, 62-63, 73-74).
PREVIOUS Leagues: Northern Alliance pre 1994 **Ground:** Storey Park, Morpeth. pre 1992
BEST SEASON FA Cup: 4th Q Rd v Burton Albion 1998-99

FACT FILE
Colours: Amber & black stripes/black/black
Change colours: Blue,white,blue
Midweek Matchday: Tuesday Programme: Yes

CLUB PERSONNEL
Chairman: Ken Beattie Tel.: 01670 515271 (H), 01670 520565 (B)
Press Officer: Secretary

NEWCASTLE BLUE STAR

GROUND: Wheatsheaf Sports Ground, Woolsington, Newcastle-on-Tyne. NE13 8DF
Tel: 0191 286 0425 **Email Address:** mark@nbsfc.co.uk **Club Website**: www.nbsfc,co,uk
Directions: From central station follow airport signs for 7 miles - ground next to Wheatsheaf Hotel on left, approx. 800yds before airport. Callerton Parkway metro station is 400yds from ground
Capacity: 2,000 Seats: 300 Cover: 500 Floodlights: Yes **Club Shop:** Yes
Clubhouse: Matchdays only. Hotdogs, soup, sandwiches available

HONOURS FA Vase 77-78; Northern Lg R-up 87-88, Lg Cup 85-86, R-up(1), Div 2 85-86; Wearside Lg 73-74 75-76 82-83 83-84 84-85, R-up 74-75 77-78 79-80, Lg Cup76-77 79-80 80-81 82-83 83-84; Sunderland Shipowners Cup 82-83 84-85; Monkwearmouth Charity Cup 74-75 79-80 82-83 88-89; Northern Comb. 62-63 68-69, Lg Cup 66-67 71-72; Northumberland Snr Cup 76-77 82-83 85-86 87-88, R-up 74-75 78-79 80-81, Minor Cup 64-65; J R Cleator Cup 86-87.
PREVIOUS Leagues: Newcastle Business Houses 32-38; North East Amateur; Tyneside Amateur; Northern Comb.; Wearside 75-85
BEST SEASON FA Trophy: Qtr-finals 88-89, 1-4 v Telford Utd (H)
FA Vase: Winners 77-78, SF 81-82 **FA Cup:** 1st Rd 84-85, 0-2 v York C. (A)
RECORD Attendance: 1,800 v Almondsbury Greenway, FA Vase SF 77-78
Appearances & Goalscorer: Ian Crumplin
Players progressing: Ian Crumplin & Tony Robinson (Hartlepool 1976 & 1986), Barry Dunn (Darlington 1979), Ian McInerney (Huddersfield Town 1988) Peter Weatherson (Queen o South)

FACT FILE
Founded: 1930 Nickname: `Star'
Sponsors: T.B.A.
Colours: All Blue
Change colours: Red/Black/red
Midweek matchday: Tuesday
Reserves' League: None
Programme:44 pages,60p Editor: M.Gault

CLUB PERSONNEL
Secretary: Jim Anderson
38 Western Ave.,West Denton,
Newcastle-on-Tyne NE5 5BU
Tel: 0191 243 1025
Chairman: Tom Brash
Press Officer: Secretary
Manager/Coach: S.Leeming
Assistant Manager: P.Johnson
Physio: T.B.A.
2000-01
Captain: Warren Fisher
Top Goalscorer & P.o.Y.: Lee Suddes

PETERLEE NEWTOWN

Secretary: Danny Cassidy, 23 Melbury Str, Seaham, Co. Durham SR7 7NF
Tel Nos: 0191 581 4591 (H) 07904 398824 (M)

Ground: Eden Lane, Peterlee, County Durham (0191 586 3004)

Directions: From town centre Fire Station, turn left into Edenhill Rd, thenright into Robson Ave. Left at the next junction and ground is on the right
Capacity: 6,000 Seats: 50 Cover: 200 Floodlights: Yes
Clubhouse: Open normal licensing hours. Sandwiches etc available **Club Shop:** No

HONOURS Northern Lg Div 2 82-83, North Eastern F'lit League, 4th Qual Rd FA Cup
PREVIOUS Leagues: Northern Alliance 76-79; Wearside 79-82

RECORD Attendance: 2,350 v Northern, Hillsborough Fund match 1989
Scorer : Keith Fairless **Appearances** : Keith Bendelow

BEST SEASON FA Cup: 4th Qual. Rd replay 85-86 **FA Vase:**

Players progressing: Keith Fairless (Scarborough) 1986, Brian Honour(Hartlepool) 1988

FACT FILE

Formed: 1976
Nickame: Newtowners
Sponsors: Artix Ltd
Colours: Sky/navy/sky
Change colours: Yellow/black/yellow
Midweek Matches: Wednesday
Programme: 10 pages, 30p
Editor: Secretary
Local Press: Hartlepool Mail, Sunderland Echo, Northern Echo

CLUB PERSONNEL
Chairman: Carl Paylor
Vice-Chairman: Bill Burnett
President: David Brown
Press Officer: Ray Matthews (0191 523 8566)
Manager: Tommy Smith
Asst Manager: Eddie Freeman
Physio: Ron Lamdrel

SEAHAM RED STAR

Secretary: John Smith, 33 Frederick Street, Seaham, Co.Durham.SR7 7HX
Tel No: 0191 5810423
Ground: Seaham Town Park, Stockton Road, Seaham, Co. Durham (0191 581 1347)
Directions: From Tyne Tunnel: A19 Teeside approx 8 miles; B1404 Seaham slip road, left at top of slip road. Right at traffic lights & first left past school into ground
Capacity: 4,000 Seats: 60 Cover: 200 Floodlights: Yes **Club Shop:** No
Clubhouse: Mon-Sat 11am-11pm, Sun 12-2, 7-10.30pm Bars & restaurant, snooke & pool
HONOURS Northern Lg Cup 92-93, Phillips F'lit Tphy 78-79, Durham Chal. Cup 79-80, Wearside Lg 81-82 (Lg Cup 81-82, Div 2 R-up 87-88, Monkwearmouth Charity Cup R-up 79-80).
PREVIOUS **Name:** Seaham Colliery Welfare Red Star 78-87
Leagues: Sunday f'tball; Houghton & Dist. 73-74; Northern Alliance74-79; Wearside 79-83.
Grounds: Deneside Recreation Recreation Park 73-75; Vane Tempest Welfare 75-78.
BEST SEASON **FA Cup:** **FA Vase:** 5th Rd 78-79 **FA Trophy** 2nd Rd 89-90
RECORDS **Attendance:** 1,500 v Guisborough, Wearside Lg
v Sunderland, floodlight opener 1979
Scorer: Tom Henderson **Appearances:** Michael Whitfield
Players progressing: Bobby Davison (Huddersfield 1980), Nigel Gleghorn (Ipswich1985), Billy Stubbs (Nottm Forest 1987), Paul Nixon (Bristol Rovers (1989), Mick Smith (Hartlepool).

FACT FILE

Formed: 1973
Nickname: The Star
Colours: All Red
Change colours: All blue
Midweek matchday: Wednesday
Reserves ' League: Banks Youth League
Programme: 20 pages
Editor: David Copeland (0191 581 8514)
Local Press : Sunderland Echo, Journal, Northern Echo, Football Echo, Washington Times

CLUB PERSONNEL
Chairman: JohnSmith
President: Michael English
Press Officer: D.Copeland (0191 5818514)
Manager: Chris Copeland
Asst Manager: Paul Walker
Physio: Allan Jackson

THORNABY

Secretary: Peter Morris, 20 Wheatear Lane, Ingleby Barwick, Stockton-on-Tees, Cleveland TS17 0TB Tel: 01642 760779
Ground: Teesdale Park, Acklam Road, Thornaby, Stockton-on-Tees TS17 8TZ (01642 606803)
Directions: A19 to Thornaby turn off, ground half mile on right. One mile fromThornaby BR station. Any Stockton-Middlesbrough bus - stop at Acklam Rd,Thornaby
Capacity: 5,000 Seats: 150 Cover: 350 Floodlights: Yes **Club Shop:** No
Clubhouse: 150+ seater social club with concert room, pool/games room and bar. Open every night and Sunday lunchtimes and all day Saturday. Sandwiches avai. in bar, canteen in ground sells pies, burgers, soup, drinks etc
PREVIOUS **Leagues:** Stockton & District 80-81; Wearside 81-85.
Names: Stockton Cricket Club 65-80; Stockton 80-99: Thornaby-on-Tees 99-00
Grounds: Grangefield Youth & Community Centre, Stockton 80-82; Tilery Sports Centre 82-83.
RECORD **Attendance:** 3,000 v Middlebrough, pre-season friendly August 1986
Appearances: Michael Watson
Win: 11-0 v Horden C.W.(H) Buchanan Cup 94-95
BEST SEASON **FA Vase:** 2nd Rd **FA Trophy:** 1st Rd
FA Cup: 4th Qual. Rd replay 92-93,1-2 v Blyth (H) after 1-1
HONOURS Northern Lg Div 2 87-88 91-92, Nth Riding Co. Cup 85-86, Inaugralwinners of Craven Cup (Northern Div 2 clubs) 94-95.

FACT FILE
Formed: 1980
Colours:Yellow and blue/Navy & white/yellow
Change colours: All sky
Midweek Matches: Wednesday
Reserves' Lge: Wearside & Teesside Lgs
Programme: 24 pages, 50p
Editor: Peter Morris (01642 585625)
Local Press : Northern Echo, Evening Gazette

CLUB PERSONNEL
Chairman: Lol Lyons
Press Officer: Peter Morris
Manager: Michael Watson
Asst Mgr: Peter May
Coach: Paul Sharkey

TOW LAW TOWN

Secretary: Bernard Fairbairn, 3 Coppice Walk, Mowden Park, Darlington, Co. Durham DL3 9DP Tel: 01325 350743
Ground: Ironworks Road, Tow Law, Bishop Auckland Tel: 01388 731443
Directions: Just of High Street in Tow Law town centre
Capacity: 6,000 Seats: 200 Cover: 300 Floodlights: Yes
Clubhouse: Every evening 8.30 -10.30 **Club Shop:** Yes
HONOURS **FA Vase R-up 97-98;** Rothmans National Cup 1977, Northern League Champions 23-24 24-25 94-95, R-up 28-29 88-89, Lg Cup 73-74; Rothmans Overseas Cup 76-77, Durham Chal. Cup 1895-96, Durham Amtr Cup 1892-93.
PREVIOUS **Leagues:** None
BEST SEASON **FA Cup:** 2nd Rd rep. 67-68, 2-6 v Shrewsbury T. (A) after 1-1. Also 1st Rd 68-69 84-85 89-90. League Clubs defeated:Mansfield Town 67-68
FA Amateur Cup: 3rd Rd rep. 70-71 **FA Trophy:** 2nd Rd rep. 82-83
FA Vase: Runners-up 1997-98
RECORD **Gate:** 5,500 v Mansfield Town, FA Cup 1967
Players progressing: Reuben Cook & Ralph Guthrie (Arsenal 1951 & 53), Gordon Hughes, Terry Melling & Chris Waddle (Newcastle 1956 & 65 & 80), EricJohnstone & Kevin Dixon (Carlisle 1963 & 83), Keith Adamson (Barnsley 1966),Tom Henderson (Bradford PA 1969), Vincent Chapman (Huddersfield 1988)

FACT FILE
Founded: 1890
Nickname: Lawyers
Colours:
Black & white stripes/black/black & white
Change colours: Red & white
Midweek Matches: Tuesday
Programme: Yes
Editor:Chairman
Local Press : Northern Echo

CLUB PERSONNEL
Chairman: John Flynn
Press Officer: John Flynn (01388 730525)
Manager: Graeme Forster
Assistant Manager: Andy Sinclair

2000-01
Leading goalscorer: Nigel Bolton 27
Captain: Michael Bailey
P.o.Y.: Scott Nicholson

WASHINGTON IKEDA HOOVER

Secretary: George Abbott,14 Grosvenor St, Southwick, Sunderland, Tyne & Wear SR5 2DG
Tel Nos: 0191 5491384 (H) 0191 4177779 (W)

Ground: Albany Park, Spout Lane, Concord, District 11, Washington
Tel: 0191 417 7779

Directions: Ground situated opposite bus station.

Capacity: 3,000 Seats: 25 Cover: Yes Floodlights: Yes Club Shop: No

Clubhouse: Open normal licensing hours, with live entertainment, pool etc

PREVIOUS **Leagues:** Washington Amateur; Northern Alliance 67-68; Wearside 68-88
Ground: Usworth Welfare Park

RECORD **Gate:** 3,800 v Bradford Park Avenue, FA Cup 1970

FACT FILE

Founded: 1949
Nickname: Mechanics
Colours: All red
Change colours: All blue
Midweek Matches: Wednesday
Programme: 8 pages, 10p
Editor: Secretary

CLUB PERSONNEL

Chairman: Derek Armstrong
Tel: 0191 416 3956 (H)
Press Officer: Ray Lish
Tel: 0191 415 7071

WEST AUCKLAND TOWN

Secretary: Allen Bayles, 11 Edith Terrace, West Auckland, Co.Durham.DL14 9JT
Tel: 01388 833783 (H) & FAX, 01388 605221 (B) 01388 661366

Ground: Darlington Road, West Auckland, Co.Durham Tel: 01388 834403

Directions: Leaving West Auckland take A68-ground on right before leavingvillage. Bus route via Bishop Auckland fron Newcastle or Darlington

Capacity: 3,000 Seats: 250 Cover: 250 Floodlights: Yes **Club Shop:** No

Clubhouse: On Gound. (The Thomas Lipton Trophy is on display at the local Working Mans Club five minutes away). Tel No: 01388 661366

HONOURS FA Amateur Cup Finalists 60-61; Northern League Champions 59-60, 60-61 Div 2 90-91,Lg Cup 59-60,62-639r-UP;48-49,61-62,63-64)
Durham Challenge Cup 63-64 Durham Benevolent Bowl 62-63; Sir Thomas Lipton Tphy`First World Cup'(as featured in `The Captains Tale') 1909, 1911.

PREVIOUS **League:** Auckland & District
Names: St Helens Utd (1919 only), West Auckland Town.

BEST SEASON **FA Cup:** 1st Rd 58-59, 61-62,98-99 **FA Trophy:** 3rd Rd. 77-78
FA Vase: **FA Amateur Cup:** Runners-up 60-61; Q-F 59-60

RECORD **Gate:** 6,000 v Dulwich Hamlet, FA Amateur Cup 58-59
Victory: 11-0 in Durham County Cup

FACT FILE

Founded: 1892
Nickname: West
Sponsors:Rushlift Mechanical Handling and F.Hudson Transport
Colours: White with black & amber band and black collar & cuffs.
Change Colours: All Yellow
Midweek Matches: Tuesday

CLUB PERSONNEL

Chairman: Jim Polfreyman
Press Officer:Stuart Alderson
Manager: Dr. Graeme Forster
Ass.Manager: Dale Swainston
Coach: T.B.A.

WHITLEY BAY

Secretary: Derek Breakwell 27 Kings Rd, Whitley Bay, Tyne & Wear, NE26 3BD 0191 252 7940

GROUND Hillheads Park, Rink Way off Hillheads Road, Whitley Bay, Tyne& Wear NE25 8HR 0191 291 3637 Club. Fax & matchday office 0191 291 3636 Website: www.whitleybayfc.co.uk

Directions: 1 mile walk from bus station - leave St Pauls Church southward, turn right at r-about, ground 3rd left at rear of ice rink.Whitley Bay (25mins from Newcastle) or Monkseaton metro stations, both 1 mile. Email: derek.breakwell@whitleybayfc.com

Capacity: 4,500 Cover: 650 Seats: 450

Clubhouse: Open 7-11pm, 7 days. Bar & concert room. Darts, pool

Club Shop: Sells progs, scarves, hats, metal badges etc. Contact Tom Moody (0191 291 1618)

PREVIOUS **Leagues:** Tyneside 09-10, Northern All. 50-55, North Eastern Lge 55-58, Northern Lge 58-88; N.P.L. 88-00 **Name:** Whitley Bay Athletic 1950-58

CLUB RECORDS **Attendance:** 7,301 v Hendon, FA Amateur Cup 1965
Win: 12-0 v Shildon 1961 **Defeat:** 1-8 v Bishop Auckland 1979 **Goalscorer:** Billy Wright 307
Appearances: Bill Chater 640 **Fee Paid:** £500 for Paul Walker from Blyth Spartans
Fee Received: £10,000 for Kevin Todd from Berwick Rangers

BEST SEASON **FA Amateur Cup:** Semi Final 65-66 68-69 **FA Trophy:** 3rd Rd 86-87
FA Cup: 3rd Rd 89-90 (0-1 v Rochdale [A]). 2nd Rd 90-91 (0-1 v Barrow [H])

HONOURS: Northern Premier Lg Div 1 90-91 (Div 1 Cup 88-89 90-91), Northern Lg 64-65 65-66 (R-up 59-60 66-67 68-69 69-70), Lg Cup 64-65 70-71 (R-up 67-68); Northern Alliance 52-53 53-54 (Lg Cup 52-53 53-54); Northumberland Sen. Cup x10, R-up x7

FACT FILE

Formed: 1897
Nickname: The Bay
Colours: Blue & white stripes/blue/blue
Change colours: Yellow
Midweek home matchday: Tuesday
Programme Pages: 24 Price: £1.00
Website: www.whitleybayfc.co.uk

CLUB PERSONNEL

Chairman: Fred Iredale
Vice Chairman: Peter Siddle
President: T.B.A.
Press Officer: Peter Fox (0779 933654 (M)
Manager: Andy Gowens
Asst Manager/Coach: Mark Cameron
Physio: Joe Jabs

2000-01

Leading goalscorer: Stee Cuggy 25
Captain: Gary Middleton
P.o.Y.: Marc Walmsley

ALNWICK TOWN

Secretary: Darren Middleton, 1 Fire Station Houses, Alnwick, NE66 2PB(1665 603781)
Ground: St James' Park, Alnwick, Northumberland Tel: 01665 603162
Directions: 35 miles north of Newcastle on A1, take the slip road to Alnwick,then first left. At roundabout turn left, ground is then on your left.
Capacity: 2,500 Seats: 100 Cover: 200 Floodlights: Yes
HONOURS Northern Lg Div 2 R-up 88-89, Northern Alliance 37-38 62-63 63-64 65-66 67-68 68-69 69-70 70-71 71-72 (R-up 59-60 61-62 66-67 72-73, Lg Cup 61-62 65-6667-68 68-69 70-71, Subsidiary Cup 80-81), Durham Central Lg Cup 64-65, Northumberland Benevolent Bowl 86-87, Northumberland SNR Cup R-up 61-62,Northumberland Amtr Cup 71-72.
PREVIOUS **League:** Northern Alliance 35-39 46-64 64-82
Names: Alnwick United Services; Alnwick United.
BEST SEASON **FA Cup:** 3rd Qual. Rd 51-52 (3-4 at Blyth), 57-58 (4-6 at Easington Coll.).
FA Trophy: 3rd Qual. Rd 90-91.
RECORD **Attendance:** 600 v Bedlington Terriers, Northern Alliance 1971.

FACT FILE
Founded: 1879
Colours: Black & white stripes/black/black
Change colours: Green and yellow
Midweek Matches: Tuesday

Local Press: Northumberland Gazette

CLUB PERSONNEL
Chairman:Iain Burns
Manager: Malcolm Beusle
Press Officer: Iain Burns

Players progressing: George Turnbull (Grimsby 1950) and Brian Pringle (1973)

CROOK TOWN

Secretary/Press Officer: Alan Stewart, 8 East Bridge Street, Crook, Co. Durham DL15 9BJ.
Tel/Fax: 01388 764 216 (H). 0191 384 3388 (W). Mobile: 07971 375095.
Ground: Millfield Ground, West Road, Crook, County Durham (01388 762959)
Directions: 400 yds west of town centre on Wolsingham Road (A689). Nearest BR station is Bishop Auckland (5 miles). Buses 1A & 1B from Bishop Auckland or X46& X47 from Durham
Capacity: 3,500 Seats: 400 Cover: 300 Floodlights: Yes
Clubhouse: Lic Bar open matchdays. Hot & Cold Food available from Shop **Club Shop:** Yes
PREVIOUS **Leagues:** Auckland & Dist. 1894-96; Northern 1896-28 29-30; Durham Central 28-29; North Eastern 30-36; Wartime Durham & Northumberland 40-41;Durham Cen. 41-45.
BEST SEASON **FA Trophy:** 3rd Rd 76-77 **FA Cup:** 3rd Rd, v Leicester 31-32. 2nd Rd (4), 1st Rd.(10) **FA Vase:** 4th Rd 99-00 **FA Amateur Cup:** Winners 5 times, plus S-F x 3
HONOURS FA Amateur Cup Winners 00-01 53-54 58-59 61-62 63-64; Northern Lg 5, (R-up 4) Lg Cup 3, (R-up 4); Durham Chall. Cup 26-27 31-32 54-55 59-60; Durham Benevolent Bowl 6; Ernest Armstrong Mem Trophy 97.
2000-01 Leading Goalscorer: Martin Blythe - 10 **Captain:** Graham Curry **P.o.Y.:** Chris Baxter

FACT FILE
Formed: 1889 Nickname: Black & Ambers
Sponsors: Bar 56
Colours: Amber/black/black
Change colours: All White
Midweek Matches: Wednesday
Programme: Yes Editor: Secretary

CLUB PERSONNEL
Chairman: Stephen Buddle
Vice-Chairman:William Neil
Chief Executive: Tom Chopra
President: Sir Tom Cowie O.B.E.
General Manager: David Buchanan
Manager: Ronan Liddane
Asst. Manager: Dennis Pinkney
Coach: Phil Leaver

EASINGTON COLLIERY

Secretary: Alan Purvis, 12 Wark Crescent, Jarrow, Tyne & Wear, NE32 4SH (0191 489 6930)
Ground: Easington Colliery Welfare Ground, CW Park, Easington, Co Durham. (0191 527 3047)
Directions: A19 Easington turn-off, B1284 thru Easington to Black Diamond PH (next to zebra crossing), ground on the right
Capacity: 2,450 Seats: 175 Cover: 475 Floodlights: Yes **Club Shop:** No
Clubhouse: Normal licensing hours. Pies, soup and sandwiches available
HONOURS Northern Lg Div 2 R-up 85-86; Wearside Lge 29-30 31-32 32-33 47-48 48-49, R-up 28-29 46-47 73-74, Lg Cup 32-33 45-46 61-62; Monkwearmouth Cup 30-31 47-48 75-76; Sunderland Shipowners Cup 74-75 79-80.
PREVIOUS **Leagues:** Wearside 13-37 39-64 73-88
BEST SEASON **FA Cup:** 1st Round Proper 55-56
FA Trophy: 2nd Qual. Rd replay 88-89 **FA Vase:** 4th Rd replay 82-83
RECORD **Attendance:** 4,500 v Tranmere Rovers, FA Cup 1st Round 1955
Scorer: Andrew McKenna **Appearances:** David Howard

FACT FILE
Founded: 1913 Nickname: The Colliery
Colours: Green & white stripes/green/green
Change colours: Yellow/black/yellow
Midweek Matches: Tuesday
Programme: Yes Editor: Charlie Dodds

CLUB PERSONNEL
Chairman: Tommy Goodrum
Press Officer: Alan Purvis
Manager: Tony Metcalfe
Asst Manager: Paul Pringle

2000-01
Leading Goalscorer: Ian Matthews 15
Captain: Andrew Davies P.o.Y.: Stephen Salvin

EPPPLETON COLLIERY WELFARE

Secretary: John Tweddle, 40 Station Road, Hetton le Hole, Tyne & Wear DH50AT
Tel No: 0191 526 9633
Ground: Eppleton Welfare Park, Park View, Hetton-le-Hole, Tyne & Wear (01915261048)
Directions: Situated behind Front Street Post Office & directly behind Hetton swimming baths, Hetton-le-Hole on A182. Buses 194, 535, 231, X5, X94 in Front Street. 8 miles from Durham BR station; buses 154 and 254 from Durham
Capacity: 2,500 Seats: 250 Cover: 500 Floodlights: Yes
Clubhouse: Bar & lounge on ground. Normal opening hours. Whitbread beers
Club Shop: Club sweaters, polo shirts, metal lapel badges available
HONOURS Northern Lg Div 2 R-up 92-93, Wearside Lg 90-91 91-92 (Lg Cup 74-75 78-79 87-88, Sunderland Shipowners Cup 47-48 85-86 90-91 (R-up 91-92), Monkwearmouth Charity Cup 89-90 90-91 91-92), Durham Challenge Cup 89-90.
PREVIOUS **Leagues:** Wearside 51-65 74-92; Houghton & District 65-74.
RECORD **Attendance:** 1,250 - Monkwearmouth Charity Cup Final 1987-88

FACT FILE
Founded: 1929
Nickname: Welfare
Club Sponsors: E & N Ritchie
Colours: Black & sky/black/black
Change colours : Yellow/green/green
Midweek matchday: Wednesday
Programme: 16 pages,50p Editor:

CLUB PERSONNEL
Chairman: Ralph Lawson
President: J.Storey
Commercial Mgr: Secretary
Press Officer: Secretary
Manager: Vin Pearson
Asst Manager: John Cullen

ESH WINNING

Secretary: Roli Bell,12 Park Rd.Central, Chester-le-Street, Co Durham 0191 388 1458 (H)
Ground: West Terrace, Waterhouses, Durham Tel: 0191 373 3872 (Fax: 0191 387 1983)
Directions: Durham to Ushaw Moor, to Esh Winning; ground 1 mile further at Waterhouses
Capacity: 3,500 Seats: 160 Cover: 500 Floodlights: Yes
Clubhouse: Open daily. Snacks served **Club Shop:** No

HONOURS Durham & Dist. Sunday Lg 78-79 79-80, Durham Co. Sun. Cup R-up 78-79,Staffieri Cup 74-75, Guards Cup 72-73, N. Durham Yth Lg 94-95, Auckland Yth Lge94-95.
PREVIOUS **Leagues:** Durham & Dist Sunday; Northern Alliance 81-82.
Grounds: None **Names:** Esh Winning Pineapple (pre-1982)
BEST SEASON **FA Cup:** 2nd Qual Rd 90-91 **FA Vase:** 2nd Round 83-84
RECORDS **Gate:** 900 v Liverpool Fantail, FA Sunday Cup 1982
Goalscorer: Mark Drake **Appearances:** Paul Hewitson 40
Win: 11-0 v Norton (H) **Defeat:** 0-10 v Shotton Comrades
Fee Paid: #350 for Mark Drake**Received:** £500 for Paul Ward (Brandon U)

FACT FILE
Formed: 1967 Nickname: `Esh'
Sponsors:Lumsden & Carroll
Colours: Yellow/green/green/ green
Change colours: Green & Navy
Midweek Matches: Tuesday
Programme: 20 pages, 50p
Editor:Nigel QuinnPress Officer: Secretary
2000-01 Top Goalscorer Mark Drake 34
Captain: Scott Oliver P.o.Y.: Brian Wray

CLUB PERSONNEL
Chairman: Charles Ryan
Vice Chairman: R.Hird
President: Jack Lumsden
Manager:Barrie Fleming Physio: Lee Sullivan

EVENWOOD TOWN

Secretary: Jim Coates, 43 Fairfield, Evenwood, Bishop Auckland, Co Durham DL14 9SE
Tel: 01388 833035 (H) 07930 213071 (M)

Ground: Welfare Ground, Stones End, Evenwood, County Durham Tel: 01388 832281

Directions: In village centre by Sports & Social club in Stones Rd
Capacity: 3,500 Seats: 32 Cover: 200 Floodlights: Yes
Clubhouse: Open lunch & evening every day

HONOURS Northern Lg 48-49 69-70 70-71 (Lg Cup 35-36), Durham Challenge Cup 69-70.
PREVIOUS **Leagues:** Barnard Castle & Dist. 1894-95; Auckland & Dist. 1894-96 1903-04 08-23 28-31; Wear Valley 1896-99 1904-06 24-25; Gauntlett Valley 06-07; South Durham 27-28. Names: None
BEST SEASON **FA Cup:** 1st Rd 1936 FA Vase:
RECORD **Gate:** 9,000 v Bishop Auckland, FA Amtr Cup 1931
Players progressing: Too numerous to record

FACT FILE
Founded: 1890
Nickname: The Wood
Sponsors: C A Roofing
Club colours: All blue
Change: Red & white sleeves/white/red
Midweek Matches: Wednesday
Programme: None

CLUB PERSONNEL
Chairman: Matt Robinson
President: N Colegrove
Press Officer: Secretary
Manager: Dr Graeme Forster

HEBBURN TOWN

Secretary: Tom Derrick, 63 Staneway, Felling, Gateshead, NE10 8LS.Tel: 0191 442 1563
Ground: Hebburn Sports & Social Ground, Victoria Road West, Hebburn Tel: 0191 483 5101
Directions: On the main road through the town about 1 mile from railway station. Hebburn lies on the Metroline - excellent bus service from Heworth Metro
Capacity: 2,000 Seats: 153 Cover: 420 Floodlights: Yes **Club Shop:** No
Clubhouse: Open 7-11pm weekdays, Sat 11am-1pm, Sun noon-2.30pm. Pool, darts etc
PREVIOUS **Leagues:** Jarrow & Dist. Jnr 12-14; S Shields Comb. 19-22; Tyneside Comb. 22-27; Tyneside 27-39; Northern Comb. 41-44 45-59; North Eastern 44-45 59-60; Wearside 60-89.
Names: Reyrolles; Hebburn Reyrolles (pre-1988), Hebburn 88-00
HONOURS Shields Gazette Cup 91-92, Wearside Lg 66-67 (Monkwearmouth Charity Cup 68-69), Durham Challenge Cup 42-43 91-92, Tyneside Lg 38-39, Northern Comb. 43-44, Gateshead Charity Cup 35-36 37-38, Palmer Hospital Cup 27-28, Hebburn Aged Miners Cup 35-36, Heddon Homes Cup 42-43, Hebburn Infirmary Cup 35-36 36-37 37-38 38-39, Craven Cup 99-00.
BEST SEASON FA Vase: 2nd Rd 91-92 **FA Cup:** 2nd Qual. Rd rep. 89-90, 0-3 v South Bank (A)
RECORD Attendance: 503 v Darwen, FA Cup Prel. Rd replay 7/9/91 **Win:** 10-1 **Defeat** 3-10

FACT FILE
Founded: 1912
Nickname: Hornets
Colours: Yellow /navy blue/yellow
Change colours:Blue and White stripes/black
Midweek Matches: Wednesday
Programme: 24 pages, 30p
Editor: Steve Newton

CLUB PERSONNEL
Chairman: Bill Laffey
Vice-Chairman: Brian Errington
Press Officer: Alan Armstrong 0191 483 2046
Manager: Tony Robinson
Coach: Norman Dryden

HORDEN COLLIERY WELFARE

Secretary: Robert Wood, 29 Morpeth St., Horden, Peterlee, County Durham SR84BE
Tel: 0191 586 8802
Ground: Welfare Park Ground, Park Road, Horden, Peterlee, Co. Durham Tel: 0191 587 3549 (Club)
Directions: A19 to Peterlee, signposted from there
Capacity: 3,000 Seats: 220 Cover: 370 Floodlights: Yes
Clubhouse: Normal licensing hours. Hot & cold snacks, darts, pool

HONOURSDurham Challenge Cup 35-36 63-64 80-81 81-82, Durham Benevolent Cup 33-34, Wearside Lg 11-12 12-13 13-14 33-34 64-65 67-68 69-70 70-71 71-72 72-73 (Lg Cup 33-34 49-50, Monkwearmouth Charity Cup 12-13 23-24 32-33 69-70 72-73,Sunderland Shipowners Cup 65-66 72-73), North Eastern Lg 37-38 63-64 (`Non-Reserve' Medal 50-51).
PREVIOUS **Leagues:** Wearside 07-35 63-75; N. Eastern 35-58 62-64; Midland (Co's)58-60; Northern Co's 60-62. **Names:** Horden Athletic
BEST SEASON FA Cup: 2nd Rd 38-39, 2-3 v Newport Co. (H)
RECORD Attendance: 8,000 - FA Cup 1937 Player progressing: Paul Dobson (Hartlepool Utd)

FACT FILE
Reformed : 1980
Nickname: Colliers
Colours: Red/black/red
Change colours:Sky,navy,navy
Reserves League: Wearside Div 2
Midweek Matches: Tuesday
Programme: 10 pages, 50p

CLUB PERSONNEL
Chairman: Norman Stephens
Press Officer: M.Burgon (041 089 064417)

KENNEK RYHOPE C.A.

Secretary: Rob Jones,17Aspatria Avenue, Blackhall, Hartlepool TS27 4EG
Tel No: 0191 5870949
Ground: Meadow Park, Stockton Road, Ryhope, Sunderland (0191 523 6555)
Directions: From Sunderland follow signs for A19 South, ground adj to Cherry Knowle Hopital in Ryhope
Capacity: 2,000 Seats: 150 Cover: 200 Floodlights: Yes

HONOURS Wearside Lg 61-62 62-63 63-64 65-66(Lg Cup 63-64 77-78), Durham Chal.Cup 77-78, Monkwearmouth Charity Cup 09-10 65-66 66-67, Sunderland Shipowners Cup 61-62 (S.C.Vaux) 86-87
PREVIOUS **Names:** Ryhope C.W. (est.1898, prev.Ryhope Villa) merged with Sporting Club Vaux (est.1968 as Monkwearmouth, later Bishopwearmouth, South Hetton) in 1988; Sunderland Vaux Ryhope C.W. 88-93. **Leagues:** S. C. Vaux: Tyne & Wear; N.Eastern Amat.
BEST SEASON **FA Cup** 1st Rd Proper 67-68 **FA Vase** 1st Rd 81-82
RECORD **Gate:** 2,000; Ryhope Colliery Welfare v Workington, FA Cup 1967

FACT FILE

Founded: 1988
Colours: Red & white stripes/black/red Change colours: All Blue

CLUB PERSONNEL

Chairman: W.Mathieson
Tel: 0191 534 5496 (H)
Press Officer: Secretary

MURTON

Secretary: Chris Fahey, 16 D'Arcy Square, Murton, Seaham, Co. Durham SR7 9LZ
Tel No: 0191 5171355
Ground: Recreation Park, Church Lane, Murton, Co. Durham (0191 517 0814)
Directions: Exit A19 onto B1285 heading west into Murton - Church Lane on left opposite catholic church
Capacity: 3,500 Seats: 100 Cover: 320 Floodlights: Yes Club Shop: No
Clubhouse: `The International' 300 yards from ground on B1285. Normal pub hours. Restaurant upstairs. Matchday snacks at ground
HONOURS Northern Lg Div 2 89-90, Wearside Lg 28-29 36-37 59-60 (Lg Cup 58-5970-71), Sunderland Shipowners Cup 59-60 69-70 70-71, Monkwearmouth Charity Cup 21-22 28-29 34-35 35-36 63-64 70-71 87-88, Durham Chall. Cup 92-93, Durham Jnr Cup 50-51.
PREVIOUS **Leagues:** Wearside 13-46 51-88; North East Counties 46-51.
RECORD **Gate:** 3,500 v Spennymoor Utd, Durham Challenge Cup 1951
Appearances: Robert Welch 500 (1962-78)

FACT FILE
Founded: 1904 Nickname: Gnashers
Club Sponsors: John Hellyns
Colours: All white with red trim
Change colours: Red/black/red
Midweek matchday: Wednesday
Programme: 12 pages, 30p
Programme Editor: Stuart Upperton
CLUB PERSONNEL
Chairman: Tom Torrence
Vice Chairman: J Hudson
President: John Hellens
Press Officer: Secretary
Commercial Mgr: T Carr
Manager: Jeff Cranson
Asst Mgr: Brian Burlinson
Coach: Richie Madden Physio: Vince Symmonds

NORTHALLERTON TOWN

Secretary: Ken Lomer, 28 Aysgarth Grove, Romanby, Northallerton, North Yorks DL7 8HY Tel No: 01609 779686(H) 01609 773970 (W) **Club Website:** www.northallertontown.co.uk
Ground: Ainderby Rd, Romanby, Northallerton, North Yorks Tel: 01609 772418
Directions: Leave A1 at Leeming Bar (A684) follow signs to Northallerton,approaching town take B1333 signed Romanby - ground 250yds on left. 3/4 a mile from Northallerton BR station - local bus from town centre(1 1/2 miles) passes ground
Capacity: 3,000 Seats: 150 Cover: 500 Floodlights: Yes
Clubhouse: Mon-Fri 7.30-11pm, Sat noon-7.30pm, Sun 12-2 & 7.30-10.30pm
Club Shop: Yes, Contact Nigel Taylor 01748 836017
HONOURS Northern Lg Cup 93-94 (Div 2 R-up 89-90), Harrogate & Dist. Lg,N.Riding Snr Cup R-up 83-84, Northern Lg.Div 2 champions 96-97 Harrogate Invit; Alverton Tpy.
PREVIOUS **Leagues:** Allertonshire; Vale of Mowbray; Ripon& Dist.; Teesside; North Yorks; Darlington & Dist.; Harrogate & Dist.
BEST SEASON **FA Cup:** 4th Qual. Rd 92-93 **FA Trophy:** 3rd Rnd 92-93
RECORD **Gate:** 671 v Farnborough, FA Tphy 3rd Rd 20/2/93

FACT FILE
Founded: 1994 Nickname: Town
Colours: Black & White stripes,white
Change Colours: All Yellow
Midweek matchday: Wednesday
Reserves ' League: Harrogate& District
Prog 16 pages, 50p Ed: Ian Bolland
CLUB PERSONNEL
Chairman: Ralph Alderson
Vice Chairman: Les Hood
Press Officer: Ian Bolland (01609 776900)
Manager: Peter Mulcaster
Physio: T.B.A.
Captain: Lee Watson P.o.Y.: Darren Poole Top Scorer: David Lawson 25

NORTON & STOCKTON ANCIENTS

Secretary: Danny Day,186 Braemar Road, Billingham, TS23 2AR (01642 899506)
Email Address: linda.day 2@ntlworld.com
Ground: Norton (Teesside) Sports Complex,Station Road, Norton, Stockton-on-Tees, Cleveland (01642 530203) Clubhouse (01642 5540310
Directions: Norton village 2 miles from Stockton centre, turn into Station Road on outskirts of village
Capacity: 2,000 Seats: 200 Cover: Yes Floodlights: Yes
Clubhouse: Full bar facilities, 150 yds from ground
HONOURS Northern Lg Cup 81-82
PREVIOUS **Leagues:** Teesside (pre-1982) **Name:** Norton & Stockton Cricket Club Trust
BEST SEASON **FA Cup:** 1st Qual Rd(4) 88-89 90-93 **FA Vase:**
RECORD **Attendance:** 1,430 v Middlesbrough, Friendly 88

FACT FILE
Formed: 1959 Nickname: Ancients
Colours: Ambe& black stripes/black & amber/black
Change: Red with green trim/red socks
Midweek Matches: Wednesday
Programme: 12 pages with entry
Club Website: nortonfootball .co.uk
CLUB PERSONNEL
Chairman: Steve Warnes
President: Barry Lee
Press Officer: Secretary
2000-01
Catain: Michael Pugh P.o.Y.: Peter Conway
Top Goalscorer: Gary Alford

Horden keeper Stephen Jewson saves from Penrith's Mike Bell. Photo: Alan Watson

This effort by Esh Winning's Mark Drake beat Shildon keeper Alan Wilkinson but hit the side netting. Photo: Alan Watson

Esh Winning. Photo: Sunderland Echo

PENRITH

Secretary: John Balmer, 58 Castle Hill Road, Penrith, Cumbria Tel: 01768 866736
Ground: Southend Road Ground, Penrith, Cumbria Tel: 01768 895990
Directions: M6 Jct 40, onto dual carriageway to Appleby & Scotch Corner, first left at next r'bout, approx 1/2 mile into Penrith on A6 into town, take 1st left for ground. 3/4 mile from Penrith (BR)
Capacity: 4,000 Seats: 200 Cover: 1,000 Floodlights: Yes Club Shop: No
Clubhouse: Open Thurs, Fri & Sat 9.30pm-2am, & Sat 2-6pm, Wed match nights 6.30-10.30pm
HONOURS Northern Lg R-up 61-62; NW Co's Lg R-up 83-84; NW Co's F/Light Trophy 95-96 96-97; Cumberland Snr Cup [12], 46-48 50-51 60-66 70-71 72-73 74-75
PREVIOUS **Leagues:** Carlisle & Dist., Northern 48-82, N.W.C. 82-87, 90-97, N.P.L. 87-90.
BEST SEASON FA Cup: 2nd Rd 81-82 League Clubs beaten: Chester 81-82
RECORDS **Attendance:** 2,100 v Chester 1981
Goalscorer: C Short **Appearances:** Lee Armstrong
Win: 13-2 v Parton Utd **Defeat:** 0-13 v Bishop Auckland

FACT FILE
Founded: 1894 Nickname: Blues
Sponsors: British Gypsum
Colours: Blue/white/blue
Change colours: White/red/white
Midweek Matches: Wednesday
Reserve team: None
Programme: 24 pages, 50p
Press Officer: Secretary
Local Press: Cumberland & Westmorland Herald, Cumberland News

CLUB PERSONNEL
Chairman: Walter Brogden
Vice Chairman: M Robson
Manager: Geoff Byers
Physio: Les Cornwell

PRUDHOE TOWN

Secretary: Brian Tulip, 12 Orchard Close, Prudhoe NE42 5LP Tel: 01661 833169
Ground: Kimberley Park, Broomhouse Road, Prudhoe, Northumberland NE42 5EH Tel/Fax: 01661 835900
Directions: Approach Prudhoe along A695, turn right at `Falcon' Inn, 200 yds down Eastwood Rd., left into Broomhouse Rd., ground on right
Capacity: 5,000 Seats: 150 Cover: Yes Floodlights: Yes
Clubhouse: Open every evening plus Sat/Sun lunchtimes
HONOURS Hexham & Dist. Lg 68-69 (Lg Cup 68-69), Newcastle & Dist. Lg 69-70 70-71, Lg Cup 69-70, Charity Shield 69-70 70-71), Northern Comb. 79-80, Northern AmtrLg 71-72, Clayton Charity Cup 68-69, Northumberland Minor Cup 78-79, Northumberland Benevolent Bowl 79-80, Heddon Homes Charity Cup 81-82
PREVIOUS **Leagues:** Hexham & Dist 59-69; Newcastle & Dist 69-71; N. Comb.; N.Amtr; Northern All. 84-88 **Names:** Ovington 1969-75; Prudhoe East End 75-94
RECORD **Attendance:** 2,500 v Blyth, Northumberland Snr Cup 1981

FACT FILE
Founded: 1959
Nickname: Citizens
Sponsors: Swinton Insurance
Colours: Purple & jade halves/purple/purple
Change: White & blue chevrons/navy/sky
Midweek Matches: Wednesday
Programme: 8 pages, 20p
Editor: J Smith

CLUB PERSONNEL
Chairman: Alex Waters
Press Officer:ErnieGoodfellow(01661 836941)
Manager: Terry Hunter
Asst Manager: Kenny Barton
Physio: Ernie Goodfellow

SHILDON

Secretary /Press Officer: Mike Armitage, 22 Hambleton Court, Byerley Park, Newton Aycliffe, Co.Durham DL5 7HR Tel: 01325 316322
Ground: Dean Street, Shildon, County DurhamTel: 01388 773877 **Directions:** In the town centre 1 mile from BR station and 300yds from Darlington-Bishop Auckland bus stop
Capacity: 4,000 Seats: 400 Cover: 500 Floodlights: Yes **Club Shop:** No
Clubhouse: Every eve. 7.30-11pm (earlier match nights), 1-11pm Sat. matchdays. Pool&Darts
HONOURS Northern Lg 33-34 34-35 35-36 36-37 39-40 (R-up 32-33 38-39, Lg Cup 33-34 34-35 37-38 38-39 39-40 52-53), Durham Challenge Cup 07-08 25-26 71-72, Durham Amateur Cup 01-02 02-03, Durham Benevelopment Bowl 24-25.
PREVIOUS **Leagues:** Auckland & District 1892-96; Wearside 96-97; North Eastern 07-32.
BEST SEASON **FA Cup:** 2nd Rd 36-37 1st Rd 27-28 29-30 34-35 36-37 55-56 59-60 61-62
FA Trophy: 3rd Qual. Rd 74-75 **FA Amateur Cup:** 4thRd 58-59 **FA Vase:** 1st Rd 86-87
RECORDS **Attendance:** 13,000 - Leeholme v Perkinsville, schoolboys game, 1920s. (Shildon game); 11,000 Shildon v Ferryhill Ath., Durham Sen. Cup 1922

FACT FILE
Founded: 1890 Nickname: Railwaymen
Sponsors:
Colours: Purple/black/black
Change: Blue&yellow halves/blue/blue
Midweek Matches: Wednesday
Programme: 48 pages, 50p
Editor: Neil Bennett (01325 332310)

CLUB PERSONNEL
Chairman: Gordon Hampton V. Chair: G. Elliott
President: John Atkinson
Manager:Ray Gowan
Assistant: John Harland Physio: Neil Jennings
2000-01 Top Scorer: Doug Grant 13
P.o.Y.: Ian Robinson
Captain: Ian Robinson

SHOTTON COMRADES

Secretary: Billy Banks, 30 Hamilton Court, Shotton Colliery, Durham DH6 2NL (0191 526 7134)
Ground: Shotton Rec. Ground, Station Road, Shotton Colliery, Co. Durham(0191 526 2859)
Directions: A19 to Peterlee to Shotton, right at the War Memorial t-junction, follow round 800yds, ground on right
Capacity: 1,700 Seats: 80 Cover: 400 Floodlights: No **Clubhouse:** No **Club Shop:** No
HONOURS Houghton & District Lg 78-79, Lg Cup x 2, Northern Alliance Lg Cup SF, Hetton Charity Cup 78-79, Peterlee Sunday Lg 75-76, Div 2 74-75; Northern Lg.Div 2 Cup R-Up. 94-95.
PREVIOUS **Leagues:** Peterlee Sunday 74-76; Houghton & Dist. 76-80; Northern Alliance 80-83
BEST SEASON FA Cup: 2nd Qual. Rd 85-86, 0-2 v Wingate(H) **FA Vase** 1st Rd 86-87 90-91
RECORDS **Attendance:** 1,726 v Dennis Waterman XI
Goalscorer: Keith Willets 50 **Win:** 8-0 v Bedlington Ter. (H), '92
Appearances: J Cudlip **Defeat:** 1-7 v Brandon Utd (A), FA Cup Prel. Rd 91-92
Transfer Fee received: £500 for G Gudlip (Shildon)

FACT FILE
Formed: 1973 Nickname: Coms
Colours: Red & white stripes/black/black
Change colours: All orange
Midweek matches: Wednesday
Reserves' Lge: Banks u-19 Yth
Programme: 12 pages, 20p Editor: E A Jones

CLUB PERSONNEL
Chairman: Colin Jobes
Vice Chairman: T Robinson
President: G Taylor
Press Officer: Secretary

Manager: B Huntingdon
Physio: W Banks

SOUTH SHIELDS F.C.

Secretary: David Fall, 50 Basil Way, South Shields NE34 8UD Tel: 0191 426 2135

Ground: Mariners Club, Filtrona Park, Shaftesbury Avenue, Jarrow, Tyne & Wear NE34 9PH. Tel: 0191 427 9839

Directions: From A1(M) take A194(M) to South Shields, A194 town centre road for 5 miles, ignore A1300 (Sunderland & coast) & turn left at next lights beside Co-op store into Simonside Ind. Est. (Shaftesbury Ave.), ground at bottom

Capacity: 2,500 Seats: 150 Cover: 400 Floodlights: Yes

Clubhouse: Two function suites, club kitchen **Club Shop:** Yes

HONOURS Northern Lge Div 2 R-up 95-96, Northern Alliance 74-75 75-76, Wearside Lg 76-77 92-93 94-95, Monkwearmouth Charity Cup 86-87 (R-up 94-95), Shipowners Cup 92-93 (R-up 83-84)), Durham Chal. Cup 76-77 R-up 94-95. **BEST SEASON** **FA Vase** QF 75-76

PREVIOUS **Leagues:** Northern Alliance 74-76 **Ground:** Jack Clarke Park 74-92

RECORD **Attendance:** 1,500 v Spennymoor, Durham Challenge Cup Final 94-95

FACT FILE

Founded: 1974 Nickname: Mariners
Colours: Claret & blue/white/white
Change: All white
Midweek matchday: Tuesday
Reserve team: None
Programme: 50p Editor: Steve Leonard

CLUB PERSONNEL

Chairman: John Rundle
Vice Chairman: George Scott
Press Officer: Secretary
Manager: David Clark
Asst Manager:Paul Brown
Physio: Jim Wilkinson

WASHINGTON NISSAN

Secretary: Harry English, 22 Rushcliffe, Fulwell , Sunderland SR6 9RG
Tel: 0191 548 7194 (H) 0191 415 2340 (W) 07889 469961 (M)

Ground: Nissan Sports Complex, Washington Road, Sunderland SR5 3NS
Tel: 0191 415 2354 or 0191 415 2773

Directions: North along A1 (M) use A690 (signed Sunderland) connect withA19, north on A19, after passing the A1231 turn off, plant on the left. Past plant & follow signs 'Nissan Offices'.

Clubhouse: Open Mon-Fri 5-11pm, Sat 11am-11pm, Sun noon-3 & 7-10.30pm

PREVIOUS **League:** Wearside to 2001

HONOURS: Wearside Lg Div 1 93-94 (Lg Cup R-up 91-92, Div 2 Cup 92-93 93-94), Nissan European Trophy 3.

FACT FILE

Founded: 1988
Colours: Blue & black stripes/ blue/blue
Change colours: Red & white/white/white.

CLUB PERSONNEL

Chairman: Alan Hill
Treasurer: J.Taylor
Press Officer: Paul Curry
Manager: Stan Fenwick
Assistant Manager: Keith Robertson.
Coach: Darren Ward

WHICKHAM

Secretary: Harry Hodgson, 2, Dockendale Hall, Dockendale Lane, Whickham, Newcastle upon Tyne,NE16 4EN Tel: 0191 488 2493

Ground: Glebe Ground, Rectory Lane, Whickham (0191 420 0186) **Directions:** A692 (Consett) from A69. Left at r'bout signed Consett/Whickham. Uphill and right at mini-r'bout. Continue along & turn left into Rectory Lane (by Lloyds Bank) for 500 yds, clubhouse on right

Capacity: 4,000 Seats: 100 Cover: Yes Floodlights: Yes

Clubhouse: Mon-Fri. 12-3 & 7-11, Sat.11-11, Sun. 12-2, 7.30-11 Souvenir Shop: No

HONOURS FA Vase 80-81, Wearside Lg 77-78 87-88 (R-up 80-81 84-85, Lg Cup 86-87, Monkwearmouth Charity Cup 76-77, Sunderland Shipowners Cup 77-78 80-81), Northern Comb. 69-70 72-73 73-74 (Lg Cup 60-61 73-74)

PREVIOUS **Leagues:** Derwent Valley -55; Northern Comb. 55-57 59-74; Tyneside Amtr 57-59; Wearside 74-88 **Ground:** Rectory Rec. Field

BEST SEASON **FA Cup:** 1st Qual. Rd. 89-90 **FA Vase:** Winners 80-81

RECORD **Gate**: 3,165 v Windsor & Eton, F.A. Vase SF 81

FACT FILE

Founded: 1944
Colours: Black & White stripes/ Black/Black
Change colours: All white
Midweek Matches: Wednesday
Programme: 20p
Local Press : Newcastle Journal, Sunday Sun, Evening Chronicle
2000-01 Top Goalscorer: Paul Wlson 22
Captain & P.o.Y.: Kriss Holmes

CLUB PERSONNEL

Chairman: Tommy Thompson
Manager: Steve Higgins
Press Officer: Secretary

WILLINGTON

Secretary: Bob Nichols, 46 Cavendish Ct, Brandon,Durham DH7 8UW Tel/ FAX 0191378 1981

Ground: Hall Lane, Hall Lane Estate, Willington, County Durham (01388 746221)

Email Address: willingtonafc@hotmail.com

Directions: Willington is on A690 7 miles west of Durham City & 2 miles east of Crook. Northern Bus Co. operates a service through Willington from Crook or Durham City

Capacity: 2,680 Seats: 350 Cover: 400 Floodlights: Yes Club shop: Occasionally

Clubhouse: Open eves 7-11pm &Sat. matchdays 1-11pm. Bar facilities.Tea shop on matchdays

HONOURS FA Amateur Cup 49-50, R-up 38-39; Northern League 13-14 25-26 29-30, R-up 12-13 57-58 75-76, Lge Cup 24-25 25-26 27-28 30-31 31-32 48-49 56-57 74-75; Durham Benevolent Cup 48-49 50-51 57-58.

BEST SEASON FA Cup: 1st Rd rep. 73-74, 1-6 v Blackburn R (A) after 0-0.Also 1st Rd 45-46 & 50-51 **FA Trophy** 3rd Rd 75-76 **FA Amat. Cup:** Winners 49-50

PREVIOUS **Leagues:** Auckland & Dist. 1906-11 **Names:** Willington Temperance 1906-11

RECORD Attendance: 10,000 v Bromley, FA Amateur Cup 2nd Rd 24/1/53 **Goalscorer:** J `Boxer' Taylor 55-69 150 approx.**Appearances:** S Rutherford 47-61 & G.Brown51-64 both 350+

FACT FILE

Founded: 1906 Nickname: Blue & Whites
Sponsor:Newfit Services
Colours: Blue & white stripes/blue/blue
Change colours: Yellow/green/green
Midweek Matches: Tuesday
Youth League: Auckland & Dist League
Programme: 50p Editor: Christina Jackson

CLUB PERSONNEL

Chai: Alistair Melville Vice-Chair: Anne Robson
President: Hilary Armstrong M.P.
Press Officer: Sec Player/Man Dave Taylor
2000-01 Captain: Geoff Young . P.o.Y. Rob Spink Top Scorer: Steve Hamil (14) Website: www.willingtonafc.free-online.co.uk

Top: Penrith keeper Gary Greenan thwarts Horden's Alan Hoey.
Photo: Alan Watson

Centre: Mike Parkinson - left (Esh Winning) and Dale White (Shildon)
Photo: Alan Watson

Bottom: Martin Kirkby (6) rises to head in Bedlington's first goal in their 5-2 victory over Unibond side Accrington Stanley in the FA Cup Third Qualifying Round tie.
Photo: Graham Brown

NISSAN WEARSIDE LEAGUE

FEEDER TO:
ARNOTT INSURANCE NORTHERN LEAGUE

President: W Robson **Chairman:** P J Maguire

Secretary: E Hargreaves, 4 South Mews, Shadforth, Durham DH6 1NS
Tel: 0191 372 2844

Season 1999-2000 saw the Wearside League operating with two divisions, sixteen teams in the First Division and eight teams in the Second Division. With the loss of four teams, Herrington CW, Sunderland Red House WMC, Wallsend Town and Workington Reserves resigining at the season's end, citing travelling and match day expense as their reasons in all but one case, it was decided to run the season just ended with a single division of twenty teams, and to suspend the League Challenge Cup competition for one season, with no new teams being admitted.

Playing 38 League games in addition to two charity cup competitions was an ambitious challenge particularly when you bear in mind that only two of our clubs had floodlights and taking into account the severe winter, which caused postponement of a total of 97 scheduled matches. The extent of the rain and flooded grounds was worse than any that can be remembered, but memory plays tricks and we can all remember playing on pitches in our youth which players would not be prepared to play on these days.

Playing three times a week at the beginning and end of the season ensured that the League was concluded by 28th May, three days before the official end of the season.

The League was dominated by two teams, Nissan FC and North Shields FC, who both qualified for, in terms of facilities, promotion to the Northern League. In the end the League was won by Nissan for the second successive season and they leave for promotion with our good wishes. North Shields, who are an example to every team for what they have achieved with their facilities, will be the team to beat next season, as they went for the last five months only being beaten in one game. Unfortunately, when they needed to win most, in the League decider against Nissan in mid May, they could only draw 0-0 and consequently finished the season in second place. They did, in addition to winning the Monkwearmouth Charity Cup, win the Brother Northumberland Senior Benevolent Bowl, their equivalent of a County Cup Final.

FINAL LEAGUE TABLE 2000-01

		P	W	D	L	F	A	GD	Pts
1	Nissan	38	31	3	4	120	29	91	96
2	North Shields	38	29	6	3	143	24	119	93
3	Wolviston	38	24	6	8	107	58	49	78
4	Windscale	38	23	6	9	99	49	50	75
5	Harton & Westoe	38	23	4	11	118	67	51	73
6	Boldon CA	38	24	4	10	104	63	41	73*
7	Redcar Town	38	21	8	9	103	61	42	68*
8	New Marske	38	19	7	12	90	58	32	64
9	Stokesley SC	38	19	6	13	116	67	49	63
10	Whitehaven	38	19	5	14	82	75	7	62
11	Ferryhill Athletic	38	16	4	18	91	89	2	52
12	Stanley United	38	12	12	14	77	76	1	48
13	Thornaby on Tees	38	14	6	18	86	101	-15	48
14	Birtley Town	38	15	4	19	79	101	-22	43*
15	Annfield Plain	38	13	3	22	87	96	-9	39
16	Cleadon SC	38	7	4	27	49	113	-64	25
17	Ryhope CW	38	6	5	27	46	102	-56	23
18	Simonside SC	38	7	2	29	33	195	-162	23
19	Jarrow	38	5	6	27	51	117	-66	21
20	Whitburn	38	2	1	35	38	178	-140	7

* points deducted

HONOURS LIST 2000-01

	Winners	Runners up
League Division One	Nissan FC	North Shields FC
Monkwearmouth Charity Cup	North Shields FC	Nissan FC
Sunderland Shipowners Charity Cup	Wolviston FC	Harton & Westoe CW FC
Tom Purvis Memorial Trophy	Windscale FC	Wolviston FC
League Leading Goalscorer	Adam Johnson (Nissan FC)	60 goals
Secretary of the Season	Keith Simpson (Wolviston FC)	

MONKWEARMOUTH CHARITY CUP 2000-01

FIRST ROUND

Simonside SC	v	Annfield Plain	2-0	Whitburn	v	Jarrow	0-4
Whitehaven	v	Stokesley SC	5-2	Windscale	v	Cleadon SC	2-0

SECOND ROUND

Thornaby on Tees	v	Stanley United	3-2	Birtley Town	v	Ferryhill Athletic	5-1
Boldon CA	v	Harton & Westoe	1-4	Simonside SC	v	Jarrow	0-3
Ryhope CW	v	Nissan	0-3	New Marske SC	v	North Shields	0-3
Windscale	v	Wolviston	2-1	Whitehaven	v	Redcar Town	

Redcar Town expelled

QUARTER FINALS

Jarrow	v	North Shields	0-4	Nissan	v	Thornaby on Tees	4-1
Windscale	v	Birtley Town		Whitehaven	v	Harton & Westoe	1-3

Birtley Town expelled

SEMI FINALS

North Shields	v	Harton & Westoe	2*1	Nissan	v	Windscale	3*0

FINAL

Nissan	v	North Shields	2-3	after extra time

SUNDERLAND SHIPOWNERS CUP 2000-01

FIRST ROUND

North Shields	v	Annfield Plain	3*2	Ferryhill Athletic	v	Whitehaven	3-1
Whitburn	v	Boldon CA	0-5	Birtley Town	v	Ryhope CW	1-0

SECOND ROUND

Simonside SC	v	Thornaby on Tees	2-3	Stokesley SC	v	Wolviston	1-3
Cleadon SC	v	North Shields	2-1	Stanley United	v	New Marske SC	3-2
Nissan	v	Jarrow	5-1	Boldon CA	v	Harton & Westoe	1-4
Windscale	v	Ferryhill Athletic	2-0	Redcar Town	v	Birtley Town	5p6, 3*3

QUARTER FINALS

Thornaby on Tees	v	Harton & Westoe	1-2	Nissan	v	Windscale	2-0
Wolviston	v	Cleadon SC	9-0	Birtley Town	v	Stanley United	1*2

SEMI FINALS

Stanley United	v	Harton & Westoe	0-2	Nissan	v	Wolviston	1-5

FINAL

Harton & Westoe	v	Wolviston	2-3	after extra time

ANNFIELD PLAIN

Secretary: M Lawson, 24 Northgate, Anfield Plain, Stanley, Co. Durham DH9 7UY
Tel: 01207
Ground: Derwent Park, Annfield Plain. **Directions:** On A693 road to Consett, 200yds west of junction with A6067. Ground behind new housing estate. 6 miles fromDurham (BR). Buses from Sunderland, Newcastle & Durham.
Capacity: 6,000 Seats: 20 Cover: 200 Floodlights: No
HONOURS Wearside Lg 84-85 (Monkwearmouth Charity Cup 92-93),
FA Cup: 1st Rd 26-27 28-29 64-65.

Founded: 1890.
Colours: Claret/white/blue
Change colours: All blue.
Programme: 16 pages, 20p

Chairman: Frank Ross
Treasurer :Marshall Lawson
Manager: D Longstaff
Press Officer: Frank Ross

BIRTLEY TOWN

Secretary: Kevin McConnell, 8 Laybourn Place, Birtley DH3 1PL Tel No: 0191 4100 495
Commercial Manager: Ray Stafford.
Ground: Birtley Sports Complex. **Directions:** (From Durham) Off A1(M) signpstedfor Chester-le-Street, take 2nd turn off r-bout signed Birtley, take last turnoff next r-bout (still signed Birtley), after one and a half miles take 1stleft after AEI Cables - ground at rear of sports complex.
Capacity: Unknown Seats: None Cover: None Floodlights: No.
Clubhouse: Matchdays only
HONOURS: Wearside Lg 45-46 (Lg Cup 35-36), Northern Alliance 23-24 (R-up 13-14).

Founded: 1890 Reformed: 1986
Colours: Green&white hoops/white/green
Change colours: Yellow/blue/red.
Midweek matches: Wednesday
Sponsors: C & C Coachworks
Chairman: John Heslington
Vice-Chairman: J Grainger.
Manager: Barry Fleming
Asst Manager: David Smith
Coach: Malcolm Thompson

BOLDON COMMUNITY ASSOCIATION

Secretary: Tom Robson, 16 Hardie Drive, West Boldon ,Tyne & Wear NE36 0JH.
Ground: Boldon Community Association, New Road, Boldon Colliery.
Directions: A19 to junc A184 Sunderland/Newcastle. Follow signs to Boldon Asdastores, then to North Road Social Club (SHACK). Ground behind. 800 yds fromEast Boldon (BR). Buses 533, 531, 319, 528.
Capacity: 3,500 Seats: 100 Cover: 400 Floodlights: No
Clubhouse: Matchdays only. Bar snacks
HONOURS: Wearside Lg 3, (Lg Cup 3), M/mouth Char Cup 2, Shipowners Cup 6.

Founded: 1892. Nickname: Villa
Colours: Black & Blue Stripes/ Black/Blue
Change: Scarlet & black
Chairman:Kevin Oliver
Vice Chairman: G Smith
President: A Brewster.
Manager: Bill Newham
Asst Manager: P Quinn
Coach: Tommy Frazer.
Press Off. / Comm. Man.: Secretary

DARLINGTON RAILWAY ATHLETIC

Secretary: Martyn Jackson, 6 Westlands Rd., Darlington,Co.Durham DL3 9JJ
Tel Nos: 01325 240495 (H) 0870 370095 (M)
Ground: Railway Social Club, Brinkburn Road,Darlington, Co Durham
Capacity: 1,000 **Seats:** None **Cover**: 50 **Floodlights** : Planned
Directions: Take A68 off A1 towards Darlington. Turn left opposite pub on right into Brinkburn Road and ground is 400 yards on left.
Clubhouse: Yes. It serves all sports at complex.
Honours: Auckland & Dist Lg & Cup, Darlington & The SacristonCharity Cups, 00-01

Reformed 1996

Colours: Dark blue & light blue stripes, blue shorts and socks.
Change Colours: Red & black quarters, black shorts and socks.

Manager: Dave Woodcock
Programme : Yes Editor: Robert Harman

FERRYHILL ATHLETIC

Secretary: Norman Bellwood, 49 Rush Park, Bishop Auckland DL14 6NS
Tel: 01388 451065 (H)
Football Secretary: Rob Ridley, 31 Ravensworth Road, Ferryhill Tel: 0780 3803335
Ground: Dean Bank Recreation Ground
Directions: The ground is situated on the old Dean & Chapter Colliery Welfare site west of the old Athletic ground at Darlington Road. From the top of Darlington Road with the Black Bull on your right, pass over the bridge crossing the A167 cutting. Dean Bank school is immediately on your left, turn left at the one way traffic restriction. Follow the signs to Dean Bank Rec.

Colours: Black & amber/amber/black & amber
Change: Red & white/red/red & white

Chairman: Secretary
Press Officer: Jimmy O'Sullivan
Tel: 01740 635524

JARROW

Secretary: Susan Scott,46 Breamish Street, Jarrow. NE32 5SH (0191 4248610)

Ground: Perth Green Community Centre.
Directions: From A19 or A1(M) followdrections to South Shields, right onto John Reid Road. First slip road ontoBrockley Whinns Estate, follow road past Red Hackle pub, third left left ontoInverness Road, then right into Perth Green Community Centre.

HONOURS: Sth Tyne Lg & Lg Cup, Washington Lg R-up 89-90 (Lg Cup 90-91, Aged Peoples Tphy R-up 90-91), Gateshead Charity Cup 90-91, Durham Tphy R-up 90-91.

Founded: 1980.
Colours: Blue & white/blue/blue
Change: Green/black/green

Chairman: B.Tyreman
Treasurer: Jimmy Kane

NEW MARSKE

Colours: Yellow & black/navy/navy or white
Change colours: Blue & black/navy/navy

Secretary: Peter Livingstone,5 Guisborough Rd,Thornaby on Tees TS17 8BE
Tel Nos: 01642 646428(H) 01642 606803 (B)

Charmain: Errol Richter
Tel: 01947 600296
Press Officer: Tony Saunders

Ground: Gurney Street, New Marske, Redcar
Directions: A19 south onto A174 Redcar- Teesport. Follow A174 towards Saltburn turn right at roundabout with footbridge over road. Ground 500 yds on left.

NORTH SHIELDS

Secretary: Dave Thompson, 38 Barnstable Road, North Shields. Tel: 0191 259 0249
Ground: Ralph Gardner Park, West Percy Rd., N.Shields, Tyne & Wear, NE29 OES
Directions: A19 northbound through Tyne Tunnel. Take 1st slip round to 1str/about & take 3rd exit & over next r/about. Take 3rd exit again at nextr/about into Waterville Rd. Over another r/about and 2nd left into Silkey'sLane. 1st right into West Percy Rd, grd on right.
Clubhouse: None
HONOURS: FA Amateur Cup 68-69, Northern Lge 68-69, N.C.E. Prem. Div. 91-92, R-up 89-90, 90-91, Lge. Cup 90-91, Presidents Cup 91-92.

Founded: 1896
Nickname: New Robins
Sponsors: Wilkinson Stores
Colours: All red
Change colours: Blue & black/black/blac

Chairman: Alan Matthews.
Treasurer:Mike Taylor
Manager: Bob Weir.Coach: Wilf Keilty.

REDCAR

Secretary: Keith Markman, 2 Riccall Court , Redcar, Cleveland TS10 4HL
Tel: 01642 481966
Ground: British Steel Club, South Ave., Dormanstown, Redcar.
Directions: Take the A19 South, then the A66 to Middlesbrough. Stay on the A66 following Teeside/Redcar. When A66 ends, at A1053 r'about, take right to Redcar. At next r'about, bear left onto A1085 to Redcar. Over next r'about, right at next r'about into Dormanstown. 1st right along the Fleet, 1st left into South Ave., ground 200 yds on right.

Colours: All red
Change colours: All royal blue

Chairman: Fred Blackburn 01642 471773
Press Officer: Allan Monghan
Tel: 01642 470962

SOUTH SHIELDS CLEADON F.C.

Secretary: Douglas Keys,3 Paragon Way,Holder Hause Estate, South Shields. NE34 8TA
Tel No: 0191 536 7434
Ground: Jack Clarke Park, South Shields.
Directions: Enter South Shields on A194 to r'bout taking you on to A1300 JohnReid Rd. 2nd left at 3rd r'bout into King George Rd then Sunderland Rd, rightat lights into Grosvenor Rd, left into Horsly Hill Rd. Ground on right
Clubhouse: Cleadon Social Club, Fulwell Ave, S Shields. Normal pub hours except Saturday.
HONOURS: Wearside Lg Div 2 90-91, Shields & Dist. Lg, Washington Lg 77-78 84-85

Nickname: The Club
Sponsors: Cleadon & Dist. Soc. Club
Colours: Yellow/black/black
Change: All red
Midweek matches: Wednesday
Chairman: Gordon Ferries
Vice-Chairman/Press Off . /Manager: David Wood (0191 455 4607).
Asst Man: Steve Duguid
Commercial Manager: Joan Wood

SOUTH SHIELDS HARTON & WESTOE

Secretary: Alan Bell, 31 Meldon avenue, South Shields, Tyne & Wear NE34 0EL
Tel Nos: 0191 4218233 (H) 0191 4301446 (W)
Groun: Harton Colliery Welfare.

Directions: A1M at Whitemare Pool take A194 to South Shields for 2 1/2 miles. At third roundabout turn right onto A1300. At 2nd roundabout turn left onto Boldon Lane. Ground 50 yards on right

Colours: All Blue
Change colours: All red

Chairman: Ronald Wightman
Treasurer: Gordon Smith

STANLEY UNITED

Secretary: Vince Kirkup, 9 Brookes Rise, Regents Green, Langley, Durham DH7 8XY
Tel: 0191 378 0921
Ground: High Road, Stanley, near Crook (nicknamed Hill Top Ground). **Directions:** Teeside on A689 to Bishop Auckland and onto Crook, turn left atMarket Place then 1st right for Tow Law to Billy Row and Stanley, right at topof bank then 1st left, grd 250 yards on left.
Clubhouse: Open matchdays. **Club Shop:** No
HONOURS: Northern Lg 3, R-up 62-63, Lg Cup 3,
BEST SEASON: FA Cup 1st Rd 53-54.FA Amateur Cup Semi Final 19-20.

Nickname: The Nops
Sponsors: Company Cars Direct
Colours: Red & white stripes/black/red
Change colours: Sky/navy/navy

President: A Westgarth
Chairman: Barry Waiting.
Asst Manager/ Coach: K Finnegan
Physio: J Burn

STOKESLEY SPORTS CLUB

Secretary: Peter Grainge, 77 Darnton Drive, Easterside, Middlesbrough TS4 3RF
Tel: 01642 273934
Ground: Stokesley Sports Ground, Broughton Road, Stokesley
Directions: A19 to Middlesbrough, then A174 turn to Whitby/Teesport. At 3rd turning up slip road A172 to Stokesley. Over 1st r'about, next r'about turn to Stokesley, 5 miles. At next r'about keep left to next r'about. Ground 100 yards on left.

Colours: Red & black/black/black
Change: White/red/red

Chairman: Eric Taylor 01642 273934
Press Officer: secretary

SUNDERLAND RYHOPE C.W.

Secretary: George McKitterick, 8 Kilburn Close, Ryhope Village, Sunderland. SR2 0QU
Tel: 0191 523 8436)
Ground: Ryhope Recreation Park, Ryhope Street, Ryhope, Sunderland Tel: 0191 521 2843
Directions: Take A19 (3 miles south of Sunderland centre) to Ryhope village, atVillage Green turn into Evelyn Terrace/Ryhope Street and carry on up bank pastPresto's for 600 yds - ground appears on left. 3 miles from Sunderland Central(BR), bus every 10 mins from Sunderland centre.
Capacity: 1,000 Seats: No Cover: No Floodlights: Yes
HONOURS: Wearside Lg 4, (Lg Cup 2), Durham Chall Cup 77-78, M/mouth Charity Cup3, S/land Shipowners Cup 2

Founded: 1988.

Colours: Yellow/black/black & red
Change colours: Red/white/red & white

Chairman:: G. Routledge
Press Officer: Peter Grainge

WHITEHAVEN AMATEURS

Secretary: Richard Stamp, Johnson House, Hillcrest Avenue, Whitehaven, CA28 6SU
Tel No: 01946 61877
Ground: Whitehaven County Ground, Coach Road, Whitehaven
Directions: Barrow on A595, ignore branch to town centre at B.P. garage turnright at t/lights on A5094. 1/2 mile turn left at Esso garage into Coach Rd.Narrow lane ent immed after l/ crossing to grd behind Rugby Lge Stadium.
HONOURS: Cumberland Cup 90-91, County League 87-88 88-89, Wearside Lg Div 2 Cup R-up 93-94.

Colours: Yellow/blue/yellow
Change colours: White/navy/white

Chairman: Bill Robson.
Press Officer: Secretary
Manager: Ian Green
Assistant Manager: Ian Atkins

WINDSCALE

Secretary: Craig Heggie, 12 Bookwell, Egremont, Cumbria CA2 2LS
Tel Nos: 01946 823587 (H) 01946 788337 (W)
Ground: Falcon Field, Egremont.
Directions: A66 to Bridgefoot. A595 Barrow,bottom of hill approaching Egremont take 3rd turn off island (signed)Smithfield/Gillfoot, ground in housing estate
HONOURS: Furness Senior Cup 1985-86

Founded: 1950
Colours:White & Navy Blue/ Navy/White
Change: Blue & white/royal/royal

Chairman: R Napier
Press Officer: Secretary
Treasurer: A Barwise

WOLVISTON

Secretary: Keith Simpson, 14 Lodore Grove, Acklam, Middlesbrough TS5 8PB 01642 823734
Ground: Metcalfe Way, Wynyard Road, Wolviston, Billingham, Cleveland TS22 5NE.
Directions: On Wynyard Road between Thorpe Thewles & Wolviston. A19 onto A689 into Wolviston village, take Wynyard Road towards Thorpe Thewles, grd left before Sir John Halls Estate.
Capacity: 2,000 Seats: None Cover: 200 Floodlights: No Club Shop: No.
Clubhouse: Licensed bar. Hot & cold meals. Open 11am-11pm on matchdays.
HONOURS: Wearside Lg Div 2 89-90, Lg Cup R-up 92-93, Teesside Lg R-up 84-85, Lg Cup 86-87, Durham FA Trophy R-up 89-90, Stockton & Dist. Lg 3, LgCup 3, Lg Charity Cup 79-80.
Record Gate: 500 v Middlesbrough 27/7/93

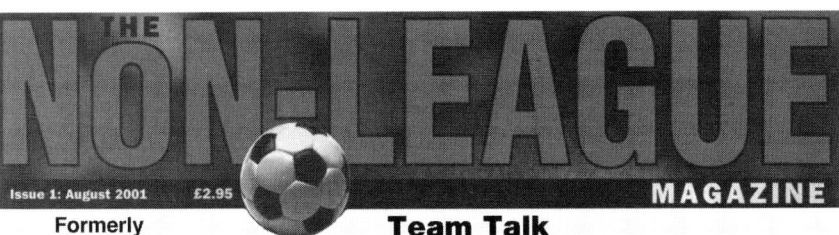

Founded: 1910 Nickname: Wolves
Sponsors: R.C.I. Industrial Cleaners
Colours: Royal blue/blue/white
Change: Red & white/red/white
Chairman: Eddie Poole President: Bob Smith
Vice Chairman: Derek Stockton
Press Officer: Andy Anderson
Manager: John Johnson
Asst Manager: Kevin Smith
Coach: Alan Lucas

You do get characters at Bognor Regis Town FC. Here "Norman Wisdom" gives linesman Richard Barnes some advice. Photo: Graham Cotterill

WADE ASSOCIATES NORTHERN FOOTBALL ALLIANCE

President: Les Todd **Chairman:** George Dobbins
Secretary: John McLackland, 92 Appletree Gardens
Walkerville, Newcastle upon Tyne NE6 4SX Tel: 0191 2621636
Press Officer: Bill Gardner Tel/Fax: 0191 4883422 Email: bill.gardner@eidosnet.co.uk

For the first time in the club's history Walker Central claimed the Premier Division title by seeing off the challenge of defending champions West Allotment Celtic. The Central did it in style and were only beaten twice in their sparkling league campaign despite losing the use of their home ground at Monkchester Green for a long spell due to the torrential downpours which marred the campaign in mid-term.

Having nothing to celebrate was a new and unwelcome experience for West Allotment who, apart from finishing as runners-up to Walker in the top flight had no trophies to collect. They came closest in the League Cup final but in extra time were beaten by the Central who completed a league and cup double in the process.

Finishing in third place - one rung lower than the previous season - Shankhouse were once again a force to be respected and although they failed to keep up the pace in the title race, Garry Kirkup's side lifted the Premier Division Challenge Cup to ease their disappointment. Once again extra time was required for Shankhouse to see off Cup final opponents Coxlodge Social Club at McKendrick Villas. Unhappily for Coxlodge they were carpeted at the end of the season for frequent rule infringements and they resigned from the league following a decision to demote them back into the First Division. They had spent only one campaign in the top flight.

Heaton Stannington and Hebburn Reyrolle were relegated from the Premier Division to be replaced for the 2001-02 season by First Division champions Amble Vikings and runners-up Harraby Catholic Club. A crowd of almost 400 saw Amble beat their visiting Cumbrian rivals on the last day of the season to settle the title issue. The Seasiders immediately indicated that they would be changing their name to Amble United to coincide with their promotion and a merger with neighbours Amble Town.

West Allotment Celtic's manager, Ken Scott, the most successful team boss in North East non-League football in the last decade announced his decision to step down on the eve of the club's move from Whitley Bay to a new ground at the Blue Flame Sports Ground in Longbenton. Scott's replacement was announced as experienced coach Terry Mitchell and there were other management changes at the end of the season. After guiding new champions Walker Central to their first ever title Allan Bell and his assistant Steve Burn have decided to join Newcastle Benfield Saints and ex-Walker chairman Bob Morton also indicated his decision to join the ambitious Saints.

In the past and since Morpeth Town's admission to the Northern League there have been few Northern Alliance outfits aiming to climb the pyramid ladder but there seems to have been a change of heart in some quarters. At least three clubs - West Allotment Celtic, Benfield Saints and Ryton - could be aiming to step up at the end of the 2001-02 season.

This will give an added edge to the title race with teams like Northbank Carlisle, Ponteland United and Shankhouse, despite having lesser short term ambitions, still hungry for silverware and expected to do well.

The close season unfortunately yielded three resignations from the league with Coxlodge Social Club (Premier Division), Heddon Institute (Division One) and Stobhill Rangers and Blyth Spartans Intermediate (both from Division Two) deciding to fold.

Bill Gardner, League Press Officer

HONOURS LIST 2000-01

Premier Division Champions	Walker Central	Runners-up	West Allotment Celtic
Division One Champions	Amble Vikings	Runners-up	Harraby Catholic Club
Division Two Champions	Wallington	Runners-up	Shankhouse Black Watch
League Cup Winners	Walker Central		
Challenge Cup Winners	Shankhouse		
Combination Cup Winners	Wark		
Amateur Cup Winners	Wallsend Town		
Durham FA Trophy Winners	Winlaton Hallgarth		
Northumberland FA Minor Cup Winners	University of Northumbria		

FINAL LEAGUE TABLES 2000-01

PREMIER DIVISION

	P	W	D	L	F	A	Pts
Walker Cental	30	23	5	2	83	27	74
West Allotment Celtic	30	21	5	4	91	36	68
Shankhouse	30	18	3	9	64	32	57
Northbank	30	17	4	9	84	58	55
Seaton Delavel	30	14	7	9	56	46	49
Ponteland	30	14	6	10	56	46	48
Benfield Saints*	30	14	4	12	69	59	43
Carlisle City	30	11	6	13	47	51	39
Coxlodge SC	30	12	2	16	53	75	38
Percy Main	30	9	10	11	38	51	37
N University*	30	12	3	15	70	67	36
Spittal Rovers	30	10	4	16	60	71	34
Winlaton Hallgarth	30	11	1	18	41	62	34
Ryton	30	9	4	17	39	59	31
Heaton Stannington	30	8	4	18	34	82	28
Hebburn Reyrolle	30	2	2	26	34	98	8

DIVISION ONE

	P	W	D	L	F	A	Pts
Amble Vikings	30	25	4	1	104	28	79
Harraby C C*	30	24	3	3	83	23	72
Newbiggin C W	30	17	3	10	78	53	54
Procter & Gamble	30	18	0	12	65	44	54
Chopwell Top Club	30	16	4	10	71	51	52
Wark*	30	16	4	10	69	57	49
Cowgate S C	30	14	3	13	83	71	45
Walker Fosse*	30	15	4	11	64	41	43
Cullercoats	30	12	3	15	57	67	39
Bedlington Terr. A	30	10	5	15	71	68	35
Amble Town	30	8	8	14	41	59	32
Heddon Institute	30	8	4	18	54	85	28
Rutherford	30	7	7	16	52	91	28
Prudhoe RTH*	30	7	4	19	28	75	22
Northern S C	30	5	4	21	31	79	19
Highfields United*	30	6	4	20	43	102	19

TOP LEAGUE GOALSCORERS - PREMIER DIVISION

Alex Benjamin	West Allotment C	37
Ben Chesters	Newcastle University	19
Iain Cavanagh	Shankhouse	19

TOP LEAGUE GOALSCORERS - DIVISION ONE

Steve Gibbard	Amble Vikings	30
John Moscrop	Amble Vikings	30
Marc Pattle	Newbiggin C W	28

STAN SEYMOUR LEAGUE CUP

SEMI-FINALS

Seaton Delaval	v	Walker Central T/A SD	2-1
Harraby CC	v	West Allotment Celtic	3-4

FINAL

Walker Central	v	West Allotment Celtic	1*0

DIVISION ONE COMBINATION CUP

SEMI-FINALS

Wark	v	Prudhoe RTH	3-1
Procter & Gamble	v	Amble Vikings	2-1

FINAL

Procter & Gamble	v	Wark	0-2

PREMIER DIVISION CHALLENGE CUP

SEMI-FINALS

Winlaton Hallgarth	v	Shankhouse	0-0, 2-5
Percy Main	v	Coxlodge Soc. Club	0-2

FINAL

Coxlodge S C	v	Shankhouse	2-3

DIVISION TWO AMATEUR CUP

SEMI-FINALS

Wallington	v	Stobhill Rangers	1-0
Horden CW Athletic	v	Wallsend Town	1-4

FINAL

Wallington	v	Wallsend Town	0-3

PREMIER DIVISION RESULTS CHART 2000-01

		1	2	3	4	5	6	7	8	9	10	11	12	13	14	15	16
1	Benfield Saints	X	5-3	4-1	5-0	4-1	2-5	3-1	1-2	2-0	1-3	5-2	0-2	2-2	0-0	2-1	3-0
2	Carlisle City	4-3	X	3-0	5-2	2-1	4-2	1-0	2-0	1-2	1-2	1-2	0-1	3-3	1-4	0-3	1-3
3	Coxlodge S C	3-1	2-1	X	1-2	3-0	3-2	1-4	2-1	1-2	5-1	0-4	2-3	2-1	2-4	2-3	2-0
4	Heaton Stannington	1-5	1-0	0-4	X	3-2	2-1	1-4	0-0	1-1	0-2	3-5	3-2	2-0	0-3	3-3	0-2
5	Hebb Reyrolle	1-1	1-2	2-3	1-1	X	1-3	2-4	1-3	1-3	3-2	0-4	2-5	1-3	1-4	2-0	3-2
6	Newcastle University	4-3	1-3	10-0	5-1	4-1	X	5-3	0-0	3-0	2-0	1-1	0-3	1-6	1-4	1-2	0-4
7	Northbank	3-1	2-2	5-1	5-0	5-4	1-0	X	3-4	0-3	4-1	4-3	0-2	5-1	1-1	2-2	6-1
8	Percy Main Ams	1-3	1-1	2-2	0-1	2-0	1-1	1-3	X	1-1	1-1	2-1	1-1	2-0	0-1	1-3	1-2
9	Ponteland Utd	2-1	1-0	1-3	3-0	5-1	3-1	2-1	6-3	X	1-1	1-3	1-1	2-4	1-3	2-1	1-1
10	Ryton	1-2	1-2	2-2	1-2	4-0	2-1	1-3	2-2	0-3	X	1-4	1-0	1-2	1-5	1-2	0-2
11	Seaton Delaval	3-0	0-0	2-1	3-1	1-0	2-4	3-2	1-1	1-1	2-0	X	0-1	3-1	1-1	1-6	1-5
12	Shankhouse	0-2	2-0	4-0	4-0	5-0	3-2	1-2	1-2	2-1	0-2	0-0	X	5-1	1-2	0-2	3-1
13	Spittal Rovers	0-0	4-0	8-1	2-0	3-1	2-4	3-3	0-1	3-1	0-2	1-3	2-7	X	1-2	1-2	0-2
14	Walker Central	4-2	1-1	1-0	3-2	7-0	6-1	2-4	4-0	1-0	4-0	2-0	1-2	5-2	X	2-2	2-0
15	West Allotment	6-1	1-1	2-0	8-1	2-0	4-3	5-2	7-1	2-1	1-2	0-0	2-1	7-0	0-2	X	2-0
16	Winlaton Hall	3-5	0-2	0-4	2-1	2-1	0-2	1-2	0-2	3-5	2-1	1-0	0-2	1-4	0-2	1-4	X

AMBLE UNITED

Secretary: Kevin Lewis, 2 Park Close, North Broomhill,Northumberland NE65 9YN(01670 761162)
Ground: Amble Welfare Park, Coquet High School, Amble..
Directions: Enter Amble after industrial estate on right. One undred yards past the zebra crossing turn left before 'The Masons arms'. Continue as if leaving Amble and Coquet High school and the ground are on the left.

Colours: Orange & Black stripes/black
Change colours: Blue & whitw/white
Chairman: Rod Henderson
Manager/Coach: Keith Douglas

CARLISLE CITY

Secretary: Jackie Williamson,14 Etterby Street, Stanwix, Carlisle Tel No: 01228 523798
Ground: The Sheepmount Sports Complex, Carlisle (01228 265599).
Directions: B6264 Brampton-Carlisle road & follow Workington signs, dual-c'way down hill (Carlisle Castle on right), where road intersects double back on yourself and take turning left just before castle, follow down hill keeping left until ground.

Colours: Sky & Navy hoops/navy
Change colours: White/navy

Chairman: Jackie Ewbank
Manage/Coach: Willie Armstrong.

HARRABY CATHOLIC CLUB 1999

Secretary: Mike Little, 34 Springfield Road, Harraby, Carlisle CA1 3QR (01228 512887)
Ground: Harrowby Community Centre, Edghill Road,Harraby
Directions: A69 over M^ to Rosehill roundabout.Second ledft on Eastern Way. First left after 3/4 mile into Arnside Road. End of road left into Edghill Road

Colours:All white
Change colours: Old gold and black

Chairman/Press Officer: Richard Wilson
Manager/Coach: Bobby Rutherford & Kevin Robson

NEWCASTLE BENFIELD PARK

Secretary: Danny Gates, 5 Winship Terrace, Byker, Newcastle-upon-Tyne (0191 2763049).

Ground: Benfield Park, Benfield Rd, Newcastle-upon-Tyne.
Directions: From Newcastle towards coast take 2nd exit after Corner House pub lights, right into Benfield Rd, ground on left opp. Walkergate Hosp. & adjacent to school.

Colours: Blue/white
Change colours: White/blue

Chairman: Jimmy Rowe
Manager: Allan Bell Coach: Steve Burn

NEWCASTLE UNIVERSITY

Secretary: Simon Kent, 8/10 Myrtle Grove,JesmondNewcastle -u-TyneNE2 3HT(0191 2093609)
Ground: Cochrane Park, Etherstone Avenue, Newcastle -u-Tyne
Directions: From Newcastle via Jesmond to coast road.Take first slip road after Jesmond Dene and immediately after lights at the Corner House.Then take first slip road and left again onto A188 and right at first roundabout at the garage into Etherstone Avenue. Ground is 200 metres on left

Colours: All blue
Change colours: White/navy

Chairman: Simon Kent
Manager: T.B.A.

NORTHBANK CARLISLE

Secretary: David Bell,4 Carlislwe Road, Dalston ,Cumbria CA5 7NG (01228 711095)
Ground: Sheepmount Sports Complex, Carlisle
Directions: B6264 from Bampton to Carlisle, follow Workington sign, past Carlisle Castle on right. Where dual carriageway intersects take next right and travel back towards Castle. Turn left before castle & keeping left follow the road to Complex

Colours: Red & white/red
Change colours: Yellow & navy/navy

Chairman: Kenny Brown
Manager: Bob Lancaster

PERCY MAIN AMATEURS

Secretary: Len Renham, 7 Stanley Crescent, Whitley Bay, Tyne & wear NE26 2 EB
Tel No: (0191 2902768)
Ground: Purvis Park , St John's Green,Percy Main, North Shields.
Directions: A19 Tyne tunnel follow signs for Royal Quays and take seconsd left after school Ground is first turning on the right adjacent to Percy Main cricket club.t after Percy Main schol

Colours: Claret & blue/claret
Change colours: All Blue

Chairman: G.Marsh
ManagerBob Rodgerson
Coach: John Humbertson

PONTELAND UNITED

Secretary: L McMahon, 1 Wardle Drive, Annitsford, Cramlingham NE23 7DB (0191250 0463).
Ground: Ponterland leisure Centre Ponteland (01661 825441)
Directions: Left at lights entering Ponteland from N'castle, ground 100m on left adjacent to Leisure Centre.
Colours: Black & White stripes/Black **Change Colours:** All yellow

Chairman:Alan Birkinshaw
Manager : Barry Wardrobe
Coach:Steve Baxter

RYTON

Secretary: Les Robson, 31 Park View Gardens, Runhead, Ryton, Tyne & wear NE40 3JD
Tel: 0191 413 7628
Ground: Kingsley Park, Crawcrook, (Tel No: 0191 413 4448)
Directions: West from Newcastle, over Scotswood Bridge and take A695to Blaydon roundabout. A617 and go through Ryton until traffic lights at Crawcrook. Turn righ when signposted to Wylam and Clara Vale ground is 400 yds on right.

Colours: Blue & black/black
Change colours: Orange/black

Chairman: Michael Williams
Manage Stevan Kendall
Coach: K.Dixon

SEATON DELAVAL AMATEURS

Secretary: Bill Fellows, 11 Ridley Street, Klondyke, Cramlington NE23 6RH (01670 731833)
Ground: Wheatridge Park, Seaton Delaval.
Directions: A189 from Newcastle, at Annitsford r'bout A190 to Seaton Delaval,left at r'bout entering village, ground 450yds on right next to Deal Garage and behind Market Garden. 3 miles from Cramlington BR station. Bus 363 from Newcastle passes ground.

Colours: Sky/black
Change colours: Yellow/blue

Chairman: Tom Ashburn
Manager/Coach: Steve Armstrong

SHANKHOUSE

Secretary: Syd Ramsey, 6 Brinkburn Ave, Cramlington, Northumberland NE23 6TB
Tel: 01670 715943
Ground: Action Park, Dudley.
Directions: Tyne Tunnel A19 to Moor Farm roundabout at Anitsford. A1 exit to Morpeth and leave at first slip road.Left at junction (to Dudley) turn right to Seaton Burn at roundabout.Then immediate right after Weetslade club and ground is signposted.

Colours: Yellow/blue
Change colours: White/blue

Chairman: George Davison
Manager: Garry Kirkup

SPITTAL ROVERS

Secretary: G Burn, 7 Sea Road, Spittal, Berwick-on-Tweed TD15 1RN (01289306049).

Ground: Newfields, Berwick-on-Tweed.
Directions: From south take Berwick by-pass to 3rd r'bout. Safeway Store on right - pitch reached by taking 2nd left on r'bout.

Chairman: Noel Evans
Vice Chairman: Paul Renton
Manager/Coach: Carl Hudson

Colours: Black & white stripes/black
Change colours: Green/Black

WALKER CENTRAL

Secretary: BobMulroy, 31 Dalton Cres., Byker Wall, Newcastle-upon-Tyne NE62DA
Tel: 0191 265 7803

Ground: Monkchester Recreation Ground, Walker, Newcastle.
Directions: From City: Shields Rd to Union Rd, to Welbeck Rd, right into Monkchester Rd, left into pitch (between houses) opposite Norbury Grove.

Club colours: White and black
Change colours: All Blue
Chairman: R T McClellan
Manager/Coach: Ray Mulroy/Billy Johnson

WEST ALLOTMENT CELTIC

Secretary: J T Jackson, 4 Rosewood Crescent, Seaton Sluice, Whitley Bay NE264BL
Tel: 0191 237 0416
Ground: Hillheads Park, Whitley Bay
Directions: From Newcastle take A1058 to Tynemouth Baths, turn left roundabout on A192 to Foxhunters Pub. Turn right follow A191 to Ice Rink on right, ground beside.

Colours: Green& white hoops, green,green
Change colours: All Blue

Chairman: J Mather
Manager/Coach: Ken Scott

WINLATON HALLGARTH

Secretary: Robert Young, Alwinton, 21B California, Winlaton Tyne & Wear NE21 6NG
Tel No: 0191 4144363)
Ground: Shibdon Park, Shibdon Road, Blaydon-on-Tyne, Tyne & Wear.
Directions: From north, over A1 Scotswood Bridge to 1st slip road, take Swalwell and Consett road to r'bout, right, Blaydon Baths car park and ground 400yds on right. From South past Metro Centre to Swalwell, then on to Blaydon and the Blaydob Baths car park.

Colours: Green & Black
Change colours: Blue & white/blue
Chairman: R obertYoung
Manager/CoachStephen Brown

DIVISION ONE CLUBS

BEDLINGTON TERRIERS 'A'; CHOPWELL TOP CLUB; COWGATE SPORTS CLUB; CRAMLINGTON TOWN; CULLERCOATS; HEATON STANNINGTON; HEBBURN SKL REYROLLE; NEWBIGGIN CENTRAL WELFARE; NEWCASTLE PROCTER & GAMBLE; NORTHERN SOCIAL CLUB ASHINGTON; PRUDHOE RTH; RUTHERFORD (NEWCASTLE); WALKER FOSSE; WALLINGTON; WARK.

SOUTH CLEVELAND GARAGES TEESSIDE FOOTBALL LEAGUE

FEEDER TO: NORTHERN LEAGUE

President: J Corner **Chairman:** L Crossman

Secretary: R D Marsay, 12 Aislaby Court, Wilton Lane, Guisborough, Cleveland TS14 6TG

Tel: 01287 637087 Fax: 01287 281051 Email: dmarsay@ntlworld.com

HONOURS LIST 2000-01

League Champions	Acklam Steelworks
Runners up	Nunthorpe Athletic
Macmillan Bowl Winners	Grangetown BC
Finalists	Thornaby FC
RT Raine Trophy Winners	Bedale Athletic
Finalists	Wolviston Reserves
JV Madden Trophy Winners	Acklam Steelworks
Finalists	Grangetown BC

FINAL LEAGUE TABLE 2000-01

		P	*W*	*D*	*L*	*F*	*A*	*Pts*	*GD*
1	Acklam SW	34	24	7	3	97	40	79	57
2	Nunthorpe Ath	34	23	4	7	106	43	73	63
3	Grangetown	34	21	7	6	80	35	70	45
4	Cargo F	34	21	5	8	112	55	68	57
5	Thornaby	34	18	9	7	69	39	63	30
6	Hollybush U	34	17	7	10	91	53	58	38
7	Bedale Ath	34	18	3	13	95	66	57	29
8	Carlin How	34	17	6	11	92	64	57	28
9	Thornaby	34	15	5	14	58	52	50	6
10	Fishburn Park	34	13	10	11	76	53	49	23
11	Wolviston Res	34	11	9	14	57	67	42	-10
12	BEADS FC	34	13	3	18	69	118	42	-49
13	Richmond Town	34	12	4	18	59	74	40	-15
14	Whitby Town Res	34	10	7	17	53	67	37	-14
15	New Marske SC	34	10	5	19	41	75	35	-34
16	Stokesley SC*	34	6	4	24	40	107	19	-67
17	Guisborough T R*	34	6	2	26	46	115	17	-69
18	Mackinlay Park	34	1	3	30	29	147	6	-118

** points deducted*

PREVIOUS HONOURS

LEAGUE CHAMPIONS

2000-01	Acklam Steelworks
1999-00	Grangetown Boys Club
1998-99	Grangetown Boys Club
1997-98	Acklam Steelworks
1996-97	Acklam Steelworks
1995-96	Acklam Steelworks

R T RAINE TROPHY WINNERS

2000-01	Bedale Athletic
1999-00	Nunthorpe Athletic
1998-99	Cargo Fleet
1997-98	Dormans Athletic
1996-97	BSC Redcar
1995-96	BSC Redcar

PLAYER OF THE YEAR

2000-01	Adam Bramley Bedale Athletic
1999-00	Nicholas Agiadis Acklam Steelworks
1998-99	John Newton Whitby Town Reserves

MACMILLAN BOWL WINNERS

2000-01	Grangetown Boys Club
1999-00	Grangetown Boys Club
1998-99	Nunthorpe Athletic
1997-98	Acklam Steelworks
1996-97	Acklam Steelworks
1995-96	Acklam Steelworks

J V MADDEN TROPHY

2000-01	Acklam Steelworks
1999-00	Nunthorpe Athletic
1998-99	Acklam Steelworks
1997-98	Acklam Steelworks
1996-97	Acklam Steelworks
1995-96	Tees Components

MATCH OFFICIAL OF THE YEAR

2000-01	Gary Coxon Middlesbrough
1999-00	Mark Tilling Guisborough
1998-99	Chris Lane Hutton Rugby

CLUBS IN MEMBERSHIP 2000-01

ACKLAM STEELWORKS
Gary Bell, 10 Avalon Court, Hemlington, Middlesbrough TS8 9HU Tel: 01642 276736

B.E.A.D.S.
Dave Kane, 27 Edgeworth Court, Hemlington, Middlesbrough TS8 9EP Tel: 01642 280586

BEDALE ATHLETIC
Mike Allen, 1 Sycamore View, Nosterfield, Bedale, North Yorks DL8 2QR Tel: 01677 470739

CARGO FLEET SC
Mick Connorton, 84 Durham Road, Eston, Middlesbrough TS6 9LZ Tel: 01642 502728

CARLIN HOW WMC
Simon Whitwell, 10 Harebell Close, North Skelton, Saltburn TS12 2FE Tel: 01287 652135

FISHBURN PARK
Richard & Karen Hutton, 14 Abbots Road, Whitby, North Yorks YO22 4EB Tel: 01947 602537

GRANGETOWN BOYS CLUB
Kevin Larkin, 19 Braemar Grove, Teesville, Middlesbrough TS6 0AN Tel: 01642 452095

GUISBOROUGH TOWN RESERVES
Chris Tilley, 4 Ash Road, Guisborough TS14 6JQ Tel: 01287 635847

HOLLYBUSH UNITED
Michael Griffiths, 7 Penryn Close, Skelton, Saltburn TS12 2ND Tel: 01287 651381

MACKINLAY PARK
Martin Coats, 221 High Street, Marske, Redcar TS11 7LR Tel: 01642 475707

NEW MARSKE SC
Errol Richter, 101 St Peters Road, Whitby, North Yorks YO22 4HX Tel: 01947 605423

NUNTHORPE ATHLETIC
Kevin Levitt, 131 Burlam Road, Middlesbrough TS5 5AX Tel: 01642 824332

RICHMOND TOWN
Linda Blackburn, 14 Westfields, Richmond, North Yorks DL10 4DD Tel: 01748 824919

STOKESLEY SC
Peter Grainge, 77 Darnton Drive, Easterside, Middlesbrough TS4 3RK Tel: 01642 273934

THORNABY FC
Sue Gardner, 25 Brotton Road, Thornaby, Stockton TS17 8EP Tel: 01642 650669

THORNABY YOUTH CLUB
Geoff Kirk, 9 Tipton Close, Thornaby, Stockton TS17 9QF Tel: 01642 676516

WHITBY TOWN RESERVES
Peter Newton, 22 Argyle Road, Whitby, North Yorks YO21 3HS Tel: 01947 602631

WOLVISTON RESERVES
Keith Simpson, 14 Lodore Grove, Acklam, Middllesbrough TS5 8PB Tel: 01642 823734

THE COUNTY SENIOR FOOTBALL LEAGUE

President: M Matthews Esq. **Chairman:** A Goodison Esq.

Secretary: R Beadsworth Esq., 32 Cockayne Place, Norton Lees, Sheffield S8 9DG
Tel/Fax: 0114 255 1275 E Mail: roy.norton@talk21.com

FINAL LEAGUE TABLES 2000-01

PREMIER DIVISION

	P	*W*	*D*	*L*	*F*	*A*	*Pts*
The Wetherby	26	17	4	5	59	30	55
Frecheville CA	26	15	5	6	60	43	50
Wombwell Main	26	12	8	6	45	36	44
Worksop Town Res	26	12	6	8	56	48	42
Hare & Hounds	25	13	3	9	51	43	42
Phoenix	25	11	6	8	55	43	39
Mexborough Main St	26	10	6	10	50	45	36
Athersley Rec	26	10	5	11	33	32	35
Hallam Reserves	26	10	5	11	58	60	35
Ecclesfield Red Rose	26	10	5	11	48	56	35
Parkgate Reserves	26	7	6	13	49	61	27
Thorpe Hesley	26	6	6	14	37	58	24
Parramore Sports	26	5	6	15	36	70	21
Wickersley	26	4	7	15	41	53	19

DIVISION ONE

	P	*W*	*D*	*L*	*F*	*A*	*Pts*
Penistone Church	24	17	4	3	63	36	55
Swinton Athletic	24	14	6	4	53	30	48
Groves Social (Sat)	24	14	4	6	64	38	46
Stocksbridge PS Res	24	13	3	8	62	36	42
Sheffield Lane Top	24	12	2	10	56	41	38
Oughtibridge WMSC	24	10	6	8	45	43	36
Grapes Roy Hancock	24	10	4	10	53	45	34
Caribbean Sports	24	10	4	10	59	64	34
Sheffield Bankers	24	9	3	12	54	54	30
Avesta Sheffield	24	7	6	11	40	61	27
High Green Villa	24	6	4	14	40	75	22
Denaby Utd Res	24	4	5	15	36	68	17
Treeton Welfare	24	2	5	17	34	77	11

PREMIER DIVISION RESULTS CHART 2000-01

		1	2	3	4	5	6	7	8	9	10	11	12	13	14
1	Athersley Recreation	X	4-0	1-0	1-1	4-3	2-1	0-2	2-0	1-0	0-1	0-2	2-0	1-0	3-2
2	Ecclesfield Red Rose	1-2	X	2-1	4-2	0-2	0-2	4-3	1-1	3-3	2-3	4-3	1-1	1-2	1-4
3	Frecheville CA	3-2	7-2	X	3-1	1-2	3-0	5-3	3-0	0-4	1-0	1-1	3-1	0-0	0-5
4	Hallam Reserves	3-2	2-3	1-2	X	1-6	4-3	0-0	1-1	2-2	1-6	9-1	3-3	0-2	2-1
5	Hare & Hounds	1-0	2-0	1-3	0-1	X	5-0	0-0	4-2	-	0-3	2-1	3-1	2-2	2-1
6	Mexborough Main St	3-3	0-1	1-1	3-2	5-0	X	4-1	1-2	1-1	2-0	2-1	2-1	1-3	3-4
7	Parkgate Reserves	0-0	1-6	3-4	4-1	2-2	2-0	X	7-1	1-7	0-4	3-3	4-2	3-1	4-0
8	Parramore Sports	2-1	1-6	1-2	2-1	2-6	2-2	3-0	X	2-3	0-3	2-0	3-3	3-3	2-4
9	Phoenix	2-0	3-0	2-6	0-4	2-0	3-2	1-1	1-0	X	1-2	4-0	3-3	1-2	2-3
10	The Wetherby	1-0	3-0	1-1	1-3	3-0	2-4	3-2	2-2	3-2	X	0-1	2-2	3-1	2-2
11	Thorpe Hesley	0-0	2-2	4-5	1-3	3-1	0-3	1-0	3-1	2-3	1-2	X	0-3	0-0	2-2
12	Wickersley	2-1	0-1	1-1	2-3	1-2	0-3	1-0	8-0	3-3	1-3	1-2	X	1-3	0-1
13	Wombwell Main	0-0	1-2	3-1	2-4	4-0	2-2	3-1	1-0	2-0	0-4	3-2	1-0	X	3-3
14	Worksop Town Res	2-1	1-1	1-3	5-3	1-5	0-0	5-2	2-1	0-2	1-2	2-1	3-0	1-1	X

COUNTY SENIOR FOOTBALL LEAGUE CUP 2000-01

FIRST ROUND

Swinton Athletic	v	Dinnington Town	3-1
Sheffield Centralians	v	Denaby United Res	2-1
Treeton Welfare	v	Davy	3-2
Sheffield Bankers	v	NCB Maltby MW	6-3

SECOND ROUND

Groves Social (Sat)	v	Phoenix	5-3
Stocksbridge PS	v	Ecclesfield Red R	4-4, 4p5
Hare & Hounds	v	Wickersley	2-5
Avesta Sheffield	v	Sheffield Centralians	4-6
Parramore Spt (excl)	v	Sheffield Banker (frft)	1-3
Frecheville CA	v	Penistone Church Res	9-0
Athersley Rec	v	Wombwell Main	2-2, 3p4
Thorpe Hesley	v	High Green Villa	3-2
Caribbean Sp (forft)	v	Hallam Res	4-4, 4p3
Worksop Town Res	v	Treeton Welfare	3-1
Penistone Church	v	Sheffield Lane Top	1-2
Old Edwardians	v	Oughtibridge WMSC	1-4
The Westherby	v	Woodhouse W End	4-2
The Forum (Sat)	v	Mexboorugh Main St	1-3
South Kirkby Colliery	v	Grapes Roy Hancock	5-0
Swinton Athletic	v	Hallam Reserves	4-4,4p3

THIRD ROUND

Groves Social	v	Parkgate Res	4-4, 5p4
Worksop Town Res	v	Wickersley (forfeit)	2-3
Oughtibridge WMSC	v	NCB Maltby MW	6-1
Mexborough Main St	v	Wombwell Main	1-0
Swinton Athletic	v	Stocksbridg ePS Rs	1-0
Sheffield Lane Top	v	Sheffield Centralians	2-1
The Wetherby	v	Frecheville CA	2-1
South Kirkby Coll	v	Thorpe Hesley	0-1

FOURTH ROUND

Groves Social (Sat)	v	Swinton Athletic	1-0
Oughtibridge WMSC	v	The Wetherby	0-1
Worksop Town Res	v	Sheffield L Top	1-1, 6p5
Mexborough Main St	v	Thorpe Hesley	2-3

SEMI FINALS

Groves Social	v	Worksop Town	1-3
The Wetherby	v	Thorpe Hesley	3-2

FINAL

Worksop Town	v	The Wetherby	3-2

WEST YORKSHIRE ASSOCIATION FOOTBALL LEAGUE

Founded 1928

President: J Hill **Chairman:** B Chaplin

Secretary: Kevin Parkinson, 9 Lake Lock Drive, Stanley, Wakefield WF3 4HN Tel: 01924 825491

With the season underway, we were all affected by both political and weather issues, which had a dramatic impact on fixtures. The national fuel crisis served to cancel a complete weekend of fixtures, but the worst autumn rainfall on record and susbsequent flooding continued to postpone matches to the year end. During this time, many clubs worked tirelessly, particularly on matchdays, to make their pitch playable and, although not all were successful, they are all to be acknowledged in respect of their efforts.

The New Year brought no respite from the elements and almost until the season end the Fixtures and Referees Appointments Secretaries had to deal with major changes to the scheduled listings. The threat of not bringing the season to a successful and complete conclusion was eliminated by a concerted effort by clubs, some of whom had to play three or four matches in a given week.

It was with great regret that the League was informed of the sudden death of Chris Foggin of Hartshead Senior. Chris was a superb example and inspiration to all in his contribution to football in the communtiy and he will be sadly and dearly missed.

In order to recognise long and distinguished service given to the local game, the Leeds & District Football Association introduced the Outstanding Service Award. I am delighted to record that K Claybrough of Carlton Athletic, R Fisher and I Kevan, both of Whitkirk Wanderers, were included to receive this honour. In addition, other recipients from the West Yorkshire League were the President, J Hill, and Council Member R Lawrence. It is a special tribute that Life Member W Keyworth of our association was presented with the Football Association Fifty Years Service to Football Medal.

Briggsports and the National Grid continued to provide valuable sponsorship to the League in respect of the Premier Division Cup and the Fair Play League respectively. This is most welcome and gratefully received.

In keeping with the times the League is featured on the internet and, through more conventional means, in newspapers and on teletext. Our thanks is extended to those agencies who assist in providing publicity.

Finally, in being adversely influenced by the weather, the season has been a long and demanding one and everyone involved shares the accolade for achieving a successful conclusion. The commitment displayed can ensure the good name of the League continues and at least maintains its status whilst providing every opportunity for progression in the future.

K Parkinson, Hon. General Secretary

HONOURS LIST 2000-01

	League Champions	League Runners-Up
PREMIER DIVISION	Carlton Athletic	Nestle Rowntrees
DIVISION ONE	Pudsey	Ripon City Magnets
DIVISION TWO	Howden Clough	Upper Armley OB
PREMIER ALLIANCE DIV	Carlton Athletic	Beeston St Anthony's
RESERVE DIVISION	Great Preston	Armley Athletic

	League Cup Winners	League Cup Runners Up
PREMIER DIVISION	Nestle Rowntrees	Carlton Athletic
DIVISION ONE	Barwick	Baildon Trintiy Athletic
DIVISION TWO	Upper Armley OB	Pontefract Town
PREMIER ALLIANCE	Whitkirk Wanderers	Horsforth St Margarets
RESERVE DIVISION	Robin Hood Athletic	Barwick

FRED WINTERBURN TROPHY TEAM AWARD Fryston Welfare

GEORGE COPE MEMORIAL TROPHY REFEREE AWARD Cyril Carlton (Selby)

FINAL LEAGUE TABLES 2000-01

PREMIER DIVISION

	P	W	D	L	F	A	GD	Pts
Carlton Athletic	30	27	1	2	106	22	84	82
Nestle Rowntrees	30	25	1	4	99	31	68	76
Horsforth St Marg.	30	21	2	7	71	42	29	65
Beeston St Ant.	30	14	2	14	59	63	-4	44
Whitkirk Wndrs	30	13	4	13	68	49	19	43
Bardsey	30	10	10	10	43	57	-14	40
Nostell Miners W	30	11	6	13	60	66	-6	39
Pontefract S & S	30	11	6	13	57	70	-13	39
Wetherby Athletic	30	11	4	15	56	63	-7	37
Knaresborough	30	11	3	16	45	64	-19	36
Mount St Marys	30	11	3	16	49	71	-22	36
Wakefield	30	9	8	13	46	51	-5	35
Aberford Albion	30	11	2	17	49	65	-16	35
Sandy Lane	30	8	7	15	55	62	-7	31
York R I	30	7	4	19	41	86	-45	25
Rothwell Athletic	30	6	5	19	31	73	-42	23

DIVISION ONE

	P	W	D	L	F	A	GD	Pts
Pudsey	26	19	4	3	59	19	40	61
Ripon City Mag.	26	17	4	5	72	33	39	55
Armley Athletic	26	16	6	4	78	35	43	54
Ossett Common R	26	12	8	6	62	36	26	44
Barwick	26	12	3	11	61	61	0	39
Baildon Trinity A	26	11	5	10	47	44	3	38
Tadcaster Mag. Sp.	26	8	11	7	46	48	-2	35
Kirk Deighton Rngrs	26	9	7	10	42	53	-11	34
Robin Hood Athletic	26	8	7	11	35	38	-3	31
Methley Rangers	26	8	6	12	62	78	-16	30
Rothwell Town	26	7	7	12	38	62	-24	28
Featherstone Coll.	26	5	7	14	37	57	-20	22
Woodhouse Hill	26	5	4	17	47	91	-44	19
Sherburn White R	26	2	7	17	36	67	-31	13

PREMIER DIVISION RESULTS CHART 2000-01

		1	2	3	4	5	6	7	8	9	10	11	12	13	14	15	16
1	Aberford Albion	X	1-1	1-0	0-4	1-4	4-0	3-0	0-3	1-2	2-3	3-1	1-5	1-3	4-1	2-1	4-2
2	Bardsey	0-3	X	3-2	0-0	2-4	2-2	1-3	0-1	1-2	2-2	3-0	1-4	1-1	2-1	3-3	3-0
3	Beeston St Anthony's	5-1	1-3	X	0-5	4-2	2-1	4-2	1-2	1-1	4-0	2-1	2-0	4-3	5-0	0-1	2-1
4	Carlton Athletic	2-1	11-0	7-1	X	1-0	5-1	1-0	3-0	4-1	1-0	7-1	2-1	5-1	2-0	1-2	3-0
5	Horsforth St Margaret's	2-3	3-0	3-1	3-2	X	2-0	1-0	2-1	2-0	5-3	0-0	2-1	3-0	5-1	0-0	1-0
6	Knaresborough Town	1-2	4-3	2-0	3-6	2-0	X	0-1	1-2	3-1	2-4	0-1	0-2	1-1	2-2	2-1	1-0
7	Mount St Marys	3-0	1-3	5-1	0-1	2-3	0-1	X	1-6	0-0	4-6	3-2	4-1	2-1	0-4	3-2	3-3
8	Nestle Rowntrees	4-2	4-0	4-1	1-3	2-3	3-2	7-0	X	-	2-1	7-1	5-0	6-1	3-2	6-0	2-0
9	Nostell Miners Welfare	4-2	0-2	7-1	0-5	2-7	3-1	3-0	2-7	X	1-2	3-3	5-3	3-1	2-2	0-4	0-1
10	Pontefract Sp & Soc.	1-0	1-1	0-4	1-2	4-1	3-1	1-2	1-3	1-4	X	-	1-2	3-2	3-3	1-4	2-2
11	Rothwell Athletic	3-0	0-0	1-5	1-3	2-1	1-3	3-1	0-1	1-1	1-3	X	1-5	2-1	0-1	0-9	0-1
12	Sandy Lane	1-3	0-0	2-0	3-5	1-4	6-0	1-1	0-1	1-1	2-2	2-3	X	1-1	2-3	0-3	0-1
13	Wakefield	2-1	-	0-0	0-1	3-0	2-0	6-1	3-1	4-3	1-1	3-1	2-2	X	1-4	2-1	3-0
14	Wetherby Athletic	1-1	0-1	0-1	0-4	3-0	0-1	3-1	1-4	2-4	2-4	4-1	5-1	1-2	X	2-1	5-3
15	Whitkirk Wanderers	3-0	1-1	3-1	0-1	4-5	3-4	1-2	0-5	5-0	6-1	1-0	0-3	0-0	2-1	X	6-1
16	York R I	3-2	2-4	2-4	1-4	2-4	2-4	2-4	1-5	1-7	4-2	0-1	3-3	-	2-1	1-2	X

FAIR PLAY LEAGUE

PREMIER DIVISION	Sandy Lane	175
	Nestle Rowntrees	225
	Wakefield	300
DIVISION ONE	Sherburn White Rose	160
	Ossett Common Rvrs	185
	Kirk Deighton Rngrs	195
DIVISION TWO	Fryston Miners Welfare	95
	Kippax Welfare	105
	Howden Clough	125
PREMIER ALLIANCE	Sandy Lane	120
	Bardsey	140
	Carlton Athletic	150
RESERVE DIVISION	Featherstone Colliery	35
	Baildon Trinity Athletic	70
	Armley Athletic	100

GOLDEN BOOT AWARD

PREMIER DIVISION		
Vernol Blair	Carlton Athletic	30
Matthew Wain	Nestle Rowntrees	28
Stephen Davey	Carlton Athletic	26
DIVISION ONE		
Paul Norris	Pudsey	31
Marcus Philpott	Ripon City Magnets	29
Craig Hewitt	Methley Rangers	27
DIVISION TWO		
James Duval	Churwell Lions	45
Robert Page	Kellingley Welfare	35
Stephen McGlone	Howden Clough	28
PREMIER ALLIANCE		
Graham Orton	Beeston St Anthony's	21
Paul Longthorne	Carlton Athletic	18
Adrian Faulkner	Nostell Miners Welfare	15
RESERVE DIVISION		
Adrian Sharpe	Great Preston	34
Graham Hirst	Armley Athletic	29
Chris Williams	Robin Hood Athletic	28

MUMTAZ WEST RIDING COUNTY AMATEUR FOOTBALL LEAGUE

President: D H Humpleby Esq.

Secretary: S Mitchell, 24 Burnsall Road, Liversedge, West Yorkshire WF15 6QF
Tel: 01924 404684

FINAL LEAGUE TABLES 2000-01

PREMIER DIVISION

	P	W	D	L	F	A	Pts
Brighouse Town	26	20	2	4	77	24	62
Ovenden West Riding	26	20	1	5	88	32	61
Golcar United	26	15	3	8	52	34	48
Hemsworth MW	26	14	5	7	57	40	47
Keighley Phoenix	25	14	0	11	60	42	42
Stump Cross	26	12	5	9	52	48	41
Storthes Hall	26	11	6	9	52	36	39
Marsden	26	9	5	12	47	55	32
Campion	26	7	7	12	47	68	28
Wibsey	26	6	10	10	23	48	28
Littletown	26	6	8	12	47	61	26
Otley Town	26	6	6	14	31	56	24
Crag Road United	26	4	6	16	30	80	18
Field	25	4	2	19	26	65	14

Keighley Phoenix v Field unplayed

DIVISION ONE

	P	W	D	L	F	A	Pt
Silsden	28	24	3	1	90	19	75
Lower Hopton	28	19	4	5	79	33	61
Keighley Shamrocks	28	15	2	11	61	42	47
Altofts	28	13	8	7	68	51	47
Eastmoor	28	11	8	9	69	62	41
Dudley Hill Athletic	28	11	8	9	58	60	41
Halifax Irish Club	28	11	6	11	59	58	39
Salt Old Boys	28	10	7	11	43	39	37
Tyersal	28	11	3	14	48	68	36
Bay Athletic	28	9	7	12	65	61	34
Hall Green United	28	9	5	14	59	64	32
Ardsley Celtic	28	9	5	14	53	67	32
Heckmondwike Town	28	9	5	14	65	84	32
Farnley	28	8	6	14	50	62	30
Ventus & Yeadon Celtic	28	1	3	24	26	123	6

Pudsey Town withdrawn - record expunged

PREMIER DIVISION CUP

SEMI FINALS

Hemsworth M W	V	Ovenden W R	2*2, 2-3p	
Littletown	v	Brighouse Town	0-2	

FINAL

Ovenden West Riding	v	Brighouse Town	1-3	at Littletown

DIVISION ONE CUP

SEMI FINALS

Bay Athletic	v	Silsden	0-1	
Lower Hopton	v	Eastmoor	1*1,7-6p	

FINAL

Silsden	v	Lower Hopton	4-0	at Littletown

DIVISION TWO CUP

SEMI FINALS

Hunsworth	v	Steeton	3-2	
Westbrook Wndrs	v	Roberttown	2-3	

FINAL

Hunsworth	v	Roberttown	3-0	at Campion

LEAGUE CONSTITUTION FOR 2001-02

PREMIER DIVISION: Brighouse Town, Campion, Golcar United, Hemsworth Miners Welfare, Keighley Phoenix, Littletown, Lower Hopton, Marsden, Otley Town, Ovenden West Riding, Silsden, Storthes Hall,Stump Cross, Wibsey,

DIVISION ONE: Altofts, Ardsley Celtic, Bay Athletic, Crag Road United, Dudley Hill Athletic, Dudley Hill Rangers, Eastmoor, Farnley, Halifax Irish Club, Hall Green United, Heckmondwike Town, Keighley Shamrocks, Rawdon Old Boys, Salt Old Boys, Steeton, Tyersal

DIVISION TWO: Barclays, Bowling, Dynamoes, Green Lane, Hunsworth, Morley Town, Roberttown, Salts, Ventus & Yeadon Celtic, Wakefield City, Westbrook Wanderers, Westwood

Maybe he's always like this!   Alan Coomes - the thinker

Photos: Garry Letts

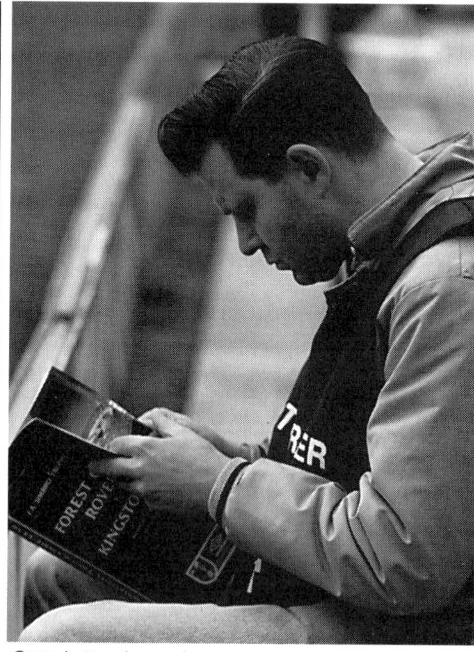

Some think, some read!   Garry Letts - the reader
Photos: Graham Cotterill and Keith Clayton who have given long and much appreciated service
Turn to page 590

NORTH EASTERN FINAL LEAGUE TABLES 2000-01

BRADFORD GRATTAN LEAGUE

PREMIER DIVISION	*P*	*W*	*D*	*L*	*F*	*A*	*Pts*
Brook Crompton	21	15	4	2	94	46	49
Smiling Mule	21	16	1	4	68	39	49
Mail Coach	21	12	5	4	70	35	41
East Bowling	21	7	5	9	65	72	26
U Save DIY	21	8	2	11	52	66	26
The Royal (Clayton)	21	6	4	11	63	69	22
Wibsey	21	5	2	14	45	50	17
Roebuck	21	2	3	16	31	101	9

SPEN VALLEY LEAGUE

PREMIER DIVISION	*P*	*W*	*D*	*L*	*F*	*A*	*Pts*
Lord Nelson	21	18	5	0	75	36	53
Thornhill	22	15	3	4	77	32	48
Saviletown Youth	22	14	2	6	78	43	44
Black Horse Batley	22	13	4	5	77	44	43
Airedale Celtic	22	10	5	7	65	57	35
Barclays	22	10	3	9	50	55	33
Bywell	22	9	4	9	50	46	31
Overthorpe SV	22	8	2	12	57	63	26
Mount SV	22	7	3	11	70	73	24
Black Labrador	22	6	4	12	49	77	22
Bosnia	21	2	4	15	44	96	10
Old Bank WMC	22	1	1	20	48	118	4

LEEDS RED TRIANGLE LEAGUE

PREMIER DIVISION	*P*	*W*	*D*	*L*	*F*	*A*	*Pts*
Wykebeck Arms Utd	24	20	3	1	97	25	63
Omnibus	24	17	0	7	76	46	51
Park Hotel (Pudsey)	24	15	4	5	79	45	49
Street Work Soc	24	15	2	7	99	68	47
Whinmoor Lions	24	12	7	5	75	51	43
Bramley Villager	24	12	3	9	80	50	39
Shoulder of Mutton	24	11	4	9	65	61	37
Old Griffin Head	24	8	4	12	54	68	28
Pudsey Sports & SC	24	8	3	13	63	75	27
Woodhouse MM	24	6	4	14	55	77	19
Scott Hall Steel	24	3	5	16	49	127	14
Headingley	24	3	4	17	51	91	13
Churwell Lion Res*	24	4	1	19	39	88	13

CRAVEN & DISTRICT LEAGUE

PREMIER DIVISION	*P*	*W*	*D*	*L*	*F*	*A*	*Pts*
Skipton Bulldogs	20	17	3	0	83	13	37
Crosshills Reserves	20	16	1	3	55	27	33
Oxenhope Recreation	20	9	5	6	48	36	23
Embsay	20	7	6	7	44	41	20
Addingham	20	6	7	7	48	58	19
Grassington United	20	8	3	9	39	51	19
Clitheroe United	20	8	4	8	48	32	18
Colne Cricket Club	20	7	2	11	42	61	14
Skipton LMS	20	6	2	12	36	64	14
Keighley Lifts	20	3	4	13	27	52	10
Cononley Sports	20	3	3	14	31	66	9
Grindleton - withdrawn							

HUDDERSFIELD & DISTRICT AFL

DIVISION ONE	*P*	*W*	*D*	*L*	*F*	*A*	*Pts*
Brackenhall United	22	16	2	4	51	25	50
Honley	22	13	6	3	71	28	45
Slaithwaite United	22	12	5	5	41	23	41
Shepley	22	10	5	7	45	34	35
Britannia Sports	22	9	6	7	42	43	33
Grange Moor	22	7	9	6	44	45	30
Wooldale Wanderers	22	7	7	8	41	38	28
Kirkburton	22	8	3	11	40	42	27
Kirkheaton Rovers	22	8	3	11	35	45	27
Sovereign Sports	22	7	3	12	42	61	24
Almondbury United	22	3	5	14	28	59	14
Skelmanthorpe	22	4	2	16	21	58	14

YORK & DISTRICT LEAGUE

PREMIER DIVISION	*P*	*W*	*D*	*L*	*F*	*A*	*Pts*
Old Malton	24	21	1	2	105	37	64
Dringhouses	24	13	8	3	63	31	47
Pocklington Town	24	13	6	5	58	24	45
Boroughbridge	24	13	5	6	66	31	44
Huntingdon Rovers	24	13	5	6	60	44	44
Bishopthorpe	24	11	8	5	57	39	41
Crayke	24	11	5	8	42	43	38
Rufforth United	24	11	3	10	42	50	36
Wigginton G'hoppers	24	7	5	12	48	52	26
Dunnington	24	4	8	12	40	53	20
Kartiers	24	5	3	16	36	79	18
New Earswick	24	2	4	18	22	67	10
CGU	24	1	1	22	16	105	4
York Sugar withdrawn							

Wade Northern Alliance action: Heaton Stannington v Benfield Saints. Photo: Graham Brown

NORTH LEICESTERSHIRE LEAGUE

PREMIER DIVISION	*P*	*W*	*D*	*L*	*F*	*A*	*Pts*
Sileby United WMC22	17	3	2	87	31	54	
Hathern	22	16	5	1	73	26	52
Ashby Ivanhoe	22	14	3	5	51	38	45
West End Rangers	22	11	6	5	61	42	39
Shelthorpe KC	22	11	3	8	77	43	36
Loughborough Town	22	8	6	8	47	59	30
Shepshed Amateurs	22	7	3	12	28	51	24
Bagworth Colliery	22	6	5	11	37	50	23
Ingles*	22	7	5	10	48	50	22
Woodhouse Imperial	22	4	4	14	39	62	16
Groby	22	3	3	16	35	78	12
Belton Villa	22	3	3	16	31	84	12

BRADFORD SUNDAY ALLIANCE

PREMIER DIVISION	*P*	*W*	*D*	*L*	*F*	*A*	*Pts*
Albion Sports	22	21	0	1	105	23	63
East Bowling Unity	22	19	2	1	82	19	59
Oakenshaw	22	11	4	7	56	42	37
Hudsons	22	10	2	10	47	36	34
Bradford Moor	22	10	4	8	52	45	34
Bolton Woods	22	8	5	9	48	49	29
Stanley Road	22	8	3	11	38	60	27
Queensbury	22	6	8	8	49	53	26
Craven Heir	22	7	3	12	40	61	24
Calverley Victoria	22	5	4	13	27	59	18
Wibsey WMC	22	5	2	15	45	82	17
Ventus United	22	1	5	16	19	85	8

WHARFEDALE SUNDAY LEAGUE

PREMIER DIVISION	*P*	*W*	*D*	*L*	*F*	*A*	*Pts*
Stanbury Rangers	16	13	3	0	95	18	42
Silsden	16	11	4	1	106	18	37
Keighley Juniors	16	9	6	1	66	34	33
Sandy Lane	16	8	2	6	58	34	26
Victoria Hotel	16	6	2	8	67	36	20
Victoria 2000	16	5	2	9	52	81	17
Royal	16	5	1	10	55	59	16
Boltmakers Arms	16	4	1	11	58	67	13
Regent Victoria	16	0	1	15	9	237	1

KEIGHLEY & AIRE SUNDAY FOOTBALL LEAGUE

PREMIER DIVISION	*P*	*W*	*D*	*L*	*F*	*A*	*Pts*
Skipton FC	20	18	2	0	85	15	56
Midlands FC	22	18	0	4	82	36	54
Keighley Victoria FC	21	14	2	5	72	34	44
Bocking AFC	22	11	3	8	61	36	36
Shoulder of Mutton K2	22	10	4	8	76	58	34
St Annes Celtic	22	9	4	9	58	35	31
Silsden Athletic FC	21	10	1	10	56	72	31
Cottingley	22	9	2	11	53	50	29
Stockbridge FC	20	5	2	13	38	88	17
Royal Oak FC	21	4	4	13	28	78	16
Keighley United	21	4	2	15	34	85	14
Brown Cow Bingley	22	2	2	18	27	83	8

Craven Athletic withdrawn

Left: Guisborough Town keeper Marty Bell prepares to block this effort from Newcastle Blue Star's Paul Hollier.
Photo: Alan Watson

Below: Northern League: Jarrow Roofing vWhitley Bay. Goalmouth action from a game which finished 1-1.
Photo: Graham Brown

SOUTHERN LEAGUE

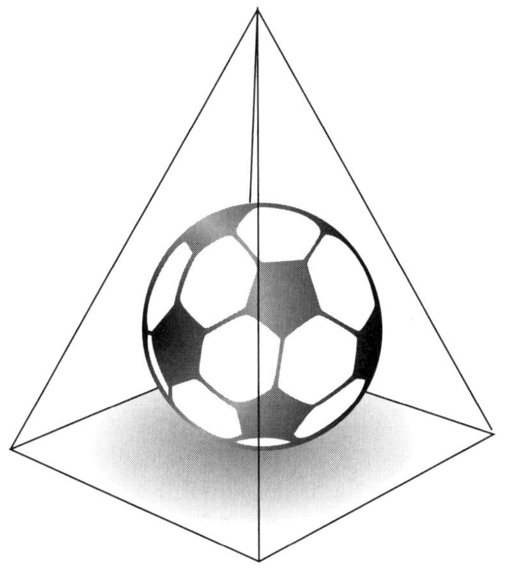

PYRAMID SECTION

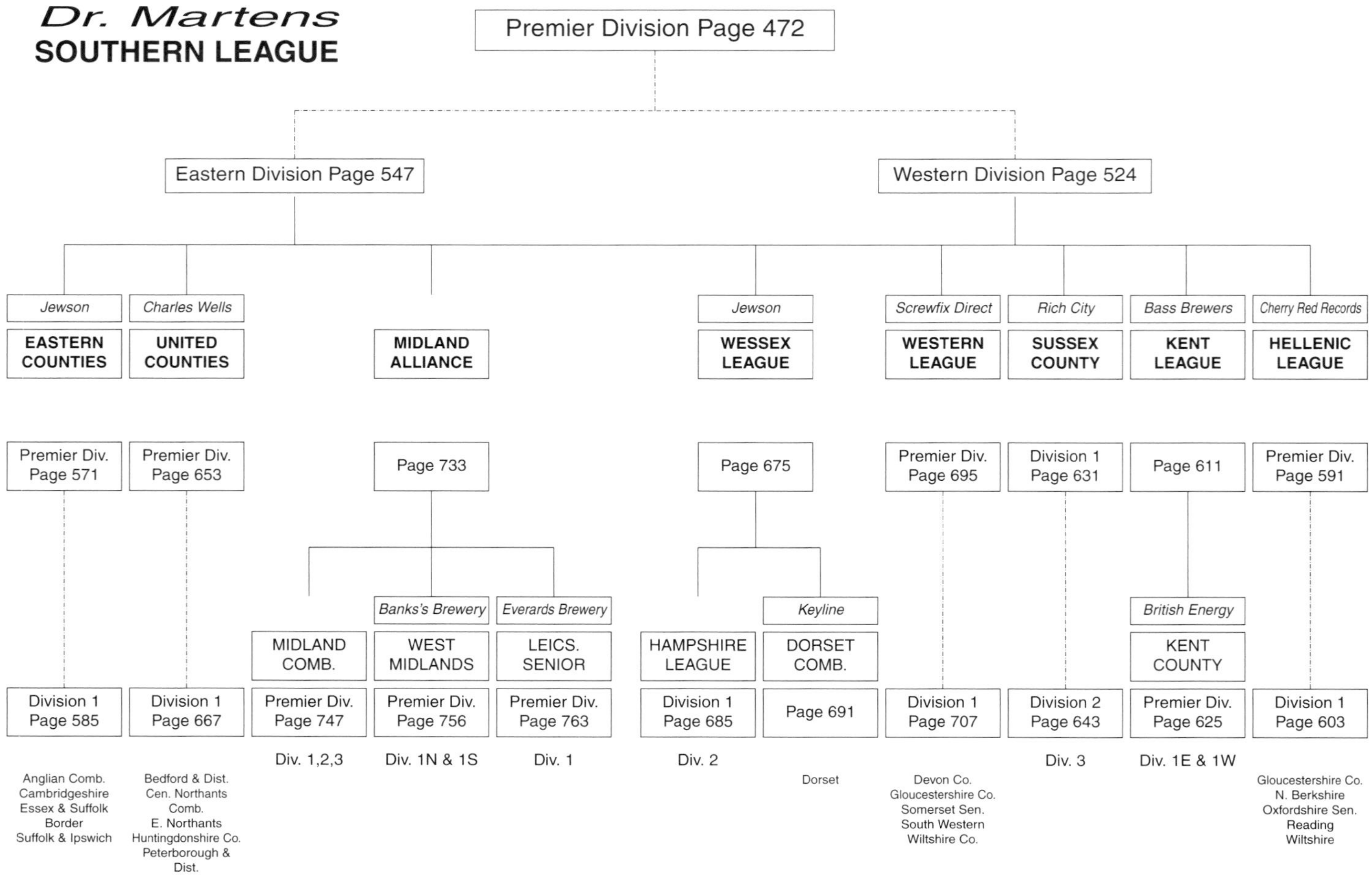

Dr. Martens
SOUTHERN LEAGUE

Premier Division Page 472

Eastern Division Page 547

Western Division Page 524

Sponsor	League	Top division	Feeder league (sponsor)	Lower division	Further divisions	Feeder leagues
Jewson	**EASTERN COUNTIES**	Premier Div. Page 571		Division 1 Page 585		Anglian Comb. Cambridgeshire Essex & Suffolk Border Suffolk & Ipswich
Charles Wells	**UNITED COUNTIES**	Premier Div. Page 653		Division 1 Page 667		Bedford & Dist. Cen. Northants Comb. E. Northants Huntingdonshire Co. Peterborough & Dist.
	MIDLAND ALLIANCE	Page 733	MIDLAND COMB.	Premier Div. Page 747	Div. 1,2,3	
			WEST MIDLANDS (*Banks's Brewery*)	Premier Div. Page 756	Div. 1N & 1S	
			LEICS. SENIOR (*Everards Brewery*)	Premier Div. Page 763	Div. 1	
Jewson	**WESSEX LEAGUE**	Page 675	HAMPSHIRE LEAGUE	Division 1 Page 685	Div. 2	
			DORSET COMB. (*Keyline*)	Page 691		Dorset
Screwfix Direct	**WESTERN LEAGUE**	Premier Div. Page 695		Division 1 Page 707		Devon Co. Gloucestershire Co. Somerset Sen. South Western Wiltshire Co.
Rich City	**SUSSEX COUNTY**	Division 1 Page 631		Division 2 Page 643	Div. 3	
Bass Brewers	**KENT LEAGUE**	Page 611	KENT COUNTY (*British Energy*)	Premier Div. Page 625	Div. 1E & 1W	
Cherry Red Records	**HELLENIC LEAGUE**	Premier Div. Page 591		Division 1 Page 603		Gloucestershire Co. N. Berkshire Oxfordshire Sen. Reading Wiltshire

Dr MARTENS LEAGUE

Chairman: D S R Gillard
Secretary: D J Strudwick
PO Box 90, Worcester WR3 8RX
Tel: 01905 757509

In a season affected by the weather, more than any other in living memory, Margate emerged from the dark clouds that threatened to disrupt the campaign to eclipse the challenge of Burton Albion. With the prospect of the Division's top two clubs clashing at Eton Park on the final day to decide the title, Margate gleaned a point from their final home match against Newport County to leave the Brewers in the shade for the second year running.

When the season opened in the customary heat of the August sunshine, nobody could forecast the obfuscation waiting around the corner. As Welling United opened their first season back in the Dr Martens League with six wins in their first eight games little did we know storm clouds were gathering somewhere out in the mid-Atlantic. By the time Crawley Town appeared from the fog of a traumatic close season to take over Welling's top spot for eight weeks, nimbus after nimbus was about to begin dropping its unwelcome load on football pitches throughout the country. The Newtowners then lost at Bath, which allowed Burton to take over at the top for one week. By the time the wet weather was upon us, Margate, after losing their opening two fixtures, topped the table for the first time on 25 November despite actually losing four of their first thirteen matches. After two weeks on cloud nine Margate began to fall a couple of fixtures behind their challengers. This allowed Burton Albion back in the frame and, apart from a ten-day spell over the New Year when Margate regained the leadership, Burton headed the table until March.

By now, though, the Brewers had dropped a shower of points at home. Fifteen points, one third of those available from their fifteen home matches completed by this stage of the season, had escaped their grasp. By comparison Margate had dropped only six home points in fourteen games and regained the leadership with a 1-0 win over Halesowen Town on 3rd March. It was a lead they refused to relinquish. In the run-in to the Championship, they lost only once in 24 games before losing what may have been a title decider at Burton on the final day of the season.

To win the Southern Football League Premier Division Title is a considerable achievement. To win two Championships is exceptional. But to win three . . .!?! Margate's manager, Chris Kinnear, had already guided Dover Athletic to two titles. Chris' previous Championship winning teams conceded 23 and 27 goals. His current team turned in another scrooge-like performance, again giving away only 27 goals to their opponents. With Regional First Division honours also under his belt, Chris is clearly one of the most successful managers at our level of the game. Congratulations Chris. Little would please us more than to see you lead Margate to the Football Conference title to make it four consecutive Ex-Southern League sides in the Football League.

The destiny of clubs at the bottom of the table was decided earlier than usual. Fisher Athletic (London) re-appearing in the Premier Division after being demoted in 1992 could not get their heads above the 'water table' that marks the relegation zone. Tamworth flirted with the foot of the table before replacing manager Paul Hendrie with Gary Mills. The former Nottingham Forest full back quickly led the Lambs to mid-table safety. And, whilst Folkestone Invicta appeared vulnerable for long periods during their first season in the Premier Division for the most part, they stayed above the trapdoor. Clevedon Town, Dorchester Town and Halesowen Town were rarely out of the bottom four all season and, with Fisher, succumbed to the depression of relegation two weeks before the close of play.

Newport IOW won the Eastern Division Championship despite a deluge of fixtures during the last few weeks of the season. The Islanders, whose pitch suffered more than most after the torrent of rain that hit the south coast, still had half their season to play at the beginning of March. At this point Newport were seventh in the table, fifteen points behind Chelmsford City.

Chelmsford had led the table since 4th November, taking over from a flurry of clubs who at various times had burst their way through to the top in the opening weeks of the season. Tonbridge Angels, Grantham Town, Newport, Spalding United, Bashley and Rothwell Town had all appeared above the clouds during the early stages but only Grantham remained in contention as the campaign moved towards its conclusion.

Grantham's chances finally faded when they dropped two points at Langney Sports on the penultimate Saturday. But, having lost only six matches at this point during the season, it would be hard to say they threw away the opportunity of promotion back to the top flight one year after being relegated. The Gingerbreads, who were already chasing Chelmsford, were finally engulfed by Newport as the Islanders stormed their way to the top of the table. Newport's surge to the top set up a Championship decider at Chelmsford on the final day of the season. Newport took the gold medals with a 1-0 win in front of the City's best crowd for several seasons. Even that magnificent goal poacher Steve Portway, who notched 38 goals this season, could not breach the Islanders' defence on this occasion.

Despite being one of the League leaders in the early weeks of the season, Spalding United's campaign ended under the low pressure of relegation. After topping the Division on 16th September with four wins in five games, the Tulips won only three further games and were finally submerged under a downpour of 22 defeats in their subsequent 37 fixtures.

Sittingbourne also found the temperature in the Eastern Division a little hot this year. The Brickies slumped to 25 defeats in this season's programme and finished in the drop zone level with Spalding on 33 points.

Wisbech Town spent much of the season on the bottom of the table. But, after evaluating its position and re-structuring its constitution, under the guidance of the Football Association's Financial Advisory Unit, the Fenmen finished six points to the good. Sound advice was wisely and gratefully accepted by the Fenmen.

Like the Premier Division, only four clubs led the Western Division throughout the whole 42-match programme. Bilston Town and Evesham United set the early pace closely followed by Mangotsfield United.

By the end of October, aided by the scoring exploits of Scott Voice, Bilston took up the 'yellow jersey' in fine style. The Steelmen seemed tempered for a serious assault on the title. But after just one defeat in the first half of their programme, it took only three defeats in their next eight matches to allow Hinckley United to take charge. Helped by a superb home record (the Knitters did not taste defeat between the first home game of last season until the last fixture of the season just ended) Hinckley pelted into top spot by 10th February and never looked back.

As dusk settled on the season, the light on Mangotsfield's campaign dimmed a little and the Bristol club finished fifth. 'Field can afford to be pleased with their first furrow into regional football.

Meanwhile, Tiverton Town, whilst being slightly better off than Newport with their fixtures, were well off the pace. With at least seventeen points to make up at the beginning of March the Devon club could only be taken seriously if they could win nearly all of their remaining eighteen fixtures. But manager Martyn Rogers is a man for all seasons. Concluding with eight games in fifteen days, Tivvy won fourteen of their last eighteen fixtures, which led to a cyclonic rise up the table. Tiverton secured the second promotion place at Blakenall on the last day of the season.

The foot of the table witnessed one of the most amazing escapes from relegation that could possibly have happened in senior football.

Storm clouds were gathering over Cinderford Town by the end of September. Although Paget Rangers and Weston-super-Mare were beneath the Foresters at this time, Cinderford had won only one game in nine. By the turn of the year they were adrift at the bottom and five points from safety. By 7th April the margin had stretched to a massive nine points with just four weeks of the season remaining. Even with four games in hand on your opponents, it's 'mission impossible' when you are bottom of the League, especially when you have only three wins to your name in 29 games. As quick as a thunderbolt (metaphorically or meteorologically speaking) the Foresters added six points to their tally, climbed above Paget and were on Bromsgrove's tail. Within another week they had made up a further six points and led the Rovers on goal difference. One week later Cinderford had completed their Houdini escape, in spite of losing their last game 4-0 at Gresley Rovers, leaving Sutton Coldfield Town in their wake and Bromsgrove and Paget in the relegation zone. And who said lightning does not strike in the same place twice? Since finishing Runners-up in the Football Conference at the end of the 1992-93 season Bromsgrove have finished in a relegation place in four of the last five years.

The wonderful Worcester Vase, the prize for winning the League Cup, effectively came home this year, to Worcester. The Faithfuls took a 4-0 first leg lead over Crawley Town into the Second Leg at the Newtowners' beautiful Broadfield Stadium. Although Crawley made amends for a disappointing result in the first game at St George's Lane, they could only breach Worcester's defence once. City's superb triumph was then toasted the following morning in the House of Commons when local MP Michael Foster tabled an Early Day Motion congratulating the club and wishing it good luck with its relocation plans.

The Semi-finals had been all Premier Division affairs. Crawley Town won their place in the Final by winning a close encounter against Kings Lynn, 3-2, Worcester followed suit by winning a wonderful match against Newport County 5-2, after extra time.

When twelve clubs reached the final qualifying round of the Football Association Cup the climate felt good for some successes in the First Round Proper. Sadly, it was an overcast day in terms of results: only four clubs made it into the Football Association's velvet bag with the full-time professionals. Burton Albion held Kidderminster Harriers to a goalless draw at Aggborough before losing the replay at Eton Park 4-2; Ilkeston Town lost at Swindon 4-1; Dorchester Town were second at Wigan 3-1 and Havant & Waterlooville went out at home to Southport 2-1. There have not been many years when the Dr Martens League has had no representation in the Second Round of the country's premier knock-out tournament but this year was one of them.

Sunny thoughts prevailed when nine Dr Martens League clubs reached the Fourth Round of the FA Trophy. But by the end of the day a low pressure had set in. Six clubs had crashed out leaving Burton Albion (who beat Scarborough 1-0), Tiverton Town (who knocked out reigning Dr Martens League Champions Boston United 2-1) and Weymouth (who defeated DM colleagues Ashford Town 3-1) in Round Five. Only Burton Albion survived at this stage. Tiverton lost to Worksop 2-1 and Southport beat Weymouth by the same score. Burton overcame Yeovil Town 2-1 before going out to Hereford United, one hurdle short of the semi-finals.

When congratulating the Winners and Runners-up and commiserating with the less fortunate it must be remembered that the margin between success and failure is narrow and relative. For the unbiased administrator success can be judged on the progress of the season and how the aims and objectives are achieved. Whilst the weather was hardly conductive to a trouble free campaign, one of the League's main objectives for the competition, to start and finish on time in an orderly and fair fashion, was achieved. No club was forced to play two games in one day. No club even faced that prospect. The League's Board unconditionally applauds all members clubs and Match Officials for their magnificent efforts to complete the fixture programme within the agreed parameters.

Talking of Match Officials, like clubs, the men in black also chase their particular rainbow of success. Six of the League's Referees have this season been promoted to the National List of Assistant Referees. This total is higher than any other Contributory League in the country. Two more Referees have been promoted to the Panel List of Referees. Another,

Kevin Pike, has been appointed to the FIFA List of Match Officials and received assignments to the Worthington Cup Final and the FA Cup Final. Seventeen Dr Martens League Assistant Referees have been promoted to the Referees' List. Well done, gentlemen.

The continued accomplishment by the League's Match Officials does not happen by coincidence or simple good luck. The Board is certain, therefore, it will be joined by the complement of Officials when it thanks and congratulates the League's List of Assessors. Barely noticed, Jimmy Hill leads his band of merry men in all weathers to matches around the country to help and advise the men in the middle and on the touchline. Unsung, but not forgotten, heroes of our game. Thank you, gentlemen. Thank you, too, Steve Tincknell and Mark Ives of the Match Officials Association. Your organisation is responsible for much success.

To organise a unit the size and stature of the Dr Martens Football League is not an inexpensive exercise. To sustain the level of success the Competition has attained over a considerable number of years is no fluke and positively absorbs substantial resources. Whilst the League has been fairly successful in self funding many of its activities, the sums of money and products it recycles back into clubs and match officials depends heavily on generous sponsorships and The Football Association.

To this end, the Board expresses its sincere thanks to R Griggs Group Limited for its fantastic sponsorship support. In thanking the Company for its obvious financial help, the Board would particularly like to thank Max and Steven Griggs, Mark Darnell, Dave Joyce and Sue Hughes for their less visible assistance and hard work. The League appreciates being associated with the great name of Dr Martens.

James Gilbert Limited has sponsored the League's Match Balls for the last two seasons and has agreed to complete its three year association with the League. The supply of Match Balls by such a high profile world-renowned company is of immense benefit to the member clubs. Thank you to the James Gilbert team. We hope you continue your interest in the football field as well as maintaining your prominence on the rugby field.

I.C.I.S. stepped into the vacuum left by Vandanel last season by supplying bench kit to clubs. I.C.I.S. is prepared to extend its commitment to those clubs taking advantage of the sponsorship agreement over the next three years. Thank you I.C.I.S. and good luck. If you do well, our clubs do well.

Significant financial assistance has also been received during the last three years from The Football Association. This year the League has received an administration grant of £20,000 and a grant of £1,500 towards the cost of the Assessing scheme. The Football Association has also allocated the League two PC's. Thank you Soho Square.

During any year there are a number of comings and goings. Sadly, this year, the Board has to report the sad passing of the League's President, George Templeman. After a brief illness, Temp's wonderful life ended on 28th January. We miss him very much and this year's AGM will not be the same without him.

More happily, the League bids farewell to Margate FC, who have won promotion to the Football Conference. Good Luck 'Gate.

At the opposite end of the spectrum we have to say goodbye to Bromsgrove Rovers, Paget Rangers and Spalding United, who have all been relegated from the Competition, and Baldock Town, who have been forced to resign. We hope there are sunnier days ahead for you soon.

In bidding Burton Albion good luck in its move to the Northern Premier League, the Board welcomes Hednesford Town and Kettering Town. The two former Conference clubs will clearly bolster our top flight.

In exchange for the clubs being relegated from the League the feeder Competitions have again come up trumps. The Board welcomes the wind of change that newcomers Chatham Town, Chippenham Town, Stourport Swifts and Swindon Supermarine will bring to the League.

And talking of 'winds of change' the League's Board is, and intends to remain, at the forefront of the proposed restructuring plans currently being discussed at the Football Association. As the most productive source of clubs to the Football Conference, the Board of The Southern Football League forged even closer ties with the League above by mutually agreeing proposals to restructure our level of the game. The Northern Premier League is also in accord with these proposals for change which recognise the national structure of the Football Conference and the semi-national level nature of the game that has been efficiently run and organised for many years by the Northern Premier League and the Southern Football League. The Football Association invited presentations from all the Leagues concerned. These have been considered at Soho Square and the Football Association has prepared its own vision for the future. This vision correlates closely with the presentations made by three of the major Leagues and further discussions are taking place.

Change will not be hastened through, but there is an air of harmony in many areas coupled with a feeling of inevitability. Despite speculation that is appearing in one or two newspapers, the Board is not at liberty to release any information about the changes being suggested. The Board intends to observe the Football Association's request for confidentiality. Needless to say, though, the Board intends to remain at the sharp end of any discussions to ensure no Dr Martens League club is disadvantaged.

The above negotiations, coupled with the wettest winter since records began, placed an increasing demand on the League's administration this year. The Board of Directors has been called upon more frequently than usual. They and the Secretariat have frequently been called upon to give up yet another Sunday. These extra demands have necessitated additional help in the office and the Board welcomes Mrs Patricia Jordan to her first Annual General Meeting. Whilst self-congratulation is no recommendation, everyone is deserving of a slap on the back at the end of a very trying but successful season.

Earlier in the report reference was made to Max Griggs and to the League's unequalled supply of clubs to the Football Conference. Those two aspects have come together this season in spectacular fashion.

Max's company also sponsor Rushden & Diamonds Football Club. This season the Diamonds became the third former Southern League club, in succession, to be promoted from the Football Conference to the Football League. Kidderminster Harriers, Cheltenham Town and now Rushden have all spent many of their bygone days, and indeed their recent past, in the Southern League. Before being promoted to the Football Conference, Rushden & Diamonds spent their entire history in the Southern League. These days are remembered fondly by Max. The Board is, therefore, unashamed in expressing its congratulations to Max and his club. We wish you all the very best of luck next season.

Dennis Strudwick, Secretary/Treasurer

PREMIER DIVISION FINAL LEAGUE TABLE 2000-01

			HOME					AWAY					TOTAL						
		P	*W*	*D*	*L*	*F*	*A*	*W*	*D*	*L*	*F*	*A*	*W*	*D*	*L*	*F*	*A*	*Pts*	*GD*
1	Margate	42	17	2	2	47	14	11	5	5	28	13	28	7	7	75	27	91	48
2	Burton Albion	42	14	6	1	36	13	11	7	3	40	23	25	13	4	76	36	88	40
3	King's Lynn	42	9	7	5	34	25	9	4	8	33	33	18	11	13	67	58	65	9
4	Welling United	42	9	6	6	29	22	8	7	6	30	33	17	13	12	59	55	64	4
5	Weymouth	42	11	6	4	41	19	6	6	9	28	32	17	12	13	69	51	63	18
6	Havant & Waterlooville	42	13	4	4	39	20	5	5	11	27	34	18	9	15	66	54	63	12
7	Stafford Rangers	42	11	3	7	42	29	7	6	8	28	30	18	9	15	70	59	63	11
8	Worcester City	42	8	7	6	29	23	10	1	10	23	30	18	8	16	52	53	62	-1
9	Moor Green	42	9	6	6	31	28	9	2	10	19	25	18	8	16	50	56	62	-3
10	Newport County	42	9	5	7	36	23	8	5	8	34	38	17	10	15	70	61	61	9
11	Crawley Town	42	13	4	4	39	22	4	6	11	22	32	17	10	15	61	54	61	7
12	Tamworth	42	11	4	6	38	24	6	4	11	20	31	17	8	17	58	55	59	3
13	Salisbury City	42	11	6	4	40	25	6	2	13	24	44	17	8	17	64	69	59	-5
14	Ilkeston Town	42	10	5	6	26	26	6	6	9	25	35	16	11	15	51	61	59	-10
15	Bath City (-3)	42	12	7	2	43	24	3	6	12	24	44	15	13	14	67	68	55	-1
16	Cambridge City	42	8	4	9	31	27	5	7	9	25	32	13	11	18	56	59	50	-3
17	Folkestone Invicta	42	9	1	11	28	37	5	5	11	21	37	14	6	22	49	74	48	-25
18	Merthyr Tydfil	42	9	6	6	32	27	2	7	12	17	35	11	13	18	49	62	46	-13
19	Clevedon Town	42	7	2	12	37	33	4	5	12	24	41	11	7	24	61	74	40	-13
20	Fisher Athletic London (-3)	42	7	4	10	24	32	5	2	14	27	53	12	6	24	51	85	39	-34
21	Dorchester Town	42	6	4	11	22	32	4	4	13	18	39	10	8	24	40	71	38	-31
22	Halesowen Town	42	4	8	9	25	33	4	5	12	22	36	8	13	21	47	69	37	-22

PREMIER DIVISION RESULTS CHART 2000-01

plus Attendance Chart

		1	2	3	4	5	6	7	8	9	10	11	12	13	14	15	16	17	18	19	20	21	22
1	**Bath City**	**X**	**3-1**	**0-0**	**4-1**	**3-2**	**3-0**	**4-3**	**2-1**	**4-0**	**3-2**	**1-1**	**2-2**	**1-1**	**1-1**	**3-1**	**2-0**	**0-1**	**2-2**	**2-1**	**0-2**	**0-0**	**3-2**
		X	1051	647	739	935	519	689	759	686	781	708	609	679	831	762	1541	710	804	832	692	1168	546
2	**Burton Albion**	**2-2**	**X**	**2-2**	**1-0**	**2-1**	**1-1**	**3-0**	**0-2**	**1-0**	**4-0**	**1-0**	**1-1**	**2-0**	**1-0**	**2-1**	**2-1**	**5-0**	**0-0**	**3-1**	**1-1**	**1-0**	**1-0**
		1376	X	946	1021	1320	1030	875	921	1006	1066	1606	1089	1464	1097	1039	1266	1085	2501	1102	1461	1155	1284
3	**Cambridge City**	**2-0**	**1-1**	**X**	**2-0**	**1-0**	**0-1**	**0-3**	**2-0**	**3-0**	**1-0**	**0-0**	**1-2**	**0-2**	**0-1**	**2-0**	**5-6**	**1-2**	**1-1**	**1-2**	**4-1**	**2-2**	**2-3**
		434	826	X	328	483	412	470	311	485	582	358	381	401	471	320	514	510	370	476	354	522	457
4	**Clevedon Town**	**0-1**	**1-2**	**3-0**	**X**	**1-2**	**4-1**	**8-1**	**0-1**	**1-4**	**0-1**	**2-3**	**1-0**	**1-2**	**2-2**	**1-2**	**2-3**	**3-1**	**2-1**	**1-1**	**2-3**	**2-1**	**0-1**
		682	519	275	X	361	286	322	428	303	248	239	271	297	341	295	534	272	222	344	336	345	247
5	**Crawley Town**	**1-2**	**2-2**	**1-2**	**1-0**	**X**	**1-0**	**4-3**	**4-1**	**2-1**	**2-0**	**1-1**	**3-0**	**0-0**	**3-1**	**1-0**	**1-2**	**5-1**	**2-2**	**0-2**	**2-1**	**2-1**	**1-0**
		692	485	823	536	X	752	327	832	451	543	402	788	978	1162	602	779	1053	858	539	1195	693	392
6	**Dorchester Town**	**4-3**	**1-3**	**1-0**	**1-0**	**2-2**	**X**	**2-2**	**1-0**	**1-2**	**0-1**	**1-2**	**0-1**	**0-1**	**4-0**	**0-3**	**0-3**	**2-1**	**0-2**	**1-1**	**0-3**	**1-1**	**0-1**
		515	605	402	500	531	X	537	482	426	523	487	486	623	502	348	701	544	547	578	484	2255	702
7	**Fisher Athletic London**	**1-0**	**0-4**	**1-2**	**1-1**	**3-2**	**1-0**	**X**	**1-2**	**0-0**	**0-3**	**1-1**	**2-3**	**1-0**	**0-2**	**3-0**	**1-3**	**1-2**	**2-3**	**2-1**	**1-1**	**1-2**	**1-0**
		148	186	135	120	396	98	X	207	129	108	209	142	131	136	150	117	143	217	137	297	98	104
8	**Folkestone Invicta**	**0-2**	**0-2**	**4-3**	**0-3**	**2-1**	**2-0**	**2-1**	**X**	**2-1**	**0-4**	**1-3**	**1-2**	**2-2**	**3-1**	**1-2**	**3-1**	**2-1**	**0-3**	**1-0**	**0-1**	**1-2**	**1-2**
		519	395	415	398	265	316	336	X	384	418	365	289	765	425	336	475	424	364	379	533	323	384
9	**Halesowen Town**	**2-0**	**1-2**	**3-0**	**1-1**	**2-2**	**1-1**	**0-2**	**4-4**	**X**	**2-2**	**0-1**	**0-4**	**0-0**	**1-1**	**0-2**	**1-3**	**3-0**	**0-1**	**1-0**	**2-2**	**0-2**	**1-3**
		471	669	316	306	411	417	413	340	X	261	503	409	363	473	535	532	402	667	504	458	294	743
10	**Havant & Waterlooville**	**2-0**	**1-1**	**4-2**	**1-0**	**0-0**	**2-1**	**3-2**	**1-4**	**0-0**	**X**	**0-1**	**4-1**	**2-3**	**1-0**	**0-0**	**3-0**	**3-1**	**2-0**	**3-2**	**0-1**	**5-1**	**2-0**
		280	416	432	328	336	475	355	260	324	X	228	540	578	301	358	420	477	425	585	495	493	317
11	**Ilkeston Town**	**3-0**	**2-1**	**0-2**	**1-1**	**1-1**	**1-0**	**1-0**	**3-0**	**1-0**	**2-1**	**X**	**1-1**	**0-3**	**2-1**	**1-0**	**0-1**	**1-1**	**1-1**	**2-1**	**0-1**	**1-6**	**2-4**
		455	1516	457	394	561	365	380	379	507	367	X	426	483	496	398	426	362	529	573	560	463	445
12	**King's Lynn**	**1-1**	**1-1**	**0-4**	**3-1**	**2-0**	**2-0**	**0-1**	**0-0**	**2-2**	**2-2**	**2-2**	**X**	**1-4**	**1-0**	**0-1**	**2-3**	**2-1**	**3-2**	**6-0**	**2-0**	**2-1**	**0-0**
		782	613	938	644	630	567	888	547	588	482	670	X	784	668	751	934	507	888	472	517	846	660
13	**Margate**	**2-0**	**1-3**	**2-1**	**2-0**	**3-0**	**3-2**	**5-0**	**3-2**	**1-0**	**1-0**	**2-0**	**3-1**	**X**	**3-2**	**0-1**	**0-0**	**1-1**	**3-1**	**1-0**	**5-0**	**3-0**	**3-0**
		706	629	428	525	1138	1006	366	950	689	336	755	406	X	395	460	2366	925	405	861	509	197	1385
14	**Merthyr Tydfil**	**3-3**	**1-5**	**2-2**	**2-0**	**0-2**	**1-2**	**2-2**	**2-0**	**0-0**	**2-1**	**4-4**	**1-0**	**0-2**	**X**	**2-0**	**2-1**	**1-0**	**3-0**	**0-0**	**0-1**	**0-1**	**4-1**
		715	581	517	381	469	631	506	364	464	463	605	438	500	X	551	707	456	663	475	504	551	667
15	**Moor Green**	**3-2**	**1-2**	**0-0**	**3-3**	**1-0**	**3-1**	**3-1**	**1-2**	**3-2**	**4-1**	**1-0**	**2-1**	**0-4**	**1-1**	**X**	**1-1**	**0-2**	**1-2**	**0-1**	**1-1**	**1-1**	**1-0**
		269	859	326	292	320	268	304	323	307	282	197	284	234	260	X	417	312	507	609	312	244	520
16	**Newport County**	**3-0**	**1-1**	**3-0**	**5-2**	**3-1**	**5-0**	**0-4**	**5-0**	**0-2**	**2-2**	**3-1**	**1-3**	**0-0**	**2-0**	**0-1**	**X**	**1-3**	**1-0**	**0-1**	**1-1**	**0-0**	**0-1**
		682	961	629	688	646	701	605	668	554	731	427	627	747	973	587	X	563	520	708	582	582	606
17	**Salisbury City**	**4-4**	**1-0**	**2-1**	**4-1**	**1-1**	**0-2**	**3-0**	**0-0**	**2-1**	**0-0**	**2-0**	**1-4**	**0-1**	**2-2**	**3-1**	**4-0**	**X**	**4-1**	**1-3**	**1-1**	**3-2**	**2-0**
		575	559	432	357	422	556	370	428	490	292	424	320	623	475	331	571	X	510	517	421	617	255
18	**Stafford Rangers**	**6-2**	**0-2**	**1-1**	**4-1**	**1-2**	**1-0**	**3-0**	**3-0**	**0-1**	**3-2**	**4-2**	**0-1**	**0-2**	**1-0**	**0-2**	**1-1**	**4-2**	**X**	**1-1**	**5-2**	**3-2**	**1-2**
		734	1674	445	645	815	549	523	608	656	746	992	668	950	516	690	840	658	X	887	769	712	697
19	**Tamworth**	**3-1**	**2-3**	**0-0**	**0-2**	**0-2**	**2-2**	**2-0**	**1-0**	**3-2**	**2-2**	**3-0**	**2-0**	**1-0**	**4-0**	**0-1**	**1-0**	**4-1**	**2-0**	**X**	**3-3**	**2-3**	**1-2**
		424	1245	526	613	430	647	577	487	602	540	446	506	422	676	684	612	535	917	X	351	406	728
20	**Welling United**	**1-0**	**1-2**	**0-2**	**2-3**	**1-1**	**1-1**	**4-0**	**1-1**	**2-2**	**2-1**	**1-2**	**1-4**	**1-0**	**1-0**	**0-0**	**3-1**	**2-1**	**0-0**	**4-0**	**X**	**2-0**	**0-1**
		500	732	551	440	777	523	575	455	525	302	600	330	619	553	514	550	432	503	644	X	735	591
21	**Weymouth**	**1-1**	**1-1**	**1-1**	**0-1**	**1-0**	**4-1**	**3-0**	**1-1**	**4-1**	**1-2**	**4-1**	**4-1**	**1-0**	**1-1**	**5-1**	**0-0**	**3-1**	**0-2**	**0-2**	**2-1**	**X**	**4-0**
		1129	1005	734	551	533	2005	627	850	730	708	740	673	1267	823	702	960	770	807	875	868	X	944
22	**Worcester City**	**0-0**	**1-1**	**2-0**	**3-3**	**2-0**	**1-2**	**1-2**	**2-0**	**4-1**	**1-0**	**1-0**	**1-1**	**0-1**	**1-1**	**1-0**	**4-4**	**0-1**	**2-4**	**1-0**	**1-2**	**0-0**	**X**
		1361	1727	765	1033	675	639	704	772	942	575	782	785	1207	1135	1003	1375	1005	1142	1003	607	827	X

DR MARTENS CHALLENGE CUP 2000-01

PRELIMINARY ROUND

Merthyr Tydfil	v	Cirencester Town	1-2	Evesham United	v	Bilston Town	1-0

FIRST ROUND

Newport County	v	Cirencester Town	1-0	Bath City	v	Witney Town	3-1
Gloucester City	v	Clevedon Town	2-1	Cinderford Town	v	Mangotsfield Utd	0-3
Bashley	v	Dorchester Town	3-2	Newport IOW	v	Weymouth	2-1
Weston super Mare	v	Tiverton Town	1-3	Salisbury City	v	Havant & W'ville^	2-2
Tamworth	v	Burton Albion	2-1	Worcester City	v	Blakenhall	4-0
Solihull Borough	v	Paget Rangers	7-1	Racing C. Warwick	v	Atherstone United	1-2
Stafford Rangers	v	Rocester	1-2	Bilston Town	v	Redditch United	2-1
Bromsgrove Rovers	v	Halesowen Town	0-2	Shepshed Dynamo	v	Moor Green	0-1
Dartford	v	Crawley Town	0-1	Chelmsford City	v	Hastings Town	1-6
Baldock Town^	v	Erith & Belvedere	3-3	Margate	v	Tonbridge Angels	4-0
St Leonards	v	Folkestone Invicta	6-4	Langney Sports	v	Welling United	3-0
Sittingbourne	v	Ashford Town^	2-2	Fisher Athletic	v	Burnham	0-2
Histon	v	VS Rugby	2-0	Stamford	v	Spalding United	2-0
Sutton Coldfield Town	v	Bedworth United	4-0	Gresley Rovers^	v	Hinckley United	2-2
Cambridge City	v	Kings Lynn	1-2	Banbury United	v	Ilkeston Town	0-1
Corby Town	v	Rothwell Town	0-7	Grantham Town	v	Wisbech Town	5-1

^ won on penalties

SECOND ROUND

Newport County	v	Bath City	5-0	Gloucester City	v	Mangotsfield Utd	0-1
Bashley	v	Newport IOW	3-2	Tiverton Town	v	Havant & W'ville	4-0
Tamworth	v	Worcester City^	0-0	Solihull Borough	v	Atherstone Utd^	3-3
Rocester	v	Bilston Town	1-4	Halesowen Town	v	Moor Green	0-1
Crawley Town	v	Hastings Town	1-0	Baldock Town	v	Margate	1-0
St Leonards	v	Langney Sports	4-2	Ashford Town	v	Burnham	4-1
Histon	v	Stamford	3-4	Sutton Coldfield Tn	v	Gresley Rovers	1-4
King's Lynn	v	Ilkeston Town	2-0	Rothwell Town	v	Grantham Town	2-1

THIRD ROUND

Newport County	v	Mangotsfield United	2-0	Bashley^	v	Tiverton Town	2-2
Worcester City	v	Atherstone United	3-2	Bilston Town	v	Moor Green	1-0
Crawley Town	v	Baldock Town	3-0	St Leonards	v	Ashford Town	1-0
Stamford	v	Gresley Rovers	1-0	King's Lynn	v	Rothwell Town	4-1

FOURTH ROUND

Newport County	v	Bashley	2-0	Worcester City	v	Bilston Town	3-2
Crawley Town	v	St Leonards	4-0	Stamford	v	King's Lynn	2-3

SEMI-FINALS

Newport County	v	Worcester City	3-5	Crawley Town	v	King's Lynn	3-2

FINAL

Worcester City	v	Crawley Town	4-1, 0-1

PREMIER DIVISION LEADING GOALSCORERS 2000-01

31	Philip Collins	Margate	17	Andrew Mainwaring	Clevedon Town
26	Gary Shepherd	Newport County	17	Martin Paul	Bath City
22	Mark Owen	Worcester City	16	Mark Hallam	Tamworth
19	Darren Rowbotham	Weymouth	15	Paul Chambers	Folkestone Invicta
18	Warren Haughton	Tamworth	15	Mark Hynes	Crawley Town
18	Lyndon Rowland	King's Lynn	15	Darren Stride	Burton Albion
18	Paul Sales	Salisbury City	15	Kevin Wilkin	Cambridge City
17	Scott Dundas	Stafford Rangers			

SOUTHERN LEAGUE - PREMIER DIVISION - LAST TEN YEARS

	91-92	92-93	93-94	94-95	95-96	96-97	97-98	98-99	99-00	00-01
Ashford Town	-	-	-	-	-	19	21r	-	-	-
Atherstone United	13	15	4	15	17	11	9	16	22r	-
Baldock Town	-	-	-	-	18	20r	-	-	-	-
Bashley	4	9	21r	-	-	-	-	-	-	-
Bath City	-	-	-	-	-	-	6	4	4	15
Boston United	-	-	-	-	-	xfer from NPL		2	1p	-
Bromsgrove Rovers	1p	-	-	-	-	-	19	22r	-	-
Burton Albion	10	8	11	3	16	6	3	13	2	2
Cambridge City	5	14	17	9	19	18	13	20	14	16
Chelmsford City	18	12	6	15	12	22r	-	-	-	-
Cheltenham Town	-	2	2	2	3	2p	-	-	-	-
Clevedon Town	-	-	-	-	-	-	-	-	8	19
Corby Town	14	3	9	22r	-	-	-	-	-	-
Crawley Town	17	=6	5	11	9	17	10	11	12	11
Dartford	6	-	-	-	-	-	-	-	-	-
Dorchester Town	11	18	18	6	13	15	4	18	18	21
Dover Athletic	2	1p	-	-	-	-	-	-	-	-
Farnborough Town	-	-	1p	-	-	-	-	-	-	-
Fisher Athletic	21r	-	-	-	-	-	-	-	-	20
Folkestone Invicta	-	-	-	-	-	-	-	-	-	17
Forest Green Rovers	-	-	-	-	-	-	-	1p	-	-
Gloucester City	12	13	10	4	4	3	11	6	20r	-
Gravesend & Northfleet	22r	-	-	14	11	14	to Isthmian Lge		-	-
Grantham Town	-	-	-	-	-	-	-	17	19r	-
Gresley Rovers	-	-	14	8	5	1	17	21r	-	-
Halesowen Town	8	10	3	13	2	4	5	8	11	22
Hastings Town	-	16	12	12	8	16	14	5r	-	-
Havant & Waterlooville							**	-	13	6
Hednesford Town	-	4	13	1p	-	-	-	-	-	-
Ilkeston Town	-	-	-	-	20r	-	-	3	9	14
King's Lynn	-	-	-	-	-	5	8	10	5	3
Leek Town	-	-	-	7	-	-	-	-	-	-
Margate	-	-	-	-	-	-	-	-	3	1p
Merthyr Tydfil	-	-	-	-	7	9	2	15	17	18
Moor Green	9	19	19r	-	-	-	-	-	-	9
Newport AFC (County from 99-00)	-	-	-	-	14	21r	-	-	7	10
Nuneaton Borough	-	-	22r	-	-	7	12	1p	-	-
Poole Town	20r	-	-	-	-	-	-	-	-	-
Rothwell Town	-	-	-	-	-	-	16	19	21r	-
Rushden & Diamonds	-	-	-	5	1p	-	-	-	-	-
St Leonards	-	-	-	-	-	-	22r	-	-	-
Salisbury City	-	-	-	-	15	12	18	12	16	13
Sittingbourne	-	-	8	20r	-	8	20r	-	-	-
Solihull Borough	-	=6	6	19r	-	-	-	-	-	-
Stafford Rangers	-	-	-	-	21r	-	-	-	-	7
Sudbury Town	-	-	-	18	10	11	to Eastern Lge.		-	-
Trowbridge Town	7	5	7	21r	-	-	-	-	-	-
Tamworth	-	-	-	-	-	-	15	9	6	12
V.S. Rugby	3	20r	-	17	22r	-	-	-	-	-
Waterlooville	15	11	20r	-	-	-	-	**		
Wealdstone	19	-	-	-	-	-	-	-	-	-
Welling	-	-	-	-	-	-	-	-	-	4
Weymouth	-	21r	-	-	-	-	-	14	10	5
Worcester City	16	17	15	10	6	10	7	7	15	8

BATH CITY

CLUB OFFICIALS

Chairman: **Stephen Hall**
Directors:
KLoach,.Todd,P.Weaver,M.Hughes.

Secretary: **Quentin Edwards** c/o the club,
01225 423087 (B) & 07785 795532 (M)

Commercial Director: **G.Todd**
Safety Officer: **J Watt**
Press Officer: **P.Weaver**

FOOTBALL MANAGEMENT TEAM

Manager: Alan Pridham
Assistant Manager: Andy Eisentrager
Physios:Terry Hardwell &Dave Monks

FACT FILE

Founded: 1889
Nickname: Stripes & The City
Midweek home matchday: Tuesday
Colours: Black & white stripes/black/b & w
Change: All yellow
Youth League: South West Counties
Ladies Team: Yes
Unofficial Club Website:www.bathcityfc,com

2000-01

Captain: Colin Towler
Top scorer:Martin Paul 19
P.o.Y.: Jon Holloway

Main Sponsor: The Bath Chronicle
BATH CITY FOOTBALL CLUB
MATCH DAY PROGRAMME
Dr Martens FOOTBALL LEAGUE
Kick-off 7.45pm Tuesday 19th September 2000
Worcester City
Season 2000/2001 Issue 4 £1.50

Pages: 48 Price £1.40

Editor: Chris Stillman
Tel: 01761 433528

GROUND Twerton Park, Twerton, Bath Avon BA2 1DB. Tel: 01225 423087/313247 Fax: 01225481391 Email Address: ofice@bathcity.freeserve,co,uk:
Directions: Twerton Park is situated on the A4/A36 Lower Bristol Road - on theBristol side of Bath City Centre (Approx 2.5 miles). The area is serviced byJ18 on the M4. From the centre of Bath the bus route is No.5 - Twerton HighStreet
Capacity: 8,840 Seated: 1,017 Covered Terracing: 4,800
Clubhouse: Several bars open all week and full service with menu on match-days catering for up to 250 people Club Shop: Contact MrM.Brush

PREVIOUS **Grounds:** The Belvoir Ground, Lambridge 1889-1932
Leagues: Southern League, Vauxhall Conference

CLUB RECORDS **Attendance:** 18,020 v Brighton & Hove Albion, FA Cup.
Defeat: 9-0 Yeovil Town 46-47 **Victory:** 8-0 v Boston United 98-99
Career goalscorer: Paul Randall. **Career appearances:** David Mogg (530)
Transfer fee paid: £15,000 for Micky Tanner from Bristol City
Transfer fee received: £80,000 for Jason Dodd from Southampton

BEST SEASON **FA Cup:** Third Round 63-64, 0-3 v Bolton W. (A) after 1-1: 93-94 **FA Trophy:** 4th Round, 89-90
HONOURS Southern League Champions 59-60, 77-78; R-up 29-33, 61-62, 89-90; Southern League Cup 78-79; Somerset Premier Cup 51-52, 52-53, 57-58, 59-60, 65-66, 69-70, 77-78, 80-81, 81-82, 83-84, 84-85, 85-86, 88-89, 89-90, 93-94, 94-95;Anglo-Italian Cup R-up 76-77, 77-78

Players progressing: Alan Skirton (Arsenal),Tony Book (Plymouth A.), Kenny Allen (Bournemouth), Peter Rogers (Exeter C.), R Bourne (Torquay), Dave Wiffil (Manchester C.), Stan Mortensen (Blackpool), Brian Wade (Swindon Town), Jeff Meacham (Bristol R.), Martin Hirst (BristolC.), Paul

L-R Back Row: Lee Vickerman, Graham Maclean, Colin Towler, Martin Paul, Ian Ganfield, Sal Bibbo, Jon Holloway, Scott Walker, Craig Hopkins, Mark Clode, Matt Hobbs. **Middle Row:** Paul Bodin (manager), Dave Monks (physio), Wayne Cleverly, Mike Davies, Jimmy Fraser, Graham Colbourne, Kevin Lloyd, Peter Tisdale, Eddie Howell, Dave Hobbs, Steve White. **Front Row:** Jason Turner, Quentin Edwards, Roy Pitman, Gilbert Walshaw, Steve Hall, Geoff Todd, Mike Hughes, Phil Weaver. **Photo:** Philip Waite.

Date	Comp.	Opponents	Att.	Score	Goalscorers
19.08	DM Prem	FOLKESTONE INVICTA	759	2 - 1	Fraser 29, McLean 75
21.08	DM Prem	Worcester City	1361	0 - 0	
26.08	DM Prem	Merthyr Tydfil	715	3 - 3	Fraser 33, Holloway 53, Colbourne 68
28.08	DM Prem	HAVANT & WATERLOOVILLE	781	3 - 2	Davis 29, Colbourne 66, McLean 72
02.09	DM Prem	Cambridge City	434	0 - 2	
05.09	DM Prem	Dorchester Town	515	3 - 4	Paul 52, Colbourne 53, Davis 57
09.09	DM Prem	FISHER ATHLETIC	689	4 - 3	Davis 11, Paul 40 66, Fraser 52
16.09	DM Prem	Ilkeston Town	455	0 - 3	
19.09	DM Prem	WORCESTER CITY	546	3 - 2	Lloyd 40, Davis 45, Hall 63
23.09	DM Prem	MARGATE	679	1 - 1	Fraser 16
30.09	FA Cup Q2	Basingstoke Town	522	1 - 1	Holloway 58
03.10	FA Cup Q2 R	BASINGSTOKE TOWN	606	2 - 0	Davis 106, McLean 115
07.10	DM Prem	Salisbury City	575	4 - 4	Paul 40 44, Allison 77, Lloyd 90
14.10	FA Cup Q3	SUTTON UNITED	897	3 - 0	Colborne 34, Holloway 65, Walker 90
21.10	DM Prem	STAFFORD RANGERS	804	2 - 2	Paul 13 74
28.10	FA Cup Q4	Forest Green Rovers	977	1 - 3	Cousins 23[og]
04.11	DM Prem	BURTON ALBION	1051	3 - 1	Colbourne 3, Walker 51, Paul 61
11.11	DM Prem	King's Lynn	782	1 - 1	Holloway 59
18.11	DM Prem	CRAWLEY TOWN	935	3 - 2	Walker 41, Paul 45 81
21.11	Som. PC 2	STREET	212	5 - 2	McLean 24 74, Walker 27, S Allison 32, F Allison 87
28.11	Lge Cup 1	WITNEY TOWN	277	3 - 1	S Allinson 24 63, Bryan 84
04.12	FA Trophy 2	Cambridge City	185	1 - 1	McLean 90
09.12	DM Prem	MOOR GREEN	762	3 - 1	Holloway 3, Paul 71, S Allison 63
12.12	FA Trophy 2 R	CAMBRIDGE CITY	403	1 - 0	Paul 43
16.12	DM Prem	Welling United	500	0 - 1	
23.12	DM Prem	NEWPORT COUNTY	1541	2 - 0	Davis 3, Paul 60
26.12	DM Prem	Clevedon Town	682	1 - 0	Fraser 45
01.01	DM Prem	WEYMOUTH	1168	0 - 0	
06.01	DM Prem	Folkestone Invicta	519	2 - 0	Towler 5, Paul 52
10.01	Lge Cup 2	Newport County	374	0 - 5	
13.01	FA Trophy 3	Yeovil Town	3507	1 - 2	Paul 50
20.01	DM Prem	MERTHYR TYDFIL	831	1 - 1	Harrington 11
27.01	DM Prem	Burton Albion	1376	2 - 2	Lloyd 29, Towler 66
30.01	DM Prem	Tamworth	424	1 - 3	Paul 49
03.02	DM Prem	ILKESTON TOWN	708	1 - 1	Walker 43
10.02	DM Prem	HALESOWEN TOWN	686	4 - 0	S Allison 13 62, Walker 18, Colbourne 88
17.02	DM Prem	Stafford Rangers	734	2 - 6	Tisdale 31, Walker 77
20.02	Som. PC QF	CLEVEDON TOWN	281	0 - 2	
24.02	DM Prem	CLEVEDON TOWN	739	4 - 1	Holloway 20, Coupe 25[og], Colbourne 34, Davis 76
28.02	DM Prem	Newport County	682	0 - 3	
03.03	DM Prem	KING'S LYNN	609	2 - 2	Holloway 63, Fraser 71
17.03	DM Prem	CAMBRIDGE CITY	647	0 - 0	
24.03	DM Prem	Margate	706	0 - 2	
27.03	DM Prem	DORCHESTER TOWN	519	3 - 0	Davis 68, Holloway 72[p], Paul 75
31.03	DM Prem	TAMWORTH	832	2 - 1	Grocutt 24[og], Paul 48
03.04	DM Prem	Havant & Waterlooville	280	0 - 2	
07.04	DM Prem	Crawley Town	692	2 - 1	Colbourne 9, Fraser 21
10.04	DM Prem	Fisher Athletic	148	0 - 1	
14.04	DM Prem	Weymouth	1129	1 - 1	Walker 70
16.04	DM Prem	SALISBURY CITY	710	0 - 1	
21.04	DM Prem	Moor Green	269	2 - 3	Davis 51, Gosling 83
28.04	DM Prem	WELLING UNITED	692	0 - 2	
05.05	DM Prem	Halesowen Town	471	0 - 2	

PLAYING SQUAD

GOALKEEPERS: Mark Hervin (Clevedon T), Liam Bull (Youth)

DEFENDERS: Colin Towler (Yate T), Gary Kemp (Newport Co), Gary Thorne (Newport Co), Ian Howell (Cinderford T), Lee Burns (Chippenham T)

MIDFIELDERS: Bradley Thomas (Cinderford T), Iain Harvey (Clevedon T), Jamie Gosling (Youth), Jamie Mills (Swindon), Joe Collins (Paulton R), Lee Vickerman (Bristol R), Marco Micciche (Clevedon T), Wayne Cleverley (Swindon)

FORWARDS: Graham Maclean (Clevedon T), Jamie Crandon (Paulton R), Owen Bryan (Youth), Paul Milsom (Clevedon T), Sam Allinson (Youth)

CAMBRIDGE CITY

CLUB OFFICIALS

Chairman: Dennis Rolph
President: Sir Neil Westbrook, CBE MA FRICS
Secretary: Stuart Hamilton
1 Parsonage Close, Highfield
Caldicote,Cambridge
Tel No: 01954 212602
email: stuart.hamilton@dial.pipex.com
Press Officer: Secretary

FOOTBALL MANAGEMENT TEAM

Manager: Chris Tovey
Asst Manager: Tom Finney
Physios: Joop Tanis and Karen White

FACT FILE

Formed: 1908
Nickname: Lilywhites
Sponsors: Lancer UK
Colours:White /black/ white. Change All Sky
Midweek matchday: Monday
Reserves' League: Eastern Counties

2000-01

Captain: Steve Holden
P.o.Y.: Martin Davies
Top Scorer: Kevin Wilkin 19

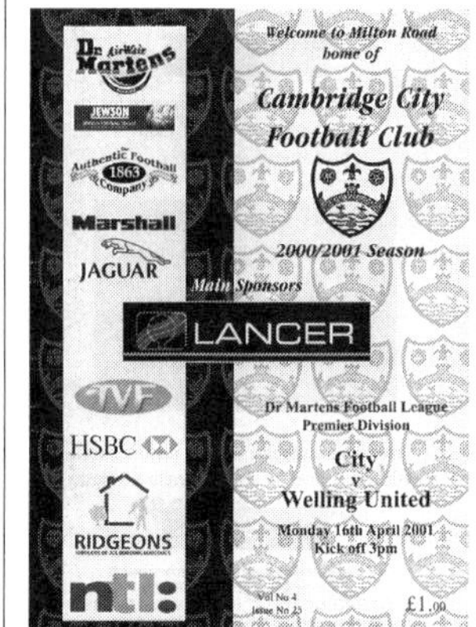

Welcome to Milton Road home of
Cambridge City Football Club
2000/2001 Season
Main Sponsors
LANCER
Dr Martens Football League Premier Division
City v Welling United
Monday 16th April 2001 Kick off 3pm
£1.00
Dr Martens
JEWSON
Marshall
JAGUAR
HSBC
RIDGEONS
ntl:

Programme
Pages: 48 Price: £1.20
Editor: Secretary

Local Press: Cambridge Evening News
Local Radio: BBC Radio Cambridge

GROUND City Ground, Milton Road, Cambridge CB4 1UY Tel: 01223 357973
Directions: Fifty yards on left from start of A1309, Cambridge to Ely Rd. (Behind Westbrook Centre). Thirty minutes walk from Cambridge BR
Capacity: 5,000 Cover: 1,400 Seats:533 Floodlights: Yes
Clubhouse: 11am-11pm Mon-Sat, 12-3 & 7pm-10.30 Sun. Bingo, Dances, Pool, Darts
Club Shop: Sells programmes, club history, badges, scarves, pennants, replica shirts Contact Neil Harvey (01223 235991)

PREVIOUS **Leagues:** Bury & Dist. 08-13 19-20, East Anglian 08-10, Southern Olympian 11-14, Southern Amateur 1913-35, Spartan 35-50, Athenian 50-58 **Name:** Cambridge Town 1908-51

CLUB RECORDS **Attendance:** 12,058 v Leytonstone, FA Amateur Cup 1st Rd, 1949-50
Scorer: Gary Grogan **Appearances:** Mal Keenan
Fee Paid: £8,000 for Paul Coe (Rushden & Diamonds) **Fee Received:**£100,000 from Millwall for Neil Harris 1998

BEST SEASON **FA Amateur Cup:** Semi Final 27-28 **FA Trophy:** 2nd Rd. 86-87 87-88
FA Cup: 1st Rd; v Ashford 66, v Swindon 46, v Walthamstow Ave. 48, v Hereford 93, v Wigan Ath. 99

HONOURS Southern Lg 62-63 (R-up 70-71, Southern Div 85-86, Div 1 R-up 69-70, Champ Cup62-63; E Anglian Cup (9); Eastern Prof Floodlit Lg 65-66 72-73, Cambs Prof Cup(6); Cambs Invitation Cup (7); Spartan Lg 47-48 48-49 (R-up 49-50); EasternDiv Champs 45-46); Southern Amat Lg 20-21 27-28 28-29 30-31 31-32; Bury & Dist.Lg (4); E Anglian Lg (6); AFA Snr Cup 30-31 46-47 47-48(shared) 48-49 49-50;AFA Invitation Cup 50-51; Hunts Prem Cup 62-63 64-65; Suffolk Sen Cup 09-10; Addenbrookes Hosp Cup 87-88; The Munns Youth Cup 82-83 83-84 84-85; ChilternYouth Lge Cup R-up 75-76; South Mids Lg Youth Trophy 82-83; Robinson Cup 87-8889-90; Jim Digney 89-90; Essex & Herts Youth Lg 89-90 Southern Lg Cup R-up 98-9

Players progressing: K Wright (West Ham 46), A Gallego(Norwich 47), A Stokes (Watford 61), D Weddle (Middlesbrough 61), D Hicksen(Bury 62), B Harvey (Blackpool 62), R Whitehead (Darlington 62), G Cummins(Hull 62), R Pearce (Peterborough 63), A Banks (Exeter 63), T Carroll (Ipswich66), Dominic Genovese (Peterborough 88), Roy Jones (Swindon), Winston Dubose(Oldham), K Wilkin (Northampton Tn 91), S Flack (Cardiff City 95), D Hedcock(Sheffield Wed 96), Neil Harris (Millwall 1998), Tesfaye Bramble, Shane Wardley (Southend United)

LEFT: Player/manager **Chris Tovey** Photo: Clive Hillier

RIGHT: Top Scorer **Kevin Wilkin** Photo: Gavin Tutcher

Date	Comp.	Opponents	Att.	Score	Goalscorers
08.08	Cambs PC F 1	Wisbech Town	n.k	1 - 1	Wilde
19.08	DM Prem	HAVANT & WATERLOOVILLE	582	1 - 0	Bramble 45
22.08	DM Prem	Folkestone Invicta	415	3 - 4	Wilkin 33 38, Cambridge 82
26.08	DM Prem	Ilkeston Town	457	2 - 0	Wilde 29, Cambridge 85
28.08	DM Prem	CRAWLEY TOWN	483	1 - 0	Cambridge 59
02.09	DM Prem	BATH CITY	434	2 - 0	Wilde 25, Cambridge 51
05.09	DM Prem	Margate	428	1 - 2	Holden 42
09.09	DM Prem	Tamworth	526	0 - 0	
16.09	DM Prem	WORCESTER CITY	457	2 - 3	Bramble 8, Wilkin 78
18.09	DM Prem	FOLKESTONE INVICTA	311	2 - 0	Wilkin 20 25
23.09	DM Prem	Weymouth	734	1 - 1	Kelly 73
30.09	FA Cup Q2	STOTFOLD	285	3 - 0	Wilkin 7 90, Bramble 33
06.10	DM Prem	BURTON ALBION	826	1 - 1	Wilde 53
14.10	FA Cup Q3	MALDON TOWN	336	3 - 2	Bramble 3, Wilkin 52 73
21.10	DM Prem	MERTHYR TYDFIL	471	0 - 1	
24.10	DM Prem	Crawley Town	823	2 - 1	Wilkin 48 78
25.10	Cambs IC P	Sawston United	57	5 - 2	Nightingale 25 92, Braybrook 37[og], Elson 100, Finney 119
31.10	FA Cup Q4	CANVEY ISLAND	575	0 - 2	
04.11	FA Trophy 1	GLOUCESTER CITY	257	1 - 0	Wilkin 72
11.11	DM Prem	NEWPORT COUNTY	514	5 - 6	Wilkin 16, Girling 21, Smith 32, Wild 36, Tovey 71
13.11	Lge Cup 1	KING'S LYNN	266	1 - 2	Salmons 65
18.11	DM Prem	Fisher Athletic	135	2 - 1	Randall 1, Tovey 60
25.11	DM Prem	Merthyr Tydfil	517	2 - 2	Salmon 41, Wilkin 75
04.12	FA Trophy 2	BATH CITY	185	1 - 1	Wardley 11
09.12	DM Prem	SALISBURY CITY	510	1 - 2	Tovey 6
12.12	FA Trophy 2 R	Bath City	403	0 - 1	
16.12	DM Prem	Newport County	629	0 - 3	
23.12	DM Prem	HALESOWEN TOWN	485	3 - 0	Cambridge 51 69, Bramble 44
26.12	DM Prem	Welling United	551	2 - 0	Nightingale 7, Cambridge 62
09.01	Cambs IC QF	MILDENHALL TOWN	93	0 - 1	
13.01	DM Prem	Clevedon Town	275	0 - 3	
23.01	DM Prem	Burton Albion	946	2 - 2	Girling 11, Wilkin 34
27.01	DM Prem	Havant & Waterlooville	432	2 - 4	Wilkin 28, Waugh 84
03.02	DM Prem	FISHER ATHLETIC	470	0 - 3	
10.02	DM Prem	TAMWORTH	476	1 - 2	Wilkin 5
17.02	DM Prem	Moor Green	326	0 - 0	
24.02	DM Prem	ILKESTON TOWN	358	0 - 0	
03.03	DM Prem	STAFFORD RANGERS	370	1 - 1	Challinor 20
10.03	DM Prem	MOOR GREEN	320	2 - 0	Wilkin 70, Cambridge 85
17.03	DM Prem	Bath City	647	0 - 0	
23.03	DM Prem	Worcester City	765	0 - 2	
26.03	DM Prem	KING'S LYNN	381	1 - 2	Hann 52[p]
31.03	DM Prem	CLEVEDON TOWN	328	2 - 0	Challinor 28, Wilde 84
03.04	DM Prem	Stafford Rangers	445	1 - 1	Challinor 50
07.04	DM Prem	Dorchester Town	402	0 - 1	
14.04	DM Prem	King's Lynn	938	4 - 0	Wilde 34 47 80, Mann 86
16.04	DM Prem	WELLING UNITED	354	4 - 1	Cambridge 39 47 68, Hann 73
21.04	DM Prem	Halesowen Town	316	0 - 3	
26.04	DM Prem	MARGATE	401	0 - 2	
28.04	DM Prem	WEYMOUTH	522	2 - 2	Chillingworth 20 26
30.04	DM Prem	DORCHESTER TOWN	412	0 - 1	
05.05	DM Prem	Salisbury City	432	1 - 2	Wilkin

Unplayed Cambs PC F(2) WISBECH TOWN

PLAYING SQUAD

GOALKEEPERS: Matt Nurse (Leicester), Aaron Benstead (Youth)

DEFENDERS: Steve Holden (Stevenage B), John Girling (Chelmsford C), Des Linton (Peterborough), Steve Wenlock (Leicester), Tim Wooding (Boston Utd), Martin Fox (Chesham Utd), Jack Wignall (Dag & Red)

MIDFIELDERS: Chris Tovey (Chelmsford C), Adam Salmons (Stockport), Adam Wilde (Camb.Utd), Jon Challinor (Stamford), Scott Taylor (Camb.Utd)

FORWARDS: Matthew Hann (Peterborough), Kevin Wilkin (Nuneaton B), Rob Nightingale (Youth)

CHELMSFORD CITY

Pages: 52 Price: £1.50
Editor: Trevor Smith (01473824782)

Local Press: Essex Chronicle, Chelmsford Weekly News, East Anglian Daily Times, Evening Gazette
Local Radio: Essex Radio/Breeze AM, BBC Essex, Chelner FM

CLUB OFFICIALS

Chairman: **Peter Stroud**
Tel: 01245 471917(H) 07900 228800M)

Secretary: **David Selby**
34 Paddock Drive,Chelmsford CM1 6SS
Tel 01245 464922

FOOTBALL MANAGEMENT TEAM

Manager: Gary Bellamy
Asst Manager: Paul Parker

FACT FILE

Formed: 1938
Nickname: City
Sponsors:Countryside Properties Plc
Colours: Claret, white trim/claret/claret
Change colours: Sky blue/navy/sky blue
Midweek matches : Monday
Club Website: www.chelmsfordcityfc.com

2000-01
Captain: Brett Girling
Top Scorer: Steve Portway 43
P.o.Y: Gary Bennett

GROUND Ground Share with Billericay Town
New Lodge, Blunts Wall Road, Billericay CM12 9SA Tel: 01277 652188

Directions: From Shenfield (A129) right at 1st lights then 2nd right. FromBasildon (A129) over 1st lights in town, then left at next lights and 2nd right. Half mile from Billericay (GER) station (London Liverpool St. - Southend line). Ground 5 mins walk from buses 222, 251, 357, 255, 551
Capacity: 3,500 Seats: 424 Cover: 600 Floodlights: Yes

Clubhouse: Open eves 8-11pm (except Mon),1pm-11pm Sat & w/e lunch noon-2.30pm.
Club Shop: Sells progs, badges, scarves, mugs etc. Contact Helen Williams via club

PREVIOUS **Leagues:** None **Grounds:** New Whittle Street 38-97, Maldon Town 97-98
Name: None (Brentwood Town were incorporated in 1970)

CLUB RECORDS **Attendance:** 16,807 v Colchester, Southern League 10/9/49
Goalscorer: Tony Butcher, 287 (1957-71) **Appearances:** Derek Tiffin, 550 (1950-63)
Win: 10-1 v Bashley (H) Dr Martens Leagu 26/4/2000
Defeat: 2-10 v Barking (A), FA Trophy, 11/11/78
Fee Paid: £10,000 for Tony Rogers (Dover Athletic, 1992) **Fee Received:** £50,000 for David Morrison (Peterborough 94)

BEST SEASON **FA Cup:** 4th Rd, 1938-39 (v Birmingham City). 1st Rd 26 times
FA Trophy: Semi-final 69-70 v Telford Utd

HONOURS Southern Lg 45-46 67-68 71-72 (R-up 48-49 60-61 63-64 65-66); Southern Div 88-89, R-up 97-98, Lg Cup 45-46 59-60 (R-up 60-61); Merit Cup 71-72; Southern Lg War-Time (East) 39-40); Essex Prof Cup 5; Essex Snr Cup 85-86 88-89 92-93; Non-League Champs Chall Cup 71-72; E Anglian Cup 48-49; Eastern Co's Lg(3) 46-49(Lg Cup 59-60); Eastern F'lit Comp 6, (Cup 72-73 74-75); Metropolitan Lg 67-68, Lg Prof Cup 67-68, Autumn Shield 70-71; Essex Snr Lg Cup 84-85; Harry Fisher Mem. Tphy 88-89

Players progressing: G Merton (Watford 48), G Adams (Orient 49), W O'Neill(Burnley 49), B Farley/S McClellan/L Dicker/P Collins (Spurs 49/49/51/68), O Hold (Everton 50), R Marden (Arsenal 50), C McCormack (Barnsley 50), D Sexton(Luton 51), W Bellet & R Mason & A Nicholas (Orient 61 & 63 & 65), R Gladwin(Norwich 66), B King (Millwall 67), J O'Mara (Bradford City 74), N Spink (Aston77), M Dziadulewicz (Wimbledon 79), M Cawston (Southend 84), P Coleman (Exeter84), J Keeley & A Owers (Brighton 86 & 87), I Brown (Bristol C 93), D Morrison (Peterborough 94)

Assistant Manager Paul Parker & Manager Gary Bellamy

Player of the Year: Gary Bennett

Photos: Gavin J Tutcher

Date	Comp.	Opponents	Att.	Score	Goalscorers
22.07	E.D.T. Trophy	Woodbridge Town	nk	3 - 0	
19.08	DM East	HASTINGS TOWN	505	2 - 2	Lakin 17, Portway 73
22.08	DM East	Wisbech Town	336	3 - 0	Dobinson 44, Portway 45, Bennett 77
26.08	DM East	Bashley	235	1 - 1	Portway 59[p]
28.08	DM East	CORBY TOWN	483	3 - 1	Berquez 9, Portway 14 39
02.09	FA Cup P	SAWBRIDGEWORTH TOWN	356	4 - 1	Fuller 31, Portway 45 69, Berquez 48
09.09	DM East	WITNEY TOWN	436	2 - 2	Berquez 40, Bishop 90
16.09	FA Cup Q1	Tilbury	293	3 - 1	Portway 40 42 47[p]
23.09	DM East	Burnham	175	5 - 1	Portway 22 37 58 61, Walker 69
25.09	DM East	TONBRIDGE ANGELS	469	4 - 1	Walker 14, Portway 25 72, Fuller 90
30.09	FA Cup Q2	GRAYS ATHLETIC	674	1 - 1	Berquez 44
03.10	FA Cup Q2 R	Grays Athletic	331	1 - 2	Hyatt 57
07.10	DM East	SITTINGBOURNE	362	1 - 0	Portway 85[p]
14.10	DM East	Histon	379	3 - 1	Dobinson 76, Walker 78, Newman 83
21.10	DM East	Erith & Belvedere	203	3 - 0	Lewis 45, Bennett 83, Berquez 85[p]
29.10	DM East	SPALDING UNITED	483	1 - 0	Bennett 76
01.11	DM East	Corby Town	97	3 - 2	Bennett 3, Portway 49 85[p]
05.11	FA Trophy 1	ST ALBANS CITY	512	0 - 2	
11.11	DM East	St Leonards	271	3 - 1	Fuller 62, Bennett 66, Portway 81
18.11	DM East	BASHLEY	466	3 - 1	Bishop 11, Portway 69[p], Fuller 78
02.12	DM East	Grantham Town	549	0 - 2	
13.12	DM East	ERITH & BELVEDERE	237	2 - 0	Fuller 64, Teneter 72
16.12	DM East	BANBURY UNITED	462	3 - 2	Caton 7, Dobinson 29, Bennett 45
19.12	Essex SC 3	Heybridge Swifts	180	0 - 8	
23.12	DM East	Newport IOW	420	0 - 0	
26.12	DM East	HISTON	454	4 - 2	Portway 22[p], Bennett 40, Taylor 67, Fuller 85
01.01	DM East	Baldock Town	528	1 - 1	Portway 49
06.01	DM East	ASHFORD TOWN	585	3 - 1	Caton 13, Portway 76[p], Walker 82
10.01	Lge Cup 1	HASTINGS TOWN	158	1 - 6	Ruddy 58[og]
13.01	DM East	DARTFORD	713	1 - 0	Bennett 82
27.01	DM East	GRANTHAM TOWN	901	1 - 2	Bennett 1
10.02	DM East	BALDOCK TOWN	606	4 - 3	Portway 2, Bennett 11, Moffatt 53, Rogers 81
17.02	DM East	Langney Sports	506	1 - 4	Bennett 65
27.02	DM East	Sittingbourne	261	3 - 0	Bennett 2 53 87
06.03	DM East	Witney Town	117	1 - 1	Walker 65
15.03	DM East	Dartford	228	1 - 0	Portway 65 F
25.03	DM East	Stamford	322	0 - 1	
31.03	DM East	ROTHWELL TOWN	481	6 - 0	Bennett 10, Berquez 26 76, Walker 28, Portway 75, Rogers 88
03.04	DM East	Hastings Town	433	2 - 2	Portway 16, Bennett 73
07.04	DM East	Spalding United	200	1 - 1	Lewis 58
10.04	DM East	Tonbridge Angels	433	1 - 1	Hayden 23[p]
12.04	DM East	WISBECH TOWN	388	6 - 0	Haydon 15, Portway 33 90, Berquez 32 68, Fuller 84
14.04	DM East	LANGNEY SPORTS	625	3 - 1	Portway 14[p] 38 41
16.04	DM East	Ashford Town	369	6 - 0	Walker 5, Portway 15 71 87, Fuller 49 71
18.04	DM East	BURNHAM	456	5 - 0	Taylor 35, Portway 41 76, Walker 57, Fuller 79
21.04	DM East	ST LEONARDS	677	2 - 1	Bennett 44, Portway 76
26.04	DM East	Rothwell Town	136	1 - 3	Portway 56[p]
28.04	DM East	Banbury United	381	3 - 2	Bennett 27, Taylor 35, Portway 65
30.04	DM East	STAMFORD	545	4 - 1	Walker 7 89, Portway 29 45
05.05	DM East	NEWPORT IOW	1441	0 - 1	

PLAYING SQUAD

GOALKEEPERS: Richard Hurst (St.Albans C)

DEFENDERS: Richard Skelly (Camb.C), Ian Wiles (Heybridge S), Mark Keen (Dag & Red), Mark Adams (Braintree T), Garry Cross (Slough T), John Bishop (Braintree T), Ben Lewis (Heybridge S), Nicky Haydon (Heybridge S), Ian Cousins (Burnham Ramblers)

MIDFIELDERS: Mark Kane (Heybridge S), Freddie Hyatt (Hendon), Russell Williamson (Southend), Kevin Dobinson (Ipswich)

FORWARDS: Ian Cambridge (Camb.C), Paul McCarthy (Baldock T)

CRAWLEY TOWN

CLUB OFFICIALS

Chairperson: **Ms Jo Gomm**
Vice Chairman: **Dave Brown**
President: **Les Turnbull**
Secretary: **Dave Haining**
20 Irving Walk, Tilgate, Crawley RH10 5BQ
Tel: 01293 535683
Chief Executive: **John Duly**
Managing Director: **Steve Duly**

FOOTBALL MANAGEMENT TEAM

Football Team Manager: Billy Smith
Coaches: Brian Owen & Ron Wilson
Asst Man: J Broughton Physio: R Massimo

FACT FILE

Formed: 1896
Nickname: The Reds
Sponsors: Providian Bank
Colours: All red Change:All blue
Midweek matchday: Tuesday
Reserves' League: Suburban
Website: www.crawley-town-fc.co.uk

2000-01

Captain: Luke Anderson
P.o.Y.: Marc Pullan
Top Scorer: Mark Hynes 19

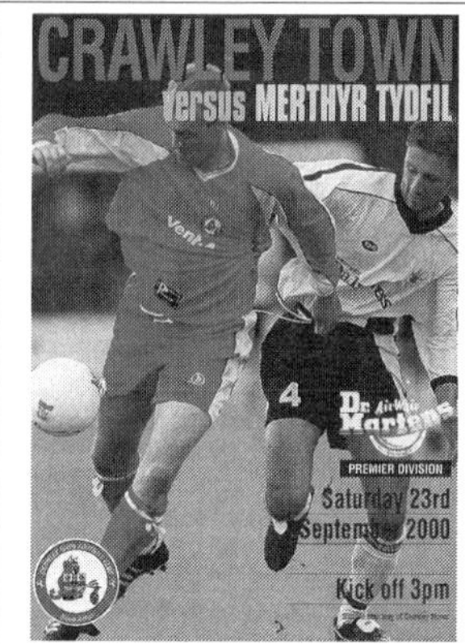

Pages: 36 Price: £1.50
Editor & Press Off: Jo Agius
Tel: 01293 432646
Local Press: Crawley Observer, Crawley News, The Argus Local Radio: Radio Mercury, BBC Southern Counties

GROUND Broadfield Stadium, Brighton Road, Crawley RH11 9RX Tel: 01293 410000

Directions: M23 exit 11, 2nd exit off roundabout, A23, towards Crawley. Turn left at next r/about into ground

Capacity: 4,996 Cover: 4,200 Seats: 1,080 Floodlights: Yes

Clubhouse: Mon-Fri: Evenings 7-11 Sat: 12-11 Sun 12-8
Club Shop: Programmes, metal badges, hats, scarves, mugs, replica kits and other items

PREVIOUS **Leagues:** Sussex County 1951-56; Metropolitan 56-63 **Grounds:** Malthouse Farm 1896-1914 38-40; Victoria Hall + Rectory Fields 18-38;Yetmans Field 45-49, Town Mead 49-53 54-97, Ifield Rec Grd 53-54

CLUB RECORDS **Attendance:** 4,104 v Barnet, FA Cup 2nd Rd 4/12/93
Goalscorer: Phil Basey 108 (68-72) **Appearances:** John Maggs 652 (63-73 75-79)
Win: 10-0 v Chichester United, Sussex Co. Lge Div. 2 17/12/55
Defeat: 0-10 v Arundel (A), Sussex County Lge 9/2/52
Fee Paid: £5,000 for David Thompson (Wokingham, May 92)
Fee Received: £75,000 for Jay Lovett from Brentford ,2000.

BEST SEASON **FA Trophy:** 3rd Rd 98-99
FA Cup: 3rd Rd Proper 91-92, 0-5 v Brighton & HA (A) League Clubs defeated: Northampton Town 91-92

HONOURS Sussex Snr Cup (2) 89-91 (R-up 58-59 95-96); Sussex I'mediate Cup 26-27; Sussex Prof. Cup 69-70; Southern Lg S Div.R-Up 83-84; Merit Cup 70-71;Sussex Floodlit Cup (3) 90-93; Sussex Lg Div 2 R-up 55-56; Gilbert RiceF'lit Cup 79-80 83-84; Southern Co's Comb. Floodlit Cup 85-86; Met Lg Chal. Cup 58-59; Mid-Sussex Snr 02-03; Montgomery Cup 25-26 Sussex Floodlit Cup 98-99 Southern Lg Cup R-up:20 00-01

Players progressing: Ray Keeley, Graham Brown (Mansfield 68), Andy Ansah (Brentford 87), Craig Whitington (Scarborough 93),Ben Abbey (Oxford United 99), John Mackie (Reading 99), Jay Lovett (Brentford 2000)

Back row. left to right: Richard Massimo (Sports Therapist), Waren Bagnall, Matt Ottley,Clinton Moore, Danny Carroll, Nigel Brake, Steve Sargent, John Timlin and Francis Vines (Reserve Team Manager). **Middle Row:** Brian Owen (First Team Coach), Rob Collins, Steve Restarick, Jimmy Dack, Jimmy Glass, Andy Little, Danny Wackett, Dave Harlow, Stewart Holmes, John Broughton (Ass. First Team Manager). **Front Row:** John Ugbah, Lee Doherty, Dean Wordsworth, Billy Smith (First Team Manager), Marc Pullan, Warren Waugh and Barrie Westgate.

Date	Comp.	Opponents	Att.	Score	Goalscorers
19.08	DM Prem	Stafford Rangers	815	2 - 1	Woolf 67, Wordsworth 84[p]
22.08	DM Prem	DORCHESTER TOWN	752	1 - 0	Woolf 89
26.08	DM Prem	KING'S LYNN	788	3 - 0	Wordsworth 38[p], Woolf 58, Hynes 86
28.08	DM Prem	Cambridge City	483	0 - 1	
02.09	DM Prem	Clevedon Town	361	2 - 1	Carroll 30, Powell 45
05.09	DM Prem	FOLKESTONE INVICTA	832	4 - 1	Hynes 55 79, Brake 59, Carroll 87
09.09	DM Prem	Halesowen Town	411	2 - 2	Anderson 86, Carroll 90
12.09	Sussex FC 1	HAILSHAM TOWN	230	6 - 2	Wordsworth 6[p] 48 68, Woolf 35, Powell 74, Vines 78
			Competition abandoned		
16.09	DM Prem	SALISBURY CITY	1053	5 - 1	Carroll 45, Wordsworth 64 80, Hynes 79, Brake 88
19.09	DM Prem	Dorchester Town	531	2 - 2	Vines 67 70
23.09	DM Prem	MERTHYR TYDFIL	1162	3 - 1	Vines 35, Wordsworth 40, Hynes 72
30.09	FA Cup Q2	ALDERSHOT TOWN	2504	1 - 2	Carroll 42
08.10	DM Prem	Fisher Athletic	396	2 - 3	Carroll 49, Wordsworth 90[p]
14.10	DM Prem	Moor Green	320	0 - 1	
21.10	DM Prem	WELLING UNITED	1195	2 - 1	Wordsworth 15, Woolf 46
24.10	DM Prem	CAMBRIDGE CITY	823	1 - 2	Carroll 23
28.10	DM Prem	Tamworth	430	2 - 0	Wordsworth 31 59
04.11	FA Trophy 1	HEYBRIDGE SWIFTS	698	2 - 1	Anderson 89, Hynes 90
11.11	DM Prem	STAFFORD RANGERS	858	2 - 2	Anderson 81, Riley 90
15.11	Lge Cup 1	Dartford	145	1 - 0	Vines 39
18.11	DM Prem	Bath City	935	2 - 3	Hynes 15, Woolf 56
09.12	DM Prem	Newport County	646	1 - 3	Hynes 90
16.12	DM Prem	WEYMOUTH	693	2 - 1	Brake 69, Mean 73
19.12	FA Trophy 2	Fisher Athletic	159	3 - 2	Mean 17, Hynes 70 81
26.12	DM Prem	MARGATE	978	0 - 0	
01.01	DM Prem	Salisbury City	422	1 - 1	Hynes 81
06.01	DM Prem	King's Lynn	630	0 - 2	
09.01	Sussex SC 2	Saltdean United	173	5 - 0	Vines 20, Carroll 27 38 68, Wordsworth 80
13.01	FA Trophy 3	ASHFORD TOWN	708	1 - 2	Carroll 38
27.01	DM Prem	Welling United	777	1 - 1	Hynes 61
29.01	Sussex SC 3	HAILSHAM TOWN	245	3 - 0	Woolf 31 45, Anderson 69
03.02	DM Prem	Worcester City	675	0 - 2	
10.02	DM Prem	MOOR GREEN	602	1 - 0	Huggins 9
15.02	Lge Cup 2	HASTINGS TOWN	306	1 - 0	Vines 86
17.02	DM Prem	Ilkeston Town	561	1 - 1	Hynes 66
27.02	Sussex SC QF	LANGNEY SPORTS	304	2 - 1	Hynes 2, Carroll 85
01.03	DM Prem	Weymouth	533	0 - 1	
03.03	DM Prem	CLEVEDON TOWN	536	1 - 0	Brake 45
06.03	Lge Cup 3	BALDOCK TOWN	288	3 - 0	Preston 21[og], Powell 83, Wordsworth 90
13.03	Sussex SC SF	Lewes	406	0 - 3	Lancing
20.03	DM Prem	FISHER ATHLETIC	327	4 - 3	Wordsworth 14, Huggins 25, Brake 54, Ugbah 61
27.03	Lge Cup QF	ST LEONARDS	267	3 - 0	Hynes 28 48, Ugbah 45
31.03	DM Prem	Burton Albion	1320	1 - 2	Carroll 47
03.04	Lge Cup SF	KING'S LYNN	414	3 - 2	Powell 39, Carroll 42, Wordsworth 98
07.04	DM Prem	BATH CITY	692	1 - 2	Ugbah 45
10.04	DM Prem	HALESOWEN TOWN	451	2 - 1	Hynes 44, Hawthorn 49
12.04	DM Prem	ILKESTON TOWN	402	1 - 1	Hynes 45
14.04	DM Prem	HAVANT & WATERLOOVILLE	543	2 - 0	Vines 27, Wordsworth 62
16.04	DM Prem	Margate	1138	0 - 3	
19.04	Lge Cup F(1)	Worcester City	986	0 - 4	
21.04	DM Prem	TAMWORTH	539	0 - 2	
22.04	DM Prem	Havant & Waterlooville	336	0 - 0	
24.04	DM Prem	Folkestone Invicta	265	1 - 2	Wordsworth 81
26.04	Lge Cup F(2)	WORCESTER CITY	644	1 - 0	Anderson 27
28.04	DM Prem	Merthyr Tydfil	469	2 - 0	Huggins 49, Hynes 57
01.05	DM Prem	BURTON ALBION	485	2 - 2	Carroll 46 75
03.05	DM Prem	WORCESTER CITY	392	1 - 0	Wordsworth 7
05.05	DM Prem	NEWPORT COUNTY	779	1 - 2	Carroll 60

PLAYING SQUAD

GOALKEEPERS: Andy Little (Banstead Ath), Jimmy Glass (Kingstonian)

DEFENDERS: Ian Payne (Vancouver 86ers), Keith Sharman (Ashford T), Danny Wackett (Youth), Stewart Holmes (Saltdean), Gus Hurdle (Dulwich Hamlet), Marc Pullan (Peacehaven & Telscombe), Lee Doherty (Grays Ath)

MIDFIELDERS: Dean Wordsworth (Ashford T), Mark Hawthorne (Slough T), Danny Carroll (Dulwich Hamlet), David Harlow (Sutton Utd), Jimmy Dack (Farnborough T), Luke Anderson (Gravesend), Matt Woolf (Bromley)

FORWARDS: Warren Bagnall (Lewes), Leroy Huggins (Fisher Ath), Steve Restarick (Welling Utd), Warren Waugh (Camb.C), Curtis Johnson (Bromley), Nigel Brake (Redhill)

FOLKESTONE INVICTA

CLUB OFFICIALS

Chairman: **Bob Dix**

President: **Bill Hewson**

Secretary: **Frank Clarke**
c/o Football club

FACT FILE

Founded: 1936
Sponsors: Eurotunnel (Le Shuttle)
& Silver Spring
Colours: Amber & black stripes/black/amber
Change Colours:white/blue/white
Midweek matchday: Tuesday
Reserves League: Winstonlead Kent Div 1
Club Website: www.folkestoneinvicta.co.uk

FOOTBALL MANAGEMENT TEAM

Manager: Neil Cugley
Asst Manager: Dave Williams
Physio: Frank Clarke

2000-01

Captain: Paul Chambers
Leading Scorer: Paul Chambers 15
P.O.Y. Dave Wietecha

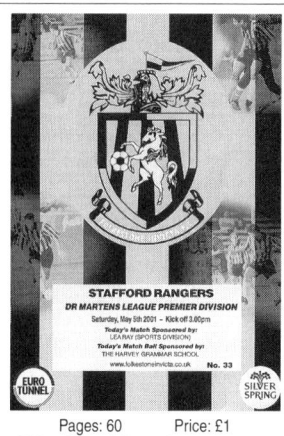

STAFFORD RANGERS
DR MARTENS LEAGUE PREMIER DIVISION
Saturday, May 5th 2001 - Kick off 3.00pm
Today's Match Sponsored by:
LEA RAY (SPORTS DIVISION)
Today's Match Ball Sponsored by:
THE HARVEY GRAMMAR SCHOOL
www.folkestoneinvicta.co.uk No. 33
EURO TUNNEL
SILVER SPRING

Pages: 60 Price: £1
Editor: Richard Morrell (01303 276517)

Local Press: Folkstone Herald
Local Radio: Neptune Radio, Radio Light

GROUND The New Pavilion, Cheriton Road, Folkestine, Kent CT20 5JU
Tel: 01303 257461

Directions: On the A20 behind Safeway foodstore, midway between Folkestone Central & West BR stations

Capacity: 6,500 Seats: 900 Cover: 3,500 Floodlights: Yes

Clubhouse: Yes, Stripes Club & Invicta Club
Club Shop: Yes

PREVIOUS **Ground:** South Rd, Hythe (pre-1991). Kent County Lg matches were played on council pitches
Leagues: Kent County (pre-1991-98) **Name:**

CLUB RECORDS **Attendance:** 2,332 v West Ham Utd Friendly Nov 96
Ground Record: 7,881 Folkestone Town v Margate, Kent Snr.Cup 1958
Win: 9-0 v Crockenhill WHL Div 1 **Defeat:** 0-7 v Crockenhill WHL Div 1

BEST SEASON **FA Vase:** Last sixteen 97-98
FA Cup: 2nd Qual Rd 95-96 Leagues Clubs Defeated: None

HONOURS (since joining Winstonlead Kent League) Kent Lge R-up 97-98, Kent Senior Trophy R-Up 93-94, 94-95,98-99,99-00
Dr.Martens League ,Eastern Division Runners-up: 99-00 Promotion to Dr.Martens Premier Division 1999-2000

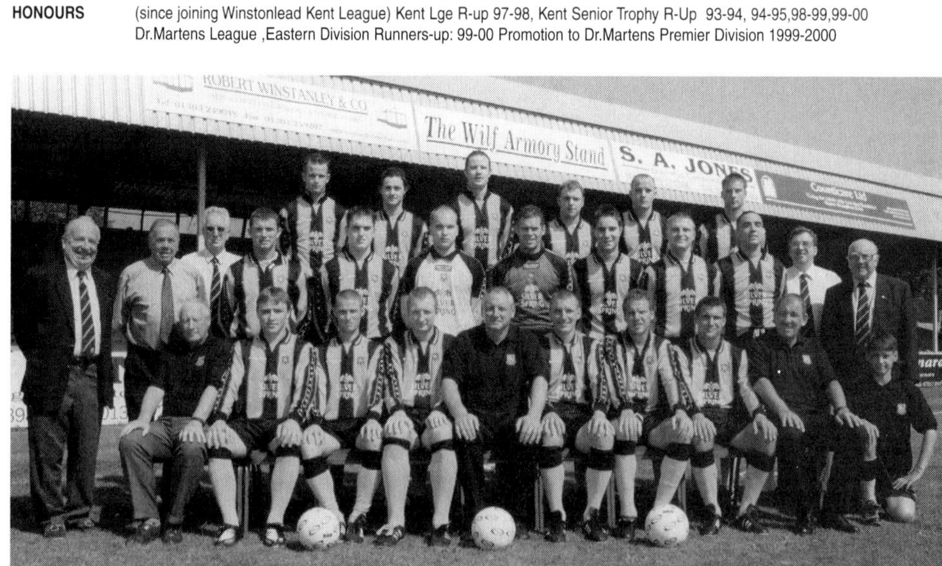

Date	Comp.	Opponents	Att.	Score	Goalscorers
19.08	DM Prem	Bath City	759	1 - 2	Chambers 19
22.08	DM Prem	CAMBRIDGE CITY	415	4 - 3	Chambers 2 17 23, Dryden 31
26.08	DM Prem	SALISBURY CITY	424	2 - 1	Lawrence 27, Morris 81
28.08	DM Prem	WELLING UNITED	533	0 - 1	
02.09	DM Prem	Moor Green	323	2 - 1	Chambers 11 18
05.09	DM Prem	Crawley Town	832	1 - 4	Dryden 4
09.09	DM Prem	HAVANT & WATERLOOVILLE	418	0 - 4	
16.09	DM Prem	Weymouth	850	1 - 1	Dryden 69
18.09	DM Prem	Cambridge City	311	0 - 2	
23.09	DM Prem	NEWPORT COUNTY	475	3 - 1	Chambers 12 55, Lawrence 29
30.09	FA Cup Q2	HASTINGS TOWN	500	1 - 1	Chambers 53
03.10	FA Cup Q2 R	Hastings Town	485	0 - 2	
08.10	DM Prem	Tamworth	487	0 - 1	
21.10	DM Prem	CLEVEDON TOWN	398	0 - 3	
24.10	DM Prem	Welling United	455	1 - 1	Chambers 43
28.10	DM Prem	King's Lynn	547	0 - 0	
11.11	DM Prem	ILKESTON TOWN	365	1 - 3	Dent 40
18.11	DM Prem	Halesowen Town	340	4 - 4	Lawrence 24 63 74, Ponsford 80
21.11	FA Trophy 1	OXFORD CITY	123	2 - 2	Dent 37 50
25.11	DM Prem	MOOR GREEN	336	1 - 2	Dent 21
27.11	FA Trophy 1 R	Oxford City	109	4 - 3	Lawrence 6, Ponsford 22, Dryden 52, Chambers 81
09.12	DM Prem	Stafford Rangers	608	0 - 3	
16.12	DM Prem	TAMWORTH	379	1 - 0	Daniels 23
18.12	FA Trophy 2	WORTHING	174	4 - 0	Daniels 20, Lawrence 27 70, Dent 50
23.12	DM Prem	Salisbury City	428	0 - 0	
26.12	DM Prem	FISHER ATHLETIC	336	2 - 1	Lawrence 15, Chambers 31
01.01	DM Prem	Margate	950	2 - 3	Briggs 12, Morris 53
06.01	DM Prem	BATH CITY	519	0 - 2	
09.01	Lge Cup 1	ST LEONARDS	142	4 - 6	Morris 70[p], Daniels 77, Moss 85, Larkin 95
13.01	FA Trophy 3	KING'S LYNN	342	1 - 3	White 55
20.01	DM Prem	Worcester City	772	0 - 2	
27.01	DM Prem	HALESOWEN TOWN	384	2 - 1	Ponsford 62[p], Dryden 63
10.02	DM Prem	Dorchester Town	482	0 - 1	
13.02	Kent SC QF	ERITH & BELVEDERE	110	3 - 2	Smith 42, Rossi 55, Dent 82
17.02	DM Prem	WEYMOUTH	373	1 - 2	Dent 88
20.02	DM Prem	Burton Albion	921	2 - 0	Dent 18, Lawrence 51
24.02	DM Prem	Newport County	668	0 - 5	
06.03	DM Prem	Havant & Waterlooville	260	4 - 1	Morris 17, Dryden 44, Hogg 63, Guiver 89
10.03	DM Prem	WORCESTER CITY	384	1 - 2	Dryden 53
17.03	DM Prem	Merthyr Tydfil	364	0 - 2	
20.03	DM Prem	DORCHESTER TOWN	316	2 - 0	Chambers 69, Chandler 78
24.03	DM Prem	BURTON ALBION	395	0 - 2	
31.03	DM Prem	KING'S LYNN	289	1 - 2	Dent 55
07.04	DM Prem	Clevedon Town	428	1 - 0	Virgo 45
14.04	DM Prem	MARGATE	765	2 - 2	Morris 60[p], Chandler 70
16.04	DM Prem	Fisher Athletic	207	2 - 1	Chambers 13 70
18.04	Kent SC SF	Gravesend & Northfleet	175	4 - 5	Reina 43 53, Hogg 57, Virgo 90[p]
21.04	DM Prem	MERTHYR TYDFIL	425	3 - 1	Chambers 16 80, Dryden 32
24.04	DM Prem	CRAWLEY TOWN	265	2 - 1	Hogg 52, Dryden 80
28.04	DM Prem	Ilkeston Town	379	0 - 3	
05.05	DM Prem	STAFFORD RANGERS	364	0 - 3	

PLAYING SQUAD

GOALKEEPERS: Dave Wietecha (Tonbridge)

DEFENDERS: Scott Daniels (Dover), Andy Morris (Ashford T), Tony Henry (Lincoln), Lee Palmer (Dover), Andy Larkin (Hastings), Tony Browne (Dover), Matt Bower (Welling)

MIDFIELDERS: Michael Everitt (Youth), Martin Chandler (West Ham), Anthony Hogg (Dover), James Virgo (Dover), James Dryden (Youth), Danny Chapman (Welling)

FORWARDS: Nicky Dent (Hastings), Ricky Reina (Ramsgate), Jon Ayling (Youth), Steve Lawrence (Dover)

HAVANT & WATERLOOVILLE

CLUB OFFICIALS

Chairman: Derek Pope

President: Arthur Saitch, Maurie Hibberd

Vice Chairman: Peter Dermott

Directors: Trevor Brock, Ray Jones, John Carter, Peter Faulkner, Sandy Peters

Secretary: Trevor Brock, 2 Betula Close, Waterlooville, Hampshire. PO7 8EJ Tel:02392 267276

FOOTBALL MANAGEMENT TEAM

Joint Managers: Mick Jenkins & Liam Daish

Physio: Phil Ashwell

FACT FILE

Formed: 1998
Nickname: Hawks
Sponsors: Thomas Sanderson
Colours: All White
Change colours: Green
Midweek matchday: Tuesday
Reserves' League:Capital

2000-01

Top Scorer: Dave Leworthy 22
Captain:Tim Hambley
P.o.Y.: Paul Wood

HAVANT & WATERLOOVILLE Football Club
Official Match Day Programme Price £1.20

Pages: 32 Price: £1
Editor: Adrian Gardiner
Local Press: News (Portsmouth)
Local Radio: Radio Victory, Radio Solent

GROUND Westleigh Park, Martin Road, West Leigh, Havant PO9 5TH Tel: 02392 787822

Directions: Take B2149 to Havant off the A27 (B2149 Petersfield Rd if coming out of Havant). 2nd turning off dual carriageway into Bartons Road then 1st right into Martins Road. 1 mile from Havant station

Capacity: 4,500 Cover: 2,500 Seats: 560 Floodlights: Yes

Clubhouse: Open every day, lunchtime and evening. 2 bars, function suites. Hot & cold food available Club Shop: Sells various souvenirs & progs

PREVIOUS (Havant) **Leagues:** Portsmouth 58-71; Hants 71-86; Wessex 86-91. **Names:** Leigh Park; Havant & Leigh Park; Havant Town
Grounds: Front Lawn 1958-83 *(Waterlooville)* ***Leagues:*** *Waterlooville & District, Portsmouth 38-53, Hants1953-71.*
Grounds: *Convent Ground 10-30, Rowlands Avenue Recreation Ground 30-63, Jubliee Park 63-98*

CLUB RECORDS **Attendance:** 3,500 v Wisbech Town, FA Vase QF 85-86
(Havant) **Win:** 10-0 x3; v Sholing Sports (H), FA Vase 4th Rd 85-86, v Portsmouth R.N. (H), Wessex League 90-91; & v Poole Town, Southern Lge SouthernDiv. 94-95. **Defeat:** 1-7 v Camberley Town (H), FA Vase 3rd Rd 88-89
Career Goalscorer: Tony Plumbley 348 **Career Appearances:** Tony Plumbley 510
Fee paid: £5,750 for John Wilson (Bashley, 90) **Fee Received:** £7,000 for Steve Tate (Waterlooville, 1993)
(Waterlooville) ***Fee paid:*** *£7,000 for Steve Tate (Havant Town, 93)* ***Received:*** *£6,000 for Dave Boyce (Gravesend & Northfleet, 93)*

BEST SEASON (Havant) **FA Cup:** 1st Rd Proper (H) 1-2 2000-01 **FA Vase:** Qtr Final 85-86 **F.A.Trophy:** 3rd Rd 98-99
(Waterlooville) ***FA Trophy:*** *3rd Rd 98-99 (lost 0-1 at Worcester City)* ***FA Amateur Cup:*** *1st Rd 59-60*
FA Cup: *1st Rd 2nd replay 83-84, 0-2 v Northampton T. (A) after two 1-1 draws*

HONOURS (Havant): FA Sunday Cup 68-69, Wessex Lg 90-91 R-up 88-89, Hampshire Lg Div 372-73 Div 4 71-72, Hampshire Sen. Cup 93-94,94-95 R-up 91-92 Hants.I'mediate Cup, Hampshire Junior Cup, Russell Cotes Cup 91-92, Portsmouth Sen. Cup 83-84 84-85 91-92, Gosport War Memorial Cup 74-75 91-92 92-93 94-95,Southern Counties F'lit Cup R-up 91-92, 00-01, Hampshire F'lit Cup 85-86, Portsmouth Lg.

(Waterlooville): Southern Lg Div 1 Sth 71-72 Lg Cup 86-87, R-up 82-83, Hants Lg R-up 69-70 Div 2 59-60 64-65, Div 3 East R-up 53-54, Hants Sen. Cup 69-7072-73 84-85 R-up 75-76 90-91,00-01, Russell Cotes Cup 88-89, Portsmouth Lg 49-50 50-51 51-52 Div 2 46-47, Div 3 38-39, Portsmouth Sen. Cup 68-69, Portsmouth Victory Cup 59-60 69-70,00-01

Players progressing: Gary MacDonald (Peterborough United 00-01)

L-R Back Row: Sean Wood (Reserves' Asst. Manager), Steve Black, Matt Leaver, Matt Jones, Alec Mason, Gary MacDonald, James Taylor, Aaron Cook,Jamie O'Rourke, Liam Daish (Joint Manager), Shaun Gale, Lee Waterman, Kevin Hayward and Mick Jenkins (Joint Manager). **Front Row:** Phil Ashwell (Physio), David Leworthy, Craig Anstey, Dave Wakefield, Paul Wood,Gary Connolly, Steve May, Neil Champion, Ben Price, Dean Blake, Mick Catlin (Reserve Team Manager).

Date	Comp.	Opponents	Att.	Score	Goalscorers
05.08	Victory Cup	PORTSMOUTH RES.	n.k	3 - 0	
08.08	S.C.CFC 99-00 F	ASH UNITED	n.k	5 - 0	Wood(2), Jones(2), Connolly
19.08	DM Prem	Cambridge City	582	0 - 1	
22.08	DM Prem	FISHER ATHLETIC	355	3 - 2	Taylor 11 24, Hambley 20
26.08	DM Prem	TAMWORTH	585	3 - 2	Hambley 35, Taylor 43, Connelly 87
28.08	DM Prem	Bath City	781	2 - 3	Taylor 5 14
02.09	DM Prem	KING'S LYNN	540	4 - 1	Taylor 12 65, Hambley 41, Leworthy 80
05.09	DM Prem	WELLING UNITED	495	0 - 1	
09.09	DM Prem	Folkestone Invicta	418	4 - 0	Hambley 33[p], Taylor 45, Wakefield 57, Blake 90
16.09	DM Prem	MARGATE	578	2 - 3	Hambley 24[p], Wood 37
23.09	DM Prem	Moor Green	282	1 - 4	O'Rourke 34
30.09	FA Cup Q2	Carterton Town	160	4 - 1	Leworthy 30, O'Rourke 36 58, Daish 57
07.10	DM Prem	NEWPORT COUNTY	420	3 - 0	O'Rourke 6, Anstey 44, Hambley 62
15.10	FA Cup Q3	Dartford	302	4 - 0	O'Rourke 9, Hambly 24 56, Taylor 90
21.10	DM Prem	Margate	336	0 - 1	
24.10	Hants SC 2	STOCKBRIDGE	150	4 - 0	Jones 45, Blake 46, Champion 64, Wakefield 71
31.10	FA Cup Q4	GLOUCESTER CITY	724	1 - 1	Donnelly 27
04.11	FA Trophy 1	CROYDON	248	2 - 1	Wakefield 33, McDonald 70
08.11	FA Cup Q4 R	Gloucester City	321	3 - 2	Taylor 16 74, Wood 47
11.11	DM Prem	Weymouth	708	2 - 1	Wood 30, Daish 34
14.11	Lge Cup 1	Salisbury City	192	2 - 2	Jones 35, Blake 90 (3-2p)
18.11	FA Cup 1	SOUTHPORT	1118	1 - 2	Wood 4
29.11	Hants RCC 2	BLACKFIELD & LANGLEY	50	3 - 0	(Competition later abandoned)
02.12	FA Trophy 2	Aldershot Town	1887	0 - 1	
05.12	Hants SC 3	Bournemouth	89	5 - 1	O'Rourke 27 43, Anstey 34, Wood 39, Jones 81
16.12	DM Prem	Clevedon Town	248	1 - 0	Wood 71
23.12	DM Prem	Ilkeston Town	367	1 - 2	Hambley 20
26.12	DM Prem	SALISBURY CITY	477	3 - 1	Hambley 8 71 81
01.01	DM Prem	Dorchester Town	523	1 - 0	Wood 4
06.01	DM Prem	Stafford Rangers	746	2 - 3	Wood 16, Leworthy 86
10.01	Lge Cup 2	Tiverton Town	371	0 - 4	
13.01	DM Prem	Merthyr Tydfil	463	1 - 2	Leworthy 24
20.01	DM Prem	Tamworth	540	2 - 2	Leworthy 7 64
27.01	DM Prem	CAMBRIDGE CITY	432	4 - 2	Leworthy 2 81, O'Rourke 25 33
10.02	DM Prem	WEYMOUTH	493	5 - 1	Leworthy 14, O'Rourke 27 57, Connolly 38, Jones 81
18.02	Hants SC QF	FARNBOROUGH TOWN	252	3 - 0	Wood 12[p] 29 76
20.02	DM Prem	HALESOWEN TOWN	324	0 - 0	
24.02	DM Prem	DORCHESTER TOWN	475	2 - 1	O'Rourke 46, Leworthy 67
27.02	DM Prem	Welling United	302	1 - 2	O'Rourke 69
06.03	DM Prem	FOLKESTONE INVICTA	260	1 - 4	Taylor 86
10.03	DM Prem	Newport County	731	2 - 2	Taylor 9, Hambley 87
15.03	Hants SC SF(1)	LYMINGTON & NEW MILTON	193	4 - 0	Daish 17, O'Rourke 58 82, Taylor 71
20.03	DM Prem	King's Lynn	482	2 - 2	Wood 58 72
29.03	DM Prem	Worcester City	575	0 - 1	
31.03	DM Prem	STAFFORD RANGERS	425	2 - 0	Daish 27, Wakefield 80
02.04	Hants SC SF(2)	Lymington & New Milton	53	2 - 1	
03.04	DM Prem	BATH CITY	280	2 - 0	Blake 32, Wood 69
10.04	DM Prem	MERTHYR TYDFIL	301	1 - 0	Leworthy 49
12.04	DM Prem	BURTON ALBION	416	1 - 1	O'Rourke 45
14.04	DM Prem	Crawley Town	543	0 - 2	
16.04	DM Prem	CLEVEDON TOWN	328	1 - 0	Leworthy 47
18.04	DM Prem	Fisher Athletic	108	3 - 0	Wood 51 90, Leworthy 70
21.04	DM Prem	Burton Albion	1066	0 - 4	
22.04	DM Prem	CRAWLEY TOWN	336	0 - 0	
24.04	DM Prem	ILKESTON TOWN	228	0 - 1	
26.04	DM Prem	Halesowen Town	261	2 - 2	Mellin 20, Taylor 56
28.04	DM Prem	MOOR GREEN	358	0 - 0	
01.05	Hants SC F	ANDOVER	1977	0 - 2	at Southampton FC
03.05	DM Prem	Salisbury City	298	0 - 0	
05.05	DM Prem	WORCESTER CITY	317	2 - 0	O'Rourke 82, Taylor 85

PLAYING SQUAD

GOALKEEPERS: Paul Nicholls (Chelsea)

DEFENDERS: Gary Connolly (Portsmouth), Liam Daish (Coventry), Ben Price (Portsmouth), Aaron Cook (Swansea), Chris Ferrett (Dorchester), Alec Masson (Bognor Regis)

MIDFIELDERS: Dean Blake (Southampton), Tim Hambley (Fisher Ath), Neil Champion (Aldershot T), Craig Anstey (Waterlooville)

FORWARDS: David Leworthy (Kingstonian), James Taylor (Bashley), Paul Wood (Happy Valley), Jamie O'Rourke (Ryde Sports)

HEDNESFORD TOWN

CLUB OFFICIALS

Directors: John Baldwin, Steve Price & Carole Price
President: Nigel Tinsley
Chairman: Steve Price
General Manager: David Degg
Football Secretary: Sue Thomas c/o club
Club Secretary: Sue Thomas
Press Officer: Neil Holde
Community Officer & Youth Development: James Thomas

FOOTBALL MANAGEMEN TE AM

Manager: Paul Raynor
Assisstant Manager: GavanWalker

FACT FILE

Founded: 1880
Nickname: The Pitmen
Club Sponsors: Extra Personnel
Club colours: White/black/white
Change colours: Royal blue/black/black
Midweek home matchday: Monday
Reserves' league: Central Conference,
Web site: www.hednesfordtownfc.co.uk
Hotline Number: 09066 555880

Season 2000-01
Leading Scorer:
P.o.Y.:
Captain:

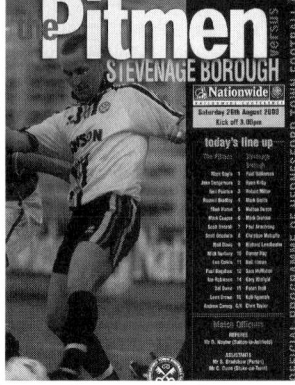

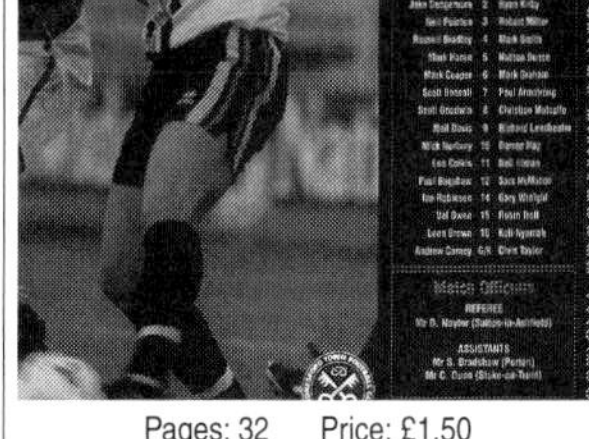

Pages: 32 Price: £1.50
Editor: James Thomas
Local Press: Express & Star; Sporting Star; Chase Post; Cannock Mercury; Birmingham Evening Mail; Sports Argus; The Chronicle
Local Radio: Radio WM; BRMB; WABC; Beacon; Signal; BBC Radio Stoke

GROUND Keys Park, Hednesford, Cannock, Staffordshire WS12 5DW
Tel: 01543 422870, Fax: 01543 428180, Hotline: 0930 555880

SIMPLE DIRECTIONS: M6 J11 to Cannock, through traffic lights to island , 3rd exit, next island, 2nd exit onto Lichfield Rd. Next island 1st exit, next island straight on, next island 3rd exit, continue to mini-island. Keys Park is straight on (signposted from 2nd island.)

CAPACITY: 6,000 **SEATED:** 1,000 **COVERED TERRACING:** 1,000

CLUB SHOP: Open throughout the week

SOCIAL FACILITIES: Strikers Bar - Open matchdays and every evening 7-11 except Sunday. No food available. Chase Suite holds functions

PREVIOUS **Leagues:** Walsall & District; Birmingham Combination 08-15, 45-53; West Midlands 19-39, 53-72, 74-84; Midland Counties 72-74; Southern League 84-95; Conference 95-01.
Grounds: The Tins (behind Anglesey Hotel) until 1904, Cross Keys until 1995. **Names:** None

HONOURS Welsh Cup R-up 91-92; Southern League - Prem. Div. 94-95; Midland Div. R-up 91-92, Lge. Cup R-up 86-87; West Midlands. Lge 77-78, R-up 83-84; Lge. Cup 83-84; Birmingham Comb. 09-10 50-51, R-up 12-13 52-53; Staffs Senior Cup 69-70, 73-74; R-up 92-93; Birmingham Sen. Cup 35-36; R-up 93-94.

CLUB RECORDS **Attendance:** 10,000 v Walsall F.A.Cup 1919-20
Win: 12-1 v Birmingham City, B'ham Wartime Lge Cup 40-41, 12-1 v Redditch United, B'ham Comb. 52-53
Defeat: 0-15 v Burton, B'ham Comb. 52-53
Career goalscorer: Tosh Griffiths, Joe O'Connor (post-war) **Career appearances:** Kevin Foster
Transfer fee paid: £12,000, for Steve Burr (Macclesfield Town 1991)
Transfer fee received: £50,000, for Dave Hanson (Leyton Orient)

BEST SEASON **FA Cup:** Fourth Round 1996-97 2-3 v Middlesbrough (A)
League clubs defeated: Blackpool 96-97, York City 96-97, Hull City 97-98, Barnet 98-99
FA Trophy: 1997-98, 3rd Round 1-2 v Grantham Town (A) **League:** 3rd, Conference 95-96

Players Progressing (Post War): Brian Horton (Port Vale 70), Vernon Allatt (Halifax T. 79); Chris Brindley (Wolverhampton W. 86), Scott Cooksey (Shrewsbury T. 98), Dave Hanson (Leyton Orient), Paul Ware (Macclesfield T.), Keith Russell (Blackpool 97)

Date	Comp.	Opponents	Att.	Score	Goalscorers
19.08	Conf.	Dover Athletic	929	0 - 4	
21.08	Conf.	RUSHDEN & DIAMONDS	1516	2 - 3	Owen 27, Bagshaw 90
26.08	Conf.	STEVENAGE BOROUGH	802	1 - 1	Davis 1
28.08	Conf.	Yeovil Town	2280	2 - 4	Goodwin 45, Davis 87
02.09	Conf.	NORTHWICH VICTORIA	800	7 - 1	Cooper 54 56 71[p], Lake 61, Goodwin 67, Sedgemore 87, Norbury 90
05.09	Conf.	Leigh RMI	475	2 - 2	Swan 19[og], Bagshaw 39
09.09	Conf.	Hereford United	2557	1 - 1	Davis 50
11.09	Conf.	MORECAMBE	942	0 - 0	
16.09	Conf.	KINGSTONIAN	881	3 - 2	Norbury 15 81, Robinson 31
18.09	Variety CT 1	TELFORD UNITED	349	1 - 0	Norbury 11
23.09	Conf.	Dagenham & Redbridge	952	1 - 6	Norbury 2
26.09	Conf.	Doncaster Rovers	2033	1 - 3	Davis 61
30.09	Conf.	CHESTER CITY	1435	0 - 0	
02.10	Conf.	WOKING	805	1 - 2	Cooper 87[p]
08.10	Conf.	Forest Green Rovers	871	2 - 0	Davis 26 51
14.10	Conf.	KETTERING TOWN	838	1 - 2	Shutt 3[og]
17.10	Variety CT 2	Chester City	584	2 - 2	Lake 59, Davis 77
21.10	Conf.	Boston United	1730	4 - 3	Bonsall 33 45 90, Bagshaw 48
28.10	FA Cup Q4	Billericay Town	721	0 - 0	
30.10	FA Cup Q4 R	BILLERICAY TOWN	450	2 - 1	Lake 33, Penn 96[og]
04.11	Conf.	SOUTHPORT	965	0 - 1	
11.11	Conf.	Nuneaton Borough	1223	1 - 5	Davis 34
18.11	FA Cup 1	OLDHAM ATHLETIC	2053	2 - 4	Pointon 19, Davis 58
02.12	Conf.	SCARBOROUGH	754	0 - 1	
09.12	Conf.	Woking	1384	1 - 1	Norbury 11
16.12	Conf.	Rushden & Diamonds	2906	1 - 5	Norbury 16
18.12	Variety CT 2 R	CHESTER CITY	147	1 - 3	Russell 48
26.12	Conf.	TELFORD UNITED	1046	1 - 1	Bagshaw 49
06.01	Conf.	Hayes	586	1 - 1	Russell 90
13.01	FA Trophy 3	Southport	1091	0 - 3	
24.01	Staffs SC 2	Stafford Town	70	3 - 0	Cooper 60, Brown 63, Russell 66
27.01	Conf.	LEIGH RMI	804	1 - 2	Davis 31
29.01	Conf.	YEOVIL TOWN	1044	1 - 2	Owen 71
03.02	Conf.	Northwich Victoria	953	2 - 2	Davis 38, Haran 73
10.02	Conf.	HEREFORD UNITED	1043	0 - 3	
13.02	Conf.	Telford United	1141	1 - 2	Robinson 33
17.02	Conf.	Morecambe	1275	0 - 0	
24.02	Conf.	DAGENHAM & REDBRIDGE	836	0 - 2	
27.02	Birm. SC 2	Evesham United	90	0 - 1	
03.03	Conf.	Kingstonian	651	0 - 1	
17.03	Conf.	Chester City	1491	1 - 0	Sedgemore 89[p]
24.03	Conf.	DONCASTER ROVERS	930	2 - 4	Norbury 55, Bagshaw 65
26.03	Conf.	DOVER ATHLETIC	693	0 - 0	
02.04	Conf.	Stevenage Borough	1450	1 - 4	Davis 81
14.04	Conf.	Kettering Town	1498	0 - 2	
16.04	Conf.	NUNEATON BOROUGH	1105	0 - 3	
19.04	Conf.	FOREST GREEN ROVERS	654	1 - 1	Brown 61
21.04	Conf.	Southport	1006	0 - 2	
23.04	Conf.	BOSTON UNITED	646	2 - 4	Owen 74, Norbury 76
28.04	Conf.	Scarborough	943	0 - 0	
01.05	Staffs SC QF	Leek CSOB	71	1 - 2	
05.05	Conf.	HAYES	925	1 - 3	Bagshaw 55

PLAYING SQUAD

GOALKEEPERS: Mark Gayle (Chesterfield)

DEFENDERS: Wayne Simpson (Nuneaton), Lennie Curtis (Boston Utd), Mark Haran (Emley), Richard Lucas (Boston Utd), Jake Sedgemore (WBA)

MIDFIELDERS: Paul Raynor (King's Lynn), Val Owen (Northwich), Paul Bagshaw (Barnsley), Stuart Lake (Walsall), Ross Rhodes (Youth), Craig Hopkins (Ilkeston)

FORWARDS: Kevin Francis (Hull), Graham Lancashire (Rochdale), Stewart Airdrie (Guiseley), Leon Brown (Lye), Neil Davis (Wycombe), Jon Pickess (Sheffield)

HINCKLEY UNITED

CLUB OFFICIALS

Chairman: **Kevin Downes**
Vice Chairman: **Rob Mayne**
Secretary: **Ray Baggott**
37 Laneside Drive, Hinckley, Leics.
LE10 1TG (01455 447278)
Press Officer: **Andy Gibbs** (01455 617828)

FOOTBALL MANAGEMENT TEAM

Manager: Dean Thomas
Coach:Charlie Palmer
Physio: Julie Hayton

FACT FILE

Formed: 1997
Sponsors: Transco
Colours: Red & blue stripes/blue/red
Change colours: Amber & black stripes/black/amber
Midweek matchday: Tuesday
Reserves' League: Mid Comb Res Div
Unofficial Website: www.hinckleyunitedfc.co.uk

2000-01

Top scorer: Andy Lucas 26
P.o.Y.: Richard Lavery
Captain: Morton Titterton

THE KNITTERS
Hinckley
U-NI-TED
F.C.
Season 2000-2001
Main Sponsor
TRINITY
TUESDAY 13TH MARCH 2001
HINCKLEY UNITED
versus
BEDWORTH UNITED
DR MARTENS LEAGUE WESTERN DIVISION
Dr Martens
OFFICIAL MATCHDAY PROGRAMME £1

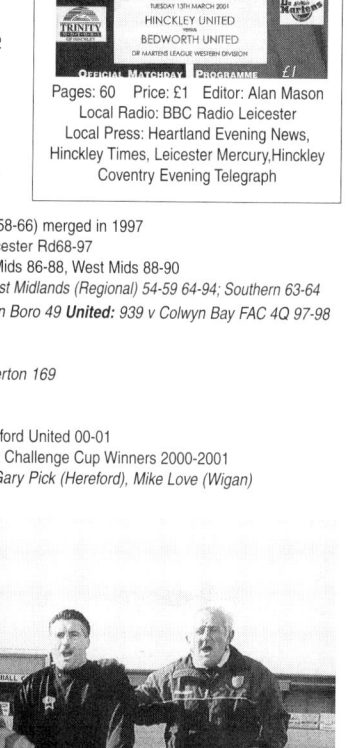

Pages: 60 Price: £1 Editor: Alan Mason
Local Radio: BBC Radio Leicester
Local Press: Heartland Evening News, Hinckley Times, Leicester Mercury,Hinckley Coventry Evening Telegraph

GROUND Middlefield Lane, Hinckley, Leics. LE10 0RB 01455 613553/615012
Directions: From M69 junction 1 take A5 north to Dodwells Island, then A47(sign Leicester). At 3rd r/about turn right (Stoke Road) then first left(Tudor Road), until crossroads. Turn left (Middlefield Lane), ground at end oflane on left
Capacity: 5,000 Cover: 1,300 Seats: 320 Floodlights: Yes
Clubhouse: Social club with lounge, games room and concert hall
Club Shop: Sells programmes, books, vidoes, badges, mugs , replica shirts,scarves, hats,etc.

PREVIOUS **Names:** Hinckley Athletic (1889) & Hinckley Town (prev. Westfield Rovers 58-66) merged in 1997
Grounds: Westfield Playing Field 58-60; Coventry Rd Rec Grd 60-68; Leicester Rd68-97
Leagues: Town: S Leicester & Nuneaton Amat, Leics Snr 72-86, Central Mids 86-88, West Mids 88-90
Athletic: Leics. & Northants; Leics. Sen.; Birmingham Comb. 14-39 47-54; West Midlands (Regional) 54-59 64-94; Southern 63-64

CLUB RECORDS **Attendance: Town:** 2,000 v Real Sociedad 86. ***Athletic:*** *5,410 v Nuneaton Boro 49* ***United:*** *939 v Colwyn Bay FAC 4Q 97-98*
Win: 7-0 v Yate Town (a) 8.4.2000.
Defeat: 0-6 v Redditch United (a) 7.11.1998
Career Goalscorer: David Sadler 53 **Career Appearances:** *Morton Titterton 169*
Fee paid: **Fee received:**

BEST SEASON **FA Trophy:** *United: 4th Rd 2-3 v Yeovil Town 98-99*
FA Cup: 4 th Q Round lost 1-2 v Colwyn Bay 97-98, lost after replay to Telford United 00-01

HONOURS Dr. Martens (Southern) Western Division Champions 2000-2001, Westerby Challenge Cup Winners 2000-2001

Players progressing: *Athletic: John Allen (Port Vale), Keith Scott (Swindon via Wycombe W.), Gary Pick (Hereford), Mike Love (Wigan)*

United celebrate the Eastern Division Championship. **Back Row**, left to right: Charlie Palmer (Assistant Manager), Niki Preston (hidden), Wayne Starkey, Danny George, Craig Smith,Julie Hayton (Physio), Stuart Storer, Guy Hadland, Ben Steane, Dean Thomas (Manager), Buster Kendall (No 1 Clubman) **Middle Row:** Jamie Lenton, Karl Brennan, and Andy Lucas (Top F.A.Cup goalscorer 2000-01) **Front Row:** David Sadler, Neil Cartwright, Richard Lavery, Morton Titterton (Captain), John Hassall, Pater Barry and Paul Hunter.

Date	Comp.	Opponents	Att.	Score	Goalscorers
19.08	DM West	Redditch United	317	1 - 2	Sadler 66
22.08	DM West	BILSTON TOWN	237	0 - 0	
26.08	DM West	PAGET RANGERS	168	4 - 1	Lavery 60, Sadler 80[p] 83, Ricketts 87
28.08	DM West	Rocester	185	9 - 1	Hunter(2),Sadler(2), Lucas 72, Ridley 77[og], Ricketts(2), Allcock 90
02.09	FA Cup P	NANTWICH TOWN	257	7 - 0	Hunter 10 67, Lucas 55 61 77, Hadland 84, Williams 88
09.09	DM West	TIVERTON TOWN	340	3 - 1	Lenton 57 82, Lucas 62
16.09	FA Cup Q1	GEDLING TOWN	265	3 - 0	Lenton 13, Lucas 61 72
23.09	DM West	Evesham United	240	1 - 0	Lenton 49
26.09	DM West	RUGBY UNITED	259	3 - 0	Lucas 18, Ricketts 78, Lenton 89[p]
30.09	FA Cup Q2	Alfreton Town	260	1 - 1	Lenton 59
03.10	FA Cup Q2 R	ALFRETON TOWN	273	2 - 1	Lucas 28, George 118
07.10	DM West	GLOUCESTER CITY	227	1 - 1	Lenton 44[p]
10.10	DM West	Bilston Town	178	2 - 0	Ricketts 80, Lenton 83
14.10	FA Cup Q3	Woodbridge Town	228	2 - 0	Hunter 5, Lucas 82
21.10	DM West	Tiverton Town	620	0 - 2	
24.10	DM West	ROCESTER	210	3 - 0	
28.10	FA Cup Q4	TELFORD UNITED	675	1 - 1	Lucas 20
04.11	FA Trophy 1	Blyth Spartans	330	0 - 2	
11.11	DM West	CINDERFORD TOWN	176	5 - 0	Hook 48[og] 54[og], Lucas 51, Hunter 70, Sadler 79
13.11	FA Cup Q4 R	Telford United	1254	1 - 4	Lucas 41
18.11	DM West	CIRENCESTER TOWN	229	2 - 2	George 53, Titterton 60
21.11	DM West	Rugby United	304	3 - 1	Sadler 22 51 72
25.11	DM West	Atherstone United	439	2 - 1	Sadler 68, Hunter 87
05.12	Lge Cup 1	Gresley Rovers	316	2 - 2	Steane 24, Titterton 84 2 3
09.12	DM West	BROMSGROVE ROVERS	245	4 - 2	Sadler 1[p], Lucas 11, Titterton 45, Hunter 70
16.12	DM West	Sutton Coldfield Town	191	2 - 2	Lucas 48, Titterton 59
19.12	DM West	Bromsgrove Rovers	179	1 - 0	Lavery 75
23.12	DM West	BLAKENALL	261	5 - 2	Titterton 9, Lucas 11, Barry 27, Lenton 28, Hassell 89
26.12	DM West	Shepshed Dynamo	394	2 - 3	Lenton 42, Lucas 82
10.01	Leics CC QF	Downes Sports	134	3 - 1	George 29, Hunter 86, Mayhew 90
13.01	DM West	RACING CLUB WARWICK	296	1 - 1	Hunter 83
24.01	DM West	REDDITCH UNITED	180	4 - 2	Sadler 8[p], Lenton 38, Lavery 40, Lucas 48
27.01	DM West	Cirencester Town	152	2 - 1	Brennan 9, Lucas 65
03.02	DM West	ATHERSTONE UNITED	367	2 - 0	Lucas 63, Hunter 83
10.02	DM West	Blakenall	149	2 - 1	Hassall 55, Brennan 90
13.02	Rollason	BIRSTALL UNITED	69	1 - 2	
17.02	DM West	GRESLEY ROVERS	358	3 - 0	Sadler 37[p], Preston 48, Titterton 61
24.02	DM West	Paget Rangers	182	2 - 0	Lucas 13 15
03.03	DM West	SOLIHULL BOROUGH	296	2 - 1	Lucas 7, Brennan 11
06.03	DM West	Gresley Rovers	378	1 - 0	Titterton 4
13.03	DM West	BEDWORTH UNITED	342	3 - 1	Brennan 52, Lenton 80, Sadler 90
17.03	DM West	Mangotsfield United	573	2 - 2	Preston 23, Hunter 50
19.03	Leics CC SF	OADBY TOWN	417	1 - 0	Lenton 66 (at Holmes Park)
24.03	DM West	SUTTON COLDFIELD TOWN	286	2 - 1	Sadler 44 52
27.03	DM West	Gloucester City	220	2 - 0	Hunter 37, Lenton 48
31.03	DM West	EVESHAM UNITED	492	1 - 1	McCartan 61[og]
07.04	DM West	Cinderford Town	127	3 - 2	Lucas 55, Sadler 65, Titterton 85
10.04	DM West	MANGOTSFIELD UNITED	455	1 - 0	Hunter 61
14.04	DM West	Bedworth United	343	3 - 0	Lenton 49, Hunter 59 76
16.04	DM West	SHEPSHED DYNAMO	497	5 - 0	Sadlert 20 90, George 35, Lenton 41[p], Titterton 72
21.04	DM West	Solihull Borough	208	3 - 0	Sadler 2 50, Hunter 61
24.04	DM West	Weston-super-Mare	125	1 - 1	Lenton 4
28.04	DM West	WESTON-SUPER-MARE	431	1 - 2	Lucas 1
30.04	Leics CC F	BARWELL	942	2 - 1	Titterton 8 45 (at Leicester City)
05.05	DM West	Racing Club Warwick	220	3 - 1	Hassell 13, Stein 87, Cartwright 88

PLAYING SQUAD

GOALKEEPERS: Scott Bentley (Leek)

DEFENDERS: Neil Cartwright (Youth), Andy Penney (Solihull), Craig Smith (Belper), Nick Preston (Youth), Bevan Browne (Camb.C), Guy Hadland (Aston Villa)

MIDFIELDERS: Moreton Titterton (Bedworth), Jamie Lenton (VS Rugby), Steve Coates (Gresley R), Gavin O'Toole (Aberystwyth), Karl Brennan (Nuneaton), Stuart Storer (Chesham)

FORWARDS: Paul Hunter (Blakenall), Andy Lucas (Shepshed Dynamo), Jermaine Gordon (Holwell Sports), Tim Wilkes (Grantham)

ILKESTON TOWN

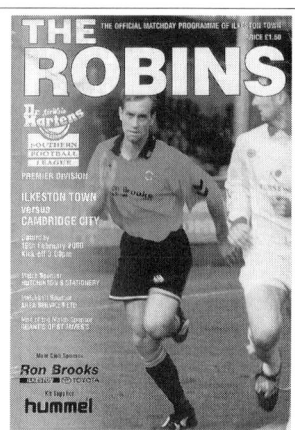

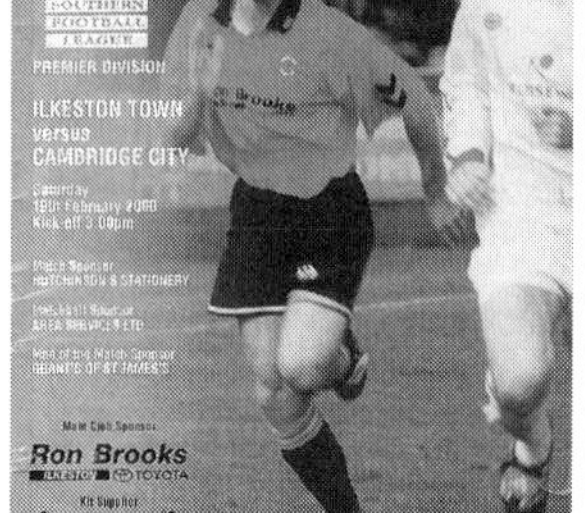

Pages: 32 Price: £1
Editors: Mic Capill, J Shiels, D Payne

CLUB OFFICIALS

Chairman: **Paul Millership**
President: **Robert Lindsay**
Secretary: **Neil Crofts,**
325 Over Lane, Belp[er,Derbys DE56 0HJ
Tel No: 01773 880611 (H)
0385 307936 (M)
Commercial Management:
J Sports Promotions Ltd

FOOTBALL MANAGEMENT TEAM

Manager / Coach: Chris Marples
Asst. Manager: Charlie Bishop

FACT FILE

Re Formed: 1945
Nickname: The Robins
Sponsors: Ron Brooks Ilkeston Toyota
Colours: Red/black/red
Change colours: All purple
Midweek matchday: Monday
Reserves' League: Midland Regional Alliance

GROUND New Manor Ground, Awsworth Rd, Ilkeston Tel: 0115 932 4094

Directions: M42 to M1 junc 23A, continue on M1 to junc 26, exit left onto A610 towards Ripley, take 1st exit signed Awsworth and Ilkeston (A6096), follow bypass signed Ilkeston A6096. Turn right after 1/2 mile signed Cotmanhay. Ground 200 yards on left
Capacity: 3,500 Seats: 270 Cover: 1,100 Floodlights: Yes

Clubhouse: Open Wed-Fri 7-11pm, Sat-Sun noon-3 & 7-11pm, and Mon or Tue if there is a match. Snacks behind bar. Large tea bar open matchdays 2-5pm (6.30-9pm for night games)
Club Shop: Sells wide range of souvenirs & programmes + `Team Talk'.
Contact club secretary

PREVIOUS **Leagues:** Midland 1894-1902 25-58 61-71; Notts & Derby Senior 1945-47; CentralAlliance 47-61; Midland Counties 1961-71 73-82; Southern League 1971-73; Northern Co.East 1982-86; Central Midlands 86-90; West Midlands (Regional) 90-94.
Ground: Manor Ground, Manor Rd (1945-92)

CLUB RECORDS **Attendance:** 2,504 v Boston United FA Cup 1st Rd 15/11/97
Win: 14-2 v Codnor M.W 46-47: 13-0 v Swanwick OB 46-47
Defeat: 1-11 v Grantham T. 47-48: 0-10 v VS Rugby 85-86
Career Goalscorer: Jackie Ward 141. **Career Appearances:** Terry Swincoe 377
Season Goalscorer: Barry Jepson 62, 1952-53
Transfer fee paid: £7,500 Justin O'Reilly (Southport 1998) **Fee received:** £25,000 for Francis Green (Peterborough Utd)

BEST SEASON **FA Cup:** 2nd Round - 1997-98 1-1, 1-2 v Scunthorpe Utd, 1999-00 0-3 (A) after 1-1 (H) v Rushden & Diamonds
FA Vase: 4th Round 88-89 1-2 v Tamworth
FA Trophy: 3rd Round 82-83 1-5 v Enfield, 94-95 2-2, 1-2 v Kidderminster H

HONOURS Southern Lge, Midland Div 94-95, (R-up 97-98); West Mids (Regional) Lg 93-94, Lg Cup 93-94, Div 1 91-92, Lg Cup 91-92; Central Mids Lg Cup 87-88; Midland Lg 67-68 (R-up 1898-99); Midland Co Lg 67-68; Central Alliance 51-52 52-53 53-54 54-55(R-up 47-48 55-56)

Back Row Left - Right: Paul Challinor, Glen Kirkwood, Emeka Nwadike, Chris Timons, Andy Love, Stuart Ford, James Baker, Matt McKenzie, John Knapper, Gary Middleton, Tony Hemmings, Ian Robinson.
Front: Charlie Bishop (Asst. Manager), Lee Newton, Anton Foster, Lennon Abbott, Chris Marples (Manager), Gareth Williams, James Whitehead, Carl Wright, George Allsop (Physio).

Date	Comp.	Opponents	Att.	Score	Goalscorers
05.08	Don Hill	Mem. Trophy Rocester	nk	0 - 1	
19.08	DM Prem	Merthyr Tydfil	605	4 - 4	Gould 45, Helliwell 49, Kirkwood 83 88
21.08	DM Prem	TAMWORTH	573	2 - 1	Kirkwood 55, Gould 90
26.08	DM Prem	CAMBRIDGE CITY	457	0 - 2	
28.08	DM Prem	Stafford Rangers	992	2 - 4	Gould 4 85
02.09	DM Prem	WORCESTER CITY	445	2 - 4	Poppleton 42[p] 56[p]
04.09	DM Prem	MOOR GREEN	398	1 - 0	Gould 23
09.09	DM Prem	Dorchester Town	487	2 - 1	Challinor 68, Eshelby 71
16.09	DM Prem	BATH CITY	455	3 - 0	Challinor 10, Gould 45, Todd 71
19.09	DM Prem	Tamworth	446	0 - 3	
23.09	DM Prem	Welling United	600	2 - 1	Gould 21, Holmes 42
30.09	FA Cup Q2	Shepshed Dynamo	479	3 - 0	Helliwell 23, Eshelby 42, Kirkwood 88
06.10	DM Prem	HALESOWEN TOWN	507	1 - 0	Gould 63
14.10	FA Cup Q3	BALDOCK TOWN	500	3 - 0	Kirkwood 37, Challinor 58[p], Kiwomya 90
21.10	DM Prem	Weymouth	740	1 - 4	Clifford 28
23.10	DM Prem	STAFFORD RANGERS	529	1 - 1	Gould 42
28.10	FA Cup Q4	Hucknall Town	1436	1 - 0	Timons 3
04.11	FA Trophy 1	ALTRINCHAM	597	1 - 1	Knapper 42[p]
07.11	FA Trophy 1 R	Altrincham	322	3 - 4	Whitehead 54 68, Clark 117
11.11	DM Prem	Folkestone Invicta	365	3 - 1	Eshelby 44 48, Clifford 75
14.11	Lge Cup 1	Banbury United	161	1 - 0	Kiwomya 86
18.11	FA Cup 1	Swindon Town	4406	1 - 4	Cox 87
21.11	DM Prem	Moor Green	197	0 - 1	
28.11	Derbys SC 3	Mickleover Sports	67	0 - 1	
09.12	DM Prem	CLEVEDON TOWN	394	1 - 1	Challinor 18
16.12	DM Prem	Worcester City	782	0 - 1	
19.12	Lge Cup 2	King's Lynn	268	0 - 2	
23.12	DM Prem	HAVANT & WATERLOOVILLE	367	2 - 1	Gould 41 81
26.12	DM Prem	King's Lynn	670	2 - 2	Gould 18, Clark 72
01.01	DM Prem	BURTON ALBION	1516	2 - 1	Helliwell 26, Gould 63
06.01	DM Prem	MERTHYR TYDFIL	496	2 - 1	Clifford 2, Clark 16
13.01	DM Prem	Halesowen Town	503	1 - 0	Clarke 45
20.01	DM Prem	WELLING UNITED	560	0 - 1	
27.01	DM Prem	WEYMOUTH	463	1 - 6	Gould 38
03.02	DM Prem	Bath City	708	1 - 1	Clarke 32
10.02	DM Prem	Fisher Athletic	209	1 - 1	Knapper 55[p]
17.02	DM Prem	CRAWLEY TOWN	561	1 - 1	Clarke 36
20.02	DM Prem	MARGATE	483	0 - 3	
24.02	DM Prem	Cambridge City	358	0 - 0	
03.03	DM Prem	NEWPORT COUNTY	426	0 - 1	
10.03	DM Prem	SALISBURY CITY	362	1 - 1	Wright 71
17.03	DM Prem	FISHER ATHLETIC	380	1 - 0	Clarke 60
31.03	DM Prem	DORCHESTER TOWN	365	1 - 0	Nwadike 76
04.04	DM Prem	Newport County	427	1 - 3	Eshelby 35
07.04	DM Prem	Margate	755	0 - 2	
12.04	DM Prem	Crawley Town	402	1 - 1	Kirkwood 16
14.04	DM Prem	Burton Albion	1606	0 - 1	
16.04	DM Prem	KING'S LYNN	426	1 - 1	Holmes 9
21.04	DM Prem	Salisbury City	424	0 - 2	
24.04	DM Prem	Havant & Waterlooville	228	1 - 0	Holmes 56
28.04	DM Prem	FOLKESTONE INVICTA	379	3 - 0	Holmes 1[p], Wright 26, Timmons 52
05.05	DM Prem	Clevedon Town	239	3 - 2	Coupe 15[og], Wright 42, Whitehead 62

PLAYING SQUAD

GOALKEEPERS: James Baker (Arnold), Stuart Ford (Hednesford)

DEFENDERS: Chris Timons (Altrincham), Gary Middleton (Arnold), Jamie Eaton (Eastwood T), Matt McKenzie (Grimsby)

MIDFIELDERS: John Knapper (Eastwood T), Ian Robinson (Hednesford), Gareth Williams (Scarborough), Paul Williams (Bury), Emeka Nwadike (King's Lynn), Carl Wright (Ipswich)

FORWARDS: Tony Hemmings (Carlisle), Glenn Kirkwood (Doncaster), David Holmes (Burton Alb), Ian Helliwell (Doncaster)

KETTERING TOWN

CLUB OFFICIALS

President Sid Chapman
Chairman: Peter Mallinger
Vice-Chairman: Michael Leech
Directors: Les Manning, Peter Webb
Club Secretary/Press Off. Graham Starmer
c/o the club Tel: 01536 483028/410815
Fax: 01536 412273
Email info@ketteringtownfc.co.uk
Assistant Secretary Andy Thomas

FOOTBALL MANAGEMENT TEAM

Manager: Carl Shutt
Physio: Peter Lake
Youth & Community Development:
Dominic Genovese

FACT FILE

Founded: 1872
Nickname: Poppies
Club Sponsors: Weldon Plant Ltd.
Club colours: Red/black/black
Change colours: All Yellow
Midweek home matchday: Tuesday
Web site: www.ketteringtownfc.co.uk

2000-2001

Top Scorer: Darren Collins
Player of the Year: Matt Fisher
Captain: Colin Vowden

Pages: 32 Price: £1.50
Editor:Graham Starmer
Other club publications:
"Poppies at the Gates of Dawn" (Fanzine)

Local Press: Evening Telegraph; Chronicle & Echo; Herald & Post; Citizen
Local Radio:
Radio Northampton; Northants 96; KCBC

GROUND: Rockingham Road, Kettering, Northants, NN16 9AW
Tel: 01536 83028/410815 (Office) Fax: 01536 412273 email: info@ketteringtownafc.co.uk

DIRECTIONS: From **south** - M1 junction 15, A43 to Kettering use A14 exit Junct. 7, follow A43 to Corby/Stamford to 1st roundabout, turn right A6003, ground half a mile.
From **north** - M1 or M6 use junction 19 then A14 to Kettering. Exit Junct. 7 then as above.
British Rail - Inter-City Midland - 50 mins from London (St.Pancras), 20 mins from Leicester

CAPACITY: 6,170 **Covered seating:** 1,800 **Covered terracing:** 2,200

CLUB SHOP: Open before and after matches, & office staff will open on request on non-match days. Situated in front of main stand. Also Alex Elmores in town centre

SOCIAL FACILITIES: Social Club (Poppies), Vice-Presidents Bar & Sponsor's Lounge 01536 410962 (Social Club)

PREVIOUS
Leagues: Southern Lge., Northants Lge., Midland Lge., Birmingham Lge. Central Alliance, United Counties Lge.
Grounds North Park; Green Lane

CLUB RECORDS
Attendance: 11,536 Kettering v Peterborough (pre-Taylor report)
Win: 16-0 v Higham YMCI (FA Cup 1909) **Defeat:** 0-13 v Mardy (Southern Lge. Div. 2, 1911/12)
Transfer fee paid: £25,000 to Macclesfield for Carl Alford, 1994
Transfer fee received: £150,000 from Newcastle United for Andy Hunt
Career goalscorer: Roy Clayton 171 (1972 - 1981) **Career appearances:** Roger Ashby

BEST SEASON
FA Cup: 4th Round - 88-89, 1-2 v Charlton Ath.; 91-92, 1-4 v Blackburn R.
League clubs defeated: Swindon T. 61-62, Millwall 63-64, Swansea C. 74-75, Halifax T. 88-89, Bristol Rovers 88-89, Maidstone U. 91-92, Hull C. 00-01
FA Trophy: Runners-up 78-79 99-00 **League:** Conference Runners-up 1980-81; 88-89; 93-94; 98-99

HONOURS
Premier Inter Lge. Cup; FA Trophy Runners-up 78-79; Alliance Premier Lge. (Conference) R-up x 4; Southern Lge., County Cup, Daventry Charity Cup x 2; Northants Senior Cup x 28; Maunsell Cup x 12

Players progressing: Billy Kellock(Peterborough), Gary Wood (Notts Co.), Dave Longhurst (Nott'm Forest), Scott Endersby (Ipswich), Steve Fallon (Cambridge U.), Andy Rogers (Plymouth), Martyn Foster (Northampton), Cohen Griffith (Cardiff C.), Andy Hunt (Newcastle), Richard Brown (Blackburn R.) Ben Wright (Bristol C.), Kofi Nyamah (Stoke C.)

Back row: Andrew Speechley, Carl Lake, Brett McNamara, Chris Perkins, Jason Lee. **Middle row:** Peter Lake (physio), Rob Yardy, Darren Collins, Steve Wilkinson, Ian Bowling, Rob Wild, Steve Lenagh, Brad Piercewright, Gary Hughes.
Front row: Shaun Murray, Martin Matthews, Dale Watkins, Carl Shutt (manager), Lee Cowling, Craig Norman, Wayne Duik.

Date	Comp.	Opponents	Att.	Score	Goalscorers
19.08	Conf.	Yeovil Town	2302	0 - 2	
22.08	Conf.	HEREFORD UNITED	1406	0 - 2	
26.08	Conf.	LEIGH RMI	1087	0 - 1	
28.08	Conf.	Dover Athletic	976	0 - 1	
02.09	Conf.	KINGSTONIAN	1203	3 - 1	Watkins 27 67, Inman 58
05.09	Conf.	Hayes	548	1 - 2	Inman 31
09.09	Conf.	Morecambe	1164	2 - 0	Watkins 68[p], Hudson 90
12.09	Conf.	DAGENHAM & REDBRIDGE	1070	0 - 0	
16.09	Conf.	SOUTHPORT	1145	1 - 1	Guyett 22[og]
19.09	Variety CT 1	FOREST GREEN ROVERS	221	3 - 0	Fisher 2, Brown 48, Shutt 81
23.09	Conf.	Rushden & Diamonds	4627	1 - 1	Codnor 7
26.09	Conf.	Telford United	386	1 - 2	Watkins 86 Worcester City
30.09	Conf.	FOREST GREEN ROVERS	1068	1 - 3	Lenagh 79
03.10	Conf.	DONCASTER ROVERS	1106	0 - 0	
08.10	Conf.	Chester City	2102	1 - 2	Brown 46
14.10	Conf.	Hednesford Town	838	2 - 1	Watkins 85, Lenagh 90
21.10	Conf.	SCARBOROUGH	1159	1 - 1	Fisher 70
28.10	FA Cup Q4	Chesham United	736	2 - 0	Adams 4, Lenagh 38
04.11	Conf.	Stevenage Borough	1845	0 - 2	
11.11	Conf.	NORTHWICH VICTORIA	1102	2 - 3	Hudson 13, Norman 45[p]
18.11	FA Cup 1	HULL CITY	2831	0 - 0	
28.11	FA Cup 1 R	Hull City	3858	1 - 0	Fisher 57
02.12	Conf.	NUNEATON BOROUGH	1791	1 - 2	Watkins 89
09.12	FA Cup 2	Bristol City	7641	1 - 3	Collins 29
16.12	Conf.	Hereford United	1561	0 - 0	
26.12	Conf.	BOSTON UNITED	2092	2 - 2	Collins 6 51
01.01	Conf.	Boston United	3108	3 - 4	McNamara 22, Watkins 55, Adams 69
06.01	Conf.	DOVER ATHLETIC	1479	0 - 2	
09.01	Variety CT QF	Yeovil Town	709	0 - 2	
14.01	FA Trophy 3	Histon	837	0 - 3	
27.01	Conf.	HAYES	1650	0 - 2	
10.02	Conf.	MORECAMBE	1217	1 - 5	Norman 43[p]
17.02	Conf.	Dagenham & Redbridge	1219	1 - 5	Collins 33
20.02	Conf.	Kingstonian	707	1 - 0	Collins 8
24.02	Conf.	Woking	1840	1 - 1	McNamara 53
27.02	N'hants SC SF	STEWARTS & LLOYDS CORBY	n.k	2 - 0	Wayte 96, Alford 105
03.03	Conf.	Southport	1258	3 - 2	Fisher 45, Norman 55[p], Inman 88
10.03	Conf.	YEOVIL TOWN	2115	2 - 1	Watkins 85 89
13.03	Conf.	RUSHDEN & DIAMONDS	4750	0 - 2	
17.03	Conf.	Forest Green Rovers	758	2 - 3	Inman 19, Collins 81
23.03	Conf.	TELFORD UNITED	1405	0 - 1	
31.03	Conf.	Doncaster Rovers	1884	0 - 0	
03.04	Conf.	Leigh RMI	351	0 - 1	
07.04	Conf.	Scarborough	1082	1 - 0	Brown 57
10.04	N'hants SC F	Rushden & Diamonds	1038	3 - 1	Perkins, Fothergill, Wilkinson
14.04	Conf.	HEDNESFORD TOWN	1498	2 - 0	Hudson 77, Collins 84
16.04	Conf.	Northwich Victoria	1011	2 - 1	Diuk 20, Collins 45
21.04	Conf.	STEVENAGE BOROUGH	1755	1 - 2	Watkins 45
24.04	Conf.	CHESTER CITY	1216	4 - 0	Collins 4 6 60, Watkins 54
28.04	Conf.	Nuneaton Borough	1865	1 - 1	Collins 71
05.05	Conf.	WOKING	2479	2 - 0	Diuk 81, Collins 90

PLAYING SQUAD

GOALKEEPERS: Ian Bowling (Mansfield), Rob Wild (Mansfield)

DEFENDERS: Chris Perkins (Southend), Garry Hughes (Northampton), Brad Piercewright (Scarborough), Craig Norman (Chelsea), Lee Cowling (Mansfield), Wayne Duik (Gedling T)

MIDFIELDERS: Ian Ridgway (Notts Co), Shaun Murray (Notts Co), Peter Fear (Oxford Utd), Martin Matthews (King's Lynn), Jason Lee (Youth), Steve Lenagh (Chesterfield)

FORWARDS: Dale Watkins (Cheltenham), Darren Collins (Rushden & Diamonds), Brett McNamara (King's Lynn), Carl Shutt (Darlington), Steve Wilkinson (Chesterfield)

KING'S LYNN

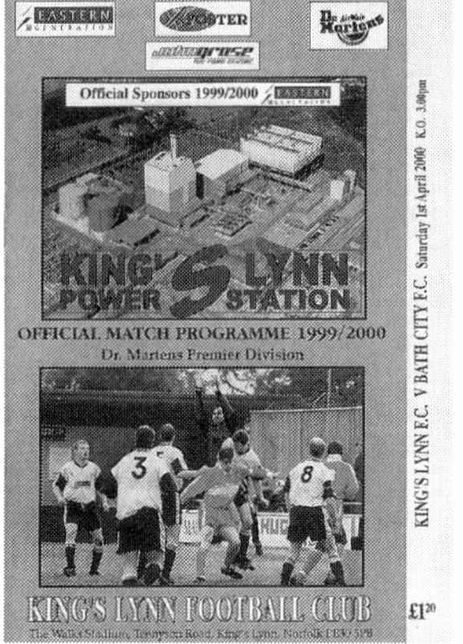

Pages: 24 Price: £1.20
Editor: Secretary
Local Press: Lynn News & Advertiser, Eastern Daily Press
Local Radio: KLFM

CLUB OFFICIALS

Chairman: **Colin Nichols**
President: **Jim Chandler**

Secretary: **Martin Davis**
158 Lynn Road, Wisbech,
Cambs PE13 3EB
Tel: 01945 583567 (H & B)
01945 588000 (FAX)

FOOTBALL MANAGEMENT TEAM

Manager: Tony Spearing
Asst Man: Darren Gee
Physio: Dave Edgeley

FACT FILE

Formed: 1879
Nickname: The Linnets
Sponsors: Eastern Group
Colours: Royal Blue with gold trim/Blue/Blue & Gold hoops
Change colours: All red
Midweek home matchday: Tuesday
Reserves League: U.C.L. Res Div 1

GROUND The Walks Stadium, Tennyson Road, King's Lynn PE30 5PB Tel: 01553 760060

Directions: At mini r-about arriving from A10/A47 take Vancouver Avenue. Ground on left after a half mile. Quarter mile from King's Lynn (BR), half mile from bus station

Capacity: 8,200 Cover: 5,000 Seats: 1,200 Floodlights: Yes

Clubhouse: Normal licensing hours, with extension on matchdays
Club Shop: Sells metal badges and other merchandise

PREVIOUS **Leagues:** Norfolk & Suffolk; Eastern Co.s 35-39 48-54; UCL 46-48; Midland Co.s54-58; NPL 80-83
Name: Lynn Town Ground: None

CLUB RECORDS **Attendance:** 12,937 v Exeter, FA Cup 1st Rd 50-51
Win: 17-0 v Beccles 29/30 **Defeat:** 0-11 v Aston Villa FA Cup 1905/6
Career Appearances: Mick Wright 1,152 (British Record) **Career Goalscorer:** Malcolm Lindsay 321
Transfer Fee Paid: Shaun Keeble Wisbech 98-99 **Transfer Fee Received:** Mark Paul , Southampton.98-99

BEST SEASON **FA Cup:** 3rd Rd 61-62 (0-4 at Everton). Competition Proper on 14 occasions; 05-06 37-38 49-50 51-52 58-63 64-65 68-69 71-72 73-74 84-85. Rd 2 97-98 League clubs defeated: Aldershot 59-60, Coventry 61-62, Halifax 68-69
FA Trophy: 2nd Rd 78-79 **FA Vase:** 5th Rd 94-95 (0-2 at Diss Town **FA Amateur Cup:** R-up 1900-01

HONOURS FA Amateur Cup R-up 1900-01, Southern Lg R-up 84-85 (Div 1 R-up 63-64), NPLPresidents Cup 82-83, Eastern Co's Lg 53-54 (R-up 49-50 52-53 (Lg Cup 53-54),Norfolk & Suffolk Lg(8)(R-up(6)), E Anglian Lg R-up(2), Norfolk Snr Cup(19)(R-up(20), Norfolk Invitation Cup 94-95, Norfolk Premier Cup 68-69(jt) 73-74, EastAnglian Cup(4)(R-up(3), Eastern Prof Floodlit Lg 68-69, Southern Lg Midland R-up 95-96 ,U.C.L. Reserve Division, League & Cup 'double', 99-00.

Players progressing: N Rowe (Derby 1949), B Taylor & P Ward (Bradford P. A. 54& 55), T Reynolds (Darlington 54), G Reed (Sunderland 55), P McCall (Bristol C55), J Neal (Swindon 57), T Dryburgh (Oldham 57), J Hunter (Barrow 59), JStevens (Swindon), G Catleugh (Watford), George Walters (Chesterfield 64), PMcNamee (Notts County 1966), W Biggins (Burnley), Jackie Gallagher(Peterborough 80), Andy Higgins (Rochdale 83), Neil Horwood (Grimsby 86),Darren Rolph (Barnsley 87), Mark Howard (Stockport 88), Andy Hunt, MalcolmLindsay

Date	Comp.	Opponents	Att.	Score	Goalscorers
27.07	Kinsella	Cup Wisbech Town	n.k	1 - 0	Palmer 50
19.08	DM Prem	WEYMOUTH	846	2 - 1	Palmer 3, Puttnam 44
22.08	DM Prem	Burton Albion	1089	1 - 1	Palmer 59
26.08	DM Prem	Crawley Town	788	0 - 3	
28.08	DM Prem	MOOR GREEN	751	0 - 1	
02.09	DM Prem	Havant & Waterlooville	540	1 - 4	Robinson 90
05.09	DM Prem	Tamworth	506	0 - 2	
09.09	DM Prem	CLEVEDON TOWN	644	3 - 1	Rowland 12, Wright 63, Robinson 88
16.09	DM Prem	Fisher Athletic	142	3 - 2	Robinson 23, Ndekwe 32, Shuttlewood 53[og]
19.09	DM Prem	BURTON ALBION	613	1 - 1	Dukes 45[og]
23.09	DM Prem	STAFFORD RANGERS	888	3 - 2	Rowland 4 31, Robinson 55
30.09	FA Cup Q2	Matlock Town	364	2 - 1	Nwadike 2, Fuff 15
07.10	DM Prem	Welling United	330	4 - 1	Mills 29, Hayes 63, Thomas 75, Rowland 87
14.10	FA Cup Q3	Canvey Island	306	1 - 2	Puttnam 78
21.10	DM Prem	NEWPORT COUNTY	934	2 - 3	Wright 45, Wilson 75[p]
24.10	DM Prem	Moor Green	284	1 - 2	Rowland 63
28.10	DM Prem	FOLKESTONE INVICTA	547	0 - 0	
04.11	DM Prem	Margate	406	1 - 3	Rowland 6
11.11	DM Prem	BATH CITY	782	1 - 1	Bush 25
13.11	Lge Cup 1	Cambridge City	266	2 - 1	Wright 55, Palmer 75[p]
18.11	DM Prem	SALISBURY CITY	507	2 - 1	Palmer 20, Rowland 70
21.11	DM Prem	TAMWORTH	472	6 - 0	Palmer 13 47 57, Howard 25[og], Rowland 61, McNeil 85
02.12	FA Trophy 2	CHESHAM UNITED	731	2 - 0	Palmer 35, Bush 87
09.12	DM Prem	Weymouth	673	1 - 4	T Wright 19
16.12	DM Prem	MARGATE	784	1 - 4	Dakin 63
19.12	Lge Cup 2	ILKESTON TOWN	268	2 - 0	March 51, Palmer 56
23.12	DM Prem	Worcester City	785	1 - 1	Palmer 39
26.12	DM Prem	ILKESTON TOWN	670	2 - 2	Rowland 57 87[p]
06.01	DM Prem	CRAWLEY TOWN	630	2 - 0	Dakin 52, Fuff 72
13.01	FA Trophy 3	Folkestone Invicta	342	3 - 1	Rowland 43 75 82
20.01	DM Prem	Clevedon Town	271	0 - 1	
27.01	DM Prem	Stafford Rangers	668	1 - 0	Dakin 74
03.02	FA Trophy 4	TELFORD UNITED	1357	1 - 2	Marsh 30
10.02	DM Prem	Merthyr Tydfil	438	0 - 1	
17.02	DM Prem	WORCESTER CITY	660	0 - 0	
20.02	Lge Cup 3	ROTHWELL TOWN	343	4 - 1	Rowlands 14, Anderson 33, Gibson 55, Bush 60
24.02	DM Prem	HALESOWEN TOWN	588	2 - 2	Fuff 26, Bush 49
27.02	Lge Cup QF	Stamford	210	3 - 2	Bush 74, Palmer 108[p], Rowland 120
03.03	DM Prem	Bath City	609	2 - 2	Bush 45, Jones 79
04.03	DM Prem	Dorchester Town	486	1 - 0	Fuff 81
10.03	DM Prem	Halesowen Town	409	4 - 0	Robinson 44, Rowland 45, Hayes 63, Gibson 90
20.03	DM Prem	HAVANT & WATERLOOVILLE	482	2 - 2	Rowland 12, Cook 22[og]
24.03	DM Prem	WELLING UNITED	517	2 - 0	Bush 65, Anderson 89
26.03	DM Prem	Cambridge City	381	2 - 1	Jones 8, Palmer 82
31.03	DM Prem	Folkestone Invicta	289	2 - 1	Palmer 2[p] 71
03.04	Lge Cup SF	Crawley Town	414	2 - 3	Rowe 36, Robinson 78
07.04	DM Prem	MERTHYR TYDFIL	668	1 - 0	Hayes 74
14.04	DM Prem	CAMBRIDGE CITY	938	0 - 4	
16.04	DM Prem	Ilkeston Town	426	1 - 1	Rowland 3
21.04	DM Prem	DORCHESTER TOWN	567	2 - 0	Rowland 17, Puttnam 69
24.04	DM Prem	Salisbury City	320	4 - 1	Hayes 30, Jones 45, Rowland 63, Palmer 90
28.04	DM Prem	Newport County	627	3 - 1	Hayes 43 66[p], Rowland 71
05.05	DM Prem	FISHER ATHLETIC	888	0 - 1	

PLAYING SQUAD

GOALKEEPERS: Steve Wilson (Kettering)

DEFENDERS: Glenn Fuff (Rushden & Diamonds), Tony Spearing (Peterborough), Simon Dakin (Grantham), Craig Clark (Stamford), Jamie March (Burton Alb), Steve Welsh (Lincoln), Dave Robinson (Grantham)

MIDFIELDERS: Simon Bush (Youth), Jason Minett (Boston Utd), Jamie Clarke (Ilkeston), Kristian Jones (Wisbech), Adie Hayes (Boston Utd), Martin Eldridge (Norwich)

FORWARDS: Lee Hudson (Kettering), Lyndon Rowland (Halesowen T), Kevin White (Swaffham), Ross McNeil (Youth), Zeke Rowe (Welling Utd), Tommy Wright (Doncaster)

MERTHYR TYDFIL

CLUB OFFICIALS

Joint Presidents:
The Archbishop of Cardiff,
His Grace John Aloysious Ward,
The Lord Bishop of Llandaff,
The Right Rev. Roy Davies

Football Sec: Anthony Hughes
Chairman: Lyn Mittell
Press Off. Robert Davies

FOOTBALL MANAGEMENT TEAM

Manager: John Lewis
Asst. Man/ Physio: David Giles

FACT FILE

Formed: 19445
Nickname: The Martyrs
Sponsors: one2one
Colours: White & black/black/black
Change colours: Royal Blue
Midweek home matchday: Tuesday
Reserves' League: None
Club Website: www.themartyrs.com

2000-01

Top scorer: Darren Ryan 11
Captain: Neil Thomas
P.o.Y.: Gareth Abraham

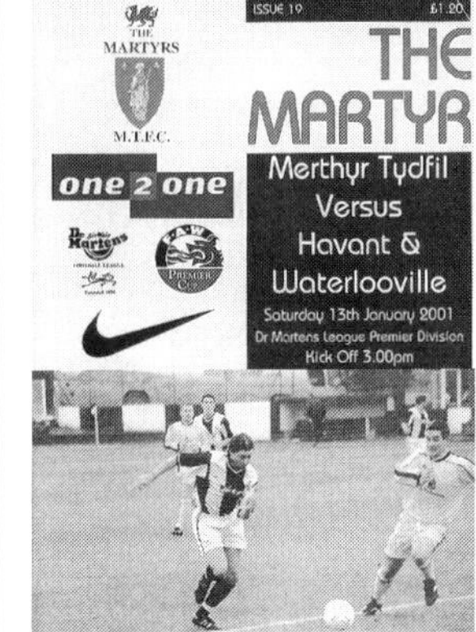

Pages: 36 Price: £1.20
Editors: Anthony Hughes Tel: 01685 359921,
Robert Davies and Mike Donovan

Local Press: Merthyr Express
Local Radio: Capitol Gold

GROUND Penndarren Park, Merthyr Tydfil, Mid Glamorgan Tel: 01685 384102
Email Address: pughy@tinyonline.co.uk

Directions: (South) A470 Express Way to Merthyr Centre to Pontmorlais (traffic lights) turn left then first right, first right at Catholic Church and right again into Park Terrace . (North) Heads of theValley road to Town Centre, to Pontmorlais(traffic lights) turn right, then as above

Capacity: 10,000 Seats: 1,500 Cover: 5,000 Floodlights: Yes

Clubhouse: Open Mon. to Sun. 6.30 - 11.00pm. 2 club cafes open on matchdays for hot food

Club Shop: Sells replica kits, club souvenirs & programmes.
Contact Mel Jenkins01443 692336

PREVIOUS **Leagues:** Southern League 46 -89 (Southern League 46-59, 1st Division 59-61, 64-71, !st Div. North 72-79, Premier Div. 61-64, 71-72, 88-89, Midland Div. 79-88), G M Conference 89-95.
Names: None **Grounds:** None

CLUB RECORDS **Attendance:** 21,000 v Reading FA Cup 2nd Rnd 1949/50
Win: 11-0 v Rushden 1987 **Defeat:** 9-2 v Altrincham 1993
Transfer fee paid: £10,000 to Cardiff City for Robbie James 1992
Transfer fee received: £12,000 for Ray Pratt from Exeter City 1981

BEST SEASON **Welsh FA Cup:** Winners 48-49 50-51 86-87
FA Trophy: 3rd Rd v Northwich Vic 95-96 **FA Cup:** 2nd Round on six occasions. League clubs defeated: Bristol Rovers

HONOURS Welsh FA Cup 48-49, 50-51, 86-87; Southern League 47-48, 49-50, 50-51, 51-52, 53-54; Southern League (Midland) 87-88; Southern League (Premier) 88-89;Southern League Cup 47-48, 50-51

Players Progressing : Syd Howarth (Aston Villa), Cyril Beech, Gilbert Beech,Bill Hullet, Ken Tucker (Cardiff City), Nick Deacy (Hereford United), Gordon Davies (Fulham), Ray Pratt (Exeter City), Peter Jones, Paul Giles (Newport County)

Date	Comp.	Opponents	Att.	Score	Goalscorers
19.08	DM Prem	ILKESTON TOWN	605	4 - 4	Abraham 11, Ryan 38, Baddeley 75, Mitchell 80[p]
22.08	DM Prem	Weymouth	823	1 - 1	Carter 82
26.08	DM Prem	BATH CITY	715	3 - 3	Abraham 8 46, Summers 90
28.08	DM Prem	WORCESTER CITY	667	4 - 1	Walker 14, Abraham 57, Mitchell 73[p], Ryan 82
02.09	DM Prem	Burton Albion	1097	0 - 1	
05.09	DM Prem	STAFFORD RANGERS	663	3 - 0	Needs 6, Loss 57, Mitchell 90[p]
09.09	DM Prem	Salisbury City	475	2 - 2	Mitchell 36, Baddeley 51
12.09	Lge Cup P	CIRENCESTER TOWN	371	1 - 0	Dunton 3[og]
16.09	DM Prem	DORCHESTER TOWN	631	1 - 2	Ryan 2
19.09	DM Prem	WEYMOUTH	551	0 - 1	
23.09	DM Prem	Crawley Town	1162	1 - 3	Loss 74
26.09	FAW Prem B	CWMBRAN TOWN	349	3 - 1	Summers 5 42, Mitchell 90[p]
30.09	FA Cup Q2	Newport County	728	4 - 0	Summers 22, Ryan 26, Baddeley 45, Mitchell 90
08.10	DM Prem	MOOR GREEN	551	2 - 0	Summers 58, Ryan 90
10.10	FAW Prem B	Cardiff City	1412	1 - 2	Summers 67
14.10	FA Cup Q3	HAMPTON & RICHMOND BOR.	569	0 - 3	
21.10	DM Prem	Cambridge City	471	1 - 0	Carter 2
23.10	DM Prem	Worcester City	1135	1 - 1	Giles 36[p]
04.11	FA Trophy 1	Rothwell Town	175	1 - 2	Thomas 45
11.11	DM Prem	FISHER ATHLETIC	506	2 - 2	Robinson 61[og], Walker 89
15.11	Lge Cup 1	Newport County	436	0 - 1	
18.11	DM Prem	Margate	395	2 - 3	Abraham 48, Walker 65
25.11	DM Prem	CAMBRIDGE CITY	517	2 - 2	Perry 57, Ryan 83
29.11	FAW Prem B	Cwmbran Town	n.k	2 - 1	Carter 60, Clarke 90
06.12	FAW Prem B	Llanelli	n.k	2 - 4	Lima 22, Perry 51
09.12	DM Prem	WELLING UNITED	404	0 - 1	
16.12	DM Prem	Halesowen Town	473	1 - 1	Carter 85
19.12	FAW Prem B	LLANELLI	n.k	2 - 1	Carter 77, Ryan 86[p]
23.12	DM Prem	BURTON ALBION	581	1 - 5	Perry 59
26.12	DM Prem	Newport County	973	0 - 2	
06.01	DM Prem	Ilkeston Town	496	1 - 2	Thomas 10
09.01	FAW Prem B	CARDIFF CITY	n.k	0 - 2	
13.01	DM Prem	HAVANT & WATERLOOVILLE	463	2 - 1	Carter 15, Perry 37
20.01	DM Prem	Bath City	831	1 - 1	Perry 90
27.01	DM Prem	MARGATE	500	0 - 2	
03.02	DM Prem	Moor Green	260	1 - 1	D Thomas 75
10.02	DM Prem	KING'S LYNN	438	1 - 0	Needs 90
17.02	DM Prem	Dorchester Town	502	0 - 4	
24.02	DM Prem	SALISBURY CITY	456	1 - 0	Ryan 6
27.02	DM Prem	Stafford Rangers	516	0 - 1	
03.03	DM Prem	Fisher Athletic	136	2 - 0	Thomas 13, Perry 82
10.03	DM Prem	Tamworth	676	0 - 4	
17.03	DM Prem	FOLKESTONE INVICTA	364	2 - 0	Carter 33, Regan 52
24.03	DM Prem	TAMWORTH	475	0 - 0	
26.03	FAW Prem QF	Cardiff City	486	1 - 0	Perry 17
31.03	DM Prem	HALESOWEN TOWN	464	0 - 0	
03.04	DM Prem	CLEVEDON TOWN	381	2 - 0	Perry 49, King 68
07.04	DM Prem	King's Lynn	668	0 - 1	
10.04	DM Prem	Havant & Waterlooville	301	0 - 1	
14.04	DM Prem	Clevedon Town	341	2 - 2	Clark 48, Regan 57
16.04	DM Prem	NEWPORT COUNTY	707	2 - 1	Abraham 13, Ryan 35
21.04	DM Prem	Folkestone Invicta	425	1 - 3	Ryan 23[p]
28.04	DM Prem	CRAWLEY TOWN	469	0 - 2	
05.05	DM Prem	Welling United	553	0 - 1	
08.05	FAW Prem SF(1)	SWANSEA CITY	617	0 - 2	
10.05	FAW Prem SF(2)	Swansea City	1235	0 - 2	

PLAYING SQUAD

GOALKEEPERS: Neil Thomas (Ton Pentre)

DEFENDERS: Rob King (Rhayader), Danny Haines (Clevedon), Adrian Needs (Ebbw Vale), Gareth Elliott (Youth)

MIDFIELDERS: Richard Jones (Barry), Dean Clarke (Newport Co), Lee Farrell (Rhayader), Tom Ramasut (Llanelli), Jim Rollo (Clevedon)

FORWARDS: Andy Mainwaring (Clevedon), Dai Thomas (Cardiff), Mark Dodds (Goytre Utd)

MOOR GREEN

CLUB OFFICIALS

Chairman: Ian Childs
Vice-Chairman: John Bassford

Secretary: Nigel Collins
7 The Morelands, West Heath,
Birmingham B31 3HA
Tel: 0121476 4944 (H) 0121 777 8961 (W)
07753 900133 (M)
Email: nigelcollins@lineone.net
Press Officer: Peter Clynes 0121 745 3262
Commercial Man.: Commercial Dept.0121 777 8961

FOOTBALL MANAGEMENT TEAM

Manager: Bob Faulkner
Coaches: Doug Griffiths & Kim Casey
Physio: Steve Shipway

FACT FILE

Formed: 1901
Nickname: The Moors
Sponsors:Alexander Forbes Insurance
Colours: Navy Blue with sky blue band
Change colours: Jade & lime
Midweek matchday: Tuesday
Reserve League: No reserve team
Website:www.moorgreenfc.co.uk

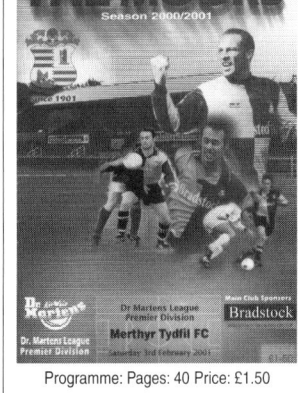

Programme: Pages: 40 Price: £1.50
Editor:Martin North(0121 603 7357)
Local Press: Solihull News, Solihull Times,
Birmingham Post & Mail, Express &Star
Local Radio: Radio WM, BRMB

GROUND `The Moorlands', Sherwood Rd., Hall Green. B28 OEX
Tel: 0121 777 8961 or 0121 624 2727

Directions: Off Highfield Rd, which is off A34 (B'ham to Stratford)
Hall Green & Yardley (BR) half mile
Capacity: 3,250 Cover: 1,200 Seats: 250 Floodlights: Yes

Clubhouse: Two bars, dance floor. Open nightly & weekend lunch

Club Shop: Selling scarves, mugs, stickers, programmes etc

PREVIOUS **Leagues:** (friendlies only 1901-21) Birmingham & Dist. A.F.A. 1908-36; Central Amateur 36-39; Birmingham Comb 45-54; West Mids 54-65; Midland Comb 65-83
Grounds: Moor Green Lane 1901-02; numerous 02-22; Windermere Road 1910-30

CLUB RECORDS **Attendance:** 5,000 v Romford, FA Amtr Cup 51
Career Goalscorer: Phil Davies 221 **Career Appearances:** Michael Hawkins 800
Transfer fee paid: £1,000 for Adrian O'Dowd (Alvechurch)
Transfer fee received: £90,000 for Ian Taylor (Port Vale)

BEST SEASON **FA Cup:** 1st Rd Proper 79-80 (lost 2-3 Stafford Rgs)
FA Trophy: 1st Rd Prop 90-91, 0-3 v Burton Albion; 96-97, 3-5 v AshtonUnited

HONOURS Southern Lg Mid Div R-up 87-88, Mids Comb 80-81 (R-up(4) 74-76 79-80 82-83, Div 185-86, Presidents Cup(2) 66-68 78-79), Mids Comb Chall Cup 80-81 (R-up 69-7082-83), Lord Mayor of B'ham Charity Cup 90-91, Mids F'lit Cup(2) 90-92, Tony Allden Tphy 81- 82, B'ham Snr Cup 57-58, Worcs Snr Cup 2000-01 R-up 86-87, B'ham Jnr Cup66-67, Worcs Jnr Cup 85-86, Solihull Charity Cup 85-86, Smedley Crook Mem.Cup 87-88, Cent Amat Lg 36-37 37-38 38-39, Verviers (Belg) Tphy 32-33 36-37,AFA Chall Cup 38-39, AFA Snr Cup 26-27 35-36, Mids F'lit Yth Lg Cup R-up 87-88,B'ham County Yth Lg Cup R-up 83-84

Players progressing: H Smith/R Jefferies (Aston Villa 47/50), F Pidcock(Walsall 53), P Woodward/B Mack (W B Abion 54), S Cooper (Birmingham City 83),K Barnes (Manchester City), P Brogan (Mansfield Town), I Taylor (Pt Vale 92), S Talbot (Pt Vale 94), D Busst (Coventry 92)

Moor Green 2000-01 Squad **Photo: Keith Clayton**

Date	Comp.	Opponents	Att.	Score	Goalscorers
19.08	DM Prem	Margate	460	1 - 0	Hall 60
22.08	DM Prem	NEWPORT COUNTY	417	1 - 1	Hall 42
26.08	DM Prem	CLEVEDON TOWN	292	3 - 3	Shepherd 44, Crisp 48, Woodley 52
28.08	DM Prem	King's Lynn	751	1 - 0	Baddams 69
02.09	DM Prem	FOLKESTONE INVICTA	323	1 - 2	Shepherd 58
04.09	DM Prem	Ilkeston Town	398	0 - 1	
09.09	DM Prem	Worcester City	1003	0 - 1	
16.09	DM Prem	STAFFORD RANGERS	507	1 - 2	Shepherd 17
20.09	DM Prem	Newport County	587	1 - 0	Crisp 35
23.09	DM Prem	HAVANT & WATERLOOVILLE	282	4 - 1	Baddams 60, Woodley 73, Shepherd 83 88
30.09	FA Cup Q2	Stafford Town	238	1 - 2	Baddams 41[p]
08.10	DM Prem	Merthyr Tydfil	551	0 - 2	
14.10	DM Prem	CRAWLEY TOWN	320	1 - 0	Crisp 67
21.10	DM Prem	FISHER ATHLETIC	304	3 - 1	Shepherd 25, Crisp 42, Softley 77
24.10	DM Prem	KING'S LYNN	284	2 - 1	Brighton 40, Martin 70
28.10	Worcs SC QF	BROMSGROVE ROVERS	123	2 - 0	Martin 17, Baddams 48
04.11	FA Trophy 1	HUCKNALL TOWN	246	0 - 1	
07.11	Birm. SC 2	Banbury United	96	5 - 3	Hall 53 58 76, Crawford 66, Baddams 85
14.11	Lge Cup 1	Shepshed Dynamo	95	1 - 0	Stanley 48
18.11	DM Prem	Clevedon Town	295	2 - 1	Baddams 79, Shepherd 89
21.11	DM Prem	ILKESTON TOWN	197	1 - 0	Martin 88
25.11	DM Prem	Folkestone Invicta	336	2 - 1	Pope 55, Softley 65
02.12	DM Prem	Salisbury City	331	1 - 3	Stanley 82
09.12	DM Prem	Bath City	762	1 - 3	Hall 33
16.12	DM Prem	BURTON ALBION	859	1 - 2	Hall 76
19.12	Lge Cup 2	Halesowen Town	234	1 - 0	Woodley 63
26.12	DM Prem	Tamworth	684	1 - 0	Hall 20
30.12	DM Prem	Welling United	514	0 - 0	
09.01	Birm. SC 3	BOLDMERE ST MICHAELS	140	3 - 0	Hall 42, Crisp 69, Charles 81[og]
13.01	DM Prem	WORCESTER CITY	520	1 - 0	Martin 49
23.01	Lge Cup 3	Bilston Town	87	0 - 1	
27.01	DM Prem	SALISBURY CITY	312	0 - 2	
03.02	DM Prem	MERTHYR TYDFIL	260	1 - 1	Shepherd 85
10.02	DM Prem	Crawley Town	602	0 - 1	
17.02	DM Prem	CAMBRIDGE CITY	326	0 - 0	
21.02	Birm. SC QF	WALSALL	158	4 - 2	Baddams 51[p] 59 85[p], Martin 64
03.03	DM Prem	WELLING UNITED	312	1 - 1	Robinson 42
06.03	DM Prem	Burton Albion	1039	1 - 2	Petty 53
10.03	DM Prem	Cambridge City	320	0 - 2	
13.03	DM Prem	HALESOWEN TOWN	307	3 - 2	Hall 25 90, Stanley 81[p]
17.03	DM Prem	Weymouth	702	1 - 5	Baddams 74
20.03	DM Prem	MARGATE	234	0 - 4	
24.03	DM Prem	Stafford Rangers	690	2 - 0	Hall 54, Martin 65
28.03	Worcs SC SF	Kidderminster Harriers	311	1 - 0	Hall 80
31.03	DM Prem	Fisher Athletic	150	0 - 3	
03.04	DM Prem	Dorchester Town	348	3 - 0	Petty 38, Collins 63, Stanley 72[p]
07.04	DM Prem	WEYMOUTH	244	1 - 1	Hall 75
09.04	Birm. SC SF	BIRMINGHAM CITY	329	3 - 1	Crisp 50, Adams 60, Collins 77
14.04	DM Prem	Halesowen Town	535	2 - 0	Petty 80, Crisp 90
16.04	DM Prem	TAMWORTH	609	0 - 1	
21.04	DM Prem	BATH CITY	269	3 - 2	Poskins 36, Martin 49, Hall 69
26.04	Worcs SC F(1)	EVESHAM UNITED	279	1 - 1	Parmenter 2[og]
28.04	DM Prem	Havant & Waterlooville	358	0 - 0	
01.05	Worcs SC F(2)	Evesham United	281	4 - 2	Stanley 7, Woodley 71, Hall 96, Martin 112
05.05	DM Prem	DORCHESTER TOWN	268	3 - 1	
07.08	Birm. SC F	TAMWORTH	n.k	3 - 1	Stanley 55, Martin 92, Lamey 116

PLAYING SQUAD

GOALKEEPERS: Andy De Bont (Stourbridge), Adam Rachel (Blackpool)

DEFENDERS: Denis Mulholland (Bromsgrove), Chris Gillard (Port Vale), Stewart Brighton (Redditch), Jai Stanley (Bedworth), Dean Peer (Shrewsbury)

MIDFIELDERS: Craig Woodley (Redditch), Richard Softley (Bromsgrove), Mick Hayde (Worcester), Martin Myers (Redditch), Jamie Petty (Solihull), Adrian Baddams (Solihull), Danny Scheppel (Worcester)

FORWARDS: Jai Martin (Woking), Wesley Joyce (Worcester), John Gayle (Shrewsbury), Richard Robinson (GMP Sports), Nathan Lamey (Hitchin), Nathan Harvey (Sandwell B), Mark Crisp (Cheltenham)

NEWPORT COUNTY A.F.C.

CLUB OFFICIALS

Chairman: Wallace Brown
Secretary: Mike Everett
43 Downing Street, Newport. NP19 0JL
Tel: 01633 669572

Club Website: www.newport-county.co.uk

Club's Email : hq.newportcounty@virgin.net

FACT FILE
Formed: 1989
Nickname: The Exiles
Sponsors: Acorn Recruitment
Colours: Amber shirts and black shorts
Change colours: All white
Midweek matchday: Monday.
Youth League: South West Counties Youth

FOOTBALL MANAGEMENT TEAM
Manager: Tim Harris
Asst Manager: Chris Hyde
Physio: John Fitzgerald
Kit Manager: Tony Gilbert

2000-01
Captain: Gary Kemp / Darren Robison
Top scorer: Garry Shephard 26
P.o.Y.: GarryShephard

Pages: 36 Price: £1.50
Editor: Wallace Brown (01633 265500)

Local Press:
South Wales Argus, South Wales Echo
Local Radio: Red Dragon, Real Radio

GROUND **Club Headquarters:**Newport Stadium, Spytty Park,Langland Way, Newport, South Wales FAX 01633 666107 Tel: 01633 662262
Directions: From Severn Bridge on M4 take 1st exit signed Newport (jct 24), 1st left at r'bout follow signs for industrial area, left at r'bout after 2 1/2miles, over 2 r'bouts, next left for ground. Ample free parking available at ground
Capacity: 3,300 Cover: 1,236 Seats: 1,236 Floodlights: Yes
Clubhouse: Small bar at ground with hot and cold snacks also available.
Club Shop: Open matchdays, sells a wide selection of souvenirs & programmes

PREVIOUS **Leagues:** Hellenic 89-90 **Grounds:** London Road, Moreton-in-Marsh 89-90; Somerton Park, Newport 90-92; Gloucester City FC 92-94 (exile period due to dispute with FAW re League of Wales)
Names: Newport AFC were formed after the demise of Newport County in1988-89, name change 1999.

CLUB RECORDS **Attendance:** 2,475 v Redditch United, Beazer (Midland) 24.8.94
Win: 9-0 v Pontlottyn Blast Furnace (A), Welsh Cup First Round 1/9/90
Defeat: 1-6 v Stafford Rangers (A) BHL 6/1/96
Career Goalscorer: Chris Lilygreen 93 **Career Appearances:** Mark Price 275 (222 Lg + 53 cup)
Transfer fee paid:£5,000 for Shaun Chapple from Forest Green Rovers £1,000 from RedditchU for Paul Burton
Transfer fee received: £5,000 from Merthyr Tydfil for Craig Lima

BEST SEASON **FA Cup:** 4th Qualifying Rd 92-93 **FA Trophy:** 3rd Rd 99-00, 00-01 **FA Vase:** N/A

HONOURS Hellenic Lge Prem Div 89-90 (Lge Cup 89-90); Glos Sen Cup Winners 93-94;Southern Lg. Mid Div Champions 94-95, R-up 98-99 Merit Cup Jnt Win 94-95, 98-99 Gwent FA Sen.Cup Winners 96-97,97-98,98-99,99-00 ,00-01Herefordshire Senior Cup. 98-99

Back Row , left to right: Glyn Jones (youth team coach), Jason Donovan,Lee Stanton, Danny Hill,Steve Benton,Andrew Thomas, Simon Pratt (coaching staff).**Middle Row:** Danny Hunt, Chris Bale, Stuart James, Matt Rose, Pat Mountain, Ryan Mackerness, Jason Matthews, Darren Robison, Shaun Chapple, Mike Flynn and Nathan Davie. **Front Row:** Darren Beckett, John Fitzgerald (Physio),Jason Eaton,Gary Kemp, Tim Harris (Manager), Chris Hyde (Assistant Manager), Gary Thorne, Garry Shephard, Lee Brown, Tony Gilbert (Kit Manager) and Ryan Dirrian

Date	Comp.	Opponents	Att.	Score	Goalscorers
19.08	DM Prem	BURTON ALBION	961	1 - 1	Rose 46
22.08	DM Prem	Moor Green	417	1 - 1	Rose 87
26.08	DM Prem	Weymouth	960	0 - 0	
28.08	DM Prem	Halesowen Town	532	3 - 1	Hunt 39, Donovan 65, Shepherd 87
02.09	DM Prem	DORCHESTER TOWN	701	5 - 0	Kemp 22, Rose 31 88, Flynn 56, Hill 79
05.09	DM Prem	Salisbury City	571	0 - 4	
09.09	DM Prem	Stafford Rangers	840	1 - 1	Hill 28
16.09	DM Prem	TAMWORTH	708	0 - 1	
20.09	DM Prem	MOOR GREEN	587	0 - 1	
23.09	DM Prem	Folkestone Invicta	475	1 - 3	Donovan 71
30.09	FA Cup Q2	MERTHYR TYDFIL	728	0 - 4	
04.10	Gwent SC 1	CHEPSTOW TOWN	145	4 - 0	Birkby 11[p] 29[p], Shepherd 44, Eaton 62
07.10	DM Prem	Havant & Waterlooville	420	0 - 3	
14.10	DM Prem	HALESOWEN TOWN	554	0 - 2	
21.10	DM Prem	King's Lynn	934	3 - 2	Thorne 21[p], Dale 50, Souter 60
04.11	FA Trophy 1	Bedford Town	713	2 - 1	Shepherd 72, Morgan 90
11.11	DM Prem	Cambridge City	514	6 - 5	Thorne 39[p], Shepherd 56 57 84, Rose 60, Eaton 76
15.11	Lge Cup 1	MERTHYR TYDFIL	436	1 - 0	Donovan 14
18.11	DM Prem	WELLING UNITED	582	1 - 1	Thorne 9
25.11	DM Prem	Dorchester Town	701	3 - 0	Shepherd 6, Donovan 30 48
02.12	FA Trophy 2	SLOUGH TOWN	627	2 - 1	Thorne 48, Souter 61
09.12	DM Prem	CRAWLEY TOWN	646	3 - 1	Eaton 5, Shepherd 23 41
16.12	DM Prem	CAMBRIDGE CITY	629	3 - 0	Eaton 63, Dale 83, Donovan 90
23.12	DM Prem	Bath City	1541	0 - 2	
26.12	DM Prem	MERTHYR TYDFIL	973	2 - 0	Shepherd 42, Kemp 68
01.01	DM Prem	Worcester City	1375	4 - 4	Thorne 31, James 34, Shephard 54, Dale 82
06.01	DM Prem	Burton Albion	1266	1 - 2	Kemp 70
10.01	Lge Cup 2	BATH CITY	374	5 - 0	Shepherd 11 25, Donovan 26, Dale 59 87
13.01	FA Trophy 3	St Albans City	604	0 - 1	
27.01	DM Prem	CLEVEDON TOWN	688	5 - 2	Shephard 40 56 87, Dale 76, Hill 82
31.01	DM Prem	FISHER ATHLETIC	605	0 - 4	
17.02	DM Prem	Clevedon Town	534	3 - 2	Dale 40, Davis 59, Hill 89
19.02	Lge Cup 3	MANGOTSFIELD UNITED	357	2 - 0	Shephard 46, Dale 63
24.02	DM Prem	FOLKESTONE INVICTA	668	5 - 0	Shepherd 17 45, Davis 20, Dale 31, Kemp 67
28.02	DM Prem	BATH CITY	682	3 - 0	Hill 60, Dale 60[p] 87
03.03	DM Prem	Ilkeston Town	426	1 - 0	Shephard 70
05.03	Lge Cup QF	BASHLEY	359	2 - 0	Shephard 45, Thomas 75
07.03	DM Prem	SALISBURY CITY	563	1 - 3	Benton 43
10.03	DM Prem	HAVANT & WATERLOOVILLE	731	2 - 2	Dale 40, Shephard 72
24.03	DM Prem	WEYMOUTH	582	0 - 0	
26.03	DM Prem	STAFFORD RANGERS	520	1 - 0	Shepherd 89
31.03	DM Prem	MARGATE	747	0 - 0	
04.04	DM Prem	ILKESTON TOWN	427	3 - 1	Dale 75, Shepherd 83 90
07.04	DM Prem	Tamworth	612	0 - 1	
10.04	Lge Cup SF	Worcester City	818	3 - 5	Dale 55, Donovan 70, Hall 119
13.04	DM Prem	WORCESTER CITY	636	0 - 1	
16.04	DM Prem	Merthyr Tydfil	707	1 - 2	Plant 51
21.04	DM Prem	Welling United	550	1 - 3	Donovan 38
24.04	DM Prem	Fisher Athletic	117	3 - 1	Sheppard 5, Dorrian 8, Thomas 51
28.04	DM Prem	KING'S LYNN	627	1 - 3	Sheppard 50
29.04	Gwent SC SF	RISCA UNITED	258	5 - 3	Plant 20 54[p] 85, Donovan 50, Dale 72
01.05	DM Prem	Margate	2366	0 - 0	
05.05	DM Prem	Crawley Town	779	2 - 1	Donovan 71, Shephard 84

PLAYING SQUAD

GOALKEEPERS: Pat Mountain (Gloucester), Matthew Taylor (Northampton)

DEFENDERS: Billy Clark (Forest Green R), Andrew Thomas (Youth), Steve Benton (Cheltenham), Jason Perry (Hull), Jeff Eckhardt (Cardiff), Ryan Souter (Bury)

MIDFIELDERS: Darren Robison (Trowbridge), Darren Ryan (Merthyr Tydfil), Scott Walker (Bath), Ryan Dorrian (Youth), Matthew Rose (Gloucester), Stuart James (Bath), Nathan Davies (Youth)

FORWARDS: Gary Shepherd (Merthyr Tydfil), Martin Paul (Bath), Carl Dale (Yeovil), Chris Bale (Youth), Steve Cowe (Swindon), Raith Plant (Cwmbran)

NEWPORT I.W.

CLUB OFFICIALS

Chairman: Bill Manuel
President: W H J Bunday
Commercial Manager: Mark Major
Secretary: Chris Cheverton
40 Whitehead Crescent, Wootton Bridge, I.o.W. PO33 4JF Tel: 01983 883879
Press Officer: Jim Baldwin
Tel: 01983 521836

FOOTBALL MANAGEMENT TEAM

Manager: Tony Mount
Assistant Manager: Neil Hards
Physio: Chris Cheverton

FACT FILE

Formed: 1888 Nickname: The Port
Colours: all Yellow with blue trim
Change colours: Sky blue with blue trim
Midweek matchday: Tuesday
Reserves' League: Wesex League

2000-01 Captain: John Price
P.o.Y: Supporters': Steve Riley
P.o.Y: Manager's: Danny Gibbons
P.o.Y: Players': Colin Matthews.
Leading goalscorer: Danny Gibbons 22

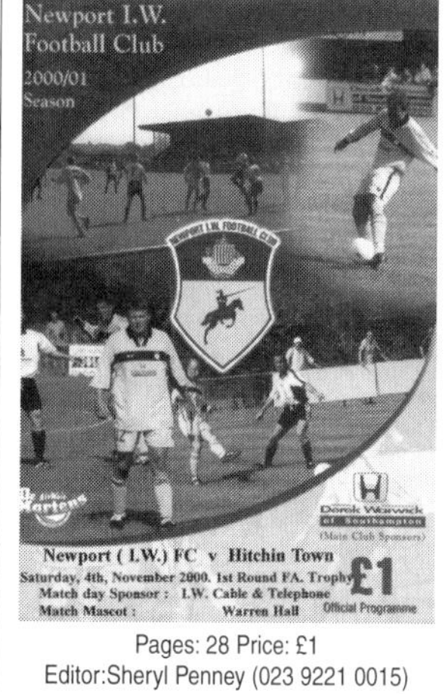

Pages: 28 Price: £1
Editor:Sheryl Penney (023 9221 0015)

Local Press: Portsmouth Evening News, I.o.W. County Press, Southampton Evening Echo
Local Radio: Solent, Isle of Wight Radio, Ocean Sound

GROUND: St. George's Park, St George's Way, Newport, Isle of Wight, PO30 2QH.
Tel: 01983 525027. Club Website: www.newportiow.freeserve.co.uk
Directions: Roads from all ferry ports lead to Coppins Bridge R-abt at eastern end of town. Take Sandown/Ventnor exit, go to small r-about, St George's way is 1st exit, ground on left 5 mins walk from Newport Bus station along Church Litten (past old ground) turn left then right at r-about.
Capacity: 5,000 Cover: 1,000 Seats: 300 Floodlights: Yes **Club Shop:** Sells souvenirs & progs. Contact Roger Sanders 01983 825925
Clubhouse: Open every evening & weekend lunch times. 2 bars, full range of hot and cold bar snacks. Buffet inside ground

PREVIOUS **Leagues:** Isle of Wight 1896-1928; Hants 28-86; Wessex 86-90
Ground: Church Litten (previously Well's Field) 1888-1988

CLUB RECORDS **Attendance:** 2,217 FA Cup 1st Rd Nov 1994 v Aylesbury U., (6,000 v Watford, FACup 1st Rd 56-57, at Church Litten)
Win: 14-1, v Thornycroft Athletic (H),Hampshire Lge Div. One, 22.12.45
Defeat: 1-11 v Emsworth(A) Hampshsire Div. Lge 1926-27 **Career Appearances:** Jeff Austin 540 (69-87)
Career Goalscorer: Roy Gilfillan 220 1951-57 **Record Goalscorer:** Frank Harrison 62 1929-30
Fee paid: £5,000 for Colin Matthews (Bognor Regis Town 00) **Fee received**: £2,250 for Mick Jenkins (Havant) 92-3

BEST SEASON **FA Trophy:** 4th Rd 99-00 **FA Vase:** Fifth Round 91-92, 92-93
FA Cup: 2nd Rd 35-36 45-46. 1st Rd another 8 times - 52-53, 53-54, 54-55, 56-57, 57-58, 58-59, 94-95, 95-96
League clubs defeated: Clapton Orient 45-46

HONOURS Dr. Martens Lge Eastern Div. 00-01, Wessex Lg R-up 89-90, Comb. 91-92, 99-00 (res 2.); Hants Lg (11), R-up (7), Div 2 R-up 70-71, Hants Snr Cup (8); Russell Cotes Cup (3); Pickford Cup (4); Isle of Wight Snr (Gold) Cup (34); Hants F'lit Cup 76-77 77-78; Isle of Wight Lg (4) 07-09 23-24; Hants I'mediate Cup 31-32 96-97; Hants Comb. Cup 38-39

Players progressing: Gary Rowatt (Cambridge United)

L-R Back Row: Spencer Brown (Asst Physio), Chris Cheverton (Physio/Secretary),Chris Collins, Steve Moss, Steve Leigh, Danny Rofe, Steve Tate, Danny Gibbons, Colin Matthews, Mark Tryon, Fraser Quirke, Ben Thomson, Ian Rew, Gary Green, Gary Sperry, Ashley Wright, Tony Mount (Manager), Neil Hands (Asst Manager) **Front Row:** Adam Holbrook, Karl Lis, John Price (Captain), Steve Watt, Steve Riley, Ian Buchman and Leigh Cole.
Photo: I.W.County Press.

Date	Comp.	Opponents	Att.	Score	Goalscorers
19.08	DM East	CORBY TOWN	430	3 - 0	Price 24, Wright 28, Riley 54
22.08	DM East	Tonbridge Angels	427	1 - 1	Gibbs 56[og]
26.08	DM East	Hastings Town	378	2 - 1	Rofe 87, Tate 89
29.08	DM East	DARTFORD	402	2 - 0	Moss 29, Gibbons 90
02.09	FA Cup P	ARUNDEL	329	5 - 2	Wright 14 46, Betteridge 17, Gibbons 85, Wilson 89
09.09	DM East	Baldock Town	185	0 - 2	
16.09	FA Cup Q1	BASHLEY	397	1 - 1	Gibbons 31
20.09	FA Cup Q1 R	Bashley	230	2 - 0	Tate 25, Leigh 27
23.09	DM East	BANBURY UNITED	397	1 - 1	Tate 53
26.09	DM East	Langney Sports	374	1 - 0	Matthews 47
30.09	FA Cup Q2	Fisher Athletic	121	2 - 4	Gibbons 13, Raw 82[p]
07.10	DM East	Spalding United	103	2 - 3	Riley 39, Gibbons 56
14.10	DM East	ST LEONARDS	344	4 - 1	Dent 1, Collins 7 34, Wright 73
21.10	DM East	Wisbech Town	238	2 - 0	Riley 65, Wright 90
25.10	DM East	Dartford	136	1 - 1	Dent 88
04.11	FA Trophy 1	HITCHIN TOWN	370	2 - 2	Gibbons 19, Riley 87
11.11	DM East	Corby Town	92	3 - 2	Gibbons 2, Collins 26, Riley 44
14.11	FA Trophy 1 R	Hitchin Town	241	1 - 4	Rofe 51
15.11	Hants SC 2	ALDERSHOT TOWN	194	5 - 0	Tate 7 38, Price 64 80 88
16.12	DM East	WISBECH TOWN	243	7 - 1	Gibbons 18 40, Wilson 38, Tate 57, Liss 83, Watt 87, Holbrook 89
23.12	DM East	CHELMSFORD CITY	420	0 - 0	
26.12	DM East	Bashley	159	1 - 1	Riley 89
06.01	DM East	Histon	191	1 - 3	Holbrook 20
09.01	Hants SC 3	BASINGSTOKE TOWN	215	5 - 1	Holbrook 5, Leigh 16, Wilson 64, Wright 73, Riley 78
16.01	Lge Cup 1	WEYMOUTH	191	2 - 1	Leigh 17, White 18
20.01	DM East	STAMFORD	319	3 - 1	Tate 15 28, Leigh 52
01.02	Hants SC QF	Lymington & New Milton	83	0 - 4	
03.02	Lge Cup 2	Bashley	154	2 - 3	Watt 89 112
10.02	DM East	Grantham Town	344	0 - 3	
15.02	DM East	Witney Town	50	5 - 0	Riley 7, Gibbons 29, Holbrook 46, Collins 50, Leigh 75
17.02	DM East	ROTHWELL TOWN	287	3 - 1	Gibbons 10 18, Leigh 53
21.02	DM East	Sittingbourne	185	2 - 1	Rofe 17, Gibbons 39
24.02	DM East	Erith & Belvedere	115	3 - 1	Leigh 45 64, Quirk 48
25.02	DM East	GRANTHAM TOWN	391	6 - 0	Gibbons 19 74, Price 37, Holbrook 69, Watt 88, Wright 90
01.03	IOW SC	EAST COWES VICTORIA ATHLETIC	n.k	3 - 4	
06.03	DM East	LANGNEY SPORTS	224	1 - 0	Tate 4
20.03	DM East	Rothwell Town	104	2 - 1	Gibbons 6 59
27.03	DM East	Banbury United	241	1 - 1	Gibbons 58
29.03	DM East	TONBRIDGE ANGELS	259	1 - 0	Gibbons 1
31.03	DM East	SITTINGBOURNE	401	4 - 0	Price 32, Holbrook 36, Wright 68 83
01.04	DM East	Stamford	207	0 - 0	
03.04	DM East	ASHFORD TOWN	304	5 - 0	Wright 19, Holbrook 39[p], Price 52, Rew 65, Tate 65
10.04	DM East	Ashford Town	159	3 - 1	Holbrook 19[p], Tate 24, Watt 33
14.04	DM East	Burnham	132	1 - 1	Yate 90[p]
16.04	DM East	BASHLEY	614	3 - 2	Holbrook 45, Watt 54 64
19.04	DM East	HASTINGS TOWN	418	2 - 0	Watt 22, Rew 24
21.04	DM East	HISTON	449	0 - 0	
22.04	DM East	St Leonards	231	3 - 0	Holbrook 15, Gibbons 24, Quirke 31
24.04	DM East	ERITH & BELVEDERE	421	2 - 0	Green 56, Riley 89
26.04	DM East	WITNEY TOWN	488	6 - 0	Quirke 8 75 83, Green 19, Holbrook 68, Tate 80
28.04	DM East	BALDOCK TOWN	610	1 - 0	Gibbons 37
29.04	DM East	SPALDING UNITED	558	2 - 0	Dear 30[og], Gibbons 72
01.05	DM East	BURNHAM	414	0 - 0	
05.05	DM East	Chelmsford City	1441	1 - 0	Green 43

PLAYING SQUAD

GOALKEEPERS: Colin Matthews (Bognor Regis T)

DEFENDERS: Dave Wilson (Bashley), Chris Collins (Stevenage), John Price (Havant T), Ian Rew (Andover), Danny Rofe (Salisbury)

MIDFIELDERS: Mark Preston (Hayes), Steve Leigh (Havant T), Adam Holbrook (Portsmouth), Adam Barsdell (Cowes Sports), Leigh Cole (Havant T), Jonathan Dodd (Portsmouth), Guy Whittingham (Wycombe)

FORWARDS: Steve Tate (Weymouth), Danny Gibbons (Weston-S-M), Dave Wakefield (Havant & W), Ben Thomson (Bashley)

SALISBURY CITY

CLUB OFFICIALS

Chairman: P R McEnhill

Secretary: Allan Finch,16 Assisi Rd, Salisbury, Wiltshire SP1 3QZ
Tel: 01722 338223 (H) 07980 506679 (M)

Press Off: Alec Hayter Tel: 01264 773765

Youth Development Off: Symon Pickett

Football in Community Off.: Andy Cook

Commercial Manager: T.B.A.

FOOTBALL MANAGEMENT TEAM

Manager: Steve Richardson
Asst. Manager: Tommy Killick
Youth Coach: Terry Hatt
Physio: Conrad Parrott

FACT FILE

Formed: 1947
Nickname: The Whites
Sponsors: T.B.A.
Colours: White/black/white
Change colours: yellow/blue/yellow
Midweek matchday: Tuesday
Reserve Team's League: Wessex Comb
Club Line: 'City Line' 0906 555 864

2000-01
Capt: Roger Emms
Top scorer: Paul Sales

Reserve Team Management
Ian Chalk & Stuart McGlashan
Masseur /Fitness Therapist : Dawn

Dr. Martens League · Premier Division
SALISBURY CITY
v.
Cambridge City
Saturday 5th May 2001 · 3.00pm
SALISBURY CITY
2000/2001 MATCHDAY PROGRAMME
£1.20
THE WESTERN DAILY PRESS
J.A. BELL HEATING & PLUMBING

Pages: 48 Price: £1.20
Editors: Dave Todd & Alec Hunter
Local Press: Salisbury Journal, Evening Echo & Sports Echo, Western DailyPress
Local Radio: Wiltshire Sound, Spire F.M

GROUND The Raymond McEnhill Stadium, Partridge Way, Old Sarum, Salisbury SP4 6PU
Tel:01722 326454, Fax 01722 323100 Club Website: www.salisbury-city-fc.com

Directions: The Stadium is situated off A345 (Salisbury - Amesbury) road on the northern edge of the city 2 miles from the City centre. Continue on this road, turn right onto A338 signed Old Sarum Business Park, Partridge Way & ground on left (well signposted)

Capacity: 4,000 Cover: 3,062 Seats: 462 Floodlights: Yes

Clubhouse: On ground, . Hot & cold snacks. Hospitality Boxes available for hire.

Club Shop: Sells replica shirts, memorabilia, programmes, scarves, metal badges, souvenirs. Contact Commercial Office (01722 326454)

PREVIOUS **Leagues:** Western 47-68 **Name:** Salisbury FC, 47-92 **Ground:** Hudson Field 47-48, Victoria Park 48-97

CLUB RECORDS **Attendance:** 8,902 v Weymouth, Western League 48
New Ground: 2,570 v Hull City F.A. Cup 1998. **Win:** 11-1 v R.A.F Colerne (H) Western League Div 2 1948
Defeat: 0-7 v Minehead, Southern League 1975
Career Goalscorer: Royston Watts 180 (59-65) **Career Appearances:** Barry Fitch 713 (63-75)
Transfer fee paid: £5,750 for Peter Loveridge (Dorchester Town, 90)
Transfer fee received: £20,,000 for Adrian Randall (Forest Green Rovers)

BEST SEASON **FA Trophy:** 2nd Rd 96-97 (lost to Dorchester Town)
FA Amateur Cup: 2nd Rd 49-50 (lost to Dulwich Hamlet)) **FA Cup:** 2nd Rd 59-60 (lost to Newport County)

HONOURS Southern Lg Southern Div Champ 94-95, R-up 85-86 92-93; Western Lg 57-58 60-61,R-up 58-59 59-60 61-62 66-67 67-68; Hants Senior Cup 61-62 63-64; Wilts PremierShield 56-57 59-60 61-62 66-67 67-68 70-71 77-78 78-79 95-96 98-99,00-01

Players progressing: Eric Fountain (Southampton 48), Cyril Smith (Arsenal 48),Tony Alexander (Fulham 65), John Evans (Stockport County 67), Graham Moxon (Exeter 75), Eric Welch (Chesterfield 76), Ian Thompson (Bournemouth 83),Trevor Wood (Port Vale 88), Denny Mundee (Bournemouth 88), Matthew Carmichael (Lincoln 90), Frank Monk (Southampton 47)George Marks 49), Joe Stocks (Millwall 64), (H)Jason Matthews (Exeter C)

Photo: Courtesy of Salisbury Newspapers (Salisbury Journal and Avon Advertiser)

L-R - Back Row: Kevin Braybrook, Robbie Matthews, Roger Emms, Clive Lyttle, Martin Shepherd, Lee Bradford.

Middle: Robbie Harbut Paul Sales Tommy Killick Steve Richardson Wayne Turk Andy Cook.

Front: Steve Witt Ben Madgwick Scott Bartlett Tyronne Bowers Matt Davies

Date	Comp.	Opponents	Att.	Score	Goalscorers
SALISBURY CITY					
19.08	DM Prem	HALESOWEN TOWN	490	2 - 1	Sales 2, Baybrooke 75
22.08	DM Prem	Clevedon Town	272	1 - 3	Sales 45
26.08	DM Prem	Folkestone Invicta	424	1 - 2	Smith 65
28.08	DM Prem	WEYMOUTH	617	3 - 2	Sales 11, Bowers 24, Corcoran 57
02.09	DM Prem	Fisher Athletic	143	2 - 1	Smith 27[p], Corcoran 55
05.09	DM Prem	NEWPORT COUNTY	571	4 - 0	Shepherd 15, Emms 18 55, Smith 39
09.09	DM Prem	MERTHYR TYDFIL	475	2 - 2	Turk 56, Smith 66
16.09	DM Prem	Crawley Town	1053	1 - 5	Sales 38
19.09	DM Prem	CLEVEDON TOWN	357	4 - 1	Sales 17 65, Shepherd 76 83
23.09	DM Prem	Worcester City	1005	1 - 0	Sales 90
30.09	FA Cup Q2	Clevedon Town	302	4 - 2	Emms 1, Smith 49 81[p], Skidmore 51[og]
07.10	DM Prem	BATH CITY	575	4 - 4	Turk 27 64, Sales 81, Lloyd 84[og]
14.10	FA Cup Q3	Dorchester Town	817	3 - 4	Sales 19 61, Smith 24
21.10	DM Prem	Burton Albion	1085	0 - 5	
24.10	Wilts PS 1	CHIPPENHAM TOWN	128	1 - 0	Tiley 28[og]
04.11	FA Trophy 1	Bashley	257	0 - 1	
11.11	DM Prem	WELLING UNITED	421	1 - 1	Harbut 56
14.11	Lge Cup 1	HAVANT & WATERLOOVILLE	192	2 - 2	Smith 44, Saunders 47 (2-3p)
18.11	DM Prem	King's Lynn	507	1 - 2	Smith 55
02.12	DM Prem	MOOR GREEN	331	3 - 1	Sales 41 67 81
09.12	DM Prem	Cambridge City	510	2 - 1	Sales 70, Shepherd 89
16.12	DM Prem	FISHER ATHLETIC	370	3 - 0	Sales 41, Smith 68, Emms 77
23.12	DM Prem	FOLKESTONE INVICTA	428	0 - 0	
26.12	DM Prem	Havant & Waterlooville	477	1 - 3	Shepherd 15
01.01	DM Prem	CRAWLEY TOWN	422	1 - 1	Sales 19
09.01	Wilts PS QF	Westbury United	n.k	4 - 0	Corcoran(2), Sales, Chalk
13.01	DM Prem	Dorchester Town	544	1 - 2	Sales 71
16.01	DM Prem	WORCESTER CITY	255	2 - 0	Sales 31, Bowers 59
20.01	DM Prem	STAFFORD RANGERS	510	4 - 1	Shepherd 4, Wakefield 7 10, Sales 90
27.01	DM Prem	Moor Green	312	2 - 0	Sales 11, Smith 77
03.02	DM Prem	Tamworth	535	1 - 4	Wakefield 36
10.02	DM Prem	MARGATE	623	0 - 1	
17.02	DM Prem	Halesowen Town	402	0 - 3	
24.02	DM Prem	Merthyr Tydfil	456	0 - 1	
03.03	DM Prem	TAMWORTH	517	1 - 3	Smith 38
07.03	DM Prem	Newport County	563	3 - 1	Bowers 2 29, Marwood 16
10.03	DM Prem	Ilkeston Town	362	1 - 1	Shepherd 35
17.03	DM Prem	Margate	925	1 - 1	Shepherd 87
31.03	DM Prem	Welling United	747	1 - 2	
03.04	DM Prem	Weymouth	770	1 - 3	Sheppard 66
07.04	DM Prem	BURTON ALBION	559	1 - 0	Cavanagh 6[og]
14.04	DM Prem	DORCHESTER TOWN	556	0 - 2	
16.04	DM Prem	Bath City	710	1 - 0	Gibbon 73
18.04	Wilts PS SF	MELKSHAM TOWN	244	2 - 1	Emms, Shepherd
21.04	DM Prem	ILKESTON TOWN	424	2 - 0	Shephard 15, Bartlett 60
24.04	DM Prem	KING'S LYNN	320	1 - 4	Smith 40
28.04	DM Prem	Stafford Rangers	658	2 - 4	Bowers 10, Smith 43
03.05	DM Prem	HAVANT & WATERLOOVILLE	298	0 - 0	
05.05	DM Prem	CAMBRIDGE CITY	432	2 - 1	Turk 36, Bowers 67
08.05	Wilts PS F	BEMERTON HEATH HARLEQUINS	n.k	1 - 0	

PLAYING SQUAD

GOALKEEPERS: Justin Shuttlewood (Forest Green R), Andy Burt (Youth)

DEFENDERS: Scott Bartlett (Cirencester), Andy Cook (Millwall), Roger Emms (Andover), Ben Madgewick (Youth), Lee Bradford (Weymouth)

MIDFIELDERS: Steve Richardson (Basingstoke), Tyrone Bowers (Fareham), Wayne Turk (Cirencester), Robbie Harbut (Bashley), Kevin Braybrook (Yeovil)

FORWARDS: Martin Sheppard (Dorchester), Paul Sales (Bashley), Phil Corcoran (Cirencester), Chris Marwood (Bashley), Rob Speakman (Exeter), Tommy Killick (Wimborne)

STAFFORD RANGERS

CLUB OFFICIALS

Chairman: B.Baker
Vice-Chairman: J.Downing
Secretary: Peter Wall
c/o Stafford Rangers FC
Tel: 01785 602430
Press Officer: T.B.A.

FOOTBALL MANAGEMENT TEAM
Manager: I Painter
Coach: A King
Physio: T.B.A.

FACT FILE
Formed: 1876
Nickname: The Boro
Colours: Black & White stripes/black/black
Change: Maroon & azure/maroon/maroon
Midweek matchday: Tuesday
Reserves' League: No reserve team

2000-01
Captain: Scott Dundas
P.o.Y.: Scott Dundas
Scott DundasR.Mitchell

Pages: 40 Price: £1.50
Editor: Peter Wall Tel. 01785 602430
Local Press: Staffordshire Newsletter, Express & Star, Evening Sentinel
Local Radio: Radio Stoke, Beacon Radio, Signal Radio

GROUND Marston Road Stafford ST16 3BX Tel: 01785 602430 Fax : 01785 602431
Club Website: www.staffordrangers.co.uk

Directions: From M6 junction 14, A34 (Stone) to roundabout, straight over into Beaconside, take third right into Common Road, ground one mile ahead. From Town Centre, follow signs for B5066 (Sandon) turn left by new housing estate. Two miles from railway station

Capacity 3,000 Cover 1,500 Seats: 426 Floodlights: Yes

Clubhouse: Yes - Open every evening
Club Shop: Two shops, one old programmes and one souvenirs run by Jim & IreneDalglish

PREVIOUS **Leagues:** Shropshire 1891-93, Birm 1893-96, 21-40, N Staffs 1896-1900, Cheshire 00-01, Birm Comb 00-12, 46-52, Cheshire Co. 52-69, N.P.L. 69-79, 83-85, Alliance Prem 79-83, GMVC 85-95
Grounds: Lammascotes, Stone Rd, Newtown, Doxey (until 1896)

CLUB RECORDS **Attendance:** 8,536 v Rotherham Utd FA Cup 3rd Rd 75
Win: 11-0 v Dudley Town FA Cup 6.9.58 **Defeat:** 0-12 v Burton Town Birmingham Lge 13.12.30
Career Goalscorer: M Cullerton 176 **Career Appearances:** Jim Sargent
Transfer fee paid: £13,000 for S Butterworth from VS Rugby 90
Transfer fee received: £100,000 for Stan Collymore from Crystal Palace 1990

BEST SEASON **FA Trophy:** Winners 1971-72 & 78-79. R-up 75-76
FA Cup: 4th Rd 74-75, 1-2 v Peterborough Utd. (H) League clubs defeated: Halifax, Stockport, Rotherham

HONOURS Birm Comb Champ 12-13; Birm Lge Champ 25-26; N.P.L. Champ 71-72, 84-85, Champ Shield 84-85; FA Trophy 71-72, 78-79, R-up 75-76; Bob Lord Trophy 85-86; Wednesday Charity Cup 20-21; Mid F/light Cup 70-71; Jim Thompson Shield 86-87; Staffs Sen Cup 54-55 56-57 62-63 71-72 77-78 86-87 91-92 Dr.Martens Western Division 99-00

Players progressing: M Aleksic (Plymouth), J Arnold (Blackburn), R Williams/MCullerton/T Bailey (Port Vale), K Barnes (Man City), A Lee (Tranmere), ECameron (Exeter), W Blunt (Wolves), G Bullock (Barnsley), K Mottershead(Doncaster), McIlvenny (WBA), S Collymore (C Palace), P Devlin (Notts Co.),R Price (Birmingham C.)

L-R Back Row: Midleton, Brindley, Spittle, Williams, Simkin, Kiely.
Middle Row: B Whittaker (physio), J Cooper (asst. physio), Carter, N Smith, Read, Boughey, Eccleston, A King (asst. manager), Dr. Dar Gupta.
Front Row: Ryder, J Smith, Craven, Dundas, I Painter (manager), Heath, Everitt, Tranter.

Date	Comp.	Opponents	Att.	Score	Goalscorers
19.08	DM Prem	CRAWLEY TOWN	815	1 - 2	Dundas 82
22.08	DM Prem	Halesowen Town	667	1 - 0	Dundas 81
26.08	DM Prem	Worcester City	1142	4 - 2	Dundas 19 27 88[p], Middleton 83
28.08	DM Prem	ILKESTON TOWN	992	4 - 2	Dundas 13, Eccleston 15 51, Kiely 77
02.09	DM Prem	MARGATE	950	0 - 2	
05.09	DM Prem	Merthyr Tydfil	663	0 - 3	
09.09	DM Prem	NEWPORT COUNTY	840	1 - 1	Craven 30
16.09	DM Prem	Moor Green	507	2 - 1	Middleton 12, Eccleston 25
19.09	DM Prem	HALESOWEN TOWN	656	0 - 1	
23.09	DM Prem	King's Lynn	888	2 - 3	Clarke 60[og], Dundas 70
30.09	FA Cup Q2	Solihull Borough	513	1 - 1	Craven 46
03.10	FA Cup Q2 R	SOLIHULL BOROUGH	432	0 - 0	(4-3p)
07.10	DM Prem	CLEVEDON TOWN	645	4 - 1	Dundas 11 61, Kiely 41 54
14.10	FA Cup Q3	CHESHAM UNITED	616	0 - 2	
21.10	DM Prem	Bath City	804	2 - 2	O'Connor 2, Dundas 84[p]
23.10	DM Prem	Ilkeston Town	529	1 - 1	Eccleston 17
04.11	FA Trophy 1	OSSETT TOWN	413	3 - 1	Middleton 17, O'Connor 52, Kiely 62
11.11	DM Prem	Crawley Town	858	2 - 2	O'Connor 20, Lovatt 31
14.11	Lge Cup 1	ROCESTER	258	1 - 2	Craven 85
18.11	DM Prem	WORCESTER CITY	697	1 - 2	Dundas 85
25.11	DM Prem	Margate	405	1 - 3	Kiely 49
28.11	Staffs SC 2	Bilston Town	262	4 - 2	Eccleston 22, Simkin 30, Brindley 39, Kiely 90
02.12	FA Trophy 2	Blyth Spartans	480	0 - 3	
09.12	DM Prem	FOLKESTONE INVICTA	608	3 - 0	Eccleston 3, Lovatt 48, O'Connor 52
16.12	DM Prem	Dorchester Town	547	2 - 0	Kiely 59, O'Connor 84
23.12	DM Prem	WEYMOUTH	712	3 - 2	Eccleston 32, Simkin 74, Lovatt 83
26.12	DM Prem	Burton Albion	2501	0 - 0	
06.01	DM Prem	HAVANT & WATERLOOVILLE	746	3 - 2	McDonald 1[og], Kiely 31, Dundas 84
13.01	DM Prem	Welling United	503	0 - 0	
20.01	DM Prem	Salisbury City	510	1 - 4	O'Connor 28
27.01	DM Prem	KING'S LYNN	668	0 - 1	
30.01	Staffs SC QF	Shifnal Town	118	4 - 1	Kiely 29, Lovatt 30, O'Connor 54, Middleton 79
03.02	DM Prem	DORCHESTER TOWN	549	1 - 0	Eccleston 39
17.02	DM Prem	BATH CITY	734	6 - 2	O'Connor 10 32 72, Dundas 15 90, Simkin 34
24.02	DM Prem	Fisher Athletic	217	3 - 2	O'Connor 19, Kiely 60, Dundas 90
27.02	DM Prem	MERTHYR TYDFIL	516	1 - 0	Simkin 35
03.03	DM Prem	Cambridge City	370	1 - 1	Simkin 68[p]
06.03	DM Prem	TAMWORTH	887	1 - 1	Barrett 85
10.03	DM Prem	WELLING UNITED	769	5 - 2	Lovatt 4, O'Connor 11, Eccleston 28, Shaw 45, Barrett 56
24.03	DM Prem	MOOR GREEN	690	0 - 2	
26.03	DM Prem	Newport County	520	0 - 1	
31.03	DM Prem	Havant & Waterlooville	425	0 - 2	
03.04	DM Prem	CAMBRIDGE CITY	445	1 - 1	Dundas 80
07.04	DM Prem	FISHER ATHLETIC	523	3 - 0	Dundas 59, Lovatt 67, Shaw 77
14.04	DM Prem	Tamworth	917	0 - 2	
16.04	DM Prem	BURTON ALBION	1674	0 - 2	
19.04	Staffs SC SF	PORT VALE	150	1 - 1	Eccleston 9 (3-4p)
21.04	DM Prem	Weymouth	807	2 - 0	Lovett 53, Shaw 70
24.04	DM Prem	Clevedon Town	222	1 - 2	Lovatt 3
28.04	DM Prem	SALISBURY CITY	658	4 - 2	Simkin 17, Shaw 39 70, O'Connor 79
05.05	DM Prem	Folkestone Invicta	364	3 - 0	Eccleston 47, Shaw 59[p], O'Connor 76

PLAYING SQUAD

GOALKEEPERS: Richard Williams (Nuneaton)

DEFENDERS: Leigh Everitt (Nuneaton), Steve Prindiville (Nuneaton), Darren Simkin (Blakenall), Craig Ludlam (Hucknall), Chris Brindley (Hednesford), Stuart Ryder (Nuneaton),

MIDFIELDERS: Scott Dundas (Leek), Daryl Wilkes (Kidsgrove), Steve Jones (Ashton Utd), Craig Lovatt (Leek), Darren Boughey (Macclesfield)

FORWARDS: Tony Eccleston (Hednesford), Joe OConnor (Kingstonian), Shaun Wray (Nuneaton), Paul Kiely (Leek)

TAMWORTH

CLUB OFFICIALS

Chairman: Bob Andrews
Vice-Chairman:
President: Len Gendle

Secretary: Rod A Hadley, 38 Godolphin, Riverside, Tamworth B79 7UF
Tel: 01827 66786 Fax: 01827 62236

Press Officer: Mark Maybury
Commercial Manager: Russell Moore

FOOTBALL MANAGEMENT TEAM

Manager: Gary Mills
Asst Man.:Darron Gee
Physio: Peter Denham

FACT FILE

Formed: 1933
Sponsors: Bloor Homes
Nickname: Lambs or Town
Colours: Red,red,white
Change colours: White,black,black
Midweek home matchday: Tuesday
Reserves' League: Central Conference

2000-01
Captain: Darren Crocutt
P.o.Y.: Darren Acton
Top scorer: Warren Haughton 25

Pages: 28 Price: £1.20
Editor: Brian & Theresa Whitehouse

Press: Tamworth Herald,Tamworth Times
Radio:Centre FM,Captal Gold/Radio WM
Club Website: www.thelambs.co.uk
Club's email address: rod@tamworthfc.co.uk

GROUND The Lamb Ground, Kettlebrook, Tamworth, Staffs B77 1AA
Tel: 01827 65798 FAX:0182762236

Directions: Follow the signs for Town Centre/Snowdome, then forKettlebrook. The entrance to the ground &car parks is in Kettlebrook Road, 50yards from the traffic island by the railway viaduct (B5000)
Capacity: 3,410 Cover: 1,191 Seats: 438 Floodlights: Yes

Clubhouse: Club on ground - open matchdays, training nights and tote night only

Clubshop: Yes

PREVIOUS **Leagues:** Birmingham Combination 33-54, West Midlands (initially Birmingham Lg) 54-72 84-88, Southern 72-79 83-84, Northern Premier 79-83
Grounds: Jolly Sailor Ground 33-34

CLUB RECORDS **Attendance:** 4,920 v Atherstone Tn, Birm Comb 48
Win: 14-4 v Holbrook Institute (H), Bass Vase 34
Defeat: 0-11 v Solihull (A), Birmingham Comb. 40
Transfer Fee paid: £5,000 for Steve Cartwright (Colchester Utd, 88)
Transfer Fee received: £7,500 for Martin Myers (Telford Utd, 90)
Career Goalscorer: Graham Jessop 195
Season Goalscorer: Percy Vials 64 (36-37)
Career Appearances: Dave Seedhouse 869

BEST SEASON **FA Cup:** 2nd Rd 69-70 (0-6 at Gillingham) **FA Trophy:** Quarter Final **FA Vase:** Winners 88-89

HONOURS FA Vase 88-89, West Mids Lg 63-64 65-66 71-72 87-88 (R-up(2) 67-69, Div 2 55-56, Lg Cup(5) 64-66 71-72 85-86 87-88 (R-up 70-71)), Birmingham Snr Cup 60-61 65-66 68-69 (R-up 36-37 63-64), Staffs Snr Cup 58-59 63-64 65-66 (R-up 55-56 66-67 70-71), Midland F'lit Cup R-up 71-72 72-73, Camkin Cup 71-72 (R-up 70-71)

Players progressing: P Hilton (WBA 49), A Godridge (Swansea 50), W Ealing (Doncaster), Higgins (Fulham), P Weir (Cardiff), S Fox (Wrexham), S Cartwright (Colchester 88), S Ryder (Walsall), D Williams (Brentford)

BackRow, left to right: Mark Hallam, Darron Gee (Assistant Manager), Gary Mills(Manager), Gavin Saxby, Darren Grocutt, David Foy, Tim Steele, Rob Warner, Darren Acton, Adam Chetwynd, Jon Howard, Michael Swan, Tom Stevenson, David Haywood and Ian McKenna. Front Row: Mark Turner, Richard Follitt, Paul Hatton, Paul Gozzard,Warren Haughton (now Woking F.C.), Nick Colley, Kirk Smith, Rob Murchell, Ryan McKenna, Adam Fletcher and Peter Denham (Physio)

Date	Comp.	Opponents	Att.	Score	Goalscorers
19.08	DM Prem	WORCESTER CITY	728	1 - 2	Hallam 28
21.08	DM Prem	Ilkeston Town	573	1 - 2	Hallam 62
26.08	DM Prem	Havant & Waterlooville	585	2 - 3	Hayes 20, Grocutt 74
28.08	DM Prem	BURTON ALBION	1245	2 - 3	Hatton 12, Haughton 88
02.09	DM Prem	Welling United	644	0 - 4	
05.09	DM Prem	KING'S LYNN	506	2 - 0	McKenzie 45, Hallam 90
09.09	DM Prem	CAMBRIDGE CITY	526	0 - 0	
16.09	DM Prem	Newport County	708	1 - 0	Haughton 83
19.09	DM Prem	ILKESTON TOWN	446	3 - 0	Hallam 51 56, Haughton 84
23.09	DM Prem	Clevedon Town	344	1 - 1	Haughton 9
30.09	FA Cup Q2	Stamford	362	1 - 1	Foy 33
03.10	FA Cup Q2 R	STAMFORD	447	1 - 1	Hallam 63 (3-2p)
08.10	DM Prem	FOLKESTONE INVICTA	487	1 - 0	Hallam 43
14.10	FA Cup Q3	BURTON ALBION	1456	1 - 1	Hallam 59
17.10	FA Cup Q3 R	Burton Albion	1579	1 - 3	Smith 63
21.10	DM Prem	Worcester City	1003	0 - 1	
24.10	DM Prem	Burton Albion	1102	1 - 3	Haughton 82
28.10	DM Prem	CRAWLEY TOWN	430	0 - 2	
04.11	FA Trophy 1	Colwyn Bay	321	3 - 3	Turner 1, Hallam 41 45
07.11	FA Trophy 1 R	COLWYN BAY	362	2 - 1	Naughton 41, Turner 83
11.11	DM Prem	Halesowen Town	504	0 - 1	
14.11	Lge Cup 1	BURTON ALBION	411	2 - 1	McKenzie 38, Haughton 89
18.11	DM Prem	WEYMOUTH	406	2 - 3	Haughton 16 65
21.11	DM Prem	King's Lynn	472	0 - 6	
25.11	DM Prem	WELLING UNITED	351	3 - 3	Haughton 18 28, Huckerby 50
28.11	Birm. SC 2	STOURBRIDGE	262	4 - 2	R Smith 40[og], Haughton 58 59 71
02.12	FA Trophy 2	BELPER TOWN	445	1 - 1	Hallam 76
05.12	FA Trophy 2 R	Belper Town	291	5 - 0	Haughton 35 81 86, Hallam 48, Foy 63
09.12	DM Prem	MARGATE	422	1 - 0	Haughton 42
16.12	DM Prem	Folkestone Invicta	379	0 - 1	
19.12	Staffs SC 2	PORT VALE	251	0 - 1	
23.12	DM Prem	Fisher Athletic	137	1 - 2	Haughton 32
26.12	DM Prem	MOOR GREEN	684	0 - 1	
06.01	DM Prem	HALESOWEN TOWN	602	3 - 2	Warner 22, Hallam 77, Foy 90
09.01	Lge Cup 2	WORCESTER CITY	302	0 - 0	(4-5p)
13.01	FA Trophy 3	BOSTON UNITED	846	0 - 3	
20.01	DM Prem	HAVANT & WATERLOOVILLE	540	2 - 2	Mills 49, Turner 72
23.01	Birm. SC 3	SOLIHULL BOROUGH	195	2 - 0	Hallam 31, Smith 71
27.01	DM Prem	Dorchester Town	578	1 - 1	Haughton 89
30.01	DM Prem	BATH CITY	424	3 - 1	Hallam 37, Mills 54, Steele 90
03.02	DM Prem	SALISBURY CITY	535	4 - 1	Hallam 20 70, Turner 29, Follett 62
10.02	DM Prem	Cambridge City	476	2 - 1	Hallam 87, Follett 90
17.02	DM Prem	FISHER ATHLETIC	577	2 - 0	Hallam 18 74
21.02	Birm. SC QF	WOLVERHAMPTON WANDERERS	575	2 - 2	Hallam 56 118 (4-1p)
24.02	DM Prem	Margate	861	0 - 1	
03.03	DM Prem	Salisbury City	517	3 - 1	Grocutt 44 57, Colley 59
06.03	DM Prem	Stafford Rangers	887	1 - 1	Haughton 48
10.03	DM Prem	MERTHYR TYDFIL	676	4 - 0	Mutchell 7, McKenna 70 90, Haughton 82
17.03	DM Prem	DORCHESTER TOWN	647	2 - 2	Hallam 45, Follett 54
24.03	DM Prem	Merthyr Tydfil	475	0 - 0	
31.03	DM Prem	Bath City	832	1 - 2	Haughton 68
07.04	DM Prem	NEWPORT COUNTY	612	1 - 0	Hallam 70
14.04	DM Prem	STAFFORD RANGERS	917	2 - 0	Follett 47, Foy 50
16.04	DM Prem	Moor Green	609	1 - 0	Haughton 89
21.04	DM Prem	Crawley Town	539	2 - 0	Follett 40, Haughton 75
28.04	DM Prem	CLEVEDON TOWN	613	0 - 2	
05.05	DM Prem	Weymouth	875	2 - 0	Turner 2, Grocutt 49
28.07	Birm. SC SF	WEST BROMWICH ALBION	598	2 - 0	Grocutt 65, Hallam 76
07.08	Birm. SC F	Moor Green	n.k	1 - 3	Wilson 63

PLAYING SQUAD

GOALKEEPERS: Darren Acton (Kidderminster)

DEFENDERS: Rob Mutchell (Kettering), Rob Warner (Hereford), David Haywood (Sutton Coldfield), David Foy (Stafford R), Rob Gould (Ilkeston), Darren Grocutt (Burton Alb), Paul Hatton (Hednesford)

MIDFIELDERS: Gary Mills (Boston Utd), David Norton (Forest Green R), Nick Colley (Telford), Mark Turner (King's Lynn), Richard Follett (RC Warwick), Paul Gozzard (Mile Oak)

FORWARDS: Mark Hallam (Forest Green R), Christy McKenzie (Stourbridge), Scott Rickards (Derby), Lee Wilson (Spalding), Darren Roberts (Barrow)

TIVERTON TOWN

CLUB OFFICIALS

President: **Dan McCauley**
Chairman: **Dave Wright**
Vice-Chairman: **Pete Buxton**

Secretary: **Ramsay Findlay**
35 Park Road, Tiverton, Devon EX16 6AY
Tel: 01884 256341

FOOTBALL MANAGEMENT TEAM

Manager: Martyn Rogers
Asst Manager: Martin Grimshaw
Physio: Alan Morgan

FACT FILE

Formed: 1920 Nickname: Tivvy
Colours: All Yellow
Change colours: All white
Midweek matches: Wednesday
Reserves' League: None

2000-01
Top Goalscorer: Phil Everett 24
Captain: Neil saunders
P.o.Y.: Steve Ovens

Pages: 56 Price: £1.50 (with colour)
Editor/ Press Officer: John Fournier
Tel: 01884 820062 & 07980 543634M

GROUND: Ladysmead, Bolham Road, Tiverton, Devon EX16 8SG Tel: 01884 252397
Website: www.tiverton-town-fc.co.uk

Directions: M5 Jct 27, west towards Tiverton on A361, continue to end of dual carriageway and turn left at r'about; ground entrance 300yds on right alongside BP petrol station

Capacity: 3,500 Seats: 300 Cover: 2,000 Floodlights: Yes

Clubhouse: Lunctimes, evenings. All day Sat during season. 3 bars. Food(burgers, chips etc)
Club Shop: Yes

HONOURS FA Vase 97-98 98-99; Western Lg 93-94 94-95 96-97 97-98 (R-up 92-93 95-96 98-99); Les Phillips Cup 92-93 94-95 95-96 96-97 97-98; Amateur Trophy 77-78 78-79, Div 1 R-up 88-89; Devon St Lukes Cup 90-91 91-92 92-93 94-95 96-97 (R-up 89-90); Devon & Exeter Lg 51-52 66-67 70-71 84-85; Devon Snr Cup 55-56 65-66; East Devon Snr Cup 35-36 37-38 52-53 55-56 60-61 62-63 66-67; North Devon Charity Cup 72-73 86-87. Devon St Luke's Bowl 99-00; Dr. Martens Western Div. R-up 2000-01

PREVIOUS **League:** Devon & Exeter; Western League **Ground:** The Elms, Blundell Road 1920-39

BEST SEASON **FA Vase:** Winners 97-98 98-99, R-up 92-93
FA Cup: 1st Rnd 90-91 91-92 94-95 97-98

RECORD **Attendance:** 3,000 v Leyton Orient, FA Cup First Round Proper 1994-95
Career Goalscorer: Phil Everett at start of 01-02 season has 339 (Kevin Smith 303 previous record holder)
Record Win: (DML) 7-1 v Cirenbcester 2001 **Record Defeat:** (DML) 1-3 v Hinckley United 2001

Players progressing: Jason Smith (Coventry City 93 & Swansea City 98), Mark Saunders (Plymouth Argyle 95), Kevin Nancekivell (00)

Back row: Martyn Grimshaw, Dave Leonard, Kevin Nancekivell, Antony Lynch, Stuart Smith, Nicky Marker, Paul Edwards, David Steele, Paul Tatterton, Phil Everett, Dave Toomey, Dai Morgan (physio). **Front row:** Luke Vinnicombe, Steve Winter, Richard Pears, Scott Rogers, Martyn Rogers (manager), Neil Saunders, Peter Conning, Paul Chenoweth, Steve Ovens

Date	Comp.	Opponents	Att.	Score	Goalscorers
19.08	DM West	SOLIHULL BOROUGH	738	2 - 2	Everett 45, Pears 63
22.08	DM West	Cinderford Town	206	3 - 1	Daly 46, Everett 54, Pears 73
26.08	DM West	Shepshed Dynamo	264	3 - 3	Leonard 30, Rogers 61, Marker 67[p]
28.08	DM West	WESTON-SUPER-MARE	701	1 - 1	Varley 37
02.09	FA Cup P	Bemerton Heath Harlequins	254	4 - 0	Rees 22, Everett 28, Marker 70[p], Ovens 72
09.09	DM West	Hinckley United	340	1 - 3	Rogers 40
16.09	FA Cup Q1	BRISTOL MANOR FARM	547	1 - 0	Varley 78
19.09	Friendly	TORQUAY UNITED	166	1 - 2	Pears
23.09	DM West	BEDWORTH UNITED	556	0 - 1	
26.09	DM West	Evesham United	169	2 - 1	Toomey 42, Ovens 63
30.09	FA Cup Q1	Bristol Manor Farm **(REMATCH)**	130	4 - 1	Everett 25, Richardson 28, Saunders 38, Marker 65
03.10	FA Cup Q2	SHORTWOOD UNITED	443	2 - 0	Everett 66, Ovens 70
08.10	DM West	REDDITCH UNITED	580	5 - 1	Knight 12[og], Daley 20, Toomey 35, Everett 73 76
14.10	FA Cup Q3	GLOUCESTER CITY	676	1 - 3	Everett 66
21.10	DM West	HINCKLEY UNITED	620	2 - 0	Toomey 51, Daly 74
24.10	DM West	Weston-super-Mare	369	2 - 1	Varley 27, Conning 36
04.11	FA Trophy 1	SITTINGBOURNE	656	3 - 0	Rogers 12, Varley 25, Marker 53
11.11	DM West	Bromsgrove Rovers	422	1 - 0	Marker 21
14.11	Lge Cup 1	Weston-super-Mare	204	3 - 1	Daly 17, Marker 22, Rogers 23
18.11	DM West	BLAKENALL	539	1 - 0	Toomey 19
25.11	DM West	Bilston Town	216	0 - 1	
02.12	FA Trophy 2	AYLESBURY UNITED	699	2 - 1	Everett 15, Speakman 44
09.12	DM West	Redditch United	238	1 - 2	Daly 90
16.12	DM West	ATHERSTONE UNITED	522	2 - 1	Everett 18, Toomey 19
23.12	DM West	Paget Rangers	145	1 - 0	Everett 49
26.12	DM West	MANGOTSFIELD UNITED	719	0 - 0	
06.01	DM West	RUGBY UNITED	672	6 - 0	Toomey 42 46 65, Everett 46 48, Nancekivell 72
10.01	Lge Cup 2	HAVANT & WATERLOOVILLE	371	4 - 0	Nancekivell 36 54, Vinnicombe 50, Ovens 71 F
13.01	FA Trophy 3	Hendon	346	2 - 1	Everett 36 52
20.01	DM West	ROCESTER	634	1 - 0	Nancekivell 84
27.01	DM West	Bedworth United	220	1 - 0	Winter 77
31.01	DM West	CINDERFORD TOWN	449	5 - 1	Everett 43, Ovens 73, Toomey 76[p] 84, Conning 86
03.02	FA Trophy 4	BOSTON UNITED	1436	2 - 1	Toomey 20 61
17.02	DM West	Rugby United	311	1 - 2	Toomey 45
20.02	Lge Cup 3	Bashley	176	2 - 2	Pears 42, Ovens 87 (4-5p)
24.02	FA Trophy 5	WORKSOP TOWN	1937	1 - 2	Everett 80
27.02	DM West	Cirencester Town	148	2 - 2	Ovens 14, Everett 84
03.03	DM West	SHEPSHED DYNAMO	542	6 - 2	Nancekivell 24 45, Rogers 27 32, Smith 55, Daly 60
13.03	DM West	Gloucester City	289	3 - 2	Daly 33, Ovens 46, Everett 67
17.03	DM West	BROMSGROVE ROVERS	568	5 - 0	Rogers 5, Ovens 23 89, Nanckivell 30, Winter 35
31.03	DM West	Atherstone United	268	1 - 2	Ovens 41
07.04	DM West	BILSTON TOWN	681	2 - 1	Smith 44, Daly 89
10.04	DM West	Rocester	82	5 - 0	Everett 7, Marker 18, Nancekivell 44, Chenoweth 65, Ovens 72
12.04	DM West	GRESLEY ROVERS	541	4 - 0	Winter 5, Marker 34[p], Ovens 59, Conning 90
14.04	DM West	GLOUCESTER CITY	828	2 - 0	Winter 69, Everett 78
16.04	DM West	Mangotsfield United	702	0 - 2	
18.04	DM West	EVESHAM UNITED	630	2 - 0	Ovens 29 81
21.04	DM West	Gresley Rovers	366	1 - 0	Ovens 29
22.04	DM West	Racing Club Warwick	125	0 - 0	
24.04	DM West	CIRENCESTER TOWN	561	7 - 1	Nancekivell 14, Chenoweth 17, Ovens 22 62 70, Marker 78[p] 83[p]
26.04	DM West	Solihull Borough	121	1 - 0	Marker 72
28.04	DM West	SUTTON COLDFIELD TOWN	832	1 - 0	Marker 56
29.04	DM West	PAGET RANGERS	1210	4 - 1	Ovens 6, Nancekivell 28, Marker 48, Pears 90
01.05	DM West	RACING CLUB WARWICK	852	7 - 2	Everett 13 41 61, Marker 37, Chenoweth 45, Toomey 49, Elvin 60[og
03.05	DM West	Sutton Coldfield Town	223	0 - 0	
05.05	DM West	Blakenall	495	3 - 0	Walker 19[og], Rogers 78, Nancekivell 84

PLAYING SQUAD

GOALKEEPERS: Paul Edwards (Bideford)

DEFENDERS: Neil Saunders (Bath), Paul Tatterton (Weston-S-M), Nicky Marker (Cheltenham), Stuart Smith (Chard), Russell Gee (Exeter), Luke Vinnicombe (Exeter)

MIDFIELDERS: Scott Rogers (Bristol C), Steve Daly (Saltash), Paul Chenoweth (Gloucester), Steve Winter (Basingstoke), Peter Conning (Bideford), Dave Leonard (Liskeard), Steve Ovens (Witney), Kevin Nancekivell (Plymouth)

FORWARDS: Antony Lynch (Taunton), Richard Pears (Clyst R), Phil Everitt (Dawlish), Dave Toomey (Cinderford)

WELLING UNITED

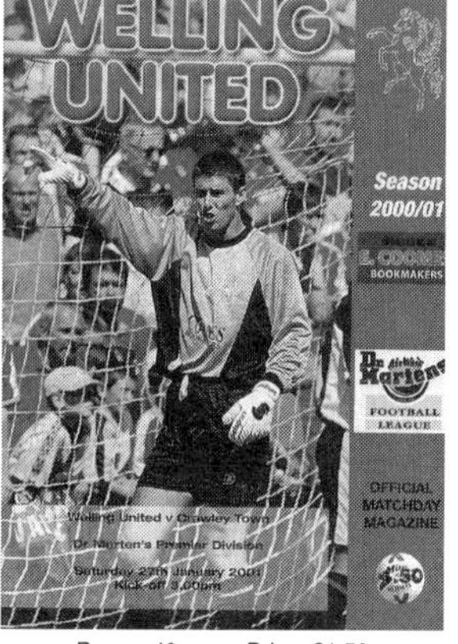

Pages: 40 Price: £1.50
Editor: Barrie Hobbins

Local Press: Kentish Times; Bexleyheath & Welling Mercury
Local Radio: Radio Kent; Radio Invicta; R.T.M.

CLUB OFFICIALS

President E Brackstone
Chairman Paul Websdale
Vice Chairman Steven Pain
General Manager Graham Hobbins
Club Secretary Barrie Hobbins c/o the club
Tel: 0181 301 1196 Fax: 0181 301 5676

Press Officer Paul Carter c/o the club

FOOTBALL MANAGEMENT TEAM

Manager: Tony Reynolds
Assistant Manager: Ray Burgess
Youth Manager: Glen Knight
Physio: Peter Green

FACT FILE

Founded: 1963
Nickname: The Wings
Club Sponsors: E.Coomes, Bookmakers

Club colours: Red/red/white
Change colours: All white
Midweek home matchday: Tuesday
Welling Wingsline: 0891 80 06 54

2000-01
Leading goalscorer: Charley Side 10
Player of the Year: Anthony Riviere
Captain: Mike Rutherford

GROUND Park View Road Ground, Welling, Kent DA16 1SY
Tel: 0181 301 1196 Fax: 0811 301 5676

DIRECTIONS: M25, then A2 towards London. Take Welling turn-off, ground 1 mile.
By rail to Welling station (BR) - ground 3/4 mile.

CAPACITY: 5,500 **SEATED:** 500 **COVERED TERRACING:** 1,500

CLUBHOUSE: Open on match days

CLUB SHOP: Sells programmes (League & non-League), scarves, mugs, caps, hats, badges, replica kits etc. Manager Peter Mason.

PREVIOUS **Leagues:** Eltham & Dist. Lge 1963-71, London Spartan Lge 1971-77, Athenian Lge 1977-79, Southern Lge 1979-86, 2001 Conference 86-2000 **Grounds:** Butterfly Lane, Eltham - 1963-78

RECORDS **Attendance:** 4,100 v Gillingham, FA Cup
Win: 7-1 v Dorking 1985-86 **Defeat:** 0-7 v Welwyn garden City 1972-73
Career Goalscorer: John Bartley - 533 **Career Appearances:** Nigel Ransom - 1,066 & Ray Burgess - 1,044
Transfer fee paid: £30,000 for Gary Abbott from Enfield
Transfer fee received: £95,000 from Birmingham City for Steve Finnan.1995

BEST SEASON **FA Cup:** Third Round 1988-89 0-1 v Blackburn Rovers League clubs defeated: Gillingham
FA Trophy: Quarter Final 1988-89 0-1 v Macclesfield

HONOURS London Spartan League 1978; Southern League Premier Division 1985/86; Kent Senior Cup 1985/86 98-99; London Senior Cup 1989/90; London Challenge Cup 1991/92, Runners-up 1993/94.

PLAYERS PROGRESSING: Paul Barron(Plymouth A), Andy Townsend (Southampton), Ian Thompson (AFC Bournemouth), John Bartley (Millwall), Dave Smith (Gillingham), Murray Jones (C. Palace), Kevin Shoemake (Peterborough), Tony Agana (Watford,), Duncan Horton (Barnet), Mark Hone (Southend), Steve Finnan & Steve Barnes (Birmingham City),Dean Standen (Luton Town)

L-R Back row: John Budden, Martin Buglione, Russell Edwards, Lew Watts, Danny Chapman, Chris Connelly, Glen Knight, Mark Hobne, John Farley, Anthony Riviere and Dean Canoville. **Front Row:** Zeke Rowe, Tony Dolby, Paul Whitmarsh, Ray Burgess, Tony Reynolds (Manager), Peter Green (Physio), Mike Rutherford, Michael Harvey, and Steve Taylor (Asst Manager).

Date	Comp.	Opponents	Att.	Score	Goalscorers
19.08	DM Prem	Clevedon Town	336	3 - 2	Rollo 28[og], Dolby 40, Cannonville 70
22.08	DM Prem	MARGATE	619	1 - 0	Canonville 70
26.08	DM Prem	DORCHESTER TOWN	253	1 - 1	Rowe 90
28.08	DM Prem	Folkestone Invicta	533	1 - 0	Dolby 37
02.09	DM Prem	TAMWORTH	644	4 - 0	Canonville 13, Dolby 22 49[p], Rutherford 47
05.09	DM Prem	Havant & Waterlooville	495	1 - 0	Glover 88
09.09	DM Prem	WEYMOUTH	735	2 - 0	Riviere 21, Dolby 27
16.09	DM Prem	Burton Albion	1461	1 - 1	Duke 50[og]
19.09	DM Prem	Margate	509	0 - 5	
23.09	DM Prem	ILKESTON TOWN	600	1 - 2	Whitmarsh 89
30.09	FA Cup Q2	Metropolitan Police	170	4 - 1	Edwards 3, Rutherford 39, Glover 42, Side 81
07.10	DM Prem	KING'S LYNN	330	1 - 4	Side 72
14.10	FA Cup Q3	TONBRIDGE ANGELS	716	1 - 0	Rowe 34
21.10	DM Prem	Crawley Town	1195	1 - 2	Budden 72
24.10	DM Prem	FOLKESTONE INVICTA	455	1 - 1	Budden 7
28.10	FA Cup Q4	Dorchester Town	759	1 - 1	Rowe 71
31.10	FA Cup Q4 R	DORCHESTER TOWN	459	2 - 4	Riviere 72 90
04.11	FA Trophy 1	UXBRIDGE	361	0 - 2	
11.11	DM Prem	Salisbury City	421	1 - 1	Rutherford 88
18.11	DM Prem	Newport County	582	1 - 1	Whitmarsh 90
25.11	DM Prem	Tamworth	351	3 - 3	Rowe 62, Riviere 78, Canoville 79
28.11	Kent SC 1	DEAL TOWN	106	4 - 0	Watts 48, Canoville 58, Whitmarsh 60, Glover 72
02.12	DM Prem	HALESOWEN TOWN	525	2 - 2	Rowe 70, Riviere 71
09.12	DM Prem	Merthyr Tydfil	404	1 - 0	Rowe 84
16.12	DM Prem	BATH CITY	500	1 - 0	Dolby 61[p]
19.12	Lge Cup 1	Langney Sports	204	0 - 3	
23.12	DM Prem	Dorchester Town	484	3 - 0	Canoville 62, Farley 81, Saunders 90
26.12	DM Prem	CAMBRIDGE CITY	551	0 - 2	
30.12	DM Prem	MOOR GREEN	514	0 - 0	
06.01	DM Prem	Weymouth	868	1 - 2	Riviere 85
13.01	DM Prem	STAFFORD RANGERS	503	0 - 0	
20.01	DM Prem	Ilkeston Town	560	1 - 0	Harland 57
27.01	DM Prem	CRAWLEY TOWN	777	1 - 1	Dolby 9
03.02	DM Prem	Halesowen Town	458	2 - 2	Bower 78, Riviere 87
10.02	DM Prem	WORCESTER CITY	591	0 - 1	
17.02	DM Prem	BURTON ALBION	732	1 - 2	Saunders 5
20.02	London SC 4	Thamesmead Town	80	0 - 0	(4-3p)
27.02	DM Prem	HAVANT & WATERLOOVILLE	302	2 - 1	Side 54, Rowe 82
03.03	DM Prem	Moor Green	312	1 - 1	Side 78
06.03	DM Prem	Fisher Athletic	297	1 - 1	Side 39
10.03	DM Prem	Stafford Rangers	769	2 - 5	Side 41, Bower 69
13.03	Kent SC QF	Gravesend & Northfleet	268	2 - 3	Rutherford, Saunders
17.03	DM Prem	CLEVEDON TOWN	440	2 - 3	Eeles 52, Budden 76[p]
24.03	DM Prem	King's Lynn	517	0 - 2	
31.03	DM Prem	SALISBURY CITY	747	2 - 1	
02.04	London SC QF	Croydon Athletic	n.k	2 - 2	Saunders 55, Restarick 57 Lost 0-3 after penalties
07.04	DM Prem	Worcester City	607	2 - 1	Side 22, Restarick 30
14.04	DM Prem	FISHER ATHLETIC	575	4 - 0	Glover 46, Canoville 71, Riviere 78 80
16.04	DM Prem	Cambridge City	354	1 - 4	Restarick 48
21.04	DM Prem	NEWPORT COUNTY	550	3 - 1	Rutherford 17, Side 45 66
28.04	DM Prem	Bath City	692	2 - 0	Restarick 44, Glover 50
05.05	DM Prem	MERTHYR TYDFIL	553	1 - 0	Side 53

PLAYING SQUAD

GOALKEEPERS: Glen Knight (Boreham Wood)

DEFENDERS: Russell Edwards (Dulwich Hamlet), Mark Hone (Kettering), Chris Currie (Gravesend), Wayne Brown (Boreham Wood), Lew Watts (Fisher Ath)

MIDFIELDERS: Mike Rutherford (QPR), Tony Riviere (Faversham), Sam Saunders (Youth), Scott Lindsey (Gravesend), David Powell (Crawley)

FORWARDS: Gary Abbott (Aldershot T), Peter Overton (Fisher Ath), Dean Canoville (Chesham Utd), Simon Glover (Ashford T)

WEYMOUTH

CLUB OFFICIALS

Chairman: **Peter Shaw**
Vice Chairmen:
Mike Archer & Dave Higson

Secretary: **Terry Northover**
2 Stoke Rd, Weymouth, Dorset DT4 9JF
Tel: 01305 771480

FOOTBALL MANAGEMENT TEAM

Manager: Andy Mason
Coach: David Laws
Physio: Bob Lucas

FACT FILE

Formed: 1890
Nickname: The Terras
Sponsors: Park Engineering
Colours: Claret & sky/claret & sky
Change colours: White with terra cotta trim
Midweek matchday: Tuesday
Reserves' League: Wessex Comb

2000-01

Captain: John Waldock
Top scorer: David Laws (21)
P.o.Y.: Mark Robinson

GROUND Wessex Stadium, Radipole Lane, Weymouth, Dorset DT4 9XJ Tel: 01305 785558

Directions: Arriving from Dorchester on A354, turn right following signs to Granby Industrial Estate at Safeway r'bout - ground on right as you enter estate
Capacity: 6,600 Cover: all sides Seats : 800 Floodlights : Yes
Clubhouse: Matchdays & functions. Hot & cold food available
Club Shop: Matchdays only. Progs & souvenirs.
During week contact Amanda (01305 815752)

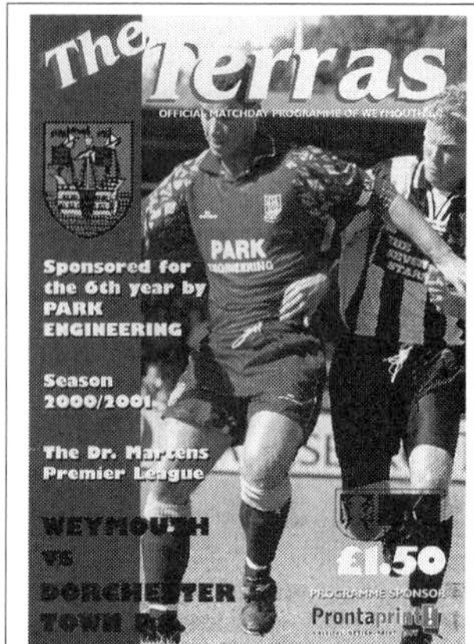

Pages: 36 Price: £1
Editor:James Murphy 01305 815656 Tel & Fax

Lcal Press: Dorset Evening Echo
Local Radio: Wessex FM

PREVIOUS **Leagues:** Dorset Lge, Western 1907-23 28-49, Southern 23-28 49-79, Alliance Premier 79-89
Ground: Recreation Ground (until 1987)

CLUB RECORDS **Attendance:** 4,995 v Manchester Utd, ground opening, 21/10/87
Career Goalscorer: W Farmer, Haynes. 275 **Career Appearances:** Tony Hobson 1,076
Transfer fee paid: £15,000 for Shaun Teale (Northwich) **Transfer fee received:** £100,000 for Peter Guthrie (Spurs, 1988)

BEST SEASON **FA Cup:** Fourth Round 61-62, 0-2 v Preston N.E. (A). 1st rd on 29 occasions
League clubs defeated: Merthyr Town 24-25, Aldershot 49-50, Shrewsbury T. 56-57,Newport County 61-62, Cardiff C. 82-83
FA Amateur Cup: First Round 1900 **FA Trophy:** Fifth Round 2000-2001

HONOURS All Prem Lg R-up 79-80 (Lg Cup 81-82); Prem Inter Lg Cup R-up 87-88 (QF 90-91);Sth Lg 64-65 65-66 (R-up 54-55 77-78), Lg Cup 72-73 (R-up 5), Sthn Div R-up 91-92; Wstn Lg 22-23, Div 2 33-34 36-37, (R-up 35-36 47-48); Dorset Sen. Cup (27);Mark Frowde Cup (13)

Players progressing: A Smith (Accrington 61), G Bond/T Spratt/A Donnelly/M Cave(Torquay 61/65/67/68), P Leggett (Swindon 62), R Fogg (Aldershot 63), B Hutchinson (Lincoln 65), A Wool (Reading 71), A Beer (Exeter 74), B Iles(Chelsea 78), G Roberts (Spurs 80), T Gulliver/R Hill/N Townsend/P Morrell/JSmeulders (Bournemouth 66/67/79/83/84), T Agana (Watford), A Townsend/D Hughes(Southampton), S Claridge (C Palace), B McGorry/S Teale (Bournemouth), T Pounder/R Evans (Bristol Rvrs), R Pethick (Portsmouth 93)

Back Row: Peter Dennis (kit manager), Mathew Hare, Mark Gammon, Ryan Cross, Danny Potter, Ian Hutchinson, Simon Browne, Darran Rowbotham, David Laws, Bob Lucas (physio). **Front:** Andy Mason (player manager), Matthew Hale, Michael Dean, John Waldock (captain), Martin Underhay, Michael Cameron, Anthony Tilley, Richie Carter (coach).

Date	Comp.	Opponents	Att.	Score	Goalscorers
25.07	Testimonial	Portland United	n.k	2 - 0	Hale 25, Waldock 87 for Darren Whyton
19.08	DM Prem	King's Lynn	846	1 - 2	Laws 89
22.08	DM Prem	MERTHYR TYDFIL	823	1 - 1	Rowbotham 66
26.08	DM Prem	NEWPORT COUNTY	960	0 - 0	
28.08	DM Prem	Salisbury City	617	2 - 3	Underhay 35, Rowbotham 47
02.09	DM Prem	HALESOWEN TOWN	730	4 - 1	Hutchinson 32, Rowbotham 50, Hale 77 85
05.09	DM Prem	Fisher Athletic	98	2 - 1	Rowbotham 7, Underhay 80
09.09	DM Prem	Welling United	735	0 - 2	
16.09	DM Prem	FOLKESTONE INVICTA	850	1 - 1	Laws 36
19.09	DM Prem	Merthyr Tydfil	551	1 - 0	Laws 14
23.09	DM Prem	CAMBRIDGE CITY	734	1 - 1	Hutchinson 5
30.09	FA Cup Q2	DORCESTER TOWN	1830	0 - 1	
07.10	DM Prem	Margate	197	0 - 3	
21.10	DM Prem	ILKESTON TOWN	740	4 - 1	Hutchinson 44, Robinson 45, Rowbotham 54, Laws 84
28.10	DM Prem	Clevedon Town	345	1 - 2	Underhay 80
04.11	FA Trophy 1	SUTTON UNITED	734	2 - 1	Robinson 39, Hale 45
11.11	DM Prem	HAVANT & WATERLOOVILLE	708	1 - 2	Robinson 60
18.11	DM Prem	Tamworth	406	3 - 2	Robinson 73, Underhay 78 85
25.11	DM Prem	Worcester City	827	0 - 0	
28.11	Dorset SC 3	WEYMOUTH SPORTS	201	7 - 2	Laws 9 35 49, Robinson 14, Hale 63, Funnell 75, Underhay 89
02.12	FA Trophy 2	HITCHIN TOWN	681	2 - 0	Robinson 77, Laws 90
09.12	DM Prem	KING'S LYNN	673	4 - 1	Rowbotham 8 65, Laws 65, Underhay 90
16.12	DM Prem	Crawley Town	693	1 - 2	Rowbotham 45
23.12	DM Prem	Stafford Rangers	712	2 - 3	Rowbotham 31, Robinson 59
26.12	DM Prem	DORCHESTER TOWN	2005	4 - 1	Phillips 8, Rowbotham 41, Robinson 51, Laws 82
01.01	DM Prem	Bath City	1168	0 - 0	
02.01	Dorset SC QF	Wimborne Town	151	2 - 1	Browne 20[p], Underhay 60
06.01	DM Prem	WELLING UNITED	868	2 - 1	Hale 47, Rowbotham 68
13.01	FA Trophy 3	Dagenham & Redbridge	1784	1 - 0	Phillips 90
16.01	Lge Cup 1	Newport IOW	191	1 - 2	Rowbotham 12
20.01	DM Prem	BURTON ALBION	1005	1 - 1	Phillips 33
27.01	DM Prem	Ilkeston Town	463	6 - 1	Phillips 9 31 62, Robinson 75, Gammon 88, Laws 90
03.02	FA Trophy 4	ASHFORD TOWN	1144	3 - 1	Laws 21, D Rowbotham 81, Phillips 88
10.02	DM Prem	Havant & Waterlooville	493	1 - 5	
17.02	DM Prem	Folkestone Invicta	373	2 - 1	Hale 7, Laws 13
24.02	FA Trophy 5	SOUTHPORT	1839	1 - 2	Laws 17
01.03	DM Prem	CRAWLEY TOWN	533	1 - 0	D Rowbotham 82
07.03	Dorset SC SF	GILLINGHAM TOWN	220	5 - 1	Robinson 6 33, Cross 23, Laws 44 55 (at Bridport)
17.03	DM Prem	MOOR GREEN	702	5 - 1	Laws 9 25 78, Robinson 13, Browne 84
20.03	DM Prem	Halesowen Town	294	2 - 0	Robinson 42, Laws 85
24.03	DM Prem	Newport County	582	0 - 0	
27.03	DM Prem	FISHER ATHLETIC	627	3 - 0	Laws 55, Rowbotham 64 75
31.03	DM Prem	WORCESTER CITY	944	4 - 0	Laws 16, Robinson 61 80 85
03.04	DM Prem	SALISBURY CITY	770	3 - 1	Hale 12, Dean 22, Cross 86
07.04	DM Prem	Moor Green	244	1 - 1	Dean 19
10.04	DM Prem	MARGATE	1267	1 - 0	Browne 90
14.04	DM Prem	BATH CITY	1129	1 - 1	Rowbotham 84
16.04	DM Prem	Dorchester Town	2255	1 - 1	Browne 9[p]
18.04	Dorset SC F	DORCHESTER TOWN	618	1 - 2	Hare 50
21.04	DM Prem	STAFFORD RANGERS	807	0 - 2	
24.04	DM Prem	Burton Albion	1155	0 - 1	
28.04	DM Prem	Cambridge City	522	2 - 2	A Browne 55[p], D Rowbotham 65
01.05	DM Prem	CLEVEDON TOWN	551	0 - 1	
05.05	DM Prem	TAMWORTH	875	0 - 2	

PLAYING SQUAD

GOALKEEPERS: Danny Potter (Exeter)

DEFENDERS: John Waldock (Sunderland), Matthew Hale (Yeovil), Alex Browne (Youth), Simon Browne (Salisbury), Ryan Cross (Dorchester), David Newland (Portland Utd)

MIDFIELDERS: Jason Rowbotham (Exeter), Ian Hutchinson (Halifax), Andy Mason (Thame Utd), Michael Dean (Bournemouth), Mark Rawlinson (Bournemouth)

FORWARDS: Leigh Phillips (Plymouth), Darren Rowbotham (Exeter), Mark Robinson (Gravesend), David Laws (Bishop Auckland), Martin Underhay (Wimborne)

WORCESTER CITY

CLUB OFFICIALS

Chairman: **Dr Michael Sorensen**
Vice Chairman: **Laurie Brown**

Secretary: **Steve Bond**
4 Ferry Close, Worcester, Worcs WR2 5PQ
Tel: 01905 423120/23003

FOOTBALL MANAGEMENT TEAM

Manager: John Barton
Assistant Manager: Mick Tuohy
Physio: Archie Richards

FACT FILE

Formed: 1902
Nickname: The City
Sponsors: Petrochem
Newsline: 0930 555 810
Colours: Blue/white/blue
Change colours: White/blue/white
Midweek matchday: Monday
Reserve Lge: Central Conference
2000-2001
Captain: Carl Heeley
P.o.Y: Carl Heeley
Top Scorer: Mark Owen (31)

Pages: 32 Price: £1.50
Editor: Julian Pugh (01905 723234)
Local Press: Berrows Journal, Worcester Evening News
Local Radio: Radio Wyvern, BBC Hereford & Worcester

GROUND St George's Lane, Barbourne, Worcester WR1 1QT Tel: 01905 23003 Fax: 26668

Directions: M5 jct 6 (Worcester North), follow signs to Worcester, right at first lights, St Georges Lane is 3rd left. 1 mile from Foregate Street (BR)station

Capacity: 4,004 Cover: 2,000 Seats: 1,125 Floodlights: Yes

Clubhouse: Open every evening and Saturday and Sunday daytime. Cold snacks available

Two shops: Outside ground (souvenirs). Inside ground (programmes) Contact club for details.

PREVIOUS
Leagues: West Mids (Birmingham) 1902-38, Southern 38-79, Alliance Premier 79-85
Names: Berwick Rangers **Grounds:** Severn Terrace, Thorneloe, Flagge Meadow

CLUB RECORDS
Attendance: 17,042 v Sheff Utd (lost 0-2), FA Cup 4th Rd 24/1/59
Win: 18-1 v Bilston, Birmingham League 21/11/31 **Defeat:** 0-10 v Wellington, Birmingham League 29/8/20
Career Goalscorer: John Inglis 189 (1970-77) **Career Appearances:** Bobby McEwan 596 (1959-75)
Transfer fee paid: £8,500 for Jim Williams (Telford United, 1981)
Transfer fee received: £27,000 for John Barton (Everton, 1979)

BEST SEASON
FA Cup: 4th Rd 58-59. 1st Rd (12)
FA Trophy: QF 69-70 73-74 80-81 81-82 **Welsh Cup:** Semi-Final 78-79

HONOURS
Southern Lg 78-79, Div 1 67-68, Div 1 Nth 76-77, Lg Cup R-up 45-46 59-60, Chal.Cup 39-40, Champs Cup 78-79; West Mids (B'ham) Lg(4) 13-14 24-25 28-30 (R-up (3) 31-34); Worcs Snr Cup (26) 07-14 28-30 32-33 45-46(jt) 48-49 55-59 60-61 62-63 64-65 69-70 77-78 79-80 81-82 83-84 87-88 96-97; B'ham Snr Cup 75-76; Staffs Snr Cup 76-77; Inter Lg Champs Cup 78-79

Players progressing: A Awford (Portsmouth 91), P King/K Ball (Cardiff C.60/65), JWilliams/M Gayle (Walsall 79/91), J Fairbrother (Peterborough 65), DTennant (Lincoln 66), R Davies (Derby 71), N Merrick (Bournemouth 74), J Barton(Everton 79), A Preece (Wrexham 90), D Lyttle (Swansea 92) M.Griffiths (Torquay United 99)

Date	Comp.	Opponents	Att.	Score	Goalscorers
19.08	DM Prem	Tamworth	728	2 - 1	Lutz 14, Cottrill 17
21.08	DM Prem	BATH CITY	1361	0 - 0	
26.08	DM Prem	STAFFORD RANGERS	1142	2 - 4	Heeley 80, Joyce 86
28.08	DM Prem	Merthyr Tydfil	667	1 - 4	Weir 39
02.09	DM Prem	Ilkeston Town	445	4 - 2	Lutz 24, Owen 25 61, Tranter 64
04.09	DM Prem	CLEVEDON TOWN	1033	3 - 3	Owen 4 90, Tranter 9
09.09	DM Prem	MOOR GREEN	1003	1 - 0	Wyatt 88
16.09	DM Prem	Cambridge City	457	3 - 2	Tranter 26, Cottrill 50, Owen 72
19.09	DM Prem	Bath City	546	2 - 3	Owen 8, Tranter 54
23.09	DM Prem	SALISBURY CITY	1005	0 - 1	
30.09	FA Cup Q2	CIRENCESTER TOWN	689	2 - 1	Heeley 60, Dukes 89
08.10	DM Prem	Dorchester Town	702	1 - 0	Owen 38
14.10	FA Cup Q3	THATCHAM TOWN	805	3 - 1	Cotterill 10, Lutz 20, Owen 79
21.10	DM Prem	TAMWORTH	1003	1 - 0	Owen 41
23.10	DM Prem	MERTHYR TYDFIL	1135	1 - 1	Wyatt 25
28.10	FA Cup Q4	Hampton & Richmond Borough	619	0 - 5	
30.10	Worcs SC QF	HALESOWEN TOWN	350	4 - 1	Owen 14 60, Cotter 67, Jefferson 81
04.11	FA Trophy 1	MANGOTSFIELD UNITED	623	3 - 0	Owen 38 57[p] 62
13.11	Lge Cup 1	BLAKENALL	343	4 - 0	Owen 26 40, Jefferson 54, Cottrill 62
18.11	DM Prem	Stafford Rangers	697	2 - 1	Owen 8, Reed 80
20.11	Worc Inf 1	WESTFIELDS	165	5 - 0	Tranter 6 9 17 67, Scheppell 69
25.11	DM Prem	WEYMOUTH	827	0 - 0	
09.12	DM Prem	Burton Albion	1284	0 - 1	
11.12	FA Trophy 2	Hendon	122	1 - 1	Owen 36 St Albans City
16.12	DM Prem	ILKESTON TOWN	782	1 - 0	Lutz 81
18.12	FA Trophy 2 R	HENDON	610	2 - 3	Carty 2 90
23.12	DM Prem	KING'S LYNN	785	1 - 1	Owen 25
26.12	DM Prem	Halesowen Town	743	3 - 1	Wyatt 3, Owen 15[p], Tranter 80
01.01	DM Prem	NEWPORT COUNTY	1375	4 - 4	Wyatt 4, Owen 10 65, Reed 59
06.01	DM Prem	MARGATE	1207	0 - 1	
09.01	Lge Cup 2	Tamworth	302	0 - 0	(5-4p)
13.01	DM Prem	Moor Green	520	0 - 1	
16.01	DM Prem	Salisbury City	255	0 - 2	
20.01	DM Prem	FOLKESTONE INVICTA	772	2 - 0	Cotter 64, Lutz 80
27.01	DM Prem	Fisher Athletic	104	0 - 1	
29.01	DM Prem	DORCHESTER TOWN	639	1 - 2	Cotter 14
03.02	DM Prem	CRAWLEY TOWN	675	2 - 0	Heeley 35, Tranter 70
05.02	Lge Cup 3	ATHERSTONE UNITED	383	3 - 2	Heeley 18 25 43
10.02	DM Prem	Welling United	591	1 - 0	Burrow 84
17.02	DM Prem	King's Lynn	660	0 - 0	
27.02	DM Prem	Clevedon Town	247	1 - 0	Owen 47
03.03	DM Prem	BURTON ALBION	1727	1 - 1	Owen 31[p]
05.03	Lge Cup QF	BILSTON TOWN	503	3 - 2	Owen 18, Lutz 82, Heeley 83
10.03	DM Prem	Folkestone Invicta	384	2 - 1	Owen 45, Heeley 56
23.03	DM Prem	CAMBRIDGE CITY	765	2 - 0	Burrow 10, Owen 38
27.03	Worcs SC SF	Evesham United	281	2 - 2	Owen 9, Shepherd 78
29.03	DM Prem	HAVANT & WATERLOOVILLE	575	1 - 0	Ellis 57
31.03	DM Prem	Weymouth	944	0 - 4	
05.04	Worcs SC SF R	EVESHAM UNITED	356	1 - 2	Owen 46
07.04	DM Prem	WELLING UNITED	607	1 - 2	Hyde 87
10.04	Lge Cup SF	NEWPORT COUNTY	818	5 - 3	Shepherd 53 82, Joyce 97 104, Carty 104
13.04	DM Prem	Newport County	636	1 - 0	Owen 55
16.04	DM Prem	HALESOWEN TOWN	942	4 - 1	Ellis 23 82, Burrow 43, Wright 87[og]
19.04	Lge Cup F(1)	CRAWLEY TOWN	986	4 - 0	Wackett 4[og], Shepherd 49 89, Hyde 74
21.04	DM Prem	FISHER ATHLETIC	704	1 - 2	Owen 35
26.04	Lge Cup F(2)	Crawley Town	644	0 - 1	
28.04	DM Prem	Margate	1385	0 - 3	
03.05	DM Prem	Crawley Town	392	0 - 1	
05.05	DM Prem	Havant & Waterlooville	317	0 - 2	

PLAYING SQUAD

GOALKEEPERS: Danny McDonnell (Halesowen T)

DEFENDERS: Martin Weir (Kidderminster), Chris Greenman (Bromsgrove), Allan Davies (Burton Alb), Marc Burrow (Bromsgrove), Carl Heeley (Sutton Coldfield), Mark Gardiner (Hereford)

MIDFIELDERS: Andy Ellis (Woking), Jon Holloway (Bath), Ian Cottrill (Nuneaton), Paul Carty (Hednesford), Ian Reed (Nuneaton), Darren Middleton (Forest Green R), Nathan Jukes (Dorchester)

FORWARDS: Phil Stant (Brighton), Mark Owen (Willenhall), Mark Shepherd (Moor Green)

CLEVEDON TOWN — Match Facts 2000-01

Date	Comp.	Opponents	Att.	Score	Goalscorers
19.08	DM Prem	WELLING UNITED	336	2 - 3	Mehew 7, Wilson 42
22.08	DM Prem	SALISBURY CITY	272	3 - 1	Milsom 1, Rollo 30, Mehew 65
26.08	DM Prem	Moor Green	292	3 - 3	Haines 15, Mainwaring 56, Lester 82
28.08	DM Prem	Dorchester Town	500	0 - 1	
02.09	DM Prem	CRAWLEY TOWN	361	1 - 2	Haines 23
04.09	DM Prem	Worcester City	1033	3 - 3	Haines 2, Milsom 7 35[p]
09.09	DM Prem	King's Lynn	644	1 - 3	Lester 20
16.09	DM Prem	HALESOWEN TOWN	303	1 - 4	Haines 23
19.09	DM Prem	Salisbury City	357	1 - 4	Ford 20
23.09	DM Prem	TAMWORTH	344	1 - 1	Mainwaring 90[p]
30.09	FA Cup Q2	SALISBURY CITY	302	2 - 4	Mainwaring 14, Mehew 45
07.10	DM Prem	Stafford Rangers	645	1 - 4	Mehew 85
21.10	DM Prem	Folkestone Invicta	398	3 - 0	Badman 17, Mainwaring 77 90[p]
24.10	DM Prem	DORCHESTER TOWN	286	4 - 1	Mainwaring 4[p], Lester 39, Coupe 67, Zabek 90
28.10	DM Prem	WEYMOUTH	345	2 - 1	Waldock 32[og], Mainwaring 54
04.11	FA Trophy 1	Cirencester Town	120	1 - 0	Mainwaring 27
11.11	DM Prem	Burton Albion	1021	0 - 1	
14.11	Lge Cup 1	Gloucester City	141	1 - 2	Mainwaring 45
18.11	DM Prem	MOOR GREEN	295	1 - 2	Mainwaring 14
25.11	DM Prem	Halesowen Town	306	1 - 1	Mainwaring 57
28.11	Som. PC 2	KEYNSHAM TOWN	160	5 - 0	Peters 2, Mainwaring 4 26[p] 44, Zabek 8
02.12	FA Trophy 2	Margate	340	1 - 2	Mainwaring 88
09.12	DM Prem	Ilkeston Town	394	1 - 1	Mainwaring 85
16.12	DM Prem	HAVANT & WATERLOOVILLE	248	0 - 1	
23.12	DM Prem	Margate	525	0 - 2	
26.12	DM Prem	BATH CITY	682	0 - 1	
06.01	DM Prem	Fisher Athletic	120	1 - 1	Milsom 86
13.01	DM Prem	CAMBRIDGE CITY	275	3 - 0	Lester 38, Wilson 40, Badman 81
20.01	DM Prem	KING'S LYNN	271	1 - 0	Milsom 89
27.01	DM Prem	Newport County	688	2 - 5	Mainwaring 10, Thorne 42
10.02	DM Prem	BURTON ALBION	519	1 - 2	Hawey 60
17.02	DM Prem	NEWPORT COUNTY	534	2 - 3	Milsom 9, Lester 78
20.02	Som. PC QF	Bath City	281	2 - 0	Milsom 2, Rollo 27
24.02	DM Prem	Bath City	739	1 - 4	Milsom 90
27.02	DM Prem	WORCESTER CITY	247	0 - 1	
03.03	DM Prem	Crawley Town	536	0 - 1	
10.03	DM Prem	FISHER ATHLETIC	322	8 - 1	Mainwaring 24 45 60 64, Harvey 29 77, Peters 48, McLean 85[p]
17.03	DM Prem	Welling United	440	3 - 2	Peters 64, Edwards 67[og], McLean 90
31.03	DM Prem	Cambridge City	328	0 - 2	
03.04	DM Prem	Merthyr Tydfil	381	0 - 2	
07.04	DM Prem	FOLKESTONE INVICTA	428	0 - 1	
11.04	Som. PC SF	Bristol City	231	1 - 0	Haines 78
14.04	DM Prem	MERTHYR TYDFIL	341	2 - 2	Harvey 15, Haines 88
16.04	DM Prem	Havant & Waterlooville	328	0 - 1	
21.04	DM Prem	MARGATE	297	1 - 2	Ball 52
24.04	DM Prem	STAFFORD RANGERS	222	2 - 1	Thorne 61 75
28.04	DM Prem	Tamworth	613	2 - 0	Ball 47, Haines 88
01.05	DM Prem	Weymouth	551	1 - 0	Haines 56
05.05	DM Prem	ILKESTON TOWN	239	2 - 3	Thorne 12, Peters 24
08.05	Som. PC F	ODD DOWN	n.k	1 - 0	Lester 27 (at Bath City)

DORCHESTER TOWN Match Facts 2000-01

Date	Comp.	Opponents	Att.	Score	Goalscorers
19.08	DM Prem	FISHER ATHLETIC	537	2 - 2	O'Hagan 12, Murray 67
22.08	DM Prem	Crawley Town	752	0 - 1	
26.08	DM Prem	Welling United	253	1 - 1	Lonnen 61
28.08	DM Prem	CLEVEDON TOWN	500	1 - 0	Harris 82
02.09	DM Prem	Newport County	701	0 - 5	
05.09	DM Prem	BATH CITY	515	4 - 3	Harris 6 38, Oldbury 44, Keeler 81
09.09	DM Prem	ILKESTON TOWN	487	1 - 2	Pickard 43
16.09	DM Prem	Merthyr Tydfil	631	2 - 1	Lonnen 48, O'Hagan 82
19.09	DM Prem	CRAWLEY TOWN	531	2 - 2	Groves 58, Keeler 90
23.09	DM Prem	Burton Albion	1030	1 - 1	Harris 32
08.10	DM Prem	WORCESTER CITY	702	0 - 1	
14.10	FA Cup Q3	SALISBURY CITY	817	4 - 3	Harris 27, Lonnen 68 76, Pickard 77
21.10	DM Prem	Halesowen Town	417	1 - 1	Holmes 58
24.10	DM Prem	Clevedon Town	286	1 - 4	O'Hagan 60[p]
28.10	FA Cup Q4	WELLING UNITED	759	1 - 1	Harris 84
31.10	FA Cup Q4 R	Welling United	459	4 - 2	Sullivan 34, Pickard 54, Groves 99 101
04.11	FA Trophy 1	BOREHAM WOOD	329	2 - 1	O'Hagan 82 84
14.11	Lge Cup 1	BASHLEY	296	2 - 3	Pickard 15 49
18.11	FA Cup 1	Wigan Athletic	3883	1 - 3	Pickard 6
25.11	DM Prem	NEWPORT COUNTY	701	0 - 3	
02.12	FA Trophy 2	Harrow Borough	256	0 - 3	
09.12	Dorset SC 3	Bournemouth Sports	112	4 - 0	O'Hagan 9 26, Pickard 52, Groves 69
16.12	DM Prem	STAFFORD RANGERS	547	0 - 2	
23.12	DM Prem	WELLING UNITED	484	0 - 3	
26.12	DM Prem	Weymouth	2005	1 - 4	Cannie 19
01.01	DM Prem	HAVANT & WATERLOOVILLE	523	0 - 1	
03.01	Dorset SC QF	HAMWORTHY RECREATION	156	7 - 1	O'Hagan 1 32 72, Sullivan 2 87, Groves 78 81
13.01	DM Prem	SALISBURY CITY	544	2 - 1	Sullivan 47[p] 72[p]
27.01	DM Prem	TAMWORTH	578	1 - 1	O'Hagan 16
29.01	DM Prem	Worcester City	639	2 - 1	Pickard 16, Lonnen 65
03.02	DM Prem	Stafford Rangers	549	0 - 1	
10.02	DM Prem	FOLKESTONE INVICTA	482	1 - 0	Pickard 1
17.02	DM Prem	MERTHYR TYDFIL	502	4 - 0	Groves 49 76, Sullivan 79, Sargeant 86
24.02	DM Prem	Havant & Waterlooville	475	1 - 2	Groves 25
27.02	DM Prem	Fisher Athletic	98	0 - 1	
04.03	DM Prem	KING'S LYNN	486	0 - 1	
07.03	Dorset SC SF	BADGER SPORTS	227	5 - 0	Harris 3, Holmes 21, Groves 44 51 86
10.03	DM Prem	MARGATE	623	0 - 1	
17.03	DM Prem	Tamworth	647	2 - 2	Sargent 26, Murray 83
20.03	DM Prem	Folkestone Invicta	316	0 - 2	
24.03	DM Prem	HALESOWEN TOWN	426	1 - 2	Groves 76
27.03	DM Prem	Bath City	519	0 - 3	
31.03	DM Prem	Ilkeston Town	365	0 - 1	
03.04	DM Prem	MOOR GREEN	348	0 - 3	
07.04	DM Prem	CAMBRIDGE CITY	402	1 - 0	Murray 28
14.04	DM Prem	Salisbury City	556	2 - 0	Holmes 17, Keeler 90
16.04	DM Prem	WEYMOUTH	2255	1 - 1	Lonon 57
18.04	Dorset SC F	Weymouth	618	2 - 1	Ferrett 7, Groves 110
21.04	DM Prem	King's Lynn	567	0 - 2	
24.04	DM Prem	Margate	1006	2 - 3	Morris 58, Lonnon 87
28.04	DM Prem	BURTON ALBION	605	1 - 3	Groves 48
30.04	DM Prem	Cambridge City	412	1 - 0	Pickard 34
05.05	DM Prem	Moor Green	268	1 - 3	

FISHER ATHLETIC Match Facts 2000-01

Date	Comp.	Opponents	Att.	Score	Goalscorers
19.08	DM Prem	Dorchester Town	537	2 - 2	Robinson 8, Adams 77
22.08	DM Prem	Havant & Waterlooville	355	2 - 3	Hume 68, Huggins 83
26.08	DM Prem	Burton Albion	875	0 - 3	
28.08	DM Prem	Margate	366	0 - 5	
02.09	DM Prem	SALISBURY CITY	143	1 - 2	Huggins 18
05.09	DM Prem	WEYMOUTH	98	1 - 2	Best 79
09.09	DM Prem	Bath City	689	3 - 4	Overton 38, Best 65, Manning 72
16.09	DM Prem	KING'S LYNN	142	2 - 3	Huggins 12, Barr 25
23.09	DM Prem	Halesowen Town	413	2 - 0	Huggins 30 65
30.09	FA Cup Q2	NEWPORT IOW	121	4 - 2	Newson 2, Huggins 17 39, Bah 42[p]
08.10	DM Prem	CRAWLEY TOWN	396	3 - 2	Huggins 7, Barr 72, Powell 81
14.10	FA Cup Q3	ALDERSHOT TOWN	514	1 - 2	Barr 90[p]
21.10	DM Prem	Moor Green	304	1 - 3	Overton 7
24.10	DM Prem	MARGATE	131	1 - 0	Tydman 46
04.11	FA Trophy 1	BURNHAM	101	3 - 2	Barr 15, Overton 24 83
11.11	DM Prem	Merthyr Tydfil	506	2 - 2	Huggins 47, Barr 58
14.11	Lge Cup 1	BURNHAM	57	0 - 2	
18.11	DM Prem	CAMBRIDGE CITY	135	1 - 2	Overton 71
27.11	Kent SC 1	Dartford	95	2 - 6	Barr 41 78
16.12	DM Prem	Salisbury City	370	0 - 3	
19.12	FA Trophy 2	CRAWLEY TOWN	159	2 - 3	Barr 2 7
23.12	DM Prem	TAMWORTH	137	2 - 1	Huggins 16, Powell 48
26.12	DM Prem	Folkestone Invicta	336	1 - 2	Huggins 40
06.01	DM Prem	CLEVEDON TOWN	120	1 - 1	Barr 32
09.01	DM Prem	BURTON ALBION	186	0 - 4	
16.01	London SC 4	THAMES POLY	67	1 - 2	Tydeman 37
27.01	DM Prem	WORCESTER CITY	104	1 - 0	Powell 55
31.01	DM Prem	Newport County	605	4 - 0	Tydeman 18 69, Barr 48[p] 79
03.02	DM Prem	Cambridge City	470	3 - 0	Powell 40 87, Barr 89
10.02	DM Prem	ILKESTON TOWN	209	1 - 1	Barr 68[p]
17.02	DM Prem	Tamworth	577	0 - 2	
24.02	DM Prem	STAFFORD RANGERS	217	2 - 3	Barr 25[p], Powell 56
27.02	DM Prem	DORCHESTER TOWN	98	1 - 0	Harris 41
03.03	DM Prem	MERTHYR TYDFIL	136	0 - 2	
06.03	DM Prem	WELLING UNITED	297	1 - 1	Tyne 41
10.03	DM Prem	Clevedon Town	322	1 - 8	Tyne 28
17.03	DM Prem	Ilkeston Town	380	0 - 1	
20.03	DM Prem	Crawley Town	327	3 - 4	Tyne 8, Barr 59 71
27.03	DM Prem	Weymouth	627	0 - 3	
31.03	DM Prem	MOOR GREEN	150	3 - 0	Tyne 22, Grant 56, Tydeman 68
07.04	DM Prem	Stafford Rangers	523	0 - 3	
10.04	DM Prem	BATH CITY	148	1 - 0	Manning 34
14.04	DM Prem	Welling United	575	0 - 4	
16.04	DM Prem	FOLKESTONE INVICTA	207	1 - 2	Edwards 9
18.04	DM Prem	HAVANT & WATERLOOVILLE	108	0 - 3	
21.04	DM Prem	Worcester City	704	2 - 1	Tyne 16 69
24.04	DM Prem	NEWPORT COUNTY	117	1 - 3	O'Neill 34
28.04	DM Prem	HALESOWEN TOWN	129	0 - 0	
05.05	DM Prem	King's Lynn	888	1 - 0	Clarke 7[og]

HALESOWEN TOWN Match Facts 2000-01

Date	Comp.	Opponents	Att.	Score	Goalscorers
19.08	DM Prem	Salisbury City	490	1 - 2	Dodds 14
22.08	DM Prem	STAFFORD RANGERS	667	0 - 1	
26.08	DM Prem	MARGATE	363	0 - 0	
28.08	DM Prem	NEWPORT COUNTY	532	1 - 3	Wood 82
02.09	DM Prem	Weymouth	730	1 - 4	Payne 44
05.09	DM Prem	BURTON ALBION	669	1 - 2	Blount 90[og]
09.09	DM Prem	CRAWLEY TOWN	411	2 - 2	Hines 55[p], Collins 79
16.09	DM Prem	Clevedon Town	303	4 - 1	Hines 9[p] 54[p], Mason 10, Darroch 44
19.09	DM Prem	Stafford Rangers	656	1 - 0	Lloyd 86
23.09	DM Prem	FISHER ATHLETIC	413	0 - 2	
30.09	FA Cup Q2	BURTON ALBION	668	0 - 2	
06.10	DM Prem	Ilkeston Town	507	0 - 1	
14.10	DM Prem	Newport County	554	2 - 0	Sutton 47 60
21.10	DM Prem	DORCHESTER TOWN	417	1 - 1	Lloyd 87
30.10	Worcs SC QF	Worcester City	350	1 - 4	Hines 23[p]
04.11	FA Trophy 1	BILSTON TOWN	323	1 - 3	Owen 40
07.11	Birm. SC 2	REDDITCH UNITED	160	0 - 1	
11.11	DM Prem	TAMWORTH	504	1 - 0	Collins 18
14.11	Lge Cup 1	Bromsgrove Rovers	233	2 - 0	Collins 44 45
18.11	DM Prem	FOLKESTONE INVICTA	340	4 - 4	Sutton 11 34, Payne 44 47
25.11	DM Prem	CLEVEDON TOWN	306	1 - 1	Collins 36
02.12	DM Prem	Welling United	525	2 - 2	Payne 64, Collins 86
16.12	DM Prem	MERTHYR TYDFIL	473	1 - 1	Bowen 68
19.12	Lge Cup 2	MOOR GREEN	234	0 - 1	
23.12	DM Prem	Cambridge City	485	0 - 3	
26.12	DM Prem	WORCESTER CITY	743	1 - 3	Bowen 87
06.01	DM Prem	Tamworth	602	2 - 3	Ford 61 65
13.01	DM Prem	ILKESTON TOWN	503	0 - 1	
27.01	DM Prem	Folkestone Invicta	384	1 - 2	Collins 17
03.02	DM Prem	WELLING UNITED	458	2 - 2	Lloyd 35, Piearce 84
10.02	DM Prem	Bath City	686	0 - 4	
13.02	DM Prem	Burton Albion	1006	0 - 1	
17.02	DM Prem	SALISBURY CITY	402	3 - 0	Bowen 35 61, Skidmore 54
20.02	DM Prem	Havant & Waterlooville	324	0 - 0	
24.02	DM Prem	King's Lynn	588	2 - 2	Sutton 16, Hines 75
03.03	DM Prem	Margate	689	0 - 1	
10.03	DM Prem	KING'S LYNN	409	0 - 4	
13.03	DM Prem	Moor Green	307	2 - 3	Ince 47, Collins 48
20.03	DM Prem	WEYMOUTH	294	0 - 2	
24.03	DM Prem	Dorchester Town	426	2 - 1	Sutton 77, Otto 84
31.03	DM Prem	Merthyr Tydfil	464	0 - 0	
10.04	DM Prem	Crawley Town	451	1 - 2	Crawford 56
14.04	DM Prem	MOOR GREEN	535	0 - 2	
16.04	DM Prem	Worcester City	942	1 - 4	Spencer 73
21.04	DM Prem	CAMBRIDGE CITY	316	3 - 0	Hines 46, Spencer 49 69
26.04	DM Prem	HAVANT & WATERLOOVILLE	261	2 - 2	Bailey 12, Otto 82
28.04	DM Prem	Fisher Athletic	129	0 - 0	
05.05	DM Prem	BATH CITY	471	2 - 0	Bailey 28 89

WESTERN DIVISION FINAL LEAGUE TABLE 2000-01

		P	W	D	L	F	A	W	D	L	F	A	Pts	GD
1	Hinckley United	42	15	5	1	55	18	15	3	3	47	20	98	64
2	Tiverton Town	42	17	3	1	65	14	11	4	6	32	22	91	61
3	Bilston Town	42	12	7	2	49	28	15	2	4	39	20	90	40
4	Evesham United	42	13	4	4	48	28	14	1	6	38	18	86	40
5	Mangotsfield United	42	12	5	4	49	22	13	4	4	42	23	84	46
6	Solihull Borough	42	11	5	5	34	21	11	7	3	39	22	78	30
7	Redditch United	42	10	6	5	46	35	7	7	7	30	34	64	7
8	Weston-super-Mare	42	7	7	7	29	24	10	3	8	39	34	61	10
9	Atherstone United	42	8	5	8	28	30	8	6	7	36	28	59	6
10	Rocester	42	8	2	11	25	45	10	3	8	32	32	59	-20
11	Cirencester Town	42	8	6	7	33	31	6	9	6	32	43	57	-9
12	Rugby United	42	8	5	8	28	28	5	5	11	32	43	49	-17
13	Gloucester City	42	5	7	9	38	41	7	4	10	38	45	47	-10
14	Blakenall (-3)	42	5	4	12	26	36	8	6	7	28	28	46	-10
15	Shepshed Dynamo	42	7	5	9	30	31	5	4	12	26	42	45	-17
16	Bedworth United	42	6	3	12	18	26	6	6	9	20	34	45	-22
17	Racing Club Warwick	42	6	4	11	23	32	7	2	12	23	45	45	-31
18	Gresley Rovers	42	7	3	11	28	33	4	5	12	18	32	41	-19
19	Cinderford Town	42	6	2	13	34	44	5	6	10	22	40	41	-28
20	Sutton Coldfield Town	42	4	7	10	21	25	3	7	11	24	41	34	-21
21	Paget Rangers	42	6	3	12	23	37	3	1	17	15	56	31	-55
22	Bromsgrove Rovers	42	4	3	14	19	42	3	6	12	28	50	30	-45

WESTERN DIVISION LEADING GOALSCORERS 2000-01

36	Scott Voice	Bilston Town	18	Lee McGlinchey	Shepshed Dynamo
25	Christopher Smith	Solihull Borough	18	Stephen Ovens	Tiverton Town
23	David Sadler	Hinckley United	17	Andrew Lucas	Hinckley United
22	Darren Edwards	Mangotsfield Utd	15	Ian Bennett	Redditch United
21	Jody Bevan	Weston super Mare	15	Jamie Lenton	Hinckley United
21	Simon Tucker	Gresley Rovers	15	Leon Mitchell	Sutton Coldfield Town
19	James Cox	Gloucester City	15	David Seal	Mangotsfield United
18	Karl Bayliss	Gloucester City			

WESTERN DIVISION RESULTS CHART 2000-01

		1	2	3	4	5	6	7	8	9	10	11	12	13	14	15	16	17	18	19	20	21	22
1	Atherstone	X	1-0	1-2	1-1	3-2	3-0	2-2	1-2	2-3	1-1	1-2	0-5	3-1	2-0	3-1	0-2	0-1	1-0	0-3	1-1	2-1	0-0
2	Bedworth U	0-0	X	0-2	2-2	4-0	1-3	1-2	0-2	1-2	2-0	0-3	0-1	2-0	1-3	1-2	0-0	1-0	1-0	0-2	1-0	0-1	0-1
3	Bilston T	2-1	4-1	X	2-0	5-5	2-1	1-1	1-0	3-0	3-1	0-2	2-4	2-0	5-2	0-0	3-3	1-1	2-2	3-3	4-0	1-0	3-1
4	Blakenall	0-2	0-0	2-3	X	3-1	3-0	1-0	0-1	3-3	0-1	1-2	1-2	4-1	0-1	1-1	3-2	0-3	1-2	1-2	2-2	0-3	0-4
5	Bromsgrove	0-2	1-2	0-2	3-3	X	1-0	1-1	1-3	0-1	1-1	0-1	1-3	2-1	1-3	0-4	2-1	1-3	1-3	0-3	3-0	0-1	0-4
6	Cinderford	2-5	3-3	0-3	1-2	0-1	X	5-1	0-1	2-3	1-0	2-3	0-2	2-2	0-2	2-0	0-4	4-0	2-1	1-3	1-3	1-3	5-2
7	Cirencester	1-1	0-3	2-0	1-0	3-1	0-2	X	1-2	4-2	0-0	1-2	2-2	0-1	2-1	3-3	1-0	4-0	1-3	1-3	3-3	2-2	1-0
8	Evesham U	1-1	2-2	0-1	2-1	3-3	3-1	1-1	X	3-2	2-1	0-1	4-0	4-2	5-1	2-3	4-1	3-2	1-0	3-2	2-1	1-2	2-0
9	Gloucester	3-4	2-2	1-3	1-3	2-2	2-2	5-0	1-3	X	2-2	0-2	0-4	4-1	0-1	0-0	0-1	2-1	4-2	2-2	3-3	2-3	2-0
10	Gresley R	1-1	1-2	3-5	0-3	1-0	4-0	2-2	1-3	1-3	X	0-1	0-1	2-0	1-0	1-1	1-2	2-1	3-1	0-2	3-2	0-1	1-2
11	Hinckley U	2-0	3-1	0-0	5-2	4-2	5-0	2-2	1-1	1-1	3-0	X	1-0	4-1	1-1	4-2	3-0	3-0	5-0	2-1	2-1	3-1	1-2
12	M'field Utd	1-3	2-0	2-1	3-0	1-3	2-2	1-1	1-2	2-1	2-1	2-2	X	8-0	0-0	2-0	7-0	1-1	3-0	0-3	4-0	2-0	3-2
13	Paget R	1-4	0-0	0-2	1-2	2-1	1-1	3-2	0-4	3-0	0-3	0-2	1-0	X	2-1	1-2	0-2	2-2	1-3	0-1	1-2	0-1	4-2
14	Warwick	3-1	4-0	0-2	0-2	1-0	0-2	2-3	2-1	1-5	2-2	1-3	1-3	1-2	X	3-1	0-2	0-1	1-0	0-0	0-0	0-0	1-2
15	Redditch U	1-5	3-1	2-3	1-2	1-1	1-1	2-2	1-0	2-1	3-4	2-1	2-2	2-1	7-0	X	2-2	2-0	2-0	2-2	4-2	2-1	2-4
16	Rocester	2-1	1-0	0-2	0-0	3-2	0-1	0-3	0-3	4-3	1-0	1-9	1-2	1-0	2-0	0-3	X	1-3	2-2	1-2	1-2	0-5	4-2
17	Rugby Utd	1-2	0-0	0-1	1-1	4-0	1-1	3-0	1-3	3-2	0-1	1-3	1-4	2-0	1-2	0-0	1-0	X	2-1	2-0	1-1	2-1	1-5
18	Shepshed	2-0	0-1	1-0	2-2	3-3	1-2	1-3	0-3	3-0	2-0	3-2	0-2	2-0	2-1	1-2	0-1	1-1	X	1-2	1-1	3-3	1-2
19	Solihull B	0-0	4-0	2-2	1-0	2-0	3-1	0-1	1-0	2-2	1-0	0-3	3-1	5-0	1-0	0-1	3-5	2-1	2-2	X	1-0	0-1	1-1
20	Sutton C T	1-0	3-0	1-2	0-1	0-1	0-0	2-2	1-3	1-2	1-0	2-2	1-2	0-1	1-2	3-1	1-2	1-1	1-1	0-0	X	0-0	1-2
21	Tiverton T	2-1	0-1	2-1	1-0	5-0	5-1	7-1	2-0	2-0	4-0	2-0	0-0	4-1	7-2	5-1	1-0	6-0	6-2	2-2	1-0	X	1-1
22	Weston s M	2-2	0-1	1-2	0-1	0-0	2-1	1-2	2-1	2-2	1-0	1-1	2-2	2-0	4-0	2-2	0-2	3-1	0-1	1-1	2-0	1-2	X

ATHERSTONE UNITED

CLUB OFFICIALS

Chairman: **Ku Akeredolu**

President: **T.B.A.**

Secretary: **Neil Dykes**
18 Greendale Close, Atherstone,
Warwickshire CV9 1PR Tel: 01827 7091223

Commercial Manager: **T Jago**

FOOTBALL MANAGEMENT TEAM

Manager: Stephen Mackenzie
Asst Manager: T.grealish
Physio: T.B.A.

FACT FILE

Formed: 1979
Nickname: The Adders
Club Sponsors: T.B.A.
Colours: Red & white stripes/red/red
Change colours: Yellow & blue/blue/blue
Midweek home matchday: Monday 7.30pm
Reserve's Lge: Midland Comb. Reserve Div.
Club Website: www.atherstoneunited.co.uk

2000-01

Captain: Danny Martin
P.o.Y.: Dale Belford
Top Goalscorer: 15

Pages: 28 Price: £1
Editor: Brian Stephenson 01827 735441

Local Press: Tamworth Herald, Evening News, Atherstone Herald, Coventry Telegraph.
Local Radio: Mercia Sound, CWR

GROUND Sheepy Road, Atherstone, Warwickshire. CV9 1HG
Tel: 01827 717829

Directions: Half mile north of town centre on B4116 Twycross/Ashby road.

Capacity: 3,500 Cover: 1,000 Seats: 373 Floodlights: Yes

Clubhouse: Open during normal licensing hours, all usual facilities.
Club Shop: Programmes, magazines, souvenirs etc. Contact: Sreve Clark 01827 712812

PREVIOUS **Leagues:** West Midlands 1979-87

CLUB RECORDS **Attendance:** 2,873 v V.S. Rugby, F.A. Cup 1st Round Proper 1987-88
Win: 12-2 vTipton Town (H), West Midlands (Regional) League Premier Division 86-87
Defeat: 1-7 v Rushden & Diamonds, Beazer League Premier Division 94-95
Goalscorer: Alan Bourton **Appearances:** Lee Spencer
Fee Paid: £4,500 toGloucester City for Gary Bradder, 1989
Fee Received: £40,000 for Andy Rammellfrom Manchester United, September 1989

HONOURS Southern Lge Midland Div 88-89; West Midlands Lge 81-82 86-87 (Lge Cup 81-82,Premier Div Cup 86-87, Div 2 Cup (Res.) 86-87); Walsall Senior Cup 83-84; Midland Combination Reserve Division 87-88; Birmingham Senior Cup R-up 89-90

BEST SEASON **FA Cup:** 2nd Rd Proper 1990-91, 0-1 v Crewe Alexandra (A)
FA Trophy: 1st Round 88-89 91-92.

Players progressing: Andy Rammell (Manchester United)

BEDWORTH UNITED

CLUB OFFICIALS

Chairman: **Peter Randle**

Vice Chairman: **Wayne Harris**

Secretary: **Graham J Bloxham**
43 Mount Pleasant Road, Bedworth,
Warwicks CV12 8EX
Mobile: 07748 640613

Press Officer: **Jamie Home**

FOOTBALL MANAGEMENT TEAM

Managers: Ian Drewitt

Assistant Manager:Marcus Law

Club Doctor: Philip Earl

Physio: John Roberts

FACT FILE

Formed: 1896 Nickname: Greenbacks

Sponsors:Bellway Homes

Colours: Green & white/Green/Green.

Change colours: Yellow & green

Midweek matchday: Tuesday

Res: Mid Comb .Youth Lg:MidFloodlit

Club website:www.bedworthunited.fwsi.com

2000-01

Captain: Ian Drewitt

Top Scorer: Adam Webster

P..o.Y.: Jamie Richardson

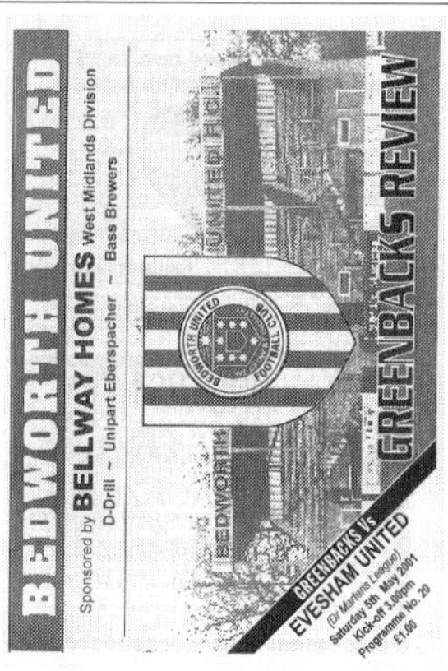

Pages: 18 Price: £1
Editor: Ron Kemp 02476 318014

Local Press: Heartland Evening News, Weekly Tribune, Bedworth Echo, Coventry Evening Telegraph
Local Radio: Mercia Sound, BBC CWR

GROUND The Oval, Miners Welfare Park, Coventry Road, Bedworth CV12 8NN
Tel: 02476 314302 **Email Address:** ronald@dkemp.3freeservice.co.uk
Directions: M6 jct 3, into Bedworth on B4113 Coventry to Bedworth road, ground200yds past past Bedworth Leisure Centre on this road. Coaches should park atthis Leisure Centre. Buses from Coventry and Nuneaton pass ground
Capacity: 7,000 Cover: 300 Seats: 300 Floodlights: Yes
Clubhouse: Social club open every day 7.30-11pm & w/e noon-3pm. Hot and cold bar food
Club Shop: Selling a wide range of souvenirs & programmes.
Contact : Ron Kemp 01203 318014

PREVIOUS **Leagues:** Birmingham Comb. 47-54; West Mids (at first Birmingham) Lg 54-72
Name: Bedworth Town 47-68 **Ground:** British Queen Ground 11-39

CLUB RECORDS **Attendance:** 5,127 v Nuneaton Borough, Southern Lg Midland Division 23/2/82
Win: 11-0 **Defeat:** 1-10
Career Goalscorer: Peter Spacey (1949-69) **Career Appearances:** Peter Spacey
Transfer fee paid: £1,750 for Colin Taylor (Hinckley Town, 1991-92)
Transfer fee received: £30,000 for Richard Landon (Plymouth Argyle, January 1994)

BEST SEASON **FA Trophy:** Second Round 80-81
FA Cup: 4th Qualifying Rd 1983/89/90

HONOURS Birmingham Comb.(2) 48-50, Birmingham Snr Cup(3) 78-79 80-82, Midland Floodlit Cup 81-82 92-93

Players progressing: Phil Huffer (Derby County 1953), Geoff Coleman(Northampton Town 1955), Ian Hathaway (Mansfield Town 1989), Richard Landon(Plymouth Argyle 1994)

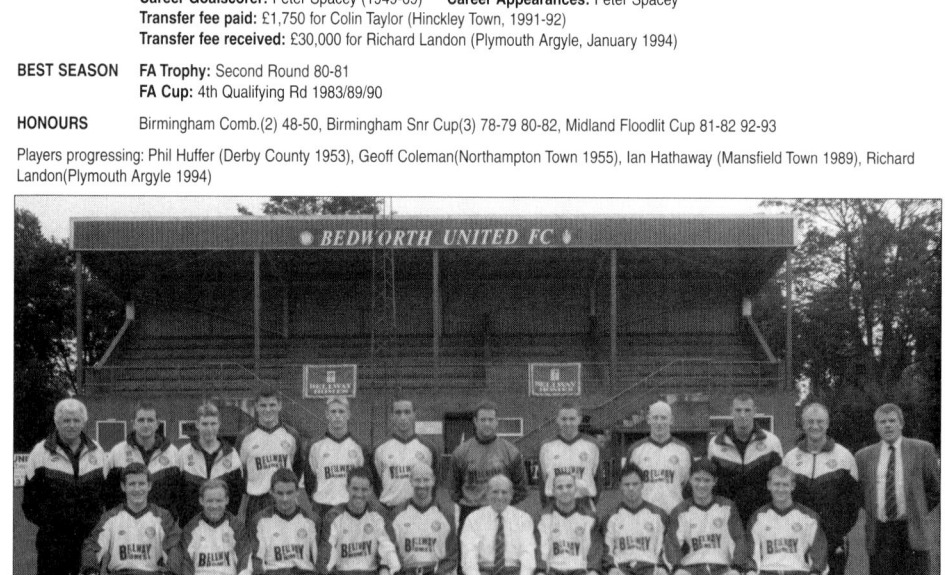

BILSTON TOWN

CLUB OFFICIALS

Chairman:Roger Williams
Vice-Chairman: **A K Hickman**
President: **Dennis Turner MP**
Press Officer: **A Owen**
Secretary:**Tony Turpin**,24 Andrew Drive,Short Heath, Willenhall, West Midlands WV12 5PP
Tel No: 01922 475541(H) 07951547870(M)

FOOTBALL MANAGEMENT TEAM

Manager: Joe Jackson
Asst Manager: Tom Stokes
Physio: Jon King

FACT FILE

Formed: 1895
Nickname: Steelmen or Boro
Sponsors: Stowlawn Ltd and Second City
Colours: Orange/white/white
Change colours: White/black/orange
Midweek matchday: Tuesday
Reserves' League: No reserve team
Youth Team:West Midland (Regional) League Youth Division

GROUND Queen Street, Bilston WV14 7EX Tel: 01902 491498
Directions: M6 junction 10, A454 towards Wolverhampton then pick up A563 towards Bilston and turn left into Beckett Street after a little over a mile,ground at bottom. 3 miles from Wolverhampton (BR), bus 45 from bus station passes ground. Buses 78 and 79 from Birmingham stop within quarter of a mile of ground
Capacity: 4,000 Cover: 350 Seats: 350 Floodlights: Yes
Clubhouse: Open evenings & weekend lunchtimes (normal pub hours). Usual club activities
Club Shop: Sells a range of souvenirs and programmes.
Contact Paul Calloway, 4 Mervyn Rd, Bradley, Bilston, West Mids WV14 8DF

PROGRAMME
Pages: 24 Price: 70p
Editor: Paul Calloway
Tel No: 01902 682476
Local Press:
Expess & Star, Evening Mail
Local Radio:
Radio West Mids, WABC, Beacon, BRMB

PREVIOUS **Leagues:** Birmingham Comb. 07-21 48-54, (Birmingham) West Mids 21-32 54-85
Names: Bilston Utd 1895-1932, Bilston **Ground:** Prouds Lane 1895-1921

CLUB RECORDS **Attendance:** 7,500 v Wolverhampton Wanderers, floodlight opening 1953
Competitive: 7,000 v Halifax Town, F.A. Cup First Round 1968
Win: 12-2 v Tipton Town **Defeat:** 0-8 v Merthyr Tydfil
Career Goalscorer: Ron McDermott 78 **Career Appearances:** Unknown
Transfer fee paid: Transfer fee received: From Southend United for Ron Poutney, 1975

BEST SEASON **FA Trophy:** 2nd Round 70-71, 74-75 **FA Vase:** Quarter Finals 92-93
FA Cup: 2nd Rd replay 72-73 (0-1 at Barnet after 1-1 draw). Also 1st Rd 68-69. League clubs defeated: None

HONOURS West Mids Lg 60-61 72-73 (R-up 22-23 70-71 73-74 74-75 75-76 84-85, Lg Cup 72-73 (R-up 65-66), Div 2 56-57), Birmingham Senior Cup 1895-96 Wednesbury Charity Cup 1981-81 81-82 82-83 84-85 (R-up 83-84)

Players progressing: R Ellows (Birmingham), James Fletcher (Birmingham 1950),Stan Crowther (A Villa 1955), Ron Pountney (Southend 1975), K Price(Gillingham), Campbell Chapman (Wolves 1984) Joe Jackson (Wolves), Mike Turner (Barnsley 1999)

L-R Back Row: Danny Watson, Neil Manton, Matthew Boswell, Gavin Stone, Kris Sage, Scott Voice, Lee Rollason, Mark Clifton, Brett Wilcox, Leon Jackson. Front Row: Nathan Rose-Laing, Jason Smith, Danny Williams, Stuart Leeding, Leon Woodley, David Read.

BLOXWICH UNITED

CLUB OFFICIALS
Chairman: Peter Langston
Vice Chairman: D Cotterill
President: M Ross
Vice President: N Smith

Secretary: David Birch, 64 Wimperis Way, Great Barr, Birmingham B43 7DF
Tel: 0121 360 3574

Press Officer: Russell Brown
40 Carrisbrooke Road, Bushbury, Wolverhampton WV10 8AB
Tel: 0121 237 4031 (W) 01902 681011 (H)
E-Mail: rwbbloxwichutd@blueyonder.co.uk

FACT FILE
Founded: 2001
Nickname: The Griffins
Sponsor: Motorland, Somerfield Rd, Bloxwich
Colours: Blue/White Halves, Blue, Blue
Change: Red & Black, Black, Red & Black
Midweek Matchday: Tuesday

2000-01
Captain: Steve Hillman
P.O.Y: Steve Hillman
Top Scorer: Jon Worsey (11)

FOOTBALL MANAGEMENT TEAM
Managers : Bob Green
Asst. Manager: Gary Webb
Coach: Alan Moore

Pages: 52 Price: 80p
Editor: Russell Brown (Press Officer)
Local Press: Express & Star, Walsall Chronicle, Walsall Advertiser, Walsall Observer, Sunday Mercury, Sports Argus, Sporting Star
Local Radio: BBC WM 95.6, Walsall FM, Beacon Radio 97.2, BRMB 96.4

GROUND The Red Lion Ground, Somerfield Rd, Bloxwich, Walsall, West Mids WS3 2EJ
Tel: 01922 405835 Fax: 01922 400600
Directions: M6 jct 10, follow signs for Walsall centre. At 1st lights turn left (about 200yds from Motorway junction) into Bloxwich Lane.At traffic island bear left. Continue thro' first set of lights to`T' junction. Turn right into Leamore Lane, at traffic island (Four Crosses pub) turn left into Somerfield Road. Ground approx. 400yds on right
Nearest Railway Station: Bloxwich (10 minutes walk from ground)
Capacity: 2,500 Seats: 250 Cover: 250 Floodlights: Yes
Clubhouse: Open 7-11 Mon-Sun, 1-11 Sat. Food available matchdays **Club Shop:** No

PREVIOUS **Leagues as Blakenall:** Bloxwich Comb.; Staffs County; Midland Comb. 60-79; W Midlands Reg Lge 79-95; Midland All 95-97
Leagues as Bloxwich Town: Bloxwich Comb., Midland Comb., Midland Football Alliance, Southern Midland, Midland Football Alliance.
Names: Amalgamation of Blakenall and Bloxwich in the Summer 2001

BLAKENAL
CLUB RECORDS **Attendance:** 1,550 v Halesowen Town 85-86 **Win:** 11-0 v Bilston United 26/4/95
Defeat: 0-7 v Macclesfield Town (Staffs Sen Cup) 31/1/95 **Fee Received**: £10,000 for Darren Simkin (Wolverhampton Wanderers, 1992)
BEST SEASON **FA Trophy:** 2nd Rd 98-99 **FA Vase:** 2nd Rd Proper 91-92
HONOURS Staffs. Sen. Cup 99-00; Midland Football Alliance 96-97, R-Up 95-96; Industrial Rewinds Lge Cup 95-96; Midlands Invit. Triangular Cup 94-95, R-Up 97-98; West Midlands Regional Premier Div. 88-89, R-Up 94-95, Prem. Div. Lge Cup 94/95; Walsall Senior Cup 63-64, 74-75, 75-76, 76-77, 80-81, 88-89, 95-96, 97-98, 98-99. Midland Comb. 76-77 **Players progressing:** Darren Simkin (Wolverhampton W.)

BLOXWICH TOWN
CLUB RECORDS: **Attendance:** 252 **Win:** 8-1 v Alvechurch **Defeat:** 0-9 v Shepshed Dynamo
BEST SEASON **FA Trophy:** 1st Q Round 98/99 **FA Vase:** 3rd Round Proper 97/98
HONOURS Midland Football Alliance 97-98, Industrial Rewinds Lge Cup R-Up 96-97, Walsall Sen. Cup 96-97; Carlsberg Challenge Cup 95-96, Midland Combination - Premier Div. 95-96, R-Up 94-95, Div. 1 89-90; Invitation Cup 89-90, Bloxwich Comb. (2), Staffs County Lge Div 1 Champions, Alan Peck Cup (x 3) **Players Progressing:** Martin O'Connor (C.Palace, Walsall, Birmingham)

CHIPPENHAM TOWN

CLUB OFFICIALS

President: Doug Webb
Chairman: Malcolm Lyus
Vice-Chairman: Les Weir
Treasurer: Richard Terrell
Press Officer: Chris Blake

Secretary: Chris Blake, 28 Sadlers Mead, Chippenham, Wilts SN15 3PB
Tel: 01249 658212

FOOTBALL MANAGEMENT TEAM

Manager: Tommy Saunders
Physio: Barnes Sports Clinic

FACT FILE

Formed: 1873
Nickname: The Bluebirds
Club Sponsors: D.L.Windows, Costcutters, Shoestrings, Crane Merchandising Systems,
Club colours: Blue & white/blue& white/blue
Change colours: All yellow
Midweek matches: Wednesday

2000-01
Captain: Lee Burns
P.o.Y.: Steve Tweddle
Leading Scorer: Steve Tweddle (49)

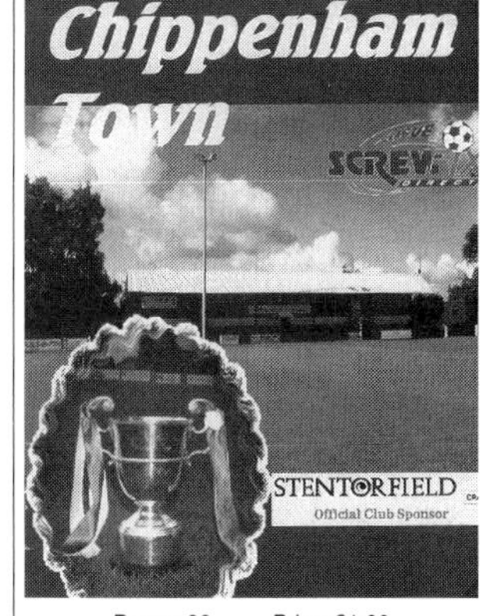

Pages: 32 Price: £1.00
Editors: Will Hulbert & Chris Blake

Local Press: Chippenham News, Wilts Gazette, Wiltshire Chronicle

GROUND Hardenhuish Park, Bristol Road, Chippenham
Tel: 01249 650400
Website: www.chippenhamtownfc.co.uk

Directions: M4 jct 17, A350 into Chippenham, follow signs for Trowbridge/Bath until r'about, left onto A420 into town, ground 800yds on left 15 mins walk from railway station on main A420 Bristol Road

Capacity: 4,000 Seats: 225 Cover: 300 Floodlights: Yes
Clubhouse: Yes, open matchdays. Food available **Club Shop:** Yes

PREVIOUS **Leagues:** Hellenic, Wiltshire Senior, Wiltshire Premier, Western League
Grounds: Westmead, Lowden, Little George Lane, Malmesbury Rd

RECORD **Gate:** 4,800 v Chippenham Utd, Western League 1951
Goalscorer: Dave Ferris**Appearances:** Ian Monnery

BEST SEASON **FA Cup:** 1st Rd 51-52 **FA Vase:** Finalists 99-00

HONOURS F.A. Vase R-up 99-00, Western Lg 51-52 R-up 00-01, Div 1 80-81, Div 2 52-53 (Res) 80-81
Wilts Shield, Wilts Senior Cup; Wilts Senior League; Les Phillips Cup (Western Lg Cup) 99-00 00-01

CINDERFORD TOWN

CLUB OFFICIALS

Chairman: **Ashley Saunders**
President: **S Watkins**
Vice Chairman: **Ray Reed**

Secretary: **Chris Warren**
9c Tusculum Way, Mitcheldean,
Glos GL17 0HZ
01594543065 (H) 01594 542421 x 2360 (B)

Press Officer: **Andy Little**

FOOTBALL MANAGEMENT TEAM

Manager: Tony Hopkins
Asst. Manager:T.B.A.
Physio: Keith Marfell

FACT FILE

Formed: 1922 Nickname: Town
Sponsors: T.B.A.
Colours: Black & white stripes/black/black
Change colours: All Red
Midweek matchday: Tuesday
Reserves' League: No reserve team
2000-01 Captain:Lyndon Tomkins
Top Scorer:Daryl Addis
P.o.Y.: Daryl Addis & Clayton Hook

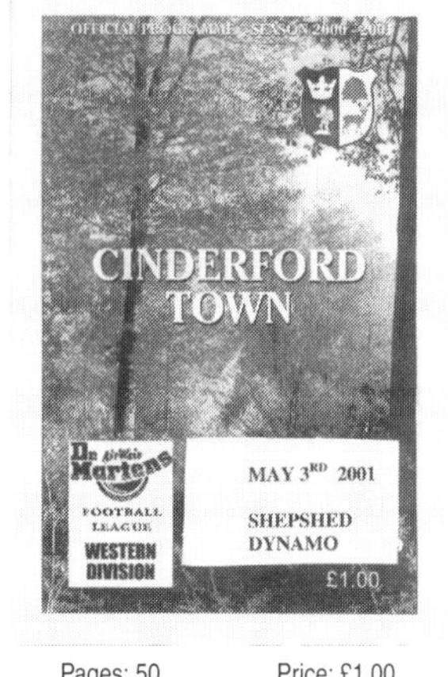

Pages: 50 Price: £1,00
Editor: Mike Bradley
Tel: 01594 824566

GROUND The Causeway, Hilldene, Cinderford, Glos. Tel: 01594 827147 or 822039

Directions: From Gloucester take A40 to Ross-on-Wye, then A48 - Chepstow. In 8miles turn right at Elton garage onto A4151 signed Cinderford, thru Littledean, up steep hill, right at crossroads, second left into Latimer Rd. Ground 5 minswalk from town centre

Capacity: 2,500 Cover: 1,000 Seats: 250 Floodlights: Yes

Clubhouse: Open every day. 2 bars, kitchen, 2 skittle alleys, darts, dancehall,committee room
Club Shop: Souvenirs, club badges (£"3.00), ties, mugs , scarves and pennants .

PREVIOUS **Leagues:** Glos Northern Snr 22-39 60-62, Western 46-59, Warwickshire Comb 63-64,West Midlands 65-69, Gloucestershire County 70-73 85-89, Midland Comb. 74-84,Hellenic 90-95
Names: None **Grounds:** Mousel Lane, Royal Oak

CLUB RECORDS **Attendance:** 4,850 v Minehead, Western League, 1955-56
Win: 13-0 v Cam Mills 38-39 **Defeat:** 0-10 v Sutton Coldfield 78-79
Career Appearances: Russell Bowles 528 **Career Goalscorer:** Unknown

BEST SEASON **FA Cup:** 2nd Rd v Gravesend 95-96 **FA Trophy:** 2nd Qual Rd
FA Vase: 2nd Rd 91-92 **FA Amateur Cup:** 3rd Qual Rd 52

HONOURS Hellenic Lg Premier Champions 94-95, Premier Lg.Cup 94-95, Floodlit Cup 93-94,Div 1 90-91; Glos Northern Snr Lg Div 1 38-39 60-61, R-up (6); Nth Glos Lg Div1 38-39 60-61; Glos Snr Amtr Cup (Nth) (6), R-up (3); Western Lg Div 2 56-57; Warwickshire Comb. 63-64; W Mids Lg Prem Div Cup 68-69; Glos Jnr Cup (Nth) 80-81; Midland Comb. 81-82; Glos Co. Lg R-up 69-70 71-72 73-74; Glos FA Trophy R-up 92-93; Hungerford Cup 94-95, Glos.Sen Cup Finalists 00-01

Back row,left to right: Kevin Coles, Gareth Hopkins, Clayton Hook, Paul Donnelly, Mark Richards, Pate Macklin, Lyndon Tomkins, Danny Iddles, Andy Fisher and Danny Hunt. **Front Row:** Daryl Addis, Steve Campbell, Ian Howell, Adie Harris, Justin Hayward, Lee Burby.

CIRENCESTER TOWN

CLUB OFFICIALS

Chairman: **Stephen Abbley**
17 Dianmer Close, Hook, Swindon. SN4 8ER.
Tel: 01743853293 (H) 01793 884900 (B)
Secretary: **Jim Saunders**
35 Chesterton Park, Cirencester, Glos. GL7 1XS
Tel: 01285 659002 (H)
Commercial Manager: **Stephen Abbley**
Press Officer: **Jim Saunders**

FOOTBALL MANAGEMENT TEAM

Manager: Ray Baverstock(01242 260619)
Coach: Mark Boyland
Physio: Laura Chamberlain

FACT FILE

Founded: 1889Nickname: Ciren
Sponsors: P.H.H./Cheltenham Windows
Colours: Red & black/ black/ red
Change colours: All Blue
Midweek Matchday: Tuesday
Reserves' League: Cirencester & District
2000-01
P.o.Y.: Kevin Sawyer
Captain & P.o.Y.: Giles Harris

GROUND The Stadium, Smithsfield, Chesterton Lane, Cirencester Tel: 01285 645783

Directions: Follow signs on by-pass to Bristol & West. At the roundabout where the Sports Centre is situated, follow the road `up the hill' and take the first left of roundaboutright. Situated 3 miles from Kemble (BR)

Capacity: 3,000 Seats: 236 Cover: 500 Floodlights: Yes

Clubhouse: Open Tuesday - Friday evenings & Saturday. Snacks are available onmatchdays.
Club Shop: None

PROGRAMME
Pages: Yes Price: £1
Editor: Margaret Marsh Tel. 01258 645783

Local Press:
Standard, Western Daily Press
Local Radio:
BBC Radio Gloucester, Severn Sound

PREVIOUS **Leagues:** Hellenic League Names: None. Grounds: None

CLUB RECORDS **Attendance:** 2,600 v Fareham 1969
Win: Unknown **Defeat:** Unknown
Career Goalscorer: Unknown **Career Appearances:** Unknown
Transfer fee paid: None **Transfer fee received:** None

BEST SEASON **FA Trophy:** 1st Qual. Round 1996-97 (1st season in comp.)
FA Vase: Never past the 1st Round **FA Cup:** 3rd Preliminary Round, 1996-97

HONOURS Gloucestershire Senior Amateur Cup 89-90; Hellenic League Div One Challenge Cup 90-91; Hellenic League Prem Div 95-96, League Cup 95-96; Gloucestershire County Cup 95-96

Players progressing: None

CLEVEDON TOWN

CLUB OFFICIALS

Chairman: John Croft

Directors: R.J.Ayers, B.W.Bradshaw, S.T.Haas G.Bradshaw T Walsh and G,Thomas

Secretary: Mike Williams
34 Robinia Walk, Whitchurch,
Bristol BS14 0SHTel: 01275 833835

Commercial Manager: Gary Bradshaw
(M) 07768 270718

FOOTBALL MANAGEMENT TEAM

Manager: Steve Fey
Coach: Gary Smart
Physio: TBA

FACT FILE

Formed: 1880
Nickname: The Seasiders
Sponsors: Bradshaw Group (Axa na)
Colours: Blue & white stripes/blue/blue
Change colours: All yellow or all green
Midweek Matches: Tuesday
Youth Team: Som Youth Floodlit SWCo
Web-site: www.clevedontownafc.co.uk

2000-01

Captain:Jim Rollo
P.o.Y.: Steve Peters
Top Goalscorer: Andy Mainwaring(23)

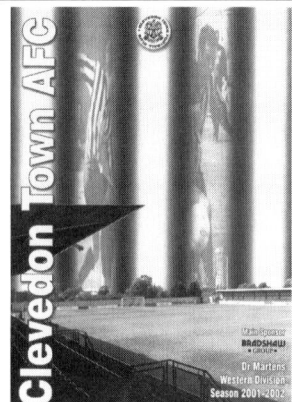

Pages: 34 Price:£1.30
Editor: Russell Isaac (01275 343000)

Local Radio: Radio Bristol
Local Press: Clevedon Mercury
Evening Post, Western Daily Press

GROUND Ha nd Stadium, Davis Lane, Clevedon
Fax: 01275 871601 Tel: 01275 871600(ground) 01275 341913 (office)

Directions: M5 Jct 20 - follow signs for Hand Stadium; first left into Central Way (at island just after motorway), 1st left at mini-r'bout into Kenn Rd, 2nd left Davis Lane; ground half mile on right. Or from Bristol(B3130) left into Court Lane (opposite Clevedon Court), turn right after 1mile, ground on left. Nearest BR station: Nailsea & Backwell. Buses from Bristol

Capacity: 3,650 Seats: 300 Cover: 1,600 Floodlights: Yes

Clubhouse: Open every day and evening. Separate function suite & lounge bar.Hot food available. Matchday refreshment bar within ground sells confectionary, teas & hot food

Club Shop: Sells all types of souvenirs, programmes and replica kit. Exchanges welcome. Contact J Anderson. **Supporters Club Chairman:** Russell Coneybeare

PREVIOUS **Leagues:** Weston & District, Somerset Senior, Bristol Charity, Bristol & District, Bristol Suburban, Western 74-93
Grounds: Dial Hill ('till early 1890's); Teignmouth Road ('till 1991)
Names: Clevedon FC, Ashtonians (clubs merged in 1974)

CLUB RECORDS **Attendance:** 1,600 v Bristol City, Friendly. 27/7/98
(At Teignmouth Road: 2,300 v Billingham Synthonia, FA Amateur Cup, 52-53)
Win: 18-0 v Dawlish Town (H), Western League Premier Division 24/4/93
Defeat: 13-3 v Yate YMCA (A), Bristol Comb 67-68

BEST SEASON **FA Cup:** 3rd Qual. Rd 2nd replay 92-93 v Newport AFC, 2-4 after two 1-1
FA Amateur Cup: 3rd Round Proper, 52-53 **FA Vase:** 6th Round 87-88, v Sudbury Town (A) **FA Trophy:** 2nd Round 98-99

HONOURS Southern League, Midland Division 98-99, Western League 92-93 (R-up 91-92), League Cup (R-up 92-93), Bristol Charity League 37-38,40-41, Somerset Senior Cup 01-02 04-05 28-29 , 00-01 Somerset Snr League 36-37, Div 1(Res.) 92-93, Bristol & suburbanLeague 25-26,27-28,28-29, Weston & District League: 39-40,43-44,44-45, Somerset Premier Cup;86-87,98-99, 00-01 Somerset Junior Cup 1897-98,Somerset Medal Competition: 87-88, Clevedon Charity Cup 26-27,30-31.

Players Progressing: Jason Eaton (Bristol City) and Jonathon Gould (Halifax Town)

L-R Back Row: Steve Fry (Manager), Gary Smart, (Ass Man), Keith Knight, Karl Bayliss, Tony Cook, Jason Matthews, Oliver Price, Lee Barless, Steve Peters, Steve Bobbins (Kit Manager) and Ian Weston (Physio).**Front Row:** Steve Lester, Mark Badman, Bradley Thomas, Tommy Callinan, Lee Jefferies, Darren Keeling, Mark Parmer, Wayne Thorne and Mark Clode.

EVESHAM UNITED

CLUB OFFICIALS

Chairman: **Jim Cockerton**
Vice Chairman: **Steve Lane**
President: **M E H Davis**
Treasurer: **Dave Wright**
Secretary/Press Officer: **Mike J Peplow**
68 Woodstock Rd, St Johns,
Worcester WR2 5NF
Tel: 01905 425993

FOOTBALL MANAGEMENT TEAM

Manager: Phil Mullen
Asst Manager: Paul Davies
Physio:Phil Greenway

FACT FILE

Nickname: The Robins
Sponsors; B anks's
Colours: Red & white/black/black
Change Colours: All blue
Formed: 1945
Midweek matches: Tuesday
Reserves' League: No reserve team
2000-01 Captain:Steve Taylor
P.o.Y: Andy smith
Top Scorer: Steve McCartan

EVESHAM UNITED F.C.
(Western) DIVISION
Official Match Day Programme
2000/2001
£1.00
EVESHAM UNITED
-V-
ROCESTER
Tuesday 24th April 2001

Pages:58 Price: £1
Editor: Mike Peplow (01905 425993)
Local Press: Evesham Journal,
Worcester Evening News, Gloucester Echo
Local Radio: Classic Gold
BBC Hereford & Worcester, FM102 The Bear

GROUND Common Road, Evesham, Worcestershire WR11 4PU Tel: 01386 442303

Directions: From Evesham High Street turn into Oat St, and join one-way system,turn right between Willmotts factory called Conduit Hill into Common Rd, ground 200yds down on right just before railway bridge. 5 minutes walk from Evesham BR station
Capacity: 2,000 Seats: 350 Cover: 600 Floodlights: Yes
Clubhouse: Open matchdays and training nights.
Cold food available in club, and hot food from tea hut on matchdays
Club Shop: Contact John Hawkins c/o the club

PREVIOUS **Leagues:** Worcester, Birmingham Combination, Midland Combination 51-55 65-92, West Midlands Regional 55-62
Name: Evesham Town **Ground:** The Crown Meadow (pre-1968)

CLUB RECORDS **Attendance:** 2,338 v West Bromwich A., friendly 18/7/92
Win: 11-3 v West Heath United **Defeat:1-8 v Ilkeston Town**
Career Goalscorer: Sid Brain **Career Appearances:** Rob Candy
Transfer fee paid: £1,500; to Hayes for Colin Day, 1992
Transfer fee received: £5,000 for Simon Brain (to Cheltenham Town)

BEST SEASON **FA Vase:** Quarter Finals 1991-92 **FA Amateur Cup:** Runners-up 1923-24
FA Trophy: 3rd Qual Rd 96-97 **FA Cup:** 2nd Qual Rd 96-97

HONOURS FA Amateur Cup R-up 23-24, Worcestershire Snr Urn(2) 76-78 (R-up 90-91), Midland Comb.(6) 52-53 54-55 65-66 67-69 91-92 (Chal. Cup 53-54 87-88 91-92 (R-up(5) 54-55 71-72 83-84 88-90)), Worcestershire Comb. 52-53 54-55; B'gham Combination R-up 30-31, Evesham Hosp. Cup 89-90, Tony Allden Mem. Cup 1973 19881992

Players progressing: Billy Tucker, Gary Stevens (Cardiff 77), Kevin Rose(Lincoln 78), Andy Preece (Northampton 86), Simon Brain (Hereford, via Cheltenham Town), Billy Turley (Northampton Tn)

Back row: Lee Neill (physio), Dean Roberts, Jay Powell, Paul West, Damien Beattie, Steve Taylor, Andrew Hodgetts, Shaun Pratt, Phil Mullen (manager), Paul Davies (asst. man.). Front row: Russell Parmenter, Lol Shaughnessy, Andy Smith, Joe Lacata, Phil Preedy, Mark Wolsey, Matt Pendleton, Steve McCartan, Stuart Payne. **Photo:** Arthur Evans

GLOUCESTER CITY

CLUB OFFICIALS

Chairman: Tracy Newport

President: R F Etheridge

Secretary: Jason Mills
25 Hewlett Road, Cheltenham,
Gloucestershire GL52 6AD
Tel/Fax: 01242 700496
Mob: 07768 750590

Club Email: mills.jason@virgin.net

Press Officer: c/o Secretary

FOOTBALL MANAGEMENT TEAM

Manager: Chris Burns
Assistant Manager: Brian Godfrey
Coach: B. Godfray
Physio: Adrian Tandy

FACT FILE

Formed: 1889
Nickname: The Tigers
Sponsors: T.B.A.
Colours: Yellow & black/black/black
Change colours: All Red
Midweek games: Tuesday

2000-01

Captain: Andy Tucker
Top Goalscorers:
Jimmy Cox & Karl Bayliss (21)
Joint P.o.Y.:
Andy Tucker & Jimmy Cox

Pages: 44 Price: £1.30
Editor: Mike Dunstan Tel: 01242 250087

Local Press: Gloucester Citizen, Western Daily Press
Local Radio: Severn Sound, BBC Radio Gloucestershire

GROUND Meadow Park, Sudmeadow Road, Hempsted, Gloucester GL2 6HS
Tel: 01452 421400

Directions: From North: A40 then then A4301 towards City Centre & Historic Docks, right into Severn Road over swingbridge, right into Llanthony Road/Hempsted Lane, 2nd right into Sudmeadow Road, ground 50yds on left

Capacity: 3,500 Cover:2,500 Seats: 560 Floodlights: Yes

Clubhouse: Meadow Park Sports & Social Club in ground. Normal licensing hours.

Club Shop: Yes

PREVIOUS

Leagues:
Bristol & Dist. (now Western) 1893-96,
Gloucester & Dist. 97-1907,
NorthGlos. 07-10,
Glos. North Senior 20-34,
Birmingham Comb. 1935-39

Grounds: Longlevens 1935-65, Horton Road 65-86

Name: Gloucester Y.M.C.A

CLUB RECORDS

Attendance: 4,000 v Dagenham & Redbridge, FA Trophy S-F 2nd Leg, 12.4.97

Win: 10-0 v Sudbury Town (H), FA Cup 3rd Rd Q., 17.10.98

Defeat: 1-12 v Gillingham 9.11.46

Goalscorer: Reg Weaver, 250

Appearances: Stan Myers & Frank Tredgett in 1950s

Fee Paid: £25,000 for S Fergusson (Worcester City), and D Holmes (Gresley R.)

Fee Received: £25,000 Ian Hedges (AFC Bournemouth, 1990)

BEST SEASON

FA Cup: 2nd Rd 89-90

FA Trophy: Semi-Final 1996-97

HONOURS

Southern Lg R-up 90-91, Lg Cup 55-56 R-up 81-82, Midland Div 88-89),
Glos NthSen Lg 33-34,
Glos Sen. Cup 37-38 49-58 65-66 68-69 70-71 74-75 78-79 79-80 81-82 82-83 83-84 90-91 92-93,
Sen Amat Cup (Nth) 31-32)

Players progressing: Numerous including William Teague (61) & Rod Thomas (64) to Swindon, John Layton (Hereford 74), Ian Main (Exeter 78), Mike Bruton (Newport 79), Mel Gwinnett (Bradford C. 84), Steve Talboys (Wimbledon 91)

Nathan Wigg Photo: Peter Barnes

GRESLEY ROVERS

CLUB OFFICIALS

Chairman: Mark Evans
President: Gordon Duggins
Vice Chairman: George Sutton
Secretary / Press Officer: Neil Betteridge, 34 Thorpe Downs Road, Church Gresley, Swadlincote, Derbys DE11 9FB
Tel: 01283 226229
Commercial Director: Mark Evans

FOOTBALL MANAGEMENT TEAM

Manager: John McGinlay
Asst Manager: Alan Titterton
Physio:

FACT FILE

Formed: 1882
Nickname: The Moatmen
Sponsors:
Colours: Red/white/red
Change colours: White/black/white
Midweek matchday: Wednesday
Reserves' League: Midland Comb (Res. Div.)

2000-01

Captain: Richard Wardle
P.o.Y.: Steve Coates
Top scorer: Simon Tucker 23

Pages: 36 Price: £1.00

Local Press: Derby Evening Telegraph, Burton Mail, Burton Trader, SwadlincoteTimes
Local Radio: BBC Radio Derby & Centre F.M.

GROUND Moat Ground, Moat Street, Church Gresley, Swadlincote, Derbys., DE11 9RE.
Tel: 01283 216315 Club Website: www.gresleyrovers.co.uk

Directions: To A444 via either the A5, A38, A5121 or M42 , Junction 11. On reaching A444 head for Castle Gresley. Take exit at large island to Church Gresley, at next island 2nd exit (Church St), then 2nd left (School St) then 1st left into Moat St. 5 miles Burton-on-Trent (BR). Buses from Swadlincote and Burton

Capacity: 2,000 Cover: 1,200 Seats: 400 Floodlights: Yes

Clubhouse: Inside ground, open Mon, Tues & Thurs eves & matchdays

Club Shop: Sells merchandise, programmes, metal badges etc.

PREVIOUS **Leagues:** Burton Lge 1892-95 97-01 09-10 43-45, Derbyshire Sen 1895-97 02-03,Leics Sen 1890-91 98-99 08-09 10-12 15-16 35-42 45-49, Notts 01-02, Midland 03-06, Central All 11-15 19-25 49-53 59-67, Birmingham Comb 25-33 53-54, Birmingham (now West Mids) 54-59 75-92, Central Comb 33-35, East Mids 67-75
Grounds: Mushroom Lane, Albert Village 1882-95, Church Str., Church, Gresley. 1895-1909

CLUB RECORDS **Attendance:** 3,950 v Burton Albion, Birmingham (now West Mids) Lg Division One 57-58
Win: 23-0 v Holy Cross Priory, Leics Jun Cup 1889-90 **Defeat:** 1-15 v Burton Crusaders 1886-87
Career Goalscorer: Gordon Duggins 306 **Career Appearances:** Dennis King 579
Transfer fee received: £30,000 for Justin O'Reilly (Port Vale 1996)
Transfer fee paid: £2,500 for David Robinson (Ilkeston Town 97)

BEST SEASON **FA Vase:** Runners-up 90-91, (SF 92-93) **FA Trophy:** Qtr Finals 95-96
FA Cup: 1st Rd Proper: 30-31 (1-3 at York City), 94-95 (1-7 at Crewe Alex.) League clubs defeated: None

HONOURS Southern Lge Champ 96-97; FA Vase R-up 90-91; West Mids Lg 90-91 91-92 (R-up 85-86 88-89); Lg Cup 88-89 R-Up. 86-87 91-92; Southern Lg Mid Div R-up 92-93; Derbys Snr Cup (7), (R-Up (3); Leics Snr Cup 1898-99 46-47 (R-Up 1899-90 45-46); Leics Sen Lg 00-01 46-47 47-48 R-Up (7); Coalville Charity Cup 46-47; Derby Senior Cup (S) (2) R-Up 00-01; Bass Vase (6); Cent All 64-65 66-67 R-Up(3) (Lg Cup 52-53); East Mids Reg Lg (2) R-Up (2); Dr.Martens (S Lge) Cup Fin 93-94

Players progressing: Phil Gee (Derby County 85), Mark Blount (Sheffield Utd 94), Colin Loss (Bristol City 94), Justin O'Reilly (Port Vale 96)

L - R - Back Row: Dave Shaw, Alex Green, Stuart Evans, Kevin Allsop, Barry Woolley, James Lindley, John Allcock, Ian Bluck, Carl Middleton, Neil Kitching and Andy Cheetham. **Middle Row:** Ernie Talbot (Kit Manager), Mark Peters, Richard Waddle, Chris Gray, Steve Bedward, Lee Westwood and Gary Norton (Res. Team Manager). **Front Row:** Jon Jenkinson, Andy Mason (coach), John McGinlay (Manager), Alan Titterton (Asst. Manager) and Matt Moran. Photo: Derrick Kinsey

HALESOWEN TOWN

CLUB OFFICIALS

Chairman:NigelPitt
President: **Laurence Wood**
Vice Chairman: **Paul Flood**
Secretary: **Stewart Tildesley**
83 Bloomfield Street, Halesowen B63 3RF
Tel: 0121 5508443(H) 07710 434708(M)
Commercial Manager & Press
Officer:**Brendan Phillips**

FOOTBALL MANAGEMENT TEAM

Manager: Brendan Phillips
Asst Manager: Alan Moore
Physio: Jeff Jones

FACT FILE

Formed: 1873
Nickname: Yeltz
Sponsors: T.B.A.
Newsline: 0930 555818
Colours: Blue with white trim
Change colours: Yellow & Black
Midweek home matchday:Tuesday
Reserve's League: None

2000-01

Captain: Phillip Wood
P.o.Y.: Les Hines
Top Scorers: Ross Collins 7

Pages: 44 Price: £1.20p Editor: R Pepper
Local Press: Sports Argus, Express & Star, Birmingham Mail, Halesowen News, Stourbridge & Halesowen Chronicle
Local Radio: BBC West Midlands, B.R.M.B., Beacon

GROUND The Grove, Old Hawne Lane, Halesowen, West Midlands B63 3TB
FAX No: 0121 602 0123 Tel No: 0121 550 2179

Directions: M5 jct 3, A456 (signed Kidderminster) to 1st island turn right (signed A459 Dudley), left at next island (signed A458 Stourbridge), at next island take 3rd left into Grammar School Lane, then Old Hawne Lane - ground 400 yds on left

Capacity: 5,000 Cover: 1,499 Seats: 499 Floodlights: Yes

Clubhouse: (0121 602 2210) 12-2.30 & 7-11 (10.30 Sun) pm daily.Cold snacks served.

Club Shop: Sells replica strips, T-shirts, waterproof tops, coats, scarves, programmes, badges etc

PREVIOUS **Leagues:** West Mids 1892-1905 06-11 46-86, Birmingham Comb. 11-39

CLUB RECORDS **Attendance:** 5,000 v Hendon F.A. Cup 1st Rd Proper 1954, (18,234 v Southall,1986 FA Vase Final at Wembley)
Goalscorer: Paul Joinson 369 **Appearances:** Paul Joinson 608
Win: 13-1 v Coventry Amateurs, Birmingham Senior Cup, 1956
Defeat: 0-8 v Bilston, West Midlands League, 7/4/62
Fee Paid: £7,250 for Stuart Evans (Gresley 1996)
Fee Received: £40,000 for Jim Rodwell (Rushden & Diamonds 96)

BEST SEASON **FA Vase:** Winners 84-85, 85-86 R-up 82-83 **FA Trophy:** 3rd Round Proper 94-95
FA Cup: 1st Rd 9 times: 54-55 then each season from 84-85 to 91-92

HONOURS Southern Lg Premier Div R-up 96, Southern Lg Midland Div 89-90, W Mids Lg(5) 46-47 82-85 85-86 (R-up 64-65, Lg Cup 82-83 84-85),B'ham Snr Cup 83-84,97-98 (R-up 51-52 67-68), Staffs Snr Cup 88-89 (R-up 83-84), FA Vase (2) 84-86 (R-up 82-3) Worcs Snr Cup 51-52 61-62 (R-up 87-88), Midland Comb. Res Div 89-90

Players progressing: Arthur Proudler (Aston Villa), Cyril Spiers (Aston Villa), Billy Morris (Wolves), Dean Spink (Aston Villa), Stuart Cash (Nottm Forest), Andrew Pearce, Tim Clarke & Sean Flynn (Coventry), Dean Stokes (Port Vale), Frank Bennett (Southampton), Julian Alsop (Bristol Rovers)

Back Row: Lee Knight, Jason Burnham, Neil Smith, Ross Collins, Jason Piearcy, Tim Clarke, Kerry Giddings, Lee Collins, Mike Crawford and Andy Jones. **Front Row:** Ryan Robertson-Little (Kit Boy), Andrew Spencer, Paul Shaw, Richard Colwell, Alfie Carter, Matthew Hall, D. Barnett (Coach), B.Phillips (Manager), C.Brookes (Gen.Man), Leslie Hines, O'Neil Donaldson, Stuart Skidmore, Ricky Otto, J.Jones (Physio)

MANGOTSFIELD UNITED

THE FIELD REVIEW
MANGOTSFIELD UNITED
FOOTBALL CLUB
FOUNDED 1951
AFFILIATED TO GLOUCESTERSHIRE F.A.
AND SOMERSET & AVON F.A.
Western Division
Season 2000/2001
Dr. AirWair Martens
FLO GAS
Official Programme £1
Sat.28th April 2001
Solihull Borough

Pages: 32 Price: 50p
Editor: Bob Smale (0117 9401926)

CLUB OFFICIALS

President: Richard Davis
Chairman: Roger Pullin
Vice Chairman: P Selway
Secretary & Press Off: Roger Gray
105 Chiltern Close, Warmley, Bristol
BS15 5UW Tel: 0117 961 6523
(Mobile) 07768 467851

FOOTBALL MANAGEMENT TEAM

Manager: Andy Black
Assistant Manager: Shaun Penny
Physio:Tammy Mullin

FACT FILE

Founded: 1950 Nickname: The Field
Sponsors: T,B,A,
Colours: Sky & maroon/maroon/sky
Change colours: Yellow/navy/yellow
Midweek matchday: Tuesday 7.45
Reserve League: Somerset Senior

2000-01

Captain: Lee Barlass
P.o.Y .& Top Scorer: Darren Edward 27

GROUND Cossham Street, Mangotsfield, Bristol BS17 3EW Tel: 0117 956 0119

Directions: M4 jct 19, M32 jct 1; A4174 marked Downend, through lights, over double mini-r'bout to Mangotsfield, left by village church onto B4465 signposted Pucklechurch, ground quarter mile on right. From central Bristol take A432 thru Fishponds, Staple Hill, to Mangotsfield and turn right by village church onto B4465. From Bath/Keynsham follow A4175, right at island at Willsbridge onto A431, then rejoin A4175 at next island (Cherry Garden Hill) to Bridge Yate, straight over double mini-r'bout and take 1st left, right into Carsons Rd after 1 mile and follow to Mangotsfield village & turn right by church onto B4465

Capacity: 2,500 Seats: 300 Cover: 800 Floodlights: Yes Club Shop: Yes

Clubhouse: Open 11-11. Snacks - hot food on matchdays. Lounge bar for functions etc

PREVIOUS **Leagues:** Bristol & District 50-67; Avon Premier Combination 67-72; Western League 72-00

RECORD **Attendance:** 2,386 v Bath City, FA Cup 77-78
Goalscorer: John Hill **Appearances:** John Hill 600+
Win: 14-0 v Dawlish (a) 1993 Western League **Defeat:** 3-13 v Bristol City United (Bristol & District Div 1)
& 17-0 v Hanham Sports (Bristol & District League `Div 6)

HONOURS Western Lg 90-91r-up 99-00, Lg Cup 73-74 r-up 86-87, Div 1 r-up 82-83; Somerset Prem. Cup 87-88, r-up 88-89 95-96; Glos Snr Cup 68-69 75-76; Glos FA Trophy 84-85 86-87 90-91 94-95 96-97; Hungerford Invitation Cup 74-75; Rothmans Nat. Cup r-up 77-78; Hanham Invit. Charity Cup 84-85 85-86;
Youth honours: Glos Yth Shield 81-82 84-85 (R-up 82-83); Somerset Floodlit Yth Lg 81-82 82-83 83-84 84-85 87-88 98-99; Somerset Yth Shield 76-77
Reserve honours Somerset Snr Lg (Res.) Div 1 98-99 Div 2 97-98 75-76, Div 3 74-75; Somerset Comb. Cup 74-75

BEST SEASON **FA Vase:** Semi Final 95-96 **FA Cup:** 4th Qualifying Rd v Gravesend & Northfleet (A) Lost 0-4 28.10.00

Players progress ing: G Megson, S White, G Penrice, P Purnell, N Tanner, M Hooper

Back row: Shaun Penny (asst. man.), Mark Summers, Adam Lewis, Dave Elsey, Dave Oyson, Dave Seal, Rob Claridge, Carwyn Thomas.
Middle row: Hadleigh Winter, Dion Vernon, Mark Allen, Will Davis.
Front row: Adam Sims, Steve Campbell, Tom Lewis, Danny Hallett, Gareth Loyden.

RACING CLUB WARWICK

CLUB OFFICIALS

Chairman: **Jim Wright**

Secretary: **Pat Murphy**
Tel: 01926 612675

FOOTBALL MANAGEMENT

Manager:Billy Hollywood

FACT FILE

Formed: 1919
Nickname: Racers
Colours: Gold & black
Change colours: Red&white/red/red
Midweek matchday: Tuesday
Youth's League: Mid F/Lit Yth Lge

2000-01
Captain: D.Weston
P.o.Y.: Paul Eden
Top scorer: Paul Eden 14

Pages: 20 Price: £1.00
Editor: Phil Street
Local Press: Warwick Advertiser, Leamington Courier, Coventry EveningTelegraph
Local Radio:C.W.R. BBC Radio Coventry, Bear Radio

GROUND Townsend Meadow, Hampton Road, Warwick CV34 6JP
Tel: 01926 495786

Directions: On the B4095 Warwick to Redditch road (via Henley in Arden) next to owners' & trainers' car park of Warwick Racecourse. From M40 jct 15 (1 1/2 miles) take A429 into Warwick, left into Shakespeare Ave., straight over island, right at T-junction into Hampton Rd, ground 300yds on left. 2 milesfrom Warwick BR station

Capacity: 1,000 Cover: 200 Seats: 250 Floodlights: Yes

Clubhouse: 01926 495786 Open every evening & Sat &Sun lunchtimes

Club Shop: Scarves, mugs, badges, programmes - contact Secretary

PREVIOUS **Leagues:** Birmingham & West Mids All., Warwickshire Comb., West Midlands (Regional) 67-72, Midland Comb. 72-89
Names: Saltisford Rovers 1919-68 **Grounds:** Coventry Road

CLUB RECORDS **Attendance:** 1,000 v Halesowen Town, FA Cup 1987
Transfer fee paid: £1,000 for Dave Whetton (Bedworth United)
Transfer fee received: £5,000 for Ben Foster (Stoke City)
Career Goalscorer: Steve Edgington 200
Win: 9-1 v Knowle
Defeat: 0-7v Redditch United
Career Appearances: Steve Cooper 600

BEST SEASON **FA Vase:** 4th Round 77-78 **FA Cup:** 3rd Qual Rd 92-93 **FA Trophy:**

HONOURS Midland Combination 87-88 (R-up 88-89); Warwick Lg 33-34 34-35 35-36; Birmingham & West Mids Alliance 48-49; Birmingham & Dist Alliance Senior Cup 49-50; Leamington & Dist Lg 37-38 45-46 46-47 47-48; Leamington Hospital Cup 37-38 46-47; Warwick Cinderella Cup 35-36 36-37 37-38 38-39 46-47; T G John Cup 36-37; Leamington Junior Cup 38-39 46-47

Players progressing: None

Racing Club Warwick's End of Season Presentation Evening.
L-R Back Row: O. Lovelock (now Rugby Utd), D. Travis, D. Weston, B. Foster (now Stoke City), T. Sidwell, and K. Elvin. **Middle Row:** D. Hollywood, S. Gray, L. Grant, and C. Dutton. **Front Row:** R. Follett (now Tamworth) K. Green, D.Titterton, C. Wells, P. Eden (now Redditch Utd), B. Hollywood (manager), D. McSheheffrey, M. Hudson, J. Wiseman, A. Green.

REDDITCH UNITED

CLUB OFFICIALS

Chairman: **Rod Laight**
President: **Major Jim Gillespie MBE**
Secretary: **Alan Wolfe,18 Packwood Close,Webheath, Redditch,Worcs. B97 5SJ**)Tel No: 01527 543044 (H)
Commercial Manager: **Pat Cremin**
Press Off:**Gordon Wilkie** Tel:01527 543999

FOOTBALL MANAGEMENT TEAM

Manager: Nicky Cross
Larry Chambers & Paul Malloy
Physio: John Kane

FACT FILE

Formed: 1900
Nickname: The Reds
Colours: Red & White
Change colours: Claret & Blue
Midweek matchday: Tuesday
Reserves' League: Midland Comb. Res Div
Programme: Pages: 50 Price: £1.50
Editor: Gordon Wilkie
Local Press: Redditch Indicator, Redditch Advertiser, Birmingham Evening Mail, Redditch Standard
Local Radio: BBC Hereford & Worcester
The Bear Radio FM102

GROUND Valley Stadium, Bromsgrove Road, Redditch B97 4RN Tel: 01527 67450
Directions: Access 7 on town centre ring-road takes you into Bromsgrove Road (via Unicorn Hill) - ground entrance 400yds past traffic lights on right.Arriving from Bromsgrove take first exit off dual carriageway. Ground 400 ydsfrom Redditch BR station and town centre
Capacity: 5,000 Cover: 2,000 Seats: 400 Floodlights: Yes
Clubhouse: Large clubroom and lounge boardroom. Open matchdays and for private hire. Food available on matchdays; steaks hot dogs, burgers, chips, bovril etc
Club Shop: Yes

PREVIOUS **Leagues:** Birmingham Comb. 05-21 29-39 46-53, West Midlands 21-29 53-72, Southern 72-79, Alliance Premier (Conf) 79-80
Name: Redditch Town **Ground:** HDA Spts Ground, Millsborough Rd

CLUB RECORDS **Attendance:** 5,500 v Bromsgrove, league match 54-55
Transfer fee paid: £3,000 for Paul Joinson from Halesowen Town
Transfer fee received: £42,000 for David Farrell (Aston Villa, 1991)

BEST SEASON **FA Cup:** 1st Rd replay 71-72, 0-4 v Peterborough U (A) after 1-1 draw. Also 1st Rd 71-72
FA Trophy: 4th Round 1998-99 0-2 v Boston Umited

HONOURS Southern Lg Div 1 Nth 75-76 (Midland Div R-up 85-86) S.Lg Cup R-up 97-98 West Mids (B'ham) Lg Southern Sect. 54-55, Birmingham Comb. 13-14 32-33 52-53 (R-up 06-07 14-15 51-52), Staffs Snr Cup 90-91, Birmingham Snr Cup 24-25 31-32 38-39 76-77, Worcs Snr Cup 894-95 1930-31 74-75 76-77 (R-up 1888-89 1929-30 52-53 73-74), Worcs Jnr Cup 90-91

Players progressing: Hugh Evans (Birmingham 1947), Trevor Lewes (Coventry1957), David Gilbert (Chesterfield 1960), Mike Tuohy (Southend Utd 1979), NeilSmith (Liverpool), David Farrell (Aston Villa 1992), Neil Davis (Aston Villa 1991)

ROCESTER

CLUB OFFICIALS

Chairman: **A.Hawksworth**

Secretary: **Gilbert Egerton**
23 Eaton Rd, Rocester, Uttoxeter,
Staffs ST145LL.
Tel: 01889 590101

FOOTBALL MANAGEMENT TEAM

Joint Managers: Martin Smith & Andy Holmes
Reserves' Manager: Alf Hawksworth

FACT FILE

Founded: 1876 Nickname: Romans
Sponsors:
Colours: Amber/black/black
Change colours: All blue
Reserves' Lge: North Staffs (North)
Midweek matchday: Tuesday

2000-2001

Captain: Richard Owen
Top scorer: Emeka Ejiofor 16
P.o.Y.: Richard Wright

32 pages £1.00
Editor: Barry Brosnan
Tel: 01889 567795

GROUND The Rivers Field, Mill Street, Rocester, Uttoxeter, Staffs Tel: 01889 590463
Email Address: rocester@floodlight org.uk
Directions: From A50 r'bout adjoining Little Chef at Uttoxeter take B5030 to Rocester & Alton Towers, right into Rocester village after 3miles over narrow bridge, in village centre bear right at sharp left-hand bend into Mill St., ground 500yds on left just past former cotton mill.

Capacity: 4,000 Seats: 230 Cover: 500 Floodlights: Yes

Clubhouse: On matchdays (normal licensing hours). Hot drinks & snacks.
Club Shop: Yes

PREVIOUS **Leagues:** Ashbourne; Leek & Moorland; Cheadle & Dist; Uttoxeter Amateur; Stafford 53-57; Staffordshire County North 57-84; Staffordshire Senior 84-87; West Midlands 87-94; Midland alliance 94-99.
Ground: Mill Street, Rocester (early 1900s-1987)

BEST SEASON **FA Cup:** 3rd Qual. Round 97-98, 1-2 v Bromsgrove Rovers (A) **FA Vase:** 5th Round 86-87, 1-3 v Garforth Town (H) aet.

RECORDS **Attendance:** 1,026 v Halesowen T., FA Vase 4th Rd Jan.'87 (at Leek Town)
Goalscorer: Mick Collins **Appearances:** Peter Swanwick.(A goalkeeper who played for 20 years -1962-82)
Fee Paid: £1,000 for Paul Ede from Burton Albion, Sept.1989.
Fee Received: £12,000 for Mark Sale from Birmingham City 1994
Win: 14-0 (twice) **Defeat:** 0-9

HONOURS West Mids Lg R-up 89-90 (Div 1 87-88, Div 1 Cup 87-88), Staffs Senior Lg (2) 85-87, Staffordshire FA Vase 85-86 87-88; Midland Alliance 98-99

Players progressing: Bert Carpenter (Manchester Utd), Joe Carpenter (Brighton), George Shepherd (Derby), Mark Sale (Birmingham, Torquay),Tony Hemmings (Wycombe via Northwich)

Back Row L-R: Michael Stark, James McCarron, Adam Bowen, Steve Stokes, Andy Bourne, Louie Whiting, Matt Smith., Alan Somerville, and Mick Ede senr (Physio). **Front Row:** Chris Rawlinson, Mark Fisher, Richard Owen, Andy Bostock and Alex Hook.
Photo by Trevor Slater of The Sentinel from whose office orders can be placed by telephoning 01782 602547

SHEPSHED DYNAMO

CLUB OFFICIALS

Chairman: **Michael Voce**
President / Vice Chairman: TBA
Secretary: **Peter Bull**
17 Welland Rd, Barrow-on-Soar,
Leicestershire LE12 8NA
Tel: 01509 413338
Press Officer: **Maurice Brindley**
Tel: 01509 267922
Commercial Manager: **T.B.A.**

FOOTBALL MANAGEMENT TEAM

Manager: Dave Williams
Coach: Frank Benjamin
Physio: Alan Cook

FACT FILE

Re-formed: 1994
Nickname: Dynamo
Sponsors: T.B.A.
Colours: All purple
Change colours: All Green
Midweek matchday: Tuesday
Reserves' League: Midland Comb.

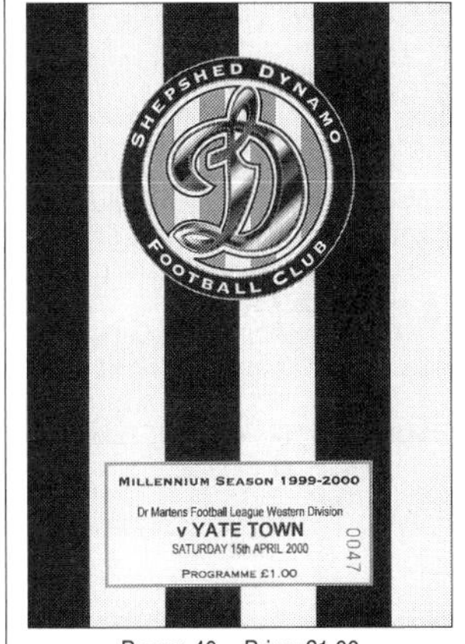

Pages: 40 Price: £1.00
Editor: Andy Reid 0116 2608295
email: andy.macmillan@ntlworld.com

Local Press: Loughborough Echo, Leicester Mercury, Coalville Times
Local Radio: Radio Leicester, Oak FM

GROUND The Dovecote, Butthole Lane, Shepshed, Leicestershire Tel: 01509 650992

Directions: M1 junction 23, A512 towards Ashby, right at first lights, right atgarage in Forest Street, right into Butthole Lane opposite Black Swan. Fivemiles from Loughborough (BR)

Capacity: 5,000 Cover: 1,500 Seats: 209 Floodlights: Yes

Clubhouse: Takes 120 in main room, 50 in others
Club Shop: Yes (Steve Straw & Alan Gibson)

PREVIOUS

Leagues:
Leicestershire Senior 07-16 19-27 46-50 51-81,
Midland Counties 81-82, Northern Counties (East) 82-83,
Southern 83-88, Northern Premier 88-93,
Midland Combination 93-94, Midland Alliance 94-96
Names: Shepshed Albion 1890-1975 91-94,
Shepshed Charterhouse 75-91
Grounds: Ashby Road (pre-1897), Little Haw Farm

CLUB RECORDS

Attendance: 2,500 v Leicester C. (friendly) 96-97
Win: 10-0 v Bloxwixh T. (H), Mid. Comb. 93-94
Defeat: 0-7 v Hyde Utd. (A) NPL 90-91
Career Goalscorer: Jeff Lissaman 104 (81-86)
Career Appearances: Austin Straker 300
Transfer fee paid: £2,000 for Doug Newton (Charterhouse)
Transfer fee received: £10,000 for John Deakin from Birmingham City (Charterhouse)

BEST SEASON

FA Vase: Semi-Finalists 78-79
FA Trophy: 3rd Rd Replay v Emley 98-99
FA Cup: 1st Rd 82-83, 1-5 v Preston North End (A),
96-97 v Carlisle United (a) 0-6

HONOURS

Southern Lge Midland Div. R-up 83-84,
N.C.E. Lge 82-83, Lge Cup 82-83;
Midland Counties Lge 81-82, Lge Cup 81- 82;
Leicestershire Senior Lge 10-11 20-21 78-79 79-80 80-81,
R-up 21-22, Div 2 53-54 65-66 77-78, Div 2 Cup 77-78;
Leicestershire Senior Cup (7);
Loughborough Charity Cup 92-93;
Midland Alliance Winners 95-96

Players progressing:
Neil Grewcock (Burnley 84), Gordon Tucker (Huddersfield 87), Devon White (Bristol R. 87), John Deakin (Birmingham City)

IBRAHIM BAH Photo: Keith Clayton

SOLIHULL BOROUGH

CLUB OFFICIALS
Chairman: **John Hewitson**
President: **Joe McGorian**
Vice Chairman: **Trevor Stevens**
Secretary: **Joe Murphy,** 2 Wilford Grove,Solihull B913FP Tel NBo: 0121 7090545 Mobile: 07811 337345
Club Fax: 0121 711 4045
Press Officer: **Richard Crawshaw**
Tel: 01564 702746 or 07712 791202(m)

FOOTBALL MANAGEMENT TEAM
Manager: Dave Busst
Coach: Paul Holleran
Physio: Graham Jones F.A.Dep.Ist

FACT FILE
Formed: 1953
Nickname: Boro
Sponsors: Carling Black Label
Colours: Red/white/red
Change colours: Yellow/blue
Midweek matchday: Tuesday
Reserve's League: Midland Comb.

2000-2001
Captain: Russell Dodd
P.o.Y.: Chris Smith
Top scorer:Chris Smith (28)

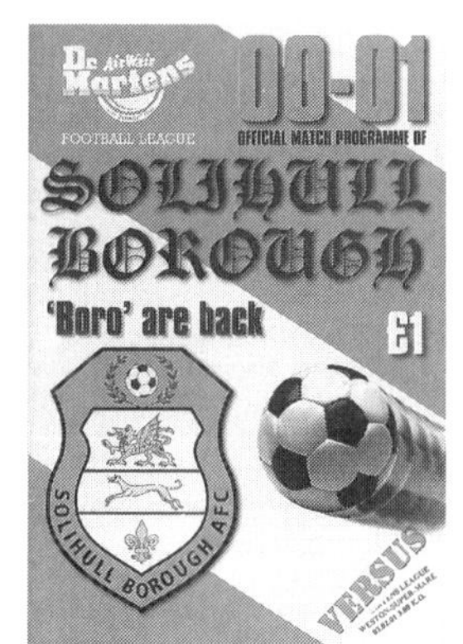

Pages: 52 Price: £1
Editors: Donna Matthews(0121 682 5783)
Local Press: Solihull Times, Solihull News, Sunday Mercury, Sports Argus
Local Radio: Radio WM, BRMB
Club Website: www.sbfc 2000,co,uk

Ground: Damson Park, Damson Parkway,Solihull,W.Mids B91 2PP(0121 705 6770)
Directions: Leave M42 at Jnct 6. A45 for 2 miles towards B'ham.Past Honda Garage and opp Forte Posthouse Hotel, left at filter to traffic lights into Damson Parkway.I mile to roundabout by Rover works.Go round, down other side of dual crriageway for 100 jds .Ground on left.Coventry use A45 to Posthouse. Solihull,A41 into Hampton Lane and Yew Tree LaneLane.
Capacity: 9,500 Cover: 2,000 Seats: 400 Floodlights: Yes
Clubhouse: Country Club facilities and all type offunctions can be booked.(0121 705 6770)

PREVIOUS **Leagues:** Mercian; Midland Combination 69-91
Name: Lincoln FC **Grounds:** Widney Stadium, Solihull 65-88,Moor Green 88-98,Redditch 98-00

CLUB RECORDS **Attendance:** 2,135 v Darlington FA Cup 1st Rd replay. At previous ground: 400 vMoor Green, Midland Comb . Div . 2 , 1971
Win: 9-1 v Alfreton Town FA Trophy 1st Rd 97-98
Defeat: 1-6 v Tiverton Town (A) Southern League (Western) 99-00
Career Goalscorer: Joe Dowling **Career Appearances:** Darrel Houghton
Transfer fee paid: £15,000 for Recky Carter, from Kettering Town
Transfer fee received: £30,000 for Andy Williams (to Coventry)

BEST SEASON **FA Cup:** 1st Rd 97-98; 1-1,3-3 (2-4pen) v Darlington and 92-93, 2-2,2-3 v V.S.Rugby
FA Vase: 5th Rd 74-75 **FA Trophy:** 1st Rd Prop 97-98

HONOURS Southern Lg Midland Div 91-92; Midland Comb. R-up 90-91, Chall Cup R-up 73-74 90-91, Presidents Cup R-up 69-70; Lord Mayor of Birmingham Charity Cup 91-92 92-93 94-95 96-97; Worcs Sen. Cup R-up 92-93 96-97 97-98; 99-00Birmingham Sen. Cup 94-95

Players Progressing: Kevin Ashley (Birmingham C.), Andy Williams (Coventry C.), Geoff Scott (Leicester C.), Danny Conway (Leicester C.), Alan Smith (LeicesterC.), Dean Spink (Aston Villa), John Frain (Northampton T.), Jamie Campbell (Walsall)

Back Row, left to right: David Busst (manager), Craig Dutton, Peter Sutton, Derek Hall, Mike Payne, Jason Pearcey, Matt Smith, Nick Amos, Simon Hollis, Paul Holleran (Assistant Manager) and Graham Jones (Physio) **Front Row:** Chris Smith, Brett Healy, Alan Ward Richard Beale, Martin Hier, Ian Cooper, Martin Crowley

STOURPORT SWIFTS

CLUB OFFICIALS

Chairman: Chris Reynolds
President: Roy Crowe
General Manager: John McDonald
Secretary: Nigel Green
32 Golden Hind Drive,
Stourport -on-Severn, Worcs. DY13 9RJ
Tel: 01299 822993
Email: n.green32@btinternet.com

FOOTBALL MANAGEMENT TEAM

Manager: Rod Brown
Coach: Gary Whild

FACT FILE

Founded: 1882.
Nickname: Swifts
Sponsors: Reynolds of Rushock
Colours: Yellow & black/yellow/yellow
Change colours: White/black/black
Midweek matchday: Tuesday
Programme: 40 pages £1.00

2000-01

Leading goalscorer: Lee Booth 52
Captain: Lea Shaw
P.o.Y.: Lee Booth

GROUND Walshes Meadow, Harold Davis Drive, Stourport-on-Severn.
Tel: 01299 825188. Club Website: http://www.fly.to/swifts

Directions: Follow one-way system through Stourport sign posted Sports Centre.Go over River Severn Bridge, turn left into Harold Davies Drive. Ground is at rear of Sports Centre. Nearest rail station is Kidderminster.

Capacity: 2,000 Seats: 250 Cover: 150 Floodlights: Yes

Clubhouse: Open matchdays. Hot snacks available. Licensed bar. **Club Shop:** No

PREVIOUS **Leagues:** Kidderminster/ Worcester/ West Midland Regional, Midland Football Alliance 1998-2001
Grounds: Bewdley Rd; Moor Hall Park; Feathers Farm; Olive Grove; Hawthorns.

RECORDS **Attendancee:** 4,000 v Birmingham, charity match.
Goalscorer: Gary Crowther **Appearances:** Ian Johnson
Win: 10-0 **Defeat:** 1-7

BEST SEASON **FA Cup** **FA Vase**

HONOURS West Mids Prem Div R-Up 94-95 96-97 97-98, Lg Div 1 R-up 87-88, Prem Div Cup 92-93, Div 2 Cup R-up 82-83;
Worcs Snr Urn 92-93 93-94 94-95 97-98
Worcs Infirmary Cup 94-95 95-96 97-98; MFA 2000-01

Back Row L-R: Mark Dearlove, Lee Booth, Matt Southwick, Ross Knight, Rob Clarke, Jan Mulders, Tim Nicholls, Simon Marsh, Brendan Hackett (Player/coach). **Front L-R:** Paul Moutford, Lea Shaw (capt), Rod Brown (Manager), Alex Cowley, Adrian Cooper.

SUTTON COLDFIELD TOWN

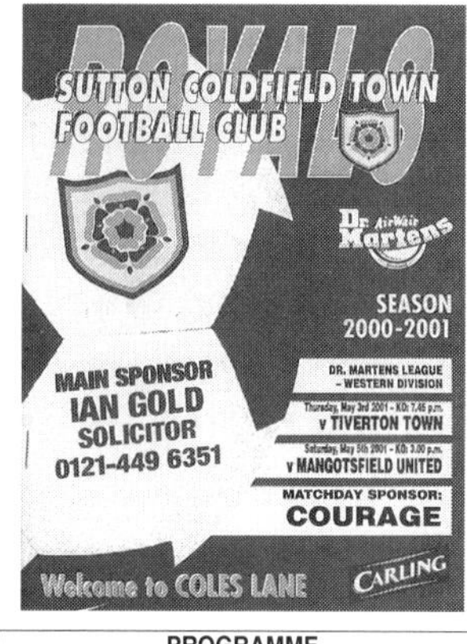

CLUB OFFICIALS

Chairman: Phillip Sharpe

Secretary: Alan Fleming, 28 Manor Road,Streetly, West Midlands B75 5PY
Tel :07970 573638 (H) 0121 354 2997 (W)

Press Officer: Peter Young
Commercial Manager: Peter Young

FOOTBALL MANAGEMENT TEAM

Manager: Chris Keogh
Asst Man: Brian Kenning
Physio: Ed Judge

FACT FILE

Formed: 1897 Nickname: Royals
Colours: Blue & White/Blue/Blue
Change colours: White/ Red/White
Midweek matchday: Tuesday
Feeder Team: Sutton Town(Mid Comb)

2000-2001
Captain: Robin Judd
P.o.Y.: Kevin Jones
Top Goalscorer: Leon Mitchell 15

GROUND Central Ground, Coles Lane, Sutton Coldfield B72 1NL Tel: 0121 354 2997 or 0121 355 5475 **Email Address:** alan.fleming1@btinternet,com
Directions: A5127 into Sutton, right at Odeon cinema (Holland Rd), then first right into Coles Lane - ground 150 yds on left. 10 mins walk from SuttonColdfield (BR), bus 104 from Birmingham
Capacity: 4,500 Cover: 500 Seats: 200 Floodlights: Yes
Clubhouse: Brick built lounge & concert room, fully carpeted and extensively decorated Open daily, food available
Club Shop: Selling metal badges, scarves, hats, pens, rosettes, progs Contact Pete Young

PROGRAMME
Pages: 20 Price: 80p
Editor: Peter Young
Local Press:
Sutton Coldfield News,
Sutton Observer
Local Radio: BRMB, Radio WM

PREVIOUS **Leagues:** Central Birmingham, Walsall Sen., Staffs Co., BirminghamComb. 50-54, West Mids (Regional) 54-65 79-82, Midlands Comb. 65-79 **Name:** Sutton Coldfield FC 1879-1921
Grounds: Meadow Plat 1879-89/ Coles Lane (site of current ambulance station) 90-1919

CLUB RECORDS **Attendance:** 2,029 v Doncaster Rovers, F.A. Cup 80-81 (Receipts £2,727)
Career Goalscorer: Eddie Hewitt 288 **Career Appearances:** Eddie Hewitt 465
Fee paid: £1,500 twice in 1991, for Lance Morrison (Gloucester) & Micky Clarke(Burton A.)
Fee received: £25,000 for Barry Cowdrill (WBA 1979)

BEST SEASON **FA Cup:** 1st Rd 80-81, 0-1 v Doncaster R (H), 92-93, 1-2 v BoltonWanderers (A)
FA Trophy: 1st Round replay 1989-90 **FA Amateur Cup:** 2nd Round 1970-71

HONOURS Southern Lg Midland Div R-up 82-83, West Mids Lg 79-80 (Lg Cup 80-81 81-82), Midland Comb.(2) 77-79 (R-up(2) 69-71, Lg Cup 69-70), Walsall Senior Lg 46-47, Walsall Sen. Cup(3) 77-80 (R-up 80-81), Staffs Sen. Cup R-up 89-90, Lord Mayor of Birmingham Charity Cup 95-96, R-up 93-94, Worcs Sen. Cup SF 88-89, Walsall Challenge Cup R-up 46-47 47-48, Sutton Charity Cup 46-47 65-66 71-72 86-87 89-90 90-91, Express & Star Cup 44-45 Dr Martens Cup 98-99

Players progressing: Arthur Corbett (Walsall 49), Paul Cooper (Manchester C.), Noel Blake (Leeds), Steve Cooper (Barnsley), Peter Latchford (WBA), Mark Smith (Wolves), John Barton (Everton), Barry Cowdrill (WBA 79),Colin Dryhurst (Halifax 79), Dale Belford (Notts Co. 87), Ellis Laight (Torquay 92)

SWINDON SUPERMARINE

CLUB OFFICIALS

Chairman: **Steve Moore**

President: **Cliff Puffit**

Secretary: **Rod Wordnam**

10, Whilestone way, Stratton, Swindon

Press Officer: **Judi Moore**

01793 790685

FOOTBALL MANAGEMENT TEAM

Manager: **Alan Dyton**

Coach: **Glynn Dubber & Tony Garland**

Physio: **Alan Jennings**

FACT FILE

Founded: 1992
Nickname: 'Marine'
Colours: Blue & white hoops/blue/white
Change colours: Yellow/navy/yellow
Midweek Matchday: Wednesday

2000-01

Top scorer: Richard Hadgkiss
P.o.Y. & Captain: Mick Casey

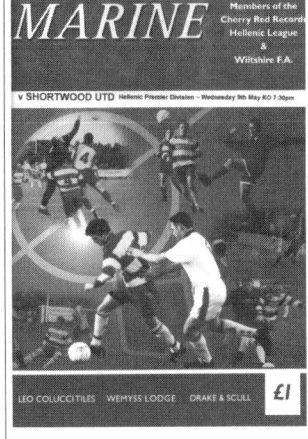

MARINE
Members of the Cherry Red Records Hellenic League & Wiltshire F.A.
v SHORTWOOD UTD Hellenic Premier Division – Wednesday 9th May KO 7:30pm
LEO COLUCCI TILES WEMYSS LODGE DRAKE & SCULL £1

Pages: 40 Price: £1.00

GROUND Hunts Copse, South Marston, Swindon
Tel: 01793 828778. E-mail: supermarinefc@aol.com.

Directions: On A361 Swindon/Highworth road, adjoining South Marston Ind. Estate. Six miles from Swindon (BR) - buses in direction of Highworth, Fairford & Lechdale. If lost ask for Honda.

Capacity: 3,000 Seats: 300 Cover: 300 Floodlights: Yes
Clubhouse: Yes

PREVIOUS

Leagues: Wiltshire Lge., Hellenic League to 2001
Names: Vickers Armstrong 46-81,Supermarine 82-91 (merged 1992) , Penhill Youth Centre 70-84, Swindon Athletic 84-89 (merged)
Ground: Supermarine: Vickers Airfield (until mid-1960s);
Swindon Ath.: Merton 70-84; `Southbrook', Pinehurst Road 84-92

RECORD **Attendance:** 498 v Highworth 2000

HONOURS: Hellenic Lge - Premier Div. 97-98, 00-01, R-up 95-96 98-99; Div. One 85-86 86-87; Reserve Section 96-97; Lge Cup 96-97,99-00; Floodlit Cup 97-98.,99-00, 00-01. Wiltshire Senior Cup 82-83, 86-87, 89-90. Wiltshire Premier Shield 96-97. Hellenic Challenge Cup 96-97, 99/00.

Back Row (L-R): Mark Teasdale (Coach), Richard Hadgkiss, Matt Saye, Steve Davis, Neil Matthews, Chris Webb, Pete Farrow, Tate Hulbert, Simon Futcher, Pete Horwat, Alan Jennings (Physio). **Middle:** Ross Moope (Mascot), Tony Garland (Asst. Manager), Tony Joyce, Michael Silvanus, Leo Colucci (Sponsor), Alan Dyton (Manager), Mick Casey (Capt), Tom Jones, Glynn Dubber (Asst. Manager). **Front:** Vinny Parker, Matt Jack.
(Hellenic Premier Division Championship Shield)

WESTON-super-MARE

CLUB OFFICIALS

President: **D A Usher**

Chairman: **Paul T Bliss**

Secretary/Press Officer: **Keith Refault**
c/o Weston Super Mare FC
Tel: 01934 635665

FOOTBALL MANAGEMENT TEAM

Coach: John Relish
Assistant Coach: Dave Mogg
Physio: Dave Lukins

FACT FILE

Formed: 1899
Nickname: Seagulls
Sponsors: 107.7 WFM
Colours: White/blue/blue
Change colours: All yellow
Midweek matches: Tuesday
Reserves' League: Somerset Senior

2000-01

Captain: & P.o.Y.: Sean Wharton
Top Scorere: Jody Bevan 24

GROUND Woodspring Park, Winterstoke Road, Weston-super-Mare BS23 3YG
Tel: 01934 635665 Directions: M5 Jct 21. A370 along dual carriageway to 4th roundabout. First left and immediately right at small roundabout, club on right. FromSouth: M5 Jct 22, follow Weston signs for approx 7 miles, right at first r'bout(by Hospital), left at next r'bout, ground 1 mile on left. Twenty minutes walk fromWeston-super-Mare (BR)
Capacity: 2,000 Seats: 250 Cover: 1,000 Floodlights: Yes
Clubhouse: Mon-Fri 7-11pm, Sat 12-11pm, Sun 12-3 & 7-11pm.
2 skittle alleys, 2bars. Bar meals and hot meals everyday
Club Shop: Selling a wide range of souvenirs & programmes.Contact Alan White at the club.

PROGRAMME

Pages: 32 Price: £1
Editors: Stuart Marshall & Phil Sheridan
Tel. 01934 635665
Local Press:
Bristol Evening Post, Western Daily Press
Local Radio: Somerset Sound, Radio Bristol
107.7 WFM

PREVIOUS **League:** Western 1900-92 (Not continuous)
Grounds: The Great Ground, Locking Road 48-55, Langford Road 55-83
Name: Borough of Weston-super-Mare

CLUB RECORDS **Attendance:** 2,623 v Woking, FA Cup First Round Proper replay 23/11/93
At Langford Road: 2,500 v Bridgwater Town, FA Cup First Round Proper replay 1961-62
Win: 11-0 v Paulton Rovers
Defeat: 1-12 v Yeovil Town Reserves
Career Goalscorer: Matthew Lazenby, 180
Career Appearances: Harry Thomas, 740
Transfer fee received: £20,000 Stuart Jones fromSheffield Wednesday 98
Transfer fee paid: None

BEST SEASON **FA Cup:** 1st Rd Proper replay 61-62, 0-1 v Bridgwater Town after 0-0; 94-95, 0-1 v Woking (A) after 2-2
FA Trophy: 14th Round 98-99 **FA Vase:** Have not entered

HONOURS Somerset Snr Cup 23-24 26-27; Western Lg Champions 91-92 (R-up 76-77), Lg Cup 76-77 (R-up 89-90), Merit Cup 76-77 77-78; Somerset Snr Lg (Reserves) Div 1 87-88 (R-up 90-91), Div 2 R-up 85-86, Div 3 84-85

Players progressing: Shaun Rouse (Carlisle United 94), Ian Maine, John Palmer(Bristol City),Wayne Brown(Chester City 97), Stuart Jones (Sheffield Wed 98), Ryan Souter (Bury 99)

Back Row, left to right: Dai Williams (Coach), Dave Lukins (Physio), Alan Bird, Mike Kilgour, Justin Pritchard, Steve Weaver, Dave Mogg (Assistant Manager), Jody Bevan, Marc Richards ,Mark Price, Dave Hunt, John Relish (Manager)
Front Row: Stuart Walford, Dave Butler,Jimmy Cox, Ryan King, Mike Pengally, Dave Watts, Andy Catley and Andy Smith

EASTERN DIVISION FINAL LEAGUE TABLE 2000-01

		P	W	D	L	F	A	W	D	L	F	A	Pts	GD
1	Newport IoW	42	17	4	0	56	7	11	6	4	35	23	94	61
2	Chelmsford City	42	17	2	2	60	21	10	7	4	42	24	90	57
3	Grantham Town	42	16	3	2	60	19	9	8	4	40	28	86	53
4	Histon	42	12	6	3	44	25	11	5	5	40	28	80	31
5	Baldock Town	42	13	5	3	37	16	10	5	6	44	28	79	37
6	Hastings Town	42	10	6	5	29	24	12	4	5	43	26	76	22
7	Stamford	42	11	7	3	35	24	9	4	8	34	35	71	10
8	Tonbridge Angels	42	11	5	5	41	26	7	6	8	38	32	65	21
9	Langney Sports	42	11	6	4	44	25	8	2	11	31	30	65	20
10	Rothwell Town (-3)	42	14	2	5	61	27	6	3	12	25	47	62	12
11	Corby Town	42	7	3	11	30	47	7	7	7	34	45	52	-28
12	Ashford Town	42	9	3	9	30	34	6	1	14	23	49	49	-30
13	Banbury United	42	4	8	9	34	33	8	3	10	23	21	47	3
14	Witney Town	42	7	6	8	33	36	5	5	11	22	35	47	-16
15	Bashley	42	6	6	9	31	32	4	8	9	26	39	44	-14
16	Dartford	42	5	7	9	24	32	6	4	11	25	35	44	-18
17	Burnham (-1)	42	6	9	6	20	28	4	5	12	19	37	43	-26
18	Wisbech Town	42	5	5	11	19	36	5	4	12	26	53	39	-44
19	St. Leonards	42	8	4	9	37	37	1	6	14	18	50	37	-32
20	Erith & Belvedere	42	6	3	12	27	44	4	4	13	22	48	37	-43
21	Sittingbourne	42	6	1	14	21	42	2	8	11	20	37	33	-38
22	Spalding United	42	4	8	9	17	33	3	4	14	18	40	33	-38

EASTERN DIVISION LEADING GOALSCORERS 2000-01

38	Stephen Portway	Chelmsford City	18	Gary Bennett	Chelmsford City
31	Gary Bull	Grantham Town	18	Daniel Gibbons	Newport IOW
31	Ashley Warner	Corby Town	17	Matthew Godderick	Banbury United
25	Wade Falana	Tonbridge Angels	17	Shaun Keeble	Stamford
25	Neil Kennedy	Histon	16	Dean Foley	Rothwell Town
22	Malcolm Ndekwe	Stamford	16	Christopher Arnold	Dartford
19	David Arter	Tonbridge Angels	15	Liam Morris	Rothwell Town
18	Dominic Barclay	St Leonards	15	Richard Ranshaw	Grantham Town

EASTERN DIVISION RESULTS CHART 2000-01

		1	2	3	4	5	6	7	8	9	10	11	12	13	14	15	16	17	18	19	20	21	22
1	Ashford T	X	1-4	1-0	3-2	1-1	0-6	1-3	1-0	4-0	1-2	0-2	2-1	3-1	1-3	2-3	4-1	2-1	1-0	0-1	0-0	1-2	1-1
2	Baldock T	2-1	X	1-0	1-0	0-1	1-1	3-0	0-0	3-1	2-1	1-1	3-2	1-0	2-0	0-1	2-1	5-0	4-1	3-1	1-1	1-1	1-2
3	Banbury U	4-0	0-1	X	3-3	1-1	2-3	1-2	1-1	2-2	2-3	0-2	1-1	0-2	1-1	2-3	1-1	2-0	4-1	3-0	1-2	2-3	1-1
4	Bashley	2-0	0-3	0-1	X	2-0	1-1	4-4	3-0	1-2	1-1	2-2	0-2	1-0	1-1	2-2	0-2	6-1	0-2	0-1	2-5	0-2	3-0
5	Burnham	0-2	1-1	0-1	2-2	X	1-5	1-0	3-1	1-0	2-1	0-2	1-3	1-1	1-1	0-0	0-0	0-0	2-2	1-1	0-5	2-0	1-0
6	Chelmsford	3-1	4-3	3-2	3-1	5-0	X	3-1	1-0	2-0	1-2	2-2	4-2	3-1	0-1	6-0	1-0	1-0	2-1	4-1	4-1	6-0	2-2
7	Corby T	1-5	1-6	2-1	2-2	2-0	2-3	X	3-4	4-2	0-2	2-1	0-3	0-2	2-3	3-2	0-2	1-1	2-1	0-1	2-2	0-4	1-0
8	Dartford	1-2	2-4	1-0	1-1	1-1	0-1	2-2	X	1-1	2-2	1-0	1-2	1-0	1-1	2-3	1-1	0-1	3-0	0-4	0-1	3-2	0-3
9	Erith & B	3-0	0-2	0-5	0-1	2-1	0-3	2-4	1-2	X	1-1	1-5	0-1	1-5	1-3	1-0	3-0	0-2	1-1	2-2	4-3	3-1	1-2
10	Grantham	6-1	1-3	1-0	6-0	2-1	2-0	5-1	4-2	1-1	X	5-0	5-2	5-0	3-0	4-3	4-2	1-1	2-1	0-1	1-0	2-0	0-0
11	Hastings T	3-1	1-1	1-0	0-1	2-0	2-2	1-1	2-1	0-2	0-5	X	0-0	1-0	1-2	3-0	1-1	3-2	0-0	3-0	0-4	2-0	3-1
12	Histon	2-0	2-2	2-0	2-1	2-0	1-3	2-2	1-1	3-0	1-1	2-5	X	2-1	3-1	0-1	0-0	4-2	2-1	2-2	3-1	5-1	3-0
13	Langney S	1-0	4-1	1-1	1-1	2-1	4-1	3-1	1-2	4-1	1-1	0-1	1-3	X	0-1	1-1	4-2	1-0	3-1	2-2	1-1	5-1	4-2
14	Newport IW	5-0	1-0	1-1	3-2	0-0	0-0	3-0	2-0	2-0	6-0	2-0	0-0	1-0	X	3-1	4-0	2-0	4-1	3-1	1-0	7-1	6-0
15	Rothwell T	3-0	2-0	3-2	1-2	5-0	3-1	2-2	2-1	7-2	2-1	0-1	1-4	3-1	1-2	X	2-2	1-0	10-2	3-1	2-3	7-0	1-0
16	S'bourne	2-1	2-3	1-0	0-1	0-2	0-3	0-0	2-5	1-2	0-5	1-5	1-2	0-4	1-2	1-2	X	1-0	3-0	1-2	1-0	3-1	0-2
17	Spalding U	0-0	0-3	0-1	0-0	0-4	1-1	0-1	1-0	1-1	3-3	0-3	1-2	0-2	3-2	2-0	2-1	X	1-1	0-4	1-3	1-1	0-0
18	St Leonards	2-1	1-0	0-1	3-3	4-1	1-3	8-2	1-2	3-1	0-2	0-1	0-4	0-0	0-3	4-1	1-1	3-1	X	2-0	3-3	0-4	1-3
19	Stamford	1-2	3-2	1-1	3-1	1-0	1-0	2-2	1-1	2-1	2-2	0-2	0-1	2-1	0-0	4-1	2-0	3-2	0-0	X	3-2	1-1	3-2
20	Tonbridge	5-0	0-0	0-2	2-1	2-3	1-1	1-2	2-0	1-0	1-1	2-4	3-3	1-2	1-1	4-0	2-1	2-1	1-0	6-2	X	2-1	2-1
21	Wisbech T	2-3	1-4	1-2	0-0	1-0	0-3	0-1	1-2	2-3	0-1	2-1	1-1	2-5	0-2	1-0	2-1	0-0	1-1	0-5	1-1	X	1-0
22	Witney T	1-3	1-1	1-2	3-1	2-2	1-1	1-3	2-0	3-0	0-3	3-3	3-1	2-3	0-5	2-1	1-1	2-3	4-1	0-2	1-0	0-0	X

We ceratinly had more than the average rainfall last season.

ASHFORD TOWN

Pages: 32 Price: £1.00
Editor: Tim Warren

Local Press: Kentish Express
Local Radio: Radio Kent, Invicta Radio

CLUB OFFICIALS

Chairman: **Andrew Tucker**
President: **Ashley M Batt**
Secretary/Press Officer: **A Lancaster**
128 Kingsnorth Rd, Ashford, Kent
TN23 2HY Tel: 01233 621325
Commercial Director: **Ernie Warron**
Tel: 01233 634125

FOOTBALL MANAGEMENT TEAM

Manager: Tim Thorogood
Asst Manager: Fary Anderson
Coach: Tim Thorogood
Physio: George Sargeant

FACT FILE

Formed: 1930
Nickname: Nuts & Bolts
Colours: Green&white/white/green
Change colours: White&green/green/white
Midweek home matchday: Tuesday
Reserves' League: Bass Brewers Kent Lge

2000-01

Leading goalscorer: Tony Eeles 10
Captains: Steve Robinson / Tom Binks

GROUND The Homelands, Ashford Road, Kingsnorth, Ashford, Kent TN26 1NJ
Tel: 01233 611838

Directions: M20 jct 10, follow A2070 signs towards Brenzett & Lydd airport, dual carriageway to junction of old A2070, ground 1 mile on left thro' village of Kingsnorth. 4 miles south of Ashford

Capacity: 3,200 Cover: 1,250 Seats: 500 Floodlights: Yes

Clubhouse: Open matchdays and for special functions. Licensed bar, function room. Limited food - sandwiches & simple snacks.

Club Shop: Sells old progs, pennants, scarves, badges etc. Contact Alan Bird(01233 662680)

PREVIOUS **Names:** Ashford United, Ashford Railway, Ashford F.C.
Leagues: Kent 30-59. Ground: Essella Park, Essella Rd 30-87

CLUB RECORDS **Attendance:** 6,525 (at Essella Park, previous ground), v Crystal Palace, FA Cup 1st Rd 1959.
3,363 (at current ground), v Fulham FA Cup 1st Round 1994.
Goalscorer: Dave Arter 197. **Appearances:** Peter McRobert 765
Win: 10-1 v Bury Town, February 1964. **Defeat:** 0-8 v Crawley Town, November1964
Fee Paid: £7,000 for J Ross & D Arter (Sittingbourne, March 94)
Fee Received: £25,000 for Jeff Ross & Dave Arter (Hythe Tn, 90). Individually: £20,000 for Lee McRobert (Sittingbourne, 93)

BEST SEASON **FA Trophy:** Semi Final 72-73, 96-97 2nd Rd
FA Cup: 2nd Rd 61-62, 0-3 v QPR (H), 66-67, 0-5 v Swindon (A). 1st Rd 7 times. League clubs defeated: None.

HONOURS FA Trophy SF 72-73; Southern Lg Southern Div R-up 86-87 95-96; Kent Lg 48-49(R-up 31-32), Lg Cup 38-39; Kent Senior Cup 58-59 62-63 92-93 95-96

Players progressing: Ollie Norris (Rochdale 61), HowardMoore (Coventry 66), Tony Godden (WBA 75), Lee McRobert (Millwall 94)

BANBURY UNITED

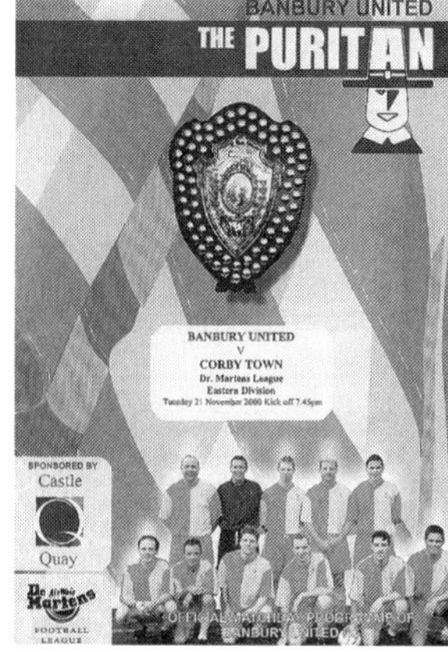

Pages: 40 Price: £1.00
Editor: Kevin Hicklin

Club Website: www.banburyunited.co.uk
Unofficial sites:
www..banbury-united.cityslide.com
www.expage.com.bufc

CLUB OFFICIALS

Chairman: Paul Saunders
Vice Chairman: Brian Kay
President: David Jesson
Commercial Mgr: Nigel Porter
Press Officer: Barry Worsley
Secretary: B Worsley, c/o Sol Systems, Unit 4 Mallorie Hse, Beaumont Rd,Banbury, OX16 7RH
Tel: 01295 265638 (H), 01295 255536 (B)
Email: bworsley@solsystems.freeserve.co.uk

FOOTBALL MANAGEMENT TEAM

Manager: Kevin Brock
Coach: Brian Robinson
Physio:Wally Hastie

FACT FILE

Founded: 1933 Reformed: 1965
Nickname: Puritans
Sponsors: T.B.A.
Colours: Red & gold/red/red
Change colours: White /white/white
Midweek matches: Tuesday
Reserves' Lge: Midland Combination

2000-01

Captain: Jonathon Corbett
P.o.Y.: Keiran Sullivan
Top Goalscorer: Matthew Gooderick 24

GROUND The Stadium, off Station Rd, Banbury, Oxon . Tel: 01295 263354

Directions: M40 jct 11, follow signs for Banbury then BR station, turn right down narrow lane before entering station forecourt; eastern end of town
Capacity: 6,500 Seats: 50 Cover: 500 Floodlights: Yes
Clubhouse: Open match days & week-ends. Mid-week on hire. Hot food available during after matches
Club Shop: Yes

HONOURS Oxon Snr Cup 78-79 87-88 (R-up7); Birmingham Comb. R-up 47-48; Oxon Prof. Cup 52-53(jt) 70-71(jt) 72-73 77-78 79-80(jt); Hellenic premier Winners 99-00 Hellenic Lg.Cup R-Up 91-92; Birmingham Snr Cup R-Up 48-49 59-60 (S.F.46-47); Oxon Snr Lg. 34-35 39-4047-48 (res); Oxon Hosp. Cup 46-47 (R-up 45-46); Oxon Benev. Cup R-up 77-78 80-8182-83; Daventry Charity Cup 88-90; Smiths Mem. Cup 68-70 (R-up 66-68); Hitchin Centenary Cup 68-69 (R-up 67-68); Leamington Charity Cup 51-52; Bucks Charity Cup 00-01
Warks Comb. R-up 57-58 60-61, Presidents Cup R-up 60-61; Midland Floodlit Cup 67-68; Wallspan Comb. 85-86

PREVIOUS **Leagues:** Banbury Jnr 33-34; Oxon Snr 34-35; Birmingham Comb. 35-54; W.Mids 54-66; Southern 66-90
Name: Banbury Spencer

BEST SEASON **FA Cup:** 1st Rd replay 73-74 (Also 1st Rd 47-48 61-62 72-73)
FA Trophy: 3rd Rd 70-71 73-74

RECORDS **Attendance:** 7,160 v Oxford City, FA Cup 3rd Qual.Rd, 30/10/48
Goalscorer: Dick Pike (1935-48), Tony Jacques (65-76) - both 222
Appearances: Ian Bowyer (557) Fee Paid : £2,000 for Phil Emsden (Oxford Utd, Jan 1980)
Fee Received: £20,000 Kevin Wilson (Derby, December 1979)
Win: 12-0 v RNAS Culham, Oxon Snr Cup 45-46
Defeat: 2-11 v West Bromwich Albion `A', Birmingham Comb. 38-39

Players progressing: Ollie Kearns (Reading), Kevin Wilson & Richard Pratley(Derby), Mick Kearns & Terry Muckleberg (Oxford), Martin Singleton (Coventry)

BASHLEY

CLUB OFFICIALS

Chairman: **David Malone**
President: **Trevor Adams**
Vice Chairman: **Fred Pingram**
Secretary: **Mrs Caroline Bailey,**
39 Ashley Lane, Hordle, Lymington,
S014 0GB Tel: 01425 620729

FOOTBALL MANAGEMENT TEAM

Manager: Derick Binns
Asst Manager: Dave Jones

FACT FILE
Formed: 1947
Nickname: The Bash
Sponsors: T.B.A.
Colours: Yellow & black
Change colours: Blue & white
Midweek matchday: Tuesday
Reserves' League: Wessex Comb

2000-01
Leading goalscorer: Dave Puckett
Captain: Andy Darnton
P.O.Y: Craig Davis

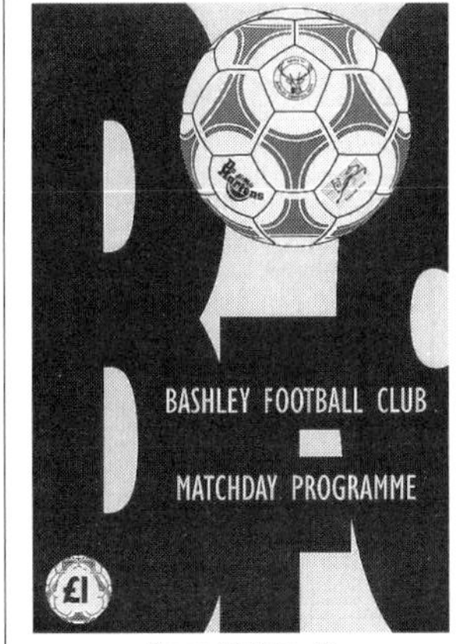

Pages: 36 Price: £1

Local Press: Bournemouth Echo, Southern Pink, New Milton Advertiser
Local Radio: 2CR,Solent, Ocean Sound

GROUND Recreation Ground, Bashley, Hampshire BH25 5RY. Tel: 01425 620280

Directions: A35 Lyndhurst towards Christchurch, turn left down B3058 towards New Milton, ground on left in Bashley village. Half hour walk from New Milton (BR) station

Capacity: 4,250 Cover: 1,200 Seats: 300 Floodlights: Yes

Clubhouse: Usual licensing hours. Snacks available
Club Shop: Open matchdays

PREVIOUS **Leagues:** Bournemouth 50-83; Hants 83-86; Wessex 86-89

CLUB RECORDS **Attendance:** 3,500 v Emley, F.A. Vase S.F. 1st Leg 87-88
Win: 21-1 v Co-operative (A), Bournemouth Lge, 64
Defeat: 2-20 v Air Speed(A), Bournemouth Lge, 57
Career Goalscorer: Colin Cummings
Career Appearances: John Bone
Transfer fee paid: £7,500 for J Stagg from Andover
Transfer fee received: £7,500 for Darren Powell from Weymouth 95

BEST SEASON **FA Cup:** 2nd Rd Proper 1994-95, 0-1 v Swansea City
FA Vase: Semi Final 87-88, Qtr Final 88-89 FA Trophy: 2nd Round 91-92

HONOURS Southern Lg Southern Division 89-90 (Lg Cup SF 89-90), Wessex Lg 86-87 87-88 88-89, Hants Lg Div 3 84-85, Hants Lg Combination 88-89, Russell Cotes Cup 88-89 90-91 92-93

Players Progressing : Wayne Brown (Bristol C 1994), David Billington Peterborough 1996), Ryan Young (Plymouth 1997), Dean Higgins (Torquay 1998), Danny Smith (Bournemouith 1998), Craig Davies (Cardiff City 1998), Tony Wallis (Cardiff C 1999), Wade Elliott (AFC Bouremouth 2000)

Action from Bashley's visit to Grantham.
Photo: Gavin J Tutcher

BURNHAM

CLUB OFFICIALS

Chairman: **Malcolm Higton**
Vice Chairman: **Mark Green**
Press Officer: **Secretary**
Secretary: **Alan King**
41 Underwood Road, High Wycombe,
Bucks HP13 6YD (01494523920 (H)
078999 41414(M)

FOOTBALL MANAGEMENT TEAM

Manager: John Griffith
Coach: Neal McLoughlin
Physio: Melanie Garrett

FACT FILE

Founded: 1878
Sponsors: Laing Homes & PKGraphics
Colours: Blue & white/blue/white
Change colours: Yellow/yellow/black
Midweek matchday: Tuesday 7.30
Reserve Team's Lge: Suburban

2000-01
Captain: Paul Brett
P.o.Y.: Mark O'Sullivan
Top Scorer: Steve Lockhart (11)

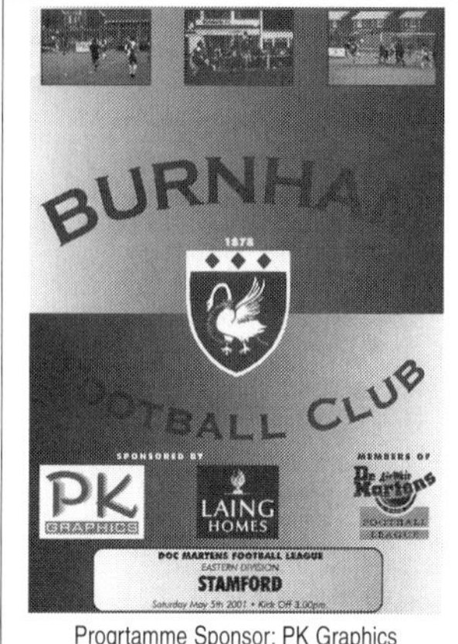

Progrtamme Sponsor: PK Graphics
32 pages Editor: Cliff Sparkes

Local Press: Slough Observer, South Bucks Express, Maidenhead Advertiser, Buckingham Advertiser
Local Radio: Star FM, BBC Thames Valley

Ground: The Gore, Wymers Wood Road, Burnham, Slough SL1 8JG
Tel: 01628 602467/602697

Directions: North west of village centre, 2 miles from Burnham BR station, 2miles from M4 junction 7, 5 miles from M40 junction 2, 100yds north of Gorecrossroads

fork right into Wymers Wood Rd and ground is immediately on right

Capacity: 2,500 Cover: 250 Seats: 250 Floodlights: Yes

Clubhouse: Open every evening and w/e lunch.

HONOURS Athenian Lg R-up(2) 78-80, Hellenic Lg 75-76 98-99 (Div 1 R-up 72-73, Lg Cup 75-76 98-99, Div 1 Cup 71-72), London Spartan Lg 84-85 (Lg Cup 84-85), Reading Comb. Lg Cup 70-71 (All Champions Cup 70-71), Wycombe Comb. R-up (4) 65-67 68-70

PREVIOUS **Leagues:** Sth Bucks & East Berks; Maidenhead Intermediate; Windsor,Slough & Dist; Gt Western Comb. 48-64; Wycombe Comb. 64-70; Reading Comb. 70-71; Hellenic 71-77; Athenian 77-84; London Spartan 84-85; Southern 85-95; Hellenic 95-99
Name: Burnham & Hillingdon 1985-87 **Ground:** Baldwin Meadow (until 20's)

BEST SEASON **FA Cup:** 3rd Qualifying Rd **FA Vase:** Semi-Final 82-83, Q-F 77-78.
FA Trophy: 4th Round Replay 99-00

RECORD **Attendance:** 2,380 v Halesowen Town, FA Vase 2/4/83
Scorer: Fraser Hughes 65, 69-70 **Win:** 18-0 v High Duty Alloys, 70-71
Defeat: 1-10 v Ernest Turners Sports, 63-64

Players progressing: D Hancock (Reading), R Rafferty (Grimsby Town), D Payne(Barnet)

CHATHAM TOWN

CLUB OFFICIALS
Chairman: **P Enright**

Secretary: **Brian Burcombe**
4 Hallwood Close, Parkwood, Rainham,
Kent ME8 9NT
Tel: 01634 363419

FOOTBALL MANAGEMENT TEAM
Manager: Steve Hearn
Asst Manager: Peter Coupland

FACT FILE
Founded: 1882
Nickname: Chats
Sponsors: Topps Scaffolding
Colours: Red & black/black/black
Change Colours: Yellow & green
Midweek matchday: Tuesday

2000-01
Captain: Phil Miles
P.o.Y.: Garry Tilley
Top Scorere: Simon Austin

GROUND Maidstone Road Sports Ground, Maidstone Road, Chatham, Kent
Tel: 01634 812194

Directions: M2, A229 Chatham turn-off, follow signs to Chatham, ground one and a half miles on right opposite garage. 1 mile from Chatham (BR).
Capacity: 5,000 Seats: 500 Cover: 1,000 Floodlights: Yes

Programme: 24 pages, £1.00
Editor: Tony Smith

Clubhouse: Matchdays and functions

PREVIOUS
Names: Chatham FC; Medway FC (1970s)
Leagues: Southern (several spells); Aetolian 59-64; Metropolitan 64-68;Kent (Sev. spells)
Ground: Great Lines, Chatham 1882-90

RECORD **Gate:** 5,000 v Gillingham, 1980

BEST SEASON **FA Cup:** QF 1888-89 (incl 2-0 v Nottm Forest 2-0) **FA Trophy:** 3rd Rd 70-71

HONOURS Kent Lg (9) 1894-95 03-05 24-25 26-27 71-72 73-74 76-77 79-80 00-01
(R-up 02-03 23-24 25-26 70-71 74-75 80-81, Lg Cup 71-72 76-77 (R-up(3)),
Thames & Medway Comb.(5) 1896-97 04-06 19-20 23-24, Kent Snr Cup 1888-89 1904-05 10-11 18-19, Kent Snr Shield 19-20

CORBY TOWN

CLUB OFFICIALS

Chairman: **James Kane C.B.E.**

President: **Vacant**

Secretary:**Gerry Lucas,**8 Richmond Avenue, Kettering, Northants NN15 5JG
Tel: 01536 513507 (H) 07932 633343 (M)

FOOTBALL MANAGEMENT TEAM

Manager:Eddie McGoldrick
Assistant Manager: Kevin Fox
Physio: Mick Mackie

FACT FILE

Formed: 1948
Nickname: The Steelmen
Sponsor: British Steel
Colours: Black& white stripes.black,black
Change colours: White& Red,white,white
Midweek matchday: Wednesday
Reserves' League: United Counties Res Div

Season 2000-2001
Captain:Tyrone Mintus
P.O.Y.: Ashley Warner
Top Goalscorer: Ashley Warner (34)

PROGRAMME

Pages: 32 Price: £1
Editor: David.Tilley
Local Press: Northampton Evening Telegraph
Local Radio: BBC Radio Northampton, Hereward, KCBC, Connect F.M.
Cllub's Email : corbytownfc@ talk21.com

GROUND Rockingham Triangle Stadium, Rockingham Road, Corby NN17 2AE Tel: 01536 406640

Directions: On northern outskirts of town at junction of A6003 and A6116,opposite entrance to Rockingham Castle grounds. One and a half miles from Corby (BR)

Capacity: 3,000 Cover: 1,150 Seats: 960 Floodlights: Yes

Clubhouse: Trackside Bar open matchdays and during the week for hot food etc.

Club Shop: Sells badges, progs etc.(Before & half time) C .Woolmer Tel: 01536 260900

PREVIOUS **Leagues:** United Counties 35-52, Midland 52-58

CLUB RECORDS **Attendance:** 2,240 v Watford, pre-season friendly 86-87
At Old Ground; 10,239 v Peterborough Utd, FA Cup 3rd Qual. Rd 52-53
Win: 14-0 v Gainsborough Trinity, 56-57 **Defeat:** 0-10 v Paget Rangers, 95-96
Career Goalscorer: David Hofbauer 141 (84-95) **Career Appearances:** Derek Walker600 (78-92)
Transfer fee paid: £2,700 for Elwyn Roberts (Barnet, 81) **Transfer fee received:** £20,000 for Matt Murphy (Oxford U. 93)

BEST SEASON **FA Cup:** 3rd Rd 65-66 (lost to Plymouth). 1st Rd on five occasions; 54-55 63-6667-68
League clubs defeated: Luton Town 65-66 **FA Trophy:** 3rd Rd, 1986-87

HONOURS UCL 50-51 51-52 (R-up 37-38), Midland Lg R-up 52-53, Southern Lg Midland Div R-up 90-91 (Merit Cup 63-64 90-91), Northants Snr Cup 6; Maunsell Cup 83-84, Daventry Charity Cup 94-95, Midland Floodlit Cup 74-75, Evans Halshaw F'lit Cup 91-92, Anglia Floodlit Trophy 68-69 72-73, Chelmsford Invitation Cup 63-64 64-65 65-66 (joint), Kettering & Dist Samaritan Cup 60-61(joint) 68-69, Wellingborough Charity Cup 50-51, Desborough Nursing Cup 48-49 50-51 (joint), Bob Cumning Cup 6

Players progressing: A McCabe (Chesterfield 55), L Chalmers (Leicester C. 56), K Brown (Nottm Forest 56), P Kearns (Aldershot 62), N Dean (Southampton 63), H Curran (Millwall 64), D McNeil/A McGowan/G Reilly (Northampton69/75/76), P Chard (Peterborough 79), T Morley (West Ham), J Flower (SheffieldUtd), M Murphy (Oxford Utd 93), C McKenzie (Hereford 94)

L-R Back Row: Sean Brennan, Paul Doherty, David Hollis, Richard Tanner (now Shepshed Dynamo), Tyrone Mintus, Des Elliott, Mark Wood, Steven Julian, Ashley Warner.
Front Row: Ian Cooper, Lane Clark, Gavin Cox, Taylor Mintus (mascot), Gary Kennedy, Grant Mawby. **Photo:** David Tilley.

DARTFORD

CLUB OFFICIALS

Chairman: **David Skinner**
Vice Chairman: **Norman Grimes**
Secretary: **Peter Martin**
10 Pembroke Place,Sutton-at-Hone,
Dartford, Kent DA4 9GN
(Match Days Only 01474 533796)
Com.Man.: **Steve Irving** 0147453379

FOOTBALL MANAGEMENT TEAM

Manager: Gary Julians
Coach:Asst-Manager: Micky Crowe
Physio:Dave Phillips

FACT FILE

Formed: 1888
Nickname: The Darts
Colours: White & black/black/black
Change colours: All Red
Midweek home matchday: Tuesday
Res League:Bass Brewers Kent Div 1
Website: www.darfordfootballclub.co.uk

2000-0

Captain: Luke Morrish
P.o.Y. & Top Scorer: Chris Arnold 21

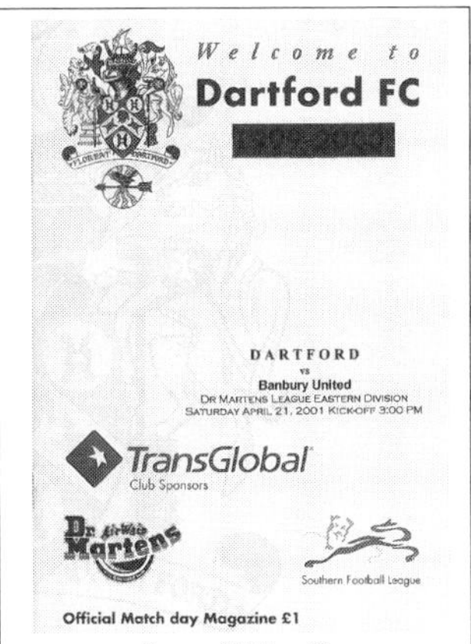

Pages: 40 Price: £1
Editor: Mike Brett-Smith Tel: 01322 277243
Press: Dartford Times, Dartford Messenger
Local Radio: Radio Kent.

GROUND As for Gravesend & Northfleet FootballClub
Directions: From Dartford Town Centre: Take A226 to Gravesend/Swanscombe for 4 miles until Swansccombe. At bottom of Galley Hill through lights and ground is immediately on left.
From A2 coastbound: Take Bluewater/Greenhithe exit (B255) and at second roundabout, with McDonalds onright) turn right towards Swanscombe junction with A226 . Then as above.
British Rail: Northfleet Station two minutes from ground
Dartford F.C. Email Address: peter@martinpe.freeserve.co.uk

PREVIOUS
Leagues: Kent (6) 1894-96 1897-8 1899-02 09-14 21-26 93-96 Southern Lg 1896-98, 99-1900, 26-81, 82-84, 86-92; GMVC 81-82, 84-86
Grounds: The Brent/ Westgate House, Potters Meadow, Engleys Meadow, Summers Meadow, Watling St, Cray Wanderers, Erith & Belverdere, and & Purfleet

CLUB RECORDS **Attendance:** 11,004 v Leyton Orient FA Cup 48
Career Appearances: Steve Robinson 653
Win: 11-1 v Faversham Tn Kent Snr Cup 65 **Defeat:** 0-10 v Guildford City SouthernLge 46
Transfer fee paid: £6,000 for John Bartley (Chelmsford 88) **Received:** £25,000 forAndy Hessenthaler (Redbridge Forest)

BEST SEASON **FA Trophy:** Runners-up 74 **FA Vase:** 2nd Qual Rd 95/96
FA Cup: 3rd Rd Prop 35-36 & 36-37 League clubs defeated: Cardiff (1935), Exeter(1961), Aldershot (1968)

HONOURS Southern Lg 1930-31, 31-32, 73-74, 83-84, R-up 87-88, 88-89, Eastern Div 30-31,31-32, Southern Div 80-81, Southern Lg Div 2 1896-97, Lg Cup 76-77, 87-88, 88-89, Championship Shield 83-84, 87-88, 88-89; Kent Lg 1995-96, Lg Cup 24-25,Kent Snr Cup 29-30, 34-35, 38-39, 69-70, Snr Trophy 95-96, Inter Lg Chall 1974;FA Trophy R-up 1974

Players progressing: Idris Hopkins (Brentford 32), Fred Dall(West Ham 36), Riley Cullum/Fred Alexander/Ted Croker (Charlton 47/48/48) Frank Coombs (Bristol C 49), James Kelly (Gillingham 51), Tom Ritchie (Grimsby 58), Dave Underwood (Watford 60), Derek Hales (Luton 72), Andy Hessenthaler (Watfordvia Redbridge F),Jimmy Bullard (West Ham United)

DORCHESTER TOWN

CLUB OFFICIALS

Chairman: **E,C,G,Belt**
President: **A.E.Miller**
Vice Chairman: **K Miller**
Comm Mgr: **Brian Benjafield**
Secretary: **David Martin**
21 Diggory Crescent, Dorchester
01305 262345
General Manager: **Keith Kellaway**

FOOTBALL MANAGEMENT TEAM

Manager: Mark Morris
Physio: Geoff Dine

FACT FILE

Formed: 1880
Nickname: The Magpies
Sponsors:Contract Motoring Services
Colours: Black & white stripes/black/black
Change colours: All red
Midweek games: Tuesdays (7.45)
Newsline (Magpies Hotline): 0839 664412
Reserves' League: Dorset Comb

2000-01

Captain: Matty Holmes
P.o.Y.:Mark Ormerod
Top Scorers:O Pickard M,Groves 6

DORCHESTER TOWN FC
Official Matchday Programme
£1.50
CARPETS DIRECT
The Magpies vs Burton Albion
Saturday 28th April
K.O. 3.00pm
Match Sponsor: The Seven Stars
Matchball Sponsor: Roger Battrick

Pages: 32 Price: £1.00
Editor: Melvin Cross (01305 848365)

Local Press: Dorset Evening Echo, Western Gazette, Western Daily Press
Local Radio: Two Counties Radio, Wessex FM

GROUND Avenue Stadium, Weymouth Avenue, Dorchester DT1 2RY Tel: 01305 262451

Directions: Situated at the junction of the town bypass (A35) and the Weymouth road (A354)
Nearest station: Dorchester South

Capacity: 5,009 Cover: 2,846 Seats: 697 Floodlights: Yes

Clubhouse: Dorchester Lounge Club - access via main entrance to stadium.
Cold food and snacks

Club Shop: Sells replica shirts, badges, mugs, etc

PREVIOUS **Leagues:** Dorset; Western 1947-72
Grounds: Council Recreation Ground, Weymouth Avenue 1880-1929; The Avenue Ground, Weymouth Avenue 29-90

CLUB RECORDS **Attendance:** 4,000 v Chelsea, official ground opening 1990. Competitive: 4, 159 v Weymouth, Southern Lge Prem Div , 99
Goalscorer: Dennis Cheney 61 (in one season) **Appearances:** Derek (Dinkie) Curtis 458 50-66
Win: 7-0 v Canterbury (A), Southern Lge Southern Div 86-87
Defeat: 0-13 v Welton Rovers Western Lge 66
Fee Paid: £12,000 for Chris Townsend (Gloucester City, 1990)
Fee Received: £35,000 for Trevor Senior (Portsmouth, 1981)

BEST SEASON **FA Trophy:** 3rd Rd replay 71-72, 96-97
FA Cup: 2nd Rd Replay 81-82, 1-2 v A.F.C. Bournemouth after 1-1. 2nd Rd 54-55 57-58; 1st Rd8 times

HONOURS Southern Lg 85-85, R-up 79-80 Div 1 Sth R-up 77-78, Lg Cup 86-87 R-up 91-92; Western Lg 54-55 R-up 60-61, Div 2 R-up 49-50, Lge Cup 54-54; Dorset Snr Cup 50-51 60-61 67-68 68-69 71-72 93-94 94-95; Dorset Lg 37-38

Players progressing: Len Drake (Bristol Rov. 57), David Noake (Luton 59), Mike Turner (Swindon 61), Trevor Senior (Portsmouth 81), David West (Liverpool 83), Mike Squire (Torquay 84), Jeremy Judd (Torquay 84),Tony White (Bournem'th 85), Graham Roberts (Spurs, Chelsea, Rangers, England) who progressed via Weymouth. Darren Garner (Rotherham U, 95), Craig Taylor (Swindon),Syfyan Ghazghazi (Club African De Tunis 98)

L-R Back Row: Mark Morris (manager), Brian Benjafield, Matt Lonnon, Danny O'Hagan , Oliver Cherrett, Matt Groves, Mark Ormerod, Andy Harris, Jamie Brown, Geoff Dine, (Physio) and Derek Taylor (Kit manager).
Middle Row: Martyn Sullivan, Paul Toms, Matty Holmes, Marcus Oldbury and Mark Jermyn.
Front Row: Simon Radcliffe, Mike White, Justin Keeler and Lee Cornick **Photo: Dorset Evening Echo**

EASTBOURNE BOROUGH

CLUB OFFICIALS

Chairman: Len Smith

President: J Stonestreet

Secretary: Mrs Myra Stephens,
7b Erica Close, Langney, Eastbourne,
East Sussex BN23 6HY
Tel/Fax: 01323 766050 0771 8027981 (M)

FOOTBALL MANAGEMENT TEAM

Manager: Garry Wilson

Coach: Nick Greenwood

Physio: Ray Tuppen

FACT FILE

Founded: 1966Nickname: Sports

Sponsors: 1st Ckass Window Systems Ltd.

Colours: Red & Black

Change: White & Red/ red/white

Midweek Matchday: Tuesday

Reserve League:Sussex Co.Prem Res.

2000-01 Captain: Daren Pearce

P.o.Y.: Ben Austin Top Scorer: Matt Allen 19

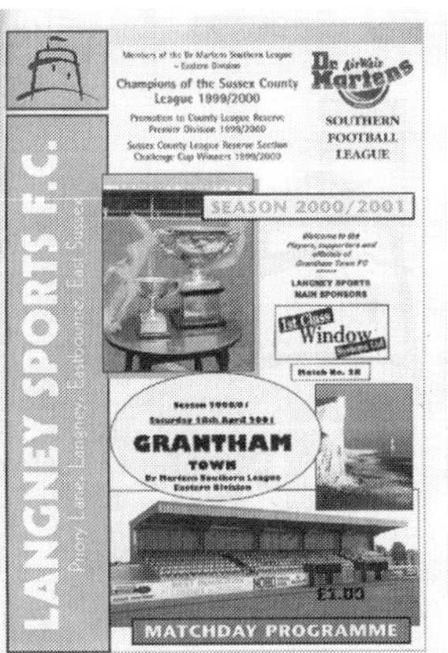

PROGRAMME

Editor: Mike Spooner

Tel./Fax: 01323 461003

Website: www.eastbourne borough fc.co.uk

Local Press: Eastbourne Gazette & Herald

GROUND Langney Sports Club, Priory Lane, Eastbourne, East Sussex Tel: 01323 766265
Email Address: head@stoucrosse-sussex.sch.uk

Capacity: 2,500 Seats: 300 Cover: 2,500 Floodlights: Yes

Directions: A22 to Polegate, A27 to Stone Cross, right onto B32104 to Langney Shopping Centre, then left and first right past crematorium.
One mile from Pevensey & Westham(BR). Buses from Eastbourne

Clubhouse: Open every evening & lunchtime with adjoining sports hall, boardroom and matchday tea bar **Club Shop:** Yes

HONOURS Unijet Sussex County League Champions 99-00, Sussex Co. Lg R-up 91-92, Div 2 87-88, Lg Cup 89-90, Div 3 86-87, Div 3 Cup 86-87, 5-aside 1990; Sussex I'mediate Cup 85-86, Eastbourne Chall. Cup 85-86 86-87 99-00 00-01 .Promotion to Southern League (Dr Martens) Eastern Division 1999-20

PREVIOUS **League:** Eastbourne & Hastings, Unijet Sussex Oo League.**Name:** Langney Sports
Grounds: Princes Park, Wartling Rd, Eastbourne/ Adjacent pitch

ECORDS **Attendance:** 1400Sussex Senior Cup Final May 2000(Brighton & H v Hastings T)
Goalscorer: Nigel Hole 146 **Appearances:** Darren Baker 435
Win: 10-1 v Haywards Heath Town, Sussex County Lg Div. 1 11/4/92
Defeat: 0-8, v Sheppey United (A), FA Vase Prel. Rd 9/10/93
v Peacehaven & Telscombe (A), Sussex County Lg Div. 1 9/11/93

ERITH & BELVEDERE

CLUB OFFICIALS

Chairman: **John McFadden**
President: **L O'Connell**
Vice Chairman: **Peter Bird**
Secretary: Miss **Kellie Discipline**
108 Chastilion Road, Dartford, Kent DA1 3LG Tel: -01322 275766
Press Off./Commecial Man.: Martin Tarrant
Tel: 01322 275766

FOOTBALL MANAGEMENT TEAM

Manager: Mike Acland 01322 225594
Asst Man ager: Dave Hough
Coach: Barry Fox
Physio: Rob Couldwell

FACT FILE

Formed: 1922
Nickname: Deres
Colours: Blue & white/blue/blue
Change colours: All red
Midweek home matchday:Tuesday
Reserves' League: None

2000-01

Captain: Paul Roberts
P.o.Y.: Martin Driscoll
Top scorer: Steve White 12

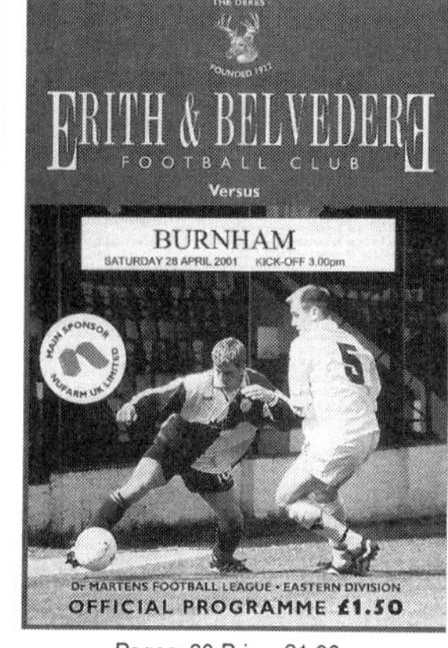

Pages: 30 Price: £1.00p
Editor: Mike Tarrant Tel: 01322 275766

Local Press:
Kentish Times, Kentish Independent
Local Radio: Radio Kent, Radio Mellenium

GROUN D Park View Rd Ground, Welling, Kent DA16 1SY Tel: 0181 301 1196
Email Address; kelliedt@tinyworld,co.uk
Directions: As for Welling United F.C.:M25,then A2 towards London.Take Welling turn-off, ground one mile. By rail to Welling stationBR (BR) ground 3/4 mile.
Capacity: 1,500 Cover: 1,000 Seats: 500 Floodlights: Yes
Club Shop: Sells programmes, badges and pens
Clubhouse: Licensed social club open matchdays and weekends. Cold snacks available. Separate canteen provides hot food on matchdays

PREVIOUS **Leagues:** Kent 22-29 31-39 78-82, London 29-31, Corinthian 45-63, Athenian 63-78
Names: Belvedere & District FC (Formed 1918, restructured 1922)

CLUB RECORDS **Attendance:** 5,573 v Crook Colliery Welfare Amt Cup 3rd Rd 1949
Win: 14-2 v Royal Marines, Kent Lge 18/11/33. (16-2 v RAF Friendly 4/9/41) **Defeat:** 0-15 v Ashford, Kent Lge 28/4/37
Career Appearances: Dennis Crawford 504, 56-71 **Career Goalscorer:** Colin Johnson284, 61-71

BEST SEASON **FA Amateur Cup:** Runners-up 1923-24, 37-38 **FA Trophy:** Third Qualifying Round second replay 89-90
FA Vase: Third Round 76-77 **FA Cup:** 4th Qual Rd 1924-25 (Equiv to 1st Rd Prop). League clubs defeated: None

HONOURS FA Amat Cup R-up 23-24 37-38; Athenian Lge Div 1 R-up 70-71 (Lge Cup 73-74), Memorial Shield 67-68; Corinthian Lge R-up 62-63, (Lge Cup 47-48 48-49 49-50); Kent Lge 81-82, (Lge Cup R-up 81-82); London Sen Cup 44-45 (R-up 38-39); KentAmat Cup 6, (R-up 4); Kent F/lit Lge R-up 67-68; Kent Interm Cup R-up 90-91; Kent Jun Cup 67-68; Kent County Yth Lge 90-91; Kent Yth Cup 87-88. Bromley Hosp Cup 38-39; Essex & Herts Border Comb Cup 73-74.

Players progressing: John Coshall (West Ham 28), Fred Ford 36/ Cyril Hammond 46/ KeithPeacock 62 (Charlton), Tommy Ord (Chelsea 72), Sean Devine (Barnet 95)

Chris Whitehouse and a packed Erith defence snuff out Grantham's Lee Marshall. Photo: Gavin J Tutcher

FISHER ATHLETIC (LONDON)

Pages: 40 Price: £1.50
Editor: Cheryl Stepton
Local Press: Southwark News, South London Press
Local Radio: Capital & Capital Gold

CLUB OFFICIALS

Chair : **Chris Georgiou**V -C : **Dave ilding**

Secretary: **John Leyden**,33 Carew Close,Chafford100,Nr Grays,Essex

Tel No: 01375 481224

General Manager: **Cheryl Stepton**

FOOTBALL MANAGEMENT TEAM

Manager: Alan Walker

Coach: Chris Hiscock

Physio: Joe Miller

FACT FILE

Formed: 1908
Nickname: The Fish
Sponsors:
Colours: Black & white stripes/white/white
Change colours: Blue/black/black
Midweek matchday: Tuesday
Reserves' League: Suburban Premier

GROUND The Surrey Docks Stadium, Salter Road, London SE16 1LQ
15 mins from Canada Water (tube)Tel: 0207 231 5144 Fax:0207 2520060

Directions: 8 minutes walk from Rotherhithe (tube).
2 miles from London Bridge (main line). Buses 381,225

Capacity: 5,300 Cover: 4,283 Seats: 400 Floodlights: Yes
Clubhouse: None Club Shop: None

PREVIOUS **Leagues:** Parthenon, West Kent, Kent Amateur, London Spartan 76-82, Southern 82-87, GMV Conference 87-91
Names: Fisher Athletic 08-93, Fisher`93 93-96 **Ground:** London Road, Mitcham

CLUB RECORDS **Attendance:** 4,283 v Barnet, GMV Conference 4/5/91
Win: 7-0 v Lewes Sept 95, FA Cup **Defeat:** 0-6 v Salisbury, 21/8/93
Career Goalscorer: Paul Shinners 205 **Career Appearances:** Dennis Sharp 720
Transfer fee paid: £2,500 for Ben Taylor (Sittingbourne)
Transfer fee received: £45,000 for Paul Gorman (Charlton 1991)

BEST SEASON **FA Cup:** 1st Rd 84-85 (0-1 at home to Bristol City), 88-89 (0-4 at BristolRovers)
FA Trophy: Third Round replay 87-88 **FA Vase:** Second Round replay 82-83 **FA Amateur Cup:**

HONOURS Southern Lg 86-87 (R-up 83-84, Southern Div 82-83, Lg Cp 84-85, Championship Cup 87-88, Merit Cup), London Spartan Lg 80-81 81-82 (R-up 78-79, Senior Div77-78, Div 2 R-up 76-77), Parthenon Lg 61-62 (Lg Cup 63-64 65-66), Kent AmateurLg 73-74 74-75 (R-up 72-73),Kent Intermediate 97-98.98-99 London Senior Cup 84-85 87-88 88-89, LondonIntermediate Cup 59-60 (R-up 75-76), Kent Senior Cp 83-84, Kent Senior Trophy 81-82 82-83, Surrey Inter Cup 61-62,Southern Lg. Eastern Div 99-00

Players progressing: John Bumstead (Chelsea), Trevor Aylott (Bournemouth), Paul Shinners (Orient 84), Dave Regis (Notts Co. - via Barnet), Paul Gorman(Charlton 91), Sean Devine (Barnet via Okonia Nicossia), George Barry (LeytonOrient), Dean Martin (West Ham Utd), Jason Lee (Charlton), Ken Charlery (Barnet), Steve Watts (Leyton Orient)

Photo: Mark Sandom

GRANTHAM TOWN

CLUB OFFICIALS

Chairman: **Barry Palmer**
President: **Michael Bird**

Secretary: **Pat Nixon**
72 Huntingtower Road, Grantham,
Lincs NG31 7AU
Tel: 01476 419391 FAX: 01476 419392

FOOTBALL MANAGEMENT TEAM

Manager:John Wilkinson
Asst Mgr:Tony Simmons
Physio: Nigel Marshall

FACT FILE

Formed: 1874
Nickname: Gingerbreads
Sponsors: Crystal Motors
Colours: White & Blac/black/black
Change: All Orange
Midweek matchday: Tuesday
Reserves' League: Lincolnshire
Club Website: www.granthamtownfc.co.uk
www.cheiroa.domon.co.uk/gtfc

2000-01
Captain: Adrian Sped
P.o.Y.: Gary Bull
Top scorer: Gary Bull 31

GROUND South Kesteven Sports Stadium, Trent Road, Grantham, Lincs Tel: 01476 402224
Directions: Midway between A1 and A52 on edge of Earlesfield Industrial Estate; from A1 take A607 to Earlsfield Ind. Est and continue into Trent Rd
Capacity: 7,500 Cover: 1,950 Seats: 750 Floodlights: Yes
Clubhouse: (01476 402225) Open evenings and weekends. Bar, darts, pool etc.Frequent live entertainment. Available for functions **Club Shop:** Programmes and a wide range of souvenirs. Contact club number.

Programme: 38 pages £1.50

Local Press: Grantham Journal, Nottingham Evening Post, Melton & GranthamTrader, Grantham Citizen, Lincolnshire Echo
Local Radio: Radio Lincolnshire, Lincs FM

PREVIOUS **Leagues:** Mid Amat All, Central All. 11-25 59-61, Midland Co's 25-59 61-72,Southern Lge 72-79, Northern Prem. 79-85
Names: Grantham FC, pre-80. Grounds: London Rd up to 90

CLUB RECORDS **Attendance:** 3,695 v Southport. F.A.Trophy Quarter Final 97-98
Win: 13-0 vRufford Colliery (H), FA Cup Preliminary Rd 15/9/34 **Career Goalscorer:** Jack McCartney 416
Defeat: 0-16 v Notts County Rovers (A), Midland Amateur All. 22/10/1892 **Career Appearances:** Chris Gardiner 664
Transfer fee paid:undisclosed for Mario Ziccari **Transfer fee received:** £20,000 for Gary Crosby (Notts Forest 87)

BEST SEASON **FA Cup:** 3rd Rd 1883-84 86-87 1973-74. Comp Proper on 23 occasions
FA Trophy: Quarter Final 1971-72, 97-98

HONOURS Southern Lg R-up 73-74 (Div 1 Nth 72-73 78-79, Merit Cup 72-73), Southern Lg Mid Div Champions 97-98. Midland Co's Lg(3) 63-64 70-72 (R-up 37-38 64-65 69-70, Lg Cup 68-69 70-71), Midland Amtr Lg10-11 (Lg Cup R-up 10-11), Central All. 24-25 (Southern Div R-up 59-60), LincsSnr Cup 1884-851936-37 (R-up(5) 34-36 39-40 45-47), Lincs Co. `A' Cup(3) 53-54 60-62 (R-up 49-50 52-53 57-58), Lincs Co. Snr Cup 71-72 82-83 (R-up 80-81)

Players progressing: E Morris (Halifax 50), P Thompson/R Cooke (Peterborough 64/80), J Rayner (Notts County 64), D Dall (Scunthorpe 79), N Jarvis/H Wood (Scunthorpe 80), D White (Bristol Rvrs 86), T Curran (Grimsby 87), G Crosby (Nottm Forest 87), A Kennedy (Wrexham 87), R Wilson (Lincoln 87)

Back Row, left to right: Tim Wilkes, Rick Ranshaw, Dave Taylor,Mario Ziccardi, Andy Gray, Mick Hogg,(Coach) and Adrian Barber. **Middle Row:** Nigel Marshal l(Trainer), Darren Dye, Wayne Hallcro, Matt Carvell, John Wilkinson (Manager), Tony Simmons,(Assistant Manager), Andy Furnell,Gary Bull, Mike Humphries (Physio). **Front Row:** Lee Marshall, Mark Harbottle, Brendon McDaid, Adrian Speed (Captain),Jiim McNeil, Kevin Ward, and John Hawley.

HASTINGS TOWN

CLUB OFFICIALS

Chairman: Peter Huggins
President: Mick Maplesden
Vice Chairman: David Bealey.
Secretary / Press Officer: R A Cosens
22 Baldslow Road, Hastings TN34 2EZ
01424 427867 (H) 01424 444635 (B)
0771 2634288 (M)

FOOTBALL MANAGEMENT TEAM

Team Managers: George Wakeling
Asst Manager: Terry White
Physio: Bob Lewis

FACT FILE

Formed: 1894
Nickname: The Town
Sponsors: Real Pine
Colours: All white
Change colours:Blue/Yellow
Midweek matchday: Tuesday
Reserves' League: Bass Kent Div 2
Newsline: 09066 555 879
00-01- Captain: Tony Burt
P.o.Y.:Duncan McArthur
Top scorer: Danny Simmonds 21

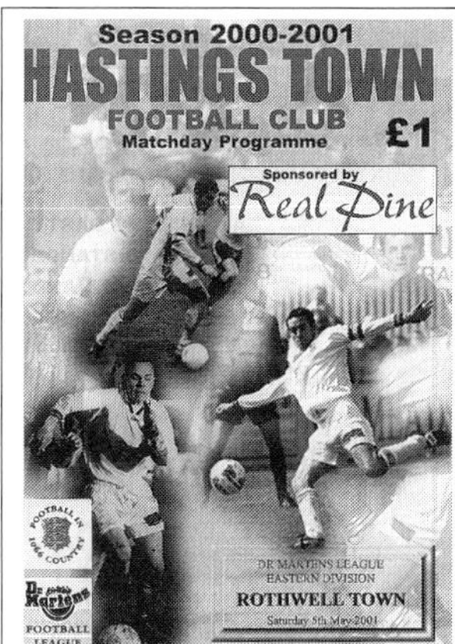

Season 2000-2001
HASTINGS TOWN
FOOTBALL CLUB
Matchday Programme
£1
Sponsored by
Real Pine
ROTHWELL TOWN

Pages: 64 Price: £1
Editor: David Bealey Tel: (01797 253310)
Local Press:Hastings Observer,Evening Argus
Local Radio: Radio Sussex,
Southern Sound, Arrow FM
Website:www.hastingstownfc.the-bench.co.uk

GROUND The Pilot Field, Elphinstone Road, Hastings TN34 2AX Tel: 01424 444635

Directions: From A21 turn left at 3rd mini-r'bout into St Helens Rd, left after 1 mile into St Helens Park Rd, this leads into Downs Rd, at end of Downs Rd (T-junction) turn left, ground 200yds on right. From town centre take Queens Road (A2101). Right at roundabout into Elphinstone Road - ground 1 mile on right.
1 1/2 miles from Hastings BR station - infrequent bus service fromtown centre to ground

Capacity: 4,050 Cover: 1,750 Seats: 800 Floodlights: Yes

Clubhouse: Open matchdays and every evening
Club Shop: Sells replica kits, scarves, programmes, pens, key-rings, badges etc

PREVIOUS **Leagues:** South Eastern 04-05, Southern 05-10, Sussex County 21-27 52-85,Southern Amateur 27-46, Corinthian 46-48
Name: Hastings & St Leonards Amateurs **Ground:** Bulverhythe Rec Gd (pre 76)

CLUB RECORDS **Attendance:** 4,888 v Notts Forest, friendly 23/6/96. Competitive: 1,774 v DoverAthletic, Southern Lge Prem. Div. 12/4/93
Goalscorer: (Season) Terry White (33) 99-00
Transfer Fee Paid: £8,000 for Nicky Dent from Ashford **Received:** £50,000 for Paul Smith from Notts Forest

BEST SEASON **FA Cup:** 4th Qual. Rd 85-86, 2-3 v Farnborough Town (A) **FA Trophy: 3rd Rd 1998-99**
FA Amateur Cup: 3rd Rd. 38-39 **FA Vase:** 5th Rd. rep. 90-91

HONOURS Southern Lg Cup 94-95, Southern Div 91-92, Div 2 R-up 08-09, Div 2(B) 09-10; Sussex Co Lg R-up 21-22 25-26, Lg Cup 80-81, Div 2 79-80 (R-up 59-60), Div 2Cup 79-80; Sussex Sen Cup 35-36 37-38 95-96 97-98; AFA Snr Cup 37-38; Gilbert Rice F/lit Cup 89-90

Players progressing: Peter Heritage (Gillingham), Paul Smith (Nottm Forest)

Back row, left to right:Peter Huggins (Chairman), dean White (Manager), Paul Hobbs, Paul Jones, Terry White, Stuart Playford, Danny Simmonds, Paul Ruddy, Steve Ferguson, Bob Lewis (Physio), David Ormerod (Treasurer), Tony Cosens (Secretary). Front Row: Charlie Pilbeam (Director), Chris Honey, Paul Tuppenney, Steve Smith, Shwan Jalal, Duncan McArthur, Steve Yates, Oti, Mick Maplesden (Director)

HISTON

CLUB OFFICIALS

Chairman: Gareth Baldwin
President: G P Muncey
Secretary: Mrs Baldwin,
5 Caxton Lane, Foxton,
Cambridge CB2 6SR (Tel: 01223 872246)
Press Officer: Streve Wells(01223 8721989)
Email:stevenwells1@ composerve.co

FOOTBALL MANAGEMENT TEAM

Manager: Steve Fallon
Coach: Bobby Broom
Physio; Lee Petrucci

FACT FILE

Founded: 1904
Sponsors:Webster Building & Civil Engineers
Colours: Red and blackstripes/black/black
Change colours: Sky & Navy/navy/sky ?
Midweek Matches: Wednesday
Reserves League: Kershaw Premier
Website: www.histonfootballclub.tripod.com

2000-01
Captain: Andrew Jeffrey
P.o.Y.: Wayne Goddard
Top Scorer: Neil Kennedy (33)

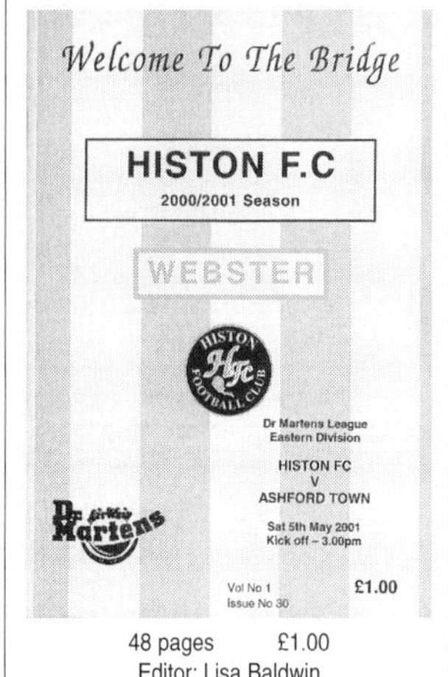

Welcome To The Bridge
HISTON F.C
2000/2001 Season
WEBSTER
Dr Martens League
Eastern Division
HISTON FC
V
ASHFORD TOWN
Sat 5th May 2001
Kick off - 3.00pm
Vol No 1
Issue No 30
£1.00

48 pages £1.00
Editor: Lisa Baldwin
Local Press : Cambridge Evening News
Local Radio: Q103
BBC Radio Cambridgeshire

GROUND Bridge Rd, Impington, Cambridge Tel: 01223 232301 Fax: 01223 237373
Club Website: http://abbey59.tripod.com
EMAIL Address: gareth@corporate innovations.co.uk

Directions: Leave A14 northern Cambridge bypass on B1049 (signposted Histon and Cottenham). Ground half a mile on right.
5 miles from Cambridge (BR). Bus No.104

Capacity: 3,250 Seats: 250 Cover: 250 Floodlights: Yes

Clubhouse: Bar/lounge open Tues-Sun eves, Sun lunch and matchdays.Snacks available

HONOURS Eastern Co's Lg - Prem. Div. 99-00, Div 1 R-up 96-97, Cup 90-91;
Cambridge Invitation Cup 77-78 79-80 96-97,00-01 (R-up 50-51 52-53 53-54);
Spartan Lg Div 1 (East) 50-51; Cambs Chall Cup; Cambs Lg Section;
Kershaw Prem Lge 00-01R-up 97-98, Sen Lge A 96-97, Cup 96-97;00-01
Auto Trader Lge & Cup (U18) 96-97 Kershaw Champions Co Cup (U18) 98-99, Colts League (U17) Champions 98-99

PREVIOUS **Leagues:** Cambridgeshire 04-48; Spartan 48-60; Delphian 60-63; Athenian 63-65; Eastern Counties 66-00
Name: Histon Institute 04-51

BEST SEASON **FA Cup:** 4th Qual. Rd. 89-90 **FA Vase:** 4th Rd 96-97, 97-98 **F.A .Trophy:** 4th Round 2000-2001

RECORD **Attendance:** 6,400 v King's Lynn, FA Cup 1956

Histon topped the Burton Fair Play table last season.

ROTHWELL TOWN

CLUB OFFICIALS

Chairman: **Keith Johnson**
President: **Ken Cheney**
Secretary: **Roger Barratt**
18 Norton St., Rothwell, Northants NN14 2DE
Tel: 01536 507744
Press Officer : **Mark Southon**
Tel: 07870 551428

FOOTBALL MANAGEMENT TEAM

Manager: Nick Platnauer
Physio: Bob Bramah

FACT FILE

Founded: 1895
Nickname: The Bones
Sponsors:Springfir Country Homes
Colours: Blue with white trim/blue/blue
Change Colours: Red, black & white trim, black/red
Midweek matchday: Tuesday
Newsline: 0930 555 829
Reserves' League: Utd Counties Res Div

GROUND Cecil Street, Rothwell, Northants NN14 2EZ Tel: 01536 710694
Directions: A14/A6 to Rothwell. At town centre r'about turn into BridgeStreet (right if north-bound, left if southbound), take 3rd left into TreshamStreet, ground is at top on left.
3 miles from Kettering (BR); Rothwell is served by Kettering to Market Harborough buses
Capacity: 3,500 Seats: 264 Cover: 1,264 Floodlights: Yes
Clubhouse: Rowellian Social Club, open every evening and weekend lunchtimes.Crisps and rolls available on matchdays (hot food and drinks available in ground). `Top of the Town Ballroom', lounge seats 200
Club Shop: Sells various souvenirs incl. metal badges.

PROGRAMME

Pages: 48 Price: £1.00 Editor & Media Relations Officer: Mark Southon
TelNo: 07860 551428

Local Press: Northants Evening Telegraph, Chronicle & Echo, Herald & Post
Local Radio: BBC Radio Northants, KCBC

PREVIOUS **Leagues:** Northants 1896-1911 21-33, Kettering Amateur 11-21 33-48, Leics.Senior 48-50, United Counties 50-56 61-94, Central Alliance 56-61 **Grounds:** Harrington Rd, Castle Hill **Name:** Rothwell Town Swifts

CLUB RECORDS **Attendance:** 2,508 v Irthlingborough Diamonds, United Counties League 1971
Win: 17-0 v Stamford, FA Cup Preliminary Round replay 1927
Defeat: 1-10 v Coalville Town, Leicestershire Sen Lge 1949
Transfer fee paid: Undisclosed for Andy Wright (Aylesbury 1992)
Transfer fee received: Undisclosed for Matty Watts (Charlton 1990)

BEST SEASON **FA Cup:** Fourth Qualifying Round 99-00
FA Trophy: Second Round Proper 94-95 **FA Vase:** Fifth Round 92-93 (1-2 v Bridlington Town)

HONOURS Northants Lg1899-1900 (R-up 1895-96 96-97 97-98), Northants Snr Cup 1899-1900 23-24 59-60 88-89 95-96 (R-up 24-25 71-72 87-88), United Counties Lg 92-93 94-95 (R-up 69-70 70-71 87-88 89-90 90-91), KO Cup 55-56 70-71 71-72 91-92 92-93 (R-up 77-78 79-80 82-83), Div 2 52-53 53-54, Div 2Cup 52-53 53-54, Benevolent Cup 92-93 94-95 (R-up 89-90 90-91), Southern League Mid Div R-up 96-97

Players progressing: Lee Glover (Nottingham Forest) 1987, Matty Watts (CharltonAth.) 1990

Photos: Gavin J Tutcher

Lewis Mogg

Dean Foley

RUGBY UNITED

CLUB OFFICIALS

Chairman: **Brian Melvin**
Secretary: **Doug Wilkins**,
298 Rocky Lane, Great Barr,
Birmingham B42 1NQ
Tel: 0121 681 1544 (H 0121 686 4068 (F)
Press Officer: **Alun Turner**
Tel: 01788 567181
Commercial Manager:**Lisa Melvin**

FOOTBALL MANAGEMENT TEAM

Manager:Tony Dobson
Asst Manager: Martin Smith
Physio: Bob Gardner

FACT FILE

Formed: 1956 Nickname: The Valley
Sponsors: Rugby Telegraph & Melbros Ltd
Colours: Navy & sky/navy/navy
Change colours: All Red
Midweek matchday: Tuesday
Club Newsline: 0930 555971
Reserves' League: Midland Combination

2000-01

Top scorer: Robbie Beard 14
Captain: Gary Redgate
P.o.Y.: Paul O'Brien

Pages: 36 Price: £1
Editor: Secretary Tel: 0121 240 4521
Local Press: Rugby Advertiser, Coventry Evening Telegraph, Rugby Observer
Local Radio: Mercia Sound, CWR

GROUND: Butlin Road, Rugby, Warks. CV21 3ST Tel: 01788 844806 www.rugbyutd.co.uk
Directions: The ground is situated off Clifton (B5414) on the north side of Rugby. 1 mile walk from the station Club Call Line: 09066 555971
Capacity: 6,000 Cover: 1,000 Seats: 240 Floodlights: Yes

Clubhouse: Open every night and weekend lunchtimes. Entertainment Saturday nights. Excellent facilities include Long Alley Skittles, darts and pool

Club Shop: Yes

PREVIOUS **Name:** Valley Sports, Valley Sports Rugby
Leagues: Rugby & District 1956-63, Coventry & Partnership, North Warks 63-69, United Counties 69-75, West Midlands 75-83

CLUB RECORDS **Attendance:** 3,961 v Northampton FA Cup 1984
Win: 10-0 v Ilkeston Tn FA Trophy 4/9/85 **Defeat:** 1-11 v Ilkeston Town (A) 18.4.98
Career Goalscorer: Danny Conway, 124 **Career Appearances:** Danny Conway, 374
Transfer fee paid: £3,500 R Smith, I Crawley, G Bradder **Transfer fee received:** £15,000 T Angus (Northampton)

BEST SEASON **FA Cup:** 2nd round 87-88, plus 1st Rd 84-85 85-86 86-87 94-95 League clubs defeated: None
FA Trophy: **FA Vase:** Winners 82-83

HONOURS Southern Lg Midland Div 86-87 (R-up 94-95, Lg Cup 89-90), FA Vase 82-83,Mid Floodlit Cup 84-85 89-90 98 -00(R-up 86-87), Birmingham Snr Cup 88-89 91-92, Utd Co's Lg Div 3 Cup 69-70.
All-time record FA Trophy win: 10-0 away to IlkestonTown, Preliminary Rd 85-86

Players progressing: S Storer (Birmingham 1985), S Bicknell (Leicester), S Norris (Scarborough), T Angus (Northampton Town), Ashley Walker (Peterborough), Ian King (Stoke City)

Back Row: Dave Watson, Peter Spacey, Jason Woodley, Steve O'Shea, Paul Berrisford, Jermaine Rainford (now Corby), John Halford.
Front: Richard Wade, Phil Murphy, Boyd Young, Keiran Sullivan, Dave Stringer, Matt Dyer, Jason Wiseman. **Photo:** Mark Sandom

SITTINGBOURNE

CLUB OFFICIALS

Chairman: **Andy Spice**

President: **E H Bennett**

Secretary:**Marilyn Bright**
c/o Sittingbourne F.C.

Commercial Manager:Brian Woodhouse

FOOTBALL MANAGEMENT TEAM

Manager:John Roles

Coach: Graham Brenton

Physio: Gary Wisdom

FACT FILE

Formed: 1881 Nickname: Brickies

Sponsors: Medway Galvanising.

Colours: Red & black stripes/black/red

Change colours: All yellow

Midweek matchday: Tuesday

Reserves' league: Winstonlead Kent

2000-01

Captain: Roy Clarke

P.o.Y.: Marc Seager

Top Scorer: Bradley Spice (10)

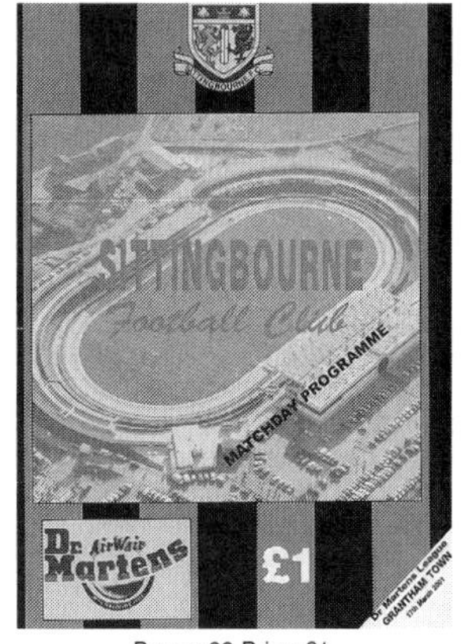

Pages: 28 Price: £1
Editor: John Pitts c/o the club
Local Press: East Kent Gazette, Kent Today, Kent Messenger Extra, Sittingbourne & Sheppy Adscene.
Local Radio: Invicta Supergold, BBC Radio Kent, Invicta FM,Medway F.M.

GROUNDCentral Park, Eurolink, Sittingbourne, Kent ME10 3SB Tel: 01795 435077
Fax: 01474 814501 Newsline: 0891333 027 Email Address: club@sittingbournefc.co.uk
Directions: Through Sittingbourne on main A2, club signposted clearly and regularly from both east and west. 1 mile from Sittingbourne BR station.
Capacity: 8,000 Cover: 3,300 Seats: 2,000 Floodlights: 420 lux
Clubhouse: The Cabin (01795 435077)
Club Shop: Sells a wide selection of souvenirs etc. Open matchdays or contact Ann Morrison (01795 664436) Official Club Website: www.sittingbournefc.co.uk

PREVIOUS **Leagues:** Kent 1894-1905 09-27 30-39 46-59 68-91, South Eastern 05-09, Southern 27-30 59-67
Grounds: SittingbourneRec. Ground 1881-90, Gore Court Cricket Ground 90-92, The Bull Ground1892-1990
Names: Sittingbourne United 1881-86

CLUB RECORDS **Attendance:** 5,951 v Tottenham Hotspur, friendly 26/1/93
Transfer fee paid: £20,000 to Ashford Town for Lee McRobert, 1993.
Transfer fee received: £210,000 from Millwall for Neil Emblen and Michael Harle, 1993

BEST SEASON **FA Cup:** 2nd Rd 25-26 (0-7 at Swindon Town), 28-29 (1-2 at Walsall), plus 1st Rd26-27 30-31 62-63
FA Trophy: **FA Vase:**

HONOURS Southern Lg Southern Div 92-93 95-96; Kent Lg 1897-98 1902-03 57-58 58-59 75-76 83-84 90-91 (Lg Cup 25-26 58-59 73-74 80-81, Div 2 Cup 54-55 57-58 83-84 86-8787-88); Kent Senior Cup 01-02 28-29 29-30 57-58; Kent Senior Shield 25-26 27-28 53-54; Kent Senior Trophy 89-90; Thames & Medway Cup 55-56 58-59; Thames & Medway Comb 02-03 07-08 11-12 24-25 25-26; Chatham Charity Cup 03-04 19-20;" Kent Midweek Lg(res) 91-92 (Lg Cup 90-91).

Players progressing: Jason Lillis (Walsall 93), Neil Emblen & Michael Harle 93, Steve Forbes 94, Lee McRobert 95 (Millwall) Jimmy Case (Brighton 93), Lee Harper (Arsenal 94)

SPALDING UNITED

CLUB OFFICIALS

Chairman: **Alan Mitchell**
President: **John Chappell**
Press Officer: **Ray Tucker**
Secretary: **Alan Clarke,** 68 Daniels Crescen t, Long Sutton,Lincs.PE12 9DR
Tel No: 01406 362582

FOOTBALL MANAGEMENT TEAM

Manager: Nick Anderson
Asst Manager: Glenn Beech
Physio: Sam Seal

FACT FILE

Founded: 1921
Nickname: Tulips
Sponsors: Geest
Colours: Tangerine & black/black/tangerine
Change: Sky/white/sky
Midweek matchday: Tuesday
Reserve League: Utd Counties Res Div

GROUND Sir Halley Stewart Playing Field, Winfrey Avenue, Spalding Tel: 01775 713328

Directions: Town centre off A16, adjacent to bus station. 250 yds from Spalding(BR) station

Capacity: 7,000 Seats: 350 Cover: 2,500 Floodlights: Yes

Clubhouse: Open matchdays, and events Club Shop: Yes

PROGRAMME
36 pages, 50p
Editor: Graham Walmsley
Local Press : Lincs Free Press, Spalding Guardian, Peterborough EveningTelegraph

HONOURS Utd Counties Lg 54-55 74-75 87-88 98-99 R-up 50-51 51-52 52-53 72-73 75-76 96-97; KO Cup 54-55 94-95; Northern Co's East Lg 83-84; Lincs Snr Cup 52-53; Hinchingbroke Cup: 98-99 Lincs Snr `A' Cup 87-88, 98-99 R-up 97-98; Snr `B' Cup 50-51; Evans Halshaw F'lit Cup 89-90

PREVIOUS **Leagues:** Peterborough; Utd Co's 31-55 68-78 86-88 91-99; Eastern Co's 55-60; Central Alliance 60-61; Midland Co's 61-68; Northern Co's East 82-86; Southern 88-91

BEST SEASON **FA Cup:** 1st Round 57-58, 1-3 v Durham City (A), 64-65, 3-5 v Newport Co. (A)
FA Trophy: 3rd Rd 99-00
FA Vase: Quarter-Finals 89-90, 1-3 v Guiseley

RECORD **Attendance:** 6,972 v Peterborough, FA Cup 1952

Players progressing: Carl Shutt (Sheffield Wed.)

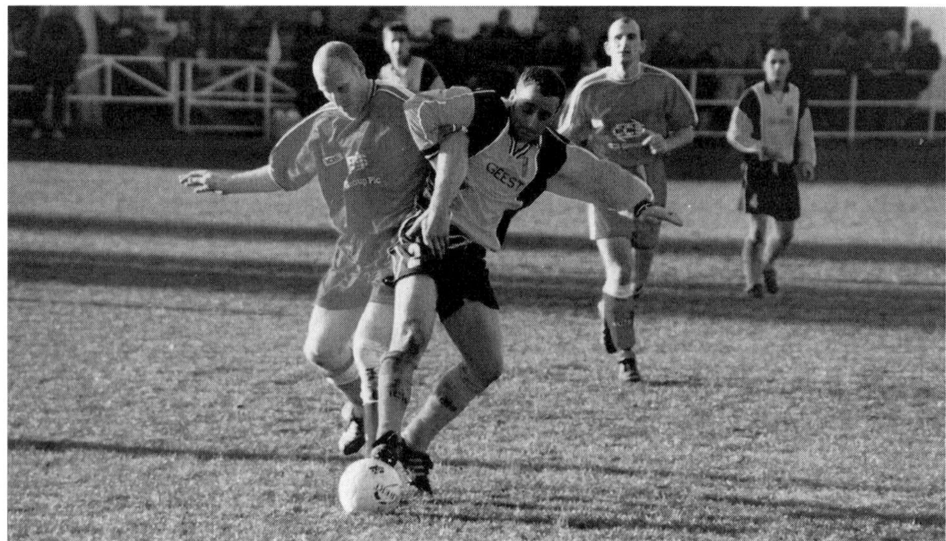

Tulips' Nigel Vince (dark shorts) tangles with Baldock's Paul McCarthy **Photo:** Gavin J Tutcher

ST. LEONARDS

CLUB OFFICIALS

Chairman: **John Cornelius**
Patron: **Leon Shepherdson**
President: **Mrs K Shepperdson**
Vice-Chairman: **Danny Bossum**
Secretary: **c/o The Club**
Business Manager: **Dale Seymour**
Tel: 01424 434755 or 07976626716
Press Officer: Roy Russell 01424846008

FOOTBALL MANAGEMENT TEAM

Manager: Andy Thomson.
Ass Managare Des McCarthy
Coach:Lloyd Bigg Physio: Rob Greig

FACT FILE

Formed: 1971
Nickname: Saints Sponsors:
Shirt Sponsor: Hastings Direct (Insurance)
Clubcall Line: T.B.A.
Colours: Blue/white/blue
Change colours: White/navy/white
Midweek Matchday: Monday
Reserves' League: Sussec County

2000-01

Captain:Simon Fox
Top Scorer: Dominic Barclay (180
P.o.Y.: Craig Willard

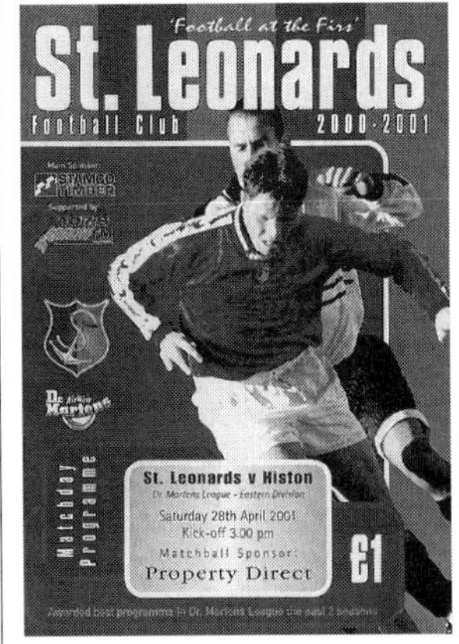

Pages: 60 Price: £1
Editor: Peter High (01424 752864)
Local Press: Hastings Observer, Eve Argus
Local Radio: Arrow FM, BBC Southern Counties Radio, Southern FM
Club Call Line: 09068 800 680

Club Website : www.freezone.co.uk/stlfc

GROUND The Firs, Elphinstone Rd, Hastings, East Sussex Tel: 01424 434755 Matchday Office 01424 716362 **Directions:** From M25 & London approach Hastings on the A21. immediately afterthe junct with the A28 on the northern borough boundary, turn right into Junction Rd. At T junct with B2093 turn right onto The Ridge. After 2 miles turn right, opposite the cemetary, into Elphinstone Rd, grd 600yards down hill on left. Nearest station; Ore (Connex South East), 1 mile uphill (no bus or taxi). Hastings (Connex South East) 1.5 miles. Bus service from town centre to ground

Capacity: 3,768 (Day), 3,015 (Even) Seats: 251 Cover: 1,000 Floodlights: Yes
Clubhouse: Licensed bar open normal pub hours. Hot food matchdays. Hot food from opening on match days.Hot foor and other refreshments available from tea bar during matches.
Club Shop: Yes, selling leisure & sports wear, souvenirs & publications, open matchdays

PREVIOUS **Leagues:** Eastbourne & Hastings 71-82, Southern Counties Comb 82-88, Sussex County 88-96
Grounds: Council pitches 71-73, Pannel Lane, Pett 73-93 **Names:** Stamco (71-96), St Leonards Stamcroft 96-98

CLUB RECORDS **Attendance:** at new ground1,798 v Tiverton Town, FA Vase 4th Rd. 15/01/95
at old ground: 527v Hastings Town, Sussex Senior Cup 2nd Rd 5/12/92
Win: 10-1 v Portfield(H), Sussex County League Div One 4/12/93 **Defeat:** 2-10 v Rothwell Town (a0 Dr Martens) 19.10.00
Career appearances: Keith Miles 292 (1995-2001) **Career Goalscorer:** Keith Miles (134) 1995-2001)
Transfer fee paid: None **Transfer fee received:** £8,000 for Jon Magee (Margate)

BEST SEASON: **FA Cup:** 3rd Qual Rd 96-97 97-98 **FA Vase:** 5th Rd 94-95 **FA Trophy:** 3rd Rd 96-97

HONOURS Sussex Sen Cup 96-97; Sussex RUR Charity Cup R-up 94-95; Hastings Snr Cup 89-90 95-96 96-97, R-up 92-93 97-98; Dr Martens Lge Southern Div R-up 96-97, Merit Cup 96-97; Sussex County Div 1 R-up 94-95 95-96, Div 2 R-up 92-93, Cup R-up 89-90 90-91, Div Three R-up 88-89, Cup R-up 88-89 Kent Midweek Lg.Cup Winners 98-99

Player progressing: Sasha Ilic (Charlton Ath 97)

L-R back Row: David Henman, Simon Fox, Danny Moody, Graham Bannatyne, Adam Flanagan, Ross Venables, Rob Greig (team attendant), Andy Thompson (manager).
Front Row: Craig Willard, Danny Fletcher, Barry Kingsford, Des Boateng, Michael O'Callaghan, Keith Miles.

STAMFORD

CLUB OFFICIALS

Chairman: **Ken Joynson**
Vice-Chairman: **Richard Jacobs**
President: **Mrs C Sturgess**
Secretary: **Jeremy Biggs**
`The Essendine', Essendine, Stamford, Lincs., PE9 4LD Tel: 01780 763048
Press Officer: **As Secretary**

FOOTBALL MANAGEMENT TEAM

Manager:Billy Jeffrey
Assistant: Nick Ashby
Physio: Pete Foskett

FACT FILE

Founded: 1896 Nickname: Daniels
Sponsors: SilverLink Restaurant/New Flame
Colours: Red
Change Colours: Yellow & green
Midweek matchday: Tuesday
Reserves League: UCL Res Div 1

2000-01
Captain: Darren Clyde
P.o.Y.: Nick Ashby
Top Scorer: Malcolm Ndokwe 25

STAMFORD A.F.C. SEASON 2000/1 Official Programme
SUPPORT THE DANIELS
Southern League Football (Eastern Division)

Pages : 44 Price:£1,00
Editor: Robin Peel
Local Newspapers: Stamford Mercury, Peterborough Evening Telegraph, Herald &Post
Local Radio:Rutland Radio,LincsFM Radio Lincolnshire & Radio Cambridgeshire

GROUND New Flame Stadium, Kettering Road,, Stamford, Lincs
Tel: 01780 763079 (Clubhouse) 01780 766027 (Pressbox)

Directions: Off A43 Kettering Rd, 1 mile east of A1. 200 yds from station
Capacity: 5,000 Seats: 250 Cover: 1,250 Floodlights: Yes
Clubhouse: Open matchdays, Sunday lunchtimes.
Food available matchdays - hot and cold
Club Shop: Wide range of Lge + non-Lge progs & club souvenirs.

PREVIOUS **Leagues:** Peterborough; Northants (UCL) 08-55; Central Alliance 55-61; Midland Co's 61-72; UCL 72-98
Grounds: None **Names:** None

CLUB RECORDS **Attendance:** 4,200 v Kettering, FA Cup 3rd Qual Rd 53
Win: 13-0 v Peterborough Reserves, Northants Lge 29-30 **Defeat:** 0-17 v Rothwell,FA Cup 27-28
Appearances: Dick Kwiatkowski 462 **Goalscorer:** Bert Knighten 248

BEST SEASON **FA Cup:** 12-13 5th Qual. Round
FA Vase: Winners 79-80, R-up 75-76 83-84 **FA Trophy: 00-01** (1st season) 2nd Round

HONOURS FA Vase 79-80 (R-up 75-76 83-84); Utd Co's Lg 75-76 77-78 79-80 80-81 81-82 96-97 97-98 (KO Cup 51-52 75-76 79-80 81-82 85-86); Northants Lg 11-12; Lincs Snr`A' Cup 78-79 82-83 97-98, 00-01; Lincs Snr `B' Cup 51-52 53-54; William Scarber Mem. Cup 70-71 82-83 85-86 88-89 93-94 94-95; Stamford Chal. Cup 89-90; Lincs Jnr Cup 48-49 Hinchbrooke Cup 1906-07, 07-08, 97-98

Players progressing: A Birchenall (Chelsea), R Chester(Aston Villa), T Tye (Chelsea), G Fell (Brighton), C Chapman (Wolves), S Collins (Peterborough), K Alexander (Grimsby), A Tillson (Grimsby), B Stubbs (Notts Co.), D Genovese (Peterborough), J Johnson, C MacCarney (Notts Co), B McNanara (Northampton), D Norris (Bolton).

Pictured with the Lincolnshire Senior Cup , back row, left to right: Richard Jacobs (Vice Chairman),Billy Jeffrey (manager), Shaun Keeble, Nick Ashby, Richard Challinor, Steve Corry, Dennis Rhule, Richard Bailey, Craig Donaldson, Martin Harrdy Ken Joynson (Chairman) **Front Row:** Jon Challinor, Warren Donald, Malcolm Ndekwe, Tom Betteridge, Darron Clyde(Captain), David Staff, Peter Foskett (Physio) and Andy Peaks. ***Photo: Gavin J Tutcher***

TONBRIDGE ANGELS

CLUB OFFICIALS

Chairman: **Colin Fry**
Vice Chairman: **Maurice Brown**
Secretary: **Ken Jarrett**
8 Faraday Ride, Tonbridge, Kent TN10 4RL
Tel: 01732 351856
Press Officer:T.B.A.
Commercial Manager:Andrew Gidley

FOOTBALL MANAGEMENT TEAM

Manager:Colin Blewden
Physio: Chris Dunk

FACT FILE

Founded: 1948
Nickname: The Angels
Sponsors: Tonbridge Coachworks
Colours: Royal Blue with white trim
Change Colours: All yellow
Midweek matchday: Tuesday
Reserves League: Suburban
2000-2001
Top Scorer: Wade Felana (27)
P.o.Y. Wade Felana
Captain: Danny Tingley

TONBRIDGE ANGELS FOOTBALL CLUB
MEMBERS OF
Dr. MARTENS SOUTHERN LEAGUE EASTERN DIVISION
SUBURBAN FOOTBALL LEAGUE
AFFILIATED TO THE KENT COUNTY FOOTBALL ASSOCIATION
MAIN SPONSORS OF TONBRIDGE ANGELS FOOTBALL CLUB
TONBRIDGE COACHWORKS

Pages: 38 Price: £1
Editor:Maurice Brown c/o Club

Local Press: Kent Messenger, Courier, Sevenoaks Leader
Local Radio: Mercury, Radio Kent, K,F.M.

GROUND Longmead Stadium, Darenth Avenue, Tonbridge, Kent TN10 3JW Tel: 01732 352417

Directions: From Tonbridge BR station, through High Street, north up Shipbourne Rd (A227 Gravesend road) to 2nd mini-r'bout (`The Pinnacles' pub), left into Darenth Avenue, ground at bottom of Avenue, far side of car park

Capacity: 5,000 Seats: 202 Cover: 400 Floodlights: Yes

Clubhouse: Open Mon-Sat evenings and Sunday lunchtimes.
Hot food on matchdays from burger bar

Club Shop: Yes, progs, replica kits etc, contact Lorraine Parks (01732 350865)

PREVIOUS **Leagues:** Southern 48-89, Kent 89-93
Ground: The Angel 48-80 **Names:** TonbridgeAngels, Tonbridge F.C., Tonbridge A.F.C

CLUB RECORDS **Attendance:** 1,463 v Yeovil Town, FA Cup 4th Qualifying Round 26/10/91.
At theAngel Ground: 8,236 v Aldershot, FA Cup 1st Round 1951
Win: 11-1 v WorthingFA Cup 1951 **Defeat:** 2-11 v Folkstone, Kent Sen Cup 1949
Career Goalscorer: Unknown **Career Appearances:** Mark Gillham, 520 to date
Transfer fee paid: **Transfer fee received:** £7,500 for Paul Emblen (Charlton Ath 97)

BEST SEASON **FA Cup:** First Round (proper) 50-51 51-52 52-53 67-68 72-73
FA Trophy: **FA Vase:**

HONOURS Kent League 94-95 (League Cup (2)), Southern League Cup Runners-up (2) (SF(1)), Kent Senior Cup 64-65 74-75 (Runners-up (2)), Kent Senior Shield 51-5255-56 57-58 58-59 63-64

Players progressing: R Saunders, M McMcDonald, T Burns, I Seymour, G Moseley, TMorgan, Neil Emblen, Paul Emblen.

Back Row: Peter Dennis (kit manager), Mathew Hare, Mark Gammon, Ryan Cross, Danny Potter, Ian Hutchinson, Simon Browne, Darran Rowbotham, David Laws, Bob Lucas (physio). Front: Andy Mason (player manager), Matthew Hale, Michael Dean, John Waldock (captain), Martin Underhay, Michael Cameron, Anthony Tilley, Richie Carter (coach).

WISBECH TOWN

CLUB OFFICIALS

Chairman: **Barry Carter**
Vice Chairman: **George Campion**
President: **J W A Chilvers**
Secretary: **John Petch**
34 Walton Rd, Wisbech, Cambs PE13 3EN
Tel: 01945 584333 &Fax)
Press Officer: **Barry Carter**

FOOTBALL MANAGEMENT TEAM

Joint Managers: TerryBack & Pat Clarke
Physio: P Ward

FACT FILE

Founded: 1920
Nickname: Fenmen
Newsline: 0930 555 865
Colours: Red with black side panel/red/red
Change colours: Blue& white,blue,blue
Midweek Matchday: Tuesday

2000-01
Captain: Chris Dear
P.o.Y.: Duncan Roberts
Top scorer: David Cobb 6

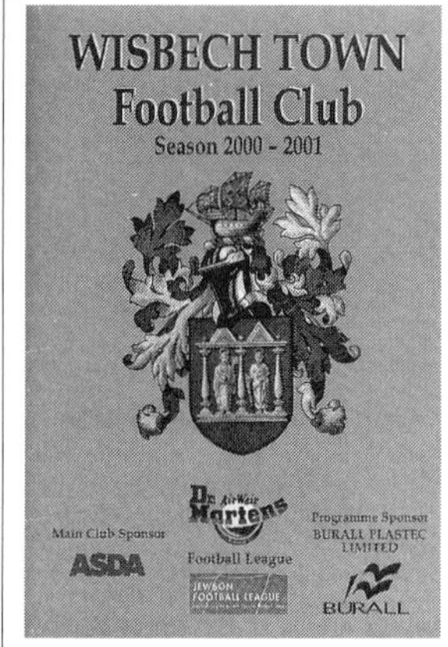

Pages: 40 Price: £1
Editor: Gordon Smith Tel: 01945 581767

Local Press: Fenland Citizen, Wisbech Standard, Eastern Daily press
Local Radio: Radio Cambridgeshire

GROUND Fenland Park, Lerowe Road, Wisbech, Cambs Tel: 01945 584176

Directions: Follow A47 bypass to the West Walton turn off roundabout where there is a Little Chef, turn left for Wisbech, Lerowe Road is first left after 30mph sign. Entering town from north along A1101 cross Freedom Bridge, atroundabout go straight over sign Walsoken/West Walton

Capacity: 3,800 Seats: 284 Cover: 1,000 Floodlights: Yes

Clubhouse: Open every day. Matchday food & drink - Tea, coffee, cold drinks, confectionary, burgers, hotdogs, soup, sandwiches, rolls

Club Shop: Sells replica shirts, caps, pennants, pens, scarves etc. Contact Club Secretary

PREVIOUS **Leagues:** Peterborough; Utd Co's 35-50; Eastern Co's 50-52 70-97; Midland 52-58;Southern 58-70
Grounds: Wisbech Park 20-21; Waisoken Rectory 21-22; Harecroft Rd 22-47

CLUB RECORDS **Attendance:** 8,004 v Peterborough United, Midland League 25/8/57
Goalscorer: Bert Titmarsh 246 (31-37) **Appearances:** Jamie Brighty (731)
Win: 18-1 v Rushden 45-46 **Defeat:** 1-10 v Brighton FA Cup 65-66
Fee Paid: £500 **Fee Received:** £4,000

BEST SEASON **FA Cup:** 2nd Rd 57-58, 97-98 League clubs defeated: Colchester
FA Trophy: 3rd Qual Rd **FA Vase:** Semi-Finals 84-85, 85-86

HONOURS Southern Lg Div 1 61-62; Utd Co's Lg (4) 46-48 49-50 61-62 (res) (R-up 48-49, Lg Cup 35-36 (R-up 46-47); Midland Lg R-up 57-58; Eastern Co's Lg 71-72 76-7790-91 (R-up 70-71 73-74 83-84 92-93 96-97), Lg Cup 50-51 70-71 71-72 (R-up 73-74 76-77 86-87); Cambs Invit Cup(8) 52-53 55-56 57-58 74-76 81-83 91-92; E Anglian Cup 87-88 (R-up 40-41 48-49); Peterborough Lg 24-25 27-28 28-29 31-3232-33; Peterborough Snr Cup 32-33 76-77 89-90 97-98

Players progressing: BryanHarvey/Terry Marshall (Newcastle), Jackie Callagher (Peterboro), Paul Scott (Blackpool), Peter Dobson (Ipswich)

Back Row left to right: Chris Dear, Mark Jimson, Ian Pledger, Duncan Roberts, Lee Hyde, Mark Thompson, PaulGoodhand and Terry Back (Manager). Front row: Nick Reeson, Paul Hill, Kevan Leggatt, Nigel Vince, Lee Ellison and Dan Steadman.

JEWSON EASTERN COUNTIES LEAGUE

Feeder to: Dr Martens League
Founded 1935

Hon. Patron: Derek Needham **President:** Roger Pauley

Secretary: Colin Lamb, 3 Land Close, Clacton-on-Sea, Essex CO16 8UJ
Tel: 01255 436398

www.jewsonleague.co.uk

PREMIER DIVISION FINAL LEAGUE TABLES 2000-01

PREMIER DIVISION

	P	W	D	L	F	A	Pts	GD
AFC Sudbury	42	32	7	3	134	37	103	97
Gorleston	42	29	8	5	99	41	95	58
Lowestoft Town	42	26	10	6	99	41	88	58
Maldon Town	42	20	10	12	68	52	70	16
Clacton Town	42	19	11	12	79	58	68	21
Wroxham	42	18	9	15	88	66	63	22
Woodbridge Town	42	17	12	13	62	67	63	-5
Gt Yarmouth Tn	42	18	8	16	64	59	62	5
Soham Town Rngrs	42	18	6	18	68	70	60	-2
Stowmarket Town	42	16	12	14	55	58	60	-3
Diss Town	42	16	10	16	69	66	58	3
Ipswich Wndrs	42	16	8	18	54	52	56	2
Fakenham Town	42	17	5	20	60	68	56	-8
Tiptree United	42	15	10	17	70	64	55	6
Mildenhall Town	42	15	9	18	58	58	54	0
Bury Town	42	15	9	18	56	73	54	-17
Ely City	42	12	10	20	61	74	46	-13
Felixstowe & W U	42	12	9	21	45	75	45	-30
Harwich & Parkeston	42	11	6	25	51	98	39	-47
Newmarket Town	42	9	9	24	50	83	36	-33
Warboys Town	42	7	9	26	38	104	30	-66
Halstead Town	42	7	7	28	42	106	28	-64

DIVISION ONE

	P	W	D	L	F	A	Pts	GD
Swaffham Town	32	24	5	3	83	27	77	56
Dereham Town	32	22	5	5	83	23	71	60
Stanway Rovers	32	22	5	5	86	29	71	57
Needham Market	32	20	5	7	70	33	65	37
Chatteris Town	32	17	6	9	73	46	57	27
Hadleigh Utd	32	16	5	11	51	46	53	5
Haverhill Rovers	32	15	7	10	67	39	52	28
Cambridge C Res	32	14	9	9	62	47	51	15
Downham Town	32	14	7	11	71	60	49	11
Norwich United	32	12	5	15	53	46	41	7
Cornard United	32	10	3	19	37	85	33	-48
Whitton United	32	8	6	18	41	64	30	-23
Somersham Tn	32	7	8	17	42	69	29	-27
Wisbech T Res	32	8	4	20	42	72	28	-30
Thetford Town	32	7	4	21	37	81	25	-44
Brightlingsea Utd	32	4	7	21	32	88	19	-56
March Tn Utd*	32	3	7	22	18	93	15	-75

* points deducted

LEADING GOALSCORERS 2000-01

PREMIER DIVISION

		Lge	KO Cup	D1 Cup	MT	Tot
Gary Ingram	Gorleston	35	0	0	2	37
Scott Witney	Maldon Town	29	5	0	0	34
Russell Stock	Wroxham	26	2	0	0	28
Andrew Claydon	AFC Sudbury	23	2	0	0	25
Brian Devereux	AFC Sudbury	25	0	0	0	25
Sam Banya*	Diss Town	17	0	0	5	22
Neal Docking	Soham Tn R	18	4	0	0	22
Stuart Roach**	Lowestoft T	17	4	0	0	21
Paul Thompson	Lowestoft T	14	0	0	5	19
Coren Hardy	Diss Town	18	0	0	0	18
David Barefield	Tiptree U	16	2	0	0	18
Gary McGee	Lowestoft T					

*including 4 goals for Felixstowe & Walton Utd
** including 18 goals for Great Yarmouth Town

DIVISION ONE

		Lge	KO Cup	D1 Cup	MT	Tot
Kevin White	Swaffham T	30	0	0	4	34
Kevin Leggett	Downham T	28	0	5	0	33
Mark Brandt	Haverhill R	18	3	6	0	27
Neil Maguire	Dereham T	17	1	4	0	22
Anthony Cracknell	Hadleigh U	20	0	1	0	21
Gavin Crane*	Stanway R	21	0	0	0	21
Simon Barnes	Dereham T	18	0	0	2	20
Andrew Sapey	Stanway R	18	1	0	0	19
Robert Back	Swaffham T	18	0	0	0	18
Jamie Hunton	Norwich U	17	0	0	0	17
David Robinson	Downham T	16	0	1	0	17
Martin Westcott	Chatteris T	17	0	0	0	17

* including 5 goals for Woodbridge Town

PREMIER DIVISION RESULTS CHART 2000-01

		1	2	3	4	5	6	7	8	9	10	11	12	13	14	15	16	17	18	19	20	21	22
1	AFC Sudbury	X	0-0	1-1	2-2	2-0	4-0	3-0	3-0	2-0	7-0	4-0	2-1	2-1	4-0	2-1	4-0	4-2	5-1	0-0	8-0	8-1	3-2
2	Bury Town	0-5	X	1-2	1-0	2-1	1-2	0-0	0-0	0-1	2-2	1-2	1-2	3-3	0-1	2-0	1-0	3-2	0-0	3-1	1-1	2-2	2-1
3	Clacton T	1-3	5-2	X	2-2	6-0	1-2	1-0	0-3	3-1	1-1	2-2	1-2	3-2	1-3	0-0	1-0	0-2	4-1	5-2	1-1	0-1	4-3
4	Diss Town	0-2	2-3	1-6	X	3-0	2-0	0-0	1-3	1-1	4-1	6-0	1-0	0-1	4-2	2-1	3-1	1-2	2-2	4-2	3-1	4-0	1-4
5	Ely City	2-2	1-1	0-1	1-1	X	4-1	0-1	0-2	0-2	2-1	3-0	0-1	1-3	0-2	2-2	2-2	1-1	1-2	2-4	5-1	2-2	4-4
6	Fakenham	1-6	5-1	0-1	2-1	0-1	X	2-1	1-3	4-0	2-1	2-2	1-0	0-1	3-1	2-0	0-2	2-1	3-2	2-1	1-1	0-2	1-4
7	Felix & W	1-5	0-1	0-0	1-0	1-2	1-0	X	0-3	1-2	3-2	3-2	0-3	0-3	0-3	1-0	5-2	1-4	0-0	2-0	2-1	1-1	0-3
8	Gorleston	4-0	5-2	3-0	3-0	4-3	4-4	5-1	X	1-1	2-0	2-1	4-3	0-1	4-1	3-1	1-0	3-1	3-1	1-0	5-1	1-2	2-2
9	Gt Yarmouth	2-3	1-3	3-3	0-1	0-2	2-0	1-1	0-1	X	1-0	2-3	2-1	0-4	1-3	0-0	2-1	2-1	0-0	3-1	4-0	3-0	0-2
10	Halstead T	0-6	0-2	0-3	0-3	3-1	1-1	4-1	0-0	0-4	X	1-3	1-1	1-5	0-0	2-0	5-1	0-3	1-3	2-1	1-3	0-1	2-4
11	Harwich & P	1-5	2-4	1-0	1-2	0-4	1-0	1-5	1-4	1-3	1-3	X	0-3	0-4	2-3	1-0	2-2	4-0	0-4	2-1	0-1	2-3	1-4
12	Ipswich W	2-4	0-1	1-2	0-1	3-1	0-2	1-1	1-3	2-1	3-0	0-2	X	0-1	1-3	2-0	0-0	0-0	1-1	1-0	5-0	1-0	2-1
13	Lowestoft T	2-2	2-0	2-3	2-2	5-0	3-0	0-0	2-0	1-1	3-0	4-1	1-2	X	3-1	2-3	4-1	6-1	3-0	2-2	2-1	1-0	1-0
14	Maldon T	0-3	2-0	1-1	3-1	0-2	1-1	2-2	1-3	0-2	3-0	3-0	1-1	1-1	X	2-2	1-0	0-2	0-1	1-1	4-0	3-0	4-1
15	Mildenhall T	1-1	2-1	3-0	3-1	0-1	2-1	1-0	0-1	1-2	4-1	2-1	2-0	0-1	0-1	X	4-2	2-4	1-3	1-2	6-0	1-1	2-1
16	Newmarket T	1-2	4-2	1-4	2-0	1-3	3-2	0-2	0-3	3-2	3-1	1-1	1-1	3-3	0-4	0-1	X	1-2	1-0	1-1	0-2	4-4	2-1
17	Soham T R	1-0	3-1	0-4	3-0	2-1	2-3	2-3	1-5	1-1	3-1	0-1	2-0	1-1	1-1	0-1	2-1	X	1-2	2-1	0-1	1-4	2-1
18	Stowmarket T	0-2	4-0	1-0	1-2	2-0	0-3	2-0	0-0	0-3	0-1	0-2	1-1	2-1	2-0	2-2	1-0	4-3	X	1-1	2-4	0-0	0-3
19	Tiptree U	1-3	1-3	1-1	2-0	1-1	2-0	4-0	3-2	7-1	2-1	4-1	1-1	1-2	4-1	2-1	1-1	0-1	X	4-0	0-2	1-3	
20	Warboys T	1-3	1-2	2-2	1-1	0-3	1-0	2-1	1-2	0-3	2-2	2-2	0-1	1-5	0-2	0-2	0-1	1-5	1-1	1-2	X	1-1	1-5
21	Woodbridge T	1-6	3-0	2-1	1-1	2-1	0-4	3-0	0-0	3-0	4-0	2-0	2-1	0-3	1-2	3-3	0-0	0-1	2-4	0-0	2-0	X	3-1
22	Wroxham	3-1	2-1	1-2	3-3	1-1	1-0	4-3	1-1	2-3	3-0	1-1	1-3	2-3	0-0	1-1	2-1	1-0	1-1	1-2	3-0	4-1	X

FIRST DIVISION RESULTS CHART 2000-01

		1	2	3	4	5	6	7	8	9	10	11	12	13	14	15	16	17
1	Brightlingsea Utd	X	2-4	1-3	4-2	0-5	2-1	3-0	1-2	1-1	1-2	1-7	1-1	1-2	0-1	2-2	1-1	2-2
2	Cambridge C Res	7-0	X	1-1	2-0	1-1	2-0	0-4	1-1	2-1	1-0	1-0	2-2	1-2	2-3	5-1	0-0	4-3
3	Chatteris Town	4-1	4-1	X	3-0	1-2	4-2	0-0	2-1	5-1	5-2	1-1	3-0	1-4	0-2	4-1	2-2	1-0
4	Cornard United	2-1	1-0	0-3	X	1-8	2-3	3-2	2-1	0-0	0-2	2-1	2-1	1-2	1-9	2-1	3-1	2-2
5	Dereham Town	7-0	3-0	1-1	4-0	X	3-2	1-3	1-0	3-0	1-1	0-2	3-0	1-0	1-0	4-0	6-0	4-0
6	Downham Town	5-1	2-2	2-1	5-1	1-1	X	2-4	3-1	2-2	2-0	0-2	2-0	0-0	2-3	0-1	4-3	5-0
7	Hadleigh United	2-0	3-3	2-0	1-0	0-1	2-4	X	2-2	2-2	0-2	0-3	2-1	1-0	0-4	3-1	2-1	4-1
8	Haverhill Rovers	4-0	0-3	3-5	4-0	1-0	4-1	0-0	X	5-0	3-2	1-0	2-0	0-1	1-1	6-0	0-0	7-0
9	March Town Utd	0-2	0-4	0-2	2-2	0-6	0-3	1-4	0-3	X	0-4	1-3	1-1	0-7	1-0	0-1	0-3	0-2
10	Needham Market	4-1	2-1	3-1	4-0	2-3	5-2	2-0	3-0	3-0	X	3-1	1-0	1-1	0-1	4-0	1-0	3-0
11	Norwich United	2-1	0-2	2-2	5-1	0-1	1-1	0-1	1-4	1-1	0-3	X	2-0	1-3	2-3	3-0	1-2	4-1
12	Somersham Town	0-0	1-1	3-2	4-0	1-3	1-3	3-1	1-1	4-1	2-4	1-0	X	1-2	3-3	0-3	5-2	3-1
13	Stanway Rovers	3-1	5-2	3-0	1-0	0-0	3-3	2-1	1-2	10-0	1-2	5-1	8-0	X	1-3	3-1	2-0	2-0
14	Swaffham Town	5-0	2-0	3-2	1-2	3-0	0-0	2-0	3-1	5-0	1-1	4-2	3-0	1-1	X	4-0	1-0	4-2
15	Thetford Town	0-0	2-2	2-5	2-4	1-3	4-5	0-1	3-2	0-1	2-1	0-0	3-0	1-3	1-4	X	2-3	2-0
16	Whitton United	3-1	1-2	0-4	2-1	0-5	4-2	2-3	0-3	3-1	1-1	0-1	2-2	1-3	1-2	3-0	X	0-2
17	Wisbech T Res	4-0	0-3	0-1	4-0	2-1	1-2	0-1	2-2	0-1	2-2	0-4	5-1	1-5	0-2	1-0	1-0	X

CHALLENGE CUP 2000-01

Lowestoft Town 5p, 0 v 0, 4p Fakenham Town

FIRST DIVISION KNOCK OUT CUP 2000-01

Haverhill Rovers 2 v 1 Needham Market

MILLENNIUM TROPHY 2000-01

Soham Town Rangers 4p, 1 v 1, 3p Diss Town

CHELL RESERVE TEAM TROPHY

Wroxham 2 v 1 Stowmarket Town

EASTERN COUNTIES FOOTBALL LEAGUE PREVIOUS SEASONS

LEAGUE CHAMPIONSHIP

2000-01	AFC Sudbury	Gorleston
1999-00	Histon	Wroxham
1998-99	Wroxham	Fakenham Town
1997-98	Wroxham	Ely City
1996-97	Wroxham	Wisbech Town
1995-96	Halstead Town	Diss Town
1994-95	Halstead Town	Wroxham
1993-94	Wroxham	Halstead Town
1992-93	Wroxham	Wisbech Town
1991-92	Wroxham	Stowmarket Town
1990-91	Wisbech Town	Braintree Town
1989-90	Sudbury Town	Thetford Town
1988-89	Sudbury Town	Braintree Town
1987-88	March Town Utd	Braintree Town
1986-87	Sudbury Town	Braintree Town
1985-86	Sudbury Town	Colchester Utd Rs
1984-85	Braintree Town	Sudbury Town
1983-84	Braintree Town	Wisbech Town
1982-83	Saffron Walden T	Gorleston
1981-82	Tiptree United	Sudbury Town
1980-81	Gorleston	Sudbury Town

FIRST DIVISION

2000-01	Swaffham Town	Dereham Town
1999-00	Tiptree United	Ely City
1998-99	Clacton Town	Mildenhall Town
1997-98	Ipswich Wndrs	Maldon Town
1996-97	Ely City	Histon
1995-96	Gorleston	Warboys Town
1994-95	Clacton Town	Sudbury Town Res
1993-94	Hadleigh United	Woodbridge Town
1992-93	Sudbury Wanderers	Soham Town Rngrs
1991-92	Diss Town	Fakenham Town
1990-91	Norwich United	Brightlingsea Utd
1989-90	Cornard United	Norwich United
1988-89	Wroxham	Halstead Town

CHALLENGE CUP

2000-01	Lowestoft Town	Fakenham Town
1999-00	Wroxham	Diss Town
1998-99	Sudbury Wndrs	Felixstowe Town
1997-98	Woodbridge Town	Warboys Town
1996-97	Harwich & P'ston	Haverhill Rovers
1995-96	Halstead Town	Fakenham Town
1994-95	Wisbech Town	Newmarket Town
1993-94	Woodbridge Town	Chatteris Town
1992-93	Wroxham	Cornard United
1991-92	Norwich United	Gorleston
1990-91	Histon	Wroxham
1989-90	Sudbury Town	Gt Yarmouth Town

CHALLENGE CUP cont.

1988-89	Sudbury Town	Halstead Town
1987-88	Braintree Town	Haverhill Rovers
1986-87	Sudbury Town	Wisbech Town
1985-86	Tiptree United	March Town United
1984-85	Tiptree United	Histon
1983-84	Lowestoft Town	Gt Yarmouth Town
1982-83	Sudbury Town	Colchester Utd Res
1981-82	Tiptree United	Gorleston Town
1980-81	Gt Yarmouth Town	Clacton Town

FIRST DIVISION KNOCK OUT CUP

2000-01	Haverhill Rovers	Needham Market
1999-00	Ely City	Downham Town
1998-99	Clacton Town	Dereham Town

LEADING GOALSCORERS

2000-01	37	Gary Ingram	Gorleston
1999-00	34	Brian Devereux	AFC Sudbury
1998-99	36	Gary Setchell	Fakenham Town
1997-98	37	Stuart Roach	Gt Yarmouth Town
	37	Neil Kennedy	Histon
1996-97	41	Peter Munns	Wisbech Town
1995-96	32	Paul Smith	Diss and Harwich
1994-95	42	Paul Smith	Harwich & P'kston
1993-94	34	Scott Snowling	Wroxham
1992-93	50	Matthew Metcalfe	Wroxham
1991-92	37	Jon Rigby	Wroxham
1990-91	25	Steve Parnell	Halstead Town
1989-90	44	Steve McGavin	Sudbury Town
1988-89	27	Danny Jay	Braintree Town

LEADING GOALSCORERS
DIVISION ONE

2000-01	34	Kevin White	Swaffham Town
1999-00	39	Stuart Jopling	Needham Market
1998-99	31	Kris Lee	Tiptree United
1997-98	27	Scott Witney	Maldon Town
1996-97	30	Glen Driver	Needham Market
1995-96	24	Ray Edwards	Ipswich Wndrs
1994-95	30	Ricky Martin	Downham Town
1993-94	25	Paul Keys	Hadleigh United
	25	Steve McKenna	Bury Town Res
1992-93	32	Adrian Bullett	Soham Town R
1991-92	25	Brendan Doe	Somersham Town
	25	Matthew Metcalfe	Diss Town
1990-91	25	Mick Money	Norwich United
1989-90	38	Andrew Smiles	Cornard United
1988-89	35	Steve Parnell	Halstead Town

BURY TOWN

Secretary: Mrs Wendy Turner, 64 Winthrop Rd., Bury-St-Edmunds, Suffolk. IP333UF
Tel Nos: 01284 753688 (H) 01284 762291 (W) Club Website: www.burytownfc.com
Ground: Ram Meadow, Cotton Lane, Bury St Edmunds, Suffolk IP33 1XP Tel: 01284 754721
Directions: Leave A14 at sign to Central Bury St Edmunds, follow signs to town centre at exit r'bout, at next r'bout 1st exit into Northgate St, L. at `T' junct (lights) into Mustow St, left immediately into Cotton Lane - ground 350 yds on right, through `Pay & Display' car park. 10 mins from station
Capacity: 3,500 Cover: 1,500 Seats: 300 Floodlights: Yes
Clubhouse: Members'/Public Bars open at matchdays **Club Shop:** Yes

HONOURS Eastern Counties Lg 63-64, R-up 37-38, Lg Cup 61-62 63-64; Metropolitan Lg 65-66, R-up 67-68 70-71, Lg Cup 67-68, Professional Cup 65-66; Suffolk Premier Cup (9); Suffolk Senior Cup 36-37 37-38 38-39 44-45 84-85
PREVIOUS **Leagues:** Norfolk & Suffolk; Essex & Suffolk Border; Eastern Co's 35-64 76-87; Metropolitan 64-71 **Names:** Bury St Edmunds 1895-1902; Bury Utd 02-06
BEST SEASON **FA Cup:** 1st Rd replay 68-69, 0-3 v AFC Bournemouth (A) after 0-0
FA Vase: Qtr Finals 88-89 **FA Trophy:** 2nd Rd 70-71
CLUB RECORDS **Attendance:** 2,500 v Enfield, FA Cup 3rd Qual. Rd 1986
Goalscorer: Doug Tooley 58 **Appearances:** Doug Tooley
Fee Paid: £1,500 for Mel Springett (Chelmsford 1990)
Fee Received: £5,500 forSimon Milton (Ipswich)

FACT FILE
Formed: 1872
Nickname: The Blues
Colours: All blue
Change colours: All yellow
Midweek matchday: Tuesday
Programme: 40 pages 80p
Editor: Mrs Wendy Turner
2000-01
Captain: D. Vince
P.o.Y.: Andy Ince
Top scorer: Andy Ince - 12
CLUB PERSONNEL
Chairman: Colin Hurley
Vice Chairman: Russel Ward
President: Cyril Elsey
Manager: Richard Wilkins
Asst Manager: Trevor Collins
Physio: Darren Gibbs

CLACTON TOWN

Secretary: Mrs Linda Pigeon c/o Club Tel: 01255 476133 email: secretary@clacton-town.com

Ground: The Rush Green Bowl, Rushgreen Road, Clacton-on-Sea, Essex CO16 7BQ
Tel/Fax: 01255 432590 email: supporters@clacton-town.com
Directions: A133 to Clacton, at r'bout right into St Johns Rd, 4th left CloesLane, 3rd right Rushgreen Rd, ground approximately half mile on right. From B1027 take main Jaywick turn off (Jaywick Lane), then 2nd left after about half a mile into Rushgreen Rd. Ground 400 yds. 2 miles from Clacton (BR), buses 3, 5or 5a to Coopers Lane/Rushgreen Rd
Capacity: 3,000 Seats: 200 Cover: Yes Floodlights: Yes Club Shop: Yes
Clubhouse: Licensed club. Open 7-11pm Mon-Fri, all day Sat & Sun.
Hot & cold food available at all times.

HONOURS Southern Lg Div 1 59-60; Eastern Co's Lg R-up 36-37 53-54 64-65 74-75 (Lg Cup 73-74), Div 1 98-99 (Lg Cup 98-99); Eastern F/lit Cup 95-96; East Anglian Cup 53-54,99-00; WorthingtonEvans Cup 56-57 67-68 74-75.
PREVIOUS **Leagues:** Eastern Co's 35-37 38-58; Southern 58-64
Grounds: Clacton Stadium, Old Road 06-87; Gainsford Av (temp)
RECORD **Attendance:** 3,505 v Romford, FA Cup 1st Qual. Rd 1952 (at Old Road)
BEST SEASON **FA Vase:** 4th Rd 74-75,99-00 ,**FA Cup:** 1st Rd,1-3 v Southend U. (H) 60-61
Players progressing: Vivian Woodward (Spurs), Mick Everitt (Arsenal), Christian McLean (Bristol R.)

FACT FILE
Founded: 1892
Nickname: Seasiders
Colours: White/white/royal blue
Change colours: yellow/yellow/royal blue
Midweek Matches: Tuesday
Programme: 40 pages, £1
Editor: Jon Gooding (01473 420731)
Local P ress: Clacton Gazette
web Site: http://www.clacton-town.com

CLUB PERSONNEL
Owner: Jeff Dewing
Chairman: Mick Brpoadbent
Commercial Manager: Michelle Stanley
Tel:01255822169
Team Manager: Mick Potter
2000-01
Captain: Steve Howe P.o.Y.: Shane Bailey
Top Goalscorer: Mitchell Springette 14

DEREHAM TOWN

Secretary: Terry Cator, 4 Yarrow Road, Dereham, Norfolk, NR20 3BH
Tel: 01362 694082(H) 01362 690459(W)

Fixtures Sec: David West Tel: 01362 693006 (H) 01362 692433 (B)

Ground: Aldiss Park, Norwich Road, Dereham, Norfolk NR20 3AL
Tel/Fax: 01362 690460
Capacity: 3,000 Seats: 250 Cover: 500 Club Shop: No

HONOURS Anglian Combination 97-98

PREVIOUS **Leagues:** Dereham & Dist., East Anglian, Anglian Combination >98
Names: Dereham, Dereham Hobbies
Grounds: Recreation Ground 1890-1998

RECORD **Defeat:** 0-13, v Gorleston, Norfolk Sen. Cup 9.1.1926

2000-01 Captain: Matthew Henman P.o.Y.: Stuart King Top Scorer: Neil McGuire 22

FACT FILE
Formed: 1890
Nickname: The Magpies
Colours: Black & white/black/white
Change colours: all Red
Midweek matchday; Tuesday
Programme - 20 pages 50p
Editor: Barnes Print
Tel: 01362 860781 Fax: 01362 860977
Website: www.derehamtownfc.com

CLUB PERSONNEL
Chairman: Tim Warner
Tel: 01362 692419 (H)

Manager: Paul Jarvis

DISS TOWN

Secretary: Pam Lattimore, 7 Station Road, Pulham St. Mary, Diss, Norfolk, IP21 4QT.
01379 608905 Tel/Fax - 07711 470858M

Ground: Brewers Green Lane, Diss Tel: 01379 651223

Directions: Just off B1066 Diss-Thetford road, near Roydon School. 1 1/2 miles from Diss (BR)
Capacity: 2,500 Seats: 280 Cover: Yes Floodlights: Yes
Club Shop: Yes, incl. pennants
Clubhouse: Open evenings (except Sunday), Sat/Sun lunchtimes, and matchdays

HONOURS FA Vase 94-95; Eastern Co's Lg Div 1 91-92, Anglian Comb. 76-77 78-79(R-up 74-75, Div 1 67-68 73-74, Lg Cup 67-68 79-80 81-82), Norfolk & Suffolk Lg R-up 55-56 (Applegate Cup 56-57 57-58(joint)(R-up 55-56)), Norfolk Snr Cup 74-75 95-96, Norfolk Jnr Cup 1891-92, Jewson Prem Lge R-up 95-96 R-up Millennium Trophy 2001

PREVIOUS **Leagues**: Norwich & District; Norfolk & Suffolk 35-64; AnglianComb. 64-82
Ground: Roydon Road 1886-1982

BEST SEASON **FA Vase:** Winners 94-95, QF 91-92

RECORDS **Attendance:** 1,731 v Atherton LR, FA Vase SF 1st leg 19/3/94

Players progressing A Thurlow (Man City), M Cawston (Norwich), T Whymark(Ipswich), C Stafford, P Gibbs (Colchester)

FACT FILE
Founded: 1888
Nickname: Tangerines
Sponsors: Apple Garages
Colours: Tangerine/navy/tangerine
Change colours: Sky blue/navy/navy
Midweek Matches: Tuesday
Reserve's League: Anglian Combination
Programme: 16 pages, 70p
Editor: Gary Enderby (01379 608767)

CLUB PERSONNEL
Chairman: Des Tebble
President: Roger Weeks
Treasurer: Noel Mullenger
Managers: Rick Neave & Alan Biley
Physio: Peter Etheridge
2000-01
Leading Goalscorer: Sam Banya 22
Captain: Lee Hunter
P.o.Y.: Gavin Pauling

ELY CITY

Secretary: Derek Oakey, 11 Frederick Talbot Close, Soham, Nr. Ely Cambs, CB7 5EY
Tel Nos: 01353 722141 (H) 01353 722179 (W) **Email Address:** derk.oakey@tesco.net

Ground: Unwin Sports Ground, Downham Road (01353 662035)

Directions: A10 Ely by-pass turn off for Downham. 3 miles (approx) from Ely(BR)

Capacity: 1,500 Seats: 150 Cover: 350 Floodlights: Yes Shop: No

Clubhouse: Open matchdays, refreshments available

Club Shop: Metal Badges: Yes

HONOURS Cambs Snr Cup 47-48, Eastern Co's Lg R-up 69-70 (Lg Cup 79-80)
Jewson Eastern Div 1 Winners 1996-97,R-up 1999-00,Cup Winners 99-00

PREVIOUS **Leagues:** Peterborough; Central Alliance 58-60
Grounds: Paradise Ground (1890 1986)

BEST SEASON **FA Cup:** 1st Rd 56-56 (2-6 v Torquay)

RECORD **Gate:** 260 v Soham, Eastern Co's Lg Div 1, 12/4/93
At old ground: 4,260 v Torquay, FA Cup 56-57

FACT FILE
Founded: 1885
Nickname: Robins
Colours: All red with white trim
Change colours: Jade/black/jade
Midweek Matches: Tuesday
Programme: 24 pages- 50p
Editor: Derek Oakley
Local Press: Ely Standard (01353 667831)
Club Website: elycityfc.com

CLUB PERSONNEL
Chairman: Brian Jordan
Manager: Steven Taylor
2000-01
Captain & P.o.Y.: Paul Jordan
Top Scorer: imon Mead 16

FAKENHAM TOWN

Secretary: Edric Linnell, 40 Warren Avenue, Fakenham, Norfolk NR21 8NP Tel: 01328 855445

Ground: Clipbush Lane, Fakenham NR21 8SW Tel/Fax: 01328 856222
Directions: Corner of A148 & Clipbush Lane
Capacity: 3,000 Seats: 264 Cover: 500 Floodlights: Yes
Clubhouse: Bar, TV. Refreshments available Tel: 01328 855859
Club Shop: Yes

HONOURS Norfolk Snr Cup 70-71 72-73 73-74 91-92 93-94 94-95;,98-99 Eastern Co's Premier Division R-up: 98-99, Lg Div1, R-up 91-92; Anglian Comb. Cup 78-79

PREVIOUS **Leagues:** N Norfolk 1884-1910; Norwich & Dist 10-35; Norfolk & Suffolk 35-64; Anglian Comb 64-87
Grounds: Hempton Green 1884-89; Star Meadow 89-1907;
Barons Hall Lawn 1907-96

BEST SEASON **FA Vase:** 98-99 3rd Rd **FA Cup:**

RECORD **Gate:** 1100 v Watford-official opening of new ground
Players progressing Nolan Keeley (Scunthorpe)
2000-01 **Captain**: Wayne Coe **P.o.Y.:** Stephen Lewis **Top Scorer:** Paul Reeve 15

FACT FILE
Founded: 1884
Nickname: Ghosts
Sponsors:Warner Paperbacks
Colours: Amber & black/black/amber
Change colours: Red & Black,red,red
Midweek Matchday: Tuesday
Reserves' League: Anglian Comb
Programme: 32 pages, 50p
Editor: John Cushion
Tel: 01328 862548
Local Press : Dereham & Fakenham Times

CLUB PERSONNEL
Chairman: Tony Fisher
President: G Middleditch
Press Officer: J Cushion
Commercial Manager: T.Vertigan
Managers: Neil Jarvis/Stuart Woodhouse

FELIXSTOWE & WALTON UNITED

Secretary: Michael Gosling, 23 Vicarage Road, Felixstowe, Suffolk IP11 2LR
Tel No: 01394 279758
Ground: Dellwood Avenue, Felixstowe IP11 9HT Tel: 01394 282917
Email Address: felixstowe@btinternet.com

Directions: A14 to Felixstowe. Turn right at 3rd r'bout then 1st left - ground100 yds on left. 5 mins walk from Felixstowe (BR) and town centre

Capacity: 2,000 Seats: 200 Cover: 200 Floodlights: Yes

Clubhouse: Bar, snack bar, TV, **Club Shop:** Yes, including enamel badges

HONOURS Suffolk Senior Cup 66-67 74-75 and 98-99 (as Walton United)

PREVIOUS **Leagues:** Essex & Suffolk Border; Ipswich & District
Names: Felixstowe Port & Town, Felixstowe Town, Felixstowe United
Merged with Walton United in 2000
Grounds: Tennis Club,Ferry Road.

RECORD **Attendance:** 1,500 v Ipswich Town, floodlight inauguration 25/1/91

2000-01 Captain & P.o.Y.: Neil Stanbridge Top Scorer: Danny Bloomfield 9,now NorwichC

FACT FILE
Founded: 1890
Nickname: Seasiders
Colours: Red & white stripes/black/red
Change: A;ll yellow
Midweek Matches: Tuesday
Programme: 48 pages, #1.00
Editor: Phil Griffiths
Tel: 01394 277156
Local Press: East Anglia Daily Times
Website: http:/www.felixstowe,btinternet.co.uk

CLUB PERSONNEL
Joint Chairmen:
Dave Ashford & Tony Barnes
Fixture Sec: MickGosling (01394 279758)
Manager:
Paul Adams (01473 404559)

GORLESTON

Secretary: Arthur Ottley,60 Peterhouse Avenue,Gorleston, Great Yarmouth, Norfolk NR31 7PZ
Tel Nos: 01493 603353 (H) 01263 738309)W) 07774 205949 (M)
Ground: Emerald Park, Woodfarm Lane, Gorleston, Great Yarmouth Tel: 01493 602802
Directions: On Magdalen Estate - follow signs to Crematorium, turn left and follow road to ground. Five and a half miles from Great Yarmouth Vauxhall (BR)
Capacity: 5,000 Seats:1000 Cover: 4,000 Floodlights: Yes
Clubhouse: Bar, colour TV, pool table, darts, snacks. Matchday Tea, coffee,cold drinks, burgers, hotdogs, rolls **Club Shop:** Yes

HONOURS Eastern Co's Lg 52-53 72-73 79-80 80-81; Lge Cup 55-56; Norfolk Snr Cup x 13, R-up x 25; Anglian Comb. 68-69, Norfolk & Suffolk Lg x 7; E Anglian Cup (3);Jewson Lge Div 1 95-96

PREVIOUS **Leagues:** Gt Yarmouth & Dist; Norfolk & Suffolk; Anglian Comb

BEST SEASON **FA Cup:** 1st Rd. 51-52, 57-58 **FA Vase:**

RECORD **Attendance:** 4,473 v Orient, FA Cup 1st Rd 29/11/51

Players progressing: J Joblins (Norwich), M Bailey (Wolves), D Stringer(Norwich), R Carter (Aston Villa), D Carter (Man City), A Brown (Charlton), S Morgan (Cambridge), P Gibbs (Colchester)

FACT FILE
Founded: 1884
Nickname: Greens
Colours: Green & White/whitw/white
Change colours: All blue
Midweek Matchday: Tuesday
Programme: 56/60 pages £1.00
Editor:Simon Barnes Printing

CLUB PERSONNEL
Chairman & President: Jimmy Jones
Managers: Robert Fleck

GREAT YARMOUTH TOWN

Secretary: Brian Smith, The Bungalow, Humberstone Farm, Cobholm, Great Yarmouth, Norfolk NR31 0AZ. Tel & Fax: 01493 656099
Ground: Wellesey Recreation Ground, Wellesey Road (01493 843373)
Directions: Just off Marine Parade, 200yds north of Britannia Pier.1/2 m from Vauxhall BR(BR)
Capacity: 3,600 Seats: 500 Cover: 2,100 Floodlights: Yes Club Shop: Yes

Clubhouse: (01493 843373). Committee Room, Sky TV, darts, pool. Hot & cold food
HONOURS Eastern Co's Lg 68-69 (R-up 56-57 67-68 77-78 78-79), Lg Cup 37-38 74-75 80-81; East Anglian Cup(3); Norfolk Senior Cup x 12, R-up x 22; Norfolk Premier Cupx 2 jt; Norfolk & Suffolk Lg 13-14 26-27 27-28; Anglian Comb. Cup 65-66(res); E Anglian Lg 56-57(res)

PREVIOUS **Leagues:** Norfolk & Suffolk

BEST SEASON **FA Cup:** 2nd Rd 52-53, 1st Rd 47-48 **FA Vase:** Semi-Final 82-83
RECORD **Attendance:** 8,944 v Crystal Palace, FA Cup 1st Rd 52-53
Appearances: Mark Vincent 538 (1984-2001)
Scorer: Gordon South 298 (1927-47) **Win:** 14-0, 2.2.10

Players progressing: R Hollis (Norwich), M Blyth & N Keeley (Scunthorpe), S Davy (West Ham), K Ready (Aston Villa), G Butcher (Blackburn)

FACT FILE
Founded: 1897
Nickname: Bloaters
Colours: Amber & black stripes/black/black
Change colours: All red
Midweek Matches: Tuesday
Programme: 40 pages, #1.00
Editor: Gerry Brown (014493 663171)

2000-01
Captain: Mark Vincent
Top Scorer: Robert George 16
P.o.Y.: Robert George

CLUB PERSONNEL
Chairman: Arthur Fiske
Manager: Paul Tong

AFC Sudbury, Champions of the Jewson Premier Division 2000 - 01. Photo: Peter Barnes

Felixstowe & Walton United FC (Jewson Eastern Counties Premier League)

Great Yarmouth Town

HARWICH & PARKESTON

Secretary: Andy Schooler, 21 The Vineway, Harwich, Essex CO12 4AX
01255 504590 (H) 01255 509700 (B) 01255 509718 (Bus. Fax)

Ground: Royal Oak, Main Road, Dovercourt, Harwich CO12 4AA Tel: 01255 503649

Directions: On main road into Dovercourt. 600 yds from Dovercourt (BR)

FLoodlights: Yes Capacity: 5,000 Seats: 350 Cover: 1,000

Clubhouse : Open every day. Dances, bingo, darts, pool, function room Club Shop: No

HONOURS FA Amateur Cup R-up 1898-99 52-53; Eastern Counties Lg 35-36 (jnt) (Lg Cup 35-36 36-37 96-97); Essex County Lg 37-38; Athenian Lg Div 1R-up 65-66 (Div 2 64-65, Lg Cup 64-65); Essex Sen. Cup 1898-99 36-37; Essex Sen. Trophy 89-90; AFA Senior Cup 35-36 36-37; Worthington Evans Cup 80-81

PREVIOUS **Leagues:** Eastern Co's 35-37 38-64; Essex County 37-38; Athenian 64-73 83-84; Isthmian 73-83 **Ground:** Phoenix Field, Seafront

BEST SEASON **FA Vase:** Q-F 90-91 **FA Cup:**
FA Amateur Cup: R-up 1898-99, 52-53

RECORD **Attendance:** 5,649 v Romford, FA Amat Cup 4th Rd 1938

Players progressing: I Gillespie (C Palace), G Waites, K Sanderson, I Brown(Bristol City 91)

FACT FILE
Founded: 1875
Nickname: Shrimpers
Colours: White & black/black/black
Change colours: Mauve & white/white/mauve
Midweek Matches: Tuesday
Reserve Lge: Essex & Suffolk Border Lge Prem. Div
Programme: 28 pages, 50p
Editor: Carl Allen
01255 552510
Club Website: hpfc.co.uk

CLUB PERSONNEL
Chairman: Graham Firth
President:Terry Rowlands
Press Officer: Carl Allan
Manager:Andy Clark
2000-01
Captain: Gary Harvey
Top Goalscorer: Matt Carmichael 17

IPSWICH WANDERERS

Secretary: Martin Head, 246 Sidelate Lane, Ipswich, Suffolk. IP4 3DH Tel: 01473 414390
Email address: headmartin@hotmail,com

Ground: Humberdoucey Lane, Ipswich, Suffolk Tel: 01473 728581

Directions: Take Woodbridge Road out of Ipswich,then left fork into Playford Road.Take first left into Humberdoucy Lane Ground 300yds on right
Capacity: 2,000 Seats: 50 Cover: Yes Floodlights: Yes

Clubhouse: Bar,Tea, coffee, cold drinks, confectionary, burgers, hotdogs,sandwiches, rolls

HONOURS Eastern Lge Div 1 97-98

BEST SEASON **FA Cup:** 2nd Q Rd 2000-01
FA Vase: 2nd Q Rd 2000-01

PREVIOUS **Leagues:** Little David SundayNames: Loadwell Ipswich

RECORD **Attendance:** 335 v Woodbridge, ECL Div 1 4/4/94

FACT FILE
Founded: 1983
Nickname: Wanderers
Sponsors:N.T.L.
Colours: All Blue
Change colours: Red & black/black/red & black
Midweek Matches: Tuesday
Programme: Yes
Editor: Alan Haste (01473 711877)
Local Press: East Anglian Daily Times, Evening Star

CLUB PERSONNEL
Chairman: A.Haste
President: P.Emmerson
Manager:Alan Dilloway
2000-01
Captain & P.o.Y.: Danny Cattermole
Top Scorer: Aren Howell 13

LOWESTOFT TOWN

Secretary: Terry Lynes, 31 Avondale Road Lowestoft, Suffolk NR32 2HU
Tel: 01502 564034 (H) 07930 872947(M) Email: terry@ltfcblues.freeserve.co.uk
Ground: Crown Meadow, Love Rd, Lowestoft Tel: 01502 573818
Directions: Just off A12, 10 mins from Lowestoft (BR)
Capacity: 3,000 Seats: 466 Cover: 500 Floodlights: Yes

Clubhouse: Pub hours, Snacks available **Club Shop:** Yes (incl metal badges)

HONOURS Eastern Co's Lg(8) 35-36(jnt) 37-38 62-63 64-65 67-68 69-71 77-78, Lg Cup(8) 38-39 54-55 65-67 68-69 75-76 83-84; 00-01Norf. & Suffolk Lg(8) 1897-99 1900-04 28-29 30-31; Suffolk Prem. Cup(7) 66-67 71-72 74-75 78-80; 99-00,00-01Suffolk Snr Cup(10) 02- 03 22-24 25-26 31-32 35-36 46-49 55-56; E Anglian Cup(10); Anglian Comb. (Res.) 77-78 79-80 (Lg Cup 76-77); E Anglian Lg (Res.) 57-58 63-64

PREVIOUS **League:** Norfolk & Suffolk 1897-1935
BEST SEASON **FA Cup:** 1st Rd 26-27 38-39 66-67, 67-68, 77-78
RECORDS **Attendance:** 5,000 v Watford, FA Cup 1st Rd 67
Goalscorer: M Tooley 383 **Appearances:** C Peck 629
Win: 19-0 v Thetford Town (H), Eastern Counties League

Players progressing: Eddie Spearitt (Ipswich 1965), Nigel Cassidy (Norwich1967), Richard Money (Scunthorpe 1973), Graham Franklin (Southend 1977)

FACT FILE
Founded: 1885
Nickname: Blues
Sponsors: Office World (Anglia) Ltd
Colours: Royal Blue/white/blue
Change colours: All red
Midweek Matches: Tuesday
Reserves' Lge: Anglian Combination
Programme:44 pages £1.00
Editor: Rachel Harrod
Website: www.lowestofttownfc.co.uk

CLUB PERSONNEL
Chairman: Shaun Cole
President: Roy Harper
Manager: Michael Chapman
2000-01
Captain: Micky Shade
P.o.Y. & Top Scorer: Paul Thompson 28

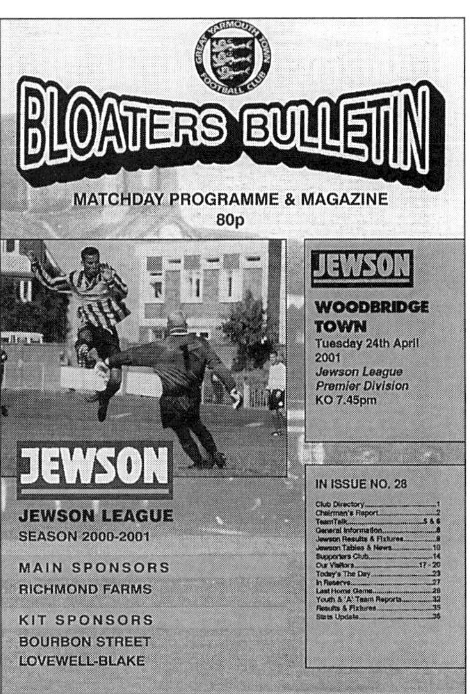

Great Yarmouth Town

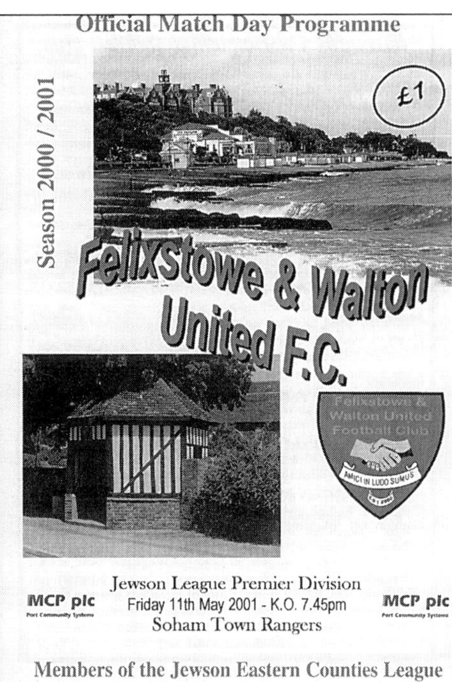

Felixstowe & Walton United FC

Lowestoft Town

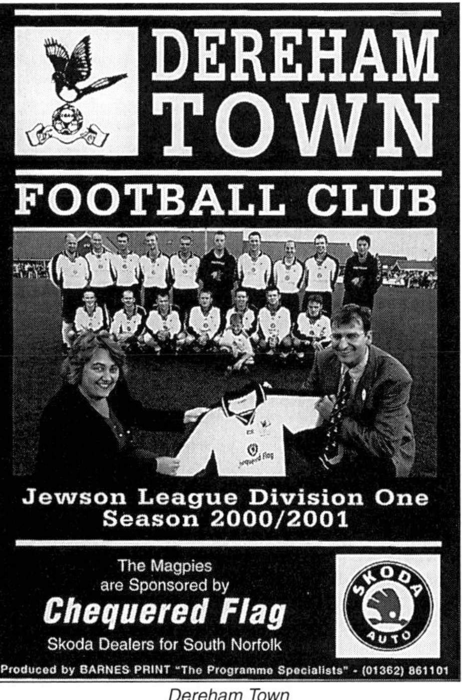

Dereham Town

MALDON TOWN

Secretary: Phil Robinson, 9 Lyndhurst Drive, Bicknacre, Essex CN3 4XL
Tel No: 01245 222633 (H) & 01206 753498 (W)
Email Address: angelina1@btinternet.com

Ground: Wallace Binder Ground, Park Drive, Maldon CM9 5XX (01621 853762)

Capacity: 2,500 Seats: 250 Cover: 500 Floodlights: Yes

HONOURS Essex Snr Lg 84-85 (Sportsmanship Award 87-88,88-89,94-95, Res Shield 93-94), Res Cup:94-95, Essex & Suffolk Border Lg 55-56 (Cup 64-65),Essex Intermediate Cup 51-52, Tolleshunt D'Arcy Cup 93-94,99-00

PREVIOUS **Leagues:** Mid Essex, N. Essex, Essex & Suffolk Border, Essex Senior
Ground: Fambridge Road (pre-1994)

BEST SEASON **FA Cup:** 2000-01 **FA Vase:** 2000-01

RECORDS **Attendance:** 33 v Millwall JUly 2000

FACT FILE

Founded: 1946 Nickname: 'The Town'
Colours: Blue & white hoops/blue/blue
Change colours: Red & black hoops/black/black
Midweek Matchday: Tuesday
Programme:24 pages £1.00
Editor: Alan Drewer
Club Website: http://www.maldontownfc.co.uk

CLUB PERSONNEL

Chairman: Bob Large
Manager: Colin Wallington

2000-01

Captain: Judd Cope P.o.Y.: Paul Younan
Top Goalscorer: Scott Whitney 40

MILDENHALL TOWN

Secretary: Karen Goodwin, 33 Kelsey Creacent,Cherry Hinton, Cambridge, Cambs.CB1 9XT Tel Nos: 01223 515330 (H) 0786 781 0944 (M)

Ground: Recreation Way, Mildenhall, Suffolk (01638 713449)

Directions: Next to swimming pool/carpark, quarter of a mile from town centre

Capacity: 2,000 Seats: 50

Clubhouse: Open matchdays & functions. Light refreshments available

HONOURS Suffolk Junior Cup 1899-1900

PREVIOUS **Leagues:** Bury & District; Cambs Lg 2B, 1B & Premier

RECORD **Attendance:** 350 v Norwich City, friendly 22/7/89

FACT FILE

Founded: 1890
Nickname: The Hall
Colours: Amber/black/black
Change colours:White/sky blue/white
Midweek Matchday: Tuesday
Programme: £1.00
Editor: Frank Marshall (01638 720616)
Local Press : Bury Free Press, Newmarket Journal, Cambridge Evening News,East Anglian Daily Times,Green 'Un

CLUB PERSONNEL

Chairman: Brian Brigden
Vice Chairman: frank Marshall
Fixture Secretary: Colin Marchant
Tel: 01842 812123
Managers: Steve O'Donoghue

NEWMARKET TOWN

Fixture Secretary: Elaine Jeakins, 140 New Cheveley Road,Newmarket CB88BY
Tel Nos: 01638 602525 (H) 01638 750201 (W) 07801 815682 (M)

Ground: Cricketfield Road, off New Cheveley Road, Newmarket (01638 663637)

Directions: 400 yds Newmarket (BR) - turn right into Green Rd, right at cross roads New Cheveley Rd, ground at top on left

Capacity: 1,750 Seats: 144 Cover: 150 Floodlights: Yes

Clubhouse: Matchdays only. Refreshments available

HONOURS Suffolk Snr Cup 34-35 93-94; Cambs Invitation Cup 58-59; Cambs Chall. Cup 21-22 26-27; Cambs Snr Lg, 19-20; Ipswich Snr Lg 30-31 31-32 32-33 33-34; Peterborough Lg 57-58; Suffolk Premier Cup 93-94 94-95 96-97

PREVIOUS **League:** Bury Snr; Ipswich Snr; Essex & Suffolk Border; Utd Co's 34-37; Eastern Co's 37-52

BEST SEASON **FA Cup:** 4th Qual. Rd 92-93, 0-2 v Hayes (H)
FA Vase: 4th Round 91-92

RECORD **Attendance:** 2,701 v Abbey Utd (now Cambridge Utd), FA Cup 1st Qual.Rd 1/10/49

Players progressing: Mick Lambert (Ipswich), M Wright (Northampton), G Tweed(Coventry), R Fuller (Charlton), Colin Vowden (Camb.Utd.)

FACT FILE

Founded: 1877
Nickname: Jockeys
Colours: Yellow & navy/navy/yellow
Change Colours: All Red
Midweek Matches: Tuesday
Programme:60p
Editor: Tony Pringle (01638 669438)

CLUB PERSONNEL

Chairman: Alan Collen
President: M J Nicholas
Manager: T.B.A.

2000-01

Captain Darren Coe
P.o.Y.: Darren O'Leary
Top Scorer: Paul Shaw 14

SOHAM TOWN RANGERS

Secretary: Mrs Wendy Gammon, 32 Broad Piece, Soham, Cambs.CB7 5EL
Tel: 01353 722139

Ground: Julius Martins Lane, Soham, Cambs. Tel: 01353 720732

Directions: A142 between Newmarket and Ely
Capacity: 2,000 Seats: 200 Cover: 1,500 Floodlights: Yes

Clubhouse: Function Room, Lounge Bar, Mail Hall, Stud Bar, Public Bar **Club Shop:** Yes

HONOURS Eastern Co's Lg Div 1 R-up 92-93; P'boro. Lg(3), Milleniuim Cup 2000-01, Cambs Invitation Cup 1990-91, 97-98, 98-99

PREVIOUS **Leagues:** Peterborough & Dist
Ground: Soham Rangers: Brook Street 1919-47
Names: Soham Town and Soham Rangers merged in 1947

RECORD **Attendance:** 3,000 v Pegasus, FA Amateur Cup 1963

2000-01 Leading goalscorer: Neal Docking 26 Captain: Kori Davis P.o.Y.: Dave Thompson

FACT FILE
Founded: 1947
Nickname: Town or Rangers
Main Sponsor: C.J.Murfitt
Colours: Green/white
Change colours: Blue/black/
Midweek Matchday: Tuesday
Reserves ' League: Cambs Prem. A
Programme: 50p Editor : Graham Eley
Local Press : Ely Standard, Newmarket Journal, Cambridge Evening News

CLUB PERSONNEL
Chairman: C.J.Murffitt
President: A. Isaacson
Managers: R Goodjohn & I. Benjamin
Coach: K. Murray
Physio: M. Drury

STOWMARKET TOWN

Secretary: Mrs Bev Mead, 59 Victoria Road, Stowmarket, Suffolk IP14 5AJ
Tel Nos: 01449 675624 (H) 07764 151351 (M) 01449 615225 (Fax)
Ground: Green Meadows Stadium, Bury Road, Stowmarket Tel: 01449 612533

Directions: About 800 yds from Stowmarket BR station - turn right at 1st lights and head out of town over r'bout into Bury Road - ground on right
Capacity: 2,000 Seats: 200 Cover: 450 Floodlights: Yes

Clubhouse: Bar open 6.30pm onwards Mon-Fri, weekends 12.0pm onwards.
Matchday food available Club Shop: Yes, incl. metal badges.
HONOURS Eastern Co's Lg R-up 91-92, Suffolk Premier Cup(4), Suffolk Snr Cup(10) Suffolk Jnr Cup., Churchman Cup: 99-00.
PREVIOUS **Leagues:** Ipswich & Dist.; Essex & Suffolk Border 25-52
Grounds: The Cricket Meadow, 1883-1984
Names: Stowupland Corinthians; Stowmarket Corinthians; Stowmarket FC
BEST SEASON **FA Cup: 2nd Q Rd 1992** **FA Vase: 4th Rd 1983-84**
RECORD **Attendance:** 1,200 v Ipswich Town, friendly July 1994
At Cricket Meadow: 3,800 v Romford, FA Amtr Cup 1st Rd 15/12/51

Players progressing: Craig Oldfield (Colchester), Les Tibbott, Ted Phillips & Brian Klug (Ipswich)

FACT FILE

Founded: 1883
Nickname: Stow
Colours: Gold & black/black/black
Change colours: All Red
Midweek Matches: Wednesday
Reserves' Lge: Essex & Suffolk Border
Programme: 20 pages,60p
Ed: Jonathon Gooding (01473 420731)
Local Press: East Anglian, Bury Free Press

CLUB PERSONNEL
Chairman: Derek Barnard
President: John Bultitude
Fixture Sec: Christine Gillingham
Tel: 01449 674507(H) 07880 732416(M)
Manager: Mel Aldis
Coach: Mark Barnard
Physio: John Chandler

AFC SUDBURY

Ground: Kingsmarsh Stadium, Brundon Lane, Sudbury, Suffolk CO10 1WQ (01787 376213)
Directions: From Sudbury centre follow Halstead/Chelmsford signs for about 1mile. 1st right after railway bridge at foot of steep hill, and 1st right after sharp left hand bend
Capacity: 2,500 Seats: 200 Cover: 150 Floodlights: Yes
Clubhouse: Matchdays/ training nights Shop: Yes Contact: Darren Witt (M) 0402 159375)

HONOURS WANDERERS - Eastern Co's Lg Div 1 92-93, Ess. & Suff. Border Lg(2) 89-91 (R-up 88-89), Suffolk Snr Cup 90-91

TOWN (Post War) Southern Lge - Lge Cup 93-94, R-up 96-97, Championship 93-94, Southern Div R-up 93-94; Eastern Counties Lg x 7, R-up x 6, Lg Cup x 6, Suffolk Prem.Cup x 13, R-up x 8, Suffolk Sen. Cup(2); E. Anglian Cup 85-86 91-92, R-up 83-84 95-96; Essex& Suffolk Border Lg x 5; E.S.B.L. Cup 49-50, R-Up 46-47; Eastern F'lit Group 93-94 94-95

PREVIOUS **Names:** Sudbury Town (1885) & Sudbury Wanderers (1958) merged 1999
Leagues: Wanderers- Essex & Suffolk Border. Town Suffolk & Ipswich; Essex & Suffolk Border; Eastern Co 55-90; Southern 91-97 Eastern Co. 98-99

BEST SEASON **FA Vase:** Quarter Final 97-98, 0-2 v Tow Law Town (A), after 1-1
WANDERERS **FA Cup:** 1st Round Proper, 00-01 (1-6 v Darlington)
TOWN **FA Vase:** Runners-up 88-89 **FA Trophy:** 3rd Rd.Proper 95-96
FA Cup: 2nd Rd Proper 96-97, 1-3 v Brentford. Played at Colchester Utd. F.C.

FACT FILE

Founded: 1st June,1999
Colours: Yellow/blue/yellow
Change Colours: All Red
Midweek Matchday: Tuesday
Programme: 48 + pages £1
Editor:T.B.A.
Local Press : Suffolk Free Press, East Anglian Daily Times

CLUB PERSONNEL

Joint Chairmen: Nick F Smith & Phil Turner

Secretary: David Webb
6 Melford Road, Sudbury, Suffolk CO10 1LS
Tel: 01787 372352 (H) 01787 886000 x6223 (B)

Manager: Keith Martin

Lowestoft Town. Back Row (l-r): Carl Chenery, Matthew Barbrook, Micky Tacon, Micky Shade, Jamie Stokeld, Stuart Roach, Paul Thompson, Iain Smith, Tosh Reeder. Front Row: Lee Pike, Grant Pierpoint, Mark Hitcham, Lee Durrant, Jamie Godbold

This goal line clearance was only a temporary reprive for Swaffham as seconds later Josh Sozzo had the ball in their net as Bedford United went on to win 3-2. FA Vase First Qualifying Round. Photo: Gordon Whittington

Dereham Town's Karl Dickerson scores a penalty in an easy FA Vase First Qualifying Round win at Long Buckby. Photo: Steve Ayre

SWAFFHAM TOWN

Secretary: D.R.Ward, 14 Mount Close,Swaffham. PE37 7BX (01760 722516(H0 01263 540402 (W) Email Address: Repward@aol,com

Ground: Shoemakers Lane, Swaffham, Norfolk (01760 722700)
Capacity: 2,000 Seats: 50 Cover: 200 Floodlights: Yes

Clubhouse: Open Tuesday, Thursday, Saturday & Sunday lunchtimes & evenings.

HONOURS Norfolk Snr Cup (2), Anglian Comb. 89-90 (Div 1 88-89)
Jewson Divison 1 Champions 00-01

PREVIOUS **Leagues:** Dereham, Anglian Combination

RECORD **Attendance:** 250 v Downham Town, Eastern Co's League Cup 3/9/91

2000-01 Captain: Marc Curson Top Scorer: Kevin White 39
Players of the Year: K.White & M Curson

FACT FILE

Founded: 1892
Nickname: Pedlars
Midweek Matchay: Tuesday
Colours: Black & white stripes/black/black
Change: All yellow
Programme: 36 pages, Free
Editor: Simon Barnes

CLUB PERSONNEL

Chairman: Kevin Burton
President: Stewart Collins
Manager: Robin Sainty

TIPTREE UNITED

Secretary: John Wisbey, 103 Peace Road, Stanway, Colchester, Essex
Tel Nos: 01206 564222 (H) 0403 585814 (M)
Email: john.wisbey@talk21.com

Ground: Chapel Road, Tiptree, Essex Tel: 01621 815213

Directions: Enter town on B1023 - Chapel Road is left at second crossroads, ground 200yds on left. 3 miles from Kelverdon (BR).
Served by Eastern NationalColchester to Maldon bus

Capacity: 2,500 Seats: 150 Cover: 300 Floodlights: Yes

Clubhouse: Open daily 7-11pm (all day Fri & Sat) & 12-2.30, 7-10.30 Sun.
Large bar, two snooker tables, pool, darts, netball, badminton, pigeon club, bingo. Dance hall seats 180, small hall seats 60. **Club Shop:** No

HONOURS Essex Snr Tphy 80-81, Eastern Co's Lg 81-82 (Lg Cup 81-82 84-85),
Essex Snr Lg R-up 75-76 77-78, Harwich Charity Cup (4),
Jewson Eastern Div 1 Champions 99-00

PREVIOUS **Leagues:** Essex & Suffolk Border; Essex Snr 78-84

RECORD **Attendance:** 1,210 v Spurs, floodlight inauguration Dec 1990

FACT FILE

Founded: 1933
Nickname:The Jam -Makers
Sponsors: Tiptree Building Supplies
Colours: Red& blackstripes/black/black
Change colours: Yellow/blue/white
Midweek Matchday: Tuesday
Reserves: Essex & Suffolk Border Lg Div 1
Programme: 32pages*, 50p Editor: Secretary
Local Press : Colchester Evening Gazette, Essex County Standard'
* Voted Eastern' Programme of the Year'
Website: www.tiptreeunited.com

CLUB PERSONNEL

Chairman: T.B.A. President: Peter Fidge
Manager: Neil Farley

2000-01: Capt: Jason Haygreen P.o.Y.: Phil Battell Top Scorer: David Barefield 24

WOODBRIDGE TOWN

Secretary: David Crowley,28 Victoria Road, Woodbridge, Suffolk.IP12 1EJ
Tel Nos: 01394 384853 (H) 01394 444630 (W)

Ground: Notcutts Park, Seckford Hall Road, Woodbridge, Suffolk IP12 4DA Tel: 01394 385308

Directions: Turning into Woodbridge off last rounda'bout from Lowestoft, or first roundabout from Ipswich. Take first turning left and first left again. Drive to ground at end of road on left.

Capacity: 3,000 **Seats:** 50 **Cover:** 200 **Floodlights**: Yes

Clubhouse: Visitors bar, lounge bar, function hall.Matchday Tea, coffee, cold drinks, hotdogs, soup, burgers, sandwiches, rolls.

HONOURS Suffolk Sen Cup(4), Jun Cup (4); Eastern Co Lg Cup 93-94 97-98, Lge Div 1 R-up 93-94; Ipswich Sen Lge (2)

PREVIOUS **Leagues:** Suffolk & Ipswich Ground: Kingston PF

BEST SEASON **FA Cup:** 3rd Rd Q 97-98 & 00-01 **FA Vase:** 6thRound 98-99

RECORD **Attendance:** 3,000 v Arsenal, floodlight opener 2/10/90

2000-01 Captain: Steve Dearsley
Top Scorer:Nigel Wallis 15 P.o.Y.: Mark Burgess& Cari David

FACT FILE

Founded: 1885
Nickname: The Woodpeckers
Sponsors: Brafe Engineering Ltd.
Colours: Black & white stripes/black/black
Change colours: All blue
Midweek Matchday: Tuesday
Reserves League: Essex & Suffolk Border
Programme: 20-24 pages ,50p
Editor: D Crowley
Local Press : East Anglian Daily Times

CLUB PERSONNEL

Chairman: Keith Dixon
President:Andrew Dalby
Football Sec: John Bennett, (01394 385973)
Commercial Manager: David Leech
Manager: David Hubbick

WROXHAM

Secretary : Chris Green, 24 Keys Drive, Wroxham, Norfolk NR12 8S Tel: 01603 783936 (H) 01603 772303 (B) Email Address: secretary@wroxhamfc.com

Ground: Trafford Park, Skinners Lane, Wroxham, Norfolk Tel: 01603 783538

Directions: Arriving from Norwich turn left at former Castle PH and keep left to ground. One and a half miles from Wroxham + Hoveton (BR). Buses 722, 724 and717

Capacity: 2,500 Seats: 50 Cover: 250 Floodlights: Yes

Clubhouse: Bar, pool, darts etc. Drinks, hot & cold food Club Shop: No

HONOURS Eastern Co's Lg 91-92 92-93 93-94 96-97 97-98, 98-99, R-Up 94-95,99-00 Lg.Cup 92-93,99-00R-up 90-91), Div 1 88-89; Norfolk Snr Cup 92-93 96-97 97-98;99-00 Anglian Comb(6) (LgCup(7); Reserves completed the double in 94-95.Jewson Res K.O. Cup 00-01

PREVIOUS **Leagues:** Norwich City; East Anglian; Norwich & Dist.; Anglian Comb. 64-88
Grounds: Norwich Road; The Avenue; Keys Hill (all pre-1947)

BEST SEASON **FA Vase:** 5th Round 99-00 v Chippenham Town

RECORDS **Attendance:** 1,011 v Wisbech Town, E. Counties Lge Prem. Div. 16/3/93
Goalscorer: Matthew Metcalf. Appearances: Stu Larter
Win: 15-2 v Thetford Town (H), E. Counties Lge Prem. Div. 17/1/92
Defeat: 1-24 v Blofield (A), Norwich & District League, early 1960s

Players progressing: Matthew Metcalf (Brentford) 93, Paul Warne (Wigan Athletic) 97

FACT FILE

Founded: 1892
Nickname: Yachtsmen
Colours: Royal & white/blue/blue
Change colours: Red & black/black/red & black
Midweek Matchday: Tuesday
Reserves ' League: Anglian Comb Prem Div
Programme: 20 pages
Editor: Matt Carpenter
Local Press : North Norfolk
Eastern Football (Norwich 628311)
Web-site:www.wroxhamfc.com

CLUB PERSONNEL

Chairman: Ray Bayles President: L King
Press Officer: Secretary
Joint Managers: Bruce Cunningham & Marty Hubble Physio: P.Terrington
2000-01 P.o.Y. & Top Scorer: Russell Stock
Captain : Darren Gill

Swaffham Town, Jewson League Division One Champions 2000-01
Back Row (l-r): R Sainty, I Nicol, P Thompson, J Turner, J Higgs, R Back, S Crawshaw, S Voutt, G Palmer
Front Row: M Blcokwell, M Fowler, A Stannard, M Curson, N Fryatt, A Seal, K White, J Hawes, S Figura

Haverhill Rovers FC. Back Row (l-r): Ted Beavis (Asst Manager), James Duke, Marcus Hunt, Dave Walton, Derrin Brindley, Paul Jenkin, Addie Hunt, Will Jones, Paul Goodman (Manager). Front Row: Mark Brandt, Alex Clarke, Neil Green, Brian Holmes, Paul Miles, Richie Walker, Neil Hammond, Ben Cowling

BRIGHTLINGSEA UNITED

Secretary: Michael Cole, The Sun, New Street, Brightlingsea, Essex, CO7 0DJ.
Tel Nos: 01206 302179H 07966 388458W
Ground: North Road, Brightlingsea, Essex (01206 304199)
Directions: B1027 Colchester - Clacton, B1029 from Thorrington Cross - follow Church Road into town, left into Spring Road, left into Church Road. Nearest station - Colchester - then bus 78 to Brighlingsea
Capacity: 2,000 Seats: 50 Cover: 250 Floodlights: Yes Club Shop: Yes
Clubhouse: Open matchadays & every evening, except Sunday. Matchday tea, coffee and snacks
HONOURS Essex Snr Lg 88-89 89-90 (Harry Fisher Mem. Tphy 89-90 (R-up 88-89), Lg Cup R-up 78-79), Eastern Co's Lg Div 1 R-up 90-91, Essex & Suffolk Border Lg Prem. Div Cup 71-72, Harwich Charity Cup 87-88, Worthington Evans Cup 76-77 77-78 78-79
PREVIOUS **Leagues:** Tendring Hundred, Essex & Suffolk Border, Essex Senior 1972-90
RECORD **Gate:** 1,200 v Colchester, friendly 68-69

FACT FILE
Founded: 1887 Nickname: Oystermen
Colours: Red & white,red,red
Change colours: Yellow & Navy, navy,navy
Midweek Matches: Tuesday
Programme: 24 pages, 30p
Editor: Kim Lay (01206 305797)
Local Press: Essex County Standard, Evening Gazette

CLUB PERSONNEL
Chairman: Michael Cole
Manager:Ken Ballard
2000-01 Leading goalscorer Bradley Hipkin 11
Captain: Lee Race
P.o.Y.: Jimmy Chatters

CAMBRIDGE CITY RESERVES

Secretary: Stuart Hamilton, 55 Crowhill, Godmanchester, Huntingdon, Cambs
Tel: 01480 382675

Ground: City Ground, Milton Road, Cambridge CB4 1UY Tel: 01223 357973
Directions: 50 yards on left from start of A1309, Cambridge to Ely Rd.
30 minswalk from Cambridge BR
Capacity: 5,000 Cover: 1,400 Seats:423 Floodlights: Yes

Clubhouse: 11am-11pm Mon-Sat, 12-3 & 7pm-10.30 Sun. Bingo, Dances, Pool, Darts

Club Shop: Sells programmes, club history, badges, scarves, pennants, replica shirts etc.
Contact Neil Harvey (01223 235991)

FACT FILE
Colours: White & black halves/black/white & black hoops
Change colours: Green & Yellow halves,green,green& yellow hoops
Midweek matchday: Monday
Programme Editor: Secretary

CLUB PERSONNEL
Chairman: Dennis Rolph
Fixtures Sec.: Andy Dewey
50 Doggett Rd., Cherry Hinton, Cambridge
01223 245694 (H) 01223 555410 (Bus. Fax)
Manager:Jeremy George
Tel; 01954 782484

CORNARD UNITED

Secretary: Chris Symes, 22 Greenacres, Mile End, Colchester, Essex CO4 (01206 851489)
Ground: Blackhouse Lane Sportsfield, Great Cornard, Suffolk (01787 376719)
Directions: Left off r'bout on A134 coming from Ipswich/Colchester intoSudbury, follow signs for Country Park - ground is immediately opposite along Blackhouse Lane
Capacity: 2,000 Seats: 250 Cover: 500 Floodlights: Yes Club Shop: No
Clubhouse: Open matchdays & Sunday lunchtimes. Matchday Tea, coffee, colddrinks, & snacks
HONOURS Eastern Co's Lg Div 1 89-90 (Lg Cup R-up 92-93), Essex & Suffolk BorderLg 88-89 (Lg Cup 88-89), Suffolk Snr Cup 89-90, Suffolk Jnr Cup R-up 84-85
PREVIOUS **Leagues:** Sudbury S/day 64-65; Bury St Edmunds & Dist 65-72; Colchester71-78; Essex Suffolk Bord 78-89. Grounds: Cornard Rec 64-71; Great CornardUpper School 71-85
RECORDS **Appearances:** Malcolm Fisher. Goalscorer : Andy Smiles
Attendance: 330 v Sudbury Town, Eastern Floodlit League 4/2/92
Win: 18-2 v St Peters House, Colchester Lge 14/9/72
Defeat: 4-10 v Finningham, Bury Lge 7/2/68

FACT FILE
Founded: 1964 Nickname: Ards
SponsorsGetech
AColours: Blue & white/white/blue
Change colours: Red
Midweek Matches: Tuesday
Reserve League: Essex & Suffolk Border
Programme: 16 pages Editor: Secretary
Local Press : Suffolk Free Press

CLUB PERSONNEL
Chairman: Chris Symes
Vice-Chairman: J.Stalker
President: Jim McLaughlin
Manager: Chris Symes
Asst Man.: Jason Stalker Physio: Mike Ford

DOWNHAM TOWN

Secretary: F. Thorne, 6 Maple Rd., Downham Market, Norfolk, PE38 9PY. (01366 382563)

Ground: Memorial Field, Lynn Road, Downham Market, Norfolk (01366 388424)

Directions: One and a quarter miles from Downham Market (BR) - continue to townclock, turn left and ground is three quarters of a mile down Lynn Road
Capacity: 1,000 Seats: 60 Cover: Yes Floodlights: Yes
Clubhouse: Bar open matchdays, refreshments & snacks available

HONOURS P'boro Lg (5) 62-63 73-74 78-79 86-88;
Norfolk Senior Cup 63-64 65-66 (R-up(3) 66-69)

PREVIOUS **Leagues:** Peterborough

RECORD **Attendance:** 325 v Wells Town Norfolk Senior Cup, 1998-99

FACT FILE
Founded: 1881
Nickname: Town
Sponsor: Lynwere Engineering
Colours: Red/white/red
Change colours: Sky/Navy/sky
Midweek Matches: Tuesday
Programme: Yes, with entry
Editor: Chairman

CLUB PERSONNEL
Chairman: John Fysh President: Louis Barker
Manager: Steve Tyres
2000-01Captain : Ian Leave
Top Scorer: Kevin Leggett 33
P.o.Y.: Martin Saddleton

HADLEIGH UNITED

Secretary: Peter Hutchings, 3 Mowlands, Capel St Mary, Ipswich. IP9 2XB Tel: 01473 311093

Ground: Millfield, Tinkers Lane, Duke Street, Hadleigh, Suffolk Tel: 01473 822165

Directions: Turn off A12 approx halfway between Ipswich & Colchester. Take B1070 & follow signs to Hadleigh. Duke Street is off the High Street - turn left by Library

Capacity: 3,000 Seats: 250 Cover: 500 Floodlights: Yes

Clubhouse: Open matchdays. **Website**: hadleigh-utd.co.uk

HONOURS Ipswich & Dist./Suffolk & Ipswich Lg 53-54 56-57 73-74 76-77 78-79 (Mick McNeil) Lg Cup 76-77 80-81 81-82 86-87; Suffolk Senior Cup 68-69 71-72 82-83. Eastern Co.Lg Champions 93-94

PREVIOUS **Leagues:** Suffolk & Ipswich (prev. Ipswich & D.)(pre-1991)
Grounds: Grays Meadow, Ipswich Road

RECORDS **Gate:** 518 v Halstead Town, FA Vase Replay 17.1.95 **Win:** 8-1 v Chatteris(A) 17/1/95 **Defeat:** 0-7 v Harwich & Parkston (H) 12/10/96, & Wisbech (H) 26/4/97

FACT FILE

Founded: 1892
Nickname: Brettsiders
Sponsors: Lancaster
Colours: White & navy/navy/navy
Change colours: All yellow
Midweek Matches: Tuesday
Reserves' Lge: Essex & Suff. Border
Programme: 12 pages, 50p
Editor: Peter Hutchings (01473 311093)

CLUB PERSONNEL

President: K.Grimsey
Chairman: John Chenery
Manager: Louis Newman

HALSTEAD TOWN

Secretary: Stephen Webber, 12 Ravens Ave, Halstead, Essex CO9 1NZ
Tel: 01787 476959 (H) 01284 767278 (B)

Ground: Rosemary Lane, Broton Ind Est, Halstead, Essex CO9 2HR Tel: 01787 472082

Directions: A131 Chelmsford to Braintree - follow signs to Halstead.
In Halstead, 1st left after Police Station, then 1st right, and first left to ground

Capacity: 2,000 Seats: 312 Cover: 400 Floodlights: Yes

Clubhouse: Open evenings and matchdays

HONOURS Eastern Co's Lg 94-95 95-96, R-up 93-94 (Div 1 R-up 89-90), Cup 95-96; Essex Senior Trophy 94-95 96-97; Knight Floodlit Cup R-up 90-91; Essex &Suffolk Border Lg 57-59 77-78 94-95(res), (R-up 49-50 54-55 60-61), Div 1(res)94-95); Essex Snr Lg Cup R-up 79-80; Essex Jnr Cup 01-02 46-47 (R-up 00-01)

PREVIOUS Lgs: Nth Essex; Halstead & Dist.; Haverhill; Essex & Suffolk Border; Essex Snr 80-88

RECORD **Attendance:** 4,000 v Walthamstow Avenue, Essex Senior Cup 1949

FACT FILE

Founded: 1879 Nickname 'The Town'
Colours: White /black/black
Change colours: All red
Midweek Matches: Tuesday
Page 24 Programme: 50p
Editor: Paul Downes
Tel: 01787 477320 (H)

CLUB PERSONNEL

Chairman: Mick Coe
Vice-Chairman:Richard Gugacz
President: Mr E J R McDowell
Fixture sec.: Andy Mizon
Tel: 01787 473898 (H) 01206 894096 (B)
Manager: Paul Grimsey
Physio: B Dunster

HAVERHILL ROVERS

Secretary: Chris Rice, 23 Ovington Place, Haverhill, Suffolk. CB9 0BA
Tel: 01440 712396 (H) 07880 966423 (M)

Ground: Hamlet Croft, Haverhill, Suffolk Tel: 01440 702137

Directions: Centre of Haverhill

Capacity: 3,000 Seats: 200 Cover: 200 Floodlights: Yes

Clubhouse: Open matchdays and functions. Snacks available

HONOURS Eastern Co's Lg 78-79 Lg Cup 64-65; Essex & Suffolk Border Lg 62-63 63-64; East Anglian Cup 90-91; Suffolk Sen Cup 96-97

PREVIOUS **League:** Essex & Suffolk Border

RECORD **Attendance:** 1,537 v Warrington Town, FA Vase QF 86-87

Players progressing: R Wilkins (Colchester)

2000-01 Captain & P.o.Y.: Paul Miles Top Scorer: Mark Brandt 34

FACT FILE

Founded: 1886 Nickname: Rovers
Colours: All red
Change colours:All yellow
Midweek Matches: Tuesday
Programme: 24 pages,50p
Editor: Ray Esdale (01440 704670)
Local Press : Haverhill Echo,Cambridge Evening News

CLUB PERSONNEL

Chairman: Terry McGerty
President: N Haylock
Press Officer: Ray Esdale
Manager: Paul Goodman
Physio: Nel Franklin

HISTON RESERVES

Secretary: Mick W Collis, 22 Haddows Close, Longstanton, Cambridge CB4 5DJ
Tel: 01954 201083 (H)

Ground Bridge Rd, Impington, Cambridge Tel: 01223 232301 Fax: 01223 237373

Club Website: http://abbey59.tripod.com

EMAIL Address: gareth@corporate innovations.co.uk

Directions: Leave A14 northern Cambridge bypass on B1049 (signposted Histon and Cottenham). Ground half a mile on right.
5 miles from Cambridge (BR). Bus No.104

Capacity: 3,250 Seats: 250 Cover: 250 Floodlights: Yes

FACT FILE

Colours: Red & black stripes/black/red & black
Change colours: Sky & navy/navy/sky & navy
Midweek matches: Wednesday

Manager: Nacer Relizani

KING'S LYNN RESERVES

Secretary: Ken Rout, Mandlyn, Fen Lane, Ashwicken, King's Lynn, Norfolk PE32 1AW
Tel: 01553 630532 (H) 01553 764494 (B) 07850 395422 (M)
email: anglian.access@btinternet.com (office hours)

GROUND The Walks Stadium, Tennyson Road, King's Lynn PE30 5PB
Tel: 01553 760060
Directions: At mini r-about arriving from A10/A47 take Vancouver Avenue. Ground on left after a half mile. Quarter mile from King's Lynn (BR), half mile from bus station
Capacity: 8,200 Cover: 5,000 Seats: 1,200 Floodlights: Yes
Clubhouse: Normal licensing hours, with extension on matchdays
Club Shop: Sells metal badges and other merchandise

FACT FILE
Colours: Blue & gold stripes/blue/blue & gold
Change colours: All purple and navy
Midweek matches: Tuesday

CLUB PERSONNEL
Manager: Darren Bloodworth

LEISTON

Chairman: Barry Spall, 'Loucarand', 5 Queen Elizabeth Close, Leiston, Suffolk IP16 4XB
Tel: 01728 831950 (H & B)

Secretary: Mark Pattinson, 'Fernhouse', 40 Eastward Ho, Leiston, Suffolk IP16 4XB
Tel: 01728 635016 (H) 01473 608230 (B) 01473 608607 (Bus. Fax)
email: mark.L.pattinson@bt.com

Ground: LTAA, Victory Road, Leiston, Suffolk IP16 4LD
Tel: 01728 830308

FACT FILE
Colours: Blue & whaite/blue/red
Change colours: Amber & red/red/red
Midweek matches: Wednesday
Programme: Yes
Editor: David Rees
Tel: 01728 833549

Manager: Mark Hood
Tel: 01502 501963

MARCH TOWN UNITED

Secretary: R S Bennett, 47 Ellingham Ave, March, Cambs PE15 9TE (01354 653271)

Ground: GER Sports Ground, Robin Goodfellows Lane, March (01354 653073)

Directions: 5 mins from town centre, 10 mins from BR station
Capacity: 4,000 Seats: 500 Cover: 2,000 Floodlights: Yes

Clubhouse: On ground, seating 150. Light refreshments available

HONOURS Eastern Co's Lg 87-88 (Lg Cup 60-61), Utd Co's Lg 53-64, Cambs Invitation Cup 54-55, East Anglian Cup 53-54 (jt withBarking)

PREVIOUS **Leagues:** Peterborough; Isle of Ely; Utd Co's 48-54
Ground: The Avenue (prior to 1946)

BEST SEASON FA Cup 1st Rd53-54 77-78,
RECORD **Gate:** 7,500 v King's Lynn, FA Cup 1956

FACT FILE
Founded: 1885
Nickname: Hares
Club colours: Orange & black/black/black
Change colours: Yellow/blue/blue
Midweek Matches: Tuesday
Programme: 30p
Editor: R Bennett
Local Press : Cambs Times, Fenland Advertiser, Peterborough Evening Telegraph

CLUB PERSONNEL
Chairman: Gary Wesley
President: D Wilkinson

NEEDHAM MARKET

Secretary: D Bloomfield, 33 Quinton Road, Needham Market, Suffolk IP6 8DA
Tel: 01449 720693

Fixture Secrtary: P Collier, Low Street, Badingham, Nr. Woodbridge, Suffolk IP3 8SS
Tel : 01728 638799

Ground: Bloomfields, Quinton Road, Needham Market, Suffolk
Tel: 01449 721000

Directions: Quinton Road is off Barretts Lane which in turn is off Needham Market High Street
Capacity: 1,000 Seats: 250 Cover: 250 Floodlights: Yes **Club Shop:** No

PREVIOUS **Leagues:** Ipswich & District; Suffolk & Ipswich >96
Grounds: Youngs Meadow; Crowley Park >96 **Names:** None

HONOURS Suffolk & Ipswich Lge 95-96

FACT FILE
Founded: 1927
Nickname: N/A
Colours: Green & Black stripes/black/black
Change Coloures: All white
Midweek Matchday: Tuesday
Programme Editor: Ian Verneau
Tel No: 01473 413957

CLUB PERSONNEL
Chairman: A.Sparkes
Managers: Colin Macrow & John Coupe
2000-01 Leading goalscorer: Simon Fryatt 15
Captain: Dean Folkard
P.o.Y.: Mat Fenn

NORWICH UNITED

Secretary: Nigel Harrowing, 43 Cawston Meadow, Poringland, Norwich NR147SX
Tel No & Fax: 0150-8 494335 (H) 01953600682 (W) Mobile: 07866 550242
Ground: Plantation Road, Blofield, Norwich, Norfolk NR13 4PL (01603 716963)
Directions: Half a mile from Blofield village - coming from Norwich on Yarmouth Rd turn left in Blofield at Kings Head pub & follow to Plantation Rd (grd on right after bridge over bypass). 1/2 hour Brundall BR (Norwich-Yarmouth line)
Capacity: 3,000 Seats: 100 Cover: 1,000 Floodlights: Yes
Clubhouse: Matchday food & drink: Tea, coffee, cold drinks, hotdogs, burgers, soup, sandwiches, rolls
Club Shop: Yes incl. metal badges & pennants
HONOURS Eastern Co's Lg Div 1 90-91 (R-up 89-89, Lg Cup 91-92), Anglian Combination 88-89
PREVIOUS **Ground:** Gothic Club, Heartsease Lane, Norwich (until end of 90-91)
RECORD **Attendance:** 401 v Wroxham, League match, 2/10/91
Goalscorer: M Money **Appearances:** Tim Sayer

FACT FILE
Founded: 1903Nickname: Planters
Colours: Yellow/blue/blue
Change colours: All red.
Midweek Matches: Tuesday
Programme: 24 pages, 50p
Editor:Barnes Print
Local Press : Eastern Counties Newspapers
2000-01 P.o.Y. & Top Scorer: Jamie Hunton

CLUB PERSONNEL
Chairman: John Hilditch, Pres Michael Miles
Vice-Chairman: Peter Powell
Managers: Paul Franklin & Donny Pye
Physio: Martyn Parker
2000-01 Captain :Brian Payne

SOMERSHAM TOWN

Secretary: Matthew Dunster, 29 Windsor Gardens,Somersham,Huntingdon, Cambs. PE17 3DY
Tel No: 01487 740786
Ground: West End Ground, St Ives Road, Somersham, Cambs (01487 843384)
Directions: On A604 St Ives to Somersham on right as you enter town
Capacity: 1,500 Seats: None Cover: 200 Floodlights: Yes
Clubhouse: Open Friday, Sat/Sun lunchtimes
HONOURS Hunts Snr Cup 72-73 94-95, Peterboro Snr Cup 84-85, Hinchingbrooke Cup 53-54, Cambs Lg Premier B Div 94-95 (reserves)
PREVIOUS **League:** Peterborough & District
RECORDS **Attendance:** 538 v Norwich City, floodlights inauguration 91
Goalscorer & Appearances: Terry Butcher
Local Press : Hunts Post, Cambs News, Citizen Express, St Ives Weekly

FACT FILE
Founded: 1893 Nickname: Westenders
Sponsors: Rapidtech (UK) Ltd
Colours: All old gold with black trim
Change colours: red&blue stripes/ blue/ red
Midweek Matchday: Tuesday
Reserve League: Kershaw Senior A
Programme: 76 pages, 50p
Editor: Tim Egan

CLUB PERSONNEL
Chairman: Alan Bailey
Vice-Chairman: Norman Burkett
President: Jack Marjason
Manager: Norman Hudson
Coach: Bob Barnett Physio: Alan Magnus

STANWAY ROVERS

Secretary: Alan Brierley, 19 Barley Way, Stanway, Colchester CO3 5YD (01206 521606 + Fax)
Ground: `Hawthorns', New Farm Road, Stanway, Colchester, Essex (01206 578187)
Directions: Take turn off marked Stanway off A12. Turn right(from London)or left from Ipsw ch+ go over flyover to Tollgate r'bout, 1st rt into Villa Rd, after 25 yds turn left into Chaple Rd, 200 yds on left into New Farm Rd, ground 400 yds on left.Nearest BR station is Colchester North
Capacity: 1,500 Seats: None Cover: 250 Floodlights: Yes Shop: No
Clubhouse: 6.45-11pm eves, 12-11pm Sats. Rolls, soup, tea, coffee etc available matchdays
Club Shop: Pennants & ties (Club website:lineone.net/ m alan brierley
HONOURS Esx Intermediate Cup R-up 89-90 90-91, Esx & Suffolk Border Lg R-up 91-2 (Div 1 86-87, Div 2 81-81 85-86), Esx Jnr Cup R-up 74-75
PREVIOUS **Leagues:** Colchester & E Essex; Essex & Suffolk. Border (pre-1992)
Ground: Stanway Secondary School, Winstree Road (20 years)
RECORD **Gate:** 166 v Sudbury Town FA Vase 4/10/97 **Win:** 8-1 v Swaffham Town (H), E. Counties Lge Div. 1 26/3/94 **Defeat:** 0-10 v Sudbury Townt (A), E.C.L. Cup

FACT FILE
Founded: 1955 Nickname: Rovers
Sponsors: David Martin Eastate Agents
Colours: Gold& black stripes/black/black
Change : Red & blue halves/ blue/yellow
Midweek matchday: Wednesday
Reserves' Lge: Essex & Suff. Border
Programme: 12 pages, 50p
Editor: Alan Brierleylocal Press:
Essex Co. Standard, Evening Gazette

CLUB PERSONNEL
Chairman: Peter Cracknell
President: Richard Deguille
Manager:Steve Ball
Physio: Stuart Bevis

THETFORD TOWN

Secretary: R.Richards, 60 Nunnery Drive, Thetford, Norfolk IP243EN Tel Nos: 01842 764282 (H) 01284 701121 (W) Email Address: omwgh@lineone.net
Ground: Mundford Road, Thetford, Norfolk Tel: 01842 766120
Directions: Off bypass (A11) at A143 junction - ground 800yds next to sports ground
Capacity: 2,000 Seats: 400 Cover: 400 Floodlights: Yes
Clubhouse: Bar, teas, refreshments, light meals & snacks **Club Shop:** No
HONOURS Eastern Co's Lg R-up 89-90, Norfolk & Suffolk Lg 54-55; Norfolk Senior Cup 47-48 90-91
PREVIOUS **Leagues:** Norfolk & Suffolk **Grounds**: None
RECORD **Attendance:** 394 v Diss Town, Norfolk Snr Cup 91
Players progressing: Dick Scott (Norwich C.), Kevin Seggie (Leeds U.),Simon Milton (Ipswich T.)
Local Press: Thetford & Watton Times, Bury Free Press
2000-01 **Capt:** Peter Smith **P.o.Y.:** David Richards **Top Scorer:** Lawrence Breen 13

FACT FILE
Founded: 1883
Sponsors: Thetford Garden Centre
Colours: Claret & blue//claret/claret
Change: Yellow & blue
Midweek Matches: Wednesday
Reserves League: Anglian Comb
Programme: 50p
Editor: Denise Jones (01842 761876)
Club Website: thetford townfc.fsnet.co.uk

CLUB PERSONNEL
Chairman: Bob Richards
Vice-Chairman: Mike Bailey
Press Officer: Paul Stevenson
Manager: Peter Jones

WARBOYS TOWN

Secretary: Martin England, 39 High Street, Warboys, Huntingdon, Cambs PE28 2TA
Tel No: 01487 822503
Ground: Sports Field, Forge Way, off High Street, Warboys, Cambs Tel: 01487 823483
Directions: Access through Forge Way, half way along south side of High Street
Capacity: 2,000 Seats: 50 Cover: 200 Floodlights: Yes
Clubhouse: Bar, lounge, function hall. Open every evening & Sunday lunchtime
Entertainment, drinks & snacks

HONOURS Utd Co's Lg Div 2 R-up 54-55, P'boro Lg R-up(2) 59-60 61-62, P'boro SnrCup 63-64, Hunts Snr Cup 26-27 28-29 31-32 32-33,94-95. (R-up 92-93,95-96), Hunts Scott Gatty Cup 30-31. Reserves: Hunts Benevolent Cup 57-58, Hunts Junior Cup 24-25 27-28 52-53, Hunts Lower Junior Cup 75-76 77-78. Eastern Lg.Cup R-up: 97-98, Eastern League Div 1 R-up: 95-96

PREVIOUS Leagues: Peterborough & Dist 46-48 56-88; Utd Co's 50-56; Huntingdonshire 48-50

RECORD Attendance: 500 v Ramsey Town, Hunts Senior Cup Semi Final

Players progressing: Alec Chamberlain (Ipswich and Watford)

FACT FILE
Founded: 1885
Nickname: Witches
Colours: Red /black/red
Change colours: White/red/white
Midweek Matches: Tuesday
Programme: 12 pages,50p
Editor: Martin England
Local Press : Hunts Post (01480 411481)

CLUB PERSONNEL
Chairman: Roger Pauley
Manager: Ian Benjamin

WHITTON UNITED

Secretary: David Gould, 7 Karen Close, Ipswich, Suffolk IP1 4LP Tel: 01473 253838

Ground: King George V Playing Field, Old Norwich Road, Ipswich, Suffolk. Tel: 01473 464030

Directions: Turn off A14, junction A1156 approx 3 miles west of A12/A14junction
Capacity: 600 Seats: No Cover: 100 Floodlights: Yes
Club Shop: No
Clubhouse: Licensed Bar. Hot & Cold Food available

HONOURS Suffolk Senior Cup 58-59 62-63 92-93; Suffolk & Ipswich Lge 46-47 47-48 65-66 67-68 91-92 92-93, Jewson Fairplay Trophy 96-97, 97-98

PREVIOUS **Leagues:** Suffolk & Ipswich Grounds: Old Norwich Rd, Ipswich

RECORD **Attendance:** 528 v Ipswich Town 29/11/95
League 244 v Ipswich Wanderers13/1/96

FACT FILE
Formed: 1926 Nickname: None
Sponsors: Speedyhire
Colours: Green & white/white/green
Change colours: All red
Midweek Matches: Wednesday
Youth's League: U18 Eastern Jun Alliance
Programme: 24pages- 50p
Editor/ Press Officer:Mark Woodward

CLUB PERSONNEL
Chairman: John Watkins
President: Russell Woodward
Fixture Sec: Alan Elliott (01473 461931)
Manager: Paul Smythe

WISBECH TOWN RESERVES

Secretary: John Petch, 34 Walton Rd, Wisbech, Cambs PE13 3EN
Tel: 01945 584333 &Fax)

Ground Fenland Park, Lerowe Road, Wisbech, Cambs Tel: 01945 584176

Directions: Follow A47 bypass to the West Walton turn off roundabout where there is a Little Chef, turn left for Wisbech, Lerowe Road is first left after 30mph sign. Entering town from north along A1101 cross Freedom Bridge, atroundabout go straight over sign Walsoken/West Walton

Capacity: 3,800 Seats: 284 Cover: 1,000 Floodlights: Yes

Clubhouse: Open every day. Matchday food & drink - Tea, coffee, cold drinks, confectionary, burgers, hotdogs, soup, sandwiches, rolls

Club Shop: Sells replica shirts, caps, pennants, pens, scarves etc. Contact Club Secretary

FACT FILE
Nickname: Fenmen
Colours: Red with black side panel/red/red
Change colours: Blue& white,blue,blue
Midweek Matchday: Tuesday

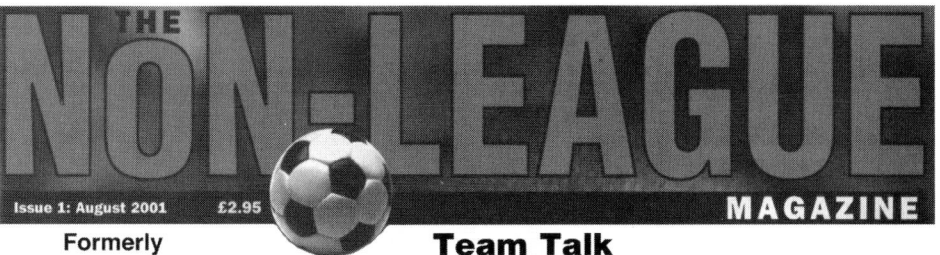

CLUB PERSONNEL
Chairman: Steve Crown
Vice Chairman: Merlin Saddleton
President: J W A Chilvers
Press Officer: John Petch

Some photographers are strangely shy of cameras themselves.
Neil Thaler supports Whitby Town so you can understand why!
Photos by Kevin Rolfe and Garry Letts.

Left: Uncle Eric' and Francis Short have often moonlighted to France for the `Tour de France', but here we see the remarkably smart looking couple at Wembley.
Right: Colin Stevens (plus helpers) is usually up north and along with the hard working Keith Clayton (for whom I can't find a sensible photo at present) has sent us a wonderful selection of photos. *Turn to page 732*

CHERRY RED RECORDS HELLENIC FOOTBALL LEAGUE

Patron: Sir Henry Cooper OBE, KSG. (2001)
Chairman: Michael Broadley

Secretary: Brian King, 83 Queens Road, Carterton, Oxon OX18 3YF
Tel/Fax: 01993 212738 **E-mail:** king.brian@ukgateway.net

A record number of clubs, 53, played in the Hellenic League during the season following the merger with the 'Chiltonian League'. These clubs were all visited and subjected to the rigours of Ground Grading, and the overall standard was very encouraging. Visits to Premier Division grounds were postponed due to the ongoing weather problems, but these inspections will be undertaken early in season 2001/2002.

I have been involved in various football capacities during the past 35 years but I have never known a season were there has been so much disruption. In September the disputes at refineries caused petrol shortages in many areas. As things seemed to be settling down the rains came and came, and came. From October right through to April postponements of matches happened all too frequently, and in total 441 fixtures were postponed during the campaign, yet all fixtures including Cup Finals were played by 19th May, only seven days later than the anticipated end of season. Much of the credit goes to the club secretaries who, in the main, acted very flexibly to ensure all matches were quickly re-fixtured when postponements did occur.

A Representative match was played at Didcot Town FC against the Combined Counties League in November that resulted in a 2-1 win for our visitors. The first Challenge match between Division One (East) and Division One (West) was played at Abingdon United in March. The players representing Div One (East) performed very well in the second half scoring four goals without reply.

Success in national cup competitions was somewhat better than of previous seasons:

FA Cup

Eight clubs competed in the competition with Yate Town going out in the Extra Preliminary Round way back in August. The first week in September saw North Leigh, Didcot Town and Brackley Town go out. Carterton Town, Abingdon United and Shortwood United needed a replay to progress to the Qualifying stage with Tuffley Rovers, who secured an excellent win against Taunton Town. The First Qualifying stage saw wins for Abingdon United, Carterton Town, who defeated Southern League club St Leonard's, and Shortwood United who beat Weston-Super-Mare after a replay. The Second Qualifying Round saw all three clubs facing opposition from the Southern League. Unfortunately, all three teams were beaten, but gave a very good account against opposition from a higher league. The reward for the three clubs was £5000 from the FA Cup television pool money that must be used in schemes for improving the ground.

FA Vase

Another excellent entry of nineteen member clubs competed in this season's competition. Almondsbury Town and Fairford Town went out in the First Qualifying Round with three winners going through to the next round. The Second Qualifying Round saw wins for Abingdon United, Bicester Town, Pegasus Juniors, Didcot Town, Cirencester Academy, Harrow Hill, Carterton Town, Tuffley Rovers and Swindon Supermarine. The First Round saw eleven clubs from the Hellenic League competing, when Cirencester Academy went out to Carterton Town 2-0 and Swindon Supermarine were seen off by Yate Town playing their first FA Vase tie for many years. Others to fall in this round were Didcot Town to Brockenhurst (4-3), Harrow Hill to former Hellenic League club Hallen (4-1), and Bicester Town to Hornchurch (2-0), while Highworth Town lost at home to Brislington (2-1) and Tuffley Rovers went out to Lymington & New Milton (2-0). The only other survivors were Abingdon United and Pegasus Juniors who had wins against East Preston and Dudley Town respectively. The Second Round produced some very interesting ties as Carterton went on their holidays to Cornwall to face St Blazey of the South Western League, Abingdon United had a home tie against Burgess Hill, whilst Pegasus Juniors faced Nantwich Town of the North West Counties League. Yate Town, having overcome 'Supermarine', were drawn against last season's losing finalists Chippenham Town, the 'Bluebells' going down 2-0. Abingdon United went to a replay before losing and Pegasus Juniors went out to Nantwich also after a replay. Carterton Town carried the Hellenic flag into the last 32 beating St Blazey after a replay and securing the Football Association regional award for the best performance of the round in the Western region. The Third Round saw Carterton on their travels to Cornwall yet again, this time facing Falmouth Town and losing 3-0 on a pitch that to say the least did not suit the Carterton method of play. It was a very good season in national competitions for Carterton, and a campaign that was destined to get better in Hellenic competition later in the season.

Premier Division

Swindon Supermarine won this season's Premier Division Championship and are promoted to the Dr Martens League, as were Banbury United last season. At the turn of the year they were in top position and never lost that position during the second half of the season.

Highworth Town had a loss of form yet again in 2001 and dropped back to finish eighth. Didcot Town maintained their improvement and finished the season in a very deserved fourth place. Yate Town made a late run and recorded a very creditable third place and will be expected to be one of the favourites for next campaign. Brackley Town under manager Peter Foley, who took over part way through the season, overhauled every other club bar Swindon Supermarine to take runners-up position. Abingdon put together an excellent run in the last six weeks to move up to fifth place.

Yate Town were the top goal-scoring club with 92 (2.42 per game) league goals closely followed by champions Swindon

Supermarine with 86 (2.26) and Brackley Town with 84 (2.21). Some excellent crowds were recorded in the division with almost 25,000 spectators watching matches with an average league gate of 63. Three clubs recorded an average league crowd in excess of 100, Highworth Town 123.95, Didcot Town 113.47 and Swindon Supermarine 104.42.

Division One (West)

The title this season was won by Gloucester United FC who, in their first season in the league, displayed a very high level of consistency throughout the campaign losing only one and drawing three of their 30 league fixtures, dropping just nine points all campaign, conceding only fifteen goals and scoring 119. They won the title by some twelve points from Bishops Cleeve who, in their first full season at Kayte Lane, were very successful eventually pushing Ardley United into third place. At the time of compiling this report it is not known whether Bishops Cleeve will be promoted to the Premier Division as a decision on their planning application has not been made. Malmesbury Victoria finished a very creditable fourth after promotion from the Wiltshire League with Headington Amateurs having a much-improved season to finish in fifth position.

Division One (East)

The newly formed Division One (East), which came about from the merger with the Chiltonian League, was won at a canter by Henley Town by some twenty points and they lost only three league matches during the season. The competition for runners-up position was very exciting and was not decided until the last week of the campaign when RS Basingstoke ensured they could not be overtaken by challengers Southall Town, Quarry Nomads, Eton Wick and Rayners Lane. Long time league leaders Finchampstead were pushed down into seventh place. The second promotion position caused many problems with RS Basingstoke not having the required facilities. Third position was good enough for Southall Town to be promoted, but this was not decided until the ill fated three-times-attempted fixture between Harrow Hill Rovers and Quarry Nomads was eventually played on 19th May. With Quarry losing 4-3 Southall secured third place with a superior goal difference of nine.

Cup Competitions

Once again Swindon Supermarine had a successful season in Hellenic cup competitions winning the Floodlit Cup and Reserve Cup. However, they were defeated in the Challenge Cup by Carterton Town.

'Cherry Red Records' Norman Matthews Floodlit Cup.

Swindon Supermarine contested the final against Division One (West) champions Gloucester United. Due to weather disruption the final was eventually played at Swindon some weeks later than originally scheduled. The match provided Gloucester United with a good test of what they will face in the Premier Division next season. Played on a bitterly cold April evening with the defence of both team's in control, extra time looked a certainty until the Gloucester goalkeeper badly mishandled the ball in time added on by the referee and presented Steve Davies with a simple tap-in to give 'Marine' the cup for the second successive season.

'RPM Records' Supplementary Cup.

Due to weather disruption this competition was cancelled for the 2000-01 season.

'Complete Music' Challenge Cup

At the end of a long hard campaign Swindon Supermarine, looking for a cup double, lined up against Carterton Town, last season's Supplementary Cup winners. The semi finals ties had seen 'Marine' beat Didcot Town 3-2 at Loop Meadow Stadium with Carterton Town securing their cup final place with a 2-1 home win over Abingdon United, who played in the semi-final for the second season running The final was played at Fairford Town and provided an entertaining match for the crowd of almost 200. Carterton took the lead in the first half with 'Marine' equalising just after half time. Carterton regained the lead from the penalty spot only for a second equaliser a few minutes from the end of the 90 minutes. Extra time produced little excitement and the destination of the cup was decided from the penalty mark with Carterton Town winning 7-6 when Supermarine missed the fourteenth penalty in the shoot-out.

Brian Wells Memorial Cup

This cup was presented to the Chiltonian League by the family of Brian Wells following the successful merger. It was agreed that this trophy would be contested annually by the leading clubs in the regional Division Ones. Again due to weather disruption this competition had to be reduced to a single match between the two divisional winners. This game summed up the season when a torrential downpour 30 minutes before kick off turned the Marriott's Stadium pitch into a lake. A delayed kick off allowed the pitch to drain enough to play the match that resulted in a win for Gloucester United over Henley Town, the score being 2-2; a penalty shoot out decided the game.

Congratulations go to all clubs who had success in Football Association and County cup competitions and in our own League and Cup competitions.

Season 2000-01 saw the first Hellenic League 'Ground Hop' with four matches being selected and played at staggered kick off times through the day and evening. The day was not the best weather-wise (how unusual) but the football that was played did great credit to the Hellenic League and provided excellent entertainment for the almost 1000 spectators at the four venues. The idea came from Iain McNay of Cherry Red Records and Iain was present throughout the day visiting each ground and watching all the matches. Work has already started on the season 2001-02 'Ground Hop'.

After three years sponsorship by 'Complete Music' the mantle was passed over to sister company 'Cherry Red Records' and I am pleased to report that agreement has been reached for a fifth season's sponsorship of the league. Thanks are extended to Iain McNay and his fellow Directors at 'Cherry Red' for their company's continued interest and support of the Hellenic Football League.

A three-year sponsorship of representative football was agreed with 'Woodstock Arts'. The league is very pleased to have attracted this sponsorship and hopes this will be another ongoing relationship as we move towards the league's 50th anniversary season.

The partnership arrangement for the use of 'Gilbert' footballs, now in the third season, proceeded without problem. A year's extension has been agreed to this arrangement that will again provide quality match balls at a greatly discounted price. Thanks are once again due to Tim Barnard for his involvement in putting this deal together. Tim was also involved in setting up the partnership arrangement with Italian sports company 'Errea'.

Brian King, General Secretary

HONOURS LIST 2000-01

PREMIER DIVISION

Winners	Swindon Supermarine
Runners-Up:	Brackley Town

DIVISION ONE WEST

Winners:	Gloucester United
Runners-Up:	Bishops Cleeve

DIVISION ONE EAST

Winners:	Henley Town
Runners-Up:	RS Basingstoke

RESERVE DIVISION ONE

Winners	Bicester Town
Runners-Up:	Didcot Town

RESERVE DIVISION TWO WEST

Winners:	Wootton Bassett Town
Runners-Up:	Almondsbury Town

RESERVE DIVISION TWO EAST

Winners:	Henley Town
Runners-Up:	Finchampstead

CHERRY RED RECORDS CHALLENGE CUP

Winners:	Carterton Town
Finalists:	Swindon Supermarine

NORMAN MATTHEWS FLOODLIT CUP

Winners:	Swindon Supermarine
Finalists:	Gloucester United

ANAGRAM RECORDS RESERVE CUP

Winners:	Swindon Supermarine
Finalists:	Finchampstead

CLUB LINESMAN OF THE SEASON

John Fellows — Wootton Bassett Town

PREMIER DIVISION FAIR PLAY AWARD

Highworth Town

DIVISION ONE FAIR PLAY AWARD

Prestwood FC

HUNGERFORD CUP

Didcot Town

SPORTS & ADMIN INCENTIVE AWARD

Premier Division

Yate Town

Division One West

Bishops Cleeve

Division One East

Henley Town

FINAL LEAGUE TABLES 2000-01

PREMIER DIVISION

	P	W	D	L	F	A	Pts
Swindon Supermarine	38	29	4	5	86	29	91
Brackley Town	38	25	8	5	84	45	83
Yate Town	38	21	9	8	92	38	72
Didcot Town	38	20	12	6	57	27	72
Abingdon United	38	21	6	11	80	53	69
North Leigh	38	20	6	12	77	51	66
Cirencester Academy	38	18	5	15	70	54	59
Highworth Town	38	19	2	17	74	68	59
Fairford Town	38	17	7	14	54	45	58
Carterton Town	38	16	9	13	64	57	57
Shortwood United	38	15	11	12	62	58	56
Tuffley Rovers	38	16	6	16	54	58	54
Wootton Bassett Town	38	14	10	14	54	60	52
Bicester Town	38	14	7	17	59	67	49
Pegasus Juniors	38	12	4	22	67	96	40
Wantage Town	38	11	4	23	49	83	37
Cheltenham Saracens	38	9	5	24	31	76	32
Harrow Hill	38	5	10	23	36	80	25
Almondsbury Town	38	7	3	28	36	76	24
Milton United	38	5	4	29	31	96	19

DIVISION ONE (WEST)

	P	W	D	L	F	A	Pts
Gloucester United	30	26	3	1	119	15	81
Bishops Cleeve	30	22	3	5	70	36	69
Ardley United	30	21	3	6	81	34	66
Malmesbury Victoria	30	15	5	10	65	59	50
Headington Amateurs	30	15	5	10	54	50	50
Easington Sports	30	12	6	12	55	61	42
Cirencester United	30	11	6	13	50	59	39
Middle Barton	30	9	11	10	45	47	38
Clanfield FC	30	8	8	14	45	58	32
Ross Town*	30	9	6	15	48	54	30
Kidlington	30	7	9	14	39	50	30
Letcombe FC	30	7	9	14	38	61	30
Purton FC	30	7	9	14	46	73	30
Witney Academy	30	8	6	16	37	82	30
Old Woodstock Town	30	6	8	16	36	61	26
Worcester Coll OB	30	5	7	18	41	69	22

* Points Deducted

DIVISION ONE (EAST)

	P	W	D	L	F	A	Pts
Henley Town	32	25	4	3	105	33	79
RS Basingstoke	32	17	8	7	63	37	59
Southall Town	32	15	10	7	63	44	55
Quarry Nomads	32	16	7	9	66	56	55
Eton Wick	32	16	6	10	71	50	54
Rayners Lane	32	15	7	10	77	58	52
Finchampstead	32	14	8	10	75	58	50
Harrow Hill Rovers	32	15	4	13	72	71	49
Englefield Green Rov	32	13	6	13	75	71	45
Binfield	32	13	6	13	56	55	45
Prestwood	32	12	9	11	60	65	45
Peppard	32	9	12	11	58	65	39
Chalfont Wasps	32	11	4	17	58	75	37
Martin Baker Sports	32	7	11	14	49	61	32
Penn & Tylers Green	32	10	2	20	47	75	32
Drayton Wanderers	32	7	3	22	44	90	24
Aston Clinton	32	3	1	28	40	115	10

COMPLETE MUSIC CHALLENGE CUP 2000-01

PRELIMINARY ROUND

Aston Clinton	2 v 4	Drayton Wanderers
Cheltenham Saracens	1 * 4	Bishops Cleeve
Cirencester United	3 * 1	Ardley United
Didcot Town	4 v 0	Chalfont Wasps
Easington Sports	1 v 2	Gloucester United
Englefield Green Rvrs	0,4 * 4,3	Wantage Town
Fairford Town	3 v 1	Middle Barton
Finchampstead	1 v 3	Brackley Town
Headington Amateurs	1 v 2	Harrow Hill
Kidlington	2 * 1	Letcombe
Malmesbury Victoria	2 v 0	Clanfield
Martin Baker Sports	1 v 3	Abingdon United
Peppard	1,1 * 1,3	Bicester Town
Prestwood	1 v 3	Southall Town
Purton	3 v 1	Witney Academy
RS Basingstoke	3 v 2	Harrow Hill Rovers
Swindon Supermarine	3 v 1	Milton United
Wootton Bassett Town	0 v 2	Cirencester Academy

FIRST ROUND

Bicester Town	0 – 6	Highworth Town
Brackley Town	9 – 3	Penn & Tylers Green
Carterton Town	2 – 0	Quarry Nomads
Cirencester Academy	1,3 * 3,2	Bishops Cleeve
Cirencester United	3,0 * 0,0	Malmesbury Victoria
Didcot Town	4 – 0	Drayton Wanderers
Eton Wick	1 – 4	North Leigh
Fairford Town	3 – 0	Yate Town
Harrow Hill	0 – 3	Ross Town
Henley Town	3 – 1	Southall Town
Kidlington	1 – 3	Tuffley Rovers

FIRST ROUND cont.

Old Woodstock Town	1 – 5	Gloucester United
Pegasus Juniors	0,2 – 2,2	Shortwood United
Purton	4p,2,4 * 4,2,3p	Almondsbury T
Swindon Supermarine	1 ab 0	RS Basingstoke
Swindon Supermarine	3 – 2	RS Basingstoke
Wantage Town	0 – 4	Abingdon United

SECOND ROUND

Abingdon United	2 – 0	Tuffley Rovers
Didcot Town	3 – 0	Fairford Town
Cirencester United	0 – 3	Carterton Town
Henley Town	2 – 5	Gloucester United
North Leigh	6 – 0	Highworth Town
Purton	1 – 4	Bishops Cleeve
Shortwood United	3 – 4	Brackley Town
Swindon Supermarine	3 – 2	Ross Town

QUARTER FINALS

Bishops Cleeve	0 – 2	Swindon Supermarine
Carterton Town	2 – 0	Brackley Town
Didcot Town	2 – 0	North Leigh
Gloucester United	3 * 1	Abingdon United

Glos Utd played an ineligible player, game awarded to Abingdon

SEMI FINALS

Carterton Town	2 – 1	Abingdon United
Didcot Town	2 – 3	Swindon Supermarine

FINAL

Carterton Town	7p,2 – 2,6p	Swindon Supermarine

NORMAN MATTHEWS FLOODLIT CUP 2000-01

PRELIMINARY ROUND

Bicester Town	5 – 3	Abingdon United
Fairford Town	3 – 1	Wootton Bassett Town
Milton United	0 – 2	Carterton Town
Pegasus Juniors	2 – 1	Ross Town
Shortwood United	1 * 1	Gloucester United
Southall Town	0 – 2	Brackley Town
Wantage Town	1 – 3	Witney Academy
Yate Town	3 – 1	Harrow Hill
	Replay	
Gloucester United	2 – 1	Shortwood United

FIRST ROUND

Almondsbury Town	1 * 2	Cirencester Academy
Bicester Town	0 – 4	Carterton Town
Cheltenham Saracens	1 – 7	Gloucester United
Fairford Town	1 – 2	Pegasus Junior's
Highworth Town	2 – 3	Brackley Town
Swindon Supermarine	2 – 0	North Leigh
Witney Academy	0 – 4	Didcot Town
Yate Town	6 – 0	Tuffley Rovers

SECOND ROUND

Brackley Town	2 – 0	Didcot Town
Pegasus Junior's	0 – 3	Gloucester United
Swindon Supermarine	3 – 2	Carterton Town
Yate Town	3 – 0	Cirencester Academy

SEMI FINALS
1st Leg

Brackley Town	0 – 1	Swindon Supermarine
Yate Town	1 – 2	Gloucester United

SEMI FINALS
2nd Leg

Gloucester United	1 – 1	Yate Town
Swindon Supermarine	0 – 0	Brackley Town

FINAL

Swindon Supermarine	1 – 0	Gloucester United

ABINGDON UNITED

Secretary: Terry Hutchinson, 41 Austin Place, Dunmore Farm Estate, Abingdon,Oxon OX14 1LT
Tel: 01235 559019

Ground: Northcourt Road, Abingdon OX14 1PL Tel: 01235 203203
Capacity: 2,000 Seats: 52 Cover: 120 Floodlights: Yes

Directions: From north (Oxford) leave A34 at Abingdon north sign and Northcourt Rd is 1st major turning after r'bout. From South, East or West leave Abingdonon A4183 and turn left into Northcourt Rd after 1 mile. 2 miles from Redley (BR)
Clubhouse: Two bars, food available. Open normal pub hours every day

HONOURS N Berks Lg 53-54 (Lg Cup R-up 53-54), Charity Shield 52-53;
Hellenic Lge - Prem Div R-up 96-97, Div 1 R-up 76-77 81-82, Res. Div 97-98,
F/Lit Cup 96-97, Lg Cup R-up 89-90, Div 1 Cup 65-66 81-82 R-up 66-67,
Reserve Cup 98-99 R-up 93-94;
Berks & Bucks Senior Cup R-up 83-84, Senior Trophy 97-98 R-up 93-94 96-97

PREVIOUS **League**: North Berks
Grounds: None

RECORD **Gate:** 1,500 v Oxford Utd 1994
Appearances: D Webb

FACT FILE
Founded: 1946
Nickname: The U's
Colours: All yellow
Change colours: Blue & white
Midweek matchday: Tuesday
Reserves' Lge: Suburban
Programme: 50p
Editor: W Fletcher, ACJI (01235 20255)
Website: abingdonunitedfc.co.uk
2000-01:
Captain: Robbie McNeil
Top Scorer Tom Larman 18

CLUB PERSONNEL
Chairman: Derek Turner
General manager: John Blackmore
Manager: Ray Hayward
Coach: Steve Morton
Physio: GrahamCorcoran & Chris Janes
Press Officer: Bill Fletche (01235 203203)

ALMONDSBURY TOWN

Secretary: Roger Perry, 61 Brookbridge House, Standfast Road, Henbury, Bristol BS10 7HW
Tel No: 0117 959 0309

Ground: Oakland Park, Gloucester Rd., Almondsbury, Bristol BS12 4AGTel: 01454 612220

Directions: Adjacent to M5 junction 16 - follow A38 Thornbury - ground first left. 4 miles from Bristol Parkway (BR). County bus services to Thornbury,Stroud and Gloucester
Capacity: 2,000 Seats: None Cover: No Floodlights: Yes
Clubhouse: 7 days, all sports, refreshments, function room, entertainment,skittles

HONOURS Glos Co. Lg(4) 76-78 79-81 (R-up 75-7681-82), GFA Chal. Tphy 78-79 (R-up 80-81), Avon Prem. Comb. 74-75, Glos SnrAmtr Cup 87-88, Hellenic Lg 83-84 (R-up 82-83, Lg Cup(2) 83-85)

PREVIOUS **Leagues:** Bristol Weslyan; Bristol Suburban; Bristol Premier Comb.; GlosCo
Ground: Almondsbury Rec. (until 1986)

BEST SEASON **FA Vase:**R-up 78-79, SF 77-78

RECORD **Gate:** 2,100,Hellenic Cup Final replay 89-90 (Newport AFC v Abingdon U)

FACT FILE

Founded: 1897
Nickname: Almonds
Colours: Royal blue/navy/navy
Change colours: Tangerine/black/black
Midweek Matchday: Tuesday
Programme: 20 pages 25p
Editor: Roger Perry
Tel: 0117 959 0309
Top Scorer 00-01: Ali El Morissy

CLUB PERSONNEL
Chairman: Brian Tufton
President: Peter Howarth
Manager: Shaun Honor
Coach: Micky Jefferies & Shaun Heyes
Physio: Peter Allen & Brian North

BICESTER TOWN

Secretary: Duncan Currie Tel No: 01869 327308 (H)

Ground: Sports Ground, Oxford Rd, BicesterTel: 01869 241036 (office& fax)
Capacity: 2,000 Seats: 250 Cover: 550 Floodlights: Yes

Directions: From Oxford; past Tescos on outskirts of Bicester - ground on right
From Aylesbury; turn left at first island on outskirts of Bicester ontobypass, right at next island, pass Tescos & ground on right
Clubhouse: One bar

HONOURS Hellenic Lg 60-1 77-78 (Lg Cup 90-91 (R-up 92-93), Div 1 76-77)

PREVIOUS **League**: Oxon Senior
Name: Slade Banbury Road (pre-1923)

RECORD **Attendance:** 955 v Portsmouth, floodlight inauguration 1/2/94

2000-01 Top Scorer & P.o.Y.: Michael Marshall

FACT FILE
Founded: 1876
Nickname: Foxhunters
Colours: Red & black/black/red or white
Change: Green & yellow/green/green
Club's Email:philip@bassett38,freeserve,co.uk
Midweek Matchday: Tuesday
Reserves' league: Hellenic Lge Res. Div.
Programme: With entry
Editor:Phil Allen (01869 252125)
CLUB PERSONNEL
Chairman: David Simpson
Vice Chairman: Ray Honour
President: Michael Kinane
Fixture Secretary: Phil Allen
Press Officer: David Simpson
Manager: Barry Grant
Coach: Kevin Leach
Physio: Ray Huntley

BISHOPS CLEEVE

Secretary: Phil Tustain, 36 Hardy Road, Bishops Cleeve, Cheltenham GL52 4BN
Tel: 01242 697281 (H) 01242 673333 x 2287 (B)
email: philiptustain@aol.com

Match Secretary: Will Pember, 11 Linworth Rd., Bishops Cleeve, Cheltenham GL52 4BN
Tel: 01242 673800 (H) 01242 843512 (B) 01242 843404 (F)

Ground: (share with Evesham Utd.) Common Road, Evesham, Worc. WR11 4PU
Tel: 01386 442303 & 07778 859722

Directions: From Evesham High Street turn into Oat St, and join one-way system, turn right between Willmotts factory called Conduit Hill into Common Rd, ground 200yds down on right just before railway bridge. 5 mins walk from Evesham BR station

Capacity: 2,000 Seats: 350 Cover: 600 Floodlights: Yes

Bishops Cleeve FC - North of Cheltenham on the A534, pass Racecourse then turn right at traffic lights and then left into Kayte Lane, ground half a mile on the left.

Clubhouse: Full facilities, bar, dance area

HONOURS Hellenic Lg Cup R-up 90-91

PREVIOUS **Leagues:** Cheltenham, Nth Glos
Grounds: The Skiller (pre-1913), Village Field (pre-1950)

RECORD **Attendance**: 1,000 v Newport AFC 89-90

00-01 Leading Goalscorer: Kevin Slack (35)

FACT FILE
Founded: 1892
Nickname: Skinners
Colours: Green/green/black
Change colours: Yellow/blue/blue
Midweek Matchday: Tuesday

CLUB PERSONNEL
President: John Davies
Chairman: David Walker
Manager: Paul Collicutt
Press Officer: David Lewis
Tel: 01386 882273
Programme Editor: John Banfield
Tel: 01242 677758

Manager: Paul Collicutt
Coach:John Banfield
Physio: Will Pember

BRACKLEY TOWN

Secretary/Press Officer: Pat Ashby, 2 Barrington Court, Ward Road, Brackley, NN13 7LE
Tel: 01327 262955(H) 01280 840900(O) 07930 143504(M)
Ground: St James Park, Churchill Way, Brackley, Northants NN13 7EJ. Tel: 01280 704077
Office: 01280 703652: Club Website: www.the-saints.co.uk Club Email: btfc1890@aol.com

Directions: Churchill Way, east off A43, south end of town
Capacity: 3,500 Cover: 150 Seats: 300 Floodlights: Yes

Clubhouse: Fully licensed. Lounge & main hall. Food available. Open all week.
Club Shop: Yes, selling club merchandise,programmes and badges etc.
PREVIOUS **Leagues:** Banbury & District; North Bucks; Hellenic 77-83; United Counties 83-94; Hellenic 94-97,Southern 97-99 **Names:** None
Ground: Banbury Road, Manor Road, Buckingham Road (up to 1974)
CLUB RECORDS **Attendance:** 720 v Kettering, Northants Senior Cup 1989
Fee Received: £2,000 for Phil Mason from Oxford City 98
BEST SEASON **FA Trophy:** 1st Qual Rd 97-98
FA Cup: 2nd Qual Rd 97-98 League clubs defeated: **HONOURS**
United Counties R-up 88-89 (Div 1 83-84); Northants Snr Cup R-up 88-89; Buckingham Charity Cup (3); Hellenic Lg Prem 96-97, Div 1 Cup 82-83. **Players progressing**: Jon Blencowe (Leicester) **Transfer Fee Paid:** None

FACT FILE
Formed: 1890 Nickname: Saints
Colours:Red & white/white/black
Change colours: All Orange
Midweek matchday: Tuesday or Wednesday
Programme: Price: £1
Editor: Brian Martin(01280 706619)
Local Press: Brackley Advertiser, Banbury Guardian, Herald & Post
Milton Keynes Citizen - Local Radio: Fox FM

CLUB PERSONNEL
Managlng Director: Mike Bosher
Chairman: Brian Ashmall
Com. Man: Ray Styles: 0772 040587
President: Clive Lomax
Press Officer: Brian Martin
Manager: Peter Foley: Coach: Matty Haycock

2000-01
Leading goalscorer: Ben Milner 30
Captain: Jason Allen
P.o.Y.: Darren Beckett

CARTERTON TOWN

Secretary: CathrynTaylor, 105 Glenmore Road, Carterton, Oxon. OX18 1TZ(01993 840628)

Ground: Kilkenny Lane, Carterton, Oxfordshire (01993 842410)

Directions: Enter Swinbrook Rd which off the Burford-Carterton road, proceed into Kilkenny Lane (one track road), ground car park 200yds on left before sharp corner. Hourly buses to Carterton from Oxford
Capacity: 1,500 Seats: 75 Cover: 100 Floodlights: Yes

Clubhouse: Lounge & fully licensed bar open every day 7.30-11pm, Sat & Sun noon-2pm, Sat 4-6pm. Snacks & meals available

HONOURS Oxon Junior Shield 85-86; Oxon Snr Cup R-up 90-91 96-97 98-99 Witney & Dist.Lg 65-66 (Div 1 84-85 76-77); Hellenic Lg Div 1 89-90 93-94 (Reserve Div 1989-90 (R-up 93-94)); Oxon Intermediate Cup R-up 93-94(res.)Hellenic Supplementary Cup 99-00,Hellenic League Challenge Cup 2000-01

PREVIOUS Leagues: Witney & District

RECORD **Gate:** 600 v Oxford Utd, Oxon Snr Cup 93-94
Goalscorer: Phil Rodney

FACT FILE
Founded: 1922
Reformed: 1946/1983
Colours: Black & white/black/black
Change colours: Yellow&blue/blue/blue
Midweek matches: Tuesday
Programme: 20 pages with admission
Editor: Jenny Maxwell (01993 212803)
Website: www.cartertontownfc.co.uk

CLUB PERSONNEL
President: G Fox
Chairman: Robert Taylor
Match Secretary: Glyn Yates

Manager: Andrew Slater
Physio: Andy Slater
Coach: Phil Rodney

20000-01
Captain: Andy Leach P.o.Y.: Kevin Lewis
Top Scorer: Scott Taylor 18

CHELTENHAM SARACENS

Secretary: Robert Attwood, 179 Arle Road, Cheltenham GL51 8LJ
Tel: 01242 515855 (H) 01242 241819 (B) 01242 222994 (Fax)

Ground: Harrow Hill FC, Larksfield Road Harrow Hill 01594 543873

Directions: Take A40 west out of Gloucester, follow A40 for 8 miles then takeA4136 to Longhope, pass by on the outskirts of Michealdean, up steep hill (Plump Hill), then second turn on the right signed Harrow Hill. At phone box on the left turn right into Larksfield Road, ground on right at top of hill.

Reserves' Ground: Petersfield Park, Tewkesbury Road, Cheltenham (01242 584134)
Directions: 1 mile from Cheltenham centre on A4019 Tewksbury Road (next to B &Q) - 1st left over railway bridge, 1st left and follow service road
Clubhouse: 2 mins away at 16-20 Swindon Rd, Cheltenham

HONOURS Glos Snr Cup 91-92 Glos Primary Cup 71-72, Winners Hellenic div 1 99-00

PREVIOUS **League:** Cheltenham 1964-86

RECORD **Attendance:** 178 v Bishops Cleeve, 1998

Players progressing: S Cotterill (Wimbledon) 88, K Knight (Reading) 89

FACT FILE

Founded: 1964
Nickname: Saras
Colours: Blue&yellow stripes/blue/blue
Change cols: Black & white stripe/black/black
Midweek Matchday: Wednesday
Reserves League: Hellenic Reserve section
Programme : 20 pages, 50p
Editor: Kevin Dix 01242 578479
Email: kevincdix@fsnet.co.uk
00-01 Top Scorer: David Macey (9)

CLUB PERSONNEL

Chairman: Jim Utteridge
Tel: 01684 273734
Match Secretary: Terry Coates
Press Officer: Terry Coates
Tel: 01242 692320

CIRENCESTER FOOTBALL ACADEMY

Secretary: Matt Sykes, 2 Stratton Brook, Gloucester Road, Cirencester GL7 2LD
Tel: 01285 653062 (H) 07768 758550 (M) 01285 643938 (F)
Email: msykes@omniwhittington.co.uk

Ground: Cirencester Town FC, Tetbury Road, Cirencester GL7 6PX
Tel: 01285 654783

Directions: From A419 head towards Cirencester town centre (follow signs for Cirencester Hospital). Turn left at Hospital roundabout, and the ground entrance is on the left at the next roundabout.

RECORD **Attendance:** 115 v Fairford Town, May 2001

Goalscorer 00-01: David Godfrey (16)

FACT FILE

Nickname: Academy
Colours: Green & white hoops/white/green
Change colours: Red & black/black/red
Midweek Matchday: Wednesday

CLUB PERSONNEL

Chairman: Alan Sykes
Tel: 01285 654783

Press Officer& Prog Ed:
Kirstine Fraser Tel: 01793 823046

Joint Managers:
John Freeth & David Hawkins

Physio: Steve Slattery

DIDCOT TOWN

Secretary: Phil Hussey c/o Loop Meadow Stadium
Ground: Loop Meadow Stadium, Bowmont Water, Didcot, OX11 7GA.
Website: http://users.tinyoline.co.uk/stevetclare/DTFC1/
Capacity: 5,000 Seats: 250 Cover: 500 Floodlights: Yes

Directions: From Town Centre: Take station road (old ground) and turn right under bridge just before station into Cow Lane. Left by Ladygrove Pub into Tamar Way. Then first left at roundabout. From A34: leave at Milton interchange and take Didcot road for approximately one mile. At roundabout take perimeter road Cross three more roundabouts and turn right at third into Avon Way
Clubhouse: Every evening and 12 noon to close at weekends and national holidys.

HONOURS Hellenic Lg 53-54,Lg Cup 1965-66 66-67 92-9397-98 Div 1 76-77,Div1 Cup 76-7, Berks & Bucks Senior Trophy 2000-01

PREVIOUS **Leagues:** Hellenic 53-54; Metropolitan League 57-63
RECORD **Attendance:** 825 v Oxford United, 2001

FACT FILE

Founded: 1907
Nickname: Railwaymen
Colours: All red & white
Change colours: Blue & yellow stripes
Midweek Matchday: Tuesday
Programme: 50p
Editor: Steve Clare & Andy Selby

CLUB PERSONNEL

President:
Chairman: John Bailey
Manager: Pete Cox
Ass.Managar: John Heapy
Player-Coach: Andy Cooper
Physio: Mark Roberts

2000-01

Leading goalscorer: Andy Marriott 17
Captain: Paul Noble
P.o.Y.: Jamie Heapy

FAIRFORD TOWN

Secretary: William Beach, 33 Park Close, Fairford, GL7 4LF Tel: 01285 712136 (H)
Email address: ftfc00@hotmail.com

Ground: Cinder Lane, London Road, Fairford, Cirencester Tel: 01285 712071

Directions: Entering Fairford on A417 from Lechlade turn left down Cinder Lane150yds after 40mph sign. From Cirencester on same road, follow thru village andturn right down Cinder Lane 400yds afterRailway Inn.
Buses from Swindon,Lechlade and Cirencester
Capacity: 2,000 Seats: 100 Cover: 150 Floodlights: Yes

Clubhouse: Open each evening, weekend lunches & before and after all games

Club Shop: Yes

HONOURS Glos Challenge Trophy 79-80, 98-99 (R-up 82-83); Hellenic Lg R-up 78-79 79- 80 90-91 94-95, (Premier Div Cup 78-79, Div 1 71-72, Div 1 Cup 71-72); Glos Jnr Cup 62-63; Swindon & Dist Lg 64-65 68-69

PREVIOUS **Leagues:** Cirencester & District (pre-1946)/ Swindon & District 46-70
Grounds: None

RECORD **Attendance:** 1,525 v Coventry City, friendly July 2000
Goalscorer: Pat Toomey **Win**: 9-0 v Moreton T **Defeat**: 0-9 v Sharpness

FACT FILE

Founded: 1891 Nickname: Town
Colours: Red/white/red
Change colours:All Blue
Midweek matchday: Wednesday
Reserves' League: Hellenic Reserve section
Programme: 20 pages with admission
Editor/Press Officer: President
Club Website: http://welcometo/ftfc

CLUB PERSONNEL

Chairman & Commercial Manager:
Stuart Pike Tel: 01285 712364
President: Michael Banner
Manager: Mark Webb
Physio: Ian Watkins

2000-01

Captain: John Hathaway
P.o.Y.: James Price
Top Scorer: Gareth Davies 16

GLOUCESTER UNITED

Secretary: Dave Phillips, 14 Woodcock Close, Abbeydale, Gloucester GL4 4WT
Tel: 01452 414766 (H/Fax) 07754 088063 (M - matchdays only)

Ground City Stadium, Meadow Park, Sudmeadow Road, Hempsted, Gloucester GL2 5HS
Tel: 01452 421400
Floodlights: Yes

Directions From junction 11 of M5 take A40 towards City Centre, follow signs for Historic Docks. On approach to docks turn right over narrow bridge into Severn Road (signposted Hempsted). Turn right into Hempsted Lane and then second right into Sudreadow Road. Ground is 50 yards on the left.

Record **Attendance:** 120 v Shortwood Utd, 25.10.00

Honours: Hellenic D1 West 99-00; Floodlite Cup R-up 99-00

2000-01 Leading goalscorer: Gary Esson 40
Captain: Andy Pritchett
P.o.Y.: Gary Esson

FACT FILE

Colours : All blue
Change colours: Red/red/white
Midweek fixtures: Wednesday

CLUB PERSONNEL

Chairman: Richard Bull
Vice Chairman: Pat Casey
Press Officer: Dave Phillips
Man: Douglas Foxwell 01452 538116
Coach: John Hamilton
Physio: Ricky Clutterbuck

HARROW HILL

Secretary/Match Sec: Robert Partridge, 20 Littledean Hill Road, Cinderford, Glos., GL14 2BE
Tel: 01594 825360 (H) 01594 542421 (B)
Club Email: geoff@tuffley33.freeserve.co.uk

Ground: Larksfield Road, Harrow Hill Tel: 01594 543873

Directions: Take A40 west out of Gloucester, follow A40 for 8 miles then takeA4136 to Longhope, pass by on the outskirts of Michealdean, up steep hill(Plump Hill), then second turn on the right signed Harrow Hill. At phone box onthe left turn right into Larksfield Road, ground on right at top of hill

RECORD **Attendance:** 350 v Cinderford Town 92

2000-01 Leading goalscorer: Andy Keveren 11
Captain: Paul Frowen
P.o.Y.: Martin Reid

FACT FILE

Founded: 1932
Nickname: Harry Hill
Colours: Claret & blue/sky/sky
Change Colours: Purple & green/black/black
Midweek Matchday: Wednesday

CLUB PERSONNEL

Chairman: Reg Taylor
President: Ken Jones
Press Officer: Geoff Tuffley
10A Bilson, Cinderford, Glos., GL14 2LJ
Tel 01594 825655(H) 01594 542421(B)
077524 75514 (M)

Manager: Phil Davies
Coach: Nick Cornwall
Physio: Martin Burford

Above: Premier Division Champions, Swindon Supermarine

Right: Division One (East) Champions, Henley Town

Below: Division One (West) Champions, Gloucester United

HENLEY TOWN

Secretary: Tony Kingston, 50 Birdhill Avenue Reading Berks. RG2 7JU
Tel: 01189 670196 (H) 07712139502 (M)
01189 844496 (B) 01189 842201 (Fax)
E-mail: ad.kingston@ntlworld.com

Ground: The Triangle Mill Lane Henley-on-Thames 01491 411083
Cover: 110 **Seats:** 60 **Floodlights:** Yes for season 2001-02

Directions: From Henley Town Centre take the A4155 Reading Road. Mill Lane is approx. 1 mile on the left past the Newtown Ind. Est. and immed. before the Garage and roundabout for Tesco. The ground is on the left, over the railway bridge.
Henley-on-Thames Railway Station ten minutes walk.
Buses 328 Reading or 329 Wycombe

Record Gate: 2000+ v Reading, 1922

Recent Honours: Hellenic Div 1 East 00-01; Oxon Senior Cup (5)

2000-01 **Captain:** Graham Jack
P.o.Y.: Phil Humphries **Top Scorer:** James Hollidge 28

FACT FILE
Founded 1871
Nickname: The Lillywhites or Town
Colours: White & black/black/black
Change cols.: Claret & blue/white/white
Midweek fixtures: Tuesday
Web site: www.henleytown.co.uk

CLUB PERSONNEL

Chairman& Match Sec: Andrew Bryan
Tel: 0118 972 3962 (H) 07730 924100 (M)
Press Officer & Youth Devel:
Jack Hollidge Tel: 0118 9341106

Managers: Bernie Harris & Kevin Davies
Coach: Keith Stiles
Physio: Richard Ellis

HIGHWORTH TOWN

Secretary: Fraser Haines, 222 Windrush, Highworth, Swindon SN6 7EB (01793861109)

Ground: Elm Recreation Ground, Highworth. (01793 766263)

Directions: Enter on A361 from Swindon, past Simpsons Garage, straight overisland, next sharp left into Green by Vet's Surgery - ground & car park 60ydson left next to Sports Hall

Capacity: 2,000 Seats: 50 Cover: 250 Floodlights: Yes Club Shop: No

Clubhouse: Sat 12-2.30 & 4.30-11pm. Mon to Fri 7-11pm. Rolls & Hot food

HONOURS Wilts Snr Cup 63-64 72-73 95-96 97-98(R-up 88-89), Hellenic Div 1 Cup 88-89,Arthur Shipway Cup 88-89 93-94, Swindon & District Lg 63-64 64-65 65-66 68-69 Hellenic Supplementary Cup Winners: 98-99, Hellenic Reserve Division Two Winners 98-99, Hellenic Premier Division R-Up 9-00

PREVIOUS **Leagues:** Wilts; Swindon & Dist

RECORD **Attendance:** 2,000 v QPR opening Floodlights
Scorer: Kevin Higgs **Appearances:** Rod Haines
Win: 12-0 v Beeches, Arthur Shipway Cup 1992
Defeat: 2-8 v Milton United, Hellenic Lge Div. 1, 1987

FACT FILE
Founded: 1894
Nickname: Worthians
Sponsors: One Stop
Colours: Red & black/black/red
Change colours: Blue/white/blue
Midweek matchday: Tuesday
Reserves Lge: Hellenic Reserve Div
Programme: 16 pages, 60p
Editor: Mike Markham (01793 763462)

CLUB PERSONNEL
President: Alan Vockins
Chairman: Rodney Haines
Match Secretary: Dave Evans (01793 763548)
Press Officer:Chairman
Manager: Chris Seagraves
Coach: Andy Wollen Physio:Clive Webb
2001-01Top Scorer: Keith Walker
Captain: Dave Webb P.o.Y.: John Reeves

NORTH LEIGH

Secretary: Peter J Dix, 8 Windmill Close, North Leigh, Nr Witney, Oxon OX8 6RP
Tel: 01993 881199

Match Secretary: Keith Huxley, The Orchard, Cote, Bampton, Oxon. OX18 2EG
Tel: 01993 851497 (H) 0118 913 3223 (B)
email: keith_huxley@fwuk.fwc.com

Ground: Eynsham Hall Park Sports Ground, North Leigh, nr Witney, Oxon OX8 6PW
Tel: 0993 881427

Directions: Ground is situated off A4095 Witney to Woodstock road 3 miles east of Witney. Entrance to ground is 300yds east of Main Park Entrance

Capacity: 2,000 Seats: 100 Cover: 200 Floodlights: Yes
Clubhouse: Bar open matches. Snacks available **Club Shop:** No

PREVIOUS **Leagues:** Witney & District 08-89

CLUB RECORDS **Attendance:** 300 v Oxford United, Friendly August 1998
Scorer: P Coles **Appearances:** P King

HONOURS Hellenic Lg Div 1 R-up 92-93 (Reserves Cup 93-94), Oxon Jnr Shield 56-57 83-84, Oxon Charity Cup 84-85 88-89, Witney & Dist. Lg(13) 50-57 84-90 LgCup (10) 47-48 51-52 53-55 56-57 81-82 85-89), Oxon Yth Cup 93-94 94-95,OxonYth u17 Lg & Cup 93-94. Oxford Sen. Cup R-Up 94-95. Marriott Cup 95-96; Oxon U-16 Youth Cup 98-99, Allied Counties Under 18 Youth (West Div)Winners

FACT FILE
Founded: 1908
Nickname: None
Sponsors: Various
Colours: Yellow & red/red/yellow
Change colours: All claret & blue
Midweek matches: Tuesday
Programme: 20 pages, £1 with entry
Editor: Janice Carter

CLUB PERSONNEL
President: Mrs Christine Smith
Chairman: Peter King
Press Officer: Barry Norton
Tel: 01993 881777

Manager: Mark Gee
Asst Manager: David Ebsworth
Physio: Andrew Davidson

PEGASUS JUNIORS

Secretary: Brian James, 7 Loder Drive, Hereford HR1 1DS
Tel: 01432 274982 (H/Fax) 01568 612367 (B) 077900 92444 (M)

Ground: Leisure Centre, Holmer Road, Hereford HR4 9UD
Tel: 01432 278178
Capacity: 1,000 Seatrs 50 Cover : Yes Floodlights: Yes Clubhouse: 48 Stowens Street

Directions: Pass through City Centre on the A49 and follow signs to the racecourse. Leave A49 at A4103 roundabout junction and entrance is approx 500 metres along Holmer Road on the left hand side, just before the racecourse entrance

PREVIOUS **Leagues:** Leisure Centre

RECORD **Attendance:** 1,400 v Newport AFC 89-90

HONOURS Herefordshire Snr Amtr Cup 71-72, Worcs Snr Urn 85-86, Herefordshire Co. Chal. Cup (6) 81-83 84-85 87-88 89-90 98-99 R-up 93-94, Hellenic Lg Div 1 84-85 98-99 R-up 93-94, Div 1 Cup R-up 93-94

00-01 Leading Goalscorer: Mark Davis (30)

FACT FILE

Founded: 1955
Colours: All red
Change colours: Blue & white/blue/blue
Midweek Matchday: Wednesday
Programme: 50p
Editor: Kevin Bishop (01432 353805)

CLUB PERSONNEL

President: Mark Ellis
Chairman: Stephen Knight
Press Officer: Chris Wells
Tel: 01432 358345

Manager: Martin Thomas
Coach: Mick Williams
Physio: Jarrod Clay & Dave Smith

SHORTWOOD UNITED

Secretary: Mark Webb, 1 The Bungalow, Shortwood, Nailsworth, Stroud, Glos GL60SD
Tel: 01453 833204 (H) 01453 835900 (B) 0781 2842724 (M)

Ground: "Meadow Bank", Shortwood, Nailsworth, Gloucestershire (01453 833936)

Directions: In Nailsworth turn into Spring Hill then first left. Continue pastshop and and keep left past "Britannia" (signposted Shortwood) - continue toend for ground. 4 miles from Stroud (BR)
Capacity: 5,000 Seats: 50 Cover: 150 Floodlights: Yes Club Shop: No
Clubhouse: Mon-Sat 7-11pm, Sun 12-2 & 7-10.30pm.. Hot food kitchen on matchdays

HONOURS Glos.Co.Lg 81-82 (R-up 80-81), Glos Tphy 83-84 91-92,94-95,(R-up 79-80), Hellenic Lg 84-85 91-92 (R-up 85-86 89-90 94-95, Div 1 R-up 83-84, Div 1Cup83-84), Prem Lge Cup R-up 95-96, Hungerford Merit Cup, Glos Snr AmCup 85-86,99-00 R-up 79-80), Stroud Charity Cup 91-92 92-93 94-95 00-01(R-up 95-96), Stroud Lg 27-28 (Div 2 26-27 64-65(res), Div 3 25-26 49-50(res) 62-63(res)), Glos Northern Snr Lg R-up (3)res)(Div 2 62-63 80-81(res) 90-91(res)), Arthur Shipway Cup 78-79 79-80, Supp'tary Cup R-up 98-99, Glos N. Sen 2 R-up 98-99

PREVIOUS **Leagues:** Stroud; Glos Northern Snr; Glos Co
Ground: Table Land, Wallow Green

RECORD **Attendance:** 1,000 v Forest Green Rovers, FA Vase 5th Rd 81-82
Goalscorer: Peter Grant **Appearances:** Peter Grant
Win: 11-0 **Defeat:** 0-9 **Fee Received:** Paul Tester (Cheltenham, 80-81)

FACT FILE
Founded: 1900
Nickname: The Wood
Sponsors: Electricity
Colours: Red & white,red,white
Change: Blue/Blue/Yellow
Midweek matchday: Wednesday
Reserves' League: Glos Northern Snr 1
Programme: 18 pages, 50p
Editor:Ashley Loveridge
2000-01Captain: Lee Driver-Dickenson
P.o.Y.: Adam Paul
Top Scorer: Matthew Gree 19

CLUB PERSONNEL
Chairman: Peter Webb
Vice C'men: W Stratford, W Lewis
President: R T Tanner
Press Officer: Ashley Loveridge
Tel: 01453 752494
Manager/Coach: John Evans/Roger Smith

SOUTHALL TOWN

Secretary: George Twyman, 119 Dormers Wells Lane Southall Middlesex UB1 3JA
Tel & Fax: 0208 574 5047(H & B)

Match Sec.: Eddie Mee, 11 Charles Hocking Hse, Bollo Bridge Rd, Acton London W3 8DA.
Tel: 0208 993 4477(H) 07940 287 985 (Bus)

Ground: Yeading FC. The Warren, Beconsfield Road, Hayes, Middx UB4 0SL
Tel 0208 848 7362

Capacity: 3,500 Cover: 1,000 Seats: 250 Floodlights: Yes

Directions: Leave M4 at junction 3, The Parkway onto Hayes by-pass. Continue to the second filter road and turn right onto A4020 Uxbridge Road, then take first turning on right into Springfield Road. Continue to end of road, turn left into Beconsfield Road, ground on right hand side at end of the road.

PREVIOUS **Leagues:** Isthmian League to 00.

RECORD **Attendance:** 45 v Finchampstead 00-01

00-01 **Leading Goalscorer:** Steve Bircham13
Captain: Stuart Freeman **P.o.Y.:** Graham Ash

FACT FILE
Formed: 2000
Nickname: The Wood
Colours: Red & white stripes/black/black
Change colours: Yellow & blue/blue/blue
Midweek Matchday: Wednesday
Programme: £1.00
Editor: Craig Brown: 020 8861 6215
email: craig@craigbrown.co.uk

CLUB PERSONNEL
Chairman: Manjit S Lit

Press Officer: Manjit S Lit
Tel: 0208 893 5373 Fax: 0208 571 9410

Manager: Dennis Bainborough
Coach: Del Deanus
Physio: Micky Croft

Spelthorne Sports after their Third Round Cherry Record Books Trophy victory over Frimley Green. Photo: Eric Marsh

Rayners Lane, winners of the Middlesex County FA Premier Cup Final against Uxbridge FC Reserves.
Back Row (l-r): Junior Smith, Graham Small, Steve Bird, Steve Cott, Simon Middleton, Peter Randall, Danny Mills, Simon Horders, Ian Woodward, Theo Handerson. Front Row: Tomy Metcalfe, Roger Carpenter, John Carpenter, Steve Heage, Greg Rice, Damien Stewart. Mascot: Simon Owens

Martin Baker Sports

TUFFLEY ROVERS

Secretary: Graham Moody, 50 Giles Cox, Quedgeley, Gloucester GL2 4YL
Tel: 01452 724083 (H & Fax) 01452 522009 (B) 07976 726075 (M)

Ground: Glevum Park, Lower Tuffley Lane, Gloucester GL2 5DT
Tel: 01452 423402

Directions: Follow Gloucester city ring-rd to traffic lights signed M5 South & Bristol. Turn right signed Hempsted & city centre, after 200yds turn right (McDonalds on corner) into Lower Tuffley Lane, ground 400yds on left
Capacity: Seats: 50 Cover: Yes Floodlights: Yes

Clubhouse: 800 yds from ground. Open before & after matches, and normal pub hours at other times. Snacks available. **Club Shop:** No

HONOURS Hellenic Lg Div 1 92-93 (Div 1 Cup 92-93, F'lit Cup 98-99), Glos Co. Lge 90-91, Glos Snr Amtr Cup 87-88, Stroud Lg 72-73, 94-95, Glos Northern Sen. Lg. Div 1 87-88 98-99 (res) Div 2 79-80.

PREVIOUS **Leagues:** Stroud; Glos Northern Senior; Glos County (pre-1991)
Grounds: Stroud Rd, Gloucester; Randwick Park, Tuffley

RECORD **Attendance:** 150 v Cinderford Town 94-95

FACT FILE

Founded: 1929
Nickname: Rovers
Club Sponsors: Port security
Colours: Claret & blue/claret/claret
Change colours: Orange/black/black or orange
Midweek Matchday: Tuesday
Reserve League: Glos.Northern Senior Lge
Programme: approx 10 pages with entry
Editor: Mrs Bev Summers (01452 417660)

CLUB PERSONNEL

President: A.W. Purdy
Chairman: Tony Newport
Manager: Geoff Medcroft
Coach: TBA
Physio: Tony Woodward

WANTAGE TOWN

Secretary: John Culley, Lorien, Winter Lane, West Hanney, Wantage, Oxon. OX12 0LF
Tel: 01235 868359 (H) 01865 850204 (B)
email: jbculleylorien@netscapeonline.co.uk

Ground: Alfredian Park, Manor Road, Wantage, Oxon Tel: 01235 764781

Directions: Take Hungerford Road from Wantage (A338)
The ground is signposted on right opposite recreation ground
Capacity: 1,500 Seats: 50 Cover: 300 Floodlights: Yes

Clubhouse: Mon-Fri 7.30-11pm, Sat noon-2.30, 4-7pm Club Shop: No

HONOURS Hellenic Lg R-up 81-82, Div 1 80-81 (R-up 69-70 87-88 91-92 95-96), Div1 Cup R-up 91-92; Oxon Snr Cup 82-83; Berks & Bucks Intermediate Cup 54-55; Swindon & District Lg 07-08 33-34 52-53 55-56

PREVIOUS **Leagues:** Swindon & Dist. 1901-12 30-35 47-56; N Berks 12-22 38-40 46-47; Reading & D. 22-30 35-38
Ground: Challow Park (pre-1922)

RECORD **Attendance:** 500 v Newport AFC 89
Win: 11-1 v Amersham Town (A), Hellenic League 60-61
Defeat: 0-14 v Thame United (A), 20/1/62
Goalscorer: A Rolls

Players progressing: Roy Burton and Colin Duncan (both Oxford United)

FACT FILE

Founded: 1892
Nickname: Alfredians
Sponsors: Broadway Motors
Colours:Green &white/white/green&white
Change Colours: Blue& white/bue/blue&white
Programme: 28 pages, 50p
Editor: Tony Woodward (01367 241328)
Midweek Matchday: Tuesday

CLUB PERSONNEL

Chairman: Tony Woodward
President: Ernie Smart
Match Secretary: Colin Blunsden
Tel: 01235 768605 (H)
Manager: Stuart Peace
Coach: Terry Delaney
Physio: Gerry Hogan

WOOTTON BASSETT TOWN

Secretary: Rod Carter, 14 Blackthorn Close, Wootton Bassett, Swindon SN4 7JE
Tel: 01793 851386 (H); 01793 494367 (B); 01793 494355 (F);
07946 034999 (M) Email: rod.carter@woolworths.co.uk

Ground: Gerard Buxton Sports Ground, Rylands Way, Wootton Bassett, Swindon 01793 853880

Directions: M4 jnct 16 to Wootton Bassett (A3102), left at 2nd r'bout (Prince of Wales pub on right), 2nd left into Longleaze (just after Mobil garage) and Rylands Way is 3rd right by shops, ground 100yds on right. From Calne/Devizes direction proceed thru town centre and turn right into Longleaze after Shell petrol station on right - Rylands Ave. is 3rd left. Coming from Malmesbury take last exit off r'bout by Prince of Wales pub and Longleaze is 2nd left

Capacity: 4,000 Seats: None Cover: 350 Floodlights: Yes Club Shop: No
Clubhouse: Open every matchday. Matchday refreshments - teas, coffees, soups & light snacks

PREVIOUS **Leagues:** Wilts (pre-1988) **Grounds:** None

RECORD **Gate:** 2,103 v Swindon T., friendly 7/91 **Win:** 11-2 **Defeat:** 0-9
Scorer: Brian (Toby) Ewing **Appearances:** Steve Thomas

HONOURS Hellenic Lg Div 1 Cup 89-90 93-94, Wilts Lg 87-88 (Div 2 84-85,Subsidiary Cup 78-79), Wilts Snr Cup R-up 02-03 03-04 87-88, Ghia Snr 83-84,Ghia Jnr Cup R-up 88-89, FA Amateur Cup QF 26-27

00-01 **Leading Goalscorer:** Lee Stodart (23)

FACT FILE

Founded: 1882
Colours: Blue & yellow/blue/yellow
Change colours: Red/black/black
Midweek matchday: Tuesday
Reserve's League: Wiltshire
Programme: 12 pages, free
Editor: Roger Williamson Tel: 01793 850751

CLUB PERSONNEL

Chairman: Paul Harrison
President: Keith Lodge
Press Officer: Rod Carter (see Sec)

Manager: Peter Yeardley
Coach: Mike Byrne
Physio: TBA

YATE TOWN

Secretary: Terry Tansley, 1 Tyning Close, Yate, Bristol. BS37 5PN
Tel: 01454 324305

Ground: Lodge Road, Yate, Bristol BS37 7LE Tel: 01454 228103

Directions: M4 jct 18, A46 towards Stroud, then A432 to Yate. Turn right at top of railway bridge into North Road, first left past traffic lights. Five miles from Bristol Parkway BR main line station, half mile from Yate BR station. Buses 329, X68 and 328

Capacity: 2,000 Cover: 400 Seats: 236 Floodlights: Yes

Clubhouse: Open every night & weekend lunchtimes. Skittles, darts, pool, live entertainment
Club Shop: Selling programmes & usual souvenirs. Contact: Secretary
HONOURS Hellenic Lg(2) 87-89 (Div 1 R-up 84-85, Lg Skol Cup R-up 87-88), Glos Chal.Tphy 88-89 (R-up 78-79), Glos Snr Amtr Cup Sth 77-78 91-92(res) 92-93(res),Glos Snr Chal. Cup (Nth) R-up 89-90 92-93 94-95, Stroud Charity Cup R-up 74-75 81-82 84-85 (Sect. A Winners(6) 76-78 79-80 82-83 87-89), Berkeley Hosp. Prem.Cup(3) 73-75 80-81, S.W. Co's Sutton Vase 85-86 Dr.Martens Fairplay award 98-99
BEST SEASON **FA Vase:** Fifth Round 1991-92
CLUB RECORDS **Win:** 13-3 v Clevedon, Bristol Premier Comb 67-68
CareerGoalscorer: Kevin Thaws **Career Appearances:** Gary Hewlett
Transfer fee - Paid: None **Received:** £15,000 for Mike Davis (Bristol Rovers 93)
PREVIOUS **Leagues:** Gloucestershire County 68-83, Hellenic 83-89, Southern Lge 89-00

FACT FILE
Formed: 1946 Nickname: The Bluebells
Colours: White/navy/navy
Change colours: All Red
Midweek matchday: Tuesday
Reserve Team's League: Bristol Suburban
Programme - Pages: 40 Price: £1
Editor: Terry Tansley c/o Club
Website:www.yatetownfc.co.uk

CLUB OFFICIALS
Chairman: Tony Phillips
President: R Hewetson
Press Officer: Secretary
Joint Managers :
Richard Thompson & Gary Hewlett
Physio:Ken Dodd

2000-01
Captain: Ben Trotman
P.o.Y.: Andy Neal (supporters)
Top Scorer & P.o.Y. (Players)
Paul Metheringham (40goals)

Milton United. Back Row (l-r): Andy Brown, Mick Stace, Darren Toomey, Paul Tuson, Gareth Walker, Colin Brind, Ashley Fell. Front Row: Tom Larman junior, Dave Bayliss, Anthony Wise, Paul Davis. Photo: Arthur Evans

Peppard FC

ARDLEY UNITED

Secretary: Alan Mitchell, 24 Orchard Road,Ardley,Bicester,Oxon OX6 9PW
Tel: 01869 346854(H) 01865 846799(B) 01865 846333(F)
email: the@mitchells99.freeserve.co.uk

Ground: The Playing Fields,Oxford Road, Ardley OX27 7PA Tel: 01869 346429
Directions: M40 junc 10 take B430 towards Middleton Stoney on the right after1/2 mile. From Oxford take A430 through Weston-on-the-Green & Middleton Stoney on the left hand side.
Floodlights: No

HONOURS Oxon Snr Lg R-up 92-93 (Pres. Cup R-up 90-91 91-92) Hellenic League Div One 96-97,97-98 Division One Cup 94-5,95-6,96-7,97-98

PREVIOUS **Leagues:** Oxon Snr (pre-1993)

RECORD **Attendance:** 91 v North Leigh (1999)

00-01 Leading Goalscorer: Steven Tucker (28)

FACT FILE
Colours: Sky/navy/navy
Change colours: All yellow
Midweek matchday: Tuesday
Programme Yes
Editor: Barbara Gow 01869 250279

CLUB PERSONNEL
President: Ben Gow
Chairman: Norman Stacey
Press Officer: Barbara Gow 01869 250279
Manager: Paul Spittle
Physio: Clive Wright

CHIPPING NORTON TOWN

Secretary: Bob Tanner, 36 Fox Close, Chipping Norton, Oxon. OX7 5BZ
Tel: 07881 712624
Match Secretary Terry Maycock, 31 Newlands, Witney, Oxon. OX28 3JL
Tel: 01993 778260

Ground: Walterbush Road, Chipping Norton, OX7 5DP
Tel: 01608 645311 or 01608 642562
Directions: From South – A361 to Chipping Norton, past school on right, take 1st left turning into Walterbush Road.
From North – drive through town and take A361 towards Burford by Kings Arms, past fire station on left, then take 1st right into Walterbush Road.
Floodlights: Yes

Record Gate: 1000 v Wolverhampton Wanderers 1981

FACT FILE
Re-formed 2001
Nickname: The Magpies
Colours: Black & white stripes/black/black & white
Change colours: Yellow/blue/yellow
Midweek fixtures: Tuesday

CLUB PERSONNEL
Chairman: Nigel Harrison
email: happyhaulier@btinternet.com
Tel: 01993 703319
Program Editor: Terry Maycock
Tel: 01993 778260
Manager: Alan Dore
Coach: TBA Physio: TBA

CIRENCESTER UNITED

Secretary: Gordon Varley, 95 Vaisey Rd, Cirencester, Glos GL7 2JW
Tel: 01285 657836 (H) 07970 748893 (M) 01367 718259 (F)
Ground: Four Acres, Chesterton Lane, Cirencester GL7 1XG Tel: 01285 885460
Directions: Follow by-pass towards Bristol, under footbridge, first left after Cirencester Town F.C., ground 200yds on left hand side Seats: None Cover: No Floodlights: No

Clubhouse: Training nights & matchdays. Rolls & sundries available Club Shop: No
HONOURS Glos Snr Amtr Cup R-up 86-87 89-90; Cirencester Lg 72-73 74-75 Div 2 (3) 71-73 74-75, Lg Cup 74-75, Res. Cup 74-75; Cheltenham Lg 76-77 83-84 Div 2 75-76, Lg Cup 83-84 R-up 86-87, Snr Charity Cup 86-87; Stroud Charity Cup 86-87 Section A 82-83 83-84; Arthur Shipway Cup 86-87 R-up 87-88 92-93; Fairford Hospital Cup R-up (4) 83-85 90-91 92-93; Hellenic Res Div 95-96, Cup96-97
PREVIOUS **Leagues:** Cirencester & Dist.(4 yrs); Cheltenham (8 yrs)
RECORDS **Attendance:** 191 v Cirencester Acad. 28.12.98
Goalscorer: M Day **Appearances:** A Smith

FACT FILE
Founded: 1970 Nickname: Herd
Colours: Red, black trim/black/black
Change colours: All Blue
Midweek Matchday: Wednesday
Programme: 40 pages, 50p
Editor: Neil Warriner (01285 656187)

CLUB PERSONNEL
President: A Day
Chairman: Paul King
Press Officer: Jason Huxtable (01285 656010)
Manager: Ivor Probert
Coach: Barry Pocock
Physio: Dave Trinder

CLANFIELD

Secretary: John Osborne, 70 Lancut Road, Witney, Oxon OX28 5AQ Tel: 01993 771631

Ground: Radcot Road, Clanfield, Oxon Tel: 01367 810314

Directions: Situated on the A4095, 8 miles west of Witney & 4 miles east of Faringdon, at the southern end of Clanfield. Buses from Witney - contact Thames Transit for details
Capacity: 2,000 Seats: No Cover: 300 Floodlights: No
Clubhouse: Every evening & Sat/Sun lunch Club Shop: No

HONOURS Oxon Jnr Shield 32-33, Oxon I'mediate Cup 67-68, Witney & Dist. Lg 66-67 (Div 1 65-66, Div 2 64-65), Hellenic Lg Div 1 69-70 (Premier Div Cup 72-73, Div1 Cup 69-70 85-86), Jim Newman Mem. Tphy 83-84 87-88, Faringdon Thursday Memorial Cup 69-70 71-72 96-97

PREVIOUS **Leagues:** Nth Berks; Witney & Dist
RECORD **Attendance:**102 v Witney Academy 2000 Top Goalscorer: D.Hamill(9)

FACT FILE
Founded: 1890
Nickname: Robins
Sponsors: Green King
Colours: All red
Change colours: Yellow & Black/black/black
Reserves' League: Hellenic Lge Res. section
Programme: 8 pages, with admission
Editor: Secretary

CLUB PERSONNEL
President: B WallisChairman: J Osborne
Managers: Jason Court & Ray Lock
Press Officer&Physio: Trevor Cuss
2000-01 Captain: Lee Kilfoyle
P.o.Y. & Top Scorer: Kevin Alcraft 11

EASINGTON SPORTS

Secretary: Matthew Wiggins, 26 Victoria Place, Banbury, OX16 3NN. Tel: 01295 256714
Ground: Addison Road, Banbury, Oxon, OX16 9DH (01295 257006)
Club Email: matt@wiggins1.freeserve.co.uk

Directions: From Oxford A423. After passing under flyover on the outskirts of Banbury take first turning left into Grange Road then third right into AddisonRd. Ground at top on left. One and a half miles from Banbury (BR)
Capacity: 1,000 Seats:0 Cover: 30Floodlights: No Programme: Yes

Clubhouse: Changing rooms, showers, bar facilities and food

HONOURS Oxon Snr Cup R-up, Oxon Intermediate League & Cup, Oxon Snr Lg

PREVIOUS **Leagues:** Banbury Jnr; Oxon Snr; Warkwick Combination
Ground: Bodicote

RECORD **Attendance:** 250 v Witney Town 68

FACT FILE
Founded: 1946
Colours: Red & white/black/red & white
Change colours: Blue/ white
Midweek Matchday: Wednesday
Reserves' League: Hellenic Res. section

CLUB PERSONNEL
Chairman: T.B.A.
President: Bob Cogbill
Manager/Coach: Andy Maguire
Physio: Bernie Jarvis
Press Officer: T.B.A.
2000-01 Leading goalscorer: Nicky Gordon 11
Captain: Allan Haynes

HEADINGTON AMATEURS

Secretary: Stephen Giles, 67 Lucerne Ave.,Bure Park,Bicester, Oxon.OX26 3EG
Tel No: 01869 246141 Email Address: steve.giles3@ btinternet.com
Ground: Barton Rec., Barton Village Road, Barton, Oxon Tel: 01865 760489
Directions: From Green Rd r'bout, Headington, (on A40) take Barton/Islip exit(1st exit coming from Witney, last coming from London), turn left into NorthWay, follow road for half mile - ground at bottom of hill on left Seats: None Cover: NoneFloodlights: No Club Shop: No
Clubhouse: Tues & Thurs 6-11, Sat matchdays 4.45-11. Rolls, chips,burgers, hot dogs, etc
HONOURS Oxon Snr League(4) 72-74 75-77 (R-up 71-72 74-75 77-78 81-82 84-85, Div1 68-69, Presidents Cup(2) 72-74 (R-up 71-72 77-78 84-85)), Oxon Charity Cup75-76 (Intermediate Cup 88-89), Hellenic League Div 1 R-up 87-88 (Res. Sect.92-93, Res. Cup 91-92)
PREVIOUS Leagues: Oxford City Junr 49-66; Oxford Sen 67-88 **Grounds:**Romanway,Cowley
RECORDS Attendance: 250 v Newport AFC 91 **Scorer:** Tony Penge **Appearances:**Kent Drackett **Win:** 6-0 v Carterton (H) 91 **Defeat:** 1-8 v Banbury United (A), Feb. 94
Player Progressing: James Light (Oxford United) 1970s

FACT FILE
Founded : 1949 Nickname: A's
Sponsors: H.B. Services
Colours: All red Change: Blue/blue/white
Midweek matchday: Tuesday
Reserves' Lge: Hellenic Res. sect
Programme: 8 pages, £1 with entry
Editor: Stan Hawkswood (01865 451869)
2000-01 Captain: Ben Wales P.o.Y.: Mark Evans Top Scorer: Matthew Phillips 11

CLUB PERSONNEL
President: N Smith Chairman: Donald Light
Press Officer: Donald Light
Manager: Phil Major
Coach/Physio: Graham McAnulf

HOOK NORTON

Secretary: Dave Macfarlane, Byeways, East End, Hook Norton, Oxon, OX15 5LG
Tel: 01608 737123(H) 07989 852632(M)

Ground: The Bourne, Hook Norton OX15 5PB 01608 737132
Directions: From Oxford – A44 to junction with A361 turn right, take 1st left to a 'T' junction, turn right & enter village, after 30 MPH turn left then 1st right into 'The Bourne', take 1st left into ground.
Floodlights No

Previous League: Oxford Senior League
Record Gate: 244 v Banbury United 12th Dec 1998
Honours: Oxford Senior League Champions 2000-01 01-02

FACT FILE
Nickname: Hooky
Colours: All maroon with silver grey trim
Change colours: White with red trim/red/red
Midweek fixtures: Tuesday

CLUB PERSONNEL
Chairman: Christopher Moores
Deputy Chairman: Michael Barlow
Press Officer: Laura Riley 01608 730108
Program Editor: Mark Willis 01608 664101
email: repro@kmslitho.co.uk
Manager David Risato
Coach: Vinny Halsall & Gerry Duggan
Physio: Steve Slaughter & John Hughes

KIDLINGTON

Secretary: David Platt, 57 Cherry Close,Kidlington, Oxon OX5 1HHJ (01865 370266 (H) 01865 244161(W) EMail Address: david@jplatt99,freeserve.co.uk
Ground: Yarnton Rd, Kidlington, Oxford Tel: 01865 375628 f loodlights: No
Clubhouse: Two bars open after matches
Directions: From Kidlington r'bout (junction of A4260 & A34) A423 north toKidlington; after 3rdlights take 2nd left (Yarnton Road), ground is 200yds onthe left ,just passes the turning to Morton Avenue.
HONOURS Oxon Snr Lg 53-54 (R-up 47-48), Hellenic Lg Cup 74-75 (R-up 68-69 73-7474-75, Div 1 R-up 63-64 78-79), Oxon Intermediate Cup 52-53 84-85 (R-up 68-69 73-74 74-75), FA Vase 5th last sixteen 76-77

PREVIOUS **League**: Oxon Snr 47-54
RECORD **Attendance:** 2500 v Showbiz XI 1973
2000-01 **Captain**: Warren Jones **Top Scorer:** Luke Holden (11) **P.o.Ys.**: Kevin Williams and Jon Twiss

FACT FILE
Founded: 1909
Colours: Green & black/black/green
Change colours: Red & white stripes/redk/red
Midweek Matchday:Tuesday/ Wednesday
Programme: 32pages £1.50
Editor: M A Canning

CLUB PERSONNEL
President: Gordon Norridge
Chairman: Geoff Talboys
Manager: Anton Vircavs
Coach: Martin Baker Physio: Michelle Hopcroft
General Manager: Karl Grossman

LETCOMBE

Secretary: Des Williams, 8 Larkdown, Wantage, Oxon. OX12 8HE
Tel: 01235 764130 (H) 01235 225714(B)

Ground: Bassett Road, Letcombe Regis, Wantage, Oxon Tel: 01235 768685

Directions: B4507 Swindon road from Wantage, left for Letcombe Regis, follow road thru Letcombe Regis; ground on right on far side of village
Seats: No Cover: No Floodlights: No Club Shop: No

Clubhouse: Open evenings except Monday. Rolls & hot food sold

HONOURS Chiltonian Lg Div 1 90-91, North Berks Lg 89-90 (Lg Cup 87-88, WarMemorial Cup 89-90, A G Kingham Cup 89-90, Faringdon Mem Cup 97-8 98-99 99-00

PREVIOUS **Leagues:** North Berks 60-90; Chiltonian 90-93 **RECORDS** **Attendance:** 90 v Courage (Reading) 03.90 **Scorer:** R Taylor **Appearances:** P Davies
Unofficial Club Website: www.letcombefc.co.uk

FACT FILE
Founded: 1960 Nickname: Brooksiders
Sponsors: T.B.A.
Colours: Blue& Green/blue/green
Change colours: Red/Green
Midweek Matchday: Wednesday
Reserves' Lge: Hellenic Res. sect
Programme: £1 with entry
Editor: Russell Stock (01235 762387)

CLUB PERSONNEL
Pres Maurice Ginniff Chairman: Dennis Stock
Vice-Chairman: G Delacoze
Manager: Patrick Allen Coach: James Simms
Physio: T.B.A.
2000-01 Captain: Liam Bren Top Scorer Ian Gordon 11 P.o.Y.: Sean McCullough

MALMESBURY VICTORIA

Secretary: Sue Neale, 30 Gastons Road, Malmesbury, Wilts. SN16 0BE
Tel: 01666 823560 E-Mail: secretary@malmesbury-victoria.com
Ground: Flying Monk Ground, Gloucester Road, Malmesbury
Tel: 01666 822141
Website: www.malmesbury-victoria.com
Directions: From A429 turning signposted Tetbury (by Nurdens Garden Centre), go past school and take next left B4014 signposted Sherston. Go down hill to mini roundabout, straight over roundabout. Go past Somerfield's super store, narrow right turning into ground behind super store.
Previous Leagues: Wiltshire >00
Honours: Wiltshire League Champions 99-00
2000-01 **Capt:** Graham Jones **P.o.Y.:** Ben Lang **Top Scorer:** Garth Walsh 20

FACT FILE
Nickname: The Vic's
Colours: Black & white stripes/black/black
Maroon, blue sleeves/blue/maroon
Midweek fixtures: Tuesday or Wednesday

CLUB PERSONNEL
Chairman: Brian Slade 01666 825705
Press Officer: Elaine Foxall 01666 841227
Programme Ed: Sue Neale 01666 823560
Manager: Lester Foxall 01249 783295
Coach: Tom Dryden

MIDDLE BARTON

Secretary: Julie Reed, 5 Hillside Road, Middle Barton, Oxon OX7 7EY
Tel: 01869 347388
Match Secretary: Jean Beale, 3 Dorne Closer, Middle Barton, Oxon OX7 7HD
Tel: 01869 340753

Ground: Worton Road, Middle Barton, Oxon. Tel: 01869 347597
Directions: Middle Barton village is situated on the B4030, 5 miles east of Enstone. 200 metres passed the Fox PH turn left at cross roads, ground 200 metres on right.
Clubhouse: Open every evening

Previous League: Oxfordshire Senior League
Record Attendance: 137 v Bishops Cleeve, 21.08.99
Honours: Oxfordshire Sen. Lge R-up 98-99
00-01 Leading Goalscorer: Ian Fraser (14)

FACT FILE
Founded: 1952
Midweek Matchday: Wednesday
Colours: Royal blue/royal blue/white
Change colours: Yellow/black/black
Programme: Yes
Editor: Geoff Lines 07779 504402

CLUB PERSONNEL
President: Derrick Jarvis
Chairman: John Hanks
Press Officer: Phil Smith (01869 347471)
Manager/Coach: Tim Fowler
Physio: Lucy Waring & Sean Long

OLD WOODSTOCK TOWN

Secretary: Ian F Lenegan c/o Workplace Systems plc.
Precedent Drive, Rooksley, Milton Keynes MK13 8PP
Tel: 07836 242300(H), 01908 251301or 251311 (B) 01908 201287 (F)
email: kim_black@lineone.net
Match Secretary: Andy Hopcraft, 4 Hensington Close, Woodstock, Oxon. OX20 1LZ
Tel: 01993 812868

Ground: New Road, Woodstock OX20 1PB
Directions: A44 from Oxford into centre of Woodstock, turn right opposite The Crown into Hensington Road. After half a mile the road bends to the right, take the first turning right into New Road, ground half-way along on the left.

HONOURS Oxfordshire Sen. Lge 98-99
PREVIOUS **Leagues:** Oxfordshire Senior League
00-01 Leading Goalscorer: Paul Stone (6)

FACT FILE
Founded:
Midweek Matchday: Tuesday
Colours: Blue & red/blue/ red
Change colours: White/green/blue
Programme: Yes Editor: Nick Mason

CLUB PERSONNEL
President: Ian F Lenagan
Chairman: Ted Saxton
Manager: Andrew Townsend
Coach: Martin Oliver & Trevor Stokes
Physio: Graham Bowerman & Trevor Stokes

PEWSEY VALE

Secretary: Liz Montague, 39 Swan Meadow, Pewsey, Wilts, SN9 5HP
E-mail: montymadhouse@btinternet.com

Ground: Recreation Ground, Ball Rd, Pewsey Tel: 01672 562990

Directions: On entering Pewsey from A345, at the Market Place proceed to end of High Street and turn right into Ball Rd, entrance to ground on right opposite pub. BR to Pewsey station
Cover: Yes Floodlights: No

PREVIOUS **League:** Wiltshire County (pre-1993), Western League 93-01
Name: Pewsey Y.M. (until late 1940s)
HONOURS Wiltshire County League 92-93

FACT FILE
Colours: Black & White]/Black/Black
Change colours:
Navy & lime green/navy/lime green & navy
Midweek matchday: Tuesday

CLUB PERSONNEL
Chairman: Rob Thompson
Manager: Don Rogers

PURTON

Secretary: Alan Eastwood, 12 Hylder Close,Woodhall Park,Swindon,Wilts. SN2 2SL
Tel: 01793 729844 **Email Address:** eastwood@hylder.fsnet.co.uk
Ground: The Red House, Purton, Tel: 01793 770262 (Saturday afternoons only)

Directions: Purton is on B4041 Wootton Bassett to Cricklade Road. Ground nearvillage hall
Capacity Seats:None Cover: None Floodlights: No
Clubhouse: Open after matches and before matches on Saturdays

HONOURS Wiltshire Lg Div One 48-49 85-86, Div 2 83-84, Div 3 86-87; Wilts Senior Cup (6) 38-39 48-49 50-51 54-55 87-89, Wilts Yth Cup 77-78 85-86 88-89, Fairford Hosp. Cup (3) 87-89 93-94 Hellenic League Div One 95-96
RECORD **Attendance:** 508 v Dorcan 5.5.85
2000-01 **Captain & P.o.Y.:** Mark McMeeking **Top Goalscorer:** Mark Cutter 15

FACT FILE
Founded: 1923
Nickname: The Reds
Sponsors: The Care Company
Colours: All red
Change colours: White & blue/blue/blue
Midweek Matchday: Wednesday
Programme: 36 pages
Editor: Alan Eastwood (01793 729844)

CLUB PERSONNEL
President: Graham Price
Chairman: Tony Brown
Press Officer: Alan Eastwood
Manager: T.B.A.

ROSS TOWN

Secretary: Chris Parsons, The Flat, Woodfields, Weston under Penyard, Ross-on-Wye HR9 7PG
Tel: 01989 566712 (H) 01242 577966 (B) 07818 096156 (M)
Ground: Ross Sports Centre, The Riverside, Wilton, Ross-on-Wye HR9 5JA (07787 573080)
Directions: From Gloucester take the A40 to Ross. After passing through Weston under Penyard you come to a mini r'about on the edge of town, take 2nd exit and proceed to next r'about onto the main A449 Ross by-pass (heading towards Monmouth). At next r'about by Esso Garage take 1st exit back towards Ross & the ground is on the right just after passing over the River Wye.
HONOURS Hereford Lge 94-95, Charity Shield 95-96; Hereford FA Charity Bowl 94-95; Worcester & Dist Lge 95-96, Baylis Cup 95-96; Hereford FA Co. Chall Cup 97-99 R-up 95-96; 98-99 Pershore Hospital Charity Cup R-up 95-96, Hellenic Lg Cup R-up: 99-00
PREVIOUS **Leagues:** Hereford Lg, Worcester & District League.
RECORD **Attendance:** 147 v Harrow Hill 26/3/97
00-01 Leading Goalscorer: Graham Jones (9)

FACT FILE
Founded:1993
Nickname: Riversiders
Colours: Red /black/black
Change colours:Green/Green/White
Midweek Matchday: Wednesday

CLUB PERSONNEL
Patron: Dave Sexton
Chairman: Geoff Jones
Press Officer: Chris Parsons
Director of Football: Chris Parsons
Manager: Ian Ford
Coach: Mark Johnson
Physio: Sylvia Durham

SHRIVENHAM

Secretary: Matthew Hampson, 12 Grange Drive, Swindon, Wilts SN3 4LD
Tel: 01793 330983(H) 01793 423033 (B 07748 804593 M
E-mail: brad@currybeast.com

Match Secretary: Robb Forty, 40 Stallpitts, Shrivenham, Swindon, Wilts
Tel: 01793 783309(H) 01793 643744(B)
Ground: The Recreation Ground, Shrivenham SN6 8BJ
Tel: 01793 784453
Directions: 'Off Highworth Road, Shrivenham' Village is signposted off A420, six miles east of Swindon, four miles west of Faringdon
Floodlights: No

Previous League: North Berks League
Record Gate 800 v Aston Villa X1 21st May 2000
Honours North Berks League Champions 00-01

FACT FILE
Colours: Blue & white hoops/blue/white.
Change colours: All Red & black
Midweek fixtures: Tuesdays

CLUB PERSONNEL

Chairman: Ian Richardson 01793 782033
Press Officer: Dan Prescott 07989 603948
Program Editor: Dan Prescott 07989 603948
Manager: Dave Clauson
Coach: Dave Clauson
Physio: P Mansfield

WINTERBOURNE UNITED

Secretary: John Lloyd, 9 Stanford Close, Frampton Cotterell, Bristol. BS36 2DG
Tel: 01454 775841(H) 0117 9552048(B) E-mail john-lloyd@1-nil.co.uk

Ground Parkside Avenue, Winterbourne, Bristol BS36 1LX 01454 850059
Directions Leave Junction 1 of M32 turn left then left again at traffic lights, sign posted Yate. Keep on road for two miles into Winterbourne After Ridings High School turn right into Parkside Avenue, ground on right.
Floodlights No

Previous League: Gloucester County League

Honours: Gloucester County League Champions 00-01

00-01 Top Scorer Scott Cameron

FACT FILE
Nickname: The Bourne
Colours: White/red/red
Change colours: Red/white/white or red
Midweek fixtures: Tuesday or Thursday

CLUB PERSONNEL
Chairman: Robyn Maggs
Tel: 01454 887338
Press Officer: as Chairman
Program Editor: John Lloyd 01454 775841
Manager Stewart Jones
Coach: Richard Dunn
Physio: Ken Purnell

WITNEY ACADEMY

Secretary: Bob Haydon, 25 Wadards Meadow, Witney, Oxon OX8 6YL
T & F. 01993 771804 (H & B)
Match Sec.: Lisa Boyer - address & tel. as Secretary

Ground: Marriotts Stadium, Down Rd, Witney, Oxon OX8 5YZ (share with Witney FC)
Tel: 01993 702549 or 01993 705930

Directions: From the centre of Witney take A4095 via Tower Hill.
At roundabout turn left onto B4047 Burford Road.
Turn left at Car Auctions, into Downs Road.
Witney Town's ground Marriotts Stadium is on the right had side.
Capacity: 3,500 Cover: 2,000 Seats: 280 Floodlights: Yes

Season 1999/2000 New Club Members of Oxfordshire F.A.

FACT FILE
Colours: All yellow
Change colours: All red
Midweek fixtures: Wednesday
Program Editor: Gary Walters
01295 270903

CLUB PERSONNEL
President: Dick Lucas
Chairman: David Wesson 01993 779842
General Manager: Steve Warburton
01865 377338
Manager: Paul Lewis 01993 704311
Coach: Kenny Clarke
Physio: Bob Haydon (FA Diploma)

DIVISION ONE EAST CLUBS

ASTON CLINTON

Secretary: John Roberts, 7 Garland Way, Aston Clinton, Bucks. HP22 5QW
Tel: 01296 630160 (H/Fax) email: john7gar@aol.com

Ground: Aston Clinton Park, London Road, Aston Clinton HP22 5HL
Tel 01296 630888
Floodlights: No
Directions: On the A41 London road opposite the Duck in Pub, signposted "Aston Clinton Park".

PREVIOUS **League:** Chiltonian League to 99
RECORD **Attendance:** 74 v Penn & Tylers Green 00-01
00-01 **Leading Goalscorer:** Neil Roberts (13)

FACT FILE
Colours: Blue & white/blue/blue
Change colours: Red & white/white/red
Midweek fixtures: Tuesday

CLUB PERSONNEL
Chairman: John Roberts
01296 630160
Press Officer & Program Editor
Michael Dedman 01296 631093
Manager: guillermo Ganet
Coach: John Roberts

BINFIELD

Secretary: Rob Challis, 49 St Mary's Rd., Sindlesham, Wokingham, Berks SL6 4XF
Tel: 01189 782220 (H) 01628 644215 (B) 07818 457808 (M)
Match Secretary: Vernon Bradshaw, 21 Audley Way Ascot Berks SL5 8EE
Tel: 01344 886144 (H); 01344 356651 (B)
Ground: Stubbs Lane, Binfield berks. RG12 1DE 01344 860822
Directions From A329 Bracknell to Wokingham Road, turn by the Travel Lodge into St. Marks Road, through the village into Terrace Road South & North, then at T junction by All Saints' Church turn right & then left into Stubbs Hill.
Record Gate: 150 v Finchampstead 1998
Previous League: Chiltonian League
00-01 Leading Goalscorer: Lee Kitching (20)

FACT FILE
Colours: All red.
Change colours: White/blue/blue
Midweek fixtures: Wednesday
Nickname: Moles
Program Editor: Bob Ellis 01344 300556

CLUB PERSONNEL
Chairman: Bob Alloway
Press Officer: Bob Ellis
Manager: Bob Ellis
Coach: Glen Duggleby

BISLEY SPORTS

Secretary Michael Clement, 3 Lower Guilford Road, Knaphill, Woking, Surrey, GU21 2EE
Tel: 01483 475003 (H) 01483 736286 (B) E-mail: mclem0@aol.com

Ground: Burghfield Sports Grnd, Church Lane, Bisley GU24 9EB
Tel: 07796 094941

Directions: Exit M3 at Junction 3. Head southbound on A322 towards West End & Bisley. Go over two roundabouts then turn left opposite the Hen & Chicken P. House into Church Lane, ground is about 400 yards on left hand side.

Floodlights: No

FACT FILE
Colours:Shirts – Blue & black/black/black
Change colours: All red
Midweek fixtures: Tuesday

CLUB PERSONNEL
Chairman: Peter Lucas
email: sales@carfiles.co.uk Tel: 01276 671314
Press Officer: See Secretary
Program Editor: Bruce Henderson
Tel: 01483 472432
Manager: Andy Clement Tel: 01276 24374
Coaches: John Cook & Bruce Henderson

CHALFONT WASPS

Secretary: Bruce Keen, 25 Albion Crescent, Chalfont St Giles, Bucks. HP8 4ET
Tel: 01494 875129 (H) email: bruce.keen@tesco.net

Match Sec/Press Off. & Prog. Editor.: Bob Isherwood 01494 871445 (H)

Ground: Crossleys, Bowstridge Lane, Chalfont. HP8 4QN Tel: 01494 875050

Directions On entering Chalfont St. Giles Village from A413 (Aylesbury - Uxbridge Road), turn left into Bolostridge Lane immediately after the shops. After a quarter of a mile turn right into Crossleys by a small green. Ground is directly ahead through the gates

Record Attendance: 50 v Harrow Hill Rovers 00-01
Previous League: Chiltonian
00-01 Leading Goalscorer: Gavin Groves (21)

FACT FILE
Colours: Yellow & black striped/black/black.
Change colours: All Green
Midweek fixtures: Tuesday
Nickname: The Stingers

CLUB PERSONNEL
Chairman: Steven Waddington
Manager: John Franks
Coach: Denis Higgs

DRAYTON WANDERERS

Web Site: http://website.lineone.net/~drayton_wanderers

Secretary: Tom Ash, 28 Stonecroft Ave., Iver, Bucks. SL0 9QF Tel: 01753 654413

Ground: Cowley Hall, Cowley Road Uxbridge 01895 258269

Directions: 1 1/2 miles south of Uxbridge town centre, follow signs to Heathrow Airport, entrance to ground opposite the Grand Union Public House.

Record Attendance: 105 v Uxbridge 1995
Previous League: Chiltonian League
00-01 Leading Goalscorer: Ian Jones (24)

FACT FILE
Colours: Black & white stripes/black/black
Change cols: Red & yellow stripes/red/red
Midweek fixtures: Wednesday
Nickname: Wanderers
Program Editor:Mick Turtle 01895 446575

CLUB PERSONNEL
Chairman: Kevin Kelly Tel: 01895 824465
email: kevin.l.kelly@bt.com
Manager: Mick Turtle
Coach: Mick Stafford & Alan Carter

ENGLEFIELD GREEN ROVERS

Secretary Jon West, 74 Lindsay Road, New Haw, Surrey KT15 3BE
Email Address: www.goode @ terry.com

Ground: Coopershill Lane Englefield Green 01784 43566

Directions: Leave M25 at junction 13, A30 by passing Egham, at top of Egham Hill turn right at traffic lights. After passing Village Green on the left take 2nd turning right at the north east of green. Ground on the right after half a mile.

Record Gate: 100 v Eton Wick, 1999

2000-01 **P.o.Y. & Top Scorer** Barney Jones **Captain :** Richards Banks

FACT FILE
Colours: All green & white
Change cols.: Red & white halves/white/white
Midweek fixtures: Tuesday
Nickname: The Rovers

CLUB PERSONNEL
Chairman: Terence David Goode
Manager:Gerry Kelly
Coach: Walter Reynolds
Physio,Press Off & Prog Ed: Peter Casey

ETON WICK

Secretary : Barrie Shurville, 21 The Wheat Butts, Eton Wick, Berks., SL4 6JH.
& Press Officer& Programme Editor 01753 862969 (H) 07860262614 (B)

Ground: 01753 852749

Directions: From M4 junction 7 follow A4 to Maidenhead. At first roundabout (Sainsbury's) take B3026 towards Eton Wick. Ground is on the right after the first road narrowing. From Eton take B3026 and ground is on the left after the 2nd road narrowing.

Record Gate 500 v Andover, 1993 FA Vase

Previous League: Chiltonian League

FACT FILE
Nickname: The Wick
Cols:Amber/black/black Change:All white
Midweek fixtures: Tuesday

CLUB PERSONNEL
Chairman: Micky Foulkes 01753 733629
Man/Coach:Rob Curtis 01753 851877
Physio: Bobby White
2000-01 Leading goalscorer: Ricky Allen
Capt: Russell Quelch P.o.Y.: Barry Pitcher

FINCHAMPSTEAD

Secretary: Richard Whitchurch-Bennett, 22 Mayflower Drive, Yateley, Hants GU46 7RR
Tel: 077740 283210 0208 738807 (B) email: whitbennrm@aol.com
Match Sec.: Michael Husk, 16 Sadlers Lane Winnersh Berks RG41 5AJ
01189 785949 (H)
Ground: Finchampstead memorial Park, The Village, Finchampstead RG11 4JR
Tel: 01189 732890
Directions: A321 from Wokingham, then fork right onto B3016. At the Greyhound pub turn right onto the B3348. The ground is 200 yards on the right.
Record Gate 425 v Sandhurst, 1958/ 9
Previous League: Chiltonian
00-01 Leading Goalscorer: Danny Humphrey (26)

FACT FILE
Web Site: www.finchampsteadfc.co.uk
Nickname: Finch
Colours: Sky blue & white/black/black
Change colours: All red
Midweek fixtures: Wednesday

CLUB PERSONNEL
Chairman: Dick West 01344 750400
E-mail: richardwest@aquaspec.fsnet.co.uk
Press Officer: Secretary
Manager: Steven McClurg
Coach: Chris Mather

HOUNSLOW BOROUGH F.C.

Secretary: Stefano Poulos, 7 Fairways Isleworth Middlesex TW7 4NS
0208 560 9763 (H); 0208 5800591 (B); 0208 560 1295 (F)
07765305003 (M) E-mail hounslowborough.f.c@lineone,net
Program Editor: Lee-John Tansey 07889 342865 E-mail: l.tansey@talk21.com
Ground: White Lodge Syon Lane Isleworth 0208 560 8829
Directions: From M25 onto M4 at junction 3 then follow signs to Central London. At Gillett Corner turn left into Syon Lane. Ground 100 metres on the left.
From A40 turn at Target Roundabout and follow A312 Hayes by pass to A4 then follow signs to Central London until Gillett Corner, turn left and ground on the left.
Record Gate 200 v Rayners Lane, 3rd January 2000
Season 1999/2000: Member of the Chiltonian League

FACT FILE
Colours: Blue & white quarters/blue/blue
Change cols.: Red & black quarters/red/red
Midweek fixtures: Tuesday
Web site: www.sportworldwide.com

CLUB PERSONNEL
Chairman: James Stefanopoulos
0208 667 1269
Manager:Jamie Rooke (07760213481)
Coach:Antony Yersley Physio: Rehana Iqbal
2000-01 Capt:Tony Yearsley, P.o.Y.:W.ayne
Tisson Top Scorer: Junior Hickson 27

MARTIN BAKER SPORTS

Secretary: Michael Hayselden, 53 Leven Way Hayes Middlesex UB3 2SS
Press Off. & Prog. Editor 0208 5732887 (H); 0208 8406992 (B)

Ground: Martins Field Tilehouse Lane Denham 01895 833077
Club Email: mick.hayselden@bt.com
Directions: A412 from the A40 London / Oxford Road. (Do not confuse the A40 with the M40 which runs parallel). The entrance to the ground is approximately 150 yards on the right between the houses.
Season 1999/2000: Member of the Chiltonian League
2000-01 Leading Goalscorer: Ray Bennett 17 Captain & P.O.Y: Paul Curd

FACT FILE
Colours: White & blue/blue/blue
Change colours: Green or gold/green or black/green or black
Midweek fixtures: Tuesday
Nickname: Baker Boys

CLUB PERSONNEL
Chairman: John Curd
Manager: Ray Flegg 0956 980880
Coach & Physio: Ron Wise

MILTON UNITED

Secretary: Sue Walker, 122 High St, Sutton Courtney, Abingdon, OX14 4AX Tel: 01235 847158 (H)
Ground: The Sportsfield,Milton Hill, Potash Lane,Milton Heights,Oxon Tel:01235 832999
Directions: Exit A34 at Milton, 10 miles south of Oxford & 12 miles north of J 13, M4. A4130 towards Wantage, after 100m 1st left, then 1st right into Milton Hill. Entrance 200m on left.
Capacity: Seats: 50 Cover:Seats Floodlights: Yes Club Shop: No
Clubhouse: On ground, open matchdays
HONOURS Hellenic Lg 90-91 (Div 1 89-90 R-Up.94-95)), Nth Berks Lg(4) 85-86 87-89(R-up 84-85 86-87, Lg Cup(3) 84-86 88-89, Div 2 80-81, Charity Shield(4) 84-86 87-89 (R-up 82-83), Nth Berks War Mem. Cup(3) 83-85 87-88, Berks & Bucks Intermediate Cup 90-91
RECORD **Attendance:** 500 v Almondsbury Picksons, Hellenic Lg 90-91
Goalscorer: Nigel Mott

FACT FILE
Founded: 1926
Colours: Sky & claret/claret/sky & claret
Change colours: Orange/white/white
Midweek matchday: Tuesday
Programme Editor / Press Officer:
David Taylor (01235 816376)

CLUB PERSONNEL
Chairman: Ken Tull President: John Cannon
Match Secretary: Sid Tindall (01491 835630)
Manager: Paul Biddle
Coach: Nigel Mott Physio: John Belcher

PENN & TYLERS GREEN

Secretary: Malcolm James, Woodlands, Forty Green Rd, Forty Green, Beaconsfield HP9 1XS
Tel: 01494 677311 (H) 0207 777 0602 (B) email: malcolm.d.james@chase.com

Ground: Elm Road, Penn, Bucks HP10 8LF Tel: 01494 815346
Directions: Entrance to ground is off the main Hazlemere to Beaconsfield road. From Beaconsfield follow the road through Penn towards Hazlemere, pass the pond on green & ground entrance is on the right before going downhill.

Record Attendance: 125 v Chalfont Wasps 00-01
Previous League: Chiltonian
00-01 Leading Goalscorer: Paul Gardner (12)

FACT FILE
Colours: Blue & white striped/blue/white
Change colours: All yellow
Midweek fixtures: Tuesday
Program Editor: Neil Bellamy 01494 812492

CLUB PERSONNEL
Chairman & Match Secretary:
Robert Dalling 01494 671424
Press Officer: Neil Bellamy

Manager: Richard Mikurenda

PEPPARD

Secretary: Chris Boyles, 14 Redwood Avenue Woodley Reading Berks RG5 4DR
0118 9699488 (H); 0118 9872473 (B); 0118 9628130 (F)
E-mail: peppardfc@dboyles.freeserve.co.uk

Ground: Bishopswood Sports Ground Horsepond Road Gallowstree Common
0118 9722675

Directions: On the Cane End to Peppard road which runs between the A4074 (Reading to Woodcote & Oxford) and the B481 (Reading to Nettlebed) roads

Club website: www.geocities.com@peppardfc

FACT FILE
Colours: All red
Change colours: Light blue/navy/navy
Midweek fixtures: Tuesday
Website: www.geocities.com@peppard

CLUB PERSONNEL
Chairman: Sean Gillett 0118 9463425

2000-01
Captain : Kevin Watkins
P.o.Y.: Mike Elwood Top Scorer: Syran Clarke (14)

PRESTWOOD

Secretary: Paul Mullen, 16 Maybush Gardens, Prestwood, Bucks HP 16 9EA
Tel No: 01494 864048 EMail: paul.mullen @the-fa,org

Ground: Prestwood Sports Centre 01494 865946

Directions: From the Chequers Public House in the Centre of Prestwood, take the road signposted to Great Hampden. The ground is approximately half a mile on the left.

Season 1999/2000: Member of the Chiltonian League

FACT FILE
Colours: Claret / claret
Change colours: orange/ blck/orange
Midweek fixtures: Tuesday

CLUB PERSONNEL
Manager:Steven Simmons 01494 725217
Res. Manager: A Henney 01494 712544

QUARRY NOMADS

Secretary: Keith Dolton, 58 Pitts Road Headington Oxford OX3 8AZ 01865 450256 (H)
Match Sec.: Linda Dolton, 58 Pitts Road Headington Oxford OX3 8AZ 01865 450256 (H)

Ground: Margaret Road Headington 07860 408769

Directions: Exit M40 J 8, then A40 towards Oxford to Green Road r'about (McDonalds on left), straight over towards Headington.Take third left into Wharton Road, then at T junction turn left into Margaret Road. Ground on left.

Record Gate 267 v Witney Town, 1994
Previous League: Chiltonian
00-01 Leading Goalscorer: Paul Kimber (11)

FACT FILE
Web Site: www.qnfc.co.uk
Colours: Black & white/black/black
Change colours: All yellow or all red
Midweek fixtures: Tuesday
Prog. Editor: Andrew Molden 01865 433686
E-mail: ac.mold@hotmart.com

CLUB PERSONNEL
Chairman: Richard Lawrence 01865 873258
Press Officer: Paul Dolton 01865 768970
Manager: Darren Henderson & Andrew
Physio: Paul Dolton

R.S. BASINGSTOKE

Secretary: Jacqui Townley, 26 Millard Close, Basingstoke RG21 5TT
Tel: 01256 357992 (H) 07802 211156 (M) 01256 330902 (F)
email: j.townley@another.com

Ground: Whiteditch Playingfield, Sherborne Rd., Basingstoke RG21 5TP 01256 814618

Directions: From M3 junction 6 cross Black Dam r'about A33/A339. At Reading Road r'about take 2nd exit into Oakridge Rd, after approx. 3/4 mile you pass school, then turn left into Sherborne Road. Ground approx. 200 metres on left.

Record Gate: 120 v Hartley Witney, 1994
Previous League: Chiltonian
00-01 Leading Goalscorer: Dale Bristow (22)

FACT FILE
Colours: Red & black/red & black/black
Change colours: All blue
Midweek fixtures: Wednesday

CLUB PERSONNEL
Chairman & Press Officer:
Mike Davis 01256 468873
Manager: Albert Fox
Asst. Man.: Kevin Haystaff
Physio: Chris Townley

RAYNERS LANE

Secretary: Tony Pratt, 4 Stirling Close Cowley Uxbridge Middx. UB8 2BA
01895 233853 (H)

Ground: 151 Rayners Lane South Harrow 0208 8669659

Directions: From A40 Polish War Memorial (First junction after Northolt Aerodrome) turn left into A4180 (West End Road), approx. 500m turn right into Station Approach, at lights turn right into Victoria Road Sainsbury's on the right). At next roundabout continue straight on to lights at junction with Alexandra Avenue (Farmers House pub on left). Continue straight on over lights and take 2nd turning on left into Rayners Lane. Ground is approx. half a mile on left.

Record Gate 550 v Wealdstone, 1983 Season 2000/2001: Member of the Hellenic Lge

2000-01 Leading goalscorer: Tommy Metcalfe 26 Captain: Steve Bird P.o.Y.: Steve Cott

FACT FILE
Colours: Yellow/yellow/green
Change colours: Green/black/black
Midweek fixtures: Tuesday
Nickname: The Lane

CLUB PERSONNEL
Chairman: Richard Mitchell 0208 4226340
Press Off/Prog.Ed: Tom Lynn
0208 8684671
Manager/Coach: Richard Hedge
0208 8480843
Physio: Ronald Fairhead

BASS BREWERS KENT LEAGUE

FEEDER TO: DR MARTENS LEAGUE

President: D D Baker **Chairman:** P C Wager **Vice Chairman:** D Richmond
Hon. Secretary & Treasurer: A R Vinter, Bakery House, The Street, Chilham, Nr Canterbury, Kent CT4 8BX Tel: 01227 730457 Fax: 01227 738880

FINAL LEAGUE TABLE 2000-01

PREMIER DIVISION

	P	W	D	L	F	A	Pts	GD
Chatham	32	23	7	2	76	28	76	48
Herne Bay	32	23	5	4	93	43	74	50
VCD Athletic	32	21	4	7	74	32	67	42
Thamesmead	32	18	8	6	63	29	62	34
Ramsgate	32	16	10	7	83	36	55	47
Tunbridge Wells	32	13	11	8	52	41	50	11
Beckenham	32	13	9	10	48	58	48	-10
Whitstable	32	12	9	11	43	44	45	-1
Greenwich Boro	32	12	8	12	46	40	44	6
Lordswood	32	12	7	13	57	55	43	2
Erith Town	32	13	4	15	42	49	43	-7
Cray Wanderers	32	10	5	17	39	46	35	-7
Slade Green	32	9	3	20	33	75	30	-42
Hythe United	32	6	11	15	41	46	29	-5
Deal Town	32	7	8	17	41	60	29	-19
Faversham	32	6	5	21	33	68	23	-35
Canterbury	32	0	4	28	15	129	4	-114

Sheppey United - record expunged
** points adjustment*

DIVISION ONE

	P	W	D	L	F	A	Pts	GD
Thamesmead Res	38	24	10	4	76	31	82	45
Margate Reserves	38	22	7	9	96	51	73	45
Folkestone Inv Res	38	20	8	10	95	61	68	34
VCD Athletic Res	38	20	8	10	87	59	68	28
Herne Bay Res	38	20	7	11	89	54	67	35
6Sittingbourne Rs*	38	17	11	10	88	55	65	33
Dover Reserves	38	18	10	10	62	45	64	17
Ramsgate Res	38	17	9	12	91	63	60	28
Ashford Town Res	38	16	11	11	67	67	59	0
Chatham Res*	38	16	8	14	87	78	58	9
Cray Wndrs Res	38	17	4	17	63	71	55	-8
Hastings Reserves*	38	14	7	17	59	78	52	-19
Lordswood Res*	38	15	5	18	67	84	50	-17
Dartford Reserves*	38	11	13	14	64	66	48	-2
Erith Town Res	38	13	7	18	65	82	46	-17
Hythe United Res	38	11	5	22	52	95	38	-43
Beckenham Res	38	9	9	20	52	66	36	-14
Whitstable Res	38	8	6	24	52	91	30	-39
Greenwich B Res*	38	10	6	22	71	112	28	-41
Swanley Furness	38	3	7	28	49	123	16	-74

HIGHEST SCORERS

Premier Division:	Herne Bay	93 goals
Division One:	Margate	96 goals

GOALS OF THE MONTH

	Premier Division	*First Division*
August	Herne Bay	Beckenham
September	Beckenham	Chatham Town Lordswood
October	Erith Town	Herne Bay
November	Ramsgate	Lordswood
December	Ramsgate	Greenwich Sittingbourne Thamesmead
January	Deal Town	Sittingbourne
February	Herne Bay	Herne Bay Ramsgate
March	Chatham Town	Ramsgate
April	Cray Wndrs	Folkestone Inv Slade Green

GOLDEN BOOT AWARD

Premier Division:	Steve Jones (Ramsgate)	35
	Liam Hatch (Herne Bay)	24
	Scott Appleton (Herne Bay)	21
Division One:	Tom Plank (Margate)	22
	Keiron Turner (Herne Bay)	20
	Antony Weir (Thamesmead)	20

MANAGER OF THE MONTH

September	N Denly	Herne Bay
October	N Denly	Herne Bay
November	G Record	Sheppey
December	No Award	
January	S Clarke	Tunbridge Wells
February	N Denly	Herne Bay
March	S Hearn	Chatham Town
April	L Hussein	Greenwich

PREMIER DIVISION RESULTS CHART 2000-01

		1	2	3	4	5	6	7	8	9	10	11	12	13	14	15	16	17
1	Beckenham	X	1-0	1-1	1-0	3-2	0-1	1-1	2-1	2-2	1-1	3-2	1-2	4-1	2-2	2-5	0-4	0-1
2	Canterbury	1-2	X	0-4	2-6	0-3	0-1	0-3	1-1	0-4	1-1	0-7	0-11	1-7	0-5	0-3	0-2	2-2
3	Chatham	5-2	4-0	X	2-1	1-0	4-0	3-1	0-4	0-1	4-0	6-0	1-1	3-1	0-0	4-2	3-2	3-3
4	Cray Wanderers	4-0	5-0	0-4	X	0-1	1-0	1-	0-1	1-1	1-1	4-4	0-1	1-2	0-2	0-4	1-3	1-0
5	Deal Town	4-1	1-1	2-2	1-0	X	0-1	1-3	1-1	5-2	1-1	1-2	1-4	1-2	1-5	0-1	1-3	0-0
6	Erith Town	3-0	2-1	2-4	2-1	2-0	X	2-0	2-1	2-4	2-3	0-2	3-5	1-2	2-2	1-1	0-3	2-2
7	Faversham	1-3	1-0	0-1	1-2	4-2	1-3	X	1-1	2-5	2-1	0-4	1-6	3-0	0-2	0-3	1-4	0-1
8	Greenwich Boro	0-1	7-0	0-1	2-0	3-2	0-2	0-0	X	2-3	3-0	2-0	3-0	1-0	2-0	0-1	0-3	0-1
9	Herne Bay	5-0	4-1	2-2	3-0	1-2	2-0	3-0	3-2	X	1-0	5-2	2-2	6-0	2-0	2-1	3-2	4-2
10	Hythe United	2-2	6-0	0-2	1-2	1-1	0-2	1-1	8-0	2-3	X	1-1	2-1	1-2	0-0	0-0	1-2	1-2
11	Lordswood	0-2	2-1	1-1	0-2	2-3	2-0	3-1	1-1	0-3	2-1	X	0-2	3-0	4-0	2-2	1-4	0-1
12	Ramsgate	1-1	12-1	0-1	0-0	4-0	1-1	4-0	1-1	2-2	3-0	1-4	X	5-0	4-1	4-1	0-2	0-0
13	Slade Green	1-2	3-0	0-4	1-5	1-1	1-0	1-0	0-2	2-6	1-4	0-0	0-2	X	1-4	0-0	0-3	3-1
14	Thamesmead	1-1	4-0	1-2	1-0	5-1	1-0	1-1	3-0	3-1	2-0	4-0	1-1	2-0	X	4-1	2-0	2-1
15	Tunbridge Wells	0-2	3-0	0-1	1-0	2-1	1-0	4-2	1-1	1-3	0-1	2-2	1-1	2-1	1-1	X	1-1	4-2
16	VCD Athletic	2-3	10-1	1-2	0-0	2-1	1-2	3-1	2-2	3-0	1-0	2-1	3-1	1-0	1-0	2-2	X	2-1
17	Whitstable	2-2	2-1	0-1	4-0	0-0	3-1	2-1	0-2	0-5	0-0	0-3	2-1	6-0	0-2	1-1	1-0	X

FIRST DIVISION RESULTS CHART 2000-01

		1	2	3	4	5	6	7	8	9	10	11	12	13	14	15	16	17	18	19	20
1	Ashford	X	5-3	2-2	3-6	2-2	0-3	2-0	2-1	2-1	2-0	1-2	4-1	1-2	0-2	1-0	3-3	3-3	0-0	4-3	1-1
2	Beckenham	d	X	d	3-1	d	a	0-1	a	d	0-1	2-1	6-1	1-2	3-4	d	3-2	3-0	d	1-4	2-2
3	Chatham	2-2	5-2	X	0-0	3-0	1-3	0-1	2-3	0-0	2-1	4-4	2-0	1-3	3-1	0-2	2-5	2-2	2-5	4-1	0-1
4	Cray Wanderers	1-2	2-1	2-6	X	1-2	0-1	2-1	2-1	1-2	4-1	1-0	1-1	0-1	3-2	1-0	1-0	5-1	0-3	0-0	4-2
5	Dartford	1-0	0-2	1-2	2-1	X	0-0	1-1	7-1	4-2	1-4	1-1	0-1	3-0	2-2	3-4	3-3	5-0	d	3-2	0-1
6	Dover	2-1	2-0	1-2	3-0	2-1	X	1-2	0-0	2-2	3-0	1-0	4-1	3-3	1-1	1-3	1-3	5-0	0-1	1-1	3-0
7	Erith Town	0-1	h	2-3	2-1	3-0	1-1	X	1-3	6-3	4-1	2-3	5-1	5-1	1-2	3-3	2-6	3-3	1-3	3-7	1-1
8	Folkestone Inv	1-3	9-1	1-4	5-0	2-0	1-1	1-0	X	15-1	2-1	4-0	4-2	1-3	4-1	4-3	0-3	5-3	2-0	0-1	4-1
9	Greenwich Boro	2-3	1-2	5-2	0-5	2-2	4-1	4-1	1-1	X	6-1	0-5	0-2	5-1	2-4	1-3	1-8	3-3	1-3	1-2	2-3
10	Hastings	3-1	1-1	0-1	2-2	2-0	0-3	4-2	0-0	1-4	X	3-3	5-1	2-1	2-1	1-1	1-5	4-2	1-1	3-1	2-1
11	Herne Bay	1-2	2-0	2-1	1-2	3-1	1-1	5-1	0-0	3-0	1-0	X	5-0	3-1	2-0	3-0	2-2	6-0	2-3	1-2	8-1
12	Hythe United	0-2	3-2	2-8	2-1	4-4	0-2	6-1	2-2	3-1	1-4	1-3	X	1-0	1-1	2-4	2-3	2-1	0-1	0-2	0-1
13	Lordswood	1-1	2-1	5-2	3-2	2-3	2-1	1-1	2-4	0-3	1-0	1-3	3-0	X	2-1	0-4	1-1	10-1	0-1	1-3	5-5
14	Margate	4-0	2-0	5-4	5-1	5-1	3-0	0-1	1-1	8-2	6-0	4-0	2-1	4-0	X	2-2	2-1	6-1	0-0	2-0	1-0
15	Ramsgate	0-0	6-3	2-5	2-3	1-1	1-2	2-0	2-2	6-1	6-0	4-3	1-3	7-0	4-2	X	1-1	0-1	0-2	3-3	4-3
16	Sittingbourne	0-2	2-2	1-0	6-1	0-0	1-1	4-1	5-2	3-1	2-1	1-2	0-1	0-3	0-0	0-2	X	1-0	2-2	3-4	2-0
17	Swanley Furness	2-3	1-2	2-3	2-3	1-3	0-3	1-3	2-3	2-3	1-1	2-4	0-2	1-4	0-4	1-5	0-5	X	0-4	1-2	5-0
18	Thamesmead	2-1	1-0	5-1	2-0	4-2	3-1	3-0	3-1	1-0	1-2	1-1	4-2	5-0	1-2	2-0	1-1	d	X	0-0	3-1
19	VCD Athletic	8-3	3-2	3-3	0-1	1-1	5-0	0-0	0-3	2-1	3-2	3-1	6-0	1-0	3-1	0-1	3-0	2-2	2-4	X	2-0
20	Whitstable	2-2	0-4	1-3	1-2	1-4	1-2	2-3	1-2	1-3	1-2	1-2	0-0	3-0	2-3	3-2	1-3	1-2	3-1	3-2	X

Unplayed matches: d = 1 point each a = 3 points to away team h = 3 points to home team

PREVIOUS HONOURS - LEAGUE CHAMPIONSHIP - PREMIER DIVISION

	Winners	*Runners Up*		*Winners*	*Runners Up*
2000-01	Chatham Town	Herne Bay	1995-96	Furness	Dartford
1999-00	Deal Town	Thamesmead Town	1994-95	Sheppey United	Chatham Town
1998-99	Ramsgate	Deal Town	1993-94	Herne Bay	Furness
1997-98	Herne Bay	Folkestone Invicta	1992-93	Tonbridge	Herne Bay
1996-97	Herne Bay	Ramsgate	1991-92	Herne Bay	Faversham

PREVIOUS HONOURS - LEAGUE CHAMPIONSHIP - FIRST DIVISION

	Winners	*Runners Up*		*Winners*	*Runners Up*
2000-01	Thamesmead Town	Margate	1995-96	Hastings Town	Furness
1999-00	Thamesmead Town	Deal Town	1994-95	Thamesmead Town	Dover Athletic
1998-99	Deal Town	Dover Athletic	1993-94	Dover Athletic	Herne Bay
1997-98	Sittingbourne	Tonbridge	1992-93	Dover Athletic	Herne Bay
1996-97	Tonbridge	Dartford	1991-92	Folkestone Invicta	Dover Athletic

PREMIER DIVISION CUP 2000-01

FIRST ROUND

Faversham Town	v	Erith Town	0-3	Tunbridge Wells	v	Deal Town	0-2

SECOND ROUND

Cray Wanderers	v	Chatham Town	0-1	Greenwich Borough	v	Beckenham Town	3-0
Herne Bay	v	Deal Town	0-2	Hythe Town	v	Whitstable Town	0-1
Ramsgate	v	Erith Town	3-0	Sheppey United	v	Slade Green	1*0
Thamesmead Town	v	Canterbury	TT T/A	VCD Athletic	v	Lordswood	0-1

THIRD ROUND

Chatham Town	v	Deal Town	0-2	Greenwich Borough	v	Thamesmead Town	2-0
Ramsgate	v	Whitstable Town	2-1	Sheppey United	v	Lordswood	1*3

SEMI-FINALS (Two legs)

Deal Town	v	Ramsgate	0-2, 0-2	Greenwich Borough	v	Lordswood	5-2, 2-1

FINAL

Greenwich Borough	v	Ramsgate	0-4

DIVISION ONE CUP 2000-01

FIRST ROUND

Ashford Reserves	v	Margate Reserves	0-2	Chatham Reserves	v	Sittingbourne Res	2-1
Herne Bay Res	v	Swanley Furness	5*5, 16-0	VCD Reserves	v	Erith Reserves	4-1

SECOND ROUND

Dartford Reserves	v	Dover Res	Dov T/A 2-1	Greenwich Reserves	v	Lordswood Res	2-1
Hastings Reserves	v	VCD Reserves	0-1	Hythe Reserves	v	Folkestone Res	2-8
Margate Reserves	v	Cray Reserves	4-0	Ramsgate Reserves	v	Beckenham Res	4-2
Thamesmead Res	v	Herne Bay Reserves	2-	Whitstable Reserves	v	Chatham Reserves	5-2

THIRD ROUND

Dover Reserves	v	Whitstable Reserves	3-2	Folkestone Reserves	v	Ramsgate Reserves	1-0
Thamesmead Res	v	Margate Reserves	2-4	VCD Reserves	v	Greenwich R	G T/A 5-1

SEMI-FINALS (Two legs)

Greenwich Reserves	v	Folkestone Res	0-1, 1-3	Margate Reserves	v	Dover Res	2-1, 4-0

FINAL

Margate Reserves	v	Folkestone Reserves	1*1

Margate Reserves won 4-2 on penalties

PREVIOUS HONOURS - LEAGUE CHALLENGE CUPS

PREMIER DIVISION CUP

	Winners	*Runners Up*
2000-01	Ramsgate	Greenwich Borough
1999-00	VCD Athletic	Faversham Town
1998-99	Deal Town	VCD Athletic
1997-98	Greenwich Borough	Herne Bay
1996-97	Herne Bay	Sheppey United
1995-96	Furness	Sheppey United
1994-95	Ramsgate	Dartford
1993-94	Ramsgate	Deal Town
1992-93	Ramsgate	Beckenham Town
1991-92	Tonbridge AFC	Whitstable Town
1990-91	Faversham Town	Alma Swanley
1989-90	Tonbridge AFC	Whitstable Town

FIRST DIVISION CUP

	Winners	*Runners Up*
2000-01	Margate	Folkestone Invicta
1999-00	Thamesmead Town	Deal Town
1998-99	Dover Athletic	Deal Town
1997-98	Thamesmead Town	Herne Bay
1996-97	Hastings Town	Deal Town
1995-96	Folkestone Invicta	Dover Athletic
1994-95	Thamesmead Town	Chatham Town
1993-94	Dover Athletic	Tonbridge AFC
1992-93	Tonbridge AFC	Canterbury City
1991-92	Folkestone Invicta	Whitstable Town
1990-91	Fisher Athletic	Beckenham Town
1989-90	Canterbury City	Dover Athletic

BECKENHAM TOWN

Secretary: Peter Palmer,36 Inglewood,Pixton Way, Selsdon, Surrey CR0 9LP
Tel: 020 86513363 Mobile 0374 728758

Ground: Eden Park Avenue, Beckenham, Kent Tel: 0181 650 1066

Directions: M25, A21 to Bromley then follow signs to Beckenham. Ground 1 mile west of town off A214, 2 mins walk from Eden Park (BR) station - trains from London Bridge. Bus 264
Capacity: 4,000 Seats: 120 Cover: 120 Floodlights: Yes
Clubhouse: All day opening at weekends. Hot & cold food, teas, etc. Bar & dance area. Pool & fruit machines Club Shop: Yes

HONOURS London Spartan Lg Cup R-up 77-78 78-79, Kent Snr Tphy R-up 81-82 93-94, Kent Lg Cup R-up 84-85 92-93 (Div 2 Cup R-up 90-91)

PREVIOUS **Leagues:** S. E. London Amtr 71-73; Metropolitan 73-75; London Spartan 75-82
Ground: Stanhope Grove, Beckenham (60 yrs)

RECORD **Gate:** 720 v Berkhamstead F.A.Cup 94-95
Scorer: Ricky Bennett **Appearances:** Lee Fabian

FACT FILE
Reformed: 1971
Nickname: Reds
Colours:All Red
Change Colours:Yellow/blue/blue
Midweek matchday: Tuesday
Programme: 8 pages, 50p
Editor:Secretary

CLUB PERSONNEL
Chairman: John Weatherhead
Vice Chairman: B Hollaway
Manager: Kevin Sugrue
Asst Manager: J Moore

CANTERBURY CITY

Secretary: Peter Sargeant. 21 Castle Road, Allington, Maidstone, Kent ME16 0PR
Tel Nos: 01622 683789 (H) 07702 425719 (M) 01622 662349 (Fax)
Ground: Salters Lane, Faversham, Kent (01795 591667).
Clubhouse: Lounge bar open on matchdays. Snack bar, burgers, hot-dogs, tea, coffee, etc
HONOURS Kent Lg Div 2 Cup 49-50 89-90, Div 1 Cup 49-50; Kent Sen. Cup 53-54; Kent Sen. Trophy 79-80; Kent I'mediate Cup 73-74; Kent Messenger Trophy 74-75; Frank Norris Mem. Shield 88-89 89-90; Kent Lge Div 2 Champ Res 90-91
PREVIOUS **Leagues:** Kent 47-59; Metropolitan 59-60; Southern 60-94
Name: Canterbury Waverley **Grounds:** Wincheap Grove, Bretts Corner 47-58 Kingsmead Stadium 58-99
BEST SEASONFA Cup: 1st Rd 64-65, 0-6 v Torquay; 68-69, 0-1 v Swindon
CLUB RECORDS Attendance: 3,542 v Chelsea, Friendly **Win:** 10-0 v Deal Town (H), Southern Lge 30/1/65 **Defeat:** 0-10 v Greenwich B(H) Kent Lg. 14.8.99. **Goalscorer:** Wilf Heathcote 113 (48-51) **Appearances:** John Carragher 627 (60-70) **Fee Paid:** £2,000 for Graham Knight (Maidstone United) **Fee Received:** £2,000 for Dave Wiltshire (Gillingham)
Players progressing: R Gawler (Southend 49), A Hughes (Grimsby 54), A Nugent (Darlington 56), J Richardson (Southport 56), T Horsfall (Cambridge Utd), J Murray (Wolves), K Hill, M Weatherley (Gillingham), T Norton (Brighton), P Hilton (Brighton 73), D Wiltshire (Gillingham 74), G Pugh (Torquay 84)

FACT FILE
Founded: 1947
Nickname: The City
Sponsors: T.B.A.
Colours: Green & white/white/green & white
Change: All Red
Midweek matchday: Tuesday
Reserve's League: Kent Lge Div 1
Programme: 32 pages, 50p
Editor: Steve Hickmott Tel: 01322 341478

CLUB PERSONNEL
Chairman: Phil Harris
Vice Chairman: TBA
President: V H Heslop
Comm Manager: T.B.A.
Managers: Meirion George/Simon Tutt
Physio: T.B.A.

CRAY WANDERERS

Secretary: Dave Brown,16 Westhurst road, Chislehurst, Kent BR7 6HT (020 8467 2128)
Ground: Bromley F.C. Hayes Lane, Bromley, Kent BR2 9EF (0181 460 5291 or 0181 313 3992)

Directions: One mile from Bromley South (BR). Buses 316, 146 and 119 passground. Junction 4 off M25, then A21 towards London
Capacity: 5,000 Cover: 2,500 Seats: 1,300 Floodlights: Yes

Clubhouse: Open pub hours (freehouse). Hot & cold food available Club Shop: Yes

HONOURS London Lg(2) 56-58 (Lg Cup 54-55), Aetolian Lg 62-63 (Lg Cup 63-64), GtrLondon Lg 65-66 (Lg Cup(2) 64-66), Metropolitan Lg Cup 70-71 (Amtr Cup(2) 66-68), London Spartan Lg(2) 76-78, Kent Lg 01-02 80-81 (R-up 79-80 90-91, Lg Cup 83-84), Kent Snr Tphy 92-93, Kent Amtr Cup(4) 30-31 62-65

PREVIOUS **Leagues:** Kent 1894-1903 6-7 9-14 34-38; W Kent 03-06 07-09; London 20-34 51-59; Kent Amtr 38-39 46-51; S London All 43-46; Aetolian 59-64; GtrLondon 64-66; Metropolitan 66-71; London Metropolitan 71-75; London Spartan 75-78
Grounds: Star Lane; Tothills; Twysden; Fordcroft; Grassmeade, St Mary Cray

CLUB RECORDS Gate: 1,523 v Stamford, F.A. Vase QF 79-80
Goalscorer: Ken Collishaw, 272 **Appearances:** John Dorey c500, 61-72
Win: 15-0 v Sevenoaks, 1894-95 **Defeat:** 1-11 v Bromley, 20-21

FACT FILE
Founded: 1860 Nickname: Wands
Sponsors: Hillman Grant
Colours: Amber & black
Change Colours: White/black/black
Midweek matchday: Wednesday
Programme: 32 pages, 50p
Editor/Press Officer: Greg Mann
Tel: 0181 318 9604(H) 0171 500 4496B)
Websites: http://hometown.aq.com\cray or wanderersfc/club.html

2000-01
Captain: Adam Heaslewood P.o.Y: Joe Vines
Top Scorer: Danny Sweeting 8

CLUB PERSONNEL
Chairman: Gary Hillman
President: Bill Faulkner
Team Manager: Ian jenkins
Asst.Manager: John Allwright
Reserve Team Manager: Sam Wright

Hythe United (now Hythe Town)

Herne Bay FC. Bass Brewers Kent Football Premier League Runners Up 2000-01. Back Row (l-r): Harry Roberts (coach), Nick Denly (Manager), Danny Maxted, Scott Appleton, Martin Collins, Daryl Broadmore, Liam Hatch, Neil Brown, Gary Pullen, Gerry Allan (Asst Manager), Joe Hodgkinson (Physio). Front Row: Justin Smale, Shane Suter, Andy Thompson, Barry Jeffreys, Lee Jones, Robbie Summers, Jon Warden

Tunbridge Wells FC. Back Row: Julian Nye, Steve Clark (Player/Manager), Wayne Balmer, Luke Hills, Gary Valli, Andy Garrett, Andy Boyle, Steve Gibbons. Front Row: Darren Walmsley, Pete McCleod, Jason Bourne, Ryan Nicklin, Grant Styles, Robin Jenner

DEAL TOWN

Secretary: Colin Adams,156 Mill Hill, Deal, Kent CT149JA (01304 372784)

Ground: Charles Sports Ground, St Leonards Road, Deal, Kent Tel: 01304 375623
Directions: A258 through Walmer, left into Cornwall Road, continue intoHamilton Road, veer left into Mill Rd, follow round to right into Manor Road, right into St Leonards Road, ground 100 yards on right. 1 mile from both Walmerand Deal BR stations. Local buses stop near ground
Capacity: 2500 Seats: 180 Cover: 180 Floodlights: Yes

Clubhouse: Matchdays & functions. Bar. Tea bar with hot & cold food Club Shop: No
HONOURS F.A.Vase Winners 99-00, Kent Lg 53-54,99-00 (R-up 88-89,98-99) Lg Cup 57-58, 81-82 , 98-99 (R-up 94-95), Kent Snr Tphy 94-95 , 99-00 R-up 82-83 90-91, Gtr London Lg Cup 67-68, Aetolian Lg R-up 59-60

PREVIOUS **Leagues:** Kent 09-59; Aetolian 59-63; Southern 63-66; Gtr London 66-71

RECORDS **Gate:**(Competitive) 2,495 v Newcastle Town F.A.Vase, S-Final 2nd Leg. 26.3.00
Scorer: Joe Brayne 175
Appearances: Alan Barrow 544 (recent times)

Player progressing: Danny Wallace (Southampton)

FACT FILE
Founded: 1908 Nickname: Town
Sponsors: Adamson Motors
Colours: Black & white hoops/white/white
Change: Yellow & Blue halves/blue/blue
Midweek matchday: Tuesday
Reserves' Lge: Bass Brewers Kent Div 1
Programme: 36 pages,70p
Editor: Colin Adams (01304 372784)

2000-01
Captain: Kevin Marsden P.o.Y.: Jason Hughes
Top Scorer: Darren Waring 16

CLUB PERSONNEL
Chairman: Graham Johns
Vice-Chairman: David Saunders
Fixture Sec: Colin Adams (01304 372784)

ERITH TOWN

Secretary: Jim Davie, 6 Dashwood Close, Broomfield Road, Bexleyheath, Kent. DA6 7NU
Tel: 020 8306 7068

Ground: Erith Sports Stadium, Avenue Road, Erith, Kent DA8 3AJ (01322 350 271)
Directions: Off the A206 at Erith, into Victoria Road, then left at T junction into Avenue Road. First right along driveway which leads to leisure car park, stadium on left.600 yards from Erith BR.
Capacity: 1,450 Seats: 1,006 Cover: 60Floodlights: Yes (156 lux)
Clubhouse: Use Leisure Facilities Shop: No

PREVIOUS **Leagues:** London Metropolitan Sunday 1959-91, London-Spartan 1991-96
Names: Woolwich Town 1959-89 and 1990-97 Woolwich Heathway 1989-90

CLUB RECORDS **Appearances:** Eric Nwaokobia 172 (9)
Victory: 7-2 v Canterbury City, Kent Sen. Trophy 20.12.00 **Defeat:** 0-8 v Deal
Goalscorer: Lee Putnam 29 **Goals in Season:** Dean Bowey 18 00-01
Attendance: 136 v Lewes F.A.Cup 1Q 99-00

HONOURS: Met Sunday Lge: Senior Section 1966, 1971, 1975.
London Spartan Lge: Intermediate Cup R-up 1994 & 1995. Div 1 R-up: 1995.
London F.A. Intermediate Cup R-up 1995. London F.A. Senior Cup R-up 2000

FACT FILE
Founded: 1959 Nickname: The Dockers
Colours: White/navy blue/red
Change Colours: Yellow/black/black
Midweek matchday: Monday
Reserve League: Kent League
Programme: 40-52 pages £1.00 (Ian Birrell)
2000-01 Captain: Alan Hanlon
Top Scorer: Dean Bowey 18
P.o.Y.: James Blyther

CLUB PERSONNEL
Chairman: Albert Putnam. V. Chair: Phil Legg
President: Cyril Rebak
Manager: John Adams Coach: Jim Hardy
General Manager: Ian Birrell
Press Secretary: David Salmon

FAVERSHAM TOWN

Secretary: Ken Black, 181 Langley Way, West Wickham, Kent BR4 0DN
Tel Nos: 020 8325 0046 (H) 07932 770485 (M)
Ground: New Stadium, Salters Lane, Faversham, Kent (01795 532738)

Directions: On A2 (Canterbury road) just west of town
Capacity: 2,000 Seats: 350 Cover: 1,500 Floodlights: Yes
Clubhouse: Open matchdays (Sat/Sun/Tues) Wed/Thurs. Snacks sold

HONOURS Kent Lg 69-70 70-71 77-78 89-90, R-up 87-88, Lg Cup 70-71 90-91, R-up 82-83,
Kent Snr Tphy 76-77 77-78 (R-up 87-88 88-89),
Kent Amtr Cup 56-57 58-59 71-72 72-73 73-74

PREVIOUS **Leagues:** Aetolian 59-64; Metropolitan 64-71; Athenian 71-76
Grounds: Ashford Rd 1901-46; Gordon Square 46-58

RECORD **Gate:** 1,400 v Sheppey Utd, 1949
Scorer: Tony Rudd 43 **Appearances:** Bob Mason
Win: 8-0 v Greenwich B., Aug'89 **Defeat:** 0-9 v Sittingbourne, Jan '82

FACT FILE
Founded: 1901
Nickname: Town
Colours: White/blue/blue
Change Colours: All Blue
Midweek matchday: Wednesday
Reserves' League: Kent Lg Div 2
Programme: 16 pages, 40p
Editor: Andy Maxted

CLUB PERSONNEL
Chairman: John Glover
President: Cris Aisani
Commercial Mgr: Terry Whitehead
Manager: John Glover
Coach: Bob Mason

Top: Thamesmead's Dave King gathers safely against Rushall Olympic in the FA Carlsberg Vase. Photo: Steve Ayre

Centre: Tunbridge Wells on the attack at Faversham. Photo: Ken Botten

Bottom: Chatham Town's Cliff Hearn out-jumps Slade Green's Rob White but heads over the bar. Photo: Alan Coomes

GREENWICH BOROUGH

Secretary: Sheila Crowhurst (Letters c/o club)
Tel Nos: 0207 3543509 07970 986537M
Ground: Harrow Meadow, Eltham Green Rd, Eltham, London SE9 Tel: 0208 8595788

Directions: South Circular (A205) to McDonalds, grd opposite.
1 mile from both Eltham and Kidbrooke BR stations
Capacity: 2,500 Seats: 5o Cover: 50Floodlights: Yes
Clubhouse: Yes

HONOURS London Spartan Lg 79-80 (Lg Cup 82-83), Kent Lg 86-87 87-88 (Lg Cup 84-85 86-87), Kent Snr Tphy 84-85, FA Vase 5th Rd 89-90

PREVIOUS **Leagues:** South London Alliance; Kent Amateur; London Spartan 77-84
Ground: Erith & Belvedere F.C. 1992-93
Name: London Borough of Greenwich

RECORD **Gate:** 2,000 v Charlton, floodlight opening, 1978
Defeat : 0-8 v Faversham Town, August 1989

FACT FILE
Founded: 1928
Nickname: Boro
Colours: All Red
Change Colours: All white
Midweek matchday: Tuesday
Programme: 16 pages, 50p
Editor: Keith Harmer
Tel: 07930 618911 (M)

CLUB PERSONNEL
Chairman: T. Hassan
Manager: L. Hussein
Asst Manager: K. Crowhurst

2000-01
Leading goalscorer: Tansel Tezel 17
Captain: J. Whitehouse
P.O.Y:: 1st Team M. Tezel
Reserves: J. Crowhurst Yth. Team: P. Hallett

HERNE BAY

Secretary: Simon Harris 72 Station Road, Herne Bay, Kent CT6 5QH
Email: roland@hernebay,co.uk

Ground: Winch's Field, Stanley Gardens, Herne Bay, Kent Tel: 01227 374156

Directions: Leave new Thanet Way at Herne Bay/Canterbury exit. Follow signs toHerne Bay via Canterbury Road. After railway bridge (1/2 mile), take first left into SpencerRoad, then first left into Stanley Gardens, Ground on left **Clubhouse:** Open matchdays **Club Shop:** Yes
Capacity: 4,000 Seats: 200 Cover: 1,500 Floodlights: Yes

HONOURS Kent Lg 91-92 94-95 96-97 97-98, (R-up 92-93 00-01), Div 2 62-63 63-64, R-up92-93(res) 94-95(res), Lg Cup 96-97, R-up 78-79 97-98, Div 2 Cup 53-54; Kent Snr Tphy 78-79, 96-97; Kent Amtr Cup 57-58 (R-up 58-59 63-64 68-69 72-73); Aetolian LgDiv 2 62-63 63-64 (Lg Cup R-up 62-63), Div 2 Cup 62-63 63-64; Athenian Lg Div 2 70-71 (Lg Cup 66-67); Kent Amtr Lg Cup 53-54 54-55; Thames & Medway Comb. CupR-up 61-62; FA Cup 4th Qual. Rd 70-71 86-87.

PREVIOUS **Leagues:** East Kent, Faversham & Dist, Canterbury & Dist, Kent Amateur, Kent 53-59, Aetolian 59-64, Athenian 64-74 **Ground:** Memorial Park 1886-1953

RECORDS **Attendance:** 2,303 v Margate, FA Cup 4th Qual. Rd 70-71
Win: 15-1; v Canterbury Gas & Water, Kent Amateur Lge 1952
Defeat: 0-11 v RAF Manston, Kent Amateur Lge 1935
Fee received: £3,000 for Mark Munday (Gravesend) 1994

FACT FILE
Founded: 1886Nickname: The Bay
Colours: Blue & white halves
Change Colours: Red & black halves
Midweek matchday: Tuesday
Reserves' League: Kent Lge Div One
Programme: 36 pages, 70p
Editor/Press Off.: Doug Smith (01227742182)
Website: www.hernebayfc.co.uk
2000-01 Captain: Barry Jeffreys
P.o.Y.: Liam Hatch
Top Scorer: Scott Appleton 26

CLUB PERSONNEL
Chairman: J Bathurst
Vice Chairman: W Dordoy
President: J Hodkinson
Manager: Nick Denly
Asst. Manager:Gerry Allen
Physio: J.Hodkinson

HYTHE TOWN (2001)

Secretary: Martin R Giles, 21 Wych Elm Way, Hythe, Kent. CT21 6QE
Tel: 01303 265962 (H) 01303 267619 (B)
Email Address: infohythetownfc.co.uk

Ground: Reachfields Stadium, Fort Rd, Hythe, Kent. Tel: 01303 264932 or 238256

Directions: On A259 west out of Hythe, turn left after light railway lights (Fort Road), entrance at end
Capacity: 3,000 Seats: 400 Cover: 2,400 Floodlights: Yes

Clubhouse: Bar open weekends/matchdays & training nights
Club Shop: No

HONOURS None as Hythe United or Hythe Town (2001)

PREVIOUS Leagues: Kent County and Southern
RECORD Attendance: 2,147 v Yeading 1990 F.A.Vase Semi-Final
Names: Hythe Town and Hythe Town 1988 Ltd

FACT FILE
Founded: 1992
Sponsor: Autorite Finishers Ltd
Colours: All Red
Change Colours: All blue
Midweek Matchday: Tuesday
Youth League :M.U.S.H. Kent Youth
Programme: 50p
Website: www.huthetownfc.co.uk
Editor: Martin Whybrow

2000-01
Captain:Gary Miller
P.o.Y. &Top Scorer: Steve Ridley

CLUB PERSONNEL
Chairman: Paul Markland
President: Rt Hon Michael Howard QC
Press Officer: Richard Giles
Manager: David Linstrem
Physio: Dave Garlinge

Cray Wanderers

Deal Town

VCD Athletic

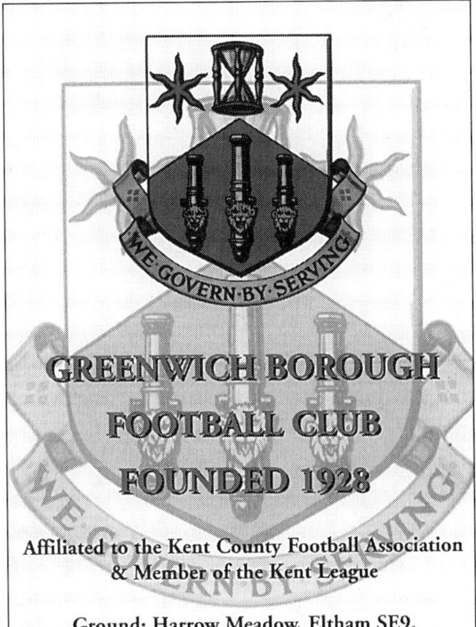

Greenwich Borough

LORDSWOOD

Secretary: Steve Lewis, Sunnybrook, Gorsewood Road, Hartley, Longfield, Kent DA3 7DF Tel: 01474 708233 (H) 01233 822300 (B) 07775 541573 (M) Email: no.9@lordswoodfc.co.uk

Ground: Lordswood Sports & Social Club Tel: 01634 669138
North Dane Way, Walderslade, Chatham, Kent ME5 9XX

Directions:

Capacity: 600 Seats: 125 Cover: No Floodlights: Yes

Clubhouse: Yes **Club Shop:** No

HONOURS None

PREVIOUS **Leagues:** Kent County Lge

RECORD **Attendance:** 386

FACT FILE
Founded: 1968
Nickname: Lords
Colours: Orange/black/black
Change Colours: All white
Midweek Matchday: Tuesday/Thursday
Reserve or Youth League: Both
Programme: Yes Editor: T.B.A.
Website: www.lordswoodfc.co.uk

CLUB PERSONNEL
Chairman: J. O'Halloran
Vice Chairman: B. Zillwood
Press Officer: T.B.A.
Manager: W.Godden

2000-01
Captain: Andy Battersby
P.o.Y.:Paul Piggott
Top Scorer: Stuart Johnson 20

MAIDSTONE UNITED

Secretary: Richard Yorke, 27 Churchill Way, Faversham, Kent ME13 7QX
Tel: 01795 534328

Ground: Ground share with Sittingbourne FC - Central Park Stadium, Eurolink Industrial Park, Church Road, Sittingbourne ME10 3SB Tel: 01795 435077

Directions: Through Sittingbourne on main A2, club signposted clearly and regularly from both east and west. 1 mile from Sittingbourne BR station.
Capacity: 8,000 Cover: 3,300 Seats: 2,000 Floodlights: 420 lux

FACT FILE
Founded: 1966
Reformed 1992
Colours: Gold/black/gold
Change Colours: All white
Midweek matchday: Tuesday
Programme: Yes
Editor: Steve Hemsley tel: 01892 514006

CLUB PERSONNEL
Chairman: Paul Bowden-Brown

RAMSGATE

Secretary/Martin Able, 164 Heath Lane, Dartford, Kent. DA1 2TW Tel No: 07958 993959 (H&M)
Ground: Southwood Stadium, Prices Avenue, Ramsgate, Kent Tel: 01843 591662

Directions: From London on A229, A253 into Ramsgate - left into Netherhill atr'bout, right into Ashburnham Rd, right into Southwood Rd. 15 mins walk from Ramsgate BR station; walk thru Warre Recreation Ground, along St Lawrence HighStr., left at `White Horse', follow Southwood Rd and turn right into PricesAvenue

Capacity: 5,000 Seats: 400 Cover: 600 Floodlights: Yes

Clubhouse: Open matchdays & private functions. Two bars, two pool tables,darts. Hot & cold food on matchdays Club Shop: No

HONOURS Kent Lg 49-50 55-56 56-57 (Lg Cup 48-49 92-93 93-94 94-95) Kent I'mediate Cup 54-55, Kent Snr Cup 63-64, Thames & Medway Cup 60-61, KentSnr Shield 60-61, Kent Floodlit Tphy 69-70, Kent Snr Tphy(2) 87-89

PREVIOUS **Leagues:** Southern 59-75
Name: Ramsgate Athletic

RECORDS **Gate:** 5,200 v Margate, 56-57
Scorer: Mick Williamson
Win: 9-1 v Crockenhill, Kent League Cup 22/1/94

FACT FILE
Founded: 1946
Nickname: Rams
Sponsors: Hoverspeed
Colours: Red & white stripes/red/red
Change Colours: Yellow & navy stripes/navy/navy
Midweek matchday: Tuesday
Reserves' League: Kent Lge Div. Two
Programme: 28 pages
Editor: Steve Redford (01843 596138)

CLUB PERSONNEL
Chairman: Richard Lawson
Vice Chairman: C Payne
President: Tom Pendry
Commercial Manager: Martin Power
Tel: 01843 597703
Manager/Coach: Lennie Lee
Asst Manager: Dave Bostock
Physio: John Burroughs

SLADE GREEN

Secretary: Bruce Smith, 15 Gumping Rd, Orpington, Kent BR5 1RX Tel: 01689 858782

Ground: The Small Glen, Moat Lane, Slade Green, Erith, Kent Tel: 01322 351077

Directions: Off A206 between Erith & Dartford.
400 yards from Slade Green BR station. Buses 89 & B13

Capacity: 3,000 Seats: 150 Cover: 400 Floodlights: Yes
Clubhouse: Yes; Hall, Directors Lounge & Canteen Club Shop: No

HONOURS Kent Snr Tphy 91-92 (R-up 80-81); Kent Lg Cup 82-83; Kent Amtr Lg 52-53 53-54 60-61 (Lg Cup 60-61); Kent Intermediate Cup 61-62; Kent Benevolent Cup46-47; West Kent 60-61 65-66; Dartford Lg R-up 48-49 (Lg Cup 47-48 (R-up 46-47)); Erith Hospitals Cup 46-47 48-49; Gtr London Lg R-up 68-69; Plumstead Challenge Cup 48-49

PREVIOUS Leagues: Dartford 46-52; Kent Amateur 52-62; Greater London 62-70
Name: Slade Green Athletic 46-86

RECORDS **Attendance:** 3,000 v Millwall, friendly 25/7/92
Goalscorer: Colin Dwyer **Appearances:** Colin Dwyer
Win: 14-0 v Island Social, Kent Amtr Lge 1953 **Defeat:** 1-9 v Whitstable Greater London 64-65

Players progressing : Roy Dwight (Nottm Forest), Alan Clark (Charlton) , Fred Lucas (Charlton)Tommy Tute (Millwall Jan. 1999)

FACT FILE
Founded: 1946
Nickname: The Green
Sponsor: T.B.A.
Colours: All white
Change Colours: Yellow /black/yellow
Midweek matchday: Tuesday
Reserve League:
Programme: 44 pages, incl. with admission
Editor: Robert Smith (01322 287982)

CLUB PERSONNEL
Chairman: Brian Smith
President: William Dudley
Press Officer: Robert Smith (01322 287982)
Manager: Srteve Waite
Coach: Micky Orme
Physio: Alan Martin

THAMESMEAD TOWN

Secretary: Albert Panting,97 Sydney Road, Bexleyheath,Kent DA6 8HQ (0208303 1350 (H)
Ground: Bayliss Avenue, Thamesmead, London SE28 8NJ Tel: 0181 311 4211

Directions: By road: From Dartford tunnel A2 to London, exit Danson Interchange and follow signs for Thamesmead and Abbey Wood. From Blackheath tunnel exit on south side and follow signs to Woolwich, to Plumstead and then to Thamesmead

From Abbey Wood (BR) north east along Harrow Manor Way, into Crossway at 3rd r'bout, Bayliss Av. is 3rd right (Bexley bus 272 stops in Crossway near Bayliss Av.

Capacity: 400 Seats: 125 Cover: 125 Floodlights: Yes Club Shop: No

Clubhouse: Mon-Fri 6-11pm, Sat 12-11pm, Sun 12-3 & 7-10.30pm. Double bar,lounge, dance-floor, children's games room, video machines, hot & cold food.New members Bar

HONOURS Spartan Lg Div 3 79-80 (Lg Cup 84-85 86-87; I'mediate champs 85-86);Kent I'mediate Cup 83-84 94-95; 4 promotions & 9 trophies (inc London & Kent FA Cups) in progress thru Spartan I'mediate Divs, 1980-87; Kent Lge Div 2 94-95, Div 2 Cup 94-95

PREVIOUS **Leagues:** London Spartan 80-91
Ground: Meridian Sports Ground, Charlton

RECORDS **Attendance:** 400 v Wimbledon, ground opening 1988
Appearances: Delroy D'Oyley **Win** : 9-0 v Kent Police, Kent League 19/4/94

FACT FILE
Founded: 1970
Nickname: The Mead
Sponsors: Courage Brewery
Colours: Green& White/Green/Green
Change Colours: All blue
Midweek matchday: Tuesday
Reserves League: Winstonlead Kent D2
Programmes: Yes. 50p
Editor: Secretary

CLUB PERSONNEL
Chairman: Brian Morris
Vice Chairman: John Kelly
President: Albert Panting
Press Officer: Matthew Panting
Manager: Terry Hill
Coach: Paul Blades
Physio: Allen Martin

TUNBRIDGE WELLS

Secretary: Mrs J.Rogers, Tappington Farm Cottage, Three oaks Lane, Wadhurst, East Sussex TN5 6PU Email Address: ronrogers@skynew.net
Ground: Culverden Stadium, Culverden Down, Tunbridge Wells, Kent TN4 Tel: 01892 520517

Directions: Leaving town on main Tonbridge rd (A26), turn left into Culverden Down ground half mile. 1 mile from Tunbridge Wells Central(BR).
Served by any Tunbridge Wells-Tonbridge bus - to St Johns

Capacity: 3,750 Seats: 250 Cover: 1,000 Floodlights: Yes
Clubhouse: Open matchdays and as required Club Shop: No

HONOURS Kent Lg 84-85 (R-up 68-69, Lg Cup 74-75 77-78 85-86 87-88)
Kent SnrTphy R-up 85-86 91-92

PREVIOUS **Names:** None. predecessors: T . Wells FC 1886-1910 47-50 T. Wells Rgrs 03-09 63-67; T. Wells Utd 51-62
Grounds: Down Lane 1906; Combley Park 06-10; Swiss Cottage 06-14;Down Farm 19-39; St Johns 47-50; Eridge Road 50-67

RECORDS **Attendance:** 967 v Maidstone United, FA Cup 1969
Goalscorer: John Wingate 151 **Appearances:** Tony Atkins 410
Win: 10-0 v Deal (H), May'86
Defeat: 1-11 v Deal Town (H), 20/2/93

FACT FILE
Founded: 1886 Reformed: 1967
Nickname: Wells
Colours: Red/White/Red
Change Colours: Yellow/navy/navy
Midweek Matchday: Tuesday
Prog: 20 pages, 50p Editor: Secretary
Web: www.@team2.com/tunbroidge wellsfc

CLUB PERSONNEL
Chairman: R.Rogers
Vice Chairman:N.Sales
Manager: Steve Clark
2000-01 Captain: Garry Valli
P.o.Y.: Wayne Balmer
Top Scorer: Steve Gibbons 16

VICKERS CRAYFORD, DARTFORD ATHLETIC

Secretary: Brian Norris, 47 Oxenden Wood Road, Chelsfield Park, Orpington, Kent, BR6 6HP
Tel: 01689 854302

Ground: Thamesmead Town FC, Bayliss Avenue, Thamesmead, London, SE28 8NJ
Tel: 0208 311 4211 (Temporary Groundshare)
Home Ground (Pending floodlights) Oakwood, Old Road, Crayford, Kent, DA1 4DN.
Home clubhouse: Lounge Bar every day and evening. Plus snack bar on matchdays.

Directions: From Abbey Wood (BR) north east along Harrow Manor Way, into Crossway at 3rd r'bout, Bayliss Av. is 3rd right (Bexley bus 272 stops in Crossway near Bayliss Av. By road: From Dartford tunnel A2 to London, exit Danson Interchange and follow signs for Thamesmead and Abbey Wood. From Blackheath tunnel exit on south side and follow signs to Woolwich, to Plumstead and then to Thamesmead.

Capacity: 400 **Seats:** 125 **Cover:** 125 **Floodlights**: Yes

PREVIOUS **League:** Kent County. **Grounds:** Flamingo Park, Sidcup (pre 1994); VCD Sports & Social Club,Old Road, Crayford

RECORD **Victory:** 8-2 v DealTown 7.2.98 **Defeat:** 1-5 v Ramsgate 25.10.97

HONOURS Kent County Cup 61-62, 63-64, 94-95, R-Up: 84-85, 89-90. Kent County Lg Div One 96-97 Kent County Premier 96-97. West Kent Cup 87-88.Kent Lge Cup R-up: Winners 99-00 ,Runners up 98-99. Kent Intermediate Shield (2) R-up(1), Erith Hosp Cup x4, R-Up x4; Kent Sen, Tphy. R-up 00-01

FACT FILE
Founded: 1916
Nickname: The Vickers
Sponsors: MB Fire Protection
Colours: Green & white/green/green
Change Colours: Blue & white/blue/blue
Midweek matchday: Wednesday
Programme: 40 pages 50p

CLUB PERSONNEL
Chairman: Michael Bonello
Man:Martin Ford Assist Man:Peter Burke
Coach: David Ward
Physio: Peter Burke

2000-01
Captain: Terry Barry
Top Scorer:Ricky Bennett 26
P.o.Y.: Nick Davis

WHITSTABLE TOWN

Secretary: George Corney, 46 Elizabeth Way, Herne Bay, Kent CT6 6ET (01227 363496)
Ground: Belmont Road, Belmont, Whitstable, Kent Tel: 01227 266012

Directions: From Thanet Way (A299), left at Tescos r'bout and down MillstroodRd - ground at bottom of road, 400yds from Whitstable (BR) station. Car park atGrimshall Rd entrance
Capacity: 2,000 Cover: 1,000 Seats: 500 Floodlights: Yes Club Shop: Yes
Clubhouse: Social & recreation purposes, open all matchdays. Bar. Hot food &drinks at tea-bar

HONOURS Kent Lg Div 2 27-28 33-34 49-50 (Lg Cup 79-80 (R-up 89-90 91-92)), KentAmtr Lg East 60-61, Kent Amtr Cup 28-29, Kent Snr Tphy R-up 78-79 89-90 92-93,Gtr London Lg Cup R-up 65-66, Kent Amtr Cup 28-29, Kent Midweek Lg Cup 92-93

PREVIOUS **Leagues:** E. Kent 1897-1909; Kent 09-59; Aetolian 59-60; Kent Amtr 60-62 63-64; S E Anglian 62-63; Gtr London 64-67; Kent Premier 67-68 (also in New Brompton, Thanet & Faversham & Dist. Lges over the years)
Names: Whitstable Utd (pre-1886); Whitstable Swifts 93-95; WhitstableTown 95-1905; Whitstable FC 08-66

RECORDS **Gate:** 2,500 v Gravesend & Northfleet, FA Cup 3rd Qual. Rd,19/10/87
Goalscorer: Barry Godfrey Appearances: Frank Cox 429 (1950-60)
Win: 18-0 v Greenstreet (H), Faversham & Dist. Lge 20-21
Defeat: 0-10 v Sittingbourne (A), FA Cup 1st Qual. Rd 62-63

FACT FILE
Founded: 1885
Nickname: Oystermen, Reds, Natives
Club Sponsors: D & J Tyres
Shirt Sponsor: McDonalds
Colours: Red & White//White/ Red
Change colours: Yellow/blue/yellow
Midweek matchday: Tuesday
Programme: 48 pages, 50p
Editor/Press Off: Bernie Thompson
Tel No: 01227 274138

CLUB PERSONNEL
Chairman: Joe Brownett
Vice Chairman: Trevor Rapley
President: George Gifford
Manager: Simon Kay/Doug Bosson
Asst Manager: John Crabbe
Physio: Tony Pattenden

Slade Green's Kevin Lee (6) and Paul Springett clear this header from Chatham's Steve Best. Photo: Alan Coomes

BRITISH ENERGY KENT COUNTY FOOTBALL LEAGUE

Founded: 1922

President: W C Manklow **Chairman:** C T C Windiate

General Secretary: B H Bundock

Press Secretary: G Jenkins

Kings View, Shottenden Lane, Molash, Canterbury, Kent CT4 8EZ

Tel: 01233 740143 Email: oldforgelane@netscapeonline.co.uk

In one of the worst seasons for many years, during which almost five hundred matches were postponed, the Management Committee were forced to extend the season twice to complete the programme following the exceptionally inclement weather. To the great credit of the fixture secretaries and much assistance from the Clubs all but six matches were played with the non-defaulting teams awarded the points in each instance.

Once again nearly all of the League's eight divisions went to the wire with either promotion or relegation issues being resolved in the final two weeks of the campaign.

In an extremely tense end to the season in the Premier Division four teams were in contention for the title right up until the final Saturday. Bearsted eventually lifted the championship trophy for the first time in the Club's history, but their joy was delayed following a protest by Snodland, who had their appeal dismissed by the Kent County Football Association, although they were confirmed as runners-up. However, no one could dispute the 'Bears' their glory, as they were undefeated in their games against nearest challengers Snodland, Maidstone United and Thames Poly. Maidstone United, who finished third, were allowed to pursue their application to join the Bass Brewers Kent League and were subsequently elected into that competition.

The only Division to be settled early was Division One East, as New Romney remained undefeated with the best defensive record in the entire League, only conceding ten goals in eighteen outings and winning the title by twelve points from old rivals Kennington. The 'Marshmen' return to the Premier Division after a gap of six years.

Another nailbiting end to the season took place in Division One West with two points separating the top three teams. Crockenhill, relegated from the Premier Division the previous season, eventually landed the title and, with three vacancies in the Premier Division, runners-up Wickham Park were also promoted to take their place in the top flight for the first time.

New Romney Reserves completed a memorable double for the Club lifting the Division Two East title. The Division Two West champions were Oakwood, who gained promotion following a superb run of nineteen unbeaten games, which started at the end of October.

The Division Three West promotion places went to two League newcomers, Danson Athletic and Bly Spartans. In fact the 'Spartans' were the leading scorers in the entire competition with 120 goals from their 22 games. In the Reserve Divisions, Stansfeld O & B Club retained the Division One title and Fleetdown United won Division Two.

The League had five clubs competing in the 'Plaaya' Kent Senior Trophy and they all acquitted themselves well. Knatchbull progressed to the third round following a notable victory over Bass Brewers Kent League Beckenham Town before bowing out away to Hythe United 4-2 after extra time. However, it was Thames Poly's performances in the London Senior Cup that really caught the eye. Victory against Harringey Borough in the first round was followed with away successes at Woodford Town, Ilford Town, Fisher Athletic and Hanwell Town. Had 'The Poly' reproduced the form that knocked out Dr Martens Southern League Fisher Athletic in the Fourth Round they undoubtedly would have gone beyond the semi-final. In the event they failed at this last hurdle after a narrow 1-0 defeat at Ryman League Croydon Athletic.

The Kent Intermediate Challenge Shield was won by Premier Division Lydd Town, who defeated fellow Premier Division Phoenix Sports by one goal to nil.

The League's domestic Cup Competitions saw Snodland lift the Inter-Regional Challenge Cup by defeating Fleetdown United 1-0 at Dr Martens League Ashford Town FC's ground. Lydd Town just failed to lift a second trophy going down by three goals to two in an exciting final in the Eastern Section Senior (Les Leckie) Cup on Hythe United's ground. There was a shock in the Western Section Reserve Divisions Cup as Division Two Holmesdale beat much-fancied Division One Greenways by the odd goal in three at Slade Green FC.

The League staged a second final at Reachfields Stadium, Hythe, when a young and talented St Margarets Reserves outfit crowned an excellent first season in the League by lifting the Eastern Junior Cup after defeating gallant Betteshanger Welfare 4-1 in another entertaining final.

The last of the League's knockout competitions was witnessed by a crowd of over 400 as Old Roan defeated Fleetdown United 2-1 in an exciting final to collect the West Kent Challenge Shield from Vice-Chairman Peter Hunter at Park View Road, the home of Dr Martens Southern League Welling United.

As a result of the atrocious weather during the season the League representative team's games scheduled against the Sussex County League and the Essex Intermediate League were cancelled.

To mark the new millennium the League were delighted to launch a unique 48 page publication entitled 'A Guide to the Kent County Football Association League', and the neat cover with the quality of the book and depth of research brought many plaudits from those who purchased it. A few copies are still available at £4.00 each by sending a cheque to League Treasurer John Weller at 52 Rogersmead, Tenterden, Kent TN30 6LF.

During the season the League Management Committee was delighted to learn that both Steve Bennett and John Underhill, two of our former Referees, had been appointed to the FIFA list of Referees.

Saturday 2nd June saw the League celebrating the end of another season with its Presentation Dinner & Dance at the Jarvis Great Danes Hotel & Country Club, Hollingbourne. Principle guests were Stuart Crooks, British Energy Dungeness 'B' Power Station's Fuel Route Manager, Barry Bright, Chairman and Managing Director of the Kent County Football Association, and Keith Masters, the Association's Chief Executive. During the evening Long Service Club Awards were presented to Chris Langley of Old Bexleians and Frank Cosgrove of Westerham.

Ian Crouch from New Eltham lifted the Referee of the Year award and the Most Promising Referee of the Year went to Matthew Boyns from Bexleyheath.

At the League's Annual General Meeting on Monday 18th June 2001, seven new teams were elected into the Competition. Cray Valley (PM), formerly of the London Intermediate League, were placed in Division One West, and Betteshanger Welfare Reserves and Norton Sports Reserves will play in Division Two East. Samuel Montagu Youth Club, Staplehurst and Town Malling United will compete in Division Three West and Town Malling United Reserves will play in Reserve Division Two West. The highlights of the AGM saw St Margarets Reserves collect the much coveted Fair Play award and a cheque for £300 from Mark Gorry, British Energy's Station Director at Dungeness 'B', as the team with the best disciplinary record in the entire League. Other clubs, who received cheques for good disciplinary records, were New Romney, Wickham Park, Oakwood, Hawkenbury, Otford United Reserves, Fleetdown United Reserves and new Romney Reserves, who each received £120 and Kennington, Larkfield & New Hythe Wanderers, Sheerness East Reserves, Oakwood Reserves and Holmesdale Reserves who each received £60.

Don Marchant of Otford United and David Bell of Palace received long service Club awards having been unable to attend the dinner.

Sean Gentle of Oakwood received the Aford Awards Manager of the Year following his club's promotion to Division One West. Press Secretary Sharon Puxty resigned unexpectedly in June 2000 and was replaced by Geoff Jenkins who joined the Management Committee in September. All Officers were re-elected unopposed.

The League continues to expand its Newsline activities and well known Radio Kent sports commentator Andrew Gidley will again be conducting interviews on the newsline this season. Why not ring 09068 800 664 and keep abreast of all the League News. The line is in operation 24 hours a day, seven days a week.

Cyril Windiate, Chairman

Thames Poly FC, London Senior Cup semi-finalists. Photo: courtesy Philip Smith

FINAL LEAGUE TABLES 2000-01

PREMIER DIVISION

	P	W	D	L	F	A	Pts
Bearsted	26	16	4	5	58	29	55
Snodland	26	16	6	3	65	28	54
Maidstone United	26	15	9	2	62	25	54
Thames Poly	26	16	5	5	57	24	53
Stansfeld O & B Club	26	14	4	8	53	30	46
Sheerness East	26	11	7	8	44	41	40
Beauwater	26	8	6	12	39	53	30
Lydd Town	26	8	5	13	43	49	29
Sevenoaks Town	26	9	2	15	41	55	29
Milton Athletic	26	8	4	14	38	59	28
Phoenix Sports	26	8	2	16	34	57	26
Knatchbull	26	8	2	16	38	63	26
Greenways	26	7	4	15	34	62	25
Norton Sports	26	5	4	17	41	72	19

DIVISION ONE WEST

	P	W	D	L	F	A	Pts
Crockenhill*	24	17	4	3	54	28	54
Wickham Park	24	16	5	3	77	31	53
Fleetdown United	24	14	7	2	54	21	52
Old Roan	24	13	4	7	48	38	43
AFC Blackheath	24	12	1	10	57	46	40
Rusthall	24	10	5	8	37	35	38
Moonshot Athletic	24	11	4	9	43	39	37
Otford United	24	10	5	9	40	36	35
Pembury	24	8	5	11	51	55	29
Westerham	24	6	3	15	27	60	21
Aylesford Paper Mills	24	5	2	17	35	71	17
Holmesdale	24	5	1	18	41	61	16
AFC Lewisham	24	2	2	17	27	70	8

DIVISION ONE EAST

	P	W	D	L	F	A	Pts
New Romney	18	17	1	0	58	10	52
Kennington	18	13	1	4	61	23	40
University of Kent	18	11	3	4	51	25	36
Bromley Green	18	7	4	7	38	41	25
St Margarets	18	6	3	9	31	42	21
Broomfield United	18	4	5	9	28	42	17
Snowdown CW	18	5	2	11	31	49	17
Iden	18	4	4	10	27	46	16
Smarden	18	4	4	10	28	53	16
Tenterden Tigers	18	4	3	11	35	57	15

** points deducted*

INTER-REGIONAL CHALLENGE CUP 2000-01

FIRST ROUND

Bearsted	v	Moonshot Athletic	1-0	Phoenix Sports	v	Sevenoaks Town	4-3
Beauwater	v	Rusthall	0-2	Snodland	v	Old Roan	2-1
Bromley Green	v	Knatchbull	2-3	Snowdown CW	v	Norton Sports	1-3
Iden	v	Sheerness East	1-3	Stansfeld O & B	v	Westerham	2-0
Kennington	v	Broomfield United	3-2	St Margarets	v	Smarden	4-0
Maidstone United	v	AFC Lewisham	2-0	Tenterden Tigers	v	Milton Athletic	3-4
New Romney	v	Lydd Town	2-4	Thames Poly	v	ST Georges	TP WO

SECOND ROUND

Aylesford Paper Mills	v	AFC Blackheath	2-5	Milton Athletic	v	St Margarets	4-0
Bearsted	v	Pembury	5-2	Otford United	v	Wickham Park	3*4
Fleetdown United	v	Phoenix Sports	3-0	Rusthall	v	Greenways	4-1
Kennington	v	Sheerness East	1-3	Stansfeld O & B	v	Holmesdale	4-1
Lydd Town	v	Knatchbull	4-0	Thames Poly	v	Snodland	1-3
Maidstone United	v	Crockenhill	2-0	University of Kent	v	Norton Sports	0-6

THIRD ROUND

Bearsted	v	Maidstone United	0-2	Rusthall	v	Fleetdown United	0-4
Snodland	v	AFC Blackheath	3-1	Stansfeld O & B	v	Wickham Park	2-0

FOURTH ROUND

Maidstone United	v	Lydd Town	2*1	Milton Athletic	v	Snodland	2-3
Sheerness East	v	Fleetdown United	0-2	Stansfeld O & B	v	Norton Sports	1-2

SEMI FINALS

Maidstone United	v	Snodland	0-1	Norton Sports	v	Fleetdown United	0-2

FINAL

Fleetdown United	v	Snodland	0-1	at The Homelands, Ashford Town FC

Right: Fleetdown United FC - Runners up in both the Inter-Regional Challenge Cup and the West Kent Challenge Shield.
Photo: courtesy Philip Smith

Left: Snodland FC - Winners of the Inter-Regional Challenge Cup.
Photo: courtesy Philip Smith

BEARSTED
Secretary: Mrs Liz Owen, 21 Copsewood Way, Bearsted, Maidstone, Kent ME15 8PL(01622 737709)
Ground: Honey Lane, Otham, Maidstone. (0411 128034)
Founded: 1895
Colours: White/blue/blue
Change Colours: Yellow/blue/blue

BEAUWATER
Founded: 1927
Secretary: Robert Taylor, 24 Sun Lane, Gravesend, Kent DA12 5HG (01474 332208)
Ground: Beauwater Leisure Club, Nelson Road, Northfleet (01474 359222)
Colours: Purple/navy/purple
Change Colours: Black & Green/black & green shorts & socks.

CROCKENHILL
Secretary: Mike Floate, Newlands Cottages, 71 Stones Cross Road, Crockenhill,Swanley, Kent BR8 8LX Tel No: 01322 668275
Ground: The Wested Meadow, Wested, Eynsford Road, Crockenhill, Kent. (01322 662097)
Founded: 1946
Colours: Red & white stripes/ black/ black
Change Colours: Black &white/ black/black

GREENWAYS
Founded: 1965
Secretary: William Miller, 14 Cygnet Gardens, Northfleet, Kent DA11 7DN (01474 560913)
Ground: Beauwater Leisure Centre, Nelson Road, Northfleet, (01474 359222)
Colours: Jade/navy / orange
Change Colours: Red & black/black/red & black

LYDD TOWN
Founded: 1885
Secretary: Bruce Marchant, 14 Quested Road, Folkestone, Kent.Ct19 4BY Tel No: 01303 275403
Ground: The Lindsey Field, Dengemarsh Road, Lydd, Romney Marsh (01797 321904)
Colours: Red/green/red
ChangeColours:Blue&white/blue/blue.

MILTON ATHLETIC
Founded: 1926
Secretary: Paul Duffin, 18 Hales Road, Tunstall, Sittingbourne, Kent ME10 1SR (01795 471260)
Ground: UK Paper Sports Ground, Gore Court Road, Sittingbourne, Kent (01795 564213)
Colours: Blue & white/navy/navy & white
Change Colours: Red & white stripes/navy/navy & white

NEW ROMNEY
Founded: 1895
Secretary: Mr Daryl Masters, 44 Fernbank Cres, Folkestone, Kent CT19 5SF (01303 253961)
Ground: The Maud Pavilion, Station Road, New Romney, Kent (01797 364858)
Colours: Navy blue & yellow/ navy/yellow
Change Colours: Orange/blue/orange

PHOENIX SPORTS
Founded: 1935
Secretary: Martyn Cole, 91 Hurst Road, Northumberland Road, Erith, Kent DA8 3EW (01322 350750)
Ground: Phoenix Spts Club, Mayplace Rd East , Bexleyheath, Kent DA7 6JT (01322 526159)
Colours: Red & white/ black/black
Change Colours: Yellow/black/black

SEVENOAKS TOWN
Founded: 1883
Secretary: Edwin Diplock, 23 Holly Bush Lane, Sevenoaks, Kent TN13 3TH (01732 454280)
Ground: Greatness Park, Seal Road, Sevenoaks (01732 741987)
Colours: Azure & black stripes/black/black
Change colours: Navy & scarlet quarters/navy/navy

SHEERNESS EAST
Founded: 1932
Secretary: Jonathan Longhurst, 16 Hilda Road, Halfway, Sheerness, Kent ME12 3BN (01795 667758)
Ground: Sheerness East Working Mens Club, 47 Queenborough Rd., Halfway, Sheerness (01795 662049)
Colours: Yellow/royal blue/royal blue
Change colours:Blue/black.blue

SNODLAND
Founded: 1940
Secretary: Terry Reeves, 136 Townsend Road, Snodland, Kent ME6 5RN (01634 240076)
Ground: Potyn's Field, Paddlesworth Road, Snodland, Kent. (01634 243961)
Colours: Yellow/ /red/black
Change colours:Sky & navy/navy/navy

STANSFELD OXFORD & BERMONDSEY CLUB
Founded: 1897
Secretary: Edward Ellis, 40 Tilbrook Road, Kidbrooke, London SE3 9QE (0208 319 0903)
Ground: Greenwich University Sports Ground,Kidbroooke Lane, Eltham,S.E.9 Tel No: 02088500210
Colours: Yellow 7 blue/blue/blue
Change Colours: All white

THAMES POLYTECHNIC
Founded: 1888
Secretary: Mrs Shirley Jarvis, 31 Monkton Road, Welling, Kent DA16 3JU (0208 854 5509)
Ground: Greenwich University Sports Ground, Kidbrooke Lane, Eltham, London SE9 (020 8850 0210)
Colours: Yellow /green/yellow
Change Colours: All blue
Previous league: Kent

WICKHAM PARK
Founded: 1934
Secretary: Brian Greenin, 145 The Avenue, West Wickham, Kent BR4 0EF (0208 777 2119)
Ground: Ten Em Bee Sports Ground, 120A Old Bromley Road, Downham. Tel No: 02083139510
Colours: Red & blacktrim/black/black
Change Colours: White/navy/white

KENT COUNTY LEAGUE DIVISION ONE WEST

A.F.C. BLACKHEATH
Secretary: Dave Wilson, 74 Shroffold Road, Bromley ,Ken BR1 5PF. Tel: 020 8698 1192
Ground: Eltham Town, The Oaks, Footscray Road,Eltham
Tel No: 020 8850 0695
Founded: 1983
Colours: Red & Black stripes/white/white
Change Colours: All white.

AYLESFORD PAPER MILLS
Founded: 1919
Secretary:Jeff Davis, 20 Penine Way, Maidstone, Kent
Tel No: 01622 717771
Ground: Cobdown Sports & Social Club, Ditton Corner, Station Road, Aylesford (01622 715552)
Colours: White with black trim/black/black
Change Colours: Red/black/black

CRAY VALLEY (PM)
Founded: 1981
Secretary: Steve Chapman, 97 Yorkland Ave., Welling DA16 2LG
Tel: 020 8304 5387 (H) 01293 802208 (B)
Ground: Badgers Sports Ground, Middle Park Ave., London SE9
Tel: 020 8850 4273
Colours: Green/black/black
Change colours: Blue & white stripes/blue/blue

EYNESFORD
Founded: 1895
Secretary: Robert Graham, 48 Goddington Lane, Orpington, Kent BR6 9DS Tel: 01689 821425
Ground: Westminster Fields, The Street, Horton Kirby.
Tel: 01322 865193
Colours: Black & white/black/black
Change Colours: Yellow & black/black/black

FLEETDOWN UNITED
Founded: 1971
Secretary: Brian Wakeman, 670 Princes Road, Dartford, Kent DA2 6JG (01322 228680)
Ground: Heath Lane, Dartford, Kent (01322 273848)
Colours: Tangerine/black/tangerine
Change colours: Blue & Black/ blue/blue

HOLMESDALE
Founded 1956
Secretary: Mark Hayes, 12 Danson Way, Rainham, Kent. ME8 7EW (01634 327954)
Ground: Holmesdale Sports & Social Club, Oakley Road, Bromley Common (020 8462 4440)
Colours: Yellow & Green/ Green/ Green
Change Colours: White/ Black/Black

MOONSHOT ATHLETIC
Founded: 1970
Secretary: Joseph Collymore, 37 Vaughan Williams Close, Deptford SE8 4AW (0208 691 2543)
Ground: Ten Em Bee Sports Ground, Bromley Road playing fields, Old Bromley Road, Downham, Kent (020 8313 9510)
Colours: Yellow/green/green
Change Colours: All burgandy

OAKWOOD
Founded: 1924
Peter Mannering, 24 Ellenswood Close, Otham, Maidstone, Kent ME15 8SQ Tel: 01622 862482
Ground: Honey Lane, Otham, Maidstone, Kent.
Colours: Red & white stripes/black/red
Change colours: White & black/black/red

OLD ROAN
Founded: 1905
Secretary: Brian Riley, 33 Buckler Gardens, Mottingham, London SE9 3BD (020 8857 0401)
Groud: John Roan PLaying Fields, Kidbrooke Park Road, KIdbrooke, London SE3 (020 8856 1915 or 020 8856 1012)
Colours: Blue & black/ black/ black & blue.
Change Colours: Red & Black/red & black/red

OTFORD UNITED
Founded: 1900
Secretary: David Dugay, 13 Monckton Road, Borough Green, Sevenoaks, Kent TN15 8SD (01732 882621)
Ground: Otford Recreation Ground, High Street, Otford, Kent (01959 524405)
Colours: Amber & black/black/black
Change Colours: All blue.

PEMBURY
Founded1908
Secretary; Michael Waterman, 26 The Coppice, Pembury, Tunbridge Wells Kent TN2 4EY 01892 824137)
Ground: Woodside Recreation Ground, Henwoods Mount, Pembury (07970 026628)
Colours: Black & White stripes/ black/black
Change Colours: All red

RUSTHALL
Founded: 1899
Secretary: Michael Mace, 'The Roos', 28 Allan Close, Rusthall, Tunbridge Wells, Kent TN4 8PL (01892 540634)
Ground: Jockey Farm, Nellington Lane, Rusthall, Tunbridge Wells
Tel : 01892 517224
Colours: Green & black/ black/ green
Change Colours: Red & black/black/black

WESTERHAM
Founded: 1888
Secretary: Doug Sayers, 16A The Green, Westerham, Kent TN16 1AX (01959 565520)
Ground: Westerham Sports Assoc., King George V Playing Fields, Costells Meadow, Westerham. (01959 561106)
Colours: Red/black/black
Change Colours: Green/white/white

KENT COUNTY LEAGUE DIVISION ONE EAST

BETTESHANGER WELFARE

Secretary: David Fairclough, 55 Tormore Park, Deal, Kent CT14 9UR Tel: 01304 366883 (H) 07714 705582 (B)
Ground: Betteshanger Welfare Ground, Cavell Square, Mill Hill, Deal. Tel: 01304 372080
Colours: Red & white hoops/navy/red & white hoops
Change colours: Yellow & black/black/black

BROMLEY GREEN

Founded: 1930
Secretary: David Stanley, 25 Carey Close, New Romney, Kent TN28 8XN Tel NO: 01797 369282
Ground: The Swan Centre, Newtown Road, South Willesborough, Ashford, Kent
Colours: All Green.
Change Colours: White/green/green

KENNINGTON

Founded: 1888
Secretary: Kevin Hayden, 36 Alec Pemble Close, Kennington, Ashford, Kent. TN24 9PF Tel No: 01233 627826
Ground: Kennington Cricket Club Club, Ulley Road, Kennington, Ashford, Kent
Colours: Yellow & sky blue/yellow/yellow
Change Colours: Dark blue and red.

NORTON SPORTS

Founded: 1927
Secretary: Colin Page, 22 Haysel, Sittingbourne, Kent ME10 4QE (01795 426675)
Ground: Norton Pk, Provender Lane,Norton,Kent (01795 520088)
Colours: Blue & white stripes/ black/ white
Change Colours: Red & black/black/white

RYE & IDEN UNMITED

Founded: 1965
Secretary: Gerard Say, 18 Parkwood, Iden, Rye, East Sussex TN31 7XE (01797 280495)
Ground: Rye Football & Cricket Salts, Fishmarket Rd., Rye, East Sussex Tel: 01797 223855
Colours: Amber/white/amber
Change Colours: All white

SMARDEN

Founded: 1984
Secrtary: Tom Carlton, The Barn, New Barn Farm, Bethersden, Ashford, Kent TN26 3EU (01233 820983)
Ground: The Minnis, Smarden, Nr Ashford, Kent
Colours: Blue & White/Blue/Blue.
Change Colours: Green & White/ Black/ Black

SNOWDOWN COLLIERY WELFARE

Founded: 1927
Secretary:Mrs Nicola Tong, 9 Ackholt Road, Aylesham, Canterbury, Kent CT3 3AF (0771 8525030))
Ground: Spinney Lane, Aylesham, Canterbury CT3 3AF (01304 840278)
Colours: Black & white stripes/black/black
Change Colours: Blue & black/white/white
Previous League: Kent

St MARGARETS

Founded: 1970 Re-formed:1993
Secretary: William Hay, 28 The Freedown, St Margarets at Cliffe, Nr Dover, Kent CT15 6BD (01304 852386)
Ground: The Alexander Field, Kingsdown Road, St Margarets at Cliffe, Nr Dover
Colours: Red, white and blue/ blue/red
Change Colours: Dark blue/white/red

TENTERDEN TIGERS

Founded: 1889
Secretary: Tony Clarke, 2 Homewood Road, Tenterden, Kent TN30 7AU Tel No: 01580 763403
Ground: Recreation Ground, Recretaion Ground Rd., Tenterden (01580 762703)
Colours: Yellow/black/black
Change Colours: Blue & white/ blue/blue

UNIVERSITY OF KENT

Founded: 1967
Secretary: Mrs Rene Simmonds, Sports Federation, Sports Centre, University of Kent, Canterbury, Kent CT2 7NL (01227 768027 or 01227 827430)
Ground: The Playing Fields, University of Kent, off Giles Lane, Canterbury
Colours: Black & white stripes/black/black
Change Colours: Blue & yellow stripes/black/black

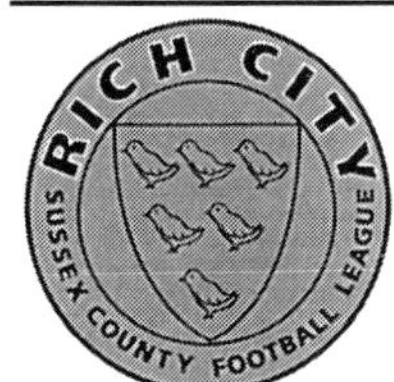

RICH CITY SUSSEX COUNTY LEAGUE

FEEDER TO: DR MARTENS LEAGUE

FOUNDED 1920

President: P H Strange **Chairman:** Peter Bentley
Secretary: P Beard, 2 Van Gogh Place, Bersted, Bognor Regis PO22 9BG
Tel: 01243 822063 (H) 07966 457908 (M) Fax: 01243 822063 Email: paul.beard@tesco.net

Some seasons are best remembered for outstanding results, others for the strength of one particular team. The 2000-01 season was memorable for an entirely different reason. It will be best remembered for breaking records for the amount of rainfall. Not since the dreadful winter of 1962-63 has a season been so threatened with abandonment because of the number of postponed matches. In 1962-63 there were no games played between 14th December and the beginning of March, by which time the League had been suspended and an Emergency Cup competition instigated. The advent of floodlighting and some adept fixture scheduling permitted the 2000-01 season to be completed, albeit with the cancellation of some of the more minor County FA Cup competitions and the late withdrawal of several Reserve teams. That the season was completed at all was testament to the hard work of the Fixtures and Referees Secretaries. I take my hat off to these gentlemen!

In the FA Cup 21 Sussex County Football League sides entered at the Preliminary Round, with Burgess Hill Town, Saltdean United, East Preston, Horsham YMCA, Littlehampton Town, Wick, Hassocks and Selsey progressing. In the First Qualifying Round Saltdean United won 3-2 at Andover, Selsey beat Reading Town 4-0, Horsham YMCA beat Cowes Sports 6-0 in a replay and Littlehampton Town won 1-0 at Hythe United in a replay. Sadly, all but one of our teams were to fall at the next hurdle, leaving Saltdean United to fly the flag in the Third Qualifying Round. Unfortunatley they did not progress any further, going down 2-1 at home to Devizes Town.

In recent years Sussex County League sides have shown signs of improving form in the FA Challenge Vase and there were high hopes of some good performances this season. The Qualifying Round saw good wins for East Preston, Arundel, Wick, Eastbourne Town, Hassocks, Redhill and Sidley United. Burgess Hill Town, Saltdean United and Horsham YMCA joined the competition in the Second Round, and the League's interest in the competition ended in the Third Round with defeat for Burgess Hill Town at Arlesey and Saltdean United at Ashford Town.

In the County FA competitions Horsham YMCA progressed to the Semi Finals of the Senior Cup, but went down 5-2 to Bognor Regis Town. The club also reached the Semi Finals of the R.U.R. Charity Cup when they were pitted against Sidlesham, and won by a solitary goal. Burgess Hill Town took on Redhill and won 3-0 to set up a thrilling Final. At the end of March Burgess Hill, so successful in recent seasons, met Horsham YMCA, who were pushing hard at the top of the Division One table, at Lancing for the Final. It was to be a great night for YM as they snatched their first senior SCFA trophy by beating their title rivals by 3-0.

The Division One League title was claimed by dark horses Sidley United. Having maintained a steady pace throughout the season they ended up five points clear of Burgess Hill Town with Wick another eleven points behind in third place. This was a League and Cup double for the East Sussex side. Previous Division One leaders, Horsham YMCA and Pagham, had drifted away to fifth and sixth places respectively. At the other end of the table, East Preston finished eleven points adrift of the rest with Eastbourne Town and Lancing filling the other two relegation places. Whitehawk only escaped relegation by one point, and had Eastbourne Town gained a result at Sidlesham in their last game of the season then Whitehawk would have gone down in their place.

Division Two side Worthing United started the season in tremendous style, recording five straight wins and only conceding two goals. At the end of August they were top of the table and stayed there until February, when the weather permitted a good number of matches to be played. Worthing slipped to fourth and the top spot was taken by Hailsham Town. By May the title race really went down to the wire. Southwick finally clinched the Division Two title by taking 72 points from their 34 matches, while just one point behind Peacehaven & Telscombe clinched second and Hailsham Town finished five points further behind in third. Lingfield ended up 25 points short of safety having taken just twelve points from their League programme. Crowborough Athletic were thirteen points above them but still filled the second relegation place.

When it came to the end of the season, Rye United were crowned Division Three Champions and return to the senior section of the Sussex County League after a long absence. They were four points ahead of Seaford who edged out Haywards Heath Town on goal difference for the second promotion place. Royal & Sun Alliance were in last place with just eighteen points. Newhaven occupied the other relegation place and both sides must wait to see if any of the clubs applying to join the League have the facilities required. Newhaven are in a slightly better state as Division Three was one team short for the season and it is possible that if two teams join the League only one may leave.

FINAL LEAGUE TABLES 2000-01

DIVISION ONE

	P	W	D	L	F	A	Pts	GD
Sidley United	38	25	8	5	65	31	83	34
Burgess Hill Town	38	23	9	6	77	46	78	31
Wick	38	19	10	9	78	51	67	27
Selsey	38	20	5	13	68	48	65	20
Horsham YMCA	38	19	6	13	74	54	63	20
Pagham	38	17	11	10	78	56	62	22
Chichester City U	38	17	6	15	82	67	57	15
Three Bridges	38	16	9	13	61	59	57	2
Sidlesham	38	17	6	15	64	64	57	0
Ringmer	38	17	5	16	55	67	56	-12
Eastbourne Utd	38	14	10	14	60	53	52	7
Hassocks	38	15	5	18	57	58	50	-1
Arundel	38	14	8	16	52	68	50	-16
Redhill	38	13	8	17	62	66	47	-4
Littlehampton T	38	11	10	17	57	61	43	-4
Saltdean Utd	38	11	8	19	54	73	41	-19
Whitehawk	38	9	11	18	53	73	38	-20
Lancing	38	9	10	19	48	77	37	-19
Eastbourne T	38	9	8	21	47	66	35	-19
East Preston	38	7	3	28	41	105	24	-64

DIVISION TWO

	P	W	D	L	F	A	Pts	GD
Southwick	34	23	3	8	76	32	72	44
Peacehaven & T	34	22	5	7	66	36	71	30
Hailsham Town	34	20	6	8	81	43	66	38
East Grinstead T	34	19	6	9	58	37	63	21
Broadbridge Hth	34	18	7	9	80	43	61	37
Worthing United	34	18	6	10	77	46	60	31
Oving	34	16	6	12	64	50	54	14
Westfield	34	13	9	12	49	52	48	-3
Oakwood	34	12	10	12	55	50	46	5
Bosham	34	13	6	15	48	73	45	-25
Wealden	34	12	8	14	61	59	44	2
Storrington	34	12	5	17	54	75	41	-21
Shoreham	34	12	4	18	67	84	40	-17
Shinewater Assn	34	12	4	18	57	78	40	-21
Mile Oak	34	11	6	17	66	69	39	-3
Crawley Down	34	10	7	17	50	68	37	-18
Crowborough Ath	34	6	7	21	49	79	25	-30
Lingfield	34	3	3	28	26	108	12	-84

DIVISION THREE

	P	W	D	L	F	A	Pts	GD
Rye United	28	21	3	4	89	38	66	51
Seaford	28	20	2	6	70	33	62	37
Haywards Heath T	28	19	5	4	62	30	62	32
Steyning Town	28	15	5	8	51	43	50	8
Franklands Village	28	12	7	9	62	38	43	24
Ifield	28	12	5	11	58	57	41	1
T.S.C.	28	10	8	10	58	53	38	5
St Francis	28	9	9	10	49	53	36	-4
Uckfield Town	28	11	2	15	45	60	35	-15
Ansty Rangers	28	10	4	14	51	63	34	-12
Bexhill Town	28	8	5	15	37	51	29	-14
Forest	28	6	10	12	39	45	28	-6
Hurstpierpoint	28	6	6	16	37	64	24	-27
Newhaven	28	7	3	18	39	69	24	-30
Royal & Sun Allnce	28	4	6	18	26	76	18	-50

DIVISION ONE RESULTS CHART 2000-01

		1	2	3	4	5	6	7	8	9	10	11	12	13	14	15	16	17	18	19	20
1	Arundel	X	0-3	0-1	2-0	1-1	2-0	2-1	1-0	3-3	0-0	4-3	1-4	0-1	2-1	0-1	1-4	2-1	1-1	4-2	0-2
2	Burgess Hill Town	3-3	X	3-1	2-1	2-0	4-2	3-0	0-5	4-2	2-1	1-1	2-1	1-1	6-1	3-2	3-0	1-1	1-1	2-1	1-1
3	Chichester City U	2-2	2-2	X	5-1	3-1	1-2	3-1	3-4	1-1	1-3	4-2	1-4	2-3	1-5	0-2	2-2	0-0	4-2	2-1	1-2
4	East Preston	0-3	1-3	0-5	X	0-4	1-8	4-0	0-0	2-1	1-3	0-4	1-1	2-1	3-1	2-1	1-2	0-1	1-4	2-2	1-4
5	Eastbourne Town	3-1	0-1	3-0	2-1	X	1-1	0-1	1-4	1-1	0-3	1-1	0-3	1-2	1-2	3-3	2-3	0-1	0-3	2-1	0-0
6	Eastbourne Utd	0-2	0-3	1-2	6-0	3-1	X	1-1	0-2	2-2	1-1	2-0	1-0	1-2	2-1	1-2	0-1	2-2	0-0	1-2	1-1
7	Hassocks	0-0	3-0	2-1	1-0	0-2	0-1	X	2-1	1-2	4-0	2-2	3-0	0-2	0-2	0-3	5-1	1-2	1-1	3-0	1-3
8	Horsham YMCA	4-0	2-1	3-2	4-3	5-0	1-3	1-0	X	5-2	4-2	1-1	1-2	3-1	2-1	0-3	0-0	0-1	2-0	1-1	3-2
9	Lancing	2-0	1-2	1-3	4-1	4-0	2-3	2-3	1-0	X	1-0	1-4	0-1	0-3	0-3	0-0	3-2	0-2	1-2	2-2	2-2
10	Littlehampton Tn	1-2	0-2	1-1	0-1	0-1	3-0	2-1	3-2	1-0	X	2-2	2-2	1-2	3-1	2-5	2-3	2-3	1-3	2-2	2-2
11	Pagham	1-2	1-1	4-1	3-0	1-0	6-1	0-3	4-3	3-3	1-0	X	2-1	4-1	3-2	2-3	4-2	0-1	2-0	7-2	1-1
12	Redhill	0-1	1-2	4-3	4-2	3-2	1-1	1-3	1-1	1-1	1-4	2-0	X	1-0	3-3	0-2	1-3	1-2	2-3	5-1	0-4
13	Ringmer	2-0	1-2	2-7	2-1	0-7	1-1	2-3	0-1	0-1	2-1	2-1	1-4	X	7-1	0-1	2-0	1-1	3-2	2-1	0-0
14	Saltdean Utd	1-2	1-4	0-2	3-2	0-0	0-4	2-0	2-1	5-1	0-1	0-2	2-2	3-1	X	2-0	0-2	1-1	1-1	1-1	0-3
15	Selsey	4-1	1-0	2-3	2-1	2-1	0-1	1-3	1-2	4-2	2-2	0-0	1-3	0-1	0-0	X	5-2	1-0	2-0	1-0	0-3
16	Sidlesham	2-0	0-1	0-5	2-3	1-0	1-2	2-0	3-3	2-2	2-1	0-1	2-0	1-0	3-1	2-1	X	4-1	2-2	2-2	1-2
17	Sidley United	4-2	4-1	1-0	1-0	2-1	2-1	0-1	2-1	1-0	0-0	0-0	2-0	6-0	1-2	2-1	2-1	X	4-0	2-2	2-0
18	Three Bridges	4-1	1-0	0-1	4-1	1-2	2-1	4-4	2-3	3-2	2-2	4-1	3-1	2-2	1-0	2-1	W/L	0-3	X	1-0	0-4
19	Whitehawk	4-2	1-1	0-4	4-0	2-2	0-0	2-1	1-0	4-2	0-2	0-1	1-1	0-2	3-1	1-2	1-4	1-2	1-0	X	1-2
20	Wick	2-2	1-4	0-2	6-1	4-1	2-1	3-2	0-1	1-3	2-1	3-3	2-0	4-0	2-2	1-6	3-0	1-2	1-0	2-3	X

JOHN O'HARA LEAGUE CUP 2000-01

FIRST ROUND

Eastbourne Utd	v	Peacehaven & Tels	3-0	Wealden	v	Lancing	2-1
Whitehawk	v	Shinewater Association	6-0	Crowborough Ath	v	Chichester City Utd	1-3
East Preston	v	Oakwood	1*0	Mile Oak	v	Arundel	0-4

SECOND ROUND

Horsham YMCA	v	Hailsham Town	2-3	Three Bridges	v	Storrington	3*2
Sidlesham	v	Oving	4-2	Eastbourne Utd	v	Wealden	4-0
Selsey	v	Broadbridge Heath	0-2	Hassocks	v	Westfield	1-0
Eastbourne Town	v	East Grinstead Town	2-1	Southwick	v	Burgess Hill Town	2-1
Whitehawk	v	Chichester City Utd	5-4	Littlehampton Town	v	Worthing United	4-2
East Preston	v	Arundel	4-2	Saltdean United	v	Shoreham	3-2
Wick	v	Crawley Down	3-0	Bosham	v	Sidley United	0-2
Redhill	v	Ringmer	1-0	Lingfield	v	Pagham (at Pag.)	0-9

THIRD ROUND

Hailsham Town	v	Three Bridges	0*1	Sidlesham	v	Eastbourne United	4-2
Broadbridge Heath	v	Hassocks	1-0	Eastbourne Town	v	Southwick	2-1
Whitehawk	v	Littlehampton Town	0-1	East Preston	v	Saltdean United	3-6
Wick	v	Sidley United	0-2	Redhill	v	Pagham	0-6

FOURTH ROUND

Three Bridges	v	Sidlesham	1-3	Broadbridge Heath	v	Eastbourne Town	3-2
Littlehampton Town	v	Saltdean United	1-3	Sidley United	v	Pagham	4*3

SEMI-FINALS

Sidlesham	v	Broadbridge Heath	3-2	Saltdean United	v	Sidley United	1-4

FINAL

Sidlesham	v	Sidley United	2-3	at Burgess Hill Town FC

DIVISION TWO CHALLENGE CUP 2000-01

FIRST ROUND

Crawley Down	v	Broadbridge Heath	2*1	Westfield	v	Southwick	1-4

SECOND ROUND

Lingfield	v	Mile Oak (at M.O.)	2-5	Shoreham	v	Shinewater Assn	1-3
Peacehaven & Tels	v	Crawley Down	2*1	Crowborough Ath	v	Wealden	2-
Bosham	v	Oving	2*2, 2*3	Southwick	v	Hailsham Town	2-4
Storrington	v	East Grinstead Town	0-4	Oakwood	v	Worthing United	1-0

THIRD ROUND

Mile Oak	v	Shinewater Assn	3-1	Peacehaven & Tels	v	Wealden	3-1
Oving	v	Hailsham Town	W-L	East Grinstead Town	v	Oakwood	2-0

SEMI-FINALS

Mile Oak	v	Peacehaven & Tels	1*4	Oving	v	East Grinstead Tn	2-1

FINAL

Peacehaven & Tels	v	Oving	2-0	at Wick FC

DIVISION THREE CHALLENGE CUP 2000-01

FIRST ROUND

Hurstpierpoint	v	Forest	1-4	Newhaven	v	Rye United	0-2
Uckfield Town	v	Seaford	1-5	Ifield	v	Royal & Sun Allnce	3-0
Ansty Rangers	v	Bexhill Town	1-4	Steyning Town	v	St Francis	5-0
Franklands Village	v	T.S.C.	2-1				

SECOND ROUND

Haywards Heath Tn	v	Forest	5-0	Rye United	v	Seaford (at Sea.)	2-0
Ifield	v	Bexhill Town	3-0	Steyning Town	v	Franklands V	2*2, 5p4

SEMI-FINALS

Haywards Heath Town	v	Rye United	1*0	Ifield	v	Steyning Town	1-2

FINAL

Haywards Heath Town	v	Steyning Town	1-0	at Burgess Hill Town FC

LEADING GOALSCORERS 2000-01

DIVISION ONE

S Poulton	Pagham	25
P Lee	Selsey	23
J Laidlaw	Chichester	21
P Churchill	Horsham YMCA	19
G Amanuel	Redhill	18
S Banks	Three Bridges	17
J Laing	Hassocks	16
D Cashman	Three Bridges	16
D Schneider	Lancing	16
L Stevens	Pagham	15
M Sheriff	Whitehawk	14
A Carr	Burgess Hill Town	14
T Ford	Selsey	14

DIVISION TWO

G Jones	Worthing United	24
L Sale	Wealden	21
P Young	Broadbridge Heath	21
D Jones	Hailsham	20
D Shepherd	Southwick	18
A Stay	Oving	18

DIVISION THREE

P Gault	Franklands Village	30
J Scriven	Haywards Heath	22
S Loughton	Seaford	16
S Young	Seaford	16
N Mortimer	Ansty Rangers	14
A Dhiman	Ifield	14

PAST RECORDS

LEAGUE DIVISION ONE

1980-81	Pagham
1981-82	Peacehaven & Tels
1982-83	Peacehaven & Tels
1983-84	Whitehawk
1984-85	Steyning Town
1985-86	Steyning Town
1986-87	Arundel
1987-88	Pagham
1988-89	Pagham
1989-90	Wick
1990-91	Littlehampton Town
1991-92	Peacehaven & Tels
1992-93	Peacehaven & Tels
1993-94	Wick
1994-95	Peacehaven & Tels
1995-96	Peacehaven & Tels
1996-97	Burgess Hill Town
1997-98	Burgess Hill Town
1998-99	Burgess Hill Town
1999-00	Langney Sports
2000.01	Sidley United

LEAGUE DIVISION TWO

1980-81	Whitehawk
1981-82	Wick
1982-83	Horsham YMCA
1983-84	Portfield
1984-85	Shoreham
1985-86	Wick
1986-87	Pagham
1987-88	Langney Sports
1988-89	Seaford
1989-90	Bexhill Town
1990-91	Newhaven
1991-92	Portfield
1992-93	Crowborough Athletic
1993-94	Shoreham
1994-95	Mile Oak
1995-96	Saltdean United
1996-97	Littlehampton Town
1997-98	East Preston
1998-99	Sidley United
1999-00	Sidlesham
2000-01	Southwick

LEAGUE DIVISION THREE

1983-84	East Preston
1984-85	Oakwood
1985-86	Seaford Town
1986-87	Langney Sports
1987-88	Midway
1988-89	Saltdean
1989-90	Worthing United
1990-91	Ifield
1991-92	Hassocks
1992-93	Withdean
1993-94	Bosham
1994-95	Midhurst & Easebourne
1995-96	Ifield
1996-97	Sidlesham
1997-98	Lingfield
1998-99	Oving SC
1999-00	Bosham
2000-01	Rye United

LEAGUE CHALLENGE CUP

1980-81	Hastings Town
1981-82	Horsham YMCA
1982-83	Whitehawk
1983-84	Steyning Town
1984-85	Littlehampton Town
1985-86	Steyning Town
1986-87	Arundel
1987-88	Wick
1988-89	Pagham
1989-90	Langney Sports
1990-91	Littlehampton Town
1991-92	Peacehaven & Tels
1992-93	Peacehaven & Tels
1993-94	Whitehawk
1994-95	Hailsham Town
1995-96	Shoreham
1996-97	Wick
1997-98	Burgess Hill Town
1998-99	Burgess Hill Town
1999-00	Saltdean United
2000-01	Sidley United

DIVISION TWO LEAGUE CUP

1980-81	Whitehawk
1981-82	Lancing
1982-83	Shoreham
1983-84	Haywards Heath
1984-85	Chichester City
1985-86	Pagham
1986-87	Selsey
1987-88	Chichester City
1988-89	Midhurst
1989-90	Oakwood
1990-91	Chichester City
1991-92	Redhill
1992-93	Lancing
1993-94	Shoreham
1994-95	Horsham YMCA
1995-96	Selsey
1996-97	Sidley United
1997-98	Three Bridges
1998-99	Sidley United
1999-00	Sidlesham
2000-01	Peacehaven & Telscombe

MERIT TABLE WINNERS

1980-81	Arundel
1981-82	Wick
1982-83	Peacehaven & Tels
1983-84	Portfield
1984-85	Steyning Town
1985-86	Wick
1986-87	Pagham
1987-88	Three Bridges
1988-89	Wick
1989-90	Wick
1990-91	Littlehampton Town
1991-92	Peacehaven & Tels
1992-93	Pagham
1993-94	Wick
1994-95	Wick
1995-96	Wick
1996-97	Wick
1997-98	Burgess Hill Town
1998-99	Horsham YMCA
1999-00	Arundel
2000-01	Redhill

Top:
SIdley United FC
Back Row (l-r):
Adie Lusted (Physio), Dickie Day (Manager), Adam Day, Danny Poole, Gerard Moyse, Peter Heritage, Chris Copley, Jimmy Watson, Matt Dadswell, Peter Baker, Chris Shoesmith (Physio). Front Row: Tim Bolton, Owen Ball, Paul Sully, Wayne Farrier, Jason Finch, David Ward. Missing from photo Brad Poole and Paul Balch.

Centre:
Three Bridges FC
Photo: Alan Bell

Bottom:
Hailsham Town.
Back Row (l-r):
Matt Smith, Paul Bennett, Mark French, Kevin Isted, Russ Tanner, Paul Richardson, Tony Mould, Dave Adams.
Front Row:
Damien Smith, Duncan Jones, Scott French, Graham Overton, Jimmy Elford, Danny Wild.
Photo:
Roger Turner

ARUNDEL

Secretary: Doug Feest, 142 Aldsworth Road, Worthing. BN12 4UU Tel: 01903 249276

Ground: Mill Road, Arundel, West Sussex. Tel: 01903 882548

Directions: A27 from Worthing to Arundel over railway bridge to roundabout. Second exit into Queen Street to town centre, turn right over bridge. Car park leading to ground 100yards right

Capacity: 2,200 Seats: 100 Cover: 200 Floodlights: 206 lux

Clubhouse: 2 bars, kitchen, toilets, telephone, pool, darts, Sky TV. Normal pub hours. No food

HONOURS Sussex Co. Lg 57-58 58-59 86-87 (Lg Cup 86-87, Div 2 Cup 76-77, Res. Sect. 78-79, Res. Sect. Cup 78-79, Merit Table 80-81,Sussex Fives 1984 1987), Sussex RUR Charity Cup 68-69 72-73 78-79 79-80, Sussex Jnr Cup 07-08, West Sussex Lg (Res.) 70-71 (Malcolm Simmonds Cup 70-71)

PREVIOUS **League** : West Sussex 1896-1975 **Grounds:** Castle Park; Station Rd Ground

RECORD **Gate:** 2,200 v Chichester, League 67-68
Scorer: Paul J Bennett **Appearances:** 537, Paul Bennett (goalkeeper)
Win : 13-0 v Horsham YMCA (H), Sussex Co. Lge Div 1 21/12/85

Players progressing: John Templeman (Brighton & Hove Albion 1966)

FACT FILE
Founded: 1889
Nickname: Mulletts
Colours: Red & white halves/white/red
Change colours: Jade & black
Midweek matchday: Tuesday
Reserves' Lge: Sussex Co. Res Div (West)
Programme: 8 pages, free Editor: P Wells
Local Press: Arun Herald

99-00- Captain: Jon Tucker
P.o.Y.:Sam Wincell

CLUB PERSONNEL
Chairman: M.Peters
Vice Chairman: S Brennan
Manager: Mike Rowland

BURGESS HILL TOWN

Secretary: The General Secretary, Burges Hill Town F.C., Leylands Park, Burgess Hill, W.Sussex RH15 8AW Tel: 0144 242429 Email : bhtfcsocial@ aol.com

Ground: Leylands Park, Burgess Hill, West Sussex RH15 8AW Tel: 01444 242429
Capacity: 2,000 Seats: 100 Cover: Yes Floodlights: Yes

Directions: Turn east from A273 London Road into Leylands Road, take 4th left (signposted) Leyland Park. Nearest station Wivelsfield

Clubhouse: Bar & social facilities. Tea bar **Club Shop:** Yes Club badges available

HONOURS Sussex County Lg 75-76 96-97, 97-98,98-99; Lg Cup 73-74 79-80 97-98 98-99 (R-up 90-91), Div 2 74-75 (Cup 73-73), F/lit Cup 96-97, Res 76-77 77-78 91-92, Res. Sect. East 77-78 82-83 84-85, Res. Cup 82-83 98-99; Yth Sect. West 91-92 East 95-96 96-97 97-98 98-99 North 96-97 97-98; Sussex Fives 80; Mid-Sussex Lg 00-01 03-04 39-4046-47 56-57 (Div 2 03-04 (res), Div 3 20-21 36-37, Div 4 (res) 56-57; Mid Sussex Snr Cup 94-95 96-97; Montgomery Cup 39-40 56-57; Mowatt Cup 45-46; Sussex RUR Charity Cup 91-92; Sussex I'mediate Cup 76-77; Sussex Yth Lge 96-97 97-98, Cup 91-92 97-98

PREVIOUS **Leagues & Grounds:** None
BEST SEASON **FA Cup:** 4th Qual. Rd. 99-00, 1-4 v Hereford United
RECORD **Gate:** 854 v Clitheroe, FA Vase 4th Rd (H)

FACT FILE
Founded: 1882
Nickname: Hillians
Sponsors: Time 24
Colours: Yellow/white/yellow
Change colours: All red
Midweek matchday: Tuesday
Programme: Yes
Website: www.bhtfc.org.uk

CLUB PERSONNEL
Chairman: Ken Somerville
President: Jack Lake
Manager: Gary Croyden

2000-01
Captain: Sean Edwards
Top Scorer: Ashley Carr 15
P.o.Y.:Aidie Downey

CHICHESTER CITY UNITED

Company Sec: John F Hutter Tel: 01243 785839
28 Stockbrigde Gdns, Donnington, Chichester, W Sussex PO19 2QT

Hon. Secretary: Gary Rustell Tel: 01243 537978 (H)
102 Churchwood Drive, Tangmere, Nr Chichester, West Sussex PO20 6GB

Ground 1: Church Road, Portfield, Chichester, West Sussex PO19 4HN Tel: 01243 779875
Capacity: 2,000 Seats: 20 Cover: 200 Floodlights: Yes

Directions: A27 from Arundel to Chichester, take road to signposted city centre then 1st left (Church Rd) after supermarket r'bout. 1 mile from Chichester(BR)

Clubhouse:2 bars, pool, snooker, seating for 100, dance floor, darts, Teabar selling h & c food.

(the club will be moving to Oaklands Park, Chichester in 2001)

Ground 2: Oaklands Park, Chichester Tel: 01243 785978
Capacity: 2,500 Seats: 50 Cover: 500 Floodlights: Yes

Directions: Half mile north of city centre adjacent to Festival Theatre. Turn into Northgate car park from Oaklands Way and entrance is beside Tennis and Squash club.
1 mile from Chichester (BR) - walk north through city centre

Clubhouse: Licensed, open matchdays and some evenings. Tea bar Club Shop: No

PREVIOUS **Names**: Chichester FC (pre-1948), Chichester City 48-00.
Amalgamated with Portfield in 2000

FACT FILE
Formed 2000
Chichester (1873) Portfield (1896)
Sponsors: McDonalds
Nickname: Lilywhites
Colours: White/black/white
Change colours:Blue &Blackstripes,blue,black
Midweek matchday: Tuesday
Programme Editor: T Wallis
Local Press: Chichester Observer

CLUB PERSONNEL

Chairman: Simon Kenny
Match Secretary:Phil Littlejohns
Tel: 01243 528007
Press Officer: T Wallis (01705 464438)
Manager: Adrian Girdler
Chief Coach: Kevin Holston
Physio: NickTaylor
Club Steward: Andy Smith(01243 775455)

EASTBOURNE UNITED

Secretary: Sid Pittman, 43 Payne Avenue, Hove, BN3 5HD Tel No: 01273 885749 (H) 01273 824686 (W) and 0777 569 5064 (M)

Ground: The Oval, Channel View Rd, Eastbourne, East Sussex (011323-726989)
Capacity: 3,000 Seats: 160 Cover: 160 Floodlights: Yes

Directions: From A22 follow signs to eastbourne East/Seafront. Turn left onto seafront. Turn left into Channel View Rd at Princess Park and ground 1st right. 2 miles from Eastbourne (BR)

Clubhouse: Bar, lounge, dancefloor, stage, tea bar, board room **Club Shop:** Yes

HONOURS Sussex Co. Lg 54-55, Div 2 R-Up 99-00 Sussex Snr Cup(5) 60-61 62-64 66-67 68-69(R-up 89-90), Sussex RUR Charity Cup 55-56,Metropolitan Lg Cup 60-61,Athenian Lg Div 2 66-67 (Div 1 R-up 68-69), Sussex I'mediate Cup 65-66 68-69

PREVIOUS **Name:** Eastbourne Old Comrades **Leagues:** Sussex Co. 21-28 35-56; Metropolitan 56-64; Athenian 64-77;Isthmian 77-92 **Ground:** Lynchmere

RECORD **Attendance:** 11,000 at Lynchmere
Players progressing: B Salvage, T Funnell, M French, L.Barnard

FACT FILE
Founded: 1894
Nickname: The 'Us'
Colours: White/black/white
Change colours: All Sky Blue.
Midweek Matchday: Wednesday
Reserve Lge: Sussex County Res. Premier
Programme: 36 pages Editor:Kevin Townsend
Local Press: Eastbourne Gazette + Herald, Evening Argus

CLUB PERSONNEL
Chairman: Peter Snashall
Vice-Chairman: Kevin Townsend
President: Doug Sissons
Press Officer: Club Secretary
Manager: Micky French
Asst Manager: Dave Shearing
Physio: Jo Henderson

2000-01
Captain: Darren Smith P.o.Y.: Jimmy Chater

HAILSHAM TOWN

Secretary/Press Officer: Derek York, 59 Anglesey Avenue, Horsebridge, Hailsham BN27 3BQ
Tel: 01323 848024 (H)

Ground: The Beaconsfield, Western Road, Hailsham, East Sussex Tel: 01323 840446
Directions: A22 to Arlington Road, turn east, then left into South Road - left into Diplocks Way until Daltons. Four miles from Polegate (BR - Brighton-Eastbourne line); regular bus service from Eastbourne
Capacity: 2,000 Seats: None Cover: 300 Floodlights: Yes
Clubhouse: Hot and cold snacks. Open every evening, matchdays and Sundays, teabar

HONOURS Sussex County Lg Div 2 R-up 80-81, Southern Co'sComb. 74-75, Sussex RUR Charity Cup, Sussex I'mediate Cup, Hastings Snr Cup,Sussex Jnr Cup, E Sussex Lg Cup, Hailsham Charity Cup, John O'Hara Cup 95-96

PREVIOUS **League:** E Sussex, Southern Comb

BEST SEASON **FA Vase:** 5th Rd 88-89

RECORD **Gate:**1,350 v Hungerford, FA Vase Feb '89
Goalscorer: H Stevens 51, 95-96
Appearances: P Comber 713

FACT FILE
Founded: 1885
Nickname: None
Colours: Yellow &Green/Green & Yellow
Change colours: All white
Midweek matchday: Tuesday
Programme: Yes
Editor: Secretary
Admission: £3.00

2000-01
Captain & P.o.Y.: Kevin Isted
Top Scorer: Duncan HJones 24

CLUB PERSONNEL
President:S.Adams
Chairman: K.Savage-Brooks
Manager: Mark Leaney

HASSOCKS

Secretary: Bob Preston, 65 Oakhall Park, Burgess Hill, West Sussex RH15 0DA
Tel: 01444 245695

Ground: The Beacon, Brighton Rd, Hassocks Tel: 01273 846040
Capacity: 1,500 Seats: None Cover: 100 Floodlights: Yes

Directions: Off A273 Pyecombe Road to Burgess Hill, 300yds south of Stonepound cross roads (B2116) to Hurstpierpoint or Hassocks

Clubhouse: Clubroom, bar, kitchen Club Shop: No

HONOURS Sussex County Lg Div 3 91-92, Div 2 R-up 94-95, Res. Sect. East R-up 92-93; Southern Counties Comb. 76-77, Lg Cup R-up 79-80; Brighton Hove & Dist. Lg 71-72; Sussex Intermediate Cup 74-75 (R-up 80-81)

PREVIOUS **Leagues:** Mid Sussex; Brighton Hove & Dist.; Southern Co's Comb
Ground: Adastra Park, Hassocks (pre-1992)

RECORD **Attendance:** 610 v Burgess Hill Town, Sussex County Lge 96-97

FACT FILE
Founded: 1902
Nickname: The Robins
Sponsors: Icon
Colours: Red/white/red
Change colours: Blue/white/blue
Midweek Matchday: Tuesday/Wednesday
Programme: 24 pages, 50p
Editor: Dave Knight
Admission: £1.50
Local Press: Mid Sussex Times, Evening Argus

CLUB PERSONNEL
President: Maurice Boxall
Chairman: Jim Goodrum
Press Off . : Dave Knight (01273 842023)
Manager: Dave John

HORSHAM YMCA

Secretary: Robin Bishop , Rosena Cottage, Brighton Road,Lower Beeding, West Sussex RH13 6NH. Tel Nos: 01408 891622 (H) 01403 322100 (W)
Email Address: rsbishop@rosenafsnet.co.uk

Ground: Gorings Mead, Horsham Tel: 01403 252689
Capacity: 1000 Seats: 150 Cover: 200 Floodlights: Yes

Directions: Approaching Horsham fron the East on A281 Brighton Road, the ground is on left & signposted opposite Gorings Mead

HONOURS Sussex Co Lge Div 2 65-66 82-83 R-up 94-95 (Lg Cup 81-82, Invitation Cup66-67 67-68, Div 2 Invit. Cup 59-60 61-62 94-95) Sussex RUR Cup Winners 2000-01

PREVIOUS **Leagues:** Horsham & Dist/Brighton & Hove/Mid Sussex
Grounds: Lyons Field, Kings Road

RECORD **Attendance:** 950 v Chelmsford City , FA Cup 2000

BEST SEASON: **FA Cup:** 4th Qual. Rd. 99-00 2-3 v Chelmsford City

FACT FILE
Founded: 1898
Nickname: YM's
Sponsors: Principal Copiers
Colours: White/black/red
Change colours: All Red
Midweek Matchday: Tuesday
Local Press: West Sussex County Times

CLUB PERSONNEL
Chairman:John Cashman
Match Secretary: Robin Bishop
Tel: 01403 891622 Manager: John Suter
Physio: Robin Bishop

2000-01
Captain: Lee Butcher
Ps.o.Y.: Ellis Hooper and Jason Dumbrill
Top Scorer:Phil Churchill 36

LITTLEHAMPTON TOWN

Secretary: John Savage, 66 Nelson Road, Worthing. BN12 6EN. (01903 502850)

Ground: The Sportsfield, St Flora's Road, Littlehampton (01903 713944)
Capacity: 4,000 Seats: 260 Cover: 260 Floodlights: Yes

Directions: 10 minutes walk from Littlehampton station (BR) - turn left alongTerminus Rd, continue through High Street and Church Rd to junction with St Flora's Rd (left)

Club Shop: No, but metal badges available
Clubhouse: Sportsman (Private Club). Separate board room & tea bar

HONOURS Sussex Co. Lg 58-59 (jt with Shoreham) 75-77 84-85 90-91 96-97
Sussex Senior Cup 73-74

RECORD **Gate:** 4,000 v Northampton, FA Cup 1st Rd Proper 90-91

BEST SEASON **FA Vase** Semi-Final 90-91
FA Cup: 1st Round 90-91

FACT FILE
Founded: 1894
Nickname: Marigolds
Colours: Gold/black/black
Change: All white
Midweek Matches: Tuesday
Programme:
Editor:
Local Press: Littlehampton Gazette

CLUB PERSONNEL
President: Ian Cunningham
Chairman:Mike Blackmore
Manager: Andy Taylor
2000-01
Captain: Barry Pidgeeon
P.o.Y.: Darren Akmenkalns
Top Scorer: deren Woods 18

PAGHAM

Secretary: Ken Randall,1Watson Way,Westergate,Nr Chichester, West Sussex PO20 6WN
Tel: 01243 5459694 (H)

Ground: Nyetimber Lane, Pagham, West Sussex Tel: 01243 266112
Capacity: 2,000 Seats: 200 Cover: 200 Floodlights: Yes

Directions: Turn off A27 Chichester by-pass (signposted A259 Pagham). Ground invillage of Nyetimber. Three miles from Bognor (BR). Buses 260 & 240

Clubhouse: Bar open matchdays and some evenings. Hot food, pool, darts,satellite TV. Tea bar
Club Shop: No

HONOURS Sussex Co. Lg R-up 80-81 87-88 88-89 92-93 (Div 2 78-79 86-87, Lg Cup88-89, Div 2 Cup 71-72 85-86, Res. Sect. West 80-81, Res Section Cup 77-78 80-81 87-88 88-89 90-91 96-97; Sussex F'lit Cup R-up 88-89; Sussex RUR Charity Cup88-89 (R-up 93-94); West Sussex Lg 65-66 68-69 69-70; Malcolm Simmonds Cup 67-68; Sussex I'mediate Cup 66-67

PREVIOUS **Leagues:** Chichester 1903-50; West Sussex 50-69 **Grounds:** None

RECORDS **Gate:** 1,200 v Bognor, 1971 **Scorer:** Mark Vickers/ R Deluca
Win: 10-1 v Seaford Town (A), Sussex County League Division Two, 1970
Defeat: 0-7 v Newport IOW (H), FA Amateur Cup, mid-1970s

FACT FILE
Founded: 1903
Nickname: Lions
Sponsors: City Sales Centre
Colours: White/black/red
Change colours: Yellow/green/green
Midweek Matchday: Tuesday
Reserve's League: Sussex Co. Res Premier
Programme: 12 pages, 50p
Editor: Rob Peach
Local Press: Bognor Observer

CLUB PERSONNEL
Chairman: Graham Peach
Vice-Chairman: Steve Newdick
President: A Peirce
Press Officer: John Rose(01243 545694)
Comm. Manager: Chairman
Manager: Richie Reynolds
Asst Manager: Kevin Hotson
2000-01 Capt: Paul Worsfold,P.o.Y.: Ashley Edwards Top scorer: Steve Poulton 33

Saltdean United. Back Row (l-r): Ian Costello, Paul Boxall, Phil Horsham, Darren Longley, Shaun Grice, Jamie Bryant, Ben Swetham, Simon Jones, Kevin Townsend. Front Row: Grant Bean, Syd Harman, Tony Flower, Sean Randall, Damian Dobbyn, Reece Head. Photo: Roger Turner

Littlehampton Town FC. Photo: Garry Letts

Sidley United, John O'Hara League Challenge Cup Winners and Division One Champions. Photo: Roger Turner

PEACEHAVEN & TELSCOMBE

Secretary: Mrs Margaret Edwards, 2,Tuscan Court, The Esplanade, Telscombe Cliffs, East Sussex BN10 7HF Tel: 01273 583022 (H) 07803 845329 (M)

Ground: Piddinghoe Avenue, Peacehaven, E. Sussex (01273 582471)
Directions: Arriving from Brighton on A259, cross r'bout and Piddinghoe Ave. is next left after 2nd set of lights - ground at end. From Newhaven Piddinghoe Ave. is first right after first set of lights. Three miles from Newhaven(BR). Peacehaven is served by Brighton to Newhaven and Eastbourne buses
Capacity: 3,000 Seats: None Cover: 250 Floodlights: Yes
Clubhouse: Bar open evenings and weekends, pool darts, hot and cold food available. Tea bar

HONOURS Sussex Co. Lg 78-79 81-82 82-83 91-92 92-93 94-95 95-96 (R-up 77-78 80-81 90-91, Lg Cup 91-92 92-93, Div 2 R-up 75-76, Div 2 Cup 75-76, Norman Wingate Tphy 82-83 91-92 92-93, Hayden Tphy 82-83 92-93, Div 2 Invitation Cup69-70, Sussex Snr Cup R-up 81-82 92-93, Sussex RUR Charity Cup 77-78 81-82 92-93 (R-up 80-81 89-90 90-91 94-95 95-96), Brighton Charity Cup 91-92 92-93 93-94, Vernon Wentworth 91-92 92-93

RECORD Attendance: 1,420 v Littlehampton, Lge 91

PREVIOUS Leagues: Lewes; Brighton

BEST SEASON FA Cup: 4th Qual. Rd 90-91 **FA Vase:** 6th Rd (Q-F) 95-96, 5th Rd 92-93

FACT FILE
Founded: 1923
Nickname: The Tye
Sponsors: Anchor Garage
Colours: All white
Change colours: Royal Blue
Midweek Matches: Tuesday
Programme: Yes
Editor: Secretary

CLUB PERSONNEL
Chairman: Jim Edwards
Match Sec: Fred Parris
Press Officer: Secretary
Manager: Peter Edwards

REDHILL

Secretary: Neil Hoad, 2b Earlswood Rd, Redhill, Surrey RH1 6HE Tel: 01737 213847
Ground: Kiln Brow, Three Arch Road, Redhill, Surrey Tel: 01737 762129
Email: michael@jbjovi.fsnet.co.uk

Directions: On left hand side of A23, two and a half miles south of Redhill
Capacity: 2,000 Seats: 150 Cover: 150 Floodlights: Yes
Club Shop: Sells usual range of souvenires. Contact Spencer Mitchell - 01737 780634
Clubhouse: Social club, bar, canteen, board room, club shop, tanoy, toilets

HONOURS Athenian Lg 24-25 83-84 (LgCup 69-70 70-71), East & West Surrey Lg. 1902-03, Southern Sub Sen West Lg. 1902-03, Surrey Snr Cup 28-29 65-66, Gilbert Rice F'lit Cup 80-81, Sussex Co. Lg Div 2 Cup 91-92, Southern Co's Comb. Cup 90-91,98-99

PREVIOUS **Leagues:** E & W Surrey; Spartan 09-10; Southern Sub; London 21-23; Athenian 23-84; Spartan 84-88
Grounds: Memorial Sports Ground, London Road 1894-1986

BEST SEASON **FA Amtr Cup:** Semi-Final 25 **FA Cup:** 1st Round 57-58

RECORDS **Attendance:** 1,200 v Crystal Palace & All Star XI, Brian Medlicott Testimonial 1989
Goalscorer: Steve Turner 119 **Appearances:** Brian Medlicott 766
Win : 10-0 v Saltdean United (H), Sussex Co. Lg Div 1 18/4/98
Defeat : 1-7 v Peacehaven & Telscombe (H), Sussex County Lg Cup 9/2/93

FACT FILE
Founded: 1894 Nickname: Reds/Lobsters
Sponsors: Trident Microsystems Ltd.
Colours: All red Change: White/black
Midweek matchday: Tuesday
Reserve League: Sussex Co.Lg
2000-01 Prog: 52-104 pages, 50p
2001-02 A4 Prog: 60 pages 50p
Editor: Michael Stewart
Local Press:Surrey Mirror/Redhill&Reigate Life

CLUB PERSONNEL
Chair: Nick Creasey V.Chair: Alan Thurlbeck
President: Malcolm Chatfield
Press Officer: Michael Stewart
Man: Russell Mason Coach: Rob O'Shaunsey
Physio: Andy Peppercorn
2000-01
Leading Goalscorer: Germain Amanuel 22
Captain: Darren Hinton
P.o.Y.: Luke Gedling

RINGMER

Secretary: Gary Bullen, 13 Browns Parth, Uckfield, East sussex TN22 1LN
Tel Nos: 07769 936272 (M) 01825 769748 (H)

Ground: Caburn Ground, Anchor Field, Ringmer Tel: 01273 812738
Capacity: 1,000 Seats: 100 Cover: Yes Floodlights: Yes

Directions: From Lewes road turn into Springett Avenue opposite Ringmer village green. Anchor Field first left. Three miles from Lewes (BR)

Clubhouse: 2 bars, function room, boardroom, tea bar
Club Shop: Club ties & metal badges

HONOURS Sussex Co. Lg 70-71, Div 2 68-69, Invit Cup 66-67; Res. Sect. East 79-80 80-81 (R-up 89-90), Yth Section 87-88, Yth SectionEast 87-88; Sussex Snr Cup 72-73 (R-up 80-81); Sussex Jnr Cup 25-26; Sussex Express Sen Charity Cup 94-95

PREVIOUS **League:** Brighton **Grounds:** None **Names:** None

BEST SEASON **FA Cup** 1st Rd Proper 70-71

RECORD **Gate:** 1,200 in FA Cup

FACT FILE
Founded: 1906
Nickname: The Blues
Colours: Sky & navy/navy/navy
Change colours: All yellow
Midweek Matchday: Tuesday
Programme: Yes
Editor: Martin BUrke (01797 230572)
Admission: £3.00
Local Press: Sussex Express

CLUB PERSONNEL
President: Sir G Christie
Chairman: Richard Soan
Manager: Glen Geard
Press Officer: Martin Burke(01797 230572)
Match Sec:John McWhirter (01323 847743)
2000-01
Captain: James Morris
P.o.Y.:Stephen Purser
Top Scorer:Jason Reid 17

SALTDEAN UNITED

Secretary: Iain Fielding, 40 Rowan Way, Rottingdean, Brighton BN2 7FP
Tel: 01273 304995

Ground: Hill Park, Combe Vale, Saltdean, Brighton Tel: 01273 309898
Capacity: 2,000 Seats: 50 Cover: Yes Floodlights: Yes
Club Website: www.the-tigers.co.uk

Directions: A259 coast road east from Brighton to Saltdean Lido, left into Arundel Drive West, and Saltdean Vale to bridle path at beginning of Combe Vale. Club 200yds along track

Club Shop: Metal badges available

Clubhouse: Licensed bar, lounge, juke box, video games, board room, tea bar.Pool table

HONOURS Sussex Co. Lg Div 3 88-89, Div 2 95-96: John O'Hara Lg Cup Winners 2000

PREVIOUS **League:** Brighton Hove & Dist Ground: None

RECORD **Attendance:** 676

FACT FILE
Founded: 1966 Nickname: Tigers
Sponsors: FDM
Colours: Red & black/black/black
Change colours: Blue & white
Programme: Yes
Editor:Greg Hadfield
Local Press: Brighton Evening Argus & Sussex Express

CLUB PERSONNEL
Chairman: Greg Hadfield
Vice Chairman:Mike Walker
President: Jim Bower
Press Officer: Iain Fielding
Manager: Steve Bean
Physio: Stan Pearce

2000-01
Leading Goalscorer: Sean Randall
Captain: Reece Head
P.o.Y: Reece Head

SELSEY

Secretary: Danny Glew, 2 Colt Street, Selsey, Chichester W.Sussex PO20 9EU
Tel: 01243 605027

Ground: High Street Ground, Selsey, Chichester, West SussexTel: 01243 603420
Capacity: 2,250 Seats: 50 Cover: Yes Floodlights: Yes

Directions: Through Selsey High Street to fire station. Take turning into car park alongside the station. Entrance is in the far corner. Regular buses from Chichester

Clubhouse: Bar, hospitality room, lounge, toilets, kitchen

HONOURS Sussex Co. Lg R-up 89-90 (Div 2 63-64 75-76 (R-up 86-87), Div 2 Cup 86-87 (R-up 84-85), Div 2 Invitation Cup 63-64, Sussex 5-aside 88-89), Sussex SnrCup R-up 63-64, Sussex I'mediate Cup 58-59, Sussex Jnr Cup(Reserves) 76-77,West Sussex Lg 54-55 55-56 57-58 58-59 60-61 (Malcolm Simmonds Cup 55-56 56-57 57-58 58-59)

PREVIOUS **Leagues:** Chichester & Dist.; West Sussex

RECORD **Gate:** 750-800 v Chichester or Portfield, 50's

FACT FILE
Founded: 1903
Nickname: Blues
Sponsors: Ariel Cars
Colours: Blue/white/blue
Change colours:All yellow
Midweek Matchday: Tuesday
Programme Editor: Secretary
Match Secretary: Mandie Glew

CLUB PERSONNEL
President: Roy Glew
Chairman: Mike Hurst
Press Officer: Secretary
Manager:Danny Hinshelwood

2000-01
Captain & P.o.Y.: Alun Morey
Top Scorer: Pau lLee 29

SIDLESHAM

WE APOLOGISE FOR THE LACK OF DETAIL AVAILABLE ABOUT THIS CLUB, BUT DESPITE REPEATED REQUESTS NOTHING HAS BEEN FORTHCOMING

Secretary: Mick Homer,2, North Common farm, Golf Links Lane,Selsey, Chichester, West Sussex. PO20 9DP Tel No: 01243 603977
Email: mbheh0428@virgin.net

Ground: Sidlesham Recreation Ground, Sidlesham. Tel: 01243 641538

Directions: From the Chichester bypass take the B2145, signposted Hunston/Selsey Head towards Selsey. Upon entering Sidlesham the ground is on the right between houses

2000-01 Captain: Calvin Hore P.o.Y.: Billy Gill Top Scorer: Lee Mould 19

FACT FILE
Colours: Yellow & Green/green/yellow
Change colours: Red /white/red

CLUB PERSONNEL
Chairman: Alan Parker
Tel: 01243 513891 (H)
Vice Chairman: Roy Parker
Manager: Richard Towers

Southwick. Rich City Sussex Division Two Champions. Photo: Roger Turner

Steve Monk scores for Hailsham Town in a top of the table clash with Southwick. Photo: Roger Turner

Oving FC. Photo: Graham Cotterill

SIDLEY UNITED

Secretary: Brian Martin, 30 Mayo Lane, Bexhill on Sea, East Sussex,TN39 5EA

Ground: Gullivers Sports Ground, Glovers Lane, Sidley, Bexhill-on-Sea
Tel: 01424 217078
Capacity: 1,500 Seats: None Cover: 150 Floodlights: Yes

Directions: From Brighton on A259 to Bexhill bypass traffic lights, left intoLondon Road, continue into Sidley, right into Glovers Lane and 1st left into North Road.
One mile from Bexhill (BR)

Clubhouse: Large bar area & function room. Tea bar
Club Shop: No, but metal badges are available.

HONOURS Sussex Co. Lg Div 1 00-01 Jphn O'Hara League Cup: 00-01Div 2 58-59 64-65 98-99, Div. 2 Cup 98-99, Div 2 Invit. Cup 57-58; Sussex Intermediate Cup 47-48, Sussex Jnr Cup 24-25

PREVIOUS **Leagues:** East Sussex; Hastings & District
Grounds: None

RECORD **Attendance:** 1,300 in 1959

FACT FILE

Founded: 1906
Nickname: Blues
Sponsors: M.T.Drains
Colours: Navy & sky/navy/navy & sky
Change colours: Yellow & Black
Midweek Matchday: Tues/ Weds
Programme: Yes Editor: Graham Weston
Local Press: Bexhill Observer, Bexhill News

CLUB PERSONNEL
President: Tom Hyland
Chairman: Dickie Day
Joint Managers: Glen Sully & Peter Heritage
2000-01
Captain & P.o.Y.: Wayne Farrier
Top Scorer: Paul Balch 12

SOUTHWICK

Secretary: Derek Earley, 1309 Poplar Ave.,Hangleton, Hove BN3 8PN Tel: 01273 328769

Ground: Old Barn Way, off Manor Hall Way, Southwick, Brighton BN43 4NT Tel: 01273 701010
Directions: Five minutes walk from either Fishergate or Southwick BR stations.By car A27 from Brighton take 1st left after `Southwick' sign to Leisure Centre. Ground adjacent.
Capacity: 3,500 Seats: 220 Cover: 1,220 Floodlights: Yes
Clubhouse: Weekdays 12-3 & 6-11, all day Sat., normal hrs Sunday. Members bar & board-room with bar. Matchday snacks from tea bar.

HONOURS Isthmian Lg Div 2 Sth 85-86, Sus. Co. Lg 25-26 27-28 29-30 47-48 68-69 74-75 (R-up x 9, Lg Cup 77-78 ,Div 1 Invit. Cup 65-66, Div 2 R-up 65-66), Combined Co's Lg R-up 84-85, Sus.Snr Cup x 10, Sus. RUR Charity Cup (10) 1896-97 08-09 10-11 24-26 27-30 37-38 76-77, W. Sus. Lg1896-97 97-98 1908-09 10-11, Sus. Jnr Cup 1891-92.

PREVIOUS **Leagues:** West Sussex 1896-1920; Sussex County 20-52 54-84; Metropolitan52-54; Combined Co's 84-85; Isthmian 85-92.

BEST SEASON **FA Cup:** 1st Round 74-75, 0-5 v Bournemouth
FA Amtr Cup: 3rd Rd. 28-29 **FA Vase:** 3rd Rd. 79-80 85-86
RECORD **Attendance:** 3,200 v Showbiz side 1971
Players progressing: Charles & William Buttenshaw (Luton 1948).

FACT FILE
Founded: 1882
Nickname: Wickers
Sponsors: Guildcare Nursing Homes
Colours: Red & black stripes/black/red
Change Colours: All white
Midweek matchday: Tuesday
Reserve League: Sussex Co. Res Div
Programme: Yes
Editor/ Press Off.: Paul Symes 01273 594142
Local Press : Evening Argus, Shoreham Herald, Adur Herald.

CLUB PERSONNEL
Chairman: Peter Keene
Vice-Chairman: Dave Cook
President: Dr D W Gordon

Manager: Malcolm Saunders
Asst Manager: Dennis Nicholl
Coach: Paul Croft

THREE BRIDGES

Secretary: Martin Clarke, 18 Mannings Close, Pound Hill, Crawley RH10 3TX
Tel: 01293 883726 (H), 07885 662940 (Mob)
Ground: Jubilee Field, Jubilee Walk,Three Bridges, Crawley, West Sussex
Tel: 01293 442000
Capacity: 3,500 Seats: 120 Cover: 600 Floodlights: Yes
Directions: From Three Bridges station, turn L. to Crawley. At 2nd T'light turn R. into Three Bridges road. Take 1st left (opp. Plough Inn) into Jubilee Walk.
Clubhouse: Open every day 12 noon - 11pm (10.30pm Sunday) Carpeted lounge. Bar serving food, Players bar, Pool, Darts, Satelite big screen TV, Dance floor. Separate Tea Bar serving hot food on match days. Disabled toilet facilities.
Club Shop: No
HONOURS Sussex I'mediate Cup 84-85 Sussex Co. Lg R-up 85-86 87-88 88-89 Div 2 54-55, R-up 68-69, 73-74, 79-80, 98-99, Invitation Cup 70-71, Div 2 Invitation Cup 62-63, 73-74, Sussex RUR Charity Cup 82-83 R-up 85-86, 87-88, 88-89. Co. Lge Div. 2 5-a-side 97-98, R-up 98-99

PREVIOUS **League s:**Mid Sussex; E. Grinstead, Redhill&District 36-52 **Grounds:** None
Names: Three Bridges 01-18, Three Bridges Worth 19-53, Three Bridges United 54-64.

RECORD **Attendance:** 2,000 v Horsham, 1948

FACT FILE
Founded: 1901
Nickname: Bridges
Sponsors: Radio Mercury
Colours: Amber & black/black/black
Change colours: Blue & white/blue/white
Midweek Matchday: Tuesday
Programme: Yes
Editor: Andy West (01293 883163)
Local Press: Crawley Observer, Crawley News

CLUB PERSONNEL
Chairman: Alan Bell
Press Officer: Alf Blackler
Manager: Daren Barker
Asst. Manager: Alan Watson

2000-01
Leading goalscorer: Steve Banks 24
Captain: Paul Leaver
P.o.Y.: Paul Leaver

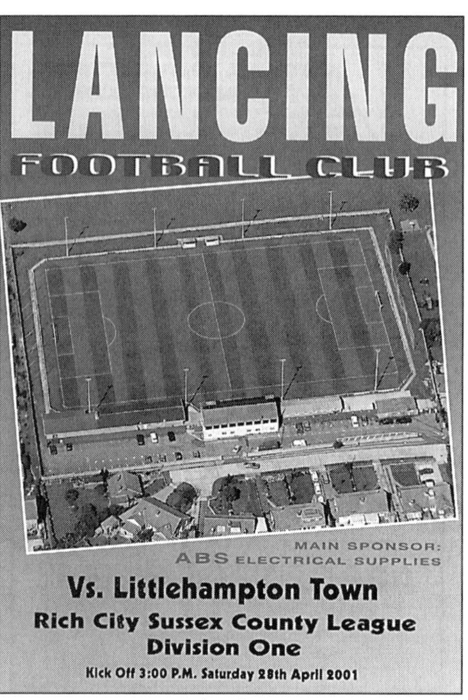

LANCING
FOOTBALL CLUB
MAIN SPONSOR:
ABS ELECTRICAL SUPPLIES
Vs. Littlehampton Town
Rich City Sussex County League
Division One
Kick Off 3:00 P.M. Saturday 28th April 2001

Lancing

Hailsham Town Football Club

(founded 1885)

RICH CITY SUSSEX COUNTY FOOTBALL LEAGUE

Monday 7th May 2001

Hailsham Town versus Crawley Down

50p

Hailsham Town

WELCOME TO KILN BROW, THE HOME OF

REDHILL

FOOTBALL CLUB

Rich City Sussex County League
Division One
REDHILL
V
EAST PRESTON
Saturday 5th May 2001.

Three Bridges

Wick Football Club
Members of the Sussex County Football Association and the Sussex County Football League
11 AM Monday 7th May
WHITEHAWK
RICH CITY COUNTY LEAGUE DIVISION ONE
SWANDEAN

Wick

WHITEHAWK

Secretary: John Rosenblatt, 25 Arundel Street, Brighton BN2 5TH Tel: 01273 680322

Ground: The Enclosed Ground, East Brighton Park Tel: 01273 609736
Capacity: 3,000 Seats: None Cover: 500 Floodlights: Yes

Directions: Follow Brighton seafront road towards Newhaven, turn inland (Arundel Road) oppo site Marina, 3rd right into Roedean Road, 1st left intoWilson Ave. 3 miles from Brighton (BR); take Newhaven, Eastbourne or Saltdean bus to Marina

Clubhouse: Licensed bar, pool, darts. Board room. Tea bar Club Shop: No

Honours: Sussex Co. Lg 61-62 63-64 83-84 (Div 2 67-68 80-81, Lg Cup 82-83 93-94, Invitation Cup 60-61 69-70, Div 2 Cup 80-81), Sussex Snr Cup 50-51 61-62,Sussex RUR Charity Cup 54-55 58-59 90-91, Sussex I'mediate Cup 49-50, Sussex Jnr Cup 48-49 51-52, Brighton Charity Cup 51-52 59-60 61-62 82-83 87-88 88-89 89-90 90-91 97-98 98-99 99-00 Worthing Charity Cup 82-83

PREVIOUS **League:** Brighton Hove & Dist**Grounds:** None
Name: Whitehawk & Manor Farm Old Boys (until 1958)

BEST SEASON **FA Vase:** 5th Round 93-94

RECORDS **Gate:** 2,100 v Bognor Regis Town, FA Cup 4th Qualifying Rd replay 88-89
Scorer: Billy Ford **Appearances:** Ken Powell 1,103

FACT FILE
Founded: 1945
Nickname: Hawks
Sponsors: Precision Metal Products
Colours: All red
Change colours: All blue
Midweek Matchday: Wednesday
Programme: £3.50 with admission
Editor: Ken Taylor (01273 735154)
Local Press: Evening Argus

CLUB PERSONNEL
President: Ron Wiltshire
Chairman/Comm Mgr: Ken Powell
Match Sec: Fred Moore
Manager: Paul Hubbard
Asst Manager: Alan Head

WICK

Secretary: Paul Beard, 2 Van Gogh Place, North Bersted, Bognor Regis, W.Sussex PO22 9BG
Tel: 01243 822063 (H)

Ground: Crabtree Park, Coomes Way, Wick, Littlehampton, W. SussexTel: 01903 713535
Capacity: 2,000 Seats: 50 Cover: 200 Floodlights: Yes

Directions: A27 to Crossbush, left at traffic lights signed Littlehampton, after 1 mile cross level crossing, turn left into Coombes Way next to Locomotive PH - ground at end. One and a half miles from Littlehampton (BR)

Clubhouse: First floor. Capacity 120. Tea bar Club Shp: No

HONOURS Sussex Snr Cup 92-93; Sussex Co. Lg 89-90 93-94, Lg Cup 87-88 96-97 (R-up 93-94 94-95), Div 2 81-82 85-86, Div 2 Cup R-up 81-82; Norman Wingate Tphy88-89 90-91, Res. Sect West 87-88 90-91 94-95; Sussex 5-aside R-up 85-86;Sussex RURCharity Cup 89-90 97-98;98-99 Gilbert Rice F'lit Cup R-up 80-81 81-82; Sussex Jnr Cup 59-60; Brighton Charity Cup 85-86; Sussex F'lit Cup R-Up 94-95

PREVIOUS **League:** West Sussex **Grounds:** Southfields Rec

RECORD **Attendance:** 900

FACT FILE
Founded: 1892Nickname: Wickers
Sponsors: Swandean
Colours: Red & black/black/black
Change colours: All white
Midweek Matchdays: Tuesday
Reserve League: Sussex Co. Reserve Div
Programme: Yes
Editor:Secretary
Local Press: Littlehampton Gazette

CLUB PERSONNEL
Chairman: Barry Wadsworth
Vice-Chairman: T.B. A.
President: Jack Croft
Manager: Carl Stabler
Asst Manager: Ian Cole

2000-01
Captain: Gary Young P.o.Y.: Gareth Green
Top Scorer: Darren annis 19

BOSHAM

Secretary: Phil Robinson, 3 Rowan Road, Havant Hampshire PO9 2UX
Tel: 02392 345276 (H) 02392 835398 (B) 0793 088 3217 (M)
Email: jennyphil@roft2.freeserve.co.uk

Ground: Bosham Recreation Ground, Walton Lane, Bosham, W. Sussex
Tel: 01243 574011

Directions: From Chichester take the A259 towards Portsmouth.
On reaching Bosham turn left at the Swan P.H. roundabout.
1/2 mile to T junction, turn left & car park 50 yds on left.

Honours: Sussex County Lge Div. 3 99-00

FACT FILE

Colours: Red/white/red

CLUB PERSONNEL

Chairman: Dick Doncaster
Tel: 01243 375184
Manager: Steve Jefkins

BROADBRIDGE HEATH

Secretary: Richard Solman, 13 Monks Court, Monks Walk, Reigate, Surrey RH2 0SR
Tel: 01737 212335

Ground: Broadbridge Heath Sports Centre, Wickhurst Lane, Horsham Tel: 01403 211311
Capacity: 1,300 Seats: 300 Cover: 300 Floodlights: Yes

Directions: Alongside A24, Horsham north/south bypass. From the A24 Horsham Bypass, at thelarge roundabout/underpass take the Broadbridge Heath Bypass towards Guildford and then at the first roundabout turn left into Wickhurst Lane.

Clubhouse: Bar. Kitchen serving meals,

HONOURS Sussex Yth Lg N. Div. 99-00, Southern Yth Lg S. Div. 00-01

PREVIOUS **Leagues:** Horsham, West Sussex, Southern Co's Comb

RECORD **Attendance:** 240

FACT FILE

Founded: 1919 Nickname: Bears
1st Team Sponsors: Identilam
Youth Sponsors: Broadbridge Heath Peugeot
Colours: All royal blue Change: All red or white
Midweek matches: Tuesday
Prog: Yes Ed: Andy Crisp (01403 252273)
Admission: £2.50

CLUB PERSONNEL

Chairman: Keith Soane
President: G W Manketelow
Manager: Sam Chapman
2000-01 Leading goalscorer: Paul Young 27
Captain: Paul Stevens
P.o.Y.: Gary Brown

CRAWLEY DOWN

Secretary: Bob Rashbrook, 3 Collier Row, Southgate, Crawley, West Sussex RH10 6ES
Tel 01293 411457 (H)

Ground: The Haven Sportsfield, Hophurst Lane, Crawley Down.
Tel: 01342 717140
Capacity: 1000 Seats: None Cover: 50 Floodlights: No

Directions: From B2028, follow signpost for village to War Memorial, turn left into Hophurst Lane, ground 100 yards on left. From A22, Felbridge, left into Crawley Down Road, ground 2 miles uphill on right.

HONOURS Sussex County Lge Div 3 R-Up 95-96
Sussex Intermediate Chall. Cup R-up 95-96

PREVIOUS **League:** Mid Sussex Football League

FACT FILE

Colours: All red Programme:Yes
Website: www.partners-solutions.co.uk / crawley down info

CLUB PERSONNEL

Chairman: Brian Suckling
Vice-Chairman: Michael Martin
President: Tony Clements
Manager : Stuart Hobbs
Match Secretary: As Secretary
Physio: Mike Green
2000-01 Captain: Bob Chambers
P.o.Y. & Top Scorer: Matt Stevenson (19)

CROWBOROUGH ATHLETIC

Secretary: Phil Sharman, High Ridge, Green Lane, Crowborough TN6 2DF

Ground: Alderbrook Recreation Ground, Fermor Road, Crowborough
Tel: 01892 661893

Directions: Turn east off A26 at Crowborough. Cross traffic lights, through High Street, right into Croft Rd, continue into Whitehall Rd and Fermor Rd, Alderbrook is 2nd right after mini-r'bout.
Capacity: 1,000 Seats: None Cover: 200 Floodlights: Yes.

Clubhous Bar facilities & tea bar on matchdays Club Shop: No, metal badges available

HONOURS Sussex Co. Lg Div 1 92-93 (Div 2 Cup 77-78, Div 3 R-up),
Sussex Intermediate Cup 86-87

PREVIOUS **League:** Brighton **Grounds:** None

RECORD **Gate:** 2,600 v Brighton & Hove Alblon (Friendly) 13.05.01

FACT FILE

Founded: 1894 Nickname: Crows.
Colours: Blue & white/white/blue
Change colours: All red.
Midweek Matchday: Tuesday
Prog. Editor: James Young: 01892 669021
Local Press: Kent & Sussex Courier,Sussex Express

CLUB PERSONNEL

President:Tony Clark Chairman: Barry J Sykes
Press Officer: Peter Crisp (01892 655470).
Manager: Harry Smith
2000-01
Captain: Adrian James
P.o.Y.: Shaun Fuller
Top Scorer: James Latimer 11

EAST GRINSTEAD TOWN

Secretar Martin Hill, The Flat,@A Saxbys Lane, Lingfield, Surrey RH7 6DN
Ground: East Court, East Grinstead Tel: 01342 325885
Directions: A264 Tunbridge Wells road (Moat Road) until mini-r'bout at bottom of Blackwell Hollow, turn immediately right by club sign then 1st left, ground 200yds down lane past rifle club on right.
Capacity: 3,000 Seats: None Cover: 400 Floodlights: Yes Club Shop: No
Clubhouse: Open 1.30-10.30 matchdays, 6-11 midweek matches. Hot food available.

HONOURS Sussex RUR Charity Cup (R-up 74-75); Sussex Co. Lg Invitation Cup 51-52; Sussex Jnr Cup (jt) 07-08; Sussex Youth Cup 86-87; Southern Amtr Lg Snr Div 3 31-32; Mid-Sussex Lg x 6, Lg Cup x 7; Brighton Lg x 3, Lg Cup x 3
PREVIOUS Leagues: Mid-Sussex 00-15 35-37; Sussex Co. 20-32; Southern Amateur 32-35.
RECORD **Attendance:** 2,006 v Lancing, FA Amateur Cup 8/11/48
Appearances: Guy Hill in 19 seasons - 1977-94
2000-01 Captain & P.o.Y.: Dave Gelattly **Top Scorers:** James Hylton & Stuart Hardy 17

FACT FILE
Founded: 1890 Nickname: Wasps
Sponsors: Rydon Group.
Colours: Gold/black/black
Change colours: All Blue
Midweek Matchday: Tuesday.
Reserves Lge: Sussex Co. Reserve Div East
Programme: 36 pages, 50p (Bruce Talbot)
Press Off.: Bruce Talbot 01293 543809
Local Press: East Grinstead Observer/East Grinstead Courier,SportsArgus
Website: www.egffc.co.uk
CLUB PERSONNEL
Chairman: Phil Cowlard Pres: Colin Dixon
Manager: Bobby Smith
Physio: Peter Kenward

EAST PRESTON

Secretary: Keith Freeman, 41 Ambersham Cres., East Preston, West Sussex BN161AJ Tel: 01903 771158
Ground: Roundstone Recreation Ground, East Preston, West Sussex Tel: 01903 776026
Capacity: Seats: None Cover: 40Floodlights: Yes
Directions: Less than a mile from Angmering (BR) station. A259 from Worthing to Roundstone Hotel (6 miles), turn south over railway crossing, left past Centurion garage, right into Roundstone Drive
Clubhouse: Open Mon-Fri eves, Sat 12-11pm, Sun 12-11pm. Light refreshments on matchdays
HONOURS Sussex Co. Lg Div 2 Champions 97-98 Div 3 83-84, (R-up 90-91), Div 3 Cup 87-88 (R-up 89-90); West Sussex Lg 77-78 80-81 81-82 82-83 (Malcolm Simmonds Cup 80-81 82-83), Div2 Sth 81-82, Div 3 Sth 79-80, Div 5 Sth 82-83; Chichester Cup 87-88; BorehamTphy 77-78 90-91 (R-up 93-94); Vernon Wentworth Cup 80-81 89-90; Worthing Lg 67-68 (Div 2 68-69 (res); Benev. Tphy 66-67 68-69; Worthing Charity Cup 68-69
PREVIOUS Leagues: Worthing; W Sussex

FACT FILE
Reformed: 1966
Nickname: None
Sponsors: Roundstone Garage
Colours: Black & white/white/white
Change: Red/white/red
Reserve's Lge: Sussex Co. Res. Div (Prem)
Programme: Yes
Editor: Andy Mott (01903 726097)
Local Press: Littlehampton Gazette
CLUB PERSONNEL
President: Greg Stanley
Chairman:Mike Barnes
Manager: Jim Quigg
Asst Manager:Jim Thompson

EASTBOURNE TOWN

Secretary: Viv Greenwood, 102 Latimer Rd., Eastbourne BN22 7DR (01323 460695)

Ground: The Saffrons, Compton Place Road, Eastbourne, East Sussex (01323723734)
Capacity: 3,000 Seats: 200 Cover: Yes Floodlights: Yes
Directions: Turn south west off the A22 into Grove Road (opposite BR station), and the ground is 1/4 mile on the right
Clubhouse: Fully licensed bar. Board room. Tea bar

HONOURS Sussex County Lg. 76-77; Sussex Sen Cup x12 1889-91, 93-95, 98-1901, 02-03, 21-22, 31-35, 52-53; Sussex RUR Charity Cup 32-33, 47-48, 49-50; SouthernAmat. Lge. x2; AFA Sen. Cup 21-22, 24-25, R-up 22-23, 23-24; AFA Invitation Cup69-70, R-up 56-57, 68-69, 70-71
PREVIOUS Leagues: Southern Amtr 07-46; Corinthian 60-63; Athenian 63-76
RECORD Attendance: 7,378 v Hastings Utd. 1953

FACT FILE
Founded: 1882
Nickname: `Bourne'
Sponsor: Eastbourne Car Auctions
Colours: Yellow & blue/blue/blue
Changes: Blue &white/black/black
Programme Editor: Chris Backhurst
Tel: 01323 505062
CLUB PERSONNEL
Chairman: Roger Addems
Manager: Pete Cherry

LANCING

Secretary: J Chisnall, 25 Amberley Court, Freshbrook Rd., Lancing, W. Sussex BN15 8DS Tel: 01903 763048 **Match Sec:** Don Stevens
Ground: Culver Road, Lancing, W. Sussex Tel: 01903 764398 Web-site: www.lancingfc.co.uk
Directions: From A27 turn south at Lancing Manor r'about into Grinstead Lane, 3rd turning on right North Farm Rd. Turn left then immed. right into Culver Rd. From railway station take 3rd turning on left heading north.
Capacity: 2,400 Seats: 350 Cover: 350 Floodlights: Yes
Clubhouse: Open matchdays & training nights. Separate tea bar. **Club Shop:** Yes
HONOURS Sussex Co. Lg R-up 49-50 64-65 (Div 2 57-58 69-70 (R-up 82-83), Div 2 Cup 81-82 92-93, Invitation Cup), Sussex RUR Charity Cup 65-66, Brighton Lg 46-47 47-48, Sussex Intermediate Cup 46-47, Brighton Charity Cup 83-84 84-85 86-87.
PREVIOUS League: Brighton Hove & District **Name:** Lancing Athletic
RECORDS - Attendance: 2,591 v Tooting, FA Amateur Cup 22/11/47 (At Culver Road: 2,340v Worthing 25/10/52) **Career Appearances:** Dave Menzies 462 **Goals:** Paul Steele 113

FACT FILE
Founded: 1941 Nickname: Yellows
Sponsors: ABS Electrical Supplies
Colours: Yellow/blue/yellow
Change colours: All red
Midweek Matches: Wed Programme: Yes
Reserves League: Sussex Co Res. Prem.
Editor/Press Off.: Len Ralph (01903 763913)
2000-01
Captain: Martin Gray
Top Scorers & P.O.Y.: Dave Schneider 16
CLUB PERSONNEL
Chairman: John Brown
President: R G Steele
Commercial Man.: Brian Hill
Manager: Andy Gander

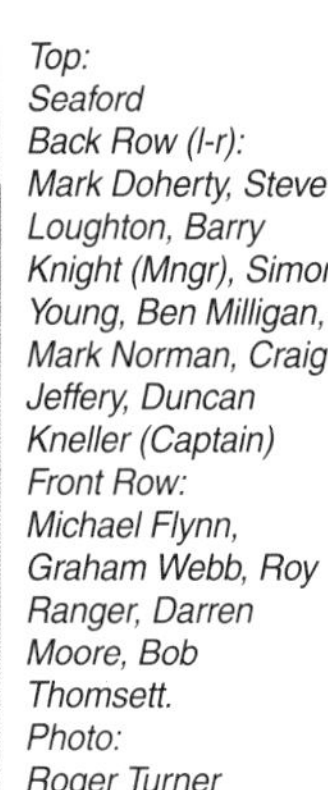

Top: Seaford
Back Row (l-r): Mark Doherty, Steve Loughton, Barry Knight (Mngr), Simon Young, Ben Milligan, Mark Norman, Craig Jeffery, Duncan Kneller (Captain)
Front Row: Michael Flynn, Graham Webb, Roy Ranger, Darren Moore, Bob Thomsett.
Photo: Roger Turner

Centre: Haywards Heath Town
Back Row (l-r): Roy Tucknott (Asst Mngr), Graeme Hatt, Nick Newman, Louis Wright, John Scriven, Martin Smith, Lee Browne, Brian Wilson (Head), Ken Swallow (Mngr), Jason McNaboe, Chris Turner, Phil Comber (Coach)
Front Row: Russell Harris, Anthony Handley, Derek Elphick (Capt), Andy Wilson, Ashley Mahoney, Marc Whitmore.
Photo: Gordon Whittington

Bottom: Hurstpierpoint
Back Row (l-r): Lee Evans, Lee Chatfield, Rodney Wilson, David Biggs, Paul Kempston, James Burrows, Graham Beveridge, Steve Fogden, Lee Saunders.
Front Row: Dave Jeanes, Richard Lester, Stuart Ritchie, Matt Charman, Ant Pitt, Tim Stevens.
Photo: Gordon Whittington

LINGFIELD

Secretary: Ron Devereux, Tanglewood, New Chapel Rd., Lingfield, Surrey RH7 6BJ
Tel No: 01342 835239

Ground: Godstone Road, Lingfield, Surrey. Tel: 01342 834269
Directions: A22, 4 miles north of East Grinstead, to Mormon Temple roundabout, take exit Lingfield (B2028) Newchapel Road for 1 1/2 miles. Left at T junction into Godstone Road (B2029) and ground is 1/2 mile on left.

FACT FILE
Colours: Red & yellow stripes/black/yellow
Change colours:Sky Blue/white/ sky blue

CLUB PERSONNEL
Chairman: Bill Blenkin
Manager: Mark Endsleigh

MILE OAK

Secretary: Colin Brown, 19 The Crescent, Southwick, West Sussex BN42 4LB
Tel: 01273 591346
Ground: Mile Oak Recreation Ground, Graham Avenue, Mile Oak. Tel: 01273 423854

Directions: From A27 take Mile Oak Road or Locks Hill & Valley Road to Chalky Road, ground 500yds on right along Graham Avenue which runs up valley fromcentre of Chalky Road
Capacity: Seats: None Cover: Yes Floodlights: Yes
Clubhouse: Mile Oak Pavillion; Hall and tea bar **Club Shop:** No

HONOURS Sussex Co.Lg.Div 2 Champions, Div 3 R-up 91-92 (Div 2 Cup R-up 92-93), Southern Counties Combination 86-87, Brighton Hove & District Lg 80-81, VernonWentworth Cup 85-86, Sussex Intermediate Cup R-up 88-89
PREVIOUS **Leagues:** Southern Counties Combination; Brighton Hove & District
Ground: Victoria Rec., Portslade
RECORD **Attendance:** 186

FACT FILE
Founded: 1960
Nickname: The Oak
Colours: Tangerine/black/tangerine
Change colours: All blue
Midweek Matchday: Tuesday
Programme: Yes
Editor: C Tew (01273 416036)
Admission: £1.50
Local Press: Brighton Evening Argus, Shoreham Herald

CLUB PERSONNEL
Chairman: L.Hamilton
President: D Bean
Manager: Tony Gratwicke

OAKWOOD

Secretary: Paula West, 12 Woodend Close,Three Bridges,Crawley W.Sussex RH101RS
Tel: 01293 401085
Ground: Tinsley Lane, Three Bridges, Crawley, West Sussex Tel: 01293 515742
Directions: From A23 to Gatwick, take 1st set of lights into Manor Royal, pass next lights, over r'bout to warehouse marked Canon, turn right signposted Oakwood. Last clubhouse down lane. Two miles north of Three Bridges (BR)
Capacity: 3,000 Seats: 20 Cover: Yes Floodlights: Yes
Club Shop: Yes, incl. metal badges
Clubhouse: Large bar area, pool tables, multidart boards. Board room & tea bar
HONOURS Sussex Snr Cup R-up 92-93, Sussex Co. Lg Div 2 R-up 89-90 (Div 2 Cup 89-90, Div 3 84-85), Southern Comb. Cup 83-84
PREVIOUS **Leagues:** Crawley & Dist., Southern Co's Comb
Ground: Park pitches
RECORD **Attendance:** 367 **Appearances:** Peter Brackpool

FACT FILE
Founded: 1966 Nickname: Oaks
Sponsors: Linden Plc
Colours: Red & black/black/black
Change colours: Blue/black/black
Midweek Matchday: Tuesday
Reserves' Lge: Sussex Co. Reserve section
Programme: 24 pages
Editor: Scott Packer Local Press: Crawley Observer, Crawley News

CLUB PERSONNEL
Chairman: Stuart Lovegrove
Press Officer & Match Sec: Scott Packer
Manager:Andy Maddox
Physio:MsS Widy ,Ass Physio:Frank Pushman

OVING

Secretary: Peter Hall, St Bruno, Prinsted Lane, Emsworth, Hants PO10 8HR
Tel: 01243 372652
Ground: Highfield Lane, Oving, Nr Chichester, W Sussex. Tel: 01243 778900
Directions: Into Oving past the Gribble Inn, follow road round to housing estate - Highfield Lane (left). Ground sign posted 50 yards on right.
Capacity: 1,000 Cover: 100 Floodlights: No
Clubhouse: Oving Social Club or Gribble Inn Contact 01243 789395 Metal Badges: Yes
HONOURS W. Sussex Lge - Div 5 Cup 81-82, Div 5S 81-82, Div 4 Cup 82-83, Div 4S 82-83, Div 3S84-85. Div 2S 87-88, 91-92, Div 1 94-95, Prem. Div 95-96 96-97; Sussex Jun Cup: 86 91; Chichester char. Cup 90-91; Sussex Co. Inter. Cup R-up 98-99; Sussex Co. Div 3 98-99, Div 3 Cup R-up 98-99
PREVIOUS **Leagues:** West Sussex
CLUB RECORDS **Attendance:** 276 v Westfield, Sussex co. Lge Div. 3 8.5.99
Win: 10-0 v S B Sports (H) Sussex Co.Iinter. Cup 10.10.98 **Defeat:** 0-5 v Lingfield (A) 13.9.97

FACT FILE
Formed: 1978-79 Nickname: "The Vikings"
Colours: Black & white/white/white
Change colours:Red& Black/Black/Black
Reserves' Lge: Sussex Co. - Res. Sect. West
Programme: 32 pages 50p
Editor: Simon Jasinski (01243 374239)
98-99Captain: John Donogue
Top Scorer: Justin Turnill (20)

CLUB PERSONNEL
Chairman: Dusty Miller
Press off.: Ade Adebayo (01903 856262)
Manager: Paul Gilbert
Asst. Manager: Adie Miles
Coach: Vijay Korgaokar
Physio: Marc Rowbottom

Lee Sale, Weladen (right), makes a challenge on John Mudge, Lingfield. Photo: Roger Turner

Midfield battle between Seaford and Thompson Sports (stripes). Photo: Roger Turner

Andy Potter, Uckfield Town, puts the ball wide of a Royal Sun Alliance defender during the first League game of the season. Photo: Roger Turner

SHINEWATER ASSOCIATION

Secretary: Brian Dowling, 79 Harebeating Drive, Hailsham BN27 1JE
Tel: 01323 442488

Ground: Shinewater Lane, Eastbourne. Tel: 01323 765880
Capacity: 1,000 Seats: None Cover: 200 Floodlights: No

Directions: A27, take B2104 to Eastbourne. At Stone Cross go under railway bridge, 1st right into Larkspur Drive, 1st left into Milfoil Drive, 3rd left into Shinewater Lane

Clubhouse: Match days (01323 765880)

RECORD **Attendance:** 302

FACT FILE
Founded:1990 Club
Colours: Navy & sky/navy/navy
Change Colours: Claret
Programme: With entry Editor: Brian Dowling
Previous League: East Sussex

CLUB PERSONNEL
Chairman: John Pinyoun
Manager: Peter Coleman

SHOREHAM

Secretary: Mrs Anne Harper, 66 Willow Crescent, Worthing. BN13 2SX Tel: 01903 267672

Ground: Middle Road, Shoreham-by-Sea, West Sussex Tel: 01273 454261
Capacity: 1,500 Seats: 20 Cover: 1 stand Floodlights: Yes

Directions: Half mile from Shoreham-by-Sea (BR) - east across level crossing, up Dolphin Road, ground 150yds on right. Or, A27 to Shoreham. At Southlands Hospital turn left down Hammy Lane, left at end, ground opposite

Clubhouse: Seats 70. Bar, pool, darts, tea bar **Club Shop:** No

HONOURS Sussex Co. Lg 51-53 77-78 (R-up 34-35, Div 2 61-62 76-77 84-85 93-94,Div 2 Cup 74-75 82-83, Invitation Cup 57-58), Sussex Snr Cup 01-02 05-06,Sussex F'lit Cup R-up 89-90, Sussex RUR Charity Cup 02-03 05-06, VernonWentworth Cup 86-87

PREVIOUS **League:** West Sussex
Ground: Buckingham Park (pre-1970)

RECORD **Gate:** 1,342 v Wimbledon (f/lt opening 86)

FACT FILE
Founded: 1892 Nickname: Musselmen
Sponsors: Len German Wholesalers
Colours:All blue
Change colours: All red
Midweek Matchday: Wednesday
Programme: Yes
Editor: Michael Wenham
Local Press: Shoreham Herald

CLUB PERSONNEL
President: Alf Bloom
Chairman: John Bell
Manager: George Parris
Press Officer: Michael Wenham
Tel: 01273 596009

STORRINGTON

Secretary: Keith Dalmon, 4 End Cottages, Turnpike Road, Amberley. BN18 9LX
Tel: 01798 831887

Ground: Recreation Ground, Storrington. Tel: 01903 745860

Directions: Turn west on A283 (off A24).
Ground is opposite the pond to the west of the village.

2000-01 : **Captain:** Rob Norris **P.o.Y.:** Richard Hack **Top Scorer:** Matthew High 11

FACT FILE
Colours: All Blue
Chanbge Colours : All yellow

CLUB PERSONNEL
Chairman: Malcolm MacMichael
Managers: Nigel Dyer & Bob Payne

WEALDEN

Secretary: Peter Byford, Chelwood, Possingworth Park, Cross in Hand, Heathfield TN21 0TN
Tel: 01435 862574 (H) 0410 944364 (M) Email: pbyford@aol.com

Ground: Wealden Sports Club, Uckfield, East Sussex. Tel: 01825 890905

Directions: Next to the Rajdutt Restaurant on the Old Eastbourne Road, south of Uckfield town centre.

Honours: Sussex County Lge Div. 3 R-up 99-00

FACT FILE
Colours: All blue
Change colours: All red

CLUB PERSONNEL
Chairman: Brian Smith Tel: 01273 812329 (H)
Manager: Tom Parker

WESTFIELD

Secretary: Mrs Jenny Drinkwater, 28 Churchfields, Westfield TN35 4SN
Tel: 01424 754032

Ground: Parish Field. Westfield Tel: 01424 751011

Directions: Take A21 towards Hastings, left onto A28. Westfield Lane, towards Ashford for 2 miles, pitch on left.

FACT FILE
Colours: White & Green/green/green
Change Colours: Yellow & Green/ green/green

CLUB PERSONNEL
Chairman: Brian Over Tel: 01424 754844
Manager: Shaun Hardy

WORTHING UNITED

Secretary: Malcolm Gamlen, 1 Westbourne Ave., Worthing, West Sussex BN14 8DE
Tel: 01903 263655

Ground: The Robert Albon Memorial Grd, Lyons Way, Worthing Tel: 01903 234466
Capacity:1,000 Seats: 100 Cover: 500 Floodlights: No

Directions: From west past Hill Barn r'about to 2nd set of lights, turn left into Lyons Way. From east 1st set of lights at end of Sompting bypass right into Lyons Way

Clubhouse: Bar (capacity 80), refreshment facilities (tea bar) Metal badges: Yes

HONOURS As Wigmore Athletic prior to 1988. Sussex Co. Lg Challenge Cup 74-75 (Invitation Cup 59-60, Div 2 52-53, Div 2 Invitation Cup 59-60, Div 3 89-90, Reserve Section West 92-93, Sussex Jnr Cup 49-50

PREVIOUS **Names:** Wigmore Athletic (founded 1948) merged with Southdown in 1988
Grounds: Harrison Road, Worthing

RECORD **Attendance:**180 v Northwood, FA Vase 3rd Rd 91-92

FACT FILE
Founded: 1988
Nickname: None
Sponsors: Tinsley Robor
Colours: Sky & white/navy/white
Change colours: All red
Programme: Yes
Editor: D.Treacy (01903 690122)
Local Newspapers: Worthing Herald

CLUB PERSONNEL
President: Bob Albon
Chairman: Len Killpatrick
Press Officer: Secretary
Manager: Geoff Raynsford

Daventry Town. Back Row (l-r): Craig Robson (Joint Mngr), Aaron Parkinson, Peter Green, Lee Ault, Paul Fountain, Ian Morgan, Steve James, Adam May (Joint Mngr), Jim Henderson (Coach). Front Row: Jimmy Simpson, Michael Christie, Casey Waldock, Wayne Brown, Julian Hakes, Dale Williams, Tony Mitten (Physio). Photo: Gordon Whittington

Irchester Town. Back Row (l-r): John Dower, Mark Downes, Phil Lawrence, Aaron Double, Liam O'Rielly, Jason D'Silva, Gareth Arzy, Bob Reed. Front Row: Gary Cotter, Curtis Watts, Mark Wheeler, Mark Dudley, Charlie Pipe, Glynn Cotter, Brian Wier

Left: Boston Town celebrate after winning the United Counties League Premier Division title with a dramatic late goal. Photo: Gordon Whittington

THE EAGLE BITTER UNITED COUNTIES LEAGUE

FEEDER TO: DR MARTENS LEAGUE

Chairman: Geoff Paul

Secretary: Roger Gamble, 8 Bostock Avenue, Northampton NN1 4LW Tel: 01604 637766

Press Officer: Jeremy Biggs Tel: 01780 763048

BOSTON CLAIM SECOND TITLE

The most difficult season in living memory was finally completed on 24 May, some 293 days after Ford Sports beat Cottingham 5-3 as the last ever Benevolent Cup final beckoned in the 2000-01 campaign. The wet weather of the winter was the main culprit, with a little bit of help from the fuel crisis in September and a thankfully brief brush with the foot and mouth epidemic in February, but it was to the great credit of the clubs that all domestic league and cup football was completed without resorting to artificial means. A few of the more minor cup competitions await resolution early in the new campaign and one or two were abandoned for the season due to the pile up of fixtures.

While most clubs will long remember the campaign for its problems, others will look back on 2000-01 with more fondness. Boston Town celebrated their second Premier Division championship on the season's final Saturday as they pipped Cogenhoe by a single point leaving the Compton Park club with the runners-up medals for the second season running. The title race could hardly have been closer as Boston's final match against Buckingham was a minute into stoppage time when substitute Ian Shooter fired home the goal which gave the Poachers a 2-2 draw and the point needed for the title. Over the season, Boston, Cogenhoe and Raunds slugged it out for supremacy with the advantage changing hands game by game.

Cogenhoe had been favourites to land their first title from the off after strengthening their squad with the summer captures of Mark Parsons and Darren Harmon from reigning champions Ford Sports and marksman supreme Steve Kuhne from Wootton. They led early on, but in October manager Steve Forbes quit after a 4-0 reverse against Desborough, Dave Conlon returning for a second spell at the helm. Boston soon took over pole position, while Holbeach and Blackstone both looked contenders early on as the goals flowed. As the season progressed Raunds emerged as strong challengers, the young side assembled by Shopmates chief Adam Sandy earning widespread praise for the quality of their football.

Some good cup runs saw Holbeach slide into mid-table as they fell behind with matches, Blackstones suffered their traditional new year slump despite some high profile signings, while St Neots and Wootton emerged as outsiders, albeit with big backlogs to clear. Desborough beat Boston twice and also added Raunds to their list of victims - but their inconsistency got the better of them once again.

Raunds were the first to slip among the big three - their inexperience showed in the last third of the seasonas just five wins in their last twelve matches proved costly. One of those wins was against Cogenhoe, who also tumbled to defeat at St Neots on cup final eve. With a week to go Boston were favourites and wins at Northampton Spencer and Eynesbury set up the final day drama.

Shane Geary's rebuilding programme at Ford Sports paid dividends as the Motormen finished the season with a nine match unbeaten run to claim fourth place. Much improved pair St Neots and Wootton both enjoyed their best seasons in years and could have laid foundations to challenge next time round.

Right from the off the relegation battle looked to be a case of perm any two from three. Eynesbury, Long Buckby and Potton all struggled from day one. Buckby handed the manager's job to Trevor Jones after Steve Renshaw stepped down in October while Eynesbury brought in Steve Galbraith after Neil King quit in December. Cue new players aplenty, and a gradual improvement at both clubs. Potton kept faith with their management and won for the first time in January. Two wins for Eynesbury at the end of February and the start of March left Long Buckby almost out of sight - but a 3-1 defeat of Cogenhoe on 6 March sparked the Bucks' own version of the great escape as their last thirteen games brought them nineteen points. Eynesbury finished bottom - late season defeats by both their rivals for the drop ended their 24 year stay in the Premier. Potton's drubbing of Rovers couldn't inspire them to pick up any reward from their last three away games, and they too bow out of the top flight after 41 seasons.

For the first time since 1987 two clubs were promoted from Division One. Both Daventry and Deeping made their intentions clear over the summer, adding batches of Premier players to squads that had gone very close in the previous season.

The pair dominated the division, although for a while champions Cottingham, rejuvenated by Willie Kelly's appointment as manager, looked like making a solid defence of the crown. Thrapston were always in close attendance, eventually finishing third, four points down on the promoted pair, while Blisworth came through the pack to finish fourth after just one defeat in their last seventeen games. Expected promotion challenges from Newport Pagnell and Rothwell Corinthians looked set fair early on only to fade away.

Daventry's greater firepower gave them a slight edge for much of the season - Jamie Cunningham, Peter Green, Paul Fountain and Jimmy Simpson managed 79 goals between them. Deeping were heavily reliant on 31 goal Robbie Williams, who topped the divisional scorecharts a second time after his move from Harrowby. When the top two met on successive Saturdays late in the season Rangers really needed to win both to stay in the championship race. The pair drew 1-1 at Outgang Road while Rangers won the return at Elderstubbs 1-0, inflicting Daventry's first home defeat and leaving the sides level on points with a game each to play. Deeping were first up with a chance of at least setting Daventry a target - but their visitors were Blisworth, one of just two sides to beat them all season. A repeat success by Simon Morrice's men lowered Rangers colours at home for the only time while handing the title to Daventry who went down 2-1 at St Ives in their finale.

Sharnbrook finished bottom of the division, but improved greatly late on as mid-season appointee John Leeson rebuilt after taking over a side badly demoralised by a series of heavy defeats. Just above them were Irchester who were similarly revitalised by management duo John Dower and Bob Reed after picking up just one point from their first sixteen outings.

Cogenhoe were emphatic winners of Reserve Division One, which ended the season two clubs light after the mid-season withdrawals of Spalding and Kings Lynn for financial reasons. Their departures saved bottom two Whitworths and Bugbrooke from the drop. Newcomers Stamford took the Reserve Division Two crown in style and move up along with ON Chenecks.

The Knockout Cup brought its usual share of upsets. Deeping beat both Ford Sports and Buckingham, while Daventry, St Ives and Woodford all toppled higher grade opponents, although Woodford were later expelled for playing the cup tied Leon Morgan in their defeat of Blackstone. The lower grade top two both reached the last eight, but the semi-finals were all-Premier affairs with holders Cogenhoe winning at Stotfold and Desborough overcoming hosts Wootton. In the final at Raunds Michael Chong's late strike gave Desborough a deserved 2-1 win over Cogenhoe.

Upsets were the order of the day in the Reserve Knockout Cup too. Lower grade Eynesbury reached the semis before losing to Rothwell on penalties, while Olney fared better in their shootout against Stotfold to go one step further. The trophy looked like going to a Reserve Division Two club for the second season running as Olney led for an hour or so in the final at Bugbrooke, but Dave Beazeley's dead ball expertise at both a penalty and free kick swung the game Rothwell's way as they won 3-1 in extra time.

Yet again it was far from a vintage year in national competitions. In the FA Cup Holbeach won three ties and Stotfold two to reach the Second Qualifying Round where they exited to Belper and Cambridge City respectively. Stotfold set the standard in the FA Vase, reaching the last 32 before bowing out 1-0 at Marlow. They were awarded result of the round accolades for wins over Great Wakering in Round Two and Lymington in Round Three.

In county cup football there was delight for Wootton who beat Dunstable 1-0 to win the Bedfordshire Senior Cup for the first time since 1970 but despair for St Neots who lost 1-0 to Somersham in the one hundredth Huntingdonshire Senior Cup final. Two all EBUCL finals saw Deeping beat Harrowby 4-1 in the Lincolnshire Senior 'B' Cup in the splendid surroundings of York Street, Boston, and Thrapston won the Northants Junior Cup for the second time in three years, beating Daventry 3-1 at the even more palatial Nene Park. Kempton crashed 4-0 to Biggleswade Town in the Huntingdonshire Premier Cup final, the Hunts Benevolent Cup went to Yaxley Reserves with a 4-1 win over Brampton, while Wootton Reserves lost 3-0 to Biggleswade United Reserves in the Beds Junior Cup final.

Other domestic awards went to Daventry (Highest Aggregate Goalscorers), Deeping (First Team's Fair Play Award winners), Bourne (Reserve Fair Play Award winners), Corby (Referee Hospitality Award winners) and Newport Pagnell (Club Hospitality Award winners). Boston manager Bob Don-Duncan made a piece of league history, winning his third Manager of the Year accolade, while Shaun Barry was Referee of the Year.

The season ended on a sad note as League President elect David Panter died on holiday in Spain the day before the AGM. David had been involved with the league since 1958, initially as a referee before embarking on a 31 year stint as Registration Secretary in 1970. He will be greatly missed by all.

Jeremy Biggs
Press Officer

FINAL LEAGUE TABLES 2000-01

PREMIER DIVISION

			Home					Away					Total					
		P	W	D	L	F	A	W	D	L	F	A	W	D	L	F	A	Pts
1	Boston Town	40	14	3	3	51	24	12	5	3	38	22	26	8	6	89	46	86
2	Cogenhoe United	40	12	3	5	55	26	15	1	4	42	25	27	4	9	97	51	85
3	Raunds Town	40	14	3	3	55	18	11	1	8	45	30	25	4	11	100	48	79
4	Ford Sports Daventry	40	13	3	4	47	29	11	1	8	31	32	24	4	12	78	61	76
5	St Neots Town	40	14	2	4	57	27	8	7	5	40	29	22	9	9	97	56	75
6	Wootton Blue Cross	40	14	4	2	52	18	7	8	5	33	30	21	12	7	85	48	75
7	Desborough Town	40	10	5	5	35	25	9	5	6	37	23	19	10	11	72	48	67
8	Northampton Spencer	40	11	4	5	39	25	8	3	9	37	35	19	7	14	76	60	64
9	Kempston Rovers	40	11	5	4	42	22	5	8	7	26	30	16	13	11	68	52	61
10	Yaxley	40	9	4	7	34	27	9	3	8	35	31	18	7	15	69	58	61
11	Stewarts & Lloyds Corby	40	8	4	8	35	27	9	5	6	29	29	17	9	14	64	56	60
12	Blackstone	40	9	4	7	64	37	6	6	8	29	34	15	10	15	93	71	55
13	Bourne Town	40	8	5	7	34	34	7	4	9	38	50	15	9	16	72	84	54
14	Holbeach United	40	8	5	7	34	26	7	3	10	35	39	15	8	17	69	65	53
15	Stotfold	40	5	6	9	36	33	7	4	9	38	33	12	10	18	74	66	46
16	Bugbrooke St Michaels	40	3	10	7	23	26	6	5	9	20	37	9	15	16	43	63	42
17	Buckingham Town	40	6	4	10	34	44	4	5	11	38	64	10	9	21	72	108	39
18	Wellingborough Town	40	4	3	13	25	47	4	6	10	32	43	8	9	23	57	90	33
19	Long Buckby	40	3	1	16	24	67	3	5	12	33	83	6	6	28	57	150	24
20	Potton United	40	2	7	11	21	54	2	0	18	17	57	4	7	29	38	111	19
21	Eynesbury Rovers	40	3	3	14	25	52	1	3	16	15	66	4	6	30	40	118	18

DIVISION ONE

		P	W	D	L	F	A	W	D	L	F	A	W	D	L	F	A	Pts
1	Daventry Town	34	12	4	1	50	13	11	2	4	54	17	23	6	5	104	30	75
2	Deeping Rangers	34	12	4	1	46	13	10	5	2	36	17	22	9	3	82	30	75
3	Thrapston Town	34	10	5	2	48	22	11	3	3	43	19	21	8	5	91	41	71
4	Blisworth	34	13	3	1	38	17	8	4	5	33	26	21	7	6	71	43	70
5	Cottingham	34	10	5	2	44	26	8	4	5	26	17	18	9	7	70	43	63
6	Newport Pagnell Town	34	9	3	5	45	27	6	2	9	34	37	15	5	14	79	64	50
7	Rothwell Corinthians	34	7	7	3	35	23	6	4	7	20	24	13	11	10	55	47	50
8	Woodford United	34	6	4	7	31	29	7	4	6	39	34	13	8	13	70	63	47
9	Harrowby United	34	10	4	3	36	15	2	6	9	19	28	12	10	12	55	43	46
10	North'ton ON Chenecks	34	7	2	8	39	34	4	6	7	26	37	11	8	15	65	71	41
11	Wellingboro Whitworths	34	5	5	7	28	29	5	5	7	28	39	10	10	14	56	68	40
12	Higham Town	34	5	5	7	20	26	4	7	6	20	23	9	12	13	40	49	39
13	St Ives Town	34	5	7	5	22	22	3	7	7	29	37	8	14	12	51	59	38
14	Burton Park Wanderers	34	5	5	7	28	32	4	3	10	25	36	9	8	17	53	68	35
15	Olney Town	34	8	3	6	29	20	1	3	13	15	38	9	6	19	44	58	33
16	Northampton Sileby Rngrs	34	3	5	9	24	35	3	6	8	28	35	6	11	17	52	70	29
17	Irchester United	34	4	4	9	18	38	1	4	12	12	48	5	8	21	30	86	23
18	Sharnbrook	34	2	2	13	19	79	2	2	13	13	88	4	4	26	32	167	16

RESERVE DIVISION ONE

(Top Five)		P	W	D	L	F	A	W	D	L	F	A	W	D	L	F	A	Pts
1	Cogenhoe United	34	13	1	3	58	17	15	0	2	46	16	28	1	5	104	33	85
2	Stewarts & Lloyds Corby	34	13	2	2	51	19	8	4	5	41	41	21	6	7	92	60	69
3	Blackstone	34	10	4	3	38	18	10	3	4	34	21	20	7	7	72	39	67
4	Yaxley	34	12	1	4	46	16	7	7	3	25	14	19	8	7	71	30	65
5	St Neots Town	34	12	4	1	35	16	8	1	8	28	26	20	5	9	63	42	65

RESERVE DIVISION TWO

(Top Five)		P	W	D	L	F	A	W	D	L	F	A	W	D	L	F	A	Pts
1	Stamford	34	15	1	1	59	15	12	3	2	42	11	27	4	3	101	26	85
2	North'ton ON Chenecks	34	13	3	1	59	15	9	2	6	36	27	22	5	7	95	42	71
3	Rothwell Corinthians	34	11	2	4	58	25	10	2	5	45	24	21	4	9	103	49	67
4	Blisworth	34	9	4	4	26	15	10	2	5	28	22	19	6	9	54	37	63
5	Wootton Blue Cross	34	10	1	6	36	28	9	2	6	37	41	19	3	12	73	69	60

PREMIER DIVISION RESULTS CHART 2000-01

		1	2	3	4	5	6	7	8	9	10	11	12	13	14	15	16	17	18	19	20	21
1	Blackstone	X	0-1	1-4	11-1	2-2	3-4	4-1	9-1	4-1	1-5	2-2	9-1	1-3	4-2	2-2	0-1	1-2	1-0	3-0	1-1	5-3
2	Boston	2-2	X	3-0	5-3	3-0	1-2	0-3	5-1	1-0	2-0	3-2	5-0	2-1	2-1	1-2	2-2	2-1	2-1	3-1	6-1	1-1
3	Bourne	1-3	1-2	X	4-0	2-0	2-4	0-1	3-0	1-4	2-1	0-2	2-2	2-1	1-0	2-1	3-1	2-2	0-0	4-4	2-2	0-4
4	Buckingham	1-2	2-2	7-2	X	2-2	1-3	0-3	3-2	0-1	2-2	0-0	3-1	2-0	4-3	0-4	0-5	0-1	3-5	3-1	1-2	0-3
5	Bugbrooke	0-0	1-2	4-0	4-4	X	0-2	2-2	0-0	0-1	0-1	2-2	2-2	2-0	2-0	0-4	1-1	0-1	1-1	1-1	1-2	0-0
6	Cogenhoe	3-1	1-2	3-1	1-2	4-0	X	0-4	6-0	7-0	2-1	2-0	7-1	3-1	4-0	2-3	2-2	1-1	2-1	2-1	2-2	1-3
7	Desborough	1-1	2-0	2-2	2-1	2-0	0-3	X	3-1	2-1	2-3	0-2	3-4	2-0	3-1	3-0	1-1	0-2	1-1	3-0	1-1	2-1
8	Eynesbury	2-3	1-2	0-4	3-1	0-1	1-2	0-3	X	1-4	1-3	2-1	2-4	2-2	2-1	1-4	1-4	2-3	0-3	3-3	1-1	0-3
9	Ford Sports	3-1	1-6	3-0	2-2	2-3	4-1	2-0	2-2	X	3-0	3-1	5-4	1-3	2-0	2-1	1-1	2-0	4-2	0-1	2-1	3-0
10	Holbeach	0-1	1-1	1-1	2-2	1-0	1-4	2-0	2-1	0-1	X	1-3	2-3	1-2	5-1	2-1	3-2	5-0	3-0	1-1	1-1	0-1
11	Kempston	3-3	0-1	4-1	3-0	4-2	1-1	0-0	6-0	0-0	4-2	X	5-1	1-3	1-0	0-1	1-0	3-1	0-3	2-2	1-0	3-1
12	Long Buckby	2-1	1-7	1-5	3-4	0-0	3-1	1-5	1-0	0-4	1-8	1-2	X	2-4	1-2	0-3	0-3	1-3	2-4	3-4	1-5	0-2
13	N'ton Spencer	3-2	1-2	2-2	3-2	1-2	1-2	0-0	2-0	3-0	3-0	1-0	3-1	X	1-3	2-0	1-2	1-1	3-1	3-2	3-1	2-2
14	Potton	2-1	1-3	2-6	0-6	0-3	0-3	0-0	4-1	1-3	0-0	3-3	1-1	1-1	X	1-6	2-2	1-2	0-4	1-6	1-1	0-2
15	Raunds	3-0	1-0	5-1	3-2	5-0	3-1	2-1	4-0	3-2	5-0	0-1	6-1	0-1	5-2	X	1-1	0-1	2-2	3-0	1-1	3-1
16	St Neots	0-2	1-1	6-1	2-2	4-0	3-0	2-1	4-1	3-0	3-1	1-0	8-1	7-5	2-0	1-3	X	3-1	1-4	3-1	0-2	3-1
17	Stewarts & L	1-2	1-1	1-2	2-1	0-1	0-1	1-2	0-0	2-1	2-0	1-1	3-1	2-2	5-0	2-3	5-2	X	2-1	1-3	1-3	3-0
18	Stotfold	2-0	1-1	2-3	1-1	1-1	1-2	1-2	2-3	2-3	2-2	1-1	8-0	1-0	3-0	2-1	0-2	1-4	X	1-1	1-2	3-4
19	Wellingboro	2-2	0-1	1-2	3-4	1-2	0-3	2-6	3-2	0-1	0-4	4-0	3-3	0-3	2-0	2-1	0-4	1-1	0-3	X	0-2	1-3
20	Wootton	1-1	5-2	0-0	5-0	3-1	0-1	2-1	5-0	1-2	3-0	2-2	5-1	3-2	3-0	3-1	4-1	1-1	4-2	1-0	X	1-0
21	Yaxley	2-1	0-1	2-1	5-0	0-0	0-2	2-2	2-0	1-2	1-2	1-1	1-1	0-3	5-1	2-4	1-3	2-1	2-0	2-0	3-2	X

DIVISION ONE RESULTS CHART 2000-01

		1	2	3	4	5	6	7	8	9	10	11	12	13	14	15	16	17	18
1	Blisworth	X	3-2	1-0	1-1	3-2	1-0	5-2	1-0	4-2	1-1	1-0	1-0	3-0	6-1	2-1	1-3	4-2	0-0
2	Burton PW	2-6	X	3-0	2-6	1-2	3-3	0-3	0-0	0-0	1-3	2-0	2-0	1-1	2-1	7-0	0-2	1-1	1-4
3	Cottingham	6-3	2-1	X	2-3	0-0	2-1	0-0	3-4	6-4	2-0	3-1	4-1	0-0	2-2	5-1	2-1	1-0	4-4
4	Daventry	0-0	3-1	0-0	X	0-1	5-0	2-0	6-1	3-1	4-0	2-2	2-1	3-1	3-1	6-0	2-2	6-1	3-1
5	Deeping	0-1	3-1	0-0	1-1	X	2-0	2-1	5-0	2-1	2-0	2-2	6-0	3-2	4-0	5-1	1-1	6-1	2-1
6	Harrowby	4-1	4-0	0-0	1-0	0-0	X	1-2	2-0	3-0	3-4	4-1	3-2	0-0	2-1	4-1	0-1	1-1	4-1
7	Higham	1-3	1-0	0-3	0-2	2-1	1-1	X	1-1	1-3	4-0	2-2	0-0	1-0	1-2	1-1	0-3	5-2	0-3
8	Irchester	0-1	0-2	1-3	1-0	1-1	0-4	0-0	X	0-4	3-2	3-2	1-0	2-2	1-1	2-3	1-7	0-1	2-5
9	Newport Pag.	2-1	2-1	1-0	0-5	0-3	0-0	1-1	5-0	X	4-0	2-4	4-3	2-0	2-2	12-0	1-2	1-2	6-3
10	N ON Chen.	1-1	1-3	0-2	2-8	0-4	4-1	2-1	4-1	2-3	X	1-1	3-1	3-1	3-2	13-0	0-2	0-2	0-1
11	N'ton Sileby	0-2	5-5	1-2	1-5	1-2	1-1	1-3	3-1	0-1	1-1	X	1-0	0-2	1-1	4-0	0-4	1-1	3-4
12	Olney	1-2	1-3	2-1	0-1	0-3	0-0	3-2	3-0	2-0	1-3	1-0	X	0-1	1-1	5-0	3-0	4-1	2-2
13	Rothwell Cor.	3-0	1-1	0-0	0-5	2-3	3-1	1-1	3-1	3-0	2-2	2-2	3-3	X	2-2	5-0	1-0	3-0	1-2
14	St Ives	1-1	1-1	1-3	2-1	0-3	1-0	1-1	4-0	0-2	0-0	0-2	2-1	3-0	X	1-2	2-2	2-2	1-1
15	Sharnbrook	0-6	0-1	1-5	1-10	2-4	1-8	0-2	1-1	0-8	3-2	3-2	1-1	1-3	1-6	X	2-6	2-8	0-6
16	Thrapston	3-1	2-0	0-4	2-0	1-1	2-0	4-1	4-1	2-2	4-4	2-2	3-0	0-1	4-3	12-1	X	1-1	2-0
17	Whitworths	0-2	3-1	1-3	1-3	2-4	0-0	0-0	2-0	6-2	1-1	2-0	1-2	0-3	2-2	2-2	2-3	X	3-1
18	Woodford	2-2	4-2	5-0	0-3	2-2	3-0	0-0	1-1	3-1	1-3	3-5	1-0	2-3	0-1	2-0	1-4	1-2	X

MONTHLY AWARDS

	Manager (Premier Div)	Manager of the Month (Div One)	Goalscorer of the Month
August	Dick Creasey (Holbeach)	Craig Robson/Adam May (Daventry)	Paul Fountain (Daventry)
September	Adam Sandy (Raunds)	Chris Beckett (Deeping)	Robbie Williams (Deeping)
October	Derek Maddox (Desboro)	Simon Morrice (Blisworth)	Mark Jameson (Wellingboro)
November	Dave Conlon (Cogenhoe)	Chris Beckett (Deeping)	Jimmy Simpson (Daventry)
December	Bob Don-Duncan (Boston)	Neil McAllister (ON Chenecks)	Jason Meeds (St Neots)
			Lee West (ON Chenecks)
January	Scott Carlin (Bugbrooke)	Lee Howard (Higham)	Richard Turner (Sileby)
February	Adam Sandy (Raunds)	Gary Petts (Thrapston)	Reuben Max-Grant (Buck'ham)
March	Jon Taylor (Wootton)	Simon Morrice (Blisworth)	Lee Ross (Ford Sports)
April/May	Shane Geary (Ford Sports)	Gary Petts (Thrapston)	Scott Coleman (N Spencer)

UHLSPORT UNITED COUNTIES LEAGUE KNOCKOUT CUP 2000-01

PRELIMINARY ROUND

Blisworth	v	Ford Sports	2-4
Olney	v	Burton PW	3-1
Desborough	v	St Neots	3-2
Woodford	v	Blackstone	1-0
Boston	v	Eynesbury	2-1
Daventry	v	Long Buckby	2-1
Wellingborough	v	Bugbrooke	1*0

Tie awarded to Blackstone, Woodford fielded ineligible player

FIRST ROUND

Cottingham	v	Newport Pagnell	0*3
Buckingham	v	Sharnbrook	4-0
Stewarts & Lloyds	v	Potton	3-0
Higham	v	Irchester	8-0
Whitworths	v	Yaxley	0-1
Desborough	v	Sileby	3-1
Wootton	v	Wellingborough	2*2, 5p4
Ford Sports	v	Deeping	2-5
North'ton Spencer	v	Harrowby	3-2
St Ives	v	Bourne	1-0
Stotfold	v	Thrapston	1*1, 4p2
Cogenhoe	v	Holbeach	4-2
ON Chenecks	v	Kempston	0-5
Rothwell Corinthians	v	Daventry	0-3
Olney	v	Raunds	1-5
Blackstone	v	Boston	1*1, 3p2

SECOND ROUND

Northampton Spencer	v	Higham	3-2
Yaxley	v	Kempston	2-1
Deeping	v	Buckingham	3-1
Wootton	v	Stewarts & Lloyds	2-1
Newport Pagnell	v	Daventry	0*1
Cogenhoe	v	Raunds	2*2, 5p4
Stotfold	v	Blackstone	6-3
St Ives	v	Desborough	0-1

THIRD ROUND

Deeping	v	Stotfold	0-1
Daventry	v	Wootton	0-3
Cogenhoe	v	North'ton Spencer	2-1
Desborough	v	Yaxley	1*1, 3p0

SEMI-FINALS

Stotfold	v	Cogenhoe	2-3
Wootton	v	Desborough	1*2

FINAL

Cogenhoe	v	Desborough	1-2	at Raunds

UNITED COUNTIES LEAGUE LEADING SCORERS/APPEARANCES 2000-01

PREMIER DIVISION

Most Appearances		*Leading Scorers*	
Blackstone			
Matt Doyle	43	Liam Harrold	19
Boston			
Mick Brown	41	Dave Scotney	19
Ross Don-Duncan	41		
Lee Rippin	41		
Dave Scotney	41		
Bourne			
Kevin Ainslie	41	Darren Munton	24
Darren Munton	41		
Buckingham			
Meshach Cole	38	Meshach Cole	20
Bugbrooke			
James Sweeney	38	James Sweeney	13
Cogenhoe			
David Bond	43	Steve Kuhne	26
Steve Kuhne	43		
Desborough			
Jamie Gilsenan	45	Richard Gilbert	18
Eynesbury			
Paul Childerley	41	Paul Childerley	7
Ford Sports			
Adrian Pestell	41	Lee Ross	21
Simon Williams	41		
Holbeach			
Phil Barnes	41	Ian Dunn	21
Steve Barnes	41		
Kempston			
Jason Mannion	37	Pete Saunders	24
Paul Stanley	37		
Long Buckby			
Sean Tiernan	39	Rick Barr	9
Northampton Spencer			
Lee O'Connor	42	Scott Coleman	19
Potton			
Keeley Thake	37	Leroy Odd	6
Raunds			
Wayne Richardson	40	Andy Evans	26
St Neots			
Andy Grieve	39	Vince Petty	25
Mick McCreanor	39		
Stewarts & Lloyds			
Kevin Byrne	40	Kevin Byrne	18
Stotfold			
Steve Young	43	Mark Phillips	21
Wellingborough			
Brett Dixon	39	Mark Jameson	23
Mark Jameson	39		
Adam Sturgess	39		
Wootton			
Andrew Carey	43	Darek Jozwiak	18
Yaxley			
Simon Acton	41	Lee Clarke	18

BLACKSTONE

Secretary: Ian McGillivry, 20 New Rd, Ryhall, Stamford, Lincs PE9 4HL
Tel: 01780 762263 (H),**Ground:** Lincoln Road, Stamford Tel: 01780 757335

Directions: A6121 Stamford to Bourne road, 2nd left past MB works

Capacity: 1,000 Seats: 100 Cover: Yes Floodlights: Yes

Clubhouse: Open evenings, lunchtimes & matchdays

HONOURS UCL Div 1 R-up 87-88 (Benevolent Cup R-up), Lincs Snr Cup `A' 92-93

PREVIOUS **Leagues:** Peterborough Works; Peterborough; Stamford & District
Names: Rutland Ironworks; Blackstone (until 1975)

RECORD **Gate:** 700 v Glinton
Win: 11-0 v Brackley, 22/1/94 (A Dunn 6 goals)
Scorer (in one game): A Dunn; 6 v Brackley Town, 22/1/94

Players progressing : Craig Goldsmith (Peterborough), Alan Neilson (Newcastle)

FACT FILE
Founded: 1920
Nickname: Stones
Sponsors: Ideal Shopfitters
Colours: All yellow & royal blue
Change Colours: All red
Midweek matchday: Tuesday
Programme: 32 pages with entry
Editor: Kevin Boor (01780 754584)
Local Press: Stamford Mercury, Herald & Post, Peterborough Evening Telegraph

CLUB PERSONNEL
President: Darren Laughton
Chairman: Bill Sewell
Manager: Vince Adams
Press Officer: Kevin Boor
Asst Manager: Pat O'Keefe
2000-01 P.o.Y. & Top Scorer: iam Harro;ld 24

BOSTON TOWN

Secretary: A Crick, Daisy Cottage, Shore Rd, Freiston, Boston, Lincs., PE22 0LN
Tel: 01205 760162. (H &Fax) 01205 313090 (W)

Ground: Tattershall Road, Boston, Lincs Tel: 01205 365470

Directions: A52 Grantham-Sleaford, 2nd left into Brotherton Rd., Argyle St. to bridge, immediately over left into Tattersall road, ground 3/4 mile on left.

Capacity: 6,000 Seats: 450 Cover: 950 Floodlights: Yes Club Shop: Yes

Clubhouse: Open evenings, except Sunday, matchdays & functions. Bar & Lounge. Darts & pool

HONOURS Midland Co's Lg 74-75 78-79 80-81 (Lg Cup 76-77); Lincs Snr `A' Cup (5)73-74 79-82 89-90 (Snr `B' Cup 65-66); Central Mids Lg 88-89; Central All 65-66; Lincs Lg 64-65; Und. Co. Lg. Prem Div 94-95, 00-01

PREVIOUS **Leagues:** Lincs 63-65; Central Alliance 65-66; Eastern Co's 66-68; Midland 68-82; Northern Co's East 82-87; Central Midlands 87-91

BEST SEASON **FA Cup:** 1st Rd Proper 76-77, 1-3 v Barnsley (A)
FA Trophy: 2nd Round 79-80, 3-6 v Mossley (A) after 0-0
FA Vase: Semi-Finals 94-95, 0-2 (agg) v Taunton Town)

RECORD **Attendance:** 2,700 v Boston Utd, FA Cup 3rd Qual. Rd 1970
Goalscorer (in a season): Carl Smaller 48, 1994-95

Players progressing: Julian Joachim (Leicester City and Aston Villa) , Neil Mann (Hull City)

FACT FILE
Founded: 1963
Nickname: Poachers
Sponsors: Barclays Brokers, Graham Gill Carpets & Boston Snooker Centre
Colours: Sky Blue/ Royal Blue/Sky
Change: Yellow/white/yellow
Midweek Matchday: Tuesday
Reserves League: None 94-95
Programme: 40 pages, 50p
Ed./ Press Off:Paul Rogerson 01205 354059H

CLUB PERSONNEL
Chairman: Mick Vines
Vice Chairman: J Rose
Treasurer: J Rose
Manager: Bob Don-Duncan
Ass.Manager: Dave Scotney
Physio: Steve Greetham
2000-01 Leading goalscorer: Dave Scotney 21
Captain: Dean Elston
P.o.Y.: Dean Elston

BOURNE TOWN

Secretary: Roger Atkins, 4 Orchard Close, Bourne, Lincs PE10 9DF Tel: 01778 424882

Ground: Abbey Lawn, Abbey Road, Bourne, Lincs Tel: 01778 422292

Directions: In market place take A151 Spalding Road, ground 500 yds on right.Public transport from Peterborough, Stamford and Grantham
Capacity: 3,000 Seats: 300 Cover: 750 Floodlights: Yes
Club Shop: Contact Sec.

Clubhouse: Small, open matchdays and specific events. Food, confectionary available

HONOURS Utd Co's Lg 68-69 69-70 71-72 90-91 (KO Cup 69-70, Benevolent Cup 90-91, Res Div 2 94-95), Lincs Snr `A' Cup 71-72 (R-up 92-93), Central Alliance Division 1 South 59-60, Lincs Intermediate Cup 85-86

PREVIOUS **Leagues:** Peterborough; UCL 47-56; Central All. 58-61; MidlandCos 61-63
Ground: Adjacent to cricket field after WW2 until 1947

RECORD **Attendance:** 3,000 v Chelmsford, FA Trophy 1970
Goalscorer: David Scotney

Players progress ing: Peter Grummit (Nottm Forest), Shaun Cunnington (Wrexham), David Palmer (Wrexham)

FACT FILE
Founded: 1883 Nickname: Wakes
Sponsors: Jaychem
Colours: Maroon & sky/sky/maroon
Change Colours: White & sky/white & sky/sky
Midweek matchday: Tuesday
Reserves' Lge: HSUCL Res Div 1
Programme: 50 pages, 50p
Editor: JimAshton (01778 440065)
Local Press: Stamford Mercury, Lincs Free Press, Peterborough EveningTelegraph, Bourne Local

CLUB PERSONNEL
Chairman: Jim Ashton
Vice-Chairman:
President: Jim Ashton
Press Officer: Jeff Hodson
Manager: Dave McNish
Physio: Dick Joy

BUCKINGHAM TOWN

Secretary: Brian Maycock, 31 Westfield, Buckingham, Bucks Tel: 01280 815529

Ground: Ford Meadow, Ford Street, Buckingham Tel: 01280 816257
Capacity: 4,000 Cover: 420 Seats: 420 Floodlights: Yes

Directions: From town centre take Aylesbury (A413) road and turn right at Phillips Garage after 400yds. Public transport: train to Milton Keynes, then bus to Buckingham

Clubhouse: Open evenings 6.30-11 (12-11 Sat & Sun) Rolls etc available on matchdays. Bingo, dominoes, darts & pool. Concert room with stage for hire,capacity 150 **Club Shop:** Yes

HONOURS Southern Lg Southern Div 90-91, Utd Co's Lg 83-84 85-86 (Div 1 R-up 75-76, Div 2 R-up 74-75, Lg Cup 83-84, Div 2 Cup R-up 74-75), Nth Bucks Lg 24-25 28-29 33-34 35-37 38-39 48-50(2) Aylesbury & Dist. Lg 02-03, Berks & Bucks Snr Cup 83-84, Berks & Bucks Jnr Cup 02-03 48-49 (R-up 38-39 72-73), Berks & Bucks Minor Cup 32-33, Buckingham Snr Charity Cup x11, r-up x 5

PREVIOUS **Leagues:** Aylesbury & Dist; Nth Bucks; Hellenic 53-57; Sth Mids 57-74; Utd Co's 74-86; Southern Lge 86-97

BEST SEASON **FA Cup:** 1st Round 1984-85 **FA Vase:** Quarter Finals 1990-91 & 92-93

RECORD **Attendance:** 2,451 v Orient, FA Cup 1st Rd 84-85
Fee paid: £7,000 for Steve Jenkins (Wealdstone, 1992)
Fee received: £1,000 for Terry Shrieves (Kettering)

FACT FILE

Formed: 1883
Nickname: The Robins
Sponsors: Wipac
Colours: All red
Change colours: All white
Midweek Matchday:
Reserves' League: No reserve team
Programme: Yes
Newsline: 0891 884 431
Local Press: Buckingham Advertiser, MK Citizen, Herald & Post
Local Radio: Chiltern Radio, Fox FM (102.6 fm), 3 Counties Radio

CLUB PERSONNEL

Chairman: Brian Maycock

BUGBROOKE ST MICHAELS

Secretary: Roger Geary, 31 Kislingbury Rd, Bugbrooke, Northampton NN7 3QG
Tel: 01604 831678

Ground: Birds Close, Gayton Road, Bugbrooke Tel: 01604 830707
Capacity: 2,500 Seats: 120 Cover: Yes Floodlights: Yes

Directions: M1. Jct 16 Take A45 to Northampton. At 1st roundabout follow signs to Bugrooke. In villagefollow road straight through to club immediately past last house on left.

Clubhouse: Yes - normal licensing hours

HONOURS Northants Junior Cup 89-90, Central Northants Comb. 68-69 69-70 70-71 71-72 76-77 85-86, UCL Res Div 2 R-up 94-95 U.C.L. Div One Champions 98-99

PREVIOUS **League** : Central Northants Combination 1952-87 **Ground:** School Close

RECORD **Attendance:** 1,156 **Scorer:** Vince Thomas **Appearances:** Jimmy Nord

Players progressing: Kevin Slinn (Watford), Craig Adams (Northampton)

FACT FILE

Founded: 1929
Nickname: Badgers
Sponsors: Unusual Industries
Club colours: Black & white/black/black
Change colours: All Red
Reserves' Lge: UCL Res. Div. 1
Programme: Eight pages
Editor: Teresa Garlick

CLUB PERSONNEL

Chairman: Tom Treacy
President: John Curtis
Manager: Chris Goodchild
Asst Manager: Jon Mundy
Press Officer:Jon Munday

COGENHOE UNITED

Secretary: Sue Wright, 6 Brafield Road, Cogenhoe, Northants NN7 1ND
Tel: 01604 890737 (H), 01604 890277 (B), Fax: 01604 890641

Ground: Compton Park, Brafield Rd, Cogenhoe, Northants (01604 890521)
Directions: Turn off A428 at Brafield-on-the-Green, first turn right toCogenhoe or A45 to Billing Aquadrome. Carry on, take second Cogenhoe turn on left

Capacity: 5,000 Seats: 100 Cover: 200 Floodlights: Yes Club Shop: No
Clubhouse: Tues-Fri 7-11, Sat 12-3 & 4-11, Sun 12-3 & 7-10.30 Snacks. Hot food on matchdays

HONOURS UCL Div 1 R-up 86-87 (Res. Div 2 88-89), K.O. Cup 96-97; Daventry Charity Cup 91-92 95-96, (R-up 79-80); Central Northants Comb 80-81 82-83 83-84 (R-up 81-82, Prem Div Cup 82-83 (R-up 78-79), Div 1 Cup R-up 77-78, Charity Shield 82-83 83-84)

PREVIOUS **League:** Central Northants Combination 1967-84
Ground: Cogenhoe Village PF 1967-84

RECORD **Gate:** 1,000 v Eastenders XI, Charity match 8/7/90
Scorer & Appearances: Tony Smith
Win: 22-0 v Ravensthorpe, Cen. Northants Comb. Prem. Div. KO Cup, 79-80
Defeat: 0-6 v Yardley United, Central Northants Comb. Div. 1, 76-77

Players progressing : Darren Bazeley (Watford 89), Darren Harmon (Notts Co. 89),Matt Murphy (Oxford Utd 93), Gary Leonard (Northampton 1978)

FACT FILE

Founded: 1967
Nickname: Cooks
Sponsors: Supertrucking
Colours: All royal
Change: Black & white/white/white
Midweek matchday: Tuesday
Reserves' Lge: UCL Res. Div 1
Programme: 32 pages with Admission
Editor:Sue Wright
Local Press: Chronicle & Echo, Northants Evening Telegraph

CLUB PERSONNEL

Chairman: Derek Wright
Vice Chairman: Bob Earl
President: Steve Brockwell
Comm. Man.: Robert Jones
Manager: Steve Forbes
Assistant Manager: Dino Cirelli
Physio: Ian Blair

Top: Boston Town Back Row (l-r): Paul Wright, Lee Orrey, Steve Parkinson, Lee Rippin, Ross Don-Duncan, Mick Brown, Rob Speechley, Deal Elston (capt), Bob Don-Duncan (manager) Front Row: John Creese, Matt Price, Ian Shooter, Graham Neal, Gavin Slater, Dave Scotney

Centre: Biggleswade United, Hinchingbrooke Cup winners Photo: Gordon Whittington

Bottom: Desborough Town, United Counties League Cup winners Photo: Gordon Whittington

DAVENTRY TOWN

Secretary: Miss Joanne Place, 30 The Cherwell, Daventry, Northants NN11 4QJ
Tel: 01327 879878 (H), 01327 300001 (B)

Ground: Elderstubbs Farm, Leamington Way, Daventry, Northants Tel: 01327 706286
Capacity: 2,000 Seats: 250 Cover: 250 Floodlights: Yes
Directions Adjacent to A45 by-pass at top of Staverton Road Sports Complex
Clubhouse: Large bar/kitchen

HONOURS UCL Div 1(2) 89-91 (Lg Cup R-up 92-93, Highest Aggregate Cup),
Northants Junior Cup 36-37 60-61 91-92
PREVIOUS **Leagues:** Northampton Town (pre-1987)/ Central Northants Combination 87-89
BEST SEASON **FA Cup:** Prel. Rd 94-95
FA Vase: Preliminary Rd 91-92 94-95
RECORD **Attendance:** 350 v Ford Sports 1991
Players Progressing: Martin Aldridge (Northampton)

FACT FILE
Founded: 1886
Sponsor: Campbell Estate Agents
Colours:White/black/black
Change colours: All red
Midweek Matchday: Tuesday
Reserves League: Central Northants Comb
Programme:
4 Pages Editor: Tony Perry
Local Press:
Daventry Weekly Express, Herald & Post

CLUB PERSONNEL
Chairman: Mel Knowles
Vice Chairman: Grant Hughes
President: Paul Webster

Managers: Kevin Flear/Craig Robson
Physio: Tony Jackson
Asst Man.: Robin Humphries, Moz Elliott

DEEPING RANGERS

Secretary: Haydon Whitham, 3 Everingham, Orton Brimbles, Peterborough PE2 5XP
Tel:01733 238539
Match Sec.: Robin Crowson
Tel: 01778 348287 (H) 07977 971796 (M) Email: rwc@excite.co.uk

Ground: Deeping Sports Club, Outgang Road, Market Deeping, Lincs.
Tel: 01778 344701 Website: www.deepingrangers.co.uk
Capacity: 1,000 Seats: 180 Cover: 180 Floodlights: yes
Directions: From Deeping town centre take the A15 towards Bourne. Turn right at Towngate Tavern following signs to Industrial Estate & club is 1/4 mile on left.
Clubhouse: Bar and lounge. Changing rooms

HONOURS Peterborough & Dist. Lge Div 3 67, Div. 2 69, Div. 1 70, Prem. Div. R-up 95-96 98-99; Lincs Junior Cup 83-84 87-88 88-89, Lincs. Sen. B Cup 00-01, R-up UCL Div 1 R-up 00-01, Fair Play Award 99-00, 00-01
Peterborough FA Senior Cup 91-92 96-97 Minor Cup 67,
PREVIOUS **League:** Peterborough & District

FACT FILE
Founded: 1966
Nickname: Rangers
Colours: Claret & blue
Change colours: White/claret/sky blue
Programme: Yes

CLUB PERSONNEL
President: Albert Lawrence
Chairman: Ed Bailey

Manager: Chris Beckett
Asst. Manager: Dave Simpson

2000-01
Leading goalscorer: Robbie Williams 31
Captain: Martin Bradley
P.o.Y.: Paul Pearson

DESBOROUGH TOWN

Secretary: John Lee, 85 Breakleys Road, Desborough, Northants NN14 2PT
Tel: 01536 760002 Email Address: johnlee@froggerycottage.fsnet.co.uk

Ground: Waterworks Field, Braybrooke Rd, Desborough Tel: 01536 761350
Capacity: 8,000 Seats: 250 Cover: 500 Floodlights: Yes

Directions: Half a mile west of A6 following signs for Braybrooke
Clubhouse: Lounge & main hall, 2 bars, games room. Every eve. & w/e lunchtimes
Club Shop: No

HONOURS Utd Co's (Prev. Northants) Lg 00-01 01-02 06-07 20-21 23-24 24-25 27-28 48-49 66-67 (R-up 02-03 10-11 19-20 22-23 79-80, 98-99), Div 2 10-11, 28-9(Res), R-up 09-10 (Res) 26-27(Res) 51-52(Res), KO Cup 77-78 96-97 00-01;
Northants Snr Cup 10-11 13-14 28-29 51-52; Desborough Charity Cup 97-98,98-99,99-00
PREVIOUS **Leagues:** None
RECORD **Attendance:** 8,000 v Kettering Town
Win: 10-1: v Huntingdon Utd (A) 1957 & v Stewarts & Lloyds (A) 1965, both UCL.
Defeat: 11-0 v Rushden Town (A) 1934
Fee received: £8,000 for Wakeley Gage, from Northampton Town
Players progressing: Wakeley Gage (Northampton), Jon Purdie & Campbell Chapman (Wolves), Andy Tillson (Grimsby), Matt Murphy (Oxford United)

FACT FILE
Founded: 1896 Nickname: Ar Tarn
Colours: Blue & white/blue/blue
Change Colours: All red
Previous Leagues: None
Midweek matchday: Tuesday
Programme: 40 pages with entry
Editor:John Lee
Local Press: Evening Telegraph,Northants Post,Chronicle & Echo,& Harborough Mail
Website: www.artarn.co.uk
2000-01 Captain:Ian Walker
Top Scorer: Richard Gilbert 22
P.o.Y.: Richard Lavin

CLUB PERSONNEL
Chairman:Alan Panter
President: T.B.A.
Press Officer: John Lee
Manager: Derek Maddox
Asst Manager: Dave McHuchinson
Physio: Dave Marlow

FORD SPORTS

Secretary: Mick Fryatt, 2 Mayfield Drive, Daventry, Northants NN11 5QB
Tel Nos: 01327 876789 (H) 01327 305407 (W)

Ground: Royal Oak Way South, Daventry, Northants Tel: 01327 709219
Capacity: 1,000 Seats: Yes Cover: Yes Floodlights: Yes

Directions: Enter Daventry on A45 or A361 and follow signs for Royal Oak Way

Clubhouse: Yes

HONOURS UCL Div 1 92-93, 95-96, Knockout Cup 97-98, Benevolent Cup R-up 92-93; Highest Agg. Goalscoring Trophy 92-93; Northants Sen Cup R-up 96-97

PREVIOUS **League:** Central Northants Comb

Player progressing: Martin Aldridge (Northampton)

FACT FILE
Founded: 1968
Nickname: Motormen
Sponsors: Ford Sports & Social Club
Colours: Blue/black/black
Change : Red & black/black/red & black
Midweek matches:
Reserves' Lge: UCL Res Div 2
Programme: 12 pages
Editor: John Hinton

CLUB PERSONNEL
Chairman: John Bailham
Managers: Darren Wood
Assistant Manager: Shane Geary
Physio: Dave Bull

HOLBEACH UNITED

Secretary: Paul Beeken, 36 West End, Holbeach, Lincs PE12 7HA Tel: 01406 425355 (H)
Email Address: secpaulathufc@aol
Ground: Carters Park, Park Road, Holbeach Tel: 01406 424761
Capacity:4,000 Seats: 200 Cover: 450 Floodlights: Yes

Directions: Second left at traffic lights in town centre, 220 yds down road on left.
From King's Lynn; sharp right at traffic lights

Clubhouse: Large bar, lounge & kitchen, open every night **Club Shop:** No

HONOURS Utd Co's Lg 89-90 (KO Cup 64-65 89-90), Benevolent Cup, Evans Halshaw Cup 97-98; Lincs Snr Cup `A' 83-84 84-85 86-87 (Senior Cup `B' 57-58)

PREVIOUS **Leagues:** Peterborough; Utd Co's 46-55; Eastern Co's 55-62; Midland Co's62-63

BEST SEASON **FA Cup:** 1st Rd Proper 82-83, 0-4 v Wrexham (at Peterborough)
FA Trophy: 2nd Qual. Round 69-70 71-72
FA Vase: 5th Round 88-89, 2-4 v Wisbech Town

RECORD **Gate:** 4,094 v Wisbech 1954

Players progressing: Peter Rawcliffe (Lincoln)

FACT FILE
Founded: 1929 Nickname: Tigers
Sponsors: Ashwood Homes
Colours: Old gold & black/black/black
Change Colours: White/blue/blue
Midweek matchday: Tuesday
Reserves' Lge: Peterborough
Prog: 44 pages, 50p Editor: David Ingle
Local Press : Lincs Free Press, Spalding Guardian, Peterborough Evening Telegraph

2000-01
Capt: Philip Barnes P.o.Y.: Martin Bunce Top Scorer: Ian Dunn 31

CLUB PERSONNEL
Chairman: Chris Cooper
President: Francis Bissadike
Manager: Dick Creasey Ass.Man. Elisio Lima
Physio: Gerald Starling

KEMPSTON ROVERS

Secretary: Alan Scott, 26 King William Rd, Kempston, Bedford MK42 7AT Tel: 01234 854875

Ground: Hillgrounds Leisure, Hillgrounds Rd, Kempston, Bedford Tel: 01234 852346.
Capacity: 2,000 Seats: 100 Cover: 250 Floodlights: Yes

Directions: M1 jct 13, A421 to Kempston, Hillgrounds Rd is off the B531 main Kempston-Bedford road. Entrance to Hillgrounds Road is opposite Sainsburys onthe B531 - ground can be found just over twi miles from Sainsburys entrance.British Rail to Bedford Thameslink/Midland then bus No.103 from Bedford town centre stops outside ground

Club Shop: No, but old programmes available from clubhouse
Clubhouse: Open 7-11pm Tues - Sun. & w/e lunch 12-3pm. Sky TV, pool, hot pies & pasties.

HONOURS United Counties Lge 73-74 (R-up 56-57 59-60), Div 1 57-58 85-86, Div 2 55-56 (R-up 67-68), KO Cup 55-56 57-58 59-60 74-75 76-77. Beds Senior Cup 08-09 37-38 76-77 91-92 (R-up 92-93)

PREVIOUS **League:** South Midlands 27-53
Grounds: Bedford Rd 1900s-1973; Hillgrounds Road 74-86 (3 grounds in same road!)

BEST SEASON **FA Cup:** **FA Vase:**

RECORD **Attendance:** Unknown **Scorer:** Doug Jack

Players progressing: Ernie Fenn (WBA), Matthew Woolgar (Luton 1994)

FACT FILE
Founded: 1884
Nickname: Walnut Boys
Club Sponsors: Audi Vindis Bedford
Colours: Red & white stripes/black/red
Change Colours: All yellow
Midweek matchday: Tuesday
Reserves's Lge: Bedford & Dist
Programme: 24 pages, 40p
Editor: Richard Coop (0378 629470)
Local Press: Bedfordshire Times, Herald & Post, Beds on Sunday

CLUB PERSONNEL
President: H Gilbert
Chairman: Mark Salsbury
Vice-Chairman: Russell Shreeves
Press Officer : Secretary
Manager:Ken Davidson
Asst Manager: Bobby Roberts
Coach: Mel Fisher

LONG BUCKBY

Secretary: Dave Austin,8 Pytchley Drive, Long Buckby, Northampton NN6 7PL 01327 842788(H)
Ground: Station Rd, Long Buckby Tel: 01327 842682
Capacity: 1,000 Seats: 200 Cover: 200 Floodlights: Yes

Directions: On Daventry - Long Buckby road. 400 yds from station (Northampton -Rugby line)

Clubhouse: Bar & concert room. Open matchdays

HONOURS UCL KO Cup 84-85, UCL Div 2 70-71 71-72, Div 2 KO Cup 71-72, Div 3 69-70; Northants Snr Cup R-up; Daventry Charity Cup 96-97

PREVIOUS **Leagues:** Rugby & D.; Central Northants Comb. (pre-1968)
Name: Long Buckby Nomads 1936

BEST SEASON **FA Vase:** 2nd Rd 85-86
FA Cup: 1st Qualifying Rd 92-93

RECORD **Gate:** 750 v Kettering, Northants Snr Cup Final 1984

Players progressing: Gary Mills (Nottm Forest), Vince Overson (Burnley), Des Waldock (Northampton),Steve Norris (Scarborough)

FACT FILE
Nickname: Bucks
Sponsors: Northampton Elec Dist
Colours: All blue
Change colours: All red
Midweek matchday: Tuesday
Reserves' Lge: HSUCL Res Div 1
Programme: 8 pages
Editor: Rod Pryor (01604 845071)
Local Press : Chronicle & Echo, Daventry Weekly News

CLUB PERSONNEL
President: Alister Bruce
Chairman: Ted Thresher
Manager: Kevin Simmonds
Assistant Manager: Martin McNulty
Physio: Robert Stafferton

NORTHAMPTON SPENCER

Secretary: Nick Hillery, Cowntess Road, Northampton
Ground: Kingsthorpe Mill, Studland Rd., Northampton NN3 1NF Tel: 01604 718898
Capacity: 2000 Seats: 100 Cover: 350 Floodlights: Yes

Directions: Turn off Kingsthorpe Road at traffic lights into Thornton Rd., 1st right into Studland Rd. and ground is at the end.

Clubhouse: Open during normal licensing hours. Lounge and bar. **Club Shop:** No

HONOURS: UCL 91-92, r-up 92-93, 97-98, Div. 1 84-85, KO Cup 88-89 93-94, r-up 87-88 96-97 97-98, Benevolent Cup 91-92; Northants Sen. Cup r-up 90-91 93-94.

PREVIOUS **League:** Northampton Town Lge 36-68
Name: Spencer School Old Boys
Grounds: Dallington Park 36-70, Duston High School 70-72

BEST SEASON **FA Cup:** 1st Qual. Rd 93-94, 96-97
FA Vase: 4th Round 87-88, 1-2 v Gresley Rovers

RECORDS **Attendance:** 800 v Nottm. Forest, dressing room opener 1993

Players progressing: Paul Stratford (Northampton), Wakeley Gage (Northampton)

FACT FILE
Founded: 1936 Nickname: Millers
Sponsors: Crisis Worldwide, International Couriers
Colours: Yellow/green/yellow
Change colours: All red
Midweek matchday: Tuesday
Reserves' League: UCL Res Div 1
Programme: 20 pages 50p
Editor: Andy Goldsmith (01604 412382)
Website: www.geocities.com/kirby42000

CLUB PERSONNEL
President: J Sampson
Joint Chairmen: Graham Wrighting & Jim Connelly
Press Off.: Andy Goldsmith (01604 412382)
Manager: Gary Sargent
Assistant. Man.: Keith Bowen
2000-01 Captain: Ian Mann
P.o.Y.: Lee O'Conner
Top Scorer: Scott Coleman 20

RAUNDS TOWN

Secretary Mrs Carol Warcup, 9 Warwick Close, Raunds, Northants Tel: 01933 626516
Ground: Kiln Park, London Road, Raunds, Northants NN9 6EQ
Tel: 01933 623351, Matchdays 01933 460941
Directions: Take Raunds turning at roundabout on A45 and ground is first left
Nearest station; Wellingborough. Bus services local
Capacity: 3,000 Seats: 250 Cover: 600 Floodlights: Yes
Clubhouse: On ground, open every day
Club Shop: Open matchdays, selling shirts, books programmes, contact Malc York, c/o club
PREVIOUS **Leagues:** Rushden & Dist., Cen. Northants Comb., U.C.L., Southern Lge 96-00
Grounds: Greenhouse Field (until 1948), The Berristers (1948-91)
BEST SEASON **FA Cup:** 4th Qual Rd, 98-99 (0-2 v Enfield),
FA Vase: Semi-final v Arlesey Tn 94-5
FA Trophy: 3rd Rd v Weston-super-Mare 98-99 (2-2, 0-1)
HONOURS UCL Prem Champions 95-96, UCL Div 1 82-83 (R-up 91-92), KO Cup 90-91, (R-up 83-84 93-94), Res Div 1 88-89 95-96 (R-up 86-87 87-88 89-90 90-91 91-92), Reserve KO Cup 84-85 88-89 93-94; Northants Snr Cup 90-91; Hunts Premier Cup R-up 92-93; Daventry Charity Cup R-up 83-84; Northants Jnr Cup 82-83 91-92 (res) 92-93 (res)
CLUB RECORDS **Attendance:** 1,500 v Crystal Palace, ground opening 23/7/91
Win: 9-0 v Potton 95, 11-2 v Brackley 93 **Defeat:** 0-6 v Baldock 83, vBuckingham 84-85
Career Goalscorer: Shaun Keeble 208 **Career Appearances:** Martin Lewis 355 (+29subs)

FACT FILE
Formed: 1946
Nickname: Shopmates
Colours: Red & black
Change Colours: Yellow
Midweek matchday: Tuesday
Reserves' League: UCL Reserve Div. One
Prog: Pages: Varies Price: £1.00
Editor: Malc York 01933 311586
2000-01-
Top Scorer: Andy Evans 29
P. of Y.: Wayne richardson
Captain: Eddie Doxford

CLUB PERSONNEL
Chairman: George Hagan
President: Mahen Perera
Manager:Adam Sandy
Asst Manager: Adam Sinclair

Cottingham FC
Back Row (l-r): Steve Marshall (Physio), Graham Leech (Asst Mngr), Adam Bell, Andy O'Neill, James Keeney, Duncan McNish, Dave Trimble, Neil Addy. Front Row: Rab Stewart, Derek Simmons, Ian Jaffrey, Gary Owen, Willie Moore, John Cairns
Photo: Gordon Whittington

Eynesbury Rovers
Back Row (l-r): Phil Whitbread (Physio), Ken Churchill (Asst Mngr), Dave Goodall, Kevin Shotter, Wayne Dickerson, Danny Workman, Paul Hickling, Damien Bavister. Front Row: Dave Samal, Andy Clark, Lee Wood, Dean Stockwell, Paul Childerley, Matt Brading, David Fisk, Stuart Humphrey. Photo: Gordon Whittington

Potton United
Back Row (l-r): Richard Piggott, Leeroy Odd, Jimmy Sweeney, Chris Humble, Keely Thake, Adam Sinclair, Andy Hughes, Martin Hammocks. Front Row: Steve Jones, Jamie Uttley, Kevin Turner, Lee Daly, Ross Harrison, John Frost, Mike Hurn.
Photo: Gordon Whittington

Raunds Town
Back Row (l-r): Adam Sandy (Manager), Graham Knight, Mark Njotsa, Lewis Collins, Luke Dowling, Peter Earl, James Mariner, Russell Douglas, Fazel Koriya, David Broomes, Bob Bramah (Physio), Adam Sinclair (Coach). Front Row: Wayne Richardson, Richard Bunting, Jamie Kearns, Steve Salisman, Eddie Boxford, Russell Dunkley
Photo: Gordon Whittington

ST. NEOTS TOWN

Secretary: Graham Izzard, c/o Football club.

Ground: Rowley Park, Cambridge Rd, St Neots, Cambs Tel: 01480 470012
Capacity: 3,000 Seats: No Cover: 250 Floodlights: Yes

Directions: Through the town centre, under the railway bridge, ground is first on the left
Capacity: 2,500 **Seating:** 160 **Covered Standing:** 300 **Floodlights :** Yes
Clubhouse: Yes with Conference,Banqueting and private functions all bookable

HONOURS Hunts Snr Cup(34), UCL 67-68 (KO Cup 67-68 68-69), Metropolitan Lg 49-50(Lg Cup 79-80), South Midlands Lg 32-33, Huntingdonshire Lg 90-91 92-92 92-93 94-95

PREVIOUS **Leagues:** South Midlands 27-36 46-49; United Counties 36-39 51-56 66-69 73-88; Metropolitan 49-51 60-66; Central Alliance 56-60; Eastern Counties 69-73; Huntingdonshire 90-94 **Name:** St Neots & District 1879-1957

BEST SEASON **FA Cup:** 1st Rd 66-67, 0-2 v Walsall (A)
FA Vase: 3rd Rd 78-79 **FA Trophy:** 2nd Qual. Rd 69-70 72-73

RECORD **Attendance:** 2,000 v Wisbech, 1966
Players progressing: Frank Atkins (Cambridge), John Gregory (Aston Villa) and Matthew Oakey (Southampton)

FACT FILE
Web site: www.stneotsfc.com
Founded: 1879 Nickname: Saints
Sponsors:Adam Kennedy, Midland Thermal, and Fleet Car Contracts
Club colours: Sky /navy/sky
Change colours:Yellow/Black/Yellow
Reserves' Lge: UCL Res Div 1
Programme: Yes Editor: MikeBirch (Tel: 01480 395505)
'Saintly Text';Revolving Information screen.
Editor: Mike Birch

CLUB PERSONNEL
Chairman: Bob Page
Vice Chairman:Bob Bridges
Commercial Man: Peter Hicks(01733 263656)
Press Officer: Neil Holmes (01480 383382)
Communic'ns Man:Rod Morris(01733 331658)
Team Manager: Chris Howell

STEWARTS & LLOYDS

Secretary: Dave Foster, 29 Tettenhall Close, Corby, Northants NN198 9PJ
Tel: 01536 746004(H) 01536 201234 (W)

Ground: Recreation Ground, Occupation Road, Corby Tel: 01536 401497
Capacity: 1,500 Seats: 100 Cover: 200 Floodlights: Yes

Directions: The ground is situated on Occupation Rd at the rear of Stewart & Lloyds Leisure Club, next to old Corby Town F.C. ground

Clubhouse: Licensed bar **Club Shop:** No

HONOURS UCL R-up 85-86, Div 1(2) 73-75; UCL KO Cup, Prem 95-96, Div 1 Cup(2)73-75, Div 2 KO Cup(2) 75-77)

PREVIOUS **Leagues:** Kettering Amateur

BEST SEASON **FA Cup:** **FA Vase:**

RECORD **Goalscorer:** Joey Martin 46 (92-93)

Players progressing : Andy McGowan (Northampton), Willie Graham (Brentford)

FACT FILE
Formed: 1935
Nickname: None
Sponsor: Weldon
Colours: Amber/ navy blue/ navy blue
Change Colours: All red
Midweek matchday: Tuesday
Programme: 12 pages with admission
Editor/Press Officer: Dave Foster

CLUB PERSONNEL
Chairman: Peter Webb
Vice Chairmen: Gordon Hall, Harry Nelson
Manager: Elwyn Roberts
Asst Manager:Stuart Carmichael
Physio: Roger White

STOTFOLD

Secretary: Bill Clegg, 12 Common Rd, Stotfold, Hitchin, Herts SG5 4BX Tel: 01462 730421
Club Email: football@stotfoldfc.freeserve.co.uk Website:www.stotfoldfc.freeserve.co.uk
Ground: Roker Park, The Green, Stotfold, Hitchin, Herts Tel: 01462 730765
Capacity: 5,000 Seats: 300 Cover: 300 Floodlights: Yes

Directions: A507 from A1, right at lights, right at T-jct.
A507 from Bedford via Shefford, left at lights, right at T-jct

Clubhouse: Clubroom, bar, refreshment bar, dressing rooms, physio room

HONOURS Utd Co's Lg R-up 93-94, KO Cup Winners 98-99 R-up 91-92, Res Div 1 87-88; Sth Mids Lg 80-81 (R-up 55-56 57-58 58-59 59-60 63-64 65-66 77-78), Div 1 53-54, Chal. Tphy 81-82; Beds Snr Cup 64-65 93-94; Beds Premier Cup 81-82; 98-99 Beds I'mediate Cup 58-59; Nth Beds Charity Cup 55-56 56-57 61-62 81-82 87-88 90-91 97-98;Beds Colts Lg 88-89; Southern Com Cup 94-95 95-96 96-97; Hinchingbrooke Cup R-up 97-98: Win. 99-00: R-up 00-01

PREVIOUS **Leagues:** Biggleswade & District/ North Herts/ South Midlands 51-84

BEST SEASON: **FA Cup: 00-01** **FA Vase: 00-01**

RECORD **Attendance:** 1,000 v Letchworth Town, FA Amtr Cup
Scorer: Roy Boon **Appearances:** Roy Boon/Dave Chellew

FACT FILE
Founded: 1904 Reformed: 1945
Nickname: Eagles Sponsors: Motorola
Colours: Amber/black/black
Change Colours: All Sky blue
Midweek matchday: Tuesday
Reserves' League: UCL Reserve Division One
Programme: 22 pages with entry
Editor: Phil Pateman (01462 834581)
Local Press: Comet, Biggleswade Chronicle

CLUB PERSONNEL
Chairman: Phil Pateman
Vice Chairman: Graham Jarman
Pres: David Chellow Man: Ken Davidson
Asst Manager: Ken Baker
Press Officer: Bill Clegg
Physio: Sarah Scoot

2000-01
Leading Goalscorer: Mark Phillips 35
Captain: Steve Young
P.o.Y.: Roy Boon

WELLINGBOROUGH TOWN

Secretary : Mick Walden, 5 Fernie Way, Wellingborough, Northants NN8 3LB Tel: 01933 279561

Ground: Dog & Duck, London Road, Wellingborough, Northants Tel: 01933 223536
Capacity: 5,000 Seats: 300 Cover: 500 Floodlights: Yes

Directions: 200yds off A45 by-pass, by Dog & Duck PH. 1 mile from Wellingborough (BR)

Clubhouse: Full facilities. Open evenings & Sat lunchtimes **Club Shop:** No

HONOURS Utd Co's Lg 10-11 62-63 64-65, Metropolitan Lge 69-70, Northants Snr Cup 1896-97 1901-02 02-03 33-34 47-48 49-50 81-82, Maunsell Cup 20-21 21-22

PREVIOUS **Leagues:** Midland 1895-97 98-1901; Southern 01-05 71-89; Northants (Utd Co's)19-34 36-56 61-68; Central Alliance 56-61; Metropolitan 68-70; West Midlands Regional 70-71

BEST SEASON **FA Cup:** 1st Round 28-29, v Bristol Rovers; 65-66, 1-2 v Aldershot Town
FA Trophy: 1st Round 71-72, 0-3 v Dartford after 1-1 & 0-0
FA Vase: 1sr Rd. 95-96

RECORD **Attendance:** 4,013 v Kettering Town
Goalscorer: S Hill **Appearances:** P Hayes 165, 1985-89

Players progressing: Phil Neal (Northampton), Fanny Walden (Spurs)

FACT FILE
Founded: 1867
Nickname: Doughboys
Sponsors: Croyland Motors
Colours: Blue & white hoops/blue/blue.
Change Colours: All red
Midweek matchday: Tuesday
Reserve League: HSUCL Res. Div. Two
Programme: 16 pages 30p
Editor: Secretary

CLUB PERSONNEL
Chairman: Martin Potton
President: T.B.A.
Press Officer: Secretary
Manager: Brian Knight
Coach: Mike Emms
Physio: Tif Felton

WOOTON BLUE CROSS

Secretary: Trevor Templeman, 3 Pollys Yard, Newport Pagnell, Bucks MK16 8YU
Tel: 0958 718482 (Mobile)

Ground: Weston Park, Bedford Road, Wootton Tel: 01234 767662
Capacity: 2,000 Seats: 50 Cover: 250 Floodlights: Yes

Directions: Four miles south of Bedford on main road through village at rear of Post Office

Clubhouse: Main hall, bar, darts, pool, bingo. Open every evening and w/e lunchtimes
Club Shop: No

HONOURS Utd Co's Lg Div 2 67-68 69-70 (KO Cup 82-83, Div 2 Cup 64-65), South Midlands Lg 47-48 (R-up 49-50), Beds Sen. Cup 70-71, Hinchinbrooke Cup(5)

PREVIOUS **Leagues:** Bedford & District; South Midlands 46-55
Grounds: Recreation Ground, Fishers Field, Rose & Crown, Cockfield

BEST SEASON **FA Vase:** 3rd Rd 74-75
FA Cup: 2nd Qual. Rd 50-51 (3-4 v Hitchin (H))

RECORD **Gate:** 838 v Luton, Beds Prem. Cup 1988

Players progressing: Tony Biggs (Arsenal)

FACT FILE
Founded: 1887
Nickname: Blue Cross
Sponsors: Vision Blinds
Colours: Blue & white/blue/blue
Change: All yellow
Reserves' League: United Counties Res. Div 1
Midweek matchday: Tuesday
Programme: 24 pages Editor: Secretary

Local Press : Bedfordshire Times, Bedford Herald, Beds Express, Beds on Sunday

CLUB PERSONNEL
President: J Clarke
Chairman: Trevor Templeman
Manager: Steve Kuhne
Assistant Manager: Phil Cavener
Physio: Trevor Templeman
Press Officer: Secretary

YAXLEY

Secretary: Alan Andrews, 3 Farringdon Close, Pterborough. PE1 4RQ 01733 342897(H) 07939 841469(M)

Ground: Holme Road, Yaxley Tel: 01733 244928
Capacity: 1,000+ Seats: 150 Cover: Yes Floodlights: Yes

Directions: A1, then A15 at Norman Cross up to traffic lights. Turn right then immediately right again. Follow the road for approx. 1 mile, then turn right into Holme Rd.. The ground is approx. 200 yards on left

HONOURS UCL Div 1 96-97, Benevolent Cup 97-98; Hunts Senior Cup (5 times Inc 98-99) Peterborough League (2); Peterborough Senior Cup (2); West Anglia League;Scott-Gatty Cup

PREVIOUS **Leagues:** Peterborough & District, Huntingdonshire, West Anglia

FACT FILE
Founded:
Sponsor: Reads Removals
Colours: All blue with white trim
Change colours: All tangerine or yellow
Programme: Yes
Editor: Malcolm Whaley

CLUB PERSONNEL
President: John Dowse
Chairman: Malcolm Whaley
Vice Chairman: Geoff Heathcote
Manager: Paul Humphries
Asst Manager: Jimmy Watson

BLISWORTH

Secretary: Peter Edwards, 31 Windmill Ave, Blisworth, Northants NN7 3EQ
Tel: 01604 858171 (H), 0585 369933 (B)

Ground: Blisworth Playing Field, Courteenhall Road, Blisworth Tel: 01604 858024
Capacity: 1,000 Seats: None Cover: None Floodlights: No

Directions: Courteenhall Road off A43

Clubhouse: Yes

HONOURS Northants Junior Cup 88-99

PREVIOUS **League:** Central Northants Combination 1978-87
Player progressing: Dave Johnson (Northampton 83-84)

FACT FILE
Founded: 1890
Sponsors: Target Furniture, JB King Plant Hire
Colours: Yellow/black/yellow
Change colours: All Blue
Reserves' Lge: UCL Res. Div. 2
Programme: Yes Editor: Liz Edwards
Tel: 01604 858171

CLUB PERSONNEL
Chairman: Pete Edwards President: L Piggott
Manager: Brian Oldham
Asst Man:Gary Edwards, Coach:RichardlLarge
Physio: Elaine Johnson

BURTON PARK WANDERERS

Secretary: David Haynes, 58 Drayton Road, Lowick, Northants NN14 3BG
Tel: 01832 735060 (H), 01933 231961 (W)

Ground: Latimer Park, Polwell Lane, Burton Latimer Tel: 01536 725841
Capacity: 1,000 Seats: 100 Cover: 150 Floodlights: No

Directions: Entering Burton Latimer, turn off A6 Station Rd and right into Powell Lane; ground on the right

HONOURS UCL Div 1 R-up, Benevolent Cup R-up
PREVIOUS **League**: Kettering Amateur
RECORD **Attendance**: 253 v Rothwell, May 1989
Players progressing : Shaun Wills (Peterborough), Laurie Dudfield (Leicester City)

FACT FILE
Founded: 1961 Nickname: The Wanderers
Sponsor: Prescott Motors
Colours:Red & Black/Black/Red
Change Colours: Blue & White
Midweek matchday: Tuesday
Prog: 16 pages with entry
Local Press : Northants Evening Telegraph, Northants Post

CLUB PERSONNEL
Chairman: Bernard Lloyd
Vice Chairman: Stuart Coles
Manager: Eddie Lynch
Asst Manager: Kelly Meagan
Physio: Stuart Coles

COTTINGHAM

Secretary: Lindsay Brownlie, 30 Bancroft Rd, Cottingham, Market Harborough LE168XA
Tel: 01536 771009 (H)

Ground: Berryfield Rd, Cottingham Tel: 01536 770051
Capacity: 1,000 Seats: None Cover: Yes Floodlights: No

Directions: One and a half miles from Corby on A427 turn right to Cottingham.At junction of B670 turn left; Berryfield Road 200 yds on right

Clubhouse: Bar & changing rooms

HONOURS UCL Div 1 R-up 97-98; Northants Junior Cup

PREVIOUS **Leagues:** Market Harborough; Kettering Amateur; East Midlands Alliance

FACT FILE
Founded:
Sponsors: B & J Decorators
Colours: Blue/Black/Blue
Change colours: Yellow/green/yellow
Reserves' Lge: UCL Res. Div. 2
Programme: No

CLUB PERSONNEL
Chairman: Mike Beadsworth
Vice Chairman: Brian Tilley
Manager: Rob Dunion
Asst Manager: Willie Kelly

EYNESBURY ROVERS

Secretary: Deryck Irons, 12 Hadleigh Close, Bedford MK41 8JW. Tel: 01234 268111
Email Address: patrick.erfc@btinternet.com

Ground: Hall Road, Eynesbury, St Neots Tel: 01480 477449
Capacity: 3,000 Seats: 200 Cover: 500 Floodlights: Yes

Directions: Two miles from A1, on South side of St Neots urban area, near Ernulf School

Clubhouse: Large bar, committee room.Available for private hire **Club Shop:** Yes

HONOURS UCL Div 1 76-77; Hunts Snr Cup 13-14 46-47 48-51 54-55 56-57 69-70 84-85 90-93 95-96,99-00; Hunts Premier Cup 50-51 90-91 95-96; Hinchingbrooke Cup (7) 46-4748-52 57-58 66-67; Cambs Invitation Cup 61-62; E Anglian Cup R-up 90-91 91-92;Hunts Scott Gatty Cup 35-36 56-57 84-85 89-90 (R-up 93-94 res); Hunts Jnr Cup 21-22 26-27
PREVIOUS **Leagues:** Sth Mids 34-39; UCL 46-52; Eastern Co's 52-63
BEST SEASON **FA Vase:** 3rd Rd 94-95 **FA Cup:** 4th Qual. Rd 54-55, 1-3 v Camb. Utd (A)
RECORD **Gate:** 5,000 v Fulham 1953 (Stanley Matthews guested for Eynesbury)
2000-01 Captain: Gavin Clark P.o.Y.: Danny Workman Top Scorer: Paul Childerley 8

FACT FILE
Founded: 1897
Nickname: Rovers
Sponsors: Classic Windows
Colours: Royal & white/royal/royal
Change Colours: Yellow/black/yellow
Midweek matchday: Tuesday
Reserves' League: Utd Counties Res. Div. 2
Prog: 32 pages, 50p Ed: Graham Mills
(Top in League 00-01 -Wirral Prog Club)
Website: www.eynesburyrovers.org.uk

CLUB PERSONNEL
Chairman: Brian Abraham
Vice Chairman:John Newland
Manager:Steve Galbarith

HARROWBY UNITED

Secretary: Paul Wilson, 3 Ascot Drive, Grantham, Lincs. 01476 402995 (H)
Email: arrowsml@aol.com

Ground: Harrowby Playing Fields, Harrowby Lane, Grantham Tel: 01476 590822
Capacity: 1,500 Seats: 100 Cover: 150 Floodlights: Yes

Directions: From A1 take B6403, go past A52 roundabout, past Ancaster turn and take road to Harrowby. Continue into Grantham, ground on right opposite Cherry Tree PH.

Clubhouse: Large bar open normal licensing hours

HONOURS Utd Co's Lg Div 1 91-92 (Benev. Cup R-up 91-92), Mids Regional All. 89-90 (Lg Cup 89-90), Lincs Snr `B' Cup(2) 90-92

PREVIOUS **Leagues:** Grantham; Lincs; East Mids Regional Alliance (pre-1990)

BEST SEASON **FA Vase:** Preliminary Round 91-92

Players progressing: Richard Liburd (Middlesbrough), Kevin Pilkington (Mansfield Town)

FACT FILE
Founded: 1949
Nickname: Arrows
Sponsor: Crystal Grantham
Colours: Red & black hoops/black/red & black
Change : Blue&white hoops/blue/blue & white
Programme: 16 pages Ed: Paul Wilson

CLUB PERSONNEL
Chairman: Paul Wilson
Vice Chairman: Robert Wilson
Match Secretary: Mick Atter
Manager: Graham Drury
Asst Mgr: Steve Joseph Coach: Tony Cook
Physio: Nigel Burton
Groundsman: Malcolm Brothwell

HIGHAM TOWN

Secretary: Chris Ruff, 23 Queensway, Higham Ferrers, Northants. NN10 8BU Tel: 01933 358862
Ground: Recreation Ground, Vine Hill Drive, Higham Ferrers Tel: 01933 353751
Capacity: 1,000 Seats: Nil Cover: 100 Floodlights: No
Directions: From Kettering 1st right on A6 after junction to St Neots. From Bedford, 3rd left after entering town on A6 from Rushden. Higham is served by London-Bedford-Corby United Counties Coachlines, and their local services Northampton-Raunds and Bedford-Kettering
Clubhouse: During season 8.30-11pm Tues, Thurs, Fri, Sat after games & 12-1.30pm Sun.
Light refreshments available after Saturday games

HONOURS UCL Div 1 97-98, R-up 70-71 71-72 89-90 92-93 93-94 94-95 95-96 98-99; Northants Lg 21-22 22-23(R-up 23-24 26-27); Northants Snr Cup 21-22 (R-up 30-31 32-33); Maunsell Premier Cup 22-23 33-34

PREVIOUS **Leagues:** Wellingborough 20-21; Northants (now UCL) 21-36; Rushden 46-50
RECORD **Attendance:** 5,700 v Chesterfield, FA Cup final qualifying round replay 22-23
Scorer: Jon Ogden 157 (Lge) **Appearances** : Brian Harbour 485

FACT FILE
Founded: 1895 Reformed: 1920 & 1946
Nickname: Lankies
Sponsors: Higham News
Colours: Sky & navy/navy/navy
Change colours: Red& white/red/red
Midweek matchday:: Tuesday
Reserves' Lge: UCL Reserve Div
Programme: 12 pages with admission
Editor: Secretary

CLUB PERSONNEL
President: Vijay Patel
Chairman: Richard Williams
Vice Chairman: Brian Kirk
Manager: Adie Mann Asst Mgr: Matt Carroll
Physio: Keith Bates

IRCHESTER UNITED

Secretary: Glyn Cotter, 26 Denford Way, Wellingborough, Northants NN8 5UB
Tel: 01933 402514

Ground: Alfred Street, Irchester Tel: 01933 312877
Capacity: 1,000 Seats: None Cover:Yes Floodlights: No

Directions: Off Rushden Road to Wollaston Road, next to recreation ground

Clubhouse: Yes

HONOURS Northants LgDiv 2 30-31 31-32,Northants Jnr.Cup 29-30,33-34,48-49 75-6, Rushden & Dis.t Lg 28-29 29-30,32-33,33-34 36-3746-47 50-51 51-52 56-57

BEST SEASON **FA Cup:** Prel. Rd 34-35
FA Vase: Preliminary Round 77-78

PREVIOUS **Leagues:** Rushden & District 1936-69

FACT FILE
Colours: Blue& Blackstripes,black,black
Change colours:Black&White stripes,black,red
Reserves' Lge: UCL Res. Div. 2
Programme: No

CLUB PERSONNEL
Chairman: Geoff Cotter
Co Managers: Bob Reed/John Dower
Physio: Mick Howarth

2000-01
Leading goalscorer: Charlie Pipe 14
Captain: Glynn Cotter
P.o.Y.: Phil Lawrence

NEWPORT PAGNELL TOWN

Secretary: John Anderson, 59 Willen Road, Newport Pagnell, Bucks MK16 0DE
Tel: 01908 610440 EMail Address: tongwell@supanet.com

Ground: Willen Road, Newport Pagnell Tel: 01908 611993
Capacity: 2,000 Seats: 100 Cover: 100 Floodlights: Yes

Directions: Adjacent to A422 Newport Pagnell by-pass

Clubhouse: Open every evening Club Shop: No

HONOURS UCL Div 1 82-83 (R-up 91-92, Div 1 Cup 77-78),Daventry Charity Cup R-up 93-94

PREVIOUS **Leagues:** North Bucks 63-71; South Midlands 71-73

BEST **FA Vase:** 2nd Round 84-85
2000-01 **Captain:** Paul Stokes **P.o.Y.:** Aiden McGlue **Top Scorer:** Paul Edgeworth 27

FACT FILE
Founded: 1963 Nickname: Swans
Sponsors: Brian Currie
Colours: White & green/green/green
Change colours: Red/green/green
Midweek Matchday: Tuesday
Reserves League: United Counties
Programme: 56 pages
Editor: Ernie Print (01908 612918)

CLUB PERSONNEL
Chairman: Gerry Ward
Vice Chairman: Ernie Print
President: Ken Inch
Manager:Danni Janes

NORTHAMPTON O.N. CHENECKS

Secretary: Ashley Clarkson, 11 Tideswell Close, West Hunsbury, Northampton NN4 9XY
Tel Nos:- 01604 708253 (H) 01234 211521 (W) 07775 940992 (M)

Ground: Old Northamptonians Sports Ground,Billing Road,Northampton Tel: 01604 34045

Capacity: 1,350 Seats: Yes Cover: Yes Floodlights: No

Directions: South ring road, exit A43 Kettering. Turn left at the lights, to the top of hill and the ground is 200 yds on right

Clubhouse: Yes

HONOURS UCL Div 1 77-78 79-80, Northants Jnr Cup R-up 93-94

PREVIOUS **Leagues:** N'pton Town (pre-1969)

FACT FILE
Founded: 1946
Colours: Yellow & Blue/Blue/yelow
Change colours: All red
Reserves' League: UCL Res Div 1
Midweek Matchday:
Prog.: 16 pages with entry
Editor: Eddie Slinn

CLUB PERSONNEL
Chairman: John Wilson
Vice Chairman: Eddie Slinn
President: Claude Hasdell
Manager: Neil McAllister
Asst Manager: Claude Hasdell
Physio: John Goodger

NORTHAMPTON SILEBY RANGERS

(formerly Northampton Vanaid)

Secretary: Tony Loveday, 28 Blueberry Rise, Ecton Brook, North'ton NN3 2AX (01604 406606)

Email Address: tony.loveday@talk21.com

Ground: Fernie Fields Sports Ground, Moulton, Northampton Tel: 01604 670366

Capacity: 700 Seats: 100 Cover: Yes Floodlights: No

Directions: R'bout at Lumbertub pub take turn to Moulton, 1st right signposted

Clubhouse: Large bar with food

HONOURS UCL Div 1 93-94, Benevolent Cup R-up 93-94;
Northants Jnr Cup 93-94 96-97 97-98; Northampton Town Lg 88-89 89-90

PREVIOUS **League:** Northampton Town (pre-1993) **Name:** Northampton Vanaid >00

RECORD **Attendance:** 78

FACT FILE
Founded: 1968Nickname: Sileby
Sponsors: Mr Removals
Colours: Red/Black/Black
Change colours: Black & white/black/red
Reserves' League: UCL Res Div 1
Programme Editors: Tony & June Loveday

CLUB PERSONNEL
Chairman: Rob Clarke Vice Chairman: G,Law
President: N.Gibbs
Manager: Nick Verity Asst Man: T.Bonner
Physio: M.Arnold
2000-01P.o.Y & Top Scorer: Richard Turner18
Captain: Mark Pepperell

OLNEY TOWN

Secretary: Andrew Baldwin, 49 Midland Road, Olney, Bucks MK46 4BP
Tel: 01234 711071 Club Website: www.olneytownfc.com

Ground: East Street, Olney , Bucks. Tel: 01234 712227
Capacity: 2,000 Seats: None Cover: Yes Floodlights: No

Clubhouse: Yes

Directions: Enter Olney on A509 from Wellingborough, 100yds on left enter East St, the ground is 200 yds on left

HONOURS UCL Div 1 72-73, Berks & Bucks I'mediate Cup 92-93

PREVIOUS **Leagues:** Nth Bucks, Rushden & Dist

2000-01 Leading Goalscorer: D. Lancaster 16 Captain: Des Cook P.o.Y: Mark Lancaster

FACT FILE
Founded: 1903
Sponsors: Cyclo Sports
Colours: Green&black/black/green
Change colours: Black&white/white/white
Programme: 8 pages - Editor: Michael Smith

CLUB PERSONNEL
Chairman: Malcom Thomas
President: Trevor Church
Manager: Russell Ward
Asst Manager: Pete Munting
Coach: Neil Bunker
Physio: Peter Munting

POTTON UNITED

Secretary: Derek Inskip, 16 Sheffield Close, Potton, Beds SG19 2NY Tel: 01767 260355
Ground: The Hollow, Biggleswade Road, Potton Tel: 01767 261100
Capacity: 2,000 Seats: 200 Cover: 250 Floodlights: Yes
Directions: Outskirts of Potton on Biggleswade Road (B1040). 3 1/2 miles from Sandy (BR).
United Counties buses from Biggleswade **Clubhouse:** Yes
HONOURS Utd Co's Lg 86-87 88-89, KO Cup 72-73, Benevolent Cup 88-89; Beds Snr Cup(5) 47-49 63-64 75-76 77-78 (R-up 94-95 96-97); Wallspan Floodlit Cup 87-88; Hinchingbrooke Cup 51-52 84-85 89-90 90-91 91-92; Hunts Premier Cup 89-90 91-92 94-95(jt) 96-97; Beds I'mediate Cup 43-44; Southern Comb. Cup 92-93; Nth Beds Charity Cup (12); East Anglian Cup 96-97; Jess Pigott Trophy 96-97

PREVIOUS **Leagues**: Sth Mids 46-55; Central Alliance 56-61
BEST SEASON **FA Cup:** 3rd Qual. Round 74-75, 1-2 v Bedford Town
FA Trophy: 3rd Qual. Round 71-72 72-73 **FA Vase:** 5th Round 89-90, 1-2 v Billericay Town
RECORD **Attendance:** 470 v Hastings Town, FA Vase 1989

FACT FILE
Founded: 1943
Nickname: Royals
Colours: White/black/black
Change Colours: Red/white/red
Midweek matchday: Tuesday
Reserves' Lge: UCL Res. Div. Two
Programme: 28 pages, 50p
Editor: Bev Strong

CLUB PERSONNEL
President: Peter Hutchinson
Chairman: Nigel Westhorp
Press Officer: Secretary
Manager: Martin Humberstone
Asst Manager: Jeff Wells

Boxing Day action as Dave Chelew nets the third goal for visitors Stotfold at Potton United. Photo: Gordon Whittington

The scorer's happy, the linsman's happy, the sub's happy as Ritchie Gilbert opens the scoring for Desborough who finally won 6-2 after a goalless first half at Wellingborough. Photo: Gordon Whittington

In off the post: Ritchie Bunting nets Raunds' equaliser on the stroke of half time, at Eynesbury. Raunds went on to beat Rovers 4-1. Photo: Gordon Whittington

ROTHWELL CORINTHIANS

Secretary: Bob Clelland, 5 Drake Close, Rothwell, Northants NN14 6DJ
Tel: 01536 710134

Ground: Seargeant's Lawn, Desborough Road, Rothwell, Northants.
Tel: 01536 418688
Capacity: Unknown Seats: 50 Cover: 200 Floodlights: Yes

Directions A6 towards Desborough, on right opposite Greening Road
Club House: Yes **Club Shop:** No

HONOURS East Midlands Alliance (2)
PREVIOUS **League** East Midlands Alliance
2000-01: **Captain:** JohnCoe **P.o.Y.:** Paul Djeneraloyic **Top Scorer:**David Harding 19

FACT FILE
Founded: 1930's
Nickname: Corinthians
Sponsor: Springfir Estates
Colours: Red,black,black
Change colours: All blue
Programme: Yes Editor: Graham Dawson

CLUB PERSONNEL
Chairman: Graham Dawson
Vice Chairmperson: May Clelland
President: Terry Smith
Joint Managers: Andy Paeluk & Tom Hanson
Physio:John Dickson

SHARNBROOK A.F.C.

Secretary: Roy Boulton, 10 St Mary's Avenue, Rushden, Northants NN10 9EP
Tel: 01933 315890

Ground: Lodge Rd, Sharnbrook, Northants. Tel: 01234 781080
Capacity: 1,000 Seats: None Cover: Yes Floodlights: No

Directions: Second sign to Sharnbrook from Rushden on A6, under railway bridge, right at T-junction, left past church, right into Lodge Road
Clubhouse: Yes

HONOURS Bedfordshire Intermediate Cup 73-74
PREVIOUS **Leagues:** Bedford & Dist (pre-1968)
Player progressing: Matt Jackson (Luton, Everton & Norwich City)

FACT FILE
Sponsor: T.B.A.
Colours: Red & Blue Stripes,Blue,Red
Change colours: Yellow,black,yellow
Programme: 12 pages
Editor:Jim Donaldson(01234 852598)
2000-01Top Goalscorer: Ian Strange
Captain:Steve Denton

CLUB PERSONNEL
Chairman: Jim Donaldson
President: John Boyles
Manager: John Leeson
Physio: Jim Donaldson

ST. IVES TOWN

Secretary: Alistair Robinson, 38 High Street,Needingworth,Huntingdon, Cambs.
Tel: 01480 460409 (H) 0585 058733 (M)
Ground: Westwood Road, St. Ives, Cambs.Tel: 01480 463207
Directions: From Huntingdon: A1123 thru Houghton, right at 2nd lighs intoRamsey Rd, after quarter mile turn right opp. Fire Station into Westwood Road
From A604: Follow Huntingdon signs past 5 r'bouts, left into Ramsey Rd at lights then follow as above.
Capacity: 5,000 Seats: 130 Cover: 300 Floodlights: Yes
Clubhouse: Bar and entertainment room. Normal licensing hours.
HONOURS Hunts Snr Cup 00-01 11-12 22-23 25-26 29-30 81-82 86-87 87-88, Cambs League 22-23 23-24 24-25.
PREVIOUS **Leagues:** Cambs; Central Amtr; Hunts; P'boro. & D. (pre-1985).
Ground: Meadow Lane
RECORD **Gate**: 400 v Saffron Walden Town, FA Vase.

FACT FILE
Founded: 1887
Nickname: Saints
Colours: White & black/black/red
Change colours: Blue/black/black
Midweek matchday: Tuesday
Reserves' Lge: UCL Res Div 2
Programme editor: Alastair Robinson
Tel: 01480 460409 (H)

CLUB PERSONNEL
Match Sec.: Alistair Robinson
38 High St., Needingworth, Huntingdon, Cambs. Tel: 01480 460409 (H)

THRAPSTON TOWN

Secretary: Barry Carter, 23 Fletcher Gardens,Thrapston, Kettering, Northants.nn1 4UJ
Tel No: 01832 735879
Ground: Chancery Lane, Thrapston, Northants Tel: 01832 732470
Capacity: 1,000 Seats: Yes Cover: Yes Floodlights: No
Directions: Chancery Lane off A605 in town centre
Clubhouse: Yes
HONOURS Northants Junior Cup 87-88, 98-99 Kettering Am Lg 70-71 72-73 73-74 77-78
UCL Div1 Runners -Up 99-00
PREVIOUS **League:** Kettering Amateur (pre-1978)

FACT FILE
Founded: 1960
Nickname: Venturas
Sponsor: IKEA
Colours: All blue & yellow
Change colours: Yellow/yellow/yellow
Programme: Yes Editor: Dave Overend

CLUB PERSONNEL
President: Derek Barber
Chairman: Dave Harris
Vice Chairman: Barry Carter
Manager: Gary Petts
Asst Manager: Barry Carter
Physio: Zoe

Rothwell Corinthians FC

Harrowby United. Back Row (l-r): Nick Andersen (Manager), Paul Kirk, Nathan Selby, Darren Glover, Simon Down, Neil Gardiner, Carl Savill, Ian Pearson, Jamie Weston, Mick Atter (Asst Mngr). Front Row: Alex Elvins, Danny Richards, Jason Harrison, Paul Clegg, Graham Drury, Robbie Greatrex, Steve Pearson. Photo: Gordon Whittington

Olney Town. Back Row (l-r): Pete Munting (Physio), Danny Munday, Guy Stewart, Paul Simpson, Des Cook, Trevor Stone, Stewart Keeping, Greg Hardie, Dave Lancaster, Asa Aldridge, Russell Ward (Manager). Front Row: Mark Lancaster, Malcolm Thomas, Scott Wrighting, Brian Stonnell, Markus Nelson, Paul Adams, Paul Pratt

WELLINGBOROUGH WHITWORTHS

Secretary: Mr R Edwards, 15 James Road, Wellingborough, Northants NN8 2LR
Tel: 01933 382376

Ground: London Road, Wellingborough, Northants. Tel: 01933 227324
Capacity: 700 Seats: None Cover: Yes Floodlights: No

Directions: Off London Road at Dog & Duck public house

Clubhouse: Yes

PREVIOUS **Leagues:** Rushden & Dist.; E. Mids All. (pre-1985)

HONOURS Rushden & District Lg 76-77; Northants Jun Cup 96

FACT FILE
Sponsor: Whitworth Brothers
Colours: Red & black/yellow/yellow
Change colours: All purple
Reserves' Lge: UCL Res Div 2
Programme: No

CLUB PERSONNEL
Chairman: Bob Jarvis
Vice Chairman: Dave Woodley
President: Terry Faulkner
Manager: Phil Harvey
Asst Manager: Mick Garrett
Physio: Andrew King

WOODFORD UNITED

Secretary: Karl Henderson,7 Swan Close, Woodford Close, Daventry, Northants. NN3 6EW
Tel: 01327 262514 (H) 01295 254555 x 220 (W)

Ground: Byfield Road, Woodford Halse, Daventry, Northants. Tel: 01327 263734
Capacity: 3,000 Seats: 25 Cover: 150 Floodlights: No

Directions Off A 361 Daventry to Banbury Rd, on Woodford Road out of Byfield

Clubhouse: Yes

PREVIOUS Leagues: Central Northants Comb pre 70, UCL 70-78, Northants Comb

HONOURS Northants Comb 66 67 90 92 95, KO Cup 66 90 93 95 98;
United Counties Lge Div 2 74, KO Cup 74;

FACT FILE
Founded: 1946
Nickname:
Sponsors: Styleglaze
Colours: All red
Change Colours: All blue
Reserves' League: Northants Comb
Programme: 16 pages
Editor: Francis Peacock (01327 263335)

CLUB PERSONNEL
Chairman: Bob Justice
Vice-Chairman: R Adams
Manager: Andy McGuire
Assistant Manager: Justin Cullen

ISLE OF WIGHT F.A.

Chairman: K R Morris
Secretary: A P Justice, 12 The Mall, Binstead, Ryde, Isle of Wight PO33 3SF
Tel: 01983 565244

FINAL LEAGUE TABLE 2000-01

DIVISION ONE	*P*	*W*	*D*	*L*	*F*	*A*	*Pts*
Red Star Spartans	22	16	2	4	59	23	50
Oakfield	22	15	4	3	66	25	49
Shanklin	22	14	6	2	41	17	48
Cowes Sports	22	15	1	6	54	30	46
Binstead	22	14	1	7	60	29	43
West Wight Mayflower	22	12	1	9	62	42	37
W B Sports	22	10	2	10	42	44	32
Seaview	22	9	1	12	47	55	28
Brading Town	22	4	6	12	28	34	18
East Cowes Vics	22	4	4	14	24	48	16
GKN Westlands	22	2	1	19	20	84	7
Northwood	22	2	1	19	21	97	7

SOUTHERN FINAL LEAGUE TABLES 2000-01

PORTSMOUTH SATURDAY LEAGUE

PREMIER DIV.	*P*	*W*	*D*	*L*	*F*	*A*	*Pts*
Southsea Town	14	8	5	1	43	13	29
Royal TML	14	8	2	4	25	19	26
Paulsgrove	14	6	4	4	27	20	22
Ship Hotel (Emsworth)	14	5	4	5	24	30	19
Shearer	14	5	3	6	35	36	18
Fareham Sacred Heart	14	2	10	2	9	13	16
Portsmouth University	14	3	4	7	20	22	13
Portchester	14	1	4	9	19	49	7

SOUTHAMPTON LEAGUE

PREMIER DIVISION	*P*	*W*	*D*	*L*	*F*	*A*	*Pts*
Brendon	24	20	2	2	64	13	62
Ford Sports	24	19	2	3	73	17	59
BTC Southampton	24	17	2	5	58	25	53
Midanbury	24	14	2	8	69	36	44
Nursling	24	12	4	8	66	33	40
Durley	24	12	2	10	55	35	38
Old Tauntonians	24	12	2	10	41	42	38
Eastleigh	24	11	2	11	43	41	35
Solent Youth	24	10	1	13	43	70	31
North Baddesley	24	7	3	14	46	57	24
Fair Oak Linden	24	5	3	16	33	79	18
Sholing	24	3	1	20	26	72	10
Braishfield	24	1	0	23	20	117	3

MEON VALLEY SUNDAY LEAGUE

DIVISION ONE	*P*	*W*	*D*	*L*	*F*	*A*	*Pts*
East Meon	18	16	1	1	58	19	49
Fareham Sacred Heart	18	13	1	4	69	27	40
Wickham Dynamo	18	12	4	2	46	20	40
Waterlooville Bobs	18	8	5	5	53	35	29
West Meon/Warnford	18	8	1	9	49	40	25
Priory Inn	18	7	3	8	34	47	24
Solent City	18	6	2	10	39	49	20
Inter Wickham Utd	18	5	2	11	27	64	17
Titchfield FC	18	3	1	14	25	60	10
Soberton Utd	18	2	0	16	26	65	6

PORTSMOUTH DOCKYARD LEAGUE

PREMIER DIVISION	*P*	*W*	*D*	*L*	*F*	*A*	*Pts*
Heron	16	13	1	2	46	22	40
Horndean	16	12	1	3	47	16	37
Bowood	16	10	1	5	44	32	31
Co-op Dragons	15	9	2	4	36	14	29
Dundas	16	6	1	9	30	47	19
Hilsea Rangers	16	4	4	8	35	42	16
Harvest Home	15	4	2	9	28	41	14
Co-op Sports	16	3	1	12	17	40	10
Portsmouth Fibre Co	16	3	1	12	28	57	10

HAVANT SUNDAY LEAGUE

SENIOR DIVISION	*P*	*W*	*D*	*L*	*F*	*A*	*Pts*
ABC Gym	16	14	1	1	45	10	43
Pop Inn	16	11	2	3	60	16	35
AFC Hayling	16	11	2	3	43	16	35
Ensinger	16	7	4	5	48	19	25
SMS	16	5	4	7	29	34	19
Kenwoods	16	4	5	7	35	45	17
Cowplain United	16	3	5	8	24	37	14
Hayling United	16	3	3	10	26	45	12
Crookhorn Social Club	16	1	0	15	23	111	3

PORTSMOUTH SUNDAY LEAGUE

PREMIER DIVISION	*P*	*W*	*D*	*L*	*F*	*A*	*Pts*
Shearer	18	17	0	1	36	9	51
Dorchester	18	12	3	3	44	19	39
Golden Hind	18	12	2	4	41	21	38
Guardsman	18	10	1	7	40	37	31
Land Port	18	5	4	9	29	32	19
HNCC	18	6	0	12	28	49	18
Pembroke	18	3	8	7	19	22	17
Prospect	18	3	7	8	16	18	16
Harvest Home	18	4	3	11	28	36	15
Pall	18	2	4	12	21	59	10

JEWSON WESSEX LEAGUE

FEEDER TO: Dr MARTENS FOOTBALL LEAGUE

President: Cyril Hurlock

Chairman: Norman Cook **Vice Chairman:** Nick Spencer

Hon. Secretary: Tom Lindon, 63 Downs Road, South Wonston
Winchester, Hampshire SO21 3EW Tel/Fax: 01962 884760

Friday 18th August seems to have been an eternity ago, but that was the start of this very difficult and prolonged season. Fuel crisis, foot and mouth, and the wettest winter on record plus floodlight failures have all made life more than difficult for all concerned with our League.

With Norman and Nick entering their first season as Chairman and Vice Chairman respectively, they could not have had a worse baptism. Blackfield & Langley became members of the League having been promoted from the Hampshire Premier League, Fleet Town rejoined the League having tasted life in the Southern Football League. Swanage Town & Herston gained promotion from the Dorset Combination, thus regaining their lost status. The Daily Echo Club of the Month was to replace the previous award, in order to consider factors other than just results.

August fixtures included an FA Cup extra Preliminary Round and more of our clubs entering the FA Youth Cup, the League Table saw Fleet Town, Andover, Thatcham Town and Lymington & New Milton at the top of the table on maximum points, with Eastleigh Reserves leading the Combination with maximum points from five matches.

FA Cup success in **September** eluded Bemerton Heath Harlequins, Brockenhurst, Bournemouth, Christchurch, Moneyfields, Portsmouth RN, Wimborne Town, and Whitchurch United, all falling at the first hurdle. They were joined by BAT, who lost on penalties, and Eastleigh by a one goal defeat. The FA Vase saw Gosport Borough and Portsmouth RN eliminated whilst Christchurch and Blackfield & Langley went out of the competition in replays. The FA Cup First Qualifying Round saw some really good attendances for our teams, but the end of the road for Downton, Lymington & New Milton and Andover. Cowes Sports had a bad day in losing to Horsham YMCA, Fareham Town also went out of the competition in a replay. Back in the FA Vase Bemerton Heath Harlequins, Downton, Andover, Whitchurch United, while Fareham Town, Moneyfields and Thatcham Town would have to wait until next season for further glory. The League positions at the end of Spetember reflected 100 per cent success for Lymington & New Milton and Andover, whilst Eastleigh Reserves continued to lead the Combination, only dropping four points.

October started well enough with County and Local Association Cup Competitions getting underway. In the FA Cup Thatcham Town went out to Worcester City 3-1 in front of a crowd of 805. In the FA Vase BAT, Fleet Town, Eastleigh, Bournemouth and AFC Newbury parted company for this season. Our own cup competitions were well under way when we started to experience the sound and feel of rain. Not only were matches postponed, but some were even abandoned. By the end of October most teams had completed a quarter of their fixture programme, with Andover and Lymington & New Milton equal on points, and in the Combination Eastleigh Reserves were still top having played fourteen matches.

November saw the weather start to cause fixture problems both domestically and in national competitions. Lymington & New Milton v Bridgwater Town was abandoned in the 65th minute of the FA Vase Second Round, but they won the replayed match, whilst Brockenhurst beat Poulton Rovers, AFC Totton beat Molesley and Wimborne Town gained victory away to Brislington. Towards the end of November we experienced almost a complete washout of fixtures. Andover and Eastleigh Reserves led their respective divisions and retained the positions through to the end of the season.

The rain was still a factor in **December**, as we did not play a League or League Cup match until the ninth. Lymington & New Milton lost to Stotfield and Cowes Sports also went out of the FA Vase to Hornchurch.

January started quite well with most of our fixtures and County Cup matches being played. AFC Totton, Brockenhurst and Wimborne Town ended their runs in the Fourth Round of the FA Vase in front of very good attendances, but it was a question of so near, yet so far! By the middle of the month the weather gained advantage once again, but we finished the month on quite a high as we only lost one fixture from full programmes from the 29th to the 31st.

Having postponed the League Cup competitions earlier in the season the decision to abandon both competitions was made in **February** due to the continuing poor weather, and to use the money allocated to the cups to provide clubs with a safe, so the money was well spent. We were able to play almost full programmes from the middle of February through to the end of the month.

March started promisingly enough, but the second Saturday saw six matches abandoned and five postponements, with no real let up in the weather until the last day of the month when we were able to complete a full fixture programme.

Would **April** be better? It was quite mixed to start with but improved as the month progressed to become a good time in which we played a vast number of matches, clearing a great deal of the backlog. The decision to extend the season was taken, the First Division was completed on 12th May, but, in spite of exceptional efforts from everyone, we failed to complete the Combination Division by just two matches.

Appreciation of a great deal of extra work and effort needs to be expressed to very many people, far too many to name, although some have been mentioned in the press. One area of difficulty that I had never considered was brought to my attention as a request of clubs at times to use a different strip as the "lady" who does the laundry has not been able to prepare the kit. Filthy wet muddy clothes must be an absolute nightmare. Fixtures, Referees, Groundsmen, Programme Editors, refreshments, advertising, travel arrangements plus many other areas have required so much more from individuals throughout this season. To those people, thank you, for your efforts cannot be measured, and the League could not be the League it is without those efforts.

Several club people are leaving office. May I mention Bob Devoy (AFC Totton), Anne Hughes (Bashley FC), Roy Newman and Jim Malloy (Portsmouth RN), and finally but by no means least, Dave Maguire (Whitchurch United). To all those mentioned, thank you for all your support and hard work. From the Management Committee Brian Trent is standing down due to ill health; our very best wishes to you Brian, please keep in touch with us and thank you for your hard work and support. Also not seeking re-election to the Committee are Stephen Churchill and Norman Cook. Thank you to you both. Norman has served the League for thirteen years in almost every capacity needed to run an efficient League. He has set high standards in every role he has fulfilled. The League will not seem the same without you, Norman; very many thanks for all your valuable work. When life is a little easier at the Dell (sorry, St Mary's) perhaps you will be able to rejoin us.

On the whole the League has had an excellent year. We have continued to operate in a professional manner and have seen some excellent football. Well done to the winners of awards and prizes, better luck next season to those who did not win this season. A special thanks to Steve Webber and Mike Warner for the continued support and interest of our valuable sponsor, Jewson.

Thank you all for your participation. See you next season.

ROLL OF HONOUR 2000-01

Champions, Jewson Wessex League	Andover FC
Runners Up	Lymington & New Milton FC
Champions, Combination League	Eastleigh FC
Runners Up	Christchurch FC
Winners, Hampshire Senior Cup	Andover FC
Finalists, Wiltshire Premier Shield	Bemerton Heath Harlequins FC
Winners, North Hants Senior Cup	Andover FC
Finalists, Aldershot Senior Cup	Fleet Town
Finalists, Greystone Cup	AFC Newbury
Finalists, Portsmouth Senior Cup	Gosport Borough FC Reserves
Winners, Fair Play Award	Downton FC
Winners, Best Programme Award	Brockenhurst FC
Winners, Longest FA Vase Run	AFC Totton, Brockenhurst FC, Wimborne Town FC

FIRST DIVISION FINAL LEAGUE TABLE 2000-01

		P	*W*	*D*	*L*	*F*	*A*	*W*	*D*	*L*	*F*	*A*	*Pts*	*GD*
1	Andover	44	20	2	0	92	17	17	3	2	61	16	116	120
2	Lymington & New M.	44	18	3	1	55	11	16	3	3	51	18	108	77
3	Wimborne Town	44	14	4	4	62	25	14	5	3	49	27	93	59
4	Fleet Town	44	16	2	4	42	24	13	1	8	49	32	90	35
5	AFC Totton	44	16	4	2	52	17	10	5	7	35	30	87	40
6	Thatcham Town	44	12	6	4	41	30	12	3	7	40	28	81	23
7	Eastleigh	44	13	4	5	46	17	10	6	6	41	31	79	39
8	Gosport Borough	44	13	3	6	38	20	10	5	7	36	24	77	30
9	Brockenhurst	44	12	3	7	50	42	11	4	7	43	30	76	21
10	Cowes Sports	44	12	2	8	47	32	10	2	10	33	38	70	10
11	Bemerton Hth Hqns	44	8	5	9	34	33	7	4	11	29	37	54	-7
12	AFC Newbury	44	12	3	7	46	37	3	5	14	25	41	53	-7
13	B.A.T.	44	5	7	10	22	38	9	3	10	30	37	52	-23
14	Bournemouth	44	8	7	7	26	24	5	5	12	25	41	51	-14
15	Fareham Town	44	8	6	8	28	35	4	4	14	20	39	46	-26
16	Moneyfields	44	6	3	13	28	38	6	6	10	24	38	45	-24
17	Christchurch	44	6	6	10	29	33	5	6	11	26	47	45	-25
18	Hamble Assc	44	7	9	6	23	31	3	5	14	16	39	44	-31
19	Whitchurch United	44	5	5	12	18	35	3	8	11	19	37	37	-35
20	Swanage T & Herston	44	8	1	13	31	48	3	3	16	21	75	37	-71
21	Blackfield & Langley	44	3	5	14	13	41	4	3	15	19	54	29	-63
22	Downton	44	2	4	16	21	54	4	4	14	24	49	26	-58
23	Portsmouth RN	44	4	5	13	26	45	0	6	16	11	62	23	-70

DAILY ECHO CLUB OF THE MONTH AWARD

August	Fleet Town FC	January	Andover FC
September	Lymington & New Milton FC	February	Andover FC
October	Brockenhurst FC	March	Andover FC
November	Gosport Borough FC	April	Gosport Borough FC
December	Andover FC		

COMBINATION DIVISION FINAL LEAGUE TABLE 2000-01

		P	W	D	L	F	A	W	D	L	F	A	Pts	GD
1	Eastleigh Res	42	17	1	3	81	19	16	3	2	66	19	103	109
2	Christchurch Res	42	17	2	2	78	24	11	5	5	50	28	91	76
3	Brockenhurst Res	42	16	3	2	55	18	12	4	5	61	33	91	65
4	Weymouth Res	42	14	2	5	59	23	11	5	5	53	39	81*	50
5	Salisbury City Res	42	14	2	5	65	32	9	9	3	52	38	80	47
6	Bashley Res	42	13	4	4	84	33	11	1	9	62	31	77	82
7	Lymington & N M Res	42	14	3	4	68	28	7	6	8	41	38	72	43
8	Newport IoW Res	40	11	4	5	59	24	11	3	6	53	33	70*	55
9	Wimborne Town Res	42	12	6	3	65	19	7	4	10	45	50	67	41
10	Moneyfields Res	42	11	6	4	48	36	9	4	8	41	44	67*	9
11	B.A.T. Res	42	11	5	5	32	25	6	4	11	36	50	60	-7
12	AFC Newbury Res	41	8	5	8	34	34	7	3	10	35	47	53	-12
13	Bemerton H H Res	42	9	3	9	41	52	6	4	11	33	59	52	-37
14	Horndean Res	41	7	8	5	38	28	6	4	11	33	72	51	-29
15	Gosport Borough Res	42	10	4	7	41	34	5	1	15	16	47	50	-24
16	AFC Totton Res	42	6	7	8	44	33	7	2	12	40	53	48	-2
17	New Street Res	42	10	1	10	39	51	4	2	15	22	60	45	-50
18	Hamble Assc Res	42	6	2	13	38	55	3	7	11	17	48	36	-48
19	Whitchurch Utd Res	42	4	3	14	21	54	4	3	14	26	50	30	-57
20	Downton Res	42	4	3	14	24	59	4	1	16	26	84	28	-93
21	Portsmouth RN Res	42	6	4	11	39	52	0	3	18	16	56	25	-53
22	Swanage T & H Res	42	3	2	16	31	106	1	2	18	15	105	16	-165

* points deducted. Please note: This league table reflects two unplayed matches

FIRST DIVISION RESULTS CHART 2000-01

	1	2	3	4	5	6	7	8	9	10	11	12	13	14	15	16	17	18	19	20	21	22	23
1	X	3-1	1-3	3-3	2-0	1-0	1-1	2-4	3-1	3-1	2-1	2-2	4-0	1-4	2-0	4-1	0-2	0-5	4-1	3-0	0-2	2-1	3-4
2	3-2	X	0-1	3-1	1-0	4-0	6-0	1-1	4-1	4-1	2-1	3-0	3-1	3-2	0-1	1-0	1-0	1-1	3-0	4-1	3-1	0-0	2-2
3	4-1	4-1	X	2-0	6-1	7-1	4-1	0-0	3-1	4-1	3-2	4-2	1-0	3-2	1-0	4-0	1-1	7-0	7-0	14-1	6-2	4-0	3-0
4	0-2	1-1	0-3	X	3-0	1-1	3-2	0-3	0-4	1-1	4-0	1-4	0-1	0-2	2-1	0-0	0-3	0-0	0-0	2-1	1-5	2-2	1-2
5	3-1	1-3	1-3	0-1	X	2-0	0-3	1-0	1-1	3-1	2-2	0-1	1-1	1-2	0-3	4-0	2-3	1-1	2-1	5-1	1-1	2-0	1-4
6	1-1	2-0	0-4	1-3	1-0	X	0-2	0-2	1-2	0-1	1-2	0-2	0-2	0-4	1-4	0-0	1-4	0-3	1-1	2-0	0-0	1-1	0-3
7	1-0	0-0	0-0	1-0	2-0	0-0	X	0-3	1-1	0-3	4-1	0-0	1-0	0-2	0-0	2-1	3-5	1-2	4-1	4-0	0-2	0-0	2-3
8	5-3	2-4	1-5	0-1	1-3	1-1	5-3	X	2-2	1-2	2-2	3-1	3-0	1-5	2-1	2-1	0-2	2-1	3-0	5-1	2-1	2-1	5-2
9	0-5	2-3	1-3	1-2	1-2	1-0	2-0	1-2	X	1-1	0-1	2-2	2-1	3-1	1-1	0-0	2-0	1-1	4-0	2-2	1-2	1-3	0-1
10	2-0	1-3	2-0	0-1	4-0	3-1	2-2	3-1	0-0	X	5-0	2-3	1-2	2-0	0-4	3-1	1-5	0-1	5-1	5-0	2-5	3-2	1-0
11	0-0	1-4	2-4	2-4	2-2	0-3	0-2	1-3	0-1	1-3	X	0-6	3-1	0-4	2-2	1-3	0-4	5-2	0-0	0-1	0-1	1-2	0-2
12	2-0	1-2	1-1	0-0	3-0	6-1	5-0	1-1	2-2	2-0	3-0	X	2-1	5-1	2-1	2-0	0-1	1-0	4-0	0-1	1-2	2-1	1-2
13	1-1	2-1	0-1	1-0	0-4	1-3	0-0	0-3	4-0	2-3	2-1	0-2	X	1-6	0-0	2-1	3-1	4-2	0-0	3-2	0-2	2-2	0-0
14	2-1	1-0	1-4	2-1	1-1	2-1	3-0	2-0	2-0	4-2	1-0	1-1	2-0	X	0-2	2-1	0-3	5-0	4-2	2-0	2-1	3-1	0-3
15	3-0	2-0	1-2	4-0	3-1	2-0	2-0	1-1	1-1	3-0	1-0	1-3	4-1	0-3	X	2-0	1-4	0-1	2-0	1-1	1-0	2-0	1-2
16	2-1	1-1	1-3	2-1	0-6	2-0	1-1	1-6	0-1	1-0	1-0	0-0	2-1	1-0	2-3	X	2-3	2-2	1-1	1-1	0-0	0-0	0-0
17	2-1	1-1	1-0	4-0	1-0	4-0	1-0	2-0	5-0	5-0	8-1	3-3	1-0	2-0	2-0	2-1	X	2-0	1-0	5-0	0-2	1-0	2-2
18	1-1	1-0	0-3	0-2	0-1	1-2	0-3	2-4	3-0	1-0	1-3	1-2	0-2	1-2	1-3	1-1	0-3	X	4-0	6-3	3-1	0-1	1-1
19	1-2	0-1	0-5	2-2	0-0	4-0	2-1	3-1	2-4	0-4	2-5	0-1	2-2	2-3	0-1	0-0	1-3	2-0	X	1-2	0-3	1-1	1-4
20	3-0	1-2	0-6	0-4	1-2	0-2	2-1	2-3	4-3	0-1	1-0	1-4	3-1	0-2	2-1	2-1	0-3	0-1	5-1	X	2-6	1-1	1-3
21	3-2	0-3	0-3	5-1	1-1	4-3	2-1	1-0	4-1	0-2	2-2	3-1	0-0	1-1	2-2	3-0	0-0	1-0	3-1	2-1	X	2-0	2-5
22	1-0	2-3	0-4	0-2	0-3	3-0	0-2	0-3	2-0	0-1	0-0	1-0	2-2	1-2	1-3	0-1	0-0	1-1	1-1	3-2	0-1	X	0-4
23	1-1	1-1	3-3	4-1	4-2	5-0	0-0	6-2	3-0	2-5	2-0	3-1	2-1	4-1	1-3	2-3	0-1	2-0	4-0	5-0	3-0	5-0	X

1 AFC Newbury
2 AFC Totton
3 Andover
4 B.A.T.
5 Bemerton Hth Hqns
6 Blackfield & Langley
7 Bournemouth
8 Brockenhurst
9 Christchurch
10 Cowes Sports
11 Downton
12 Eastleigh
13 Fareham Town
14 Fleet Town
15 Gosport Borough
16 Hamble Assc
17 Lymington & N M
18 Moneyfields
19 Portsmouth RN
20 Swanage Town & H
21 Thatcham Town
22 Whitchurch United
23 Wimborne Town

LEADING LEAGUE GOALSCORERS

FIRST DIVISION

44	Andrew Forbes	Andover FC
31	Vince Rusher	Andover FC
28	Leigh Phillips	Lymington & New Milton FC
28	Kevin Reacord	AFC Totton
25	Phillip McDonald	Cowes Sports FC

COMBINATION DIVISION

33	Steve Wheatland	Eastleigh FC
29	Martin Beck	Bashley FC
27	Kevin James	Bashley FC
22	Stuart Cannie	Wimborne Town FC
22	Alex Rossi	Brockenhurst FC

A.F.C. NEWBURY

History: The club was formed in 1996 from the resources of Ecchinswell Football Club (1906), Shaw Boys and Belles Junior Football Club (established in 1972) and Wickham U17 Youth Team. The club operates from Faraday Road Stadium but this is the only link with Newbury Town F.C.

Secretary: Mike Hall,17 Moores Place, Hungerford, Berks. RG17 0JS
Tel: 01488 685241 (H) 07714 953784 (W)
Email Address: mike.hall o @ talk21.com

Ground: Faraday Road, Newbury, Berks. Tel: 01635 523222

Directions: A34 to Robin Hood roundabout, then A4 towards Reading.
Right at lights after 100 yards into Faraday Road. Ground at end of road.

FACT FILE
Formed: 1996
Colours: Green & white/white/green & white
Change: Red & white/red/red & white
Reserves:Wessex Combination
Midweek Matches: Tuesday
Website (under construction)
www.@fcnewbury.com

CLUB PERSONNEL

Chairman: Steve Hartley Tel: 01488 683783(H) 0118 9304030 (W)

Manager: Andy Lyne

2000-01
Captain: James Caswell
P.o.Y.: Paul Marchant
Top Scorer: Anthony Alleyne 14

A.F.C. TOTTON

Secretary: Mrs Sheila Benfield, 35 Fishers Road, Totton, Southampton SO40 9HW
Tel: 023 80865421
GROUND: Testwood Park, Testwood Place, Totton, Southampton Tel:023 80868981
Directions: Five minutes walk from Totton station. Turn off at roundabout in Totton centre into Library Road.Then first left and second right into Testwood Place.

Capacity: 2,500 Seats: 200 Cover: 250 Floodlights: Yes Club Shop: No

Clubhouse: Open for matches and training sessions. Burgers, sandwiches, tea,coffee, biscuits etc available

HONOURS : Hampshire League 2, Russell Cotes Cup 98-99

PREVIOUS : **League:** Hants 1886-1986
Name: Totton FC until merger with Totton Athletic 1979
Grounds: Downs Park; Mayfield Park

RECORD: **Gate:** 600 v Windsor & Eton, F.A. Cup 4th Qual Rd 82-83

FACT FILE

Founded: 1886
Nickname: Stags
Colours: Blue with white trim/blue/blue
Change colours: Lime/Black/Black
Midweek Matches: Tuesday
Programme: 30 pages 50p

CLUB PERSONNEL

Chairman: John Dawson
Vice Chairman: R.Thurston
President: D Maton
Manager: Ian Robinson
Press Officer: P Chilcott (023 80860453)

ANDOVER

Secretary: Chris Jeremy, 23 Stubbs Court, Artists Way, Andover, Hants SP10 3QR
Tel: 01264 361973
Ground: Portway Stadium, West Portway Ind. Estate, Andover SP10 3LF Tel: 01264 391341
Directions: From the Andover By-pass A303 follow signs to Portway Ind. estate. On exiting the A303 turn right at r/about & over bridge, bear off left at next mini r/about and after 150yds turn right onto estate. Straight on until you enter Hopkinson Way, ground on left 4-500 yds
Capacity: 3,000 Cover: 250 Seats: 250 Floodlights: Yes
Clubhouse: Open matchdays & private function Club Shop: No Metal Badges: Yes

HONOURS Wessex Lg 00-01 R-up 94-95,97-98 Western Lg R-up 69-70 70-71; Hants Lg 13-14 24-25 33-34 44-45 48-49 50-51 61-62 (R-up 42-43), Northern Div 13-14, Div 2 R-up 37-38; Salisbury & Dist Lg (7) Hants Sen Cup (5); Russell Cotes Cup 23-24 31-32 37-38 44-45 52-53 58-59 60-61 61-62; Pickfords Cup 50-51; Hants Interm Cup 59-60 60-61; Hants Jun Cup 19-20 (R-up 1894-95 1910-11 12-13) N.Hants Cup 99-00 00-01

PREVIOUS **Leagues:** Salisbury & D.; Hants 1896-98, 1899-1901, 02-62; Southern 1898-99,1971-93 98-99; Western 1962-71; Wessex Lge 93-98

BEST SEASON **FA Cup:** 1st Rd 62-63, 0-1 v Gillingham
FA Trophy: 3rd Qual Rd 69-70, 70-71
FA Vase: 4th Rd 94-95, 1-3 v Falmouth Town (A)

FACT FILE

Founded: 1883
Nickname: The Lions
Colours: Red & black/black/red
Change cols: All Purple.
Midweek matchday: Tuesday
Reserve Team's League: None
Programme: 50 pages #1.00
CLUB PERSONNEL
Chairman: John Cunningham-Brown

President: R Coleman

Manager: Ken Cunningham-Brown
Asst Manager: Mike Burford
Physio: Chris Burford
2000-01
Captain: Danny Barker
P.o.Y.: Vince Rusher
Top Goalscorer: Andrew Forbes 56

B.A.T. SPORTS

Secretary: Mike Geddes, Tel: 023 80337460(H) 07799 482302
39 Pacific Close, Victoria Quay, Ocean Village,Southampton, SO14 3 TX

Ground: BAT Sports Ground, Southern Gdns, off Ringwood Road, Totton SO 40 8RW
Tel: 023 8086243

Directions: Into centre of Totton, proceed up Ringwood Rd past small r'bout,2nd left into Southern Gardens. Half mile from Totton (BR), bus X2(Southampton-Bournemouth)

Capacity: 3,000 Seats: 150 Cover: 150 Floodlights: Yes

Clubhouse: Normal licensing hrs, all day for members' sports facilities. Hot & cold snacks

BEST SEASON **FA Vase:** 3rd Rd 99-00

2000-01 Captain: Lee Hodder P.o.Y.: Richard Hurst Top Scorer: Tommy Pegler 14

FACT FILE
Founded: 1925
Colours: All blue
Change: Red & black/red/red
Midweek Matches: Tuesday
Programme: 20 pages, 30p

CLUB PERSONNEL
Chairman: Ray Roberts
Manager: Andy Leader & Ray Collins

BEMERTON HEATH HARLEQUINS

Secretary: Andy Hardwick, 2 Ashley Rd, Salisbury, Wilts. SP2 7BZ Tel: 01722 333015 & 07931 284658 (M)

Ground: Western Way, Bemerton Heath, Salisbury, Wilts Tel: 01722 331925 Fax: 01722 331218

Directions: Turn off A36 Salisbury-Bristol Rd at Skew Bridge (right turn if coming out of Salisbury), 1st left into Pembroke Rd for half mile, 2nd left along Western Way - ground quarter mile at end. 40 mins walk from Salisbury(BR) station.
Bus 51 or 52 from city centre stops at junction of Pembroke Rd/Western Way

Capacity : 2,100 Seats: 200 Cover: 350 Floodlights: Yes Clubhouse: Yes

HONOURS Wilts Snr Cup 92-93, Wilts Lg(3) as Bemerton Athletic

PREVIOUS **Names:** Bemerton Athletic, Moon FC & Bemerton Boys; all merged in 1989
Leagues: Bem. Ath.: Salisbury. & Wilts Comb.
Moon: Salisbury. & Andover Sunday Bem.Boys: Mid Wilts

RECORD **Attendance:** 1,118 v Aldershot Town FA Cup 1st Qual Rd Aug 94
Appearances: Keith Richardson

FACT FILE
Founded: May 1989
Nickname: Quins
Colours: Black & white hoops/black/black & white hoops
Change colours: Yellow/white/white
Midweek Matches: Tuesday
Programme: 32 pages, 50p

CLUB PERSONNEL
Chairman: George Parker
President: Peter Say
Manager: Steve Slade
Coach:Andy Nash
Physio: Andy Nash

BLACKFIELD & LANGLEY

Secretary: Doug Sangster, 3 Fir Tree Grove, Butts Ash Lane, Hythe, Hants SO45 3RA
Tel: 023 80844911 (H) 023 80313721 (B) Email: doug.sangster@tesco.net

Ground: Gang Warily Rec., Newlands Rd, Blackfield, Southampton, Hants SO45 1GA
Tel: 01703 893603

Directions: A326 from Totton. At Holbury mini roundabout take right fork signposted to Lepe and Fawley. After the 1st set of lights (170m) turn left into ground.

Previous League: Hampshire League

2000-01 Leading goalscorer: Nathan Renyard 10 Captain: Simon Eagle P.o.Y.: Jimmy Hooper

FACT FILE
Colours: Green & white/green/green
Change colours: Red & white/red/red
Midweek home matchday: Tuesday

CLUB PERSONNEL
Chairman: Ian Hore
5 Foxhayes Lane, Blackfield,
Southampton, Hants SO45 2QD
Tel: 023 8089 3325 (H) 023 8084 7659 (B)

BOURNEMOUTH

Secretary: John Field,33 Stanton Road, Bournemouth, Dorset BH10 5DS
Tel No: 01202 388486

Ground: Victoria Park, Namu Rd., Winton, Bournemouth, Dorset Tel: 01202 515123

Directions: Any bus to Wimborne Road, Winton. 2 miles from Bournemouth Central(BR)

Capacity: 3,000 Seats: 250 Cover: 250 Floodlights: Yes Shop: No

Clubhouse: Open daily 7-11pm. Sandwiches & hot snacks available.

HONOURS Hants Lg 13-13 21-22, B'mouth Snr Cup 66-67 89-90, Texaco F'lit Cup R-up 91-92, Hants I'mediate Cup 49-50 69-70, Hants Yth Cup 54-55 57-58 67-68

PREVIOUS **Leagues:** Hampshire **Ground:** Dene Park 1888-90
Names: Bournemouth Rovers 1875-88; Bournemouth Dene Park 1888-90

RECORD **Scorer:** B Head
Fee Received: £1,500 for Chike Onourah (Wimborne 93-94)

FACT FILE
Founded: 1875
Nickname: Poppies
Sponsors: Chapel Carpets
Colours: All white
Change colours: All blue.
Midweek Matches: Tuesday
Reserves' League: Jewson Wessex Comb
Programme: 58 pages, 50p
Editor: Mark Willis
Local Press: Evening Echo

CLUB PERSONNEL
Chairman:Robert Corbin
Vice Chairman: J B Wood
President: D Nippard
Comm. Manager: Alex Pike
Press Officer: Mark Willis
Manager: Alex Pike
Asst Manager: Nick Jennings
Coach: Chris Weller
Physio: Irvin Brown

Andover FC - Wessex Champions

Moneyfields FC

Fleet Town. Back Row (l-r): Scott Mitchell, Neil Roberts, Martin Whiddet, Tommy Taylor, John Richards, John Williams, Mark Watson, Lee Raby, Mark Frampton, John Murphy, Dylan Pearson, Adam Deller-Smith. Front Row: Ricky Jones, Steve Franks, Matty Miller, David Keir (Physio), Nidel Bateman, Wayne Wanklyn, Jesse Bone, Aidan Kilne, Lewis Field, Gavin Smith

BROCKENHURST

Secretary: Peter Plowman, 6 Cherry Tree Close, Everton, Lymington, Hampshire Tel No: (01590 644535)

Ground: Grigg Lane, Brockenhurst, Hants Tel: 01590 623544
Capacity: 2,000 **Seats:** 200 **Cover:** 300 **Floodlights:** Yes
Clubhouse: Every evening plus Tues, Sat & Sun lunchtimes

Directions: M27 Junc 1, A337 to Lyndhurst, A337 to Brockenhurst, turn right at Carey's Manor Hotel into Grigg Lane, ground 200 yds on the right

HONOURS Hants Intermediate Cup 61-62; Bournemouth Senior Cup 60-61; Hampshire Lg 75-76, R-up 73-74 79-80, Div 2 70-71 R-up 60-61, Div 3 59-60.

PREVIOUS **League:** Hampshire Lge 24-26 47-86

RECORDS **FA Amateur Cup:** 2nd Round 73-7
Attendance: 1,104 v St Albans City F.A.Amateur Cup January 1974

2000-01 **Captain:** Jimmy Sheppard **P.o.Y.**:Pete Gardner **Top Scorer:** Phill Stone 27

FACT FILE
Founded: 1898 Nickname: The Badgers
Sponsor: Parkcrest
Colours: Blue & white/blue/blue
Change colours: Green/black/green
Midweek Matches: Wednesday
Reserves League: Wessex Comb
Programme: 36 pages, #1.00
Editor/Press Officer: Dave Stansbridge

CLUB PERSONNEL
Chairman: Keith Collins
President: Mike Kimber
Vice Chairman: Alex Chalmers
Manager: Chris Collinge
Asst. Mgr: J.Sheppard Res Mgr: M.Lobb

CHRISTCHURCH

Secretary: Mrs Dawn Page, 87 The Albany, Manor Road, Bournemouth BH1 3EJ Tel: 01202 551977

Ground: Hurn Bridge Sports Club, Hurn Bridge, Avon Causeway, Christchurch Tel: 01202 473792

Directions: A338 from Ringwood, turn off signed Hurn Airport on left. Before Airport use mini roundabout & take exit signed Sopley & ground is immed. on the right. 3 miles from Christchurch (BR)

Capacity: 2,000 Seats: 215 Cover: 265 Floodlights: Yes
Clubhouse: Normal pub hours. Cooked food at lunchtimes

HONOURS Hants Jnr Cup 1892-93 1911-12 20-21; Hants Int. Cup 86-87; Pickford Cup 91; Hants Lg Div 2 37-38 47-48 85-86 (Div 3 56-57); B'mouth Snr Cup (5) 56-57 59-60 67-70; B'mouth Page-Croft Cup 94-95

PREVIOUS **League:** Hampshire **Ground:** Barrack Rd Recreation Grd (>1984)

RECORD **Appearances** : John Haynes

Players progressing: Jody Craddock (Cambridge Utd 93), Dan West (Aston Villa 94)

2000-01 Captain: Philip Langdown P.o.Y.: Neil Massie

FACT FILE
Founded: 1885
Nickname: Priory
Sponsors: Franklin Transport
Colours: All royal blue (white trim)
Change colours: All Red
Midweek Matches: Tuesday
Programme: 16 pages, 50p
Editor: Dennis Miller

CLUB PERSONNEL
Chairman: Robin Osborne
Vice Chairman: Mick Ryan Pres Joss Jenkins
Press Officer: Robin Osborne
Joint Managers: Nigel Cripps & Tony Brown
Physio: Emma Walsh

COWES SPORTS

Secretary: Bill Murray, 3 Firs Close, Cowes, Isle of Wight PO31 7NF Tel: 01983 294445

Ground: Westwood Park, Reynolds Close, off Park Rd, Cowes, Isle of Wight PO31 7NT Tel: 01983 293793

Directions: Take Park Rd out of Cowes . Reynolds Close is a right turn half mile up hill
Capacity: 1695 Seats: Yes Cover: Stand Floodlights: Yes

Clubhouse: Yes Club Shop: No

HONOURS Hampshire League 93-94, Isle of Wight Gold Cup 94-95,Wessex Lg.Cup 98-9

PREVIOUS **League:** Hampshire (pre-1994)

BEST SEASON **FA Cup:** 4th Qual. Rd replay 57-58, 1-4 v Trowbridge (A) after 2-2
FA Vase: 5th Rd 99-00

FACT FILE
Founded:
Colours: Blue & white stripes,black,blue
Change colours: All Yellow
Midweek Fixtures: Wednesday
Reserves' Lge: I.O.W. Saturday Lg.
Programme Editor: Roger Hendey

CLUB PERSONNEL
President: Ada Leigh
Chairman: Ian Lee
Manager: Derek Ohren

DOWNTON

Secretary: Brian Ford, 11 Chantry Road, Wilton, Salisbury, Wilts. Tel No: 01722 743314

Ground: Brian Whitehead Sports Ground, Wick Lane, Downton Tel: 01725 512162

Directions: Travel south from Salisbury on A338 for about 7 miles. Turn right intoWick Lane, and the ground is a qtr mile on left
Capacity: 1600 Seats: 250 Cover: Nil Floodlights: Yes

Clubhouse: Bar with kitchen facilities Club Shop: No

HONOURS Wilts Sen Cup 79-80 80-81, (R-up 55-56 91-92 94-95); Wilts Jun Cup 49-50; Bournemouth Sen Lge 60 61 62 64 65 67 68, Sen Lge Cup 61-62 63-64 66-67, Cup 62-63 79-80; Wessex Lge Cup 95-96; Wessex Comb Cup (R-up 95-96); RussellCotes Cup 95-96; Hayward Cup 64-65

PREVIOUS **League:** Bournemouth, Hants (pre-1993)

FACT FILE
Founded: 1905
Nickname: The Robins
Sponsor: Lex Vauxhall Salisbury
Colours: Red/white/red
Change colours:Yellow/blue/yellow
Midweek Matchday: Tuesday
Programme: Yes
Editor: James Blake

CLUB PERSONNEL
Chairman: James Blake
President: R Tanner
Manager: M Savage
Coach: C Huxford
Physio: T Ship

EASTLEIGH

Secretary: Richard Vowles, 28 Franklyn Avenue, Sholing, Southampton, Hants SO19 8AP
Tel: 02380 447802
Ground: `Ten Acres', Stoneham Lane, North Stoneham, Eastleigh SO50 -9HT Tel: 02380 613361
Directions: M27, Jct 5, to r'bout - exit marked Stoneham Lane. Carry on to r'bout & come back down Stoneham Lane, turning right opp. Concord Club. Ground 400 yds on left. Southampton Parkway (BR) 3/4 mile. Bus 48 (S'hampton-Winchester) to Stoneham Church stop
Capacity: 2,300 Seats: 175 Cover: 210 Floodlights: Yes Club Shop: No
Clubhouse: 11-11 Mon-Sat plus Sundays. Extensive function facilities. All catering undertaken

HONOURS Wessex Lg Cup R-up 91-92, Hants Lg Div 2 69-70 (R-up 54-55 60-61 62-63 64-65(Res), Div 3(W) 50-51 53-54 70-71(Res), Comb.(Res) (3) R-up 96-Hants, Comb Cup (Res) 96-7,97-8 Midweek F'lit Cup 78-79, Soton Snr Lg(W) 49-50 (R-up 51-52(Res), Div 1 56- 57) 57-58(Res)), Russell Cotes R-up 76-77 80-81 89-90,
PREVIOUS **Leagues:** Southampton Jnr & Snr 46-59/ Hants 50-86
Names: Swaythling Ath. 46-73; Swaythling 73-80
Grounds: Southampton Common 46-47; Walnut Avenue, Swaythling 47-75
BEST SEASON **FA Vase:** 4th Round 82-83,90-91, 94-95
RECORDS **Gate:** 2,500 v Southampton, floodlight opener 30/9/75
Scorer : Johnny Williams, 177 **Appearances** : Ian Knight, 611
Win: 12-1 v Hythe & Dibden (H) 11/12/48 **Defeat:** 0-11 v Austin Spts (A) 1/1/47

FACT FILE
Founded: 1946
Nickname: None
Sponsors: Southern Exhaust Services
Colours: All blue
Change colours: All red
Midweek matches: Wednesday
Programme: 32 pages with admission
Editor: Mark Pearce & Tommy Whale

CLUB PERSONNEL
Chairman: Roger Sherwood
President: Clive Wilson
Manager:Trevor Parker
Asst Manager: Joan Diaper
Physio: Bert Wyatt

2000-01 Leading goalscorer: Reza Sotoudeh
Captain: Dean Dyrne
P.o.Y.: Robin Abbott

FAREHAM TOWN

Secretary: Malcolm Harper OBE, 20 Hampton Grove, Catisfield, Fareham, Hants PO15 5NL
Tel: 01329 8413476 (H) 01329 844074 (Fax) 0410 689939 (M)
Ground: Cams Alders, Highfield Avenue, Fareham, Hants PO14 1JA Tel: 01329 231151
Directions: M27, J11, follow A27 towards Southampton. After passing Fareham station turn left at traffic lights (2nd left) into Redlands Ave.. Turn right at Redlands Inn then left into Highfields Ave.
Capacity: 5,500 Cover: 500 Seats: 450 Floodlights: Yes
Clubhouse: Open every evening except Sundays. Food available
Club Shop: Sells programmes, scarves & fanzines
HONOURS Hants Lg (8) 59-60 62-67 72-73 74-75 (R-up 55-56 60-61 67-68 71-72 76-77 78-79, Div 2 R-up 52-53, Eastern Div 24-25, Div 3 East 49-50), Hants Snr Cup 56-57 62-63 67-68 92-93, Russell Cotes Cup (6) 64-65 72-77, Gosport War Memorial Cup, SW Co's Cup (2), Pickford Cup (2),
PREVIOUS **Leagues:** Portsmouth 47-49, Hants 49-79, Southern 79-98
Name: Fareham FC **Ground:** Bath Lane
BEST SEASON **FA Trophy:** Semi Final 86-87 **FA Amateur Cup:** 2nd Rd 63-64 66-67 73-74
FA Vase: 1st Rd 98-9 **FA Cup:** 1st Rd replay 88-89, 2-3 v Torquay U. (H) after 2-2
RECORDS **Attendance:** 2,650 v Wimbledon, FA Cup 1965.
(at Southampton F.C.) 6,035 v Kidderminster H., FAT S-F 2nd leg 86-87
Fee received: £43,000 for David Leworthy (Spurs)

FACT FILE
Formed: 1947
Nickname: The Town
Sponsors: Portsmouth Evening News
Colours: Red/white/red
Change colours: Whiteblack/black
Midweek matchday: Wednesday
Reserves' League: Hampshire Comb
Programme: 36 pages £1
Editor: Ian Tewson Tel. 01329 662624

CLUB PERSONNEL
Chairman: Bob Ralls
Director of Football: John Green
President: Ken Atkins
General Manager: Tony Adams (01705 615931)
Press Officer: M Willis
Manager: Mark Chamberlain (01705 327527)
Physio: James McKay

FLEET TOWN

Secretary: John Goodyear, 25 Velmead Road,Fleet,Hants GU52 7LJ
Email: goodyear.john@btinternet.com
Ground: Calthorpe Park, Crookham Road, Fleet, Hants Tel: 01252 623804
Directions: Leave the M3 at Junction 4A. Follow signs to Fleet via A3013.
At 5th roundabout (a T-junction), turn left over railway bridge.
Carry on past `Oatsheaf' pub on the right - ground is 1/4 mile further on right.
Capacity: 2,000 Seats: 200 Cover: 250 Floodlights: Yes
Clubhouse: Yes. Hot & cold food served **Club Shop**: No

PREVIOUS **Leagues:** Hampsire 61-77, Athenian, Combined Co's, Chiltonian, Wessex 89-95, Southern 95-00, Wessex 00-
Names: None **Grounds:** None

CLUB RECORDS **Win:** 15-0
Transfer fee paid: £3,000 to Aldershot Dec 99 for Mark Russell 1991

Career Goalscorer: Mark Frampton 428 **Career Appearances:** Mark Frampton250

HONOURS Wessex Lg 94-95 , Lg Cup R-up 92-93,
Hants Lg Div 2 R-up 61-62 (Div 1 R-up 60-61), Aldershot Snr Cup 92-93, 99-00
Simpsonair Challenge Shield 1993, Hants Yth LgDiv 3 92-93.

FACT FILE
Founded: 1890 Re-Formed: 1947
Nickname: The Blues
Sponsors: Southern Coating Contractors Ltd.
Colours: Navy & sky/sky/navy & sky
Change: Red & Black
Midweek Matches: Tuesday
Reserves' League: Suburban(Wednesdays)
Prog: : 20 Pages:£1.00 Editor: Stuart Reeves
Website: www.fleettownfc.co.uk

CLUB PERSONNEL
Chairman: Martn Griffiths
President: Tony Frost
Vice Chairman: Jon Goodyear
Manager: Tommy Taylor
Assistant Manager: Jess Bone
Coach: John Richards Physio: David Keir

2000-01
Captain: John Williams
P.o.Y.: Mark Watson
Top Scorer:Mark Frampton 34

Top:
Brockenhurst FC
Back Row (l-r): Mark Adams, Pete Gardner, Cliff Huxford (Manager), Richard Cort, Phil Stone, Andy Colverson, Steve Limpow, Sam Perceval, Steve Hillier, Robin Bates (Physio).
Front Row: Andy Knighton, Tim Constable, Mark Dancer, Mark Jones, Ben Thompson, Dave Knighton, Steve Leigh-Bryant.

Centre:
An aerial duel during the first half at Testwood Park as Totton defend their penalty box against Chippenham Town.
Photo: Martin Wray

Bottom:
Guy Dipper (Wimborne) with Gavin Smith (Fleet) ready to pounce!
Photo: Mark Sandom

GOSPORT BOROUGH

Secretary: B V Cosgrave, 2 Cavanna Close, Rowner, Gosport PO13 0PE Tel: 01329314117
Ground: Privett Park, Privett Road, Gosport, Hants Tel: 01705 501042 (Office)
Directions: M27 Junct 11, A32 Fareham to Gosport. At Brockhurst r-about (about 3 miles) right into Military Rd passing thru H.M.S. Sultan, left into Privett Rd at next r-about, ground 300yds left signed `Privett Park Enclosure'. 2 miles from Portsmouth Harbour (BR) or Fareham (BR)
Capacity: 4,500 Cover: 500 Seats: 450 Floodlights: Yes Club Shop: No
Clubhouse: Matchdays only - from 1.30 Sat., 6.30 Wed. Refreshment hut sells hot food & drinks
HONOURS Wessex Lg Cup 92-93, Southern Lg Div 1 South R-up 84-85, Hants Lg 45-46 76-77 77-78 (Div 3 (Res.) 70-71 75-76), Portsmouth Lg R-up 44-45, HantsSenior Cup 87-88, Russell Cotes Cup R-up 94-95, Hants Intermediate Cup 70-71, Portsmouth Senior Cup 61-62 69-70 70-71 94-95, South West Counties PrattenChallenge Cup 77-78
BEST SEASON **FA Trophy:** 1st Rd 88-89 **FA Amateur Cup:** 3rd Rd 47-48 66-67
FA Vase: 6th Rd rep 77-78 **FA Cup:** 4th Qual. Rd 80-81 (lost to Windsor & Eton)
PREVIOUS **Leagues:** Portsmouth 44-45; Hants 45-78; Southern 78-92
Name: Gosport Borough Athletic
RECORD **Attendance:** 4,770 v Pegasus, FA Amtr Cup 1951
Scorer: Richie Coulbert 192 **Appearances**: Tony Mahoney 764
Win: 14-0 v Cunliffe-Owen, Hampshire Lg Div 1 45-46
Defeat: 0-9 twice v Newport, Hants Lg Div 1 47-48.
v Gloucester (A), SouthernLg Prem Div 89-90

FACT FILE
Founded: 1944 Nickname: The Boro'
Sponsors: Cawte & Elms
Colours: Yellow/blue/yellow
Change colours: All red
Midweek matchday: Tuesday
Reserves ' League: Wessex Combination
Programme: 20 pages, 50p
Editor: Ian Hay (01329 314601)
Local Press: Portsmouth Evening News, Southampton Evening Echo
A club record 14 consecutive victories were achieved last season

CLUB PERSONNEL
Chairman: JohnStimpson
President: H.Mizen
Manager: Mick Marsh Coach Hugh Doyle
Physio: Dave Topliss

2000-01
Captain & P.o.Y.: Stuart Hensman
Top Scorer: Jon Wallsgrove 31

HAMBLE AEROSTRUCTURES SPORTS & SOCIAL CLUB

Secretary: Matthew Newbold, Flat 6, 70-72 Portsmouth Road, Woolsten, Southampton, Hants. SO19 9AN Tel: 023 803 24147 (H) 023 804 53371(W)

Ground: Folland Park, Kings Avenue, Hamble.,Southampton SO31 4NF Tel: 01703 452173

Directions: M27 junction 8, then B3397 to Hamble. Half mile fromHamble (BR); turn right out of station, proceed for one mile then turn right before shops into Kings Avenue. Ground 1000 yards on right in works sports ground.

Capacity: 1000 Seats: 150 Cover: 150 Floodlights: Yes
Clubhouse: 300 capacity social club. Cricket & bowls

HONOURS: Hampshire Lg Div 3 80-81 (Div 4 79-80), Hampshire Intermediate Cup 79-90, Southampton Senior Cup 84-85 86-87 91-92
As Hamble AS&SC: Jewson Wessex League Cup 97-98
PREVIOUS **Name:** Folland Sports (pre-1990), Aerostructures SSC 90-97
RECORD **Defeat:** 1-10 v Andover (A), Wessex League 93-94

FACT FILE

Colours: Maroon
Change colours: All navy blue
Midweek Matches: Tuesdays & Wednesdays
Reserves ' League: Wessex Comb
Under 18 & Under16: So'ton Youth Lgs

CLUB PERSONNEL

President: Alistair Tritten
Assistant Secretary: Matthew Newbold
Treasurer:Barry Morse
SeniorManagers: Nigel Kent &Dick Donohoe

LYMINGTON & NEW MILTON

Secretary: John Osey, 9 Samphire Close, Lymington, Hants SO41 9LR Tel: 01590 676995
Ground: Fawcett Fields,Christchurch Rd., New Milton,Hants BH25 6QF (01425 6281910
Directions: M27 Jct 1 follow A337 to Lyndhurst one way system(A35) towards Christchurch. Left in Hinton Admiral at Cat & Fiddle.Follow Ringwood road ,then left at A337 roundabout to New Milton. Ground one mile on left past Chewton Glen Hotel.
Capacity: 3,000 Seats: 262 Cover: 262 Floodlights: Yes
Clubhouse: Open seven days a week 11.0 am to 11.0 pm. Hot food and functions availab le
HONOURS Wessex Lg 92-93 96-97 97-98, 98-99 R-up 91-92 95-96, Wessex Lg Cup 88-89, R-up 94-95, 98-99 Wessex Comb. 92-93, Hants Snr Cup R-up 89-90, Texaco Cup 91-92, Bournemouth Snr Cup 92-93, R-up 96-97, Russell Cotes Cup 93-94 94-95, R-up91-92 92-93; Pickford Cup R-up 92-93. Jewson Champions Shield 98-99
BEST SEASON **FA Cup:** 4th Qual. Rd. 99-00, 1-3 v Aldershot Town (H)
FA Vase: 98-99 Quarter Final, 1-3 v Taunton Town (A)
PREVIOUS **Names:** Lymington Town (until 1988 merger with Wellworthy Ath.),
AFC Lymington 88-98 (until merger with New Milton Town)
Ground: Ampress Ground (Wellworthy Ath.), until 1988 merger
RECORD **Attendance:** 2,900 v Karen Mills Memorial Day 12.3.95
Scorer: Darren Pitter 197 **Appearances:** Graham Kemp 322
Win: 11-1 v Romsey Town (H), Wessex League 9/11/92
Defeat: 0-8 v Basingstoke Town (A), Hampshire Senior Cup 10/4/90

FACT FILE

Founded as Lymington & New Milton: 1998
Nickname: Linnets
Sponsors: Sewards
Colours: Red & blue stripes/blue/red
Change colours: Yellow /green/green
Midweek Matches: Tuesday
Reserves ' League: Wessex Comb

Programme: 48 pages, £1.00
Editor/Press Officer: Richard Milbery

CLUB PERSONNEL

Chairman: Terry Morris
V - Chairmen: Richard Millbery/Bob Philpott
President: Jack Holliday & Ted Goodyer

Manager: Derek Binns
Coach: Alan Farrar

MONEYFIELDS

Secretary: Peter Shires, 242 Grafton Street, Mile End, Portsmouth.PO2 7LH
Tel: 023 9264 5813(H) 023 9261 1363 (B) 077141 76138(M)

Ground: Moneyfields Sports Ground, Moneyfields Avenue, Copnor, Portsmouth,Hants.
Tel: 023 9266 5260 Club), 023 9265 2424 (Office) **Club Shop**: Yes
Capacity: 1,500 Seats: 150 Cover: 150 Floodlights: Yes

Clubhouse: Daily 7-11 p.m. Saturday 11-11p.m. (food from 1.0 pm)

Directions: From Southampton & the west - travel east on M27 onto A27. Take exit marked Southsea A2030. (From east take the same exit). Head south along A2030 exit and turn right into Tangier Road (4th right). Follow until`Tangiers' PH & take next right into Folkestone Road. Carry on into Martin Rd & club is in front of you.

RECORDS: **Appearances:** Matthew Lafferty 156 (Jewson Wessex)
Goalscorer: Kevin Marsh 49 (Jewson Wessex)
Attendance: 152 v Fareham Town, Jewson Wessex League, 98-99

BEST SEASON F.A.Cup: 1st Prelim Rd 00-01
F.A.Vase: 2nd Qual Rd. 00-01

HONOURS: Portsmouth Senior Cup: 90-91 R-up 91-92 Hampshire League Div 3 91-92, Div 2 92-93,Div 196-97,R-Up 97-98 Portsmouth Premier champions 90-91,91-92 Billy Hill Cup 90-91 Hampshire Intermediate Cup Winners 91-92, 92-93 Russell Cotes Cup Finalists 98-99 Hants Youth Cup (under 18) (4), Under 16 (98-99), Hants Youth League 00-01 R-up 98-99

FACT FILE
Founded:1987 Nickname: Moneys
Sponsors: Icee Ltd
Colours: Yellow/& navyblue/yellow
Change: Green & white/ green/green.
Midweek Fixtures: Wednesday
Reserves League: Wessex Combination
Prog 20pages 50p Eds: David & Michelle Hayter(023 9264 3986)

CLUB PERSONNEL
Chairman: David Jupe
Tel: 023 9235 9571
Manager: Calvin Hore
Assistant Manager: Terry Arnold
Physio: Adie Hylands

2000-01
Captain: Matthew Lafferty
Ps.o.Y: DeanWarerman & James Dunk
Top Scorer: Kevin Marsh 14

PORTLAND UNITED

Secretary: David Naerger, 5 Three Yards Close, Portland
Tel Nos: 01305 821553 (H) 01305 768888 (B) 07811 518453 (M)

Ground: New Grove Corner, Grove Road, Portland, Dorset
Tel: 01305 861489

Directions A354 to Portland, follow one way system to the top of island, roundabout (hotel on left, garage on right), over roundabout for 500m, turn left into Grove Road, ground on left hand side.

Cover: Yes **Clubhouse:** Yes

FACT FILE
Colours: All blue
Change colours: Red/black/red
Midweek matches: Tuesday
Programme: Yes
Chairman: Phillip Laming
Acorn Bungalow, 1b, Straits, Portland, Dorset.
Tel: 01305 822756 (B)

SWANAGE TOWN & HERSTON

Secretary: Eric Webster, 24 James Day Mead, Ulwell Road, Swanage BH191NQ
Tel: 01929 423522 (H & Fax)

Ground: Days Park, off De Moulham Road, Swanage, Dorset BH19 Tel: 01929 424633

Directions: A35 to Wareham - at roundabout on the Wareham bypass take the A351 to Corfe Castle & Swanage, bear left for the beach and town, along Victoria Avenue, until traffic lights - cross over lights, first turning on left before the seafront, into De Moulham Road. Carry on into North Beach car park, enter car park and turn left into ground.

Capacity: Cover: Yes Floodlights: Yes Clubhouse: Yes

Previous League: Dorset Combination

FACT FILE
Colours:White,black and blue.
Change colours: All yellow & sky blue
Midweek matchday: Tuesday
Programme: Yes

CLUB PERSONNEL
Chairman: Len Marsh
204D High Street, Swanage, Dorset BH19 2PQ
Tel: 0129 424152
President: Mayor of Swanage

THATCHAM TOWN

Football Secretary: Peter Woodage, 5 Elm Grove, Thatcham, Berks. RG18 3DJ
Tel: 01635 861937

Ground: Waterside Park, Crookham Rd, Thatcham, Berks Tel: 01635 862016
Capacity: 3,000 Seats: 300 Cover: 300 Floodlights: Yes

Directions: M4 junc 13, take A34 to Newbury, then left onto A4 towards Reading InThatcham turn right to the railway station. The ground is on the left beyond the station - 2 minutes walk.From South A34 to Newbury,take A339 to Basingstoke,left to Thatcham then left again down Crookham Rd. Ground on right just before station

Clubhouse: Open every evening & lunchtimes **Club Shop:** Yes

HONOURS Wessex Lg 95-96,R-up 98-99, Cup 90-91 91-92 94-95 96-97, (R-up twice)

PREVIOUS Ground: Station Road 46-52; Lancaster Close 52-92

BEST SEASON **FA Cup:** 4th Qual Rd 96-97

RECORD **Attendnace:** 1,400 v Aldershot, FA Vase

FACT FILE
Founded: 1895
Sponsors: Panasonic Gsm Mobile Phones
Colours: Blue & white stripes/blue/blue
Change colours:Red,black,black
Midweek Matches: Tuesday
Programme: 28 pages, 50p
Editor: Les Wiunkworth

CLUB PERSONNEL
Chairman: Phil Holdway
General Secretary: John Haines
Press Officer: Phil Holdway (*01635 867803)
Manager:Neil Baker
Coach:Jason Braidwood

WHITCHURCH UNITED

Secretary: Joanna Cozzi, 39 Hartley Meadow, Whitchurch,Hants RG26 892579(H)

Ground: Longmeadow, Winchester Road, Whitchurch Tel: 01256 892493

Directions: From Whitchurch (BR) station; turn left after Railway Inn, follow road to end, turn right into main road, arriving in town turn left alongWinchester Road. Ground three quarters of a mile on left

Capacity: 2,000 Seats: 200 Cover: Yes Floodlights: Yes

Clubhouse: Hot food on matchdays. Sports hall with squash courts and indoor bowling green

PREVIOUS **Leagues:** Hampshire (pre-1992)

BEST SEASON **FA Vase:** Extra-Preliminary Rd 93-94, 1-3 v Peppard (H)

FACT FILE

Founded: 1903
Colours: Red &white/black/black
Change colours: White/blue/blue.
Midweek Matches: Tuesday
Programme: 24 pages

CLUB PERSONNEL

Chairman: Gary Shaughnessy
Tel No: 01256 893237

WIMBORNE TOWN

Secretary: Paul Christopher, 31 Brookside Rd, Bronsgore, Christchurch, Dorset. Bh23 8NA Tel No: 01425 674084 (H) 07901 892182 (M)
Ground: The Cuthbury, Cowgrove Road, Wimborne, Dorset BH21 4EL Tel: 01202 884821
Capacity: 3,250 Seats: 275 Cover: 150 Floodlights: Yes
Directions: Wimborne to Blandford Road, behind Victoria Hospital
Clubhouse: Eves 7-11, Sat noon-11, Sun 12-6 Bar & Skittle alley **Club Shop:** Yes
HONOURS FA Vase 91-92; Wessex Lg 91-92 93-94 ,99-00(R-up 92-93 96-97), Lg Cup 93-94,99-00 (R-up 90-91 95-96); Dorset Lg Div 1 80-81 81-82 (R-up 38-39 72-73), Div 2 31-32 34-35 36-37(R-up 35-36), Lg Cup R-up (4) 72-74 80-82; Dorset Snr Cup 91-92 96-97, (R-up 80-82 85-86 98-99,99-00); Mark Frowde Cup 92-93 94-95; Dorset Snr Amateur Cup 36-37 63-64;Dorset Jnr Cup 31-32 36-37 (R-up 13-14 34-35); Dorset Minor Cup 12-13; Dorset Jnr Amateur Cup (3) 34-36 38-39; Bankes Charity Cup 89-90 94-95 95-96, TexacoF/Light Cup 90-91

PREVIOUS **Leagues:** Dorset Lge, Dorset Comb, Western 81-86

BEST SEASON **FA Vase:** Winners 91-92 **FA Cup:** 1st Rd Proper 82-83

RECORDS **Attendance:** 3,250 v Bamberbridge FA Vase Semi-Final 28/3/92
Goalscorer: Jason Lovell **Win** (Wessex Lg): 9-0 v E.Cowes V 98-99, Brockenhurst 99-00
Appearances: James Sturgess **Defeat** (Wessex Lg): 2-6 v Thatcham Town 91-92
Fee paid: £5,500 for J P Lovell (Bashley, 1992)
Fee received: £6,000; for J P Lovell (Bashley, 1989) & for Tommy Killick(Dorchester, 1993)

FACT FILE
Founded: 1878 Nickname: Magpies
Sponsors: Nicolas O'Hara
Colours: Black & white stripes/black/black
Change colours: Yellow/green/yellow
Midweek Matches: Tuesday
Reserve League: Wessex Combination
Programme: 24 pages, 50p
Editor: L.Fergus
2000-01 Captain: Danny Robbins
Top Scorer: Darren Elmes 30
P.o.Y.: Andy Barham

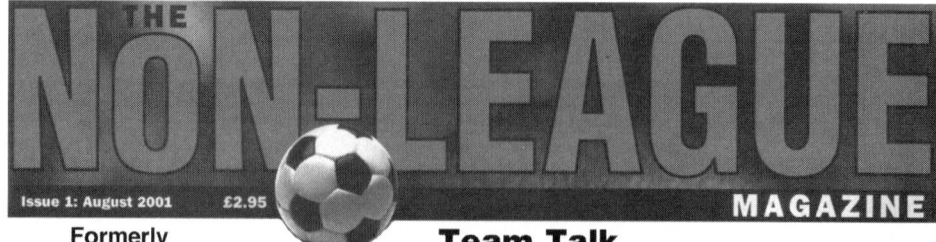

CLUB PERSONNEL
Chairman: Nicholas O'Hara
President: Brian Maidment
Press Officer: Secretary
Manager: Alex Pike
Asst, Mgr: Mike Buxton
Coach: John Macey
Physio: Irvin Brown

HAMPSHIRE FOOTBALL LEAGUE

Established: 1896

President: N L White
Chairman: G Cox
Secretary: I J Craig
56 Ecton Lane, Anchorage Park, Hilsea, Portsmouth PO3 5TA
Tel: 023 9267 1155 Fax: 023 9265 1147 Email: iancraig@eurobell.co.uk

League Development Officer: J Moody

At last season's AGM in June a number of changes were made in the Honorary positions of the League. John Moody was appointed the League Development Officer, I moved from Fixtures Secretary to League Secretary, and Stewart Springer took on the Fixtures.

On the playing side, Fareham Sacred Hearts were making their County debut, whilst Alresford Town returned to the League after a short absence and East Cowes Victoria joined us from the Wessex League. AFC Basingstoke withdrew both their sides from the competition without a ball being kicked, due to the lack of a major sponsor.

In September Gerry Sutton, who once served on the League Committee, passed away and the League sent their condolences. Also, the first fixtures problem arose when the League decided to call off all scheduled fixtures due to the petrol crisis. An unusual deluge of rain came early this season and caused havoc with County and local Association Cup matches being called off, meaning the League fixtures had to be re-arranged on a weekly basis.

From 7th October my wife Julie and daughter Kerri joined the League and became the Results Secretaries. A week after they took the job on they both went shopping for the day - guess who had to stay in and take the results?

In November Colden Common Secretary Mark Budden resigned from the League Management Committee and we thank him for his contribution to the League. An invitation went to David Munday, Secretary of Brading Town, to join the Committee, which he accepted. Continual bad weather hit the League and Cup programme, with only two League games played on the 25th of the month.

December continued in the same vein, rain in the first three weeks, then snow and frost, combining to allow only 70 of the 149 scheduled games to be played during the month.

January saw the League's last representatives, Horndean, knocked out of the Hampshire Senior Cup by Lymington & New Milton of the Jewson Wessex League.

The Committee agreed in February to cancel this season's Trophyman Cups due to the continuing bad weather. The Hampshire League went "on the net", teaming up with Yellow Jersey. This allows the League to show fixtures, results, league tables, and news in general about the League.

Saturday 24th February saw the first full League fixture list since Saturday 30th September and it proved notable for Yateley Green and Romsey Town Reserves who both recorded their first wins of the season.

Winchester City and Fleet Spurs reached the semi-finals of the Hampshire Intermediate Cup and with both teams being kept apart in the draw an all Hampshire League final was a nice prospect. The first cup winners of the season were Fareham Sacred Hearts who beat Gosport Borough Reserves 3-2 in the Portsmouth Senior Cup at Moneyfields.

With the rain still falling, and the foot and mouth epidemic, it left mammoth tasks for a number of clubs to complete their fixtures. In April, 433 matches still had to be played. A meeting to discuss the problem of fixtures was held, and the clubs agreed to extend the season to 31st May with any matches that couldn't be played due to unavailability of pitches to be made a 0-0 draw and one point awarded to each side.

Winchester City reached the final of the Southampton Senior Cup beating Brendon 2-0, the side that had knocked them out of the Hampshire Intermediate Cup two days earlier. In the final they met Southampton Premier Division side Nursling, who were surprise winners over Locksheath. Fleet Spurs beat Oakfield after extra time to secure a place in the final of the Hampshire Intermediate Cup. Winchester City went on to beat Nursling 2-0 at The Dell to lift the Southampton Senior Cup, but Fleet Spurs lost 2-1 against Brendon in the final of the Hampshire Intermediate Cup.

On 7th May Vosper Thornycroft won the Premier Division after drawing 1-1 with Brading Town. Two days later they collected another trophy after beating Bishops Waltham Reserves and then won the newly formed Combination Two Division in their first season in the League. Stockbridge lost in their efforts to lift the North Hants Senior Cup when they were beaten 5-3 by Wessex League champions, Andover.

Farnborough North End won Division Two without kicking a ball as closest rivals Fareham Sacred Hearts lost 3-2 to Laverstock & Ford, and Winchester City beat Tadley Town 5-1 to win Division One. Congratulations go to Colden Common Reserves who won the Combination Division One Trophy for the third season running, beating Winchester City Reserves 3-0.

Two well established clubs leave the League this season, AC Delco and Winchester Castle and we wish them well in the future.

Finally I would like to thank all the clubs who have soldiered through what has been a very difficult season, John Moody for his advice, when needed, in my first season as League Secretary, and last but not least my wife, Julie, who has put up with a lot of phone calls, paperwork, and me, throughout the season.

It can only get better, can't it?

Ian J Craig, Hon League Secretary

FINAL LEAGUE TABLES 2000-01

PREMIER DIVISION

	P	W	D	L	F	A	Pts
Vosper Thornycroft	40	27	8	5	98	43	89
Poole Town	40	26	7	7	128	54	85
Stockbridge	40	23	9	8	107	70	78
East Cowes Vics	40	23	8	9	116	53	77
Pirelli General	40	19	8	13	65	50	65
Brading Town	40	19	8	13	83	71	65
Alton Town	40	19	8	13	78	66	65
Locksheath	40	18	10	12	74	70	64
Petersfield Town	40	17	10	13	98	74	61
Colden Common	40	17	10	13	72	60	61
West Wight Mayflower	40	19	4	17	70	68	61
Amesbury Town	40	16	11	13	77	61	59
Horndean	40	15	8	17	68	79	53
Liss Athletic	40	12	11	17	75	75	47
Ringwood Town	40	12	9	19	66	87	45
Hythe & Dibden	40	11	9	20	58	91	42
Lymington Town	40	11	7	22	50	71	40
New Street	40	11	7	22	57	89	40
Bishops Waltham Town	40	7	12	21	45	91	33
Esso (Fawley)	40	6	8	26	42	112	26
AFC Aldermaston	40	2	8	30	45	137	14

DIVISION ONE

	P	W	D	L	F	A	Pts
Winchester City	30	20	4	6	84	34	64
Winchester Castle	30	18	7	5	72	31	61
Clanfield	30	17	7	6	91	45	58
Hayling United	30	17	6	7	58	28	57
AFC Portchester	30	16	9	5	59	34	57
Fleet Spurs	30	17	5	8	63	28	56
Paulsgrove	30	15	5	10	64	42	49
Hilsea	30	14	4	12	52	59	45
Fleetlands	30	11	9	10	38	39	42
Verwood Town	30	9	4	17	35	67	31
Tadley Town	30	8	5	17	36	64	29
Co-op Sports	30	7	6	17	22	43	27
Micheldever	30	6	7	17	42	72	25
AC Delco	30	7	4	19	40	86	25
Yateley Green	30	6	6	18	36	79	24
Romsey Town	30	5	6	19	32	73	21

DIVISION TWO

	P	W	D	L	F	A	Pts
Farnborough NE	30	26	1	3	113	30	79
Fareham Sacred Heart	30	23	4	3	97	26	70
Alresford Town	30	22	1	7	71	41	67
Laverstock & Ford	30	21	3	6	66	39	66
Otterbourne	30	15	6	9	60	47	51
Hadleigh	30	14	9	7	52	47	51
Overton United	30	14	5	11	71	57	47
Hamble Club	30	11	4	15	40	46	37
Awbridge	30	10	6	14	50	46	36
Netley Central	30	7	10	13	41	51	30
Ordnance Survey	30	6	11	13	33	44	28
QK Southampton	30	6	9	15	29	61	27
Broughton	30	7	7	16	41	84	27
Compton	30	4	7	19	44	99	19
Hedge End	30	4	6	20	32	66	18
Bishopstoke Social	30	3	5	22	25	81	14

PREMIER DIVISION RESULTS CHART 2000-01

		1	2	3	4	5	6	7	8	9	10	11	12	13	14	15	16	17	18	19	20	21
1	AFC Alder'ton	X	0-2	3-5	2-3	3-6	1-3	0-6	1-1	0-2	4-3	2-3	1-1	0-2	0-3	2-9	1-2	1-4	3-3	0-5	1-1	1-5
2	Alton Town	1-1	X	2-1	7-0	1-4	2-1	0-4	2-1	2-4	1-0	4-2	1-2	1-0	0-0	3-0	2-1	3-2	5-0	3-1	0-1	4-0
3	Amesbury Tn	2-2	3-1	X	5-0	3-2	0-0	1-1	2-0	1-1	1-1	0-1	4-2	2-3	5-0	1-0	5-0	1-2	3-0	3-3	0-0	2-0
4	Bishops W. Tn	0-0	3-3	2-2	X	4-2	4-5	0-2	1-0	1-1	0-1	0-0	0-0	0-0	1-0	4-2	1-2	3-2	1-4	2-2	0-3	2-2
5	Brading Town	2-0	1-5	1-0	6-3	X	0-0	1-1	4-0	3-0	1-0	2-0	4-4	1-0	7-2	3-2	2-3	2-2	0-0	2-2	1-1	3-2
6	Colden Com.	4-1	4-2	1-2	3-0	1-0	X	4-0	3-0	3-1	5-2	2-0	1-3	3-0	5-1	2-2	0-2	0-0	2-2	2-3	0-1	1-3
7	East Cowes V	9-1	4-1	5-1	2-0	4-1	0-0	X	2-2	4-2	10-0	2-2	2-3	5-1	5-2	1-3	0-2	8-1	3-1	4-1	1-2	3-2
8	Esso (Fawley)	2-1	1-1	0-4	2-1	4-2	2-6	0-4	X	1-1	0-0	3-3	2-3	0-2	3-1	1-3	0-3	0-3	1-0	0-5	0-6	1-0
9	Horndean	6-1	2-2	2-6	2-0	0-1	0-1	0-2	6-0	X	5-1	3-2	3-1	1-0	3-3	1-2	3-1	1-3	0-3	2-4	1-2	0-2
10	Hythe & Dibden	2-2	2-2	0-0	2-2	3-0	0-0	2-2	4-3	4-2	X	0-3	4-1	3-0	1-3	1-0	2-1	0-3	4-1	3-4	1-2	1-1
11	Liss Athletic	6-1	2-4	2-3	0-0	1-2	3-0	0-2	0-0	2-2	3-1	X	2-2	6-2	0-0	2-2	0-0	2-2	2-5	2-5	3-1	3-1
12	Locksheath	4-0	1-0	1-2	4-0	0-2	2-2	1-2	5-2	0-0	3-1	1-0	X	2-0	0-0	2-1	1-1	1-8	2-1	1-3	1-1	3-0
13	Lymington Tn	3-0	2-0	1-1	2-3	2-2	0-1	1-1	4-4	0-1	1-2	0-3	1-0	X	5-0	0-5	2-0	1-1	3-1	1-2	0-2	1-3
14	New Street	2-0	0-2	4-1	4-1	0-2	3-0	0-4	1-0	1-3	3-1	1-2	2-2	0-2	X	0-2	0-2	0-3	7-1	3-6	1-1	1-4
15	Petersfield Tn	5-1	3-3	3-0	1-1	4-2	5-1	1-4	5-0	1-1	5-1	1-3	2-1	6-3	3-3	X	1-1	4-4	2-2	1-5	0-3	0-2
16	Pirelli General	4-0	1-1	2-0	4-1	3-2	3-0	3-3	1-0	0-1	3-0	2-1	1-3	1-0	4-1	3-0	X	0-4	1-1	2-1	2-3	1-1
17	Poole Town	2-0	1-2	2-0	4-0	3-0	5-1	4-0	6-0	7-1	7-4	4-3	6-0	2-0	3-0	1-2	3-1	X	1-1	4-0	6-1	4-2
18	Ringwood Tn	4-2	1-0	2-2	3-1	0-4	2-0	0-2	5-2	1-2	0-1	2-1	2-4	2-1	1-2	1-4	2-1	1-3	X	1-3	2-2	6-3
19	Stockbridge	4-3	5-0	2-0	2-0	5-1	1-1	4-1	4-2	4-0	1-0	2-1	4-3	1-1	1-3	2-1	1-1	2-2	1-1	X	0-4	3-5
20	Vosper Th.	5-1	5-1	5-2	1-0	3-2	1-3	1-0	6-1	6-0	2-0	5-2	1-2	3-2	3-0	3-3	1-0	2-1	3-0	2-2	X	3-0
21	West Wight M	1-2	0-3	3-1	2-1	0-1	1-1	2-1	2-1	1-2	5-0	4-2	1-2	0-1	1-0	0-2	1-0	4-3	3-1	2-1	1-0	X

AFC ALDERMASTON
Ground: Aldermaston Rec. Society, Automatic Weapons Establishment, Aldermaston, Reading, Berks. Tel: 0118 982 4544

ALTON TOWN
Secretary: A J M Hillman, 19a Beechwood Rd, Alton, Hants GU34 1RL (0142087103)
Ground: Bass Spts Ground, Anstey Rd, Alton (01420 82465)
Colours: Black & red/black/black
Midweek home matchday: Any

AMESBURY TOWN
Ground: Amesbury Recreation Ground, Amesbury, Wiltshire.
Tel: 01980 623489

ANDOVER NEW STREET
Secretary: Mrs F J Waterman, `Jorin Bay' 2 Pine Walk, Andover, Hants SP10 3PW(01264 362751)
Ground: Foxcotte Park, Charlton Down, Andover.(01264 358358)
Colours: Green & black/black/green
Midweek home matchday: Tuesday or Wednesday

BISHOPS WALTHAM TOWN
Ground: priory Park, Elizabeth Way, Bishops Waltham, Southampton, Hant. Tel: 01489 894269

BRADING TOWN
Secretary: Mick Edmondston, Seawinds, Nunwell St., Sandown.I.O.W. PO36 9DE(01983 404770)
Ground: Vicarage Lane, Brading, Isle of Wight (01983 405217)
Cols: All red

EAST COWES VICTORIA ATHLETIC
Secretary: J Stone, 99 High Park Rd., Ryde, Isle of Wight PO33 1BZ
Tel: 01983 565269 (H) 07970 009901 (M)
email: John@Stoners.demon.co.uk
Ground: Beatrice Avenue Ground, East Cowes, I.O.W. Tel: 01938 297165 Directions: From the ferry: 1 mile from town centre on lower main road to Newport or Ryde near Whippingham Church adjacent to Osborne Middle School Colours: Red/black/white

ESSO (FAWLEY)
Secretary: Mr A Haws, 40 Hollybank Rd, Hythe, Southampton, Hants SO45 5FQ (01703 843402)
Ground: Esso Recreation Club, Long Lane, Holbury, Southampton, Hant (01705893750)
Colours: White/blue/red

HORNDEAN
Secretary: Mrs Gladys Berry, 74 Five Heads Road, Horndean PO8 9NZ (01705 591698)
Ground: Five Heads Park, Five Heads Road, Horndean (01705 591363)
Colours: Black & Red/black/black

HYTHE & DIBDEN
Secretary: Mr A Moyst, 105 Hobart Drive, Hythe, Southampton, Hants SO40 6FD (01703 847335)
Ground: Ewart Rec Ground, Jones Lane, Hythe, Southampton (01703 845264 -matchdays only)
Colours: Green/green/yellow

LISS ATHLETIC
Secretary: W.E.Moseley, 3 Yew Tree Place, Liss, Hants. GU33 7ET (01730 894631)
Ground: Newman Collard PF, Hill Brow Rd, Liss, Hants (01730 894022)
Colours: All Blue & White
Midweek home matchday: Thursday

LOCKS HE ATH
Secretary: Michael Harrison, 30 Whitebeam Road, Hedge End, Southampton, Hants.SO30 OPZ (01489 784470)
Ground: Locksheath Rec, Warsash Rd, Titchfield Common, Eastleigh (01489600932)
Colours: Red/black/black

LYMINGTON TOWN
Ground: Sports Ground, Southampton Road, Lymington, Hants. Tel: 01590 671305

PETERSFIELD TOWN
Secretary: M Nicholl, 49 Durford Rd, Petersfield, Hants GU31 4ER (01730300518)
Ground: Love Lane, Petersfield, Hants (01730 233416)
Colours: Red & Black/Black/Black
Midweek Matches: Wednesday

PIRELLI GENERAL
Secretary: Miss Bernice Fox 31 Spring Close, Fair Oak, Eastleigh, Hants SO507BB (01703 693537)
Ground: Jubilee Spts Ground, Chestnut Ave., Eastleigh (01703 612721)
Colours: Blue & white/white/white
Midweek home matchday: Tuesday

POOLE TOWN
Secretary: Bill Read, 15 Addison Close, Romsey, Hants SO51 7TL (01794 517991)
Ground: Petersham Lane, Gants Common, Holt, Wimborne, Dorset (01258 840379)
Colours: Red & white/red/white
Change Colours: Yellow & black/blue/yellow

PORTSMOUTH ROYAL NAVY
Secretary: Roy Newman 8 Kimpton Close, Lee-on-Solent, Hants PO13 8JY Tel: 02392 799198 (H)
Ground: The Navy Stadium, HMS Temeraire, Burnaby Road, Portsmouth PO1 2EJ Tel: 0239 272 4235, (Clubhouse 023 92291660)
Directions: From Portsmouth Harbour (BR), turn right onto The Hard, pass under the rail bridge and turn left into Park Road, after approx 200yards take 1st right into Burnaby Road. Entrance to ground 100 mtrs on the right
Colours: All blue Midweek Matches: Monday

RINGWOOD TOWN
Ground: The Clubhouse, Long Lane, Ringwood, Hants.
Tel: 01425 473448

STOCKBRIDGE
Secretary: Graham Howard, 1 Moat Cottages, Longstock,Stockbridge, Hants.SO20 6EP (01264 810753)
Ground: The Recreation Ground, High Street, Stockbridge, Hants
Colours: All red

VOSPER THORNYCROFT
Secretary: Peter Prin, 454 Bursledon Road, Sholing, Southampton, Hants. SO19 8QQ (01703 403829)
Ground: Vosper Thornycroft Spts Ground, Portsmouth Rd, Sholing, Southampton(01489 403829)
Colours: All royal

WINCHESTER CITY
Secretary: Geoffrey Cox, 9 Burnetts Gdns, Horton Heath, Eastleigh, Hants SO57BY (01703 693021)
Ground: Hillier Way, Abbotts Barton, Winchester (01962 863553)
Colours: Red & white/black/red
Change: White/green/green

DIVISION ONE CLUBS

AFC PORTCHESTER
Ground: Portchester Community School, White Hart Lane, Portchester, Hants. Tel: 02392 364399

CLANFIELD
Ground: Peel Park, Charlton Lane, Clanfield, Waterlooville, Hants.

COLDEN COMMON
Secretary: M.Budden, 44 Orchard Close, Colden Common, Winchester,Hampshire.SO21 1ST (01962 713813)
Ground: Colden Common Recreation Ground, Main Road, Colden Common (01962712365)
Colours: Red & white/black/red
Midweek home matchday: Wednesday

CO-OP SPORTS
Ground: Langstone College, Fyurze Lane, off Lockways Rd., Milton, Portsmouth. Tel: 02390 824798

FAREHAM SACRED HEARTS
Ground: Bakers barracks, Thorney Island, West Sussex.

FARNBOROUGH NORTH END
Ground: Farnborough Gate, Ringwood Rd., Farnborough, Hants.

FLEETLANDS
Secretary: David Bell, 72 White Hart Lane, Portchester, Hants. PO16 9BQ.(01705321781)
Ground: Lederle Lane, Gosport, Hants (01329 239723)
Colours: Red & black/white/white
Change: All white
Midweek home matchday: Any

FLEET SPURS
Secretary: C R Filkins, 5 Byron Close, Fleet, Hants GU13 9QD (01252 627385)
Ground: Ancells Farm, Fleet, Hants
Colours: Red & black/black/red
Change: Blue or green or purple/turqu/white

HAYLING UNITED
Secretary: Mrs S Westfield, 14 Harold Road, Hayling Island, Hants PO11 9LT (01705 463305)
Ground: Hayling Park, Hayling Island, Hants
Colours: Red & navy/navy/navy
Midweek home matchday: Tuesday

DIVISION TWO CLUBS

ALRESFORD TOWN
Ground: Alrebury Park, The Avenue, Alresford, Hants.
Tel: 01962 735100
AWBRIDGE
Ground: Village Hall Field, Crossroads, Awbridge, Romsey, Hants.
BISHOPSTOKE SOCIAL
Ground: Chicken Hall Lane, Bishopstoke, Eastleigh, Hants
Tel: 01860 612038
BROUGHTON
Ground: The Sportsfield, Buckholt rd., Broughton, Stockbridge, Hants.
Tel: 01794 301150
COMPTON
Ground: Shepherds Lane, Compton Down, Winchester
Tel: 01962 712083
HADLEIGH
Ground: Taverner Close, Basingstoke, Hants.
HAMBLE CLUB
Ground: Mount Pleasant Rec, Hamble Lane, Hamble, Southampton.
Tel: 01703 452327

HILSEA
Secretary: Mr Terry Harwood, 147 Manners Rd, Southsea, Hants PO4 0BD (01705785140)
Ground: Portsmouth Sailing Centre, Eastern Rd, Portsmouth PO3 5LY (01705670119)
Colours: Yellow/blue/white Change: Blue/blue/white

MICHELDEVER VILLAGE
Ground: Lord Rank Playing Fields, Duke St., Micheldever, Winchester.

PAULSGROVE
Secretary: S J Cox, 22 Alameda Road, Purbrook, Waterlooville, Hants. PO7 5HD (01705 785110)
Ground: The Grove Club, Marsden Rd (off Allaway Avenue), Paulsgrove, Portsmouth (01705 324102)
Colours: Red & black stripes/black/red
Change: Blue & white/blue/black
Midweek home matchday: Wednesday

ROMSEY TOWN
Secretary: Andy Spreadbury, 13 Tanners Road, North Baddesley Southampton SO52 9FD (01703 739034)
Ground: The By-Pass Ground, South Front, Romsey (01794 512003)
Colours: Yellow & black/black/black
Midweek Matchday: Wednesday

TADLEY TOWN
Secretary: Mike Miller, Meadow View, West Heath, Baughurst, Hants RG26 5LE(01256 850700)
Ground: The Green, Tadley, Hants
Cols: Blue & maroon stripes/maroon/maroon
Change: Yellow/blue/blue

VERWOOD TOWN
Secretary: Mrs J A Fry, 19a Noon Hill Rd, Verwood, Dorset BH31 7DB (01202822826)
Ground: Pottern Park, Pottern Way, Verwood, Dorset
Colours: All red Change: All blue
Midweek home matchday: Tuesday

YATELEY GREEN
Secretary: Alan Baynes, 7 Borderside, Yateley, Camberley Surrey GU17 7LJ
Ground: Yateley Recreation Ground, Reading Road, Yateley, Camberley, Surrey
Colours: Green/black/black Change: Red/black/black

HEADLEY ATHLETIC
HEDGE END
Ground: Norman Rodaway Sports Ground, Heathouse Lane, Hedge End, Southampton. Tel: 02380 798027
KING'S SOMBORNE
LAVERSTOCK & FORD
Ground: The Dell, Laverstock & Ford SC, 23 Church Rd., Laverstock, Salisbury. Tel: 01722 327401
NETLEY CENT. SPORTS
Ground: Netley Rec, Station Rd, Netley Abbey, Southampton
Tel: 01703 452267
ORDNANCE SURVEY
Ground: Lordshill Rec. Ground, Southampton. Tel: 02380 732531
OTTERBOURNE
Ground: Oakwood Park, off Oakwood Ave., Otterbourne
Tel: 01962 714681
OVERTON UNITED
Ground: Recreation Centre, Bridge Street, Overton
Tel: 01256 770561
Q.K. SOUTHAMPTON
Ground: Civil Service Club, off Malmesbury Road, Shirley, Southampton. Tel: 01703 771950

KEYLINE DORSET COMBINATION LEAGUE

Founded: 1957

President: Jack Cruickshank **Chairman:** Alan Burt

Secretary: Geoff Theobald, 41 South Road, Corfe Mullen
Wimborne, Dorset BH21 3HZ Tel: 01202 697994

Prior to the commencement of the playing season Parley Sports Football Club, members of the league since 1962, shocked all concerned by withdrawing from the competition for financial reasons. It was a great disappointment to lose the competition's most successful club in such circumstances.

The 2000-01 season will probably be remembered mainly for the number of postponed matches, in excess of 70 League and Cup matches were deferred for one reason or another. The trend started in September with the 'petrol crisis', continued with what turned out to be the wettest ever winter since records began, and concluded with the 'foot and mouth crisis'. For the first time since the League was founded in 1957 the league programme was not completed. One fixture, Gillingham Town FC versus Westland Sports FC, remained unplayed.

The chase for League Championship honours once again proved to be a two horse race, this time between Hamworthy Recreation FC and Portland United FC, with Hamworthy Recreation eventually being crowned Champions, denying Portland United a hat-trick of Championship wins. Westland Sports FC and Dorchester Town FC Reserves finished in third and fourth places respectively.

At the other end of the table, Witchampton United FC once again found life in the Combination League difficult, finishing in bottom place.

Hamworthy Recreation FC and Hamworthy United FC contested the Combination Cup Final, played at Bournemouth Sports Club in front of a very good crowd. The match saw Hamworthy Recreation win by two goals to nil. This victory gave 'Recreation' a League and Cup double.

This season's Representative fixture against the Wiltshire League was not played due to the bad weather. However, the Under 21 squad under manager Phil Simpkin (Dorchester Town) did manage to play their fixture against the Bournemouth FA, winning the game on penalties.

During the season Dorchester Town FC Reserves gave notice of their withdrawal from the Dorset Combination League, intending to join the Jewson Wessex Combination League. However, this decision was reversed when the Wessex League would not accept them, due to their ground sharing agreement with AFC Bournemouth.

Portland United FC, having finished as Runners-up in the League, successfully applied to join the Jewson Wessex League for the 2001-02 season.

Having completed the season as Dorset League Champions, Holt United FC will be returning to the Combination League for the coming season after an absence of five years.

Geoff Theobald, Secretary

FINAL LEAGUE TABLE 2000-01

	P	W	D	L	F	A	Pts
Hamworthy Recreation	34	29	3	2	115	27	90
Portland United	34	27	6	1	101	29	87
Westland Sports	33	21	2	10	81	61	65
Dorchester Town*	34	21	2	11	74	35	62
Hamworthy United	34	18	5	11	58	37	59
Bridport	34	18	5	11	63	50	59
Wareham Rangers	34	15	8	11	55	58	53
Gillingham Town*	33	12	10	11	63	58	43
Shaftesbury	34	11	8	15	50	50	41
Blandford United*	34	12	8	14	46	54	41
Stourpaine	34	12	3	19	63	71	39
Sherborne Town	34	11	3	20	52	69	36
Sturminster Newton	34	9	8	17	44	66	35
Flight Refuelling	34	10	4	20	63	90	34
Allendale	34	9	4	21	32	63	31
Bournemouth Sports	34	8	6	20	38	69	30
Weymouth Sports*	34	9	6	19	47	82	30
Witchampton United	34	4	7	23	38	114	19

* points deducted

LEADING GOALSCORERS 2000-01

Crispin Rigler	Hamworthy Recreation	42
James Reeve	Portland United	30
Simon Freak	Stourpaine	26
Mark Fitch	Portland United	23
Darren Orchard	Hamworthy United	21
Aaron Turner	Hamworthy Recreation	20
Stacey White	Westland Sports	19
Trevor Harmer	Sherborne Town	17
Christian Evans	Dorchester Town	15
Paul Honeybun	Flight Refuelling	15
Christopher Reader	Portland United	14

RESULTS CHART 2000-01

		1	2	3	4	5	6	7	8	9	10	11	12	13	14	15	16	17	18
1	Allendale	X	0-3	2-0	1-0	1-3	3-2	1-0	1-3	0-1	0-2	1-4	1-4	0-2	0-1	0-0	0-2	3-2	1-1
2	Blandford U	1-0	X	1-2	4-0	0-2	4-0	0-0	3-4	1-3	3-3	0-1	3-2	1-0	1-0	1-1	0-6	2-1	2-1
3	Bournemouth	2-0	1-1	X	0-0	0-3	4-3	0-4	0-2	0-0	0-2	2-1	1-1	3-1	1-3	3-5	1-0	2-0	0-0
4	Bridport	2-2	2-0	1-0	X	0-2	2-3	6-1	3-2	1-2	1-0	2-3	2-0	2-1	2-0	6-0	1-3	3-0	2-1
5	Dorchester T	0-1	4-1	2-0	0-1	X	1-3	1-3	0-4	3-2	0-0	1-2	2-0	2-0	3-1	5-0	2-4	5-0	4-0
6	Flight Refuel.	3-1	1-3	3-2	2-2	0-1	X	2-2	0-4	1-0	1-4	1-1	3-5	1-2	4-1	1-2	2-4	2-2	0-1
7	Gillingham T	2-1	1-1	2-0	5-3	0-3	6-1	X	0-4	3-3	1-1	2-2	1-2	1-2	3-0	1-1	n/p	1-0	4-1
8	Hamworthy R	5-2	4-0	2-1	1-0	2-2	6-0	3-1	X	5-0	1-1	4-1	4-2	3-1	3-0	4-0	2-0	7-0	5-0
9	Hamworthy U	4-0	2-1	4-0	1-2	1-0	4-0	2-1	1-2	X	0-2	2-0	2-0	3-0	1-2	2-1	1-2	2-1	5-0
10	Portland Utd	5-1	3-0	3-0	2-1	2-0	4-2	2-1	3-0	4-0	X	3-1	6-1	2-1	5-1	3-1	1-1	6-1	8-1
11	Shaftesbury	0-1	1-4	3-0	5-1	2-3	1-2	1-1	0-1	0-2	2-2	X	3-0	2-1	2-2	0-1	0-1	0-0	1-1
12	Sherborne T	0-1	3-0	3-1	1-2	0-3	4-0	2-3	1-2	0-5	0-2	0-1	X	3-1	2-1	1-3	2-0	0-0	2-1
13	Stourpaine	3-0	1-1	4-1	0-1	3-1	3-2	3-2	0-4	2-0	2-3	2-1	3-4	X	1-3	1-4	1-1	2-4	2-2
14	Sturminster N	2-1	0-0	0-0	0-2	0-3	3-1	1-1	0-1	1-1	1-4	1-1	3-2	4-1	X	2-2	0-3	1-1	0-1
15	Wareham Rngrs	1-0	1-0	3-0	2-2	1-0	1-3	1-1	2-2	0-0	0-1	2-1	2-1	3-2	4-3	X	2-3	0-1	0-1
16	Westland Sp	2-0	3-1	5-4	2-3	1-6	2-6	4-1	0-2	1-0	2-5	2-1	3-1	3-1	3-2	4-5	X	3-2	3-0
17	Weymouth Sp	0-0	1-3	4-1	1-2	0-1	2-1	2-3	2-7	1-1	0-4	1-4	3-2	2-6	3-1	2-1	4-2	X	3-2
18	Witchampton U	1-6	0-0	1-6	3-3	0-6	3-7	2-5	0-10	0-1	2-3	1-2	1-1	2-8	3-4	1-3	2-6	2-1	X

COMBINATION LEAGUE CUP 2000-01

FIRST ROUND

Allendale	v	Portland United	2-5
Sherborne Town	v	Wareham Rangers	5-2
Shaftesbury	v	Westland Sports	0-1

SECOND ROUND

Bridport	v	Hamworthy United	1-3
Sherborne Town	v	Dorchester Town	1-2
Westland Sports	v	Blandford United	5-0
Witchampton United	v	Bournemouth S	2-2, 0-5
Hamworthy Rec.	v	Stourpaine	6-2
Sturminster Newton	v	Portland United	1-1, 1-3
Weymouth Sports	v	Gillingham Town	0-2
FLIGHT REFUELLING		PARLEY S. W.D	

THIRD ROUND

Dorchester Town	v	Hamworthy United	1-2
Gillingham Town	v	Westland Sp	3-3, 2-2, 1-3
Flight Refuelling	v	Hamworthy Rec.	2-4
Portland United	v	Bournemouth S	1-1, 2-0

SEMI FINALS

Hamworthy Rec.	v	Westland Sports	7-0
Hamworthy United	v	Portland United	1-0

FINAL

Hamworthy Rec.	v	Hamworthy United	2-0

TREVOR WILLIAMS FAIR PLAY TROPHY 2000-01

Allendale	13	Bridport	29	Sturminster Newton	35
Dorchester Town	25	Blandford United	30	Witchampton United	35
Sherborne Town	26	Portland United	34	Hamworthy United	36
Wareham Rangers	26	Westland Sports	34	Shaftesbury	39
Hamworthy Engineering	27	Bournemouth Sports	35	Gillingham Town	40
Weymouth Sports	28	Flight Refuelling	35	Stourpaine	50

PREVIOUS RECORDS

	Combination League		Combination Cup	
	Champions	*Runners Up*	*Champions*	*Runners Up*
2000-01	Hamworthy Rec.	Portland United	Hamworthy Rec.	Hamworthy United
1999-00	Portland United	Dorchester Town Res	Portland United	Gillingham Town
1998-99	Portland United	Parley Sports	Portland United	Parley Sports
1997-98	Sturminster Marshall	Portland United	Portland United	Westland Sports
1996-97	Shaftesbury	Bournemouth Sports	Bournemouth Sports	Hamworthy Engineering
1995-96	Hamworthy Eng.	Bridport Reserves	Sturminster Newton	Sherborne Town
1994-95	Hamworthy Eng.	Bournemouth Sports	Shaftesbury	Hamworthy Engineering
1993-94	Hamworthy Eng.	Westland Sports	Westland Sports	Sherborne Town
1992-93	Westland Sports	Sherborne Town	Westland Sports	Portland United
1991-92	Blandford United	Westland Sports	Dorchester Town	Parley Sports

ALLENDALE

Chairman: E Case (01202 887920 H, 01258 857191 B)

Secretary: Rod Pope, 51 Dalkeith Road, Corfe Mullen Wimborne, BH21 3PQ (01202602922 H, 01929 424601 B)

Ground: Redcotts Recreation Ground, School Lane, Wimborne

Colours: White/blue/blue Change Colours: All red

GILLINGHAM TOWN

Chairman: E Murphy
Secretary: David J Ayles, 37 Sylvan Way, Bay Road, Gillingham SP8 4EQ (01747822065)
Ground: Hardings Lane, Gillingham (01747 823673)
Cover: Yes
Programme: Yes Clubhouse: Yes
Colours: Tangerine/black/tangerine
Change colours: Yellow & green/green/green

BLANDFORD UNITED

Chairman:M.Westwood
Secretary: Mrs Catherine Johnson, 37 Damory Street,Blandford Forum, Dorset DT117EU (01258 455899)
Ground: Recreation Ground, Park Road, Blandford Forum, Dorset. (HQ Tel: 01258456374)
Cover: No Clubhouse: No Programme: Yes
Colours: All Royal Blue
Change colours: Red/black/green

HAMWORTHY RECREATION

Chairman: M,Robson
Secretary: Ray Willis ,52 Heckford Road, Poole BH15 2LY (01202 773 290)
Ground: Hamworthy Rec. Club, Magna Rd, Canford Magna, Wimborne, Dorset BH21 3AE(01202 881922)
Cover: No Clubhouse: Yes Programme: No
Colours: All green.
Change colours: Blue & White stripes/blue/blue.

BOURNEMOUTH SPORTS CLUB

Chairman: I.Hansford

Secretary: Mrs June Johnson,19 Lawns Road, Wimborne,. Bh21 2JP Tel No: 01202 887195
Ground: Chapel Gate, East Parley, Christchurch, Dorset BH23 6BD (01202 581933)
Cover: No Clubhouse: Yes Programme: Yes
Colours: Gold/black/gold Change colours: All blue

HAMWORTHY UNITED

Chairman: D.Manuel
Secretary: Peter Gallop, 51A Symes Road, Hamworthy, Poole, Dorset BH15 4PR(01202 670792)
Ground: The County Ground, Blandford Close, Hamworthy, Poole, Dorset (01202674974)
Cover: Yes Floodlights: Yes
Programme: Yes Clubhouse: Yes
Colours: Maroon & Sky Blue stripes/maroon/maroon
Change colours:Yellow & black stripes/black/black

BRIDPORT Reserves

Chairman: David Fowler
Secretary: Keith Morgan, 95 Orchard Crescent, Bridport DT6 5HA 01308 456142 (H) 01308 424 269 (W)
Ground: The Beehive, St Mary's Field, Bridport, Dorset (01308 423834)
Colours: Red & black/black/red & black
Change colours:All blue.

HOLT UNITED

Ground: Gaunts Common, Holt, Wimborne, Dorset.
Tel: 01258 840379

Previous League: Dorset County League

COBHAM SPORTS (formerly Flight Refuelling)

Chairman: A Miles
Secretary: Harry W Doyle, 27 Fairview Crescent, Broadstone, Poole BH18 9AL Tel: 01202 698393 (H) 07718 896211 (M)
Ground: Merley Park, Merley, Wimborne, Dorset (01202 885773)
Cover: No Clubhouse: Yes Programme: Yes
Colours:Sky blue/navy blue/navyblue.
Change colours: All red

SHAFTESBURY

Chairman: A.P.Humphries
Secretary: Phil Watts, 4 Willow Cottages, Compton Abbas, Shaftesbury SP70NF (01747 811037)
Ground: Cockrams, Coppice Street, Shaftesbury (01747 853990)
Cover: Yes Floodlights: Yes Clubhouse: Yes
Colours: Red & white striped/Red/Red
Change colours: Yellow/black/black

DORCHESTER TOWN Reserves

Chairman: C E Clarke
Secretary: David Martin, 21 Diggory Crescent, Dorchester DT1 2SP Tel: 01305 262345 (H) 07971 172795 (M)
Ground: The Avenue Stadium, Dorchester. (01305 262451)
Cover: Yes Floodlights: Yes Clubhouse: Yes
Programme: Yes
Colours: Black & white stripes/black/black
Change: All red.

SHERBORNE TOWN

Chairman: F Henderson
Secretary: Mike Mock, 67 Yew TRe Close, Yeovil. BA20 2PB Tel Nos: 01935 426219 (H) 01935 703934 (W)
Ground: Raleigh Grove, The Terrace Playing Fields, Sherborne (01935 816110)
Cover: Yes Clubhouse: Yes Programme: Yes
Colours: Yellow/black/yellow
Change colours: Black& white/white/black.

STOURPAINE

Chairman: C.Hardiman
Secretary: Rob Turner, 35 Hod View, Stourpaine, BLandford DT11 8TN Tel : 01258 451691
Ground: Dick Draper Memorial Fields, Stourpaine, Blandford Forum, Dorset Tel: None
Previous league: Dorset County League
Colours: Navy blue & Yellow/navy blue/ yellow & navy blue.
Change Colours: Red & white stripes/red & white/red & white

WESTLAND SPORTS

Chairman:A.Fisher
Secretary: Dean Vincent, 8 Whitemead, Abbey Manor Park, Yeovil. BA21 3RX Tel NOs: 01935 479971 (H) 01935 705381 (W)
Ground: Westland Sports Ground, Westbourne Close, Yeovil (01935 703810)
Cover: No Clubhouse: No Programme: Yes
Colours: Red & Black/Black/Black
C hange colours: All White

STURMINSTER NEWTON UNITED

Chairman: A.Stockley
Secretary: Richard Frear 44 Green Close, Sturminster Newton DT10 1BL (01258473036)
Ground: Barnetts Field, Honeymead Lane, Sturminster Newton, Dorset. (01258471406)
Cover: Yes Clubhouse: No Programme: Yes
Colours:Red & Black stripes /red/red
Change colours:Blue & Black stripes/blue/blue.

WEYMOUTH SPORTS

Chairman: M.Richards
Secretary: Alan Burt, 32 Preston Road, Weymouth, DT3 6PZ Tel Nos: 01305 833256 (H) 01305 773536 (W)
Ground: Weymouth College, Cranford Ave., Weymouth, Dorset (01305 208859/208860)
Colours: Blue & yellow stripes/yellow/blue.
Change: Red/black/red
Prev. Lge: Dorset (champs 1993)

WAREHAM RANGERS

Chairman: G.Hawkes
Secretary: Mrs Carol White, 18 Folly Lane, Wareham, Dorset BH20 4HH (01929551765)
Ground: Purbeck Sports Centre,Worgret Rd, Wareham, Dorset
Cover: No Clubhouse: No Programme: Yes
Colours: Amber & black/black/black
Change colours:Navy & light blue/ navy/ light blue

WINCHAMPTON UNITED

Chairman: A Wrixon

Secretary: Geoff Parnell, 28 Bovington Close, Canford Heath, Poole, BH17 8AZ .Tel Nos: 01202 600382(H) 07976 331369 (M)

Ground: Critchell Park, Winchampton, Wimborne. Tel: 01258 840986
Colours: Yellow/green/yellow
Change Colours: Claret/navy blue/navy blue.

SCREWFIX DIRECT WESTERN LEAGUE

President: Rod Webber **Chairman:** Cliff Ashton

Secretary: Ken Clarke, 32 Westmead Lane, Chippenham, Wiltshire SN15 3HZ
Tel: 01249 464467 **Fax:** 01249 652952 **Email:** westernleague@aol.com
www.firsteleven.co.uk/western

A season dominated by floods, fuel shortages and foot and mouth disease saw the Western League clubs emerge with credit for completing fixtures with a minimum of fuss.

Although Chippenham Town pushed Taunton Town to the end of the season, the Somerset outfit showed their class in the end and picked up the League Champions trophy yet again. Following a decision by the Taunton directors not to seek promotion, Chippenham Town were handed the opportunity to progress to the Dr Marten's Southern League. With the hard work off the pitch, matching the players' achievement, the Bluebirds proved worthy of promotion and will be playing at the higher level for the first time in their history.

Russell Musker took Taunton Town all the way to Villa Park and lifted the FA Carlsberg Vase. Tommy Saunders, his rival manager at Chippenham Town, must now aim higher as his charges will be competing for the FA Umbro Trophy next term.

Although Paulton Rovers posed no late threat to the leaders there was a time in the season that they looked threatening.

Four points separated the following trio, Yeovil Town Reserves, Bideford and Backwell United. Backwell United's feat was remarkable in that they overcame a ground closure order – caused by the Foot & Mouth crisis.

Devizes Town, Melksham Town, Brislington, Welton Rovers and Dawlish Town were mid table for most of the season, and were capable of providing entertaining football. Devizes Town and Welton Rovers equipped themselves well on their return to the higher division.

The next quartet of Bridport, Elmore, Barnstaple Town and Bridgwater Town never faced the real possibility of relegation, but a few supporters' hearts fluttered at some disappointing results.

With the season drawing to a close Odd Down, Bristol Manor Farm and Bishop Sutton started adding up the points available and there were many sighs of relief around those three clubs when they pulled themselves away from the danger zone.

Westbury United faced manager related problems, and, although finishing in a relegation position, they avoided the drop thanks to Chippenham Town's elevation.

Minehead Town were finally forced into bottom spot by the deduction of three points for failing to field a team for a late season fixture at Devizes Town.

In the First Division Team Bath proved that the brave decision of the clubs to accept them into membership of the league was correct. Following early season, when they had to adjust to the league, on and off pitch difficulties were soon sorted and both Team Bath and Keynsham Town were pushing for top spot. Hallen, in their first season since jumping across the pyramid, showed their class in the league and were unlucky not to have proceeded further in the FA Carlsberg Vase.

Frome Town, Bitton, Bath City Reserves, Warminster Town, Corsham Town, Torrington and Exmouth Town provided a solid mid table group with all sides displaying some considerable skills - at times - but not always able to produce the results that mattered.

Pewsey Vale was the surprise team in the new year. Under Don Rogers' leadership they achieved their aim to finish above relegation so that they could jump in the opposite direction to Hallen, and join the Hellenic League, in a bid to reduce travelling.

Chard Town faced problems off the pitch, which they overcame, and look like improving in the future.

Street, Wellington, Larkhall Athletic, Ilfracombe, Cadbury Heath, Worle St Johns and Calne Town all faced an end of season, where any two could have ended in the relegation zone. As luck would have it for the bottom two there were no suitable places in the lower leagues, and so Worle St Johns and Calne Town live to fight for another Western League season.

Without question the biggest loser to Foot & Mouth in the league was Clyst Rovers. The club was forced to abandon its season, and negotiation between club, league and The FA ensured their existence for the new campaign.

FINAL LEAGUE TABLES 2000-01

PREMIER DIVISION

			Home					Away					Total						
		P	W	D	L	F	A	W	D	L	F	A	W	D	L	F	A	GD	Pts
1	Taunton Town	38	15	3	1	68	15	16	1	2	65	26	31	4	3	133	41	92	97
2	Chippenham Town	38	15	1	3	54	12	15	4	0	55	15	30	5	3	109	27	82	95
3	Paulton Rovers	38	12	3	4	46	21	11	7	1	46	23	23	10	5	92	44	48	79
4	Yeovil Town	38	12	4	3	54	17	9	4	6	30	29	21	8	9	84	46	38	71
5	Bideford	38	10	6	3	39	23	9	4	6	32	22	19	10	9	71	45	26	67
6	Backwell United	38	11	2	6	35	17	8	5	6	24	20	19	7	12	59	37	22	64
7	Devizes Town	38	11	1	7	48	26	8	4	7	40	36	19	5	14	88	62	26	62
8	Brislington	38	10	6	3	34	15	7	4	8	33	33	17	10	11	67	48	19	61
9	Melksham Town	38	11	1	7	31	25	6	5	8	27	29	17	6	15	58	54	4	57
10	Welton Rovers	38	6	7	6	37	22	9	1	9	26	31	15	8	15	63	53	10	53
11	Dawlish Town	38	10	1	8	34	37	4	5	10	16	31	14	6	18	50	68	-18	48
12	Elmore	38	6	4	9	36	44	8	0	11	31	36	14	4	20	67	80	-13	46
13	Bridport	38	6	5	8	28	31	4	8	7	23	32	10	13	15	51	63	-12	43
14	Barnstaple Town	38	7	3	9	25	30	5	4	10	20	49	12	7	19	45	79	-34	43
15	Bridgwater Town*	38	7	6	6	27	30	4	5	10	18	28	11	11	16	45	58	-13	41
16	Odd Down	38	9	3	7	24	21	1	5	13	10	36	10	8	20	34	57	-23	38
17	Bishop Sutton	38	5	8	6	33	42	4	3	12	24	44	9	11	18	57	86	-29	38
18	Bristol Manor Farm	38	5	6	8	21	25	3	2	14	16	41	8	8	22	37	66	-29	32
19	Westbury United	38	3	3	13	20	42	0	2	17	7	59	3	5	30	27	101	-74	14
20	Minehead Town*	38	5	0	14	22	60	0	0	19	12	96	5	0	33	34	156	-122	12

** Points deducted*

FIRST DIVISION

			Home					Away					Total						
		P	W	D	L	F	A	W	D	L	F	A	W	D	L	F	A	GD	Pts
1	Team Bath	36	15	1	2	54	8	11	5	2	54	14	26	6	4	108	22	86	84
2	Keynsham Town	36	11	6	1	34	16	14	1	3	45	19	25	7	4	79	35	44	82
3	Frome Town	36	12	2	4	46	19	9	2	7	31	26	21	4	11	77	45	32	67
4	Hallen	36	11	2	5	42	23	9	4	5	39	29	20	6	10	81	52	29	66
5	Bitton	36	9	2	7	33	25	10	5	3	33	24	19	7	10	66	49	17	64
6	Bath City Reserves	36	11	3	4	48	37	6	3	9	26	33	17	6	13	74	70	4	57
7	Exmouth Town	36	9	4	5	36	18	6	3	9	40	36	15	7	14	76	54	22	52
8	Warminster Town	36	7	6	5	25	20	7	4	7	23	33	14	10	12	48	53	-5	52
9	Corsham Town	36	6	3	9	26	34	10	1	7	34	33	16	4	16	60	67	-7	52
10	Torrington	36	6	5	7	36	35	8	3	7	33	37	14	8	14	69	72	-3	50
11	Chard Town	36	6	3	9	28	46	5	6	7	24	29	11	9	16	52	75	-23	42
12	Pewsey Vale	36	6	3	9	29	42	6	3	9	19	37	12	6	18	48	79	-31	42
13	Street	36	5	6	7	20	22	5	3	10	20	41	10	9	17	40	63	-23	39
14	Wellington	36	6	3	9	24	32	5	2	11	16	31	11	5	20	40	63	-23	38
15	Larkhall Athletic	36	9	1	8	30	32	2	4	12	16	41	11	5	20	46	73	-27	38
16	Ilfracombe	36	5	4	9	30	36	4	6	8	18	28	9	10	17	48	64	-16	37
17	Cadbury Heath	36	5	1	12	21	34	5	4	9	27	34	10	5	21	48	68	-20	35
18	Worle St Johns	36	5	3	10	35	39	5	2	11	29	48	10	5	21	64	87	-23	35
19	Calne Town	36	3	5	10	16	28	5	2	11	19	40	8	7	21	35	68	-33	31

Clyst Rovers record expunged

TOP GOALSCORERS 2000-01

Antony Lynch	Taunton Town	36
Steven Tweddle	Chippenham Town	35
Mark Salter	Frome Town	25
Lee Langmead	Torrington	24
Barry Flippance	Devizes Town	24
Ellis Laight	Taunton Town	23
Gary Lewis	Warminster Town	22
Matthew Rawlins	Chippenham Town	21
Chris Giles	Yeovil Town	20
Matthew Fricker	Frome Town	20
Adam Cole	Bitton	20
Leon Hapgood	Taunton Town	20

PREMIER DIVISION RESULTS CHART 2000-01

		1	2	3	4	5	6	7	8	9	10	11	12	13	14	15	16	17	18	19	20
1	Backwell U	X	3-0	3-1	3-1	3-0	0-0	0-2	1-0	1-2	2-0	1-2	3-1	1-1	5-0	2-0	1-2	0-1	0-1	3-1	3-2
2	Barnstaple T	1-0	X	2-0	0-2	1-3	1-1	3-3	1-0	1-2	1-1	2-6	0-1	2-1	3-0	2-0	1-3	1-4	0-1	3-0	0-2
3	Bideford	3-0	2-2	X	3-2	1-0	2-1	4-1	6-1	2-2	2-0	2-2	2-0	3-3	3-0	2-0	0-0	0-5	1-2	1-1	0-1
4	Bishop Sutton	1-1	1-1	1-1	X	2-2	2-2	2-2	2-1	1-5	1-1	0-4	3-1	0-2	2-1	4-2	2-2	1-4	2-6	5-1	1-3
5	Bridgwater T	1-2	0-1	0-5	1-1	X	1-0	4-2	1-2	1-5	1-1	0-0	3-0	2-1	5-3	1-0	2-2	2-4	1-0	0-0	1-1
6	Bridport	1-3	5-1	1-1	1-1	1-1	X	1-0	3-0	1-1	0-2	1-1	0-2	0-3	6-0	1-0	0-2	1-7	3-4	2-1	0-1
7	Brislington	0-1	4-0	0-0	2-1	3-0	1-0	X	0-0	0-3	3-0	1-2	2-1	3-0	5-1	1-1	1-1	1-1	2-0	2-0	3-3
8	Bristol M F	1-2	1-1	1-3	2-0	1-1	1-1	0-3	X	1-4	2-0	3-2	1-2	1-1	4-1	0-0	0-1	0-1	0-0	2-0	0-2
9	Chippenham T	2-1	0-1	0-1	4-0	1-0	5-0	1-1	3-1	X	2-0	5-1	3-0	2-1	8-0	2-0	0-2	5-3	2-0	4-0	5-0
10	Dawlish T	0-4	1-4	2-1	4-1	2-0	1-1	1-2	3-0	1-6	X	2-1	2-0	0-1	3-1	4-2	1-5	2-4	2-0	3-1	0-3
11	Devizes T	1-4	6-0	0-3	5-0	3-0	4-3	2-1	2-0	2-3	1-1	X	0-4	3-2	7-0	1-0	0-1	1-2	1-2	3-0	6-0
12	Elmore	2-2	2-4	3-0	1-3	1-2	2-2	0-4	3-0	1-4	1-2	2-4	X	2-4	2-0	2-2	3-3	1-6	2-0	4-1	2-1
13	Melksham T	0-1	1-0	1-2	3-2	1-0	1-1	2-1	2-1	0-3	0-1	3-2	3-0	X	3-0	2-0	2-3	2-5	2-1	2-0	1-2
14	Minehead T	1-0	2-3	0-5	0-3	0-4	1-5	3-1	1-3	0-3	4-2	1-4	0-8	0-3	X	2-1	0-6	1-2	2-3	4-1	0-3
15	Odd Down	3-1	1-0	1-2	3-0	0-0	2-0	1-2	2-1	0-1	1-0	0-1	1-0	0-0	4-1	X	2-4	0-4	1-4	2-0	0-0
16	Paulton R	0-0	6-0	1-1	3-2	2-0	5-0	2-1	2-1	1-2	4-2	1-4	1-2	3-1	6-0	1-1	X	2-3	2-0	2-0	2-1
17	Taunton T	1-1	4-0	3-1	2-1	1-0	1-2	5-1	4-0	1-1	4-1	4-1	2-0	3-2	8-1	7-0	2-2	X	2-0	11-0	3-1
18	Welton R	2-0	7-0	2-0	1-1	2-3	1-2	1-1	1-1	0-3	0-1	1-1	2-3	0-0	9-1	0-0	4-0	1-3	X	1-0	2-2
19	Westbury U	0-1	0-0	1-2	1-2	2-1	1-1	0-3	1-3	1-5	0-0	3-2	2-4	0-1	4-1	0-1	1-6	2-5	1-2	X	0-2
20	Yeovil T	0-0	3-2	0-3	5-1	1-1	0-1	1-2	3-1	0-0	2-1	4-0	6-2	4-0	9-1	2-0	1-1	3-1	5-0	5-0	X

LES PHILLIPS CHALLENGE CUP 2000-01

PRELIMINARY ROUND

Bridgwater Town	v	Calne Town	5-0
Devizes Town	v	Frome Town	1-4
Ilfracombe	v	Cadbury Heath	4-2
Street	v	Paulton Rovers	0-2
Chippenham Town	v	Warminster Town	2-0
Exmouth Town	v	Bath City Reserves	4-1
Odd Down	v	Taunton Town	0-8
Wellington	v	Bitton	0-1

FIRST ROUND

Barnstaple	v	Welton Rovers	2-5
Bishop Sutton	v	Dawlish Town	1-2
Bridgwater Town	v	Minehead Town	6-0
Corsham Town	v	Melksham Town	3-3, 4p2
Frome Town	v	Bristol Manor Farm	1-3
Ilfracombe Town	v	Keynsham Town	4-3
Paulton Rovers	v	Team Bath	3-2
Worle St Johns	v	Clyst Rovers	8-1
Bideford	v	Chard Town	3-1
Bitton	v	Torrington	4-6
Brislington	v	Bridport	0-2
Elmore	v	Taunton Town	0-6
Hallen	v	Chippenham Town	0-2
Larkhall Athletic	v	Exmouth Town	0-1
Westbury United	v	Backwell United	1-5
Yeovil Town Reserves	v	Pewsey Vale	2-1

SECOND ROUND

Bristol Manor Farm	v	Dawlish Town	3-4
Corsham Town	v	Bridport	0-3
Paulton Rovers	v	Bideford	1-1, 3p4
Welton Rovers	v	Bridgwater Town	1-0
Chippenham Town	v	Yeovil Town Reserves	3-2
Exmouth Town	v	Ilfracombe	6-5
Taunton Town	v	Torrington	4-2
Worle St Johns	v	Backwell United	0-5

QUARTER FINALS

Chippenham Town	v	Bridport	3-2
Taunton Town	v	Welton Rovers	0-1
Dawlish Town	v	Exmouth Town	1-1, 6p7
Backwell United	v	Bideford	0-2

SEMI FINALS

Chippenham Town	v	Bideford	2-1
Exmouth Town	v	Welton Rovers	2-0

FINAL

Chippenham Town	v	Exmouth Town	1-0	at Bideford FC

HIGHEST LEAGUE ATTENDANCES 2000-01

Taunton Town	v	Chippenham Town	803	21.04.01
Chippenham Town	v	Taunton Town	756	06.01.01
Melksham Town	v	Chippenham Town	710	13.04.01
Chippenham Town	v	Devizes Town	611	16.04.01
Taunton Town	v	Bridgwater Town	581	16.04.01
Chippenham Town	v	Melksham Town	581	26.12.00
Chippenham Town	v	Bideford	524	10.03.01
Chippenham Town	v	Yeovil Town Reserves	502	17.02.01
Chippenham Town	v	Paulton Rovers	502	09.09.00
Devizes Town	v	Chippenham Town	483	20.02.01
Chippenham Town	v	Elmore	480	28.04.01
Bideford	v	Barnstaple Town	430	13.04.01
Chippenham Town	v	Minehead Town	420	31.03.01
Bridgwater Town	v	Taunton Town	415	26.12.00
Chippenham Town	v	Westbury United	414	14.04.01
Taunton Town	v	Bideford	423	10.05.01
Chippenham Town	v	Odd Down	404	29.09.00
Chippenham Town	v	Dawlish Town	403	07.04.01
Welton Rovers	v	Paulton Rovers	396	13.04.01
Chippenham Town	v	Barnstaple Town	395	14.10.00

PAST RECORDS

WESTERN FOOTBALL LEAGUE CHAMPIONS

1981-82	Bideford	1991-92	Clevedon Town
1982-83	Bideford	1992-93	Tiverton Town
1983-84	Exmouth Town	1993-94	Tiverton Town
1984-85	Saltash United	1994-95	Tiverton Town
1985-86	Exmouth Town	1995-96	Taunton Town
1986-87	Saltash United	1996-97	Tiverton Town
1987-88	Liskeard Athletic	1997-98	Tiverton Town
1988-89	Saltash United	1998-99	Taunton Town
1989-90	Taunton Town	1999-00	Taunton Town
1990-91	Weston-super-Mare	2000-01	Taunton Town

WESTERN FOOTBALL LEAGUE FIRST DIVISION CHAMPIONS

1981-82	Shepton Mallet	1991-92	Westbury United
1982-83	Bristol Manor Farm	1992-93	Odd Down
1983-84	Bristol City Reserves	1993-94	Barnstaple Town
1984-85	Portway-Bristol	1994-95	Brislington
1985-86	Portway-Bristol	1995-96	Bridgwater Town
1986-87	Swanage Town & Herston	1996-97	Melksham Town
1987-88	Welton Rovers	1997-98	Bishop Sutton
1988-89	Larkhall Athletic	1998-99	Minehead
1989-90	Ottery St Mary	1999-00	Devizes Town
1990-91	Minehead	2000-01	Team Bath

LES PHILLIPS CHALLENGE CUP WINNERS

1989-90	Plymouth Argyle Reserves	1995-96	Tiverton Town
1990-91	Elmore	1996-97	Tiverton Town
1991-92	Plymouth Argyle Reserves	1997-98	Tiverton Town
1992-93	Tiverton Town	1998-99	Yeovil Town Reserves
1993-94	Tiverton Town	1999-00	Chippenham Town
1994-95	Elmore	2000-01	Chippenham Town

BACKWELL UNITED

Secretary:Doug Coles, 156 Rodway Road, Patchway, Bristol BS34 5ED (0117 985 7089)

Ground: Backwell Recreation Ground, West Town Rd, Backwell, Avon Tel: 1275 462612

Directions: Near centre of Backwell on main A370 Bristol to Weston-super-Mare road. Buses from Bristol or Weston, or 20 mins walk from Nailsea & Backwell(BR) station; turn right out of station, right at traffic lights (half mile),ground quarter mile on right just past car sales

Capacity: 1,000 Seats: 60 Cover: 150 Floodlights: Yes

Clubhouse: Open 6-11pm weekdays, 12.30-11pm Sat. Snacks available Club Shop: No

HONOURS Somerset Snr Lg 77-78 79-80 80-81 81-82 82-83 (Lg Cup 82-83 (R-up 79-80) Div 1 72-73); Somerset Snr Cup 81-82; SW Co.'s Sutton Transformer Cup 81-82. Western Lge Div 1 89-90 Champions, 94-95 promoted in 3rd place

PREVIOUS **Leagues**: Clevedon & Dist; Bristol C. of E.; Bristol Surburban (pre 1970); Somerset Senior 70-83
Grounds: Two in Backwell prior to 1939. Club reformed in 1946

RECORD **Attendance**: 487 v Brislington, Gt Mills Lg. 2/5/94
Goalscorer: Steve Spalding **Appearances:** Wayne Buxton
Win: 10-1 v Dowton, F.A.Cup 1st Qualifying Round. 1998-99
Defeat: 2-6 v Tiverton Town (H), Les Phillips Cup QF 1.2.94

FACT FILE
Founded: 1911
Nickname: Stags
Club Sponsors: C W Jones Carpets
Colours: All red
Change colours: All Gold
Midweek Matches: Tuesday
Programme: 42 pages, 50p
Editor: Dick Cole (01275 463627)

CLUB PERSONNEL
Chairman: Richard Cole
Vice-Chairman: Peter Higgins
President: John Southern
Press Officer:Mike Naylor (01275 858576)
Manager:Jamie Patch
Asst Manager: Shaun Penny
Physio: Steve Tregale

BARNSTAPLE TOWN

Secretary: David Cooke, 51 Walnut Way, Whiddon Valley, Barnstaple, Devon. EX32 7RF Tel: 01271 326088
Ground: Mill Road, Barnstaple, North Devon Tel: 01271 343469
Directions: A361 towards Ilfracombe (from M5 Jct 26), in Barnstaple follow A361Ilfracombe signs, second left after crossing small bridge is Mill Road
Capacity: 5,000 Seats: 250 Cover: 1,000 Floodlights: Yes
Clubhouse: Full license. Bar snacks Club Shop: Yes

HONOURS Western Lg 52-53 79-80 (R-up 80-81 81-82, Div 1 49-50 94-95, Merit Cup74-75 83-84 84-85, Comb. 92-93), Devon Professional Cup 62-63 64-65 67-68 69-70 71-73 (X2) 74-75 76-81 (X5), Devon Lg, Devon St Lukes Cup 87-88, Devon Snr Cup 92-93, Devon Youth Cup 48-49 51-52

PREVIOUS **Leagues:** Nth Devon, Devon & Exeter, S. Western **Name:** Pilton Yeo Vale
Grounds: Town Wharf (> 1920); Highfield Rd, Newport (> 35), Pilton Pk, Rock Pk

RECORDS **Attendance:** 6,200 v Bournemouth, FA Cup 1st Rd, 54 **Appearances:** Ian Pope
Win: 12-1 v Tavistock (H), FA Cup 3rd Qual. Rd 1954
Defeat: 1-10 v Mangotsfield Utd (A), Western Lge Prem. Div. 90-91

BEST SEASON **FA Cup:** 1st Rd replay 51-52 **FA Vase:** 4th Rd 94-95

Players progressing: Len Pickard (Bristol R. 51), John Neale (Exeter72), Barrie Vassallo (Torquay 77), Ian Doyle (Bristol C. 78), Ryan Souter (Swindon 94), Jason Cadie (Reading 94)

FACT FILE
Founded: 1906
Nickname: Barum
Sponsors:Edmund Walker
Colours: Red/red/red
Change colours: Yellow/black/yellow
Midweek Matches: Wednesday
Reserve League: Devon & Exeter
Programme: 70p
Programme Editor: David Cooke
Local Press: N. Devon Journal Herald

CLUB PERSONNEL
President: Wilf Harris
Chairman: John Cann
Manager: John Hore
Physio: Amanda James
2000-01
Captain: Simon Dawe
P.o.Y.: Andy Stevens
Top Scorer: Steve Burton 12

BIDEFORD

Secretary: Kevin Tyrrell, 69 Laurel Ave., Bideford, devon EX39 3AZ Tel: 01237 4707747

Ground: The Sports Ground, Kingsley Road, Bideford Tel: 01237 474975

Directions: A361 for Bideford - ground on right as you enter the town
Capacity: 6,000 Seats: 120 Cover: 1,000 Floodlights: Yes
Clubhouse: `Robins Nest' - on ground. Open lunchtimes and evenings, snacks and bar menu. Mgr: Mrs Sue Tyrell

HONOURS Western Lg 63-64 70-7171-72 81-82 82-83, Div 1 51-52, Div 3 49-50, Lg Cup 71-72 84-85; Alan Young Cup 64-65 69-70; Merit Cup 68-69; Subsidiary Cup 71-72; Devon Snr Cup 79-80; Devon St Lukes Cup 81-82 83-84 85-86 95-96 (R-up 86-87 91-92 94-95)

PREVIOUS **Leagues:** Devon & Exeter 47-49; Western 49-72; Southern 72-75
Name: Bideford Town **Ground:** Hansen Ground (1 season)

BEST SEASON **FA Cup:** 1st Rd 64-65(replay) 73-74 77-78 81-82. **FA Vase:**

RECORD **Gate:** 6,000 v Gloucester C., FA Cup 4th Qual. Rd 60
Scorer: Tommy Robinson 259 **Appearances:** Derek May 527
Win: 16-0 v Soundwell 50-51 **Defeat:** 0-12 v Paulton 96-97

Players progressing: Shaun Taylor (Swindon Town) Tony Dennis (Cambridge)

FACT FILE
Founded: 1949
Nickname: Robins
Colours: All Red
Change colours: Blue/blue/white
Midweek Matchday: Tuesday
Programme: 32 pages, 50p
Editor: Ian Knight

CLUB PERSONNEL
President: C Prust
Chairman: Ian Knight
Manager:Sean Joyce
Reserve Manager: Barry Hooper

BISHOP SUTTON

Secretary: Roy Penney, 53 Ridgway Lane, Whitchurch, Bristol BS14 9PJ Tel: 01275 541392

Ground: Lakeview Football Field, Bishop Sutton Tel: 01275 333097

Directions: On A368 at rear of Butchers Arms pub - ground signposted on left entering village from the West

Capacity: 1,500 Seats: None Cover: 200 Floodlights: yes

Clubhouse: Open matchdays. Rolls, pies and usual pub food available Club Shop: No

HONOURS Somerset Snr Lg R-up 89-90 (Div 1 83-84 (R-up 81-82), Div 2 82-83), Bristol & Avon Lg 80-81 (Div 2 79-80), Somerset Jnr Cup 80-81, Weston Yth Lg77-78, Chew Valley KO Cup 83-84, Mid-Somerset Lg(Res) R-up 82-83 (Div 3 81-82)

PREVIOUS **Leagues:** Weston & Dist. Yth; Bristol & Avon; Somerset Snr (pre 1991)
Ground: Adjacent cricket field

BEST SEASON **FA Cup:** **FA Vase: 3rd Rd 1998**

CLUB RECORDS **Attendance:** 400 v Bristol City, friendly
Win: 15-0 v Glastonbury Res

Players progressing: David Lee (Chelsea), S Williams (Southampton), J French(Bristol R.)

FACT FILE

Founded: 1977
Nickname: Bishops
Sponsors: Symes Off License
Colours: All blue
Change colours: All yellow
Midweek Matches: Tuesday
Youth team's League: Somerset Mid Week
Programme: Yes
Editor: G Williams

CLUB PERSONNEL

Chairman: G.Williams
Vice Chairman: Roy Penney
President: Bob Redding
Manager: Tony Corneling
Coach: Peter Wills
Physio: Chris Bailes

BRIDGWATER TOWN '84

General Secretary: Mrs Glenda Fletcher,18 Dunkery Road, Bridgwater Tel:01278 425599
Football Secretary: Miss Sally Wright, 37 Kidsbury Rd, Bridgwater, Som. TA6 7AQ
Tel: 01278 421189

Ground: Fairfax Park, College Way, Bath Road, Bridgwater Tel: 01278 446899 (matchdays and weekday mornings only)

Directions: M5 jct 23, follow signs to Glastonbury (A39), turn right for Bridgwater (A39).
Look for sign to Bridgwater College via College Way
One mile from Bridgwater (BR) station

Capacity: 2,000 **Seats:** 150 **Cover**: Yes **Floodlights**: Yes

Clubhouse: On the Ground

HONOURS Somerset Senioir Cup 93-94, Somerset Senior Lge 90-91 91-92 ,
Western Lge Div 1 95-96

PREVIOUS **League:** Somerset Snr (pre-1994)**Names:** None

BEST SEASONFA Cup: 2nd Q Rd **FA Vase:** First Round

RECORDS **Attendance:** 1,112 v Taunton Town 26.2. 97

FACT FILE

Founded: 1984
Nickname: The Robins
Sponsor: TMB Patterns
Colours: Red&white stripes/red/white
Change colours: All blue
Midweek Matchday: Tuesday
Youth Team's League: U18 Floodlight
Programme: Yes
Eds:G ordon Nelson,MarkHollidge& Andy Cole

CLUB PERSONNEL

Chairman: Keith Setter
President: Tom Pearce
Press Officer: GordonNelson
Manager: Jon Bowering
Sports Injury Therapist: Dave Callow
L.C.S.P., F.A.Dip.

BRIDPORT

Secretary: Ian Hallett,Brookside, Burstock, Beaminster, Dorset DT8 3LJ (01308 868795)
Email Address: ian@newsport.freeserve.co.uk and FAX: 01308 867422
Ground: The Beehive, St Mary's Field, Bridport, Dorset Tel: 01308 423834

Directions: Take West Bay road from town centre, turn right just before Palmers Brewery

Capacity: 2,000 Seats: 200 Cover: 400 Floodlights: Yes Club Shop: No

Clubhouse: Yes, open matchdays and for functions. Hot and cold snacks available

HONOURS Western Lg Cup 70-71 72-73 77-78 (R-up 76-77, Div 1 R-up 94-95, Merit Cup 69-70 71-72 73-74); Dorset Comb.(3) 85-88 (Lg Cup 86-87 87-88); Dorset Snr Cup(8) 63-64 69-71 75-76 78-81 87-88; Dorset Snr Amtr Cup(6) 48-50 54-55 56-57 70-72; W. Dorset Chal. Bowl 07-08; Perry Str. Lg 22-23; Mark Frowde Cup 76-77 88-89

PREVIOUS **Leagues:** Perry Street; Western 61-84; Dorset Combination 84-88
Grounds: Pymore (pre 1930s); Crown Field (pre 1953)

BEST SEASON **FA Cup:** **FA Vase:**5th Round 88-89

RECORD **Attendance:** 1,150 v Exeter City, 1981; 3,000 v Chelsea, at Crown, 1950
Scorer (in a season): Ellis Hoole 36
Fee received: £2,000 for Tommy Henderson
Fee paid: £1,000 for Steve Crabb

FACT FILE

Founded: 1885
Nickname: Bees
Sponsors:Nerwlands Holidays
Colours: Red & black/black/red & black
Change colours: Blue & black/blue/blue
Midweek Matches: Tuesday
Reserves ' League: Dorset Combination
Programme: 40pages, #1.00
Editor: Ian Hallett (01308 868795)

CLUB PERSONNEL

President: B Williams
Chairman: David Fowler
Manager: Derek Walkey
Asst Manager:Adrian Chance

2000-01

Captain: Paul Toms
P.o.Y.: Paul Gadsby
Top Scorer: Peter Knox 17

BRISLINGTON

Secretary: David Braithwaite, 3 Ashcott, Whitchurch, Bristol BS14 0AG
Tel: 01275 542040 (H) 0794 701 2253 (M) Email: brizzsec@aol.com

Ground: Ironmould Lane, Brislington, Bristol Tel: 0117 977 4030
Directions: 4 miles out of Bristol on main A4 to Bath - turn left up lane opposite Garden Centre just before dual carriageway (500 yards past Park & Ride on right)

Capacity: 2000 Seats: 144 Cover: 1500 Floodlights: Yes

Clubhouse: Yes - on ground, open matchdays **Club Shop:** No

HONOURS Somerset Senior Cup 92-93 R-up 93-94;
Somerset Senior League, Les Phillips Cup SF 93-94 99-00, Premier Cup 95-96 Semi-Final 00-01

PREVIOUS **League:** Somerset Senior (pre-1991)

BEST SEASON **FA Vase**: 3rd Rd 89-90, 2-3 v Abingdon T. (A)

FACT FILE
Formed:
Nickname: Bris
Sponsors: Trade Windows
Colours: Red & black/black/black & red
Change colours: Yellow & blue/blue/blue
Midweek matches: Tuesday
Reserves ' League: Somerset Senior
Programme: 50p
Editor: Laserset (0117 969 5487)

CLUB PERSONNEL
President: Paul Bishop
Chairman: M.Richardson
Vice-Chairman:B.Perrott
Manager: Nigel Webb
Asst Manager: David Mehew
Physio: Samantha Durrant

2000-01
Leading goalscorer: Dave Morrissey 25
Captain: Craig Russell
P.o.Y.: Craig Russell

BRISTOL MANOR FARM

Secretary: Chris Davis, 52 The Crescent, Sea Mills, Bristol, BS9 2JS. 0117 968 2174 (H)
0117 968 3571 (W) Email: christopher-davis2000@hotmail.com
Ground: `The Creek', Portway, Sea Mills, Bristol BS9 2HS Tel: 0117 968 3571

Directions: M5 jct 18 (Avonmouth Bridge), follow A4 for Bristol - U-turn on dual carriageway by Bristol & West sports ground and return for half mile on A4- ground entrance is down narrow lane on left (hidden entrance). Near to Sea Mills station (BR Temple Meads-Severn Beach line)

Capacity: 2,000 Seats: 84 Cover: 350 Floodlights: Yes Club Shop: No

Clubhouse: Open every evening & lunchtime Sat & Sun. Lounge bar, skittle alley, bar meals.

HONOURS Western Lge Prem 00-01 Sportsman Awards, Western Lg Div 1 82-83, Glos Tphy 87-88, Glos Amtr Cup 89-90, Somerset Snr Lg Div 1 (Lg Cup, Div 2)
PREVIOUS **Leagues:** Bristol Suburban 64-69; Somerset Snr 69-77
Name: Manor Farm O.B. 1964-68 **Grounds:** None
BEST SEASON **FA Cup:** **FA Vase:**
RECORD **Attendance:** 500 v Portway, Western Lg 1974
Goalscorer: Chris Rex, 222 **Appearances:** Paul Williams, 821
Win: 8-2, v Frome (A), 2/9/84 **Defeat:** 1-8, v Exmouth (A), 5/5/86
Fee paid: Nil **Fee received:** £3,000 for Nicky Dent (Yeovil Town, 1989)
Players progressing: Ian Hedges (Newport) 88-89, Gary Smart (Bristol Rovers)

FACT FILE
Formed: 1964
Nickname: The Farm
Club Sponsors: M.T.I. Ltd
Colours: Yellow
Change colours: Red/black/red
Midweek Matchday: Tuesday
Reserve s' League: Suburban League
Programme: 28 pages, 50p
Editor: Natalie & Michelle Lawrence

CLUB PERSONNEL
Chairman: Tim Estcourt
Manager: Geoff Bryant
Assistant Manager: Pete McCall

2000-01
Leading goalscorer: Mike Airs 12
Captain: Mike Airs
P.o.Y.: Dean Smart

DAWLISH TOWN

Secretary: Graham Jones, 133 Kingsdown Crescent, Dawlish, Devon, EX7 0HB
Tel: 01626 866004 07850 284423(M) Email: dawlishtown@jonesdawlish.freeserve.co.uk.

Ground: Playing Fields, Sandy Lane, Exeter Road, Dawlish Tel: 01626 863110
Website: www.dawlishtownfc.co.uk

Directions: Approx 1 mile from centre of town, off main Exeter road (A379)
Capacity: 2,000 Seats: 200 Cover: 200 Floodlights: Yes
Clubhouse: Open nightly, all day Saturday and Sunday situated in car park opposite ground

HONOURS Western Lg Div 1 R-up 98-99, Lg Cup 80-81 83-84, Devon Premier Cup 69-70 72-73 80-81, Devon Snr Cup 57-58 67-68, Devon St Lukes Cup 82-83 (R-up 81-82), Carlsberg Cup 96

BEST SEASON **FA Cup:** **FA Vase:** Quarter Finals 86-87

PREVIOUS **League:** Devon & Exeter **Ground:** Barley Bank 1875-1900

RECORD **Gate:** 1,500 v Heavitree Utd, Devon Prem. Cup Q-Final
Defeat: 0-18 v Clevedon (A), Western Lge Prem. Div. 92-93

FACT FILE
Founded: 1889
Colours: Green /black/green
Change Colours:Blue/white/white
Midweek matchday: Wednesday
Programme: 34 pages, 50p
Programme Editor: Roy Bolt

CLUB PERSONNEL
President: Bob Webster
Manager: Tony Bowker

2000-01 Leading Goalscorer: Sean Friend 20
Captain: Jason Heath
P.o.Y.: Jason Heath

Barnstaple Town. Back Row (l-r): Stephen Hensor, Kevin Squire, Daniel Harris, Dave Penberthy, Nick Murray, Steve Gibson, Simon Ovey, Kevin Darch. Front Row: Shaun Watts, Martin Davey, David Amooie, Dave Cooke (Sec), John Hore (Manager), Neil Pointing, Craig Dann, Russell Hayes

Bideford AFC. Back Row (l-r): Owen Pickard, Alex Crook, Rob Gough, Glen Duff, Mark Coombe, Matt Hare, Carl Armstrong, Chris Slough. Front Row: Alan Chapman, Matt Joslynn, Richard Gomm, Darren Polhill, Paul Mitchell (Chairman), Shaun Joyce (Manager), Simon Langmead, Shane Powell, Mike Southgate, Kevin Darch

Bridgwater Town. Back Row (l-r): Jon Bowering (Manager), Dave Callow (Physio), Gordon Nelson (Treasurer), Shaun Strange, Rob Snook, Shaun Pople, Kevin Hurd, Ben Fellows, Lea Hurford, Chris Young, Kevin Milson (Asst Manager), Danny Mira, Colin Paczoski (Asst Physio). Front Row: Tim Dyer, Paul Heyward, Richard Smith, Dave Pope, Craig Rice, Keith Setter (President), Dave Clark, Dan Ford, Piers Gouier, Chris May

DEVIZES TOWN

Secretary: Chris Dodd, 69 Broadleas Park, Devizes, Wilts. SN10 5JG.
Tel: 01380 726205

Ground: Nursteed Road, Devizes. Tel: 01380 722817

Directions: Off Nursteed Road (A342 signposted Andover); leaving town ground on right opposite Eastleigh Rd
Capacity: 2,500 Seats: 130 Cover: 400 Floodlights: Yes

HONOURS Western League Div. 1 99-00; Wilts Snr Cup 07-08 49-50 56-57 57-58 58-59 60-61 61-62 62-63 65-66 67-68 70-71 71-72 73-74 78-79

PREVIOUS **Leagues:** Wilts Comb.; Wilts Premier
Name: Southbroom (until early 1900s)
Ground: London Rd (pre 1946)

FACT FILE

Founded: 1883

Colours: Red & white stripes/black/red
Change colours: All yellow
Midweek Matchday: Tuesday

CLUB PERSONNEL

Chairman:Les Moore

Manager: Brian Newlands

ELMORE

Secretary: Neville Crocker, Flat 1, 9 Belmont Road, Tiverton, Devon
Tel: 07968 642094 (H) 07968 642094 (M) 01884 253687 (W)

Ground: Horsdon Park, Tiverton, Devon EX16 4DE Tel: 01884 252341

Directions: M5 Jct 27, A373 towards Tiverton, leave at 1st sign for Tiverton &Business Park, ground 500yds on right
Capacity: 2,000 Seats: 200 Cover: Floodlights: Yes

Clubhouse: 11am-11pm Mon-Sat. Full canteen service - hot & cold meals & snacks
Club Shop: Yes

HONOURS East Devon Snr Cup 72-73 75-76, Western Lge R-up 94-95. Lge Cup 90-91,94-95, Div 1 R-up 90-91, Prem Div Merit Cup R-up 91-92, Div 1 Merit Cup 86-87 89-90 90-91, Devon St Lukes Cup R-up 90-91, Devon Snr Cup 87-88, Devon Intermediate Cup 60-61, Football Express Cup 60-61, Devon & Exeter Lg Div 2A 73-74 86-87(res)(Div 1A 76-77(res)), Devon Yth Cup 77-78.

PREVIOUS **Leagues:** Devon & Exeter 47-74; South Western 74-78 Grounds: None

RECORD **Attendance:** 1,713 v Tiverton Town Fri.April 14th 95
Appearances: P Webber **Goalscorer:**
Win: 17-0 **Defeat:** 2-7

FACT FILE

Founded: 1947
Nickname: Eagles
Club Sponsors: Ken White Signs
Colours: All Green
Change colours: Red & black/black/black
Midweek matches: Tuesday
Reserve League: None
Programme: 12 pages, 30p
Editor: Richard Tapp(01884 252341)

CLUB PERSONNEL

Chairman: Alan J Cockram
Vice Chairman: P.J.Garnsworthy
Manager: Peter Buckingham
Asst Manager: R Moore
Physio: M Crocker

KEYNSHAM TOWN

Secretary: Iain Anderson, 195 Mount Hill Road, Hanham, Bristol BS15 9SU
Tel: 0117 961 6426

Ground: Crown Field, Bristol Road, Keynsham Tel: 0117 986 5876
Directions: A4 from Bristol to Bath, ground on left before entering village opp. Crown Inn. Bus service every 30 mins from Bristol passes ground. 10mins walk from Keynsham BR station
Capacity: 2,000 Seats: 120 Cover: 500 Floodlights: Yes
Clubhouse: Evenings & before & after games. Snacks
Club Shop: No

HONOURS Somerset Lg Div 1 77-78; Somerset Snr Cup 51-52 57-58, 00-01; Div. 2 00-01 GFA Jnr Cup 25-26; Somerset & Avon (South) Premier Cup 79-80 (SF 93-94);

BEST SEASON **FA Cup:** 4th Qual. Rd **FA Vase:**

PREVIOUS **Leagues:** Bristol District, Bristol Comb., Bristol Premier, Somerset Senior
Grounds: The Hams 1886-1910; Gaston 1910-25; Park Road 25-30; Charlton Rd 30-39

RECORD **Attendance:** 3,000 v Chelsea, f'light opening 88-89.
Competitive:2,160 v Saltash, Amateur Cup, Oct 1952

FACT FILE
Founded: 1895
Nickname: K's
Sponsors: Ace Building Services Ltd
Colours: All amber
Change colours: All blue
Midweek matchday: Wednesday
Reserves ' League: Somerset Senior
Programme: 32 pages, 50p
Editor: Mark Brown (0117 969 5487)

CLUB PERSONNEL
Chair: Steve Brindle Pres: Lester Clements
Press Officer: Ray Parker Manager: Nigel Lee
Physio: Malcolm Trainer

2000-01
Leading goalscorer: Paul Payne 20
Captain: Mark Jones

Devizes Town. Back Row (l-r): Jason Hillier, Dave Hopkins, Justin King, Dave Marfleet, Barry Flippance, Nathan Perkins, Nigel Curtis, Jim Griffin, Spencer Wilmot, Allister Belcher (Reserve Manager), Phil Fry (Physio). Front Row: Robin Moore, Gary Campbell, Danny Maslin, Andy Coombes, Bud Walters, Ashton Turner, Nathan Sheridan, Andy Stone

Paulton Rovers. Back Row (l-r): Phil Underhill, Mike Brown, Tony Carr, Allan Bull, Paul Harrison, Mark Made, Aaron Day, Marcus Bloomfield, Tarik Whitcliffe, John Rendell, Craig Russell, Arthur Appleton, Phil Sergeant, Paul Hirson (Manager). Front Row: Rob Frost, Paul Tovey, Adam Fricker, Scott Woodman, John Peart, Matty Brown, Ian Symons, Nick Tiley, Richard Perry, Mark Buxton, Ben Pope, Matt Sweet.

Taunton Town. Back Row (l-r): Darren Hawkings, Mark Forrester, Simon Ingram, Ellis Laight, Ryan Draper, Paul West, Russel Musker (Manager), Tom Kelly (Asst Manager), Steve Kidd. Front Row: Matt Francis, Lee Tucker, Russell Jee, Nick Noon, Paul Edwards, Sean Kenny

MELKSHAM TOWN

Secretary: David Phillips, 25 Duxford Close, Bowerhill,Melksham,Wlts. SN12 6XN
Ground: The Conigre, Melksham (01225 702843)
Capacity: 3,000 Seats: 150 Cover: 1,500 Floodlights: Yes

Directions: Just off main square in grounds of Melksham House

Clubhouse: Inside ground, open every evening & weekend lunchtimes

HONOURS Wilts Lg 03-04 93-94 (R-up 24-25 29-30 59-60 67-68 68-69 71-72), Western Lg Div 1 79-80, 96-97, Wilts Snr Cup 03-04 69-70 77-78 (R-up 57-58 67-68 68-69), Wilts Shield 80-81 81-82 84-85 ,85-86,97-98 ,99-00(R-up 86-87).

PREVIOUS **Leagues:** Wiltshire 1894-1974 93-94; Western 74-93
Grounds: Challymead; Old Broughton Road Field

BEST SEASON **FA Cup:** 2nd Q Rd 57-58 **FA Vase:** 3rd Rd 81-82,98-99
FA Amateur Cup: 1st Rd 68-69

RECORD **Attendance:** 2,821 v Trowbridge Town, FA Cup 57-58

FACT FILE

Founded: 1876
Sponsors: Cooper Avon Tyres
Colours:yellow/black/yellow
Change colours: All white
Midweek Matchday: Tuesday
Prog Editor: Mike Miller ()1225 791873)

CLUB PERSONNEL

President: Mike Harris
Chairman: Mike Perrin
Vice Chairman: Paul Smith
Manager:Robert Lardner
Ass.Manager: Keith McCrum
Physio: Paul B rickley
2000-01 Captain: Steven Seals
P.o.Y & Top Scorer: Matt Messenger

ODD DOWN ATHLETIC

Secretary: Mike Mancini, 36 Caledonian Rd., East Twerton, Bath BA2 3RD
Tel: 01225 423293 Mobile: 07788 635560

Ground: Coombe Hay Lane, Odd Down, Bath Tel: 01225 832491

Directions: On main Bath/Exeter road - leaving Bath turn left into Combe Hay Lane opposite Lamplighters Pub.opposite Park & Ride car park. 40 mins walk from Bath (BR)

Capacity: 1,000 Seats: 160 Cover: 250 Floodlights: Yes

Clubhouse: Yes, open noon-3 & 7-11pm. Hot & cold food available
Club Shop: No

HONOURS Western Lg Div 1 92-93, Somerset Snr Cup 91-92

PREVIOUS **Leagues:** Wilts Premier, Bath & District, Somerset Senior

BEST SEASON **FA Cup:** **FA Vase:**

RECORD **Appearances:** Steve Fuller 424
Scorer: Joe Matano 104
Win: 11-1 v Minehead (H), Western Lge Prem. Div. 19/3/94

FACT FILE

Founded: 1901
Sponsors: First Bus/Streamline
Colours: Black & white stripes/black/black
Change :All Yellow
Midweek Matches: Tuesday (7-30)
Reserves ' League: Somerset Senior
Programme: 12 pages with admission
Editor: Secretary

CLUB PERSONNEL

President: P A L Hill
Chairman: N Fenwick
Vice Chairman: Eric Clarke
Manager: Chris Mountford

PAULTON ROVERS

Secretary: John Pool, 111 Charlton Park, Midsomer Norton,Bath BA3 4BP Tel: 0176 1415190

Ground: Athletic Ground, Winterfield Road, Paulton Tel: 01761 412907

Directions: Leave A39 at Farrington Gurney (approx 15 miles south of Bristol),follow A362 marked Radstock for two miles, left at junction B3355 to Paulton,ground on right. Bus services from Bristol and Bath

Capacity: 5,000 Seats: 138 Cover: 200 Floodlights: Yes

Club Shop: Old programmes available - contact Chairman
Clubhouse: 3 bars, lounge, skittle alley, dance hall. Capacity 300. Cateringfacilities

HONOURS Western Lg Div 2 R-up 1900-01; Somerset Snr Cup 00-01 02-03 03-04 07-08 08-09 09-10 34-35 67-68 68-69 71-72 72-73 74-75; Somerset Snr Lg 00-01 03-04 04-05 70-71 71-72 72-73 73-74; Somerset F/Lit Youth Lge 96-97

PREVIOUS **Leagues:** Wilts Premier; Somerset Snr
Grounds: Chapel Field; Cricket Ground; Recreation Ground 1946-48

BEST SEASON **FA Cup:** **FA Vase:**

RECORDS **Attendance:** 2,000 v Crewe, FA Cup, 1906-07
Appearances: Steve Tovey **Goalscorer:** D Clark

FACT FILE

Founded: 1881
Nickname: Rovers
Sponsors: Barons Property Centre/Bass Breweries
Colours: White/maroon/maroon
Change colours: Yellow/navy/navy
Midweek matches: Tuesday
Reserves' League: Somerset Snr
Programme: 20 pages, 50p
Editor: D Bissex (01761 412463)
Local Press: Bath Evening Chronicle, Bristol Evening Post, Western Daily Press

CLUB PERSONNEL

President: Mr T Pow
Chairman: David Bissex
Vice Chairman: Mr D Carter
Manager: Alan Pridham
Physio: Mike Brown

TAUNTON TOWN

Ground: Wordsworth Drive, Taunton, Somerset TA1 2HG Tel: 01823 278191
Directions: Leave M5 Jct 25, follow signs to town centre, at 2nd set of lights turn left into Wordsworth Drive; ground on left. 25 mins walk from Taunton (BR); turn left out of station and follow road right through town centre bearing left into East Reach. Follow road down and turn right into Wordsworth Drive shortly after Victoria pub
Capacity: 4,000 Seats:400 Cover: 1,000 Floodlights: Yes Club Shop: Yes
Clubhouse: Social club to accommodate 300, full bar facilities, separate bar & hall for private functions
HONOURS FA Vase Winners 00-01 R-up 93-94, Western Lge Champions 68-69 89-90,95-6,98-9,99-00, 00-01 (R-up 93-94 97-98, Les Phillips R-up 93-94 97-98, Alan Young Cup 73-74 75-76 (jt with Falmouth), Charity Chall. Cup 49-50, 50-51), Somerset Snr Lg 52-53, Som Prem.Cup R-up 82-83 89-90 92-93 98-99
PREVIOUS **Leagues:** Western 54-77; Southern 77-83 **Grounds:** Several prior to 1953
BEST SEASON **FA Cup:** 1st Rd Proper 81-82, 1-2 v Swindon T. (A) **FA Trophy:** 1st Rd Proper 80-81, 1-5 v Hendon at Q.P.R **FA Vase:** Winners 00-01, R-up 93-94, S-F 97-98 98-99
RECORDS **Attendance:** 3,284 v Tiverton Town, **FA Vase:** Winners 00-01
Appearances: Tony Payne **Scorer** (in a season) : Reg Oram 67
Win: 12-0 v Dawlish Town (A), FA Cup Prel. Rd, 28/8/93
Defeat: 0-8 v Cheltenham Town (A), FA Cup 2nd Qual. Rd, 28/9/91
Players progressing: Charlie Rutter (Cardiff), Stuart Brace (Southend), Steve Winter (Torquay) Kevin Maloy (Exeter C.)

FACT FILE
Formed: 1947 Nickname: Peacocks
Club Sponsors: T.G.Roofing
Colours: Sky blue & claret/claret/sky blue
Change colours: Yellow/sky blue/yellow
Midweek matches: Tuesdays
Reserves ' League: None
Programme: 32 pages, £1 Editor: Les Gill
Newsline: 0930 555 849

CLUB PERSONNEL
Chairman: T F Harris
Secretary: Joan Ellis
c/o the club, Tel: 01823 333833 (H)
Press Officer: Les Gill
Manager: Russell Musker
Asst. Man: Tom Kelly
Physio: Kevin Matthews

2000-01
Captain: Paul West
P.o.Y.: Darren Hawkings
Top Scorer: Antony Lynch 51

TEAM BATH

Secretary: Matt Birch, Barn Cottage, Esgar Rise, Worle, Weston-super-Mare, Som. BS22 9JG
Tel: 01934 521466 (H) 01225 826656 (B) 01225 826755 (F)
e-mail: m.birch@bath.ac.uk

Ground: University of Bath, Sports Training Village, Claverton Down, Bath.
Tel: 01225 826339

Directions: Follow signs to Claverton Down and Park & Ride (University).
Take the Norwood Ave. entrance to the campus and as you drive towards the university you will approach two "hanger" like buildings on the right.
This is the Sports Training Village. Follow signs to free car park.

Honours Western League Div. 1 Champions 00-01

FACT FILE

Formed: 2000

Colours: Gold/blue/gold
Change colours: All blue
Midweek Matchday: Monday

CLUB PERSONNEL
Chairman: Ivor Powell
c/o Univ. of Bath, Sports Development, Claverton Down, Bath BA2 7AY
Tel: 01225 826656

Manager: Ged Roddy
Tel: 01225 826339

WELTON ROVERS

Secretary: Geoff Baker, 6 Longfellow Road, Westfield Road, Westfield, Radstock BA3 3YZ
Email Address: weltonrovers@ yahoo.com

Ground: West Clewes, North Road, Midsomer Norton, Somerset Tel: 01761 412097

Directions: A367 Bath to Radstock õ right at lights at foot of hill onto A362,ground on right.

Capacity: 2,400 Seats: 300 Cover: 300 Floodlights: Yes Club Shop: No

Clubhouse: 7.30-11pm daily, plus Sat matchdays 1.30-2.45pm, Sun 12-2pm

HONOURS Western Lg 11-12 64-65 65-66 66-67 73-74, Div 1 59-60 87-88,Amateur Cup 56-57 57-58 58-59 59-60, Alan Young Cup 65-66 66-67 67-68(jt); Somerset Snr Cup 06-07 11-12 12-13 13-14 19-20 24-25 25-26 60-61 61-62 62-63, Som. I'mediate Cup 77-78, Som. Jnr Cup 06-07(jt) 24-25 30-31, WBC Clares City of Wells Cup 78-79

PREVIOUS **Leagues:** None **Names:** None **Grounds:** None
BEST SEASON **FA Cup:** **FA Vase:** **FA Amateur Cup:**
RECORD **Attendance:** 2,000 v Bromley, FA Amateur Cup 1963
Goalscorer: Ian Henderson, 51

FACT FILE
Formed: 1887
Nickname: Rovers
Sponsors: Young Bros (Roofing)
Colours: Green & navy/navy &green/green
Change colours: Yellow/black/yellow
Midweek matchday: Wednesday
Reserve s' League: Somerset Senior
Programme: 12 pages, 25p
Editor: M Brown
Website: www.geocities.com/weltonrovers

2000-01
Captain: Mark Evans P.o.Y.: Steve Jenkins
Top Scorer: Gareth Wright 16

CLUB PERSONNEL
Chairman: Rae James
Manager: Stuart Minall Asst Man: Steve Tovey
Physio: John Carver

WESTBURY UNITED

Secretary: Michael Taylor, 31 Gryphon Close, Westury, Wiltshire BA13 (01373 865406)

Ground: Meadow Lane, Westbury Tel: 01373 823409

Directions: In town centre, A350, follow signs for BR station, Meadow Lane on right (club signposted). Ten mins walk from railway station (on main London-South West and South Coast-Bristol lines)

Capacity: 3,500 Seats: 150 Cover: 150 Floodlights: Yes

Clubhouse: Evenings 7-11pm, Fri, Sat & Sun lunchtimes 12-3pm Club Shop: No

HONOURS Western Lg Div 1 91-92, Wilts Senior Cup 31-32 32-33 47-48 51-52, Wilts Combination, Wilts Lg 34-35 37-38 38-39 49-50 50-51 55-56, Wilts Premier Shield R-up 92-93

PREVIOUS **Leagues:** Wilts Comb.; Wilts Co. (pre-1984)
Ground: Redland Lane (pre-1935)

RECORD Gate: 4,000 - v Llanelli, FA Cup 1st Rd 37 & v Walthamstow Ave. FA Cup 37

Players progressing: John Atyeo (Bristol City)

FACT FILE
Formed: 1921
Nickname: White Horsemen
Colours: Green & white/white/green
Change colours: Sky & navy/blue/blue
Midweek Matches: Wednesday
Reserves' league: Wilts County Lg.
Programme: 16 pages, 50p
Editor: Mike Taylor (01373 865406)

2000-01
Captain: Mark Pearce
P.o.Y.: Mark Batters
Top Scorer: Steve Perkins 8

CLUB PERSONNEL
Chairman: Phillip Alford
Vice Chairman: Bert Back
President: Ernie Barber
Managers: T.B.A.
Physio: Dave Prescott

YEOVIL TOWN RESERVES

Secretary: Jean Cotton, c/o Club.
Tel: 01935 428130 (H) 01935 423662 (B) Fax: 01935 473956

Ground: Huish Park, Lufton Way, Yeovil Somerset, BA22 8YF.
Tel: 01935 23662 Fax 01935 73956

Directions: Leave A303 at Cartgate roundabout and take A3088 signposted Yeovil.Take first exit at next roundabout and first exit at next roundabout intoLufton Way. Railway station - Yeovil Pen Mill (Bristol/Westbury to Weymouth)2.5 miles from ground. Yeovil Junction (Waterloo to Exeter) 4 miles.
Bus service from both stations on Saturday - matchdays

Capacity: 8,720 Seats: 5,212 Terracing: 3,508 Floodlights: Yes

Club Shop: Open on matchdays selling full range of souvenirs, match programmes etc

Clubhouse: Matchdays hot + cold food available. Meals can be ordered with advance notice. All weather astro turf pitch available for bookings9am-10pm

HONOURS: Western League: Champions 58-59, Div. 1 R-up 97-98

FACT FILE

Founded: 1895
Nickname: Glovers
Sponsors: Precision Publishing Papers
Colours: Green/white/green
Change colours: Navy & red/navy/navy & red
Midweek matchday: Wednesday
Programme: Yes

CLUB PERSONNEL

Chairman: John Fry
President: S N Burfield
Manager: Terry Rowles
Physio: Maurice O'Donnell

Yeovil Town Reserves: Back Row (l-r): Tom White, Ross Newell, Paul Heinbest, James Thompson, Luke Buckinghamshire, Stephen Collis, Fisal Mali, Matthew Davis, Simon Baker, Shivar Thompson, Richard Parkinson. Front Row: Chris Luke, Richard Lindegaard, Glenn Poole, Maurice O'Donnell (Manager), Andy Lindegaard, James Bent, Stuart Hussey.

BATH CITY RESERVES

Secretary: Quentin Edwards c/o the club.
Tel: 01225 359087 (H) 01225 423087 (B) & 07785 795532 (M)
Email Address: offi ce@bathcityfc.freeserve.co.uk

Ground: Twerton Park, Twerton, Bath Avon BA2 1DB
Tel: 01225 423087/313247 Fax: 01225 481391

Directions: Twerton Park is situated on the A4/A36 Lower Bristol Road - on the Bristol side of Bath City Centre (Approx 2.5 miles). The area is serviced by J18 on the M4. From the centre of Bath the bus route is No.5 - Twerton High Street
Capacity: 8,840 Seated: 1,017 Covered Terracing: 4,800

Clubhouse: Several bars open all week and full service with menu on match-days catering for up to 250 people **Club Shop:** Contact MrM.Brush

FACT FILE
Founded: 1889
Nickname: Stripes & The City
Midweek matchday: Wednesday
Colours: Black & white stripes/black/b & w
Change: All yellow
Website: www.bathcityfc.com

CLUB PERSONNEL
Chairman: Stephen Hall
Commercial Director: G Todd
Press Officer: P Weaver

Manager: Dave Hobb s Tel: 01225 840619
2000-01 Capt., P.o.Y. & Top Scorer: Wayne Cleverly

BITTON

Secretary: Michael Hall, 14 Pillingers Road, Kingswood, Bristol BS15 8DE Tel: 0117 960 3627

Ground: The Recreation Ground, Bath Road, Bitton, Tel: 0117 932 3222
Capacity: 500 Cover: 80Seats: 48 Floodlights: Yes

Directions: M4 junc 18. Take A46 towards Bath, at first roundabout take A420 for Wick/ Bridgeyate. On approach to Bridgeyate turn left at mini-r'about onto A4175 and follow for 2.2 miles, then left for Bath on the A431. The ground is 100 yards on right. Nearest station: Keynsham Bristol

Clubhouse: Weekdays 7.30-11, Sat. all day, Sun 12-3 & 7.30-10.30 Club Shop: No

HONOURS Glos. Jun Cup r-up 90; Avon Prem. Lg r-up 94, 95; Glos Sen amat Cup 95; Glos Chall Trophy r-up 97; Glos County Lg r-up 97.

PREVIOUS **Leagues:** Avon Premier Comb., Glos County

FACT FILE
Founded: 1922
Sponsors: John Dean Builders
Colours: Red & white stripes/black/black
Change colours: Yellow/green/yellow
Midweek Matcday : Monday 7.45
Programme: 36 pages Editor: Paul Cater

CLUB PERSONNEL
Chairman: John Langdon
V- Chairman: Steve Webb Pres: Roy Ewans
Com Man.: Paul Cater (0117 932 5205)
Manager: Martyn Dyer
Captain: John Lester
P.o.Y. & Top Scorer: Adam Cole 23

CADBURY HEATH

Secretary: Colin Trotman, 51 Deanery Road, Kingswood, Bristol BS15 9JB
Tel: 0117 983 7510 (H)

Ground: Springfield, Cadbury Heath Road, Warmley, Bristol. Tel: 0117 967 5731

Directions: Situated in East Bristol on the road between Warmley & Oldeland.
Tower Road (North & South) runs from Warmley to Oldland and passes Cadbury Heath road. Look for Spar shop and King William P.H..
Turn into Cadbury Heath Road. 20 yds on right entrance to Social Club.

PREVIOUS **League:** Gloucestershire County Lge.

HONOURS Glos. County Lge 98-99, R-up 99-00

FACT FILE
Colours: Red & white/red/red
Change Cols.: yellow/black/black
Midweek Matchday: Wednesday

CLUB PERSONNEL
Chairman: Dave Smart
1 Farm Close, Emerson Green,
Bristol BS16 7RU
Tel: 0117 956 1223

Manager: Steve Plenty
Tel: 0117 957 3053

CALNE TOWN

Secretary: Laurie Drake, 22 Falcon Rd, Calne, Wilts SN11 8PL . Tel: 01249 819186
Ground: Bremhill View, Lickhill Rd., North End, Calne. 01249 816716.
Directions: Take A4 from Chippenham near Calne turn L. at 1st R'abt onto A3102 Calne B'pass at next R'abt turn R., next L, then R and R. again. Email: calnetownfc@btinternet.com
Capacity: 2,500 **Seats:** 78 **Cover**: 250 **Floodlights**: Yes **Club Shop**: No
Clubhouse: Mon-Fri 7-11pm, Sat-Sun 12-11pm. Filled rolls, hot food, tea,coffee, sweets etc
HONOURS Western Lg Div 1 R-up 92-93; Wilts Snr Cup 12-13 34-35 84-85 (R-up1894-95 94-95 1911-12 49-50); Wilts Lg 33-34, (`Ghia' Cup 8) 1-81 85-86, Div 279-81, Div 3 85-86, Div 4 81-82
PREVIOUS **League:** Wilts Co. (pre-1986) **Ground:** Anchor Road Rec. 1887-1967
Names: Calne Town (1886) & Harris Utd merged; Calne & Harris Utd (1921-67)
RECORD **Attendance:** 1,100 v Swindon, Friendly 25/7/1987
Scorer: Robbie Lardner **Appearances:** Gary Swallow, 259
Win: 11-1 v Heavitree (H) **Defeat:** 2-7 v Odd Down (A)

FACT FILE
Founded: 1887 Nickname: Lilywhites
Sponsors: The Bug & Spider
Colours: White/black/black
Change colours: All Blue
Midweek Matchday: Tuesday 7.45
Programme: 20 pages, 50p
Editor: Kath Brindle (01249 815198)

2000-01
Captain: Martin Wheeler
Top Scorer: Toby Colebourne
P.o.Y.: Nick Taylor

CLUB PERSONNEL
Chair: Steve Walker Pres: Bill Burt
Managers: Steve Hale & Paul Rankin

CHARD TOWN

Secretary: Michael Froom,30 Helliers Close, Chard , Somerset TA20 1LJ (01460 63670)
Ground: Town Ground, Zembard Lane, Chard TA20 1JL Tel: 01460 61402
Capacity: 1,500 Seats: 60 Cover: 200 Floodlights: Yes

Directions: Follow sports centre signs off main A30 High Street along Helliers Road. Right into Upper Combe Street and left into Zembard Lane . BR 7miles Axminster or 8 miles Crewkerne
Clubhouse: Matchdays & most evenings. Snacks served

HONOURS Som. Snr Lg 49-50 53-54 59-60 67-68 69-70 (Lg Cup 61-62 71-72 76-77); Western Lg Div 1 R-up 83-84 87-88 95-96, (Merit Cup 82-83, Comb. Cup(Res) 91-92 (R-up 92-93)); Som. Snr Cup 52-53 66-67; S W Co's Cup 88-89; Western Com Lge 96-97, Cup 96-97.

BEST SEASON **FA Cup:** 2nd Qual Rd. 77-78 82-83 **FA Vase:**

PREVIOUS **Leagues:** Somerset Snr 20-24 48-75; Perry Street 25-48 **Grounds:** None
2000-01 Players.o.Year: Paul Nicholls & Adam Downes
Top Scorer: Adam Downes 13 Captain: Steve Sivell

FACT FILE
Founded: 1920
Nickname: Robins
Colours: Scarlet/black/black
Change colours: White/white/red
Midweek matches: Wednesday
Programme: 24 pages with entry
Editor: Mike Froom

CLUB PERSONNEL
Chairman: Brian Beer
Gen Man: Malcolm Adcock
Vice Chairman: Jim Loveryn
Manager: Steve Ritchie
Asst.Man: Wiliam Morris
Physio: Kevin Morgan

CLYST ROVERS

Secretary: Bob Chamberlain, Orchard Cottage, Clyst St George, Exeter EX3 0NZ(01392 873498)
Ground: Waterslade Park, Clyst Honiton, Devon Tel: 01392 366424
Directions: A30 following signs for Exeter Airport. Coming from Exeter take 1st right after airport turning (ground signposted) up narrow 200yds past Duke of York Pub
Capacity: 3,000 Seats: 130 Cover: 300 Floodlights: Yes
Club Shop: Yes, Programmes, souvenirs etc
Clubhouse: Open one and a half hours before kick off and after game. Excellent food available
HONOURS Devon St Lukes Cup R-up 92-93, Western Lg Cup SF 92-93
PREVIOUS **Leagues:** Exeter & District 26-44 51-66; Exeter & District Sunday 67-82; South Western 81-92 **Grounds:** Fair Oak 1926-44
RECORD **Gate:** 768 v Tiverton, Devon St Lukes final 11/5/93
Win: 6-0 v Heavitree United, 1993
Defeat: 0-12 v Torpoint Athletic, South Western League, October 1990

FACT FILE
Founded: 1926 Reformed: 1951
Nickname: Rovers
Sponsors: Vantage Pharmacy, Paignton
Colours: All yellow
Change colours: Blue/black/black
Midweek Matches: Wednesday
Programme: 32 pages, 30p
Editor: Ray Dack (01392 215075)

CLUB PERSONNEL
President: Mr P W Brown
Chairman: Bob Chamberlain
Vice Chairman: Colin Dadson
Manager:Bill Potter
Physio: Bill Wreford

CORSHAM TOWN

Secretary: Richard Taylor, 7 Cresswells, Corsham, Wilts SN13 9NJ Tel: 01249 714406
Website: www.corshamtownfc.co.uk Email: cup@corshamtownfc.co.uk

Ground: Southbank Ground, Lacock Road, Corsham, Wilts. SN13 9HS Tel: 01249 715609
Directions From the A4 turn into Corsham at the Hare & Hounds PH roundabout, taking the Melksham Road, B3353, past the Methuen Arms PH then straight across the next mini-r'about into Lacock Road. The ground is situated 1/2 mile on right
Capacity:1,500 Seats: No Cover: Yes Floodlights: Yes
Clubhouse: Yes Club Shop: No

HONOURS Wiltshire Lge. 97-98, Wiltshire FA Sen. Cup 75-76 96-97, Wiltshire Lge. KO Cup 95-96 96-97
PREVIOUS **League:** Wiltshire Co. Lge

FACT FILE
Founded: 1893
Sponsors: Hong Kong House & Addkey Print
Colours: All red
Change colours: Yellow/blue/blue
Midweek matchday: Tuesday

CLUB PERSONNEL
Chairman: Colin Hudd
Manager: Mark Godley
Assistant Manager: Rob Humphreys
2000-01
Leading goalscorer: David Kilmurray 17
Captain: Craig Chaplin
P.o.Y.: David Kilmurray

EXMOUTH TOWN

Secretary: David Richardson J.P.,44 Whitchurch Avenue, Exeter. EX2 1NT (01392 430985)
Ground: King George V Ground, Southern Road, Exmouth Tel: 01395 263348
Email Address: davidrich43@hotmail.com

Directions: On right side of main Exeter to Exmouth road (A376). Half mile from Exmouth (BR)

Capacity: 2,500 Seats: 100 Cover: 250 Floodlights: Yes Club Shop: Yes
Clubhouse: Open every night and weekend lunchtimes. Snacks available

HONOURS Western Lg (3) R-up (2) Lg Cup 88-89; Div 1 R-up 81-82; Sportmanship Tphy (2); Devon Premier Cup (2) Devon St Lukes Cup (3); Devon Snr Cup 50-51; East Devon Snr Cup (2 Harry Wood Mem. Cup 81-82; Exmouth Chal. Cup [7]
PREVIOUS **League:** Devon & Exeter 1933-73 **BEST SEASON** **FA Vase:** SF 84-85
RECORD **Gate:** 2,395 v Liverpool XI, friendly in 1987 **Scorer:** Mel Pym, 117
Appearances: Keith Sprague, Geoff Weeks 410 (Western Lg)
Victory: 11-0 v Pewsey Vale 7/10/00 (A) 10-0 v Glastonbury 27'3/99 (H)

FACT FILE
Formed: 1933
Nickname: `Town' or `Blues'
Colours: Blue & white/blue/blue
Change cols: Red & white/black/red & white
Midweek matchday: Tuesday
Reserves' League: Devon & Exeter
Prog: 36 pages, 30p Editor: A.Hooker
Website: www.eclipse.co,uk/exmouth.afc

CLUB PERSONNEL
Prest: Brian Bradley Chair: Malcolm Hale
Vice Chairman: Philip Rugg
Manager:Russell Wilson
2000-01 Capt: Steve Taylor
Top Scorer: Danny Williams 15

Chard Town. Back Row (l-r): Adam Downes, Stuart Larcombe, Josh Stunnell, Craig Parker, Steve Casey, Matt Corrick. Middle Row: Tim John, Kevin Warren (goalkeeping coach), Steve Ritchie (Manager), Billy Morris (Coach), Andy Morris. Front Row: Lewis Bacon, John Ritchie, Paul Nichols, Steve Sivell, Dan Wilson, James Steer, Steve Burr.

Frome Town. Back Row (l-r): Sean Baker, Tony Pounder, Matt Fricker, Gary Lewis, Nick Mansfield, Paul Thorpe, Mark Salter, Jerry Gooding, Billy Robinson, Dick Pickersall, Ken Randell. Front Row: John Miller, Darren Squire, Bradley Peters, Neil Smith, Simon White, Wayne Bradshaw, Matt Harris, Arron Blacker, Kieron White.

Hallen. Back Row (l-r): Mel Beavan (Kit Manager), Matthew Baird, John Evans, Dave Sweeney, Alex Stocker, Robert Clarke, Robert Pritchard, Paul Owen, Simon Backwell, Nick Scarrett, James Tilley. Front Row: Daniel Pitt, Justin Backwell, Sean Sage, Nick Johns (Coach), Shaun Bond (Player-Manager), Eddie Howells, Tom Knight, Andrew Cook, Mark Cutler.

FROME TOWN

Secretary: Geoff Norris, 10 Clumber Drive, Frome, Somerset BA11 2LG (01373 464 803)
Ground: Badgers Hill, Berkeley Road, Frome Tel: 01373 453643

Directions: On the Westbury Road, 1 mile from town centre and Frome BR station
Capacity: 5,000 Seats: 250 Cover: 800 Floodlights: Yes Club Shop: No
Clubhouse: Evenings & weekends. Cold food only

HONOURS Wiltshire Lge 1909-10,1910-11,Western Lg 78-79 (Div 2 19-20, Div 2R-up 54-55, Lg Cup 79-80 82-83, Merit Cup 82-83, Alan Young Cup 79-80,Subsidiary Cup 59-60), Somerset Prem Cup 66-67 68-69 82-83, Wilts Prem Lg 62-63, Western Co's F'lit Cup 83-84, Somerset Snr Cup 32-33 33-34 50-51, Somerset Snr Lg 06-07 08-09 10-11

PREVIOUS **League:** Somerset Senior, Wilts League and Wilts Premier
BEST SEASON **FA Trophy:** 2nd Rd v Boston Utd (a) 0-4, 1984-85
FA Cup: 1st Rd Proper v L.Orient 1954-55 **FA Vase:** 2nd Rd v Paulton R (a) 1-2
RECORD **Attendance:** 8,000 v Leyton Orient, F.A.Cup 1st Rd. 58

FACT FILE
Founded: 1904 Nickname: Robins
Sponsors: Telewest Communications
Colours: All red
Change colours: Purple/navy/navy
Midweek matchday: Tuesday
Reserves ' League: Somerset Senior
Programme: 24 pages, 50p
Editor: Secretary

CLUB PERSONNEL
President: Mr C W M Norton
Chairman: Paul McGuinness
Vice Chairman: Steve Porter, Geoff Norris
Manager: Simon White
Physio: Bob Stokes

HALLEN

Secretary: Jonathon Rogers, 114 Wellington Hill West, Westbury on Trym, Bristol BS9 4QY
Tel: 0117 985 6138 (H) 0117 900 1811 (B)
Email Address jrogers.gosw@go-region.gsi.gov.ok
Ground: Hallen Playing Fields, Moorhouse Lane, Hallen, Nr Bristol Tel: 0117 950 2265
Directions: M5 jct 17, A4018 to Henbury r'bout, right, right again at junction,next right to Station Road, left into Avonmouth Road at r'bout. One mile toHallen, ground first left, then right into lane to ground
Capacity: 2,000 Seats: 200 Cover: 200 Clubhouse: **YHO-**
HONOURS Glos County Lg 92-93, Glos Snr Trophy 92-93
PREVIOUS **League:** Glos County (pre-1993), Hellenic 93-00
Names: Lawrence Weston Athletic (80's), Lawrence Weston Hallen (pre-1991)
Ground: Kings Weston (early 1980's)
RECORD **Attendance:** 803 v Bristol Rovers 1997

FACT FILE
Founded: 1949
Colours: All Royal Blue
Change Colours: All Yellow
Midweek Matchday: Wednesday
Programme: No
CLUB PERSONNEL
Chairman: Barrie Phillips
Tel: 0117 950 1754
President: Ken Naish
Manager: Sean BondCoach: Nick Johns
Physio: Charlie Baldwin
2000-01
Captain: Paul Owen P.o.Y.: Robert Pritchard
Top Scorer: Mark Cutler 16

ILFRACOMBE TOWN

Secretary: Tony Alcock, 2 Worth Road, Ilfracombe, North Devon EX34 9JA Tel: 01271 862686. Mobile: 07977 589199

Ground: Marlborough Park, Ilfracombe, Devon Tel: 01271 865939
Directions: A361 to Ilfracombe. Turn1st right in town after lights and follow Marlborough Rd to the top, ground on left.**Capacity:** 2,000 **Seats:** 60 Cover: 450Floodlights: Yes Club Shop: No
Clubhouse: Every night 7-11pm and weekend lunchtimes. Hot & cold meals on matchdays
HONOURS E Devon Prem Lg 25-26 28-29 29-30, N Devon Senior Lg, N Devon Prem Lg 66-67 70-71 81-82 82-83, Western Lg Div 2 R-up 52-53, Les Phillips Cup R-up 91
PREVIOUS Leagues: North Devon 04-14 20-22 60-84; EDevon Premier 22-31;Exeter & District t 32-39 46-49; Western 49-59 **Grounds:** Shaftesbury Field; Brimlands; Killacleave (all pre-1924)
Names: Ilfracombe FC 02-09; Ilfracombe Utd 09-14; Ilfracombe Comrades 14-20
RECORDS **Attendance:** 3,000 v Bristol City, Ground opening, 2/10/24
Goalscorer: Paul Jenkins 77 **Appearances:** Bobby Hancock 45
Players progressing: Jason Smith (Coventry City and Swansea City via Tiverton Town)

FACT FILE
Founded: 1902 Nickname: Bluebirds
Sponsors: K&J Electrical
Colours: All Blue Change : All Green
Midweek matchday: Tuesday
Reserves ' League: North Devon
Programme: 8 pages, 40p Editor: Phil Hill
2000-01
Captain: Kevin Pickard P.oY.: Steve Hobbs
Top Scorer: Kevin Squire 22

CLUB PERSONNEL
Chairman: Phil Hill V-Chair BarryJones
President: Mrs Jo Rose
Manager: Kevin Constantine
Physio: Ray Wooff

LARKHALL ATHLETIC

Secretary: Garry Davy, 84 London Road West, Batheaston, Bath, BA1 7DA 01225 852729
Email: garrydvy@aol.com

Ground: "Plain Ham", Charlcombe Lane, Larkhall, Bath. 01225 334952
Directions A4 from Bath, 1 mile from city centre turn left into St Saviours Rd. In Larkhall Square fork left, and right at junction, road bears into Charlcombe Lane. Ground on right as lane narrows

Capacity: 1,000 Seats: None Cover: 50Floodlights: No

HONOURS Somerset Senior Cup 75-76, Somerset Senior Lg,; Western Lg Div 1 88-89 93-94 94-95(Div 1 Merit Cup (4) 83-86 87-88 (jt with Yeovil Res)

PREVIOUS **League:** Somerset Senior

FACT FILE
Founded: 1914
Nickname: Larks
Colours: Royal & white/royal & white/royal
Change colours: Red & white/red & white/red
Midweek Matches: Tuesday
Programme: Yes
CLUB PERSONNEL
President: Tony Codd
Chairman: Jim McLay Tel: 01373 834050
Manager: Chris Jeffrey
2000-01
Leading goalscorer: Shaun Wiles-Richards 13
Captain: Julian Bowen
P.o.Y.: Matt Peters

MINEHEAD

Secretary: Mike Till, 6 Badger Park, Minehead, Som. TA24 6LL Tel: 01643 706309
Ground: The Recreation Ground, Irnham Road, Minehead, Somerset (01643 704989)
Directions: Entering town from east on A39 turn right into King Edward Road at Police station, first left into Alexandra Rd and follow signs to car park;ground entrance within. Regular buses to Minehead from Taunton, the nearestrailhead. (Steam train 'holiday route' Taunton to Minehead)
Capacity: 3,500 Seats: 350 Cover: 400 Floodlights: Yes
Clubhouse: Yes **Club Shop:** No
HONOURS: Southern Lg R-up 76-77, Div 1 Sth 75-76, Merit Cup 75-76; Western Lg R-up 66-67 71-72, Div 1 90-91 98-99, Alan Young Cup 67-68 (jt with Glastonbury), Somerset Prem. Cup 60-61 73-74 76-77
PREVIOUS **Leagues:** Somerset Senior; Southern 72-83
RECORD **Attendance:** 3,600 v Exeter City, FA Cup 2nd Rd, 77
Defeat: 1-11 v Odd Down (A), Western Lge Prem. Div. 19/3/94
Longest unbeaten run of league games 36, May 1998-May 1999
BEST SEASON **FA Cup:** 2nd Round 76-77, 1-2 v Portsmouth (A); 77-78, 0-3 v Exeter City (H).

FACT FILE
Founded: 1889
Colours: Blue & white/blue/blue
Change colours: Yellow/black/black
Midweek Matches: Tuesday
Programme: Yes
Editor: Brian Walder

CLUB PERSONNEL
Chairman: Colin Gardner
Tel: 01984 633932
Manager: Andy Hodgson
2000-01
Captain: Dave Burr
P.o.Y.: Adrian Giblett
Top Scorer: Sean Kenny 11

SHEPTON MALLETT

Secretary: Ken Hurrell, 3 Buckland Road, Shepton Mallett, Somerset BA4 5TQ
Tel: 01749 344037 email: hurrell503@aol.com

Ground: The Playing Fields, Old Wells Rd., West Shepton, Shepton Mallett, Som. BA4 5XN
Tel: 01749 344609
Capacity: 2500 Covered Seating: 120 Floodlights: Yes

Directions: Take the Glastonbury road from Shepton Mallett town centre then turn right at the junction with Old Wells Rd (approx. 1/2 mile) - the ground is 400 yards on the left.

PREVIOUS **League:** Somerset Senior

HONOURS Somerset Senior League 2000-01

FACT FILE
Founded: 1986
Colours: Black & white
Change colours: All green
Midweek matchday: Tuesday

CLUB PERSONNEL
Chairman: Brian Blinman
Manager: Roger Smith

STREET

Secretary: Mark Clarke, Ostia, Overleigh,Street,Somerset BA16
Tel Nos: 01458 447353 (H) 0800252418 (W) 07979 514181 (M)
Ground: The Tannery Ground, Middlebrooks, Street, Somerset
Tel: 01458 445987 Matchdays 01458 448227
Directions: Sign posted from both ends of A39 & B3151, Station Castle Cary
Capacity: 2,000 Seating: 120 Cover: 25 Floodlights: Yes Club Shop: No

HONOURS: Western Lge R-up 52-53

RECORDS: **Attendance:** 4,300 v Yeovil Town FA Cup 17/11/47

PREVIOUS: **Grounds:** Victoria Field, Tunpike Ground

FACT FILE
Founded: 1880 Nickname The Cobblers
Sponsors C I C A
Colours: Green & white/white/white
Change colours: Red & black/black/black
Midweek home matchday: Tuesday
Programme: 44 pages 50p
Editor: M Clarke

CLUB PERSONNEL
Chairman: Andrew Walton
Manager: Simon White
Asst Mgr: Simon Culliford
Physios: Dick Pickersgill, Andrew Lee

TORRINGTON

Secretary: David Priscott, 6 Highfield Terrace, Bishops Talton, Barnstaple EX32 0AN
Tel: 01271 328316 (H) 07751-149900 (M) e-mail AFC. torrington@bushinternet.com
Ground: Vicarage Field, School Lane, Great Torrington Tel: 01805 622853 **Directions:** In town centre turn left by parish church, right at swimming pool, ground behind swimming pool. Good parking. Red Bus from Bideford & Barnstaple (nearest BR station).Bus stop 300yds from ground
Capacity: 4,000 Seats: 100 Cover: 1,000 Floodlights: Yes Shop: No
Clubhouse: Weekdays 7-11pm, Sat 11-11 & Sun 12-3. Light snacks available on matchdays.
HONOURS Western Lg R-up 90-91; Merit Cup 91-92 93-94 95-96; South Western Lg Cup 81; Devon St Lukes Cup R-up 95-96 96-97; Devon & Exeter Lg & Cup 73-74; Festival of Britain Cup 96-97; Les Phillips Cup R-up 91-92; Torridge Cup (13) Somerset Youth Floodlight League 99-00
PREVIOUS **Leagues:** N Devon; Devon & Exeter; S Western 77-84 Grounds: None
BEST SEASON **FA Vase:** 5th Rd 84-85 FA Cup: 2nd Qual Rd. 81-82,94-95,96-97
RECORDS:Scorer: Trevor Watkins, 254 **Apps:**Mike Gilbert 527 **Fee Rcd:** £3,000 D.Walter(Yeovil)

FACT FILE
Formed: 1908
Nickname: Torrie or Supergreens
Sponsors: R & S Ware
Colours: Green & white Change : All white.
Midweek Matches: Wednesday
Programme: 64 pages, 50p Editor: Secretary
Local Press: North Devon Journal

CLUB PERSONNEL
Pres: Keith Curtis Chairman: Winston Martin
Manager: Jeff Evans Coach: Paul Hutchings
Physio: Albert Williams
2000-01 Captain: Karl Baggaley
P.o.Y.: Trevor Haslet
Top Scorer:Lee Langmead 30

WARMINSTER TOWN

Secretary: Mrs Joy Brown
23 Leighton Park oad, Westbury, Wilts. BA13 3RX
Tel: 01373 823987 (H) 01373 468326 (B) 07703 460539 (M - matchdays only)

Ground: Weymouth Street, Warminster, Wilts BA12 9NS, Tel: 01985 217828

Directions: Take A350 for Weymouth from lights at centre of town - ground on left at brow of hill

Capacity: 2,000 Seats: 75 Cover: 150 Floodlights: Yes

Clubhouse: Yes. Evenings & matchdays Club Shop: No

HONOURS Wilts Snr Cup 1900-01 02-03 10-11, R-up 09-10 26-27 32-33 53-54; Wilts Prem. Lg 56-57; Wilts Jnr Cup R-up 21-22 27-28 55-56 58-59; Central Wilts Lg 08-09

PREVIOUS **League:** Wiltshire**Grounds:** None

RECORD **Attendance:** 1,500 for Ladies International, England v Wales, mid-1970s

BEST SEASON **FA Cup:** 2nd Qual. Rd.(x5) **FA Vase:** 2nd Qual Rd

FACT FILE
Founded: 1878
Nickname: Red & blacks
Sponsors: The Assam
Colours:Blue & Black
Change: All white
Midweek Matchday: Tuesday
Reserve League: Wiltshire
Programme: 50p
Editor: Harry Theobald

CLUB PERSONNEL
Chairman: Glen Shuttlewood
Tel: 01985 212033

Manager: Andy Crabtree

WELLINGTON

Secretary: Dave Grabham, 12 Drakes Park, Wellington, SomersetTA21 8TB
Tel: 01823 664946 (H), 01823 355687 (B)

Ground: Wellington Playing Field, North Street, Wellington, Somerset Tel: 01823 664810

Directions: At town centre traffic lights turn into North St., then first left by Fire Station into the public car park that adjoins the ground

Capacity: 3,000 **Seats:** None **Cover:** 200 **Floodlights:** Yes **Clubhouse:** Yes **Club Shop:** No

HONOURS Western Lg Div 1 R-up 80-81, Merit Cup 91-92, Comb Lge 95-96;Comb Lge KO Cup 95-96 98-99; Somerset Snr Lg Div 1 R-up; Rowbarton & Seward Cup, Bill Slee Trophy

PREVIOUS **Leagues:** Taunton Saturday, Somerset Senior

RECORD **Attendance:** **Goalscorer:** Ken Jones

BEST SEASON **FA Cup:** 1st Qual Rd. 81-82, 84-85 **FA Vase:** 2nd rd Prop 98-99

99-00 Captain: Stuart Parris P.o.Y.: Matthew Burfield Top Scorer: Simon Towler

Players progressing: Nick Jennings and Ian Stonebridge (Plymouth)

FACT FILE
Founded: 1892
Sponsors: A J Shire & Wadham Fencing
Colours: All tangerine
Change cols: Blue & claret stripes/blue/blue
Midweek Matches: Wednesday
Reserve Lge: Devon & Exeter Sen Div
Programme: Yes Editor: Jane Brown

CLUB PERSONNEL
Chairman: Selwyn Aspin
Vice-Chair: Mke Bull President: Alan Shire
Manr: Dave Sheehan Res Man: Ian Jackson
Physio: Ken Pearson
2000-01: Capt: Matthew Brereton
P.O.Y & Top Scorer:Christian Woon

WILLAND ROVERS

Secretary: Andy Jarrett, 2 College Court, Uffcombe, Cullompton, Devon EX15 3EQ
Tel: 01884 841210

Ground: Silver Street, Willand, Devon. Tel: 01884 33885
Capacity: 2000 Covered Seating: 75 Floodlights: Yes

Directions: leave the M5 at Junction 27 (signed Tiverton & N. Devon).
Follow signs to Willand and the ground is on the left hand side about 1/4 mile after passing Willand village sign.

PREVIOUS **League:** Devon County League >01

BEST SEASON **FA Vase:** 1st Round proper 00-01, 1-4 v Falmouth Town (A)

FACT FILE
Founded: 1946
Colours: White/black/black
Change colours: Red/white/red
Midweek matchday: Tuesday

CLUB PERSONNEL
Chairman: Mike Mitchell
Manager: Clive Jones

WORLE ST. JOHNS

Secretary: Gail Norton, 101 Devonshire Road, Weston-super-Mare, Somerset BS23 4NY
Tel: 01934 413843 (H) 01934 621167 (B) 0794 730661 (M) 01934 420048 (F)
e-mail: jahiley@aol.com

Ground: Coleridge Road, Bournville Estate, Weston-s-Mare, Somerset
Tel: 01934 612862

Directions: Leave M5 at J21and take main road into Weston-s-Mare.
Turn left at the 4th r'about into Winterstoke Road, then take the 2nd right into Byron Road and then 1st left into Coleridge Road.

PREVIOUS **League:** Somerset Senior Lge.
Names: Worle & Weston St. Johns amalgamated 2000

HONOURS R-up Somerset Sen. Lge. 99-00 (Worle)

FACT FILE
Colours: blue & black/black/blue & black
Change Colours: Claret & blue/claret/claret
Midweek Matchday: Tuesday

CLUB PERSONNEL
Chairman: John Hiley
101 Devonshire Road, Weston-s-Mare,
Somerset BS23 4NY
Tel: 01934 413843 (H)

Manager: Martin Dancey
Tel: 01934 517792

SOUTH WESTERN FINAL LEAGUE TABLES 2000-01

BRISTOL PREMIER COMBINATION

PREMIER DIVISION	P	W	D	L	F	A	Pts
Highbridge Utd Res	26	17	7	2	63	25	58
Sea Mills Park	26	18	3	5	68	41	57
Bristol Union	26	15	5	6	59	26	50
Thornbury Town	26	16	2	8	59	36	50
Longwell Green Sports	26	11	10	5	49	30	43
Bristol 5 OB	26	11	3	12	43	41	36
Bitton Reserves	26	9	9	8	39	44	36
Hillfields OB	26	9	9	8	50	56	36
Chipping Sodbury	26	10	4	12	50	56	34
Hartcliffe	24	7	6	11	42	50	27
Hallen Reserves	26	5	8	13	46	64	23
St Philips Mas	24	4	5	15	46	69	17
Nicholas Wndrs	26	4	5	17	26	65	17
AEK Rangers	26	1	10	15	28	64	13

BRISTOL & AVON LEAGUE

PREMIER DIVISION	P	W	D	L	F	A	Pts
Filwood Sports	24	20	3	1	91	33	60
Bristol Spartak	24	16	4	4	65	34	52
CTK Southside	24	15	4	5	89	35	49
Southmead YC	24	15	3	6	72	39	48
Nailsea Town Res	24	13	2	9	55	49	41
Parkway Rangers	24	12	2	10	81	55	38
QS Bedminster	24	10	3	11	54	55	33
Patchway Sports	24	9	5	10	71	72	32
Dundry Athletic Res	24	8	3	13	42	59	27
Easton Cowboys	24	7	2	15	43	66	23
Clevedon Sports	24	7	1	16	44	74	22
Chipping Sodbury A	24	5	2	17	33	65	17
Bristol Parkway	24	2	0	22	30	143	3

BRISTOL DOWNS LEAGUE

DIVISION ONE	P	W	D	L	F	A	Pts
Clifton St Vincents	26	20	2	4	85	19	62
Sneyd Park	26	19	5	2	68	22	62
Torpedo	26	17	5	4	73	29	56
Prince of Wales	26	17	3	6	55	28	54
Retainers	26	12	4	10	62	50	40
DDAS	26	11	4	11	42	49	37
Cotswool	26	10	5	11	55	42	35
Clifton Rockets	26	10	5	11	53	58	35
Ashley	26	9	6	11	60	52	33
The Albion	26	9	3	14	55	59	30
Compass Athletic	26	9	2	15	48	58	29
St Andrews	26	5	4	17	34	82	19
Pump House	26	5	1	20	33	111	16
Tebby	26	2	5	19	32	96	11

SOMETECH TAUNTON LEAGUE

DIVISION ONE	P	W	D	L	F	A	Pts
Sydenham Rangers	16	13	2	153	26	47	
Bishops Lydeard	16	13	1	2	39	20	40
Staplegrove	16	9	1	6	37	29	28
Galmington	16	7	4	5	31	20	25
Bridgwater Sports	16	6	4	6	22	26	22
Wyvern	16	6	3	7	36	35	21
Redgate*	16	4	3	9	35	34	12
Highbridge Town	16	2	3	11	27	49	9
Alcombe Rovers	16	1	1	14	22	63	4

BRISTOL & DISTRICT LEAGUE

SENIOR DIVISION	P	W	D	L	F	A	Pts
Rangeworthy	27	21	4	2	71	19	67
Long Shore	28	15	9	4	59	34	54
Hartcliffe CC	28	15	7	6	51	28	52
Highbridge Utd A	28	15	4	9	47	34	49
Fishponds Athletic	28	14	6	8	52	40	48
Brimsham Green	28	12	8	8	46	36	44
Pucklechurch Spts Res	28	11	6	11	46	45	39
Seymour United	28	11	4	13	50	48	37
BAWA Aces	27	10	6	11	65	53	36
Knowle United	28	9	5	14	52	62	32
South Bristol Central	27	9	4	14	49	62	31
Oldland Abbot'ns Rs	28	8	5	15	37	57	29
Lawrence Rovers	28	8	4	16	52	81	28
Nicholas Wands. Res	27	4	9	14	26	55	21
Frampton Ath Rngrs Rs	28	4	3	21	33	82	15

BRISTOL & SUBURBAN LEAGUE

PREMIER DIV ONE	P	W	D	L	F	A	Pts
Almondsbury	28	23	3	2	76	15	49
Stoke Gifford Utd	28	19	4	5	76	36	42
P & W United	28	16	5	7	52	31	37
St Aldhelms	27	14	6	7	59	45	34
Yate Town Reserves	27	14	5	8	55	39	33
Exeter United	28	14	5	9	48	40	33
Ridings High	28	9	10	9	51	46	28
Avonmouth	28	10	7	11	52	59	27
Avonside Court	28	11	4	13	47	51	26
Cadbury Heath Res	28	8	6	14	47	56	22
Glenside FC	28	9	2	17	38	62	20
Southmead Athletic	28	3	13	12	24	39	19
Broad House Plain Res	28	6	5	17	34	71	17
Bristol Telephones	28	6	4	18	40	76	16
Filton Athletic	28	5	5	18	30	63	15

SALISBURY & DISTRICT LEAGUE

PREMIER DIVISION	P	W	D	L	F	A	Pts
Tisbury United	22	16	3	3	58	28	51
Damerham	21	15	1	5	71	34	46
Dave Coleman AFC	22	13	6	3	54	25	45
Shrewton United	22	12	2	8	56	38	38
Bemerton HH	22	12	2	8	66	52	38
South Newton	21	11	2	8	69	51	35
Bulford	22	10	1	11	51	54	31
Friends Provident	22	7	5	10	60	51	26
Stockton & Codford	22	7	4	11	29	43	25
Porton Sports	22	8	1	13	48	68	25
Nomansland	22	2	4	16	41	70	10
PFC Durrington	22	2	1	19	27	116	7

DORSET COUNTY SATURDAY LEAGUE

DIVISION ONE	P	W	D	L	F	A	Pts
Poole Borough	30	24	4	2	125	31	76
Weymouth United	29	19	2	8	90	56	59
Badger Sports	30	18	4	8	65	55	58
Dorchester United	29	16	5	8	75	46	53
Chickerell United	30	14	1	15	72	59	43
Gillingham Town Res	29	12	7	10	63	56	43
Hamworthy United Res	30	12	7	11	63	64	43
Beaminster	30	9	6	15	55	66	33
Portland United Res	30	11	0	19	54	82	33
Blandford United Res	29	9	5	15	40	63	32
Lytchett Red Triangle	29	9	4	16	64	73	31
Shaftesbury Reserves	30	8	6	16	42	80	30
Flight Refuelling Res	30	8	4	18	65	78	25
Okeford United	30	6	5	19	50	117	23
Dorchester YMCA	29	3	5	21	40	104	14

CARLSBERG SOUTH WESTERN FOOTBALL LEAGUE

Sponsored by The St Austell Brewery Co Ltd

President: Tristan H Scott **Chairman:** Bob Bell

Secretary: Ray Rowe, 5 Alverton Gardens, Truro, Cornwall TR1 1JA
Tel/Fax: 01872 242190 Email: ray@rowe57.FSbusinessco.uk

Press Officer: Mrs Wendy Donohue, 115 Longfield, Falmouth, Cornwall TR11 4SL
Tel: 01326 316642 **Fax:** 01326 219022 **Email:** wendyresultsouthwest@talk21.com

This has been the most difficult season since the League was founded in 1951. It is a great achievement that all fixtures were completed and this was all down to the attitude of the clubs to accept all situations and drive towards an acceptable situation. This was the first season for Secretary Ray Rowe, and it certainly was a baptism of fire. Some 50 per cent of fixtures needed to be re-arranged; the reasons are well documented - fuel crisis, serious bad weather (100 days of continuous rain) and foot and mouth. Weekly meetings with MAFF were the order of the day, with every club entrance and car park being disinfected.

The season was extended by fourteen days, finishing on 23rd May with St Blazey being crowned champions having led from September, Porthleven being runners-up. Holsworthy were the surprise package finishing fourth.

The League Cup final was played at St Blazey where Porthleven finally lost their 'bridesmaid' status by defeating Saltash United 4-2.

Falmouth Town and Porthleven represented the League in the FA Vase in an excellent fashion, eventually going out to Bedlington Terriers and Marske respectively. Falmouth created a bit of history by travelling the greatest distance for any FA competition.

Bodmin Town and St Austell needed to seek re-election and they were re-elected at the AGM. The League hope to attract the twentieth club which would then mean that promotion and relegation would 'kick in'.

The 50th Anniversary Dinner was held in May and was a great success. Jewson, the League's sponsors for the past fifteen years, gave notice that they did not wish to continue. The League will be continually grateful for their contribution to the success of the League. The good news is that Carlsberg, with the support of St Austell Brewery, are the new sponsors with an excellent three year deal. The League will now be known as The Carlsberg South Western Football League.

FINAL LEAGUE TABLE 2000-01

	P	*W*	*D*	*L*	*F*	*A*	*Pts*
St Blazey	36	27	6	3	124	33	87
Porthleven	36	25	8	3	90	26	83
Liskeard Athletic	36	24	7	5	97	55	79
Holsworthy	36	24	3	9	84	44	75
Millbrook	36	22	6	8	94	45	72
Saltash United	36	21	8	7	85	43	71
Falmouth Town	36	18	10	8	72	46	64
Penzance	36	16	9	11	65	59	57
Tavistock	36	14	7	14	50	52	50
Torpoint Athletic	36	14	7	15	56	60	50
Plymouth Parkway	36	12	4	20	53	77	40
Callington Town	36	11	6	19	63	93	39
Newquay	36	10	8	18	58	81	38
Truro City	36	11	4	21	58	81	37
Penryn Athletic	36	10	5	21	49	80	35
St Austell	36	7	6	22	41	76	27
Launceston	36	8	3	25	39	92	27
Wadebridge Town	36	6	4	26	51	115	22
Bodmin	36	5	2	29	39	110	17

ROLE OF HONOUR 2000-01

South Western Football League Champions
St Blazey

Runners Up Porthleven

League Challenge Cup Winners
Porthleven

Runners Up Saltash United

Sporting Trophy
1st Liskeard Athletic
2nd Penzance
3rd Launceston

Ground Trophy
1st Penryn Athletic
2nd Liskeard Athletic
3rd St Blazey

Jack Hawke Trophy
for the Leading Goalscorer
Ian Rowe (Holsworthy) 36

Top Referee
Colin Spence

Best Programme
Saltash United

RESULTS CHART 2000-01

		1	2	3	4	5	6	7	8	9	10	11	12	13	14	15	16	17	18	19
1	Bodmin Town	X	4-3	0-9	0-1	4-2	1-4	0-3	0-2	0-2	0-3	1-2	1-3	2-3	2-2	0-2	1-2	2-1	3-1	1-3
2	Callington Town	4-1	X	3-1	1-3	2-4	3-4	0-0	2-5	3-3	4-0	1-2	0-5	2-6	0-3	1-0	4-1	0-2	4-1	3-0
3	Falmouth Town	3-0	9-3	X	2-1	3-2	4-2	1-0	3-0	1-2	1-1	3-0	2-2	2-1	1-4	1-1	0-0	4-1	3-1	1-1
4	Holsworthy	7-2	3-1	4-0	X	3-2	4-2	0-1	3-1	0-0	3-1	3-0	0-2	5-2	2-1	0-1	0-2	5-2	4-0	4-1
5	Launceston	3-0	1-3	0-3	1-3	X	0-4	0-6	1-3	3-1	0-0	1-2	0-1	1-1	0-4	1-4	0-1	2-1	0-1	6-1
6	Liskeard Athletic	2-1	3-0	2-1	3-2	5-0	X	4-2	4-2	2-1	2-0	2-2	2-2	4-0	0-4	4-4	2-0	1-1	3-2	4-0
7	Millbrook	2-1	2-2	2-0	6-2	4-1	1-1	X	6-2	4-1	2-0	1-0	1-1	4-2	1-5	4-1	1-2	5-0	2-1	3-0
8	Newquay	4-1	2-3	0-2	0-1	2-0	1-2	2-3	X	2-0	1-2	2-3	0-3	2-0	0-6	1-1	2-2	2-2	2-4	1-1
9	Penryn Athletic	3-3	3-0	1-2	1-3	2-1	1-2	2-3	3-0	X	1-2	2-1	0-3	2-0	1-5	1-6	2-3	2-1	1-0	2-1
10	Penzance	1-0	7-0	1-1	0-0	2-0	6-6	0-3	3-0	4-1	X	1-0	0-1	2-0	1-2	1-4	1-1	1-2	2-2	6-1
11	Plymouth Parkway	3-0	3-2	2-2	3-4	0-2	1-5	0-5	5-1	3-2	2-4	X	0-0	0-1	1-6	1-3	0-2	3-2	0-3	0-2
12	Porthleven	5-0	6-1	5-0	2-1	9-0	2-0	2-1	1-1	1-0	8-0	1-0	X	2-1	1-1	2-4	1-0	0-2	3-0	3-1
13	St Austell	2-0	2-2	0-2	0-0	0-1	1-4	1-1	0-1	1-1	2-3	2-5	1-1	X	1-3	1-0	1-2	0-3	0-2	5-2
14	St Blazey	7-1	0-0	3-1	0-1	8-0	2-2	3-2	5-0	4-0	3-1	3-0	2-1	6-1	X	2-1	2-0	4-1	4-0	4-1
15	Saltash United	4-1	3-0	0-0	1-0	1-0	1-2	1-0	1-1	3-1	1-3	2-1	1-1	2-0	2-2	X	3-2	1-1	0-1	10-1
16	Tavistock	3-1	0-1	0-0	0-3	1-2	0-3	3-3	0-1	3-0	0-0	1-1	0-2	3-0	2-1	2-3	X	1-2	4-3	3-2
17	Torpoint Athletic	3-0	2-1	1-1	0-3	4-0	0-1	2-0	0-3	5-1	1-1	0-3	1-2	1-0	1-1	2-5	0-0	X	3-1	2-0
18	Truro City	3-4	0-0	0-1	2-3	0-0	3-1	0-3	3-3	3-1	2-3	4-2	1-3	2-1	1-5	1-5	3-2	1-3	X	4-0
19	Wadebridge Town	3-1	2-4	0-2	1-3	3-2	0-3	2-7	5-5	2-2	1-2	1-2	1-3	1-2	3-7	1-3	1-2	3-1	3-2	X

CARLSBERG SOUTH WESTERN LEAGUE CHALLENGE CUP 2000-01

PRELIMINARY ROUND

Bodmin Town	v	Torpoint Athletic	1-2
Saltash United	v	Liskeard Athletic	2-1
Holsworthy	v	Truro City	3-4

FIRST ROUND

Callington Town	v	St Blazey	1-6
Newquay	v	Wadebridge Town	3-2
Plymouth Parkway	v	St Austell	4-3
Tavistock	v	Millbrook	1-1, 3-2
Falmouth Town	v	Porthleven	1-2
Penzance	v	Launceston	2-0
Saltash United	v	Penryn Athletic	4-1
Torpoint Athletic	v	Truro City	3-3, 4*3

QUARTER FINALS

Newquay	v	Torpoint Athletic	2-1
Saltash United	v	Penzance	2-2, 1*1, 4p3
Porthleven	v	St Blazey	2-1
Tavistock	v	Plymouth Parkway	2-5

SEMI FINALS

Newquay	v	Saltash United	1-2
Plymouth Parkway	v	Porthleven	2-2, 0-3

FINAL

Porthleven v Saltash United 4-2 at St Blazey

LEADING GOALSCORERS 2000-01

Ian Rowe	Holsworthy	36
Justin Harrington	St Blazey	29
Andy Sargent	Liskeard Athletic	29
Jeff Babb	Millbrook	25
Dominic Richardson	Porthleven *(6 with Saltash United)*	25
Glyn Hooper	St Blazey	23
Dave Burt	Penzance	20

SPORTING TROPHY

average from a mark of 5

Liskeard Athletic	4.121
Penzance	4.089
Launceston	4.02
Truro City	4.00
Holsworthy	3.95
St Austell	3.89

GROUND TROPHY

average from a mark of 5

Penryn Athletic	4.94
Liskeard Athletic	4.86
St Blazey	4.50
Torpoint Athletic	3.97
Porthleven	3.95
Newquay	3.80

BODMIN TOWN

Secretary: Sheila Chapman, c/o Bodmin AFC, Bodmin, Cornwall PL31 2AF
Tel: 01208 77974 (H)

Ground: Priory Park, Bodmin. Tel: 01208 269033 or 021208 78165
Directions: Just off town centre in Priory Park complex, at rear of town car park

Capacity: 2,000 Cover: Grandstand Seats: Yes Floodlights: Yes

Clubhouse: Mon-Thu 6.30-11pm (matchdays 6-11), Fri-Sat 12-11pm,
Sun 12-3 & 7-10.30pm, unless Sky matches are on then 12 -10.30 pm
Bar snacks available most times Club Shop: No

Honours: South Western Lg 90-91 93-94 (R-up 76-77, 92-93, 94-95, Lg Cup 93-94 ,97-98 (R-up 7-78 88-89 94-95,95-96), Cornwall Snr Cup Winners 98-99 R-up 93-94, Cornwall Charity Cup 86-87 89-90,96-97.Cornish Guardian E.C.P.L.Supplimentary Cup 91-92 (R-Up. 93-94)- GordonSweet Cup 90-91,92-93,98-99

FACT FILE
Founded: 1889 Nickname: Black & Ambers
Sponsors: Gynn Construction
Colours: Black & amber/black/amber
Change colours: All white
Midweek Matchday: Wednesday
Reserves' League: East Cornwall Premier
Programme: 64pages, 40p
Programme Editor: Secretary

CLUB PERSONNEL
Chairman: Colin.Hooper
Vice-Chairman: P.Lee
President: A.Gynn
Manager: Sean Hooper
Asst Manager: Phil Brown
Physio: Jim Brewer

CALLINGTON TOWN

Secretary: Philip Brown, Mount Pleasant Cottage, Harrowbarrow, Callington PL17 8JL
Tel: 01822 833851 (H) 01752 307102 (B)

Ground: Ginsters Marshfield Park, Callington Comm. College, Launceston Rd., Callington, Cornwall Tel: 01579 382647 **Directions** Turn into Callington Community College from the A388, Callington to Launceston road. Go to the top of the drive and bear left - the ground is 100m ahead.

2000-01: Captain & P.o.Y.: Matthew Hawke Top Goalscorers: Gary Smith 13

FACT FILE
Colours: Red & black/black/red & black
Change Cols.: Blue & yellow/blue/blue & yellow
Midweek Fixtures: Wednesday

CLUB PERSONNEL
Chairman: Andrew Long
34 Coombe Road, Callington
Tel: 01579 383982 (H) 01752 220881 (B)

Manager: Ian Southcott
Tel: 01579 383561 (H) 07973 109609

FALMOUTH TOWN

Secretary: John E Thompson, 45 Woodland Avenue, Penryn, Cornwall TR10 8PG
Tel: 01326 372972(H) 01326 372778 (W)
Club's Website http://www.users.globalnet.co.uk/~cgdf

Ground: Bickland Park, Bickland Vale, Falmouth, Cornwall Tel: 01326 375156
Directions: Follow A39 to Tregoniggie Industrial Estate - will pass ground on left.
1 1/2 miles from Penmere Halt (BR) on Falmouth-Truro branch line. Bus service from town centre
Capacity: 6,000 Seats: 300 Cover: 1,200 Floodlights: Yes Club Shop: TBA
Clubhouse: Mon-Fri 7-11pm, Sat 12-11pm, Sun 12-3 & 7-10.30pm. Meals available

HONOURS: Cornish Senior Cup x 11 R-up x 8; Western Lg x 4, Lg Cup 74-75, Alan Young Cup x 3; South Western Lg x 14 R-up x 5, Lg Cup x 13 R-up x 5; Pratten Cup 73-74, Cornwall Charity Cup 59-60 94-95 99/00 R-up 00-01

BEST SEASON **FA Cup:** 1st Round 62-63 & 67-68 & 69-70
FA Vase: Quarter Final 86-87 **FA Trophy:** 2nd Round 77-78

PREVIOUS **Leagues:** Cornish Snr 50-51; South Western 51-74; Western 74-83
RECORDS **Gate:** 6,300 v Oxford United, FA Cup 1st Round 3/11/62
Scorer: Joe Scott 198, 72-78
Appearances: Keith Manley 580 (appr) 70-83

FACT FILE
Founded: 1949 Nickname: Town
Club Sponsors: Stralfors
Colours: Amber/black
Change colours: Red/white
Midweek Matchday: Tues/Wed
Reserves' League: Cornwall Comb
Programme: 16 pages, 50p
Editor/ Press Off.: Mike Odgers 01209 715766

CLUB PERSONNEL
Chairman:Roger Fenner
V.Chair:Trevor Jones
President: Sid RidgeoN
Manager: David Bal
Coach: Keith Barker

2000-01
Leading goalscorer: Bryn Wheeler 20
Captain: Adrian Street
P.O.Y: Dave Sweet

HOLSWORTHY

Secretary: Mel Goodenough, 114B New Street, Torrington, Devon EX38 8BT

Tel Nos: 01805 625049(H) 01805 622315 (emergency W)
078117 32422 (M)

Ground: Upcott Field Tel: 01409 254295
Cover: Yes Floodlights: Yes

Directions: Leave town on A388 towards Bideford, 100 yds past mini-roundabout on left.

Honours: Devon Senior Cup 53-54 (Prem. Cup 71-72 78-79), Devon Junior Cup 38-39

2000-01: Captain: Danny Bryant P.o.Y.: Matt Penry Top Goalscorer: Ian Rowe 36

FACT FILE
Nickname: Magpies
Colours: Black & White/Black/black & red
Change colours:yellow/green/green & yellow
Programme: 20 pages, "2 with entry
Editor: Terry Trewin.& Bob Thomson

CLUB PERSONNEL
Chairman: Mike Pett
Manager: Leigh Cooper
Assistant Manager: Joe Scott

LAUNCESTON

Secretary: Chris Martin, 3 Tavistock Road, Launceston, Cornwall PL15 9HA
Tel: 01566 776175 (H) Email: launcestonfc.co.uk

Ground: Pennygillam, Pennygillam Industrial Estate, Launceston PL15 7ED
Tel: 01566 773279 **Web site:** www.launcestonfc.co.uk

Directions: Follow signs to Pennygillam Ind. Est., just off main A30 -ground 400yds on left

Capacity: Seats: 150 Cover: 150 Floodlights: Yes

Clubhouse: Open after every game. Bar meals available. Club Shop: No

HONOURS South Western Lg Winners 94-95, R-up 84-85, S.W Lg.Cup Winners: 95-96
Cornish Snr Cup 1899-1900 00-01 82-83 (R-up 92-93, Charity Cup R-up 88-89)

FACT FILE
Founded: 1891 Nickname: Clarets
Colours: Claret & blue/blue/claret
Change colours: Sky/Sky/claret
Midweek matchday: Tues/Wed
Reserves' League:East Cornwall Prem.
Programme: Yes

CLUB PERSONNEL
Chairman: Keith Ellacott
President: Mr.S.Dawe
General Manager: Keith Ellacott
Joint Managers: Keith Ellacott & Gary Shirley
Physio: B.Medland
2000-01. Capt: Steve Jago. P.o.Y.: JohnTape
Top Goalscorer: Liam Tilley 12

LISKEARD ATHLETIC

Football Secretary: Brian Olver, Windrush, Tremeddan Lane, Liskeard, Cornwall PL14 3DS
Gen. Secretary: D J Rawlings, Bradwood, Woodgate Rd., Liskeard PL14 6DY
Ground: Lux Park, Liskeard, Cornwall (01579 42665) **Directions:** Take Tavistock Road (A390) from town centre, after 1/2 mile turn left on St Cleer Road (follow signs to Lux Park Sports Complex) & ground is 200 yards on left. Half mile from Liskeard BR station
Capacity: 2,000 Seats: 100 Cover: 300 Floodlights: Yes Club Shop: No
Clubhouse: (01579 342665) Normal licensing hours. Hot & cold food available
HONOURS: South Western Lg 76-77 78-79 (R-up 75-76 77-78; Lg Cup 76-77 78-79) Western Lg 87-88 (R-up 85-86 89-90, Merit Cup 80-81); Cornwall Snr Cup 04-05 83-84 84-85 85-86 88-89 89-90 93-94 (R-up 70-71 75-76 76-77 78-79 94-95); Cornwall Charity Cup 21-22 79-80, Cornwall Jnr Cup 05-06 13-14 26-27; SWPratten Cup 78-79; E Cornwall Prem RAOB Cup 67-68, Plymouth & Dist. Lg 60-61(Div 1 59-60 (R-up 54-55 73-74), Div 2 76-77(Res)), Victory Cup 60-61, Charity Cup 59-60), E Cornl Prem. Lg (Res) 84-85 92-93 93-94 R-up: 98-99,99-00(Lg.Cup 88-89 93-94,99-00)
PREVIOUS Leagues: E. Cornwall Prem., Plymouth & Dist., South Western 66-79, Western 79-95
RECORDS **Goalscorer:** T Turner 59, 60-61 **Appearances:** Brian Bunney, 500+

FACT FILE
Formed: 1889 Nickname: Blues
Sponsors: J P Leisure & Gilbert Outfitters
Colours: Blue & White/blue/blue & white
Change colours: Yellow & blue
Midweek matchday: Tuesday
Prog: 40 pages, 50p Editor: I.Pook

CLUB PERSONNEL
Chairman: David Hick V. Chair: B.Harding
President: W.N.Rawlings
Man: Chris Burchell Asst Man: John Hillson
Physio:
2000-01
Leading goalscorer: Andy Sargent 29
Captalns: G. MacMillan & Dave Leonard
P.o.Y.: Jamie Ahearne & J. Dawe

MILLBROOK

Secretary: Lee Collins, Goosaford Cottage, St John, Torpoint, Cornwall PL11 3AR
Tel No: 01752 822892 (H)
Ground: Mill Park, Millbrook, Cornwall (01752 822113)

Directions: From Torpoint Ferry - 3 miles to Antony on A374, fork left, after 1 mile turn left again and follow B3247 to Millbrook (3 miles), take road marked `Town Centre Southdown', right at mini-r'bout after 1/4 mile, ground clearly visible. From Tamar Bridge - follow signs for Torpoint, 2 miles after Polbathic right turning marked Millbrook, 5 miles to Millbrook then proceed as above
Capacity: 2,000 Seats: None Cover: 200 Floodlights: Yes Club Shop: No
Clubhouse: Weekdays 7-11pm, Sat 11am-11pm, Sun noon-3 & 7.30-10.30. Hot food (chips, burgers etc) available during and after matchdays
HONOURS: South Western Lg R-up 81-82, Cornwall Snr Cup R-up 83-84 (Charity Cup 84-85, Jnr Cup 75-76), Plymouth & District Lg 80-81 (Div 1 R-up 76-77)
PREVIOUS **Leagues:** Plymouth Comb.(8yrs)/ Plymouth & Dist.(6yrs)
CLUB RECORDS **Scorer:** Unknown **Appearances:** John Horne 215

FACT FILE
Founded: 1973 Nickname: The Brook
Sponsors: Plymouth Boat Cruises Ltd
Colours: White & Black/black/red
Change colours: All Royal blue
Midweek matchday: Tuesday
Reserve's League: Plymouth & District
Programme: 20 pages, 10p
Editor: J Weekes (01752 822637)

CLUB PERSONNEL
President: Mrs E Weekes
Chairman: Martin Bettridge
Vice Chairman: K Townsend
Press Officer: W Linney
Manager: Paul Stewart
Asst Manager: S Matthews

NEWQUAY

Secretary: Bob Steggles, 12 Clemens Close, Newquay, Cornwall, TR7 2SG. Tel: 01637 872677
Ground: Mount Wise, Newquay 01637 872935
Directions: .5 mile from Newquay BR, follow 1-way system for .5 mile grd sign on L.eft at Clevedon Road Website: www.newquayafc.com Email: bob@steggles.net
Capacity: 4,000 Seats: 250 Cover: 500 Floodlights: Yes Club Shop: No
Clubhouse: 7-11pm w/days, 12-11pm Sat, 12-10.30 Sun. Hot & cold snacks during matches
HONOURS: Cornish Snr Cup 34-35 52-53 54-55 56-57 91-92(R-up(10) 05-07 08-09 25-26 33-34 35-36 57-58 69-70 84-85 87-88), S. Western Lg(7) 58-60 77-78 79-80 81-82 83-84 87-88 (R-up 57-58 85-86 94-95, Lg Cup 55-56 88-89(R-up(4) 56-58 79-81), Cornwall Charity Cup(13) 06-07 08-09 53-56 57-59 62-63 69-70 74-75 76-78 88-89 (R-up(10) 07-08 20-21 56-57 60-61 73-74 75-76 81-82 84-87), W. Cornwall Lg 06-07 (R-up(2) 07-09), Cornish Snr Lg Herald Cup 34-35 (R-up(7) 33-34 35-36 49-51 55-57 58-59)
PREVIOUS **Leagues:** West Cornwall; Plymouth & District 21-27; Cornish Senior 31-51
BEST SEASON **FA Vase:** 3rd Round 90-91

FACT FILE
Founded: 1890 Nickname: Peppermints
Sponsors:Hunters Sports
Colours: Red & white stripes/white/white
Change colours: Blue & white/white/white
Midweek Matchday: Tuesday
Reserve League: Cornwall Combination
Programme: 24 pages, 50p Editor: J Hawkey

CLUB PERSONNEL
Chairman: Eric.Tummon V.-Chairman: M.Jago
President: A.Kendall Manager: Conrad Robins
Physio: Ross McOnie Coach: Kelvin Hunkin
2000-01 Leading goalscorer: Kieron Avery 12
Captain: Bradley Ralph
P.o.Y.: Justin Miles

Launceston FC

Porthleven. Back Row (l-r): V James (Team Sec), D Hart (Physio), I Hodges, A Hart, A Avery, G Penhalion, B Hayden, W Britton, R Triggs, L Williams (Chairman), A Carey (Manager). Front Row: P Ainscough, A Bleasdall, A Roberts, N Hedlyn, T Burrows (Captain), D Phillips, R Daley, C France (Asst Manager).

St Blazey AFC, South Western League and Cornwall Senior Cup winners 2000-01. Back Row (l-r): Damian Mulready, Chris Hawke, Matt Parsons, Dave Philp, Nigel Pugh, Neil Burton, Paul Smith. Front Row: Trevor Mewton (Mngr), Mike Southgate, Graham Waters, Ian Gosling, Mark Rowe (Capt), Justin Harrington, Sam McKune, Terry Huddy (Trainer)

PENRYN ATHLETIC

Secretary: Mike Young, 1 Dunvegan Road, Penryn, Cornwall TR10 8HJ
Tel: 01326 374098 (H) 01326 212974 (B) 01326 374098 (F)

Ground: "Kernick", Kernick Road, Penryn, Cornwall Tel: 01736 75182 (Clubhouse)

Directions: From Truro take the NEW Falmouth road at Treluswell and at the Treleiver roundabout follow signs for Kernick Industrial Estate.
Turn left at the new Asda store.

PREVIOUS **League:** Cornwall Comb.

2000-20001 **Captain:** Steve Jewell **P.o.Y.:** Steve Coggin
Top Goalscorer: Paul Kneebone (central defender) 10

FACT FILE
Colours: Red & black stripes/black/red & black
Change colours: Light & dark blue stripes/ dark blue/dark blue
Midweek matchday: Wednesday

CLUB PERSONNEL
Chairman: Peter Young
146 Little Oaks, Penryn
Tel: 01326 378035 (H)

Manager: David Jenkin
Tel: 01326 377582 (B) 07968 93258 (M)

PENZANCE

Secretary: John Mead, 8 Chyanclare, St Clare Street, Penzance TR18 2PG
Tel./Fax: 01736 369066 (H)

Ground: Penlee Park, Alexandra Place, Penzance Tel: 01736 361964
No Floodlights

Directions: Seafront road past harbour, after amusement arcade turn right at r'bout (Alexander Rd), ground second right.
Fifteen minutes walk from Penzance(BR); directions as above

HONOURS Cornish Snr Cup 1892-93 95-96 97-98 98-99 1903-04 07-08 47-48 60-61 72-73 80-81 (R-up 1896-97 99-1900 00-01 04-05 48-49 49-50 54-55 56-57 74-75), South Western Lg 55-56 56-57 74-75 (Lg Cup R-up 60-61), Cornwall Charity Cup 47-48 48-49 (R-up 21-22 63-64), Cornwall Snr Lg Div 2 57-58 (Div 2 Cup 53-54 54-55), Cornwall Comb. R-up 65-66 (Lg Cup 69-70 (R-up 81-82)), Cornwall Jnr Cup(West) 03-04 04-05 05-06 07-08 09-10

Players progressing: Gerry Gazzard (West Ham), Tony Kellow (Exeter)

FACT FILE
Founded: 1888
Nickname: Magpies
Colours: Black & white/black/black
Change colours: All sky blue
Midweek matchday: Tuesday - no lights
Reserves' league: Cornwall Comb

CLUB PERSONNEL
President: Jim Dann
Chairman: Peter George
Man:Gary Marks Trainer: John Mead

2000-01
Leading Goalscorer: David Burt 23
Captain: Nigel Thwaites
P.o.Y: Lee Bushby

PLYMOUTH PARKWAY

Secretary: Stuart Cadmore, 71 Trelawny Road, Menheniot, Liskeard, Plymouth PL14 3TS
Tel: 01579 340820 (H) 01752 304096 (B) 07776 14102 (M)

Ground: Brickfields, Cumberland Road, Devonport, Plymouth

Directions: Torpoint Ferry - Ferry Road and right to Park Avenue- Chapel Street- the le then bear into Cumberland Road. Ground is on left in Madden Road

FACT FILE

Colours: Yellow/royal blue/white
Change colours: Azure blue/black/blue

CLUB PERSONNEL

Chairman: Mark Rowles
Tel: 01752 790436 (H) 01752 201918 (B)

Manager: Gez Baggott
Tel: 01752 302596 (H) 0966 542982 (M)

PORTHLEVEN

Team Secretary: Vidal James, 23 Parc-an -Bans,Camborne, TR14 7RW (01209 710618)
Ground: Gala Parc, Mill Lane, Porthleven (0208 574181) Clubhouse (01326 574754)
Directions: From Penzance on A394, B3304 into Porthleven, ground on left immediately before town. From Helston on B3304 ground on right as you exit town. Buses from Helston & Penzance
Capacity: 1,500 Seats: None Cover: Yes Floodlights: Yes Shop: No
Clubhouse: Mon-Fri 7-11pm, Sat 11am-8pm, Sun 11-3 & 7-10.30pm. Full food menu at wek-ends
PREVIOUS Grounds: Treza Downs; Sunset Farm
Leagues: West Penwith; Cornwall Snr; South Western 66-77; Cornwall Comb. 77-89
HONOURS S outh Western League R-up 72-73, 98-99 00-0 Lg Cup R-up Winners 00-01 98-99, Cornwall Comb.ination (6), (Lg Cup(6), Cornwall Charity Cup 70-71, 97-98 Cornwall Senior Cup R-up 68-69, 97-98 ,99-00 ,00-01 George Evely Cup 64-65 65-66 83-84 86-87, West Penwith Lg, Penzance Hosp. Cup, Penzance Charity Cup
Best Performance: F.A.Vase: Quarter Finalists 1997-98
Season 2000-01: Captain: John Burrows P.o.Y.:Nicky Medlyn Top Scorer:Dominic Richardson 34

FACT FILE
Founded: 1896
Nickname: Fishermen
Colours: Yellow & black/ black/yellow & black
Change colours: All blue
Midweek Matchday: Wednesday
Reserves' League: Cornwall Combination
Programme: 50p

CLUB PERSONNEL
President: P F Johns
Chairman: Len.Williams
Vice Chairman: J.Cowles
Manager: Alan Carey
Assistant Manager: T.B.A.
Coach: Gary Bannister

SALTASH UNITED

Secretary: P J Gammage, 23 Spire Hill Park, Saltash, Cornwall, PL12 4SR Tel: 01752 844046

Ground: Kimberley Stadium, Callington Road, Saltash, Cornwall Tel: 01752 845746

Directions: First left after crossing Tamar Bridge, through town centre, at top of town fork right at min- roundabout, ground 400 yds ahead on left.
Capacity: 3,000 Seats: 250 Cover: 250 Floodlights: Yes
Clubhouse: Club attached to stand and caters for dancing and clubactivities.Sapphire Lounge caters for wedding receptions,quiz nights and private functions etc

PREVIOUS **Leagues:** Cornwall Snr; Sth Western 51-59 62-76; E Cornwall Prem 59-62; Western 76-95

HONOURS Cornwall Snr Lg 49-50 50-51, Western Lg 84-85 86-87 88-89 (R-up 83-84 87-88, Lg Cup 86-87 87-88 (R-up 88-89), Div 1 76-77, Merit Cup 79-80 87-88), Sth Western Lg 53-54 75-76 (R-up 3), Lg Cup 3, Cornwall Snr Cup 6

FACT FILE
Formed: 1945
Nickname: The Ashes
Colours: Red & white/black/red
Change: Blue & yellow/blue/blue
Midweek Matchday:Tuesday/ Wednesday
Programme: 52 pages,50p
Editor: Marian Gammage

CLUB PERSONNEL
President: P Skinnard
Chairman: Michael Howard
Manager:Mike Doel & Chris Wakeham

St. AUSTELL

Secretary: Peter Beard, 24 Alexandra Rd, St Austell, Cornwall PL25 4QP
Tel: 01726 64138 (H) 07867 675460(M)

Ground: Poltair Park, Poltair Road, St. Austell Tel: 01726 66099

Directions: 5 mins walk north of St Austell (BR)

Capacity: 8,000 Seats: 200 Cover: 300 Floodlights: No

Clubhouse: Mon-Fri 7-10.30 & Sat 12-11pm Food is available

PREVIOUS **Leagues:** Rocky Park (1890s)

RECORD **Gate:** 15,000 v Penzance, Senior Cup 49

HONOURS South Western Lg 68-69 (R-up 4), Lg Cup 64-65 71-73 87-88 (R-up 4), Cornish Senior Cup(11)

FACT FILE

Founded: 1890
Sponsors: Kwik Print
Colours: White/black/red
Change colours: Yellow/Red/Black
Midweek Matchday: Tuesday
Reserves' League: East Cornwall Prem.

CLUB PERSONNEL

Chairman: B.Powell
Asst Chairman: Alan Lucas
Manager: Tony Nancarrow
Asst Manager: Keith Hosbani

St. BLAZEY

Secretary: Martin RichardsChristalea, Doubletrees,St Blazey PL2H 2LE 01726 817156
Email Address: admin@stblazey-football.co.uk
Ground: St Blaise Park, Station Road, St Blazey Tel: 01726 814110

Directions: A390 Liskeard-St Austell road, turn into Station Road at lights inSt Blazey village; ground 100 yards on left. One and a half miles from Par (BR)

Capacity: 3,500 Seats: 180 Cover: 700 Floodlights: Yes Club Shop: No
Clubhouse:Mon- Sat 11-6.00pm, Sun 12-11pm. Bar snacks

HONOURS SWestern Lg (8), R-up (10), Lg Cup 5, (R-up 5), Cornish Snr Cup (10),Cornish Charity Cup (5) Cornwall Snr Lg Cup (Herald Cup) 35-3648-49

RECORDS **Gate:** 6,500 v St Austell, Cornwall Snr Cup 48-49
Goalscorer: B Tallamy **Appearances:** W Isbell

2000-01: Capt: Dave Philp **P.o.Y.:** Nigel Pugh **Top Iscorers** Justin Harrington &Glyn Hooper 35

FACT FILE
Founded: 1896 Nickname: Saints
Sponsors: Eden Project
Colours: Green, Black & White
Change colours: Blue & white/blue/blue
Midweek matchday: Wednesday
Reserve's League: East Cornwall Premier
Prog: 24 pages,50p Editor: Steve Paynter
Website: stblazey-football.co.uk

CLUB PERSONNEL
Chairman: Mr H Cooke.V- Chair: MrA Putt
Manager: Trevor Mewton
Assistant Manager: Dave Jones
Treasurer Brian Brokenshire
Football Secretary: Martin Richards

TAVISTOCK AFC

Secretary: Philip Lowe, 14 Anderton Court, Whitchurch, Tavistock PL19 9EX
Tel: 01822 614447(H) 01752 206700(W)

Ground: Langsford Park, Crowndale Rd, Tavistock (01822 614447)

Directions: A386 from Plymouth, 2nd left after Ford garage into Crowndale Road and the ground is half mile on left opposite Tavistock College

Capacity: 2,000 Seats: 200 Cover: 200 Floodlights: Yes Club Shop: No

Clubhouse: Open all day Saturday and evenings 6.30-10.30 or 11pm. Hot & cold food

HONOURS Devon Premier Cup R-up 94-95, Devon Snr Cup 1889-90 1968-69 77-78 81-82, South Western Lg Cup 68-69 (R-up 76-77 83-84), Bedford Cup -numerous times; Devon Charity Cup 78-79, R-up 77-78

RECORDS **Gate:** 5,000 v Calstock, Bedford Cup final 1952
Appearances: A Pethick 1,000+

Players progressing: Peter & Neil Langman (Plymouth A., 51 & 53); Robbie Pethick (Portsmouth); Mike Trebilcock (Plymouth A. 65); Harold Redmond & Danny Sullivan (Crystal Pal. 57 - £100)

FACT FILE
Founded: 1888
Nickname: `Tavy' or `Lambs'
Sponsors: SMC / Applied Automation
Colours: Red/black/black Change : All Blue
Midweek matchday: Wednesday
Reserves' Lge: Plymouth & Dist Comb. (Prem)
Programme: 32 pages, with entry
Editor: Vice Chairman
Website: www.tavistock.afc.co.uk

CLUB PERSONNEL
Chairman: Robin Fenner
Vice Chairman: Eric Pinch (Press Officer)
Managers:Chris Abbott & Craig Smith
Asst Manager: Gary Tiffany
Physio: Les Mewton

TORPOINT ATHLETIC

Secretary: Vic Grimwood, 43 Hemerdon Heights, Plympton PL7 3EY Tel: 01752 344263 (H)

Ground: The Mill, Mill Lane, Torpoint, Cornwall Tel: 01752 812889

Directions: Bear left from Torpoint ferry, ground down hill on left after half a mile

Capacity: Seats: Yes Cover: Yes Floodlights: No
Clubhouse: Yes

PREVIOUS **League:** Plymouth & District League.(Premier)

BEST SEASON **FA Vase**: 4th Round 93-94, 0-3 v Diss Town (H), eventual winners

HONOURS South Western Lg 64-65 66-67 (Lg Cup R-up 65-66), Cornish Snr Cup 8

FACT FILE

Colours: Gold & black stripes/gold/gold
Change colours: Red & white/white/red
Programme: Yes

CLUB PERSONNEL

Chairman: Colin Phillips
Tel: 01752 705845 (H)

Manager: Phil Cardew
Tel: 01752 812721 (H)

TRURO CITY

Secretary: Brian Fisher, 33 Southview Road, Biscosey, Par Pl24 2HJ(01726 812238)

Ground: Treyew Road, Truro, Cornwall (01872 278853)

Capacity: 5,000 Seats: 250 Cover:Yes Floodlights: Yes

Directions: On A39 by-pass south of city.
10 mins walk from BR station; up hill and left at junction

HONOURS South Western Lg 60-61 69-70 92-93 95-96 97-98, (R-up 54-55 62-63 66-67 67-68 70-71 96-97), Lg Cup 59-60 66-67(jt) 92-93 (R-up 54-55 58-59 67-68 93-94 95-96 97-98); Cornish Snr Cup x13; Cornish Charity Cup x7; Cornish Snr Lg 31-32 32-33; Cornwall Combination 94-95 98-99 League Cup: 1968,78,86,88,99

FACT FILE
Formed: 1889
Colours: Red & black/black/black
Change colours: Yellow/blue/blue
Midweek Matchday: Tuesday
Programme: Yes

Reserve s' League: Cornwall Combination

CLUB PERSONNEL
Chairman: Des Coad
Manager: Chris Webb

WADEBRIDGE TOWN

Secretary: Brian Williams, 4 School Walk, Wadebridge, PL27 6DY
Ground: Bodieve Park, Bodieve Road, Wadebridge (01208 812537)

Capacity 2,000 Seats: No Cover: Some Floodlights: No

Directions: At junction of A39 and B3314 to east of Wadebridge

HONOURS South Western Lg R-up 68-69 78-79 79-80 (Lg Cup 5), (R-up 3),
CornishSenior Cup 79-80, Cornish Charity Cup 8

FACT FILE

Nickname: Bridgers
Colours:All red/white
Change colours: All blue/white
Reserve s' League: East Cornwall Premier

CLUB PERSONNEL

Chairman: Steve Cudmore
Manager:Robbie Black

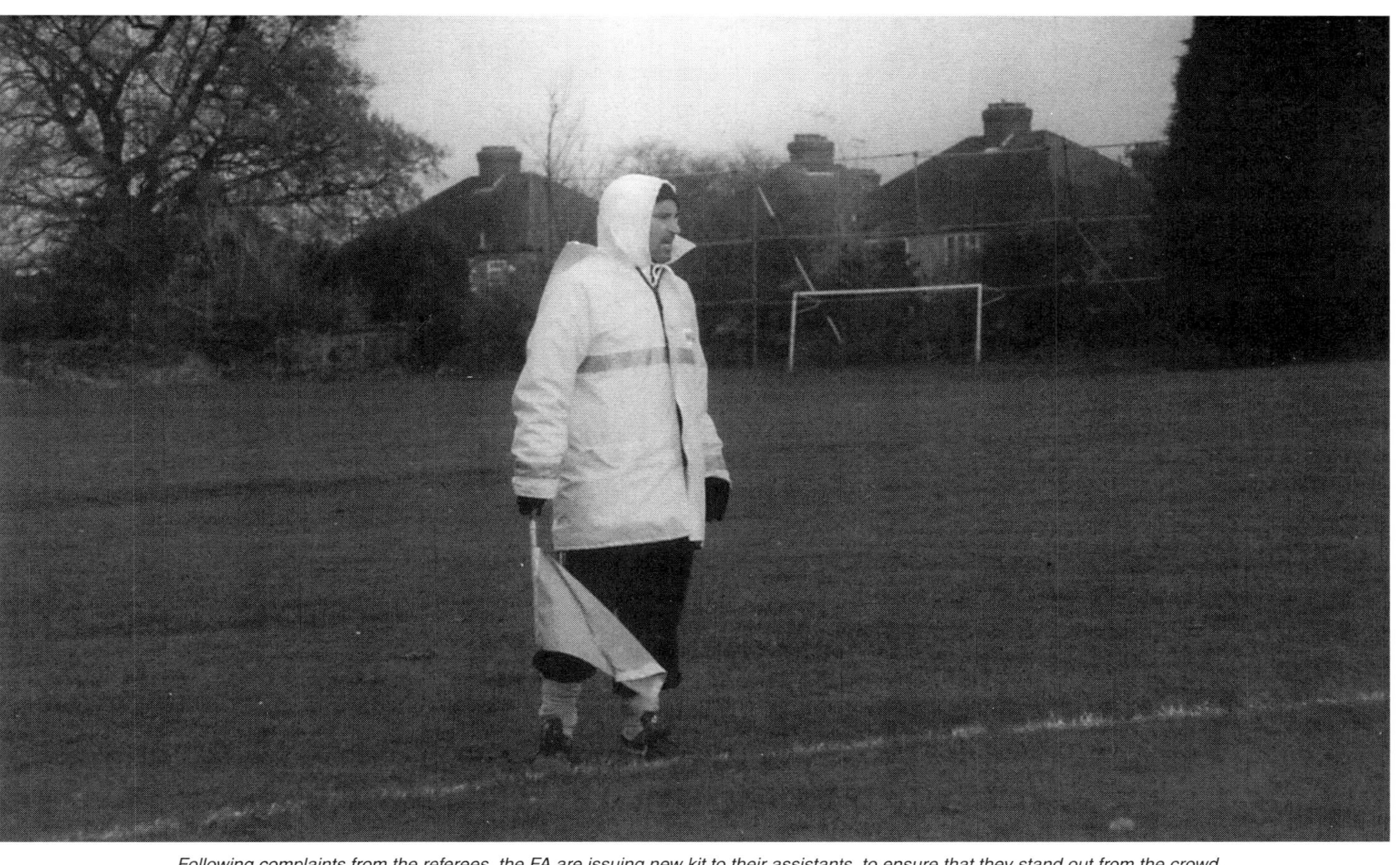

Following complaints from the referees, the FA are issuing new kit to their assistants, to ensure that they stand out from the crowd.
Photo: Francis Short

JOLLY'S CORNWALL COMBINATION LEAGUE

Club	Ground	Capacity	Seats	Cover	Floodlights	Clubhouse
FALMOUTH TOWN	Bickland Park	6000	300	1200	Yes	Yes
GOONHAVERN	Reen Manor Parc	700	No	Overhang	No	Yes
HAYLE	Trevassack Park	800	No	No	No	Yes
HELSTON ATHLETIC	Kellaway Parc	1000	No	Overhang	No	Yes
ILLOGAN RBL	Oxland Parc	2000	100	Yes	No	Yes
LUDGVAN	Fairfield	800	No	Overhang	No	Village Hall
MARAZION BLUES	Trevenner	1000	No	Overhang	Yes	Village Hall
MOUSEHOLE	Trungle Parc	1000	No	50	No	Yes
MULLION	Clifden Parc	2200	No	30	No	Yes
NEWQUAY	Mount Wise	3500	250	500	Yes	Yes
PENRYN ATHLETIC	Kernick Road	800	20	Yes	No	Yes
PENZANCE	Penlee Park	3000	250	Yes	No	Yes
PERRANWELL	Village Playing Field	700	No	100	No	Village Hall
PORTHLEVEN	Gala Parc	1500	25	Yes	Yes	Yes
RNAS CULDROSE	Sportsfield	500	No	No	No	Yes
ST AGNES	Enys Parc	1000	No	No	No	Yes
ST IVES TOWN	The Saltings	500	No	No	No	No
ST JUST	Lafrowda Park	1000	No	100	No	Yes
TRURO CITY	Treyew Road	3000	20	Yes	Yes	Yes
WENDRON	Underlane	400	No	No	No	Yes

CORNISH GUARDIAN EAST CORNWALL PREMIER LEAGUE

Club	Ground	Capacity	Seats	Cover	Floodlights	Clubhouse
BODMIN TOWN	Priory Park	3000	400	400	Yes	Yes
BUDE TOWN	Broadclose	1000	No	30	No	Yes
CAMELFORD	Tregoodwell	1000	No	100	No	No
FOXHOLE STARS	Goverseth	800	No	No	No	Yes
LAUNCESTON	Pennygillam	1000	150	150	Yes	Yes
LISKEARD ATH	Lux Park	2000	50	300	Yes	Yes
MILLBROOK	Mill Park	2000	50	200	Yes	Yes
NANPEAN ROVERS	Victoria Bottoms	1500	No	100	No	Yes
PADSTOW UNITED	Jury Park	500	No	No	No	No
PROBUS	St Georges Field	500	No	No	No	No
ROCHE	Trezaise Road	500	No	No	No	Yes
ST AUSTELL	Poltair Park	4000	200	200	No	Yes
ST BLAZEY	Blaise Park	3500	200	600	Yes	Yes
ST BREWARD	Brake Park	1000	No	20	No	Yes
ST CLEER	Recreation Field	1000	No	100	No	Yes
ST DENNIS	Boscawen Park	900	No	No	No	Yes
SALTASH UNITED	Kimberley Stadium	3000	250	250	Yes	Yes
STICKER	Ennis Farm	1000	No	30	No	Yes
TORPOINT ATH	Mill Field	1000	100	100	No	Yes
WADEBRIDGE TN	Bodieve Park	1500	20	80	No	Yes

WESTWARD DEVELOPMENTS
DEVON COUNTY LEAGUE

President: Carl Throgmorton

Chairman: Stephen Ware **Vice Chairman:** John Brett

Hon. Secretary: Philip Hiscox, 19 Ivy Close, Wonford, Exeter EX2 5LX

Tel/Fax: 01392 493995 Email: pahiscox@hotmail.com

Another day in Ivy Close. Imagine the scene. It's anytime from October to March, it's cold, it's wet and I'm sat at my desk looking at websites. My favourites? - No, sorry, nothing that exciting - the Met Office Weather Site that says it's raining. The local forecast - gloomy, the five day advanced forecast positively depressing. A quick click with my mouse and I'm at the BBC Devon Site. "Three more cases in Devon of Foot & Mouth" reads the headline. Veterinary Officer says no end in sight. I light another cigar and log off the internet. The postman has been with two results sheets, five registration forms and seven pink postponement forms from last weekend. Finally, over a distinctly dark mug of coffee I look at last weekend's postponed games and see if there is anywhere to fit in new dates. A wry smile - one game can be played on the last Saturday in April, the other six? - Midweek including Appledore at home to Topsham and Crediton away to Dartmouth. Things are really that bad . . .

The time machine moves on to 19th May. It's sunny, it's Topsham and it's the last game! One wise crack in the crowd says, "Bet you're glad it's all over". I stand waiting until the final whistle blows. Ivybridge management invade the pitch with screams of delight. But me? Yes, you guessed it - I look to the heavens and think to myself in 1966 mode, "yep, it is now".

On the pitch, well the playable ones anyway, it was a good season. Willand Rovers deservedly won the League having got off to a flier back in August and never really let it slip. Some chased, Heavitree and Buckland notably, but it was Willand's year.

Willand leave us for pastures new and it was the new club that provided much of the season's entertainment, Buckland Athletic deserving their Runners Up award for playing the game with flair and passion and the right way too, winning the Sportsmanship Cup with a record of just 22 yellows and no reds at all.

Alphington clinched third spot in the League and at the bottom end Plymstock United can be thankful that foot & mouth stopped some clubs' legitimate ambitions and saved others' skins.

In the Cups, homeless side Newton Abbot went all the way, the hard way, twice winning on penalties to win the Pertemps Devon Cup, Dartmouth being the most unlucky as losing finalists. Darts striker Mark Collins set a record as he scored 46 goals this season, more than any other player has managed before.

Ivybridge Town triumphed in the Throgmorton Cup after a run of games that never saw a home tie and they didn't even get a First Round bye. In some ways it was a deserved reward, for Ivybridge lost more than any other club due to foot & mouth. Indeed, they played three home matches "away" to get their fixtures played.

Heavitree United were beaten finalists in the Cup and managed fourth in the League, and back almost twelve months ago Budleigh and Exeter Civil Service shared the Charity Shield.

So there you have it, the ninth season of Devon League soccer. In many ways just finishing the season was enough, but, yes, we did enjoy it too (well, when it wasn't raining).

Philip Hiscox, Secretary

Martyn King, captain of Ivybridge Town, lifting the Throgmorton Cup with Valerie Throgmorton.

Photo: John Hawkes

FINAL LEAGUE TABLE 2000-01

	P	W	D	L	F	A	W	D	L	F	A	Pts
Willand Rovers	38	15	2	2	54	19	11	7	1	44	22	87
Buckland Athletic	38	11	5	3	61	29	13	0	6	46	25	77
Alphington	38	12	4	3	47	30	9	6	4	40	28	73
Heavitree United	38	14	2	3	61	28	8	3	8	36	33	71
Dartmouth	38	11	6	2	61	27	8	5	6	47	33	68
Vospers Oak Villa	38	10	2	7	46	38	10	4	5	34	23	66
Ottery St Mary	38	11	2	6	43	27	9	3	7	39	30	65
Budleigh Salterton	38	12	5	2	38	14	7	3	9	39	46	65
Newton Abbot Spurs	38	10	4	5	42	20	6	8	5	47	36	60
Newton Abbot	38	8	6	5	48	24	9	2	8	48	34	59
Elburton Villa	38	7	3	9	32	38	7	5	7	27	45	50
Ivybridge Town	38	9	7	3	51	31	4	3	12	23	43	49
Cullompton Rangers	38	6	5	8	19	33	5	7	7	32	36	45
Appledore	38	9	1	9	48	41	3	5	11	25	46	42
Topsham Town	38	6	3	10	36	41	4	3	12	31	64	36
Crediton United	38	7	5	7	41	38	3	1	15	20	66	36
Exeter Civil Service	38	6	4	9	31	38	2	5	12	24	44	33
Buckfastleigh Rangers	38	5	1	13	22	53	4	2	13	17	65	30
Stoke Gabriel	38	3	6	10	28	41	4	2	13	29	52	29
Plymstock United	38	3	5	11	29	56	1	4	14	18	67	21

RESULTS CHART 2000-01

		1	2	3	4	5	6	7	8	9	10	11	12	13	14	15	16	17	18	19	20
1	Alphington	X	4-1	4-0	2-1	3-2	3-0	4-6	3-3	0-0	1-0	4-1	2-0	0-5	1-1	1-5	5-0	2-1	3-1	3-1	2-2
2	Appledore	4-5	X	4-0	0-1	4-1	4-4	4-1	2-3	2-4	5-2	2-6	2-1	2-1	2-1	1-2	0-1	6-1	3-0	1-3	0-4
3	Buckfastleigh Rngrs	0-2	2-2	X	0-3	0-4	2-3	2-0	1-4	2-0	1-6	1-2	0-1	1-4	1-4	0-9	2-0	2-5	3-1	1-0	1-2
4	Buckland Athletic	4-4	4-1	5-0	X	4-2	8-0	1-1	2-2	1-1	1-0	3-2	5-0	4-3	3-3	2-0	7-2	2-3	4-1	0-2	1-2
5	Budleigh Salterton	3-3	1-1	2-0	0-2	X	2-0	0-0	3-1	1-2	1-0	3-1	3-1	2-1	2-0	4-0	5-0	2-0	2-0	1-1	1-1
6	Crediton United	1-5	1-0	2-3	2-4	0-3	X	3-3	4-3	2-3	0-1	1-2	5-0	3-3	1-1	3-2	4-0	3-2	1-1	3-0	2-2
7	Cullompton Rngrs	0-1	0-0	1-0	0-2	1-7	2-1	X	0-3	3-0	2-0	2-0	0-3	1-5	2-2	2-1	0-0	1-1	1-3	0-0	1-2
8	Dartmouth	0-0	5-2	5-0	6-2	2-2	4-1	3-1	X	4-0	1-1	3-0	2-3	4-1	3-3	2-2	4-2	4-1	5-1	2-3	2-2
9	Elburton Villa	1-0	4-1	0-1	2-0	4-2	4-0	0-2	1-3	X	1-1	2-6	1-1	1-5	1-3	0-1	2-2	2-0	4-2	2-4	0-4
10	Exeter Civil Service	1-1	3-2	1-2	1-3	1-2	4-0	2-2	1-0	0-2	X	1-1	3-3	3-5	0-1	1-3	2-1	2-1	3-4	2-1	0-4
11	Heavitree United	1-2	4-1	3-0	1-5	4-0	6-2	4-1	2-1	2-2	5-2	X	1-0	3-1	5-3	0-0	7-0	2-0	5-1	1-4	5-3
12	Ivybridge Town	2-2	5-3	4-1	3-2	6-1	3-0	1-1	1-4	1-3	2-1	0-0	X	1-2	4-1	5-0	2-2	5-2	3-3	1-1	2-2
13	Newton Abbot	5-1	2-0	0-0	2-0	1-1	1-2	1-1	2-1	11-0	7-0	0-2	1-1	X	2-2	1-2	3-2	1-4	6-1	1-1	1-3
14	Newton Abbot Spurs	1-0	0-1	6-0	0-1	1-1	6-1	3-1	1-1	7-1	2-0	0-3	4-1	0-0	X	1-1	3-1	0-3	4-1	3-2	0-1
15	Ottery St Mary	0-3	1-1	10-0	0-2	5-2	2-1	1-0	2-5	0-2	1-0	2-1	3-1	2-1	2-2	X	6-1	2-1	4-1	0-1	0-2
16	Plymstock United	2-2	3-2	1-4	1-6	1-2	3-1	1-6	0-3	1-1	3-3	1-2	1-0	2-4	2-7	2-3	X	1-1	4-4	0-3	0-2
17	Stoke Gabriel	1-3	1-2	2-2	0-3	1-3	2-3	2-2	3-3	3-0	1-1	0-2	3-1	0-5	1-1	1-3	4-0	X	1-4	1-2	1-1
18	Topsham Town	0-1	1-2	3-1	3-4	4-1	2-0	2-3	2-1	2-0	2-2	0-0	1-4	1-2	2-9	0-4	2-2	8-0	X	0-2	1-3
19	Vospers Oak Villa	0-4	3-3	6-3	0-4	3-0	6-0	0-1	1-4	1-2	3-2	5-3	4-1	2-0	0-2	2-1	4-2	4-2	0-2	X	2-2
20	Willand Rovers	2-1	2-0	6-0	2-1	1-3	2-1	2-0	2-2	2-2	5-2	3-2	2-0	2-0	2-1	2-0	5-0	3-1	8-0	1-3	X

LEADING GOALSCORERS 2000-01

Mark Collins	Dartmouth	46
Gary Fisher	Buckland Athletic	41
Tony Hendy	Ivybridge Town	28
Tom Sercombe	Newton Abbot Spurs	27
Roger Bonaparte	Vospers Oak Villa	26
Mark Loram	Dartmouth	26
Dave Stocker	Newton Abbot	26
Nick Murray	Heavitree United	25
Justin Osborne	Newton Abbot	24
David Steel	Willand Rovers	24

BASS SPORTING TROPHY 2000-01

Position	*Club*	*Marks*
1	Buckland Athletic	279
2	Newton Abbot	269
3	Ottery St Mary	267
4	Willand Rovers	265
5	Exeter Civil Service	252
6	Vospers Oak Villa	250
7	Crediton United	248
8	Ivybridge Town	239

LEAGUE ALL TIME RECORDS

		P	W	D	L	F	A	Pts	P/G
1	Willand Rovers	318	183	61	74	755	429	610	1.91
2	Stoke Gabriel	318	177	64	77	766	421	595	1.87
3	Newton Abbot	318	158	66	94	731	466	540	1.69
4	Alphington	318	145	64	109	626	558	499	1.56
5	Cullompton Rngrs	318	141	57	120	590	518	480	1.50
6	Vospers Oak Villa	318	141	52	125	690	603	475	1.49
7	Budleigh Salterton	226	131	42	53	556	312	435	1.92
8	Buckfastleigh Rngrs	318	127	51	140	579	643	432	1.35

ALL TIME LEADING GOALSCORERS

Justin Osborne	156
Mark Seatherton	150
David Downing	109
Alan Clarke	102
Leon Newnham	101
Roger Bonaparte	100
Jason Warren	100

SOMERSET COUNTY FOOTBALL LEAGUE

President: L J C Heal **Chairman:** Miss S A Wright

Hon Secretary: C R J Rose, Sutley House, Pilton, Shepton Mallet BA4 4BL
Telephone: 01749 890767

FINAL LEAGUE TABLES 2000-01

PREMIER DIVISION

		P	*W*	*D*	*L*	*F*	*A*	*Pts*
1	Shepton Mallet T	34	23	8	3	73	28	77
2	Shirehampton	34	20	9	5	73	41	69
3	Clevedon United	34	19	9	6	84	41	66
4	Backwell Res	34	15	12	7	59	46	57
5	Radstock Town	34	16	6	12	62	50	54
6	Mangotsfield Res	34	14	7	13	58	47	49
7	Brislington Res	34	12	10	12	52	48	46
8	Nailsea United	34	13	7	14	59	58	46
9	Bridgwater Res	34	13	6	15	55	59	45
10	Wells City	34	12	9	13	58	65	45
11	Portishead	34	10	12	12	43	38	42
12	Burnham United*	34	12	7	15	52	57	42
13	Timsbury Athletic	34	10	12	12	48	53	42
14	Fry Club	34	11	9	14	43	50	42
15	Welton Rovers Res	34	9	9	16	48	77	36
16	Robinsons	34	10	5	19	47	79	35
17	Watchet Town	34	6	11	17	30	59	29
18	Long Sutton	34	3	8	23	47	95	17

FIRST DIVISION

		P	*W*	*D*	*L*	*F*	*A*	*Pts*
1	Castle Cary	34	23	7	4	99	32	76
2	Peasedown Athletic	34	19	10	5	80	43	67
3	Nailsea Town	34	20	7	7	77	46	67
4	Paulton Rovers	34	17	10	7	84	51	61
5	Glastonbury	34	14	10	10	51	42	52
6	Stockwood Green	34	14	10	10	56	52	52
7	Cheddar	34	15	4	15	71	61	49
8	Clevedon United Reserves	34	14	7	13	47	52	49
9	Cleeve West Town	34	14	5	15	55	55	47
10	Banwell	34	12	9	13	67	70	45
11	Oldland Abbotonians	34	12	8	14	56	55	44
12	Congresbury	34	12	8	14	55	60	44
13	Hengrove Athletic	34	13	5	16	44	60	44
14	Clandown	34	10	5	19	51	71	35
15	Winscombe	34	9	7	18	38	66	34
16	Westland United	34	8	8	18	44	82	32
17	Bishop Sutton	34	8	7	19	36	65	31
18	Saltford	34	6	5	23	31	79	23

FINAL LEAGUE TABLES 2000-01

SECOND DIVISION

	P	W	D	L	F	A	Pts
Keynsham Town	34	23	3	8	85	43	72
Blackbrook	34	22	4	8	102	54	70
University of Bath	34	21	5	8	91	50	*67
Imperial FC	34	18	10	6	75	36	64
Portishead Res	34	17	10	7	84	48	61
Ilminster Town	34	15	9	10	81	55	54
Cutters Friday (B)	34	15	8	11	82	52	53
Frome Town	34	14	11	9	68	58	*51
Crewkerne	34	14	9	11	67	66	*50
Nailsea United Res	34	15	5	14	68	69	50
Larkhall Athletic	34	12	7	15	44	61	43
Frome Collegians	34	12	7	15	62	58	*41
Odd Down	34	11	7	16	58	52	40
Dundry Athletic 82	34	11	8	15	83	88	*40
Churchill Club 70	34	11	7	16	59	74	40
Peasedown Athletic Res	33	6	2	25	32	109	20
Wrington Redhill	34	4	4	26	36	114	16
Burnham United Res	33	4	4	25	49	139	*15

* points deducted

THIRD DIVISION

	P	W	D	L	F	A	Pts
Weston Super Mare	38	30	5	3	137	41	95
Tunley Athletic	38	26	4	8	115	58	82
Wells City Res	38	24	4	10	95	53	76
Shepton Mallet Res	38	21	7	10	101	58	70
Langford Rovers 2000	38	21	7	10	82	56	70
Long Ashton	36	19	6	11	76	40	*62
Kewstoke	38	16	11	11	102	96	59
Street	38	15	13	10	88	64	*57
Worle St Johns	38	16	5	17	99	111	53
St George (East in G.)	38	13	8	17	68	88	47
Timsbury Athletic Res	38	13	7	18	73	72	46
Yatton Athletic	37	14	4	19	76	89	46
Clutton	38	13	7	18	66	84	46
Robinsons Reserves	38	14	4	20	78	101	46
Frys Club Reserves	37	12	5	20	71	81	*40
Backwell United A	38	12	4	22	55	97	40
Hengrove Athletic Res	38	10	9	19	60	95	39
Cheddar Reserves	38	9	7	22	70	90	34
Impreial FC Reserves	38	7	9	22	54	101	30
Westland Utd Reserves	36	9	0	27	63	154	*25

PAST WINNERS

	PREMIER DIVISION	DIVISION ONE	DIVISION TWO	DIVISION THREE
1999-00	Shirehampton	Welton Rovers	Nailsea Town	University of Bath
1998-99	Clevedon United	Mangotsfield Utd	Paulton Rovers	Dundry Athletic 82
1997-98	Portishead	Timsbury Athletic	Mangotsfield Utd	Wrington Redhill
1996-97	Street	Radstock Town	Worle	Clevedon Utd Res
1995-96	Portishead	Nailsea United	Ilminster Town	Worle
1994-95	Portishead	Stockwood Green	Robinsons	Shepton Mallet Res
1993-94	Portishead	Longwell Green	Odd Down	Street
1992-93	Long Sutton	Clevedon Town	Saltford	Keynsham Cricketers
1991-92	Bridgwater T (1984)	Portishead	Bishop Sutton	Blackbrook
1990-91	Bridgwater T (1984)	Frome Town	St George E in G	Bishop Sutton Res
1989-90	Bridgwater T (1984)	Clevedon Town	Keynsham Town	Clutton
1988-89	Brislington	Stockwood Green	Ilminster Town	Fry's Club
1987-88	Robinson's DRG	Weston super Mare	Stockwood Green	Mendip Hospital
1986-87	Robinson's DRG	Bridgwater T (1984)	Shepton Mallet	Stockwood Green
1985-86	Robinson's DRG	Imperial United	Clevedon Town	Frome Town

LEAGUE CONSTITUTION 2001-02

Backwell United
Banwell
Bishop Sutton
Blackbrook
Bridgwater Town
Brislington
Bristol Spartak
Burnham United
Castle Cary
Cheddar
Churchill Club 70
Clandown
Cleeve West Town
Clevedon United
Clutton
Congresbury
Crewkerne
Cutters Friday (Bristol)
Dundry Athletic
Frome Collegians
Frome Town
Fry's Club
Glastonbury
Hengrove Athletic
Ilminster Town
Imperial Bristol
Kewstoke AFC
Keynsham Town
Langford Rovers 2000
Larkhall Athletic
Long Ashton
Long Sutton
Mangotsfield United
Nailsea Town
Nailsea United
Odd Down
Oldland Abbotonians
Paulton Rovers
Peasedown Athletic
Portishead
Radstock Town
Robinsons
Saltford
Shepton Mallet
Shirehampton
Stockwood Green
St George E-in Gordano
Street
Timsbury Athletic
Tunley Athletic
University of Bath
Watchet Town
Wells City
Welton Rovers
Westland United
Weston St John

GLOUCESTERSHIRE COUNTY LEAGUE

Chairman: A C Barrett

Hon. Secretary: D J Herbert, 8 Fernhurst Road, St George, Bristol BS5 7TQ
Tel: 0117 951 7696

FINAL LEAGUE TABLES 2000-01

PREMIER DIVISION

		P	*W*	*D*	*L*	*F*	*A*	*Pts*
1	Winterbourne United	34	24	4	6	89	48	76
2	Highridge United	34	22	4	8	71	28	70
3	Patchway Town	34	20	9	5	66	31	69
4	Tytherington Rocks*	34	17	7	10	75	48	58
5	Whitminster	34	15	9	10	59	44	54
6	Brockworth	34	15	9	10	59	52	54
7	Roman Glass St George	34	16	6	12	52	49	54
8	DRG Stapleton	34	12	11	11	59	52	47
9	Pucklechurch Sports	34	14	5	15	50	47	47
10	Totterdown P O B	34	13	7	14	56	63	46
11	AXA	34	13	5	16	62	72	44
12	Hardwicke	34	11	7	16	61	70	40
13	Viney St Swithins	34	10	10	14	51	63	40
14	Ellwood	34	10	6	18	46	66	36
15	Henbury O B	34	10	5	19	46	64	35
16	Broad Plain House	34	9	7	18	43	65	34
17	Old Georgians	34	9	6	19	45	75	33
18	Frampton Athletic Rgs	34	7	1	26	40	93	22

* Points adjustment

GLOUCESTER NORTHERN SENIOR LEAGUE

DIVISION ONE

	P	*W*	*D*	*L*	*F*	*A*	*Pts*
Sharpness	30	21	4	5	81	28	67
Slimbridge	30	19	6	5	68	26	63
Taverners	30	18	7	5	49	21	61
Smiths Athletic	30	17	5	8	52	40	56
Lydbrook Athletic	30	14	11	5	58	31	53
Broadwell Amateurs	30	12	8	10	47	38	44
Shortwood Utd Res	30	12	8	10	55	49	44
Kings Stanley	30	12	5	13	50	53	41
Bourton Rovers	30	11	5	14	51	54	38
Tuffley Rovers Res	30	8	11	11	49	51	35
Wooton Rovers	30	6	8	16	38	59	26
Cam Bulldogs	30	7	7	16	36	64	25
Dursley Town	30	5	8	17	34	68	23
Kingswood	30	5	7	18	32	74	22
Brimscombe & Thrupp	30	3	6	21	34	88	15

Holding? Never, Ref
Michael Bartley (Thatcham) about to lose his shirt to Fleet's John Murphy.
Photo: Andrew Chitty

SKURRAYS WILTSHIRE FOOTBALL LEAGUE

Secretary: Peter Ackrill, 3 Dallas Avenue, Swindon SN3 3NP
Tel: 01793 520334

FINAL LEAGUE TABLES 2000-01

PREMIER DIVISION

	P	W	D	L	F	A	Pts
Cricklade Town	34	23	6	5	104	42	75
Shrewton United	34	22	8	4	109	35	74
Devizes Town Res	34	21	5	8	88	47	68
Melksham Town Res	34	18	10	6	73	51	64
Biddestone	34	18	7	9	76	57	61
Trowbridge Town	34	17	10	7	57	41	61
Stratton Crosslink	34	17	5	12	79	49	56
Bradford Town	34	16	4	14	60	53	52
Chiseldon Southbrook	34	12	8	14	77	79	44
Pewsey Vale Res	34	12	8	14	55	75	44
Warminster Town Res	34	12	7	15	42	57	43
Wroughton	34	12	4	18	56	67	40
Aldbourne	34	8	15	11	40	62	39
Purton Reserves	34	8	7	19	46	74	31
Malmesbury Vic Res	34	9	4	21	47	82	31
Westbury Utd Res	34	6	11	17	47	86	29
Corsham Town Res	34	7	4	23	52	92	25
Marlborough Town	34	5	3	26	46	105	18

INTERMEDIATE DIVISION

	P	W	D	L	F	A	Pts
Wanborough Utd	24	14	6	4	68	31	48
Blunsdon United	24	13	6	5	78	42	45
Burmah Castrol	24	13	5	6	61	30	44
Dunbar Westside	24	12	4	8	73	45	40
Stratton C'link Res	24	7	8	9	33	44	29
Down Ampney	24	8	4	12	33	62	28
Cricklade Town Res	24	7	5	12	37	76	26
Mitel	24	7	4	13	55	65	25
Biddestone Res	24	4	4	16	39	79	16

JUNIOR DIVISION ONE

(Top 2)	P	W	D	L	F	A	Pts
Aston Keynes	24	21	2	1	101	33	65
Wroughton Res	24	19	2	3	94	31	59

JUNIOR DIVISION TWO

(Top 2)	P	W	D	L	F	A	Pts
Swindon Eagles	24	21	1	2	98	22	64
Wootton Bassett Utd	24	16	3	5	70	38	51

E.C. MILLS SPORTSMANSHIP WINNERS

Shrewton United

ADDKEY SENIOR K.O. CUP

Winners: Cricklade Town
Finalists: Devizes Town Reserves

PLAISTER AUTO'S INTERMEDIATE CUP

Winners: Wanborough United
Finalists: Blunsden United

FOUNTAIN TROPHIES JUNIOR K.O. CUP

Winners: Swindon Eagles
Finalists: Wootton Bassett United

REFEREE'S AWARD

P Alexander

SECRETARY'S AWARD

D Phillips (Melksham Town)

CONSTITUTION OF LEAGUE 2001-02

PREMIER DIVISION

(17 teams)

Aldbourne
Biddestone
Bradford Town
Corsham Town Reserves
Cricklade Town
Devizes Town Reserves
Malmesbury Victoria Reserves
Marlborough Town
Melksham Town Reserves
Pewsey Vale Reserves
Purton Reserves
Shrewton United
Stratton Crosslink
Trowbridge Town
Warminster Town Reserves
Westbury United Reserves
Wroughton

INTERMEDITATE DIVISION

(11 teams)

Teams will play each other 3 times

Ashton Keynes
Biddestone Reserves
Blunsdon United
Burmah Castrol
Calne Town Reserves
Down Ampney
Dunbar Westside AFC
Sherston
Stratton Crosslink Reserves
Wanborough United
Zarlink

JUNIOR DIVISION

(18 teams)

Aldbourne Reserves
Blunsdon United Reserves
Bromham
Burmah Castrol Reserves
Cricklade Town Reserves
Down Ampney Reserves
Dunbar Westside AFC Reserves
Ferndale Rodbourne
Marlborough Town Reserves
Minety
Purton A
Sporting HKQ
Swindon Eagles
Wanborough United Reserves
West Swindon
Wootton Bassett Town A
Wootton Bassett United
Wroughton Reserves

We all enjoyed the end of season functions at the Ringway Hotel, Basingstoke (thanks to hotel manager John Yarrall) and it was noticeable that the lads took every opportunity to get themselves into team groups, I suppose they had photographed so many club squads for the Directory perhaps they began to think they too were a squad - (bit sad?).

Left: Graham Cotterill, Garry Letts, Andrew Chitty, Gordon Whittington and Peter Lirettoc on the way up - Photo by Eric Marsh.

Centre: Peter Barnes was mascot for Mildenhall F.C. - Photo by Gordon Whittington.
Photographers often double up at big games!

Bottom: Here we go again:
Left to right back row: Alan Coomes, Neil Thaler, Gordon Whittington and Graham Cotterill. Front Row: Peter Lirettoc, Peter Barnes,`The Old Pro' and Roger Turner. Photo by Paul Dennis who has also supplied some much appreciated quality photos over the years.

Turn to page 746

MIDLAND FOOTBALL ALLIANCE

President: Bernard Davis **Chairman:** Pat Fellows

Secretary: Peter Dagger, 32 Drysdale Close,
Wickhamford, Worcestershire WR11 6RZ
Tel: 01386 831763 Fax: 01386 833488
E-mail: PDagger@talk21.com

This is the seventh annual report of the Midland Football Alliance since its inception in 1994. Season 2000-01 will be remembered not for one of the most exciting finishes to a league season, with Stourport Swifts winning the championship by one goal, but for the numerous problems, including a petrol strike, foot and mouth disease and most significantly the wettest winter for nearly 250 years, which meant the season had to be extended by three weeks.

Many matches were postponed during the season, indeed even in the middle of May nearly a full day's fixture list was lost to the weather. It is a tribute to both club and league officials that the season was completed and, although it was difficult to please everyone, particularly in hindsight, lessons will have been learned and the experience will have been beneficial if we should ever encounter a similar season again.

2000-01 was the first campaign without the support of Interlink Express, who had been our generous main sponsors since 1994. Despite many hours of hard work by members of the Management Committee, the league does not have a sponsor and this will be one of the aims and hopes for 2001-02. However, we remain grateful to Bernard and Irene Davis for sponsoring the League Cup, Rameses Associates the Invitation Cup, and Baker and Joiner the Hospitality Award. Malcolm Lycett, a life member of the League through his company Polymac Services, continues to sponsor the annual awards for the Team Manager and the highest goalscorer and Clubcall provide awards for the team of the month.

Stourport Swifts needed to win their final match by two clear goals to equal Rushall Olympic on points and goal difference and become champions on the number of goals scored. A 3-0 win meant that the championship, after nearly ten months, was decided by one goal. Commiserations must go to Rushall Olympic and also to Barwell who had lead the table for most of the season and looked likely to be champions until the last two or three weeks of the season. Stourport have been rewarded with promotion to the Dr Martens League and the only consolation to both Rushall Olympic and Barwell is that after a lot of hard work, and a considerable amount of money, both clubs achieved the required ground grading to be considered for promotion to the Dr Martens League in future seasons.

The League Cup was keenly contested, the semi-finalists being Bridgnorth Town, Stafford Town, Stourport Swifts and Stourbridge. The final saw Stourbridge defeat Bridgnorth Town on penalties, after the match had finished 1-1 after extra time.

Once again we had high hopes of success in the FA Cup and particularly the FA Vase, with the final being played locally at Villa Park. Three clubs, Oadby Town, Rushall Olympic and Stourport Swifts, reached the fifth round but were unable to make the ultimate push to the final.

The Midland Invitation Cup sponsored by Rameses Associates is a competition for clubs in the Midland Football Alliance and its three feeder leagues. The weather caused major problems to the competition but the final was eventually played on 2nd June between Stratford Town and Willenhall Town and resulted in a victory for Willenhall with a 1-0 scoreline.

Prior to the start of the season the match for the Joe McGorian Trophy competed for by the previous season's League Champions and League Cup winners saw Oadby Town take the trophy after defeating Willenhall Town.

As usual our Referees and Assistant Referees received many prestigious appointments during the season. At the end of the season Kevin Friend was promoted to the national panel league of referees and David Cooke, Adam Dewfield, Michael Murphy and Richard Smith were promoted to the national list of Assistant Referees.

They say that football is now an all year round sport, after this season I think we all know what they mean.

P G Dagger, General Secretary/Treasurer

Stourport Swifts.

Back Row: Richard Taylor, Lee Booth, Brendan Hackett, Mark Dearlove, Rob Clarke, Lee Ayres, Matt Southwick, Jan Moulders, Alex Cowley. Front Row: Paul Mountford, Adrian Cooper, Ross Knight, Lee Shaw, Paul Moore, Simon Marsh.

Photo: Marshall's Sports Services (Birmingham)

FINAL LEAGUE TABLE 2000-01

		P	W	D	L	F	A	Pts	GD
1	Stourport Swifts	42	28	9	5	109	38	93	71
2	Rushall Olympic	42	28	9	5	98	28	93	70
3	Barwell	42	26	11	5	74	35	89	39
4	Oadby Town	42	26	7	9	89	45	*82	44
5	Stourbridge	42	23	10	9	93	52	79	41
6	Stratford Town	42	20	10	12	96	58	70	38
7	Boldmere St Michaels	42	19	13	10	73	49	70	24
8	Willenhall Town	42	19	8	15	76	62	65	14
9	Bridgnorth Town	42	17	8	17	79	66	59	13
10	Chasetown	42	15	10	17	55	78	55	-23
11	Oldbury United	42	14	11	17	70	71	53	-1
12	Cradley Town	42	15	4	23	52	80	49	-28
13	Stafford Town	42	12	12	18	68	83	48	-15
14	Bloxwich Town	42	14	6	22	54	80	48	-26
15	Wednesfield	42	14	6	22	60	91	48	-31
16	Shifnal Town	42	12	11	19	56	75	47	-19
17	Halesowen Harriers	42	13	7	22	55	73	46	-18
18	Stapenhill	42	12	8	22	58	91	44	-33
19	Pelsall Villa	42	12	6	24	60	90	42	-30
20	Knypersley Victoria	42	10	10	22	64	100	*37	-36
21	West Mids Police	42	9	7	26	67	112	34	-45
22	Sandwell Borough	42	9	7	26	62	111	34	-49

Centre: Stourbridge Back Row (l-r): Lewis Baker, Michael Moore, Nick Hyde, Darren Alden, Anthony Robinson, Brian Robinson, Simon Black, Kevin Brookes, Andy Dale, Kevin Stanley. Front Row: Nathan Pulisgiano, Ian Jones, Leon Blake, Paul Corden, David Unitt, Stuart Hamilton, Leroy Murphy, Derek Kodua

Bottom: Boldmere St Michaels Back Row (l-r): John Hanson, Neil Holloway, Andrew Spencer, Richard Evans, Jim Arnold, Darren Owen, Luke Jones, Andrew Charles. Front Row: Neal Watkins, Nicky Richardson, Christain Kelsall, Paul Gregory, Garraint Eivars, Paul Wetburn. Photos: Marshall's Sports Services (Birmingham)

CLUBCALL TEAM OF THE MONTH AWARDS 2000-01

August/September	Stourport Swifts	January	Stourport Swifts
October	Barwell	February	Stapenhill
November	Pelsall Villa	March	Rushall Olympic
December	Boldmere St Michaels	April/May	Stourport Swifts

LIST OF HONOURS

	1994-95	1995-96	1996-97	1997-98	1998-99	1999-00	2000-01
LEAGUE CHAMPIONSHIP							
Winners	Paget Rgrs	Shepshed D	Blakenall	Bloxwich T	Rocester	Oadby Town	Stourport Swifts
Runners up	Hinckley Ath	Blakenall	Hinckley Ath	Rocester	Kings Norton	Stratford T	Rushall Olympic
LEAGUE CUP							
Winners	Sandwell Boro	Blakenall	Willenhall T	Knypersley V	Oldbury Utd	Willenhall T	Stourbridge
Runners up	Halesowen H	Oldbury Utd	Bloxwich T	Bloxwich T	West Mids Pol.	Knypersley V	Bridgnorth T
INVITATION CUP							
Winners	Blakenall	Pelsall Villa	Oldbury Utd	Atherstone U	Atherstone U	Bridgnorth T	Willenhall T
Runners up	Shifnal Town	Oldbury Utd	Bridgnorth T	Blakenall	Bandon	Darlaston T	Stratford T
HOSPITALITY CUP							
Winners	Rushall Olympic	Halesowen H	West Mids Pol.	Halesowen H	Halesowen H	Halesown H	Halesowen H
KEVIN KEEGAN - PLAYER OF THE YEAR							
Player	Anthony Smith	Simon Hyden	Adrian Horne	John Powell	Ian Long	David Davis	John Powell
Club	Stratford T	Rushall O	Pelsall Villa	Shifnal Town	Oldbury Utd	Oldbury Utd	Shifnal Town
TOP GOALSCORER - THE GOLDEN BOOT							
Player	J Bundred	M Biddle	C Blakemore	S Bradbury	A Lucas	S Bradbury	L Booth
Club	Knypersley V	Knypersley V	Willenhall T	Chasetown	Barwell	Chasetown	Stourport S
BEST DISCIPLINARY AWARD							
Club	Oldbury Utd	Barwell	Barwell	Stapenhill	Rocester	Boldmere St M	Stafford Town
BEST PROGRAMME AWARD							
Club		Boldmere St M	Pelsall Villa	Rocester	Willenhall T	Shifnal Town	West Mids Pol.
MANAGER OF THE YEAR							
Manager	E Caulfield	M O'Kane	B Green	Knox/Folland	T Greer	T Hussy	R Brown
Club	Paget Rgrs	Shepshed D	Blakenall	Bloxwich T	Rocester	Oadby T	Stourport S
J McGORIAN CUP							
			Shepshed D	Willenhall T	Knypersley V	Oldbury Utd	Oadby Town

BARWELL

Secretary: Mrs Shirley Brown, 101 Eskdale Road, Hinckley, LE10 0NW (01455 446048)
Email address: steven.brown16@ntlworld.com

Ground: Kirkby Rd, Barwell, Leics (01455 843067)
Directions: M42 jct 10 (Tamworth Services), A5 towards Nuneaton. Remain on A5for approx 11 miles, go straight on at traffic lights at the Longshoot Motelthe 400 yards at r/about take 1st exit left sign A47 Earl Shilton, in 3 milesat traffic lights go straight ahead and in 1 mile at r/about take first leftexit sign Barwell in village centre 1/2 mile go straight over mini r/about, 20yards turn right into Kirkby Rd, ground 400 yards on right.
Capacity: 2,500 Seats: 256 Cover: 750 Floodlights: Yes
Clubhouse: Evenings & lunchtimes. Snacks available. **Club Shop:** No

HONOURS: Barwell Ath.: Leics Snr Lg Tebbutt Brown Cup 91-92, Leics Sen Cup 96-97.

PREVIOUS **Names:** Barwell Athletic F.C., Hinckley F.C. - amalgamated in 1992.
Leagues: Midland Combination 92-94
(Barwell Ath.: Leics Senior. Hinckley: Central Midlands 86-88)
Ground: Barwell Ath.: Kirkby Road pre 1992, Hinckley: groundshare at Hinckley Ath. pre-'92

RECORDS **Goalscorer:** Andy Lucas
Appearances: Kevin Johnson.

FACT FILE

Founded: 1992.
Nickname: Canaries
Sponsors: Megadrive
Colours: All yellow with green trim
Change colours: All blue with white trim
Midweek matchday: Tuesday
Programme: 36 pages #1.00
Editor: I Backhouse
2000-01 Captain: Darren Grassby
Top Scorer: Jason Percival
P.o.Y.: Paul Grears

CLUB PERSONNEL
Chairman: David Laing.
Vice Chairman: Ron Boorman.
President: Derek Withers
Press Officer: Merv Nash.
Manager: Paul Purser
Asst Manager: Mark Rosegreen
Physio: Viv Coleman

BOLDMERE St. MICHAEL

Secretary: Dave Holvey, 38 Aldridge Road, Streetly, Sutton Coldfield, B743TT
Tel: 0121 353 6321 (H & FAX) 07787 106698 950102 (M)
Ground: Church Road, Boldmere, Sutton Coldfield
Tel: 0121 373 4435 or 0121 384 7531
Directions: A38 & A5127 from City towards S. Coldfield, left at Yenton lights onto A452 (Chester Rd), Church Rd is 6th turning on the right.
Nearest station: 400yds from Chester Road (BR).
Capacity: 2,500 Seats: 230 Covered: 400 Floodlights: Yes
Clubhouse: , Bar & lounge, every evening and four lunchtimes.

HONOURS: Birmingham AFA 36-37; Birmingham AFA Snr Cup; Birmingham Jnr Cup, FA Amtr Cup SF 47-48; AFA Snr Cup 47-48; Central Amtr Lg 48-49; Midland Comb 85-86 88-89 89-90, Challenge Cup 77-78 89-90; Tony Allden Mem. Cup 78-79 88-89 91-92; Challenge Trophy 86-87; Sutton Charity Cup 96-97.
PREVIOUS: **Leagues:** West Mids 49-63; Midland Combination 63-94.

Players Progressing: John Barton (Everton, Derby County),Kevin Collins (Shrewsbury), Jack Lane (Birmingham City, Notts Co.), John Lewis(Walsall), Don Moss (Cardiff, C Palace), Harry Parkes (Aston Villa), Wally Soden (Coventry). Mike Griffiths (Torquay Un ited) , Robin Elmes and Jinmy Quiggin (Hereford United)

FACT FILE
Founded: 1883 Nickname: Mikes.
Sponsor: Swift Forwarding
Colours: White/black/black
Change Colours: Yellow/green/yellow
Midweek matches: Tuesday
Programme: 32 pages, 90p
Editor: D.Holvey (0121 3536321)

CLUB PERSONNEL
Chairman: Keith Fielding
Match Secretary: as secretary
Manager: Alan Parsons
2000-01
Captain: Andrew Richardson
P.o.Y.: Darren Owen
Top Goalscorer: Jimmy Quiggin 15

BRIDGNORTH TOWN

Secretary: Mary Boot, 68 Wellmeadow,Bridgenorth,Shropshire WV15 6DE (01746 764204)
Ground: Crown Meadow, Innage Lane, Bridgnorth, Salop WV16 6PZ (01746 762747)
Directions: Follow signs for Shrewsbury (A458) over river bridge on by-pass,turn right for town centre at island, right at T junction, 1st left into Victoria Road, right at cross-road, follow road into Innage Lane, ground on left.
Capacity: 1,600 Shop: Yes Seats: 250 Cover: 700 Floodlights: Yes
Clubhouse: Evenings & weekend lunches, Dancehall, darts, pool, hot food on matchdays
Record Fee Recieved: £10,000 for Delwyn Humphries from Kidderminster Harriers
Players Progressing: Roger Davies (Derby county) and Paul Jones (Wolves via Kidd'ter H)

HONOURS: Midland Comb 79-80 82-83 (R-up 76-77 80-81); Lg Cup 78-79, Tony Allden Mem Cup R-up, Kidderminster & Dist Lge,Shropshire Snr Cup 85-86; Shropshire County Cup 70-71 75-76 76-77 78-79 79-80;Welsh Amt Cup 70-71; Shropshire County Jun Cup 98-99.
BEST SEASON: FA Cup: 3rd Qual Rd 64-65FA Vase: 5th Rd 75-76, 94-95
PREVIOUS Leagues: Kidderminster & Dist until 68; Midland Comb 68-83; Southern Lge, Midland Div. 83-96 Names: St Leonards Old Boys pre 46
RECORDS Goalscorer: Roger Davies 157 Appearances: Kevin Harris 426
Attendance: 1,600 v South Shields FA Vase 5th Rd 1976

FACT FILE
Founded: 1946
Nickname: The Town
Sponsors:
Colours: All Blue
Change colours: All red
Midweek matchday: Tuesday
Programme: 24 pages,60p
Editor: Simon Bromley
Local Press : Shropshire Star, Bridgnorth Journal, Express & Star.. Local Radio: Beacon, BBC Radio Shropshire
Youth League: West Mids Regional Regional

CLUB PERSONNEL
Chairman: Simon Bromley
Vice Chairman: Ian Thomas
President: Mike Williams
Manager:Les Bristow
Asst Manager: Paul Blakeley
Physio: Andy Perry

BROMSGROVE ROVERS

Ground Victoria Ground, Birmingham Road, Bromsgrove, Worcs, B61 0DR Tel: 01527 876949
Directions: Ground is situated on the north side of Bromsgrove on the Birmingham Road, off the A38 Bromsgrove by pass. The M5 and M42 join theA38 to the north of the town making it easy to get to the ground without havingto go into town. The 144 Midland Red bus runs from New Street StationBirmingham and passes the ground.
Capacity: 4,893 Seated: 394 Covered Terracing: 1,344
Clubhouse: Victoria Club (01527 878260) - Serves hot & cold food. Big screenTV, pool table & darts. Open matchdays and week-day evenings.
Club Shop: Selling replica clothing & souvenirs. Contact Doug Bratt (01527 874997).
PREVIOUS Leagues: Birmingham Lge 1898-08 53-65, Birmingham Comb. 1908-53, West Midlands 65-72, Southern Lge - Northern Div. 73-79, Midland Div.79-86, Premier Div. 86-92, GMVC 92-97, Southern 97-01
HONOURS: Vauxhall Conference R-up 92-93, Lge Cup 94-95 95-96; Southern Lge Prem 91-92, R-up 86-87, Cup 92-93, R-up 86-87,Midland Div 85-86, Merit Cup 85-86, Cup 85-86, R-up 73-74 87-88; Bill Dellow Cup 85-86; Worcester Sen Cup (8), R-up (10); Birmingham Sen Cup 46-47, R-up 47-48 88-89; W Mid Lge R-up 67-70, Cup 67-68 70-71; Birminham Lge 59-60, R-up 04-05 56-57 60-61; Birmingham Comb 46-47, R-up 49-50 50-51; Hereford Charity Chall Cup 46-47, R-up 47-48.
CLUB RECORDS Attendance: 7,389 v Worcester City - 1957
Career - Goalscorer: Chris Hanks 238, 83-84 **Appearances:** Shaun O'Meara 763, 75-94

FACT FILE
Formed: 1885
Sponsors: All Saints Masterfit (Bromsgrove).
Nickname: Rovers or Greens
Colours: White with gren trim/white/white
Change colours:red withGreen trim
Midweek matchday: Tuesday
Reserves' league: Central Conference.
Newsline: 0891 88 44 96
Programme: Pages: 40 Price: £1.20
Editors: Brian Perry 0121 628 6009
Alan Saunders 01527 833838

CLUB PERSONNEL
Chairman: Keith McMaster
President: Charles W Poole
Secretary: c/o Bromsgrove Rovers FC
Commercial Manager: Rebecca O'Neill
Manager:George Rooney
Trainer: Stewart Pinfold
Physio: Paul Sunners

CHASETOWN

Secretary: Chris Harris, 38 Naden House, Stafford Rd., Cannock, Staffs. WS12 4NU
tel; 01543 572927 (H) 01889 583306 (B)

Ground: The Scholars, Church Street, Chasetown, Walsall WS7 8QL Tel: 01543 682222/684609

Directions: Follow Motorways M5, M6 or M42 and follow signs for A5. A5 to White Horse Road/Wharf Lane, left into Highfields Rd (B5011), left into Church Street at top of hill, ground at end just beyond church. Buses 394 or 395 W Mids Travel, 94 Chase Bus,from Walsall, 860 Midland Red from Cannock.
Capacity: 2,000 Seats: 112 Cover: 250 Floodlights: Yes **Club Shop:** Yes
Clubhouse: Mon-Fri 7.30-11pm, Sat 11.30am-11pm, Sun 8-10.30pm. Basic snacks

HONOURS West Mids Lg R-up 90-91 92-93 (Lg Cup 89-90 90-91, Div 1 77-78 (R-up73-74 74-75 75-76 80-81 82-83), Div 1 Cup R-up 80-81 82-83, Div 2 R-up 87-88,Div 2 Cup R-up 86-87); Walsall Snr Cup 90-91 92-93; Staffs Snr Cup R-up 91-92.

PREVIOUS Name: Chase Terrace Old Scholars 54-72 Ground: Burntwood Rec Cte (pre'83)
Leagues: Cannock Yth 54-58; Lichfield & Dist. 58-61; Staffs Co. 61-72; West Mids 72-94.

RECORDS Attendance: 659 v Tamworth, FA Cup 2nd Qual Rd 1/10/88.
Appearances: A Cox 469 (+15) **Win:** 14-1 v Hanford (H), Walsall Snr Cup 17/10/92.
Goalscorer: T Dixon 172 **Defeat:** 1-8 v Telford U Res., West Mids (Reg.) Lge Div. 1

FACT FILE
Founded: 1954.
Nickname: Scholars
Colours: All blue
Change Colours: All Red.
Sponsors: Aynsley Windows
Midweek matchday: Tuesday
Reserves League: West Midlands
Programme: 26 pages, 50p
Editor/Press Officer: Mike Fletcher

CLUB PERSONNEL
Chairman: Brian Baker
Vice Chairman: B Simpson
President: A Scorey.
Manager: Cliff Painter
Asst Manager: Brian Fox
Physio: E Highfield.

CRADLEY TOWN

Secretary: David Attwood, 4 Birch Coppice, Quarry Bank, Brierley Hill, W Midlands DY5 1AP
Tel: 01384 637430
Ground: Beeches View, Beeches View Ave, Cradley, Halesowen, B63 2HB. (01384 569658)
Directions: M5-jct3.A456 right at 2nd island into Gaglet Rd. Third left to Rosemary Rd. Straigh into Lansdowne Rd/Dunstall Rd then left at T jct into Huntingtree Rd/Luffley Mill Rd.Left at next T jct into Stourbridge Rd and left into Beecher Rd East.First left into Abbey Rd and right into Beeches View Avenue at end .Ground entrance is between houses 48 & 59,20yyds on left.
Capacity: 3,000 Seats: 200 Cover: 1,500 Floodlights: Yes
Clubhouse: Open matchdays only. Food available Club Shop: No

HONOURS West Mids Lg Div 1 90-91, Midland Comb. Div 2 72-73 R-up 75-76 77-78, Presidents Cup 74-75 75-76, Invitation Cup 72-73); Metropolitan Lg 70-71, Wednesbury Charity Cup 90-91, Dudley Guest Hosp. Cup 71-72 72-73 75-76 90-91
PREVIOUS Leagues: Metropolitan; Brierley Hill; Kidderminster; West Mids Amtr; Midland Comb. 71-82; West Midlands 82-99 **Name:** Albion Haden United **Grounds:** None
RECORDS Gate: 1,000 v Aston Villa, friendly **Goalscorer:** Jim Nugent **Apps:** R J Haywood
Win: 9-1 v Wolverhampton United (H), West Midlands Lge 1990
Defeat: 0-9 v Paget Rangers (A) Midland Invitation Cup 97
Transfer fee paid: £1,000 for Darren Marsh (Oldswinford, 1992)
Received: £20,000 for John Williams (Swansea, 1991)

FACT FILE
Founded: 1948
Nickname: Lukes
Sponsors:Commercial Risk Insurance
Colours: White/black/black
Change colours: Yellow/blue/blue
Midweek matchday: Tuesday
Programme: Yes

CLUB PERSONNEL
President: Alf Hill
Chairman: Graham Taylor
Vice Chairman: Trevor Thomas
Press Officer: Trevor Thomas (01384 569658)
Manager: Trevor Thomas
Asst Mgr: Andy Mole
Physio: Chris Knight

2000-01
Captain: Matthew Aston
P.o.Y.: Paul Probert
Top Goalscorer: Robert Hiscox 8

HALESOWEN HARRIERS

Secretary: Mrs Christine Beasley, 43 Hawne Lane, Halesowen, West Midlands, B63 3RN. Tel: 0121 550 3788 (H) 01384 896748 (B) 07788 697167 (M)

Ground: Hayes Park, Park Rd, Colley Gate, Halesowen Tel: 01384 896748

Directions: On A458 Birmingham to Stourbridge Rd (B'ham 10 miles, Stourbridge 4 miles). M5 Jct 3 (towards Kidderminster), right at 1st island (towards Dudley), turn left at island (towards Stourbridge), straight over next island then 3m to ground on left side, 200yds past Park Lane. 1 mile from Lye BR

Capacity: 4,000 Seats: 350 Cover: 500 Floodlights: Yes **Club Shop:** Yes

Clubhouse: Open every evening. Limited range of hot snacks, but full cold snack kitchen.

HONOURS West Mids League Div 1 85-86 (Div 2 84-85, Div 2 Cup 84-85), Inter City Bowl 67-68 68-69, Festival League x5, R-up x9, FA Sunday Cup SF 79-80, Midland Sunday Cup, Birmingham Sunday Cup.

PREVIOUS **Leagues:** Festival (Sunday)/ West Midlands (pre-1994)

Grounds: Birmingham Parks 61-70/ Halesowen Town FC 70-84 (both whilst in Sunday football).

RECORDS **Attendance:** Friendly matches 750 v Walsall and Wolves in 1985
Competitive: 450 v Lye, Lge 1988
Defeat: 2-8 v Frickley Athletic (A), F.A. Cup 2nd Qual Rd 26/9/92.

Win: 12-1 v Lichfield & v Malvern Town, 1986. **Fee paid:** £750 to Oldswinford for L Booth, 1991.

FACT FILE

Founded: 1961
Nickname: None
Sponsors:Ludlow Coaches,Bevan Contracts
Colours: White/black/white
Change colours: Yellow/Blue/Yellow
Midweek matchday: Tuesday or Wednesday.
Programme: 28-36 pages
Editor: Rob Shinfield 01922 42205
7

CLUB PERSONNEL

Chairman: Derek Beasley
Tel: 01384 896748(W) 0771 855 2337(M)

2000-01

Leading goalscorer: Mark Clarke 12
Captain: Giles Parry
P.o.Y.: Stuart Butler

KNYPERSLEY VICTORIA

Secretary: Steve Chawner, 18 John St., Biddulph, Stoke on Trent. ST6 6BB (01782 518998)
Email Address: secretary@knypersleyvics.co.uk

Ground: Tunstall Road, Knypersley, Stoke-on-Trent, (01782 522737 club).

Directions: M6 Jct 15 join A500, 4th exit, pick up A527, follow through Tunstall, Chell, to Biddulph. Ground is situated on A527 just before Biddulph. From M6 jct 18 follow signs to Holmes Chapel then Congleton, A527 to Biddulph,continue thru lights, ground on left.

Capacity: 1,200 Seats: 200 Cover: 200 Floodlights: Yes **Club Shop:** Yes

Clubhouse: Open from 1pm Saturdays, 7pm weekdays. Hot snacks at tea bar

HONOURS West Mids Lg Div 1 92-93, Staffs Snr Lg 84-85 (Lg Cup 84-85 85-86), Staffs Co. Lg R-up 79-80, Staffs FA Vase 83-84 86-87, Sentinel Cup 86-87, Leek & Moorlands Lg 72-73 (Div 2 71-72). Industrial Rewinds Cup 98, Joe McGorian Cup 88.

BEST SEASON **FA Cup** 3rd Qual Rd 96-97 **FA Vase:**

PREVIOUS **Leagues:** Leek & Moorlands 69-78; Staffs Co. (North) 78-83; Staffs Sen 83-90; W Midland (Reg) 90-94. **Grounds:** None

RECORDS **Attendance:** 1,100 v Port Vale, friendly 1989
Goalscorer: J Burndred 128 **Appearances:** Terry Stanway 601
Fee paid: £1,000 M Biddle (Congleton 93) **Defeat:** 0-9 v Meir KA, Staffs Sen.
Win: 10-0 v Clancey Dudley, West Midls (Reg.) Div. 1 90-91

FACT FILE

Founded: 1969.
Nickname: The Vics.
Sponsors: Chrysalis Fibres
Colours: Claret & sky/claret/claret & sky.
Change colours; Blue & Yelow/ Blue/Yellow
Midweek matchday: Tues/Thurs
Reserve League: Staffs Senior.
Programme: 40 pages 60p.
Editor/ Press Officer: J A Shenton (01782 517962).
Website: www.knypersleyvics.co.uk

CLUB PERSONNEL

Chairman: Alan farr
President: G Quinn

Manager: Terry Stanway
Coach: Mick Biddle
Physio: T.B.A.

LUDLOW TOWN

Secretary: Mr J Nash, 58 Hucklemarsh Road, Ludlow, Shropshire (01584 874337)

Ground: Blakenall F.C., Red Lion Ground, Bloxwich, Walsall

Directions: From Kidderminster A4117, straight over r'bout into Henley Rd, 2nd left into Sandpits Rd, follow road for 1/4 mile until road bears round to the left into Ridding Rd - ground on right

Capacity: Seats: No Cover: 150 Floodlights: Yes Clubhouse: Yes

HONOURS: West Mids. Lg. Prem 00-01, Div. 2 78-79, Lg. Cup R-up 94-95. Div 1 Cup 90-91; Shropshire Co. Cup: 73-7493-94, 94-95 96-97; Presteigne-Otway Cup 90-91.94-95:

PREVIOUS: League: Kidderminster League 1961-63, Shropshire Co. Lg.: 1963-1978
Ground: Riddings Park, Riddings Road, Ludlow, Shropshire

BEST SEASON **F.A.Vase:** 1st Q Rd. 98-99 (1st season) **F.A.Cup:** Never Entered

FACT FILE

Formed: 1890
Colours: Red & white/black/black
Change colours: Blue & white/white/blue
Midweek Matchdays: Tuesday
Reserve League: West Midlands
Programme: Yes

2000-01

Leading goalscorer: Ashley Davies 58
Captain: Shaun Parker
P.o.Y.: Shaun Parker

CLUB PERSONNEL

Chairman: P.Gwilliam
Vice Chaiman: Robert Leech
Co Managers: Steve Frisby - Les Bristow
Asst Manager: Bob Jones
Physio: Miss J Stretton

Bridgnorth Town. Back Row (l-r): Ryan Daley, Kevin Thompson, Shaun Williams, Eric Smith, Simon Bryan, Ian Perry, Jason Treharne, Phil Embrey, Carl Bradley. Front Row: Tony Collins, Dave Titterton, Steve Ball, Steve Hanmer, Kenny Drakeford, Matt Bytheway, Neil Meredith, Charlie Blakemoore, Rob Simcox. Photo: Marshall's Sports Service (Birmingham)

Halesowen Harriers. Back Row (l-r): John Powell, Lee Brown, Martin Jeffs, Steve Lawson, Richard Knott, Giles Parry, Paul Hampton, Paul Round, Chris Busby, Richard Colwell, Andy Jones, Simon Evans, Darren Taylor. Front Row: Spencer Truslove, Stephen Harris, Mark Clarke, Stuart Butle, Clint Hughes, Indi Rai, Daniel Mumford, Neil Smith. Photo: Marshall's Sports Service

Left: Oldbury United Back Row (l-r): Steve Watson, Stuart Grosvenor, Tony Davis, Steve Johnson, Neil Hesson, Dave Davies, Dave Titterton. Front Row: Steve Wilkinson, Katie Moor (mascot), Mark Jones, Dave Jackson, Brett Clarke, Alan Kuilla.

Photo: Marshall's Sports Service (Birmingham)

OADBY TOWN

Secretary: Ken Farrant c/o Club. Tel Nos: 0116 2716007 (H) 0794 1584017 (M)
Ground: Invicta Park, Wigston Road, Oadby, Leics LE2 5QG Tel: 0116 271 5728

Directions: Oadby is situated 4 miles south of Leicester on the A6. from Oadby church in the centre of town, follow signposts for Wigston. The ground is 3/4 mile from the church on the left.
Capacity: Cover: 224 Seating: 224 Floodlights: Yes
Clubhouse: Yes Shop: Yes

HONOURS Leicestershire Senior Lge: (8) Midland Football Alliance 99-00
Div. 2 51-52; Lge Cup 77-78 93-94 94-95;
Leics Senior Cup 62-63 63-64 75-76 76-77 80-81
Charity Cups Rolleston 58-59 59-60 68-69 74-75 88-89 93-94 96-97 97-98;
Coalville 60-61 63-64 65-66 69-70; Harborough 83-84 88-89; Oadby 70-71;
Battle of Britain 93-94 94-95 96-97
PREVIOUS **Leagues:** Leicestershire Senior League

FACT FILE

Founded:1939
Colours: All red
Change colours: All white
Midweek matchday: Wednesday
Programme Editor: Rob Campion

CLUB PERSONNEL

Chairman: Brian Ford Powell
Vice Chairman: Stuart Blyth
President: Bob Mallet
Vice President: Alan Hussey

Manager: Lee Adam
Asst. Manager: T.B.A.
Physio: Derek Hewitt

OLDBURY UNITED

Secretary: Lee Tomkinson, 36 Bryan Road, Walsall,WS2 9DW
Tel. Nos: 01922-447834 (H) 0121 3034468 (W) 07790 295141 (M)

Ground: The Cricketts, York Road, Rowley Regis, Warley, West Midlands (0121 5595564)

Directions: M5 jct 2, follow Blackheath & Halesowen signs, first left at lights and fourth right into York Road (turning before motorway flyover), ground 200yds on left. One and a half miles from Sandwell & Dudley and Rowley Regis BR stations. Bus 404 from West Bromwich, Oldbury and Blackheath.
Capacity: 3,000 Seats: 300 Cover: 1,000 Floodlights: Yes
Clubhouse: Mon-Fri 7.30-11pm, Sat-Sun 12-2.30 (12-11pm Sat matchdays). Snacks available on matchdays. **Club Shop:** No

HONOURS West Mids Lg 92-93, Staffs Snr Cup 87-88, Midland Comb. R-up 78-79(Presidents Cup 72-73(res), Div 3 R-up 82-83(res), Chal. Vase 82-83(res)),Walsall Snr Cup 82-83, B'ham Snr Amtr Cup, Oldbury Lg Div 2 61-62, Worcs Snr Urn 86-87, Sandwell Charity Cup 86-87, Interlink Invitation Cup 96-97. Industrial Rewinds League Cup: 98-99
PREVIOUS **Leagues**: Oldbury 58-62/ Warwick & W Mids All. 62-65/ Worcs (later Midland) Comb. 65-82/ Southern 82-86.**Names:** Queens Colts 58-62/ Whiteheath Utd 62-65
Grounds: Brittania Park 61-63/ Newbury Lane (Oldbury Stadium) 63-78.
RECORDS **Attendance:** 2,200 v Walsall Wood, Walsall Snr Cup Final 1982.
Win: 10-1 v Blakenall **Defeat:** 1-9 v Moor Green.

FACT FILE

Founded: 1958
Nickname: Cricketts,The Blues.
Sponsors: Beswick Paper Group, Oldbury.
Colours: Navy with sky trim/blue/blue
Change colours: All amber
Midweek matchday: Tuesday
Programme: 28 pages, 60p
Editor: Football Secretary.

CLUB PERSONNEL

Chairman: Roy Keeling.
Vice Chairman: Ken Harris.
Press Officer: Ian Whitmore

Manager: John Morris
Asst Mgr: Kevin Sweeney
Physio: Paul Millard

PAGET RANGERS

GROUND Vale Stadium, Farnborough Rd., Castle Vale, Birmingham B35 7BE
Tel: 0121 747 6969 Fax: 0121 747 6862 Press/Matchdays: 0121 749 7707
Directions: M6 North to Junct. 5. Turn right onto A452. Turn right at 1st r'about into Tangmere Drive. Fork right into Farnborough Rd. 800 yds turn right signed Fort centre.
M6 South to Spaghetti junction. Take signs for Tyburn Rd (A38) Turn right onto A452. Turn left opposite Jaguar factory then as above (Tangmere Drive)
Capacity: 5000 Cover: 200 Seats: 280 Floodlights: Yes 257 Lux
Clubhouse: 'Spitfire Club'. Open daily. Capacity 150. Servery from kitchen to ground.
No club shop - metal badges, ties etc avail. from committee.
PREVIOUS **Leagues:** Birmingham Suburban; Central Amateur; Midland Comb. 50-81; Southern 87-88 95-01; West Midlands (Regional) 88-94; Midland Alliance 94-95.
Grounds: Pype Hayes Park 38-46; Springfield Road, Walmley 46-93, Ground Share Sutton Coldfield Town >98.
HONOURS West Mids Lg R-up 91-92 (Lg Cup 91-92); Midland Comb.(6) 59-61 69-71 82-83 85-86 (R-up 77-78, Lg Cup 59-60 66-67, Div 1 Cup 70-71, Div 3 82-83 (res)); B'ham Jnr Cup 51-52; Walsall Snr Cup 85-86; Midland Alliance 94-95; Lord Mayor of Birmingham Charity Cup 94-95; Staffs Sen Cup R-up 94-95
BEST SEASON **FA Cup:** Third Qual Round 94-95
FA Vase: Fourth Rd 88-89, 0-1 v Wisbech **FA Trophy:** 2nd Rd 98-99, 0-2 v Accrington Stanley

FACT FILE

Formed: 1938 Nickname: The 'Bears'
Sponsors: INA Bearing Co. Ltd.
Colours: Gold/black/gold
Change colours: All red
Midweek matchday: Tuesday
Reserves' League: No reserve team

PROGRAMME
Pages: 24 Price: £1
Editor: R R Ruddick 0121 747 6969

CLUB OFFICIALS
Chairman: Derek Culling
Secretary: Stephen Whale, 30 Innsworth Drive, Castle Vale, Birmingham B35 6BB Tel: 0121 749 2919 (h) 0790 1960446 (M)
Press Officer: Chris Inman
Commercial Manager: Chairman
Manager: Chris Sharp
Asst Manager: Paul Edwards
Coach: Chris Sharpe
Physio: D J Culling

PELSALL VILLA

Secretary: Gareth J Evans, 72 St Pauls Crescent, Pelsall, Walsall WS3 4ET(01922 693114).
Ground: The Bush, Walsall Road, Pelsall, Walsall
Tel: 01922 682018 Club, 01922 692748 Ground
Directions: M6 jct 7 marked A34 B'ham. Take A34 towards Walsall to 1st island,turn right (marked Ring Road), cross two islands. At large island at bottom of hill take last exit marked Lichfield, up hill, cross next island to lights.Continue to next set of lights and turn left (B4154 Pelsall). Over railway bridge to Old Bush pub on right (next to Pelsall Cricket & Sports Club).
Capacity: 2,000 Seats: Yes Cover: 624 Floodlights: Yes **Club Shop:** Yes
Clubhouse: Mon-Fri 7-11pm, Sat noon-11pm, Sun noon-3 & 7-10.30pm. Hot &cold meals.

HONOURS West Mids Lg - Prem. Lge 94-95 (R-up 95-96) Div Cup 95-96, Div 1 Cup 88-89 (R-up 89-90, Div 2 Cup R-up 83-84, Walsall Snr Cup R-up 89-90 92-93, Wednesbury Charity Cup 6, (R-up 7), D Stanton Shield(2) 73-75 (R-up 75-76), Sporting Star Cup 76-77 (R-up 61-62), Prem Div Tphy(res)89-90), Rugeley Charity Cup 78-79 (R-up 69-70), Bloxwich Charity Cup(2), Edge Cup 83-84, Ike Cooper Tphy R-up 89-90. Midland Triangle Cup 95-96.
BEST SEASON **FA Cup:** 3rd Qual. Rd 92-93, 2-4 V Gainsborough T. (A).
FA Vase: 5th Rd 92-93, 0-1 v Buckingham T. (A)
PREVIOUS **League:** Staffs County (South) 61-81, West Midlands 82-96 Grounds: None
RECORDS **Attendance** 2,060 v Aston Villa 29.7.98
Goalscorer: Dean Walters 231 **Appearances:** Neil Coles 588

FACT FILE

Reformed: 1961
Nickname: Villians
Sponsor: Metelec
Colours: Red & black/black/red
Change colours: Blue & white/white/white
Midweek home matchday: Tuesday
Programme: 68 pages, 80p
Editor: Secretary

CLUB PERSONNEL

Chairman: RonNew
Vice Chairman: J H Gough
President: B J Hill
Press Officer: B J Hill

Manager: Kevin Gough
Asst Manager: A.Dixon
Physio: R.Pickering

QUORN

Secretary: Margaret Berry, 214 BarrowRd.Sileby,Leics.LE12 7LR Tel: 01509 813259
Ground: Farley Way, Quorn, Leics (01509 620232)Colours: Red/white/red

RUSHALL OLYMPIC

Secretary: Peter Athersmith, 46 Blakenall Lane, Leamore, Walsall, W Mids WS31HG
Tel: 01922 712632 (H) 0121 553 5525 (W) 07909 792422(M)
Ground: Dales Lane, off Daw End Lane, Rushall, Nr Walsall (01922 641021).
Directions: From Rushall centre (A461) take B4154 signed Aldridge. Approx., 1mile on right, directly opposite Royal Oak P.H., in Daw End Lane. Grd on right. 2 miles Walsall (BR) station.
Capacity: 2,500 Seats: 200 Cover: 200 Floodlights: Yes **Club Shop:** No
Clubhouse: Bar/lounge, every night 8-11pm, Sat matchdays, Sun noon-2.30pm
HONOURS West Mids Lge Div 1 79-80; Walsall Amtr Lge Div 1 55-56, Div 2 52-53, Snr Cup 54-55 55-56, Jabez Cliff Cup 55-56 ; Staffs Co. Lge Div 1(4) (Div 2 56-57); Walsall Charity Cup 52-53; Walsall Chal.Cup (2).Walsall Mem. Charity Cup (x7) 55-62; W Preston Chal. Cup 56-57; Cannock & Dist. Charity Cup 56-57; Wednesbury Snr Cup (3) Sporting Star Cup (5) J W Edge 62-63 66-67; Walsall Snr Cup 64-65;99-00 Lichfield Charity64-65 66-67; Staffs Yth Cup 81-82. Mid Alliance R-up 00-01
PREVIOUS **Leagues:** Walsall Amateur 52-55/ Staffs County (South) 56-78/ West Midlands (Reg) 78-94. **Grounds:** Rowley Place 51-75/ Aston University 76-79.
RECORDS **Attendance:** 2,000 v Leeds Utd Old Boys **Goalscorer:** Graham Wiggin
Appearances: Alan Dawson (400+ apps) **Players progressing:** Lee Sinnott (Watford), Lee Palin (Aston Villa),Stuart Watkiss (Walsall), Steve Taylor (Crystal Palace via Bromsgrove £1,500 + £18,000 sell on-record club fee)

FACT FILE

Founded: 1951Nickname: Pics.
Sponsors: Staus Systems
Colours: Amber with black trim/black/black
Change colours: White & Black/white/white
Midweek matchday: Tuesday
Youth League: West Mids (Reg.)
Programme: 36 pages, 50p
Editor/ Press Officer: Darren Stockall (01922 379153).

CLUB PERSONNEL

Chairman: John Burks
Vice Chairman: Trevor Westwood
President: Brian Greenwood.
Manager: John Allen
Asst Manager:Kevin Foster
Physio: Lee Horrocks
2000-01 Capt: Martin Leadbeater
P.o.Y.: Limmy Conway
Top Scorer: AsaCharlton 14

SHIFNAL TOWN

Secretary: Glyn Davies, 30 Drayton Road, Shifnal, Shropshire, TF11 8BT (01952460326 H)
Ground: Phoenix Park, Coppice Green Lane, Shifnal, Shropshire.
Directions: M54 jct 3, A41 towards Newport, 1st left for Shifnal (3 miles), in Shifnal take 1st right, and sharp right again up Coppice Green Lane, ground800yds on left past Idsall School.
Capacity: 3,000 Seats: 224 Cover: 300 Floodlights: Yes
Clubhouse: Open Mon-Sat 7.30-11pm (matchdays 12-11pm), Sun 12-3 & 7.30-10-30
Not on ground but in Newport Rd, Shifnal. **Club Shop:** No
HONOURS: West Mids Lg 80-81 81-82 Div 1 78-79,
Shropshire Snr Cup 80-81 90-91 92-93.
BEST SEASON **FA Cup:** 1982-83 **FA Vase:** 1983-84
PREVIOUS **Leagues:** Wellington (Dist.) 64-69; Shropshire County 69-77 85-93; West Midlands 77-85; Midland Combination 94-95.
Grounds: Admirals Park 80-85
RECORDS **Attendance:** 1,002 v Bridgnorth T., FA Vase 3rd Rd 83-84 (Admirals Park)
Goalscorer: Steve Kelly 35 **Appearances:** John Powell 321
Win: 10-1 v Malvern, 82-83 **Defeat:** 1-6

FACT FILE

Founded: 1964 Nickname: None.
Sponsors: Assoc. Cold Stores & Transport Ltd.
Colours:All Red & white
Change cols: Blue & white/white/blue & white
Midweek matchday: Tuesday
Reserves' League: West Midlands
Programme: 32 pages, 60p
Editor: J.Wilson (01952 274855).

CLUB PERSONNEL

Chairman: Mr. A.Dodd
Vice Chairman: Mr. R Owen
President: Mr.D.Millward
Press Off:K.Fullerton 01952 405274
Manager: Ken Howells
Asst Manager: John Powell
Physio: Charlott Lewis

STAFFORD TOWN

Secretary: Dave Rowley, 32 Lodge Rd, Brereton, Rugely, Staffs WS15 1HG
Tel: 01889 800779 (H) 07971 454217 (Mobile) Email: info@staffordtownfc.co.uk

Ground: Stafford Rangers FC, Marston Road, Stafford

Directions: From M6 junction 14, Take 3rd left to Red Hill Roundabout and follow signs for Aston Fields Ind Est along Beaconside. Aston Fields is signposted 3rd right along Common Road, having travelled over railway bridge, Stafford Rangers FC ground is on the right

Capacity: 6,000 Cover: 3,000 Seats: 426 Floodlights: Yes Club Shop: No

Club address: Chamley Club, Beconside, Stafford Tel: 01785 665739 (Mr N Payne)

HONOURS WMRL Div 1 93-94, Staffs Snr Lg R-up 91-92, Midland Comb. Div 2 78-79, Staffs Vase 84-85 92-93 (R-up 87-88,99-00, Bourne Sports Trophy 84-85, Walsall Sen Cup SF 91-92 W.Mids Champions 99-00 Lg.Cup R-up 99-00 Laegue Discipline Award 00-01

PREVIOUS **Leagues:** Staffs Co. (North) 74-77 82-84; Midland Comb. 77-82; Staffs Sen. 84-93, W.M.R.L. 93-2000
Grounds: Silkmore Lane 74-77 Burton Manor Spts 77-88; Riverway 88-91 Park Stadium 91-94 ;

RECORD **Win:** 14-0 v Leek CSOB (H), Staffs Senior League 8/10/88
Goalscorer: Mick Stark : 54 goals in the 1999-2000 season

FACT FILE
Founded: 1974
Nickname: Reds or Town
Colours: All red
Change colours:All Blue
Midweek matches: Mon/Wed
Programme: 36 pages, #1.00
Editor: Chris Curtis & Graham Whitehall (01785 605561)
Website: www.staffordtownfc.co.uk

CLUB PERSONNEL
Chairman: Gordon Evans
01785 254073 (H) 01785 283863 (B)
President: Graham Hollinshead
Press Officer: Chris Curtis/Alan Bowers
Manager: Dave Downing

2000-01
Captain: Nick Anthony
P.o.Y.: Mark Tilston
Top Scorer: Russell Demmatteo 25

STAPENHILL

Secretary: Peter Begent, 22 Grasmere Close, Stapenhill, Burton-on-Trent DE159DS
Tel: 01283 540583

Ground: Edge Hill, Maple Grove, Stapenhill, Burton-on-Trent (01283 562471).

Directions: 3 miles from Burton on A444 Measham Rd, turn right (coming from Burton) at Copperhearth Pub Hse into Sycamore Rd, Maple Grove is 5th left. 3miles from Burton-on-Trent (BR) buses 15, 16 from opposite station.

Capacity: 2,000 Seats: 200 Covered: 500 Floodlights: Yes

Clubhouse: In ground. Pub hours. Matchday tea bar. **Club Shop:** No

HONOURS Midland Combination R-up 92-93 Div 1 89-90, Challenge Cup 92-93 93-94, Leics Snr Lg 59-60 86-87 88-89 (Tebbutt Brown Cup (2) 87-89), Leics Snr Cup 69-70 86-87, Derby Snr Cup R-up 88-89 91-92.

BEST SEASON **FA Cup:** **FA Vase:**

PREVIOUS **League:** Leics Snr 58-89/ Midland Combination 89-94.
Name: Stapenhill Waterside Community Centre.

RECORDS **Attendance:** 2,000 v Gresley, Derbys Snr Cup final 88-89.
Goalscorer: Brian Beresford 123 **Appearances:** Ian Pearsall 172.
Win: 11-0 v Alcester Town (H), Midland Comb. Prem. Div.,1992-93.
Defeat: 0-7 v Bridgnorth Town, FA Vase.

FACT FILE
Founded: 1947
Nickname: Swans
Sponsors: TAG Football Kits
Colours: Red & Green
Change Colours: All blue
Midweek matchday: Tuesday
Programme: 50p
Editor: Secretary

CLUB PERSONNEL
Chairman: Tony Smith
Vice Chairman: Ken Hulland
President: Fred Sleigh.
Press Officer: Secretary.
Manager: Steve Coburn
Asst Manager: Gary Norton

STOURBRIDGE

Secretary: Hugh Clark,10 Burnt Oak Drive, Stourbridge, W. Mids DY8 1HL Tel: 01384 392975

Ground: War Memorial Ath. Grd, High St., Amblecote, Stourbridge DY8 4HN (01384 394040)

Directions: Take A491, signposted Wolverhampton, from Stourbridge ring-road -ground 300yds on left immediately beyond traffic lights and opposite `RoyalOak' pub. Buses 311, 313 from Dudley, and 256 from Wolverhampton, pass ground. 1 mile from Stourbridge Town (BR)

Capacity: 2,000 Cover: 1,250 Seats: 250 Floodlights: Yes

Clubhouse: Open every evening from 8pm and Sunday lunchtimes

Club Shop: Programmes & souvenirs. Contact Nigel Gregg

PREVIOUS Name: Stourbridge Standard **Leagues:** West Midlands (prev. Birmingham) 1892-1939 54-71, Birmingham Comb. 45-53, Southern 71-00

HONOURS Welsh Cup R-up 73-74; Southern Lg Midland Div 90-91 (Lg Cup 92-93), Div 1 North73-74, Merit Cup 73-74; West Mids (prev. B'ham) Lg 23-24 (R-up 4); B'ham Comb. R-up 51-52; B'ham Snr Cup 49-50 45-46 75-76 (R-up 3); Worcs Snr Cup 9, (R-up 12); Herefordshire Snr Cup 54-55; Camkin Cup R-up 69-70; Camkin Presidents Cup 70-71; Albion Shield 43-44; Keys Cup 37-38 62-63, Worcs Comb. R-up 27-28; Worcs Jnr Cup R-up 27-28; Tillotson Cup R-up 39-40, MFC Davis League Cup 00-01.

BEST SEASON **FA Cup:** 4th Qual Rd: 67-68, 84-85 85-86 98-99 **FA Trophy:** Qtr Final 70-71

CLUB RECORDS **Career Goalscorer:** Ron Page 269 **Career Appearances:** Ron Page 427

FACT FILE
Formed: 1876 Nickname: The Glassboys
Sponsors: Carlsberg
Colours: Red & white stripes
Change colours: Yellow & blue
Midweek matchday: Tuesday
Programme: Pages: 28 Price: £1
Editors: Hugh Clark & Nigel Gregg

CLUB PERSONNEL
Chairman: Mark Serrell
Chief Executive: Nick Pratt
Press Officer: Richard Clark
Manager/Coach: Mark Harrison
Assistant Manager: Steve Brown
Physio: Mark Farrington

2000-01
Leading goalscorer: Michael Moore 41
Captain: Stuart Hamilton
Supporters' P.O.Y: Michael Moore
Players' P.O.Y: Lewis Baker

STRATFORD TOWN

Secretary: Roger Liggins, 17 Hammerton way, Wellesbourne, Warwicks. CV35 9NS
Tel Nos: 01789 840755 (H) 02476 539401 (W)
Ground: Masons Road, off Alcester Road, Stratford-upon-Avon, Warks (01789 297479).
Directions: Follow the signs for Alcester/Worcester A422 from the town centre.
Masons Road is the 1st right afterthe railway bridge.
400 yards from Stratford-on-Avon (BR)station.
Local buses for West Green Drive.
Capacity: 1,100 Seating/Cover: 200 Floodlights: Yes

Clubhouse: Open every night except Sunday **Club Shop:** No.

HONOURS Midland Comb 56-57 86-87; Chal. Cup 86-87 88-89 (R-up 55-56); Chal. Vase 81-82; Jack Mould Tphy 81-82; Tony Allden Mem. Cup 86-87; B'ham Snr Cup62-63.

BEST SEASON **FAVase:** **FA Cup:**

PREVIOUS **Leagues:** W Mids 57-70/ Mid Com. 70-73 75-94/ Hellenic 70-75.

RECORDS **Attendance:** 1,078 v Aston Villa, Birmingham Snr Cup, Oct 1996

Players progressing: Martin Hicks (Charlton '77), Roy Proverbs (Coventry, '56)

FACT FILE

Founded: 1944
Nickname: The Town
Sponsors: Porters Precision Products
Colours: All Blue
Change Colours: All Tangerine
Midweek Matchday: Tuesday
Reserves' League: Midland Comb. Res. Div..
Programme: 20 pages, 50p
Editor:

CLUB PERSONNEL

Chairman: Stuart Dixon
Vice-Chairman: T.B.A.
President: P Chatburn
Commercial Mgr: J Carruthers.
Manager: S Dixon
Physio: N Dixon

STUDLEY B.K.L.

Secretary: Mark Sealey c/o club.

Ground: Beehive, BKL Sports Ground, Abbeyfields,Birmingham Rd., Studley, Warwicks
Tel: 01527 853817
Directions: M42 Jct.3 onto A435 to Redditch.Over island at Dog Pub on left continue towards Studley. Ground on left signposted to Abbeyfields.
Capacity : 1,500 **Seats:** 200 **Cover :** Yes **Floodlights**:Yes **Clubhouse:** Yes,on ground.

HONOURS Midland Comb. Div 1 91-92, Chall Cup R-up 91-92,
Presidents Cup R-up 91-92, Div2 Cup 87-88;
Smedley Crooke Char. Cup 90-91 91-92;
Birmingham Vase R-up 96-97

PREVIOUS **League:** Redditch & South Warwickshire Sunday Combination 71-87
Name: BKL Works

CLUB RECORDS **Appearances:** Lee Adams
Goalscorer: Brian Powell
Attendance: 500 v Feckenham 31.8.98

FACT FILE

Founded: 1971
Nickname: Bees
Sponsors: BKL Fittings
Colours: All Skyblue & navy blue.
Change colours: All Yellow
Programme: 50p Editor: Gordon Wilkie
Reserve's League:

CLUB PERSONNEL

Chairman: David Robinson
Vice-Chairman: Alec James
Press Officer: Dave Chiswell

Manager: John Adams
Asst Manager: Alan Scarfe & Glen Adams
Physio: Dave Middleton

WEDNESFIELD

Secretary: Brian Saville, 74 Dunstall Hill, Wolverhampton WV6 0SP (01902 653266)

Ground: Cottage Ground, Amos Lane, Wednesfield, Wolverhampton (01902 735506).
Directions: From Wolverhampton on the A4124 Wednesfield Rd. Stay on road right through Wednesfield until island. Leave island at 1st exit (Wood End Rd), left after 200yds into Amos Lane. Ground on right, approx. 400yds along. 3 miles Wolverhampton BR station. Bus 559 to Wood End or 560 to Red Lion.
Capacity: 1,000 Seats: 148 Cover: 250 Floodlights: Yes

Clubhouse: Evenings 7-11pm. Food (burgers, chips etc) on 1st team matchdays.
Club Shop: No.

HONOURS West Mids Lg Div 1 76-77 (R-up 77-78).

BEST SEASON **FA Vase:** **FA Cup:**

PREVIOUS **League:** Wolverhampton & District Amateur 61-76/West Midlands 77-97.
Ground: St Georges PF 61-76 **Name:** Wednesfield Social 61-89.

RECORDS **Attendance:** 480 v Burton Albion, FA Cup 1981.

FACT FILE

Founded: 1961.
Nickname: Cottagers.
Sponsors: Ansells
Colours: Red/black/black& white
Change colours: Black & White
Stripes/white/black & white
Midweek matchday: Tuesday
Programme: 50p
Editor: TBA

CLUB PERSONNEL

Chairman: Surinda Ghattaura
Vice Chairman: J Massey
Manager/Coach: Ken Hall
Physio: M Andrews
Commercial Mgr: D Clayton
Press Officer: J Massey (01902 781819).

WILLENHALL TOWN

Secretary: Neil Arrowsmith,73 Parklands Road,Wolverhampton, W.Midlands
Ground: Noose Lane, Willenhall, West Midlands (01902 605132-club, 636586-office).
Directions: M6 Jnc 10 follow 'new' Black Country route and then 'Keyway'. On leaving 'Keyway' follow signs to Wolverhampton(A454). At 'Neachells' P H house right into Neachells Lane, and first right again into Watery Lane. At island turn left onto Noose Lane, ground is 200yds on left.
Capacity: 5,000 Seats: 324 Cover: 500 Floodlights: Yes

Clubhouse: Open Mon-Thurs 12-3 & 7-11pm, Fri-Sat 11am-11pm, Sun 12-2 & 7-10.30pm.
Snacks available. **Club Shop:** Yes

HONOURS FA Vase R-up 80-81; West Mids Lg 78-79, Div 1 75-76, Prem. Div Cup 79-80, Div 2 Cup 78-79(res); Southern Midland 83-84; Birmingham Snr Cup R-up 82-83; J W Hunt Cup 73-74., Mid Alliance Cup R-up 99-00, Rameses Invitation Cup 2000-01.
BEST SEASON **FA Vase:** Runners-up 80-81 **FA Cup:**
PREVIOUS **Leagues:** Wolverhampton Amateur/ Staffs County/ West Mids 75-82 91-94/Southern 82-91.
RECORDS Attendance: 3,454 v Crewe Alexandra, FA Cup 1st Rd 1981.
Goalscorer: Gary Matthews Appearances: Gary Matthews.
Players progressing: Sean O'Driscoll (Fulham),Joe Jackson (Wolves), Stuart Watkiss (Wolves), Tony Moore (Sheff U), Andy Reece (Bristol R.), Wayne O'Sullivan (Swindon).

FACT FILE

Founded: 1953 Nickname: Reds
Colours: All Red
Sponsors: Aspray Transport
Change colours: White & Blue/Blue/Blue
Midweek matchday: Tuesday.
Reserves League: Midland Comb.
Programme: 40 pages, 70p
Editor: Simon Hayes (01902 411758)

CLUB PERSONNEL

President: Jack Williams
Chairman: David Homer V-Chair: Keith Badger
Manager: Martin Thomas
Asst Manager:Kelvin Sullivan
Physios: Mike Andrews & Garyt McHale

2000-01

Capt: Russell Brown P.o.Y.: Aaron Skelding
Top Scorer: Gary Piggott 16

Pelsall Villa. Back Row (l-r): Nick Lovett, Ian Brown, John Williams, Craig Davidson, Steve Corbett, Matt Cartwright, Adrian Horne, Steve Lyons, Tony Dixon. Front Row: Gary Moore, Mark Bentley, Peter Howells, Chris Wilkins, Tom Bergin, Shaun Derry, Andrew Read. Photo: Marshall's Sports Service (Birmingham)

Shifnal Town. Back Row (l-r): Richard Finney, John Powell, Jason Treharne, Lee Turton, Anthony O'Connor, Craig Ashley, Mick Kiernan, Glen Rooney, Greg Owen. Front Row: Nick Guy, Nick Stokes, Michael Flavell, Jeff Hull, Dave Phillips, Lee Roberts, Gavin Hancox. Photo: Marshall's Sports Service (Birmingham)

Three more of the best!

Top left: Would you trust this man? Andrew Chitty in action at Tow Law!

Top right: Of course photographers have to be on the ball at all times and we can all see Garry Letts knew exactly what was going on here! Photo - Ian Morsman whose Aldershot and Wembley photos have also been appreciated.

Bottom left: Gordon Whittington really thought he'd won the cup and wouldn't be parted! - Photo Roger Turner

Turn to page 906

RAPIDE MIDLAND FOOTBALL COMBINATION

FEEDER TO: MIDLAND FOOTBALL ALLIANCE

Chairman & Treasurer: David Prust

Hon Secretary: Norman Harvey

115 Millfield Road, Handsworth Wood, Birmingham B20 1ED   Tel: 0121 357 4172

What a year it has been for two newcomers who were re-born, Leamington after an absence of a dozen years and Rugby Town whose spell away from football lasted 28 years, even though they were placed in the Second Division. Whilst the Brakes' opening game attracted 730 fans with gate receipts of £1212 and all 500 programmes sold out, Rugby were winning eight nil in front of 500 fans to set the scene for the rest of the season.

We say farewell to Dave Robinson and everyone at Studley BKL who are promoted to the MFA and we hope their stay is a long one. It has been fun having them with us and watching their ambitions grow.

The first side to be claimed champions were West Hagley in the Third Division who were the only club in the whole league to remain unbeaten to the end. Alvechurch Reserves were second and newcomers Wilnecote Sports enjoyed a marvellous time to finish third, as well as having excellent cup runs.

In the Premier Division, Nuneaton Griff fought off the determined challenge of Studley BKL to retain the title by a single point, and manager Mark Green is out to complete a hat-trick of championships.

The closest finish was in the First Division where the top three went into the final game even-stevens and all three won to leave Shirley Town top, County Sports second and Knowle third, all on 74 points. Town took the title on goal difference.

Leamington took the Second Division honours despite losing to Rugby Town at the New Windmill ground watched by 1,263 fans and record receipts of £2046.60, plus another sell out in both the programmes and the club shop stock. Rugby Town ended runners up having led the table for most of the season.

Boldmere St Michaels won the Reserve Division five points ahead of Barwell, with Shepshed Dynamo ending up in third spot.

On the cup scene, the Endsleigh Challenge Cup final at Villa Park was won by Nuneaton Griff who beat Sutton Town by the game's only goal, a neat reversal of the result in the Birmingham County FA Vase final. Griff also collected the Coventry Evening Telegraph Cup to round off a memorable season.

The President's Cup was won by Old Hill Town who defeated Knowle, the Challenge Vase went to Cadbury Athletic who overcame Rugby Town and Wilnecote Sports collected the Challenge Urn after beating Alvechurch Reserves.

Barwell won the Challenge Trophy and Ilkeston Town picked up the Challenge Bowl after beating Shepshed Dynamo and Bilston Town respectively, and Romulus won the Invitation Cup against Brownhills Town.

Kings Heath reached the fourth round of the Birmingham Senior Cup before losing at home to West Bromwich Albion and Studley BKL won the Worcestershire Senior Urn for the first time ever.

The Wirral Programme of the Year award went to Blackheath Ivensys with Loughborough Athletic second and in joint third spot were Alvechurch and Rugby Town. Our own awards saw Loughborough top overall with Pershore Town collecting the Premier Division honours. Rugby Town took the Second Division and Cadbury Athletic Reserves won the Third Division.

We cannot end without going back to Leamington Football Club and their phenomenal support - a last few statistics - 11,223 fans passed through the New Windmill turnstiles for the 22 matches at an average of 510 per game, beating some Conference and most Southern League clubs by the proverbial mile.

Incidentally, when Roy Baxter of Southam, a Brakes fan of 30 years standing, turned up for the game with Kenilworth Wardens, he was presented with a ball autographed by the entire Leamington squad. The reason? He was visitor number 10,000 for the season.

Paul Vanes, Press Officer

FINAL LEAGUE TABLES 2000-01

PREMIER DIVISION

	P	W	D	L	F	A	Pts
Nuneaton Griff	40	31	4	5	83	34	97
Studley BKL	40	30	6	4	98	32	96
Romulus	40	27	6	79	34	88	
Pershore Town	40	22	8	10	82	62	74
Coventry Sphinx	39	20	6	13	63	38	66
Meir KA	39	20	6	13	67	56	66
Alvechurch	40	21	3	16	77	64	66
Coventry Marconi	40	19	8	13	87	61	65
Kings Heath	40	15	12	13	61	53	57
Sutton Town	40	16	7	17	67	57	55
Bolehall Swifts	40	15	9	16	77	76	54
Massey-Ferguson	40	15	8	17	81	81	53
Handrahan Timbers	40	12	7	21	51	69	43
Cheslyn Hay	40	11	9	20	53	71	42
Alveston	40	11	9	20	53	87	42
Feckenham	40	9	11	20	49	80	38
Blackheath Inv.	40	10	7	23	51	91	37
Northfield Town	40	8	12	20	44	83	36
Southam United*	40	10	5	25	53	79	32
Cont. Star*	40	10	4	26	64	98	31
>HIGHGATE UNITED	40	11	4	25	49	96	37

DIVISION ONE

	P	W	D	L	F	A	Pts
Shirley Town	36	23	5	8	104	47	74
County Sports	36	23	5	8	108	61	74
Knowle	36	22	8	6	78	33	74
Coleshill Town	36	20	5	11	72	56	65
Brownhills Town	36	19	6	11	76	48	63
Handsaker	36	19	9	8	63	35	63
Alvis Oak Cov.	36	17	9	10	80	59	60
Old Hill Town	36	19	3	14	86	73	60
Thimblemill Rec.	36	17	7	12	88	63	58
Fairfield Villa	36	17	7	12	81	57	58
Dudley Sports	36	14	8	14	52	63	50
Polesworth NW	36	11	6	19	64	74	39
Holly Lane	36	8	13	15	62	76	37
Mile Oak Rovers	26	10	7	1	59	90	37
Burntwood Town	36	9	8	19	45	81	35
Loughborough Ath	36	10	4	22	47	85	34
Hams Hall	36	10	3	23	51	85	33
Kenilworth Town	36	10	2	24	72	121	32
Wellesbourne	36	6	1	29	38	119	10

** points deducted*

DIVISION TWO

	P	W	D	L	F	A	Pts
Leamington	34	28	4	2	96	31	88
Rugby Town	34	25	6	3	106	24	81
Wilmcote S & S	34	22	8	4	87	28	74
Cadbury Athletic	34	21	6	7	71	34	69
Archdale	34	19	8	7	82	43	65
Leamington Hibs	34	18	7	9	102	76	61
Droitwich Spa	34	17	3	14	64	55	54
Enville Athletic	34	16	6	12	53	49	54
Burman Hi-Ton	34	13	6	15	59	61	45
Earlswood Town	34	11	7	16	58	73	40
Chelmsley Town	34	11	5	18	43	72	38
WM Police Res	34	9	8	17	50	77	35
Barnt G Spartak	34	10	5	19	46	75	35
Lichfield Enots	34	9	7	18	43	72	34
Rugby	34	7	10	17	55	81	31
Kenilworth Wardens	34	7	3	24	48	94	24
Malvern Athletic	34	6	3	25	50	112	21
County Sports Res	34	4	4	26	61	117	16

RESULTS CHART 2000-01

		1	2	3	4	5	6	7	8	9	10	11	12	13	14	15	16	17	18	19	20	21
1	Alvechurch	X	2-2	2-0	2-3	5-2	2-3	2-1	0-2	3-0	1-2	2-0	1-2	2-1	0-2	1-0	0-1	2-3	0-3	2-0	2-3	1-2
2	Alveston	0-3	X	2-1	2-1	2-2	3-2	3-3	0-3	0-0	3-1	3-2	1-0	2-2	2-3	1-1	0-1	1-1	2-4	0-1	0-1	0-4
3	Blackheath I	2-3	2-2	X	1-0	0-0	3-3	2-6	0-6	1-1	3-2	5-2	1-0	1-2	3-4	2-2	0-3	2-1	1-3	1-0	2-7	0-3
4	Bolehall S	3-5	4-0	1-0	X	2-2	1-8	3-3	2-1	1-0	2-0	1-1	4-1	4-1	0-2	0-0	1-3	2-1	0-2	0-0	0-1	2-2
5	Cheslyn Hay	1-2	0-1	0-1	2-2	X	1-0	1-1	2-1	4-1	0-3	0-1	0-2	3-1	1-1	2-1	0-1	1-4	1-2	3-1	2-1	0-1
6	Conti. Star	1-3	1-0	0-3	3-1	5-1	X	0-6	0-4	2-3	4-2	1-4	0-1	3-1	2-0	6-0	1-6	1-2	1-1	2-0	1-6	0-2
7	C Marconi	2-1	6-1	4-1	4-3	2-0	1-0	X	0-2	4-0	1-1	4-0	1-0	1-2	2-1	0-1	2-2	2-2	1-3	4-2	1-2	2-1
8	C Sphinx	0-1	1-2	2-0	2-1	2-0	5-0	2-4	X	2-0	1-0	1-0	2-3	3-0	-	0-1	0-2	0-0	0-3	2-0	0-0	4-1
9	Feckenham	1-4	2-1	3-1	0-5	2-2	3-2	0-5	1-2	X	2-1	5-2	0-2	2-1	1-0	1-2	1-2	2-2	0-4	2-2	1-1	0-0
10	H Timbers	0-3	3-1	1-2	1-0	1-0	3-1	1-2	1-1	3-2	X	4-0	1-0	2-2	0-3	1-2	0-4	0-1	0-0	0-3	0-2	1-0
11	Highgate U	1-3	5-2	3-0	0-4	1-3	1-1	3-1	0-1	3-3	3-2	X	0-3	0-0	1-3	0-2	0-3	1-0	1-3	3-0	0-5	1-3
12	Kings Heath	2-4	3-1	3-2	3-1	1-0	4-4	1-1	0-3	1-1	3-3	1-0	X	1-2	2-1	5-0	1-1	1-2	0-1	1-1	0-0	1-2
13	Massey F	2-4	5-2	2-1	6-4	3-1	6-2	2-1	0-0	2-4	1-1	4-0	1-3	X	2-3	3-0	1-4	5-4	1-2	1-2	1-3	7-1
14	Meir K.A.	0-0	3-0	4-0	1-1	3-2	3-0	1-0	1-2	3-2	1-0	1-2	2-0	2-2	X	1-0	2-3	2-0	0-5	3-1	1-5	4-0
15	Northfield T	2-2	2-6	2-3	0-2	2-3	1-0	1-4	0-0	1-1	3-2	0-3	0-0	1-1	0-0	X	0-1	3-5	0-1	0-3	1-4	0-0
16	Nuneaton G	3-0	3-0	2-0	1-3	4-2	1-0	1-0	3-1	1-0	3-0	7-1	2-4	5-0	2-0	3-3	X	0-1	2-1	2-2	3-2	1-0
17	Pershore T	2-1	2-0	3-1	4-4	2-2	5-1	4-1	1-3	1-0	2-1	5-0	0-0	3-2	3-1	3-3	2-1	X	2-0	3-2	1-5	2-1
18	Romulus	5-3	0-0	1-1	0-2	2-2	1-0	3-0	0-0	2-0	2-0	6-1	1-0	3-1	1-1	3-1	0-1	1-0	X	4-1	1-0	2-1
19	Southam U	0-1	2-3	2-0	2-3	1-2	2-1	1-3	3-2	3-1	2-3	0-3	3-3	0-1	0-2	2-5	1-2	1-3	1-2	X	0-2	2-1
20	Studley B.K.L.	5-1	4-0	2-0	4-3	1-0	4-1	4-0	3-0	1-0	2-2	2-0	1-1	0-0	3-2	4-0	1-0	1-0	3-0	3-2	X	0-3
20	Sutton Town	0-1	1-2	2-2	5-1	2-3	3-1	1-1	2-0	1-1	1-2	2-20	2-2	1-3	3-0	4-1	1-3	5-0	3-2	0-2	0-1	X

2000-01 CUP RESULTS

PRESIDENTS CUP FINAL

Old Hill Town	v	Knowle	1*0

CHALLENGE VASE FINAL

Cadbury Athletic	v	Rugby Town	1-0

CHALLENGE TROPHY FINAL

Barwell	v	Shepshed Dynamo	2-1

DIVISIONAL LEADING SCORERS

Premier	Chris Partridge (Coventry Marconi)	39
First	Carl Fairhurst (County Sports)	37
Second	Delroy Brown (Leamington Hib)	32
Third	Richard Perry (West Hagley)	35
Reserves	Justin Jenkins (Hinckley United)	18

ALVECHURCH F.C.

Secretary: Stephen Denny,11 Shawhurst Croft,Hollywood,Birmingham.B47 5PB (01564 822302)
Ground: Lye Meadow, Redditch Rd, Alvechurch, Worcs (0121 445 2929)
Directions: M42 jct 2, follow signs to Redditch, taking dual carriageway. At island turn right (signed Alvechurch) ground approx one mile on right. Ground is actually on Redditch Road, just south of Alvechurch village
Capacity: 3,000 **Seats**:100 **Cover:**Yes **Floodlights:**Yes
Clubhouse: Evenings and matchdays **Club shop:** No
HONOURS Mid Comb Chall Cup R-up 95-96, Smedley Crooke Cup R-up 94-95
CLUB RECORDS **Goalscorer:** Dean Meyrick **Appearances:** Dean Meyrick
PREVIOUS **Leagues:** None
Name: None (predecessors, Alvechurch FC, founded 1929, folded in 1992)

Founded: 1994
Nickname: The Church
Sponsors: Centreprint
Colours: Gold/black/black
Change colours: Black &White,white/black
Midweek matchday: Wednesday
Chairman: Michael Rowley
Director of Football: Lee Shaw
Patron: Roy Yardley
Manager:Mick Preece

ALVESTON

Secretary: Martin Beese, 16 The Smallholdings, Bubbenhall Road, Baginton, CV8 3BB
Tel: 02476 305294H 077744 23641M

Ground: Home Guard Club, Main Street, Tiddington, Stratford-upon-Avon. Tel: 01789 297718
Social Club Telephone : 01789 297718 Club Email martin.beese@fleet.gecapital.com

Floodlights: Yes

Directions: ground is on the Stratford - Wellesbourne Road (B 40860) Home Guard Club is last building on right through Tiddington

Chairman: Martin Beese (02476 305294)

Colours: Maroon & Sky Blue/Sky Blue/ Maroon & Sky Blue
Change Colours: Black & White Stripes/ White/White
2000-01
Leading Goalscorer: Reuben Wilson 15
Captain: John O'Brien
Player of the Year: Andy Beechy

BOLEHALL SWIFTS

Secretary: Philip Hill, 64 Rene Road, Bolehall,Tamworth,Staffs. B77 3NN (07812 449054- M)
Ground: Rene Road, Bolehall, Tamworth (01827 62637)
Directions: A51 signs south to Bolebridge island, left under railway archesinto Amington Rd, 4th left into Leedham Ave, fork right into Rene Rd, ground onright by school. From Tamworth BR station walk up Victoria Road for threequarters of a mile and catch No.3 or No.6 mini-bus to Bolehall. Alight atLeedham Avenue or Rene Road and follow as above
Capacity: 2,000 Seats: 500 Cover: 600 Floodlights: Yes Club Shop: No
Clubhouse: Large Social Club. Open evenings 7-11 & lunchtimes. Snacks available
HONOURS: Midland Comb. Div 2 84-85, F/Lit Cup R-up 96-97, Chall. Vase 84-85, Presidents Cup R-up 85-86; Fazeley Char Cup 84-85 (R-up 85-86); Ernie Brown Mem. Cup R-up 89-90 90-91 91-92 92-93 94-95 98-99, Jack Mould Cup R-up 85-86 Tony Allden Nenorial Cup 98-99

Founded: 1953 Nickname: Swifts
Colours: Yellow/black/yellow
Change Colours: All Blue
Sponsors: Need -A-Skip-Hire Ltd.
Midweek matches: Tuesday
Programme: 24 pages, 70p
Editor: W Gould (01827 64530)
President: mr.L. Fitzpatrick
Chairman: James Latham
Vice-Chairman: K.Norchi
Manager: Ron Tranter Ass.Man: D.Finney
Coach: J.Capaldi
Physio: D.Crump

CHESLYN HAY

Secretary: J Rogers, 22 John Riley Dr., New Invention, Willenhall WV12 5AS (01922 860064)
Ground: Scholars Ground, Chasetown F.C., Church St., Chasetown, Walsall. 01543 682222
Directions: M6 Junct 11, A460 to Cannock, A5 to Brownhills, to Whitehouse Rd and Wharf Lane, at junction turn left into Highfield Rd., leading to Church St., ground on left.
Capacity: 2,000 Seats: 200 Cover: 300 Floodlights: Yes Club Shop: Yes
Clubhouse: Evenings 7-11pm. Food (burgers, chips etc) on 1st team matchdays
HONOURS: Midland Comb. Prem Div. R-up 98-99, Div. 3 R-up 94-95;
Wolves Cup 86-87 87-88, Staffs. Chall. Cup 96-97; Walsall Chall. Cup 96-97;
W H Johns Mem. Cup 96-97; J W Hunt Cup R-up 96-97
CLUB RECORDS **Appearances:** Gary Osborne 522
Goalscorer: Ian Morgan 142 (in 113 games)

Founded: 1984
Sponsors: Pro Clean Ind. Services
Colours: Orange/white/black
Change colours: Blue & white stripes/blue/white
Programme: Yes
Editor/Press Off: As Sec. Fax: 01922 421460
Chairman: Ivor Osborne (01922 414755)
Manager: Carl Oulton Assistant: Paul Baker
Physio: M Bailey
2000-01 Leading goalscorer: Dave Marriott 15
Captain: Paul Miller
P.o,Y.: Everton Francis

COLESHILL TOWN

Secretary: George Phillips,49 Circus Avenue, Chelmsley Wood, Birmingham (0121 770 9513)
Ground: Pack Meadow, Packington Lane, Coleshill, Birmingham B46 3JQ (0167563259)
Directions: A446 to A4117 towards Coleshill, Packington Lane forks from A4117,south of village and ground is 150 yds on right. M6 jct 4, 1 mile away
Capacity: 3,000Seats: 50Cover: 50 Floodlights: Yes
Clubhouse: Bar open 7 nights a week. Bar manager resident
HONOURS: Mercian Lg 75-76, Walsall Snr Cup 82-83 R-up 83-84, Midland Comb. R-up 83-84, Div 2 69-70 R-up 74-75, Invitation Cup 70, Presidents Cup R-up x2 67-69
CLUB RECORDS: **Attendance:** 1,000
Players progressing: Gary Shaw (Aston Villa)

Founded: 1894
Nickname: Coalmen
Colours: Green & white/green/green
Change Colours: All blue
Midweek matches: Tues/Thurs
Programme: 30p,
Editor: Mavis Gordon

Chairman:
Manager: Christopher Davies

COUNTY SPORTS

Secretary: Geoff Woodward, 2 Lansdowne Road, Worcester WR1 1ST
Tel: 01905 23341 (H) 01905 612342 (B)
email: sports@woodward2.worldonline.co.uk

Ground: King George V Playing Fields, King George Way, Pershore, Worcs.
Tel: 01386 556902

Directions: Leave M5 at Junction 7 (Worcester South) - take first left A44 to Pershore. On entering town at second set of lights turn left. Ground 300 yards on left.

Clubhouse: Yes Floodlights: No

Founded: 1968
Colours: Yellow/blue/blue
Change Colours: White/jade green/black
Midweek matches:

Chairman: Martin Pinches
Tel: 01905 457944 (H)
Match Secretary: Brian Evans
Tel: 01905 456122 (H)

COVENTRY MARCONI F.C.

Chairman: B Olsen **Vice-Chairman:** D Ryan **Press Officer:** P Scanlon

Secretary: P Scanlon, 61 Norton Hill Drive, Wyken, Coventry, West Mids CV2 3AX
Tel: 02476 616576

Ground: Allard way, Copswood, Coventry Tel: 01203 451361
Capacity 1,500 **Seats**: 92 **Cover:** Yes, Seats and standing **Floodlights:**Yes

Clubhouse: 12-11 Saturdays 6.00-11.00 weekdays

HONOURS: Midland Comb Div 1 96-97, Presidents Cup 96-97.
Only winners of Coventry Evening Telegraph Cup (3 years), R-up Endslegh Comb Cup 99-00

Formed: 1923
Sponsors: Marconi
Colours: White with blue trim/bluewhite
Change colours: All red
Programme: 20pages Price:
Editor P.Scanlon 75p

Manager: C.Davies
Assistant Manager: J.McGinty
Physio: P.Tovey

COVENTRY SPHINX

Secretary: David Rees. 15 Pleydell Close, Willenhall Wood, Coventry CV3 3EF2 (02476 305921)

Match Secretary: Kevin Monks: Tel Nos: 02476 659249 (H) 0403 508358 (M)

Ground: Sphinx Drive, off Siddeley Avenue, Stoke Aldermoor, Coventry Tel: 01203 451361
Social Club Telephone Number: 02476 451361

Chairman: Vic Jones
Manager: Willie Knibbs

Colours:
Sky blue & white/black/white
Change Colours
White/white/Sky Blue

FECKENHAM

Secretary: M G Hawkes4 Mill Lane, Feckenhamk, Redditch, Worcs B96 6HY (01527 893341)

Ground: Redditch United F.C. See details in Dr. Martens Section **Floodlights**: Yes

Directions: M42 , Junction 4 take A38 towards Bromsgrov to Golf Course. Left at roundabout - A448 towards Redditch. Aftyer five miles take third exit off roundabout, cross over dual carriage-way, . First right into Birchfield Road, pastthe Foxlydiate Pubkic House.. First left into Red Lane leading into Bromsgrove rRoad. Valley Stadium is approx 3/4 mile on the left

Acting Chairman: R.Freeman
28 Milford Close,Walkwood,Redditch B97 5PZ
Tel Nos: 01527 67450 (H) 01527 401819 (W)

Colours: Green & White Hoops/Green/Green
Change Colours: All Yellow

GROSVENOR PARK (formerly Sutton Town)

Secretary: Peter Yates, 8 Crome Road, Great Barr, Birmingham B43 7NL
Tel: 0121 360 1611 (H) email: py@otal.com

Ground: The Central Ground. Coles Lane, Sutton Coldfield
Tel: 0121 354 2997

Directions: From M6 J5 (Spaghetti Junction), take A5127 along Gravelyy Hill. Follow into Sutton New Rd then Birmingham Rd. Turn right into Holland Rd at junction with Odeon Cinema then 1st right into Coles Lane. Ground 400m on left.

Clubhouse: 0121 354 2997

Honours: Mid Comb Div 1 99-00, B'ham County Cup R-up 99-00, Endsleigh Cup 99-00 (first non Premier club for 30 years), 00-01 R-up B'ham County Vase 00-01, MFC team of 99-00

Founded: 1959
Colours: Tangerine/black/tangerine
Change colours: White/black/white

Chairman: Ron Evans
Tel: 01543 673620 (H)
Match Secretary: Ray Fisher
Tel: 0121 360 9904

2000-01
Captain: Mel Henry P.o.Y.: Chris Bryan
Top Scorer: Linz Taylor 22

HANDRAHAN TIMBERS

Secretary: Darren Mansell, 56 Windermere Drive, Kingswinford DY6 8AN (01384 830815)

Ground: Mile Flat Sports Ground, Mile Flat, Wallheath, Kingswinford, W. Mids (01381 484755)

Cover: 200 Seats: 40 Floodlights: Yes

Clubhouse: Teas and refreshments Club Shop: No

HONOURS Midland Comb. Div 1 R-up 93-94, Birmingham Chall. Vase R-up 93-94, Wednesbury Charity Cup 91-92, J W Hunt Cup 92-93 R-up 93-94; Invitation Cup 94-95

PREVIOUS **Leagues:** Staffs County Lg (South) 82-86 **Grounds:** None

CLUB RECORDS **Goalscorer:** Paul Baker **Appearances:** Jonathan Pole

Win: 9-0 **Defeat:** 0-6

Founded: 1982
Nickname: Timbers
Sponsors: W J Handrahan & Son
Colours: Red & black stripes/black/black
Change colours: Blue & white stripes/navy/navy
Midweek matchday: Wednesday
Programme: All games except outside cups
Chairman: E J Smith
President: W J Handrahan
Manager: Glen Taylor/Nigel Kirkham
Asst Manager: Phillip McNally
Press Officer: E J Smith (01384 295394)

HANDSWORTH CONTINENTAL STAR

Secretary: Gary Christie, 21 Spouthouse Lane, Great Barr B43 5PX
Tel: 0121 357 1044 (H) 07752 202802 (M)
email: soccer@continentalstar.fsnet.co.uk

Ground: Oldbury Leisure Centre, Newbury Road, Oldbury, West Mids.
Tel: 0121 552 1818

Clubhouse: Bar open 7 nights a week. Bar manager resident

HONOURS: Midland Comb Div One R-up 96-97; Birmingham Vase

Founded: 1975
Colours: Yellow with blue band/blue/blue
Change Colours: Blue & Yellow/ Black/ Black
Website:
www..continentalstar.fsnet.co.uk

Chairman: Roger John
Tel: 0121 686 2692 (H)

HIGHGATE UNITED

Secretary: Simon Pretty,8 Monastry Drive,Solihull,B91 1DN (0121 706 0933)

Ground: The Coppice, Tythe Barn Lane, Shirley, Solihull B90 1PH (0121 7444194)

Directions: A34 from City through Shirley, fork right B4102 (Tanworth Lane), half mile then right into Dickens Heath Rd, then first right & ground on the left. 100yds from Whitlocks End (BR)

Capacity: 5,000 Seats: 250 Covered: 750 Floodlights: Yes

Clubhouse: Members Club open Tue to Thur, Sat & Sun. Light refreshments available weekends

HONOURS Midland Comb (3) 72-75 (Div 2 66-67 68-69 71-72), Lg Cup (5) 72-74 75-77 84-85 (R-up 78-79 92-93); Presidents Cup 70-71 85-86); Tony Allden Mem. Cup 74-75; Invit. Cup 68-69 71-72 85-86; West Mids All. 63-64; Birmingham Snr Cup 73-74

CLUB RECORDS **Attendance:** 4,000 v Enfield, FA Amateur Cup QF 1967

Players progressing: John Gayle (Wimbledon), Keith Leonard (A Villa), Geoff Scott (Leicester C.)

Founded: 1947 Nickname: The Gate
Colours:Red/Black/Red & Black
Change Colours: All white
Midweek matches: Tuesday
Programme: 28 pages, 50p
Editor: Terry Bishop (0676 22788)

Chairman: Terry Bishop
Treasurer: G Read
Press Officer: N C Sawyer
Manager: Jim Simms
Physio: Richard Flynn

KINGS HEATH

Secretary: Stuart Maddocks, 37 Rowheath Road, Cotteridge, Birmingham B30 2EP

Tel No: 0121 604 7543

Ground: Alvechurch F.C. See their section for details

Directions: As for Alvechurch F.C.

HONOURS Midland Comb. Div 1 R-up 92-93, Div 2 R-up 82-83, Presidents Cup R-up 79-80 81-82 92-93; Birmingham Chall. Vase R-up 86-87; Worcester Sen Urn 96-97,Chall. Cup R-up 96-97

PREVIOUS **Names:** Horse Shoe FC/ Kings Heath Amateur

Ground: Shirley Town (pre-1994)

Player progressing: Geoff Scott (Stoke C.)

Founded: 1964
Nickname: The Kings
Colours: Old Gold/black/gold
Change Colours: All white
Midweek Matchday:
Programme: 12 pages
Editor: M Kite

Chairman: Ray Kite
Manager: Clive Seeley

MASSEY-FERGUSON

Secretary: Terry Borras, Masey Ferguson, c/o Massey Ferguson social Club, Broad Lane, Coventry CV5 9LA. Tel Nos: 02476 675745 (H) 07909 685137 (M)

Ground: Massey-Ferguson Sports Ground, Banner Lane, Tile Hill, Coventry (01203 694400)

Directions: A45 to Meridan turn (B4104). Over two traffic islands, turn rightat 3rd island into Pickford Grange Lane, continue to Pickford Green Lane, &Hockley Lane, left into Broad Lane, right into Banner Lane, 3rd entrance right

Seats: 70 Cover: 200 Floodlights: Yes Clubhouse: Not on ground

HONOURS Midland Comb. Div 1 94-95, Div 2 93-94, Chall. Vase 93-94, Chall Cup 94-95, Presidents Cup 94-95; Coventry Evening Telegraph Cup 95-96

PREVIOUS **League:** Coventry Alliance (pre-1993)

Colours: Red & Black stripes,Black,Black
Change Colours: Yellow/ Blue / White
Programme: Yes

Chairman: Joe Swords

Manager: John Halford, Geoff Brassington
Coach: Carl Lascelles
Physio: Joe Doolan

MEIR K.A.

Secretary: Chris Robinson , 19 Tthe Square, Meir, Stoke -on- Trent, Staffs ST3 6DW
Tel No: 01782 332152
Ground: Kings Park, Hilderstone Road, Meir Heath, Stoke-on-Trent (01782 388465)
Directions: M6 jct 14, A34 to Stone, A520 to Rough Close then Meir Heath, turnright (B5066) ground approx 1 mile on right. 3m Blythe Bridge (BR)
Capacity: 5,000 Seats: 200 Cover: 250 Floodlights: YesClub Shop: No
Clubhouse: open matchdays. Hot food
HONOURS: Staffs Snr Lg 88-89, 90-91; Staffs FA Vase 93-94; Walsall & Dist Sen Cup 89-90;Mid Comb Prem Lge R-up 96-97; Mid Comb Lge Chall Cup R-up 97-98
PREVIOUSLeagues: Staffs Alliance/ Staffs Snr 84-92
Ground: Normacot Rec **Name:** 'The Station'&'Shoulder of Mutton.'

Founded: 1972 Nickname: Kings
Colours: Yellow/navy/navy
Change colours: All Red
Midweek matchday: Wednesday
Programme: 32 pages 50p
Editor: Kelly Reaney (01782 325624)
President: Peter Bott
Chairman: Des Reaney
Vice Chairman: Graham Lovatt
Manager: Des Reaney Coach: Bernie Bramwell
Press Officer: Mark Allen (01782 304472)
Commercial Mgr: Paul Robinson

NUNEATON GRIFF

Secretary: Bob Archer, 27 Park Lane, Robinsons End, Nuneaton, Warwicks. CV10 8LX
Tel: 024 76 74 1831 (H) Email Address: a.archer3@ntlworld.com
Ground: The Pingles Stadium, Avenue Road, Nuneaton. Tel: 024 76 37 0688
Directions: Avenue Road (A4252) leads to Cedar Tree Pub traffic lights, where you turn left into the stadium car park service road - unsuitable for coaches.
Capacity: 2,000 **Seats:** 238 **Cover:** 400 **Floodlights:** Yes
Clubhouse: Yes / Usual Licensing hours Tel: 024 7673 5344 (Social Club) **Club Shop:** No
HONOURS: Coventry Alliance 97-98, Coventry Telegraph Cup 98, Cov. Charity Cup 99, BCFA Junior Cup Winners 98-99 R-up 99-00, Midland Comb Prem Div 99-00 00-01 (NB Only club to be placed in Premier Division on application and win title in first season.) Cov Tel Challenge Cup 00-01, Endsleigh Challenge Cup 00-01, BCFC Challenge Vase R-up 00-01

Founded: 1972-73
Nickname: Griff
Colours: Blue & white/blue/red & blue
Change colours: All yellow
Midweek Matchday:Wednesday
Programme:16 pages £1.00

Chairman: John Gore
Manager: Mark Green
2000-01
Captain: Lee Bateman P.o.Y.: Adam Banks
Top Scorers: Dave Aston & Mark Whitehead (33)

PERSHORE TOWN 88

Secretary: Don Roberts, 6 Gardens Close, Upton-on-Severn, Worcs.WRS 0LT (01684 593439)
Ground: King George V Playing Fields, King Georges Way, Pershore, Worcs (01386556902).
Directions: M5 jct 7, A44 to Pershore (8 miles) cross 1st lights in Pershore,at 2nd lights turn left & fold road round into King Georges Way, ground immediately on left.
Capacity: 4,000 Seats: 200 Cover: 200 Floodlights: Yes (138 lux) Club Shop:No
Clubhouse: Open every evening, Sun lunch & all day Sat. Snack available during matches.
HONOURS Midland Comb Prem 93-94, Div 2 89-90; Worcs Jnr Cup 90-91, Robert Biggart Cup (5), R-up (3); Worcs Snr Urn 95-96, R-up 92-93, Jack Mould Cup 90-91, Alfred Terry Cup 90-91 Martley Hosp. Cup(`A') 90-91
RECORDS **Atttendance:** 1,356 v Yeading, FA Cup 4th Qual. Rd 23/10/93
PREVIOUS League: Midland Comb 89-90 90-94

Founded: 1988 Nickname: The Town
Colours: Blue & White,blue,blue
Change colours:Red,black, red
Midweek matchday: Tuesday
Programme: 20 pages,60p
Editor: Terry Conway (01386554390)
2000-01 Captain: Dean Emerson
P.o.Y.:Niel Turner Top Scorer: Paul Jones 24
Chairman: Anthony Bradstock
Manager: Colin Shepherd
Asst Mgr: Mike Pugh
Coach: Frank Concannon

ROMULUS

Secretary: Andy Fitchett, 7 Saveker Drive, Sutton Coldfield, Birm. B76 1FT Tel: 0121 3111115H 07768 852784M
Ground: Vale Stadium, Farnborough Road, Castle Vale, Birm. B35 7BE. Tel: 0121 7476969 Fax: 0121 7476868 Email: information@romulus-fc.co.uk Website: www.romulus-fc.co.uk

Directions: From Birmingham City Centre take No. 67 bus alight at terminus. Ground is 3 mins walk. Train - exit at New Street station. Catch No. 67 bus from City centre. If travelling by car contact the secretary for directions.

Capacity: 2,000 Seats: 500 Cover: 600 Floodlights: Yes

Founded: 1979
Colours: Red & white stripes/red/red
Change colours: White/white/black
Chairman: John Matthews
Tel: 01827 899583 (H) 0121 693 4747 (B)

2000-01
Leading goalscorer: S. Gossage 18
Captain: J. Preston
P.o.Y.: S. Gossage

SHIRLEY TOWN

Secretary: Jimmy Merry, 20 Maddens Hill Road, Shirley, Solihull B90 4QQ
Tel: 0121 603 3989 (H) 0121 705 4695 (B) 07813 346857 (M)

Ground: Kenilworth Town FC, Gypsy Lane (off Rouncil Lane), Kenilworth.
Tel: 01926 850851
Directions: M42 J 4 - A34. Follow A34 signed Shirley. Follow Stratford road take 2nd left into Dog Kennel lane. End of road at island turn left then 1st right into Dickens Heath Road. Then 1st right into Tythe Barn Lane. At end of road turn right at junction into Tile House Lane. Ground situated 60 yards on right.
Floodlights: No

Founded: 1926
Colours: Blue,white trim/blue/blue
Change Colours: All red

Chairman: Peter Sysum
14 St. Heliers Rd., Northfield,
Birmingham B31 1QT Tel: 0121 477 7765 (H)

SOUTHAM UNITED

Secretary: Alan D Freeman,3 Old Road, Southam, Warwickshire Cv47 1GF (01926 817711)

Ground: Banbury Road Ground, Southam, Leamington Spa. Tel: 01926 812091

Directions: A423 - 12 miles south of coventry on the Banbury side of Southam

Capacity: 2000 Seats: 200 Cover: 250 Floodlights: Yes

Clubhouse: Yes, with food available Club Shop: No

HONOURS Midland Comb. Prem. Div. R-up 97-98: Birmingham County Sat. Vase 97-98; Coventry Chall. Cup; Coventry City Cup; Coventry & N. Warwicks. Lge Pre. Div.

RECORD **Attendance:** 1,500 v Coventry City, friendly 86-87

Founded: 1905
Colours: White & black/black/black
Change colours:Red & black/white/white
Midweek Matchday: Tuesday
Programme: 10 pages 50p Editor: Ian Jowsey

Chairman: Charles Hill
Presss Officer: Vic Shepherd
Manager: Bobby Hancocks & Ashley Alexander
Physio: Bill Rutledge

WEST MIDLANDS POLICE

Secretary: John Black, 57 Grosvenor Close, Sutton Coldfield, W.Mids. B75 6RP. 0121 308 7673

Ground: Police Sports Ground, `Tally Ho', Pershore Road, Edgbaston, Birmingham B57RN
Tel: 0121 472 2944

Directions: 2 miles south west of city on A441 Pershore Road. Ground is on the left 50yds past Priory Road lights (Warks County Cricket Ground).
3 miles from Birmingham New Street (BR) - buses 41, 45 & 47 from city.

Capacity: 2,500 Seats: 224 Covered: 224 Floodlights: Yes

Clubhouse: 3 bars including snooker room, ballroom, kitchen. Hot &cold food. Open all day.

Club Shop: 0121 472 2944

BEST SEASON **FA Vase:** Quarter Final 91-92 **FA Cup:** 2nd Q ual Rd 91-92

Founded: 1974
Colours: Red & black/ black/black
Change Colours: All Blue
Midweek matchday: Tues/Thurs.
Programme: 16 pages, 50p
Editor: D.Coulsop (01283 533791)
President: Chief Constable E.Crew
Chairman: Dep. Chief Constable Anne Summers
Manager: Jim Scott

2000-01

Captain: Paul Shaw P.o.Y.: Neil Tiller
Top Scorer: Mark Bellingham 42

Nuneaton Griff FC. Back Row (l-r): Gary Smith (Asst Mngr), Mick Upton, Ian Brain, Roman Kurzny, Dave Gawman, Mark Dunn, Lee Bateman (Capt), Scott Moore, Jamie Hood, David Aston, Mark Green (Manager). Front Row: James Proctor (Physio), Ruban Field, Darren Wright, Adam Banks, Wayne Hadley, Daniel Wright, Mark Wright, Mark 'Oggy' Whitehead.

Leamington FC on their big day. Back Row (l-r): Rob Morey, Nick Mort, Mark Simmonds, Paul O'Keefe, Liam McGovern, Will Payne, Ian Billington. Front Row: Simon Gulliver, Tim Romback, John Burgess, Simon Wickson, Kevin Ariss, Adam Ball, Josh Blake. Photo: Gordon Whittington

DIVISION ONE CLUBS

BLACKHEATH INVENSYS
Secretary: Paul Boswell, 34 Princes Rd., Tividale, W. Mids. B69 2LR
Tel: 0121 532 4032 (H) 07720 956309 (M)
Ground: Invensys Brook Crompton Sports Ground, Oakemore Rd., Rowley Regis Tel: 0121 698 3253
Colours: Red & white/red/red

BROWNHILLS TOWN
Secretary: Paul Dixon, 263 Chase Road, Burntwood, Staffs WS7 0EA
Tel: 01543 683730
Ground: Holland `Park, The Parade, Brownhills, Walsall(0956535545)
Colours: All Blue

BURNTWOOD
Secretary: David Cox, 12 Galway Road,Burntwood, Staffs. WS7 8DT
Tel No: 07931 626887 (M)
Ground: Memorial Institute, Rugeley Road, Burntwood.
Tel: 01543 675578
Colours: Red and Blue stripes/Blue/Red

CADBURY ATHLETIC
Secretary: Gerry Boyle,1 Greenway Gardens, Kings Norton,Birmingham B38 9RY (0121 628 6533 (H) 07974 382986 (M)
Ground: Cadbury Recreation Ground, Bournville Lane, B'ham. B14 6DL Tel No: 0121 458 2000 x 3316 or 01§21 454 4264
Colours: All Purple.

DUDLEY SPORTS
Secretary: John Lewis, 6 Hern Rd., Brieley Hill, West Mids DY5 2PW
Tel: 01384 895782
Ground: Hillcrest Avenue, Brierley Hill, West Mids (01384 826420)
Colours: Green & white /white/ green

FAIRFIELD VILLA
Secretary/Press Officer: C W Harris, 28 ShelleyClose, Catshill, Bromsgrove B61 0NH Tel: 01527 877203
Ground: Bromsgrove Rovers F.C. See their details.
Colours: All Red & Black

HANDSAKER
Secretary: Claire Handsaker, 43 Bridle Lane, Streetly, Sutton Coldfield.
Tel: 0121 580 9308 (H) 07956 517258 (M)
Ground: Hollyfields Centre Club Ltd., Woodacre Road, Erdington Birmingham B24 0JT Tel: 0121 373 1018
Colours: Navy & white stripes/navy & red trim/navy & red trim

HOLLY LANE '92
Secretary: R G Ashton, 19 Grange Road, Erdington, Birmingham B24 0DG Tel: 0121 350 2352
Ground: Holly Sports & Social Centre, Holly Lane, Erdington, Birmingham B249LH. tel: 01213 730979
Colours: Yellow/black/yellow

KENILWORTH TOWN
Secretary: Mrs Sally McKenzie, K.T.F.C.,Marlborough House, Holly Walk, Leamington Spa CV32 4JA 01926 855247 (H) 886632 (W)
Ground: K.T.F.C. Gypsy Lane (off Rouncil Lane), Kenilworth, Warwicks. Tel: 01926 50851
Colours: All blue

KNOWLE
Secretary: Roger Whittick, 149 Richmond Road, Solihull B92 7RZ
Tel No :0121 684 2753 (H) 07944 753551 (M)
Ground: Hampton Rd, Knowle, Solihull , W.Mid B93 0NX
Tel: 01564 779807
Colours: Red/black/black

LEAMINGTON
Secretary: Brian Knibb, 61 Villiers Street, Leamington Spa,Warwicks. Cv32 5YA Tel No: 01926 429066
Ground: New Windmill Ground,Harbury Lane, Whitnash,Leamington Spa Warwicks Cv33 9JR (07866 348712)
Colours: Gold/ Black/ Gold.

LOUGHBOROUGH F.C.
Secretary: John Belton: 51 Farndale Drive, Loughborough, Leics.LE112RG Tel No: 01509 231583 (H) 01509 231583 (W)
Ground: The Drome, Derby Road Playing Fields, Derby Road, Loughborough Tel: 01509 610022
Colours: All white and blue.

MILE OAK ROVERS
Secretary: Keith Lycett, 1 Price Avenue, Mile Oak, Tamworth, Staffs. B78 3NL Tel Nos 018267 708735 (H)01827 89614(W)
Ground: Recreation Ground,Price Avenue,Mile Oak,Tamworth, Staffs. B78 3NL 01827 289614 or 01827 289614
Colours: All Blue.

NORTHFIELD TOWN
Secretary: Matthew Kirby, 53 Park Dale Drive, Birmingham B31 4RN
Tel: 0121 604 2202 (H) 07876 143121 (M)
Ground: Shenley Lane Comm. Assoc. & Sports Centre, 472 Shenley Lane, Birmingham B29 4HZ Tel: 0121 478 3900
Colours: yellow/blue/yellow

OLD HILL TOWN
Secretary: Scott Wilshaw, 10 Rowley Hill View, Cradley Heath, West Midlands. B64 7ER 01384 564466 (H) 07976 849022 (M)
Ground: Hingleys, Bluebell Road, Cradley Heath, West Midlands. (01384 566827)
Colours: All maroon

POLESWORTH NORTH WARWICK
Secretary: Mrs Lynn Wright, 69 Chaytor Rd,.Polesworth, Tamworth Staffs. B78 1JS (01827 892896 or 0797 389 8523)
Ground: North Warwick Sports Ground, Hermitage Hill, Tamworth Road, Polesworth, Warks.
Colours: Green/ Black/ Black

RUGBY TOWN
Secretary: David Badger: New House, Halfway Lane, Dunchurch Nr Rugby, Warwicks.CV22 6RP 01788 522538 (H) 01812 392842 M)
Ground: The Rugby Lions R.F.C. Webb Ellis Rd., Rugby, Warwicks. Cv22 7AU (01788 334466)
Colours: All Tangerine and Black

THIMBLEMILL R.E.C.
Secretary: Gerry Houten, 86 Gower Road, Halesowen, W.Midlands, B62 9BT Tel Nos: 0121 422 3357 (H) 07966 374771 (M)
Ground: Thimblemill Recreation, Thimblemill Road, Smethwick, Warley. Tel: 0121 429 2459
Colours: Red & Blue/ Blue/ Blue.

WILMCOTE SPORTS & SOCIAL
Secretary: Jennifer Smith, 19 Nightingale Close, Spernal Lane, Great Alne, Warwicks. B49 6PE 01789 488077 (H)
Ground: The Patch, Rear of Wilmcote S.S.Club, Astton Cantlow Road, Wilmcote, Stratford on Avon (01789 297895)
Colours: Green & yellow / Green / Yellow

BANKS'S BREWERY WEST MIDLANDS (REGIONAL) LEAGUE

FEEDER TO: MIDLAND ALLIANCE

Hon Secretary: Neil Juggins
14 Badgers Lane, Blackwell, Bromsgrove

The 2000-01 season will be remembered above all else for the dreadful weather that plagued virtually the whole campaign, resulting in the extension of the league programme until May 26th, and the cancellation of the league cup competitions. This was the first time since 1964 that a league cup competition had not been contested, whilst it was the latest finish to a league programme since 1947. In addition, the Foot and Mouth crisis affected the Herefordshire based clubs, particularly Bromyard Town who did not fulfil any fixtures between March 3rd and April 26th. This left them with fourteen games to play in the final month of the specially extended campaign.

The season had also commenced in unsatisfactory fashion when Walsall Wood's appeal to the Football Association against relegation to Division One was finally heard and upheld just a little over a week before the start of the league fixtures. The outcome was that Wood's hastily admitted reserve side fulfilled the games allocated to the first XI in Division One (North), whilst the reinstated first XI finally commenced its Premier Division fixtures a fortnight later than everyone else on 2nd September. The Oak Park club struggled initially, taking only three points from its first twelve games, but recovered sufficiently to avoid the relegation places, which were ultimately filled by Brierley Hill Town and Tipton Town in a tight finish that saw just a single point covering four clubs. Brierley Hill fell into the bottom two places on the same day that Walsall Wood commenced their league programme, and never managed to escape, whilst Tipton hovered just above for much of the campaign. A dismal haul of just a single point from five games in the closing days of the season proved costly, victory in the last game coming too late to save them from bottom place.

The success story of the season was undoubtedly Ludlow Town. Although Darlaston Town made the early running with nine consecutive victories, they were eventually overtaken by the Riddings Park club at the end of October, and there Ludlow remained, apart from a short spell in mid-November when Warley Rangers took over, eventually clinching the championship as early as Easter Monday with a 3-1 victory at Wolverhampton Casuals. Ludlow still had five games to play at this stage, but it was the club's first championship success since 1979, when they finished top of Division Two. The margin of victory was also a considerable surprise for a club that had never previously finished higher than ninth in the Premier Division. A record breaking season saw Ludlow just fail to equal the league record of 35 wins in a season, set by Stafford Town a year earlier, though they did exceed Stafford's points tally to create a new record of 111. The unusually large programme of fixtures played a part in this, though no other club has ever played so many league games in a season whilst suffering just a single defeat.

The Keys Cup went to Warley Rangers, who clinched the runners up spot in their penultimate game, whilst Little Drayton Rangers came with a late run to finish third. Both clubs thus enjoyed their most successful seasons in the WMRL to date, with Warley's scoring exploits including the unusual feat of registering double figures in both meetings wtih Brierley Hill Town (11-0 away, then 10-1 at home).

Both of the regionalised sections of Division One were disrupted by late withdrawals. In the North, Borgfeld Celtic and Cannock Chase withdrew on the eve of the season, whilst Heath Hayes belatedly entered a reserve side which began its fixtures later than everyone else. This side made one of the worst starts to a season in the WMRL's 112 year history by losing its first twelve games. The first point did not arrive until January, and the first win was not secured until fellow strugglers Chasetown Reserves were beaten on March 10th in their eighteenth game. Remarkably, this victory heralded a massive turnaround in fortunes for a nine game unbeaten run, which included five victories, and meant the bottom two places were avoided. Chasetown Reserves, meanwhile, failed to win any of their last eighteen games, picking up just four points in the process and finishing bottom.

At the other end of the table Newport Town were the early pacesetters, leading the way until being overhauled by Wolverhampton United in mid January. The Wolves then went on to hold off a late challenge by newcomers Ounsdale to clinch the championship with a 4-0 victory over Newport Town in their final fixture on May 19th. Ounsdale matched the old record for the highest percentage of games won in a season, whilst United went on to set new records for the highest percentage of games won and points won in a season at this level. They also achieved the unusual distinction of completing their league programme without registering even a single draw.

Dudley Town FC. Back Row (l-r): Ian Davis (Manager), Joel Blake, Jason Attwell, Ian Cornfield, Ben Curley, Richard Taylor, John Carmichael (C), Brian Carmichael, Noel Haye, Richard Cooper, Albert Johnson, Phil Male, Tony Higgins, Tom Botfield, Adam Farmer, Craig Barnett, Tom Johnson. Front Row: John Farmer, Stuart Turner, Phil Mills, Neil Henn, Martin Hassam, Bernie Gethins, Stewart Marshall, Wayne Crumpton, Mick Dixon, Geoff Dixon.

Star FC. Back Row (l-r): Chris Perry (Reserves Manager), Matt Flanagan, Matt Illingworth, Kenny Sheldon, Matt Lunn, Andy Farrell, Chris Jordan, Dean Yates, Gareth Vaughan. Middle Row: Craig Harris, Andy Pritchard, Kevin Nokes, Adam Pritchard, Neil Turford, Russell Morris, John Fawcett, Steve Crann. Front Row: Duncan Horier, Tony Instones, Mark Neville, Tim Crann, Nigel Vaughan (Manager), Steve Aston, Gareth Horier, Matt Ellis, Kyle Hodson, Stuart Hill

Westfields FC. Back Row (l-r): Sean Edwards (Joint Manager), Matt Morris, Kevin Jinks, Adam Godwin, Dave Howes, Jon Pugh, Darren Hall, Steve Berry, Keith Hobby, Owain Meale (Coach). Front Row: Clive Harris (Joint Manager), Derrek Craddock, Darren Gwilliam, Danny Phillips, Mark Hibbard, Sam Clarke, Jack Gwillim, Neil J Prece (Physio)

In the South Division there was much disruption. Gornal Athletic Reserves withdrew their reserve side after just a couple of games, whilst judging the standings of the clubs became rather difficult due to major differences in the number of league fixtures fulfilled by the various clubs. By way of example, mid November saw one club having played ten games, whilst another had played as few as three. By mid January it varied between five and fourteen!

Bustleholme Reserves were the early leaders before being overtaken by Bewdley Town, who won their opening six games. However, they played no WMRL games between October 21st and December 23rd, when a seventh consecutive victory was secured, but by then newcomers Brinton's Athletic had taken over as leaders. Brinton's, in fact, led the way from December 16th to April 28th (apart from one week in February) until they were finally overtaken by Ledbury Town. Ledbury had started the campaign modestly and had only appeared as contenders in the closing weeks of the season, having had as many as five games in hand at one stage. However, despite losing only one of their last fifteen games, Ledbury only secured the title with a 4-3 victory at Bustleholme in their final fixture on 19th May, having overcome a points deduction. Goalscoring was the notable feature of their play, shattering the previous record by averaging some 4.5 goals per game and falling just short of a century of goals in only 22 games.

Bottom place befell Lye Town Reserves. Lye ended the season with seven straight defeats and, despite being ahead with their fixtures, they reached bottom place on March 3rd and remained there. Higher up, Mahal was another club to complete the league season without drawing any games, and having only registered a single draw the previous season it is just as well that the WMRL does not feature on the pools coupons!

On a national level the days when the WMRL's finest could match the country's best are long gone. A dozen clubs entered the FA Vase, mostly starting in the Second Qualifying Round, but, although half of these reached the First Round Proper, none went on to progress further.

FINAL LEAGUE TABLES 2000-01

PREMIER DIVISION

	P	*W*	*D*	*L*	*F*	*A*	*Pts*
Ludlow Town	44	34	9	1	100	35	111
Warley Rangers	44	29	7	8	129	54	94
Little Drayton Rangers	44	27	7	10	91	53	88
Darlaston Town	44	24	7	13	111	76	79
Causeway United	44	22	11	11	78	47	77
Shawbury United	44	22	6	16	77	59	72
Malvern Town	44	19	16	9	83	67	72*
Kington Town	44	19	9	16	92	78	66
Lye Town	44	18	12	14	68	63	66
W'ton Casuals	44	17	12	15	82	67	63
Wellington	44	19	6	19	69	75	63
Tividale	44	16	11	17	72	74	59
Star	44	15	12	17	77	69	57
Westfields	44	14	14	16	60	63	56
Heath Hayes	44	15	8	21	63	74	53
Bustleholme	44	15	6	23	79	91	51
Ettingshall Holy Trinity	44	14	9	21	58	80	51
Dudley Town	44	13	8	23	48	72	47
Bromyard Town	44	10	10	24	51	97	40
Walsall Wood	44	9	10	25	54	78	37
Gornal Athletic	44	10	7	27	59	105	37
Brierley Hill Town	44	10	7	27	48	125	37
Tipton Town	44	10	6	28	61	108	36

* points adjustment

DIVISION ONE NORTH

	P	*W*	*D*	*L*	*F*	*A*	*Pts*
W'ton United	26	23	0	3	101	27	69
Ounsdale	26	22	1	3	85	21	67
Brereton Social	26	18	1	7	63	29	55
Newport Town	26	14	4	8	60	47	46
Lucas Sports	26	13	6	7	80	46	45
Great Wyrley	26	14	2	10	65	50	38*
Eccleshall Res	26	10	5	11	37	37	35
Morda United	26	10	2	14	29	62	32
Walsall Wood Res	26	8	5	13	41	64	25*
Sikh Hunters	26	8	1	17	45	71	25
Shifnal Town Res	26	7	3	16	39	67	23*
Heath Hayes Res	26	5	5	16	34	72	20
W'ton Sports Gnst	26	5	4	17	30	74	19
Chasetown Res	26	2	7	17	31	73	13

DIVISION ONE SOUTH

	P	*W*	*D*	*L*	*F*	*A*	*Pts*
Ledbury Town	22	16	2	4	99	37	49*
Brintons Athletic	22	14	4	4	66	40	46
Sedgley White Lions	22	13	2	7	61	29	41
Chaddesley Corbett	22	11	6	5	55	39	39
Bewdley Town	22	12	2	8	58	37	38
Mahal	22	11	0	11	50	57	33
Hinton	22	8	6	8	36	47	30
Bustleholme Res	22	7	4	11	41	44	25
Malvern Town Res	22	9	1	12	37	55	25*
Leominster Town	22	5	4	13	39	66	19
Lye Town Res	22	5	1	16	29	74	16
Pershore Town Res	22	4	2	16	19	65	14

* points adjustment

PREMIER DIVISION RESULTS CHART 2000-01

	1	2	3	4	5	6	7	8	9	10	11	12	13	14	15	16	17	18	19	20	21	22	23
1	X	0-1	1-1	0-1	1-3	0-4	2-0	1-1	3-2	1-5	2-4	2-4	0-3	2-3	0-5	2-1	1-3	1-5	0-5	2-0	0-11	2-1	1-0
2	1-2	X	5-0	1-1	1-0	1-2	0-3	5-0	0-0	1-2	2-2	0-3	1-3	1-1	1-3	3-1	2-2	1-3	2-2	3-2	0-6	0-2	1-5
3	3-0	1-0	X	1-2	2-3	2-1	5-1	1-1	1-2	6-1	6-3	2-1	0-3	3-1	0-1	0-7	2-0	1-3	1-1	2-1	1-2	4-0	0-1
4	3-3	4-0	2-0	X	2-2	1-0	5-0	2-1	1-0	1-0	1-1	0-2	2-0	0-0	0-1	2-2	4-0	1-1	3-1	0-1	3-4	1-2	3-0
5	8-2	5-0	5-5	1-0	X	4-0	1-0	6-0	3-1	1-1	3-1	1-1	5-1	4-4	3-2	1-3	5-0	4-2	1-1	2-1	1-3	6-2	1-5
6	1-1	1-1	0-0	1-2	1-0	X	1-0	1-2	1-0	0-0	2-3	2-4	0-1	0-1	2-1	0-3	0-1	1-3	0-1	1-0	2-2	2-3	0-1
7	2-1	5-1	0-1	0-5	1-2	0-1	X	3-0	3-3	2-1	1-3	1-1	2-3	0-0	3-0	3-0	1-4	1-0	3-1	2-2	1-5	1-2	1-1
8	3-1	0-1	4-3	1-1	2-3	1-2	1-2	X	3-0	3-5	3-4	1-1	2-2	0-1	0-3	4-2	3-2	2-2	2-4	2-0	2-4	0-2	1-2
9	3-0	2-1	2-1	2-0	3-1	0-1	0-1	1-2	X	3-2	1-2	2-3	0-2	1-1	2-1	0-3	1-4	4-1	2-3	1-1	2-2	2-1	0-0
10	3-0	6-4	2-0	1-1	1-4	4-2	0-2	3-0	3-4	X	1-3	0-2	2-2	1-2	2-0	5-2	1-0	4-1	4-6	2-0	0-0	1-0	1-1
11	0-1	3-0	5-0	3-1	3-0	1-0	4-0	3-2	1-0	1-1	X	0-2	2-1	1-2	2-3	3-2	2-1	1-0	0-0	2-3	3-1	3-0	3-1
12	2-0	4-0	3-2	2-0	3-2	2-2	1-1	5-0	0-0	1-0	2-0	X	1-1	6-0	2-1	1-0	2-1	1-0	4-2	3-1	1-1	3-2	5-0
13	1-1	1-0	1-0	1-2	1-2	2-2	3-4	2-2	2-0	2-4	1-1	0-1	X	1-2	2-1	0-0	2-1	1-0	2-0	4-0	2-1	1-1	3-1
14	3-0	1-1	4-3	1-2	1-5	4-1	1-1	4-0	2-2	3-1	0-0	2-3	3-3	X	1-1	4-1	2-2	3-0	1-0	2-0	2-3	4-0	4-1
15	3-1	1-2	5-1	2-3	2-1	2-0	4-1	2-1	2-3	0-4	0-2	1-1	3-0	1-1	X	0-1	4-1	1-0	0-1	2-1	1-1	0-2	2-4
16	3-4	1-2	4-0	2-0	2-1	3-4	1-1	1-2	1-3	3-1	1-0	0-2	1-1	1-1	2-3	X	4-1	1-3	1-1	1-0	0-1	3-1	2-2
17	1-2	2-1	1-3	0-4	2-3	2-3	3-1	0-2	3-0	3-3	0-3	0-1	2-2	2-3	0-3	0-0	X	2-3	2-2	2-6	1-3	3-2	2-4
18	4-2	1-1	0-3	1-1	0-0	2-2	3-1	1-0	4-3	0-2	0-3	1-3	1-2	0-0	2-2	1-3	6-0	X	1-1	2-1	2-5	3-0	1-1
19	4-0	4-0	2-1	0-1	4-2	3-1	2-0	4-0	1-2	1-3	2-4	1-3	2-1	1-1	1-1	2-2	6-1	0-1	X	1-0	0-2	3-3	0-2
20	1-1	1-1	1-6	1-3	4-1	4-0	0-1	4-1	1-0	0-0	1-3	1-2	3-0	4-1	0-2	1-1	1-2	1-1	1-2	X	0-2	0-5	2-2
21	10-1	7-0	6-3	1-4	2-3	2-0	3-0	2-1	3-2	3-2	1-2	1-2	2-0	4-2	1-2	1-3	3-0	4-1	2-1	4-1	X	4-0	4-0
22	1-1	0-1	1-0	3-2	2-0	2-0	2-1	5-1	3-1	3-5	1-0	1-2	3-1	1-3	1-2	2-2	2-1	1-3	2-1	0-0	0-0	X	2-1
23	2-0	2-1	2-2	1-1	1-2	0-1	1-1	2-0	0-1	4-2	1-1	0-2	0-1	3-1	0-1	0-0	0-1	2-3	2-2	1-1	0-0	1-0	X

1	Brierley Hill Town	**7**	Ettingshall Holy Trinity	**13**	Lye Town	**19**	W'ton Casuals
2	Bromyard Town	**8**	Gornal Athletic	**14**	Malvern Town	**20**	Walsall Wood
3	Bustleholme	**9**	Heath Hayes	**15**	Shawbury Town	**21**	Warley Rangers
4	Causeway United	**10**	Kington Town	**16**	Star	**22**	Wellington
5	Darlaston Town	**11**	Little Drayton Rangers	**17**	Tipton Town	**23**	Westfields
6	Dudley Town	**12**	Ludlow Town	**18**	Tividale		

DIVISION ONE NORTH RESULTS CHART 2000-01

		1	2	3	4	5	6	7	8	9	10	11	12	13	14
1	Brereton Social	X	3-0	1-0	2-1	6-1	2-0	1-0	0-3	0-1	5-1	4-0	4-0	2-3	5-0
2	Chasetown Res	1-2	X	1-1	4-4	0-2	0-5	2-3	2-3	0-4	2-3	4-2	0-3	4-3	2-2
3	Eccleshall Res	0-2	0-0	X	2-1	3-0	1-3	3-0	1-3	2-3	2-1	2-1	0-1	2-3	1-1
4	Great Wyrley	3-1	8-1	2-3	X	7-0	2-1	4-0	3-1	3-1	0-1	3-2	0-1	1-4	3-1
5	Heath Hayes Res	1-1	1-0	1-1	3-7	X	2-2	4-1	0-3	0-2	1-0	0-0	2-2	0-5	3-5
6	Lucas Sports	4-2	3-3	0-0	5-1	2-1	X	7-0	3-3	2-3	6-0	4-0	7-1	1-3	0-2
7	Morda United	1-0	1-0	1-3	1-0	5-2	0-2	X	0-2	1-6	4-2	2-0	4-1	0-4	2-1
8	Newport Town	2-3	4-1	2-0	2-3	3-1	6-6	1-1	X	0-4	4-1	0-3	5-3	0-4	2-0
9	Ounsdale	1-2	3-0	2-0	3-0	5-1	0-0	8-0	3-0	X	4-2	3-1	5-0	1-0	4-0
10	Shifnal Town Res	0-3	2-2	2-1	2-3	2-1	1-5	1-1	0-1	1-3	X	1-4	2-2	3-6	3-0
11	Sikh Hunters	0-3	2-0	1-3	0-3	3-1	3-4	3-0	2-6	2-4	4-1	X	4-2	0-4	2-6
12	W'ton Sports Gnst	1-4	1-1	0-2	0-1	0-4	1-6	4-0	1-0	0-5	1-2	2-3	X	0-2	2-2
13	W'ton United	4-0	6-0	3-1	7-0	5-2	5-2	1-0	1-3	4-2	2-0	6-2	6-0	X	8-0
14	Walsall Wood Res	1-5	2-1	2-3	2-2	2-1	4-0	0-1	1-1	0-5	0-5	3-1	3-1	1-2	X

DIVISION ONE SOUTH RESULTS CHART 2000-01

		1	2	3	4	5	6	7	8	9	10	11	12
1	Bewdley Town	X	1-5	3-2	9-4	3-0	3-0	3-0	2-1	7-0	0-3	2-3	2-3
2	Brintons Athletic	0-3	X	2-2	3-3	2-1	2-7	4-1	3-1	8-1	5-1	3-1	1-0
3	Bustleholme Res	1-2	0-4	X	2-0	2-0	3-4	4-1	1-1	4-0	1-3	4-1	1-0
4	Chaddesley Corbett	2-0	1-4	2-1	X	1-1	3-3	6-1	5-1	5-2	3-1	2-3	3-2
5	Hinton	2-2	2-2	1-1	1-5	X	2-10	1-1	3-1	3-2	1-0	2-0	1-3
6	Ledbury Town	4-2	3-4	2-0	2-2	5-1	X	8-2	12-1	6-3	5-1	3-0	3-2
7	Leominster Town	1-5	5-2	4-4	1-1	1-2	0-4	X	6-2	0-2	3-4	3-1	1-4
8	Lye Town Res	1-0	1-4	1-2	0-3	0-4	1-8	2-4	X	2-0	1-2	3-1	3-2
9	Mahal	2-1	3-0	4-2	0-2	1-2	3-2	2-1	5-2	X	3-2	8-0	2-4
10	Malvern Town Res	2-4	2-6	2-1	0-1	3-2	0-5	1-1	4-1	1-2	X	2-0	0-3
11	Pershore Town Res	0-3	0-0	3-2	1-0	1-1	0-2	0-2	1-2	1-4	1-3	X	1-3
12	Sedgley White Lions	1-1	1-2	4-1	1-1	1-3	2-1	4-0	2-1	2-1	6-0	11-0	X

BRIERLEY HILL & HAGLEY ALLIANCE

Secretary: Tony Gore, 114 Dobbins Oak Road, Pedmore, Stourbridge, W.Mids DY9 0XY
Tel: 01562 720158 (H) 07932 493128 (M)

Ground: Halesowen Harriers FC, Park Road, Halesowen, West Mids.
Tel: 01384 896748

Directions: From M5 junction 3, follow A456 towards Kidderminster to first island. Turn right onto A459 towards Dudley. Turn left at next island onto A458 towards Stourbridge. Follow this road for 2 miles. Ground is on left-hand side.

Founded: 1955
Nickname: Lions
Colours: Blue & white shirts & shorts, white socks
Change colours: Green & white hoops, white shorts, black socks

Programme: 20 pages, 50p
Editor: Secretary

Chairman: Lee Robson

BROMYARD TOWN

Secretary: Tony Haverfield, 16 Highwell Avenue, Bromyard, Hereford HR7 4EL
Tel: 01885 483655 (H) 01855 483655 0585 849948 (M)
Ground: Delahay Meadow, Stourport Road, Bromyard HR7 4NT Tel: 01885 483974
Directions: 1/4 mile outside Bromyard on the Stourport/Kidderminster road (B4203). The ground is on the right through iron gates, adjacent to O'Malleys Irish restaurant.

Founded: 1893

Colours: Blue & black/black/blue
Change colours: Green & white/white/green
Chairman: Tony Watkins
Tel: 01885 483509

BUSTLEHOME

Secretary: Geoff Benbow, 123 Coles Lane,Hill Top, West Bromwich B71 2QW
Tel Nos: 0121 556 9625 (H) 0121 569 6073 (W) 07836 265300 (M)
Ground: Tipton Sports Academy, Wednesbury Oak Road, Tipton DY4 0BS
Directions: From M6 Junction 9, take A461, through Wednesbury Town centre to Ocker Hill Island. Follow signpost here taking a full right turn towards Bilston A4098 for half a mile, turning left at traffic lights A4037. Ground is 50 yards on left.

FACT FILE
Founded: 1975
Colours: Yellow/green/green
Change colours: All white
CLUB PERSONNEL
Chairman: Colin Hall

CAUSEWAY UNITED

Secretary: Frank Webb, 10 Moorfield Drive, Halesowen, West Midlands B63 3TG Tel: 0121 550 5219 (H) 0121 550 9916 (B)
Ground: Halesowen Town F.C., The Grove, Old hawne Lane, Halesowen Tel: 0121 550 2179
Directions: M5 jct 3, A456 (signed Kidderminster) to 1st island turn right (signed A459 Dudley), left at next island (signed A458 Stourbridge), at next island take 3rd left into Grammar School Lane, then Old Hawne Lane - ground 400 yds on left
Capacity: 5,000 Cover: 1,420 Seats: 420 Floodlights: Yes

Colours: All white

Change Colours: All blue.

Chairman:Steven Hulston

DARLASTON TOWN

Secretary: David Powers,Flat 1, Waverley Rd,Darlaston, West Mids WS10 8ED(0121 526 5708)
Ground: City Ground, Waverley Rd, Darlaston (0121 526 4423) **Directions:** M6 Jct 10, A454 towards Willenhall, left at lights outside`Lane Arms' into Bentley Rd North, follow this down hill & over the railway & canal bridges to traffic lights. Cross over the lights into Richards St and along into Victoria Rd, 1st right into Slater St and ground on left but entrance is next left in Waverley Rd
Capacity: 2,000 Seats: Yes Cover: Yes Floodlights: Yes Club Shop: Yes
Clubhouse: Open matchdays. Tues/Wed/Thur evenings & Sunday Lunch. Hot/colddrinks/snacks
HONOURS: West Mids Lg Div 1 89-90 (R-up 91-92 92-93, Div 1 Cup Cup 89-90), B irmingham Snr Cup 72-73, B'ham Vase 90-91 91-92, B'ham Jnr Lg 07-08, B'hamComb. 10-11 37-38 45-46 (Tillotson Cup 36-37 37-38 38-39 45-46), Keys Cup 11-12), Wednesbury Lg(5) 1896-1901
PREVIOUS Leagues:(inc Wedn'bury Lg) pre-1908/ B'gham Comb. 08-11 28-54/ WMids 11-28

Founded: 1874 Nickname: Blues
Sponsors: Rubery owen
Colours: Blue & white stripes/blue/blue
Change colours: Yellow/black/black
Midweek matchday: Tuesday
Prog. Editor: Dave Stevenson (0121 526 2465)
Chairman: Mrs D Ratcliffe
Match Sec: Neil Arrowsmith (01902 450612)
Press Officer: 'Scotch Bob'
Manager: Jim McMorran
Assistant Manager: Colin Johnson
Physio: Michelle Cookson

DUDLEY TOWN

Secretary: Margaret Turner, 3,Straits Road, Lower Gornal, Dudley, DY3 2UY Tel: 01384 214741
Ground: The Beeches, Packwood Road, Tividale W,Mids Tel : 01384 211743
Directions: M5 Jct 2 signs to Dudley (A4123). One mile past school and playing fields under walkway to lights. Left into Regent Road.,left into Elm Terrace then left again into BirchTerrace and 2nd left into Pakewood Road. Ground is at end of cul-de-sac.
Capacity: 500 Cover: 1000 Seats: 100 Floodlights: Yes Club Shop: No
Clubhouse:Social club open on matchday . Food available from snackbar
HONOURS Southern Lg Midland Div 84-85, Birmingham Comb 33-34 (R-up 34-35 47-48), Midland (Worcs) Comb 31-32 (R-up 29-30 30-31), West Mids Lg Cp R-up 75-76 (Div2 Cp R-up 80-81), Birmingham Senior Cup 85-86 (R-up 64-65 83-84)Worcs SeniorCp 45-46(joint)(R-up 84-85), Camkin Cp 64-65, Worcs Junior Cp 83-84

FACT FILE
Formed: 1893 Nickname: The Robins
Colours: Red/black/black
Change: Yellow/black oryellow/grey or red
Midweek matchday: Tuesday 7.45pm
Progr: Pages:28 Price75p Editor: T.B.A.
Website: www.dtfc.net
Chairman: Nevil Jeynes V Chair: Alan Guest
President: N D Jeynes
Manager: Ian Davis Asst Man:Tommy Johnson
2000-01 Captain & P.o.Y.: John Carmichael
Top Scorer; Tony Higgins 12

ETTINGSHALL HOLY TRINITY

Secretary: Graham Mills, 27 Ashen Close, Sedgley, Dudley, West Mids DY3 3UZ(01902 66222)
Ground: Aldersley Stadium, Aldersley Road, Tettenhal, Wolverhampton (01902 556200)
Directions: From Wolverhampton take A41 Tettenhall Road, 1.5 miles turn right into Lower Street, then right into Aldersley Road, ground on right
HONOURS West Mids Lg Div 1 Cup R-up 85-86 (Div 2 R-up 84-85), Sporting Award 85-86,Staffs Co. Lg R-up 82-83 (Lg Shield 82-83 83-84), Ike Cooper Cup 82-84 83-84,Sporting Club Award 81-82, Wolverhampton & District Amateur Lg 80-81 (Div 1 65-66, Div 2 64-65), Div 1/2 Cup 64-65 65-66, A H Oakley Cup 80-81, J W Hunt Cup 82-83 83-84 (R-up 79-80), Wolverhampton Cup 83-84 (R-up 82-83)
PREVIOUS **League:** Wednesbury Church & Chapel (early 1900s), Bilston Youth (1950s),Wolverhampton & District Amateur (1960s), Staffs County (South)

FACT FILE
Founded: 1920 Nickname: Trins
Club Sponsors: DKB Electric/ John O'Dell
Colours: All Green/white
Change colours: All Blue
Midweek matchday: Wednesday
Prog. Editor: John Edwards (01785 713458)
Chairman:John Robinson Pres: David Gadd
Manager: Graham Mills Physio: David Gads
2000-01
Captain; Riad Erraji P.o.Y.: Scott Bamford Top Scorer: Lee Elliottt 30

GORNAL ATHLETIC

Secretary: Richard Gwinnett,166 Wolverhampton Rd.,Sedgley, DudleyW.Mids(01902 825191 (H)
Ground: Garden Walk Stadium, Lower Gornal, Dudley, West Midlands (01384 358398)
Directions: From Dudley take A459 to Sedgley past the Burton Rd Hospital. 1ston left at the Green Dragon public house on the B4175 (Jews Lane). Follow theroad until you come to the Old Bull's Head, turn left into Rednall Road, 2ndleft to Garden Walk
Capacity: 3,000 Seats: 100 Cover: 500 Floodlights: Yes Club Shop: No
HONOURS West Mids Lg Div 1 R-up 83-84 (Div 1 Cup 92-93), Birmingham Vase 91-92
PREVIOUS **League:** Midland Comb. 51-63
Name: Lower Gornal Ath
RECORDS **Transfer fees received:** £1,500 for Gary Bell and for George Andrews both toCardiff City, 1965

FACT FILE
Founded: 1945 Nickname: Peacocks
Sponsors: Jasper Steels
Colours: All blue
Change colours: All white
Reserves' Lge: West Mids (Reg.) Lge Res. Div
Chairman: Ian Hall
Commercial Manager: Martin Wedgebury
Manager: John Gwinnell
Coach: Ian Clark/ Ross Hill
Reserves' Manager: Ian Davies

HEATH HAYES

Secretary: John Deans, 280 Hednesford Rd., Heath Hayes, Cannock, Staffs. WS12 5DS Tel: 01543 278430 (H) 01543 378181 (B)

Ground: Coppice Colliery Ground,Newlands Lane, Heath Hayes, Cannock,Staffs.(07976 269280)

Directions: From Cannoc, take Lichfield Rd. After 2.5 miles first right past Texaco garage on right
Seaon 2000-01: Captain: Stuart Turnbull Player of the Year: Lyndon Davies
Top Scorer: Warren Inskip (27)

FACT FILE
Colours: Blue & white stripes/blue/blue
Change Colours: All white

Chairman John Weldon
Manager: Paul Kent
Coach: Geraint Jones
Reserve Team Manager: Andrew Cox
Physio: John Thacker

KINGTON ATHLETIC

Secretary: Mrs Pauline Shaw, 9 Banley Drive, Headbrook, Kington, Hereford HR5 3NL
Tel: 01544 231777

Ground: Park Road Ground, Mill Street, Kington, Hereford (01544 231007)

Directions: Follow signs for kington Town Centre, look for left turn betweenthe Town Clock and the Burton Hotel. Carry on this road for 500 metres, groundon left as road bends

FACT FILE

Colours: Yellow /black/black
Change colours: All Red

CLUB PERSONNEL
Chairman: William Mayglothing

LEDBURY TOWN

Secretary: Mike Clueit, 55 Lawnside Road, Ledbury, Herefordshire, HR8 2AE.
Tel: 01531 633 182

Ground: New Street, Ledbury, Hertfordshire Tel: 01531 631 463

Directions: Leave M50 at junction 2. Take A417 to Ledbury. At first island take first exit and at second island take fourth exit. ground is 100 yards on right.

FACT FILE
Formed: 1893
Colours: Black & white//black/black.
Change colours: Red & blue/red/red

CLUB PERSONNEL
Chairman: Ken Powell

LITTLE DRAYTON RANGERS

Secretary: Brian Garratt, 4 Quarry Bank Road, Market Drayton, Shropshire TF9 1DR Tel: 01630 654618 (H)
Ground: Greenfield Sports Club, Greenfield Lane, Market Drayton. Tel: 01630 655088
Directions: A41 to Tern Hill island, turn right for Newcastle-u-Lyme. Over 1st island and turn right at next, by Gingerbread P.H. towards town centre. After 200 yds turn right, before going over bridge, into Greenfields Lane. Ground is 150 yds down lane on right.

FACT FILE
Colours: Royal & pale blue stripes/royal/royal
Change Colours: red & Blue stripes/blue/red

Chairman: John Thorneycroft

LYE TOWN

Secretary: John Woodhouse, 46 Surfeit Hill, Cradley Heath, Warley, West Midlands. B64 7EB
Tel Nos: 01384 633976(H) 0121 627 6600(W) 07703 244804(M)
Ground: Sports Ground, Stourbridge Road, Lye (01384 422672) **Directions:** On A458 Birmingham-Stourbridge road about 400yds afterlights/crossroads at Lye. From M5 jct 3 take road marked Kidderminster as faras lights at bottom of Hagley Hill, right at island, 3rd turn off at nextis-land,turn off left at crossroads/lights, ground about 400yds on left. Quarter mile from Lye (BR)
Capacity: 5,000 Seats: 200 Cover: 600 Floodlights: Yes **Clubhouse:** Yes (01384 822672)
HONOURS West Mids Lg R-up 76-77 78-79 79-80 80-81 (Prem. Div Cup 75-76), Midland Comb.35-36 (R-up 32-33 34-35 37-38), B'ham Snr Cup R-up 80-81
PREVIOUS **Leagues:** Midland Combination 31-39
RECORD **Gate:** 6,000 v Brierley Alliance

FACT FILE
Founded: 1930 Nickname: Flyers
Colours: All Blue
Change Colours: Yellow/green/yellow
Programme: 24 pages, 40p
Editor: J.Galloway
Chairman: Roy Pearson
President: Ian Cole
Manager: David Beasley
Coach: Alan Moore
Physio: Harry Hill

MALVERN TOWN

Secretary: Margaret Caldicott, 20 Nixon Court, Callow End, Worcester WR2 4UU 01905 831327
Ground: Langland Stadium, Langland Avenue, Malvern, Worcs Tel: 01684 574068
Directions: From Worcester take A449 to Malvern.Turn left at roundabout signposted B4208 to Welland. Left at traffic lights into Pickersleigh Road. Turn left at Longford Arms Pub, into Maddesfield R oad. 2nd left into Langland Ave., ground 100yds on right. 1 mile from Malvern (BR)
Capacity: 4,000 **Seats:** 140 **Cover:** 310 **Floodlights:** Yes **Shop:** No
Clubhouse: 2 bars, large dance area, teabar matchdays **Best F.A.Vase Season:** 99-00 2nd Rd
HONOURS Worcester/ Midland Comb. 55-56 Mid Comb Cup R-up 75-76, WFA Senior Urn (7), WFA Sat Junior Cup Winners (4) Banks's Brewery Premier League Cup R-up 87-88 WFA Nursing Cup Winners 97-98, Robert Biggart Cup Winners 97-98, 98-99 ,Evesham Hosp Cup 99-00
PREVIOUS League: Midland Comb. 55-79 **RECORD Gate:** 1,221 v Worcester, FA Cup

FACT FILE
Founded:1947 Sponsors: Malvern Instruments
Colours: Claret/white/sky
Change:White/black/maroon
Reserves League: Banks's Brewery Div 1 S
Midweek Matchday: Tuesday
Programme: 28 pages 50p Editor: Brian Scott
Chairman: Geoff Brewer President: R H Mann
Manager: Joe Rawle
Asst. Manager: Richard Anson
2000-01 Leading goalscorer: Andrew Shepherd
Captain: Sean Cotterill P.o.Y.: Philip Slade

SHAWBURY UNITED

Secretary: Dave Thomas, 183 Cordwell Park,Wem, Shropshire SY3 9JB
Tel: 01743 245457 (H)

Ground: The Butler's Sports Centre, Bowen's Field, Wem. Tel: 01939 233287

Directions: Go into Wem town centre and at the Church junction turn right. Take the first left after pedestrian crossing, then first left with Hawkestone pub on corner. 2nd left into car park and ground.

FACT FILE

Formed: 1992
Colours: Blue & yellow/blue/blue
Change Colours: All yellow

CLUB PERSONNEL

Chairman: Ron Humphreys
Tel: 01939 251076

SMETHWICK RANGERS

Secretary: Mohan S Gill, 11 Middlesmoor, Wilnecote, Tamworth, Staffs B77 4PL (01827 330702)

Ground: Hadley Stadium, Wilson Road, Smethwick Tel No: 0121 434 4848

Directions: From Wolverhampton Centre, proceed along A459 to junc Parkfields Rd & Sedgley Rd. Turn left at the main Parkfield traffic lights A4039, sign Ettingshall, travel 500yds, left into Myatt Ave, 1st right into Lawn Rd. Ground on right

FACT FILE

Founded: 1972
Colours: Blue & white/blue/blue
Change colours: Red & black/black/black

CLUB PERSONNEL

Chairman: Sukbinder Binning

STAR

Secretary: David Rymer, 6 Callaughton, Much Wenlock, Shropshire TF13 6PT
Tel: 01952 727542 (H) 01746 713000 (B)
Ground: Lawson Mardon Star, Stourbridge Road, Bridgnorth.
Directions: **Please phone secretary.**
Capacity: 2,000 **Seats**:130 **Cover:**Yes **Floodlights**:Yes
Clubhouse: Not at present **Club shop:** No
PREVIOUS **Leagues:** Shropshire County, Bridgnorth and Kidderminster Leagues
Names: Lawson Marclon Star F.C. and Star Aluminium F.C.
HONOURS Won promotion from all their previous Leagues.

Founded: 1964
Nickname: Star
Colours: Sky blue/navyblue/sky blue.
Change: Red & black stripes/black/black
Midweek matchday: Wednesday
Programme: Yes (free) Ed: James Banks
CLUB PERSONNEL
Chairman: B.Upton
Match Secreatary: G.Honey
Manager: Nigel Vaughan
Asst Man: Alan Pope
Press Officer: J.Baylis 01952 73020

TIPTON TOWN

Secretary: Ruth Shinfield,21 Blue Rock Place, Tower Road, Tividale. B69 1PB(0777 904 3929)
Ground: Tipton Sports Acadamy, Wednesbury Oak Road, Tipton, West Midlands
Directions: M6 Jct 9 through Wednesbury taking A461 until right at island signto Tipton. At next island - Ocker Hill - turn full right owards Bilston & Wolverhampton. After 1/3 mile turn left at traffic lights and ground is on left.
Capacity: 1000 **Seats:** 200 **Cover:** New covered stand and dressing rooms **Floodlights**:Yes
Clubhouse: Open with excellent food available week-ends. 12noon - 7.00 p.m.**Club Shop:** no
Honours: West Mid Reg. Lge DIv 1 Champions & Lge Cup, Wednesbury Senior Charity Cup (5)
Record Attendance: Approx 1100 v Wolverhampton Wanderers in a pre season friendly 1.8.88

FACT FILE
Founded: 1948
Sponsors: Tipton & Cseley Building Society
Colours: Black & white stripes/black/black
Change colours: White/blue/blue
Midweek Matchday: Wednesday
Programme Editor: Ruth Shinfield

CLUB PERSONNEL
Chairman: Kevin Jenning
Manager:Neil Hickinbottom

TIVIDALE

Secretary: Leon Murray ,59 Peel Way, Tividale, Oldbury, W.Mids B69 3JZ(0121 532 6979)
Ground: The Beeches, Packwood Rd, Tividale, Warley, W. Midlands B69 1UL tel: 01384 211743
Directions: Dudley Port Station to Burnt tree, left towards Birmingham, ground1 mile on right. Or, M5 jct 2, follow Dudley signs A4123, after approx 2 miles turn left into Regent Rd & left again into Elm Terraces, 1st left into Birch Crescent. Packwood Rd is second left - ground at end of cul-de-sac
Capacity: 3,500 Seats: 200 Cover: 1,000 Floodlights: Yes Club Shop: No
Clubhouse: Mon-Fri 8-11pm, Sat 12-11pm, Sun 12-3 & 8-10.30. Cobs, rolls,sandwiches available
HONOURS West Midlands Lg Div 1 72-73 (Prem. Div Cup 76-77, Div 1 Cup 72-73), Wednesbury Charity Cup 76-77
PREVIOUS Ground: City Road **Leagues:** Handsworth & District 56-60; inactive 60-62; West Mids Alliance 62-66 **RECORD Attendance:** 2,400 v Telford United, FA Cup

Founded: 1954 Nickname: Dales
Sponsors: Midland & North Security Consultants
Colours: All Yellow
Change colours:White/white/blsck
Midweek matchday: Tuesday
Programme: 40 pages, 60p Editor: c/o Club
Newsline: 0891 66 42 52
Chairman: Donald Ashton
President: Lord Peter Archer
Press Officer: T Clark
Manager: Paul Madders
Asst Manager: Ron Blackwood
Physio: John Cotton

WALSALL WOOD

Secretary: David Cartwright, 299 Walsall Road, Stone Cross, West Bromwich B71 3LN
Tel: 0121 588 6021 (H) 01922 652633 (B) 07932 390381 (M)
Ground: Oak Park, Lichfield Rd, Walsall Tel: 01543 361084 **Directions:** Off A461 Walsall-Lichfield Rd, 4 miles from Walsall town centre and 100yds south of junction with A4152 Aldridge-Brownhills. If travelling via M6/M5 exit motorway at jct 7 (Post House) and continue on A34 towards Walsall before joining A4148 which connects with the A461. 4 miles from Walsall (BR) station - regular buses pass ground Capacity: 3,000 Seats: 400 Cover: 400 Floodlights: Yes
Clubhouse: Evenings, matchdays and Sunday lunchtimes. Darts, pool. Hot snacks on matchdays
HONOURS Midland Comb. 51-52 (R-up 53-54 54-55 57-58 58-59 60-61, Lg Cup 54-55 60-61 (R-up 56-57 58-59)), B'ham Jnr Cup 76-77. Walsall Sportsco: Mids Comb. Lg Cup 79-80

FACT FILE
Founded: 1924
Colours: All red
Change colours: White/blue/white & blue

Chairman: Scott Drew
Match Secretary: David Collins
Tel: 01922 428417 (H)

Previous Leagues
Mids Comb. 51-92
Staffs Snr 92-93

WELLINGTON

Secretary: Michael Perkins, haworth, Wellington, Hereford HR4 8AZ
Tel: 01432 830523 (H) 01432 345432 (B) 07974 447817 (M)
Ground: Wellington Playing Fields, Wellington. No telephone.
Directions: The ground is situated off the A49, 8 miles south of Leominster & 5 miles north of Hereford. At the end of the dual carriageway turn for Wellington. The ground is 1/4 mile from A49, on the left , behind Wellington School and opposite the Church.
2000-0001: Captain: Mark Fish P.o.Y.: Pete Wallace Top Scorer: Peter Wallace 21

Formed: 1968
Colours: tangerine/blue/tangerine
Change colours: Blue & white/blue/blue
Chairman: Philip Smith
Tel: 01432 830096 (H)
Match Secretary: Colin Williams
Tel: 01432 830620 (H) 0374 101316 (M)

WESTFIELDS

Secretary:& Chief Executive: Andrew Morris, 17 Fayre Oaks Green, Kings Acre, Hereford HR4 0QT(01432 264711)
Ground: Thorn Lighting, Holme Lacy Rd, Rotherwas, Hereford Tel: 0860410548
Directions: Proceed 1.5 mile from Hereford on A49, left in Home Lacy Rd at Broadleys Inn.One mile to Thorn Lighting Rotherwas, ground on the right on Ind. Estate. 2 miles from Hereford (BR)
Capacity: 2,000 Seats: 100 Cover: 150 Floodlights: Yes Club Shop: Yes
Clubhouse: 'Broadleys Inn' Holme Lacey Rd. Hereford (1/2 mile from ground)
HONOURS West Mids Lg Div 1 86-87, Div 2 R-up 83-84 (Div 2 Cup 79-80 83-84), Herefordshire Snr Cup 85-86 88-89 91-92 95-96 (Yth Cup 92-93 95-96), Kington Chall. Cup x5; Kington Invit. Cup x4; Presteigne Ottway Cup x4, Worcs Jnr Cup 79-80, Wye Guild Cup x2, Hereford Sunday Lg Prem 75-76 76-77 (Div 1 71-72, Div 2 76-77, Div 3 75-76, Prem Div Cup x2, Div 1 Cup x2, Div 3 Cup 72-73), Smart Brown Cup 67-68, Fair Play Cup 67-68. Dennis Hartland Mem Trophy 95-96,99-00 00-01 R Biggart Trophy 95-96,99-00

Founded: 1966 Nickname: The Fields
Sponsors: Left Bank Village
Colours: Maroon & sky/sky/sky
Change colours: Sky/white/sky & maroon
Midweek matchday: Tuesday
Programme: Yes Editor: Andy Morris
Chairman: Alan Dunsford V .Chair: Neil Preece
President: Graham Preece
Joint Managers: Sean Edwards & Clive Harris
Coach:Dwain Meale Physio: Neil Preece
2000-01 Capt: Matt Phillips P.o.Y.: Mark Hinbbard Top Scorer: Derek Craddock 29

WOLVERHAMPTON CASUALS

Secretary: Michael Green, 63 St Phillips Avenue, Pennfields Wolverhampton WV67ED
Tel: 01902 333677
Ground: Brinsford StadiumBrinsford Lane, Coven Heath, Wolverhampton (01902 783214)
Directions: Onto M54 from M6 North, at Junc 2 turn right (A449 to Stafford).Ground half a mile, turn right into Brinsford Lane. Billbrooke (BR) 2 miles
Seats: 50Cover: 50Capacity: 2,000Floodlights: No
Clubhouse: Bar & snacks, open Tues/Wed/Thurs/Sat/Sun & alternate Mondays
HONOURS WMRL Div 1 94-95, R-up (3) 85-88, Div 1 Cup 85-86
PREVIOUS Name: Staffs Casuals (pre 81) Ground: Aldersley Stadium

FACT FILE
Founded: 1899
Colours: All Green & White
Change colours: Gold/black/gold
Programme: 28pages 30p
Editor: G Smith

CLUB PERSONNEL
Chairman: Barry Austin
President: Clive Hammond
Manager: Gary Walters

WOLVERHAMPTON UNITED

Secretary: John Lee, 105 Milton Road, Fallings Park, Wolverhampton WV10 0NE
Tel: 01902 723 940 (H) 07774 299 628 (M)
Ground: Wednesfield FC, Amos Lane, Wednesfield, Wolverhampton. Tel: 01902 735 506
Directions: From Wolverhampton, leave on B4124 Wednesfield Road. Stay on this road until you come to a traffic island. Straight over into Wood End Lane, then immediately left into Amos Lane. Ground is 400 yards on right.

FACT FILE
Formed: 1976
Colours: Yellow/black/yellow
Change colours: All blue
Chairman: Clifford Dulstone
Match Secretary: Tom Ryan
Tel: 01543 422 012 (H)

Lye Town. Back Row (l-r): Mark Philpotts, John Constable, Jim Darby, Paul Hampton, James Constable, Darren Smith, Stuart Hensman, Mark Bache. Front Row: David Moss (mascot), Mark Smart, Adam Eveson, Paul Parker, John Hurst, Matt Blakemore, Paul Tomlinson. Photo: Marshall's Sports Services

Tividale. Back Row (l-r): Paul Davis, Stephan Worley, Stuart Clarke, Shaun Healey, Paul Millard, Luke Reynolds, Dean Smith. Front Row: Spencer Trulove, Andy Checketts, Jamie Price, Jason Downing, David Brookes. Photo: Marshall's Sports Services

First half action as Hulcop for Kidlington shields the ball from Headington's Norris at Yarnton Road.
Photo: Martin Wray

Quorn FC. Photo: Gordon Whittington

EVERARDS BREWERY
LEICESTERSHIRE SENIOR FOOTBALL LEAGUE

Founded 1896

President: John M Elsom F.C.A. **Chairman:** David Jamieson
Hon Secretary: Robert J Holmes, 8 Huntsman Close, Markfield, Leics LE67 9XE
Tel: 01530 243093
www.leicestershireseniorfootballleague.com www.oxfordshire.demon.co.uk/leic1.htm
Press Officer: Dave Lumley, 8 Pinewood Close, Coutnesthorpe, Leicsester LE8 5TS
Tel: 0116 277 8455 Email: davelumley@leicssenior.freeserve.co.uk

FINAL LEAGUE TABLES 2000-01

PREMIER DIVISION

	P	*W*	*D*	*L*	*F*	*A*	*GD*	*Pts*
Quorn	34	25	7	2	86	22	64	82
Holwell Sports	34	22	10	2	79	38	41	76
Highfield Rangers	34	19	10	5	78	38	40	67
St Andrews	34	20	6	8	72	38	34	66
Thringstone	34	20	5	9	73	50	23	65
Downes Sports	34	19	6	9	69	40	29	63
Coalville Town	34	18	3	13	69	56	13	57
Ibstock Welfare	34	15	5	14	50	44	6	50
Barrow Town	34	14	5	15	45	58	-13	47
Anstey Nomads	34	14	3	17	68	65	3	45
Leics YMCA	34	11	9	14	47	50	-3	42
Thurmaston Tn	34	12	6	16	49	57	-8	42
Kirby Muxloe	32	12	5	15	54	50	4	41
Friar Lane OB	33	9	6	18	55	65	-10	33
Blaby Whetstone	34	7	8	19	38	72	-34	29
Birstall Utd	34	8	4	22	55	81	-26	28
Aylestone Park	34	6	5	23	30	84	-54	23
Cottesmore*	33	1	1	31	24	133	-109	0

DIVISION ONE

	P	*W*	*D*	*L*	*F*	*A*	*GD*	*Pts*
Thurnby Rangers	32	20	7	5	92	42	50	67
Ellistown	32	21	4	7	79	33	46	67
Ratby Sports	32	20	6	6	85	43	42	66
Earl Shilton Alb	32	19	5	8	61	33	28	62
Sileby Town	31	16	9	6	67	35	32	57
Huncote S & S	31	14	8	9	63	45	18	50
Stoney Stanton	32	14	4	14	67	50	17	46
Bardon Hill	29	13	7	9	72	61	11	46
Asfordby Ams*	31	15	4	12	55	52	3	46
Lutterworth Town	32	13	6	13	64	50	14	45
Fosse Imps	31	11	10	10	60	47	13	43
Leics Constab.	32	11	3	18	47	61	-14	36
Narborough*	27	9	6	12	31	50	-19	30
Saffron Dynamo	30	9	2	19	53	77	-24	29
North Kilworth	32	7	2	23	45	128	-83	23
Anstey Town	32	5	3	24	38	88	-50	18
Loughboro D'mo	30	3	2	25	32	116	-84	11

Harborough Town - record expunged. **points deducted*

RECENT WINNERS OF THE LEAGUE CUPS

	PREMIER DIVISION	DIVISION ONE	BEACON BITTER LEAGUE CUP
2000-01	Quorn	Thurnby Rangers	Quorn
1999-00	Highfield Rangers	Leicester YMCA	Saffron Dynamo
1998-99	Oadby Town	Thurmaston Town	Thurmaston Town
1997-98	Oadby Town	Thurby Rangers	Friar Lane OB
1996-97	Oadby Town	Leicester Constabulary	Cottesmore Amateurs
1995-96	St Andrews	Quorn	St Andrews
1994-95	Oadby Town	Kirby Muxloe	St Andrews
1993-94	St Andrews	Asfordby Amateurs	Oadby Town
1992-93	Holwell Sports	Barrow Town	St Andrews
1991-92	Holwell Sports	Burbage Old Boys	Barwell Athletic
1990-91	Lutterworth Town	Houghton Rangers	Houghton Rangers

ANSTEY NOMADS

Secretary: Mervyn Miles, 66 CharlesDrive, Anstey, Leics.LE7 7BG Tel No: 0116 236 2909
Ground: Llimah International Park, Cropston Road, Anstey (0116 236 4868) Colours: Red/white/white

AYLESTONE PARK OLD BOYS

Secretary: Pete Burrows, 27 Cartwight Drive, Oadby, Leicester Tel: 0116 271 2682
Ground: Dorset Avenue, Fairfield Estate, Wigston, Leics (0116 277 5307)
Capacity: 2,000 **Seats**: 40**Cover:** 100 **Floodlights**:Yes
Clubhouse: Open matchdays 2pm -11pm **Club shop:** No
Previous League : Leicester District
HONOURS: Leics. Senior League Runners-up 94-95

Founded: 1967 Nickname: The Park
Colours: Red / white/ red
Change colours: White
Midweek matchday: Tuesday Prog: Yes
Hon.Chief Executive: Bob Stretton M.B.E.
President: Gary Lineker
Chairman: John Nutt
Treasurer: Jan Williams
Managers: Carl Williams & Gary Franks

BARROW TOWN

Secretary: Alan Dawkins, 72 Beaumont Road, Barrow-on-Soar, Loughborough, Leics LE12 8PJ (01509 413288) Email Address; alan@dawkins9-freeserve.co.uk
Ground: Riverside Park, Meynell Road, Quorn, Leics (01509 620650)
Directions: Access via Quorn Lodge Drive & Barrow road.
Capacity: 2,000 **Seats**: None **Cover:** 50 **Floodlights**:Yes **Clubhouse:** Yes **Club shop:** No
HONOURS: Leics Sen Lg. 92-93 R-up 94-95.Loughboro.Charity Cup 68-69,96-97,98-99,00-**BEST SEASON FA Vase:** 2nd Rd Proper. 2000-01
2000-01: Captain: Darren Wagg **Ps.o.Y**.D.Wagg & L.Johnson **Top Scorer**: Leroy Johnson 22

Re-formed 1947
Nickname: Riversiders
Colours: Red & black/black/red
Change colours: Navy Blue
Midweek matchday: Tuesday
Club Personnel
Chairman: Michael Bland
Manager: Richard Pitman
Vice Chairman, Treasurer, President, Press Officer : A.Dawkins

BIRSTALL UNITED

Secretary: Bob Gerrard, 58 Halstead Rd, Mountsorrel, Leicester LE12 7HF (0116 237 6886)
Ground: Meadow Lane, Birstall (0116 267 1230)**Colours:** White/navy/navy

BLABY & WHETSTONE ATHLETIC

Secretary: Mrs Sandra Morris, 10 Winchester Road, Blaby, Leics LE8 3HJ Tel: 0116 277 3208
Ground: Blaby & Whetstone Boys Club, Warwick Road, Whetstone (0116 286 4852) **Colours:** Navy & white/navy/navy

COALVILLE TOWN

Secretary: Robert Brooks, 17 Ashland Drive, Coalville, Leics LE67 3NH (01530 833269)
Ground: Owen Street Sports Ground, Owen Street, Coalville (01530 833365) Colours: Black&White/black/black

DOWNES SPORTS

Secretary: Tony Jacques, 17 Merton Close, Broughton, Astley Leicester LE9 6QP
Tel No: 01455 28402 (H) 01455 282028 (W)

Ground: Leicester Rd,Hinckley (01455 615062)
Directions: Off northern perimeter road round Leicester
Capacity: 2000 **Seats**:1 **Cover:**Yes **Floodlights**:Yes
Clubhouse: Yes **Club shop:** No
Honours: Leics. Sen. Lge. Div Two R-up 1986-87

Founded: 1968
Nickname: The Builders
Colours: Tangerine/black/tangerine
Change colours:t.b.a.
Midweek matchday: Tuesday
Programme:No
Club Personnel
Chairman: F. Down
Manager: S. Greenhill

ELLISTOWN

Secretary: John Measom, 29 Standard Hill, Coalville, Leicster LE67 3HN Tel: 01530 810941
Ground: 1 Terrace Road, Ellistown **Colours:** Yellow/blue/yellow/blue **Change colours:** Red/black/red

FRIAR LANE OLD BOYS

Secretary: Kevin Brooks, 299 Milligan Rd, Leicester LE4 2RJ Tel: 0116 224 3854
Ground: Knighton Lane East, Leicester (0116 283 3629) **Colours:** Black & white stripes/black/black

HIGHFIELD RANGERS

Secretary: Maurice Christian, 18 Blanklyn Avenue, Leicester LE5 5FA Tel: 0116 273 4002
Ground: 443 Gleneagles Ave., Rushey Mead, Leicester Tel: 0116 266 0009 **Colours:** Yellow/blackyellow

HOLWELL SPORTS

Secretary: Mrs Anne Marriott, 24 Church Lane, Croxton Kerrial, Grantham, Lincs NG32 1PZ Tel: 01476 870658
Ground: Welby Road, Asfordby Hill, Melton Mowbray, Leics Tel: 01664 812663 **Colours:** Green & gold/green/green

IBSTOCK WELFARE

Secretary: Ralph A Wilkinson, 6 Valley Rd, Ibstock, Leicester LE67 6NY (01530 450243)
Ground: The Welfare, Leicester Road, Ibstock (01530 260656)
Capacity: Unlimited **Seats**: 50**Cover:** 150 **Floodlights**:No
Clubhouse: Yes **Club shop:** No **Colours:** Red/black/red
HONOURS: Leics Sen Cup 93-94 R-Up 97-98; Leics Sen Lg Div 1 R-Up 90-91; Coalville Ch Cup x3 R-up x4; Loughborough Ch.Cup (4) R-up (2)

KIRBY MUXLOE S.C.

Secretary: Philip Moloney, 16 Church Lane, Ratby, Leics LE6 0JE (0116 239 2916)
Ground: Ratby Lane, Kirby Muxloe (0116 239 3201) **Colours:** Blue/black/black

LEICESTER YMCA

Secretary: Colin Chappell, 132 South Knighton Rd, Leicester, LE2 3LQ Tel: 0116 270 2721
Ground: YMCA Sports Ground, Belvoir Drive, Leicester Tel: 0116 244 0740
Directions: M1 Jct21 (M69) onto A563, Soarvalley Way, Aylestone Rd. Left at lights, to city. Belvoir Drive 2nd Right after next lights.
Capacity: 1,500 **Seats**No **Cover:** 100 **Floodlights**:Yes **Club shop:** No
Clubhouse: Yes . Sats & Suns 12.30p.m. onwards
HONOURS Leics. Sen. Lge. Div. 1 99-00; **PREVIOUS Leagues:**Mid Comb. 97-9
BEST SEASON **FA Vase:** N/A **FA Cup:** N/A

Founded: 1910
Nickname: Beavers
Colours: Red & black/black/black
Change colours: Sky blue/white/white
Midweek matchday: Wednesday
Programme: No
Club Personne
Chairman: B. Irwin
Manager: Tony Yeoman

St ANDREWS SOCIAL CLUB

Secretary: Les Botting, 2 Neston Road, Saffron Lane, Leicester LE2 6RD Tel: 0116 224 3961
Ground: Canal Street, off Aylestone Rd, Old Aylestone,Leicester Tel: 0116 283 9298
Directions: Next to Big City Tyres
HONOURS: Leics Sen Lg. Premier Champions: 89-90,93-94,95-96 **Colours:** Black & white/black/black

THRINGSTONE MINERS WELFARE

Secretary: Peter Hordley,The Willows, 9 Main Street, Thringstone, Leics. LE67 8ND
Ground: Homestead Road, Thringstone Tel: 01530 223367 **Colours:** Blue , white, red.

THURMASTON TOWN

Secretary: Kevin Sadler, 81 Woodgreen Road, Leicester LE4 9UD Tel: 0116 246 0093
Ground: Elizabeth Park, Checklands Road, Thurmaston. Tel: 0116 260 2519
HONOURS: Dist. Lg Champs 97-99, Page & Moy Junior Cup Winners 97-98 Leics Div One Champions & Beacon Bitter Cup Winners 98-99
Colours: Black & white stripes, black,black.

THURNBY RANGERS

Secretary: Ian Henson, 13 Dudley Avenue, Thurnby Lodge, Leicester LE5 2EE Tel: 0116 241 2741 07761 227 586 (M)
Ground: Dakyn Road, Thurnby Lodge, Leicester. Tel: 0116 243 3698
Colours: All green **Change colours:** All red

DIVISION ONE CLUBS

ANSTEY TOWN
Secretary:Stephen Staniforth, 38 Woodgon Road, Anstey , Leics. LE7 7EQ Tel No: 0116 210 0091 (H)
Ground: Leicester Road, Thurcaston (0116 236 8231)
Colours: All blue

ASFORDBY AMATEURS
Secretary: Stephen Hazeldine,19 Mildmay Close,Melton Mowbray,LeicsLE13 1AH Tel No:01664 857362
Ground: Hoby Road Sports Ground, Asfordby, Melton Mowbray
Tel: 01664 434545
Colours: red/black/black

BARDON HILL
Secretary: Adrian Bishop, 138 Bradgate Drive, Coalville, Leics LE67 4HG (01530815560)
Ground: Bardon Close, Coalville, Leicester (01530 815569)
Colours: Red/blue/blue

COTTESMORE AMATEURS
Secretary: Kevin Nimmons, 17 Redwing Close, Oakham, Rutland LE15 6DA Tel: 01572 724582
Ground: Rogues Park, Main Street, Cottesmore, Rutland
Tel: 01572 813486
Directions: Rear of Sun Inn.
Colours: Green/black/green

EARL SHILTON ALBION
Secretary: Graham Redshaw,3 Lucas Way,Earl Shilton,Leics.LE9 7GL
Tel No: 01455 847822
Ground: Stoneycroft Park, New St., Earl Shilton, Leics (01455 844277)
Colours: Green & gold/green/gold

HUNCOTE SPORTS & SOCIAL
Secretary: D Russell, 72 Sycamore Way, Littlethorpe, Leics LE9 5HU (0116 2841952)
Ground: Enderby Lane, Thurlaston, Leics (01455 888430).
Seating: No Cover: No Clubhouse: Yes Directions: 3 miles from exit 21 on M1. Via Enderby on B582. Thurston Lane onto Endersby Road.
Colours: Yellow & blue/blue/blue

LEICESTERSHIRE CONSTABULARY
Secretary: Mick Allard, 8 Evelyn Rd., Braunstone, Leicester LE3 3BA
Tel No: 0116 289 0027
Ground: Police HQ, St Johns, Enderby (0116 248 2198)
Colours: Blue & yellow/ blue/blue

LOUGHBOROUGH DYNAMO
Secretary: Max Hutchinson, 3 Wythburn Close, Loughborough, Leics LE11 3SZ(01509 266092)
Ground: Nanpanton Sport Ground, Loughborough (01509 612144)
Colours: Gold/black/gold

LUTTERWORTH TOWN
Secretary:Maureen Maguire c/o Hall Lane <Bitteswell, Lutterworth. Leics. LE17 4LN Tel No: 01455 554046
Ground: Hall Lane, Bitteswell, Lutterworth, Leics (01455 554046)
Colours: White & blue/blue/blue.

NARBOROUGH & LITTLETHORPE
Secretary: Barry Garner, 7 Riverside Court, Littlethorpe, Leicester LE9 5HU (0116 286 7632)
Ground: Ray Hurd Pavilion, Leicester Road, Narborough (Near M1 bridge) (0116275 1855)
Colours: Sky Blue/Navy Blue/Navy Blue.

NORTH KILWORTH
Secretary: Mrs Hilary Cheney, 109 Queens Drive, Enderby , Leics. LE9 5LL Tel No: 0116 275 1460
Ground: Rugby Road, North Kilworth, Lutterworth, Leics
Tel: 01858 880890
Colours: Navy & white/navy/navy

RATBY SPORTS
Secretary: John Rowe, 57 Danehill, Ratby, Leicester LE6 0NG
Tel: 0116 238 6806
Ground: Ratby Sports Club, Desford Lane, Ratby
Tel: 0116 239 2474
Colours: All red

SAFFRON DYNAMO
Secretary: Bob King, 14 Bramley Close, Broughton Astley, Leicester LE9 6QU(01455 284270)
Ground: Cambridge Road, Whetstone, (0116 284 9695)
Directions: Near County on road from Whetstone to Cosby..
Honours : Many as a Sunday club in last 25 years.
Colours: Red/black/black

SILEBY TOWN
Secretary: Ann Bettles, 6 Jubilee Avenue, Sileby, Leics LE12 7TH (01509 813864)
Ground: Memorial Park, Seagrave Road, Sileby, Leics
Tel: 01509 816104
Colours: All Red

STONEY STANTON
Secretary: Nigel Bradbury,144 Sketchley ,Burbage,Leics
Tel: 01455 615305
Ground: Highfields Farm, Huncote Road, Stoney Stanton,Leics.
Directions: M69 Jct 2 towards Sapcote.1st left toStoney Stanton.Right at mini roundabout and left into Long Street.Follow road out of village Highfield Farm on left.(Clubhouse open but no cover or seats)
Honours: Leics Sen Lg Div 1 R-Up 98
Colours: White/black/black

ISTHMIAN LEAGUE

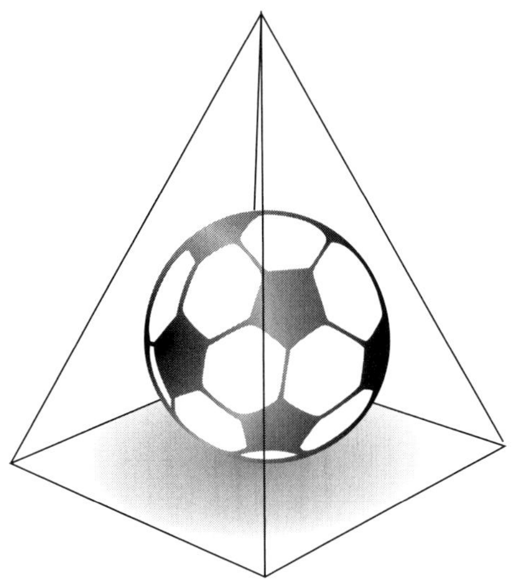

PYRAMID SECTION

Ryman
ISTHMIAN LEAGUE

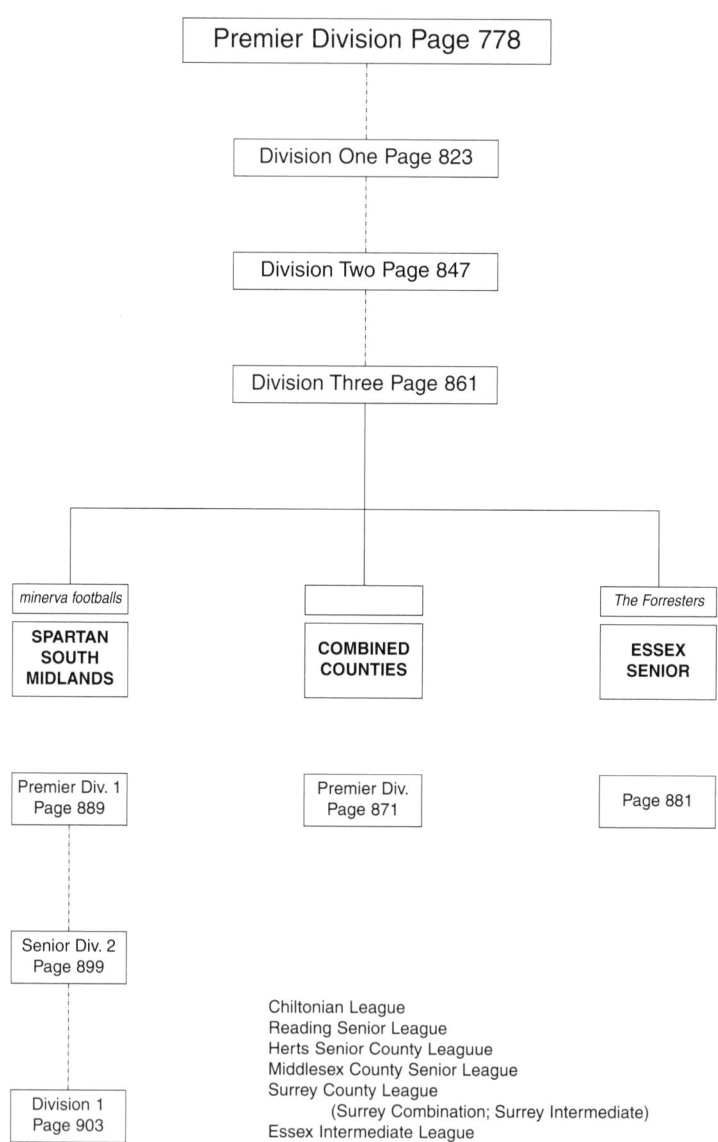

Premier Division Page 778
Division One Page 823
Division Two Page 847
Division Three Page 861
minerva footballs
SPARTAN SOUTH MIDLANDS
COMBINED COUNTIES
The Forresters
ESSEX SENIOR
Premier Div. 1 Page 889
Premier Div. Page 871
Page 881
Senior Div. 2 Page 899
Division 1 Page 903
Chiltonian League
Reading Senior League
Herts Senior County Leaguue
Middlesex County Senior League
Surrey County League
(Surrey Combination; Surrey Intermediate)
Essex Intermediate League

RYMAN LEAGUE

Chairman: A C F Turvey, MCIM, 18 Apple Way, Old Basing, Basingstoke, Hants RG24 7HA

Secretary: N R Robinson FCRArb, 226 Rye Lane, Peckham, London SE15 4NL

Tel: 020 8409 1978 (H) 020 7639 5726 (B) Fax: 020 8409 1979 (H) 020 7277 6061 (B)

Email: nickrob@clara.net secretary@isthmian.co.uk

The 'F' Word Season - Flood, Frost and Foot and Mouth

This was one of the most exacting seasons since the winter of 1963. The net result was that five matches were unplayed and the Associate Members Trophy Final was held over to next season.

Following the F word connection, it is Farewell to Farnborough Town, who were worthy champions, although their performance was almost eclipsed by Jeff King's Canvey Island, who not only finished as runners up but magnificently went to Villa Park seven days after Berkhamsted Town were runners up in The FA Challenge Vase and won The FA Challenge Trophy, the first time an Isthmian side had won the Compeititon since Bishop's Stortford in 1981.

In Division One it was not so much the 'F' which was important but the 'B', because Boreham Wood, Bedford Town and Braintree Town occupied the top three spaces and even Bishop's Stortford were fourth with Barton Rovers getting in on the act and getting relegated! Boreham Wood's promotion was an immediate return to the Premier Division, while Bedford Town sought their return to the highest Division following their re-emergence as a senior football team and Braintree Town finally justified their transfer from our sister league with their promotion to the top Division.

In Division Two there were more clubs returning to higher places, this time Tooting & Mitcham United, Windsor & Eton and Barking all going back to the Division from which they had been relegated in previous seasons.

Arlesey Town and Ashford Town Middlesex were the two new clubs in Division Three last year and they occupied places one and three in the Division at the end of the season with Lewes separating them. Arlesey Town won 108 points out of a possible 126 and in scoring 138 goals achieved a whopping goal difference of 101, the first time in the League's history that this has been achieved.

In Cup Competitions the League Cup saw a new name on the trophy in Heybridge Swifts, who defeated Croydon in the final at Purfleet on May Day Bank Holiday, while three days later Purfleet themselves went to Gravesend to contest the Full Members Cup Final, but were beaten in a thoroughly entertaining final and Gravesend & Northfleet therefore also became the new name on that trophy and, when the Associate Members Trophy final is finally played in August, yet another new name will be engraved because this final will take place between Marlow and Hemel Hempstead Town.

Returning to the original theme, we are not unhappy to say Farewell to the season!

Nick Robinson

PREMIER DIVISION FINAL LEAGUE TABLE 2000-01

			HOME					AWAY					TOTAL						
		P	*W*	*D*	*L*	*F*	*A*	*W*	*D*	*L*	*F*	*A*	*W*	*D*	*L*	*F*	*A*	*Pts*	*GD*
1	**Farnborough Town**	**42**	**14**	**5**	**2**	**43**	**13**	**17**	**1**	**3**	**43**	**14**	**31**	**6**	**5**	**86**	**27**	**99**	**59**
2	Canvey Island	42	16	4	1	46	17	11	4	6	33	24	27	8	7	79	41	89	38
3	Basingstoke Town	42	13	6	2	40	19	9	7	5	33	21	22	13	7	73	40	79	33
4	Aldershot Town	41	15	4	1	41	11	6	7	8	32	28	21	11	9	73	39	74	34
5	Chesham United	42	13	3	5	42	22	9	3	9	36	30	22	6	14	78	52	72	26
6	Gravesend & Northfleet	42	12	3	6	32	21	10	2	9	31	25	22	5	15	63	46	71	17
7	Heybridge Swifts	42	11	7	3	47	29	7	6	8	27	31	18	13	11	74	60	67	14
8	Billericay Town	41	10	8	3	34	22	8	5	7	28	32	18	13	10	62	54	67	8
9	Hampton & Richmond Borough	42	14	3	4	43	22	4	9	8	30	38	18	12	12	73	60	66	13
10	Hitchin Town	42	10	2	9	40	32	8	3	10	32	37	18	5	19	72	69	59	3
11	Purfleet	42	8	8	5	31	21	6	5	10	24	34	14	13	15	55	55	55	0
12	Hendon	40	9	2	9	32	28	7	4	9	30	34	16	6	18	62	62	54	0
13	Sutton United	41	7	6	7	40	35	7	5	9	34	35	14	11	16	74	70	53	4
14	St. Albans City	42	7	2	12	25	33	8	3	10	25	36	15	5	22	50	69	50	-19
15	Grays Athletic	42	9	6	6	32	28	5	2	14	17	40	14	8	20	49	68	50	-19
16	Maidenhead United	42	10	1	10	28	27	5	1	15	19	36	15	2	25	47	63	47	-16
17	Croydon	42	9	6	6	34	24	3	4	14	21	53	12	10	20	55	77	46	-22
18	Enfield	42	9	5	7	31	32	3	4	14	17	42	12	9	21	48	74	45	-26
19	Harrow Borough	41	6	4	11	32	48	4	7	9	30	43	10	11	20	62	91	41	-29
20	Slough Town	42	8	4	9	26	29	2	5	15	14	33	10	9	23	40	62	39	-22
21	Carshalton Athletic	42	9	3	9	26	36	1	3	17	14	49	10	6	26	40	85	36	-45
22	Dulwich Hamlet	42	4	4	13	18	36	0	6	15	15	48	4	10	28	33	84	22	-51

PREMIER DIVISION RESULTS AND ATTENDANCES 2000-01

		1	2	3	4	5	6	7	8	9	10	11	12	13	14	15	16	17	18	19	20	21	22
1	Aldershot Town	X X	1-0 1822	NP NP	1-0 2489	4-0 2175	1-0 1218	4-0 2010	1-0 2031	2-1 1625	1-1 3197	1-0 2065	6-0 1750	2-2 1753	3-0 1226	1-1 2241	2-1 2145	2-0 1804	2-1 2026	3-0 1410	1-0 2264	2-3 1877	1-1 2547
2	Basingstoke Town	2-1 1161	X X	1-1 504	0-0 501	1-1 226	2-1 285	1-1 444	2-2 488	4-0 296	0-1 946	4-0 445	1-0 428	1-0 497	2-2 268	5-0 353	3-2 420	2-1 370	2-1 309	1-2 404	3-2 475	2-1 538	1-0 477
3	Billericay Town	2-2 922	2-2 419	X X	2-1 1056	0-0 244	1-1 357	0-0 179	3-0 430	0-2 490	1-2 726	1-0 408	3-1 475	3-1 278	1-1 338	2-0 510	5-1 495	3-1 422	2-0 413	1-1 346	0-0 339	2-1 363	0-5 566
4	Canvey Island	1-1 861	0-0 718	2-1 1190	X X	3-2 282	2-1 725	5-0 340	3-2 410	4-1 416	0-1 643	1-1 630	1-0 410	1-0 333	3-0 642	3-2 411	3-0 414	2-2 491	1-0 282	1-0 542	1-0 802	3-1 653	6-2 331
5	Carshalton Athletic	2-1 670	1-0 303	5-0 337	1-4 356	X X	0-4 324	4-2 269	3-1 344	2-1 356	0-5 440	1-3 336	1-0 289	0-3 345	1-1 281	1-2 265	1-1 330	0-5 260	1-0 285	1-0 284	0-1 377	1-1 224	0-1 1067
6	Chesham United	0-3 329	1-2 364	2-0 397	1-1 455	3-1 295	X X	4-1 323	2-0 280	0-0 153	1-4 511	3-0 314	3-1 276	1-0 303	1-1 402	4-1 378	2-3 263	3-0 309	2-1 225	5-0 140	2-0 621	2-0 449	0-3 306
7	Croydon	2-2 554	2-2 109	1-2 106	2-1 118	3-0 165	2-1 109	X X	1-1 185	2-2 219	0-1 175	1-2 136	1-0 107	1-1 131	2-0 121	2-0 121	1-2 148	5-1 112	0-2 109	0-0 130	4-1 138	0-2 119	2-1 204
8	Dulwich Hamlet	2-4 924	0-2 268	0-1 322	2-3 312	1-0 285	0-1 338	1-4 271	X X	1-1 361	0-2 517	0-2 427	1-2 412	1-1 133	0-1 287	0-3 325	1-0 204	0-2 277	2-3 217	1-1 205	2-2 283	1-0 284	2-1 420
9	Enfield	1-0 346	1-4 188	1-0 206	3-0 119	2-1 151	3-1 224	1-0 156	1-1 196	X X	0-3 313	0-1 252	2-1 117	2-2 129	1-2 211	0-2 177	1-1 148	2-5 206	3-1 228	2-1 188	1-1 229	2-3 306	2-2 231
10	Farnborough Town	1-0 3478	1-1 764	3-0 497	1-2 1124	3-0 521	0-0 517	3-1 700	3-0 502	1-1 725	X X	1-0 452	3-0 736	1-1 1097	3-1 534	2-0 684	0-1 367	3-0 488	4-1 685	3-2 502	1-1 677	4-0 688	2-1 781
11	Gravesend & Northfleet	2-0 789	0-2 275	1-1 443	1-2 662	3-0 524	3-2 463	2-0 525	2-1 443	1-0 473	2-1 681	X X	0-1 363	3-4 412	2-1 363	2-1 227	0-0 391	3-0 468	0-1 203	1-0 222	1-2 481	1-0 468	2-2 499
12	Grays Athletic	1-1 316	0-0 224	2-3 386	0-3 267	3-1 208	0-2 199	2-2 181	1-1 210	2-0 312	0-3 284	2-1 295	X X	1-3 221	1-1 194	3-2 207	1-0 188	2-1 211	2-1 195	1-1 279	1-0 169	6-0 193	1-2 250
13	Hampton & Richmond Borough	1-0 838	3-2 433	1-2 254	2-2 166	4-2 184	3-1 292	3-0 178	4-0 157	4-0 278	1-0 609	1-0 485	0-0 205	X X	3-3 258	0-2 201	2-1 250	2-4 271	1-0 274	2-0 367	2-0 151	1-2 458	3-1 550
14	Harrow Borough	1-1 825	1-4 188	4-2 193	0-2 215	2-2 215	3-2 151	0-1 165	2-1 134	2-1 240	2-3 376	0-6 253	1-2 173	4-5 217	X X	1-4 289	1-1 222	1-4 149	1-2 207	1-2 248	1-0 305	2-2 382	2-1 182
15	Hendon	0-5 273	2-3 161	0-2 123	2-1 240	1-0 135	2-2 328	4-0 304	4-0 138	3-0 306	0-2 303	1-2 207	1-1 210	2-0 201	NP NP	X X	1-4 147	4-0 157	2-1 228	1-2 203	2-1 183	0-1 347	0-1 370
16	Heybridge Swifts	2-1 479	1-1 170	2-2 444	1-1 312	2-1 232	3-1 254	1-2 195	3-1 139	2-0 295	2-3 457	2-2 298	4-0 208	3-2 214	4-2 219	2-2 204	X X	0-0 284	4-0 173	4-3 264	3-2 337	0-1 184	2-2 310
17	Hitchin Town	2-5 336	0-1 350	2-1 382	4-1 301	3-0 301	1-2 258	7-3 280	1-0 277	2-1 457	1-2 391	1-2 388	2-0 271	2-0 331	3-6 286	3-3 363	0-2 201	X X	0-2 252	0-1 176	3-0 242	0-0 334	3-0 413
18	Maidenhead United	3-0 1213	3-2 263	1-2 191	0-2 173	2-0 306	0-2 329	3-1 217	1-0 217	2-1 292	0-1 459	1-3 203	3-2 138	0-0 248	4-1 279	1-2 187	1-2 155	0-1 241	X X	1-2 194	1-0 256	1-0 613	0-2 258
19	Purfleet	2-2 653	0-0 197	1-1 340	0-1 443	3-0 178	1-2 239	3-0 162	1-1 231	3-0 264	0-2 301	1-0 201	3-1 302	2-2 173	4-2 186	0-0 162	1-1 163	0-1 201	1-1 169	X X	2-0 257	1-3 201	2-1 182
20	Slough Town	0-1 982	0-2 295	2-3 501	0-1 438	3-1 333	0-2 385	1-0 326	1-1 637	3-1 1009	0-2 708	2-0 233	1-0 292	1-1 457	1-2 486	1-0 522	1-1 284	0-3 647	1-0 628	3-2 351	X X	1-2 436	4-4 452
21	St Albans City	0-1 1230	0-3 402	0-0 330	1-4 333	0-1 528	1-5 517	2-2 380	2-1 368	0-1 490	2-4 582	0-2 312	1-2 503	5-0 469	1-0 232	1-3 433	3-0 353	2-0 414	3-1 726	0-2 452	1-0 509	X X	0-1 556
22	Sutton United	1-1 659	2-0 645	1-4 389	0-1 552	3-1 902	2-3 387	2-1 584	7-1 509	2-3 446	1-0 644	1-4 543	2-3 390	2-2 564	3-3 466	NP NP	1-2 574	1-1 520	2-0 476	2-2 503	1-1 385	4-2 648	X X

RYMAN LEAGUE CUP 2000-01

PRELIMINARY ROUND

Leatherhead	1	v	0	Romford
Marlow	1	v	0	Wivenhoe Town
Berkhamsted Town	2	v	3	Flackwell Heath
Aveley	4	*	2	Tooting & Mitcham
Leyton Pennant	2	v	1	Abingdon Town
Egham Town	3,2	*	2,1	Hemel Hempstead
Great Wakering R	2	v	0	Tilbury
Edgware Town	1,0	*	0,0	Met Police
Wembley	4	v	0	Camberley Town
Dorking	1	v	2	Hungerford Town
Ford United	1	v	0	Hornchurch
Hertford Town	4	v	0	Witham Town
Leighton Town	1	v	2	Epsom & Ewell
Barking	1,0	*	0,3	Arlesey Town
Chertsey Town	0	v	3	East Thurrock Utd
Ashford Town (Mx)	5	v	3	Croydon Athletic
Tring Town	0	v	2	Wingate & Finchley
Chalfont St Peter	2	v	4	Northwood
Clapton	0	v	1	Corinthian Casuals
Lewes	5	v	0	Kingsbury Town
Molesey	2,0	*	0,1	Cheshunt
Ware	2	v	1	Windsor & Eton
Banstead Athletic	4	*	2	Bracknell Town
Wokingham Town	1	v	3	Horsham

FIRST ROUND

St Albans City	3,1	*	1,2	Boreham Wood
Maidenhead United	1	v	3	Leatherhead
Yeading	0	*	1	Marlow
Flackwell Heath	1	v	3	Slough Town
Dulwich Hamlet	5	*	2	Aveley
Carshalton Athletic	1	*	0	Hitchin Town
Leyton Pennant	0	v	4	Hampton & Rich B
Bognor Regis Tn	5	v	3	Harlow Town
Farnborough Town	2	*	1	Enfield
Hemel Hemp. Town	2	*	0	Great Wakering R
Thame United	4	v	3	Wealdstone
Edgware Town	0	v	1	Basingstoke Town
Harrow Borough	2	v	3	Croydon
Wembley	2	v	1	Staines Town
Bishop's Stortford	2	*	5	Canvey Island
Gravesend & N	6	v	1	Hungerford Town
Ford United	0	v	2	Heybridge Swifts
Hertford Town	2	v	3	Oxford City
Walton & Hersham	2	*	1	Aldershot Town
Bedford Town	1	v	0	Epsom & Ewell
Arlesey Town	3	v	4	Hendon
East Thurrock Utd	1	*	2	Braintree Town
Ashford Town (Mx)	1	v	3	Bromley
Wingate & Finchley	1	v	3	Chesham United
Whyteleafe	2	*	3	Worthing
Grays Athletic	0	v	4	Northwood
Billericay Town	3	v	1	Barton Rovers
Corinthian Casuals	1	v	0	Sutton United
Lewes	1,0	*	0,2	Aylesbury United
Molesey	2	v	4	Ware
Uxbridge	2	v	3	Purfleet
Banstead Athletic	0	v	2	Horsham

SECOND ROUND

St Albans City	3	v	1	Leatherhead
Marlow	0	v	2	Slough Town (R)
Dulwich Hamlet	1	*	2	Carshalton Athletic
Hampton & Rich. B	3	v	2	Bognor Regis Town
Farnborough Town	5	*	1	Hemel Hemp. Tn
Thame United	0	v	4	Basingstoke Town
Croydon	3	v	0	Wembley
Canvey Island	2	v	0	Gravesend & N
Heybridge Swifts	3	v	0	Oxford City
Walton & Hersham	0	v	5	Bedford Town
Hendon	3	*	2	Braintree Town
Bromley	1	v	3	Chesham United
Worthing	0	v	2	Northwood
Billericay Town	4	v	0	Corinthian Casuals
Aylesbury United	1	v	0	Ware
Purfleet	4	v	0	Horsham

THIRD ROUND

St Albans City	3	v	1	Marlow
Carshalton Athletic	0	v	3	Hampton & Rich. B
Farnborough Town	1	v	3	Basingstoke Town
Croydon	5	v	0	Canvey Island
Heybridge Swifts	3	v	0	Bedford Town
Hendon	2	v	3	Chesham United
Northwood	4	v	3	Billericay Town
Aylesbury United	0	v	1	Purfleet

FOURTH ROUND

St Albans City	0,3	*	3,3	Hampton & Rich. B
Basingstoke Town	0	v	2	Croydon
Heybridge Swifts	3	v	0	Chesham United
Northwood	4	v	1	Purfleet

SEMI-FINALS

Hampton & Rich. B	2,2	v	3,3	Croydon
Heybridge Swifts	4,2	v	1,1	Northwood

FINAL

CROYDON	0	v	3	HEYBRIDGE SWIFTS

* after extra time

(R) Removed from competition

FULL MEMBERS CUP 2000-01

FIRST ROUND

Walton & Hersham	1	v	0	Farnborough
Carshalton Athletic	3	p	3	Basingstoke
Worthing	2	v	0	Hampton & Rich. B
Hitchin Town	2	v	1	Bedford Town
Braintree Town	5	v	0	Enfield
Aylesbury United	1	v	2	Thame United
Slough Town	4	v	3	Aldershot Town
Staines Town	4	p	4	Sutton United
Harrow Borough	1	v	2	Romford
Heybridge Swifts	2	v	0	Billericay Town
Harlow Town	0	v	2	Hendon
Purfleet	3	v	1	Boreham Wood

SECOND ROUND

Dulwich Hamlet	2	v	1	Walton & Hersham
Basingstoke Town	2	v	1	Whyteleafe
Worthing	2	v	4	Bognor Regis Town
Maidenhead Utd	2	*	1	Leatherhead
Gravesend & N.	4	v	0	Ford United
Wealdstone	0	v	3	Hitchin Town
Chesham United	4	*	2	Braintree Town
Northwood	3	v	4	St Albans City
Thame United	2	v	3	Oxford City
Bromley	1	v	0	Slough Town
Yeading	1	v	4	Uxbridge
Sutton United	2	p	2	Croydon
Romford	0	v	2	Barton Rovers
Grays Athletic	4	*	4	Bishop's Stortford
Heybridge Swifts	6	*	5	Hendon
Purfleet	1	v	0	Canvey Island

THIRD ROUND

Dulwich Hamlet	0	v	2	Basingstoke Town
Bognor Regis Town	2	v	3	Maidenhead United
Gravesend & N.	7	v	1	Hitchin Town
Chesham United	0	v	2	St Albans City
Oxford City	2	v	0	Bromley
Uxbridge	2	v	0	Sutton United
Barton Rovers	2	v	0	Grays Athletic
Heybridge Swifts	1	v	3	Purfleet

FOURTH ROUND

Basingstoke Town	1	v	3	Bognor Regis Town
Gravesend & N.	1	p	1	St Albans City
Oxford City	4	v	1	Uxbridge
Barton Rovers	0	v	1	Purfleet

SEMI-FINALS

Bognor Regis Town	0	v	2	Gravesend & N.
Oxford City	1	v	2	Purfleet

FINAL

GRAVESEND & N	3	v	1	PURFLEET

*: after extra time
p: match decided by penalties

ASSOCIATE MEMBERS TROPHY 2000-01

FIRST ROUND

Berkhamsted Town	1	v	3	Edgware Town
Hertford Town	2	v	3	Cheshunt
Leyton Pennant	2	v	1	Wembley
Arlesey Town	4	v	0	Tring Town
East Thurrock Utd	3	v	1	Clapton
Abingdon Town	2	p	2	Hungerford Town
Dorking	2	v	1	Croydon Athletic
Bracknell Town	1	p	1	Wokingham Town
Witham Town	0	v	2	Tilbury
Flackwell Heath	3	v	0	Chalfont
Molesey	1	p	1	Tooting & Mitcham
Windsor & Eton	4	v	1	Ashford Town

SECOND ROUND

Edgware Town	2	v	1	Cheshunt
Leyton Pennant	2	v	3	Hornchurch
Ware	2	v	1	Arlesey Town
East Thurrock Utd	4	v	0	Aveley
Marlow	4	v	2	Camberley Town
Hungerford Town	0	v	5	Banstead Athletic
Dorking	3	v	2	Corinthian Casuals
Chertsey Town	1	v	2	Bracknell Town
Great Wakering R	1	v	2	Barking
Kingsbury Town	2	v	0	Leighton Town
Tilbury	1	v	4	Wivenhoe Town
Hemel Hemp. T	4	v	1	Wingate & Finchley
Met Police	1	p	1	Egham Town
Horsham	5	v	2	Flackwell Heath
Molesey	0	v	1	Windsor & Eton
Lewes	2	v	1	Epsom & Ewell

THIRD ROUND

Edgware Town	1	v	0	Hornchurch
Ware	0	v	4	East Thurrock Utd
Marlow	2	v	1	Banstead Athletic
Dorking	1	v	0	Bracknell Town
Barking	4	v	0	Kingsbury Town
Wivenhoe Town	2	v	4	Hemel Hemp. Tn
Egham Town	0	v	1	Horsham
Windsor & Eton	0	v	5	Lewes

FOURTH ROUND

Edgware Town	1	v	2	East Thurrock Utd
Marlow	3	p	3	Dorking
Barking	0	v	1	Hemel Hemp. Tn
Horsham	3	v	1	Lewes

SEMI-FINALS

East Thurrock Utd	1	v	4	Marlow
Hemel Hempstead	5	*	2	Horsham

FINAL

MARLOW		v		HEMEL HEMP. T

*: after extra time
p: match decided by penalties

ALDERSHOT TOWN

CLUB OFFICIALS

Chairman: Karl Prentice

Vice Chairman: John McGinty

Company Secretary: Graham Brookland
c/o Aldershot Town FC, (07973 172073)

Press Officer: Nick Fryer Tel:01483 563570

FOOTBALL MANAGEMENT TEAM

Manager: George Borg
Asst Man.: Stuart Cash
Physio: Alan Mc Creanney

FACT FILE

Formed: 1992 Nickname: The Shots
Sponsors: Charters Peugeot
Colours: Red / white & red
Change : Black & white/black & red/black
Midweek matchday: Tuesday
Reserves' League: Suburban league
Club Newsline: 09066 55585
Official Website: www.theshots.net
Unofficial Website: www.shotsweb.co.uk

2000-01

Captain: Ollie Adedeji
Top Scorer: Gary Abbott (27)
P.o.Y.: Mark Bentley

Pages: 44 Price: £1.50
Editors: Karl Prentice/Graham Brookland
Tel: 01256 471630

Local Press: Aldershot News, Farnham Herald
Local Radio: County Sound (96.4, 1476 khz), BBC Southern Counties(104.6 fm)

GROUND Recreation Ground, High Street, Aldershot, Hants GU11 1TW
Tel: 0870 112 4112Fax: 0870 112 5112

Directions: Ground situated on eastern end of High Street next to large multi-storey B.T. building. From M3 (jct 4) take A325 to Aldershot. After five milesat r'bout take 1st exit marked town centre (A323) into Wellington Ave. At Burger King r'bout take 2nd exit into High Street - ground on left, large carpark adjacent. 5 mins walk from Aldershot (BR)

Capacity: 7,500 Cover: 6,850 Seats: 1,800 Floodlights: Yes

Clubhouse: Matchdays and special functions Steward: Wally Clarke 01252 320211 x212

Club Shop: Range of souvenirs, programmes, replica kits.
Open matchdays or contact Janet Guess (01252-528007) for mail order

PREVIOUS **Leagues:** None **Names:** None **Grounds:** None

CLUB RECORDS **Attendance:** 7,500 v Brighton & Hove Albion F.A.C. First Round 18.11.00
"Ground record: 19,138 Aldershot FC v CarlisleUnited, FA Cup 4th Rd replay 28/1/70
Win: 8-0 v Bishop's Stortford (a) League 5.9.98 **Defeat:** 0-6v Worthing (a) Puma Cup 2.3.99
9-1 v Andover (n) Hants Senior Cup Final 99-00
Career Goalscorer: Mark Butler 155. (92-98) **Career Appearances:** Mark Butler 303. (92-98)
Transfer Fee Paid: £20,000 to Woking for Grant Payne (11.99)
Transfer Fee Received: £6,000 for Leon Gutzmore from Bedford Town (11.99)

BEST SEASON **FA Cup:** Second Round 99-00 v Exeter City **FA Trophy:** Fourth Rd Replay 99-00
FA Vase: Quarter Final 93-94

HONOURS Isthmian League Prem. Div. R-up 99-2000, Div 1 97-98, Div 3 92-93; Simpsonair Trophy 92-93; Skol Invitation Trophy 92-93; Hants Senior Cup SF 92-93; 98-99, 99-00. Suburban Lge Western Div 94-95; Allied Counties Youth Lge 1994-95; Guardian Insurance Lge Cup 98-99 R-up 95-96

Date	Comp.	Opponents	Att.	Score	Goalscorers
19.08	Ryman P	SUTTON UNITED	2547	1 - 1	Protheroe 23
22.08	Ryman P	Harrow Borough	825	1 - 1	Abbott 70[p]
26.08	Ryman P	Billericay Town	922	2 - 2	Gell 14, Fielder 84
28.08	Ryman P	HITCHIN TOWN	1804	2 - 0	Abbott 27[p], Andrews 83
02.09	Ryman P	DULWICH HAMLET	2031	1 - 0	Abbott 28[p]
05.09	Ryman P	Slough Town	1230	1 - 0	Abbott 67
09.09	Ryman P	CROYDON	2010	4 - 0	Andrews 45, Abbott 72 87, Abbey 90
12.09	Lge Cup 1	Walton & Hersham	325	1 - 2	Lloyd 90
16.09	Ryman P	St Albans City	982	1 - 0	Coll 3
23.09	Ryman P	HENDON	2241	1 - 1	Coll 90
30.09	FA Cup Q2	Crawley Town	2504	2 - 1	Ullathorne 48, Abbott 78[p]
07.10	Ryman P	GRAYS ATHLETIC	1750	6 - 0	Crossley 2, Abbott 9 18 47 59, Holsgrove 76
10.10	Ryman P	Hampton & Richmond Borough	838	0 - 1	
14.10	FA Cup Q3	Fisher Athletic	514	2 - 1	Abbott 13 26[p]
21.10	Ryman P	GRAVESEND & NORTHFLEET	2065	1 - 0	Browne 3
24.10	FMC 1	Slough Town	271	3 - 4	Pearson, Peters(2)
31.10	FA Cup Q4	DOVER ATHLETIC	2873	1 - 0	Abbott 52
04.11	Ryman P	Purfleet	653	2 - 2	Protheroe 13, Abbott 17
11.11	Ryman P	MAIDENHEAD UNITED	2026	2 - 1	Abbott 25, Protheroe 52
15.11	Hants SC 2	Newport IOW	194	0 - 5	
18.11	FA Cup 1	BRIGHTON & HOVE ALBION	7500	2 - 6	Abbott 26[p] 88
25.11	Ryman P	CANVEY ISLAND	2489	1 - 0	Andrews 55
02.12	FA Trophy 2	HAVANT & WATERLOOVILLE	1887	1 - 0	Browne 37
09.12	Ryman P	HEYBRIDGE SWIFTS	2145	2 - 1	Bentley 84, Protheroe 90
16.12	Ryman P	Dulwich Hamlet	924	4 - 2	Bentley 19, Protheroe 33, Abbott 53, Browne 69
23.12	Ryman P	CARSHALTON ATHLETIC	2175	4 - 0	Abbott 18 25[p] 42, Andrews 90
26.12	Ryman P	Farnborough Town	3478	0 - 1	
06.01	Ryman P	Maidenhead United	1213	0 - 3	
13.01	FA Trophy 3	STEVENAGE BOROUGH	2965	1 - 5	Browne 23
27.01	Ryman P	ST ALBANS CITY	2264	2 - 3	Graham 12, Abbott 90
10.02	Ryman P	SLOUGH TOWN	1762	1 - 0	Bentley 4
17.02	Ryman P	Croydon	554	2 - 2	Kirby 3, Bentley 27
20.02	Ryman P	Enfield	346	0 - 1	
24.02	Ryman P	HAMPTON & RICHMOND BOR.	1753	2 - 2	Crossley 45, Browne 83
27.02	Ryman P	Basingstoke Town	1161	1 - 2	Browne 90
06.03	Ryman P	HARROW BOROUGH	1226	3 - 0	Bentley 11, Browne 31 67
31.03	Ryman P	Gravesend & Northfleet	789	0 - 2	
03.04	Ryman P	Hitchin Town	336	5 - 2	Browne 8 61 85, Coll 73, Gell 89
07.04	Ryman P	ENFIELD	1625	2 - 1	Holsgrove 77, Bentley 82
10.04	Ryman P	Sutton United	659	1 - 1	Protheroe 58
12.04	Ryman P	PURFLEET	1410	3 - 0	Browne 12, Abbott 76, Protheroe 81
14.04	Ryman P	Carshalton Athletic	670	1 - 2	Holsgrove 11
16.04	Ryman P	FARNBOROUGH TOWN	3197	1 - 1	Protheroe 84
18.04	Ryman P	Chesham United	329	3 - 0	Browne 25 82, Chewins 88
21.04	Ryman P	Canvey Island	861	1 - 1	Graham 10
26.04	Ryman P	CHESHAM UNITED	1220	1 - 0	Browne 56
28.04	Ryman P	BASINGSTOKE TOWN	1722	1 - 0	Abbott 43
03.05	Ryman P	Grays Athletic	316	1 - 1	Forrester 20
04.05	Ryman P	Hendon	273	5 - 0	Browne 26, Holsgrove 51, Protheroe 55, Chewins 84, Abbott 90
05.05	Ryman P	Heybridge Swifts	479	1 - 2	Coll 62
Unplayed	Ryman P	BILLERICAY TOWN			

PLAYING SQUAD

GOALKEEPERS: Gareth Howells (Sutton Utd), Andy Pape (Sutton Utd), Chris Knowles (Tamworth)

DEFENDERS: Lee Protheroe (Enfield), Jason Chewins (Wealdstone), Leon Townley (Slough), Ryan Kirby (Stevenage), Ollie Adedeji (Bromley), Owen Coll (Stevenage)

MIDFIELDERS: Mark Bentley (Enfield), Ricgard Gell (Chesham Utd), John Nutter (Wycombe), Lee Holsgrove (Wycombe), Mark Graham (Barry), Paul Harford (Sutton Utd), Jimmy Sugrue (Dulwich Hamlet)

FORWARDS: Grant Payne (Woking), Scott Forrester (Dulwich Hamlet), Mark Watson (Chesham Utd), Stafford Browne (Dag & Red)

BASINGSTOKE TOWN

CLUB OFFICIALS

Chairman: David Knight
President: Rafi Razzack
Secretary: Richard Trodd
5 Lehar Close, Brighton Hill,
Basingstoke RG22 4HT
Tel: 01256 413076
Press Officer: John Gray
Commercial Manager: AlanHumphries

FOOTBALL MANAGEMENT TEAM

Manager: Ernie Howe
Asst Manager: Pete Peters
Coach: Steve Richardson
Physio: Mark Randall

FACT FILE

Formed: 1896
Nickname: Stoke
Sponsors: Centerprise International & Ericsson
Colours: Blue & gold stripes/blue/blue
Change colours: All Red
Midweek home matchday: Tuesday
Reserves' League: Suburban (Prem Div) and Capital league

2000-01

Captain : Dominic Naylor
Top Scorer: Sean Gorman
P.o.Y.:Paul Wilkinson

£1.50
THE CAMROSE
CALL THE CAMROSE 'BLUES' CALL LINE 09066 555828
Basingstoke Town Official Club Sponsor: Centerprise International
Ryman Premier Division – Saturday 5th May 2001 – Kick off 3:00pm
BASINGSTOKE TOWN v GRAVESEND & NORTHFLEET
Programme Sponsors: Ericsson Mobile Communications Ltd Gazette Newspapers Ryman
OFFICIAL PROGRAMME OF BASINGSTOKE TOWN F.C.

Pages: 24 Price: £1.50
Editor: T.B.A. Local Press: Basingstoke Gazette (461131)
Local Radio: Radio 210 (01189 413131), Kestrel Radio (01256 694000)

GROUND Camrose Road, Western Way, Basingstoke RG24 6HWTel: 01256 325063 or 01256 or01256 327575 Email Address: info@btfc.co.uk Club Website http // www.btfc.co.uk

Directions: Exit 6 off M3 and follow A30 west, ground off Winchester Road. Two miles from bus and rail stations

Capacity: 6,000 Cover:2,000 Seats: 651 Floodlights: Yes

Clubhouse: Open every day (incl. lunchtime) Steward: Cheryl Fox (01256 464353)
Club Shop: Open daily 10-5pm, selling programmes, books, scarves, shirts, badges etc.

PREVIOUS **Leagues:** Hants 1900-40 45-71; Southern 71-87 **Ground:** Castle Field 1896-1947

CLUB RECORDS **Attendance:** 5,085 v Wycombe Wanderers, FA Cup 1st Rd replay 97-98
Win: 10-0 v Chichester City (H), FA Cup 1st Qualifying Round, September 1976
Defeat: 0-8 v Aylesbury United, Southern League, April 1979.
Goalscorer: Paul Coombs 159 (Oct 91 99) **Appearances:** Billy Coombs
TransferFees - Paid: £4,750 for Steve Ingham (Gosport Borough) **Received:** £6,750 for Steve Ingham (Bashley)

BEST SEASON **FA Trophy:** 3rd Rd 98-99, 0-2 v Yeovil T. (H)
FA Cup: 2nd Rd replay 97-98, 3-4 pens aet 0 -0 v Northampton (H) after 1-1; 2nd Rd 89-90, 2-3 v Torquay U. (H)
League clubs defeated: Wycombe Wanderers 97-98

HONOURS Southern Lge Southern Div 85-86; Isthmian League Div 1 R-up 88-89 96-97; Hants League 67-68 69-70 70-71 (R-up 65-66 66-67 68-69, North Div 11-12 19-20); HantsSenior Cup 70-71 89-90 95-96 96-97

Players progressing: Tony Godfrey (Southampton 58), John Neale (Exeter 72),Mike Doherty (Reading 82), Micky Cheetham (Ipswich 88), Matt Carmichael(Lincoln), Tony Franklin (Exeter), Steve Welsh (Peterborough 90)

Date	Comp.	Opponents	Att.	Score	Goalscorers
19.08	Ryman P	HEYBRIDGE SWIFTS	420	3 - 2	Gorman 4 45, T Sills 63
22.08	Ryman P	Sutton United	645	0 - 2	
26.08	Ryman P	Harrow Borough	167	4 - 1	Girdler 40, Cook 45, Gorman 85, Newbery 90
28.08	Ryman P	DULWICH HAMLET	488	2 - 2	Newbury 46, Mings 65
02.09	Ryman P	CROYDON	444	1 - 1	Chudy 55
05.09	Ryman P	Farnborough Town	764	1 - 1	Mings 49
09.09	Ryman P	BILLERICAY TOWN	504	1 - 1	Gorman 6
16.09	Ryman P	Chesham United	364	2 - 1	Mings 35, Newbery 68[p]
23.09	Ryman P	Canvey Island	718	0 - 0	
30.09	FA Cup Q2	BATH CITY	522	1 - 1	Mings 8
03.10	FA Cup Q2 R	Bath City	606	0 - 2	
07.10	Ryman P	St Albans City	295	3 - 0	Chudy 23, Girdler 30, Mycroft 89
10.10	Lge Cup 1	Edgware Town	110	1 - 0	Bassett 53
21.10	Ryman P	GRAYS ATHLETIC	428	1 - 0	Newbery 59
24.10	FMC 1	Carshalton Athletic	102	3 - 3	Newbery 49[p], Gorman 59, Bassett 108 4 -2p
28.10	Ryman P	Maidenhead United	263	2 - 3	Chudy 29, Newbery 90
31.10	Hants SC 2	EAST COWES VICTORIA ATHLETIC	0	4 - 1	T Sills 34 40 74, Gorman 46
04.11	FA Trophy 1	Harlow Town	179	1 - 2	Gorman 24[p]
11.11	Ryman P	Slough Town	402	2 - 0	Newbery 64 84
14.11	Lge Cup 2	Thame United	126	4 - 0	J Sills 45, T Sills 48 50, Gorman 78
18.11	Ryman P	PURFLEET	404	1 - 2	Baker 43
02.12	FMC 2	WHYTELEAFE	180	2 - 1	Mings 85, J Sills 90
16.12	Ryman P	SUTTON UNITED	477	1 - 0	Gorman 90
23.12	Ryman P	Hitchin Town	350	1 - 0	Naylor 34
26.12	Ryman P	HAMPTON & RICHMOND BOR.	497	1 - 0	Gorman 11
06.01	Ryman P	SLOUGH TOWN	538	3 - 2	Mings 45 57, Newbery 90
09.01	Hants SC 3	Newport IOW	215	1 - 5	Gorman 57
13.01	Ryman P	Hampton & Richmond Borough	433	2 - 3	Cook 42, T Sills 82
16.01	Lge Cup 3	Farnborough Town	282	3 - 1	T Sills 30, Gorman 46, J Sills 65
27.01	Ryman P	FARNBOROUGH TOWN	946	0 - 1	
30.01	Ryman P	ENFIELD	296	4 - 0	T Sills 5, Naylor 26, J Sills 40 52
03.02	Ryman P	Dulwich Hamlet	268	2 - 0	J Sills 29 74
17.02	Ryman P	Billericay Town	419	2 - 2	Howes 55, Gorman 80[p]
22.02	FMC 3	Dulwich Hamlet	55	2 - 0	Howes 5, Cook 75
24.02	Ryman P	Enfield	188	4 - 1	Naylor 61, Gorman 23 81, Baker 86
27.02	Ryman P	ALDERSHOT TOWN	1161	2 - 1	Cook 58, Gorman 72
03.03	Ryman P	ST ALBANS CITY	475	2 - 1	Howes 64, T Sills 90
05.03	Ryman P	Hendon	161	3 - 2	Gorman 13 69[p], T Sills 38
10.03	Ryman P	Carshalton Athletic	303	0 - 1	
20.03	Ryman P	Gravesend & Northfleet	275	2 - 0	T Sills 53 57
29.03	Lge Cup QF	CROYDON	145	0 - 2	
31.03	Ryman P	Grays Athletic	224	0 - 0	
03.04	Ryman P	CARSHALTON ATHLETIC	226	1 - 1	Bristow 77
07.04	Ryman P	Purfleet	197	0 - 0	
10.04	Ryman P	Heybridge Swifts	170	1 - 1	T Sills 71
12.04	FMC QF	BOGNOR REGIS TOWN	148	1 - 3	Mings 59
14.04	Ryman P	HITCHIN TOWN	370	2 - 1	T Sills 45, Gorman 69
18.04	Ryman P	Croydon	109	2 - 2	T Sills 27, Bristow 76
21.04	Ryman P	HENDON	353	5 - 0	Gorman 3 43 45, T Sills 9 37
24.04	Ryman P	CHESHAM UNITED	285	2 - 1	Gorman 39, T Sills 53
26.04	Ryman P	MAIDENHEAD UNITED	309	2 - 1	Cook 9, Sumner 58
28.04	Ryman P	Aldershot Town	1722	0 - 1	
29.04	Ryman P	CANVEY ISLAND	501	0 - 0	
01.05	Ryman P	HARROW BOROUGH	268	2 - 2	Gorman 37, Naylor 86
05.05	Ryman P	GRAVESEND & NORTHFLEET	445	4 - 0	Gorman 1 6 33, Lisk 22

PLAYING SQUAD

GOALKEEPERS: Clive Lyttle (Reading), Scott Tarr (Yeading)

DEFENDERS: Mark Lisk (Dorchester), Steve Baker (Farnborough), Don Forbes (Forest Green R), Chris Honor (Forest Green R), Jason Bristow (Reading)

MIDFIELDERS: Stuart Girdler (Woking), Rob Cook (Forest Green R), Jimmy Fraser (Bath), Glenn Howes (Eastleigh), Dominic Naylor (Dag & Red), Toby Sumner (Aldershot)

FORWARDS: Tim Sills (Camberley), Sean Gorman (Godalming & Guildford), Lee Chudy (Burnham), Mike Davis (Bath), Richard Newbery (Carshalton)

BEDFORD TOWN

CLUB OFFICIALS

Chairman: **David Howell**

Vice Chairman: **Paul Brown**

President:

Secretary: **Barry Stephenson**
9 Aspen Ave., Bedford, Beds MK41 8BX
Tel: 01234 342276

FOOTBALL MANAGEMENT TEAM

Manager: Roger Ashby
Asst. Manager: Andy Lomas
Physio: John Clare

FACT FILE

Founded: 1908 Reformed: 1989
Nickname: Eagles
Sponsors: Charles Wells & Asda
Colours: Blue, white trim/blue/blue
Change Colours: White
Midweek Matchday: Tuesday
Reserves' League: Capital

2000-01

Captain: Gary Williams
Top Scorer: Kevin Slinn 27
P.o.Y.: Paul Covington

Pages: 40 Price: £1.50
Editor: Dave Swallow

Local Press:Beds Times, Beds on Sunday
Local Radio: Chiltern Radio,Three Counties

GROUND: The New Eyrie, Meadow Lane, Cardington, Bedford MK44. 3SB Fax: 01234 831990
Tel: 01234 838448. Club Website: www.eagles.co.uk

Directions: BR station Bedford Midland 3miles from ground. Bus station 5 mins walk from BR station. Service 171 & 172 stop outside ground (Canvins stop). Trains from London Thameslink run every 30 mins to Bedford. By road:**A1** going north take L. turn Bedford A603 at Sandy r'abt. Over small bridge keep on this road for 5 miles, ground on right. **M1** going North A603. Next r'abt straight over to Cambridge A1 & Bedford A603. Take 3rd turn to Bedford. At r'abt take 4th exit to Sandy A603. Ground is half a mile on left.

Capacity: 3,000 Seats: 300 Cover: 1000 Floodlights: Yes

Clubhouse: Matchdays bar snacks **Club Shop:** Good range of merchandise incl. programmes. Mick Spavins (01234 402822)

PREVIOUS **Leagues:** South Midlands 91-94 (predecessors: Utd Co's 08-39; Southern 46-82)
Grounds: Allen Park, Queens Park, Bedford (park pitch) 1991-93
(predecessors: London Rd; Gasworks; Queens Pk; The Eyrie, Raleigh Street)

CLUB RECORDS **Attendance:** 3,000 v Peterborough Utd, ground opening 6/8/93. (predecessors: 18,407 v Everton, FA Cup 4th Round 12/2/66)
At Allen Park: 1,227 v Bedford Utd, South Midlands Lge Div. One, 26/12/91
Career scorer: Jason Reed **Career appearances:** Jason Reed
Win: 9-0 v Ickleford, and Caddington **Defeat:** 1-5 v Toddington

BEST SEASON **FA Cup:** 2nd Q 98-99 , 99-00 **FA Vase:** 5th Round 1998-99, 1-2 v Tiverton Town (H) **F.A.Trophy:** 4th Rd v Yeovil Town 99-00

HONOURS: Isthmian League Div. 2 98-99; South Midlands Lg 94-95 (Div 1 92-93, F'lit Cup 94-95); Hinchingbrook Cup 94-95 94-95; Beds Sen Cup 94-95. (Predecessors: Southern Lg 58-59 (Div 1 69-70), Utd Co's Lg 30-31 32-33 33-34 (R-up 7 Times) Vandanal Cup 97-8 Beds Prem , Beds Premier Cup 97-98 **FA Cup** 4th Rd 63-64 65-66. **FA Trophy** Semi-Final 74-75.

Players progressing: Bill Garner (Southend 69), Nicky Platnaeur (Bristol Rovers 77). Ray Bailey/Derek Bellotti/Billy Brown/Bert Carberry/PeterHall/Dave Quirke/Bobby Fold (Gillingham 56-67), Phil Driver (Wimbledon 78), Joe Dubois (Grimsby T 53), Ted Duggan (Luton T 56), Harry Duke (Noprwich C 46),John Fahy (Oxford U 64), Ken Flint (Spurs 47), Joe Hooley (Accrington 61), Joe Kirkup (Reading 55), Graham Moxon (Exeter C 75), Bela Olah (Northampton 58),Gary Sergeant (Peterborough U 77), Neil Townsend (Southend U 73)

Back Row L-R: John Clare (Physio), Grant Haley, Paul Wilson, Eddie Lawley, Gary Williams, Wayne Dyer, James Heeps, Gavin Jaggard, Paul Covington, Paul Sherlock, Daniel French, Chris Payne and Andy Lomas (Assistant Manager). Adam Hancock, Josh Sozzo, Carl Drew, Paul Turner, Roger Ashb y (Manager), Steve Heard, Mark Paul, Kevin Slinn,and Steve Jackman.

Date	Comp.	Opponents	Att.	Score	Goalscorers
19.08	Ryman 1	THAME UNITED	500	1 - 0	Lawley 24
22.08	Ryman 1	Boreham Wood	327	0 - 3	
26.08	Ryman 1	Northwood	308	2 - 2	Drew 44, Paul 45
28.08	Ryman 1	ROMFORD	525	3 - 1	Slinn 6, Drew 45, Williams 76
02.09	FA Cup P	Witham Town	197	3 - 0	Lawley, Heard, Wilson
05.09	Ryman 1	Bromley	187	1 - 1	Slinn 65[p]
09.09	Ryman 1	STAINES TOWN	439	4 - 4	Lawley 52, Slinn 57, Drew 66 72
12.09	Lge Cup 1	EPSOM & EWELL	210	1 - 0	Lawley 77
16.09	FA Cup Q1	STAINES TOWN	442	3 - 1	Drew 7, Slinn 26, Wilson 88[p]
19.09	Ryman 1	BRAINTREE TOWN	289	2 - 2	Williams 4, Drew 61
23.09	Ryman 1	Bishop's Stortford	393	3 - 2	Slinn 7, Drew 50 60
30.09	FA Cup Q2	ENFIELD	804	0 - 0	
04.10	FA Cup Q2 R	Enfield	289	1 - 1	Drew 89 3 4
07.10	Ryman 1	Worthing	354	1 - 0	Paul 49
14.10	FMC 1	Hitchin Town	327	1 - 2	Slinn
17.10	Ryman 1	Whyteleafe	129	2 - 1	Jaggard 22, Lawley 25
21.10	Ryman 1	WALTON & HERSHAM	472	2 - 1	Paul 18 47
31.10	Beds SC 2	AMPTHILL TOWN	0	3 - 0	Jaggard 12, Paul 27, O'Buck 87[og]
04.11	FA Trophy 1	NEWPORT COUNTY	713	1 - 2	Drew 11
11.11	Ryman 1	YEADING	428	5 - 1	Paul 34 73, Drew 40 58, Jaggard 80
14.11	Lge Cup 2	Walton & Hersham	105	5 - 0	Payne(3), Slinn(2)
18.11	Ryman 1	Leatherhead	257	2 - 0	Covington 14, Wilson 22
25.11	Ryman 1	AYLESBURY UNITED	607	1 - 0	Paul 31
28.11	Ryman 1	FORD UNITED	423	2 - 3	Drew 89, Dyer 90
05.12	Beds PC 1	LEIGHTON TOWN	168	2 - 1	Slinn 45 88
09.12	Ryman 1	HARLOW TOWN	567	4 - 0	Paul 17, Slinn 27 42, Jaggard 43
23.12	Ryman 1	OXFORD CITY	584	2 - 1	Turner 14, Paul 70
01.01	Ryman 1	BROMLEY	676	3 - 0	Jaggard 10, Williams 78, Slinn 90
06.01	Ryman 1	Yeading	241	1 - 1	Slinn 83[p]
13.01	Ryman 1	BOREHAM WOOD	818	1 - 0	Dyer 45
20.01	Ryman 1	Thame United	771	0 - 0	
23.01	Ryman 1	WEALDSTONE	458	4 - 1	Slinn 62 71 72, Williams 90
25.01	Beds SC QF	Leighton Town	n.k	2 - 3	Moss, Sozzo
27.01	Ryman 1	NORTHWOOD	628	6 - 1	Gell 13[og], Slinn 14, Williams 45, Lawley 50 58, Drew 62
10.02	Ryman 1	WHYTELEAFE	607	1 - 1	Drew 68[p]
17.02	Ryman 1	Staines Town	347	5 - 1	Drew 39 88, Slinn 73 78, Turner 90
20.02	Lge Cup 3	Heybridge Swifts	148	0 - 3	
24.02	Ryman 1	Wealdstone	407	1 - 1	Drew 50
06.03	Ryman 1	Braintree Town	329	1 - 2	Williams 2
10.03	Ryman 1	Ford United	338	1 - 1	Jolley 40[og]
13.03	Beds PC QF	ARLESEY TOWN	249	2 - 1	Jaggard, Heard
17.03	Ryman 1	BISHOP'S STORTFORD	659	3 - 1	Lawley 55, Turner 64, Dyer 87
20.03	Ryman 1	Uxbridge	176	2 - 2	Slinn 81, Wilson 86
24.03	Ryman 1	BOGNOR REGIS TOWN	495	1 - 1	Slinn 62
31.03	Ryman 1	Walton & Hersham	312	1 - 1	Slinn 32
07.04	Ryman 1	LEATHERHEAD	623	3 - 0	Wilson 15[p], Dyer 19, Turner 61
14.04	Ryman 1	Oxford City	427	0 - 0	
16.04	Ryman 1	BARTON ROVERS	835	1 - 1	Wilson 84
19.04	Ryman 1	Barton Rovers	382	1 - 0	Lawley 31
21.04	Ryman 1	Aylesbury United	822	0 - 3	
24.04	Ryman 1	Romford	176	6 - 0	Slinn 6 80 84, Drew 30 32 90
26.04	Ryman 1	Bognor Regis Town	196	1 - 0	Williams 39
28.04	Ryman 1	UXBRIDGE	813	0 - 0	
01.05	Ryman 1	WORTHING	675	1 - 0	Slinn 16
05.05	Ryman 1	Harlow Town	366	0 - 0	

PLAYING SQUAD

GOALKEEPERS: Jimmy Heeps (Leighton), Matt Finlay (Raunds), Andy Lomas (St.Albans)

DEFENDERS: Gary Williams (Hitchin), Lee Harvey (Stevenage), Steve Jackman (Raunds), Gavin Covington (Hitchin), Eddie Lawley (Buckingham), Grant Haley (Peterborough), Paul Wilson (Boston Utd), Rob Miller (Stevenage)

MIDFIELDERS: Paul Turner (St.Albans), Carl Adams (Kettering), Wayne Dyer (Stevenage), Steve Heard (Aylesbury), Ross Harrison (Stevenage)

FORWARDS: Carl Drew (Harlow), Kevin Slinn (Raunds), Nando Perna (Thame), Mark Paul (Kettering)

BILLERICAY TOWN

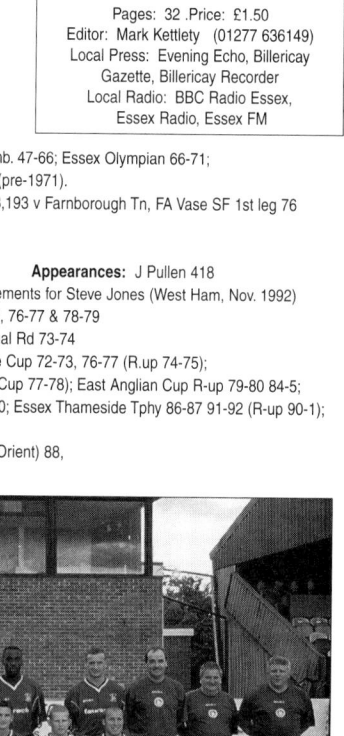

CLUB OFFICIALS

Chairman: Rod Moore

V. Chair: John Stacey **Pres:** Jim Hall

Secretary: Len Dewson
14 Graham Close, Billericay,
Essex CM12 0QW Tel: 01277 622375
Email: lendewson@cwcom.net

Press Officer: T.B.A.

FOOTBALL MANAGEMENT TEAM

Manager: Gary Calder
Asst. Man.: Chris Snowsill
Coach: Joe Dunwell
Physio: Dave Lawson

FACT FILE

Formed: 1880 Nickname: The Town
Sponsors: (Home) Faurecia Ltd
(Away) City Deal Services Ltd.
Colours: Royal Blue/White/ Royal Blue
Change colours: T.B.A.
Midweek Matches: Tuesday

2000-01 Captain: Chris Moore
P.o.Y.: Joe Baker
Top Scorer: Joe Baker 27

Pages: 32 .Price: £1.50
Editor: Mark Kettlety (01277 636149)
Local Press: Evening Echo, Billericay Gazette, Billericay Recorder
Local Radio: BBC Radio Essex, Essex Radio, Essex FM

GROUND: New Lodge, Blunts Wall Rd, Billericay CM12 9SA. 01277 652188
Directions: From Shenfield (A129) right at 1st lights then 2nd right. FromBasildon (A129) over 1st lights in town, then left at next lights and 2nd right. Half mile from Billericay (GER) (London Liverpool St. - Southend line). 5 mins walk from buses 222, 251, 357, 255, 551
Capacity: 3,500 Seats: 424 Cover: 2000 Floodlights: Yes
Clubhouse: Open every evening 8-11pm (except Monday)(1pm-11pm Sat) and weekend-lunch times noon-2.30pm. Discos, live entertainment
Club Shop: Open matchdays for souvenirs, metal badges, old progs, programme swaps Nigel Harris (01268 558114) Club Website: www.billericaytownfc.co.uk

PREVIOUS **Leagues:** Romford & Dist. 1890-1914; Mid Essex 18-47; South Essex Comb. 47-66; Essex Olympian 66-71; Essex Snr 71-77; Athenian 77-79 **Grounds**: Laindon Road (pre-1971).

CLUB RECORDS **Attendance:** 3,841 v West Ham Utd, Floodlight opener 77. Comp match: 3,193 v Farnborough Tn, FA Vase SF 1st leg 76
Win: 11-0 v Stansted (A), Essex Senior League 5/5/76
Defeat: 3-10 v Chelmsford City (A), Essex Senior Cup 4/1/93
Goalscorer: (career) F Clayden 273, (season) Leon Gutmore 51 (97-98) **Appearances:** J Pullen 418
Fees - Paid: Undisclosed **Received:** £22,500+ increments for Steve Jones (West Ham, Nov. 1992)

BEST SEASON **FA Cup:** 1st Rd Proper 97-98 **FA Vase:** Winners - 75-76, 76-77 & 78-79
FA Trophy: 5th Rd 00-01 **FA Amateur Cup:** 3rd Qual Rd 73-74

HONOURS: Essex Snr Lg 72-73 74-75 75-76, R-up 71-2 73-4, Lg Cup 71-72, Challenge Cup 72-73, 76-77 (R.up 74-75); Isthmian Lge Div 2 79-80, Div 1 R-up 80-81, 97-98; Athenian Lg 77-79 (Lg Cup 77-78); East Anglian Cup R-up 79-80 84-5; Essex Snr Cup 75-76 (R-up 85-6 93-4,4-5,5-6); Essex Snr Tphy 77-78 79-80; Essex Thameside Tphy 86-87 91-92 (R-up 90-1); Essex F'lit Tphy 77-78; Phillips F'lit Tphy 76-77; Rothmans Merit Award 1978

Players progressing: D Westwood (QPR) 75, A Hull, D Carter (Peterborough,Orient), D Cass (Orient) 88, D Ludden (Orient) 92, S Jones (West Ham Utd) 92

Back Row, left to right: Gary Henty, Dean Parratt, Kevin Jordan, Simon Spencer, Paul Newell, Gavin King, Joe Baker, Paul Linger, Justin Gentle and Brian Hammatt. **Front Row:** Kirk Game, Robert Gosney, Chris Moore, Dave Culverhouse, Russell, Penn, Lee Williams, Jeff Woolsey and Glenn Southgate.
Photo: Evening Echo

Date	Comp.	Opponents	Att.	Score	Goalscorers
19.08	Ryman P	Hampton & Richmond Borough	254	2 - 1	Spencer 10 56
22.08	Ryman P	MAIDENHEAD UNITED	413	2 - 0	Baker 17, Linger 24
26.08	Ryman P	ALDERSHOT TOWN	922	2 - 2	Dunwell 23, Linger 33
28.08	Ryman P	Purfleet	340	1 - 1	Williams 60
02.09	Ryman P	Carshalton Athletic	337	0 - 5	
05.09	Ryman P	GRAVESEND & NORTHFLEET	408	1 - 0	Linger 41
09.09	Ryman P	Basingstoke Town	504	1 - 1	Dunwell 45
12.09	Lge Cup 1	BARTON ROVERS	130	3 - 1	Linger 15, Penn 49, Shiret 74
16.09	Ryman P	HENDON	510	2 - 0	Linger 44 82
19.09	Ryman P	ST ALBANS CITY	339	2 - 1	Hannigan 64[og], Dunwell 87
23.09	Ryman P	Hitchin Town	382	1 - 2	Baker 60
03.10	FA Cup Q2	WINGATE & FINCHLEY	278	5 - 1	Linger 56 67, Gentle 54, Spencer 72, Shiret 88
07.10	Ryman P	Harrow Borough	193	2 - 4	Southgate 75, Parratt 87
14.10	FA Cup Q3	Bishop's Stortford	636	2 - 1	Linger 77, Baker 90[p]
21.10	Ryman P	SUTTON UNITED	566	0 - 5	
24.10	FMC 1	Heybridge Swifts	152	0 - 2	
28.10	FA Cup Q4	HEDNESFORD TOWN	721	0 - 0	
30.10	FA Cup Q4 R	Hednesford Town	450	1 - 2	Baker 57
04.11	FA Trophy 1	FARNBOROUGH TOWN	453	2 - 0	Linger 29, Baker 46[p]
11.11	Ryman P	DULWICH HAMLET	430	3 - 0	Palmer 14[og], Dunwell 21, Williams 41
14.11	Lge Cup 2	CORINTHIAN CASUALS	156	4 - 0	Woolsey 39, Spencer 56, Williams 74 90
18.11	Ryman P	Chesham United	397	0 - 2	
25.11	Ryman P	ENFIELD	490	0 - 2	
02.12	FA Trophy 2	HASTINGS TOWN	401	2 - 2	Baker 30, Moore 71
09.12	Ryman P	GRAYS ATHLETIC	475	3 - 1	Baker 63 69, Boateng 27
16.12	Ryman P	Maidenhead United	191	2 - 1	Baker 89, Linger 90
19.12	FA Trophy 2 R	Hastings Town	317	2 - 1	Baker 10[p], Gentle 80
23.12	Ryman P	CANVEY ISLAND	1100	2 - 1	Baker 76 90
26.12	Ryman P	Heybridge Swifts	444	2 - 2	Williams 90, Spencer 90
02.01	Essex SC 3	HULLBRIDGE SPORTS	191	3 - 2	Shiret, Spencer, Linger
06.01	Ryman P	Dulwich Hamlet	322	1 - 0	Baker 19[p]
09.01	Essex SC 4	WALTHAM ABBEY	151	4 - 1	Spencer, Henty(2), Boateng
13.01	FA Trophy 3	Bognor Regis Town	411	2 - 0	Woolsey 45, Baker 78
30.01	Ryman P	Farnborough Town	497	0 - 3	
17.02	Ryman P	BASINGSTOKE TOWN	419	2 - 2	Woolsey 44, Williams 64
19.02	FA Trophy 4	Histon	433	3 - 0	D Gentle 3 64, Baker 90
24.02	FA Trophy 5	TELFORD UNITED	709	2 - 3	Moore 23, Spencer 82
27.02	Essex SC QF	Heybridge Swifts	114	0 - 2	
03.03	Ryman P	HARROW BOROUGH	338	1 - 1	Gentle 6
06.03	Ryman P	Gravesend & Northfleet	443	1 - 1	Williams 70
10.03	Ryman P	St Albans City	501	0 - 0	
13.03	Lge Cup 3	Northwood	118	3 - 4	Linger, D Gentle, Own-Goal
17.03	Ryman P	HITCHIN TOWN	422	3 - 1	Piscopides 24, Baker 58 75
20.03	Ryman P	CROYDON	174	0 - 0	
24.03	Ryman P	SLOUGH TOWN	363	0 - 0	
27.03	Ryman P	CARSHALTON ATHLETIC	244	0 - 0	
03.04	Ryman P	HAMPTON & RICHMOND BOR.	278	3 - 1	Linger 6, Piscopides 42, Baker 67
07.04	Ryman P	CHESHAM UNITED	357	1 - 1	D Gentle 30
10.04	Ryman P	Slough Town	330	3 - 2	D Gentle 29, Woolsey 37, Linger 83
13.04	Ryman P	Canvey Island	1190	1 - 2	Baker 75
16.04	Ryman P	HEYBRIDGE SWIFTS	495	5 - 1	Baker 22 26 45, Henty 60 77
19.04	Ryman P	Sutton United	389	4 - 1	Baker 13 36, Horner 44[og], D Gentle 47
21.04	Ryman P	Enfield	206	0 - 1	
24.04	Ryman P	PURFLEET	346	1 - 1	J Gentle 27
26.04	Ryman P	Hendon	123	2 - 0	D Gentle 3, Baker 75
28.04	Ryman P	FARNBOROUGH TOWN	726	1 - 2	Williams 61
03.05	Ryman P	Croydon	106	2 - 1	Baker 6, Moore 16
05.05	Ryman P	Grays Athletic	386	3 - 2	Linger 30[p], D Gentle 60, Tomlinson 70

PLAYING SQUAD

GOALKEEPERS: Gavin King (Bishop's Stortford), Adam Hart (Bishop's Stortford)

DEFENDERS: Kevin Jordan (Bishop's Stortford), Jeff Woolsey (Dag & Red), Chris Moore (Canvey Is), Nicky Savage (Ford Utd), Steve Dickinson (Grays Ath)

MIDFIELDERS: Andy Tomlinson (Heybridge), Martin Carthy (Purfleet), Russell Penn (Enfield), Joe Baker (Sutton Utd)

FORWARDS: Amara Simba (St.Albans), Jamie Wallace (Ford Utd), Lee Williams (Enfield), Justin Gentle (Dag & Red)

BOREHAM WOOD

CLUB OFFICIALS

Chairman: **Danny Hunter**
President: **W F O'Neill**
Secretary:**Peter Smith**,26 Briarwood Road,Stoneleigh,Epsom, Surrey KT19 2LYTel: 020 8393 2902(H) 07711745987(W)
Press Officer: **John D Gill** (020 8723 6407)

FOOTBALL MANAGEMENT TEAM

Manager:Graham Roberts
Asst Manager: Roger Goodhind
Physio: Dave Dickens

FACT FILE

Formed: 1948 Nickname: The Wood
Sponsors: One 2 One
Colours: All white Change : Alll yellow
Midweek matchday: Tuesday

2000-01

Captain: Garry Woton
P.o.Y.: Dominic Grime
Top Scorer: John Lawford 30

BOREHAM WOOD FOOTBALL CLUB
THE OFFICIAL MATCHDAY PROGRAMME
2000/2001 SEASON
Ryman
one 2 one
£1.50
TUESDAY 1st MAY 2001 - Kick Off 7.45pm
V BOGNOR REGIS TOWN
Ryman Football League Division One

Pages: 44 Price: £1.50
Editor: John Gill
(020 8723 6407)
Local Radio: Chiltern Radio
Local Press: Boreham Wood Times, Watford Observer, Herts Advertiser

GROUND: Meadow Park, Broughinge Rd, Boreham Wood,Herts WD6 5AL (020 8953 5097)
Directions: A1 towards London from M25, 1st turn for Boreham Wood, head for town centre, into Brook Rd at r'bout before town centre, Broughinge Rd is 1st right. 1 mile from Elstree & Boreham Wood station (Thameslink),or bus 292 or107 to McDonalds (5 minutes walk)
Capacity: 4,502 Cover: 1,568 Seats: 600 Floodlights: Yes
Clubhouse: (020 8953 5097). Open during normal licensing hours. Snacks available. Function room (250) available for hire
Club Shop: Sells good selection of souvenirs & programmes. Contact: Dell Ward (020 8363 7345)

PREVIOUS **Leagues:** Mid Herts 48-52, Parthenon 52-57, Spartan 56-66, Athenian 66-74
Ground: Eldon Avenue 1948-63 **Names:** Boreham Wood Rovers and Royal Retournez, amalgamated in 1948
CLUB RECORDS **Attendance:** 3,892 v Arsenal , 9 July 99 (friendly) **Goalscorer:** Micky Jackson, 208
Appearances: Dave Hatchett, 714
BEST SEASON **FA Amateur Cup:** 3rd Rd. replay 70-71 **FA Trophy:** 3rd Rd 1995-96. Replay at Chorley 3-4, 3rd Rd replay 97-98
FA Cup: 2nd Round v Luton Town 1996-97. v Cheltenham Town 97-98
HONOURS: Isthmian Lg.Prem Div R-Up 97-98 Div I 94-95, 00-01 Isthmian Lg Div 2 76-77 (Yth Cup R-up 80-81), Isthmian Lge. Cup 96-97; R-Up 94-95,95-96 ,98-99 Athenian Lg 73-74 (Div 2 68-69, Div 1 R-up 69-70), Spartan Lg R-up 65-66, Herts Senior Cup 71-72 ,98-99 (R-up 66-67 74-75 79-80 87-88,96-97,97-98), Herts Junior Cup 51-52, Parthenon Lg 55-56 (R-up(2) 53-55 56-57, Herts Charity Shield 64-65, Herts Interm Cup 69-70, Herts Charity Cup (5) 80-81 83-84 85-86 88-90 (R-up 71-72 84-85 86-87 90-91 91-92 92-93), London Senior Cup R-up89-90, London Intermediate Cup 70-71, Neale Trophy 69-70, Essex & Herts BorderComb 72-73 (Lg Cup 72-73, Western Div R-up 82-83 89-90), Mithras Cup 76-77, Middx Border Lg 81-82 (Lg Cup 79-80), Wallspan Floodlit 86-87, London Challenge Cup 97-98
Players progressing: Colin Franks (Watford & Sheff Utd), Charles Ntamark (Walsall), Dean Samuels (Barnet 96),Justin gentle (Colchester U),Kenny Veyse (Plymouth Argyle), Matthew Brady (Wycombe Wanderers)

Back Row, left to right: Steve Gracie (Physio), AlanParis, Dominic Grime, Andre Delisser, Wayne Brown, Tony Samuels, John Lawford, Lee Harvey, Darren Bonfield, Micky Engwell, Otis Hutchins, Jeran Meah, Graham Roberts (Manager 2000-01), Danny Hunter (Chairman) and Roger Goodhind (Ass.Manager 00-01) **Front Row:** Les Littlechild, Dave Dickens, (Physio), Charlie Hunter (Mascot), Andy Polston, Neil Selby, Gary Dixon, Garry Wotton (club captain), Youness Nabil, Paul Kelly, Daniel Costeloe, Bryan Hammatt and Micky Hunter (mascot) **Photo:** John D Gill

Date	Comp.	Opponents	Att.	Score	Goalscorers
19.08	Ryman 1	Bognor Regis Town	246	2 - 0	Hutchins 49, Lawford 61
22.08	Ryman 1	BEDFORD TOWN	327	3 - 0	Selby 44, Lawford 66, Nabil 79
26.08	Ryman 1	WALTON & HERSHAM	206	3 - 0	Lawford 7 89, Baker 79
28.08	Ryman 1	Worthing	401	2 - 1	Lawford 52 65[p]
02.09	FA Cup P	GREAT WAKERING ROVERS	203	3 - 0	
05.09	Ryman 1	BARTON ROVERS	201	2 - 0	Delisser 15, Adams 67
09.09	Ryman 1	Wealdstone	383	3 - 2	Lawford 5[p] 22, Adam 23
12.09	Lge Cup 1	St Albans City	157	1 - 1	Selby
16.09	FA Cup Q1	St Margaretsbury	128	0 - 1	
19.09	Ryman 1	Oxford City	140	2 - 2	Delisser 12, Pierson 64[og]
23.09	Ryman 1	WHYTELEAFE	206	0 - 3	
30.09	Ryman 1	Staines Town	230	2 - 1	Lawford 64, Delisser 80
07.10	Ryman 1	Bishop's Stortford	304	0 - 4	
14.10	Ryman 1	STAINES TOWN	214	2 - 0	Imber 26, Nartey 82
17.10	Ryman 1	Northwood	221	1 - 1	Nartey 49
21.10	Ryman 1	Thame United	491	0 - 1	
23.10	FMC 1	Purfleet	68	1 - 3	Nartey
28.10	Ryman 1	BRAINTREE TOWN	225	1 - 4	Savage 63
31.10	Lge Cup 1 R	ST ALBANS CITY	151	2 - 3	
04.11	FA Trophy 1	Dorchester Town	329	1 - 2	Lawford 4
11.11	Ryman 1	LEATHERHEAD	184	2 - 1	Boyce 41, Bayliss 76
18.11	Ryman 1	Bromley	205	4 - 2	Grime 19 29, Simpson 38, Lawford 59
02.12	Ryman 1	THAME UNITED	249	1 - 0	Lawford 39
05.12	Herts SC 2	BARNET	100	3 - 4	Harvey 8, Delisser 25 55
09.12	Ryman 1	UXBRIDGE	248	2 - 3	Lawford 43 52[p]
26.12	Ryman 1	Aylesbury United	411	2 - 2	Lawford 70, Harvey 76
13.01	Ryman 1	Bedford Town	818	0 - 1	
16.01	Ryman 1	FORD UNITED	188	1 - 1	Wood 70[og]
23.01	Ryman 1	Yeading	145	2 - 1	Lawford 15 57
03.02	Ryman 1	OXFORD CITY	203	1 - 1	Grime 90
15.02	Ryman 1	Walton & Hersham	83	0 - 1	
17.02	Ryman 1	WEALDSTONE	401	2 - 1	Hammatt 59, Wotton 90
20.02	Ryman 1	Leatherhead	119	2 - 0	Lawford 22, Holsgrove 29
03.03	Ryman 1	BISHOP'S STORTFORD	268	0 - 3	
10.03	Ryman 1	NORTHWOOD	279	2 - 0	Lawford 2, Bennetts 78
13.03	Ryman 1	ROMFORD	208	3 - 0	Engwell 40[p], Lawford 45, Meah 90
20.03	Ryman 1	HARLOW TOWN	166	6 - 3	Engwell 17[p], Grime 53, Meah 74 90, Lawford 86 90
24.03	Ryman 1	Braintree Town	374	3 - 0	Meah 38, Dixon 69, Paris 80
27.03	Ryman 1	WORTHING	214	4 - 2	Engwell 3[p], Lawford 13 20, Greene 73
03.04	Ryman 1	Barton Rovers	137	2 - 0	Lawford 4, Engwell 51[p]
07.04	Ryman 1	BROMLEY	242	1 - 0	Dixon 88
14.04	Ryman 1	Romford	183	4 - 0	Dixon 2 25 49, Hammatt 90
16.04	Ryman 1	AYLESBURY UNITED	380	3 - 2	Meah 15, Lawford 35, Brown 70
18.04	Ryman 1	Whyteleafe	154	1 - 0	Lawford 24
21.04	Ryman 1	Harlow Town	198	1 - 1	Engwell 10[p]
24.04	Ryman 1	Ford United	153	1 - 1	Meah 8
28.04	Ryman 1	YEADING	306	6 - 2	Nabil 5, Lawford 17, Walker 28[og], Dixon 63, Hammatt 83 84
01.05	Ryman 1	BOGNOR REGIS TOWN	405	3 - 1	Wotton 51, Meah 55[p], Dixon 90
05.05	Ryman 1	Uxbridge	210	0 - 1	

PLAYING SQUAD

GOALKEEPERS: Noel Imber (St.Albans)

DEFENDERS: Lee Harvey (St.Albans), Gary Wotton (Aylesbury), Andy Polston (Braintree), Micky Engwell (Purfleet), David McDonald (Enfield)

MIDFIELDERS: Andre Delisser (Hayes), Mark Pye (Aldershot), Phil Mason (Aylesbury), Kieran Gallagher (Dag & Red), Julian Capone (Enfield)

FORWARDS: John Lawford (Chesham Utd), Gary Dixon (Hitchin), Neil Selby (Aylesbury), Tony Samuels (St.Albans), Brian Jones (Wealdstone)

BRAINTREE TOWN

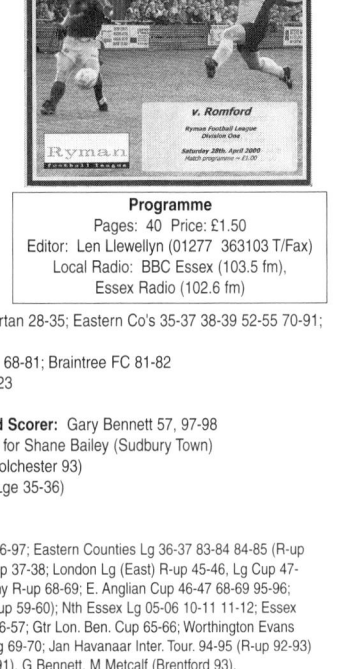

CLUB OFFICIALS

Chairman: **George Rosling**
Vice Chairman: **Ivan Kibble**
President: **Ron Webb**
Secretary: **T A Woodley,** 19a Bailey Bridge Rd., Braintree, Essex CM7 5TT (01376 326234)
Press Officer: **Ron Webb** (01376 325338)

FOOTBALL MANAGEMENT TEAM

Manager:John Embery
Ass Manr Steve Jackson Coach:Ken Varney
Physio: Tony Brightwell

FACT FILE

Founded: 1898
Nickname: The Iron
Sponsors: T.B.A.
Colours:Yellow with navy side panel
Change colours: White
Reserves' Lg: Essex/Herts Border Comb
Email Address:
10665.3036@ compuserve.com

2000-2001

Captain: Nicky Smith
P.o.Y.: Nicky Smith
Top Goalscorer: Robbie Reinelt 42

GROUND Cressing Road Stadium, Clockhouse Way, Braintree, Essex (01376 345617)
Directions: From Braintree by-pass, turn into Braintree at the McDonalds r'bout, follow signs for East Braintree Ind. Est. - floodlights on left 3/4 mile into town just past. Orange Tree Pub. Entrance next left in Clockhouse Way, then left again. 1 mile from Braintree & Bocking (BR). Bus 353 from Witham or town centre Town centre 20 mins walk
Capacity: 4,000 Cover 1,500 Seats 250 Floodlights:Yes
Clubhouse: Open evenings 7-30-11, Sun 12-3, Sat matchday 12.00- 11.00 Full bar facilities
Club shop: ContactTom Marshall 01376 347920 (75 year History of Braintree £15.99)

Programme
Pages: 40 Price: £1.50
Editor: Len Llewellyn (01277 363103 T/Fax)
Local Radio: BBC Essex (103.5 fm),
Essex Radio (102.6 fm)

PREVIOUS **Leagues:** North Essex 1898-1925; Essex & Suffolk Border 25-28 55-64; Spartan 28-35; Eastern Co's 35-37 38-39 52-55 70-91; Essex Co. 37-38; London 45-52; GtrLondon 64-66; Metropolitan 66-70; Southern 91-96
Names: Manor Works 1898-1921; Crittall Ath. 21-68; Braintree & Crittall Ath. 68-81; Braintree FC 81-82
Grounds: The Fair Field 1898-1903; Spaldings Meadow, Panfield Lane 03-23

CLUB RECORDS **Attendance:** 4,000 v Spurs, charity challenge match, May 1952
Career Goalscorer: Chris Guy 211, 63-90. **Seasonal Record Scorer:** Gary Bennett 57, 97-98
Career Appearances: Paul Young 524, 66-77 **Fee Paid:** £2,000 for Shane Bailey (Sudbury Town)
Fee Received: £10,000 Matt Metcalf (Brentford 93) & John Cheesewright(Colchester 93)
Win: 15-3 v Hopes (Birmingham Friendly 39), 12-0 v Thetford Tn (Eastern Lge 35-36)
Defeat: 0-14 v Chelmsford City A (Nth Essex Lge 23)

BEST SEASON **FA Cup:** 4th Qual. Rd 69-70 85-86 94-95 97-98

HONOURS: Isthmian Lge Div 2 R-up 97-98, Div 3 R-up 96-97; Guardian Insurance Cup R-up 96-97; Eastern Counties Lg 36-37 83-84 84-85 (R-up 86-87 87-88 88-89 90-91), Lg Cup 87-88 (R-up 35-36 74-75); Essex County Lg R-up 37-38; London Lg (East) R-up 45-46, Lg Cup 47-48(jt) 48-49 51-52 (R-up 49-50); Metropolitan Lg Cup 69-70; Essex Elizabethan Tphy R-up 68-69; E. Anglian Cup 46-47 68-69 95-96; Essex Sen.Tphy 86-87 (R-up 90-91); Essex & Suffolk Border Lg 59-60 84-85 (Lg Cup 59-60); Nth Essex Lg 05-06 10-11 11-12; Essex Sen Cup 95-96 R-up 96-97; Essex Jnr Cup R-up 04-05 05-06 22-23; RAFA Cup 56-57; Gtr Lon. Ben. Cup 65-66; Worthington Evans Cup (3) R-up (4); Eastern F'lit Cup 85-86 96-97 (R-up 94-95 97-98); Anglian F'lit Lg 69-70; Jan Havanaar Inter. Tour. 94-95 (R-up 92-93)

Players progressing: J Dick (West Ham 53), S Wright (Wrexham 83), J Cheesewright (Birmingham C. 91), G Bennett, M Metcalf (Brentford 93), R Reinhelt (Gillingham 93), M de Souza (Birmingham C.), G Culling (Colchester U94)

Back Row, left to right: K.Varney (coach), K.Budge, J.Leek, M.Jones, B.Quinton, A.Keeper, G.Cowan, P.Catley, G.Walters, L.Gutzmore, C.Davidson, R. Reinelt, S.Jackson(Assistant Manager), B.Embury (Manager). **Front Row:** T.Brightwell (Physio), D.Parrett, D.Stanley, N.Simpson, N.Smith, R.Blackery, T.Howard and B.Girling

Date	Comp.	Opponents	Att.	Score	Goalscorers
19.08	Ryman 1	Walton & Hersham	151	4 - 0	Reinelt 18[p] 47, Noble 50, Gutzmore 87
26.08	Ryman 1	WEALDSTONE	312	1 - 1	Noble 17
28.08	Ryman 1	Yeading	133	2 - 5	Reinelt 36, Jones 49
02.09	FA Cup P	BANBURY UNITED	212	6 - 0	Cowan 33, Gutzmore 42, Quinton 53, Noble 85 89, Fuller 9
05.09	Ryman 1	AYLESBURY UNITED	227	3 - 2	Noble 7, Naylor 77, Jones 81
09.09	Ryman 1	Leatherhead	203	2 - 1	Game 50, Reinelt 68
12.09	Lge Cup 1	East Thurrock United	59	2 - 1	Jones, Buckley
16.09	FA Cup Q1	CLAPTON	201	5 - 0	Noble 19, Howard 26, Stanley 51, Gutzmore 86, Smith 89
19.09	Ryman 1	Bedford Town	289	2 - 2	Smith 17, Gutzmore 81
23.09	Ryman 1	Thame United	181	1 - 4	Noble 90
30.09	FA Cup Q2	Canvey Island	240	1 - 1	Gutzmore 90
03.10	FA Cup Q2 R	CANVEY ISLAND	242	2 - 3	Noble 80, Reinelt 89[p]
07.10	Ryman 1	Harlow Town	171	0 - 0	
17.10	Ryman 1	Romford	110	4 - 2	Grayburn 3[og], Noble 48 85 88
21.10	Ryman 1	NORTHWOOD	262	1 - 2	Quinton 10
24.10	FMC 1	ENFIELD	162	5 - 0	Noble(2), Quinton, Reinelt, Cowan
28.10	Ryman 1	Boreham Wood	225	4 - 1	Noble 19, Reinelt 36 78 79
31.10	Ryman 1	BOGNOR REGIS TOWN	170	2 - 1	Reinelt 67 69
05.11	FA Trophy 1	Romford	226	2 - 2	Reinelt 15[p], Noble 73
11.11	Ryman 1	BROMLEY	301	5 - 0	Reinelt 12 80, Smith 46, Stanley 54, Leek 58
14.11	FA Trophy 1 R	ROMFORD	183	2 - 0	Jones 27, Stanley 78
18.11	Ryman 1	Uxbridge	141	1 - 3	Reinelt 37
25.11	Ryman 1	OXFORD CITY	239	3 - 1	Reinelt 39 89, Smith 47
02.12	FA Trophy 2	ROTHWELL TOWN	210	1 - 1	Reinelt 55
09.12	Ryman 1	BARTON ROVERS	330	2 - 1	Stanley 58, Quinton 90
16.12	Ryman 1	Aylesbury United	530	2 - 1	Reinelt 26, Game 43
19.12	Essex SC 3	East Thurrock United	61	0 - 7	
23.12	Ryman 1	WORTHING	298	2 - 2	Reinelt 54, Smith 59
06.01	Ryman 1	Bromley	234	6 - 0	Howard 15, Noble 27 32, Leek 50, Stanley 84, Gutzmore 88
08.01	FA Trophy 2 R	Rothwell Town	157	2 - 2	Gutzmore 4, Reinelt 107 Won 4-3 after penalties
13.01	FA Trophy 3	MAIDENHEAD UNITED	403	1 - 2	Stanley 19
27.01	Ryman 1	Wealdstone	271	3 - 2	Noble 24, Howard 40, Naylor 75
29.01	Lge Cup 2	Hendon	86	2 - 3	Gutzmore 35, Leeke 86
01.02	FMC 2	Chesham United	85	2 - 4	Merten, Davey
10.02	Ryman 1	Bognor Regis Town	190	0 - 2	
13.02	Ryman 1	Bishop's Stortford	238	3 - 5	Noble 21, Reinelt 54[p] 78
17.02	Ryman 1	LEATHERHEAD	303	4 - 0	Quinton 16, Reinelt 27 75, Gutzmore 65
20.02	Ryman 1	FORD UNITED	205	2 - 4	Stanley 14, Quinton 22
24.02	Ryman 1	Whyteleafe	200	1 - 2	Game 33
27.02	Ryman 1	YEADING	152	3 - 1	Stanley 44, Reinelt 51, Noble 74
03.03	Ryman 1	HARLOW TOWN	474	2 - 1	Reinelt 22 89
06.03	Ryman 1	BEDFORD TOWN	329	2 - 1	Stanley 41, Smith 81
13.03	Ryman 1	WHYTELEAFE	153	5 - 0	Reinelt 44 49 56 71, Gutzmore 80
24.03	Ryman 1	BOREHAM WOOD	374	0 - 3	
31.03	Ryman 1	Northwood	197	2 - 3	Parratt 8, Noble 80
03.04	Ryman 1	STAINES TOWN	197	4 - 1	Spencer 7, Noble 54, Reinelt 64, Gutzmore 90
07.04	Ryman 1	UXBRIDGE	323	3 - 0	Spencer 4, Gutzmore 72 80
10.04	Ryman 1	Ford United	134	3 - 0	Simpson 68, Reinelt 78 85
14.04	Ryman 1	Worthing	301	3 - 0	Gutzmore 22 38, Bray 67[og]
16.04	Ryman 1	BISHOP'S STORTFORD	538	1 - 1	Cowan 32
18.04	Ryman 1	THAME UNITED	238	4 - 1	OG 1, Reinelt 50 82, Gutzmore 90
21.04	Ryman 1	Oxford City	205	0 - 1	
24.04	Ryman 1	WALTON & HERSHAM	266	5 - 1	Spencer 1, Noble 18 41, Reinelt 20, Gutzmore 55
28.04	Ryman 1	ROMFORD	440	10 - 0	Smith 1 25, Gutzmore 6 14 59, Simpson 11 82 88, Jones 47,Spencer 73
03.05	Ryman 1	Staines Town	134	2 - 2	Simpson 7, Reinelt 21
05.05	Ryman 1	Barton Rovers	195	3 - 0	Reinelt 42 76[p], Simpson 84

PLAYING SQUAD

GOALKEEPERS: Paul Catley (Chelmsford)

DEFENDERS: Mark Jones (Romford), Craig Davidson (Canvey Is), Gavin Cowan (Youth), Terry Howard (Boreham Wood), Kirk Game (Billericay), Gary Waters (Heybridge), Brett Girling (Chelmsford)

MIDFIELDERS: Dean Parratt (Billericay), Nicky Smith (Camb.C), Josh Leeke (Maldon T), Danny Stanley (Maldon T), Nicky Simpson (Heybridge)

FORWARDS: Tom Noble (Maldon T), Robbie Reinelt (St.Albans), Leon Gutzmore (Bedford), Brad Quinton (Bishop's Stortford)

CANVEY ISLAND

CLUB OFFICIALS

Chairman: **Ray Cross,** 95 Lakeside Path, Canvey Island, Essex SS8 5PD.
Tel: 01268 684357 (H)
Secretary: **Mrs Frances Roche,** 56 Harvest Road, Canvey Island SS8 9RP.
Tel: 01268 698586 (H/Fax)
Press Officer: **Tony Roche**
Tel: 01268 698586

FOOTBALL MANAGEMENT TEAM

Manager: Jeff King. 01268 511555 (B) 07850654321 (Mobile)
Asst Manager: Glenn Pennyfather
Physio: Harry Johnson

FACT FILE

Formed: 1926
Nickname: Gulls
Sponsors: Kings The Clubs
Colours: Yellow/blue/white
Change colours: Red & Blue/White/white
Midweek matchday: Tuesday
Reserves' League:
Essex & Herts Border Comb
Club Website: www.canveyfc.com

2000-01

Captain Steve Tilson
Supporters P.o.Y.: Ashley Harrison
Top Goalscorer: Wayne Vaughan (18)

Pages: 52 Price: £1.30
Editor: Keith Johnson (01268 682991)
Local Press: Evening Echo
Local Radio: Essex FM, BBC Essex

GROUND: Park Lane, Canvey Island, Essex SS8 7PXTel: 01268 682991
Directions: A130 from A13 or A127 at Sadlers Farm r/about, 1 mile through town centre, 1st right past old bus garage. Bus 3 or 151 fromBenfleet (BR) to stop after Admiral Jellicoe (PH)
Capacity: 4,308 Seats: 500 Cover: 827 Floodlights: Yes
Clubhouse: Open Tues, Thurs & Sats. Full licence. Food avaiable
Club Shop: Open matchdays. Selling programmes, badges, shirts etc. Contact Keith Johnson (07773 959125)

PREVIOUS **Leagues:** Southend & Dist.; Thurrock & Thameside Comb.; Parthenon; Metropolitan;Gtr London 64-71; Essex Senior
Grounds: None **Names:** None

CLUB RECORDS **Attendance:** 3,250 v Brighton & Hove Albion F.A. Cup 95-96
Win: 7-1 v Bedford **Defeat:** 7-0 v Halstead
Career Appearances: Steve Price (407) **Career Goalscorer:** Andy Jones (200)?
Fee received: £3,000 for Ian Durrant from Grays Athletic
Fee paid: £ 5,000 for Chris Duffy to Northwich Victoria

BEST SEASON **FA Cup:** 2nd Round, 1-2 v Southend Utd. (at Southend) 00-01 League clubs defeated: Port Vale 2-1(A) after 1-1 (H)
FA Vase: Semi-final v Tiverton 27/3/93 **FA Trophy:** Winners 2000-01 v Forset Green Rovers 1-0

HONOURS: Ryman Lge - Div 2 95-96, 97-98,R-up 98-99 Div 3 R-up 94-95; Carlton Trophy 95-96; Essex Sen Lg 86-87 92-93 (Lg Cup 79-80 92-93),Trophy R-up 93-94; Harry Fisher Mem.Tphy 93-94; Essex Thameside Trophy 93-94; Parthenon Lge Cup 58-59; Metropolian Lge 67-68 68-69, Cup 67-68 68-69; Thameside 95-96 97-98; Res. Lge 95-96, Cup 95-96, Essex Senior Cup 98-99

Players progressing: Peter Taylor (Spurs), Gary Heale (Luton T)

Photo: Darren C Thomas

Date	Comp.	Opponents	Att.	Score	Goalscorers
19.08	Ryman P	FARNBOROUGH TOWN	643	0 - 1	
22.08	Ryman P	St Albans City	424	4 - 1	Clark 49 80, Duffy 61, Jones 90
26.08	Ryman P	Sutton United	652	1 - 0	Vaughan 47
28.08	Ryman P	HARROW BOROUGH	541	3 - 0	Parmenter 50, Tilson 61[p], Kennedy 75
02.09	Ryman P	SLOUGH TOWN	653	1 - 0	Vaughan 43
05.09	Ryman P	Heybridge Swifts	312	1 - 1	Jones 80
09.09	Ryman P	CHESHAM UNITED	725	2 - 1	Smith 16, Clark 75
12.09	Lge Cup 1	Bishop's Stortford	181	5 - 3	Clark 2 113, Brazier 15 106, Jones 22
16.09	Ryman P	Dulwich Hamlet	343	3 - 2	Vaughan 3 20 80
19.09	Ryman P	Maidenhead United	172	2 - 0	Vaughan 43, Gregory 46
23.09	Ryman P	BASINGSTOKE TOWN	718	0 - 0	
30.09	FA Cup Q2	BRAINTREE TOWN	240	1 - 1	Game 43[og]
03.10	FA Cup Q2 R	Braintree Town	242	3 - 2	Gregory 4, Tilson 26[p] 85[p]
06.10	Ryman P	PURFLEET	542	1 - 0	Bodley 24
14.10	FA Cup Q3	KING'S LYNN	306	2 - 1	Parmenter 35, Vaughan 44
21.10	Ryman P	Carshalton Athletic	356	4 - 1	Parmenter 45, Tilson 60, Vaughan 62, Gregory 75
31.10	FA Cup Q4	Cambridge City	575	2 - 0	Tilson 32[p], Vaughan 85
07.11	Ryman P	ENFIELD	416	4 - 1	Tilson 23, Vaughan 41 58, Clark 90
11.11	Ryman P	Hendon	246	1 - 2	Gregory 66
19.11	FA Cup 1	PORT VALE	2282	4 - 4	Smith 49, Vaughan 54[p] 90, Jones 89
25.11	Ryman P	Aldershot Town	2489	0 - 1	
28.11	FA Cup 1 R	Port Vale	3566	2 - 1	Gregory 105, Vaughan 119
02.12	FA Trophy 2	Harlow Town	327	2 - 2	Bennett 6, Parmenter 61
05.12	FA Trophy 2 R	HARLOW TOWN	238	2 - 0	Drury 46[og], Tilson 81
10.12	FA Cup 2	Southend United	11402	1 - 2	Jones 90
16.12	Ryman P	ST ALBANS CITY	805	3 - 1	Vaughan 60, Bennett 83, Tilson 88[p]
19.12	Essex SC 3	BARKINGSIDE	177	3 - 0	Parmenter 7, Duffy 8, Clark 65
23.12	Ryman P	Billericay Town	1100	1 - 2	Gregory 3
26.12	Ryman P	GRAVESEND & NORTHFLEET	620	1 - 1	Davidson 66
02.01	Essex SC 4	Barking	145	5 - 2	Jones 31, Gregory 38, Tilson 42 85, Kennedy 52
06.01	Ryman P	HENDON	411	3 - 2	Kennedy 2, N Gregory 56 59
13.01	FA Trophy 3	NORTHWOOD	302	5 - 1	Tilson 7, Kennedy 52, Gregory 55 60, Jones 79
16.01	Ryman P	HAMPTON & RICHMOND BOR.	333	1 - 0	Gregory 5
23.01	Lge Cup 2	GRAVESEND & NORTHFLEET	221	2 - 0	Jones 44 46
27.01	Ryman P	DULWICH HAMLET	410	3 - 2	Gregory 1, Tilson 75 82
29.01	FMC 2	Purfleet	180	0 - 1	
03.02	FA Trophy 4	Bilston Town	536	1 - 0	Parmenter 32
10.02	Ryman P	HEYBRIDGE SWIFTS	414	3 - 0	Jones 32, Bodley 45, Tilson 85
13.02	Ryman P	SUTTON UNITED	331	6 - 2	Vaughan 21 46, Gregory 52, Tilson 78, Duffy 81, Clark 84
17.02	Ryman P	Chesham United	455	1 - 1	Parmenter 32
20.02	Essex SC QF	GREAT WAKERING ROVERS	214	3 - 1	
24.02	FA Trophy 5	STEVENAGE BOROUGH	1010	1 - 1	Vaughan 7
26.02	FA Trophy 5 R	Stevenage Borough	1148	0 - 0	(4-2p)
03.03	Ryman P	Purfleet	443	1 - 0	Duffy 2
06.03	Ryman P	GRAYS ATHLETIC	410	1 - 0	Vaughan 7
10.03	FA Trophy QF	TELFORD UNITED	807	1 - 0	Jones 20
14.03	Lge Cup 3	Croydon	74	0 - 5	
20.03	Ryman P	Grays Athletic	267	3 - 0	Gregory 8, Vaughan 42, Tilson 60[p]
31.03	F.A.T. SF(1)	CHESTER CITY	1221	2 - 0	Tilson 28, Vaughan 73
03.04	Ryman P	Harrow Borough	215	2 - 0	Tanner 42 85
07.04	F.A.T. SF(2)	Chester City	2647	2 - 0	Parmenter 30, Stimson 60
10.04	Essex SC SF	Purfleet	202	1 - 0	Parmenter 33
13.04	Ryman P	BILLERICAY TOWN	1190	2 - 1	Tilson 36, Thompson 90
16.04	Ryman P	Gravesend & Northfleet	662	2 - 1	Vaughan 9 84
18.04	Ryman P	MAIDENHEAD UNITED	282	1 - 0	Vaughan 69
19.04	Ryman P	Slough Town	333	1 - 0	Vaughan 24
21.04	Ryman P	ALDERSHOT TOWN	861	1 - 1	Kennedy 55
24.04	Ryman P	Hitchin Town	301	1 - 4	Tanner 45
27.04	Ryman P	Enfield	119	0 - 3	
28.04	Ryman P	Croydon	118	1 - 2	Clark 45
29.04	Ryman P	Basingstoke Town	501	0 - 0	
01.05	Ryman P	Farnborough Town	1124	2 - 1	Duffy 13, Miller 26
02.05	Ryman P	Hampton & Richmond Borough	166	2 - 2	Parmenter 7, Vaughan 67
03.05	Ryman P	CARSHALTON ATHLETIC	282	3 - 2	Jones 28[p], Miller 36, Duffy 38
04.05	Ryman P	CROYDON	340	5 - 0	Vaughan 40 60, Duffy 43, Tilson 50, Clark 75
05.05	Ryman P	HITCHIN TOWN	491	2 - 2	Law 13[og], Gregory 57
13.05	FA Trophy Final	Forest Green Rovers	10007	1 - 0	Chenery 16 (at Aston Villa)
04.08	Essex SC F	Dagenham & Redbridge	1095	2 - 2	Duffy 2, Kennedy 95 (4-5p)

PLAYING SQUAD

GOALKEEPERS: Ashley Harrison (Dover)

DEFENDERS: Peter Smith (Woking), Garry Britnell (Enfield), Ben Chenery (Kettering), Micky Bennett (Brighton), Steve Ward (Grays Ath), Mick Bodley (Dag & Red)

MIDFIELDERS: Adam Miller (Ipswich), Adam Tanner (Colchester), Steve Tilson (Southend), Mark Stimson (Leyton Orient), Steve Parmenter (Dorchester), Ian Thompson (Norwich), Chris Duffy (Northwich), John Kennedy (Ipswich)

FORWARDS: Neil Gregory (Colchester), Paul Cobb (Dag & Red), Wayne Vaughan (Tottenham), Andy Jones (Billericay)

CHESHAM UNITED

CLUB OFFICIALS

President: **Bill Wells**
Chairman: **Tony O'Driscoll**
Secretary: **Jim Chambers**
c/o Chesham United FC.
Tel: 01494 775490 (H) 0181327 4016(B)
Commercial Manager: **Brian McCarthy**
Press Officer: **Heather Jan Brunt**

FOOTBALL MANAGEMENT TEAM

Manager: Bob Dowie
Physio: Karl Jones

FACT FILE

Formed: 1886 Nickname: The Generals
Sponsors: Carlsberg
Colours: Claret & blue quarters/claret/claret
Change colours: White & blue/blue/white
Midweek home matchday: Tuesday
Reserve Team's League: Suburban North
Match information: 09068 335505

2000-2001

Captain & P.o.Y.: Brian Stathem
Top Scorer: Dudley Campbell 18

CHESHAM UNITED
FOOTBALL CLUB
Ryman football league
PREMIER DIVISION
PURFLEET
Tuesday 1st May 2001 7.45pm
RYMAN PREMIER DIVISION
Match Sponsored by
McDonalds Chesham
2000/01 Season - Official Programme £1.20

Pages: 52 Price: £1.50
Editors: Alan Calder
(01442 230420 [H])

Local Radio: Three Counties
Local Press: Bucks Examiner, Bucks Advertiser, Bucks Free Press

GROUND: The Meadow, Amy Lane, Amersham Road, Chesham, Bucks. HP5 1NE
Tel: 01494 783964 (ground clubhouse) Fax: 01494 794244 Club Website: www.cheshamunitedfc.co.uk Email Address: jimchamberschesham@talk21.com

Directions: M25 junction 18, A404 to Amersham, A416 to Chesham - go down to r-about at foot of Amersham Hill, then sharp left. 10 mins walk from Chesham station (Metropolitan Line)
Capacity: 5,000 Cover: 2,500 Seats: 284 Floodlights: Yes

Clubhouse: Open every evening & matchdays. Bar snacks. Available for hire(business training meetings, weddings etc)
Club Shop: Open matchdays Metal Badges: Yes

PREVIOUS **Leagues:** Spartan 17-47; Corinthian 47-63; Athenian 63-73

CLUB RECORDS **Attendance:** 5,000 v Cambridge Utd, FA 3rd Rd 5/12/79
Goalscorer: John Willis **Appearances:** Martin Baguley (600+)
Record Fees - Paid & Received: Undisclosed (club policy)

BEST SEASON **FA Cup:** 3rd Rd 79-80. 1st Rd 66-67 68-69 76-77 82-83
FA Amtr Cup: R-up 67-68 **FA Trophy:** 3rd Rd 92-93 (1-3 v Sutton United [H])

HONOURS: FA Amtr Cup R-up 67-68, Isthmian Lg 92-93 (Div 1 90-91 96-97), Div 2 Nth 86-87, Associate Members Cup R-up 90-91, Charity Shield 94-95; Athenian Lg Div 1 Cup 63-64 68-69; Corinthian Lg R-up (2) 60-62 (Lg Cup 60-61); Spartan Lg(4) 21-23 24-25 32-33 (R-up 26-27 29-30 33-34); Berks & Bucks Snr Cup 21-22 25-26 28-29 33-34 47-48 50-51 64-65 66-67 75-76 92-93 (R-up 94-95)

Players progressing: Bill Shipwright & Jimmy Strain (Watford 53 & 55), StewartScullion (Charlton 65), John Pyatt (L'pool 67), Brian Carter (Brentford 68),Kerry Dixon (Spurs 78), Tony Currie (Torquay 84), Dwayne Plummer (Bristol Rovers)

Back Row, left to right: Drax Hippolyte (Reserve Team Manager), Paul Vockins, James Pinnock, Mark Watson, Fitz Hall, Delroy Preddie, Jason Court, Lee Kersey, Victor Renner, Dereck Brown, Pete Lawrence (Assistant Manager), Karl Jones (Physio) and Bob Dowie (Manager) **Front Row:** Dave Clark, Ernie Cooksey, D.J.Campbell, Brian Statham, Martin Fox, Terry Bowes, Kelechi Durv and Craig Farley

Date	Comp.	Opponents	Att.	Score	Goalscorers
19.08	Ryman P	Enfield	224	1 - 3	Abrahams 14
22.08	Ryman P	HAMPTON & RICHMOND BOR.	303	1 - 0	Statham 43
26.08	Ryman P	GRAYS ATHLETIC	275	3 - 1	Simpson 6, Brown 28 39
28.08	Ryman P	Maidenhead United	329	2 - 0	Storer 73 86
02.09	Ryman P	Hendon	328	2 - 2	Renner 47, Bowes 71
05.09	Ryman P	CARSHALTON ATHLETIC	295	3 - 1	Hall 16, Harland 48, Renner 59
09.09	Ryman P	Canvey Island	725	1 - 2	Harland 10
12.09	Lge Cup 1	Wingate & Finchley	161	3 - 1	Renner, Simpson(2)
16.09	Ryman P	BASINGSTOKE TOWN	364	1 - 2	Bowes 62
19.09	Ryman P	Harrow Borough	144	2 - 3	Renner 38, Hall 46
23.09	Ryman P	FARNBOROUGH TOWN	511	1 - 4	Harland 77
30.09	FA Cup Q2	WALLINGFORD	290	3 - 2	Stephenson 40, Campbell 49, Harland 61
07.10	Ryman P	Hitchin Town	258	2 - 1	Campbell 37 42
14.10	FA Cup Q3	Stafford Rangers	616	2 - 0	Campbell 51, Simpson 90
21.10	Ryman P	Dulwich Hamlet	338	1 - 0	Renner 71
28.10	FA Cup Q4	KETTERING TOWN	736	0 - 2	
07.11	Ryman P	HEYBRIDGE SWIFTS	263	2 - 3	Kersey 63, Campbell 69
11.11	Ryman P	Croydon	109	1 - 2	Campbell 90
14.11	Lge Cup 2	Bromley	133	3 - 1	Brown, Watson(2)
18.11	Ryman P	BILLERICAY TOWN	397	2 - 0	Watson 5, Storer 36[p]
29.11	Friendly	QUEENS PARK RANGERS	n.k	1 - 0	
02.12	FA Trophy 2	King's Lynn	731	0 - 2	
09.12	Ryman P	Slough Town	517	2 - 0	Campbell 48, Storer 85[p]
16.12	Ryman P	HENDON	378	4 - 1	Campbell 15, Watson 16, Kelly 39[og], Towler 78
23.12	Ryman P	Gravesend & Northfleet	463	2 - 3	Storer 23, Campbell 63
26.12	Ryman P	ST ALBANS CITY	621	2 - 0	Watson 13, Brown 28
02.01	Ryman P	Hampton & Richmond Borough	292	1 - 3	Bowes 73
06.01	Ryman P	CROYDON	323	4 - 1	Gorman 4, Watson 14, Farley 53 77
13.01	Ryman P	Grays Athletic	199	2 - 0	Bowes 7, Statham 87[p]
27.01	Ryman P	Carshalton Athletic	324	4 - 0	Pinnock 55, Fox 62, Watson 80, Cowes 81
01.02	FMC 2	BRAINTREE TOWN	85	4 - 2	Renner(3), Bowes
17.02	Ryman P	CANVEY ISLAND	455	1 - 1	Bowes 45
20.02	FMC 3	ST ALBANS CITY	288	0 - 2	
22.02	Lge Cup 3	Hendon	99	3 - 2	Farley 37, Campbell 70, Brown 90
24.02	Ryman P	Heybridge Swifts	254	1 - 3	Statham 37
27.02	Ryman P	Sutton United	387	3 - 2	Renner 47, Brown 66, Statham 84[p]
03.03	Ryman P	HITCHIN TOWN	309	3 - 0	Watson 44, Statham 52, Campbell 75
06.03	B&B SC QF	AYLESBURY UNITED	n.k	4 - 0	Brown 13, Statham 40[p], Watson 48 53
10.03	Ryman P	HARROW BOROUGH	402	1 - 1	Brown 69
15.03	Lge Cup QF	Heybridge Swifts	119	1 - 3	Statham 38[p]
20.03	Ryman P	ENFIELD	153	0 - 0	
31.03	Ryman P	DULWICH HAMLET	280	2 - 0	Watson 59, Duru 89
03.04	B&B SC SF	BURNHAM	n.k	6 - 2	Statham 26, Bowes 30 39, Cooksey 47, Watson 90
07.04	Ryman P	Billericay Town	357	1 - 1	Renner 39
10.04	Ryman P	MAIDENHEAD UNITED	225	2 - 1	Campbell 18, Hall 68
14.04	Ryman P	GRAVESEND & NORTHFLEET	314	3 - 0	Fox 22 85, Statham 53[p]
16.04	Ryman P	St Albans City	385	5 - 1	Gorman 17, Campbell 22 40, Cooksey 60, Fox 75
18.04	Ryman P	ALDERSHOT TOWN	329	0 - 3	
19.04	Ryman P	Farnborough Town	517	0 - 0	
21.04	Ryman P	SUTTON UNITED	306	0 - 3	
24.04	Ryman P	Basingstoke Town	285	1 - 2	Campbell 25
26.04	Ryman P	Aldershot Town	1220	0 - 1	
28.04	Ryman P	Purfleet	239	2 - 1	Watson 44, Beeton 55
01.05	Ryman P	PURFLEET	140	5 - 0	Cooksey 31, Watson 34, Campbell 45 86, Hall 90
05.05	Ryman P	SLOUGH TOWN	449	2 - 0	Statham 19[p], Brown 44
07.05	B&B SC F	MAIDENHEAD UNITED	805	1 - 0	Statham 59[p](at Slough Town)

PLAYING SQUAD

GOALKEEPERS: Delroy Preddie (Walton & Hersham)

DEFENDERS: Brian Statham (Gillingham), Richard Horner (Sutton Utd), Fitz Hall (Barbet), Alan Beeton (Wycombe), Lee Kersey (Enfield), Victor Renner (Gravesend)

MIDFIELDERS: Terry Bowes (Wisbech), Corey Browne (Harrow), Steve Barnes (Welling), Michael Gorman (Edgware), Gary Issott (Northwood), Kelechi Duru (Harrow), David Pratt (St.Albans)

FORWARDS: Paul Fewings (Boston Utd), Wayne Andrews (Aldershot), Danny Boateng (Arsenal)

CROYDON

CLUB OFFICIALS

Chairman: Ken Jarvie
Secretary: Mrs Jacqueline Jarvie
2 Spa Close, London SE25 6DS
Tel: 020 86537250(H),
Press Officer: Russell Chandler
26 Dartnell Rd, Croydon, Surrey. CR0 6JA
Tel: 0208 406 4573 (H) 0208 654 8555 (B)
Match Secretary: Gordon Tennant

FOOTBALL MANAGEMENT TEAM

Manager: Ken Jarvie
Coach: John Finch
Physio: Ian Fairs

FACT FILE

Formed: 1953
Nickname: The Trams
Sponsors:
Colours: Sky & navy / navy & sky/navy & sky
Change colours: Whte
Midweek home matchday: Wednesday
Reserve Team's League: Suburban Capital

2000-01

Captain: Ally Reeve
P.o.Y.: NickMcDonell
Top Scorer: Nick McDonell

Pages: 28 Price: £1.00
Editor: Russell Chandler (0181 406 4573 H)

Local Press: Whyteleafe Advertiser, Croydon Midweek Post, Times, Guardian

GROUND Croydon Sports Arena, Albert Road, South Norwood, London. SE25 4QL
Tel: 0208 654 3462/8555

Directions: Train to East Croydon or Norwood Junction, then bus 12 to eitherBelmont or Dundee Road. Walk down either - ground at bottom. 5 mins walk fromWoodside (BR)

Capacity: 8,000 Cover: 1,000 Seats: 450 Floodlights: Yes

Clubhouse: Open every evening and lunchtime, holds 250, snacks available
Dancing, discos, bingo. Lounge bar available for private hire

Club Shop: Yes Badges £2.50, Croydon Women's F.C. Champions badges £3.00

PREVIOUS **Leagues:** Surrey Senior 53-63; Spartan 63-64; Athenian 64-74
Name: Croydon Amateurs 1953-74

CLUB RECORDS **Attendance:** 1,450 v Wycombe, FA Cup 4th Qualifying Rd 1975
Career appearances: Alec Jackson (1977-88) 452 + 111goals and Tony Luckett(1962-73) 411 appearances + 411 goals
Transfer fee paid: Steve Brown **Transfer fee received:** Peter Evans (to Sutton Utd)

BEST SEASON **FA Cup:** 2nd Round replay 79-80, 2-3 v Millwall after 1-1
FA Trophy: 2nd Round 81-82, 82-83 **FA Amateur Cup:** 3rd round 71-72

HONOURS Isthmian Lg Div. 1 99-2000, Div 2 R-up 75-76 95-96, Lg Cup: R-up 74-75 FM Cup 99-2000; Surrey Snr Cup 81-82 (R-up 76-77 99-00), Surrey Prem Cup 86-87, Spartan Lg 63-64, Athenian Lg R-up 71-72 (Div 2 65-66 (R-up 70-71)), Surrey Snr Lg R-up 56-57 60-61 62-63 (Lg Cup 60-61, Charity Cup 53-54 62-63, Res Section 57-58), London Senior Cup R-up 77-78, Suburban Lg South 86-87(Lg Cup(2), Southern Yth Lg 85-86 (Lg Cup 85-86 87-88), Berger Yth Cup 78-79, Southern Youth Lg Cup 96-97. Womens F.A.Cup 95-6,99-00 R-up 97-98 Premier Lg 99-00

Players progressing: Alan Barnett (Plymouth 1955), Peter Bonetti (Chelsea), Leroy Ambrose (Charlton 1979), Steve Milton (Fulham - via Whyteleafe), Murray Jones (Crystal Pal. - via Carshalton)

Croydon's ace goalscorer, Nic McDonnell, has to watch in vain as his shot is blocked by Al-James hannigan of Dulwich Hamlet.
Photo: Alan Coomes

Date	Comp.	Opponents	Att.	Score	Goalscorers
19.08	Ryman P	Hendon	304	0 - 4	
21.08	Ryman P	ENFIELD	219	2 - 2	Agudosi 40, McDonnell 52
26.08	Ryman P	GRAVESEND & NORTHFLEET	136	1 - 2	McDonnell 82
28.08	Ryman P	Hampton & Richmond Borough	178	0 - 3	
02.09	Ryman P	Basingstoke Town	444	1 - 1	Ellan 23
04.09	Ryman P	PURFLEET	130	0 - 0	
09.09	Ryman P	Aldershot Town	2010	0 - 4	
12.09	Lge Cup 1	Harrow Borough	93	3 - 2	McDonnell 55, Sugrue 59, Dickinson 80
16.09	Ryman P	MAIDENHEAD UNITED	109	0 - 2	
18.09	Ryman P	HITCHIN TOWN	112	5 - 1	Coleman 10 32, Agudosi 35 48 60
23.09	Ryman P	Slough Town	380	0 - 1	
30.09	FA Cup Q2	Carshalton Athletic	312	1 - 1	Coleman 11
02.10	FA Cup Q2 R	CARSHALTON ATHLETIC	194	2 - 2	Dickson 50, McDonnell 89 (3-1p)
07.10	Ryman P	FARNBOROUGH TOWN	175	0 - 1	
14.10	FA Cup Q3	Gravesend & Northfleet	402	1 - 4	McDonnell 89
21.10	Ryman P	ST ALBANS CITY	138	0 - 2	
28.10	Ryman P	Sutton United	584	1 - 2	McDonnell 67
04.11	FA Trophy 1	Havant & Waterlooville	248	1 - 2	McDonnell 17
11.11	Ryman P	CHESHAM UNITED	109	2 - 1	McDonnell 65 79
13.11	Lge Cup 2	WEMBLEY	72	3 - 0	Reeve, Allen, Sugrue
05.12	FMC 2	Sutton United	194	2 - 2	Allen, Garland (3-4p)
09.12	Ryman P	CARSHALTON ATHLETIC	165	3 - 0	Judge 9 60, Harper 90
16.12	Ryman P	Enfield	156	0 - 1	
23.12	Ryman P	HARROW BOROUGH	121	2 - 0	Judge 38, McDonnell 90
26.12	Ryman P	Dulwich Hamlet	271	4 - 1	Cleevely 48[og], McDonnell 69, Allen 81, Dundas 90
06.01	Ryman P	Chesham United	323	1 - 4	Dickinson 71
13.01	Ryman P	Gravesend & Northfleet	525	0 - 2	
16.01	London SC 4	Croydon Athletic	0	3 - 4	Bower[p], Davenport[og], Clark
27.01	Ryman P	Maidenhead United	219	1 - 3	McDonnell 79
31.01	Surrey SC 1	CHERTSEY TOWN	65	2 - 0	Dundas, McDonnell
10.02	Ryman P	Purfleet	162	0 - 3	
17.02	Ryman P	ALDERSHOT TOWN	554	2 - 2	McDonnell 7, Allen 22
20.02	Ryman P	Grays Athletic	182	2 - 2	Garland 30, McDonnell 84
23.02	Surrey SC QF	CRYSTAL PALACE	0	2 - 3	McDonnell, Garland
03.03	Ryman P	Farnborough Town	700	1 - 3	McDonnell 22
05.03	Ryman P	HEYBRIDGE SWIFTS	148	1 - 2	Judge 3
10.03	Ryman P	Hitchin Town	260	3 - 7	Thompson 42, Coleman 44 54
14.03	Lge Cup 3	CANVEY ISLAND	74	5 - 0	Coleman 10 90, Dickinson 55, Dunbar 60, Currie 89
20.03	Ryman P	Billericay Town	174	0 - 0	
26.03	Ryman P	HAMPTON & RICHMOND BOR.	131	1 - 1	McDonnell 67
29.03	Lge Cup QF	Basingstoke Town	145	2 - 0	Thompson 7, Dundas 45[p]
31.03	Ryman P	St Albans City	326	2 - 2	McDonnell 33, Garland 87
02.04	Ryman P	SLOUGH TOWN	119	4 - 1	McDonnell 40 50, Garland 57, Thompson 86
04.04	Ryman P	SUTTON UNITED	204	2 - 1	Coleman 41, McDonnell 83
07.04	Ryman P	GRAYS ATHLETIC	107	1 - 0	McDonnell 33
12.04	Lge Cup SF(1)	Hampton & Richmond Borough	240	3 - 2	Coleman(2), Dickinson
14.04	Ryman P	Harrow Borough	165	1 - 0	Dickson 89
16.04	Ryman P	DULWICH HAMLET	185	1 - 1	McDonnell 83
18.04	Ryman P	BASINGSTOKE TOWN	109	2 - 2	Thompson 45 90
21.04	Ryman P	Heybridge Swifts	195	2 - 1	Thompson 61, Dickinson 90
23.04	Ryman P	HENDON	121	2 - 0	Dickson 36, Harper 69
28.04	Ryman P	CANVEY ISLAND	118	2 - 1	Thompson 70[p] 77
30.04	Lge Cup SF(2)	HAMPTON & RICHMOND BOR.	143	3 - 2	Dickinson 9, Thompson 71, Coleman 74
03.05	Ryman P	BILLERICAY TOWN	106	1 - 2	Garland 35
04.05	Ryman P	Canvey Island	340	0 - 5	
05.05	Ryman P	Carshalton Athletic	269	2 - 4	Garland 3, Thompson 47
07.05	Lge Cup F	HEYBRIDGE SWIFTS	318	0 - 3	(at Purfleet)

PLAYING SQUAD

GOALKEEPERS: Les Cleevely (Dulwich Hamlet)

DEFENDERS: Dave Richards (Dulwich Hamlet), Tony Chin (Dulwich Hamlet), Danny Bower (Dulwich Hamlet), Ross Edwrads (Fisher Ath)

MIDFIELDERS: Omari Coleman (Millwall), Barry Kingsford (St.Leonards), Craig Dundas (Local), Graham Harper (Portsmouth), Chris Dickson (Tooting & Mitcham), Luke Basford (Woking)

FORWARDS: Nic McDonnell (Farnborough), Peter Garland (Dulwich Hamlet), Eben Allen (Molesey)

ENFIELD

CLUB OFFICIALS

Chairman: **A Lazarou** Pres: **R.Prosser**
Secretary: **Keith Hughes**,28 Peace Close, Rosedale, Cheshunt, Herts. EN7 5EQ
Tel No & Fax:: 01992 301109
Match Sec: **Derek Bird**,17 Fishers Close, Waltham Cross,Herts.
Tel No: 01992 301741

FOOTBALL MANAGEMENT TEAM

Manager: **Tom Loizou** Coach: **John Sitton**
Asst Man/Coach: **Frank Fuschillo**
Physio: **Steve Quinton & K.Elliott**

FACT FILE

Formed: 1893
Nickname: The E's
Sponsors: Enfield Gazette & Advertiser
Newsline: 0930 555845
Colours: White/blue/white
Change colours: Blue/white/blue
Midweek matchday: Tuesday
Reserves' League: Middlesex Co.
2000-01: Captain Danny Jones
P.O.Y.: Danny Jones
Top Scorer: James Bunn 10

Pages: 48 Price: £1.50
Editor: Steven Edwards,Derek Bird and Edward Penn
Local Press: Enfield Gazette, Enfield Advertiser, Enfield Independent

GROUND: Boreham Wood FC. Meadow Park, Broughinge Rd, Boreham Wood, Herts WD6 5AL. Tel: 0208 9535097 Email: efcltd@lineone.net Website: www.enfieldfc.com
Directions: A1 towards London from M25, 1st turn for Boreham Wood, head for town centre, into Brook Rd at r'bout before town centre, Broughinge Rd is 1st right. 1 mile from Elstree & Boreham Wood station (Thameslink), or bus 292 or 107 to McDonalds (5 minutes walk)
Capacity: 4,502 Cover: 1,568 Seats: 500 Floodlights: Yes
Club Shop: Contact office or see website

PREVIOUS **Leagues**: Tottenham & Dist 1894-95; Nth Middx 96-1903; London 03-13 20-21; Middx 08-12, 19-20; Athenian 12-14 21-39 45-63; Herts & Middx Comb 39-42; Isthmian 63-81; GMV Conference 81-90
Name: Enfield Spartans 1893-1900 **Grounds:** Baileys Field 1893-96; Tuckers Field 96-1900; Cherry Orchard Lane1900-36 Southbury Road 1936-1999

CLUB RECORDS **Attendance:** 10,000 (10/10/62) v Spurs, floodlight opener
Win: 18-0 v Stevenage FA Cup 2nd Qual 22/10/27 (H) **Defeat:** 0-12 v Woolwich Polytechnic, London Lge Div 2 27/4/04
Fee Paid: for Gary Abbott (Barnet) **Fee Received:** for Paul Furlong (Coventry City)
Scorer: Tommy Lawrence, 191 1959-1964. **Appearances:** Steve King 617 (77-89)

BEST SEASON **FA Amateur Cup:** Winners 66-7 69-70 R-up 63-4 71-2 **FA Trophy:** Winners 81-2 87-8
FA Cup: 4th Rd replay 80-81, 0-3 v Barnsley (at Spurs), Att 35,244, after 1-1.
League clubs beaten: Wimbledon, Northampton 77-78, Hereford, Port Vale 80-81, Wimbledon 81-82, Exeter 84-85, Orient 88-89, Aldershot 91-92, Cardiff City 94-95, Torquay Utd 94-95, Chesterfield 99-00

HONOURS: Alliance Premier Lge 82-83 85-86 (R-up 81-82), Lg Cup R-up 81-82; IsthmianLg(8) 67-70 75-78 79-80 94-95 (R-up 64-65 71-72 74-75 80-81 90-92 95-96), LgCup(2) 78-80 (R-up 91-92 94-95); Athenian Lg(2) 61-63 (R-up 34-35); London LgDiv 1 11-12 (R-up 04-05 06-07); Middx Snr Cup 13-14 46-47 61-62 65-66 68-71 77-81 88-89 90-91 97-98, (R-up 10-11 20-21 47-48 51-52 57-60 62-63 66-67 72-73 75-76 84-85); London Snr Cup 34-35 60-61 66-67 71-73 75-76 (R-up 63-64 67-68 70-71); Middx Lg (West) 09-10 (R-up 10-11); European Amtr Cup Winners Cup 69-70

Players progressing: Terry McQuade (Millwall 61), Roger Day (Watford 61), Jeff Harris (Orient 64), Peter Feely (Chelsea 70), Carl Richards & Jon Bailey (B'mouth 80 & 95), Paul Furlong (Coventry 91), Andy Pape (Barnet 91), GregHeald (Peterborough 94), Lee Marshall (Norwich City 97)

Back Row,left to right: M Rodothenous, D reddington, G. Cooper, J. Ayres, M.Weilbnowski (Assistant), T.Loizou (Manager), F.Fuschillo (Assistant Manager), M.Whittamore, N.Gyoury, G.Georgiou, S.Peddle and S Magona.
Middle Row: D.Lewis, L Hall, J.Loomes, O.Petersen, A.Grant, G.Wilkie, G.Hoy, M.Rufus, M. Koularmanou.
Front Row: S.Quinton (Physio), L.Allen, M.Shirley, C.Perifimou and K.Elliott (Physio)

Date	Comp.	Opponents	Att.	Score	Goalscorers
19.08	Ryman P	CHESHAM UNITED	224	3 - 1	Bunn 79, Morgan 81, Alleyne 85
21.08	Ryman P	Croydon	219	2 - 2	Geraghty 20, Dickinson 90[og]
26.08	Ryman P	Dulwich Hamlet	360	1 - 1	Rattray 20
28.08	Ryman P	SLOUGH TOWN	306	1 - 1	Bunn 83[p]
02.09	Ryman P	ST ALBANS CITY	229	2 - 3	Hammatt 38 43
05.09	Ryman P	Harrow Borough	240	1 - 2	Morris 72
09.09	Ryman P	HEYBRIDGE SWIFTS	148	1 - 1	Flemming 9
12.09	Lge Cup 1	Farnborough Town	260	1 - 2	Bunn 101
16.09	Ryman P	Farnborough Town	725	1 - 1	Dack 15[og]
19.09	Ryman P	GRAYS ATHLETIC	117	2 - 1	Flemming 37 52
23.09	Ryman P	Carshalton Athletic	356	1 - 2	D Gentle 74
30.09	FA Cup Q2	Bedford Town	804	0 - 0	
04.10	FA Cup Q2 R	BEDFORD TOWN	289	1 - 1	Fleming 79 (4-3p)
07.10	Ryman P	HAMPTON & RICHMOND BOR.	129	2 - 2	Allen 56, Hammatt 70
15.10	FA Cup Q3	STOURPORT SWIFTS	247	3 - 1	McDonald 12, Morgan 35, Bunn 57
21.10	Ryman P	MAIDENHEAD UNITED	228	3 - 1	Bunn 55, Rattray 70, McDonald 88
24.10	FMC 1	Braintree Town	162	0 - 5	
28.10	FA Cup Q4	Harrow Borough	504	1 - 2	Bunn 91
04.11	FA Trophy 1	ERITH & BELVEDERE	179	4 - 2	Allen 39, Bunn 45[p], Hammatt 76 90
07.11	Ryman P	Canvey Island	416	1 - 4	Rattray 5
11.11	Ryman P	Gravesend & Northfleet	473	0 - 1	
25.11	Ryman P	Billericay Town	490	2 - 0	Bunn 19 39[p]
16.12	Ryman P	CROYDON	156	1 - 0	Hammatt 35
23.12	Ryman P	Purfleet	264	0 - 3	
26.12	Ryman P	HITCHIN TOWN	206	2 - 5	Flemming 22, Hammatt 78
01.01	Ryman P	St Albans City	1009	1 - 0	Hammatt 90
06.01	Ryman P	GRAVESEND & NORTHFLEET	252	0 - 1	
08.01	FA Trophy 2	Maidenhead United	182	0 - 1	
13.01	Ryman P	DULWICH HAMLET	196	1 - 1	Flemming 72
23.01	Middx SC 2	Uxbridge	80	2 - 3	Devereux 3, Bunn 40
27.01	Ryman P	HARROW BOROUGH	211	1 - 2	Morris 57
30.01	Ryman P	Basingstoke Town	296	0 - 4	
03.02	Ryman P	Slough Town	490	1 - 3	Boyce 18
10.02	Ryman P	FARNBOROUGH TOWN	313	0 - 3	
17.02	Ryman P	Heybridge Swifts	295	0 - 2	
20.02	Ryman P	ALDERSHOT TOWN	346	1 - 0	Jones 13
24.02	Ryman P	BASINGSTOKE TOWN	188	1 - 4	Johnson 38
27.02	Ryman P	HENDON	177	0 - 2	
03.03	Ryman P	Hampton & Richmond Borough	278	0 - 4	
06.03	Ryman P	Sutton United	446	3 - 2	Allen 18 27, Chandler 30
10.03	Ryman P	Grays Athletic	312	0 - 2	
20.03	Ryman P	Chesham United	153	0 - 0	
31.03	Ryman P	Maidenhead United	292	1 - 2	Georgiou 24
07.04	Ryman P	Aldershot Town	1625	1 - 2	Georgiou 6
10.04	Ryman P	CARSHALTON ATHLETIC	151	2 - 1	Allen 39, Jones 62[p]
14.04	Ryman P	PURFLEET	185	2 - 1	Georgiou 33 46
16.04	Ryman P	Hitchin Town	457	1 - 2	Georgiou 47
21.04	Ryman P	BILLERICAY TOWN	206	1 - 0	Boyce 24
27.04	Ryman P	CANVEY ISLAND	119	3 - 0	Jones 68 79[p], Georgiou 86
28.04	Ryman P	Hendon	306	0 - 3	
05.05	Ryman P	SUTTON UNITED	231	2 - 2	Ayres 28 43

PLAYING SQUAD

GOALKEEPERS: Kenny Addai (Beaconsfield SYCOB), Mark Whittamore (Edgware)

DEFENDERS: Simon Peddie (Youth), Gary Hoy (Arlesey), James Ayres (Kettering), Steve Magona (Boreham Wood), Grant Cooper (Youth), Dave Reddington (Cheshunt)

MIDFIELDERS: Chris Perifimou (Cheshunt), Adam Gant (Witham), Oliver Petersen (Harrow), Nicky Gyoury (Colchester), Michael Rodosthenous (Cheshunt), Lee Allen (Chesham Utd), Marvin Rufus (Romford), Glen Wilkie (Cheshunt)

FORWARDS: Mike Koulamanou (Wembley), Joe Nartey (Dulwich Hamlet), Jody Loomes (Cheshunt), George Gregorio (Cheshunt), George Georgiou (Purfleet), Dwayne Lewis (Harrow), Leon Hall (Cheshunt)

GRAVESEND & NORTHFLEET

CLUB OFFICIALS

Chairman: Brian Kilcullen
Secretary: Roly Edwards
c/o Football Club

Press Officer: Paul Cossom
Tel: 01474 533796

FOOTBALL MANAGEMENT TEAM

Manager: Andy Ford
Assistant Manager: Phil Handford
Physio: Martin Allen

FACT FILE

Formed: 1946
Nickname: The Fleet
Sponsors: Shepherd Neame
Colours: Red/white/red
Change colours: yellow & Blue
Midweek matchday: Tuesday
Youth Team: P.A.S.E. League

2000-01

Captain: Scortt Lindsey
P.o.Y.: Jimmy Jackson
Top Scorer: Che Stadhart 16

Gravesend & Northfleet F.C. est. 1946
v
Dulwich Hamlet F.C.
Saturday 28th April 2001
Kick Off 3.00pm
Gravesend & Northfleet Football Club
Ryman football league
Ryman Premier League
SHEPHERD NEAME
FIRST TEAM SPONSORS
Official Matchday Magazine Price £1.50

Pages: 32 Price: £1.50
Editor: Paul Cossom
Local Press: Gravesend Reporter, Kent Messenger. Gravesend Messenger The News Shopper
Local Radio: Invicta Radio, Radio Kent, RTM, Mercury FM

GROUND: Stonebridge Road, Northfleet, Kent DA11 9BA Tel: 01474 533796
Directions: From A2 take Northfleet/Southfleet exit (B262), follow toNorthfleet then B2175 (Springhead Rd) to junc A226, turn left (The Hill, Northfleet), road becomes Stonebridge Rd, grd on right at bottom of steep hill after 1 mile - car parking for 400-500. 2 mins from Northfleet BR station
Capacity: 3,300 Cover: 2,200 Seats: 600 Floodlights: Yes
Clubhouse: Fleet Social Centre. Hot and cold food available at tea bars onmatchdays
Club Shop: Sells progs, hats, scarves, badges etc, & other memorabilia.
Contact John Still or Angela Still

PREVIOUS **Leagues:** Kent (Gravesend Utd), Southern 46-79, Alliance Prem. 79-82
Names: Gravesend Utd, Northfleet Utd (merged 1946)
Ground: Central Avenue (Gravesend Utd) (Northfleet always played at StonebridgeRd)

CLUB RECORDS **Attendance:** 12,036 v Sunderland, FA Cup 4th Rd 12.2.63. 26.081 v Aston Villa FACup 3rd Rd 95-96 at Villa Park
Goalscorer (career): Steve Portway 150+ (92-94, 97-present) **Appearances:** Ken Burrett 537
Win: 8-1 v Clacton Tn, Sth Lge 62-63, 7-0 Godalming 95-96 FAC. **Defeat:** 0-9 v Trowbridge Tn, Southern Lge Prem Div 91-92
Fee Paid: £8,000 for Richard Newbery (Wokingham 96), £8,000 for Craig Williams(Tonbridge 97)
Fee Received: £35,000 for Jimmy Bullard (West Ham 1998)

BEST SEASON **FA Cup:** 4th Rd Replay 1963, 2-5 v Sunderland (A), 1-1 (H) **FA Trophy:** 3rd Rd 88-89 , 99-00

HONOURS: Southern Lg 57-58, Southern Div 94-95, Div 1 Sth 74-75 (R-up 70-71 88-89), Lg Cup 77-78 (R-up 57-58), Champ Cup 77-78; Kent Sen Cup Winners 48-49 52-53 80-81, 99-00 (R-up 47-48 76-77 90-91 97-98); Kent Floodlit Cup 69-70 (R-up 72-73); Kent Sen Shield R-up 47-48 51-52; Kent Interm Cup R-up 87-88; Kent Midweek Lg 95-96, R-up 92-93 93-94 94-95; Kent Youth Lg Cup 82-83 86-87 96-97; Kent Youth Lg 95-96 96-97; John Ullman Cup 82-83

Players progressing: Several incl. most recently: K Baron (Aldershot 60), R Dwight (Coventry 62), R Cameron (Southend 63), R McNichol (Carlisle 65), A Humphreys (Mansfield 64), B Thornley (Brentford 65), P Jeavons (Lincoln 66), B Fry (Orient 66), B Gordine (Sheffield Utd 68), TBaldwin (Brentford 77), L Smelt (Nottm Forest 80), T Warrilow (Torquay 87),J.Bullard(W.H.U.98)

Back Row, left to right: Martin Allen (Physio), Aaron Barnett, Paul Booth, Robert Owen, Danny Lye, Francis Duku, Jamie Turner,Gavin Rose, Matt Lee, Liam Hatch, Craig Wilkins, Aiden O'Brien and Phil Handford (Assistant Manager) **Front Row:** Carl Bartley, Eliot Martin, Che Stadhart, Ryan Briggs, Darren Smith, Andy Ford (Manager), Jimmy Jackson (Captain), Danny Jeffery, Lee Spiller, Mitch Crawley and Justin Skinner

Date	Comp.	Opponents	Att.	Score	Goalscorers
02.08	Testimonial	CHARLTON ATHLETIC	634	3 - 5	Restarick 3, Jackson 65 73[p] for Jim Jackson
19.08	Ryman P	SLOUGH TOWN	468	1 - 2	Barnett 85
22.08	Ryman P	Farnborough Town	452	0 - 1	
26.08	Ryman P	Croydon	136	2 - 1	Booth 36, Stadhart 79
28.08	Ryman P	ST ALBANS CITY	481	1 - 0	Stadhart 71
02.09	Ryman P	HEYBRIDGE SWIFTS	391	0 - 0	
05.09	Ryman P	Billericay Town	408	0 - 1	
09.09	Ryman P	SUTTON UNITED	499	2 - 2	Hegley 80, Booth 84
16.09	Ryman P	Hitchin Town	388	2 - 1	Barnett 56, Booth 62
18.09	Ryman P	Hendon	207	2 - 1	Restarick 72, Owen 78
23.09	Ryman P	HAMPTON & RICHMOND BOR.	412	3 - 4	Booth 11, Jackson 20[p], Stadhart 55
30.09	FA Cup Q2	NEWBURY	254	4 - 0	Lee 12, Jackson 41 74, Stadhart 77
03.10	Lge Cup 1	HUNGERFORD TOWN	121	6 - 1	OG 6, Stadhart 15, Spiller 65, Jeffrey 72, Barnett 79,Restarick 83p
06.10	Ryman P	Carshalton Athletic	336	3 - 1	Wilkins 29, Barnett 62, Stadhart 86
14.10	FA Cup Q3	CROYDON	402	4 - 1	Wilkins 21, Spiller 44, Booth 60, Stadhart 67
21.10	Ryman P	Aldershot Town	2065	0 - 1	
28.10	FA Cup Q4	MANGOTSFIELD UNITED	736	4 - 0	Duku 9, Stadhart 34 78, Restarick 83
11.11	Ryman P	ENFIELD	473	1 - 0	Restarick 78
14.11	FA Trophy 1	HASTINGS TOWN	232	0 - 1	
02.12	Ryman P	Dulwich Hamlet	427	2 - 0	Booth 18, Brown 75[og]
08.12	FA Cup 1	NOTTS COUNTY	2376	1 - 2	Jackson 75 Gillingham
16.12	Ryman P	Heybridge Swifts	298	2 - 2	Walters 9[og], Restarick 55
23.12	Ryman P	CHESHAM UNITED	463	3 - 2	Jackson 16, Restarick 43, Hegley 74
26.12	Ryman P	Canvey Island	620	1 - 1	Wilkins 69
30.12	Ryman P	FARNBOROUGH TOWN	681	2 - 1	Wilkins 23, Jackson 53
06.01	Ryman P	Enfield	252	1 - 0	Stadhart 8
09.01	Ryman P	PURFLEET	454	1 - 0	Stadhart 7
13.01	Ryman P	CROYDON	525	2 - 0	Judge 20[og], Stadhart 68
16.01	Ryman P	HARROW BOROUGH	363	2 - 1	Wilkins 29, Booth 67
23.01	Lge Cup 2	Canvey Island	221	0 - 2	
30.01	Ryman P	Maidenhead United	203	3 - 1	Crawley 31, Duku 35, Barnett 73
15.02	FMC 2	FORD UNITED	73	4 - 0	Booth(2), Jackson, Stadhart
17.02	Ryman P	Sutton United	543	4 - 1	Stadhart 6 73, Jackson 20[p], Barnett 85
20.02	Ryman P	HITCHIN TOWN	468	3 - 0	Booth 29, Hegley 57, Stadhart 84
24.02	Ryman P	Harrow Borough	247	6 - 0	Jackson 15 49, Stadhart 26, Smith 44, Hegley 89 90
03.03	Ryman P	CARSHALTON ATHLETIC	524	3 - 0	Duku 21, Jackson 29, Lee 31
06.03	Ryman P	BILLERICAY TOWN	443	1 - 1	Jackson 43
13.03	Kent SC QF	WELLING UNITED	268	3 - 2	Owen, Stadhart, Jackson
15.03	FMC 3	Hitchin Town	68	7 - 1	Restarick(5), Jeffrey, Hegley
17.03	Ryman P	Hampton & Richmond Borough	485	0 - 1	
20.03	Ryman P	BASINGSTOKE TOWN	275	0 - 2	
24.03	Ryman P	Purfleet	201	0 - 1	
31.03	Ryman P	ALDERSHOT TOWN	789	2 - 0	Stadhart 15, Hegley 32
03.04	Ryman P	GRAYS ATHLETIC	363	0 - 1	
10.04	Ryman P	St Albans City	233	2 - 0	Owen 2, Smith 44
12.04	FMC QF	ST ALBANS CITY	119	1 - 1	Jeffrey (4-3p)
14.04	Ryman P	Chesham United	314	0 - 3	
16.04	Ryman P	CANVEY ISLAND	662	1 - 2	Owen 19
18.04	Kent SC SF	FOLKESTONE INVICTA	175	5 - 4	Jackson 11 118, Smith 23, Jeffrey 36, Stadhart 52
21.04	Ryman P	Grays Athletic	295	1 - 2	Currie 12
22.04	Ryman P	MAIDENHEAD UNITED	222	0 - 1	
24.04	Ryman P	Slough Town	312	0 - 2	
28.04	Ryman P	DULWICH HAMLET	443	2 - 1	Wilkins 3 52
02.05	FMC SF	Bognor Regis Town	200	2 - 0	Duku(2)
03.05	Ryman P	HENDON	227	2 - 1	Currie 14, Wilkins 66
05.05	Ryman P	Basingstoke Town	445	0 - 4	
07.05	Kent SC F	Dover Athletic	1002	4 - 0	Stadhart 3, Wilkins 20, Barnett 57, Jackson 68[p]
10.05	FMC F	PURFLEET	511	3 - 1	Jackson 31 76[p], Owen 45

PLAYING SQUAD

GOALKEEPERS: Jamie Turner (Deal)

DEFENDERS: Craig Wilkins (Tonbridge), Matthew Lee (Sutton Utd), Justin Skinner (Aylesbury), Aaron Barnett (Erith & Belvedere), Francis Duku (Dulwich Hamlet)

MIDFIELDERS: Elliot Martin (Margate), Jimmy Jackson (Charlton), Darren Smith (Sittingbourne), Lee Spiller (Margate), Robert Owen (Sittingbourne), Gavin Rose (Bromley)

FORWARDS: Che Stadhart (Hampton & R), Carl Bartley (Dulwich Hamlet), Paul Booth (Tunbridge Wells), Liam Hatch (Herne Bay), Tom Planck (Margate)

GRAYS ATHLETIC

CLUB OFFICIALS

Chairman: **Frank Harris**
Secretary: **Jeff Saxton**
216 Thundersley Park Road,
South Benfleet, Essex SS71HP
Tel: 01268 756964
Press Officer: **Gordon Norman**
Tel: 014024 51733

FOOTBALL MANAGEMENT TEAM

Manager: Craig Edwards
Asst Man.:John Frostick Coach: Lyndon Lynch Physio: Marrtin Stevens

FACT FILE

Formed: 1890
Nickname: The Blues
Sponsors: Harris Commercials
Colours: Royal & white
Change colours: Red/white
Midweek matchday: Tuesday

2000-2001 Captain: Billy Manuel
P.o.Y.:Andy Douglas
Top Scorer: Andy Douglas 11

Grays Athletic Football Club
Ryman Football League PREMIER DIVISION
SEASON 2000-2001
Main Sponsors: HARRIS GROUP OF COMPANIES

Pages: 48 Price: £1
Editor: Jeremy Mason (01375 400188)
Local Press: Thurrock Gazette
Local Radio: BBC Essex, Radio Essex

Club Website: grays.ath.btinternet,co,uk

GROUND Recreation Ground, Bridge Road, Grays RM17 6BZ (01375 391649)
Directions: Seven minutes walk from Grays station - turn right round one way system, right into Clarence Road, and at end into Bridge Road. Bus No. 370. By road - A13 towards Southend from London, take Grays exit and follow signs to town centre, keep left on one-way system, continue up hill for about 1/2 mile, turn right into Bridge Road, ground 1/2 mile on right
Capacity: 4,500 Cover: 1,200 Seats: 300 Floodlights: Yes
Clubhouse: Bar, pool, darts, bar snacks available. Indoor sports hall.
Stewardess: Sue Riley (01375 377753)
Club Shop: Sells `The First Hundred Years', sweaters, T-shirts, replica shirts, scarves, ties, etc.
Contact Bill Grove 01375 391649

PREVIOUS **Leagues:** Athenian 12-14, 58-83; London 14-24, 26-39; Kent 24-26; Corinthian 45-58

CLUB RECORDS **Attendance:** 9,500 v Chelmsford City, FA Cup 4th Qual. Round 1959
Win: 12-0 v Tooting (H) London Lge 24/2/23 **Defeat:** 0-12 v Enfield (A) Athenian Lge 20/4/63
Goalscorer: Harry Brand 269 (1944-52) **Appearances:** Phil Sammons, 673. 1982-97
Fee Paid: For Ian Durant (Canvey Island 85)
Fee Received: Undisclosed for Tony Witter (C. Palace), Dwight Marshall(Plymouth 1991) and Matthew Lawrence(Wycombe W)

BEST SEASON **FA Cup:** 1st Rd 51-52 88-89 ,00-01 **FA Trophy:** 3rd Rd 92-93 **FA Amateur Cup:** 3rd Rd 63-64

HONOURS Isthmian Div 1 R-up 87-88 ,99-00(Div 2 Sth 84-85, Lg Cup 91-92); Athenian Lg R-up 82-83, Res. Sect. R-up 58-59 (Cup R-up 59-60); Corinthian Lg 45-46 (R-up 51-52 54-55 56-57), Lg Cup(2) 45-47, Mem. Shield(4) ; Essex Snr Cup 8(R-up 9; Essex SenTr 98-99; East Ang Cup 44-45 (R-up 43-44 54-55); Essex Thameside Tphy x 7 (R-up 7); Essex Elizabeth Tphy 76-77 (R-up 65-66); Claridge Tphy 87-88 88-89; Mithras Cup 79-80; Essex Int Cup(3) 56-57 58-60 (Jun Cup 19-20 (R-up 58-59); Essex & Herts ,Border Comb. East 87-88 (Ancillary Cup 78-79, Comb Cup 82-83); Fred Budden Tphy 86-87; Hornchurch Charity Cup 78-79 86-87; Neale Tphy 50-51; Ford Rate Tphy 83-84 85-86 87-88 (R-up 84-85 86-87); Stan Veness Mem. Tphy (8) 87-96

Players progressing: J Jordan (Spurs 47), R Kemp (Reading 49), B Silkman & TBanfield (Orient), G O'Reilly (Spurs), W Entwhistle (Bury 83), M Welch(Wimbledon 84), T Witter (C Palace 90), D Marshall (Plymouth 91), M Lawrence(Wycombe W. 96-97)

Steve Dickinson and John O'Sullivan clear the danger from Purfleet's Martin Carthy. **Photo:** Alan Coomes

Date	Comp.	Opponents	Att.	Score	Goalscorers
19.08	Ryman P	DULWICH HAMLET	210	1 - 1	Wright 85
22.08	Ryman P	Slough Town	503	0 - 1	
26.08	Ryman P	Chesham United	275	1 - 3	Hayzelden 39
28.08	Ryman P	FARNBOROUGH TOWN	284	0 - 3	
02.09	Ryman P	SUTTON UNITED	302	1 - 2	D Hazel 8
05.09	Ryman P	Hitchin Town	271	0 - 2	
09.09	Ryman P	HARROW BOROUGH	194	1 - 1	Risley 54
12.09	Lge Cup 1	NORTHWOOD	88	0 - 4	
16.09	Ryman P	Heybridge Swifts	208	0 - 4	
19.09	Ryman P	Enfield	117	1 - 2	Blaney 65
23.09	Ryman P	MAIDENHEAD UNITED	195	2 - 1	Blaney 36, Nesling 90
30.09	FA Cup Q2	Chelmsford City	674	1 - 1	Hazle 4
03.10	FA Cup Q2 R	CHELMSFORD CITY	331	2 - 1	Fiddes 69, Hayzelden 75
07.10	Ryman P	Aldershot Town	1750	0 - 6	
14.10	FA Cup Q3	Mildenhall Town	343	2 - 0	Critoph 67[og], O'Sullivan 89
21.10	Ryman P	Basingstoke Town	428	0 - 1	
28.10	FA Cup Q4	Northwood	467	1 - 1	Dickinson 90
31.10	FA Cup Q4 R	NORTHWOOD	313	1 - 0	O'Sullivan 48
04.11	FA Trophy 1	ASHFORD TOWN	209	3 - 4	Hazle 37, Wright 41, Wallace 45
11.11	Ryman P	Hampton & Richmond Borough	205	0 - 0	
18.11	FA Cup 1	Reading	5643	0 - 4	
28.11	Essex SC 3	LEYTON PENNANT	51	4 - 2	Risley, Wright, Blaney, A N Other
05.12	FMC 2	BISHOP'S STORTFORD	86	4 - 2	Dickinson, Gentle, Hayzelden, Wallace
09.12	Ryman P	Billericay Town	475	1 - 3	D Gentle 34
16.12	Ryman P	SLOUGH TOWN	193	1 - 0	Gentle 8
23.12	Ryman P	Hendon	210	1 - 1	Hazelden 90
26.12	Ryman P	PURFLEET	289	1 - 1	Gentle 64
06.01	Essex SC 4	GREAT WAKERING ROVERS	w.o for Great Wakering		
06.01	Ryman P	HAMPTON & RICHMOND BOR.	221	1 - 3	Hazleden 75
13.01	Ryman P	CHESHAM UNITED	199	0 - 2	
20.01	Ryman P	Dulwich Hamlet	412	2 - 1	Douglas 47 52
03.02	Ryman P	Farnborough Town	736	0 - 3	
10.02	Ryman P	HITCHIN TOWN	211	2 - 1	Cooper 15, Southgate 43
13.02	Ryman P	CARSHALTON ATHLETIC	208	3 - 1	Edwards 2, Sogbe 22, Southgate 89
17.02	Ryman P	Harrow Borough	173	2 - 1	Douglas 1, Cooper 18
20.02	Ryman P	CROYDON	182	2 - 2	Southgate 52[p], OG 87
01.03	FMC 3	Barton Rovers	45	0 - 2	
06.03	Ryman P	Canvey Island	410	0 - 1	
10.03	Ryman P	ENFIELD	312	2 - 0	Abraham 44, Southgate 58[p]
20.03	Ryman P	CANVEY ISLAND	267	0 - 3	
24.03	Ryman P	Carshalton Athletic	289	0 - 1	
27.03	Ryman P	Sutton United	390	3 - 2	Douglas 40, McCloud 55, Baker 76[og]
31.03	Ryman P	BASINGSTOKE TOWN	224	0 - 0	
03.04	Ryman P	Gravesend & Northfleet	363	1 - 0	Southgate 57
07.04	Ryman P	Croydon	107	0 - 1	
12.04	Ryman P	Maidenhead United	138	2 - 3	Cooper 6, Foddis 90
14.04	Ryman P	HENDON	207	3 - 2	Douglas 1 76, Manuel 45
16.04	Ryman P	Purfleet	302	1 - 3	O'Sullivan 44
21.04	Ryman P	GRAVESEND & NORTHFLEET	295	2 - 1	Douglas 23, Brazier 79
24.04	Ryman P	HEYBRIDGE SWIFTS	188	1 - 0	Fiddes 76
28.04	Ryman P	St Albans City	292	2 - 1	Southgate 29, Douglas 52
01.05	Ryman P	ST ALBANS CITY	169	6 - 0	Manuel 15 44, Douglas 40 53, Fiddes 51, Cooper 85
03.05	Ryman P	ALDERSHOT TOWN	316	1 - 1	Douglas 85
05.05	Ryman P	BILLERICAY TOWN	386	2 - 3	Manuel 75[p], McCloud 85

PLAYING SQUAD

GOALKEEPERS: Dean Mahoney (Braintree), Paul Newell (Billericay)

DEFENDERS: Steve Robinson (Edgware), Richard Halls (Barking), Alan Keeper (Braintree), Kevin Ramsay (Barking), Andy Sussex (Barking)

MIDFIELDERS: Dave Rainford (Slough), Glenn Southgate (Barking), Alex Fiddes (Heybridge), John O'Sullivan (Braintree), Sam Cooper (Canvey Is)

FORWARDS: Mervin Abraham (Dulwich Hamlet), Dean Allen (Ford Utd), Craig Edwards (Southend), Andy Douglas (Arsenal), Nathan Thomas (Barking)

HAMPTON & RICHMOND BOROUGH

CLUB OFFICIALS

Chairman: Victor Searle **Pres:** AlanSimpson
Vice Chairman: Michael Holland
Press Officer: Les Rance
Secretary: Adrian Mann,
30 Burniston Court, Manor Rd, Wallington,
Surrey SM6 0AD (0208 773 0858)
Email:anthony@nash6.freeserve.co.uk

FOOTBALL MANAGEMENT TEAM

Manager: Steve Cordery
Assistant Manager: Tony Coombe
Coach: Craig Maskell
Physio: Gareth Workman

FACT FILE

Formed: 1921
Nickname: Beavers/Borough
Sponsors: M.M Cox.Properties Ltd.
Colours: Red & blue/white/blue
Change Colours: White/blue/white
Midweek Matchday: Tuesday

2000-01

Captain: Jason Shaw
Top scorer: Craig Maskell 27
P.o.Y.: Craig Maskell

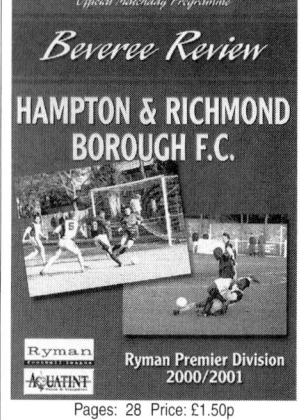

Official Matchday Programme
Beveree Review
HAMPTON & RICHMOND BOROUGH F.C.
Ryman
AQUATINT
Ryman Premier Division 2000/2001

Pages: 28 Price: £1.50p
Editor: Tony Nash

Local Press: Middx Chronicle, Surrey Comet, Richmond & Twickenham Times, The Informer
Website: http://www.hamptonfc.co.uk

GROUND: Beveree Stadium, Beaver Close, off Station Rd, Hampton TW12 2BX
Tel: Office 020 8979 2456(matchdays only) Club: 020 8941 4936 Boardroom: 020 8941 2838
Directions: A3 out of London, fork left (signed Staines/Esher/Sandown Pk) onto A243, A309 Staines exit to Hampton Ct at `Scilly Isles' r'bout, left at r'bout after Hampton Court Bridge onto A308, after 1 mile right into Church St (A311), left after White Hart after 200yds into High St, Station Rd on right just before junction with A308
Capacity: 3,000 Seats: 300 Cover: 800 Floodlights: Yes
Clubhouse: (020 8979 2456). Lounge bar and hall, open on matchdays and training nights. Hall available for hire. Steward: Steve Penny
Club Shop: Sells various souvenirs & prog. Contact: David Rees

PREVIOUS **Leagues:** Kingston & District 21-33; South West Middx 33-59; Surrey Snr 59-64; Spartan 64-71; Athenian 71-73
Grounds: Hatherop Rec (until 1959)

CLUB RECORDS **Win:** 11-1 v Eastbourne Utd, Isthmian Lge Div 2 (S), 90-91 **Defeat:** 0-13 v Hounslow Town, Middlesex Senior Cup 62-63
Goalscorer: Peter Allen (176) 1964-73 **Appearances:** Tim Hollands (700) 1977-95
Fees - Paid: £3,000 for Matt Flitter (Chesham United) June 2000
Fees - Received: £40,000 for Leroy Griffiths from Q.P.R.May 2001

BEST SEASON **FA Cup:** 1st Rd Proper 00-01 (1-2 v Barnet) **FA Amateur Cup:** 1st Rd Prop 73-74 (2-4 v Leytonstone)
FA Trophy: 1st Rd Prop 83-84 (0-2 v Maidstone Utd)
FA Vase: 3rd Rd 91-92 (0-1 v Newport IOW), 95-96 (0-1 v Colllier Row)

HONOURS: London Snr Cup(2) 86-88; Spartan Lg(4) 64-67 69-70, (R-up 67-68), Lg Cup(4) 64-68 (R-up 2); Surrey Snr Lg 63-64 (Lg Cup R-up 60-61); Middx Charity Cup 69-70 95-96 97-98,98-99 (R-up 68-69 71-72 89-90 94-95); Middx Snr Cup R-up 71-72 76-77 95-96; Athenian Lg Div 2 R-up 72-73; Southern Comb. Cup 68-69 71-72 76-77 81-82 83-84 85-86 96-97 (R-up 77-78 79-80 97-98); Isthmian Lge promotion from Div 1 97-98, Div 2 95-96, Div 3 91-92

Players progressing: Andy Rogers (Southampton), Dwight Marshall (Plymouth), Paul Rogers (Sheffield Utd via Sutton Utd), Derek Bryan Brentford 97), Darren Powell (Brentford 98), Julian Charles (Brentford 99.), Leroy Griffiths (Q.P.R., 01)

Back row, left to right: Steve Cordery (Manager),Gareth Workman (Physio), Craig Maskell (Player-Coach), Martin Carter, Matt Flitter, Dean Green, Tony Houghton, Nick Burton, Peter Barnsby, Warren Williams, Richard Taylor, Tony Coombe (Assistant Manager),and Malcolm Taylor (Assistant Coach) Front Row: Fiston Manuella, Ronnie Givvan, Gary Holloway, Eric Talbot, Jason Shaw (Captain), Dudley Gardner, Jamie Morris, Luke Dowling, Ryan Hillary, and Marc Coates. Mascot Peter Nash and reclining,Leroy Griffiths (now Queens Park Rangers)

Date	Comp.	Opponents	Att.	Score	Goalscorers
19.08	Ryman P	BILLERICAY TOWN	254	1 - 2	Barnsby 67
22.08	Ryman P	Chesham United	303	0 - 1	
26.08	Ryman P	St Albans City	457	0 - 5	
28.08	Ryman P	CROYDON	178	3 - 0	Maskell 25, Griffiths 86, Williams 89
02.09	Ryman P	HARROW BOROUGH	258	3 - 3	Carter 60 76, Maskell 77
05.09	Ryman P	Sutton United	564	2 - 2	Williams 38, Simpson 86
06.09	S Comb Cup 1	CHESSINGTON & HOOK UNITED	n.k	3 - 1	
09.09	Ryman P	HITCHIN TOWN	271	2 - 4	Maskell 3, Griffiths 90
12.09	Lge Cup 1	Leyton Pennant	56	4 - 0	Maskell 20 69, Leenders 30, Barnes 46[og]
16.09	Ryman P	Slough Town	469	1 - 1	Simpson 41
19.09	Ryman P	DULWICH HAMLET	157	4 - 0	Maskell 24[p] 33[p] 61[p], Williams 56
23.09	Ryman P	Gravesend & Northfleet	412	4 - 3	Maskell 7, Griffiths 57, Williams 65 75
30.09	FA Cup Q2	Windsor & Eton	165	3 - 0	Maskell 59, Green 70 73
07.10	Ryman P	Enfield	129	2 - 2	Green 6, Maskell 38
10.10	Ryman P	ALDERSHOT TOWN	838	1 - 0	Williams 80
14.10	FA Cup Q3	Merthyr Tydfil	569	3 - 0	Green 10, Griffith 21 85
21.10	Ryman P	Purfleet	173	2 - 2	Barnsby 12, Maskell 53
24.10	FMC 1	Worthing	139	0 - 2	
28.10	FA Cup Q4	WORCESTER CITY	619	5 - 0	Flitter 2, Holloway 54 86, Griffith 80, Williams 89
04.11	FA Trophy 1	MAIDENHEAD UNITED	278	1 - 4	Simpson 27
08.11	Lge Cup 2	BOGNOR REGIS TOWN	87	3 - 2	Leenders 27 50, Maskell 75
11.11	Ryman P	GRAYS ATHLETIC	205	0 - 0	
18.11	FA Cup 1	Barnet	2340	1 - 2	Maskell 21
28.11	Ryman P	CARSHALTON ATHLETIC	184	4 - 2	Maskell 51, Griffith 63, Green 69, Asamoah 89
02.12	Ryman P	Heybridge Swifts	214	2 - 3	Wood 30, Asamoah 88
09.12	Ryman P	FARNBOROUGH TOWN	609	1 - 0	Holloway 80
16.12	Ryman P	Harrow Borough	217	5 - 4	Flitter 17, Griffiths 37 47 75[p] 85
19.12	Lge Cup 3	Carshalton Athletic	101	3 - 0	OG, Maskell, Asamoah
23.12	Ryman P	MAIDENHEAD UNITED	274	1 - 0	Green 84
26.12	Ryman P	Basingstoke Town	497	0 - 1	
02.01	Ryman P	CHESHAM UNITED	292	3 - 1	Green 49, Griffiths 72, Holloway 89
06.01	Ryman P	Grays Athletic	221	3 - 1	Griffiths 15 61, Williams 79
09.01	Middx SC 1	STAINES TOWN	180	2 - 3	Maskell, Williams
13.01	Ryman P	BASINGSTOKE TOWN	433	3 - 2	Maskell 2 68, Williams 28
16.01	Ryman P	Canvey Island	333	0 - 1	
27.01	Ryman P	SLOUGH TOWN	458	2 - 0	Holloway 2, Williams 62
10.02	Ryman P	SUTTON UNITED	550	3 - 1	Barnsby 28, Williams 70 89
14.02	Lge Cup QF	St Albans City	120	3 - 3	
17.02	Ryman P	Hitchin Town	331	0 - 2	
20.02	Ryman P	HENDON	201	0 - 2	
24.02	Ryman P	Aldershot Town	1753	2 - 2	Green 9, Asamoah 90
27.02	Lge Cup QF R	ST ALBANS CITY	157	3 - 0	Carter, Williams, Holloway
03.03	Ryman P	ENFIELD	278	4 - 0	Maskell 27 50, Griffiths 40, Williams 76
17.03	Ryman P	GRAVESEND & NORTHFLEET	485	1 - 0	Holloway 30
20.03	Ryman P	ST ALBANS CITY	151	1 - 2	Griffiths 55
26.03	Ryman P	Croydon	131	1 - 1	Griffiths 15
31.03	Ryman P	PURFLEET	367	2 - 0	Griffiths 46, Maskell 87
03.04	Ryman P	Billericay Town	278	1 - 3	Woolsey 74[og]
10.04	Ryman P	Dulwich Hamlet	133	1 - 1	Maskell 43
12.04	Lge Cup SF(1)	CROYDON	240	2 - 3	Maskell, Williams
14.04	Ryman P	Maidenhead United	248	0 - 0	
16.04	Ryman P	Hendon	201	0 - 2	
21.04	Ryman P	Carshalton Athletic	325	3 - 0	Williams 17, Holloway 19, Green 80
28.04	Ryman P	HEYBRIDGE SWIFTS	250	2 - 1	Green 35, Griffiths 43
30.04	Lge Cup SF(2)	Croydon	143	2 - 3	Maskell 39[p], Griffiths 75
02.05	Ryman P	CANVEY ISLAND	166	2 - 2	Gardner 6, Griffiths 45
05.05	Ryman P	Farnborough Town	1097	1 - 1	Flitter 57

PLAYING SQUAD

GOALKEEPERS: Stuart Mackenzie (Farnborough)

DEFENDERS: Anthony Howard (Fulham), Nick Burton (Aldershot), Fiston Manuella (Brentford), Matt Flitter (Chesham Utd), Tom Upsher (Fulham), Tony Houghton (Dulwich Hamlet)

MIDFIELDERS: Gary Holloway (Walton & Hersham), Richard O'Connor (Leatherhead), Martin Carter (Chertsey), Dudley Gardner (Slough)

FORWARDS: Craig Maskell (Leyton Orient), Dean Green (Leyton Pennant), Danny Alleyne (Yeading), Warren Williams (Hanwell T), Marc Coates (Walton & Hersham)

HARROW BOROUGH

CLUB OFFICIALS

Chairman: Jim Ripley **President:** Jim Rogers
Secretary: Peter Rogers,
21 Ludlow Close, South Harrow, Middx HA2 8SR (0208 248 8003H)(0208 4230157W)
Commercial Manager:
Jim Hayes c/o the club
Press Officer: Paul Carter (07971 848385)

FOOTBALL MANAGEMENT TEAM

Manager: Edwin Stein
Asst Manager: David Howell
Physio: Chas E Cox

FACT FILE

Formed: 1933
Nickname: The Boro
Sponsors: Sodexho Land Technology
Colours: Red, white trim/white/red, white hoops
Change cols: White/navy blue trim/navy/navy
Midweek matchday: Tuesday

2000-01

Captain: Mark Cooper/Pat Gavin
P.o.Y.: Pat Gavin
Top Scorer: Pat Gavin 19

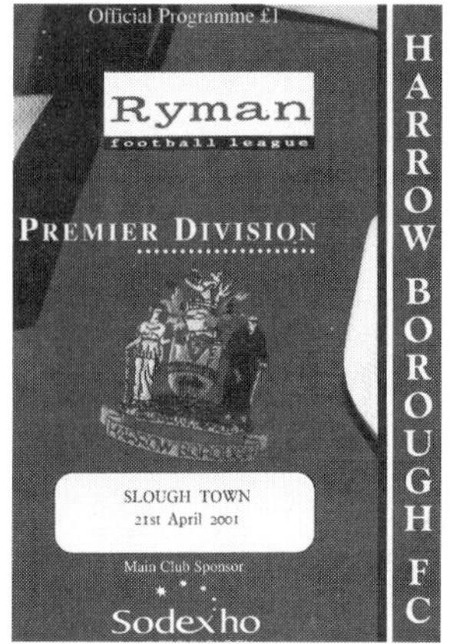

Official Programme £1
Ryman
football league
PREMIER DIVISION
SLOUGH TOWN
21st April 2001
Main Club Sponsor
Sodexho
HARROW BOROUGH FC

Pages: 32 Price: £1.00p
Editor: Paul Carter (07971 848385)

Local Press: Harrow Observer

GROUND: Earlsmead, Carlyon Avenue, South Harrow, Middx HA2 8SS Tel: 0208 422 5989 or 5221. Website: www.harrowboro.com Email: paul@harrowboro.com
Directions: Underground to Northolt (Central Line) then 140 bus to Northolt Park BR, 282 bus, to Eastcote Arms or to South Harrow (Piccadilly Line) then 114 or H10 to Kings Rd.Junction. By road leave A40 at Macdonalds roundabout towards Northolt station (A312 north), left at lights, right at next island (Eastcote Arms pub), ground 5th turning on right.
Capacity: 3,070 Cover: 1,000 Seats: 350 Floodlights: Yes
Clubhouse: Open daily, normal pub hours. Four bars, games room, equipped for all social events. Hot and coldfood available, buffets by prior request
Club Shop: Sells progs, scarves, badges, T-shirts, etc. Contact Tony Trowbridge c/o club

PREVIOUS **Leagues:** Harrow & Dist 33-4; Spartan 34-40, 45-58; W Middx Comb 40-1; Middx Sen41-45; Delphian 58-63; Athenian 63-75;
Names: Roxonian 1933-8; Harrow Town 38-66 **Ground:** Northolt Road 33-4

CLUB RECORDS **Attendance:** 3,000 v Wealdstone, F.A. Cup 1st Qualifying Round 1946 Fee Received: £16,000 for Lee Endersby (Enfield 97)
Scorer: Dave Pearce, 153 **Appearances:** Steve Emmanuel 522 (1st team only), Les Currell 582, Colin Payne 557
Fee Paid: Unspecified to Dagenham for George Duck & Steve Jones, Summer 81
Win: 13-0 v Handley Page (A), Middlesex Snr Lg 18/10/41. **Defeat:** 0-8 5 times: Wood Green T. (A) Middx Lge 40, Met Police (A) Spartan Lg 52, Briggs Spts (A) Spartan Lg 53, Hertford T. (A) Spartan Lge 53, Hendon (A) Middx Snr Cup 65

BEST SEASON **FA Trophy:** Semi final 82-83 **FA Cup:** 2nd Rd 83-84 (1-3 at home to Newport Co)

HONOURS: Isthmian Lg 83-84 (Div 1 R-up 78-79); Athenian Lg Div 2 R-up 63-64; Spartan Lg R-up 57-58 (Div 2 West 38-39 (R-up 37-38); Middx Senior Cup 82-83 92-93; Harrow & Dist. Lg Div 1 R-up 33-34; Middx Charity Cup 79-80 92-93 (R-up 78-79); Middx Intermediate Cup 55-56,R-up 75-76, Middx Premier Cup 81-82,R-up 82-83, Harrow Sen Cup 95 97, London Interm'te C 78-79

Players progressing: D.Russell (Arsenal), M.Lucas (L.Orient), R.Shaw (Torquay U), T.Eden (Raith R), T. Carpenter (Watford), M Bottoms (QPR 60), C Hutchings (Chelsea 80), R Holland (Crewe 85), J Kerr (Portsmouth 87), D Howell, A Pape & E Stein, (Barnet), D .Byrne (Gillingham), R.Rosario (Norwich), D Kemp (Crystal Palace), M Doherty (Reading), D Bassett (Wimbledon), G Borthwick (Bournemouth), B.Shaw, Torquay U),T.Evans (Scunthorpe U), L.Charles (Q.P.R.), P.Barrowcliff (Brentford).

L-R Back Row: David Howell (1st team coach), Paul Scott, Dwayne Lewis, Joe Lyons, Lee Broughton, David Hook, Marc Walsh, Pat Gavin, Carl Levene, Leon Woodruffe, Edwin Stein (manager), Chas Cox (physio).
Front Row: Emond Protain, Christian Hyslop, John Hurlock, Jon Barrie Bates, Fabio Valenti, Andy Rose. **Photo:** Paul Carter

Date	Comp.	Opponents	Att.	Score	Goalscorers
19.08	Ryman P	Maidenhead United	279	1 - 4	Gavin 44
22.08	Ryman P	ALDERSHOT TOWN	825	1 - 1	Xavier 41[p]
26.08	Ryman P	BASINGSTOKE TOWN	167	1 - 4	Gavin 48
28.08	Ryman P	Canvey Island	541	0 - 3	
02.09	Ryman P	Hampton & Richmond Borough	258	3 - 3	Gavin 20, Xavier 27 44
05.09	Ryman P	ENFIELD	240	2 - 1	Oktay 2, Gavin 69
09.09	Ryman P	Grays Athletic	194	1 - 1	Gavin 22
12.09	Lge Cup 1	CROYDON	93	2 - 3	McCormack 57 79
16.09	Ryman P	CARSHALTON ATHLETIC	208	2 - 2	Xavier 20, Lund 90
19.09	Ryman P	CHESHAM UNITED	144	3 - 2	Xavier 36 65 90[p]
23.09	Ryman P	Dulwich Hamlet	287	1 - 0	McCormack 4
30.09	FA Cup Q2	TRING TOWN	190	4 - 0	Lund 52, Gavin 58, Xavier 59
07.10	Ryman P	BILLERICAY TOWN	193	4 - 2	Xavier 30, Moore 43[og], Hurlock 79, Gavin 90
14.10	FA Cup Q3	STAFFORD TOWN	184	0 - 0	
18.10	FA Cup Q3 R	Stafford Town	321	3 - 1	Walters 50[og], Hurlock 54[p], Roberts 88
21.10	Ryman P	HEYBRIDGE SWIFTS	216	1 - 1	Hurlock 65
24.10	FMC 1	ROMFORD	104	1 - 2	Gavin
28.10	FA Cup Q4	ENFIELD	504	2 - 1	Oktay 75, Lund 93
11.11	Ryman P	St Albans City	486	0 - 1	
14.11	FA Trophy 1	Witney Town	75	3 - 2	Gavin 37 41 90
18.11	FA Cup 1	Wycombe Wanderers	2681	0 - 3	
28.11	Ryman P	Slough Town	237	2 - 1	Xavier 8 19
02.12	FA Trophy 2	DORCHESTER TOWN	256	3 - 0	Payne 40, Xavier 68, Hurlock 71
16.12	Ryman P	HAMPTON & RICHMOND BOR.	217	4 - 5	Newby 40, Oktay 52, Duru 80 86
23.12	Ryman P	Croydon	121	0 - 2	
26.12	Ryman P	HENDON	289	1 - 4	Payne 55
06.01	Ryman P	ST ALBANS CITY	305	2 - 2	Hurlock 11[p], Rose 60
13.01	FA Trophy 3	Evesham United	154	2 - 4	Petersen 70, Xavier 80[p]
16.01	Ryman P	Gravesend & Northfleet	363	1 - 2	Rose 48
27.01	Ryman P	Enfield	211	2 - 1	Hurlock 27[p], Richardson 68
30.01	Middx SC 2	RUISLIP MANOR	130	7 - 0	Hurlock, Cooper, Roberts, Richardson, Heyrettin, Barnes
02.02	Ryman P	Purfleet	186	2 - 4	Petersen 53, Roberts 87
10.02	Ryman P	Carshalton Athletic	281	1 - 1	Cooper 35
13.02	Middx SC QF	YEADING	160	6 - 1	Gavin 30, Cooper 92, Richardson 94 110 120, Newby 115
17.02	Ryman P	GRAYS ATHLETIC	173	1 - 2	Gavin 3
20.02	Ryman P	Farnborough Town	534	1 - 3	Hurlock 9
24.02	Ryman P	GRAVESEND & NORTHFLEET	247	0 - 6	
27.02	Ryman P	HITCHIN TOWN	149	1 - 4	Newby 76
03.03	Ryman P	Billericay Town	338	1 - 1	Lewis 84
06.03	Ryman P	Aldershot Town	1226	0 - 3	
10.03	Ryman P	Chesham United	402	1 - 1	Hurlock 8
13.03	Ryman P	MAIDENHEAD UNITED	207	1 - 2	Rose 80
20.03	Ryman P	SUTTON UNITED	180	2 - 1	Bates 31, Valenti 57
24.03	Ryman P	FARNBOROUGH TOWN	376	2 - 3	Rose 65, Scott 73
27.03	Middx SC SF	Hayes	0	2 - 1	Gavin 44, Hurlock 94
31.03	Ryman P	Heybridge Swifts	219	2 - 4	Woodrowse 4, Levene 40
03.04	Ryman P	CANVEY ISLAND	215	0 - 2	
07.04	Ryman P	Sutton United	466	3 - 3	Howell 4, Woodruffe 37, Gavin 82
14.04	Ryman P	CROYDON	165	0 - 1	
16.04	Middx SC F	Uxbridge	438	0 - 3	
19.04	Ryman P	DULWICH HAMLET	128	2 - 1	Scott 70 73
21.04	Ryman P	SLOUGH TOWN	386	1 - 0	Woodruffe 39
28.04	Ryman P	Hitchin Town	286	6 - 3	Valenti 27 50 90, Cooper 45, Gavin 52, Woodruff 80
01.05	Ryman P	Basingstoke Town	268	2 - 2	Gavin 61 63
05.05	Ryman P	PURFLEET	248	1 - 2	Hyslop 62

Unplayed Ryman P Hendon

PLAYING SQUAD

GOALKEEPERS: Keita Karamoko (Wembley)

DEFENDERS: Christian Hyslop (Baldock), Aiden O'Brien (Gravesend), Richard Clarke (Scunthorpe), Wayne Walters (W embley), Darren Bloor (Trafford)

MIDFIELDERS: John Hurlock (Chesham Utd), Fabio Valenti (Edgware), Carlton Mitchell (Wembley), Leon Woodruffe (Yeading)

FORWARDS: Mark Xavier (Dulwich Hamlet), Pat Gavin (Farnborough), Spencer Knight (St.Albans)

HENDON

CLUB OFFICIALS

Chairman: **Ivor Arbiter**

Secretary: **Graham Etchell,** c/o Hendon FC.
Tel: 020 8201 9494(Club)
Press Officer: Club Secretary

Marketingl Manager: **T.B.A.**
PressOfficer**: David Ballheimer**

FOOTBALL MANAGEMENT TEAM

Manager: Dave Anderson
Ass.Man: John Turner
Player/Coach: Warren Kelly Physio: T.B.A.

FACT FILE

Formed: 1908 Nickname: Dons or Greens
Sponsors: UK Packaging
Colours: Green& white stripes/black/black
Change Colours: Tangerine/Royal /royal
Midweek matchday: Tuesday
Reserve League: Suburban (Premier)
Club Line: 09066 555 836
Club Website: www.hendonfc.net

2000-01

Captain: Gary Fitzgerald
P.o.Y & Top Scorer: Dale Binns

Pages: 40 Price: £1.50p
Editor: Secretary
Local Press: Hendon Times, Willesden & Brent Chronicle, Hampstead & Highgate Express
Local Radio: Capital, GLR, LBC

GROUND: Claremont Road, Cricklewood, London NW2 1AE.
Tel: 020 8201 9494 Fax: 020 8905 5966

Directions: From Brent Cross station (Northern Line) to the east take first left after flyover on North Circular - Claremont Rd is then left at 3rd mini-r'bout. Buses 102, 210, 226 and C11 pass ground

Capacity: 3,029 Cover: 601 Seats: 329 Floodlights: Yes

Clubhouse: (contact Sue Damary 020 8455 9185). Two banqueting suites,conference centre, room hire, restaurant & bars open licensing hours 7 days aweek. Hot & cold food, pool, darts, bingo, members club, satelite TV,entertainments

Club Shop: Contact Derek Furmedge, 020 8459 2042 (H) Sells football souvenirs

PREVIOUS
Leagues: Finchley & Dist. 08-11, Middx 10-11, London 11-14, Athenian 14-63.
Names: Christ Church Hampstead to 08, Hampstead Town to 26, Hampstead to 33,Golders Green to 46
Grounds: Kensal Rise 08-12; Avenue Ground, Cricklewood Lane 12-26

CLUB RECORDS
Attendance: 9,000 v Northampton, FA Cup 1st Rd 1952
Goalscorer: Freddie Evans 176 (1929-35) **Appearances:** Bill Fisher 787 (1940-
Defeat: 2-11 v Walthamstow Ave. (A), Athenian Lge 9/11/35 **Win:** 13-1 v Wingate (H), Middx Senior Cup 2/2/57
Fee Paid: Paul Whitmarsh (undisclosed) **Fee Received:** £30,000 for Iain Dowie (Luton)

BEST SEASON
F.A. Cup: First Rd 20 times, Second Rd 5 times **F.A.Trophy:** 5th Rd 98-99

HONOURS: European Am Champions 72-3; Isthmian Lg 64-5 72-3 (R-up 63-4 65-6 73-4) Lg Cup 76-7 (R-up 86-7), Full Members Cup 94-5 97-8 98-99, Premier Inter-Lge Cup R-up 86-7; Middx Lge 12-3 13-4; Athenian Lg 52-3 55-6 60-1 (R-up 28-9 32-3 47-8 48-9 51-2); London Lg Div 1 R-up 12-13 (Amtr Div 13-4); Finchley & Dist. Lg 10-1; London Snr Cup 63-4 68-9 (R-up 35-6 50-1 54-5 58-9 71-2); Middx Snr Cup (12) (R-up 83-4), Middx Interm 64-5 66-7 72-3, Middx Charity Cup(14); London IntermCup (4) (R-up (2); Suburban Lg 92-3 (R-up 84-5 97-8)

Players progressing: Peter Shearing (WHU 60), Iain Dowie (Luton 88), PeterAnderson (Luton), Jeff Harris (Orient), Phil Gridelet (Barnsley 90), GerrySoloman (Leyton O 91), Junior Hunter & Micah Hyde (both Cambridge 94-95),Simon Clark (Peterboro' 94-95),Junior Lewis(Gillingham 99-00)

L-R Back Row: Jason Soloman, Simon Clarke, Bontcho Guentchev, Paul Johnson, Paul Towler, Warren Kelly, Gary McCann, Gary Fitzgerald, Ross Pickett, Matthew Bartholomew, Jon Daly, David Adekola, Marvyn Watson.
Front: Fernanda Chiappinelli (asst. physio), David Haule, Dale Binns, Gary Anderson (physio), Dave Anderson (coach), Frank Murphy (manager), Curtis Warmington (player/coach), Paul Adolphe, Iain Duncan, John Johnson (coach).

Date	Comp.	Opponents	Att.	Score	Goalscorers
19.08	Ryman P	CROYDON	304	4 - 0	Clarke 2, Pickett 35, Adolphe 40, Watson 84
22.08	Ryman P	Heybridge Swifts	204	2 - 2	Daly 70, Kelly 85[p]
26.08	Ryman P	Hitchin Town	363	3 - 3	Kelly 62[p] 83[p], Binns 70
28.08	Ryman P	SUTTON UNITED	370	0 - 1	
02.09	Ryman P	CHESHAM UNITED	328	2 - 2	Pickett 48, Daly 85
05.09	Ryman P	St Albans City	522	3 - 1	Guentchev 6, Clarke 53, Haule 57
09.09	Ryman P	SLOUGH TOWN	347	2 - 1	Binns 40, Haule 66
12.09	Lge Cup 1	Arlesey Town	196	4 - 3	Guentchev 10, Binns 14 58, Adekola 39,
16.09	Ryman P	Billericay Town	510	0 - 2	
18.09	Ryman P	GRAVESEND & NORTHFLEET	207	1 - 2	Adekola 50
23.09	Ryman P	Aldershot Town	2241	1 - 1	Haule 33
30.09	FA Cup Q2	ST MARGARETSBURY	236	3 - 2	Clarke 18, Pickett 37 79
06.10	Ryman P	MAIDENHEAD UNITED	228	2 - 1	Haule 27, Fitzgerald 60
14.10	FA Cup Q3	FORD UNITED	242	2 - 1	Adekola 12 72
25.10	FMC 1	Harlow Town	93	2 - 0	Watson, OG
04.11	FA Trophy 1	TONBRIDGE ANGELS	195	2 - 0	Duncan 10, Clout 42[og]
11.11	Ryman P	CANVEY ISLAND	246	2 - 1	Adekola 6, Haule 85
13.11	FA Cup Q4	DAGENHAM & REDBRIDGE	519	1 - 3	Pickett 26
18.11	Ryman P	Carshalton Athletic	265	2 - 1	Pickett 53, Binns 82
11.12	FA Trophy 2	WORCESTER CITY	122	1 - 1	Binns 68 St Albans City
16.12	Ryman P	Chesham United	378	1 - 4	Pickett 47
18.12	FA Trophy 2 R	Worcester City	610	3 - 2	Heeley 47[og], Binns 52, Pickett 90
23.12	Ryman P	GRAYS ATHLETIC	210	1 - 1	Haule 65
26.12	Ryman P	Harrow Borough	289	4 - 1	Adekola 27 45, Adolphe 29, Haule 65
30.12	FMC 2	Heybridge Swifts	125	5 - 6	Obiji 13 24, Johnson 20, Bridges 70[og], Edwards 93
06.01	Ryman P	Canvey Island	411	2 - 3	Edwards 63, Binns 83
13.01	FA Trophy 3	TIVERTON TOWN	346	1 - 2	Adekola 17
15.01	Middx SC 2	WEMBLEY	84	1 - 1	Solomon 28
29.01	Lge Cup 2	BRAINTREE TOWN	86	3 - 2	Adekola 9 59, Daly 120
15.02	Middx SC 2 R	Wembley	82	2 - 0	Haule 13, Adekola 45
17.02	Ryman P	Slough Town	433	0 - 1	
20.02	Ryman P	Hampton & Richmond Borough	201	2 - 0	Binns 67 78
22.02	Lge Cup 3	CHESHAM UNITED	99	2 - 3	Binns 45 57
24.02	Ryman P	PURFLEET	203	1 - 2	Binns 22
27.02	Ryman P	Enfield	177	2 - 0	Watson 60, Street 83
01.03	Middx SC QF	Uxbridge	73	0 - 2	
03.03	Ryman P	Maidenhead United	187	2 - 1	Kelly 49[p], Binns 57
05.03	Ryman P	BASINGSTOKE TOWN	161	2 - 3	Binns 63, Pickett 90
19.03	Ryman P	Purfleet	162	0 - 0	
31.03	Ryman P	Farnborough Town	684	0 - 2	
02.04	Ryman P	HEYBRIDGE SWIFTS	147	1 - 4	Pickett 28[p]
09.04	Ryman P	FARNBOROUGH TOWN	303	0 - 2	
11.04	Ryman P	HITCHIN TOWN	157	4 - 0	Pickett 48 62, Haule 73, Adekola 90
14.04	Ryman P	Grays Athletic	207	2 - 3	Haule 49, Daly 75
16.04	Ryman P	HAMPTON & RICHMOND BOR.	201	2 - 0	Guentchev 30, Binns 66
18.04	Ryman P	ST ALBANS CITY	183	0 - 1	
19.04	Ryman P	CARSHALTON ATHLETIC	135	1 - 0	Guentchev 2
21.04	Ryman P	Basingstoke Town	353	0 - 5	
23.04	Ryman P	Croydon	121	0 - 2	
25.04	Ryman P	DULWICH HAMLET	138	4 - 0	Adekola 1 63, Guentchev 39, Binns 58
26.04	Ryman P	BILLERICAY TOWN	123	0 - 2	
28.04	Ryman P	ENFIELD	306	3 - 0	Adolphe 56, Solomon 62, Guentchev 77
03.05	Ryman P	Gravesend & Northfleet	227	1 - 2	Solomon 86
04.05	Ryman P	ALDERSHOT TOWN	273	0 - 5	
05.05	Ryman P	Dulwich Hamlet	325	3 - 0	Streete 37, Guentchev 42, Binns 83
Unplayed	Ryman P	HARROW BOROUGH			
Unplayed	Ryman P	Sutton United			

PLAYING SQUAD

GOALKEEPERS: David Hook (Harrow), Gary McCann (Dulwich Hamlet)

DEFENDERS: Iain Duncan (Aylesbury), Pat Sappleton (Youth), Rene Street (Northwood), Mark Turner (Yeading), Simon Clarke (Kettering), Warren Kelly (St.Albans), Paul Towler (Met.Police), Chris Sparks (Yeading), Gary Fitzgerald (Enfield)

MIDFIELDERS: Dale Binns (Youth), Jon-Barrie Bates (Harrow), Paul Yates (Brook House), Lee O'Donnell (Woking), Michael Woolmer (Ruislip Manor), Mervyn Watson (Youth)

FORWARDS: Davis Haule (Wembley), Nathan Edwards (Youth), Ricci Crace (Ware), Ross Pickett (Walton & Hersham), Eugene Ofari (Liberty Professionals)

HEYBRIDGE SWIFTS

CLUB OFFICIALS

Chairman: Mike Springett

President: T.B.A.

Vice Chairman: Michael Gibson

Secretary: Dennis Fenn
31 Saxon Way, Maldon, Essex CM9 7JN Tel: 01621 854798

Match Secretary: Terry Stowers
74 Wood Road, Heybridge, Maldon, Essex CM9 4AW Tel: 01621 857226

Press Offr: Tony Foster (M) 07931 330756 (H) 01376 519712

Treasurer: John Russell

FACT FILE

Formed: 1880 Nickname: Swifts
Sponsors: Towermaster.
Lighting Towers Systems
Midweek matchday: Tuesday
Colours: Black & white stripes/black/black
Change colours: All Red or Amber/ white
Reserves' Lge: Essex & Herts Border Comb

2000-2001

Captain & P.o.Y: Kris Lee
Captain: Gary Waters

FOOTBALL MANAGEMENT TEAM

Manager Liam Cutbush. Asst M: Robbie Nihill
Coach: Keith Hull Physio: Glenn Churchet

HEYBRIDGE SWIFTS F.C.
2000/2001 season
Ryman Football League
flying high
Sponsored by TOWERMASTER LIGHTING TOWER SYSTEMS
HEYBRIDGE SWIFTS v ALDERSHOT TOWN
Saturday 5th May Kick-off 3.00pm
ROBERT E LEE
£1·50 OFFICIAL MATCHDAY MAGAZINE

Pages: 40 Price: £1.50
Editors: Tony Foster
Local Press: Maldon & Burnham Standard
: BBC Essex, Essex FM,Essex Chronicle,Green Un
Chelmer FM
Club Website: www.robert-e-lee.couk\swifts

GROUND: Scraley Road, Heybridge, Maldon, Essex Tel: 01621 852978

Directions: Leave Maldon on the main road to Colchester, pass through Heybridge then turn right at the sign to Tolleshunt Major (Scraley Road). The ground on the right. Six miles from nearest station (Witham). By bus via Chelmsfordand Maldon

Capacity: 3,000 Cover: 1,200 Seats: 550 Floodlights: Yes

Clubhouse: Two bars open every night. Games room, boardroom, kitchen (on matchdays)

Club Shop: Open matchdays, selling club sweaters, shirts, scarves, baseball hats, enamel badges, old programmes etc. Contact Chris Daines, c/o club.

PREVIOUS **Leagues:** Essex & Suffolk Border, North Essex, South Essex, Essex Senior 1971-84

CLUB RECORDS **Attendance:** 2,477 v Woking FA Trophy 97 and pre season v West Ham United , 3,000 +, 99-00.
Goalscorer: Julian Lamb 115 (post war), Dave Matthews 112 (Isthmian)
Appearances: Hec Askew 500+, Robbie Sach 358 (Isthmian)
Fee Paid: None **Fee Received:** £35,000, Simon Royce (Southend Utd)

BEST SEASON **FA Trophy:** Qtr finals v Woking 22/3/97 (lost 0-1)
FA Cup: First round 0-2 v Gillingham 11/11/94, 0-3 v Bournemouth 15.11.97 **League clubs defeated:** None

HONOURS: Isthmian Lg Div 1 R-up 95-96, Div 2 North 89-90; Essex Senior Lg 81-82 82-83 83-84, Lg Cup 82-83, Trophy 81-82; JT Clarke Cup 82-83; Thorn EMI National Floodlit Competition R-up 82-83; Eastern Floodlit Cup 93-94; East Anglian Cup 93-94 94-95; Essex & Suffolk Border Lge 31-32; Essex Jun Cup 31-32; North Essex Lge 46-47 Ryman League Cup 00-01

Players progressing: Simon Royce (Southend United & Charlton Athletic), Peter Cawley & Ben Lewis (Colchester Utd), Alan Hull (Leyton Orient), Jonathan Hunt (Birmingham City), Dominic Naylor (Leyton Orient), Haken Hayrettin (Doncaster Rovers), Derek Payne & Tom Meredith (Peterborough Utd), Ben Barnett, Eddie Stein & Tim Alexander (Barnet), Ashley Vickers (Peterborough United), James Pullen (18 year old ,goal-keeper to Ipswich Town) 99-00.

Back Row: Left to right: Steve Dowman (Manager), Sean Caton, Kingsley Banks, Louis Baille, Andy Potter, Hecko Hesse, Mark Cranfield, Dave Kreyling, Colin Wall, John Pollard, Gino Defoe, Matt Greenley **Front Row**: Sean Campbell, Paul Abrahams, Danny Roberts, Robbie Bate, Phil Leggatt, Ronnie Bridges, Russell Tanner, Dave Streetley. Mascots: Luke Nihill and James Love.

Date	Comp.	Opponents	Att.	Score	Goalscorers
19.08	Ryman P	Basingstoke Town	420	2 - 3	Lee 81, Payne 88
22.08	Ryman P	HENDON	204	2 - 2	Parker 20, Lee 27
26.08	Ryman P	MAIDENHEAD UNITED	173	4 - 0	Cook 10[og], Streetley 63, Gillespie 78, Lee 79
28.08	Ryman P	Carshalton Athletic	230	1 - 1	Parker 74
02.09	Ryman P	Gravesend & Northfleet	391	0 - 0	
05.09	Ryman P	CANVEY ISLAND	312	1 - 1	Payne 17
09.09	Ryman P	Enfield	148	1 - 1	Pollard 52
12.09	Lge Cup 1	Ford United	74	2 - 0	Defeo 1 66
16.09	Ryman P	GRAYS ATHLETIC	208	4 - 0	Lee 10 85, Parker 48, Miyoba 90
19.09	Ryman P	Farnborough Town	367	1 - 0	Parker 38
23.09	Ryman P	PURFLEET	254	4 - 3	Kane 69, Lee 75, Parker 90, Wiles 90
30.09	FA Cup Q2	SUDBURY	278	1 - 1	Lee 22
03.10	FA Cup Q2 R	Sudbury	409	2 - 3	Haydon 58[p], Tomlinson 61
07.10	Ryman P	SLOUGH TOWN	168	3 - 2	Lee 28, Gillespie 46, Miyoba 90
21.10	Ryman P	Harrow Borough	216	1 - 1	Lyons 48[og]
24.10	FMC 1	BILLERICAY TOWN	152	2 - 0	Potter, Rogers
28.10	Ryman P	CARSHALTON ATHLETIC	232	2 - 1	Rogers 45, Parker 90
04.11	FA Trophy 1	Crawley Town	698	1 - 2	Lee 59
07.11	Ryman P	Chesham United	263	3 - 2	Waters 20, Gillespie 55, Rogers 84
18.11	Ryman P	ST ALBANS CITY	337	0 - 1	
02.12	Ryman P	HAMPTON & RICHMOND BOR.	214	3 - 2	Lee 5 18, Parker 19
09.12	Ryman P	Aldershot Town	2145	1 - 2	Parker 90
16.12	Ryman P	GRAVESEND & NORTHFLEET	298	2 - 2	Parker 7, Lee 60
19.12	Essex SC 3	CHELMSFORD CITY	180	8 - 0	Wall 17, Miyoba 25, Tomlinson 27, Payne 42, Warwick 68, Kane 69, Rogers73
23.12	Ryman P	Sutton United	574	2 - 1	Lee 27, Parker 78
26.12	Ryman P	BILLERICAY TOWN	444	2 - 2	Lee 25, Parker 55
30.12	FMC 2	HENDON	125	6 - 5	Warwick 38 94, Moss 65, Wall 75, Miyoba 84, Rogers 120
06.01	Ryman P	HITCHIN TOWN	284	0 - 0	
09.01	Lge Cup 2	OXFORD CITY	118	3 - 0	Warwick 40, Lee 44, Rogers 88
30.01	Ryman P	Hitchin Town	201	2 - 0	Parker 29, Lee 45
10.02	Ryman P	Canvey Island	414	0 - 3	
15.02	Essex SC 4	TIPTREE UNITED	n.k	4 - 3	Moss, Creasy(2), Warwick[p],
17.02	Ryman P	ENFIELD	295	2 - 0	Lee 50, Wall 72
20.02	Lge Cup 3	BEDFORD TOWN	148	3 - 0	Wall 48, Lee 58 86
22.02	FMC 3	PURFLEET	67	1 - 3	Walker
24.02	Ryman P	CHESHAM UNITED	254	3 - 1	Parker 78 88, Payne 83
27.02	Essex SC QF	BILLERICAY TOWN	114	2 - 0	Lee, Parker
03.03	Ryman P	Slough Town	353	1 - 1	Wall 11
05.03	Ryman P	Croydon	148	2 - 1	Pollard 45, Parker 90
10.03	Ryman P	FARNBOROUGH TOWN	457	2 - 3	Lee 80, Parker 85
13.03	Essex SC SF	Dagenham & Redbridge	412	1 - 2	Caton 80
15.03	Lge Cup QF	CHESHAM UNITED	119	3 - 1	Wall 15 17, Pollard
24.03	Ryman P	Dulwich Hamlet	204	0 - 1	
27.03	Ryman P	Maidenhead United	175	3 - 1	Lee 45 65, Caton 54
31.03	Ryman P	HARROW BOROUGH	219	4 - 2	Parker 11 80 85, Lee 22
02.04	Ryman P	Hendon	147	4 - 1	Warwick 35 90, Moss 59, Wall 84
07.04	Ryman P	St Albans City	284	0 - 3	
10.04	Ryman P	BASINGSTOKE TOWN	170	1 - 1	Parker 5
12.04	Lge Cup SF(1)	NORTHWOOD	166	4 - 1	Parker 10 42 84, Gillespie 58
14.04	Ryman P	SUTTON UNITED	310	2 - 2	Lee 25, Warwick 84
16.04	Ryman P	Billericay Town	495	1 - 5	Lee 85
19.04	Ryman P	Purfleet	163	1 - 1	Boylan 65
21.04	Ryman P	CROYDON	195	1 - 2	Lee 15
24.04	Ryman P	Grays Athletic	188	0 - 1	
28.04	Ryman P	Hampton & Richmond Borough	250	1 - 2	Payne 42
01.05	Ryman P	DULWICH HAMLET	139	3 - 1	Parker 43 48, Caton 89
03.05	Lge Cup SF(2)	Northwood	n.k	2 - 1	Boylan 60, Wall 90
05.05	Ryman P	ALDERSHOT TOWN	479	2 - 1	Lee 45, Parker 54
07.05	Lge Cup F	Croydon	318	3 - 0	Parker 40, Lee 56, Wall 65 (at Purfleet)

PLAYING SQUAD

GOALKEEPERS: Kingsley Banks (Witham)

DEFENDERS: Mark Cranfield (Braintree), Russell Tanner (Braintree), Colin Wall (Gravesend), Ray Filby (Youth), Ross Taylor (Chelmsford)

MIDFIELDERS: Dave Streetley (Halstead), John Pollard (St.Albans), Dave Kreyling (Billericay), Sean Caton (Wivenhoe), Robbie Bate (Stanway R), Robbie May (Wivenhoe), Adam Gillespie (Youth), Lewis Baillie (Wivenhoe)

FORWARDS: Kris Lee (Tiptree), Simon Parker (Stowmarket), Paul Abrahams (Wivenhoe), Danny Roberts (Wivenhoe)

HITCHIN TOWN

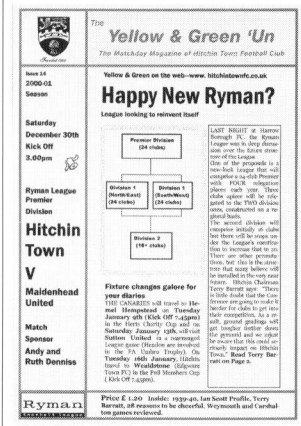

CLUB OFFICIALS

Chairman: **Terry Barratt**
Secretary: **Roy Izzard**
2 Bedford Road, Ickleford, Hitchin, Herts
Tel: 01462 433171

Media Officer: **Neil Jensen**
Tel: 01462 454678 0207 5457921
Email: neiljensen@hitchintownfc.co.uk

FOOTBALL MANAGEMENT TEAM

Manager: Andy Melvin
Physio: Peter Prince
Coach: Robbie O'Keefe

FACT FILE

Formed: 1865 Reformed 1928
Nickname: The Canaries
Sponsors: Alma Engineering
Colours: Yellow/green/green
Change colours: white/black/black
Midweek matchday: Tuesday
Clubcall Line: 09066 555 817
Website: www.hitchintownfc.co.uk

2000-01

Captain: Adam Parker
P.o.Y.: Tim Allpress
Top Scorer: Adam Parker 27

The
Yellow & Green 'Un
The Matchday Magazine of Hitchin Town Football Club

Issue 14
2000-01
Season

Saturday
December 30th
Kick Off
3.00pm

Ryman League
Premier
Division

Hitchin
Town
V
Maidenhead
United

Match
Sponsor
Andy and
Ruth Denniss

Yellow & Green on the web--www. hitchintownfc.co.uk

Happy New Ryman?

League looking to reinvent itself

Premier Division (24 clubs)
Division 1 (North/East) (24 clubs)
Division 1 (South/West) (24 clubs)
Division 2 (16+ clubs)

LAST NIGHT at Harrow Borough FC, the Ryman League was in deep discussion over the future structure of the League. One of the proposals is a new-look League that will comprise a 24-club Premier with FOUR relegation places each year. Three clubs apiece will be relegated to the TWO division ones, constructed on a regional basis. The second division will comprise initially 16 clubs but there will be scope under the League's constitution to increase that to 20. There are other permutations, but this is the structure that many believe will be installed in the very near future. Hitchin Chairman Terry Barratt says: "There is little doubt that the Conference are going to make it harder for clubs to get into their competition. As a result, ground gradings will get tougher further down the pyramid and we must be aware that this could seriously impact on Hitchin Town." Read Terry Barratt on Page 2.

Fixture changes galore for your diaries

THE CANARIES will travel to Hemel Hempstead on Tuesday January 9th (Kick Off 7.45pm) in the Herts Charity Cup and on Saturday January 13th, will visit Sutton United in a rearranged League game (Hendon are involved in the FA Umbro Trophy). On Tuesday 16th January, Hitchin travel to Wealdstone (Edgware Town FC) in the Full Members Cup (Kick Off 7.45pm).

Ryman

Price £1.20 Inside: 1939-40, Ian Scott Profile, Terry Barratt, 28 reasons to be cheerful, Weymouth and Carshalton games reviewed.

Pages: 24 (A4) Price: £1.20 Ed: Neil Jensen
Local Press: Hitchin Comet, Herts on Sunday
Local Radio: Chiltern, BBC Three Counties

GROUND: Top Field, Fishponds Road, Hitchin SG5 1NU (01462 459028-matchdays only)
Directions: On A505 near town centre opposite large green. 1 mile from Hitchin(BR). From A1(M) Jct 8,A602 towards Bedford into Hitchin.Over two roundabouts through lights on one way system. Turn right at next roundabout for Fishponds Road.
Capacity: Cover: 1,250 Seats: Floodlights: Yes
Clubhouse: (01462 434483). Members bar, Function Hall (available for hire). Open everyday. Steward: Eamonn Watson/ Nigel Collins
Club Shop: Yes, Contact - Chris Newbold on chris@bewvikd013.freeserve.co.uk

PREVIOUS **Leagues:** Spartan 28-39; Hert & Middx 39-45; Athenian 39,45-63

CLUB RECORDS **Attendance:** 7,878 v Wycombe Wanderers, FA Amateur Cup 3rd Rd 18/2/56
Win: Spartan Lge 29-30 13-0 v Cowley, 13-0 v RAF
Defeat (Isthmian Lge): 0-10 v Kingstonian (A) 65-66, v Slough T. (A) 79-80
Career (Isthmian Lge) **appearances:** Paul Giggle 67-88 **Career** (Isthmian Lge) **goals:** Paul Giggle, 129
Fee paid: £2,000 Ray Seeking Potton United, July 1989 **Fee received:** £30,000 Zema Abbey to Cambridge Utd Jan 00

BEST SEASON **FA Trophy:** 5th Rd 98-99 **FA Amateur Cup:** Semi Final 60-61, 62-63
FA Cup: 2nd Rd on four occasions -
v Swindon 1-3 (A) 76-77, v Boston Utd, 0-1 (A) 73-74, v Wycombe Wand. 0-5 (H) 94-95, v Gillingham 0-3 (A) 95-9

HONOURS: Isthmian Lge R-up 68-69Div 1 92-93 R-up 98-99, Spartan Lge 34-35; AFA Sen Cup 30-31; Herts Snr Cup (19-record); London Sen Cup 69-70 (R-up 72-73); E Anglian Cup 72-73; Herts Charity Cup(17), Herts I'mediate Cup (8); Woolwich Trophy 82-83; Televised Sport International Cup 88-89 90-91; Southern Comb. Senior Floodlit Cup 90-91

Back Row Left to right: Del McKoy,*Jermaine Daley,James Dillnutt,Tim Allpress, Darren Sarll, Shaun Marshall, Enzo Silvestre*,and Rob Kean **Middle Row:** Peter Prince (Physio), Jon Bone, Jeran Meah*, Darren Bonfield*, Richard Wilmot,* James Robinson, Marc Burke, Sam Turner*, Bunny Dear (Physio). **Front Row:** Sid Springett (Kit Man), Robbie O"keefe (Coach), Ian Scott, Stuart Beevor, Carl Williams, Adam Parker, Gary Dixon*, Andy Melvin (Manager), Nick Sopowski (Physio). * left club in 00-01

Date	Comp.	Opponents	Att.	Score	Goalscorers
19.08	Ryman P	Purfleet	201	1 - 0	Beevor 65
22.08	Ryman P	CARSHALTON ATHLETIC	301	3 - 0	Marshall 39 41, Akurang 90
26.08	Ryman P	HENDON	363	3 - 3	Dixon 42 50, Parker 81
28.08	Ryman P	Aldershot Town	1804	0 - 2	
02.09	Ryman P	Maidenhead United	241	1 - 0	Marshall 42
05.09	Ryman P	GRAYS ATHLETIC	271	2 - 0	Dixon 5 64
09.09	Ryman P	Hampton & Richmond Borough	271	4 - 2	Allpress 72, Parker 73, Beevor 78, Williams 83
12.09	Lge Cup 1	Carshalton Athletic	82	0 - 1	
16.09	Ryman P	GRAVESEND & NORTHFLEET	388	1 - 2	Marshall 21[p]
18.09	Ryman P	Croydon	112	1 - 5	Keen 28
23.09	Ryman P	BILLERICAY TOWN	382	2 - 1	Marshall 27, Meah 88
30.09	FA Cup Q2	MAIDENHEAD UNITED	336	1 - 1	Dixon 84[p]
03.10	FA Cup Q2 R	Maidenhead United	190	1 - 1	Parker 90 (6-7p)
07.10	Ryman P	CHESHAM UNITED	258	1 - 2	Parker 25
10.10	Herts SC 1	HEMEL HEMPSTEAD TOWN	117	5 - 1	Parker(3), Akurang, Nolan
14.10	FMC 1	BEDFORD TOWN	327	2 - 1	Parker, Akurang
21.10	Ryman P	SLOUGH TOWN	334	3 - 0	Beevor 51, Williams 55, Akurang 75
24.10	Herts SC 2	LONDON COLNEY	121	7 - 0	Marshall, Parker(2), Meah, Kean, Nolan(2)
28.10	Ryman P	St Albans City	647	0 - 2	
04.11	FA Trophy 1	Newport IOW	370	2 - 2	Parker 49 83
14.11	FA Trophy 1 R	NEWPORT IOW	241	4 - 1	Parker 37 44, Scott 59, Williams 90
18.11	Ryman P	Farnborough Town	488	0 - 3	
25.11	Ryman P	DULWICH HAMLET	237	1 - 0	Beevor 13[p]
02.12	FA Trophy 2	Weymouth	681	0 - 2	
16.12	Ryman P	Carshalton Athletic	260	5 - 0	Marshall 19 30 52, Williams 28, Dixon 38
23.12	Ryman P	BASINGSTOKE TOWN	350	0 - 1	
26.12	Ryman P	Enfield	206	5 - 2	Dixon 7, Parker 70 79 88, Williams 72
30.12	Ryman P	MAIDENHEAD UNITED	252	0 - 2	
06.01	Ryman P	Heybridge Swifts	284	0 - 0	
09.01	Herts SC QF	STEVENAGE BOROUGH	405	1 - 2	Rydeheard 65
13.01	Ryman P	Sutton United	520	1 - 1	Parker 56
23.01	Herts CC QF	Hemel Hempstead Town	n.k	3 - 1	Dixon 18 52[p], Parker 75
30.01	Ryman P	HEYBRIDGE SWIFTS	201	0 - 2	
10.02	Ryman P	Grays Athletic	211	1 - 2	Williams 50
15.02	FMC 2	Wealdstone	120	3 - 0	Kean, Akurang, Nolan
17.02	Ryman P	HAMPTON & RICHMOND BOR.	331	2 - 0	Lamey 54, Parker 71
20.02	Ryman P	Gravesend & Northfleet	468	0 - 3	
24.02	Ryman P	SUTTON UNITED	413	3 - 0	Nolan 50 86, Parker 78
27.02	Ryman P	Harrow Borough	149	4 - 1	Parker 71 90, Allpress 79, Meah 88
03.03	Ryman P	Chesham United	309	0 - 3	
06.03	Ryman P	PURFLEET	176	0 - 1	
10.03	Ryman P	CROYDON	260	7 - 3	Dixon 5 49, Allpress 8, Kean 39, Akurang 60, Laney 83, Nolan 87
15.03	FMC 3	GRAVESEND & NORTHFLEET	68	1 - 7	Rydeheard
17.03	Ryman P	Billericay Town	422	1 - 3	Parker 74
31.03	Ryman P	Slough Town	414	3 - 0	Parker 9, Lamey 57 79
03.04	Ryman P	ALDERSHOT TOWN	336	2 - 5	Akurang 22, Beevor 80[p]
07.04	Ryman P	FARNBOROUGH TOWN	391	1 - 2	Akurang 36
11.04	Ryman P	Hendon	157	0 - 4	
14.04	Ryman P	Basingstoke Town	370	1 - 2	Rydeheard 62
16.04	Ryman P	ENFIELD	457	2 - 1	Marshall 8, Simpson 32
21.04	Ryman P	Dulwich Hamlet	277	2 - 0	Simpson 65, Nolan 79
24.04	Ryman P	CANVEY ISLAND	301	4 - 1	Nolan 51 62 89, Marshall 89[p]
28.04	Ryman P	HARROW BOROUGH	286	3 - 6	Parker 35 90, Hyslop 82[og]
01.05	Herts CC SF	STEVENAGE BOROUGH	102	6 - 1	Rydeheard 31, Marshall 33 41, Nolan 51 65 78
03.05	Ryman P	ST ALBANS CITY	242	0 - 0	
05.05	Ryman P	Canvey Island	491	2 - 2	Marshall 30, Parker 33
12.05	Herts CC F	TRING TOWN	n.k	3 - 0	Marshall[p], Nolan, Akurang

PLAYING SQUAD

GOALKEEPERS:	James Robinson (Youth), Nick Webb (Harlow)
DEFENDERS:	Scott Cretton (Stevenage), Tim Allpress (St.Albans), Nick Grime (Boreham Wood), Jon Bone (Barton R), Mark Burke (Luton), Russell Lawes (Luton
MIDFIELDERS:	Ian Scott (St.Albans), Carl Williams (Carshalton), Adam Parker (Stevenage), Cliff Akurang (Chesham Utd), Louie Evans (Peterborough), Stuart Beevor (Aylesbury)
FORWARDS:	Shaun Marshall (Boreham Wood), Matthew Nolan (Youth), Lee Endersby (Bishop's Stortford)

KINGSTONIAN

CLUB OFFICIALS
Chairman: Alan Kingston
General Manager: Chris Kelly
Directors : G Chapple, L Cooley, T Dixon, M Grant, C Kelly, A Kingston,K.Phillips N Verbruggen,
Football Secretary:
Graham Richards, 1 Bridge Court, Bridge Street, Leatherhead, Surrey KT22 8BWTel No: 01372 377076
Commercial Man.: Chris Richardson
Press Officer: Alan Kingston 01737 210032

FOOTBALL MANAGEMENT TEAM
Manager: Bill Williams
Coach: Steve Sedgley

FACT FILE

Founded: 1885
Nickname: The Ks
Sponsors: Bass Brewers
Club Colours: Red & white hooped shirts, white shorts, white socks
Change Colours: Yellow shirts, royal blue shorts, red socks
Midweek matchday: Tuesday
Reserves' League: Suburban

20000-01
Leading Scorer: Geoff Pitcher
Captain: Gary Patterson

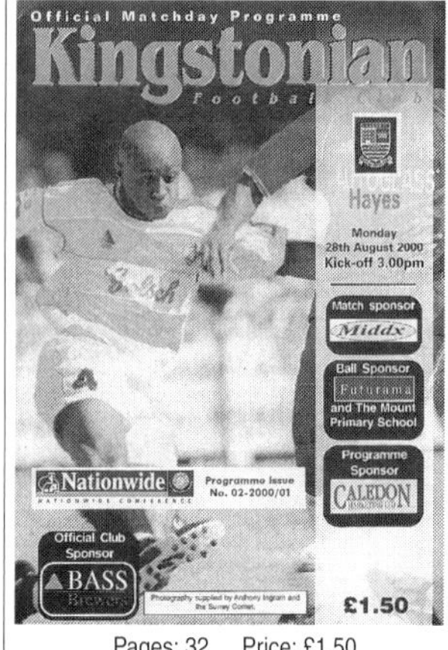

Pages: 32 Price: £1.50
Editor: Robert Wooldridge Tel: 020 8669 3824

Local Press: Surrey Comet 020 8546 2261
Local Radio: County Sound; Southern Counties

GROUND: Kingsmeadow Stadium, Kingston Road, Kingston-upon-Thames, Surrey. KT13PB
Tel: 0208 547 3335/6 Fax: 0208 974 5713
DIRECTIONS: From town centre - Cambridge Rd on to Kingston Rd (A2043) to Malden Rd. From A3, turn off at New Malden, turn left on to A2043 - grd 1 mile on left. Half mile from Norbiton (BR)
CAPACITY: 9,000 **COVERED TERRACING:** 3,500 **SEATED:** 690
SOCIAL FACILITIES: Banqueting centre, open 7 days. 3 bars capacity 400. Contact Chris Kelly (0208 547 3335).
CLUB SHOP: Sells programmes, shirts, badges etc. Contact Chris Dickinson Tel: 0208 747 3336

RECORDS **Win:** 15-1 v Delft, friendly 5/9/51; Competitive 10-0 v Hitchin (H) Isthmian Lge 19/3/66)
Attendance: 4,582 v Chelsea (Friendly) 22.7.95
Defeat: 0-11 v Ilford (A) Isthmian Lge 13/2/37
Fee Paid: £18,000 for David Leworthy to Rushden & Diamonds '97
Goalscorer: Johnny Whing 295
Fee Received: £150,000 for Gavin Holligan from West Ham Utd. '99
Appearances: Micky Preston 555

PREVIOUS **Leagues:** Kingston & Dist.; West Surrey; Southern Suburban; Athenian 1919-29; Isthmian League 29-98; Conference 98-01
Names: Kingston & Surbiton YMCA 1885-87, Saxons 87-90, Kingston Wanderers 1893-1904, Old Kingstonians 08-19
Grounds: Several to 1921; Richmond Rd 21-89

HONOURS FA Trophy 98-99 99-00; Isthmian League 33-34, 36-37, 97-98, R-up 47-48 62-63, Div 1 R-up 84-85, League Cup 95-96; Athenian Lge 23-24 25-26, R-up 26-27; London Senior Cup 62-63 64-65 86-87, R-up x 5; Surrey Senior Cup x 9, R-up 90-91.

BEST SEASON **FA Amateur Cup:** Winners 32-33 R-up 59-60
FA Trophy: Winners 98-99 99-00
FA Cup: 4th Round replay 00-01, 0-1 v Bristol City (H), after 1-1
League: 5th Conference 99-00
League clubs defeated: Brighton & H.A. 94-95, Brentford & Southend Utd. 00-01

PAST PLAYERS: C Nastri (C Palace), H Lindsay (Southampton 65), G Still (Brighton 79), D Byrne (Gillingham 1985), J Power (Brentford 87), Jamie Ndah (Torquay), Gavin Holligan (West Ham '99)

Back row (left to right): Steve McKimm, Peter Barnsby, Sean Thurgood, Adrian Blake, Simon Stewart, Lance Key, Eddie Saunders, Colin Luckett, Phil Wingfield **Middle row:** Frank Brooks (physio), Stuart Munday, Mark Jones, David Bass, Mark Beard, Steve Brown, Billy Mead, Chris Williams (fitness coach) **Front row:** Ronnie Green, James Pinnock, Dave Clarke, Steve Sedgley (coach), Danny Bolt, Sammy Winston, Mark Boyce
Not pictured: Bill Williams (manager), David Sadler

Date	Comp.	Opponents	Att.	Score	Goalscorers
19.08	Conf.	NORTHWICH VICTORIA	942	1 - 0	Luckett 89[p]
22.08	Conf.	Dagenham & Redbridge	1252	2 - 1	Akuamoah 28, Winston 66
26.08	Conf.	Scarborough	1275	0 - 1	
28.08	Conf.	HAYES	902	0 - 1	
02.09	Conf.	Kettering Town	1203	1 - 3	Pitcher 75
05.09	Conf.	NUNEATON BOROUGH	788	2 - 2	Stewart 15, Simba 77
09.09	Conf.	DONCASTER ROVERS	1321	1 - 1	Simba 58
13.09	Conf.	Forest Green Rovers	547	1 - 3	Boyce 75
16.09	Conf.	Hednesford Town	881	2 - 3	Simba 21, Winston 60
23.09	Conf.	CHESTER CITY	1125	1 - 3	Luckett 67[p]
26.09	Conf.	Dover Athletic	632	3 - 1	Bass 4, Harris 48, Pitcher 90
30.09	Conf.	RUSHDEN & DIAMONDS	1363	2 - 4	Pitcher 50, Winston 77
03.10	Conf.	HEREFORD UNITED	833	0 - 3	
08.10	Conf.	Morecambe	1060	2 - 3	Kadi 55, Akuamoah 83
10.10	Variety CT 2	Dover Athletic	312	1 - 0	Luckett 84
14.10	Conf.	SOUTHPORT	904	3 - 1	Duerden 71 89, Pitcher
21.10	Conf.	Yeovil Town	2902	1 - 3	Allan 42
28.10	FA Cup Q4	DEVIZES TOWN	619	5 - 2	Allan 12 73, Pitcher 37 82 86[p]
04.11	Conf.	BOSTON UNITED	842	0 - 0	
07.11	JC Thompson Shield	Kidderminster Harriers	609	1 - 2	Wingfield 39
18.11	FA Cup 1	Brentford	3809	3 - 1	Pitcher 46, Winston 62 77
25.11	Conf.	Stevenage Borough	2007	5 - 2	Pitcher 10 13, Luckett 16 30, Winston 86
02.12	Conf.	LEIGH RMI	929	0 - 2	
09.12	FA Cup 2	Southport	3659	2 - 1	Harris 20, Pitcher 33
16.12	Conf.	DAGENHAM & REDBRIDGE	809	2 - 3	Vickers 61[og], Wingfield 64
19.12	Variety CT QF	RUSHDEN & DIAMONDS	190	1 - 0	Akuamoah 11
26.12	Conf.	Woking	2246	0 - 0	
01.01	Conf.	WOKING	1717	0 - 3	
06.01	FA Cup 3	Southend United	7270	1 - 0	Akuamoah 8
13.01	FA Trophy 3	Staines Town	767	2 - 2	Pitcher 46 86
22.01	FA Trophy 3 R	STAINES TOWN	426	2 - 0	Luckett 56, Pitcher 90
27.01	FA Cup 4	Bristol City	14787	1 - 1	Wingfield 57
03.02	FA Trophy 4	SOUTHPORT	1245	0 - 1	
07.02	FA Cup 4 R	BRISTOL CITY	3341	0 - 1	
10.02	Conf.	Doncaster Rovers	1787	2 - 0	Duerden 53 84
17.02	Conf.	STEVENAGE BOROUGH	990	0 - 2	
20.02	Conf.	KETTERING TOWN	707	0 - 1	
27.02	Conf.	Hayes	738	1 - 1	Patterson 90
03.03	Conf.	HEDNESFORD TOWN	651	1 - 0	Jones 23
10.03	Conf.	MORECAMBE	885	1 - 6	Allan 31
13.03	Conf.	Telford United	860	1 - 0	Green 7
17.03	Conf.	Rushden & Diamonds	3842	1 - 2	Duerden 9
31.03	Conf.	Nuneaton Borough	1423	1 - 2	Akuamoah 66
03.04	Conf.	SCARBOROUGH	694	2 - 2	Green 28, Luckett 51[p]
05.04	Surrey SC 1	CROYDON ATHLETIC	0	0 - 0	(w.o for Kingstonian)
07.04	Conf.	YEOVIL TOWN	1613	3 - 4	Holligan 22, Allan 54, Green 77
10.04	Conf.	Northwich Victoria	788	1 - 2	Green 29
12.04	Surrey SC QF	TOOTING & MITCHAM UNITED	103	3 - 1	Wingfield, Mead, Akuamoah
		(Kingstonian were removed for fielding an ineligible player)			
14.04	Conf.	Southport	1153	2 - 2	Holligan 52, Pitcher 85
16.04	Conf.	TELFORD UNITED	867	0 - 1	
18.04	Conf.	Hereford United	867	0 - 0	
21.04	Conf.	Boston United	2145	1 - 2	Luckett 56[p]
24.04	Conf.	DOVER ATHLETIC	723	0 - 0	
26.04	Conf.	Chester City	834	0 - 0	
28.04	Conf.	Leigh RMI	402	1 - 2	Luckett 60[p]
30.04	Variety CT SF	Yeovil Town	295	5 - 0	Pitcher 8, Luckett 13, Winston 17[p] 22, Saunders 75
05.05	Conf.	FOREST GREEN ROVERS	774	0 - 1	
07.05	Variety CT F	CHESTER CITY	495	0 - 0	Lost 2-4 after penalties

PLAYING SQUAD

GOALKEEPERS: Lance Key (Northwich), Adrian Blake (Walton & Hersham)

DEFENDERS: Mark Boyce (Hayes), Peter Barnsby (Hampton & R), Stuart Munday (Dover), Simon Stewart (Fulham), Colin Luckett (Millwall), Eddie Saunders (Woking), Mark Beard (Southend)

MIDFIELDERS: Mark Jones (Wimbledon), David Bass (Scarborough), Phil Wingfield (Farnborough), Steve McKimm (Hayes), David Clarke (Dover), Billy Mead (Millwall), Danny Bolt (Sutton Utd)

FORWARDS: Sammy Winston (Sutton Utd), James Pinnock (Gillingham). Steve Brown (Dover), David Sadler (Hinckley Utd), Ronnie Green (Youth)

MAIDENHEAD UNITED

CLUB OFFICIALS

Chairman: **Roger Coombs**
Vice Chairman: **Jon Swan**
President: Jim Parsons
Secretary: **Ken Chandler**
c/o Maidenhead United
Press Off .: **Jon Swan** (01344 723750)

FOOTBALL MANAGEMENT TEAM

Manager: Alan Devonshire
Asst. Man. & Coaches: Carl Taylor,Phil Parkes & Dave Harrison
Physios:Jon Urry & Bryan Clements

FACT FILE

Formed: 1870
Nickname: Magpies
Sponsors: Trademark Windows
Colours: Black & white stripes/black/black
Change colours: Red/white/white
Midweek matchday: Tuesday
Reserve League: Suburban
Local Press: Maidenhead Advertiser, Reading Evening Post, Slough Observer

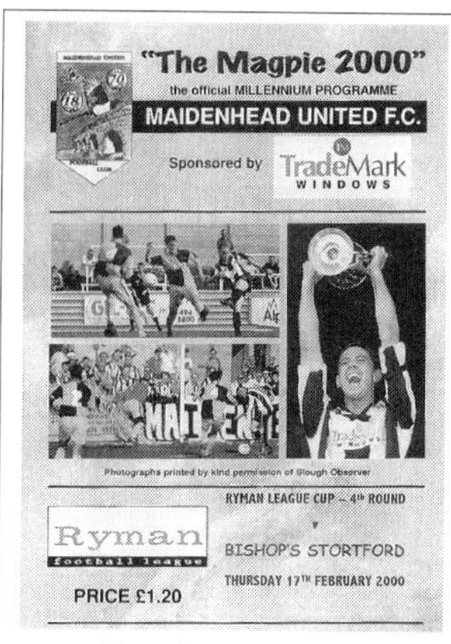

Pages: 36 Price: £1
Editor: J Swan/R Jackson Tel: 01344 723750

Local Radio: 2-Ten FM, Star FM, Thames Valley FM

GROUND York Road, Maidenhead, Berks SL6 1SQ Tel: 01628 624739/636314

Directions: From Maidenhead BR station proceed eastwards down Bell St - 500 yds
Ground is 5 miles from M4 in town centre.
Capacity: 4,000 Cover: 1,500 Seats: 400 Floodlights: Yes
Clubhouse: Open evenings & matchdays. Some hot food
Club Shop: Wide range of programmes and club souvenirs.
Contact Mark Smith (01753 854674)

PREVIOUS **Leagues:** Southern 1894-1902; West Berks 02-04; Grt West Sub 04-22; Spartan 22-39; Grt West Comb 39-45; Corinthian 45-63; Athenian 63-73, Isthmian 1973-
Names: Maidenhead FC, Maidenhead Norfolkians. **Grounds:** None

CLUB RECORDS **Attendance:** 7,920 v Southall, FA Amat Cup Q/F 7/3/36
Season's goalscorer: Jack Palethorpe 66, 1929-30
Career appearances: Bert Randall 532, 1950-64
Career goalscorer: George Copas 270, 1924-35
Win: 14-1 v Buckingham Town (H), FA Amat. Cup 6/9/52
Defeat: 0-14 v Chesham United (A), Spartan Lge 31/3/23
Transfer fee paid: Undisclosed **Transfer fee received:** £5,000 from Norwich for Alan Cordice, 79

BEST SEASON **FA Cup:** Qtr Finals 1873-74 74-75 75-76 **F A Trophy:** 3rd Qual Rd **FA Amateur Cup:** Semi Final 35-36

HONOURS Isthmian Lg Div 2 Sth R-up 90-91,Promotion to Premier Division 99-00 Full Members Cup 96-97; Spartan Lg x3 R-upx2; Corinthian Lg 57-58 60-61 61-62 R-up 58-59 59-60, Mem. Shield 56-57 61-62,R-up x4, Neale Cup 48-49 57-58 60-61; Gt Western Suburban Lg 19-20 R-up 20-21; Berks & Bucks Snr Cup x17, Berks & Bucks Benev. Cup x6 R-up x2; Mithras Cup R-up x4; Southern Comb. Cup R-up 81-82; Sub Lge West 97-98; Allied Counties Champ 97-98

Players progressing: A Cordice (Norwich 79), P Priddy (Brentford 72), D Kemp (Plymouth), L Sanchez (Reading),E Kelsey, J Palethorpe (Reading 30), B Laryea(Torquay), R Davies (Torquay), Mark Harris (C.Palace & Swansea C 1985),Ben Abbey (Oxford U via Crawley 99)

Back Row, left to right: Paul Kelly, Adam Durrant, Steve Atkins, Darren Grieves, Richard Barnard, Lewis Craker, Jamie Jarvis, Matt Glynn, Chris Ferdinabd, Tim Cook, and Paull Scott **.Front Row:** Steve Croxford, Obinna Ulasi, Simon Goodram, Andy Rose, Brian Connor, Adrian Allen, Paul Woodhouse, Nick Hart. Missing from squad: Lee Channell, Andy Morley and Craig Webster

Photo: Peter Wilson of The News Desk

Date	Comp.	Opponents	Att.	Score	Goalscorers
19.08	Ryman P	HARROW BOROUGH	279	4 - 1	Morley 17, Croxford 31, Glynn 61, Allen 67
22.08	Ryman P	Billericay Town	413	0 - 2	
26.08	Ryman P	Heybridge Swifts	173	0 - 4	
28.08	Ryman P	CHESHAM UNITED	329	0 - 2	
02.09	Ryman P	HITCHIN TOWN	241	0 - 1	
05.09	Ryman P	Dulwich Hamlet	217	3 - 2	Allen 34, Ferdinand 51, Cove 77
09.09	Ryman P	FARNBOROUGH TOWN	459	0 - 1	
12.09	Lge Cup 1	LEATHERHEAD	105	1 - 3	Glynn 74
16.09	Ryman P	Croydon	109	2 - 0	Channell 41, Hickey 81
19.09	Ryman P	CANVEY ISLAND	172	0 - 2	
23.09	Ryman P	Grays Athletic	195	1 - 2	Ferdinand 64
30.09	FA Cup Q2	Hitchin Town	336	1 - 1	Channell 82
03.10	FA Cup Q2 R	HITCHIN TOWN	190	1 - 1	Harkness 37[p] Won 7-6 after penalties
06.10	Ryman P	Hendon	228	1 - 2	Channell 88
14.10	FA Cup Q3	Hucknall Town	380	2 - 3	Arkins 27, Brown 81
21.10	Ryman P	Enfield	228	1 - 3	John 73[og]
28.10	Ryman P	BASINGSTOKE TOWN	263	3 - 2	Brown 9, Morley 10, Channell 65
04.11	FA Trophy 1	Hampton & Richmond Borough	278	4 - 1	Channell 57 89, Croxford 75, Domingos 90
11.11	Ryman P	Aldershot Town	2026	1 - 2	Channell 82[p]
18.11	Ryman P	SUTTON UNITED	258	0 - 2	
25.11	Ryman P	Purfleet	169	1 - 1	Nartey 8
09.12	Ryman P	St Albans City	628	1 - 3	Channell 26
16.12	Ryman P	BILLERICAY TOWN	191	1 - 2	Channell 54
23.12	Ryman P	Hampton & Richmond Borough	274	0 - 1	
26.12	Ryman P	SLOUGH TOWN	615	1 - 0	Ulasi 71
30.12	Ryman P	Hitchin Town	252	2 - 0	Nartey 58, Glynn 67
06.01	Ryman P	ALDERSHOT TOWN	1213	3 - 0	Nartey 3, Channell 69, Allen 79
08.01	FA Trophy 2	ENFIELD	182	1 - 0	Nartey 21
13.01	FA Trophy 3	Braintree Town	403	2 - 1	Ulasi 39, Nartey 89
16.01	FMC 2	LEATHERHEAD	116	2 - 1	Woodhouse 18, Channell 92
27.01	Ryman P	CROYDON	219	3 - 1	Cook 21, Glynn 12, Croxford 41
30.01	Ryman P	GRAVESEND & NORTHFLEET	203	1 - 3	Driscoll 53
03.02	FA Trophy 4	Blyth Spartans	902	1 - 2	Glynn 18
17.02	Ryman P	Farnborough Town	685	1 - 4	Channell 88
20.02	B&B SC 3	SLOUGH TOWN	0	2 - 0	
24.02	Ryman P	Carshalton Athletic	285	0 - 1	
27.02	FMC 3	Bognor Regis Town	156	1 - 2	Channell 43
03.03	Ryman P	HENDON	187	1 - 2	Channell 25[p]
07.03	B&B SC QF	READING	0	1 - 0	Channell
13.03	Ryman P	Harrow Borough	207	2 - 1	Cook 47, Tyson 49
27.03	Ryman P	HEYBRIDGE SWIFTS	175	1 - 3	Tyson 76
31.03	Ryman P	ENFIELD	292	2 - 1	Channell 35 44
03.04	B&B SC SF	WINDSOR & ETON	0	2 - 1	Glynn 24, Channell 90
10.04	Ryman P	Chesham United	225	1 - 2	Arkins 81
12.04	Ryman P	GRAYS ATHLETIC	138	3 - 2	Tyson 8, Rake 45, Cook 47
14.04	Ryman P	HAMPTON & RICHMOND BOR.	248	0 - 0	
16.04	Ryman P	Slough Town	726	0 - 1	
18.04	Ryman P	Canvey Island	282	0 - 1	
21.04	Ryman P	PURFLEET	194	1 - 2	Glynn 28
22.04	Ryman P	Gravesend & Northfleet	222	1 - 0	Tyson 23
24.04	Ryman P	DULWICH HAMLET	217	1 - 0	Dickson 41[og]
26.04	Ryman P	Basingstoke Town	309	1 - 2	Morley 87
28.04	Ryman P	Sutton United	476	0 - 2	
01.05	Ryman P	CARSHALTON ATHLETIC	306	2 - 0	Glynn 12 47
05.05	Ryman P	ST ALBANS CITY	256	1 - 0	Rake 63
07.05	B&B SC F	Chesham United	805	0 - 1	(at Slough Town)

PLAYING SQUAD

GOALKEEPERS: Richard Barnard (Millwall)

DEFENDERS: Andy Morley (Basingstoke), Tyrone Houston (Slough), Andy Rose (Harrow), Adam Durrant (Youth), Brian Connor (Marlow), Steve Croxford (Hampton & R), Paul Woodhouse (Brentford), Lewis Craker (Walton & Hersham)

MIDFIELDERS: Tom Cook (Thame), Matt Glynn (Windsor), Paul Kelly (Boreham Wood), Steve Brown (Feltham), Craig Webster (Youth), Jamie Jarvis (Burnham), Chris Ferdinand (Oxford C)

FORWARDS: Adrian Allen (Leyton Pennant), Paul Scott (Harrow), Micky Creighton (Uxbridge), Darren Grieves (Boreham Wood), Lee Channell (Feltham), Steve Arkins (Slough)

PURFLEET

CLUB OFFICIALS

Chairman: **Grant Beglan**
V/Chairman/Chief Executive: **Tommy Smith**
Secretary: Norman Posner, 1 Chase House Gardens, Hornchurch, Essex, RM11 2PJ, Tel: 01708 458301
Match Secretary/Press Officer: **Norman Posner**
Comm Mger: **Tony Joy** (01375 392906)

FOOTBALL MANAGEMENT TEAM

Manager: Colin McBride
Asst Manager: Jimmy McFarlane
Coach: Ronnie Hanley
Physio: Michelle Sheehan

FACT FILE

Founded: 1985
Nickname: Fleet
Colours: Green&yellow/green/green&yellow
Change colours: All white
Midweek home matchday: Monday
Reserve's League: None
Sponsors: Nat. West. Bank, Lakeside Shopping Cntr and T & P Lead Roofing Ltd

2000-00

Leading Goal Scorers:
Martin Carthy & George Georgiou 16
Captain: Jimmy McFarlane
P.o.Y.: Jimmy McFarlane

Pages: 44 Price: £1
Editor: Norman Posner (01708 458301 H)

Local Press: Romford, Thurrock Recorder, Thurrock Gazette
Local Radio: Essex Radio, BBC Radio Essex

GROUND: Thurrock Hotel, Ship Lane, Grays, Essex. 01708 868901 Fax: 01708 866703
Webside: www.purfleetfootballclub.com
Directions: M25 or A13 to Dartford tunnel r'bout. Ground is fifty yards on right down Ship Lane. Nearest station is Purfleet, two miles from ground
Capacity: 4,500 Cover: 1,000 Seats: 300 Floodlights: Yes
Clubhouse: Steward: Tommy South
Club Shop: Selling programmes & magazines. Contact Tommy South (01708 868901)

PREVIOUS **League:** Essex Senior 85-89. **Grounds:** None

CLUB RECORDS **Attendance:** 2,572 v West Ham United, friendly 1998.
Goalscorer: George Georgiou 106. **Appearances:** Jimmy McFarlane 399
Win: 10-0 v Stansted (H) 86-87, v East Ham Utd (A) 87-88 (both Essex Senior League)
Defeat: 0-6 v St Leonards Stamco(A), FA Trophy 96-97. 0-6 v Sutton United(H) Isthmian Lge 97-98

BEST SEASON **FA Cup:** Fourth Qual Replay 95-96 (lost 1-3 away to Rushden & D)
FA Trophy: Second Rd Prop 95-96 (lost 1-2 away to Macclesfield Tn)

HONOURS: Isthmian Lg Div 2 91-92 Div 1 R-up 93-94, Div 2 Nth R-up 88-89, Associate Members Tphy 91-92; Essex Snr Lg 87-88 (Lg Cup (2) 86-88; Essex Snr. Cup R-up 97-98, 99-00, Stanford Charity Cup 87-88 (R-up 85-86); Essex Thames-Side Trophy 94-95; Essex Bus Houses Sen L/Cup 93-94; F Budden Trophy 94-95; Essex & HertsBorder Comb R-up 94-95; Full Members Cup R-up 99-00, 00-01.

Players progressing to Football League: Paul Cobb & Lee Williams (Leyton O.)

John Keeling (light shirt) Purfleet's No. 8 in an aerial tussle with Jamie Wallace of Grays. **Photo:** Alan Coomes

Date	Comp.	Opponents	Att.	Score	Goalscorers
19.08	Ryman P	HITCHIN TOWN	201	0 - 1	
22.08	Ryman P	Dulwich Hamlet	205	1 - 1	Southon 35
26.08	Ryman P	Slough Town	452	2 - 3	Southon 18, Carthy 26
28.08	Ryman P	BILLERICAY TOWN	340	1 - 1	Carthy 42
02.09	Ryman P	FARNBOROUGH TOWN	301	0 - 2	
04.09	Ryman P	Croydon	130	0 - 0	
09.09	Ryman P	ST ALBANS CITY	257	1 - 3	Keeling 78
12.09	Lge Cup 1	Uxbridge	77	3 - 2	Georgiou 22, Carthy 44, McFarlane 82
16.09	Ryman P	Sutton United	503	2 - 2	Coombs 4, Georgiou 45
23.09	Ryman P	Heybridge Swifts	254	3 - 4	Carthy 16, Georgiou 45 67
30.09	FA Cup Q2	IPSWICH WANDERERS	108	3 - 1	Georgiou 30 46[p], Coombs 60
06.10	Ryman P	Canvey Island	542	0 - 1	
14.10	FA Cup Q3	GRANTHAM TOWN	207	2 - 2	Georgiou 18[p], Coombs 35
17.10	FA Cup Q3 R	Grantham Town	506	0 - 1	
21.10	Ryman P	HAMPTON & RICHMOND BOR.	173	2 - 2	Carthy 30 71
23.10	FMC 1	BOREHAM WOOD	68	3 - 1	McFarlane, Engwell, Carthy
04.11	Ryman P	ALDERSHOT TOWN	653	2 - 2	Buglione 75, Adedeji 79[og]
11.11	Ryman P	CARSHALTON ATHLETIC	178	3 - 0	Buglione 20, Carthy 35, Georgiou 67
18.11	Ryman P	Basingstoke Town	404	2 - 1	Buglione 11 58
25.11	Ryman P	MAIDENHEAD UNITED	169	1 - 1	Carthy 59
28.11	Essex SC 3	Aveley	77	4 - 0	Carthy(2), Georgiou(2)
02.12	FA Trophy 2	Northwood	218	1 - 3	Pashley 80
11.12	Lge Cup 2	HORSHAM	72	4 - 0	Georgiou 8 86, Buglione 18, Engwell 80
16.12	Ryman P	Farnborough Town	502	2 - 3	Ling 3, Simpson 6
23.12	Ryman P	ENFIELD	264	3 - 0	Georgiou 16, Carthy 35, Simpson 43
26.12	Ryman P	Grays Athletic	289	1 - 1	Adams 90
06.01	Ryman P	Carshalton Athletic	284	0 - 1	
09.01	Ryman P	Gravesend & Northfleet	454	0 - 1	
13.01	Ryman P	SLOUGH TOWN	201	2 - 0	Adams 7, Simpson 82
15.01	Essex SC 4	SOUTHEND UNITED	124	4 - 0	McFarlane, Carthy, Simpson, Keeling
29.01	FMC 2	CANVEY ISLAND	180	1 - 0	Ling 61
02.02	Ryman P	HARROW BOROUGH	186	4 - 2	Simpson 2[p] 19 45 57
10.02	Ryman P	CROYDON	162	3 - 0	Buglione 10, Adams 17, Simpson 35
17.02	Ryman P	St Albans City	323	2 - 0	Simpson 27, Adams 45
19.02	Ryman P	DULWICH HAMLET	231	1 - 1	Ling 39
22.02	FMC 3	Heybridge Swifts	67	3 - 1	Georgiou(2), A N Other
24.02	Ryman P	Hendon	203	2 - 1	Southon 44, Georgiou 59
03.03	Ryman P	CANVEY ISLAND	443	0 - 1	
06.03	Ryman P	Hitchin Town	176	1 - 0	Carthy 84
13.03	Essex SC QF	TILBURY	n.k	1 - 0	Carthy
15.03	FMC QF	Barton Rovers	61	1 - 0	Martin 8[p]
19.03	Ryman P	HENDON	162	0 - 0	
24.03	Ryman P	GRAVESEND & NORTHFLEET	201	1 - 0	McFarlane 29
26.03	Lge Cup 3	Aylesbury United	133	1 - 0	McFarlane 70
29.03	Lge Cup QF	Northwood	129	1 - 4	Ullathorne
31.03	Ryman P	Hampton & Richmond Borough	367	0 - 2	
02.04	Ryman P	SUTTON UNITED	189	2 - 1	McFarlane 19, Carthy 70
07.04	Ryman P	BASINGSTOKE TOWN	197	0 - 0	
10.04	Essex SC SF	CANVEY ISLAND	202	0 - 1	
12.04	Ryman P	Aldershot Town	1410	0 - 3	
14.04	Ryman P	Enfield	185	1 - 2	Greaves 47
16.04	Ryman P	GRAYS ATHLETIC	302	3 - 1	Blunden 36 54, Sains 63
19.04	Ryman P	HEYBRIDGE SWIFTS	163	1 - 1	Martin 45
21.04	Ryman P	Maidenhead United	194	2 - 1	McFarlane 10, Keeling 83
24.04	Ryman P	Billericay Town	346	1 - 1	Martin 59
28.04	Ryman P	CHESHAM UNITED	239	1 - 2	Martin 41
01.05	Ryman P	Chesham United	140	0 - 5	
03.05	FMC SF	Oxford City	103	3 - 1	Heighway, Blunden, Keeling
05.05	Ryman P	Harrow Borough	248	2 - 1	Keeling 24, Blunden 87
10.05	FMC F	Gravesend & Northfleet	511	1 - 3	Simpson 7

PLAYING SQUAD

GOALKEEPERS: Steve Mead (Concord R)

DEFENDERS: Jim McFarlane (Concord R), Gary Howard (Dag & Red), Jamie Southon (Chelmsford), Greg Berry (Millwall), John Purdie (Billericay)

MIDFIELDERS: Kierna Adams (Boreham Wood), Jon Keeling (Tilbury), Martin Ling (Leyton Orient), Paul Cole (Tilbury), Paul Linger (Billericay)

FORWARDS: Martin Buglione (Ashford T), Keith Martin (Tilbury), Simon Ullathorne (Aldershot), Colin Simpson (Chesham Utd)

St ALBANS CITY

CLUB OFFICIALS

Chairman: **Lee Harding**
President: **Cllr Malcolm MacMillan**
Vice Chairman: **Paul Farmer**
Secretary: **Steve Eames** c/o Club
Safety Officer: **Rex Winn** 0966 175124 (M)
Comm. Man: **Roberta Rolland**

FOOTBALL MANAGEMENT TEAM

Manager: John Kendall
Physio: T.B.A.

FACT FILE

Formed: 1908
Nickname: The Saints
Colours: Yellow , blue & white
Change colours: Sky Blue, white & red
Midweek home matchday: Tuesday
Newsline: 0930 555822
Club Website:http://www.scfc.co.uk
E-Mail: info@sacfc,co,uk

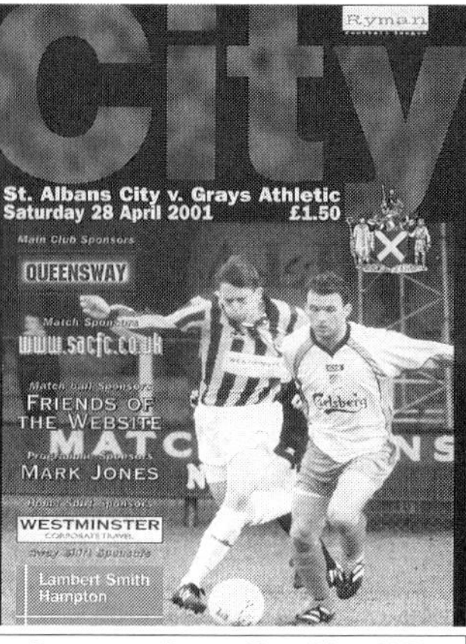

Programme: Pages: 32 Price: £1.50
Published by Queensway Publishing
Local Press: St Albans & District Observer, Herts Advertiser
Local Radio: BBC Three Counties, Chiltern Radio, Oasis

GROUND: Clarence Park, York Rd, St Albans, Herts AL1 4PL Tel: 01727 864296
Directions: Left out of St Albans station - Clarence Pk 200yds ahead acrossHatfield Rd. M25, jct 21 to Noke Hotel island, straight on thru Chiswell Green towards St Albans, straight over 2 mini-r'bouts and one larger island, thru 2sets of lights and right at island at far end of city centre (St Peters St.) into Hatfield Rd, over mini-r'bout, left at 2nd lights into Clarence Rd, ground on left
Capacity: 6,000 Cover: 1,900 Seats: 904 Floodlights: Yes
Clubhouse: Open matchdays and available for functions. Manager: Keri Farmer(01727 866819) Tea bar within ground serves hot food
Club Shop: Club merchandise & League & non-League progs,magazines, videos etc
Managers: Lee Woods c/o club

PREVIOUS **Leagues:** Herts County 08-10; Spartan 08-20; Athenian 20-23

CLUB RECORDS **Attendance:** 9,757 v Ferryhill Ath., FA Amtr Cup QF 27/2/26
Appearances: Phil Wood 900 (62-85) Goalscorer: W H (Billy) Minter 356 (top scorer for 12 consecutive seasons 1920-32)
Win: 14-0 v Aylesbury United (H) Spartan Lge 19/10/12 **Defeat:** 0-11 v Wimbledon (H), Isthmian Lge 9/11/46.
Fee Paid: £6,000 for Paul Turner (Yeovil Town Aug 97) **Fee Received:** £92,750 for Dean Austin (Southend 90/Spurs 92)

BEST SEASON **FA Amateur Cup:** Semi final 22-23 24-25 25-26 69-70. **FA Trophy:** Semi-Final 1998-99 1-2 & 2-3 v Forest Green Rovers
FA Cup: 2nd Rd replay 68-69 (1-3 at Walsall after 1-1 draw), 80-81 (1-4 atTorquay after 1-1 draw), 96-97 (9-2 at Bristol City)

HONOURS: Isthmian Lg 23-24 26-27 27-28 (R-up 54-55 92-93), Div 1 85-86, Div 2 R-up 83-84, Lg Cup R-up 89-90, Res. Sect. R-up 48-49 60-61 61-62; Athenian Lg 20-21 21-22 (R-up 22-23); Spartan Lg 11-12 (R-up 12-13, East Div 09-10); Herts Co. Lg 09-10 (West Div 08-09, Aubrey Cup(res) 61-62); London Snr Cup 70-71 (R-up 69-70); AFA Snr Cup 33-34 (R-up 30-31 32-33 34-35); E Anglian Cup 92-93; Herts SnrCup(13) (R-up 10), Herts Snr Tphy 86-87, Herts Charity Cup(25) (R-up(18);Mithras Cup 64-65 71-72 (R-up 76-77); Wycombe F'lit Cup(2) 68-70; St AlbansHosp Cup 45-46; Hitchin Centenary Cup 70-71 (R-up 71-72); Victory Cup 25-26 27-28, Liege Cup 26-27; Billy Minter Invit. Cup (3) 90-93

Players progressing: A Grimsdell (Spurs 11), G Edmonds (Watford 14), R Burke(Man Utd 46), J Meadows (Watford 51), M Rose (Charlton 63), J Kinnear (Spurs 65), J Mitchell (Fulham 72), A Cockram (Brentford 88), D Austin (Southend 90),T Kelly (Stoke 90), M Danzey (Cambridge 92), D Williams (Brentford 93),

L - R - Back row: Danny Honeyball, Mike Bignall, Rob Smith, Younis Nabil, Gary Wraight, John Rattle.
Middle Row: Darren Fenton, Richard Evans, Christian Metcalfe, Gary Ansell, Corey Campbell, Richard Wilmot
Front Row: Derek Brown, Andy Linighan, Steve Cook & Gary Roberts *(Co-managers)* Steve Rutter *(Coach)* Richard Goddard, Ryan Moran

Date	Comp.	Opponents	Att.	Score	Goalscorers
04.08	Herts CC 1	STEVENAGE BOROUGH	n.k	1 - 3	Moran
19.08	Ryman P	Carshalton Athletic	377	1 - 1	Campbell 69
22.08	Ryman P	CANVEY ISLAND	424	1 - 4	Ansell 21
26.08	Ryman P	HAMPTON & RICHMOND BOR.	457	5 - 0	Piper 13, Ansell 52, Samuels 49, Randall 77, Hannigan 79
28.08	Ryman P	Gravesend & Northfleet	481	0 - 1	
02.09	Ryman P	Enfield	229	3 - 2	Piper 12, Samuels 23, Ansell 56[p]
05.09	Ryman P	HENDON	522	1 - 3	Ansell 22
09.09	Ryman P	Purfleet	257	3 - 1	Piper 64 75, Jones 66
12.09	Lge Cup 1	BOREHAM WOOD	157	1 - 1	Jones
16.09	Ryman P	ALDERSHOT TOWN	982	0 - 1	
19.09	Ryman P	Billericay Town	339	1 - 2	Piper 14
23.09	Ryman P	SUTTON UNITED	452	0 - 1	
30.09	FA Cup Q2	Baldock Town	432	0 - 0	
03.10	FA Cup Q2 R	BALDOCK TOWN	185	1 - 2	Evans 29
07.10	Ryman P	BASINGSTOKE TOWN	295	0 - 3	
14.10	Ryman P	Slough Town	509	2 - 1	Samuels 73, Piper 79
21.10	Ryman P	Croydon	138	2 - 0	Simba 75, Piper 90
28.10	Ryman P	HITCHIN TOWN	647	2 - 0	Piper 34 84
31.10	Lge Cup 1 R	Boreham Wood	151	3 - 2	Samuels(2), Ansell
05.11	FA Trophy 1	Chelmsford City	512	2 - 0	Simba 25 32
11.11	Ryman P	HARROW BOROUGH	486	1 - 0	Simpson 87
18.11	Ryman P	Heybridge Swifts	337	1 - 0	Simba 89
21.11	Herts SC 2	Royston Town	114	6 - 0	Knight, Maynard(2), Simpson(2), Campbell
25.11	Ryman P	FARNBOROUGH TOWN	708	2 - 4	Simpson 65, Piper 84
28.11	Lge Cup 2	LEATHERHEAD	101	3 - 1	Cook 24 71, Knight 60
02.12	FA Trophy 2	Bashley	283	7 - 1	Ansell 4[p] 59, Piper 32 56, Wraight 62, Knight 69, Pratt 80
05.12	FMC 2	Northwood	161	4 - 3	Wraight, Piper, Ansell, OG
09.12	Ryman P	MAIDENHEAD UNITED	628	3 - 1	Moran 6, Ansell 27, Knight 47
16.12	Ryman P	Canvey Island	805	1 - 3	Ansell 76
23.12	Ryman P	DULWICH HAMLET	637	2 - 1	Simpson 60, Ansell 90
26.12	Ryman P	Chesham United	621	0 - 2	
01.01	Ryman P	ENFIELD	1009	0 - 1	
06.01	Ryman P	Harrow Borough	305	2 - 2	Moran 28, Strevens 45
09.01	Lge Cup 3	MARLOW	109	3 - 1	Goddard, Strevens, Cooper
13.01	FA Trophy 3	NEWPORT COUNTY	604	1 - 0	Strevens 13
27.01	Ryman P	Aldershot Town	2264	3 - 2	Davis 37, Blaney 43, Simba 66
03.02	FA Trophy 4	Chester City	1442	2 - 3	Simba 25 90
06.02	Ryman P	CARSHALTON ATHLETIC	333	0 - 1	
14.02	Lge Cup QF	HAMPTON & RICHMOND BOR.	120	3 - 3	Hillier, Simba(2)
17.02	Ryman P	PURFLEET	323	0 - 2	
20.02	FMC 3	Chesham United	288	2 - 0	Roach(2)
24.02	Ryman P	SLOUGH TOWN	436	1 - 0	Simpson 29
27.02	Lge Cup QF R	Hampton & Richmond Borough	157	0 - 3	
03.03	Ryman P	Basingstoke Town	475	1 - 2	Blaney 57
10.03	Ryman P	BILLERICAY TOWN	501	0 - 0	
20.03	Ryman P	Hampton & Richmond Borough	151	2 - 1	Davis 13, Blaney 65[p]
31.03	Ryman P	CROYDON	326	2 - 2	Moran 46, Goddard 70
07.04	Ryman P	HEYBRIDGE SWIFTS	284	3 - 0	Evans 3, Morrison 32, Wraight 40
10.04	Ryman P	GRAVESEND & NORTHFLEET	233	0 - 2	
12.04	FMC QF	Gravesend & Northfleet	119	1 - 1	Dawes (3-4p)
14.04	Ryman P	Dulwich Hamlet	283	0 - 1	
16.04	Ryman P	CHESHAM UNITED	385	1 - 5	Blaney 30
18.04	Ryman P	Hendon	183	1 - 0	Davis 14
21.04	Ryman P	Farnborough Town	677	0 - 4	
24.04	Ryman P	Sutton United	385	2 - 4	Andrews 30, Pratt 60
28.04	Ryman P	GRAYS ATHLETIC	292	1 - 2	Wraight 36
01.05	Ryman P	Grays Athletic	169	0 - 6	
03.05	Ryman P	Hitchin Town	242	0 - 0	
05.05	Ryman P	Maidenhead United	256	0 - 1	

PLAYING SQUAD

GOALKEEPERS: Richard Wilmot (Hendon)

DEFENDERS: Richard Goddard (Woking), Derek Brown (Baldock), Andy Linighan (Oxford Utd), Ryan Moran (Luton), Richard Preston (Baldock), Danny Honeyball (Aylesbury), Jon Rattle (Baldock), Corey Campbell (Gravesend)

MIDFIELDERS: Gary Wraight (Stevenage), Simon Dunlop (Baldock), Rob Smith (Baldock), Steve Cook (Baldock), Richard Evans (Chertsey), Darren Fenton (Baldock), Christian Metcalfe (Hayes)

FORWARDS: Youness Nabil (Boreham W.), Mike Bignall (Baldock), Dominic Gentle (Billericay), Gary Ansell (Barnet)

SUTTON UNITED

CLUB OFFICIALS
Chairman: Bruce Elliott
President: Andrew W Letts
Secretary: Dave Farebrother,
38 Plevna Rd Hampton.TW12 2BP
Tel: 0771 2682415 (M)
Press Officer: Tony Dolbear
Tel: Mobile 07966 507023

FOOTBALL MANAGEMENT TEAM
Manager: John Rains
Assistant Manager: Tony Rains
Coach: Micky Cook **Physio:** Dennis Rose
Youth& Res Team Manager: Phil Dunne

FACT FILE
Formed: 1898 Nickname: The U's
Sponsors: Securicor
Colours:
Amber & chocolate/chocolate/amber & chocolate
Change colours: Green & white/black/black
Midweek matchday: Tuesday
Reserve League: Suburban League
Local Press: Sutton Advertiser, Sutton Guardian, Sutton Independent, Sutton Comet
Local Radio: Thames Radio, County Sound
2000-01
Leading Scorer: Danny Bolt 24
Player of the Year: Ryan Palmer
Captain: Dave Harlow

RYMAN LEAGUE PREMIER DIVISION
-v- MAIDENHEAD UNITED
ALLDERS of SUTTON
Ryman football league
Sutton United FC
Main Club Sponsors
securicor

Pages: 48 Price: £1.50
Editor: Mackrory - Iain Jamieson
Email iainmj@hotmail.com

Other club publications:
'Touchliner' (Supporters' Club)

GROUND: Borough Sports Ground, Gander Green Lane, Sutton, Surrey SM1 2EY Tel: 0208 6444440 Fax: 0208 6445120 Website: www.btinternet.com/~suttonunited
Directions: Gander Green Lane runs between A232 (Cheam Road - turn by Sutton Cricket Club) and A217 (Oldfields Road - turn at`Goose & Granite' PH lights). Ground opposite `The Plough' 50 yards from West Sutton BR station. Bus 413 passes ground
Capacity: 7,032 **Seated**: 765 **Terracing - Covered:** 1,250 **Uncovered:** 5,000
Clubhouse: Open every day, food. Available for hire with five function rooms
Club Shop: Open matchdays selling a full range of souvenirs, etc, contact Tony Cove via club

PREVIOUS **Leagues:** Sutton Junior, Southern Sub 10-21, Athenian 21-63, Isthmian 63-86, 91-99, GMVC 86-91, 99-00
Names: Sutton Association, Sutton Guild Rovers **Grounds:** Western Road, Manor Lane, London Road, The Find.

CLUB RECORDS **Attendance:** 14,000 v Leeds United,FA Cup 4th Rd 24/1/70
Victory: 11-1 v Clapton 66, & leatherhead 82-83 **Defeat:** 13-0 v Barking 25-26
Scorer: Paul McKinnon (279) **Appearances:** Larry Pritchard 781 (65-84)
Fee Paid: to Malmo FF for Paul McKinnon 83 **Fee Received:** £100,000 for Efan Ekoku (Bournemouth 90)

BEST SEASON **FA Amateur Cup:** Runners-up 62-63 68-69; SF 28-29 36-37 67-68 **FA Trophy:** Runners-up 80-81; SF 92-93,99-00 **FA Cup:** 4th Rd-69-70, 0-6 v Leeds Utd (H); 88-89, 0-8 v Norwich C.(A), 3rd Rd 87-88 v Middlesbrough 1-1, 0-1, 93-94 v Notts Co(A)2-3

HONOURS Bob Lord Trophy 90-91; **Isthmian League** 66-67 84-86 98-99 R-up 67-68 70-71 81-82, Lge Cup (3) 82-84 85-86 97-98 R-up 79-80; Loctite Cup 91-92; Carlton Cup 95-96; **Athenian Lge** 27-28 45-46 57-58 R-up 46-47, Lg Cup 45-46 55-56 61-62 62-63, Res Sec 61-62 R-up 32-33; Anglo Italian Semi-Pro Cup 79 R-up 80 82; London Snr Cup 57-58 82-83; London Charity Cup 69-70 R-up 67-68 68-69 72-73; Surrey Snr Cup x14 R-up x9; Surrey Interm. Cup x4 R-up x6; Surrey Jnr Cup R-up 09-10; Surrey Snr Char. Sh. x3 R-up x6; Surrey Interm Char. Cup 31-32 R-up 34-35 38-39; Dylon Char. Sh. 84 R-up 80 82 83 85; Groningen Yth tournament 83 85 R-up 79 81 89 91; John Ullman Invit. Cup 88-89

Past Players progressing: Numerous including the following since 1980 - S Galloway (C Palace 84), P McKinnon (Blackburn 86), R Fearon (Ipswich 87), PHarding (Notts Co), E Ekoku (Bournemouth 91), M Golley (Maidstone), A Barnes (C Palace 91), P Rogers (Sheff U 92), S Massey (C Palace 92), A & R Scott (Sheff U 93), O Morah (Cambridge 94), M Watson (West Ham 95), E Hutchinson (Brentford 2000)

Back row (l-r): Chris Boothe, Nko Ekoku (now Chesham Utd), Chuck Martini, Danny Arkwright, Tommy Dunn, Rob Haworth, Michael Mison.
Middle row: Tony Rains (asst. man.), Ryan Palmer, Scott Corbett, John Rains (manager), Richard Taylor, Stuart Hammonds, Mick Cook (coach).
Front row: Jon Palmer, Eddie Akuamoah, Matt Fowler, Dave Timothy, Paul Honey, Danny Brooker, Gary Drewett **Photo:** Gary Letts

Date	Comp.	Opponents	Att.	Score	Goalscorers
19.08	Ryman P	Aldershot Town	2547	1 - 1	Salako 76
22.08	Ryman P	BASINGSTOKE TOWN	645	2 - 0	Bolt 17, Salako 62
26.08	Ryman P	CANVEY ISLAND	652	0 - 1	
28.08	Ryman P	Hendon	370	1 - 0	Ekoku 90
02.09	Ryman P	Grays Athletic	302	2 - 1	Nartey 65, Sears 81
05.09	Ryman P	HAMPTON & RICHMOND BOR.	564	2 - 2	Bolt 30 75
09.09	Ryman P	Gravesend & Northfleet	499	2 - 2	Barnett 29[og], Nartey 79
12.09	Lge Cup 1	Corinthian Casuals	166	0 - 1	
16.09	Ryman P	PURFLEET	503	2 - 2	Forrester 39, Thompson 90
19.09	Ryman P	SLOUGH TOWN	468	1 - 1	Hobson 84
23.09	Ryman P	St Albans City	452	1 - 0	Thompson 90
30.09	FA Cup Q2	Littlehampton Town	396	5 - 0	Forrester 46, Thompson 48 90, Bolt 71[p], Sears 86
07.10	Ryman P	Dulwich Hamlet	420	1 - 2	Panter 75
14.10	FA Cup Q3	Bath City	897	0 - 3	
21.10	Ryman P	Billericay Town	566	5 - 0	Boothe 7, Thompson 17 51, Palmer 26, Bolt 86
24.10	FMC 1	Staines Town	158	4 - 4	Harford(2), Palmer, Bolt[p] 6 5
28.10	Ryman P	CROYDON	584	2 - 1	Haworth 6, Bolt 43[p]
04.11	FA Trophy 1	Weymouth	734	1 - 2	Boothe 66
11.11	Ryman P	FARNBOROUGH TOWN	644	1 - 0	Bolt 58
18.11	Ryman P	Maidenhead United	258	2 - 0	Bolt 4 10
05.12	FMC 2	CROYDON	194	2 - 2	Bolt(2) 4 3
16.12	Ryman P	Basingstoke Town	477	0 - 1	
23.12	Ryman P	HEYBRIDGE SWIFTS	574	1 - 2	Bolt 51
26.12	Ryman P	Carshalton Athletic	1064	1 - 0	Thompson 27
06.01	Ryman P	Farnborough Town	781	1 - 2	Boothe 24
13.01	Ryman P	HITCHIN TOWN	520	1 - 1	Bolt 84
30.01	Surrey SC 1	DULWICH HAMLET	206	1 - 0	Whitmarsh
06.02	FMC 3	Uxbridge	110	0 - 2	
10.02	Ryman P	Hampton & Richmond Borough	550	1 - 3	Haworth 23
13.02	Ryman P	Canvey Island	331	2 - 6	Williams 48, Whitmarsh 54
17.02	Ryman P	GRAVESEND & NORTHFLEET	543	1 - 4	Ekoku 10
20.02	Surrey SC QF	Whyteleafe	180	0 - 2	
24.02	Ryman P	Hitchin Town	413	0 - 3	
27.02	Ryman P	CHESHAM UNITED	387	2 - 3	Bolt 63[p] 68
03.03	Ryman P	DULWICH HAMLET	509	7 - 1	Boothe 23, Whitmarsh 25, Haworth 35 75, Bolt 60 66 86
06.03	Ryman P	ENFIELD	446	2 - 3	Haworth 49, Ekoku 55
10.03	Ryman P	Slough Town	556	4 - 4	Ekoku 12, Bolt 53, Whitmarsh 59 84
20.03	Ryman P	Harrow Borough	180	1 - 2	Bolt 43
27.03	Ryman P	GRAYS ATHLETIC	390	2 - 3	Haworth 31, Boothe 56
02.04	Ryman P	Purfleet	189	1 - 2	Boothe 78
04.04	Ryman P	Croydon	204	1 - 2	Haworth 56
07.04	Ryman P	HARROW BOROUGH	466	3 - 3	Bolt 3, Honey 49, Gray 90
10.04	Ryman P	ALDERSHOT TOWN	659	1 - 1	Whitmarsh 78
14.04	Ryman P	Heybridge Swifts	310	2 - 2	Bolt 40, Haworth 89
16.04	Ryman P	CARSHALTON ATHLETIC	902	3 - 1	Whitmarsh 15 52, Harlow 44
19.04	Ryman P	BILLERICAY TOWN	389	1 - 4	Boothe 53
21.04	Ryman P	Chesham United	306	3 - 0	Whitmarsh 50, Haworth 60, Gray 90
24.04	Ryman P	ST ALBANS CITY	385	4 - 2	McCormack 25, Palmer 51, Boothe 53, Baker 63
28.04	Ryman P	MAIDENHEAD UNITED	476	2 - 0	Haworth 63, Bolt 87
05.05	Ryman P	Enfield	231	2 - 2	Haworth 50, Whitmarsh 79
15.05	Friendly	CHELSEA XI	1022	3 - 3	Bolt, Haworth, Whitmarsh

Unplayed Ryman P HENDON

PLAYING SQUAD

GOALKEEPERS: Tommy Dunn (Youth), Chuck Martini (King's Lynn)

DEFENDERS: Stuart Hammonds (Lincoln Utd), Ryan Palmer (Brighton), Danny Arkwright (Whyteleafe), Neil Baker (Boreham Wood), Michael Mison (St.Albans), Danny Brooker (Kingstonian)

MIDFIELDERS: Scott Corbett (Farnborough), Gary Drewett)Kingstonian), Paul Honey (Youth), David Timothy (Woking)

FORWARDS: Rob Haworth (Dag & Red), Eddie Akuamoah (Kingstonian), Matt Gray (Youth), Chris Boothe (Farnborough), Matt Fowler (Carshalton), Jon Palmer (King's Lynn)

CARSHALTON ATHLETIC Match Facts 2000-01

Date	Comp.	Opponents	Att.	Score	Goalscorers
12.08	Tom Fuller	Cup Tooting & Mitcham United	n.k	0 - 4	
19.08	Ryman P	ST ALBANS CITY	377	1 - 1	Elverson 11[p]
22.08	Ryman P	Hitchin Town	301	0 - 3	
26.08	Ryman P	Farnborough Town	521	0 - 3	
28.08	Ryman P	HEYBRIDGE SWIFTS	230	1 - 1	Jones 68
02.09	Ryman P	BILLERICAY TOWN	337	5 - 0	Liddle 6, Pace 32, Jones 38, Thomas 76, Elverson 79
05.09	Ryman P	Chesham United	295	1 - 3	Brodrick 40
09.09	Ryman P	DULWICH HAMLET	344	3 - 1	Elverson 25, Thomas 78 88
12.09	Lge Cup 1	HITCHIN TOWN	82	1 - 0	Jones
16.09	Ryman P	Harrow Borough	208	2 - 2	Thomas 42 90
23.09	Ryman P	ENFIELD	356	2 - 1	N Robson 48, Thomas 76[p]
30.09	FA Cup Q2	CROYDON	312	1 - 1	Thomas 18
02.10	FA Cup Q2 R	Croydon	194	2 - 2	Robson 13, Thomas 63 (1-3p)
06.10	Ryman P	GRAVESEND & NORTHFLEET	336	1 - 3	Elverson 55
21.10	Ryman P	CANVEY ISLAND	356	1 - 4	Pace 21
24.10	FMC 1	BASINGSTOKE TOWN	102	3 - 3	Pace 31, Elverson 90, Liddle 95 (2-4p)
28.10	Ryman P	Heybridge Swifts	232	1 - 2	Liddle 38
04.11	FA Trophy 1	Wisbech Town	253	2 - 1	Liddle 32, Page 51
11.11	Ryman P	Purfleet	178	0 - 3	
14.11	Lge Cup 2	Dulwich Hamlet	103	2 - 1	Pace 56, Tanner 101
18.11	Ryman P	HENDON	265	1 - 2	Pace 24
28.11	Ryman P	Hampton & Richmond Borough	184	2 - 4	Bartley 1, Brodrick 52
02.12	FA Trophy 2	HISTON	237	3 - 4	Bartley 36 66, Tanner 87
09.12	Ryman P	Croydon	165	0 - 3	
16.12	Ryman P	HITCHIN TOWN	260	0 - 5	
19.12	Lge Cup 3	HAMPTON & RICHMOND BOR.	101	0 - 3	
23.12	Ryman P	Aldershot Town	2175	0 - 4	
26.12	Ryman P	SUTTON UNITED	1064	0 - 1	
06.01	Ryman P	PURFLEET	284	1 - 0	Liddle 81
13.01	Ryman P	FARNBOROUGH TOWN	440	0 - 5	
23.01	Surrey SC 1	Metropolitan Police	n.k	4 - 1	Pace, Fairbrother, Drewett, Jones
27.01	Ryman P	CHESHAM UNITED	324	0 - 4	
30.01	Ryman P	SLOUGH TOWN	224	0 - 1	
06.02	Ryman P	St Albans City	333	1 - 0	Fowler 30
10.02	Ryman P	HARROW BOROUGH	281	1 - 1	Fowler 83
13.02	Ryman P	Grays Athletic	208	1 - 3	Fowler 29
17.02	Ryman P	Dulwich Hamlet	285	0 - 1	
24.02	Ryman P	MAIDENHEAD UNITED	285	1 - 0	Pace 24
03.03	Ryman P	Gravesend & Northfleet	524	0 - 3	
10.03	Ryman P	BASINGSTOKE TOWN	303	1 - 0	Pabrowa 61
20.03	Surrey SC QF	WOKING	103	1 - 4	Glasgow 4
24.03	Ryman P	GRAYS ATHLETIC	289	1 - 0	Pace 64
27.03	Ryman P	Billericay Town	244	0 - 0	
03.04	Ryman P	Basingstoke Town	226	1 - 1	Fowler 42
10.04	Ryman P	Enfield	151	1 - 2	Elverson 51
14.04	Ryman P	ALDERSHOT TOWN	670	2 - 1	Fowler 25[p], Pace 83
16.04	Ryman P	Sutton United	902	1 - 3	Fowler 29[p]
19.04	Ryman P	Hendon	135	0 - 1	
21.04	Ryman P	HAMPTON & RICHMOND BOR.	325	0 - 3	
28.04	Ryman P	Slough Town	528	1 - 3	Dabrowa 54
01.05	Ryman P	Maidenhead United	306	0 - 2	
03.05	Ryman P	Canvey Island	282	2 - 3	Pace 8, Fowler 50
05.05	Ryman P	CROYDON	269	4 - 2	Fowler 17 39, Glasgow 62, Pace 45

DULWICH HAMLET   Match Facts 2000-01

Date	Comp.	Opponents	Att.	Score	Goalscorers
19.08	Ryman P	Grays Athletic	210	1 - 1	Palmer 43
22.08	Ryman P	PURFLEET	205	1 - 1	Perkins 47
26.08	Ryman P	ENFIELD	360	1 - 1	Fowler 79
28.08	Ryman P	Basingstoke Town	488	2 - 2	Fowler 52 87
02.09	Ryman P	Aldershot Town	2031	0 - 1	
05.09	Ryman P	MAIDENHEAD UNITED	217	2 - 3	Fowler 38[p], P Garland 88
09.09	Ryman P	Carshalton Athletic	344	1 - 3	Fowler 48
12.09	Lge Cup 1	AVELEY	82	5 - 2	Fowler 15[p] 92, Palmer 33, Perkins 99, Dussard 115
16.09	Ryman P	CANVEY ISLAND	343	2 - 3	Fowler 67, Chin 83
19.09	Ryman P	Hampton & Richmond Borough	157	0 - 4	
23.09	Ryman P	HARROW BOROUGH	287	0 - 1	
30.09	FA Cup Q2	Selsey	318	2 - 1	P Garland 32, Perkins 34
07.10	Ryman P	SUTTON UNITED	420	2 - 1	Perkins 53 90
14.10	FA Cup Q3	LEWES	245	1 - 1	P Garland 53
17.10	FA Cup Q3 R	Lewes	228	0 - 0	3 1
21.10	Ryman P	CHESHAM UNITED	338	0 - 1	
28.10	FA Cup Q4	Hayes	464	2 - 4	Perkins 45, Fowler 45
04.11	FA Trophy 1	Cinderford Town	131	1 - 1	Webb 65
07.11	FA Trophy 1 R	CINDERFORD TOWN	137	1 - 2	Fowler 58
11.11	Ryman P	Billericay Town	430	0 - 3	
14.11	Lge Cup 2	CARSHALTON ATHLETIC	103	1 - 2	Perkins 59
18.11	Ryman P	SLOUGH TOWN	284	2 - 2	Webb 62, Fowler 90
25.11	Ryman P	Hitchin Town	237	0 - 1	
28.11	London SC 4	Bromley	n.k	6 - 3	Fowler(6)
02.12	Ryman P	GRAVESEND & NORTHFLEET	427	0 - 2	
16.12	Ryman P	ALDERSHOT TOWN	924	2 - 4	Abraham 63, Webb 90
23.12	Ryman P	St Albans City	637	1 - 2	O'Brien 90
26.12	Ryman P	CROYDON	271	1 - 4	Forrester 72
06.01	Ryman P	BILLERICAY TOWN	322	0 - 1	
09.01	FMC 2	WALTON & HERSHAM	74	2 - 1	Bartley 30, Perkins 85
13.01	Ryman P	Enfield	196	1 - 1	Perkins 56
20.01	Ryman P	GRAYS ATHLETIC	412	1 - 2	Abraham 80
27.01	Ryman P	Canvey Island	410	2 - 3	Richards 21 28
30.01	Surrey SC 1	Sutton United	206	0 - 1	
03.02	Ryman P	BASINGSTOKE TOWN	268	0 - 2	
17.02	Ryman P	CARSHALTON ATHLETIC	285	1 - 0	Bartley 76
19.02	Ryman P	Purfleet	231	1 - 1	Bartley 49
22.02	FMC 3	BASINGSTOKE TOWN	55	0 - 2	
24.02	Ryman P	FARNBOROUGH TOWN	517	0 - 2	
27.02	London SC QF		Ford United	n.k	1 - 3
03.03	Ryman P	Sutton United	509	1 - 7	Sears 31
06.03	Ryman P	Farnborough Town	502	0 - 3	
24.03	Ryman P	HEYBRIDGE SWIFTS	204	1 - 0	Richards 88
31.03	Ryman P	Chesham United	280	0 - 2	
07.04	Ryman P	Slough Town	368	1 - 1	Dyer 3
10.04	Ryman P	HAMPTON & RICHMOND BOR.	133	1 - 1	Nartey 77
14.04	Ryman P	ST ALBANS CITY	283	1 - 0	Chin 54
16.04	Ryman P	Croydon	185	1 - 1	Gray 19
19.04	Ryman P	Harrow Borough	128	1 - 2	Bartley 63
21.04	Ryman P	HITCHIN TOWN	277	0 - 2	
24.04	Ryman P	Maidenhead United	217	0 - 1	
25.04	Ryman P	Hendon	138	0 - 4	
28.04	Ryman P	Gravesend & Northfleet	443	1 - 2	Dyer 12
01.05	Ryman P	Heybridge Swifts	139	1 - 3	Goyle 20
05.05	Ryman P	HENDON	325	0 - 3	

SLOUGH TOWN — Match Facts 2000-01

Date	Comp.	Opponents	Att.	Score	Goalscorers
19.08	Ryman P	Gravesend & Northfleet	468	2 - 1	Allen 10, Barnett 75[og]
22.08	Ryman P	GRAYS ATHLETIC	503	1 - 0	Hawthorne 20
26.08	Ryman P	PURFLEET	452	3 - 2	Hall 6, Markman 57, Marshall 89
28.08	Ryman P	Enfield	306	1 - 1	Haynes 82
02.09	Ryman P	Canvey Island	653	0 - 1	
05.09	Ryman P	ALDERSHOT TOWN	1230	0 - 1	
09.09	Ryman P	Hendon	347	1 - 2	Hall 2
12.09	Lge Cup 1	Flackwell Heath	170	3 - 1	Hall[p], Rainford, McPherson
16.09	Ryman P	HAMPTON & RICHMOND BOR.	469	1 - 1	Marshall 90
19.09	Ryman P	Sutton United	468	1 - 1	Deaner 28
23.09	Ryman P	CROYDON	380	1 - 0	Markman 31
30.09	FA Cup Q2	Tonbridge Angels	578	0 - 2	
07.10	Ryman P	Heybridge Swifts	168	2 - 3	Markman 45, Townley 81
14.10	Ryman P	ST ALBANS CITY	509	1 - 2	Marshall 26
21.10	Ryman P	Hitchin Town	334	0 - 3	
24.10	FMC 1	ALDERSHOT TOWN	271	4 - 3	Kerr, Barrowcliff, Holsgrove, James
04.11	FA Trophy 1	BISHOP'S STORTFORD	426	5 - 0	Marshall 27 65 67, Hall 31 49
11.11	Ryman P	BASINGSTOKE TOWN	402	0 - 2	
14.11	Lge Cup 2	Marlow	226	2 - 0	Marshall 48, Holsgrove 81
18.11	Ryman P	Dulwich Hamlet	284	2 - 2	Archer 10, Rainford 82
28.11	Ryman P	HARROW BOROUGH	237	1 - 2	Black 27
02.12	FA Trophy 2	Newport County	627	1 - 2	Black 34
05.12	FMC 2	Bromley	106	0 - 1	
09.12	Ryman P	CHESHAM UNITED	517	0 - 2	
16.12	Ryman P	Grays Athletic	193	0 - 1	
23.12	Ryman P	FARNBOROUGH TOWN	582	0 - 2	
26.12	Ryman P	Maidenhead United	615	0 - 1	
06.01	Ryman P	Basingstoke Town	538	2 - 3	Lambert 45, Archer 76
13.01	Ryman P	Purfleet	201	0 - 2	
27.01	Ryman P	Hampton & Richmond Borough	458	0 - 2	
30.01	Ryman P	Carshalton Athletic	224	1 - 0	Holsgrove 87
03.02	Ryman P	ENFIELD	490	3 - 1	Allen 10, Hall 65, Lambert 86
10.02	Ryman P	Aldershot Town	1762	0 - 1	
17.02	Ryman P	HENDON	433	1 - 0	McPherson 87
20.02	B&B SC 3	Maidenhead United	n.k	0 - 2	
24.02	Ryman P	St Albans City	436	0 - 1	
03.03	Ryman P	HEYBRIDGE SWIFTS	353	1 - 1	Marshall 67
10.03	Ryman P	SUTTON UNITED	556	4 - 4	Marshall 21 37, Cross 22, Hall 86
24.03	Ryman P	Billericay Town	363	0 - 0	
31.03	Ryman P	HITCHIN TOWN	414	0 - 3	
02.04	Ryman P	Croydon	119	1 - 4	Timothy 74
07.04	Ryman P	DULWICH HAMLET	368	1 - 1	Marshall 37
10.04	Ryman P	BILLERICAY TOWN	330	2 - 3	Rainford 67[p] 88
14.04	Ryman P	Farnborough Town	688	1 - 1	Coombes 88
16.04	Ryman P	MAIDENHEAD UNITED	726	1 - 0	Markman 89
19.04	Ryman P	CANVEY ISLAND	333	0 - 1	
21.04	Ryman P	Harrow Borough	386	0 - 1	
24.04	Ryman P	GRAVESEND & NORTHFLEET	312	2 - 0	Asamdoh 67 82
28.04	Ryman P	CARSHALTON ATHLETIC	528	3 - 1	Coombes 84, Rainford 90[p], Asamoh 90
05.05	Ryman P	Chesham United	449	0 - 2	

DIVISION ONE FINAL LEAGUE TABLE 2000-01

		P	W	D	L	F	A	W	D	L	F	A	Pts	GD
1	Boreham Wood	42	15	2	4	48	27	11	5	5	34	22	85	33
2	Bedford Town	42	14	6	1	50	19	8	10	3	31	21	82	41
3	Braintree Town	42	15	3	3	64	24	10	3	8	48	36	81	52
4	Bishop's Stortford	42	13	2	6	58	37	11	4	6	45	39	78	27
5	Thame United	42	13	3	5	50	27	9	5	7	36	27	74	32
6	Ford United	42	9	6	6	30	26	10	6	5	40	32	69	12
7	Uxbridge	42	12	2	7	44	24	9	3	9	29	31	68	18
8	Northwood	42	11	4	6	50	39	9	4	8	39	42	68	8
9	Whyteleafe	42	11	2	8	33	32	9	4	8	29	37	66	-7
10	Oxford City	42	8	7	6	37	25	8	6	7	27	24	61	15
11	Harlow Town	42	10	9	2	34	22	5	7	9	36	44	61	4
12	Worthing	42	7	6	8	35	32	9	3	9	34	37	57	0
13	Staines Town	42	7	6	8	30	30	9	2	10	30	36	56	-6
14	Aylesbury United	42	8	3	10	34	29	9	1	11	31	26	55	10
15	Yeading	42	8	5	8	38	34	7	4	10	34	40	54	-2
16	Bognor Regis Town	42	9	4	8	40	31	4	7	10	31	40	50	0
17	Walton & Hersham	42	6	5	10	22	35	8	3	10	37	45	50	-21
18	Bromley	42	7	3	11	28	40	7	3	11	35	46	48	-23
19	Wealdstone	42	5	6	10	30	34	7	3	11	24	39	45	-19
20	Leatherhead	42	8	3	10	30	38	4	1	16	7	49	40	-50
21	Romford	42	6	2	13	33	54	3	2	16	20	59	31	-60
22	Barton Rovers	42	1	3	17	10	38	1	6	14	20	56	15	-64

DIVISION ONE RESULTS CHART 2000-01

		1	2	3	4	5	6	7	8	9	10	11	12	13	14	15	16	17	18	19	20	21	22
1	Aylesbury U	X	0-0	3-0	1-2	2-0	2-2	1-2	1-4	1-1	1-3	1-0	5-1	1-0	0-1	0-4	1-2	3-0	0-1	0-2	5-1	1-2	5-1
2	Barton R	0-4	X	0-1	0-1	2-2	0-2	0-3	1-2	0-1	1-3	0-1	0-1	0-0	2-1	0-1	1-2	1-3	0-0	0-1	0-2	2-4	0-3
3	Bedford T	1-0	1-1	X	3-1	1-1	1-0	2-2	3-0	2-3	4-0	3-0	6-1	2-1	3-1	4-4	1-0	0-0	2-1	4-1	1-1	1-0	5-1
4	Bishop's S	2-3	2-2	2-3	X	2-4	4-0	5-3	0-1	4-0	4-3	4-0	1-3	1-2	3-2	2-1	1-0	2-1	4-3	2-2	4-1	4-2	5-1
5	Bognor R T	2-1	2-0	0-1	2-5	X	0-2	2-0	1-2	2-3	1-1	5-0	2-2	2-0	5-0	4-5	1-1	1-0	2-3	2-3	1-1	1-0	2-1
6	Boreham W	3-2	2-0	3-0	0-3	3-1	X	1-4	1-0	1-1	6-3	2-1	2-0	1-1	3-0	2-0	1-0	2-3	3-0	2-1	0-3	4-2	6-2
7	Braintree T	3-2	2-1	2-1	1-1	2-1	0-3	X	5-0	2-4	2-1	4-0	1-2	3-1	10-0	4-1	4-1	3-0	5-1	1-1	5-0	2-2	3-1
8	Bromley	3-2	0-2	1-1	3-0	0-1	2-4	0-6	X	1-3	1-1	1-0	0-4	2-3	1-0	0-1	1-1	3-2	1-3	4-0	2-3	0-3	2-0
9	Ford Utd	2-0	4-2	1-1	0-0	0-0	1-1	0-3	3-1	X	0-3	2-1	2-0	0-0	1-0	3-0	1-3	2-2	0-2	2-1	5-1	1-2	0-3
10	Harlow T	0-0	3-0	0-0	2-2	0-0	1-1	0-0	3-1	3-2	X	3-0	3-2	0-2	2-2	1-3	0-0	1-1	3-2	3-1	2-1	3-2	1-0
11	Leatherhead	3-0	2-1	0-2	1-2	2-1	0-2	1-2	3-3	0-2	1-1	X	1-5	1-0	4-1	3-1	0-2	0-2	5-1	1-0	1-3	1-1	0-6
12	Northwood	1-3	1-0	2-2	7-3	2-2	1-1	3-2	3-2	2-3	4-2	4-1	X	1-1	2-0	1-0	1-5	0-1	5-3	3-1	4-1	2-4	1-2
13	Oxford C	0-2	5-1	0-0	2-2	2-1	2-2	1-0	3-2	1-1	1-1	3-0	2-5	X	0-1	5-0	0-0	0-1	2-2	3-0	1-2	4-1	0-1
14	Romford	0-1	2-2	0-6	1-2	1-4	0-4	2-4	2-3	1-3	5-2	2-0	3-1	3-2	X	1-0	2-4	2-6	2-3	0-2	0-3	3-1	1-1
15	Staines T	0-3	3-1	1-5	2-3	3-3	1-2	2-2	1-1	0-0	0-1	3-0	3-1	0-2	3-0	X	2-1	0-2	1-1	4-1	1-0	0-1	0-0
16	Thame U	1-0	11-3	0-0	3-2	2-1	1-0	4-1	1-0	1-4	2-2	4-0	1-2	1-1	3-1	0-4	X	5-0	1-3	4-0	0-1	3-1	2-1
17	Uxbridge	2-0	8-2	2-2	1-0	3-0	1-0	3-1	3-1	0-2	2-1	3-0	3-0	4-0	2-4	0-1	4-1	X	1-2	0-2	1-2	1-1	0-2
18	Walton & H	0-2	1-0	1-1	2-4	5-2	1-0	0-4	1-4	1-1	3-2	0-0	1-2	1-1	1-0	2-0	0-2	0-2	X	0-2	0-0	0-1	2-5
19	Wealdstone	1-3	2-0	1-1	1-2	2-0	2-3	2-3	4-1	3-1	2-2	0-1	2-2	0-1	3-3	1-1	0-4	1-0	2-3	X	1-2	0-1	0-0
20	Whyteleafe	1-0	4-1	1-2	5-4	2-4	0-1	2-1	3-1	1-0	0-0	0-1	1-2	0-2	2-1	2-0	1-5	2-1	2-1	2-0	X	0-3	2-2
21	Worthing	0-3	1-1	0-1	2-3	3-3	1-2	0-3	2-2	3-3	4-1	5-0	1-1	1-5	2-0	0-1	3-0	3-1	1-0	0-1	0-0	X	3-1
22	Yeading	1-0	0-0	1-1	0-3	1-0	1-2	5-2	2-4	3-2	0-3	0-1	2-2	0-2	7-2	1-2	2-2	0-1	3-2	2-2	3-1	4-0	X

AYLESBURY UNITED

CLUB OFFICIALS

Chairman: **Bill Greenwell**
Vice Chairman: **Les Baycroft**
Secretary: **Tony Graham**
c/o the club.
Press Officer: **Tony Graham**
Email: info@aylesburyutd.co.uk

FOOTBALL MANAGEMENT TEAM

Manager: Cliff Hercules
Assistant Manager: Floyd Street
Physios: Tyrone Matthews & Jon Hay

FACT FILE

Formed: 1897 Nickname: The Ducks
Sponsors: Driftgate Press
Colours: Green & w hite/white/white
Change colours: Yellow & black, black,black
Midweek home matchday: Tuesday
Reserve Team's League: Suburban
Newsline: 0906 655 5811

2000-01

Captain: Phil Mason
P.o.Y.: Peter Clifford
Top Scorer: Roni Joe 15

GROUND The Stadium, Buckingham Road, Aylesbury HP20 2AQ Tel: 01296 436350/436891
Fax: 01296 395667

Directions: On A413 to Buckingham, just off ring road opposite Horse & Jockey PH. Arriving from Buckingham ground is on left - from all other directions follow Buckingham signs and ground on right. Half hour walk from Aylesbury rail and bus stations

Capacity 4,000 Cover: 1000 Seats: 500 Floodlights: Yes

Clubhouse: Pub hours, but shut during matches. Bar snacks available
Function room available for hire(01296 428000).

Club Shop: Sells programmes, magazines, leisurewear, badges etc.
Contact DebbieGamage c/o The Club

Programme
Pages: 36 Price: £1.50
Editor: 21st Century Ducks.

Local Press: Bucks Herald, Bucks Advertiser
Local Radio: Three Counties Radio, Chiltern Radio, Mix 96

PREVIOUS
Leagues: Bucks Contiguous 1897-1903, South Eastern 03-07, Spartan 07-51, Delphian 51-63, Athenian 63-76, Southern 76-88, GMV Conference 88-89
Grounds: Printing Works Ground 1897-1935, Sports Stadium, Wendover Rd (ground name changed to The Stadium, Turnfurlong Lane) 35-85, shared grounds 85-86 **Name:** Night School, Printing Works (merged in 1897)

CLUB RECORDS
Attendance: 6,000 v England 1988 (at old ground: 7,500 v Watford, FA Cup 1st Rd1951)
Career goalscorer: Cliff Hercules **Career appearances:** Cliff Hercules
Transfer fee paid: £15,000 for Glenville Donegal (Northampton, 1990)
Transfer fee received: Undisclosed forJermaine Darlington (Q.P.R. 1999)

BEST SEASON
FA Trophy: Quarter-Final replay 80-81 **FA Cup:** 3rd Rd 95. League clubs defeated: Southend Utd 89-90

HONOURS
Southern Lg 87-88 (Mids Div R-up 84-85, Sth Div R-up 79-80); Athenian Lg Div 2 R-up 67-68; Delphian Lg 53-54 (R-up 52-53, Lg Cup 59-60); Spartan Lg 08-09 (R-up 52-53), West Div 28-29 (R-up 45-46), Div 1 38-39 (R-up 34-35); Berks & Bucks Snr Cup 13-14 85-86 96-97; Isthmian League Cup 94-95, Isthmian Charity Shield 95-96 Isthmian League R-up 98-99

Players progressing: Ray Mabbutt (Bristol Rovers), Phil Barber (Crystal Palace 1986), Jermaine Darlington (Q.P.R. 99),Lee Cook

United's Steve Callinan looking for a chance to cross during the FA Umbro Trophy match against Rugby United. Photo: Steve Ayre

BARKING & EAST HAM UNITED

CLUB OFFICIALS

Chairman: John Edgeworth

Vice-Chairman: Paul Lovell

President: Terry Lovell

Secretary: Roger Chilvers
50 Harrow Rd, Barking, Essex IG11 7RA
Tel: 020 8591 5313

Press Officer: Derek Pedder
Tel: 020 8592483

FOOTBALL MANAGEMENT TEAM

Manager: Craig Edwards
Asst Manager .Paul Downes
Coach: Martin Stevens
Physio: Martin Stevens

FACT FILE

Founded: 1880
Nickname: The Blues
Sponsors: Capital Coin Ltd
Colours: Blue & white
Change colours: Yellow/red/white
Midweek matchday: Tuesday
Reserves' League: None

PROGRAMME
Pages: 16 Price: 80p
Editor: Roger Chilvers

GROUND Mayesbrook Park, Lodge Avenue, Dagenham RM8 2JR Tel: 020 8595 6900

Directions: Off A13 on A1153 (Lodge Ave), and ground 1 mile on left. Bus 162 from Barking station. Nearest tube Becontree.

Capacity: 2,500 Cover: 600 Seats: 200 Floodlights: Yes

Clubhouse: 2 large bars, open daily 11am-11pm (Sundays Noon-11pm). Hot & cold food and drinks.

Club Shop: No

PREVIOUS
Grounds: Eastbury Field, Kennedy Estate,Movers Lane, Barking Rec. Ground Merry Fiddlers,Vicarage Field (until 1973)
Names: Barking Rovers, Barking Institute, Barking Woodville, Barking Town.
Leagues: London 1896-98 09-23, South Essex 1898-21, Leyton & Dist 1899-1900,Athenian 23-52

CLUB RECORDS
Attendance: (At Mayesbrook) 1,972 v Aldershot FA Cup 2nd Rd 78
Win: 14-0 v Sheppey Utd Mithras Cup 69-70 **Defeat:** 0-8 v Marlow.
Fee received: £6,000 for Alan Hull (Orient) **Fee paid:** None over £1,000
Goal scorer: Neville Fox 241 (65-73) **Appearances:** Bob Makin 566

BEST SEASON
FA Vase: 96-97 **FA Amateur Cup:** Runners-up 26-27
FA Cup: 2nd Rd rep. 81-82 1-3v Gillingham (A) after 1-1. Also 2nd Rd 78-79 79-80 83-84, and 1st Rd 26-27 28-29 78-80.
League clubs defeated: Oxford Utd 79-80.

HONOURS FA Amateur Cup R-up 26-27; Isthmian Lg 78-79 (Lg Cup R-up 76-77); Athenian Lg 34-35 (R-up 24-25); London Lg 20-21 (Div 1 (A) 09-10); South Essex Lg Div 1 1898-99,R-up (2), Div 2 (4); London Senior Cup (4), R-up (3); Essex Senior Cup (7), R-up (8); Dylon Shield 79-80; Eastern Floodlit R-up (3); Essex Elizabethean 66-67, R-up (2); Essex Thameside (4), R-up (4); London Charity Cup 61-62 R-up 21-22; London Intermediate Cup 85-86; East Anglian Cup 37-38 53-54;Mithras Cup (3), R-up (2); Premier Midweek (2). Vandenel Trophy R-up 99-00

Players progressing: 21 players since 1908 - 1956; Peter Carey (Orient 57), Lawrie Abrahams (Charlton 77), Kevin Hitchcock (Nottm Forest 83), Dennis Bailey (Fulham 86), Alan Hull (Orient 87) Joe Sibley 1939, Hedley Sheppard 1932, Paul Wilson (Barnet) John Still(Manager Barnet),

BISHOPS STORTFORD

CLUB OFFICIALS

Chairman: John Goodwin
President: B W A Bayford
Vice-Chairman: T.B.A.
Secretary: Martin Stone
15 Thornbera Gardens, Bishop's Stortford,
Herts. CM23 3NP
01279 466931 (H) 0207 653 4858 (B)
Press Officer: Martin Stone

FOOTBALL MANAGEMENT TEAM

Team Manager: Martin Hayes
Assistant Manager: Tim Moylette
Physio: Peter Fox & Brian Curtis

FACT FILE

Formed: 1874 Nickname: Blues or Bishops
Colours: White & blue stripes/blue/blue
Change colours: Yellow/yellow/yellow
Midweek matchday: Tuesday
Local Press: B.Stortford Citizen,
Herts & Essex Observer, Herald
Local Radio: BBC Essex, Essex FM,
Breeze AM, Mercury FM

2000-2001
Captain: Mark Risley
P.o.Y.: Glen Southam
Top Scorer: Vinnie John 38

Pages: 72 Price: £1.50
Editor: Roy Kemp
Tel: 01279 300647

GROUND Woodside Park, Dunmow Road, Bishop 's Stortford (01279 306456)
Directions: M11 jct 8, A1250 towards town centre, left at first roundabout. Woodside is first on right opposite Golf Club. Entrance is between industrial units on right. By rail: British Rail: W. Anglia Line (London, Liverpool Str.-Cambridge)
Capacity: 4,000 Cover: 700 Seats: 298 Floodlights: Yes
Clubhouse: Open lunchtimes,evenings and matchdays
Function room(seating 250) available for hire .
Club Shop: Full stock inc. scarves, badges and other souvenirs.
Massive stock of programmes and books etc. Contact Mark Pulfervia club.

PREVIOUS **Leagues:** East Herts 1896-97, 02-06, 19-21; Stansted & Dist. Lg 06-19; HertsCounty 21-25 27-29; Herts & Essex Border 25-27; Spartan 29-51; Delphian 51-63;Athenian 63-73

CLUB RECORDS **Attendance:** 6,000 v Peterborough Utd, FA Cup 2nd Rd 1972 & v Middlesbrough FACup 3rd Rd replay, 1983
Win: 11-0: Nettleswell & Butntmill, Herts Jun Cup 2nd Rd 1911 **Defeat:** 0-13 v Cheshunt (H), Herts Sen. Cup 1st Rd 9/1/26
Fee Paid: For Vinnie John to Grays Athletic (1999) **Fee Received:** £10,000 for Carl Hoddle (Leyton O., 89)
Scorer: (Since 29) Jimmy Badcock 123 **Appearances:** Phil Hopkins 543

BEST SEASON **FA Amateur Cup:** Winners 73-74 **FA Trophy:** Winners 80-81
FA Cup: 3rd Rd rep. 82-83 (above) - League clubs beaten: Reading 82-83

HONOURS Isthmian Lg Div 1 80-1 94-5 (Lg Cup 88-9, Full Mem. Cup 90-1), Prem. Inter Lg Cup 89-90; Athenian Lg 69-70 (R-up 66-7, Div 1 65-6, Div 2 R-up 64-5); Delphian Lg 54-5; London Snr Cup 73-4; Herts Snr Cup 58-9 59-0 63-4 70-1 72-3 73-4 75-686-7; E Anglian Cup 81-2; Herts Charity Cup 62-3 65-6 73-4 81-2 82-3 84-5 87-896-7; Herts Charity Shield 54-5; Herts I'mediate Cup (res) 94-95; Eastern F'lit Cup 84-5; Essex F'lit Cup 67-8; Essex & Herts Border Comb 81-2 88-9 R-up (2) 92-4; Fred Budden Tphy R-up 78-9 90-1 92-3

Players progressing: P Phelan (Southend 61), M Hollow (Orient 62), P Phillips(Luton 69), T Baker (Colchester 86), T Sorrell (Maidstone, Colchester, Barnet 88), C Hoddle (Leyton O., Barnet 89), T English (Colchester 89), L Fortune-West (Gillingham 95), L Braithwaite (Exeter City 96)

Back Row, left to right: Brian Handford (Chiropodist), Tim Moylette (Assistant Manager), Danny Wolf, Tyronne Hercules, Martin Hayes (Player/Manager), Micky Desborough, Vinnie John, Mark Harman, Tim Langer, Steve Taylor, Trevor Paul, Peter Fox (physio), Brian Curtis (physio) Front Row: Paul Kyriacou, Ray Taylor, Gary Kimble, Ryan Gunn, Mark Risley, Carl Fannon, Lee Endersby, Troy Braham and Glen Southam

BOGNOR REGIS TOWN

CLUB OFFICIALS

Chairman: **T.Martin**
President: **S Rowlands**
Secretary: **Peter Helsby,** c/o The Club.
02392 291388
Press Officer: Jack Pearce
Comm. Manager: **Maurice Warner**

FOOTBALL MANAGEMENT TEAM

Manager: Jack Pearce
Coach: Paul Holden M.B.E.
Physios: S Sidaway & Heidi Simpson

FACT FILE

Founded: 1883
Nickname: The Rocks
Sponsors: Butlins South Coast World
Colours: White (green trim)/green/white
Change colours: Blue/white/red
Midweek home matchday: Tuesday
Reserves ' League: None

2000-01

Captain: M.Bimingham
P.o.Y.: D.Wright
Top Scorer: M.Russell

Programme
Pages: 36 Price: £1
Editor: Maurice Warner Tel: 01243 822325

Local Press: Bognor Regis Journal & Guardian, Bognor Observer, Brighton Argus, Portsmouth News
Local Radio: Radio Sussex, Ocean Sound, Radio Solent, Southern Sound, Spirit FM

GROUND Nyewood Lane, Bognor Regis PO21 2TY
Tel: 01243 822325

Directions: West along sea front from pier, past Aldwick shopping centre then turn right into Nyewood Lane

Capacity: 6,000 Cover: 3,800 Seats: 243 Floodlights: Yes

Clubhouse: Open every night, matchdays and Sunday lunchtimes. Hot food available

Club Shop: Selling programmes and normal club items

PREVIOUS **Leagues:** W Sussex Lge 1896-1926; Brighton, Hove & District Lge 26-27; Sussex County Lge 27-72; Southern Lge 72-81

CLUB RECORDS **Attendance:** 3,642 v Swansea FA Cup 1st Rd replay, '84
Goalscorer: Kevin Clements (206) **Appearances:** Mick Pullen, 967 (20 seasons)
Transfer Fee Paid: £2,200 Guy Rutherford 95-96
Fee Received: £10,500 for John Crumplin & Geoff Cooper (Brighton & Hove Alb, 87) & Simon Rodger (C Palace 89)

BEST SEASON **FA Amateur Cup:** 1st Round 71-72 **F A Trophy:** 3rd Round 95-96
F A Cup: 2nd Rd on four occasions - League clubs beaten: Swansea 84-85, Exeter 88-89
84-85 2-6 v Reading (A), 85-86 1-6 v Gillingham (A), 88-89 0-1 v Cambridge (H), 95-96 0-4 v Peterborough (A)

HONOURS: Isthmian Lg Div 1 R-up 81-82, (Lg Cup 86-87); Southern Lg R-up 80-81 (Lg Cup R-up 80-81), Merit Cup 80-81; Sussex Lg 48-49 71-72 (R-up 38-39 51-52), Div 2 70-71, Invitation Cup 40-41 49-50 62-63 71-72; Brighton Lg R-up 26-27; W Sussex Lg (5) 20-25 (R-up 1896-97, 25-26), Jnr Lg 10-11 13-14; Southern Co's Comb 78-79; Sussex Snr Cup(9) 54-56 79-84 86-87 94-95 (R-up 51-52 58-59 84-85 00-01); Sussex Prof. Cup 73-74, Sussex RUR Cup 71-72; Sussex I'mediate Cup 52-53, Littlehampton Hosp. Cup 29-30 33-34; Bognor Charity Cup(8) 28-29 30-31 32-33 37-38 47-48 58-59 71-73; Gosport War Mem. Cup (2) 81-83 (R-up 86-87); Snr Midweek F'lit Cup R-up 74-75

Players progressing: E Randall (Chelsea 50), J Standing (Brighton 61), A Woon (Brentford 72), J Crumplin & G Cooper (Brighton 87), Simon Rodger (C Palace 89)

BROMLEY

CLUB OFFICIALS

Chairman: **Glyn Beverly**

Secretary: **John Self**
22 Faringdon Avenue, Bromley,
Kent BR2 8BS

FOOTBALL MANAGEMENT TEAM

Manager: Dave Garland
Ass.Manager:Mike Reid
Coach: Stuart McIntyre

FACT FILE

Formed: 1892
Nickname: The Lilywhites
Colours: White/black/black
Change colours: All red
Midweek home matchday: Tuesday
Reserve's League: None
Youth League: Kent Youth League
Newsline: 0930 555 838

2000-01

Captain: Mark Tompkins
P.o.Y.: Danny Harwood
Top Scorer: Mark Tompkins 20

Pages: 32 Price: £1.20
Editor: Colin Russell(020 8405 0738)

Local Press: Bromley Times
Local Radio: Radio Kent,
Bromley Local Radio

GROUND Hayes Lane, Bromley, Kent BR2 9EF Tel: 0208 460 5291 or 0208 313 3992

Directions: One mile from Bromley South (BR). Buses 314, 146 and 119 pass ground. Junction 4 off M25, then A21 towards London
Capacity: 5,000 Cover: 2,500 Seats: 1,300 Floodlights: Yes

Clubhouse: Open matchdays. Food available

Club Shop: Yes. contact Jim Brown

PREVIOUS **Leagues:** South London - 1894; Southern 94-96; London 96-98 99-1901; West Kent 01-04; Southern Suburban 04-07; Kent 1898-99, 11-14; Spartan 07-08; Isthmian 08-11; Athenian 19-52
Grounds:White Hart Field Cricket Ground, Widmore Rd & Plaistow Cricket Field (pre-1904),Hayes Lane 1904-37 .New Ground

RECORDS **Attendance:** 12,000 v Nigeria, 1950
Goalscorer: George Brown 570 (1938-61) **Appearances:** George Brown
Win: 131 v Redhill, Athenian League 1945-46 **Defeat:** v Barking ,Athenian League 1933-34
Fee Paid: Unknown **Fee Received:** £50,000 for Jon Goodman (from Millwall 90)

BEST SEASON **FA Amateur Cup:** Winners 10-11, 37-38, 48-49
FA Trophy: Second Round 91-92 **FA Cup:** 2nd Rd replay v Scarborough 37-38, Lincoln 38-39, Watford 45-46

HONOURS: Isthmian League(4) 08-10 53-54 60-61 (R-up 52-53 55-56 87-88), Div 1 R-up 79-80 5-86 90-91, Prince Phillip 5-a-side Cup 1979; Athenian League 22-23 48-49 50-51 (R-up 35-36); London League Div 2 1896-97; Spartan League 07-08; London Snr Cup 09-10 45-46 50-51; Kent Senior Cup 49-50 76-77 91-92 96-97; Kent AmateurCup (12) 07-08 31-32 35-36 36-37 38-39 46-47 48-49 50-51 52-53 53-54 54-55 59-60; LondonChallenge Cup 1995-96.

Players progressing: Roy Merryfield (Chelsea), Stan Charlton (Arsenal 52), RonHeckman (Orient 55), John Gregory (West Ham 51), Bill Lloyd (Millwall 56), Brian Kinsey (Charlton 56), Harold Hobbs (Charlton & England), Matt Carmichael (Lincoln 90), Leslie Locke (QPR 56), Jon Goodman (Millwall 90), Dean Wordsworth (Crystal Palace 97), Landry Zahana-ONI (Luton Town 98)

Bromley's Mark Tompkins watches in vain as he just fails to connect with this cross. Yeading 'keeper Adam Dunsby looks on in relief. Photo: Alan Coomes.

CARSHALTON ATHLETIC

CLUB OFFICIALS

Chairman: Steve Friend
President: John Carpentiere
Vice Chairman:T.B.A.
Secretary: Janey Gould,394 Winchcombe Road, Carshalton, Surrey SM5 1SB
General Manager: Andy Abrehart
Press Officer: Roger Fear
Commercial Manager: Roger Fear

FOOTBALL MANAGEMENT TEAM

Man: Frank Murphy Ass Man:John Johnson
Coaches:Curtis Warmington & Clive Gartell
Physios: Tanya Clarke & Mark Davis

FACT FILE

Formed: 1905 Nickname: Robins
Sponsors: CDL Exhibition Contractors
Colours: White, maroon trim/maroon/white
Change colours: Maroon/white
Midweek matchday: Tuesday
Reserve League: Suburban
Newsline: 0930 555 877

2000-01

Captain & P.o.Y.: Matt Everson
Top Scorer: Jamie Pace

Pages: 20 Price: £1.20p
Editor: Andy Hill (020 8644 7928)

Local Press: Sutton Comet, Sutton Herald
Local Radio: BBc Southern Counties

GROUND War Memorial Sports Ground, Colston Av, Carshalton SM5 2PW
Tel: 0181 642 8658

Directions: Turn right out of Carshalton BR Station, and Colston Avenue is first left. Entrance 150 yards on right. London Transport bus 151 from Morden to Wrythe Green Lane
Capacity: 8,000 Cover: 4,500 Seats: 240 Floodlights: Yes
Clubhouse: Open every evening and lunchtime. Licenced bar, pool, darts,machines, discos on Saturday. Separate function hall (bookings taken). Food:sandwiches, rolls, burgers, hot dogs, teas, coffees and soft drinks. (0181 642 8658)
Club Shop: Sells hats, scarves, T-shirts, badges, programmes etc

PREVIOUS **Leagues:** Southern Sub (pre-1911); Surrey Snr 22-23; London 23-46; Corinthian46-56; Athenian 56-73
Grounds: Wrythe Recreation Ground 1907-14; Culvers Park 19-20

CLUB RECORDS **Attendance:** 7,800 v Wimbledon, London Senior Cup
Career goalscorer: Jimmy Bolton(242) **Career appearances:** Jon Warden (504)
Transfer fee paid: £5,000 for Junior Haynes 1998 **Transfer fee received:** £15,000 for Curtis Warmington (Enfield)
Win: 13-0 v Worthing, Loctite Cup Third Round 28/2/91
F.A.Trophy : 3rd Rd 95-96 lodst away at Hyde United (2-3)
FA Cup: 2nd Rd 82-83, lost 1-4 at Torquay. - League clubs defeated: None

HONOURS: Isthmian League Div 2 R-up 76-77, Corinthian League 52-53 53-54, Surrey Senior League R-up 22-23, Surrey Senior Cup(3) Runners-up (5) Surrey Senior Shield 75-76 Runners-up (2)), London Challenge Cup 91-92 Isthmian Lg Cup R-up 90-91

Players progressing: Roy Lunnes (Crystal Pal. 60), Les Burns (Charlton 67), Ron Walker (Watford), Nobby Warren (Exeter),Terry Stacey (Plymouth A.), Frank GeorgelLeyton Orient) ,Tommy Williams (Colchester U), Alan Eagles (Leyton Orient), Derek Razzell (Q.PR),Muray Jones Crystal Pal.) Gus Caesar (Arsenal), Darren Annon (Brentford) 94, Ian Cox (Crystal Pal.) 94, Carl Asaba (Brentford)

Photo: Kevin W Rolfe

DULWICH HAMLET

CLUB OFFICIALS

Chairman: **Martin Eede**
President: **Tommy Jover**
Vice Chairman: **Brian Shears**
Secretary:: **Jack Payne: 11 Teversham Lane, London SW8 2DJ (020 7622 4828)**
Press Officer: **John Lawrence**
Tel: 020 8761 2091

FOOTBALL MANAGEMENT TEAM

Manager: Gwynne Berry
Physio: Danny Keenan

FACT FILE

Formed: 1893 Nickname: The Hamlet
Sponsors: Domino's Pizza
Colours: Navy blue & pink stripes/navy/navy
Change colours: Red & light blue squares/red/red
Midweek matchday: Tuesday
Reserve League: Suburban

2000-01 Captain: Ian Savage
P.o.Y.: Dave Richards
Top Scorer: Matt Fowler 17

GROUND: Champion Hill Stadium, Edgar Kail Way, East Dulwich, London SE22 8BD Tel: 020 7274 8707

Directions: East Dulwich station, 200yds. Denmark Hill station, 10 mins walk. Herne Hill station then bus 37 stops near grd. Buses 40 & 176 from Elephant & Castle, 185 from Victoria

Capacity: 3,000 Cover: 1,000 Seats: 500 Floodlights: Yes

Clubhouse: Open 7 days a week, bar. Function rooms and meeting room available for hire Health Club,Gymnasium,Squash courts (020 7274 8707)

Club Shop: Sells programmes, pennants, badges, scarves, baseball caps, replica shirts (by order only). New shop opening in 2001-02.

Pages: 48 Price: £1.20
Editor: John Lawrence
Local Press: South London Press, Southwark News

PREVIOUS **Leagues:** Camberwell 1894-97; S/thern Sub 1897-1900 01-07; Dulwich 00-01; Spartan 07-08
Grounds: Woodwarde Rd 1893-95; College Farm 95-96; Sunray Avenue 96-1902; Freeman's Ground, Champion Hill 02-12; Champion Hill (old ground) 1912-92; Sandy Lane (groundshare with Tooting & Mitcham F.C.) 91-92

CLUB RECORDS **Attendance:** 20,744, Kingstonian v Stockton, FA Am Cup Final 1933 (at refurbished ground): 1,835 v Southport FAC 98-99
Career Goalscorer: Edgar Kail 427 (1919-33) **Career Appearances:** Reg Merritt 571 (50-66)
Fee Paid: T Eames (Wimbledon), G Allen (Carshalton Ath 80) **Fee Received**: E Nwajiobi (Luton 83)
Win: 13-0 v Walton-on-Thames, 37-38 **Defeat:** 1-10 v Hendon, 63-64

BEST SEASON **FA Amateur Cup:** Winners 19-20 31-2 33-4 36-7 **FA Trophy:** Quarter Final 79-80
FA Cup: 1st Rd replay 30-31 33-34. 1st Rd on 14 occasions

HONOURS: Isthmian League 19-20 25-26 32-33 48-49, (R-up(7) Div 1 77-78; London Senior Cup 24-25 38-39 49-50 83-84 (R-up 05-06 07-08 20-21 27-28); Surrey Senior Cup 14 (R-up -6); London Chal. Cup 98-9 R-up 91-92; 99-00 London Charity Cup(12); Surrey Senior Shield 72-73; Surrey Centen. Shld 77-78; Sth of the Thames Cup (4) 56-60; Southern Comb Cup 73-74

Players progressing: W Bellamy (Spurs), A Solly (Arsenal), L Fishlock/A Gray/APardew (C Palace), J Moseley & E Toser (Millwall), R Dicks (Middlesborough), GJago/J Ryan (Charlton Ath 51/63), G Pearce (Plymouth), R Crisp (Watford 61), ENwajiobi (Luton 83), C Richards & J Glass (Bournemouth), P Coleman (Millwall86), A Perry (Portsmouth 86), N Kelly (Stoke City), C Emberson (Rotherham), CAsaba (Brentford)S.Watts (Leyton O), M.King (Barnet),J Darlington (Q.P.R.), D.McEwen (Spurs)

DULWICH HAMLET 18.8.01

Back Row L-R
Luke Edgehill
Al-James Hannigan
Oliver Hunt
Declan Perkins
Nick Leach
James Mercer.

Front Row L-R
Michael Ebanks
Ryan Gray
Francis Quarm
Julian Old
Rob Fench.

Photo by Peter Singh

FORD UNITED

CLUB OFFICIALS

Chairman: Jimmy Chapman
President : Nick Scheeler
Secretary: Mick Ewen
215 Rush Green Rd, Rush Green,
Romford, Essex. RM7 0JR
Tel: 01708 724178 (H) 07939 879295 (M)
Chief Execs: John Rowe & George Adams

FOOTBALL MANAGEMENT TEAM

Manager: Dennis Elliott
Coach: Stevie Brice
Assistant Coach: Johnny Burrows
Physio.: Alan Jeyes

FACT FILE

Founded: 1934
Nickname: Motormen
Sponsor: Sky Sports
Colours: Blue/white/blue
Change: All red
Midweek home matchday: Tuesday
Res Lg. Essex & Herts Border Comb

2000-01
Captain: Glen Thomas
Top Scorer: Dean Allen 24

Pages: 72 Price: £1
Editor: Michael Ewen
Tel: 01708 724178 (H)

GROUND Oakside Stadium,Station Road, Barkingside, Ilford, Essex
Directions: From London Take A12 ,Eastern Avenue and turn left into Horns Road., Barkingside (Greengate). Right into Craven Gardens, right again into Carlton Drive and left into Station Road..Go over bridge and ground is on right next to Barkingside (Central Line). From Ilford BR station take 169 bus to Craven Gardens.
Capacity: 3,000 Seats: 316 Cover: 1000 Floodlights: Yes Club Shop: Yes
Clubhouse: Large bar which is open every day 12.00 midday until 11.00 p.m.

HONOURS: London Snr Cup 55-56 56-57 94-95 97-98; 00-01 Essex Snr Lge 91-92 96-97,R-up 94-95, Essex Sen. Trophy 90-91 91-92,00-01 Essex Senior Cup 39-40 49-50 50-51 51-52 85-86, R-up Spartan Lg 49-50 50-51 55-56 56-57 57-58; London Lg 36-37 38-39; Essex Elizabethan 59-60 60-61 70-71; Gtr London Lg 70-71; Sportsmanship Award 77-78 79-80 80-81; Essex Thameside Trophy: 98-=99Essex & Herts Border Comb.(res) 94-95 (Lg Cup 94-95); Isthmian League Div 3 98-99, Promoted from Div 2 99-00

RECORDS: **Attendance:** 58,000 Briggs Sports v Bishop Auckland, at St James Park, Newcastle, FA Amateur Cup
Appearances: Roger Bond **Goalscorer:** Jeff Wood 196
Win: Unknown **Defeat:** Unknown

PREVIOUS: **Leagues:** Spartan, Spartan, Aetolian, Metropolitan, Essex Senior
Names: Brigg Sports (1934) & Ford Sports (1934) amalgamated in 1958 **Grounds:** Ford Sports & Social Club, Rush Green Road, Romford.

BEST SEASON: **FA Vase:** 98-99, 5th Round, 1-2 v Bedlington Terriers (H)
FA Amateur Cup: Semi-Final 53-54

Players progressing: Les Allen (Spurs), Mick Flanagan (QPR, Charlton, Crystal Palace), Jim Stannard (Fulham, Southend, Millwall), Nicky Hammond (Arsenal,Swindon), Laurie Abrahams (Charlton), Doug Barton (Reading, Newport)

Back Row, left to right: Mark Lord, Paul Salmon, Glen Thomas, Billy Cove, Kevin Hoddy, Jamie Wallace, Jimmy Chapman, Dean Allen and Jamie Bly. **Front Row:** George Durrant, Danny Benstock, Ben Wood, Billy Read, Dennis Elliott (Manager), Les Whitton (Coach) and Stevie Brice (Coach).

HARLOW TOWN

CLUB OFFICIALS

Chairman: **Jeff Bothwell**

President: **Ron Bruce**

Press Officer: **Gavin McWilliams**
Tel: 01279 441894

Secretary: **Graeme Auger**
58 Braziers Quey, South Street,Bishop's Stortford, Herts (01279 465998)

FOOTBALL MANAGEMENT TEAM

Manager: Ian Allinson
Coach: Geoff Livingstone
Physio: Mickey Stevens

FACT FILE

Founded: 1879
Nickname: Hawks
Sponsors: BritSec Int. Ltd
Colours: Red & white/white/white
Change: White & yellow/yellow/yellow
Midweek matches: Wednesday
Reserves' Lge: Essex & Herts Border Comb
Website:www.harlowtown.co.uk

2000-01

Captain: Tony McNally
P.o.Y.: Danny Cowley
Top Scorer: Marc Salmon 20

HARLOW
TOWN F.C.
BritSec
Ryman
OFFICIAL MATCHDAY MAGAZINE 2000 - 2001
BEDFORD TOWN
Ryman League Division One
Saturday 5th May 2001, K.O. 3.00 pm.
Official Programme £1-50
HAWKS HOTLINE: 09066 555 889

36 pages £1.00
Editor: Phil Tuson (01279 416743)

Local Press: Harlow Citizen, Harlow Star, Harlow Herald & Post
Local Radio: Essex Radio, BBC Essex, Ten 17

GROUND Harlow Sports Centre, Hammarskjold Rd, Harlow CM20 2JF Tel: 01279 445319
Email: jeff.bothwell@ britsec.co.uk

Directions: Near town centre, 10 mins walk from Harlow Town (BR) station

Capacity: 10,000 Cover: 500 Seats: 400 Floodlights: Yes

Club Shop: Yes

Clubhouse: Open daily 11-11 (10.30 Sundays). Hot & cold food available

PREVIOUS **Leagues:** East Herts (pre-1932); Spartan 32-39 46-54; London 54-61; Delphian 61-63; Athenian 63-73; Isthmian 73-92; Inactive 92-93
Grounds: Marigolds 1919-22; Green Man Field 22-60

CLUB RECORDS **A ttendance:** 9,723 v Leicester, FA Cup 3rd Rd replay 8/1/80
Goalscorer: Jeff Wood (45 in 88-89) **Appearances:** Norman Gladwin 646 (1949-70)
Win: 12-0 v Hertford Ath. (H), E. Herts Lge 5/10/29 **Defeat:** 0-11 v Ware (A), Spartan Lge Div. One (East) 6/3/48

BEST SEASON **FA Amateur Cup:** 2nd Rd 72-73 **FA Trophy:** 2nd Rd(2) 80-82 **FA Vase:** 3rd Rd 88-89
FA Cup: 4th Rd 79-80 (lost 3-4 at Watford). Also 1st Rd 80-81 81-82 League clubs defeated: Southend, Leicester 79-80

HONOURS Isthmian Lg Div 1 78-79 (R-up 82-83, Div 2 Nth 88-89, Yth Cup 77-78), Ath'n LgDiv 1 71-72, E Angl. Cup 89-90, Knight F'lit Cup R-up 87-88, Essex Snr Cup 78-79, Essex F'lit Competition R-up 71-72, London Lg Chal. Cup 59-60, Spartan LgCup 52-53, Epping Hosp. Cup (3) 46-49, Essex & Herts Border Comb Cup 75-76, Fred Budden Trophy 88-89 89-90, Chelmsford Yth Lg 86-87 (Lg Cup 86-87 87-88)

Players progressing: Jeff Wood (Charlton 75), Neil Prosser (B'mouth 80)

Back Row: ,left to right: John Coley, Danny Cowley, Andy Purcell, Dave Drury, Leon Ettienne, Nick Webb, Darryl Trigg, Tony McNally, Dave Cook, Neil Moore, Mark Pearcey and Lee Claridge. Front Row: Geoff Livingstone (Coach), Marc Salmon, Phil Leggatt, Marvin Samuel, Martin Young,, Jon Hooker, Richard Wilcox, Dennis Greene and Neil Thompson.

NORTHWOOD

CLUB OFFICIALS

Secretary: Steve Williams, 35 Evelyn Drive
Hatch End, Pinner, Middx HA5 4RL
Tel: (02088 428 1533 - H & fax)

Chairman: Andy Johnson

Vice Chairman: Geoff Foster

President: Lothar Hahn

Press Off: M Russell (01923 827690)

FOOTBALL MANAGEMENT TEAM

Manager: Tony Choules
Coaches: Gerry Henry & John Toogood
Physio: George Price

FACT FILE

Founded: 1899
Nickname: Woods
Sponsors: IFS Freight Forwarding
Colours: All red
Change colours: All yellow
Midweek Matches: Tuesday
Reserve League: Suburban

2000-01

Captain: Chris Gell
P.o.Y: Gary Williams
Top Scorer: Lawrence Yaku 47

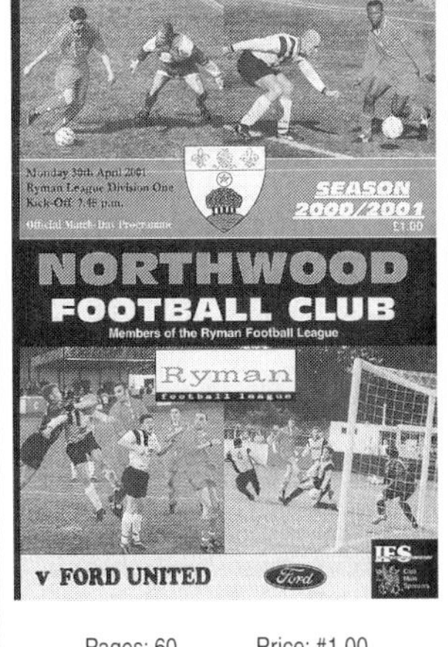

Pages: 60 Price: #1.00
Editor: A Evans (0208 8566 2880)
Local Press: Ruislip & Northwood Gazette, Watford Observer

GROUNDNorthwood Park, Chestnut Avenue, Northwood (01923 827148)
Email Address: evansa@ealing, gov,uk **Club Website:** www.northwoodfc.com
Directions: A404 (Pinner-Rickmansworth) - Chestnut Ave. on left by large grey iron rail way bridge. Third of a mile from Northwood Hills station (Metropolitan Line) - turn right out of station to r'bout, left into Pinner Road, left into Chestnut Avenue after 300yds. Buses 282 and H11 to Northwood Hills **Club Shop:** No
Capacity: 2,580 Seats: 200 Cover: 500 Floodlights: Yes
Clubhouse: Weekends & most eves from 6pm. Bar. Hot and cold food. Pool, juke-box

HONOURS: Isthmian Lg Associate Members Cup 92-93,99-00; London Spartan Lg 91-92 (R-up 89-90), Lg Cup 89-90 91-92; Hellenic Lg Div 1 78-79 (Prem Div Cup R-up 81-82); Middx Lg 77-78 (R-up 72-73 76-77), Div 1 R-up 71-72, Challenge Cup 74-75 76-77 77-78; Middx Snr Charity Cup R-up 93-94; Middx Snr Cup SF 91-92 92-93 98-99; R-up 99-00 Jnr Cup 46-47 47-48 48-49; Harrow & Wembley Lg (9); Middlesex Premier Cup 94-95.Isthmian Div 2 R-up 99-00

PREVIOUS: **Leagues:** Harrow & Wembley 32-69; Middlesex 69-78; Hellenic 79-84; London Spartan 84-92
Names: Northwood Town **Grounds:** None

CLUB RECORDS: **Attendance:** 1,642 v Chelsea Friendly July 1997
Goal Scorerin Season: Lawrence Yaku 61 (99-00) **Career Appearances:** Chris Gell
Win: 15-0 v Dateline (H) Middlesex Inter Cup 1973 **Defeat:** 0-8 v Bedfont (Middlesex Lg.1975)

BEST SEASON: **FA Cup:** 2nd Qual Rd 94-95, 99-00 **F.A.Trophy:** 3rd Rd 00-01
FA Vase: Qtr finals 96-97

Players progressing: Gavin Maguire, Derek Payne (Barnet), Warren Patmore (Cambridge United)

OXFORD CITY

CLUB OFFICIALS

Chairman: **M Woodley**
President: T.B.A.
Vice Chairman: **T.B.A.**
Press Officer/Secretary: **John Shepperd**
20 Howe Close, Wheatley, Oxford OX33 1SS
Tel: 01865 872181 (& Fax)

FOOTBALL MANAGEMENT TEAM

Manager: Paul Lee
Asst Manager:
Physio: C. Perkins

FACT FILE

Formed: 1882
Nickname: City
Sponsors: S.M.C.
Colours: Blue & white hoops/blue/blue
Change colours: yellow,black,black
Midweek Matchday: Tuesday
Reserves Lge: Suburban Lge Prem Div.
Website: oxfordcityfc.co.uk

2000-01
Captain Richarde Peirson
Top Scorer: Danny Wise 26
P.o.Y.: Julian Dark

OXFORD CITY Football Club
SEASON 2000/01
£1
Ryman football league
UNIPART DCM

Pages: 60 Price: £1
Editor: John Sheppard

Local Press: Oxford Mail
Local Radio: Radio Oxford FM, Fox FM

GROUND Court Place Farm, Marsh Lane, Marston, Oxford. OX3 0NQ.
Tel: 01865 744493.01865 742394 (Clubhouse)

Directions: From London M40/A40, ring-road to North, take 1st slip road, follow signs to John Radcliffe hospital and Court Place Farm Stadium, ground on left after leaving flyover. From the north same ring-road.
Capacity: 3,000 Seats: 300 Cover: 400 Floodlights: Yes
Clubhouse: Open matchdays, most refreshments available
Club Shop: Yes, open matchdays, selling souvenirs. Contact Paul Cotterell

PREVIOUS **Leagues:** Isthmian 07-88; South Midlands 90-93
Grounds: The White House 1882-1988; Cuttleslowe Pk 90-91; Pressed Steel,Romanway 91-93

CLUB RECORDS **Attendance:** 9,500 v Leytonstone, FA Amateur Cup 50
Win: 9-0 v Harlow Town, Isthmian League 9/10/76
Defeat: 0-8 v Wycombe Wanderers, Isthmian League - date unknown
Scorer: John Woodley **Appearances:** John Woodley
Fee Paid: £3,000 for S Adams (Woking) **Fee Received:** £17,500 for Howard Forinton (Yeovil T. 1.97)

BEST SEASON **FA Amateur Cup:** Winners 05-06 Runners-up 02-03 12-13 **FA Vase:** Runners-up 94-95
FA Cup: Second Round 69-70, 1-5 v Swansea City (H) **FA Trophy:** 1st Rd Prop 96 v Merthyr Tydfil

HONOURS FA Amateur Cup 05-06 (R-up 02-03 12-13); F.A.Vase R-Up 94-95; Isthmian Lg R-up 34-35 45-46, Div 1 95-96 R-up 77-78 South MidlandsLg 92-93; Oxon Senior Cup - 28 times

Players progressing: A Blakeman (Brentford 46), C Holton (Arsenal 50), K Savin(Derby 50), R Adams (Blackpool 48), A Jeffries (Brentford 49), P James (Luton 49), D Gordon/E Wilcox (WBA 47/48), V Mobley (Sheffield Wed 63), J Varney (Hull 50), P Lee (Hereford 73), H Poole (Port Vale 55), G Parker (Luton 81), M Keown(Arsenal 84), D Meeson (Wolves 52)

Back row, left to right: Paul Bradford (Asst. Physio), Paul Lee (Manager), Steve Kenny (kit man), Gary Goodwiin (Coach), Jermaine Ferreira, Alan Foster, Kamran Abbasi, Chris Johnson, Mark Bruce, Lee Joshua, Steve Gray, Lee Hewlett, Chris Perkins (Physio), John McMahon, and Michael Thorp. **Front Row:** Tom Waterhouse, Kelvin Alens, Craig Farley, Shaun Wimble, Julian Dark (Captain), Nigel Emsden, John Mitchell and Andy Smith.

SLOUGH TOWN

CLUB OFFICIALS

Chairman: Martin Deaner
Secretary / Press Off.: Roy Merryweather
Tel: 01753 554833 (Ground)
01735 534033(W)
01189 722871(H)

FOOTBALL MANAGEMENT TEAM

Manager: Steve Browne
Physio: Kevin McGoldrick

FACT FILE

Formed: 1890
Nickname: The Rebels
Sponsor: T.B.A.
Colours: Amber/navy blue/amber
Change colours: All white
Midweek home matchday: Tuesdays
Website: www.sloughtownfc.net

2000-01

Captain: Steve Daly
P.o.Y.: Steve Mautone
Top Scorer: Dwight Marshall 9

SLOUGH TOWN
FOOTBALL CLUB
TODAY'S MATCH SPONSOR
SLOUGH TOWN SUPPORTERS CLUB
SLOUGH TOWN F.C.
SERVE WITH HONOUR
Versus GRAVESEND & NORTHFLEET
20th January 2001
K.O. 3.00pm
Ryman League Premier Division
Ryman

Pages: 36 Price: £1.50
Editor: John Tebbit
Local Press: Slough Observer Slough Express
Local Radio: Thames Valley FM, Star FM
Radio Berkshire

GROUND: Wexham Park Stadium, Wexham Road, Slough, Berkshire. SL2 5QR.
Tel: 01753 554833 Fax: 01753 533949

Directions: From North : M25 J16 East London M40 J1 - South A412 through Iver Heath to George Green. 2nd set lights turn right by George PH, George Green.Church Lane 1 mile to end, then small roundabout, turn left, ground 1/4 mile onright

Capacity: 5,000 Cover: 1,890 Seats: 450 Floodlights: Yes

Clubhouse: Lounge bar open weekdays 7pm-11pm, weekends, lunchtimes, evenings. Banqueting hall for all types of functions

Club Shop: Contact: Graham Gowland 01252 873620

PREVIOUS **Leagues:** Southern Alliance 1892-93; Berks & Bucks 1901-05; Gt Western Suburban1906-19; Spartan 1920-39; Herts & Middx 1940-45; Corinthian 1946-63; Athenian1963-73; Isthmian 1973-90, 94-95; Alliance Prem. (GMVC) 90-94
Grounds: Dolphin Playing Fields & Stadium, Chalvey Rd Sports Grd, YorkRd Maidenhead 1920, Centre Sports Ground 36-42

CLUB RECORDS **Attendance:** 8,000 - Schoolboys u15 Final Slough v Liverpool - 1976
Win: 17-0 v Railway Clearing House - 1921-22
Defeat: 1-11 v Chesham Town 1909/10
Transfer fee paid: £18,000 for Colin Fielder from Farnborough - 1991
Career appearances: Terry Reardon 458 - 64/81
Received: £22,000 from Wycombe Wanderers for Steve Thompson
Career goalscorer: E.J.C. Tory Norris 84 - 25/26

BEST SEASON **FA Cup:** 2nd Round Proper, 79-80 (Yeovil T), 82-83 (Bishop's Stortford), 85-86 (Leyton O.), 86-87 (Swansea C.).
League clubs defeated: Millwall, 1-0 (H) Jan. 1983
FA Trophy: Semi-Final 1976-77, 2-6(agg) v Dagenham; 97-98, 1-2(agg) v Southport

HONOURS: FA Amateur Cup R-up 72-73; Great Western Suburban League R-up 19-20: Spartan League R-up 20-21 21-22 31-32 32-33 38-39; Herts & Middx League R-up 43-44; Corinthian League 50-51 (R-up 45-46 46-47 57-58); Athenian League 67-68 71-72 72-73 (R-up 68-69),LgCup 71-2 72-3 Div 1 64-65, Memorial Shield 64-65 71-72 72-73); Isthmian League 80-81 89-90 R-up 94-95, (Div 2 R-up 73-74),Lg Cup 75-76 80-81 R-up 94-95 Lge Shield 89-90 ; Berks & Bucks Sen Cup (10) 02-03 19-20 23-24 26-27 35-36 54-55 70-72 76-77 80-81

Back Row, left to right:Steve Stott (Player-Coach), Dave Timothy, Chris Allen (now Brighton), Dave Rainford, Leon Townley, Danny Honey, Chris Andrews, Andrew Deaner, Mark Hawthorne (now Crawley Town), Aaron Patton (now Hemel Hempstead), Phil Simpson, Kevin McGoldrick(Physio), Graham Kemp (Player-Coach). **Front Row:** Keith McPherson, Dwight Marshall, Chris White, Steve Daly (Captain), Steve Browns,(Manager),Paul Barrowcliff, Junior Haynes, Mark Halland Damien Markman.

STAINES TOWN

CLUB OFFICIALS

Chairman: **Alan Boon**
President: **T.B.A.**
Vice Chairman: **Ken Williams**
Secretary: **Steve Parsons**
3 Birch Green, Staines, Middx TW18 4HA
Tel: 01784 450420
Commercial Mgr: **Ken Williams**
Press Officer: **Stuart Moore** (01784 421118)

FOOTBALL MANAGEMENT TEAM

Manager: Ken BallardAsst Man: Danny Pipe
Physios: Chris Wiltcher,Mike Critchall,Mike Savage and Des Collins

FACT FILE

Formed: 1892
Nickname: The Swans
Sponsors: The Exchange Nightclub
Colours: Old gold (blue trim)/royal/royal
Change colours: All white
Midweek matchday: Tuesday
Reserve league: none

2000-01

Captain & P.o.Y : Jon Underwood
Top Scorer: Nick Hooper (18)

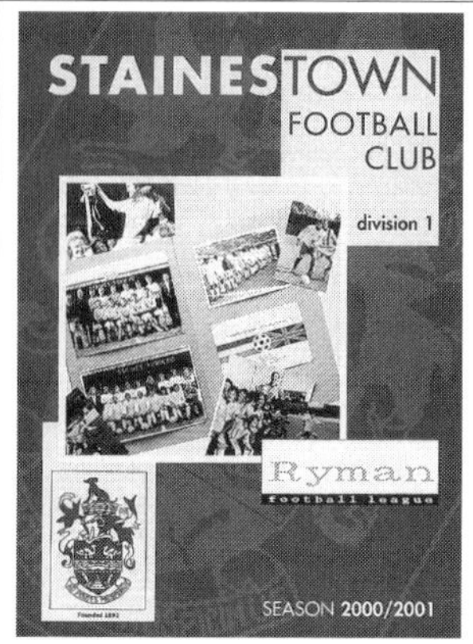

Pages: 44 Price: £1.50
Editor: Sec. & Stuart Moore (01784 421118)
Local Press: Staines & Ashford News, Middx Chronicle, Informer,Staines Gaurdian
Local Radio: County Sound, GLR, Capital, Star FM, Radio Wey.

GROUNDWheatsheaf Park, Wheatsheafe Lane,Staines,Middlesex TW18 2PD(01784 455988)
Directions: M25 Jct13 to A30 Staines by-pass to Crooked Billet roundabout.Take town centre exit(A308) and left into South St., at iron bridge. Pass bus staion and bear left into Laleham Rd. Wheatsheafe Lane is 1km on right Buses 481, 570,and 573 pass Wheatsheaf Lane.
Capacity: 2,500 **Cover:** 850 **Seats:** 250 **Floodlights**:Yes **Food:** Rolls and snacks available
Club HQ & Clubhouse: Staines Town FC, Wheatsheaf Lane, Staines (01784 455988).
During first half of 2000-02 season all facilitries will be renovated so matches will be played elsewhere for several months.
Club Shop: Souvenirs available from Ray Moore c/o STFC.

PREVIOUS **Leagues:** W London All (pre-1900), W London, W Middx (pre-1905), Gt WesternSuburban 05-13 20-24, Gt Western Comb, Munitions Lg (World War 1), London Works(World War 1), Hounslow & Dist 19-20, Spartan 24-35 58-71, Middx Sen 43-52; Parthenon 52-53, Hellenic 53-58, Athenian 71-73
Names: Staines Albany and St Peters Institute (merged) in 1895, Staines 05-18,Staines Lagonda 18-25, Staines Vale (2nd World War)
Grounds: Edgell Rd (St Peters Inst); The Lammas, Shortwood Common, Mill Mead(Hammonds/Wicks/Pursers Farm); Shepperton Road (to 51); Wheatsheaf Lane (51-96) ,Alwyns Lane Chertsey (1996-8)

CLUB RECORDS **Attendance:** 2,750 v Banco di Roma (Barassi Cup) 1975 (70,000 saw 1st leg in Rome)
Goalscorer: Alan Gregory 122 **Appearances:** Dickie Watmore 840
Win: 14-0 v Croydon (A), Isthmian League Div. 1 19/3/94 **Defeat:** 1-18 v Wycombe Wanderers (A), G West Sub Lge 1909
Fee Paid: For R Teale (Slough 81) **Fee Received:** For Scott Taylor (Millwall 95-96)

BEST SEASON **FA Amateur Cup:** 3rd Rd 23-24 **FA Trophy:** 2nd Rd 2nd Replay 76-77l (Last 32)
FA Cup: 1st Rd 84-85, 0-2 v Burton Alb (A) & 1879-80 & 80-81 (as St Peters Institute)

HONOURS Isthmian Lg Div 1 74-75 88-89 (Div 2 74-75); Athenian Lg Div 2 71-72 (Div 1 R-up 72-73); Spartan Lg 59-60 (R-up 70-71), Lg Cup 68-69 (R-up 60-61 70-71); Hellenic Lg R-up 55-56 (Lg Cup R-up 53-54 55-56); Gt Western Suburban Lg Div 1R-up 11-12 22-24 (Div 2 (Middx) 20-21); W London All Div 1 1899-1900; W LondonLg Div 1 00-01; W Middx Lg 04-05 (R-up 03-04); London Snr Cup R-up 76-77 80-81; Middx Snr Cup(7), (R-up 09-10 32-33 79-80), Snr Charity Cup 94-95; Barassi Cup76; Southern Comb. Chall. Cup 64-65 66-67 68-69 94-95 96-97,(R-up 67-68 94-95,99-00);W Middx Cup 23-24; Staines Cottage Hosp Cup 24-25; Merthyr Middx Charity Shield 90-91,(R-up 94-95); El Canuelo Trophy 92-93 94-95 94-95; Carlsberg Cup 94-95; Melksham Middx Charity Shield 96-97 Jim Lawford Memorial Cup 99-00

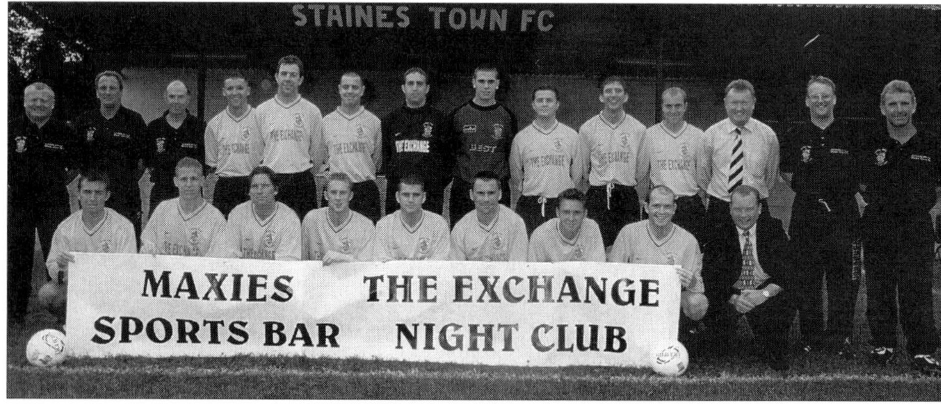

Back row, left to right: Craig Reilly, Steve Battams, Derek Walters, David Evereitt, Danny Hayward, Lloyd Wye, Nick Hooper, Mark Butler and Max Angliss (Sponsor) **Front Row:** Dave Beard (Coach), Reg Payne (Assistant Coach), Chris Wiltcher (physio), Mark Costello, Jon Underwood, Danny Roberts, Matthew Lovett, Paul Seake, Andrew Sullivan, Peter Terry, James Glynn, Ken Ballard (Manager), Danny Pipe (Assistant Manager) and Mike Savage (Coach)

THAME UNITED

CLUB OFFICIALS

Chairman: **Jim Tite**

Vice Chairman: **Mike Dyer**

Secretary: **Sally Hunt**
c/o Thame United.

FOOTBALL MANAGEMENT TEAM

Manager: Andy Sinott
Assistant Manager: Mark West

FACT FILE

Founded: 1883
Sponsors:F.M.C.G.
Nickname: United
Colours: Red & blacks/black/red & black.
Change colours: Green & white
Midweek Matchday: Tuesday
Reserves' League: Suburban

2000-2001

Top Scorer: Mark West 26
P.o.Y.:Mark West
Captain: Martin Brown

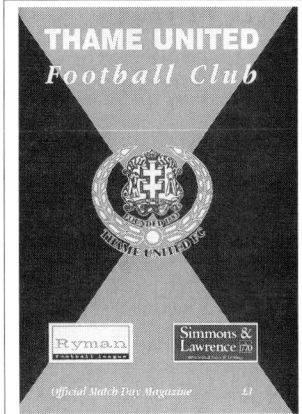

THAME UNITED
Football Club
Ryman
Simmons & Lawrence
Official Match Day Magazine £1

Pages: 24 Price: £1
Editor: Sally Turner (c/o Club)
Local Press: Oxford Mail, Thame Gazette, Bucks Free Press
Local Radio: Radio Oxford, Fox FM, Mix 96

GROUND: Windmill Road, Thame, Oxon OX9 2DR (01844 213017)
Club Website: www.thameunitedfc.co.uk

Directions: Into Nelson Street from Market Square. 3 miles from Haddenham &Thame Parkway (BR). Nearest bus stop at Town Hall (half mile away)

Capacity: 3,600 Seats: 284 Cover: 850 Floodlights: Yes

Clubhouse: Open every evening and weekend lunch times **Club Shop:** No -
Banqueting facilities for 200 (weddings, dinners, dances etc)

PREVIOUS **Leagues:** Oxon Senior; Hellenic 1959-87; South Midlands 1987-91
Name: Thame FC **Ground:** None

CLUB RECORDS **Attendance:** 1,035 v Aldershot, Isthmian Div 2 4/4/94
Win:11-3 v Barton Rovers 16/09/01 **Defeat:** 2-11 v Hungerford, FA Cup Prelim. Rd 1984
Career Goalscorer: Not known **Career Appearances:** Steve Mayhew
Transfer Fee received: **Fee paid:**

BEST SEASON **FA Cup:** Third Qualifying Round 91-92, 0-4 v Salisbury
FA Vase: Semi Final 1998/99

HONOURS Isthmian Lg Div 2 94-95, Div 2 R-up 98-99 Div 3 R-up 92-93; Hellenic Lg 61-62 69-70, Premier Div Cup (4); Sth Mids Lg 90-91; Oxon Snr Cup 1894-95 05-06 08-09 09-10 75-76 80-81 92-93;00-01 Oxon Interm Cup 76-77 78-79 91-92,99-00; Oxon Charity Cup

Players progressing to the Football League: None

Back row, left to right: Justin Merritt, Steve Smith, Andy Williams, Alex Stewart, Wayne Cort, Martin Brown (captain), Chris Brain, Micky Swaysland, Mark Avery and Bob Rayner **Front Row:** Daniel Welsh, Mark Simms, Chris Fontaine, representatives of FMCG, the main club sponsors, on either side of manager Andy Sinnott, Mark West (Assistant Player Manager) Mark Jones and James Saulsbury.

TOOTING & MITCHAM UTD

CLUB OFFICIALS

Chairman: John Buffoni
President: Cliff Bilham
Vice Chairman: Alan Simpson

Secretary: Les Roberts, 91 Fernlea Road, Mitcham, Surrey CR4 2HG (01816 465275)

Commercial Manager: John Pollard
Press Officer: Steve Taylor c/o club

FOOTBALL MANAGEMENT TEAM

Managers: Keith Boanes & Ian Hazell
Coach: Peter Shaw
Physio: Danny Keenan

FACT FILE

Formed: 1932
Nickname: Terrors
Sponsors: Claremont Coaches
Colours: Black & white stripes/black/white
Change colours: All red
Midweek matchday: Tuesday
Reserve League: Suburban

Programme: Pages: 24 Price: 80p
Editor: Steve Taylor
Local Press: Mitcham News, South London Press, South London Guardian
Local Radio: Capital

GROUND

Address: Sandy Lane, Mitcham, Surrey CR4 2HD Tel: 0181 648 3248

Directions: Tooting (BR) quarter mile.
Sandy Lane is off Streatham Road near the Swan Hotel

Capacity: 8,000 Cover: 1,990 Seats: 1,990 Floodlights: Yes
Clubhouse: Open every evening and weekend lunchtimes. Wide variety of food available
Club Shop: Sells souvenirs & confectionary

PREVIOUS: **Leagues:** London 32-37, Athenian 37-56 **Ground:** None **Name:** None

CLUB RECORDS: **Attendance:** 17,500 v QPR, FA Cup 2nd Rd 56-57
Goalscorer: Alan Ives 92 (1972-78) **Appearances:** Danny Godwin 470
Win: 11-0 v Welton Rovers, FA Amateur Cup 62-63
Defeat: 1-8 v Kingstonian, Surrey Snr Cup 66-67 v Redbridge Forest (H), LoctiteCup 3rd Rd 19/2/91
Fee Paid: £9,000 for Dave Flint (Enfield) **Fee Received:** £10,000 for Herbie Smith (Luton)

BEST SEASON: **FA Trophy:** 2nd Qualifying Rd Replay 71-72 81-82
FA Amateur Cup: 1st Rd replay 22-23 **FA Vase:**
FA Cup: 4th Rd 75-76, 1-3 v Bradford C. (A) 3rd Rd 58-59; 2nd Rd 56-57 76-77;1st Rd 5 other occasions
League clubs defeated: Bournemouth & Boscombe Ath, Northampton 58-59, Swindon 75-76

HONOURS: Isthmian League 57-58 59-60 (Full Members Cup 92-93); Athenian League 49-50 54-55; London Challenge Cup R-up 59-60; Surrey Senior Cup 37-38 43-44 44-45 52-53 59-60 75-76 76-77 77-78; Surrey Senior Shield 51-52 60-61 61-62 65-66 London Senior Cup 42-43 48-49 58-59 59-60 (R-up 43-44 44-45); South Thames Cup 69-70;

Players progressing: Trevor Owen (Orient 58), Dave Bumpstead (Millwall 58), Paddy Hasty (Aldersot 58), Walter Pearson(Aldershot), Richie Ward & Alex Stepney (Millwall 62 & 63), Vic Akers(Watford 75), Paul Priddy (Wimbledon 78), Carlton Fairweather & Brian Gayle(Wimbledon 84)

Tooting & Mitcham celebrate promotion back to Division One. **Photo: Peter Singh**

UXBRIDGE

Pages: 44 Price: £1.00
Editor: Richard Russell

Local Press: Uxbridge Gazette & Leader, Uxbridge Recorder
Local Radio: Capital, G L R, Star FM

CLUB OFFICIALS

Chairman: Alan Holloway
President: Alan Odell
Secretary: Roger Stevens
9 Bourne Ave, Hillingdon, Middx UB8 3AR
Tel: 01895 236879
Match Sec: Mick Burrell Tel: 01895 443094
Res & Youth Sec: Bob Clayton
Tel: 01895 857001
Press Officer /Commercial Manager:
Derek Marshall

FACT FILE

Formed: 1871
Nickname: The Reds
Sponsor:
Colours: Red/white/red
Change: Sky & navy blue/white & red
Midweek matchday: Tuesday
Reserves' League: Suburban (Prem Div)

2000-01
Captain: Gavin Bamford
P.o.Y: Kevin Cleary: Supp's: Kevin Cleary
Player's: Dean Clark
Top Scorer: Chris Moore (28)

FOOTBALL MANAGEMENT TEAM

Manager: George Talbot Ass. Manager: Sean Dawson
Coach: Mark Gill Physios:Catherine Horne/Stuart Everley
Res Manager: Andy Everley Youth Manager: Barry Warner

GROUND Honeycroft, Horton Road, West Drayton, Middx UB7 8HX Tel: 01895 443557
Directions: From West Drayton (BR) turn right then 1st right (Horton Road).Ground 1 mile on left. From Uxbridge (LT) take 222 or U3 bus to West Draytonstation, then follow as above. By road, ground 1 mile north of M4 jct 4 takingroad to Uxbridge and leaving by first junction and turning left into Horton Rd- ground 500yds on right
Capacity: 3,770 Cover: 760 Seats: 339 Floodlights: Yes
Club Shop: Good selection of souvenirs & programmes. Contact Averill Hinde
Clubhouse: Open every evening and weekend/bank holiday lunchtimes. (01895 443557)
Hot & cold snacks available on matchdays
Large clubhouse with bar and function room availablefor hire.

PREVIOUS **Leagues:** Southern 1894-99; Gt Western Suburban 1906-19, 20-23; Athenian 1919-20, 24-37, 63-82; Spartan 37-38; London 38-46; Gt Western Comb. 39-45;Corinthian 46-63
Name: Uxbridge Town 23-45 **Grounds:** RAF Stadium 23-48, Cleveland Rd 48-78

CLUB RECORDS **Attendance:** 1,000 v Arsenal, opening of floodlights 1981
Career Scorer: Phil Duff, 153 **Career Appearances:** Roger Nicholls, 1054

BEST SEASON **FA Trophy:** 2nd Rd.1998-99, 99-00, 00-01 **FA Vase:** 4th Rd 83-84
FA Cup: 2nd Rd 1873-74. Also 1st Rd 1883-84 84-85 85-86 **FA Amateur Cup:** Runners-up 1897-98

HONOURS FA Amateur Cup R-up 1897-98; London Chall. Cup 93-94 96-97 98-99, R-up 97-98; IsthLge Div 2 S. R-up 84-85; Athenian Lge Cup R-up 81-82, Res. Sect. 69-70, Res. Cup R-up 68-69; Corinthian Lge 59-60 (R-up 48-49), Lge Mem. Shield 50-51 52-53; Middx Sen.Cup 1893-94 95-96 1950-51, 2000-01 R-up 97-98; Middx Sen. Charity Cup 07-08 12-13 35-36 81-82 (R-up 69-70 82-83 85-86); Middx PremCup 95-96 (R-up 2000-01; Allied Counties Yth Lge [East] 92-93 (Lge Cup R-up 86-87), Lge Shield 88-89 92-93, R-up 97-98; AC Delco Cup R-up 85-86; Suburban Lge North Div 95-96 97-98, R-up 96-97; Middx Sen Yth Cup 96-97

Players progressing: William Hill (QPR 51), Lee Stapleton (Fulham 52), Gary Churchouse (Charlton A.), Tony Witter (QPR), Guy Butters (Spurs), Michael Meaker (QPR)

Back Row L-R: Mike Nicks (coach), Mark Weedon, Gavin Bamford, Stuart Bamford, Simon Poulter, Kevin Cleary, Mark Gill (capt.), Phil Glanville, Sean Dawson, Dean Clark, George Talbot (manager). **Front Row R-L:** Catherine Horne (physio), Leyton Brooks, Paul Mills, Jamie Cleary, Nicky Ryder, Lee Tunnell, Chris Moore.Photo: Roy Green

WALTON & HERSHAM

CLUB OFFICIALS

Chairman: **A.Smith**
President: TBA
Secretary: **Mark Massingham,** 7b Sidney Rd., Walton-on-Thames, Surrey. KT12 2NP
Tel: 01932 885814
Press Officer: **Mervyn Rees**
Tel: 01932 245756

FOOTBALL MANAGEMENT TEAM

Manager: Matt Alexander

Physio: Stuart Smith

FACT FILE

Formed: 18960 Nickname: Swans
Sponsors: T.B.A
Colours: White with red band/white/red
Change colours: Yellow/Blue/yellow
Midweek home matchday: Tuesday
Reserve Team's League: Suburban
Club Website:
www.waltonandhershamfc.co.uk
2000-2001 Captain: Chris Whelan
P.o.Y.: David Cory
Top Scorer: David Cory 14

Official Match Day Programme
Walton Hersham F.C.
The Ryman Football League
£1.20
RYMAN LEAGUE DIVISION ONE
WALTON & HERSHAM v. STAINES TOWN
Thursday 5th April 2001 Kick off 7.45 p.m.
Ryman
The Ryman Football League

Pages: 36 Price: £1.20
Editor: Mark Massingham Tel: 01932 885814

Local Press: Surrey Herald, Surrey Comet
Local Radio: County Sound, BBC Southern Counties

GROUND: Sports Ground, Stompond Lane, Walton-on-Thames Tel: 01932 245263 (club)

Directions: From North: Over Walton Bridge & along New Zealand Ave., down 1-way street and up A244 Hersham Rd - grd 2nd right. From Esher: Down Lammas Lane then Esher Rd, straight over 1st r'bout, 4th exit at next r'bout (WestGrove) 2nd left at end of Hersham Rd and Stompond Lane 1/2 mile on left.Ten min walk Walton-on-Thames (BR). Bus 218 passes grd

Capacity: 6,500 Cover: 2,500 Seats: 500 Floodlights: Yes

Clubhouse: (01932 245263). Open every night. TV, darts, pool, refreshments on matchdays

Club Shop: Open matchdays. Contact Richard Old, c/o the club

PREVIOUS **Leagues:** Surrey Senior; Corinthian 45-50; Athenian 50-71

CLUB RECORDS **Attendance:** 6,500 v Brighton, FA Cup First Round 73-74
Scorer: Reg Sentance 220 in 11 seasons
Appearances: Terry Keen 449 in 11 seasons
Win: 10-0 v Clevedon, FA Amateur Cup 1960
Defeat: 11-3 v Kingstonian Surrey Sen Shield 58
Transfer fee paid: £6,000
Transfer fee received: £150,000 for Nathan Ellington 99

BEST SEASON **FA Trophy:** 4th Round 99-00 **FA Amateur Cup:** Winners 72-73, (SF 51-52, 52-53)
FA Cup: 2nd Rd 72-73 (v Margate), 73-74 (v Hereford). League clubs defeated: Exeter 72-73, Brighton 73-74

HONOURS: Isthmian Lg R-up 72-73, Barassi Cup 73-74; Athenian Lg 68-69 (R-up 50-51 69-70 70-71, Lg Cup 69-70); Corinthian Lg 46-49 (R-up 49-50), Premier Midweek F'litLg 67-69 70-71 (R-up 71-72); Surrey Snr Cup 47-48 50-51 60-61 61-62 70-71 72-73(R-up 46-47 51-52 59-60 69-70 71-72 73-74); London Snr Cup R-up 73-74; SouthernComb. Cup 82-83 88-89 91-92; 99-00 Surrey Comb.Cup 49-50 91-92; John Livey Memorial Trophy 91-92

Players progressing: Andy McCulloch (QPR 1970), Mick Heath (Brentford 1971),Paul Priddy (Brentford 1972), Richard Teale (Q.P.R. 1973), SteveParsons (Wimbledon 1977), Stuart Massey (Crystal Palace), Ross Davidson(Sheffield Utd), Nathan Ellington (Bristol Rovers), Tommy Williams (West Ham United)

Des Boateng (white shorts), 'Swans' No.5, clashes with Fleet's Dylan Pearson in their FA Cup meeting. Photo: Mark V Sandom

WEALDSTONE

CLUB OFFICIALS

Chairman: **Paul Rumens**
Vice Chairman: **Nick Dugard**
Secretary: **Roger Slater,** c/o 31 Jersey Avenue,Stanmore,Middlesex HA7 2JG
Tel: 0208 552 3595
Commercial Director: **Howard Krais**
Press Officer: **Roger Slater**
Company Secretary: **Graham Clark**

FOOTBALL MANAGEMENT TEAM

Manager: Gordon Bartlett
Asst Mgr: Leo Morris Coach: Chris Walton
Physio: Matt Watton

FACT FILE

Formed: 1899
Nickname: The Stones
Sponsors: Warwick Wright
Colours: Blue & white quarters
Change colours: Yellow
Midweek matches: Tuesday
Reserves' League: None
Club Website: http://come.to/wealdstonefc

2000-01

Captain: Paul Lamb
P.o.Y: Paul Lamb
Top Scorer: Carl Holmes 17

Pages: 36 Price: £1.50
Editor: Roy Couch (0208 907 4421)

Local Press: Harrow Observer, Harrow Times
Local Radio: Capital, G.L.R., L..B.C.
Stones Soccerline: 09003 800 160

GROUND: (Sharing with Edgware FC) White Lion Ground, High Street,Edgware,Middlesex (Ground Tel No: 020 8952 6799) Email Address: roge@ dircon.co.uk
Directions: Left out of Edgware station(Northern Line), left again at crossroads and ground is on right , 300 yards down Edgware High Street opposite Warwick Wright
Clubhouse: Open nightly and Friday, Saturday and Sunday lunch time. Hot and cold food on matchdays.

PREVIOUS **Leagues:** Willesden & Dist. 1899-1906 08-13; London 1911-22; Middx 13-22; Spartan 22-28; Athenian 28-64; Isthmian 64-71; Southern 71-79 81-82,88-95; GMVConference 79-81 82-88
Grounds: College Farm 03-10; Belmont Rd 10-22; Lower Mead Stad 22-91; Vicarage Rd (Watford FC) 91-93; The Warren (Yeading F.C.) 93-95

CLUB RECORDS **Attendance:** 13,504 v Leytonstone FA Amateur Cup Fourth Round replay 5/3/49
Goalscorer: George Duck, 251 **Appearances:** Charlie Townsend, 514
Win: 22-0 v The 12th London Regiment (The Rangers)(H), FA Amateur Cup 13/10/23
Defeat: 0-14 v Edgware Town (A), London Senior Cup 9/12/44
Fees Paid: £15,000 for David Gipp (Barnet, 90) **Received:** £25,000 for Stuart Pearce (Coventry City 83); for Sean Norman (Chesham, 1989)

BEST SEASON **FA Amateur Cup:** Winners 1965-66 **FA Trophy:** Winners 1984-85
FA Cup: Third Round 77-78, 0-4 v Q.P.R. (A). 1st Rd on 13 occasions. League clubs defeated: Hereford Utd and Reading, 77-78

HONOURS: FA Trophy 84-85; FA Amateur Cup 65-66; GMV Conference 84-85; Isthmian Lge - Div3 96-97; Southern Lg Southern Div 81-82, Div 1 South 73-74, Lg Cup 81-82; Athenian Lg 51-52 (R-up 52-53 58-59 60-61); Spartan Lg R-up 22-23; London LgDiv 2 12-13 (R-up 11-12); London Snr Cup 61-62 (jt) (R-up 39-40 51-52 60-61); Middx Snr Cup (11); Middx Senior Charity Cup (11); Capital League 84-85 86-87

Players progressing: Stuart Pearce (Coventry City 83), Vinnie Jones(Wimbledon 86), Danny Bailey (Exeter 89), Phil White (Orient 53), Tom McGhee & John Ashworth (Portsmouth 54 & 62), Charlie Sells (Exeter City 62), Eddie Dilsworth (LincolnCity 67), Colin Franks (Watford 69)

Photo: James Smith

WHYTELEAFE

CLUB OFFICIALS

Chairman: **Tony Lidbury**
Secretary: **Robin Clements,** 7 Orchard End, Caterham, Surrey CR3 5UR
TelNo: 01883 3400-77 (H) 07767 233698 (M)
Press Officer: **Brian Davis,**
Tel: 020 8651 2999 (H)
Commercial Manager: **T Dounce**
Tel: 01883 343450

FACT FILE

Formed: 1946
Nickname: Leafe
Sponsors: Sunday Sport
Colours: Green & white/white/white
Change colours: Yellow & black/black/black
Midweek matchday: Tuesday
Reserve Team's League: Suburban

FOOTBALL MANAGEMENT TEAM

Manager: Lee Richardson — Assistant Man.: Bernie Donnelly
Coach: Mark Coote — Physio: John Knapton

GROUND 15 Church Road, Whyteleafe, Surrey CR3 0AR
Tel: 0181 660 5491 (Ground) 0181645 0422 (Boardroom)

Directions: Five minutes walk from Whyteleafe (BR) - turn right from station, and left into Church Road

Capacity: 5,000 Cover: 600 Seats:400 Floodlights: Yes

Clubhouse: Open every lunchtime & evening. Hot & cold food, pool, darts, gaming machines
Clubshop: No

Programme
Pages: 36 Price: £1.00
Editor: Warren Filmer (0181 660 3255)

Local Press: Croydon Advertiser
Local Radio: Mercury

PREVIOUS **Leagues**: Caterham & Edenbridge, Croydon, Thornton Heath & Dist., SurreyIntermediate (East) 54-58, Surrey Senior 58-75, Spartan 75-81, Athenian 81-84
Names: None **Grounds:** None

CLUB RECORDS **Attendance:** 2,210 v Chester City F.A.Cup 1st Rd 99-00.
Transfer fee paid: £1,000 for Gary Bowyer (Carshalton)**Transfer fee received:** £25,000 for Steve Milton

BEST SEASON **FA Vase:** 5th Rd 80-81 85-86
FA Trophy: 3rd Qualifying Rd 89-90 **FA Cup:** First Round proper, 99-00 v Chester City (H)

HONOURS Isthmian Lge Div 2 South R-up 88-89; Surrey Senior Lge 68-69 (Lge Cup R-up 68-69, Lge Charity Cup 71-72, Res Sect 62-63 (Chall. Cup 62-63 (R-up 59-60); Surrey Sen. Cup 68-69 (R-up 87-88); Surrey Prem. Cup R-up 84-85; E. Surrey Charity Cup 79-80 (R-up 76-77 77-78); Thornton Heath & Dist Lge 51-52(Lge Cup 51-52) Div 4 R-up 51-52; Edenbridge Charity Cup 51-52; Caterham & Purley Hospital Cup 51-52; Surrey County Interm Lge East Sect 1 55-56; Surrey Jun. Cup R-up 51-52; Caterham & Edenbridge Lge Div 3 51-52;
Borough of Croydon Charity Cup 56-57; Southern Yth Lge 89-90 (R-up 88-89), Lge Cup 88-89 89-90; Southern Counties M'week F'lit Cup 95-96

Players progressing: Steve Milton (Fulham)

Back Row, left to right: Lee Richardson, Gary Bowyer,Stephen Vidal, Eric Kaira, Matt Martin, Danny Mason, Daniel Nwanze, David Stares,Gary Fisher, Bernie Donnelly (COach) and Tony Lidbury (Chairman) **Front Row:** Mark Redfern, Mark Fawke, Paul McKay, Ben Jones, Stuart Massey (Captain), Matt Kember, Leion Dillon, Dean Lock and Gary Odlum

WINDSOR & ETON

CLUB OFFICIALS

Chairman: Peter Simpson

President: Sir David Hill-Wood, Bt

Secretary: Steve Rowland, c/o Football Club
Tel No: 07887 770630 (M)

Press Officer: Secretary

FOOTBALL MANAGEMENT TEAM

Manager: Byron Walton
Asst Manager:Trevor Baron
Physio: Des Hunt

FACT FILE

Founded: 1892
Nickname: Royalists
Sponsors: Murex Welding Products
Colours: All red with green trim
Change colours: White/black/black
Midweek matches: Tuesday
Reserves' League: Suburban (North)

2000-01

Captain: Colin Ferguson
P.o.Y.: Trevor Bunting
Top Scorer: Chuk Agudosi

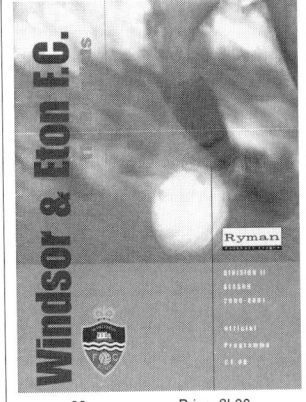

28 pages Price: £!.00
Editor: Malcolm Williams

Local Press: Windsor & Eton Express, Windsor & East Berks Observer, Evening Post
Local Radio:

GROUND Stag Meadow, St Leonards Road, Windsor, Berkshire SL4 3DR (01753 860656)

Directions: A332 from M4 junct 6. Left at r'bout (B3173), left into St Leonards Rd at lights on T-junction, ground 500 yards on right on B3022 opposite Stag &Hounds PH. 1 mile from town centre - pass available to St Leonards Rd. BR to Windsor Central station (from) Slough or Windsor Riverside (change at Staines from Waterloo)

Capacity: 4,500 Cover: 650 Seats: 400 Floodlights: Yes

Clubhouse: Yes **Club Shop:** Yes

PREVIOUS **Leagues:** Southern 1895-96; West Berks; Great Western Suburban 1907-22; Athenian 22-29 63-81; Spartan 29-32; Great Western Comb; Corinthian 45-50; Metropolitan 50-60; Delphian 60-63 **Ground:** Ballon Meadow 1892-1912

CLUB RECORDS **Attendance:** 8,500 (Charity match) **Appearances:** Kevin Mitchell
Fee Paid: £9,000 for Keith White (Slough Town)
Fee Received: £45,000 for Michael Banton & Michael Barnes (Barnet)

BEST SEASON **FA Amateur Cup:** 4th Rd 21-22 **FA Vase:** Semi-Final 80-81 (QF 79-80) **FA Trophy:** 3rd Rd 88-89
FA Cup: 2nd Rd replay 83-84. 1st Rd 7 times 25-26 80-81 82-86 91-92. League clubs defeated: None

HONOURS Isthmian Lg Div 1 83-84 Div 2 R-up 82-83 2000-01,
Athenian Lg 79-80 80-81 Lg Cup 79-80 R-up 78-79 80-81, Div 2 Cup 63-64 R-up 68-69, Spartan Lg R-up 36-37 37-38 Div 1 30-31,
Metropolitan Lg R-up 53-54 Lg Amtr Cup 51-52 52-53, Lg Cup 52-53 R-up 53-54 54-55, Gt Western Suburban Lg R-up 21-22,
Berks & Bucks Snr Cup (11) 10-11 36-38 40-45 61-62 87-89 R-up 07-08 24-25 26-27 38-39 46-47 62-63,
Berks & Bucks Benev. Cup 35-36 37-38 46-47 62-63 R-up 38-39 47-48 49-50

Players progressing: Reg Dare (Southampton 1949), Steve Adams (Charlton 1979), Dave Barnett (Colchester 1988), Vic Woodley (Chelsea & England), Billy Coward (QPR, Walsall), Ken Groves (Preston), Dave Regis (Notts County)

Back Row: Tony Perry (Director of Football), Mark Fiore, Colin Ferguson, Terry Mitchell, Trevor Bunting, Gary Duffy, Matty James, R White. Front Row: Mark Holzman, Byron Walton (player-manager), Gavin Murnagh, John Mitchell, Eddie Gray, Adam Crittenden. **Photo:** Graham Brown

WORTHING

CLUB OFFICIALS

Chairman: **Beau Reynolds**
President: **Morty Hollis**
Vice Chairman: **Ray Smith**

Secretary/Press Off.: **Paul Damper**
19 Fletcher Road, Worthing,
West Sussex BN14 8EX
Tel: 01903 210290

FOOTBALL MANAGEMENT TEAM

Manager: Brian Donnelly
Assistant Manager:Andy Proto
Physio: Alan Robertson

FACT FILE

Formed: 1886
Nickname: The Rebels
Sponsors: Lionvest Trading
Colours: Red, with white trim/red/red
Change colours: Blue with white trim/blue/blue
Midweek matches: Tuesday

2000-01

Captain: Mark Burt
P.o.Y: Stuart Tuck
Top Scorer: Marc Rice (16)

Pages: 40 Price: £1 Editor: Ian Fowler
Local Press: Evening Argus, Worthing Herald
Worthing Guardian
Local Radio: Southern FM,
Southern Counties Radio

GROUND Woodside Road, Worthing, West Sussex BN14 7HQ (01903 239575)

Directions: Follow A24 to town, at end of Broadwater Rd having gone over railway bridge, 1st right into Teville Rd, right into South Farm RD, 2nd left into Pavilion Rd, Woodside Rd is first right. Half a mile fromWorthing (BR)

Capacity: 4,500 Seats: 450 Cover: 1,500 Floodlights: Yes

Clubhouse: Open 2 hrs before kick-off & closes 11pm. Hot & cold food available

Club Shop: Yes

PREVIOUS **Leagues:** West Sussex Sen 1896-04, 05-14, 19-20; Brighton, Hove & Dist 19-20; Sussex County 20-40, 45-48; Corinthian 48-63; Athenian 63-77 **Names:** None **Grounds:** Homefield Park, Beach House Park

CLUB RECORDS **Attendance:** Claimed to be 4,500 v Depot Battalion Royal Engineers, FA Amtr Cup 07-08
Transfer fee paid: Undisclosed fee forMarc Rice (Havant & Waterlooville1998)
Transfer fee received: £7,500 for Tim Read (Woking, 1990)
Win: 25-0 v Littlehampton (H) West Sussex Lge 1911-12 **Defeat:** 0-14 v Southwick (A), Sussex County Lge 1946-47
Career Goalscorer: Mick Edmonds 276 **Career Appearances:** David Bloom 397

BEST SEASON **FA Vase:** 5th Rd 78-79 **FA Trophy:** 4th rd Replay 85-86 **FA Amateur Cup:** Quarter-Final replay 07-08
FA Cup: 2nd Rd 82-83, 0-4 v Oxford Utd; 1st Rd 36-37, 94-95 (1-3 v AFC Bournemouth), 99-00 (0-3 v Rotherham United)

HONOURS Isthmian Lg R-up(2) 83-85 (Div 1 82-83, Div 2 81-82 92-93);Isth Full members Cup r-up98-99, Athenian Lg Div 1 R-up 63-64, Div 2 R-up 71-72, Lg Cup R-up 72-73, Mem. Shield R-up 63-64; SussexSnr Cup (21); Sussex RUR Char. Cup (13); Sussex Co. Lg(8) 20-22 26-27 28-29 30-31 33-34 38-40; W Sussex Lg (7); Brighton Char. Cup(9) 29-31 34-35 62-63 69-7173-74(jt) 80-82; Worthing Char. Cup (11); AFA Invit. Cup 63-64 68-69 73-74 75-76 (Snr Cup R-up 36-37 46-47 48-49); Corinth. Lg Mem. Shield R-up 49-50 (NealeTphy 58-59); Roy Hayden Mem. Tphy 75(jt), 77 78,79. Don Morecraft Tphy 72 73 76 8182; Sussex F'lit Cup(3) 88-90 97-98; Sussex I'mediate Cup 34-35 64-65; BrightonChal. Shield 29-30 31-32

Players progressing: Ken Suttle (Chelsea 48), Alan Arnell & Fred Perry (Liverpool 54), Craig Whitington (Scarborough, via Crawley Town) 93, Darren Freeman (Gillingham), Paul Musselwhite (Scunthorpe), Trevor Wood (Port Vale), Richard Tiltman (Brighton), David Cameron (Lincoln C)

BackRow, left to right: Simon James, Gavin Geddes, Paul Kennett, James wastell, Mark Burt (captain), Ben Carrington, Andrew Beech, Warren Smart and Lee Weston. **Front Row:** Peter Brackley (now Lewes), Stuart Tuck, Danny Davis, Charlie Mays (mascot), Marc Rice and Neil Francis.

Photo: Richard Grange of The Argus, Brighton

YEADING

CLUB OFFICIALS

Chairman: Philip Spurden
President: T.B.A.
Secretary: Joanne Powell,42 Roberts Ride, hazlemere,Bucks. HP15 7AF
Tel No: 01494 712442
Email: yeading@yeadingfc.co.uk

Press Officer: Tim Fuell (0709 1214576)

FOOTBALL MANAGEMENT TEAM

Managers: Johnson Hippolyte & Naz Bashir
Physios: Eddie Cole & Denis Collins

FACT FILE

Formed: 1965 Nickname: The Ding
Sponsors: T.B.A.
Colours: Red & black stripes/black/black
Change colours: White/black/black
Midweek matchday: Tuesday
Reserves League: Capital

Website: www.yeadingfc.co.uk
Local Newspapers: Hayes Gazette

2000-01

Leading goalscorer: Matt Edwards 17
Captain: Steve Ashley

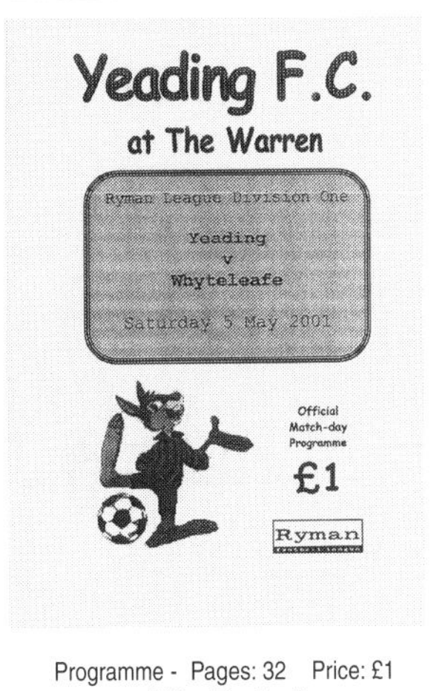

Programme - Pages: 32 Price: £1
Editor: Tim Fuell

GROUND The Warren, Beaconsfield Rd.Hayes, Middx.(0208 8487362/7369.Fx:0208 5611063)
Directions: 2 miles from Hayes (BR) - take Uxbridge Road and turn right towards Southall, right into Springfield Rd and then left into Beaconsfield Rd. Bus 207 stops 1/2 mile from ground
Capacity: 3,500 Cover: 1,000 Seats: 250 Floodlights: Yes
Clubhouse: Open normal pub hours.' The Warren' Conference & Banquetting suite available for hire .(Social Secretary: William Gritt)
Club Shop: Planned Metal Badges: Yes
Well stocked football bookshop at internet site: http://welcome.to/yeadingfc

PREVIOUS **Leagues:** Hayes & District Yth; Uxbridge; S W Middx 1967-74; Middx 74-84;Spartan 1984-87

CLUB RECORDS **Attendance:** 3,000; v Hythe Town, FA Vase SF 1990; v Tottenham Hotspur, friendly
Career Goalscorer: Dave Burt 327 **Career Appearances:** Norman Frape
Fee Paid: Unknown **Fee Received:** £45,000 for Andrew Impey (QPR)

BEST SEASON **FA Cup:** First Round Proper (93-94 & 94-95)
FA Vase: Winners 89-90
FA Trophy: 2ndRd (97-98 & 98-99)

HONOURS FA Vase 89-90; Isthmian League Div 2 Sth 89-90 (Div 1 R-up 91-92);Spartan League 86-87 (R-up 85-86, Senior Div R-up 84-85, League Cup 85-86 86-87); Middlesex Snr League (6) 71-73 74-76 81-82 83-84 (R-up 73-74 74-75 78-79, LeagueCup (6) 72-73 75-76 79-83); South West Middlesex League (2) 69-71; Middlesex Snr Cup 89-90 91-92, Middlesex Prem. Cup 80-81, Middlesex I'mediate Cup (5) 70-7274-76 77-78, Middlesex Jnr Cup (4) 68-69 70-72 74-75; Uxbridge League 66-67; Middlesex Border League Cup 86-87 (AJA Cup 86-87); Suburban League Nth 87-88; Allied Counties Yth League 89-90 (Lge Cup 89-90)

Players progressing: Andrew Impey (Leicester City ,West Ham United , QPR and England U 21) and Lee Charles (Q.P.R.via Chertsey Town)

Yeading's Chris Sparks (light shorts) successfully clears the danger from Bromley's Tom Beech. **Photo:** Alan Coomes.

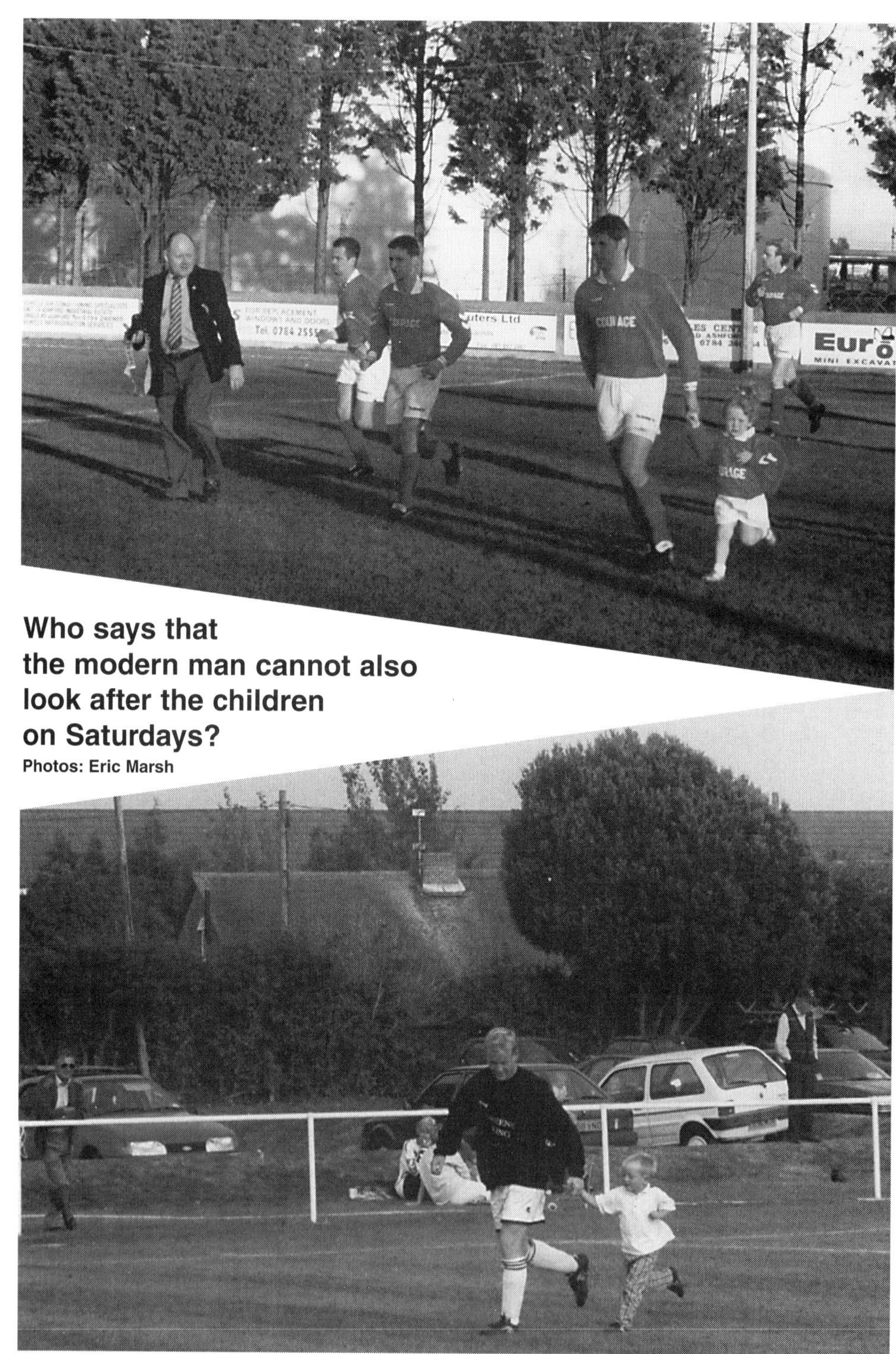

Who says that the modern man cannot also look after the children on Saturdays?

Photos: Eric Marsh

DIVISION TWO FINAL LEAGUE TABLE 2000-01

		P	W	D	L	F	A	W	D	L	F	A	Pts	GD
1	Tooting & Mitcham United	42	14	6	1	48	15	12	5	4	44	20	89	57
2	Windsor & Eton	42	11	5	5	33	22	13	5	3	37	18	82	30
3	Barking	42	15	4	2	43	25	8	9	4	39	29	82	28
4	Berkhamsted Town	42	13	4	4	52	20	11	4	6	47	29	80	50
5	Wivenhoe Town	42	11	7	3	39	22	12	4	5	39	30	80	26
6	Hemel Hempstead Town	42	10	5	6	35	28	12	5	4	39	16	76	30
7	Horsham	42	12	4	5	47	30	7	5	9	37	31	66	23
8	Chertsey Town	42	10	6	5	33	21	8	3	10	26	38	63	0
9	Great Wakering Rovers	42	11	8	2	45	22	5	5	11	24	37	61	10
10	Tilbury	42	11	4	6	36	28	7	2	12	25	39	60	-6
11	Banstead Athletic	42	10	2	9	37	27	7	6	8	32	31	59	11
12	East Thurrock United	42	10	5	6	37	28	6	6	9	35	36	59	8
13	Metropolitan police	42	10	1	10	32	43	8	3	10	32	34	58	-13
14	Marlow	42	7	7	7	29	30	8	4	9	33	31	56	1
15	Molesey	42	8	5	8	31	30	6	4	11	22	31	51	-8
16	Wembley	42	6	5	10	18	35	6	5	10	21	28	46	-24
17	Hungerford Town	42	4	4	13	17	44	7	5	9	23	29	42	-33
18	Leyton Pennant	42	5	5	11	21	36	5	6	10	26	38	41	-27
19	Cheshunt	42	6	3	12	24	38	5	3	13	24	39	39	-29
20	Edgware Town	42	5	4	12	24	37	4	5	12	17	40	36	-36
21	Leighton Town	42	4	7	10	21	38	4	3	14	23	49	34	-43
22	Wokingham Town	42	3	4	14	20	45	0	8	13	19	49	21	-55

DIVISION TWO RESULTS CHART 2000-01

		1	2	3	4	5	6	7	8	9	10	11	12	13	14	15	16	17	18	19	20	21	22
1	Banstead A	X	1-1	6-3	4-0	1-4	0-2	1-2	1-0	0-1	2-0	2-0	2-0	0-1	2-2	6-1	0-1	3-0	0-3	3-1	0-2	1-2	2-1
2	Barking	2-0	X	1-6	2-1	2-1	2-2	4-1	2-0	1-0	2-1	2-0	1-1	3-2	2-1	2-0	0-0	3-5	3-1	2-0	2-1	2-2	3-0
3	Berkhamsted	1-1	0-0	X	2-0	5-0	4-0	5-0	5-2	2-2	2-1	0-1	4-2	0-0	4-1	3-0	4-1	2-0	2-0	0-1	0-3	1-2	5-2
4	Chertsey T	3-1	2-4	2-3	X	2-2	0-0	1-0	0-1	1-1	0-0	4-2	4-1	3-0	2-1	2-1	1-0	3-0	1-1	0-2	0-1	0-0	2-0
5	Cheshunt	2-1	1-2	1-1	1-0	X	2-4	3-1	1-2	0-3	1-0	0-0	1-4	2-1	2-3	0-4	0-3	3-1	1-2	0-1	1-2	1-2	1-1
6	E Thurrock	1-1	2-1	0-0	3-1	3-1	X	2-1	1-1	1-2	1-1	2-1	4-2	1-2	3-2	4-2	0-1	0-1	0-1	2-1	2-2	1-3	4-1
7	Edgware T	2-1	0-0	1-3	1-2	1-2	3-1	X	2-1	1-2	0-1	1-2	1-1	2-1	0-2	0-1	1-1	2-4	2-2	0-2	1-2	1-5	2-1
8	G Wakering	1-1	1-1	1-4	2-1	2-1	4-2	1-1	X	0-0	1-1	4-0	3-0	3-1	2-1	3-3	0-0	3-0	2-2	3-1	0-1	2-1	7-0
9	Hemel H T	2-1	0-1	0-2	0-2	1-3	3-3	2-0	2-0	X	1-1	1-1	3-1	3-1	1-2	2-2	3-1	1-0	0-3	2-1	2-1	2-2	4-0
10	Horsham	1-4	4-0	1-6	6-0	4-0	2-1	2-0	3-0	0-2	X	2-0	2-0	3-0	3-2	0-1	2-2	2-2	3-2	1-1	0-3	3-1	3-3
11	Hungerford	0-3	0-3	1-4	1-0	3-1	2-1	1-1	1-1	1-4	0-4	X	0-2	0-1	0-2	1-1	2-0	0-3	0-4	0-1	1-2	1-4	2-2
12	Leighton T	2-0	0-3	1-3	2-2	1-1	4-3	0-1	1-5	0-0	1-5	1-0	X	1-1	0-1	0-3	1-3	1-2	0-3	0-0	0-0	4-1	1-1
13	Leyton P	1-3	1-3	0-2	0-0	0-2	1-3	2-0	2-0	1-6	1-1	0-1	4-0	X	0-0	0-2	2-1	3-3	0-3	0-0	0-2	2-4	1-0
14	Marlow	3-4	2-2	2-0	1-3	1-1	3-0	2-1	1-2	0-4	4-1	1-3	1-1	1-1	X	1-0	1-0	2-1	1-2	0-0	1-3	0-0	1-1
15	Met Police	0-1	2-0	1-4	1-2	2-1	0-1	3-2	5-3	1-0	1-6	1-1	2-1	4-2	0-4	X	1-3	3-0	0-5	1-0	1-2	0-3	3-2
16	Molesey	1-1	1-2	0-0	1-0	2-0	1-5	3-0	1-2	1-3	4-2	1-3	0-1	0-0	2-2	2-1	X	1-0	0-2	1-2	3-3	4-1	2-0
17	Tilbury	3-2	2-1	1-1	1-2	1-2	1-1	2-3	3-0	2-0	2-1	0-0	3-2	2-1	0-1	4-3	2-1	X	1-1	3-2	0-1	0-1	3-2
18	Tooting & M	3-0	2-2	3-0	1-1	2-0	1-1	1-1	1-1	2-0	2-3	2-1	4-0	3-3	1-0	2-0	4-0	4-0	X	2-1	1-0	5-0	2-1
19	Wembley	1-2	2-2	3-2	2-4	2-1	1-0	1-1	1-1	0-1	0-4	0-0	2-1	0-3	1-0	1-4	1-0	0-1	0-3	X	0-3	0-2	0-0
20	Windsor & E	0-3	2-2	1-2	5-0	2-1	1-0	0-0	1-0	1-2	2-1	2-3	3-0	2-2	2-1	1-0	4-2	1-0	1-1	2-0	X	0-2	0-0
21	Wivenhoe T	2-2	2-2	1-0	1-3	1-0	1-5	4-0	0-0	1-1	4-0	2-0	3-0	3-0	2-2	0-1	1-0	1-0	3-1	4-2	2-2	X	1-1
22	Wokingham	0-0	2-7	2-1	1-2	1-0	0-0	0-1	3-2	0-5	0-3	1-4	2-3	1-2	2-3	0-2	1-2	1-2	0-2	2-2	1-1	0-1	X

ARLESEY TOWN

GROUND: Hitchin Rd, Arlesey, Beds SG15 6RS Tel: 01462 734504

Directions: A1 take A507 to Shefford, at 3rd roundabout turn left, 1st left follow road through village, ground 1.5 miles on left

Capacity: 2,096 Seats: 150 Cover: 300 Floodlights: Yes

Club Shop: Yes

Clubhouse: Open daily 7- 11.30, Sat 12-11.30, Sun 12-2.30 7-11.30
Members bar & function suite

HONOURS: FA Vase Winners 1994-5; Isthmian League (Ryman) Div 3 Champions 00-01, Beds Sen Cup 65-66 78-79 96-97, Prem Cup 83-84,Interm Cup 57-58; S Mids Lge Prem Div 51-52 52-53 94-95 95-96.99-00, Div 2 29-30 31-32 35-36, Chall Trophy 79-80, Prem Shield 64-65, O'Brien Prem Cup 93-94, Flood-LitCup 90-91; Utd Co Lge Prem Div 84-85, KO Cup 87-88; Hinchingbrooke Cup 77-78 79-80 81-82 96-97; Biggleswade KO Cup 77-78 80-81

PREVIOUS: **Leagues:** Biggleswade & Dist.; Beds. Co. (S. Mids) 22-26 ,27-28; Parthenon; London 58-60; Utd Co's 33-36 82-92. Spartan South Midlands 92-99

RECORDS: **Attendance:** 2,000 v Luton Res, Beds Snr Cup 1906
Appearances: Gary Marshall

BEST SEASON: **FA Vase:** Winners 94-95 **FA Cup:** 3rd Qual.

Players Progressing: Roland Legate (Luton), Pat Kruse (Brentford, Leicester) & Dave Kitson(Camb U)

FACT FILE
Founded: 1891
Nickname: Blues
Colours: Sky & navy/navy/navy
Change Colours: All white.
Midweek matchday: Tuesday
Reserves' Lge: S. Midlands Lge Res Div 1
Programme: £1.00
Editor: Pete Brennan (01462 834455)
Club Website: www.arleseyfc.co.uk/

CLUB PERSONNEL
Secretary: John Albon
13 St Johns Rd, Arlesey, Beds SG15 6ST.
Tel: 01462 731318 (H & B),
Mob 07711 566044
Email: j.albon1@ntlworld.com

Chairman: Eddie Haetzman
(01462 816836)
Vice-Chairman: Scott Geekie
(01462 732396)
President: Maurice Crouch

Manager: Nicky Ironton
Asst Man:Alan Dawson
Physio: Eric Turner

2000-01
Captain & P.o.Y.: Dave `Hatchett
Top Scorers: Dave Kitson & Lee Tekell (24)

ASHFORD TOWN (Middlesex)

Ground: Short Lane, Stanwell, Staines, Middx Tel: 01784 245908
Club Website: www.ashfordtownmxfootballclub.co.uk

Directions: M25 jct 13, A30 towards London, 3rd left at footbridge after Ashford Hospital crossroads - ground signposted after 1/4 a mile on right down Short Lane.
2 miles from Ashford (BR) & Hatton Cross (tube) stations.
Bus route - Westlink 116
Capacity: 2,000 Seats: 100 Cover: 100 Floodlights: Yes

Clubhouse: Open 7 days a week. Refreshments always available - hot food on matchdays
Club Shop: No

HONOURS: Combined Co's Lg Champions 94-95, 95-96, 96-97, 97-8, 99-00; Chall Cup R-up 92-93 94-95, Lg Vase Cup R-up 91-92 94-95; Surrey I'mediate Lg, Surrey Prem. Cup 89-90; Middx Prem. Cup R-up 89-90; Southern Comb Cup 95-96, World Wide Carpets Prem Ch Cup 98-99

PREVIOUS **Ground:** Clockhouse Lane Rec
Leagues: Hounslow & Dist. 64-68; Surrey Intermediate 68-82; Surrey Premier 82-90 Combined Counties League 90-00

RECORD **Appearances:** Alan Constable 650
Attendance: 750 v Brentford, friendly 29/7/8
Goalscorer: Andy Smith

FACT FILE

Formed: 1964
Nickname: Ash Trees
Colours: Tangerine & white/white/tangerine
Change colours:Blue/Black/Blue
Midweek matchday: Tuesday
Programme: 24 pages, £1
Editor: Secretary

CLUB PERSONNEL

Secretary: Alan B J Constable
3 Craigwell Close, Chertsey Lane,
Staines, Middx. TW18 3NP
Tel: 01784 440613 (H) 07956 930719 (M)
01784 451614 (Fax)
Email: alanc52@aol.com
Chairman: Robert Parker
Vice Chairman: Des Vertannes
President: T.B.A.
Press Secretary: Kerry Vertannes
Manager: Dave Kent

2000-2001
Captain: Steve Scott
Top Scorer:Scott Todd (26)
P.o.Y .Ian Miles

BANSTEAD ATHLETIC

GROUND
Address: Merland Rise, Tadworth, Surrey KT20 5JG (01737 350982)

Directions: Follow signs to Tattenham Corner (Epsom racecourse), then to Banstead Sports Centre. Ground adjacent to swimming pool.
Half a mile fromTattenham Corner (BR)
Bus 420 from Sutton stops outside ground. Also buses 406 & 727 from Epsom

Capacity: 3,500 Seats: 250 Cover: 800 Floodlights: Yes
Clubhouse A ll week 11am-11pm. 2 bars, real ale, bar snacks Club Shop: Yes

HONOURS: Surrey Snr Lg(6) 50-54 56-57 64-65, R-up(5) 49-50 54-56 57-59, Lg Cup 57-58, Charity Cup 52-53 58-59; London Spartan Lg R-up 77-78 (Lg Cup(2) 65-67);Surrey Prem. Cup R-up 91-92, 95-96; Surrey Snr Shield 55-56; Gilbert Rice F'lit Cup 81-82 86-87 (R-up(4) 82-86); Athenian Lg Cup(2) 80-82 (R-up 82-83 (SF 79-80); Surrey Int. Lg(2) 47-49, Cup 46-47 54-55; E. Surrey Charity Cup (4) 59-6066-67 76-78, R-up 79-80, I'mediate Sect. 75-76 (R-up 76-77), Jnr Sect. 81-82;Southern Comb. Cup R-up 69-70; Suburban Lg R-up 86-87; Carlton T.V. Trophy R-Up 95-96

PREVIOUS **Leagues:** Surrey Int., Surrey Snr 49-65, Spartan 65-75, London Spartan 75-79, Athenian 79-84

RECORDS **Attendance:** 1,400 v Leytonstone, FA Amateur 1953
Win: 11-0 **Defeat:** 0-11
Career goalscorer: Harry Clark **Career appearances:** Dennis Wall
Transfer fee received: None **Transfer fee paid:** None

BEST SEASON **FA Cup:** 3rd Qual.Rd. 86-87. 00-01 FA Vase: Semi - finals 96-97

Players to Lg: W Chesney & B Robinson (Crystal Palace)

FACT FILE
Founded: 1944
Nickname: A's
Sponsors: PDM Marketing
Colours: Amber/black/black
Change colours: Red & white
Programme : Pages: 38 Price: £1.00
Editor: Colin Darby (0181 643 5437)
Midweek Matchday: Tuesday
Club Website: www.bansteadathletic.co.uk

2000-01
Captain: Geoff Taylor
P.o.Y.: Mark Leahy
Top scorer: Marcel Dennis 26

CLUB PERSONNEL

Secretary: Gordon Taylor
116 Kingston Avenue, North Cheam,
Surrey SM3 9UF
TEL: 0181 641 2957

Chairman: Terry Molloy
President: T.B.A.
Press Officer: Colin Darby
Manager: Bob Langford
Coaches: Ray Best & Michael Stratford
Physio: John Steerwood

BARTON ROVERS

GROUND Sharpenhoe Road, Barton-le-Clay, Bedford MK45 4SD (01582 707772)

Directions: M1 Jct 12, from London exit turn right, take 2nd right through Harlington and Sharpenhoe. Entrance to ground 44 yds on right down concrete drive entering village. 41/2 miles from Harlington (BR), 6 miles from Luton (BR), good bus or taxis service from Luton
Capacity: 4,000 Seats: 160 Cover: 1,120 Floodlights: Yes

Clubhouse: Noon-3pm weekends (no football), noon-11pm (matchdays), 7-11pm weekdays. Real ale, hot & cold snacks, pool, darts, gaming machines
Club Shop: Yes (contact 01582 751013)

PREVIOUS **Leagues:** Luton & Dist. 47-54; Sth Midlands 54-79
Grounds: Church Pitch 1898-1912; Barton Cutting 1912; Sharpenhoe Rd 12-33;Faldo Rd 33-38; Barton Rec. 46-75

CLUB RECORDS **Attendance:** 1,900 v Nuneaton, FA Cup 4th Qual. Rd 1976
Win: 17-1 v Flitwick Athletic (H), S Midlands Lge Div 1 55-56
Defeat: 1-11 v Leighton United (H), S Midlands Lge Prem Div 62-63
Scorer: Richard Camp 152, 1989-98
Appearances: Tony McNally 514 (1988-2000)
Fees - Paid: £1,000 for B Baldry (Hitchin Town, 1980)
Received: £1,000 for BBaldry (Bishop's Stortford, 1981)

BEST SEASON **FA Cup:** 1st Round 1980-81, 0-2 v Torquay United (A)
FA Vase: Runners-up 77-78 (SF 76-77 81-82, QF 75-76 78-79)
FA Trophy: 2nd Rd 98-99,99-00

HONOURS: Sth Mids Lg(8) 70-73 74-79 (R-up 67-68), Div 1 64-65 (R-up 55-56), Div 2 54-55, Lg Shield 57-58 60-61 68-69, Chal. Tphy 71-72 74-75 77-78 78-79; Beds Snr Cup (7), R-up (5); Beds Premier Cup 95-96, R-up 81-82 83-84 88-89, 99-00 Beds Intermediate Cup 53-54; Luton & Dist. Lg Div 3 47-48; North Beds Charity Cup 72-73 74-75 76-77 77-78 79-80 80-81 (R-up 70-71); Isthmian Lge Div 2 R-Up 94-95, Assoc. Members Trophy R-up 92-93; South Midlands Floodlight Cup 98-99. Hinchingbroke Cup R-up: 98-99,99-00

Players progressing: Kevin Blackwell (Huddersfield T.)

FACT FILE

Formed: 1898
Nickname: Rovers
Sponsors: SRC Contractors
Colours: All royal blue with white trim
Change colours: All yellow
Midweek Matchday: Tuesday
Reserves' League: None
PROGRAMME
Pages: 64 Price: £1
Editor: Sec & Nick Rhodes (01582 881865)
Local Press: Luton News, Herald, Beds on Sunday
Local Radio: Radio Chiltern, Radio Beds
Three Counties Radio

CLUB OFFICIALS
Chairman: John Milton
President: P Howarth
Vice Chairman: Ken Burr
Secretary: Owen Clark, 108 Manor Road, Barton-le-Clay, Bedford MK45 4NS
Tel: 01582 882398
Press Officer: Nick Rhodes
Tel: 01582 881865

FOOTBALL MANAGEMENT TEAM
Manager: Dick Newman
Physio: Mark Boulding

BERKHAMSTED TOWN

GROUND:
Address: Broadwater, Lower Kings Road, Berkhamsted, Herts HP4 2AA Tel: 01442 862815

Directions: Adjacent to Berkhamsted station (Euston-Birmingham line). A41 toBerkhamsted town centre traffic lights, left into Lower Kings Road

Capacity: 2,500 Seats: 170 Cover: 350 Floodlights: Yes

Clubhouse: Open 7 days a week. Pool & darts - Big screen

Club Shop: Contact Lee Whybrow

PREVIOUS **Leagues:** Herts Co. 1895-1922; Herts Co: 1921 ,Spartan 22-51, 66-75; Delphian 51-63; Athenian 63-66,83-84; London Spartan 75-83
Grounds: Sunnyside Enclosure 1895-1919, Sports Ground 1919-83
Name: Bekhamsted Comrades 1919-22

CLUB RECORDS **Attendance:** 1,732 v Bedlington Terriers F.A.Vase Semi Final 2nd Leg 2001
Career appearances: Ray Jeffrey (612)
Victory: 14-0 **Defeat:** 2-12

BEST SEASON **FA Cup:** 3rd Qual Rd v Barnet 87-88, v Slough 91-92, v Chesham U. 92-93
FA Vase: Finalists 2000-01
FA Trophy: 1st Rd v Kidderminster Harriers 97-98

HONOURS Herts Senior Cup 52-53; London Spartan Lge 79-80 (Div 2 26-27); Herts Charity Shield 50-51(jt) 73-74 79-80 84-85 90-91; Herts Senior County Lge Aubrey Cup 52-53; St Marys Cup(13); Apsley Senior Charity Cup (9); Southern Comb 84-85(F/lit Cup 84-85)

Players progressing: Frank Broome(Aston Villa & England), Maurice Cook (Fulham), Keith Ryan(Wycombe), Maurice Telling (Millwall)

2000-01 Captain: Paul Lowe Top scorer: Ben Smith 24 P.o.Y.: Ben Smith

FACT FILE
Formed: 1895
Nickname: Job Opportunities
Sponsors: C D Wright Elect Wholesalers
Colours: White/black/black
Change Colours: Yellow/blue/blue
Midweek Matchday: Tuesday
Reserves' Lge: Suburban League Prem Div
PROGRAMME
Pages: 64 Price: £1
Editor: Editor
Local Press: Berkhamsted Herald, Berkhamsted Gazette
Local Radio: Chiltern Radio, Mix '96', Three Counties Radio
Website: www.berkhamstedfc.co.uk

CLUB PERSONNEL
Chairman: Danny Jennings

Secretary:David Stanley, 17 Old Vicarage Gardens, Markyate, St Albans, Herts. AL3 8PW. Tel No: 01582 840707

Press Off.: Bob Sear (01442 864547 H & B)

Manager: Steve Bateman
Coach: Mark Pearson
Physio: Brian Hardy

CHERTSEY TOWN

GROUND
Address: Alwyns Lane, Chertsey, Surrey KT16 9DW Tel:01932 561774 Email: tfc.freeserve.co.uk

Directions: Alwyns Lane is off Windsor Street at north end of shopping centre. 10 mins walk from Chertsey (BR). London Country bus

Capacity: 3,000 Seats: 250 Cover: 1000 Floodlights: Yes

Clubhouse: Open weekday evenings and weekend lunchtimes
Club Shop: Open matchdays, selling club & football souvenirs. Contact Blake Robins

HONOURS Isthmian Lge Cup 94-95 (Assoc. Members Trophy 94-95), Div 2 R-up 94-95, Div 3 R-up 91-92; Surrey Snr Lge 59-60 61-62 62-63 (Lge Cup 59-60 61-62); Combined Co's Lge R-up 85-86 (Concours Tphy 85-86); Surrey Snr Cup R-up 85-86; Spartan Lge & Lge Cup R-up 74-75

PREVIOUS **Leagues:** West Surrey (pre-1899); Surrey Jnr 1899-1920; Surrey Intermediate 20-46; Surrey Snr 46-63; Metropolitan 63-66; Gtr London 66-67; Spartan 67-75; London Spartan 75-76; Athenian 76-84; Isthmian 84-85; Combined Counties 85-86.
Grounds: The Grange (pre-World War 1), The Hollows (pre-1929)

CLUB RECORDS **Attendance:** 2,150 v Aldershot, Isthmian Lge Div. 2 4/12/93
Goalscorer: Alan Brown 54, 1962-63
Win: 10-1 v Clapton (H), Isthmian Lge Div. 3, 91-92
Defeat: 1-12 v Bromley (H), FA Cup Preliminary Rd, 82-83
Transfer fee received: £67,500. Paid: Nil

BEST SEASON **FA Vase:** Quarter Final 87-88 91-92
FA Cup: 3rd Qual. Rd 92-93, 1-3 v Kingstonian (H)
FA Trophy: 2nd Qual Rd 95-96 **FA Amateur Cup:** 3rd Qual Rd 61-62

Players progressing: Rachid Harkouk (Crystal Palace), Peter Cawley (Wimbledon 87), Lee Charles (Q.P.R. 95)

FACT FILE
Formed: 1890 Nickname: Curfews
Sponsors: Holly Tree
Colours: Blue & white stripes/white/white
Change colours: Yellow & Black
Midweek Matchday: Tuesday
PROGRAMME: Pages: 36 Price: £1
Editor: Chris Gay (01276 20745)
Local Press: Surrey Herald
Local Radio: BBC Southern Counties, County Sound
Club Website: www.curfews.com

2000-01
Captain: Jack McKinlay
Top Scorer: Marlon Stuart 20
P.o.Y.: Paul Gower

CLUB PERSONNEL
Chairman: Nick Keel
President: Cllr Chris Norman
Vice Chairman: Steve Powers
Press Officer/Secretary: Chris Gay
23 Richmond Close, Frimley, Camberley,Surrey GU16 8NR
Tel: 01276 20745

FOOTBALL MANAGEMENT TEAM
Manager: Paul Walker
Asst Manager: T.B.A.
Coach:Steve Johnson
Physio: T.B.A.

CHESHUNT

GROUND Address: The Stadium, Theobalds Lane, Cheshunt, Herts . Tel: 01992 626752
Email address: alfie@cheshubtfc.fsnet.co.uk

Directions: M25 to junction 25, A10 north towards Hertford, next roundaboutthird exit to next roundabout, turn left proceed under railway bridge, turnleft, ground approx 400 yards on right. 400yds from Theobalds Grove BR station,Buses 310, 242, 311 & 363 to Theobalds Grove station

Seats: 285 Cover: 600 Capacity: 2,500 Floodlights: Yes
Clubhouse: Yes Club Shop: No

HONOURS:
Athenian Lg 75-76 (R-up 73-74), Div 1 67-68, Div 2 R-up 65-66, Lg Cup74-75 75-76; Spartan Lg 62-63, Lg Cup 63-64 92-93, (R-up 89-90); London Lg 49-50 (R-up 56-57), Div 1 47-48 48-49 (R-up 46-47), Div 1 Cup 46-47, Lg Cup R-up58-59, Park Royal Cup 46-47; Isthmian Lg Div 2 R-up 81-82 (Div 3 R-up 94-95);Herts Snr Cup 23-24 (R-up 48-49 49-50 68-69 69-70 71-72 73-74); Herts CharityCup 00-01 05-06 (R-up 70-71 74-75 80-81); Herts Charity Shield 46-47 65-66 (52-53 53-54 54-55 63-64 64-65); Herts Snr Centenary Tphy 91-92; East Anglian Cup74-75 (R-up 75-76); Mithras Floodlit Cup 69-70 (R-up 75-76); London Charity Cup73-74; Roy Bailey Tphy 90-91 94-95 97-98 98-99 99-00

PREVIOUS: **Leagues:** Athenian 19-20 21-31 64-77; London 20-21 24-25 46-51 55-59; Delphian51-55; Aetolian 59-62; Spartan 62-64; Isthmian 77-87
Name: None **Ground:** None

RECORDS: Attendance: 7,000 v Bromley, London Senior Cup 1947

BEST SEASON: **FA Vase:** Quarter Final 81-82
FA Cup: 4th Qual. Rd(4)

Players progressing: Ian Dowie, Ruben Abgula, SteveSedgeley, Lee Hodges, Paul Marquis, Steve Terry, Neil Prosser, Mario Walsh

FACT FILE

Founded: 1946
Nickname: Ambers
Sponsors: Brasilia
Colours: Gold & black/Black/Black
Change colours: All blue
Midweek matchday: Tuesday
Reserves' Lge: Essex & Herts Border Comb
Programme: Pages: 28 Price: £1
Editor: Alfie Norman
Website: www.cheshuntfc.com

CLUB PERSONNEL

Secretary:
Mr F.Beer,10 Hyde Court Parkside,
Waltham Cross EN8 TTL
Chairman:Vince Satori
Vice Chairman: Paul Cully
President: Paul Philips
Press Officer: Alfie Norman
Manager: Troy Townsend
Asst Manager: Kevin O'Dell
Physio: Paul Largerman

2000-01

Captain:Glenn Wilkie
P.o.Y.: Omar Dervish
Top Scorer: Tom Moody

EAST THURROCK UNITED

Ground: Rookery Hill, Corringham, Essex Tel: 01375 644166-club
Directions: A13 London-Southend, take 1014 at Stanford-le-Hope for two and a half miles - ground on left. Two miles from Stanford-le-Hope and Basildon BR stations

Capacity: 3,000 Seats: 160 Cover: 360 Floodlights: Yes Club Shop: No
Clubhouse: Open all day seven days a week. Hot and cold snacks

HONOURS: Metropolitan Lg Div 2 72-73, Essex Snr Lg R-up 88-89 (Lg Cup 88-89 91-92, Harry Fisher Mem. Tphy 83-84 90-91, Sportsmanship Award 81-82 86-87 89-89), Essex SnrTphy R-up 91-92 95-96, Fred Budden Tphy R-up 89-90, Essex & Herts Border Comb.89-90 (Lg Cup 89-90) , Isthmian League Div. Three 99-00

PREVIOUS **Leagues:** Sth Essex Comb.; Gtr London; Metropolitan 72-75; London Spartan 75-79; Essex Snr 79-92
Grounds: Billet, Stanford-le-Hope 70-73 74-76; Grays Athletic 73-74; Tilbury FC 77-82; New Thames Club 82-84
Name: Corringham Social (pre-1969 Sunday side)

CLUB RECORDS **Attendance:** 947 v Trevor Brooking XI, May 1987.
Competitive: 845 v Bashley, FA Vase 1989
Goalscorer: Graham Stewart 102 **Appearances:** Glen Case 600+
Win: 7-0 v Coggeshall (H) 1984
Defeat: 0-9 v Eton Manor (A) 1982, both Essex Snr League
Transfer Fee Paid: £22,000 (Orient & Wimbledon)

BEST SEASON **FA Cup:** 3rd Qual 93-94 **FA Vase:** 5th Rd 84-85

Players progressing to Football League: Greg Berry (Leyton Orient & Wimbledon)

2000-01 Leading Goalscorer: Rikki Finning 20
Player of the Year: Rikki Finning Captain: Tony Pizzey

FACT FILE

Founded: 1969
Nickname: Rocks
Colours: Amber/black/black
Change: all White
Midweek Matchday: Monday
Reserves' Lge: Essex/Herts Border Com
Programme: 36 pages £1.00
Editor: Tony Smith (01375 892855)
Local Press:
Thurrock Gazette/ Thurrock Recorder
Local Radio: BBC Essex

CLUB PERSONNEL

Secretary: Peter Lambert
30 Thames Cres., Corringham,
Essex, SS17 9DU.
Tel: 01375 643418
Chairman: Gary Snell
Vice Chairman: Alan Gower
President: Alan Gower
Press Officer: Malcolm Harris
Manager: Lee Patterson
Asst. Man.: Dave Card
Physio: Richard Mainwaring

GREAT WAKERING ROVERS

Ground: Borroughs Park,Little Wakering Hall Lane, Gt.Wakering, Souithend SS3 OHQ
Tel: 01702 217812

Directions: 4a bus from Shoeburyness (BR), 4a or 4b from Southend - alight at British Legion in Gt Wakering alongside which runs Little Wakering Hall Lane. A127 past Southend signposted Gt Wakering. In Gt Wakering, half mile past large Esso garage along High Street is Little Wakering Hall Lane, ground 250 yds along on left

Capacity: 2,100 Cover: 300 Seats: 150 Floodlights: Yes

Clubhouse: Every eve., Sat 11-11, Sun 12-3 & 7.30-10.30. Hot meals, snacks etc matchdays only
Club Shop: No

HONOURS Isthmian League div. 3 R-iup 99-00; Essex I'mediate Cup 91-92, Essex I'mediate Lg Div 2 91-92, Div 3 90-91, Lg Cup 91-92, Southend Charity Shld 90-91 91-92, Essex Snr Lg. 94-95, Lg Res. Sect. 94-95 (Wirral Programme Essex Sen. Lg. Award 92-93 94-95)

PREVIOUS **Leagues:** Southend & Dist. 19-81, Southend All. 81-89, Essex I'mediate 89-92
Ground: Gt Wakering Rec

BEST SEASON **FA Cup:** 2nd Qual 98-99
FA Vase: 5th Round 97-98

RECORDS **Attendance:** 659 v Potters Bar FA Vase 5th Rd 7-2-98
Win (in Senior Football): 9-0 v Eton Manor 27/12/93
Defeat (in Senior Football): 1-7 v Bowers Utd, Essex Snr Lge 1-4-98

Players progressing: Les Stubbs (Southend, Chelsea) 1947, Jackie Bridge(Southend Utd) 1948, Kevin Maddocks (Maidstone Utd)

FACT FILE
Founded: 1919
Nickname: Rovers
Sponsors:I.M.S.
ColoursGreen & white stripes/whte/green
Change Coours: All Red
Midweek Matchday: Tuesday
Reserves' Lge: Essex & Herts Border Comb
Programme: 24-32 pages, £1.00
Editor: Keith Perryman 01245 354084
Website: great wakeringroversfc.co.uk

2000-01
Captain:John Heffer
P.o.Y.: Paul Wheeler
Leading Goalscorers: Mark Hampshire (18)

CLUB PERSONNEL

Secretary: Roger Sampson
37 Lee Lotts, Gt. Wakering,
Southend SS3 0HA
Tel: 01702 217812

Chairman: Fred Smith
Vice-Chairman: Barry Beadle
President: Eddie Ellis
Manager:T.B.A.
Physio: Clive Taylor
Press Officer: Nobby Johnson
Tel: 01702 297840

HEMEL HEMPSTEAD TOWN

Ground: Vauxhall Ground, Adeyfield Rd, Hemel Hempstead HP2 4HW Tel: 01442 259777

Directions: Euston to Hemel Hempstead Station. H2 or H3 bus to Windmill Rd., Longlands

Capacity: 3,000 Seats: 175 Cover: Yes Floodlights: Yes
Clubhouse: Tel: 01442 259777. Open 7-11pm weekdays, 12-11pm w/ends & Bank Hols. Tea bar open matchdays
Club Shop: No

HONOURS Ryman Lge Div 3 98-99; Herts Snr Cup 05-06 07-08 08-09 25-26 61-62 65-66 91-92, Herts Charity Cup/Shield 25-26 34-35 51-52 63-64 76-77 83-84 (R-up 90-91), Spartan Lg 33-34, Herts Intermediate Cup 54-55 65-66 83-84, West Herts St Mary Cup 70-71 75-76 82-83 85-86 90-91 91-92 93-94, Athenian Lg Div 1 R-up 64-65 (Res Cup 65-66), Delphian Lg (res) 54-55 (Res Cup 54-55 61-62)

PREVIOUS **Leagues:** Spartan 22-52; Delphian 52-63; Athenian 63-77
Names: Apsley 1885-1947; Hemel Hempstead Town (merged with Hemel Hempstead Utd in1947) **Grounds:** Crabtree Lane (til '71)

CLUB RECORDS **Attendance:** 2,000 v Watford 1985
(at Crabtree Lane: 3,500 v Tooting, FA AmtrCup 1st Rd 1962)
Goalscorer: Dai Price **Appearances:** John Wallace, 1012

BEST SEASON **FA Cup:** Never past Qualifying Rounds
FA Vase: 4th Rd 98-99 v Taunton Town

FACT FILE

Founded: 1885
Nickname: Hemel
Sponsors: Barling
Colours: All red with white trim
Change colours: Green/white trim
Midweek Matches: Tuesday

Programme: 48 pages, 80p
Editor/Press Off.: Paul Bullen
Local Press: Hemel Gazette, Herald
Local Radio: Beds Radio, Chiltern, Three Counties Radio

CLUB PERSONNEL

Secretary & Press Officer: Leo Glynn
4 Little Catherells, Gadebridge, Hemel Hempstead, Herts HP1 3QB

Chairman: David Boggins
President:
Vice President: Dave Lloyd

Manager: Gary Phillips
Asst Manager: Roy Butler
Physio: Zoey

TOP: BANSTEAD ATHLETIC

OPPOSITE:
Arlesey's Neil Trebble sends aheader goalwards in the final match at Kingsbury. Photo: D. Nicholson

BELOW:
BERKHAMSTED TOWN
Back: Bryan Hardy (physio), John Richardson, Graham Hall, Paul Lowe (capt.), Sean O'Connor, Paul Aldridge, Andy Adebowale, Darren Coleman, Mark Pearson (coach), Nancy Bryant (asst. Physio). Seated: Mark Dawber, Andy Mullins, Terry Nightingale, Ben Smith, Steve bateman (manager), Neil Yates, Kevin Franklin, Mark Knight, Luke Brockett. Photo: Bob Sear

HORSHAM

GROUND: Queen St, Horsham RH12 5AD (01403 252310) E mail address : c/o Sec

Directions: From the station turn left into North Street. Pass the Arts Centreto the traffic lights and turn left. At the next set of lights (200 yards) turn left again into East Street. East Street becomes Queen Street after the IronBridge and the ground lies opposite Queens Head public house

Capacity: 4,500 Seats: 300 Cover: 3,000 Floodlights: Yes
Clubhouse: Matchdays only. Hot and cold snacks. Dancehall
Club Shop: Yes

HONOURS Sussex Snr Cup 33-34 38-39 49-50 53-54 71-72 73-74 75-76; Sussex RUR Cup (13); Sussex Floodlight Cup 77-78; Sussex County Lg (7), R-up (4), Lg Cup 45-46 46-47; Metropolitan Lg 51-52; Athenian Lg Div 1 72-73, Div 2 69-70 72-73; West Sussex Sen Lge (4); ICIS Div 3 95-96

CLUB RECORDS **Attendance:** 8,000 v Swindon, FA Cup 1st Rd, November 1966
Victory: 16-1 v Southwick Sususssex Co Lg 1945-46
Defeat: 1-11 v Worthing Sussex Sen Cup 1913-14

BEST SEASON **FA Cup:** 1st Rd 47-48 (lost 1-9 at Notts County), 66-67 (lost 0-3 v Swindon)
F.A. Trophy: 1st Rd Proper Replay 76-77 **F.A.Vase:** 4th Rd Replay 85-86

PREVIOUS **Leagues:** W Sussex Sen; Sussex County 26-51; Metropolitan 51-57; Corinthian 57-63; Athenian 63-73
Grounds: Horsham Park, Hurst Park, Springfield Park

Players progressing: Jamie Ndah (Barnet), Darren Freeman (Fulham)

2000-01 **Captain:** Matt Smart **P.o.Y.:** Ian Chatfield **Top scorer:** Gavin Geddes 35

FACT FILE

Founded: 1885
Nickname: Hornets
Club Sponsors: Sunley Homes
Colours: Anber & Green
Change colours: All white
Midweek Matches: Tuesday
Reserves' League: Suburban

Programme: 40 pages, £1.20
Editor:Adam Hammond (01403 217316)
Local Press: West Sussex County Times: Market Square, Horsham (01403 253371)

CLUB PERSONNEL

Secretary: Jef Barrett, 3Bunting Close, Horsham, West Sussex RH13 5PA.
Tel No 01403 267730
Email : jeff.barrett@btinternet.com

Chairman: Frank King
Vice Chairman: Tim Hewlett
President: Geoff Holtom
Press Officer: Jeff Barrett (01403 267730)

Manager: John Maggs
Asst Mgr/Coach:Ali Rennie
Physio: Geoff Brittain

HUNGERFORD TOWN

GROUND
Address: Town Ground, Bulpit Lane, Hungerford RG17 0AY
Tel: 01488 682939 (club) 01488 684597 (boardroom) 01488 684597 (Fax)

Directions: M4 jct 14 to A4, right and left at Bear Hotel, through town centre on A338, left into Priory Rd, second left into Bulpit Lane, over crossroads, ground on left. 3/4 mile from Hungerford BR station

Capacity: 3,000 Seats: 172 Cover: 200 Floodlights: Yes Club Shop: Yes

Clubhouse: Open every evening and lunchtimes including Sunday. 2 bars,dancehall, boardroom/committee room, darts, pool, fruit machines. Hot & coldsnacks. Steward: Dianne Tanner (01488 682939)

HONOURS: Berks & Bucks Snr Cup 81-82 (R-up 75-76 76-77); Hellenic Lg Div 1 70-71, PremDiv Cup 77-78, Div 1 Cup 70-71, Benevolent Cup 60-61; Hungerford Cup 96-97, Isthmian Lge Representatives in Anglo-Italian Tournament 81.

PREVIOUS **Leagues:** Newbury & D.; Swindon & D.; Hellenic 58-78
Names: None **Grounds:** None

CLUB RECORDS **Attendance:** 1,684 v Sudbury Town, FA Vase SF 1st leg 88-89
(20,000 v Modena inItaly 1981) Anglo-Italian Tournament
Scorer: Ian Farr (268) **Appearances:** Dean Bailey (approx 400)
Transfer Fee Paid: £4,000 for Joe Scott (Yeovil Town)
Received: £3,800 for Joe Scott (Barnstaple Town)

BEST SEASON **FA Cup:** 1st Rd 79-80, 1-3 v Slough T. (A)
FA Vase: Semi-Final 77-78 79-80 88-89

Players progressing to Football League: Steve Hetzke (Reading, Blackpool,Sunderland), Bruce Walker (Swindon, Blackpool), Des McMahon (Reading), BrianMundee (Bournemouth, North'ton)

FACT FILE

Founded: 1886
Nickname: Crusaders
Club Sponsors: Kerridge Insurance
Colours: White/navy blue/blue
Change colours: All yeoow
Midweek Matchday: Tuesday
Reserves' League: Suburban (North)
Programme: 24 pages, 50p
Editor:Martyn Leach (01488 683682)
Local Press: Newbury Weekly News, Newbury Evening Post
Local Radio: Radio Berkshire , Radio 210 Kick F.M.

CLUB PERSONNEL

Chairman: Alan Holland
Vice Chairman: Ron Tarry
President: Sir Seton Wills
General Secretary: Eric Richardson
Match Secretary: Norman Matthews
Press Officer: Ron Tarry (01488 682539)
Manager: Gary Ackling
Asst.Man: Tim North
Reserve Team Managers:
Nicky Harrison & Mike Butler
Youth Team Manager: Dave Curtis
Physio: Gerald Smith

LEATHERHEAD

GROUND Fetcham Grove, Guildford Rd, Leatherhead, Surrey KT22 9AS
Tel: 01372 360151, Fax: 01372 362705

Directions: M25 jct 9 to Leatherhead; follow signs to Leisure Centre, ground adjacent. Half mile from Leatherhead (BR)
London Country Buses 479 and 408 - ground opposite bus garage

Capacity: 3,400 Seats: 200 Cover: 445 Floodlights: Yes

Clubhouse: Bar open 12-11pm matchdays. Full catering. Tel: 01372 360151

Club Shop: Yes. Tel: 01372 362705

PREVIOUS **Leagues:** Surrey Snr 46-50; Metropolitan 50-51; Delphian 51-58; Corinthian 58-63; Athenian 63-72

CLUB RECORDS **Attendance:** 5,500 v Wimbledon, 1976
Win: 13-1 v Leyland Motors 46-47 Surrey Sen Lge
Defeat: 1-11 v Sutton United
Career goalscorer: Steve Lunn 96-97 (46)
Career appearances: P Caswell
Fee paid: £1,500 to Croydon (B Salkeld)
Fee received: £1,500 from Croydon (B Salkeld)

BEST SEASON **FA Amateur Cup:** Semi finalists 70-71 73-74
FA Trophy: Runners-up 77-78
F A Cup: 4th Round 74-75, 2-3 v Leicester C.(A).
Also 2nd Rd 75-76 76-77 78-79,1st Rd 77-78 80-81

League clubs defeated: Colchester, Brighton 74-75, Cambridge Utd 75-76,Northampton 76-77

HONOURS FA Trophy R-up 77-78; Isthmian Lg Cup 77-78; Corinthian Lg 62-63; Athenian Lg Div 1 63-64; Surrey Snr Cup 68-69 (R-up 64-65 66-67 74-75 78-79); Surrey Snr Lg 46-47 47-48 48-49 49-50(Lg Cup 49-50), Snr Shield 68-69, Charity Cup 46-47 49-50); E. Surrey Charity Cup 68-69 (R-up 67-68); London Snr Cup R-up 74-75 77-78; Surrey Inter Cup 89-90; Southern Comb. Cup 89-90

Players progressing: Chris Kelly (Millwall), B Friend (Fulham), L Harwood (Port Vale), John Humphrey (Millwall)

FACT FILE
Founded: 1946
Nickname: Tanners
Sponsors: The Beer Seller
Colours: Green and White/green/green
Change colours: Blue & white
Midweek Matchday: Tuesday
PROGRAMME
Pages: 24 Price: £1
Edito: Robert Wooldridge (0208 669 3824)
Local Press: Leatherhead Advertiser, Surrey Advertiser
Local Radio: County Sound

CLUB OFFICIALS
Chairman: Tim Edwards
President: Gerald Darby
General Manager: Keith Wenham (at club)
Secretary: Gerald Darby
Ranmore, 31 Harriots Lane, Ashtead, Surrey, KT21 2QG
Press Office/Comm. Director: Tim Edwards

FOOTBALL MANAGEMENT TEAM
Manager: Chick Botley
Asst. Manager: Clive Howse
Youth Team Manager: Alex Inglethorpe
Physio: Steve Young

LEWES

GROUND: The Dripping Pan, Mountfield Road, Lewes BN7 1XN Tel: 01273 472100

Directions: Two minute walk from Lewes (BR) - turn left out of station and left into Mountfield Road. Ground 100 yards on right

Capacity: 2,600 Cover: 400 Seats: 400 Floodlights: Yes Club Shop: Yes
Clubhouse: (01273 472100). Bar, tea bar

HONOURS: Isthmian Lg Div 2 R-up 79-80 91-92; Ath'n Lg Div 1 69-70 (Div 2 67-68); Sussex Co. Lg 64-65 (R-up 24-25 33-34 58-59 63-64, Lg Cup 39-40); Mid Sussex Lg 10-11 13-14; Sussex Snr Cup 64-65 70-71 84-85 (R-up 79-80 82-83 87-88); Sussex Royal Ulster Rifles Charity Cup(3) 61-63 64-65; Gilbert Rice F'lit Cup 82-83 88-89; Neale Tphy 68-69; Sussex F'lit Cup 76-77 (SF 83-84); Southern Counties Comb Div1 80-81

PREVIOUS: **Leagues:** Mid Sussex 1886-1920; Sussex Co 20-65; Athenian 65-77

RECORDS: **Attendance:** 2,500 v Newhaven, Sussex County Lg 26/12/47
Goalscorer: Mark Stafford 192
Appearances: Terry Parris 662
Transfer Fee Paid: None
Transfer Fee Received: £2,500 for Grant Horscroft (Brighton)

BEST SEASON: **FA Cup:** 4th Qual. Rd, lost to Harwich & Parkeston
FA Trophy: 1st Rd 82-83 **FA Amateur Cup:** 2nd Rd 67-68
FA Vase: 2nd Rd 00-01

Players progressing to Football League: (to Brighton unless stated) Don Bates(1950), Peter Knight (1964), Terry Stanley (1969), Colin Woffuden (1970), GElphick & Steve Ford (Stoke 1981), Glen Geard, Grant Horscroft (1987), J Hammond (Fulham), S Funnell, L Allen (Wimbledon), M Rice (Watford)

FACT FILE

Founded: 1885
Nickname: Rooks
Colours: Red & Black stripes/black/black
Change colours: All white
Midweek matches: Tuesday
Reserves' League: Sussex Co. Res. Sect

PROGRAMME
Pages: 32 pages Price: £1.50
Editor: Martin Burke
Local Press: Evening Argus, Sussex Express
Local Radio: Southern F.M.,B.B.C. Southern Counties

CLUB PERSONNEL

Secretary: Steve Kitchener
8 Malling Down, Lewes, East Sussex BN7 2BN
Tel: 01273 475228

President: T. Carr
Chairman: T. Parris

Manager: Jimmy Quinn

LEYTON PENNANT

GROUND Wadham Lodge Sports Ground, Kitchener Rd, Walthamstow, London. E17 4JP
Tel:0208 527 2444 **Website:** www.leyton-pennant.net **Email:** andy.perkins@btinternet,com
Directions: North Circular Road to Crooked Billet,turn into Chingford Road,then into Brookscroft Road, first on left. Walthamstow Central (Victoria Line tube) 1 mile away, then buses W21 or 256
Capacity: 2,000 Cover: 600 Seats: 200 Floodlights: Yes

Clubhouse: (0208 527 2444). Open 11-11 Mon-Sat, 12-3 & 7-10.30 Sun. No hot food. Hot snacks from tea bar on matchdays
Club Shop: Sells progs, pennants, scarves, badges etc. Contact Ian Ansell c/o the club

HONOURS Isthmian Lg Div 1 R-up 86-87 (Div 2 North 84-85); Essex Snr Tphy R-up 84-85; National Floodlight Cup 84-85; London Sen. Cup 03-04 (R-up 33-34 37-38 45-46); London Charity Cup 34-35 36-37 R-up (4) London Lg 23-24 24-25 25-26 (R-up 26-27), Lg Cup 56-57; Athenian Lg 28-29 65-66 66-67 76-77 81-82 ,R-up (3), Div 2 Cup R-up 69-70; London Chall. Cup R-up 09-10 27-28 95-96; East Anglian Cup R-up 45-46 72-73; Essex Thameside Trophy 64-65 66-67 81-2 (R-up 63-64); Leyton & Dist. All 1892-93 94-95; Eastern F'lit Comp 97-98, 99-00

PREVIOUS **Name:** Leyton FC, Leyton Wingate (75-92), Walthamstow Pennant (64-92)
Leagues: Leyton & Dist. Alliance, South Essex, Southern 05-11, London 20-26, Athenian 27-82, Spartan (Walthamstow Pennant)
Grounds: Brisbane Rd (Home of Leyton Orient), Hare & Hounds Leabridge Rd

CLUB RECORDS **Attendance:** 676 v Aldershot, Isthmian Lge 10/2/96
(100,000, Leyton v Walthamstow Ave., FA Amateur Cup final, Wembley, April 26th 1952)
Win: 10-2 v Horsham 1982 **Career goalscorer:** Steve Lane 118
Defeat: 1-11 v Barnet 1946 **Career appearances:** Steve Hamberger 387
Transfer fee paid: £200 for Dwight Marshall (Hampton)
Transfer fee received: £6,000 for T Williams (Redbridge Forest)

BEST SEASON **FA Amateur Cup:** Winners 26-27 27-28, R-up x6
FA Vase: Sixth Rd 83-84 **FA Trophy:** 3rd Rd 86-87
FA Cup: 3rd Rd 09-10 League clubs defeated: None

Players progressing: C Buchan (Sunderland 10), Casey (Chelsea 52), K Facey (Orient 52), M Costello (Aldershot 56), D Clark (Orient 61), D Marshall (Luton)

FACT FILE
Formed: 1868
Nickname: Lilywhites
Sponsors: Kay Sports
Colours: White/navy/navy
Change colours: All navy
Midweek home matchday: Tuesday
Reserves' Lge: Essex & Herts Border Comb
PROGRAMME
Pages: 32 Price: £1
Editor: Andy Perkins
Local Press: Waltham Forest Guardian, Hackney Gazette
Local Radio: LBC

CLUB PERSONNEL
Chairman: Dave Salmon
Vice-Chairman: T.B.A.
President: George Cross
Secretary: Andy Perkins, 4 Chestnut Drive, Wanstead, London E11 2TA, Tel: 0208 530 4551
Web site: www.btinternet.com/~andy.perkins
Press Officer: Andy Perkins
FOOTBALL MANAGEMENT TEAM

Team Manager/Coach:Tommy Lee
Physio: T.B.A.

2000-01
Captain: Simon Tickner
P.o.Y.: Andy Silk
Top Scorer: Jay Notley 10

MARLOW

GROUND:
Address: Alfred Davis Memorial Ground, Oak Tree Road, Marlow SL7 3ED (01628 483970)

Directions: A404 to Marlow (from M4 or M40), then A4155 towards town centre.Turn right into Maple Rise (by ESSO garage), ground in road opposite (Oak Tree Rd). 1/2 mile from Marlow (BR). 1/4 mile from Chapel Street bus stops

Capacity: 3,000 Cover: 600 Seats: 250 Floodlights: Yes
Clubhouse: Open matchdays & most evenings. Snack bar open matchdays
Club Shop: Sells badges, ties, pens, videos etc

HONOURS: Isthmian Lg Div 1 87-88, Div 2 South R-up 86-87, Lg Cup 92-93; SpartanLg Div 1 37-38 (Div 2 West 29-30); Berks & Bucks Sen Cup (11)

PREVIOUS: **Leagues:** Reading & Dist.; Spartan 1908-10 28-65; Great Western Suburban;Athenian 65-84
Name: Great Marlow
Grounds: Crown Ground 1870-1919); Star Meadow 19-24

CLUB RECORDS: **Attendance:** 3,000 v Oxford United, FA Cup 1st Rd 1994. (Ground - 8,000 SloughT. v Wycombe W., Berks & Bucks Snr Cup Final, 1972)
Goalscorer: Kevin Stone 31
Appearances: Mick McKeown 500+
Fees - Paid: £5,000 for Richard Evans (Sutton Utd. 94)
Received: £8,000 for David Lay from Slought Town 94

BEST SEASON: **FA Cup:** Semi-Finals 1882; 3rd Rd 94-95 (0-2 v Swindon) 92-93 (1-5 v Tottenham); 1st Rd - 19 times -1871-85 86-88 92-93 1991-92 94-95
FA Trophy: 1st Rd 1987-88, 91-92
FA Vase: 5th Rd replay 74-75, 5th Rd 00-01

Players progressing: Leo Markham (Watford 1972), NaseemBashir (Reading)

FACT FILE

Formed: 1870
Nickname: The Blues
Sponsors: North West Estates
Colours: Royal, white trim/royal/royal
Change colours: White & black
Midweek matchday: Tuesday
Reserves' League: Suburban Premier
Programme: Pages: 40 Price: £1
Editor: Terry Staines
Local Press: Bucks Free Press, Maidenhead Advertiser, Evening Post
Local Radio: Eleven 70, Radio 210, Thames Valley Radio
Information Line (normal call rates) : 01932 710215
2000-01 Captain: Grant Goodall
P.o.Y.: James Pritchard
Top scorer:James Pritchard 20

CLUB PERSONNEL

Secretary: Paul Burdell, 69 Wycombe Rd., Marlow. (01628 890540)

Chairman: Terry Staines
Press Off./Comm. Man.: Terry Staines
Manager: Graham Pritchard
Coach: Derek Sweetman
Physio: Mark Skoyles

METROPOLITAN POLICE

GROUND:
Metropolitan Police Sports Ground, Imber Court, East Molesey (0181 3987358)
Directions: From London: A3 then A309 to Scilly Isles r'bout, right into Hampton Court Way, left at 1st r'bout into Ember Court Rd - ground faces in 300yds. From M25 jct 10: A3 towards London for 1 mile, A307 through Cobham, left immediately after Sandown Park into Station Rd - ground 1 mile on left. Half mile from either Thames Ditton or Esher BR stations

Capacity: 3,000 Seats: 297 Cover: 1,800 Floodlights: Yes Club Shop: No

Clubhouse: (0181 398 1267). Four bars, dancehall, cafeteria open 9am-11pm. Hot & cold food

HONOURS: Isthmian Lg Div 2 R-up 77-78 87-88; Spartan Lg 28-29 29-30 36-37 38-39 45-46 53-54 54-55, (R-up 47-48), Lg Cup 59-60 (R-up 57-58); Middx Snr Cup 27-28;Surrey Snr Cup 32-33, Charity Shield 38-39; Metropolitan Lg Cup 68-69 (Amtr Cup 68-69 69-70); London Snr Cup R-up 34-35 40-41; Herts & Middx Comb. 39-40;Diadora Lg Carlsberg Trophy 94-95

PREVIOUS:
Leagues: Spartan 28-60; Metropolitan 60-71; Southern 71-78
Grounds: None
Name: None

CLUB RECORDS:
Attendance: 4,500 v Kingstonian, FA Cup 1934
Goal Scorer: Mario Russo
Appearances: Pat Robert
Win: 10-1 v Tilbury 1995
Defeat: 1-11 v Wimbledon, 1956

BEST SEASON **FA Cup:** 1st Rd - 32-33, 0-9 v Northampton T. (A); 84-85, 0-3 v Dartford (H); 94-95, 0-3 v Crawley T. (H)

FACT FILE
Founded: 1919
Nickname: Blues
Club Sponsors: Hatch Associates
Colours: All blue
Change colours: Black & White stripes
Midweek Matches: Tuesday
Reserves' League: Suburban

Programme: 10 pages, 50p
Editor/ Press Officer:
Cliff Travis (01932 782215)

Local Press: Surrey Comet, Surrey Herald
Local Radio: County Sounds

2000-01
Leading Goalscorer: Jason Prins 25
Captain: Adam Wickens
P.o.Y.: Ian Batten

CLUB PERSONNEL

Secretary: Tony Brooking,
15 Westmoreland Ave, Hornchurch, Essex.
RM112EJ. Tel: (01708 450715)

Chairman: Des Flanders QPM
Vice Chairman:Dave Smith
President: Sir John Stevens QPM

Manager: Ian Fleming
Physio: Dick Pierce

MOLESEY

GROUND **Address:** 412 Walton Road, West Molesey, Surrey KT8 0JG
Tel: 0181 941 7989 (Boardroom) 0181 979 4823 (Clubhouse)

Directions: A3 from London to Hook, thenA309 to Marquis of Granby pub, right to Hampton Court station, turn left forWest Molesey, ground one mile on left

Capacity: 4,000 Cover: 600 Seats: 400 Floodlights: Yes
Clubhouse: Open every evening and weekend lunchtimes
2 bars, discos, live artists, darts, bingo, pool. Steward: John Chambers
Club Shop: Contact John Chambers

PREVIOUS **Name:** Molesey St Pauls 1950-53. **Grounds:** None
Leagues: Surrey Intermediate 53-56; Surrey Snr 56-59; Spartan 59-72; Athenian72-77

CLUB RECORDS **Attendance:** 1,255 v Sutton United, Surrey Senior Cup Semi-Final 1966
CareerGoalscorer: Michael Rose, 139
Career Appearances: Frank Hanley, 453
Transfer fee paid: £500 for Chris Vidal (Leatherhead 88)
Transfer fee received: £5,000 for Chris Vidal (Hythe Town 89)

BEST SEASON **FA Vase:** 6th Rd 81-82. **FA Trophy:** 1st Rd replay 90-91
FA Cup: First Round Proper 94-95, 0-4 v Bath City (H)

HONOURS Isthmian Lg Div 1 R-up 92-93 (Div 2 South R-up 89-90, Lg Cup R-up 92-93), Surrey Senior Lg 57-58, (Lg Charity Cup 56-57), Spartan Lg R-up 59-60 (Lg Cup 61-62 (R-up 63-64)), Surrey Senior Shield R-up 74-75, Southern Combination Cup 90-91 94-95

Players progressing: John Finch (Fulham), Cyrille Regis (WBA, Coventry &England)

2000-2001 Captain 0MattCorbould P.o.Y.: Phil Dean Top Scorer: Phil Dean (14)

FACT FILE

Formed: 1950
Nickname: The Moles
Colours: White/black/black
Change colours: Yellow/royal
Midweek home matchday: Tuesday
Reserve Team's League: Suburban
Youth Team: Southern Yth Lge

Programme - Pages:16 Price: £1
Editor: Ben O'Connor
c/o the club
Local Press: Surrey Comet, Surrey Herald, Molesey News
Local Radio: Thames 107.8 FM
Hospital Radio, County Sound, Three Counties, Star FM.

CLUB PERSONNEL

Secretary/Press Officer:
Ben O'Connor (c/o the club)

Chairman: Norman Clark
President: Fred Maynard

Manager: Clive Walker
Coach: Lawrence Batty
Reserve Manager: Andy Graves

HORSHAM F.C. L- R Back: J Maggs (manager), G Brittain (physio), S Payne, S Vincent, R Barnes, G Mackay, I Chatfield, J Kirby, S Flain, M Lempriere, A Rennie (asst. man.). Front: G Chapman, B Short, M Smart, J Clark, R Andrews, D Bastian. **Photo:** Clive Turner.

LEYTON PENNANT F.C.

ROMFORD F.C. L-R Back: Martin St Hilaire, Antony Warren, Stuart Horne, Wayne Roff (asst. man.), Paul Withey (manager), Scott Ballard, Danny Church, Craig Bristow, Kevin Warre, Paul Joynes (player-coach). Front: Kevin Clark, Scott Withey, Danny Read, Matt Burr, Micky Rogan, Dean Harding, Steve Good.

ROMFORD

GROUND 'Sungate', Collier Row Road, Collier Row, Romford, Essex. Tel: 01708 722766
Website: www.romfordfc.co.uk Email: derek@romfordfc.freeserve.co.uk

Directions: Take the A12 from London as far as the Moby Dick junction.
Turn left and then right at the 1st roundabout into Collier Row Road.
The ground entrance is signposted 200 yards on the right.
Nearest station is Romford (BR).
From directly outside the station the London bus 247 passes the ground.

Capacity: 2,500 Cover: 300 Seats: 175 Floodlights: Yes
Clubhouse: T.B.A.
Club Shop: Open matchdays, selling replica shirts, programmes etc.

PREVIOUS **Leagues:** Essex Senior 92-96 **Grounds:** Hornchurch 92-95, Ford Utd 95-96
Names: Romford FC, formed 1876, folded in the Great War. Reformed 1929 until 78. Restarted in 1992 & in 96 merged with Collier Row - both names being used for that season only. Name changed to Romford in 1997

CLUB RECORDS **Attendance:** 820 v Leatherhead (IL2) 15/4/97
Career Goalscorer: Micky Ross 57
Season goalscorer: Vinny John 45 (97-98)
Career Appearances: Danny Benstock 197
Win: 9-0 v Hullbridge (H) ESL 21/10/95
Defeat: 0-10 v Braintree Town(A) Div. 1 28.4.01
Transfer fee paid: £1,500 for Wade Falana (Braintree) June 97
Fee received: £4,000 for Vinny John from Grays A. July 98

BEST SEASON **FA Cup:** 4th Qual Rd 97-98 v Bromsgrove Rov. (A), 99-2000 v Ilkeston T. (A)
FA Vase: 5th Rd 96-97 v Bedlington Terriers 2-1
FA Trophy: 2nd Round v Worthing 98-99

HONOURS Essex Senior Lge Champ 95-96, Lge Cup 95-96;
Isthmian Div 2 Champ 96-97; East Anglian Cup 97-98

FACT FILE
Reformed: 1992
Nickname: The Boro
Sponsors: TBA
Colours: Blue & old gold/blue/blue
Change colours: Red & black/black/black
Midweek home matchday: Tuesday (7.45)
Reserves' Lge: Essex & Herts Border Prem
Club Call: 09066 555 841
PROGRAMME
Pages: 40 Price: £1.20
Editor: Derek RobinsonTel: 01708 507803
Local Press: Romford Recorder
Local Radio:Active FM

CLUB OFFICIALS
President: Dave Howie
Chairman: Dave Howie
Vice-Chairman: Steve Gardener
Secretary: Derek Robinson
Tel: 01708 507803
Press Officer: Steve Gardener

FOOTBALL MANAGEMENT TEAM
Team Manager: Paul Withey
Physio: Colin Maherson

2000-01
Captain: Micky Rogan
P.o.Y.: Steve Good
Top Scorer: Mervin Abraham 13

TILBURY

GROUND: Chadfields, St Chad's Rd, Tilbury, Essex RM18 8NL Tel: 01375 843093

Directions: BR from Fenchurch Street to Tilbury Town then one mile walk.
By road: M25 (jct 30 or 31) - A13 Southend bound, Tilbury Docks turn off after 4 miles, Chadwell St Mary turn off (left) after another 1.5 miles, right after 400 metres, rt at r'bout (signed Tilbury), right into St Chad's Rd after .5 mile, 1st rt into Chadfields for ground.

Capacity: 4,000 Seats: 350 Cover: 1,000 Floodlights: Yes Club Shop: No
Clubhouse: Open evening, all day Fri. & Sat. and Sun. lunchtimes. Hot &cold food

HONOURS: Isthmian Lg Div 1 75-76, (Div 1 Cup 74-75), Div 3 Prom.: 91-92, 99-00; Athenian Lg 68-69 (Div 2 62-63); London Lg 58-59 59-60 60-61 61-62, Lg Cup 58-59 60-61 61-62, R-up (3); DelphianLg 67-68 (Div 2 62-63); Essex Snr Cup 60-61 63-64 72-73 74-75 (R-up 46-47 47-48 69-70 71-72 78-79);

PREVIOUS **Leagues:** Grays & Dist.& Sth Essex (simultaneously); Kent 27-31; London 31-39 46-50 57-62; Sth Essex Comb. (war-time); Corinthian 50-57; Delphian 62-63; Athenian 63-73 **Names:** None
Grounds: Green & Silley Weir Ground 1900-11; Orient Field 19-38

RECORDS **Attendance:** 5,500 v Gorleston, FA Cup 4th Q Rd 19/11/49
Goalscorer: Ross Livermore 305 (in 282 games, 1958-66)
Appearances: Nicky Smith 424 (1975-85)
Fee received: £2,000, Tony Macklin to Grays A. 1990 & for Steve Conner to Dartford, 1985
Win: 17-0 v No.9 Coy Royal Artillery (H), South Essex Lg 4/10/02.
In Senior Football; 13-2 v Chalfont National (A), London Lg 28/4/92
Defeat: 1-10 v Maidstone U. (A), Corinthian Lge 4.9.62
v Met. Police (A), Isthmian Lg. 6.5.95

BEST SEASON **FA Cup:** 3rd Rd 77-78, 0-4 v Stoke City (A)
FA Amateur Cup: Quarter Final v Wimbledon 46-7
FA Vase: Round 4 v Cowes Sports (a) 99-00

Players progressing to Football League: L Le May, T Scannell, T Oakley, JEvans

FACT FILE
Founded: 1900
Nickname: Dockers
Colours: Black& white stripes,black,black
Change colours: All red
Midweek Matches: Tuesday
Reserves' League:
Essex & Herts Border Comb
PROGRAMME
36 pages, £1.00
Editor: Lloyd Brown
Local Press:
Thurrock Gazette, Thurrock Recorder
Local Radio: Essex Radio, BBC Essex

CLUB PERSONNEL
Chairman: Robin Nash
Vice Chairman: Daniel Nash
President: T.B.A.
Secretary: Lloyd Brown
2 High Ash Close,Linford, Essex
SS17 ORB
Tel: 01375 409938 (H)
0776 232 6519 (M)
Press Officer: as Secretary

Manager: Tony Cross
Physio: Roger Hutton

WEMBLEY

GROUND **Address:** Vale Farm, Watford Road, Sudbury, Wembley HA0 4UR
Tel: 0181 908 8169
Directions: Sudbury Town station (Underground) 400 yds, or 10 mins walk from North Wembley (BR) station. Buses 18, 92, 245 & 182
Capacity: 2,000 Cover: 350 Seats: 350 Floodlights: Yes
Clubhouse: Open every night & weekend lunchtimes.
Hot food on matchdays (0181 904 8169). Club Shop: No

PREVIOUS **Leagues:** Middx 46-49; Spartan 49-51; Delphian 51-56; Corinthian 56-63; Athenian 63-75

CLUB RECORDS **Attendance:** 2,654 v Wealdstone, FA Amateur Cup 52-53
Career goalscorer: Bill Handrahan 105 (1946-52)
Career appearances: Spud Murphy 505 (78-88)
Win: 11-1 v Hermes, London Senior Cup 1963
Defeat: 0-16 v Chelsea, London Challenge Cup 59-60
Transfer Fee paid: Nil
Fee received: £10,000 for Gary Roberts (Brentford, 1981)

BEST SEASON **FA Trophy:** 1st Round proper 91-92
FA Amateur Cup: 2nd Round 66-67, 68-69
FA Cup: 1st Round Proper 1980-81, 0-3 v Enfield (A)

HONOURS Middx Sen Cup 83-84 86-87 (R-up 55-56 68-69 78-79 87-88 91-92 92-93 98-99);Middx Lge 47-48 (Lge Cup 46-47), Middx Charity Cup 67-68 (jnt) 80-81(jnt) 82-83 86-87 94-95,(R-up 83-84 87-88 96-97); Middx Invitation Cup 56-57; Athenian Lge R-up 74-75 (Div 1 R-up 67-68); Corinthian Lge Mem Shield R- up 58-59; Delphian Lge R-up 55-56; Spartan Lge Div 1 West 50-51 (Dunkel Trophy 50-51 jnt); London Sen Cup R-up 55-56; Hitachi Cup SF 83-84; Suburban Lge North 85-86, Lge Cup 84-85 (R-up 83-84)

Players progressing: Keith Cassells (Watford 1977), MikeO'Donague (Southampton 1979), A McGonigle (Olympiakos), Gary Roberts (Brentford1980), Richard Cadette (Orient 1984)

FACT FILE

Formed: 1946
Nickname: The Lions
Sponsors: G & B Builders
Colours: Red & white/red/red
Change colours: All gold
Midweek matchday: Tuesday
Reserves' League: Suburban

Programme - Pages: 28 Price: £1
Editor: Richard Markiewicz
(0181 902 0541 - before 9pm)
Local Press: Wembley & Harrow Observer
Local Radio: Capital, G.L.R

CLUB PERSONNEL

Secretary: Mrs Jean Gumm, 14 Woodfield Avenue, North Wembley, Middx HA0 3NR(0181 908 3353)

Chairman: Brian Gumm
President: Eric Stringer
Press Officer: Richard Markiewicz
(0181 902 0541 before 9pm)
Commercial Manager: Nick Bennett

Manager:Scott Cousins
Asst. Manager: Roger Linton

WIVENHOE TOWN

GROUND: Broad Lane Ground, Elmstead Road, Wivenhoe CO7 7HA Tel: 01206 825380
Directions: Coming out of Colchester towards Clacton take first turning (right) towards Wivenhoe, 1st left and ground clearly visible on right at cross-roads. 1 mile from Wivenhoe (BR)
Capacity: 3,000 Cover: 1,300 Seats: 250 Floodlights: Yes
Clubhouse: (01206 825380) Open normal pub hours Club Shop: A full range of souvenirs etc

PREVIOUS: **Leagues:** Brighlingsea & District 1927-50; Colchester & East Essex 50-71; Essex & Suffolk Border 71-79; Essex Senior 79-86 **Name:** Wivenhoe Rangers
Grounds: Spion Kop; Broomfield; Claude Watcham's Meadow; Vine Farm; Spion Kop; Broomfield; King George V Playing Fields; Essex University

CLUB RECORD **Attendance:** 1,912 v Runcorn, FA Trophy 1st Rd, Feb 1990
Transfer fee received: £5,875 for Bobby Mayes (Redbridge Forest)
Win: 18-0 v Nayland. **Defeat:** 0-8 v Carshalton A. (H), Isthmian Lg 28/8/93
Career goalscorer: Paul Harrison, 258 in 350 games
Career appearances: Keith Bain, 536

BEST SEASON **FA Cup:** 4th Qual Rd 89-90 2-3 v Halesowen Tn (A), 94-95 1-2 v Enfield (H)
FA Trophy: 2nd Rd replay 89-90 **FA Vase:** 5th Rd 82-83;

HONOURS Isthmian Lg Div 1 89-90 (Div 2 Nth 87-88); Essex Snr Lg R-up 79-80 81-82 85-86(Harry Fisher Tphy 83-84 85-86); Essex & Suffolk Border Lg 78-79, Div 1 72-73,Div 2 71-72, Lg Cup R-up(2); Colchester & East Essex Lg 52-53 55-56 (R-up 70-71), Div 1 59-60 69-70, Div 2 R-up 68-69, Lg KO Cup 51-52 52-53 54-55 55-56 (R-up 59-60), Challenge Cup 52-53); Brighlingsea & Dist Lg Div 1 35-36 36-37 47-48(R-up 37-38), Lg KO Cup 36-37 37-38 47-48, Challenge Cup 36-37; Essex Snr Tphy87-88 Essex Jnr Cup R-up 55-56 78-79; Amos Charity Cup(7) (R-up 72-73); StokesCup(3); Wivenhoe Charity Cup (4), (R-up [4]); Cristal Monopole Cup (5), (R-up 2); Sidney James Mem. Tphy 69-70 (R-up 72-73), Tolleshunt D'Arcy Mem. Cup(3)(R-up 2); Walton & District Charity Cup 73-74 78-79; Coggeshall Brotherhood Cup80-81; Brantham Charity Cup R-up 82-83; Worthington Evans Cup 81-82 (R-up 80-8185-86); Harwich Snr Cup R-up 84-85; Woodbridge Chal. Cup 91-92; Mat FowlerShield 92-93 94-95

Players progressing: Robert Reinelt (Gillingham) 1993

FACT FILE

Formed: 1925
Nickname: The Dragons
Colours: Royal blue/yellow
Change colours: Red/black
Reserves' League: Essex & Suffolk Border
Midweek matchday: Tuesday
Programme: 36 pages £1.00
Editor: P Reeve
Local Press: East Anglian Daily Times, Colchester Evening Gazette
Local Radio:
BBC Radio Essex, S.G.R.

CLUB PERSONNEL

Secretary//Press Officer: Mike Boyle, 15 Daniell Drive, Colchester, Essex (01206 573223)

Chairman: Kevin Foskett
Vice Chairman: Max Brook
Manager: Julian Hazel
Asst Manager: Steve Pitt
Physio: Matt Manning

2000-2001

Captain:Steve Henson
P.o.Y.:Robbie May
Captain: Steve Henson

DIVISION THREE FINAL LEAGUE TABLE 2000-01

		P	W	D	L	F	A	W	D	L	F	A	Pts	GD
1	Arlesey Town	42	17	3	1	75	22	17	3	1	63	15	108	101
2	Lewes	41	12	6	2	63	18	13	5	3	41	16	86	70
3	Ashford Town (Middx)	42	10	4	7	50	27	16	3	2	52	22	85	53
4	Flackwell Heath	42	14	5	2	47	18	10	5	6	46	33	82	42
5	Corinthian Casuals	42	12	5	4	43	24	12	5	4	40	26	82	33
6	Aveley	42	13	2	6	44	26	11	1	9	41	35	75	24
7	Epsom & Ewell	42	9	2	10	40	29	14	2	5	36	23	73	24
8	Witham Town	42	12	6	3	44	23	9	3	9	32	34	72	19
9	Bracknell Town	41	11	5	5	50	37	8	5	7	40	33	67	20
10	Croydon Athletic	41	10	5	5	45	20	5	7	9	33	43	57	15
11	Ware	42	8	4	9	33	33	9	2	10	42	43	57	-1
12	Tring Town	42	5	6	10	26	31	11	3	7	34	40	57	-11
13	Egham Town	42	7	5	9	33	28	8	6	7	27	32	56	0
14	Hornchurch	42	7	5	9	35	29	7	8	6	38	31	55	13
15	Wingate & finchley	42	9	5	7	43	32	6	2	13	32	43	52	0
16	Kingsbury Town	42	6	5	10	40	46	5	3	13	34	54	41	-26
17	Abingdon Town	42	6	4	11	28	49	6	3	12	25	53	*40	-49
18	Dorking	42	8	2	11	37	56	2	7	12	22	43	39	-40
19	Hertford Town	41	6	1	14	29	44	3	7	10	28	53	35	-40
20	Camberley Town	42	4	4	13	28	57	4	4	13	25	50	32	-54
21	Clapton	42	3	4	14	25	63	2	5	14	23	58	24	-73
22	Chalfont St. Peter	42	3	1	17	18	54	1	0	20	12	96	13	-120

Abingdon Town deducted 3 points

DIVISION THREE RESULTS CHART 2000-01

		1	2	3	4	5	6	7	8	9	10	11	12	13	14	15	16	17	18	19	20	21	22
1	Abingdon T	X	0-5	0-3	1-6	3-1	2-1	1-0	1-1	0-4	3-2	3-1	0-1	2-1	1-4	2-2	2-3	1-3	1-1	1-1	1-2	1-3	2-4
2	Arlesey T	5-0	X	2-0	2-1	2-1	4-1	9-1	3-0	4-0	2-1	3-3	3-0	2-1	2-3	8-1	3-3	5-1	1-1	6-0	4-3	3-1	2-0
3	Ashford T	1-2	1-2	X	2-1	2-2	3-0	8-0	3-2	2-0	2-2	5-1	1-1	0-1	0-1	1-1	3-0	5-1	1-3	3-4	3-0	1-2	3-1
4	Aveley	4-0	1-1	0-4	X	6-1	1-0	3-1	3-1	1-3	2-0	3-1	2-0	0-1	0-3	5-2	2-1	5-2	0-1	4-2	1-0	1-1	0-1
5	Bracknell T	4-1	0-3	2-2	2-2	X	2-1	3-0	2-1	2-2	3-3	0-3	3-3	2-3	3-2	2-0	0-1	3-1	3-1	0-2	3-2	5-1	6-3
6	Camberley T	2-1	1-3	0-4	2-0	1-5	X	4-2	0-3	2-4	2-2	2-2	1-1	0-4	1-2	1-3	0-5	1-2	0-5	2-3	0-3	5-2	1-1
7	Chalfont S P	1-2	0-5	2-3	1-5	0-6	0-2	X	3-0	0-1	1-2	2-1	1-1	1-2	0-5	1-2	0-3	1-2	0-3	0-2	1-4	2-1	1-2
8	Clapton	1-1	2-8	0-4	2-4	1-0	1-3	2-0	X	1-1	1-3	3-1	1-2	0-4	2-6	2-2	2-2	0-2	0-1	2-4	1-5	0-5	1-5
9	Corinthian C	4-0	0-6	0-1	3-0	2-2	3-2	4-0	8-1	X	3-2	0-0	1-0	0-1	2-0	3-1	1-1	3-1	0-0	2-2	1-3	2-1	1-0
10	Croydon A	0-1	0-2	0-2	4-1	NP	5-1	4-0	3-1	0-0	X	4-0	2-2	0-1	2-2	1-1	2-2	4-1	3-0	4-0	5-0	0-2	2-1
11	Dorking	3-2	2-3	1-3	1-2	0-5	3-2	2-1	1-0	0-2	0-3	X	2-1	0-2	4-3	4-3	0-1	4-4	2-7	1-3	4-4	3-2	0-3
12	Egham T	2-1	3-2	1-2	2-1	1-2	0-1	7-0	1-1	1-1	4-2	1-1	X	1-2	0-1	4-0	0-4	0-1	1-1	1-2	0-0	2-1	1-2
13	Epsom & E	1-2	0-2	1-2	3-1	0-2	4-0	1-2	5-0	1-2	0-1	3-0	1-2	X	1-1	3-1	4-1	2-2	1-2	3-1	2-1	0-4	4-0
14	Flackwell H	2-2	1-1	2-3	1-2	4-0	2-1	4-0	2-2	2-0	2-2	2-2	2-1	3-0	X	3-1	1-0	2-1	1-0	4-0	2-0	3-0	2-0
15	Hertford T	1-3	0-3	0-3	2-3	0-3	3-3	6-1	2-1	0-1	1-3	3-1	1-2	2-3	2-0	X	0-3	3-2	0-1	0-1	1-4	1-0	1-3
16	Hornchurch	5-1	0-3	4-0	0-2	2-0	1-2	4-1	1-3	0-3	2-2	0-0	4-0	2-2	2-2	0-1	X	3-2	0-1	0-1	1-2	3-0	1-1
17	Kingsbury T	6-2	2-3	0-5	3-1	0-3	1-1	5-2	1-1	1-5	5-0	2-1	2-2	1-2	2-2	1-1	3-2	X	0-4	0-1	2-3	2-3	1-2
18	Lewes	3-0	1-1	4-4	0-1	3-0	6-0	13-0	5-1	1-1	4-0	4-2	3-0	0-1	1-0	NP	3-3	4-2	X	2-2	4-0	2-0	0-0
19	Tring T	2-3	0-3	1-2	0-2	1-2	1-1	1-0	2-1	2-4	2-0	1-1	0-1	1-1	1-2	5-1	1-1	1-1	0-1	X	2-0	2-2	0-2
20	Ware	1-0	1-5	1-3	0-3	2-2	4-0	2-1	1-1	2-3	3-3	0-1	0-2	1-2	1-1	3-1	2-0	1-0	1-3	1-2	X	3-0	3-0
21	Wingate & F	4-0	0-1	0-1	1-2	1-1	4-3	8-0	5-1	2-3	0-0	1-0	1-3	1-0	1-2	2-2	1-1	5-3	1-1	2-1	1-6	X	2-1
22	Witham T	1-1	0-1	1-1	3-1	2-2	0-0	5-0	6-1	2-0	1-0	1-0	1-2	4-2	5-4	2-2	1-1	1-0	0-4	2-0	4-0	2-1	X

ABINGDON TOWN

Secretary: Ted Quail, 107 Park Lane, Thatcham, Newbury, Berks RG18 3BZ (01635868967)
GROUND Address: Culham Road, Abingdon OX14 3BT (01235 521684)
Directions: On A415 road to Dorchester-on-Thames half a mile south of town centre. Nearest rail station is Culham. Main line: Didcot Parkway or Oxford. Bus service from Didcot & London
Capacity: 3,000 Cover: 1,771 Seats: 271 Floodlights: Yes
Clubhouse: (01235 521684). 7.30-11pm. 6pm matchdays. 12.30-2.30, 4-11 Sat. Hot food on matchdays. Pool, darts, jukebox, canteen
Club Shop: Selling programmes, magazines, scarves. Metal Badges: £2
HONOURS Berks & Bucks Sen Cup 58-59 (R-up 88-89 92-93); Isthmian League Div 2 (Sth) 90-91 (Assoc. Mem. Tphy R-up 90-91); London Spartan Lg 88-89 Hellenic Lge(4) 56-57 58-60 86-87, R-up(3) 70-72 87-88,Lg Cup 57-58 70-71 81-82 (R-up 83-84 86-87), Div 1 75-76, Div 1 Cup 75-76,Res. Div(3) 69-71 86-87, Res. Div Cup 70-71 85-86, Res. Div Suppl. Cup 74-75;Oxford & Dist. Lg (3) 1898-1901; Reading & Dist. Lg 47-48; Berks & Bucks Jnr Cup 06-07; Abingdon Centenary Cup 58-59; Joan Lee Mem. Cup 69-70 70-71 86-87
PREVIOUS **Leagues:** Oxford & Dist.; West Berks; Reading Temperance; North Berks; Reading & Dist. 1927-50; Spartan 50-53; Hellenic 53-88; London Spartan 88-89
RECORDS **Attendance:** 1,400 v Oxford City, FA Cup September 1960
BEST SEASON **FA Vase:** Fifth Round, replay, 199-90. **FA Cup:** 4th Qual. Rd 60-61 0-2 v Hitchin, 89-90 1-3 v Slough(H), 92-93 1-2 v Merthyr T.(A) after 0-0

FACT FILE
Formed: 1870 Nickname: The Abbotts
Sponsors: Morlands
Colours: Yellow & green/green/yellow
Change colours: Black & white
Programme: Pages: 40 Price:£1.00
Editor: Kevin Rowland(01235 522115)
Midweek Matchday: Wednesday
Reserves ' League: Suburban (West)
Local Press: Oxford Mail, Oxford Times, Abingdon Herald, South Oxon Guardian

CLUB PERSONNEL
Chairman: Phil Evans
President: Dr Tim Reynolds
Vice Chairman: Craig Norcliffe
Press Off : Roger Nicholls: 07768 427268 (M)
Manager: Alan Thorne
Asst Manager:T.B.A.
Physio:T.B.A.
Coach: T.B.A.

AVELEY

Secretary: Craig Johnston,62 Brimfield Rd., Watts Wood,Purfleet, Essex RM19 1RG (01708 864313)
GROUND: `Mill Field', Mill Road, Aveley, Essex RM15 4TR (01708 865940)
Directions: London - Southend A1306, turn into Sandy Lane at Avele .Rainham or Purfleet BR stations then bus No. 723 to the ground. Bus from Rainham No 324
Capacity: 4,000 Cover: 400 Seats: 400 Floodlights: Yes
Clubhouse: Normal pub hours. Bar snacks and hot food available Club Shop: No
HONOURS: Isthmian Lg Div 2 (North) R-up 89-90, Lg (AC Delco) Cup 89-90; London Lg 51-5254-55 (R-up 55-56, Lg Cup 53-54); Delphian Lg R-up 57-58 (Lg Cup 61-62);Athenian Lg 70-71 (Div 2 R-up 68-69); Essex Junior Cup 47-48 48-49; Essex Thameside Trophy 79-80 R-up 97-98; Hornchurch Charity Cup 81-82 (R-up 83-84); East Anglian Cup 88-89, R-up 97-98
PREVIOUS **Leagues:** Thurrock Com 46-49; London 49-57; Delphian 57-63; Athenian 63-73
RECORDS **Attendance:** 3,741 v Slough T., FA Amateur Cup 27.2.71
Goalscorer: Jotty Wilks, 214 **Appearances:** Ken Riley, 422
Win: 11-1 v Histon, 24/8/63
Defeat: 0-8 v Orient, Essex Thameside Trophy, 11/4/85
BEST SEASON **FA Cup:** 1st Rd 70-71, 0-1 v Yeovil League clubs defeated: None
FA Amateur Cup QF 70-71 **FA Trophy** 3rd Qual Rd replay 74-75 **F.A.Vase** 3rd Rd 89-90
2000-01 Captain & P.o.Y.: Billy Goldstone Top Scorer: Kenny Leslie 20

FACT FILE
Founded: 1927
Sponsors: Dagenham Motors
Colours: All Royal blue
Change: All Red
Midweek matches: Tuesday
Reserves' Lge: Essex & Herts Border Comb
Programme: 48 pages Price: £1
Editor: Terry King
Local Press: Thurrock Gazette
Romford Recorder
Local Radio: Radio Essex, Essex Radio

CLUB PERSONNEL
Chairman: David Patient
President: Ken Clay
Press Officer: Terry King
Manager: Steve Mosely
Asst Mg:r Ian Bodley
Coach: Lee Malcolm
Physio Phil Hunter

BRACKNELL TOWN

Ground: Larges Lane, Bracknell RG12 9AN. Tel: 01344 412305 (club), 01344 300933 (office)
Directions: Off A329 just before Met Office r'bout by Bracknell College, ground 200 yards. From Bracknell (BR)/bus station - right out of station, follow pathover bridge, left down steps and follow cycle path ahead, after 300yds follow curve over footbridge, right and follow lane to end, left and ground on leftafter bend
Capacity: 2,500 Seats: 190 Cover: 400 Floodlights: Yes
Clubhouse: Members' bar open 11am-11pm Mon-Sat, 12-3 & 7-10.30pm Sun.
Club Shop: Yes, selling metal badges, programmes, scarves, club sweaters, club ties
PREVIOUS **Leagues:** Great Western Comb.; Surrey Snr 63-70; London Spartan 70-75
Grounds: None **Names:** None
CLUB RECORDS **Attendance:** 2,500 v Newquay, FA Amateur Cup 1971
Career Goalscorer: Richard Whitty **Career Appearances:** James Woodcock
BEST SEASON **FA Cup:** 1st Round Proper, 00-01 (0-4 v Lincoln City)
HONOURS: Isthmian Lg Div 3 93-94; Berks & Bucks Snr Cup R-up; Spartan Lg 74-75, (Lg Cup 81-82 82-83); Surrey Snr Lg 68-69 (Lg Cup 68-69 69-70)
Players progressing: Willie Graham (Brentford)

FACT FILE
Founded: 1896
Nickname: Robins
Reserve's League: Suburban (west)
Colours: Red & white quarters/red/red
Change colours: Blue & white stripes/blue/blue
Midweek Matchday: Tuesday
Programme: Pages: 32 Price: £1.00
Editor/Press Off.: Robert Scully 01344 640721

CLUB PERSONNEL
Secretary: David Mihell, 51 Upshire Gdns., The Warren,Bracknell, Berks RG12 9YZ
Tel: 01344 488369 (H) 07712 489415 (M)

Chairman: Chris Nixon
President: Jack Quinton

Manager: Alan Taylor
Asst Manager:Mark Tallentire
Physio: Geoff Jones

CAMBERLEY TOWN

Secretary: David Clifford 63 Inglewood Ave, Camberley, Surrey. GU15 1RS
Tel & Fax: 01276 516613 Website: www.cambrleytownfc .co.uk
Ground: Krooner Park, Krooner Road, off Frimley Rd, Camberley, Surrey, GU15 2QP.
Tel: 01276 65392 **Directions:** M3 Jct 4, follow signs to Frimley, then B3411 towards Camberley, ground on left opposite `The Standard' pub
Capacity: 3,000 Seats: 195 Cover: 280 Floodlights: Yes Club Shop: Yes
Clubhouse: Open matchdays & 2 evenings. Food available from burger bar matchdays

HONOURS: Isthmian Lg Div 2 R-up 78-79; Surrey Snr Lg 30-31 31-32 32-33 (R-up 46-47 61-62), Lg Charity Cup 37-38 51-52 (R-up 31-32 36-37 54-55 72-73); Surrey Snr Cup 78-79 (R-up 35-36); W. Surrey Lg 13-14 (R-up 12-13); Ascot & Dist Lg 03-04; Surrey Jnr Charity Cup R-up 08-09; Surrey Jnr Cup 1897-98 1909-10 (R-up 07-08); Aldershot Snr Lg 12-13 (Lg Charity Cup R-up 21-22); Southern Comb. Cup 80-81 (R-up 78-79 85-86 87-88); Aldershot Sen Cup 96-97 97-98

PREVIOUS **Leagues:** Ascot & District; West Surrey; Aldershot Snr; Surrey Snr 22-73 Spartan 73-75; Athenian 75-77 82-84; Isthmian 77-82
CLUB RECORDS: **Attendance:** 3,500 v Crystal Pal. friendly 14.10.74
Competitive: 2,066 v Aldershot Town, Isthmian Lge Div. 3, 10.11.92
BEST SEASON: **FA Vase:** Quarter Final 85-86, 98-99 v Woodbridge
FA Cup: 1st Rd Prop 98-99 v Brentford 4th Qual. 32-33 33-34 97-98

FACT FILE
Founded: 1896
Nickname: Krooners, Reds or Town
Colours:Red & White Stripes/ Red/Red
Change colours: L & D Blue strips
Midweek Matches: Tuesday
Reserve's League: Suburban
Programme: 24 pages, £1
Local Press: Camberley News
Bracknell News

CLUB PERSONNEL
Chairman: Ian Waldren
Press Office & Prog.Ed,: Andy Vaughan
Managers: Martin Paterson
Physio: T.B.A.
2000-01 Leading goalscorer: Tony Wood 23
Captain: Justin Gray
P.o.Y.: Justin Gray

CHALFONT ST PETER

Secretary: Alan Thompson, 4 Dane Close, Amersham, Bucks. HP7 9LZ (01494 724260)
Ground: Mill Meadow, Amersham Road, Chalfont St Peter SL9 7BQ Tel: 01753 885797
Directions: A413 from Uxbridge (London) to Chalfont. Turn left 100 yds after 2nd major roundabout (between Ambulance station and Community Centre. Two miles from Gerrards Cross (BR), regular buses from Slough & Uxbridge
Capacity: 4,500 Cover: 120 Seats: 220 Floodlights: Yes Club Shop: Yes
Clubhouse: Open every evening, Saturday afternoons and Sunday lunchtimes
PREVIOUS **Leagues:** Great Western Combination 1948-58; Parthenon 58-59; London 60-62; Spartan 62-75; London Spartan 75-76; Athenian 76-84
BEST SEASON **FA Trophy:** 3rd Qual Rd 89-90 91-92 **FA Vase:** 4th Rd 87-88
FA Cup: 3rd Qual Rd85-86 (wins over Banbury, King's Lynn and Barking)
HONOURS Isthmian Lg Div 2 87-88; Athenian Lg R-up 83-84 (Lg Cup 76-77 82-83); London Spartan Lg Div 2 75-76; Berks & Bucks Intermediate Cup 52-53; Berks & Bucks Benevolent Cup 64-65
CLUB RECORDS **Attendance:** 2,550 v Watford, benefit match 85
Career Goalscorer: Unknown **Career Appearances:** Colin Davies
Transfer Fee Paid: £750 to Chertsey (Steve Church, March 1989)
Players progressing to Football League: Paul Barrowcliff (Brentford), Dean Hooper (Swindon)

FACT FILE
Founded: 1926
Nickname: Saints
Colours: Red, green trim/green/green & red
Change colours: Yellow/black/black
Midweek matchday: Tuesday
Reserves' League:
Programme: Pages: 30 Price: 50p
Editor: Mal Keenan
Local Press: Bucks Advertiser,
Bucks Examiner, Bucks Free Press,
Wycombe Midweek
Local Radio: Chiltern Radio

CLUB PERSONNEL
Chairman:Nigel Payne
Press Officer: Chairman (01494 875195)
Manager: Martin Dean

CLAPTON

Secretary: Linda Ambrose, 8 Silvin Hill, Crystal Palace, SQ19 2QF Tel: 0208 6531010
Ground: The Old Spotted Dog, Upton Lane, Forest Gate, London E7 9NP
Tel: 0208 4720822
Directions: BR to Forest Gate.Tube to Plaistow (District Line). Official entrance in Upton Lane. Docklands Light Railway to Prince Regent then 325 bus to ground
Capacity: 2,000 Seats: 100 Cover: 180 Floodlights: Yes Club Shop: No
Clubhouse: Match days. Light snacks available. To hire please contact club
HONOURS: FA Amateur Cup: 06-07 08-09 14-15 23-24 24-25 (R-up 04-05); Isthmian Lg 10-11 22-23 (R-up 05-06 07-08 09-10 24-25), Div 2 82-83; Essex Thames-side Tphy(2); A.F.A.Invitation Cup (2); London Snr Cup (2); London Charity Cup; Essex Snr Cup (4); Middlesex Snr Cup; Essex Sen Trophy; First English team to play on the continent, beating a Belgian Select XI over Easter 1890.
PREVIOUS **Leagues:** Southern 1894-96 (founder members); London 1896-97
CLUB RECORDS **Attendance:** 12,000 v Tottenham Hotspur, FA Cup 1898-99
BEST SEASON **FA Cup:** 3rd Rd Proper 25-26 (lost 2-3 to Swindon at Upton Park)
League clubs defeated Norwich City 25-26.
FA Amateur Cup: 06-07 08-09 14-15 23-24 24-25 (R-up 04-05);

FACT FILE
Founded: 1878
Nickname: Tons
Sponsors: T.B.A.
Colours: Red & white stripes/black/black
Change colours: All blue
Midweek Matchday: Tuesday
Programme: 12-16 pages £1.00
Editor: Match Secretary

CLUB PERSONNEL
Chairman: Neville Watson
Chief Executive: Vince McBean
Press Officer: Alexander Cole
Manager: Tony Blackwell
2000-01
Leading goalscorer: Joel Sapiro 12

Photo: Alan Coomes.

Aveley's Kenny Leslie gets up well in between Flackwell Heath defenders Jason Eaton and Neil Catlan, but his header hit the post.

LEIGHTON TOWN FC

Left to Right

Back Row:
Adrian Nesbeth
Adrian Browne
Alan Jordan
Gary Duffy
Matt James
Trevor Bunting

Front Row:
Alex Jeffries
Garry Smart
Gavin Mernagh
Grant Eaton
Gordon Hill

CORINTHIAN-CASUALS

Secretary: Brian Wakefield, 5 Martingales Close, Richmond, Surrey Tel: 020 8940 9208

Ground: King George's Field, Hook Rise South, Tolworth, Surrey KT6 7NA
Tel: 020 8397 3368 Email Address: rob@corinthians.freeserve.co.uk
Directions: A3 to Tolworth r'bout (The Toby Jug). Hook Rise is slip road immediately after the Toby Jug pub. Turn left under railway bridge after a 1/4mile - grd on right. Half mile from Tolworth (BR); turn left, continue to Toby Jug, then as above. K2 Hoppa bus from Kingston passes ground
Capacity: 1,700 Seats: 126 Cover: 500 Floodlights: Yes Club Shop: Yes
Clubhouse: Evenings, matchdays, Sunday lunchtimes. Hot & coldsnacks on matchdays

HONOURS FA Amateur Cup R-up 55-56 (SF 56-57), London Spartan Lg R-up 92-93 (Lg Cup R-up 91-92); Combined Counties Lg R-up 96-97

PREVIOUS **Leagues:** Isthmian 39-84, Spartan 84-96; Combined Counties 96-97

BEST SEASON **FA Cup:** 1st Rd 65-66 1st Rd replay 85-86 **FA Vase:** 5th Rd 83-84
FA Amateur Cup: Runners-up 55-56

Career Records: Goals Cliff West 219 **Appearances** Bruce Martin 504

Players progressing: Peter Phillips (Luton Town),Andy Gray, Tony Finnegan, Alan Pardew to Crystal Palace

FACT FILE
Founded: 1939
Sponsors: London Catering Services
Colours: Chocalte & Pink/sky/sky
Change colours: White/navy/white Midweek
Matchday: Tuesday
Reserves' League: Suburban
Programme: 24-48 pages, £1
Editor: Rob Cavallini
Club Website:
www.corinthians.freeserve.co.uk
CLUB PERSONNEL
Chairman: David Harrison
President: Jimmy Hill
Team Manager: Trevor Waller
Press Officer & MatchSecretary
Rob Cavallini (0208 4042763)
2000-01
Captain: Bruce Martin
Top Goalscorer: Iain Waghorn 20

CROYDON ATHLETIC

Secretary: Dean Fisher, 153 Chipstead Valley Road, Coulsdon, Surrey CR5 3BQ
Tel: 020 84073296 (H & Fax) 020 7556 6092
Ground: Mayfields, off Mayfield Road, Thornton Heath, Surrey, CR7 6DN. Tel: 0208 6648343: Club Website: www.croydonathletic.co.uk Email: dfisher@croydonathletic.co.uk
Directions: Follow A23 from London & continue on A23 into Thornton Road. After roundabout take !st on right into Silverleigh Road, left fork into Trafford Road which continues into Mayfield Road. To end and turn left and follow narrow road to ground. 1 mile from Norbury (BR). Buses 109, 154
Capacity: 3,000 Seats: 163 Cover: 300 Floodlights: Yes
Clubhouse: Open every evening & weekends Club Shop: Yes

HONOURS: London Spartan Lg winners 94-95, R-up 88-89 93-94, (Reserve Div 88-89, R-up 88-89); London Snr Cup R-up 91-92; Southern Youth Lg 92-93; Bearman Harber MemTrophy 87-88; Wirral Prog 86-87 96-97; Umbro Fair Play Winners 97-98

PREVIOUS **Leagues:** None

RECORDS **Attendance:** 550 **Goalscorer:** Graham Edginton
Appearances: Graham Edginton/ Paul Gall/Leon Maxwell

BEST SEASON **FA Vase:** 3rd Rd 94-95 **FA Cup:** 2nd Qual. Rd 94-95

Players progressing to Football League: Jamie Ndah (Torquay Utd)

FACT FILE
Founded: 1990 Sponsors: T.C.S. Media
Colours: Maroon & white/maroon/maroon
Change colours: Yellow/royal/royal/royal
Midweek matches: Tuesday
Reserve League: Suburban (S)
Programme: 52 pages, £1
Editor: Secretary
CLUB PERSONNEL
Chairman: Keith Tuckey
V Chairman/ Press Officer: Clive Thompson
Manager: Haydon Bird
Asst Man.: Peter Thomas
1st Team Coach: Peter Burdett
Chief Scout: John Langford
Physio: Mick Reed
2000-01
Leading Goalscorer: John Fowler 41
Captain: Dean Davenport
P.o.Y: Robert Frankland

DORKING

Secretary: Ray Collins,11 Richmond Way, Fetcham, Surrey KT22 9NP (01372 453867)
Ground: Meadowbank, Mill Lane, Dorking, Surrey RH4 1DX (01306 884112)

Directions: Mill Lane is off Dorking High St. next to Woolworths and Marks &Spencers opposite the White Horse pub. Fork right in Mill Lane past theMalthouse pub. 1/2 mile from both Dorking and Deepdene (BR) stations
Capacity: 3,600 Cover: 800 Seats: 200 Floodlights: Yes Club Shop: Yes
Clubhouse: All week &Sun. 4-11 p.m. Sats 12-11pm Hot & cold food on matchdays

HONOURS Isthmian Lge Div 2 Sth 88-89, (Full Members Cup R-up 92-93); Surrey Sen Cup R-up 1885-86 1989-90; Surrey Senior Shield (2), R-up (3); Surrey Sen Lge (4), R-up (2), Lge Cup (3); Lge Charity Cup (4), R-up (5); Gilbert Rice F'lit Cup 87-88 (R-up 89-90); Surrey I'mediate Cup 56-57 (R-up 54-55); Southern Comb.Challenge Cup 92-93

PREVIOUS **Ground:** Prixham Lane (until 1953) **Leagues:** Surrey Senior 22-56 77-78; Corinthian 56-63; Athenian 63-74 78-80; Southern 74-77

CLUB RECORDS **Attendance:** 4,500 v Folkestone Town, FA Cup 1st Qual. Rd 1955 and v Plymouth Argyle 1st Rd F.A.Cup 92-93

BEST SEASON **FA Cup:** 1st Round Proper 92-93, 2-3 v Plymouth A. (H)
FA Vase: 3rd Rd (3) 83-84 86-88 **FA Trophy:** 2nd Rd 91-92

FACT FILE
Formed: 1880 Nickname: The Chicks
Colours: Green & white hoops/green/green
Change colours: All navy blue
Midweek matches: Tuesday
Reserve League: Suburban
Programme: 48 pages £1 Editor: Paul Mason
Press: Dorking Advertiser, Surrey Mirror
Surrey Advertiser
Local Radio: County Sound, Radio Surrey, Radio Mercury
CLUB PERSONNEL
Chairman: Jack Collins
President: Ingram Whittingham
Vice-Chairman: Ray Collins
Co. Sec.: Martin Collins
Press Officer: Bryan Bletso
Manager: Ian Dawes
Asst Manager: Chick Banes
Physio: Bennie Fishlock

EDGWARE TOWN

Ground: White Lion Ground, High Street, Edgware HA8 5AQ. Tel: 0181 9526799

Directions: Left out of Edgware tube station (Northern Line), left again at crossroads and ground is 300yds on right in Edgware High St. behind White Lion pub. Buses 32, 288 142

Capacity: 5,000 Seats: 220 Cover: 1,500 Floodlights: Yes Club Shop: No

Clubhouse: Open nightly and Fri, Sat, Sun lunchtimes.
Hot & cold food matchdays, cold food lunchtimes

HONOURS: Isthmian Lg Div 3 91-92; London Spartan Lg 87-88 89-90 (Lg Cup 87-88); Corinthian Lg R-up 53-54, Memorial Shield 52-53 61-62; Athenian Lge R-up 81-82; Middx Snr Lg 40-41 41-42 42-43 43-44 44-45, Cup 47- 48 (R-up 73-74 94-95); London Snr Cup R-up 47-48; Middx Border Lg Cup 79-80; Suburban Lg Div R-up 89-90

PREVIOUS Leagues: Corinthian 46-63; Athenian 64-84; London Spartan 84-90
Names: Edgware F.C. **Grounds:** None

CLUB RECORDS **Attendance:** 8,500 v Wealdstone, FA Cup 1948

Career Appearances: John Mangan **Career Goalscorer:** Steve Newing

BEST SEASON **FA Vase:** 5th Round, 1991-92

Players progressing: Brian Stein (Luton), Dave Beasant (Wimbledon), Scott McGleish (Charlton 94)

2000-01 Captain & P.o.Y.: Dave Tilbury Top Goalscorer: Tony Reid 8

FACT FILE

Founded: 1939 Nickname: Wares
Colours: Green & white quarters/green/green
Change colours: All yellow
Midweek Matchday: Tuesday
Reserve League: Suburban
Sponsor: Philiam Construction
Programme: Pages: 16 Price: 50p
Editor: Paul Gregory (0181 959 2535)
Website: www.edgwaretownfc.com

CLUB PERSONNEL

Chairman: Paul Karaiskos
President: Mr V Deritis
Patron: Russell Grant
Manager: John Harding
Asst Manager: Noel Blackwell
Physio: Sarah Gow
Secretary: Peter Evans,5 Windmill Ct., Windmill Lane, Bushey, Herts WD23 1NG
Tel: 0208 420 4750 Fax: 0208 950 8924

EGHAM TOWN

Club Administrator: Alison Thompson, 138A Thorpe Lea Rd, Egham, Surrey. TW20 8BL
Tel: 01784 463562

GROUND: Runnymeade Stadium, Tempest Road, Egham, Surrey TW20 8HX (01784 435226)

Directions: M25 jct 13, follow signs to Egham, under M25 at r'bout, left to end, left at mini-r'bout, over railway crossing, left to end (Pooley Green Rd), right, Tempest Rd 2nd right. Bus 41 43 441 from Staines to Pooley Green Rd. 30 mins Egham or Staines (BR)

Capacity: 5,635 Seats: 335 Cover: 1,120 Floodlights: Yes Club Shop: No

Clubhouse: (01784 435226) 7-11pm daily & weekend lunchtimes. Function hall

HONOURS Isthmian Lg Assoc Members Tphy R-up 91-92; Spartan Lg 71-72 (Lg Cup R-up 67-68); Athenian Lg R-up 75-76 (Div 2 74-75); Surrey Snr Cup R-up 91-92, Surrey Snr Lg 22-23, Lg Charity Cup 22-23 (R-up 26-27 34-35); Surrey Intermediate Lg20-21, Charity Cup 19-20 20-21 (R-up 26-27); North West Surrey Charity Cup 20-21; Egham Twinning Tournament 67-68 71-72 74-75 75-76 76-77 80-81; SouthernComb. Floodlit Cup 77-78 (R-up 83-84)

RECORD **Attendance:** 1,400 v Wycombe Wanderers, FA Cup 2ndQual Rd 72
Scorer: Mark Butler 50 (91-92) Career record scorer as well
Appearances: Dave Jones 850+ **Win:** 10-1 v Camberley, 81-82

PREVIOUS **Leagues:** Hounslow & District 1896-1914; Surrey Intermediate 19-22; Surrey Senior 22-28 65-67; Spartan 29-33 67-74; Parthenon 64-65; Athenian 74-77

BEST SEASON FA Cup: 4th Qual Rd 90-91, 0-2 v Telford Utd (A)

FACT FILE

Founded: 1877
Nickname: Sarnies/Town
Colours: Yellow & Green/green/yellow
Change colours: All white
Midweek Matches: Tuesday
Reserves' League: Suburban
Programme: 40 pages, £1
Editor: A lisonThompson (01784 463562 H)
Local Press: Herald & News
Local Radio: County Sound

CLUB PERSONNEL

Chairman: Patrick Bennett
Vice Chairman: Peter Barnes
President: Peter Barnes
Press Officer: Secretary
Manager:Paul Walker
Coaches: Glynn Stephens & Adam Dale
Physio: Ken Weaver

EPSOM & EWELL

Secretary: D Wilson, 33 Delaporte Close, Epsom, Surrey KT17 4AF (01372 729817)
email: d,wilson@nbad.co.uk

GROUND: Share with Banstead A. Merland Rise, Tadworth, Surrey KT20 5JG(01737 350982)

Directions: Follow instructions to Banstead Athlketic (BR). Bus 420 from Sutton stops outside ground. Also bus 460 from Epsom

Capacity: 3,500 Seats: 250 Cover: 800 Floodlights: Yes Club Shop: No

Clubhouse: Normal licensing hours, food available

HONOURS FA Vase R-up 74-75; London Lg 27-28, R-up (5); Corinthian Lg Memorial Shield 59-60 (R-up 51-52 56-57); Athenian Lg Div 2 R-up 75-76 (Lg Cup R-up 76-77, Div2 Cup R-up 67-68); Isthmian Lg Div 2 77-78 (Div 1 R-up 83-84), Vanranel Ass Members Trophy R-up 97-98; Surrey Snr Lg 25-26 26-27 74-75 (R-up 73-74), Lg Cup73-74 74-75, Charity Cup 26-27 (R-up 73-74), Surrey Snr Cup 80-81 (R-up 3); Surrey Snr Shield 32-33 54-55; Surrey Intermediate Cup 29-30,Charity Cup 57-58; Southern Comb. Cup 79-80 (R-up 82-83 92-93)

PREVIOUS Leagues: Surrey Snr 24-27 73-75; London 27-49; Corinthian 49-63; Athenian 63-73 75-77 **Record Goalscorer:** Tommy Tuite

CLUB RECORDS Attendance: 5,000 v Kingstonian, F.A. Cup 2nd Qual. Rd, 15/10/49

BEST SEASON FA Cup: 1st Rd 33-34, **FA Vase:** R-up 74-75 **FA Trophy:** 2nd Rd 81-82

Players progressing: Matt Elliott (Leicester), Chris Powell(Derby), Paul Harding (Notts County, Birmingham), Murray Jones (Grimsby), Alan Pardew (Charlton), Mick Leonard (Chesterfield)

FACT FILE

Founded: 1917
Nickname: E's
Colours: Royal & white
Change: All yellow
Midweek Matches: Tuesday
Reserves' League: Suburban
Programme: 28/32 pages, £1.00
Editor: Stella Lamont (01737 356245)
Club Website www.@eefc.net

2000-01

Captain: Graham Morris
Top Scorer: Ben Forey (30)
P.o.Y.: Dave Hyatt

CLUB PERSONNEL

President: Stella Lamont
Chairman: Peter Atkins
Vice Chairman: Peter Lumm
Manager: Adrian Hill
Coaches: Barry Barnes
Physio: Kevin Taylor

FLACKWELL HEATH

Secretary: Mrs Christine Hobbs, 23 Southfield Rd., Flackwell Heath, Bucks. HP10 9BT
Tel: 01628 521051

GROUND: Wilks Park, Heath End Rd, Flackwell Heath, High Wycombe. HP10 9EA
Tel: 01628 523892

Directions: M40 jct 3 Wycombe East, follow signs for F/Heath left up Treadway Hill & right at top of hill at roundabout. Wilks park 800yds on right, grd at rear of Magpie (PH). Bus 301 either from bus station or High Street near bottom of Crendon Street which comes from BR station. Ask for Oakland Way

Capacity: 2,000 Seats: 150 Cover: Yes Floodlights: Yes Club Shop: No

Clubhouse: Open every night 6.30-11pm & before & after matches. Hot food in tea bar

HONOURS: Gt Western Combination 57-58 62-63; Hellenic Lg Div 1 R-up 76-77; Berks & Bucks Snr Cup SF 85-86

PREVIOUS: **Leagues:** Wycombe & District; Gt Western Comb.; Hellenic 76-82; Athenian 82-84

RECORDS: **Attendance:** 4,500 v Oxford U., charity game 1986 (competitive: 700 v Aldershot Town, 27/10/92)
Goalscorer: Tony Wood **Appearamces:** Ben Richards
Win: 6-0 v Clapton & v Petersfield (both away) **Defeat:** 0-7 v Aveley (H)

BEST SEASON: **FA Cup:** 2nd Qual. Rd replay 90-91, 0-3 v Grays A (A) after 2-2

FACT FILE

Founded: 1907
Colours: Red/black
Change colours: Yellow/black/black
Midweek Matches: Tuesday
Reserves' League: Suburban
Programme: 18 pages £1

CLUB PERSONNEL

Chairman: T Glynn
Vice Chairman: J.Driscoll
President: Ken Crook

Arlesey 'keeper Martyn Patching deals comfortably with this Egham Town attack. Photo: Roger Turner.

Which way now? Clapton's Davey Armstrong looking for a way to avoid the Flackwell Heath midfield. Photo: Francis Short.

HERTFORD TOWN

Ground: Hertingfordbury Park, West Street, Hertford Tel: 01992 583716

Directions: Rail to Hertford Nth (from Moorgate) or Hertford East (LiverpoolStr.); both 15 mins walk. Green Line bus to town centre then 10 mins walk.

By road; off bypass heading east, turn off at Ford garage

Capacity: 6,500 Seats: 200 Cover: 1,500 Floodlights: Yes

Club Shop: Souvenirs **Clubhouse:** Yes **Sponsors:** Simply Health

HONOURS Herts Char. Cup 72-73, 89-90, Herts Snr Cup 66-67, Hertford Char.Shd 19-20 20-21 35-36 49-50 55-56 59-60, Eastern Co's Lg Cup 72-73, East Anglian Cup 62-63 69-70, Southern Co's Comb. F-lit Cup 94-95, Mithras Cup SF 85-86, Ryman Div 3 R-up 97-98

PREVIOUS **Leagues:** Herts Co.; Spartan 21-47 48-59; Delphian 59-63; Athenian 63-72; Eastern Co's 72-73 **Names:** None **Grounds:** None

BEST SEASON **FA Cup:** 4th Qual. Rd. 73-74 (lost 1-2 at Hillingdon Borough)

CLUB RECORDS **Gate:** 5,000 v Kingstonian, F.A. Amateur Cup 2nd Rd 55-56

Appearances: Robbie Burns

Players progressing to Football League: G Mazzon (Aldershot), J.Hooker (Brentford)

2000-01 Captain: David Crate P.o.Y. & Top Scorer: Danny Fitzpatrick 19

FACT FILE

Founded: 1908
Nickname: The Blues
Colours: Blue & yellow stripes/blue/blue
Change colours: Orange & Black
Midweek Matches: Tuesday
Reserves' Lge: Essex & Herts Border Comb
Programme: 28 pages, £1.50
Editor: Matt Darrington (01992 447927)
Local Newspapers: Hertfordshire Mercury

CLUB PERSONNEL

Secretary & Press Officer: Stephen Hedley, 29 Upper field Road,Wewyn Garden City, Herts AL7 3LP(01707 333712)
President: John Hedley
Chairman: David Thomas
01992 500123 (H) 07777 556 6771 (M)
Manager: Andy Prutton
Physio: David Crate

HORNCHURCH

Secretary: Rob Monger,1 PIckwick Close,Laindon,Basildon Essex SS15 5SW(01268 490847)

GROUND: The Stadium, Bridge Avenue, Upminster, Essex RM14 2LX (01708 220080)
Website: www.urchins.org Email: enquiries@urchins.org

Directions: Fenchurch Street to Upminster (BR) then 10 mins walk. Or tube toUpminster Bridge (LT), right outside station, 2nd right into Bridge Ave. ground 150yds on right. By road Bridge Avenue is off A124 between Hornchurch and Upminster. Buses 248, 348, 370, 373 from Romford or Upminster BR stations

Capacity: 3,000 Seats: 300 Cover: 350 Floodlights: Yes Club Shop: Yes,

Clubhouse: Mon-Fri 7.30-11, Sat 12-11, Sun 12-3. Cafeteria open matchdays

Club Shop: Yes, selling programmes, handbooks, scarves, hats, souvenirs etc.
Contact : Peter Harris(01268 544151)

HONOURS: Athenian Lg 66-67, Romford Lg(2), Essex Snr Trophy R-up 86-87, Essex Jnr Cup Essex Thameside Tphy 84-85, Isthmian Yth Cup, CarlsbergTrophy R-up 93-94

PREVIOUS: **Leagues:** Romford 25-38; Spartan 38-52; Delphian 52-59; Athenian 59-75

Names: Hornchurch & Upminster (Upminster FC pre-1950s) merged with Upminster Wanderers in 1961

RECORDS: **Attendance**: 3,000 v Chelmsford, FA Cup 66-67

BEST SEASON: **FA Cup:** 4th Qual Rd 66-67, lost 0-4 at home to Chelmsford City
F.A. Vase: 5th Rd 74-75

FACT FILE

Founded: 1923
Nickname: Urchins
Sponsors: Premier Snacks
Colours: Red & white/red/red
Change Colours: Yellow/blue
Midweek Matches: Tuesday
Reserve Lge: Essex & Herts Border Comb
Programme: 16-20 pages with admission
Editor: Peter Harris (01268 544151)
Local Press: Romford Recorder
Local Radio: Essex Radio, Active FM

CLUB PERSONNEL

Chairman: Tony Wallace
Vice Chairman: Brian Davie
Manager: Mick Marsden
Physio: D Edkins

2000-01

Leading goalscorer: Craig Cripps 20
Captain: Nick Lowery
P.o.Y.: Craig Cripps

KINGSBURY TOWN

Secretary: David Thomas, 9 Hillview Gardens, Kingsbury, NW9 0DE

GROUND: Silver Jubilee Park, Townsend Lane, Kingsbury, London NW9 7NE
Tel: 0208 2051645 Website:www.madasafish.com/~kingsbury-town

Directions: Underground to Kingsbury, cross road and take bus 183 to TownsendLane (2 miles) - ground in far left-hand corner of Silver Jubilee Park

Capacity: 2,500 Seats: 165 Cover: 400 Floodlights: Yes Club Shop: Yes

Clubhouse: Mon-Fri 7-11, Sat 12-11, Sun 12-2.30 & 7-10.30. Food on matchdays

HONOURS: Isthmian Lg Div 2 Nth R-up 85-86; Spartan Lg Cup R-up 59-60 64-65; Parthenon Lg 51-52 (Prem Charity Cup 52-53 53-54; Snr Charity Cup 53-54); Middx Snr Cup R-up 88-89; Middx Charity Cup 85-86 (R-up 88-89); Middx Lg Charity Cup (3) 44-47; Willesden & Dist. Lg R-up 30-31 (Div 2 34-35)

PREVIOUS: **Leagues:** Hellenic 27-30 (as Davis Sports); Willesden & District 30-43; MiddxSnr 44-47; Parthenon 47-59; Spartan 59-76 78-81; Athenian 76-78 81-84

RECORDS: **Attendance:** 1 ,300 v Wealdstone, FA Amateur Cup 1971

BEST SEASON: **FA Vase:** 4th Rd 74-75
FA Cup: 3rd Qual. Rd. 87-88, 0-1 v Leytonstone-Ilford (H)

FACT FILE

Founded: 1927 Nickname: Kings
Sponsors: VPA Entertainment Technology
Colours: Royal blue & White/white/royal
Change colours: Yellow/navy/yellow
Midweek Matches: Tuesday
Reserves' League: Suburban
Programme 16-20 pages 50p
Editor: Dave Thomas
Local Press: Harrow Observer, Willesden Chronicle, Allsport Weekly, Edgware &Finchley Times

CLUB PERSONNEL

Chairman: Mark Harrt
Press Officer: Dave Thoomas
Manager: Toni Kelly
Physio: Ann Bryan

2000-01

Captain: Mark Burgess
P.o.Y.: Mark Ivers
Top Goalscorer: Ben Porter 28

LEIGHTON TOWN

GROUND: Bell Close, Lake Street, Leighton Buzzard, Beds Tel: 01525 373311

Directions: From bypass (A505) take A4146 (Billington Rd) towards Leighton Buzzard, straight overfirst roundabout then straight over mini-r'bout & 1st left into car park - ground behind Camden Motors just before town centre. Half mile from Leighton Buzzard (BR) station. Buses from Luton, Aylesbury and Milton Keynes

Capacity: 2,800 Seats: 155 Cover: 300 Floodlights: Yes Club Shop: No

Clubhouse: Normal licensing hours. Snack bar on matchdays - full range of hot snacks & drinks

HONOURS Isthmian Lge Div 3 R-up 95-96; Sth Midlands Lg 66-67 91-92, Lg Cup 90-91, O'Brien Tphy 90-91, Reserve Div 1 87-88 91-92 94-95, Res Div 2 76-77, Res Challenge Cup 93-94 94-95; Beds Snr Cup 26-27 67-68 68-69 69-70 92-93; Bucks Charity Cup 94-95;98-99 Spartan Lg Div 2 23-24 27-28; Leighton & District Lg, Beds Intermediate Cup (res) 90-91; Beds Yth Cup 91-92 92-93,94-95 94-95; Chiltern Youth Lg 94-95, Lg Cup 93-94; East Anglian Yth. Cup 94-95; Assoc Mem. Cup 96-97.98-99, S.E. Co. Youth F'lit Lge (Corinthian Div.) 1999-00

BEST SEASON **FA Cup:** Third Qual. Round 70-71, 1-2 v St Albans City (A)
FA Vase: 2nd Round 1980-81, 94-95, 95-96, 00-01

PREVIOUS **Leagues:** Leighton & Dist,; South Midlands 22-24 26-29 46-54 55-56 76-92; Spartan 22-53 67-74; United Counties 74-76
Name: Leighton United 1922-63 **Ground:** Wayside

CLUB RECORDS **Attendance:** 1,522 v Aldershot T., Isthmian Lg Div 3, 30/1/93

FACT FILE

Founded: 1885 Nickname: Reds
Colours: Red & white
Change colours: Orange & black
Midweek Matchday: Tuesday
Reserve's League: Suburban
Programme: £1.00
Editor: Adrian Howells (01525 758258)
2000-01 Captain:Danny Power
P.o.Y.: Kenny Hollis
Top scorer: James Tatham 9

CLUB PERSONNEL

Secretary: Adrian Howells, 43 Carina Drive, Leighton Buzzard, Beds., LU7 3XG.
Tel: 01525 758258 Fax: 01525 633268
Chairman: Iain S McGregor
President: M.Hide
Press Officer: Iain S McGregor
Tel: 01525 370142
Manager: T.B.A.
Physio: Dawn Thomas

TRING TOWN

Secretary: Laurie McParland, 125 Bennetts End Rd, Hemel Hempstead, Herts HP3 8DX
Tel Nos:01442 263902 (H) 07836 265105 (M)

GROUND: Pendley Sports Centre, Cow Lane, Tring, Herts HP23 5NS (01442 824018)

Directions: One mile from Tring centre on A41 - direct connection to M25 (jct20) via new A41 bypass. One and a half miles from Tring (BR). Numerous busesfrom station and Watford-Aylesbury routes serve ground

Capacity: 2,500 Seats: 150 Cover: 250 Floodlights: Yes Club Shop: No
Clubhouse: All licensing hours. Dancehall, pool, darts, kitchen.

HONOURS: Spartan Lg 67-68, R-up 68-69. Herts Charity Shield winners 4, R-up 2. Athenian Lg Div 2 R-up 76-77, Herts Snr Cup R-up 77-78

PREVIOUS: **Leagues:** Gt Western Combination; Spartan 53-75; Athenian 75-77
Names: None Ground: Tring Cricket Ground (40 yrs)

RECORD: **Attendance:** 2,500 v West Ham, friendly
Goalscorer & Appearances: Gary Harthill

BEST SEASON: **FA Cup:** 3rd Qual. Rd replay 84-85, 0-5 v Fisher(A) after 1-1
FA Vase: 5th Rd 76-77, 0-2 v Farnborough Town (H)

FACT FILE

Founded: 1904
Nickname: T's
Colours: Red & white /red/red
Change: Yellow & blue stripes/blue/yellow
Midweek Matchday: Tuesday
Reserves' Lge: Suburban Lge
Programme: 24 pages £1
Editor/Press Officer:
Alan Lee (01702 216063)

Local Radio: Chiltern, Mix 96
BBC Three Counties Radio

CLUB PERSONNEL

Chairman: Harry Bowden

Manager: Howard Cowley
Physio: Keith Hardy

WARE

Secretary: Ian Bush, 42 Burnett Squ, Hertford, Herts SG14 2HD (01992 587334)

GROUND: Wodson Park, Wadesmill Road, Ware Herts SG12 0HZ (01920 463247)

Directions: A10 off at junction A602 & B1001 (Ware North), turn right at roundabout 300yds, and follow Ware sign, past Rank factory, turn left at main roundabout onto A1170 (Wadesmill Rd). After 3/4 mile stadium on right

Capacity: 3,300 Seats: 312 Cover: 500 Floodlights: Yes Club Shop: Yes
Clubhouse: Licensed bar open matchdays. Light snacks at refreshment bar

HONOURS: Herts Snr Cup 1898-99 03-04 06-07 21-22 53-54, Herts Char. Shield 26-27 56-57 58-59 62-63 85-86, Herts Char. Cup R-up 64-65 65-66 78-79 89-90, Spartan Lg 52-53 (Div 1 Sect.B 51-52, Div 2 Sect.A 26-27), Athenian Lg Div 2 Cup 65-66 72-73,East Anglian Cup 73-74, Herts Co. Lg 08-09 21-22, East Herts Lg 04-05 06-07 (LgCup 06-07), Perry Cup 26-27 28-29 37-38 51-52 52-53 53-54 55-56, Dunkels Cup 52-53, Rolleston Cup 39-40 51-52

PREVIOUS: **Leagues:** East Herts; North Middx 07-08; Herts County 08-25; Spartan 25-55;Delphian 55-63; Athenian 63-75

RECORDS **Attendance:** 3,800 v Hendon Amt Cup 56-57

BEST SEASON: **FA Cup:** First Round Proper 68-69 (lost 6-1 to Luton Town)

FACT FILE

Founded: 1892
Nickname: Blues
Sponsors: Charvill Bros Ltd
Colours: Blue & white stripes/blue/blue
Change colours: Amber/black
Midweek Matchday: Tuesday
Reserves' Lge:
Essex & Herts Border Comb
Programme: 24 pages, 50p
Editor : K.Mynott (01992 551605
Local Press: Herts Mercury, Herts Star, Herald & Post

CLUB PERSONNEL

Chairman: W ally Luck
Press Officer: Secretary
Manager: Grah am Norcott
Coach: Dermot Drummy
Physio: Frank Roberts

WINGATE & FINCHLEY

Secretary: Micky Dulin,C/o Club. Tel Nos: Club below. 01992 584780(H) 07961 849265 (M)
GROUND: The Abrahams Stadium, Summers Lane, Finchley, London N12 0PD
Tel: 0208 446 2217 Fax: 020 8343 8194
Directions: North Circular (A406) to junction with High Road Finchley (A1000).
Go north and Summers Lane is 200 yds on right - parking for 80 cars.
Tube to East Finchley (Northern Line) and then 263 bus to Summers Lane towards North Finchley
Capacity: 8,500 **Seats:** 500 **Cover:** 500 **Floodlights:** Yes **Club Shop:** No
Clubhouse: Open during matches. Also tea-bar selling most refreshments

HONOURS: Isthmian League Div. 3 R-up 98-99, London Senior Cup Winners 94-95

CLUB RECORDS: Attendance: 9,555 - Finchley v Bishop Auckland, F.A. Amat Cup QF 49-50
Career Goalscorer: Marc Morris 578
Career Appearances: Marc Morris 587(1975-93)
Win: 9-0, Wingate v Sarratt, Herts Co. Lge Div. 1, 20/4/85
Defeat: 0-9 v Edgware,Ryman League Division Two. 15.1.2000

BEST SEASON **FA Vase:** 74-75 Quarter Final (Wingate)
FA Amateur Cup: Semi-Final (Finchley)
PREVIOUS: **Names:** Wingate (founded 46), Finchley (founded late 1800s) merged in 91
Leagues: (as Wingate & Finchley) South Mids 89-95

FACT FILE
Founded: 1991
Nickname: Blues
Colours: Blue/white/blue
Change Colours: All yellow
Midweek matches: Tuesday
Reserve's Lge: Sub Lge U18
Programme: 32pages, £1.00
Editor: Peter Rebak (0208 8371 6001)

CLUB PERSONNEL
Chairman: StevenAstaire
Vice Chairman: David Ackerman
President: Kenneth Aston
Press Off.: Adam Rynhold
(Tel No: 0208 888 7530)
Manager: John Bolle
Player/Coach: Clive Wilson
Coach: Physio: Jim Connolly

WITHAM TOWN

Secretary: Jim Claydon, 58 Silver Street, Silver End, Witham, Essex CM8 3QG
Tel: 01376 584086 H, 01376 583241 x 426 B
Ground: Spa Road, Witham, Essex CM8 1UN
Tel: 01376 511198 (lounge) 500146 (reception) 520996 (boardroom)
Directions: From Witham BR (network S.E.) station; through pub car park and follow road to Faulkbourne, at main r'bout turn left and ground is on the right.
By road: Off A12 at Witham sign, left at 1st lights (Spinks Lane), right at end of road, follow road under railway bridge - ground 100yds on left
Capacity: 2,500 Seats: 150 Cover: 300 Floodlights: Yes
Clubhouse: Open every night and weekend lunctimes.Hot bar snacks. **Club Shop:** No

HONOURS: Essex Snr Lg 70-71 85-86 (R-up 84-85 86-87), Tphy 85-86 (R-up 88-89); Essex Thameside Trophy R-up 95-96; Loctite Tphy SF 90-91
PREVIOUS: **Leagues:** Mid Essex; Essex & Suffolk Border; Essex Senior 71-87
CLUB RECORDS **Attendance:** 800 v Billericay Town, Essex Senior League, May 1976
Win: 7-0 v Banstead 27/9/94 **Defeat:** 0-9 v Collier Row 21/10/95
Goalscorer: Colin Mitchell **Appearances:** Keith Dent (16 years)
Fee received: for Steve Tilson (Southend)
BEST SEASON: **FA Vase:** 5th Round, 85-86
FA Cup: 2nd Qual. Rd 87-88 (v Gravesend), 88-89 (v B. Stortford), 89-90 (v Dartford)

FACT FILE
Founded: 1947 Nickname: Town
Colours: Red & black stripes/black/black
Change colours: Blue & white
Midweek Matchday: Tuesday
Essex & Herts Border Comb
Programme: 24 pages, 60p
Editor: Nigel Dudley
2000-01
Captain: Alan Vincent
P.o.Y.: Glen Driver
Top Scorer: Glen Driver 31

CLUB PERSONNEL
Chairman: Dave Knott
Vice Chairman: Dave Puttock
President: B Olley
Press Officer: G Vale (01376 513861)
Manager: Tony Kinsella
Asst Mgr: Derek Robinson
Physio: Derek Robinson

WOKINGHAM TOWN

Secretary: John Aulsberry, 8 Paice Green, Wokingham RG40 1YN Tel: 01189 790441

Ground: c/o Windsor & Eton FC, Stag Meadow, St Leonards Rd, Windsor, Berks SL4 3DR
Tel: 01753 860656

Directions: A332 from M4 junct 6. Left at r'bout (B3173), left into St Leonards Rd at lights on T-junction, ground 500 yards on right on B3022 opposite Stag & Hounds PH. 1 mile from town centre - pass available to St Leonards Rd. BR to Windsor Central station (from) Slough or Windsor Riverside (change at Staines from Waterloo)
Capacity: 4,500 Cover: 650 Seats: 400 Floodlights: Yes
Clubhouse: Yes Club Shop: No

HONOURS Isthmian Lg R-up 89-90 (Div 1 81-82, Full Members Cup R-up 94-95), Berks & Bucks Snr Cup 68-69 82-83 84-85 95-96, Berks & Bucks I'mediate Cup 52-53

PREVIOUS **Leagues:** Reading & Dist.; Great Western Comb 07-54; Metropolitan 54-57; Delphian 57-59; Corinthian 59-63; Athenian 63-73.

BEST SEASON **FA Trophy:** Semi finals 87-88 **FA Amateur Cup:** 4th Rd 57-58
FA Cup: 1st Rd replay 82-83, 0-3 v Cardiff (A) after 1-1 League clubs defeated: None

CLUB RECORDS **Attendance:** 3,473 v Norton Woodseats, FA Amateur Cup 57-58
Career Goalscorer: Terry Brown 91
Career Appearances: Dave Cox, 533

FACT FILE
Formed: 1875 Nickname: The Town
Sponsors: Swan Hill Homes
Colours: Amber & black/black/black
Change colours: All w hite
Midweek matchday: Tuesday
Programme: Pages: 32 Price: £1
Editor: Alan Glenny
Local Press: Wokingham Times, Wokingham News, Reading Evening Post
Local Radio: 210 FM
2000-2001
Captain: Simon Turner
P.o.Y.: Jon Horsted
Top scorer: Gary Blake (15)
CLUB PERSONNEL
Chairman: Richard Brown
President: G Gale
Manager: Steve Mellor
Assistant Manager: Dave Wakefield
Physio: Melanie Garratt

COMBINED COUNTIES LEAGUE

President: Ron Monkley **Chairman:** John Bennett
General Secretary: Clive Tidey, 22 Silo Road, Farncombe, Godalming, Surrey GU7 3PA
Tel: 01483 428453 Fax: 01483 426117

The season started on a difficult note, when Withdean 2000 FC, having finally been accepted into membership, found themselves removed just two days before the start of the season when the Football Association refused to sanction the League with Withdean in it.

The League started therefore with just one change from the previous season, with Southall coming in from the Ryman League to replace promoted Ashford Town. The pre-season favourites were, without doubt, Ash United whose experienced squad under the stewardship of Jamie Horton started like an express train, winning seventeen of their first eighteen league games and not many would have bet against them winning the championship at the turn of the year.

AFC Wallingford and Cove were never too far away though, and as time went on a three horse race developed with none of the three giving an inch. Wallingford, under ex-Reading Town boss Dave Crowdy, had assembled a strong squad including the mercurial Andy Shildrick, whose goal scoring exploits in the League with Peppard FC a few seasons back were well remembered. With several ex-Reading Town players in his squad, including the vastly experienced Craig Rutherford in goal, they were well equipped to give anyone a run for their money and, in the midst of a tremendous run of form, they broke the league scoring record when they beat bottom club Cranleigh by a massive thirteen goals to nil. Cranleigh must have been sick of the sight of their Oxfordshire opponents as they had already also conceded eleven at home to them.

The greatest transformation through had taken place at Cove. The arrival of the untested Steve Beeks, managing a club for the first time, assisted by ex-Chobham manager John Meopham, turned into an immediate success story for the club as they swept all their challengers away with an unbeaten run of 30 league matches from December through to the end of the season. Beeks, who combined playing with managing, had assembled an impressive looking squad, including a number of ex-Basingstoke Town players. There were no weak links, but two players caught the eye, being Ian Mancie who scored an incredible 53 league goals, and goalkeeper Adrian Creamer, who had scouts flocking to Oak Farm.

Cove had spent two seasons as the basement club before the arrival of Beeks but, in one season of total success, they did not just win the League, but they also won the League's Premier Challenge Cup, beating Walton Casuals 3-0 in the Final at Woking, also reaching the Fifth Round of the FA Carlsberg Vase where they lost controversially to Chippenham Town. Cove had raced into a two goal lead and scored a third just before half-time only to have it disallowed following a hideous refereeing error when the Chippenham keeper was knocked over but by one of his own players with no Cove player within yards of playing distance. The official, clearly unsighted, deemed that the keeper had been fouled and Chippenham eventually pulled the two goals back and notched the winner in a devastating eight minute spell near the end of the game. If the third goal had counted, though, Cove would surely have hung on.

Prior to the start both Bedfont, their ground now up to Ryman standard, and Chipstead looked as if they would mount a challenge but, although both enjoyed reasonable seasons, neither was in the race as the end of the season approached.

Westfield also flattered to deceive, winning eleven on the trot at one stage, and reaching the Fourth Round of the Vase in their first season of entry. They finally went out, when a midweek trip to runaway Division Three Ryman leaders, Arlesey Town, proved too much and a 0-6 defeat was a disappointing end to a creditable run.

At the other end of the league, it was a surprise to see usually strong outfits, Farnham Town and Reading Town, struggling. Farnham had lost their manager to neighbours Sandhurst Town before the start of the season and most of their squad defected with him, leaving the club with a very inexperienced squad of young players.

Rock bottom once again though were Cranleigh and, coupled with several significant administrative shortcomings, the club will need to show an improvement if its membership of the League is to be retained for too much longer.

Cove were unable to meet the Ryman deadline for promotion applications so there will be no movement between the two leagues. Although, nominally, there are three feeder leagues to the Combined Counties, the requirement for floodlights remains a major stumbling block for intermediate clubs hoping to make the grade and this is a matter of concern. One idea that is now being explored is to allow intermediate clubs into Division One, where they would compete against Reserve teams from the League. This would give a foothold for ambitious outfits to achieve senior football and will be followed up next season.

The League sets the end of its season as 31 May as a matter of course, and as a result was able to complete its fixtures, despite the incessant rain that dogged the season. Two clubs in particular, Chessington & Hook and Viking Greenford, barely played at home for several months and it is pleasing that both teams are actively preparing to undertake drainage improvements.

At the Presentation Evening, Times journalist Russell Kempson, who had featured Wallingford throughout the season in a series of articles, was on hand to present the various winners with their trophies. It was fitting that Wallingford were worthy winners of the Fair Play Award, with just twenty cautions all season, whilst League President Ron Monkley deemed that, amongst a very good crop, the programme of the season was that of Ash United, with honourable mentions for Merstham and Southall.

cont.

At the AGM, with the wheel apparently having turned full circle, Withdean FC were finally elected to the League for season 2001-02, having secured an acceptable ground sharing arrangement with Horsham FC. This time they come with the blessing of the Football Association and will bring the League's constitution up to 22. There are no other changes.

At Reserve level, both Godalming and Walton Casuals have left to join the Suburban League, but Hartley Wintney Reserves are coming in from the Aldershot League.

One other important change is that the League will issue an annual fixture list for the first time. With clubs split almost 50/50 over its introduction, the matter will be further reviewed in a year's time.

Alan Constable, Hon. Fixture Secretary

FINAL LEAGUE TABLES 2000-01

PREMIER DIVISION

	P	W	D	L	F	A	Pts
Cove	40	35	2	3	146	28	107
AFC Wallingford	40	30	6	4	128	39	96
Ash United	40	28	4	8	121	53	88
Bedfont	40	24	4	12	96	64	76
Chipstead	40	23	5	12	92	48	74
Westfield	40	19	6	15	66	56	63
Walton Casuals	40	19	5	16	73	68	62
Merstham	40	16	9	15	86	64	*59
Feltham	40	17	7	16	74	75	58
Chessington & Hook	40	15	7	18	83	92	*58
Southall	40	17	8	15	84	70	*56
Godalming & G'ford	40	15	10	15	73	80	55
Sandhurst Town	39	17	6	16	75	61	*54
Cobham	40	16	6	18	69	72	54
Chessington Utd	40	14	13	13	67	57	*51
Raynes Park Vale	40	15	5	20	63	78	50
Hartley Wintney	40	12	4	24	73	99	40
Viking Greenford	40	8	8	24	58	101	32
Reading Town	40	6	9	25	43	97	*30
Farnham Town	39	4	3	32	30	145	15
Cranleigh	40	4	3	33	28	181	15

DIVISION ONE

	P	W	D	L	F	A	Pts
Bedfont	28	19	3	6	73	28	60
Godalming & G'ford	28	18	3	7	63	35	*60
Ash United	28	17	6	5	98	50	57
Walton Casuals	28	16	5	7	66	39	53
Cove	28	13	8	7	60	46	47
Merstham	28	14	4	10	65	41	46
Sandhurst Town	28	12	6	10	60	45	*44
Raynes Park Vale	28	13	3	12	46	39	42
Westfield	28	12	7	9	60	52	*40
AFC Wallingford	28	11	2	15	63	80	35
Chessington United	28	9	5	14	48	66	32
Chessington & Hook	28	8	5	15	49	59	29
Cobham	28	8	2	18	43	68	*28
Feltham	28	8	4	16	37	56	*25
Farnham Town	28	0	1	27	18	145	1

* points adjustment

PREMIER DIVISION RESULTS CHART 2000-01

		1	2	3	4	5	6	7	8	9	10	11	12	13	14	15	16	17	18	19	20	21
1	AFC Wallingford	X	2-1	3-1	1-1	5-1	2-2	4-0	2-3	13-0	9-0	3-1	5-0	3-0	1-3	4-1	2-1	4-1	2-1	1-0	3-1	2-1
2	Ash United	3-3	X	4-0	3-0	0-2	5-4	6-3	1-5	5-1	2-0	8-0	4-1	3-0	2-0	5-2	4-1	3-1	3-0	4-1	5-0	2-1
3	Bedfont	1-2	2-0	X	1-2	2-1	3-2	2-2	3-1	5-0	2-1	4-0	1-2	2-3	4-2	2-0	0-4	4-2	2-1	4-2	2-0	2-3
4	Chess & Hook	1-4	0-3	0-2	X	1-1	4-1	5-1	0-4	7-2	5-0	3-3	4-3	1-3	2-1	0-2	0-2	3-4	2-2	7-1	1-2	3-2
5	Chess. Utd	1-3	0-2	3-4	1-1	X	0-2	0-2	0-2	10-0	4-0	3-1	0-1	6-4	3-3	2-0	0-0	2-1	1-0	3-3	3-1	0-1
6	Chipstead	1-0	3-2	3-2	5-2	3-1	X	0-1	2-1	2-0	1-0	1-2	1-0	5-1	3-2	0-1	1-1	1-0	5-0	9-0	3-1	4-0
7	Cobham	1-2	3-3	1-4	3-1	0-0	0-3	X	1-3	6-0	0-0	4-1	0-2	2-3	5-1	0-0	3-0	1-0	1-1	1-0	1-3	2-0
8	Cove	3-0	2-2	2-0	6-0	0-0	3-1	4-0	X	4-0	11-0	4-2	2-0	5-0	2-0	4-1	9-0	5-2	1-0	3-1	2-3	1-0
9	Cranleigh	0-11	1-8	1-3	0-5	2-0	2-0	3-2	0-7	X	0-1	0-3	0-0	1-3	1-7	1-5	1-3	1-4	1-1	1-2	0-6	0-4
10	Farnham T	0-3	0-6	0-8	3-3	1-3	0-5	1-2	0-4	4-2	X	4-6	0-5	2-2	1-0	0-3	0-4	n/p	1-7	0-1	0-2	0-3
11	Feltham	0-2	2-3	4-2	2-4	0-0	1-1	4-0	0-3	4-0	2-1	X	1-2	5-1	1-1	2-0	4-2	0-0	0-2	1-1	3-0	3-1
12	Godalming & G	2-2	1-1	0-1	3-4	2-3	2-2	1-3	0-6	2-1	2-1	1-1	X	0-4	1-4	4-2	2-0	0-5	4-4	3-2	4-0	5-0
13	Hartley W	1-5	3-2	1-3	1-2	0-3	0-2	2-1	1-4	8-2	4-5	1-2	2-2	X	1-3	1-2	7-0	1-3	2-4	5-1	1-4	2-0
14	Merstham	2-3	0-1	2-2	2-1	0-0	1-0	1-2	1-2	10-0	8-1	2-0	1-2	1-0	X	4-3	2-0	1-1	7-0	4-3	1-1	1-3
15	R P Vale	1-1	1-0	3-1	1-1	0-0	0-2	1-3	1-5	5-1	4-1	1-2	1-3	4-1	0-2	X	2-1	1-0	0-3	2-1	1-4	0-3
16	Reading	0-2	1-2	0-1	0-2	2-3	1-1	1-7	0-2	0-2	3-1	2-4	1-4	1-1	1-1	1-2	X	0-5	0-4	3-2	1-1	1-2
17	Sandhurst	1-3	1-2	0-0	2-3	1-2	2-1	4-1	1-4	3-0	3-1	3-1	3-3	1-0	1-2	3-1	1-1	X	3-1	4-0	2-1	3-3
18	Southall	2-2	4-1	0-4	4-0	1-1	3-2	2-0	0-3	1-1	8-0	2-3	1-0	0-2	5-0	3-5	2-2	3-1	X	4-2	2-0	2-0
19	Viking Gr	0-3	0-1	2-4	4-1	4-4	0-4	1-0	1-3	8-0	2-0	0-3	2-2	1-1	3-3	2-1	1-1	0-2	2-1	X	2-3	0-3
20	Walton Cas	0-2	1-6	3-3	3-0	2-0	2-1	1-3	0-6	3-0	3-0	1-0	3-0	4-0	2-0	3-3	4-1	0-1	2-3	2-0	X	0-0
21	Westfield	0-4	1-3	2-3	4-1	0-0	0-3	2-1	2-5	6-0	3-0	2-0	2-2	2-0	0-0	2-0	3-0	1-0	2-0	0-0	2-1	X

LEADING GOALSCORERS 2000-01

PREMIER DIVISION

53	I Mancey	Cove
38	I Concannon	AFC Wallingford
35	M Nolan	Chipstead
26	S Mitchell	Ash United
24	S Joyce	Ash United
23	S Jenns	Merstham

DIVISION ONE

24	S Shepherd	Ash United
21	G Huddison	Cove
20	B Campbell	Walton Casuals
18	A Morgan	Sandhurst Town
16	P Reader	Bedfont
14	G Salmon	Raynes Park Vale

PREMIER CHALLENGE CUP 2000-01

FIRST ROUND

Chipstead	v	Chessington Utd	0*0, 0-3
Cove	v	Reading Town	2-0
Raynes Park Vale	v	AFC Wallingford	0-5
Cobham	v	Merstham	0-3
Godalming & G'ford	v	Walton Casuals	1*2

SECOND ROUND

Chessington & Hook	v	Chessington Utd	5-2
Cranleigh	v	Walton Casuals	0-2
Feltham	v	Sandhurst Town	2-3
Southall	v	AFC Wallingford	0-6
Cove	v	Ash United	2-1
Farnham Town	v	Hartley Wintney	2-1
Merstham	v	Bedfont	0*0
Westfield	v	Viking Greenford	4-0

THIRD ROUND

AFC Wallingford	v	Cove	2-3
Farnham Town	v	Walton Casuals	1-6
Chessington & Hook	v	Westfield	1*1, 0-2
Sandhurst Town	v	Bedfont	0-3

SEMI-FINALS

Bedfont	v	Cove	0-3
Walton Casuals	v	Westfield	1-0

FINAL

Cove	v	Walton Casuals	3-0	at Woking

DIVISION ONE CHALLENGE CUP 2000-01

FIRST ROUND

Feltham	v	AFC Wallingford	2-3

SECOND ROUND

Cranleigh (scr)	v	Godalming & G (bye)	
Bedfont	v	Merstham	3-1
Farnham Town	v	Cobham	1-3
Walton Casuals	v	Sandhurst Town	2-4
Ash United	v	Chessington Utd	1-2
Cove	v	Chessington & Hook	4-1
Viking Greenford	v	Raynes Park Vale	4-1
Westfield	v	AFC Wallingford	2-0

THIRD ROUND

Chessington United	v	Cove	1-3
Sandhurst Town	v	Cobham	5*5
Godalming & G'ford	v	Bedfont	0*1
Westfield	v	Viking Greenford	1-4

Cobham removed from competition - ineligible player

SEMI-FINALS

Bedfont	v	Viking Greenford	4*0
Sandhurst	v	Cove	3-2

FINAL

Bedfont	v	Sandhurst Town	2*3	at Ashford Town (Middlesex)

FAIR PLAY TABLE 2000-01

PREMIER DIVISION	Points
AFC Wallingford	26
Cove	38
Westfield	38
Farnham Town	44
Hartley Wintney	46
Chipstead	47
Bedfont	48

DIVISION ONE	Points
Westfield	20
Merstham	26
Raynes Park Vale	26
Chessington & Hook	30
Chessington United	31
Walton Casuals	34
Farnham Town	36

AFC WALLINGFORD

Secretary: Richard may, 27 Chiltern Crescent, Wallingford, Oxon OX100PG
Tel Nos: 01491 837391 (H) 01491 823612 (W) 07748 828574(M)
Ground: Wallingford Sports Park, Hithercroft Road,Wallingford,Oxon.(Tel:01491 835044
Directions : Nearest Railway station: Cholsey & Moulsford. Bus - Thames Transit.
Capacity: 1,500 Cover: 100 Seats: 40 Floodlights: Yes Club Shop: Yes

Clubhouse: Open evenings 7.30-11.00, Sat & Sun Tea & snacks available 01491 835044
HONOURS: Chiltonian Prem Lge 97-98; Bon Accord Trophy 95-96 Combined Counties League Premier Division Runners Up 2000-01, Berks & Bucks Senior Trophy Finalists 2000-01, North Bucks Nairne Paul Cup Winners 2000-01
RECORDS: **Attendance:** 280 v Reading Town **Goalscorer:** Carl Henry 68 97-98
Appearances: Anthony Hill 240
PREVIOUS: **Leagues:** Chiltonian Lge 95-98
2000-01 Captain: Gary Stevens P.o.Y.: Barry Primmer Top Scorer: Ian Concannon 4

FACT FILE
Founded: 1995
Colours: Red & black hoops/black/red & black
Change colours: Blue & white
Midweek matchday: Tuesday
Programme: 20 pages; price 50p
Editor: Andy Ham (01491 837608)

CLUB PERSONNEL
President: K Lester
Chairman: E L Townsend
Tel: 01491 839103 (H)
Match Secretary: G Lee
21 Orchard Close, Brightwell, Wallingford, Oxon. Tel: 01491 836921 (H)
Manager: Dave Crowdy Coach: Gary Elkins

ASH UNITED

Secretary: Alex Smith-Gander, 41 Ash Street,Ash,Surrey Tel: 01252 345221 (H & Fax)
Email: alex@smith-gander.freeserve.co.uk. or:
Alan Haderle, 30 Longfield Rd.,Ash, Aldershot.Hants GU12 6ND : 01252 345747 (Tel & Fax)
Ground: Youngs Drive, off Shawfield Rd, Ash, Nr Aldershot Tel: 01252 745747
Directions: A323 towards Ash, left into Shawfield Rd, left into Youngs Drive
1 mile from both Ash and Ash Vale BR stations. Bus - Stagecoach 20A, 550
Capacity: 1,500 Seats: None Cover: Yes Floodlights: Yes

HONOURS: Prem Chall Cup 97-98; Comb Co Lge 98-99; Aldershot Sen Cup 98-99
CLUB RECORDS **Attendance;** 650 v Tiverton Town FA Vase
Goalscorer: Scott Joyce 40 **Appearances:** Tommy Burton 540
BEST SEASON **FA Cup:** 2nd Qual Rd v Walton & Hersham 98-99
FA Vase: 4th Rd v Tiverton Town 98-99
PREVIOUS **Ground:** Ash Common Rec. 70-71 **Leagues:** Surrey Snr, Aldershot Snr

FACT FILE
Founded: 1911
Colours: Red & green/green/green
Change colours: All blue
Midweek Matchday: Tuesday
Programme: 36 pages, #1.00
Editor: Garth Watmore 01252 657944
Captain & P.o.Y.: Mattie Everard
Top Scorer: Shaun Mitchell (31)

CLUB PERSONNEL
President; Mr E Britzman Chairman: Robert J Atkins Vice Chairman: Geoff Hills
Gen Manager: Alex Smith-Gander
Manager: Steve Atkins Asst.Man Jamie Horton

BEDFONT

Secretar Leslie King, 14 Harlequin Close, Isleworth, Middlesex. TW7 7LA
Tel No: 0208 894 5525 (H) 0208 392 3021 (W)
Ground: The Orchard, Hatton Rd, Bedfont, Middx. Tel: 0208 8907264
Directions: Turn down Faggs Rd opposite Hatton Cross (Picadilly Line) station on Great South Western Rd (A30), then sharp right into Hatton Rd. Ground opposite Duke of Wellington pub. Bus - Westlink 203
Capacity:2,000 Seats: 100 Cover: 50Floodlights: Yes Clubhouse: Yes

HONOURS Comb. Co's Chal. Vase 92-93 (Res. Div R-up 88-89, Res. Cup R-up 89-90, Grant McClennan Yth Cup 91-92), Middx Lg 73-74 76-77 (Div 1 (Res) & Div 1 Cup 71-72 78-79 79-80, Surrey Prem. Lg 84-85 86-87, Middx I'mediate Cup 69-70 76-77, Inter. Contois Tour. 1992, Liege Euromann Tour. 89, Harold Clayton Cup 90-91, Hounslow & Dist. Div 1 (Res) 86-87

PREVIOUS Names: Bedfont Inst.(1900), Bedfont Rangers(1950) & Fairholme Utd(1953) merged 1968. Club later merged with Interharvester(1973) & Bedfont Eagles(1988). **Ground:** Bedfont Rec.

FACT FILE
Founded: 1968
Colours: Yellow & blue stripes/blue/blue
Change colours: All red or White/navy/navy
Midweek matches: Tuesday
Programme: 20 pages, 50p. Editors: Les King (020 8891 1985)

CLUB PERSONNEL
President: Roger Cooper
Chairman: John Dollimore
Vice Chairman: Mick Carroll
Manager: John Morris
Coach: Ron Griffin
Asst. Man.: Mark Wilson

CHESSINGTON & HOOK UNITED

Secretary: Alan Warwick, 38 Hartfield Road, Chessington, Surrey. KT9 2PW
Tel:020 8397 1843(H)
Ground: Chalky Lane, Chessington, Surrey. Tel: 01372 729892

Directions: Turn off A243 into Chalky Lane opposite Chessington World of Adventure Theme Park Railway - Chessington South. Bus - London Transport 71.
Capacity: Seats: Cover: Floodlights: Yes

HONOURS: Combined Counties Lge Prem Cup R-up 97-98, Surrey County Lge Prem Div R-up 96-97, Div 1 70-71,

PREVIOUS **Leagues:** Middx Lge 68-69, Surrey County 69-72, Home Counties 72-78 Comb Co 78-81, Surrey Prem, Surrey Comb, Surrey Prem.

FACT FILE
Founded: 1968
Colours: All blue
Change colours: Yellow/black/yellow
Midweek Matchday:
Programme: Yes

CLUB PERSONNEL
Chairman: Graham Ellis
63 Stormont Way, Chessington, Surrey. KT9 2QW
Tel: 020 8391 4829(H)
Manager: Paul Ellis 020 8397 8499 (H)

CHESSINGTON UNITED

Secretary: Michael Smith, 34 Sopwith Avenue, Chessington, Surrey KT9 1QE
Tel: 020 8255 8847 (H) 0797 9606125 (M)

Ground: Fetcham Park Utd., Riverlane, Leatherhead, Surrey. Tel: 01372 363995
Nearest Railway Station: Leatherhead
Buses: London Country 465 & 479

2000-01: Captain: David Sutton P.o.Y.: Paul O'Sullivan Top Scorer: Dan Martin 18

FACT FILE

Colours: All Green

CLUB PERSONNEL

President:R.Jaramillo

Chairman: Richard Jaramillo
19 Purbeck Close, Merstham, Redhill
Surrey RH1 1PG
Tel: 01737 644588

Match Secretary: as Secretary

CHIPSTEAD

Secretary: Geoff Corner, 20 Sunnymede Avenue, Carshalton Beeches, Surrey SM54JF
Tel: 0181 642 0827 (H)

Ground: High Road, Chipstead, Surrey. Tel: 01737 553250
Directions: Brighton Road northbound, left into Church Lane, left into HogcrossLane, right High Road. 1 1/2/ miles from Chipstead (BR). Bus -London County 405, 407
Capacity: 2,000 Seats: 30 Cover: 100 Floodlights: Yes

HONOURS Surrey Premier Lg R-up 82-83 83-84 85-86 (Lg Cup 82-83 84-85 85-86), Combined Co's Lg 89-90 (R-up 90-91 92-93, Lg Cup 86-87 90-91 92-93, Elite Class Cup R-up 89-90, Reserve Section Cup 92-93)

BEST SEASON **FA Cup:** 1998-99 **FA Vase:** 1998-99

CLUB RECORDS Attendance: 903
Goalscorer: Appearances:

PREVIOUS **Leagues:** Surrey Intermediate 62-82; Surrey Premier 82-86

FACT FILE

Founded: 1906 Nickname: Chips
Colours: Green & white/black/black
Change colours: Purple/yellow/yellow
Midweek matchday: Tuesday
Programme: 44 pages

2000-01

Captain: Russell Harmsworth P.o.Y.: Steve Eggleton Top Scorer: Mick Nolan 35

CLUB PERSONNEL

President: Clive Wood
Chairman:D.Faircloth, 156 St Andrews Road, Coulsdon,Surrey CR5 3HF(0208 668 8348)
Manager: S Bangs Coach:M.Ford

Cove FC, Premier Division Champions. Photo: Eric Marsh

COBHAM

Secretary: Ken Reed, 29 Waterer Gardens, Tadworth, Surrey. KT20 5PB
Tel: 01737352641 (H) Fax: 01737 352259

Ground: Leg O'Mutton Field, Anvil Lane, Downside Bridge Rd, Cobham, Surrey
Tel: 01932 865959

Directions: A3 turnoff A245, A307 (Portsmouth) towards Leatherhead, right intoBetween Streets, rt into Downside Rd then rt opposite car park. Cobham & StokeD'Abernon (BR) 2 miles. Bus - Green Line 715, London Country 501, 513

Capacity: 2,000 Seats: None Cover: Yes Floodlights: Yes Club Shop: No
Clubhouse: Yes

HONOURS Combined Co's Lge Cup, Res Lge (3)

BEST SEASON **FA Cup:** **FA Vase:** 1998-99 3rd Rd.

CLUB RECORDS **Attendance:** 2,000 v Showbiz XI, charity game 1975

PREVIOUS **League:** Surrey Senior **Grounds:** Cobham Rec

FACT FILE
Founded: 1892
Nickname: Hammers
Sponsor: Peter Haworth Consultancy
Colours: Red /black/black
Change colours:Black & White stripes
Midweek matchday: Tuesday
Programme: Yes

CLUB PERSONNEL
Chairman:Chris Woolston
President: E D Strange
Manager: Gary Block
Coach: Tony Wilson
Physio: C Bird

COVE

Secretary: Graham Brown, 6 Longfield Close,Haley Estate, Farnborough. GU14 8HQ
Tel: 01252 650920 - Club Email: covefc1897@aol.com

Ground: 7 Squirrels Lane, Farnborough, Hants GU14 8PB. Tel.: 01252 543615

Directions: Farnborough (BR) 2 miles; right into Union Street, right at lights into Prospect Rd, left into West Heath Rd, right into Romayne Close and follow signs to Cove FC. Or, M3 jct 4, follow A325 signed Aldershot & Farnham, right into Prospect Rd. (signed Cove FC & Farnborough Town FC), then as above

Capacity: 3,500 Seats: 75 Cover: 475 Floodlights: Yes Club Shop: No
Clubhouse: Mon-Fri 7-11, Sat 12-11, Sunday 12-3 & 7-11. Hot food on matchdays

HONOURS: Surrey I'mediate Lg; Surrey Prem. Lg x5, R-up x3, Lg Cup x3, Res.Section x4 ,R-up x4, Res. Cup x2; Combined Co's Lg Cup 81-82; Hants Lg Div 3, Div 4, Div 2 R-up; Aldershot - Snr Cup x5, R-up, Snr Shield x4, Snr Lg, Div 2x3, Div 2 Cup, Div 4 Cup

PREVIOUS Leagues: Aldershot Jnr; Aldershot I'mediate 45-48; Surrey I'mediate 48-71; Surrey Snr 71-73; Hants 74-81; Combined Counties 81-90 &95-01; Isthmian 90-95;

CLUB RECORDS **Attendance:** 1,798 v Aldershot, Isthmian Lg Div 3, 1/5/93

BEST SEASON **FA Cup**: 2nd Rd 2000-01 **FA Vase:** 5th Rd 00-01 2-3 v Chippenham Tn. (H)

FACT FILE
Founded: 1897
Sponsors: Sunnyside Removals
Colours: Yellow & black stripes/black/yellow
Change colours: Red & white stripes/red/red
Midweek Matches: Tuesday
Reserves' League: Comb. Cos. 1st Div
Programme: 30 pages, 50p
Editor: Graham Brown (01252 650920)

CLUB PERSONNEL
Chairman: T. Bannister
President: Ron Brown

2000-01
Leading Goalscorer: Ian Mancey 66
Captain & P.o.Y : Alan Carey

CRANLEIGH

Secretary: Steve Dawe, 2 Seltops Close,Cranleigh, Surrey GU6 7JW (01483 427100)

Match Secretary: Alan Pavia Tel: 01483 271233 (H) 01483 894248 (B)

Ground: Snoxall Playing Fields, Knowle Lane, Cranleigh Tel: 01483 275295

Directions: A281 from Guildford towards Horsham, at Shalford take B2128 to Cranleigh High St., right opposite Onslow Arms into Knowle Lane, ground half mile on left. Public transport: Guildford (BR) then bus (Alder Valley) 273 or 283

Capacity: 450 Seats: None Cover: 50Floodlights: No
Clubhouse: Licensed bar. Hot food on matchdays Club Shop: No

HONOURS W Sussex County Times Cup 92-93

BEST SEASON **FA Vase** 3rd Rd 92-93 **FA Cup:**

CLUB RECORDS **Attendance:** 450 v C Palace, friendly 1989
Competitive: 285 v Hailsham,FA Vase 3rd Rd 12/12/92

PREVIOUS **League:** Surrey Intermediate

FACT FILE
Founded: 1893
Nickname: Cranes
Sponsors: Roger Coupe, Est. Agents
Colours:Blue & Yellow/blue/blue & yellow
Change colours: Yellow/green/yellow
Midweek matchday: Tuesday
Programme: £1.50
Editor: Peter Slater (01483 894245)

CLUB PERSONNEL
Chairman: Roy Kelsey (01483 427100)
President: Alan Pavia
Manager: Roy Kelsey
Asst Manager: Paul Jones
Coach: Andy Clements

FARNHAM TOWN

Secretary: Mrs Barbara Fripp, 70 Lower Farnham Rd., Aldershot. GU12 4EA (01252 657184)

Ground: Memorial Ground, Babbs Mead, West Street, Farnham, Surrey (01252 715305)

Directions: From A31, direction Winchester, take 2nd turning into town at Coxbridge roundabout. Follow West Street until you come to new mini roundabout - the Memorial Ground is on the right.

Capacity: 2,000 Seats: None Cover: 150 Floodlights: Yes
Clubhouse: Open every evening and match daysClub Shop: No

HONOURS Combined Counties Lg 90-91 91-92, Challenge Cup Prem Div 95-96, Challenge Tphy 91-92 (R-up 89-90).

CLUB RECORDS **Attendance:** 500 v Kingstonian, Surrey Snr Cup 1960.

PREVIOUS **Leagues:** Surrey Intermediate; Surrey Snr 47-71: Spartan 71-75: London Spartan 75-80: Combined Counties 80-92.

BEST SEASON **FA Cup:** Never past Qualifying Rounds

FACT FILE
Founded: 1921 Nickname: The Town
Sponsors: Frazer Freight.
Colours: All claret & blue.
Change: White, pale blue & claret/claret/claret
Midweek Matchday: Tuesday
Reserve League: Comb Counties Res Div
Programme: 32 pages 50p
Editor: Ann Butters

CLUB PERSONNEL
Chairman: DerekWythe
President; Paul Cooper
Press Officer: Charlie White
Manager: Peter Browning
Asst Manager: Roy Atkin
Coach: A Wyciechowski/A Metcalfe

FELTHAM

Secretary: John Cronk,Flat 8 Wyvern Court, 24 Gordon Rd, Ashford, Middsx TW15 3EZ
Tel: 01784 243122 (H) 0208 839 2104 (B) Website: http://www.felthamfc.freeserve.co.uk/
Ground: Feltham Arena(All weather surface), Shakespeare Ave., Feltham, Middx.Tel: 0208 890 6164 (club), 0208 890 6905 (ground)**Directions:** BR to Feltham & 5 mins walk thro' Glebelands Park. Buses 90, 285,117, 237, H24 or H25 to Feltham station, or 116 to top of Shakespeare Ave. By car: M3, M4, A312 Staines road towards Bedfont, 2nd left is Shakespeare Ave
Capacity: 10,000 Seats: 650 Cover: 1,500 Floodlights: Yes
Clubhouse: Open 7 days a week. 2 bars, dancehall available for hire Club Shop: No
HONOURS Surrey Snr Lg R-up 65-66 (Lg Cup 65-66, Charity Cup 63-64 65-66),Southern Comb. Cup(2)(R-up(2)), Middx Summer Cup, Isthmian Div 2 80-81, Comb.Cos. Lge Co. 96-97
PREVIOUS **Leagues:** Feltham: West Middx Sunday; Staines & Dist.; Hounslow & Dist.; Surrey Snr 63-68; Spartan 68-73; Athenian 74-77; Isthmian 78-95
CLUB RECORDS **Attendance:** 1,9 38 v Hampton,Middlesex Senior Cup 1968
Goalscorer: Paul Clarke 130**Appearances:** Paul Clarke 326
BEST SEASON **FA Cup:** 3rd Qual.Rd.77-78, 1-4 v Tilbury; 82-83, 0-1 v Chesham U

FACT FILE
Founded: 1946 Sponsors: Feltham first
Colours: Royal blue & white halves/blue/blue
Change colours: Red /White or Blue/White
Midweek Matches: Wednesday
Programme: 20 pages, 50p
Editor:Chris Thompso
Email: cjthompson-uk@yahoo.co.uk

CLUB PERSONNEL
Chairman: Eric Robins (07956 964207)
Press Off.: Richard Seuke
01932 - 761544(Tel) 761744 (Fax)
Managers: Sammy Boyd & Dave Patience
Players progressing:Rachid Harkouk,Tony Witter(CrystalP) Andy Pape (QPR), Pat Gavin (Gillingham) Bobby Wilson (Brentford)

GODALMING & GUILDFORD

Secretary: Eddie Russell, 31 Harts Gardens, Guildford, Surrey GU2 9QB. 01483 535287 (H & B)

Ground: Weycourt, Meadrow, Godalming, Surrey (01483 417520)
Directions: A3100 from Guildford - past Beefeater Hotel on left, then 'Save' petrol station on right, then 1st right 50 yards on. From Godalming on A3100, grd on left by Leathern Bottle pub. Three quarters of a mile from Farncombe BR station

Capacity: 3,000 Seats: 200 Cover: 200 Floodlights: Yes Club Shop: No
Clubhouse: Open Tues, Thurs eves, matchdays. Hot & cold snacks available
HONOURS Combined Co's Lg 83-84, Lge Chall. Trophy 82-83, Res Lge 95-96 96-97, Res Chall Cup 92-93 97-98, Chall Shield 96-97: Southern Comb Chall Cup 97-98
PREVIOUS **Leagues:** Guildford & Dist 50-71; Surrey Intermediate 71-78; Surrey Co. Senior 78-79
RECORDS **Attendance:** 600+ ex-Guildford City XI v ex-Football Lg XI. Tony Burge benefit 91
Goalscorer: Sean Gorman 127 **Appearances:** Paul Monger 356
BEST SEASON FA Cup: 1st Q.Rd. **FA Vase:** 2nd Rd.
Players progressing: John Humphreys (MIllwall)

FACT FILE
Founded: 1950
Nickname: The Gees
Colours: Green & yellow/green/green
Change colours: Blue & white/white/blue.
Midweek matchday: Tuesday
Programme: Yes

CLUB PERSONNEL
Chairman: Jane Phillips
Life President: W F Kyte
Press Officer: Secretary
Manager: Roger Steer
Asst Managers: Andy Dear
Physio: Dennis Rose

HARTLEY WINTNEY

Secretary: Mick Bradley, 8 Dairy Walk, High St., Hartley Wintney, Hampshire RG27 8XX Tel No: 01252 845745(H/Fax) 07754782189 (M)
Ground: Memorial Playing Fields, Green Lane, Hartley Wintney, Hants
Tel: 01252 843586
Directions: A30 west through Camberley, left at parade of shops at beginning of village then sharp right - ground on right. Two miles from Winchfield (BR)
Buses: Stagecoach 200, Bee Line 111, 112
Capacity:4,000 Seats: None Cover: Yes Floodlights: Yes

HONOURS: Aldershot Senior League winners: 73-74,74-75,75-76. Alderhot Senior Cup Winners 76-77,80-81 CoCo.League Winners 82-83,R-up 80-81
BEST SEASON **FA Cup:** Do not compete **FA Vase:** Do not compete
PREVIOUS **Leagues:** Basingstoke/ Aldershot

ACT FILE
Founded: 1897
Nickname: The Row
Colours: Orange/black/black
Change colours: All white or Red/black/black
Midweek matchday: Tuesday
Programme: Yes

CLUB PERSONNEL
Chairman: as Secretary
President: W A Mitchell
Treasurer: D.Willoughby
2000-01
Captain: Wayne Cracknell
P.o.Y.: Ian Dorkin
Top Scorer: Ian Dorkin 32

MERSTHAM

Secretary: Richard Baxter, 2 Wood Street, Merstham, Surrey. RH1 3PF
Tel: 01737 645748 (H) 01293 450890 (B) Email: the.baxters@virgin.net
Ground: Merstham Rec., Weldon Way, Merstham, Redhill, Surrey RH1 3QB (01737 644046)
Directions: Leave Merstham village (A23) by School Hill, take 5th right (WeldonWay), clubhouse and car park 100m on right. 10 mins walk from Merstham (BR);down School Hill, under railway bridge, then 5th turning on right into WeldonWay. Bu98-99s - London Country 430, 432 & 435
Capacity: 2,000 Seats: 100 Cover: 100 Floodlights: Yes Club Shop: No
Clubhouse: Across adjacent footpath. Open daily (am & pm). Snacks available
HONOURS Combined Co's Lg R-up 87-88 89-90 (Elite Class Cup 89-90 (R-up 90-91), Res. Sect. 90-91), Spartan Lg 79-89 (Lg Cup 79-80), Surrey Snr Lg 71-72, Surrey Snr Char. Cup 79-80, E. Surrey Char. Cup 80-8 98-99, Surrey I'mediate Lg 52-3
CLUB RECORDS **Attendance:** 532
BEST SEASON **FA Cup:** 3rd Q Rd **FA Vase:** 4th Rd.
PREVIOUS **Leagues:** Redhill & Dist.; Surrey Co.S.E. I'mediate; Surrey Snr 64-78; London Spartan 78-85 **Grounds:**None

FACT FILE
Founded: 1892
Club Sponsors: Brewers
Colours: Amber & black stripes/black/amber
Change colours:White,navy, red.
Midweek matches: Tuesday/Thursday
Programme: Yes Editor:Mrs S Fish

CLUB PERSONNEL
Chairman:Ted Hickman President: Bill Lawton
Press Officer: ChrisBrock
Manager:Alan Gallagher
Asst Manager: Graeme Crawford
2000-2001 Captain: Lennie Satchell
P.o.Y.: Anthony Jupp
Top Goalscorer Steve Jenns 23:

AFC Wallingford, Combined Counties League Premier Division Runners Up. Photo: Gordon Whittington

Sandhurst Town. Back Row (l-r): Simon Harrison, Howard Bristow, Steve Stairs, Colin Bland, Richard Ronchetti, Grant Nesbitt, Errol Hutchings, Martyn Fairminer, Tommy Powers, Bernie Bridger (Physio). Front Row: David Browning (Mascot), Dave Ward (Coach), Gavin Matthews, Darren Wilson, Dave Hawtin (Asst Manager), Pete Browning (Manager), Ben Neville, John Edwards, Tom Powers, Robbie McKinnon (Mascot).

Hartley Wintney

RAYNES PARK VALE

Secretary: Dave Brenen, 22 The Crescent, Belmont, Surrey SM2 6BJ
Tel No: 0208 296 8626 (H) 01932 853500 (W)

Ground: Grand Drive, Raynes Park. SW20 9NB Tel: 07714 339747
Directions: Bus - London Transport 131 & 152
Nearest railway station - Raynes Park.

HONOURS: None

FACT FILE

Colours:Maroon & blue stripes/blue/maroon
Change colours: Green & white hoops/green/white

CLUB PERSONNEL

President: Robert Hallett

Chairman: Nigel Thorn
43 Granville Avenue, Hounslow, Middlesex
Tel No: 0208 572 2331

READING TOWN

Secretary: Richard Grey, 6 Milestone View Court, Lowfield Road, Caversham Park, Reading RG4 6ND Tel: 07970 253785 Email: rgrey.cia@btinternet.com
Ground: Reading Town Spts Ground, Scours Lane, Tilehurst, Reading, Berks (0118 945 3555)
Directions: Out of Reading on Oxford road (A329), past Battle Hosp. Scours Lane 1st right after r'bout. Nearest station - Tilehurst or Reading (General). Bus -Reading Bus 17

Capacity: 2,000 Seats: No Cover: Yes Floodlights: Yes Clubhouse: Yes

PREVIOUS **Leagues:** Chiltonian 89-95, Reading 66-89
Names: Lower Burghfield, XL United, Vincents Utd, Reading Garage, ITS Reading Town

CLUB RECORDS **Attendance:** 253 v Banstead Ath FA Vase 96-97
Defeat: 0-10 v Feltham(A) 96-97
Win: 7-0 v Cranleigh/Viking Spts/AFC Wallingford all Home 97-98

BEST SEASON **FA Cup:** 1st Qual. Rd. 00-01 **FA Vase:** 4th Rd 96-97

HONOURS Comb. Counties Lge R-up 97-98; Chiltonian Lge Champions 94-95, Berks &Bucks Sen. Trophy 95-96, R-up 96-97

FACT FILE
Founded: 1968
Colours: Red & black stripes/black/black
Change colours: Navy/navy/red
Midweek Matchday: Tuesday
Programme: 20 pages 50p
Editor: Richard Grey

CLUB PERSONNEL
Chairman: Roland Ford, 103 Little Heath Road, Tilehurst, Berkshire RG31 5TG
Tel: 0118 941 2270
Fixture Sec.: As Secretary
Manager:Neil Webb (Ex Man. Utd. & England)
2000-01 Leading goalscorer: Nathan Broad 13
Captain: Tommy Boylan
P.o.Y.: Tommy Boylan

SANDHURST TOWN

Secretary: Tony Ford, Pennings Cottage, Aldershot Road, Guildford, Surrey GU3 3AA
Tel Nos: 01483 567284 (H) 07778 628547(M)
Ground: Bottom Meadow, Memorial Ground, Yorktown Rd, Sandhurst (01252 873767)

Directions: M3 Jn$ - A331 -A321 or M4 Jn10 -A329M -A321.Park in maincouncil offices cr park off A321. Walk down tarmac path to ground. Nearest station: Sandhurst. Buses: 174,193 & 194

Capacity: 2,000 Seats: Eight Cover: Yes Floodlights: Yes Clubhouse: open 6 days

PREVIOUS **Leagues:** Reading & Dist.; East Berks; Aldershot Snr 79-84; Chiltonian84-90

CLUB RECORDS **Attendance:** 353 v Aldershot Town (Friendly)
Win: 9-1 v Cranleigh (08.01.2000) **Defeat:** 0-8 v Cobham 26.10.1991)
Goalscorer: Glenn Price **Appearances:** John Parker

BEST SEASON **FA Vase:** 1st Rd 93-94 **FA Cup:** 1st Rd Qualifying

HONOURS Combined Co's Lge Chal. Vase R-up 92-93 (Reserve Chal. Cup R-up 91-92), Chiltonian Lg R-up 86-87, Aldershot Snr Lg R-up 83-84; Berks & Bucks Sen.Trophy R-up 92-93 Aldershot Senior Cup: 00-01 , Co.Co. Res Cup 00-01,

FACT FILE
Founded: 1910
Nickname: Fizzers
Colours: Red/black/black
Change colours: Yellow,blue,yellow
Midweek matchday: Tuesday
Programme: Yes Editor:Tony Ford

CLUB PERSONNEL
Chairman:Phil Sigley (01276 32742)
President: Malcolm Watts
Match Sec.: as Secretary
Manager:Peter Browning
Coach: Paul McKinnon
2000-01 Capt: Martyn Fairminer P.o.Y.: Tommy Powers Top Scorer: Steve Stairs 18

SOUTHALL

Secretary: Andy Fitzsimons, PR Office, PO Box 110, Feltham, Middx. TW13 4YA
Tel: 0208 751 3107 (H & Fax) Email: freespace@musicbase@virgin.net
Ground: Ground share with Chalfont St. Peter FC, The Playing Fields, Amersham Road, Chalfont St Peter SL9 7BQ Tel: 01753 885797 **Directions:** A413 from Uxbridge (London) to Chalfont. Turn left 100 yds after2nd major roundabout (between Ambulance station and Community Centre. 2 miles from Gerrards Cross (BR), regular buses from Slough & Uxbridge
Capacity: 4,500 Cover: 120 Seats: 220 Floodlights: Yes

PREVIOUS: **Leagues**: Southern 1896-1905; Gt Western Suburban; Herts & Middx; Athenian 19-73, Ryman 73-00

BEST SEASON: **FA Cup:** 3rd Round 35-36, 1-4 v Watford (H)
FA Vase: Runners-up 85-86 **FA Amateur Cup:** Runners-up 24-25

HONOURS: FA Amtr Cup R-up 24-25, FA Vase R-up 85-86, Isthmian Lg Div 2 R-up 74-75, Gt Western Suburban Lg 12-13, Athenian Lg 26-27 R-up 54-55, Middx Snr Cup x12, Middx Charity Cup x9

FACT FILE
Founded: 1871 Nickname: Fowlers
Colours: Red & white stripes/white/rwhite
Change: Yellow & black
Midweek Matchday: Wednesday
Res' Lge: Middx County
Prog: 6 pages, 50p Ed: Steve Hawkins
2000-01 P.o.Y.: Andre Robinson
Top Scorer: Andre Robinson 12

CLUB PERSONNEL
Chairman: B T Wadlow
Manager: Keith Chamberlin
Physio: Keith Chamberlin
Club Website: www.southallfootballclub.co.uk
Club Email: geoff@southallfootballclub..co.uk

VIKING GREENFORD

Secretary: Stephen Hosmer, 27 St Georges Rd., Hanworth, Middlesex. TW13 6RD
Tel. & Fax: 0208 894 1244 (M) 0831 393559

Ground: Avenue Park, Western Avenue, Greenford, Middx (020 8578 2706)

Directions: On London-bound carriageway of A40, 300 yds before Greenford flyover and slip road to A4127. 12 mins walk from Greenford (Central Line) station - turn right out of station to A40, turn right - grd 1/4 mile on rght

Capacity: 450 Seats: 50 Cover: 100 Floodlights: Yes Club Shop: No

Clubhouse: Open every evening except Sunday. Hot & cold snacks on matchdays

HONOURS Hellenic Lg Div 1 85-86 (Div 1 Cup R-up 90-91).Co.Counties Lg.(R-Up.94-95)

CLUB RECORDS **Att:** 180 v Wealdstone,Middx.SenCup,Sept.96 **Goalscorer**: Frank Healy, 43

PREVIOUS **Leagues:** Middlesex 70-80; Hellenic 80-91

BEST SEASON **FA Cup:** 1st Q Rd 96 F,A.Vase: 2nd Rd v Diss Town 1991

Players progressing: Gordon Bartlett (Portsmouth), AlanDevonshire (West Ham), Peter Shaw (Charlton A.)

FACT FILE

Founded: 1945 Nickname: Vikings
Sponsors: Measham Self-Drive/ Greeene King
Colours: All tangerine, black trim
Change colours: Sky blue & maroon/sky/sky
Midweek matchday: Tuesday
Programme: 12 pages, 50p
Editor: John Bennett

CLUB PERSONNEL

Chairman: Terry Cross
President: Roy Bartlett
Press Officer: T.B.A.
Manager: Wayne Haley
Asst Man.:Steve Parsons
Physio: Ernie Stockwell

WALTON CASUALS

Secretary: Stuart Roberts, 47 Foxholes, Weybridge, Surrey. KT13 0BN. Tel: 01932845923
Email: sroberts@cattronuk.com

Ground: Franklyn Road Sports Ground, Waterside Drive, Walton-on-Thames, Surrey KT12 2JG
Tel No: 01932 787749 Website: http://www.waltoncasualsfc.co.uk

Directions: Next to Elmbridge Leisure Centre, left off Terrace Rd at first roundabout out of Walton centre. Hersham (BR), then bus 564 to Elmbridge Leisure Centre.

Capacity: 1,500 Seats: None Cover: 80Floodlights: Yes
Clubhouse: Matchdays only. Hot food available from Tea Bar Club Shop: No

HONOURS Suburban Lge (South) 82-83, (R-up 83-84); Surrey Prem Lge R-up 94-95, S.P.L. Chall Cup 93-94, (R-up 94-95); Surrey Premier Cup R-up 86-87

BEST SEASON **FA Vase:** 1Q 96-97(only Game) **FA Cup:** Never entered

PREVIOUS **Leagues:** Surrey Premier, Surrey Senior, Surrey Intermediate, Suburban.

CLUB RECORDS **Attendance:** 178 v Pagham FA Vase 96/97

FACT FILE

Founded: 1948
Nickname: The Stags
Sponsors: Tallents Bar
Colours: Tangerine/black/tangerine
Change colours: Red & black/white/red
Midweek Matchday: Tuesday
Programme: 36 pages 50p
Editor/Press Officer: Stuart Roberts

CLUB PERSONNEL

Chairman:Graham James (01932 227921)
General Manager: David Symonds
President: Grahan James
Managers: Mick Sullivan & Garry Clark

WESTFIELD

Secretary: Michael Lawrence, 19 Ash Road, Barnsbury Estate, Woking, Surrey. GU22 0BJ
Tel/Fax: 01483 722184 (H)

GROUND Woking Park, Kingfield, Woking, Surrey Tel: 01483 771106

Directions: (Adjacent to Woking FC.)
M25 J10 or 11, signposted from outskirts of Town.Ground 1 mile.
Woking B.R.Station & buses from Woking
Capacity: 1,000 Seats: None Cover: Yes Floodlights: Yes

Clubhouse Yes - open matchdays when snacks are available.

Club Shop No

PREVIOUS **League:** Surrey County Senior League

FACT FILE

Founded: 1953
Colours: All yellow
Change colours:Yellow/Black/Yellow
Midweek Matchday:Tuesday
Programme: No

CLUB PERSONNEL

President: R Hill
Chairman: Steven Perkins
160 Coleford Bridge Road, Mytchett, Camberley, Surrey
Tel: 01252 547900 (B)
Manager: John Cassidy
Asst. Managers:
Alan Morton & Brian Hennessy

WITHDEAN 2000

Secretary: Brian Davies, 119 Church Road, Hove BN3 2AF
Tel: 01272 272776 (H) 01273 764874 (B)
Email: briand@bdinsurance.demon.co.uk

Ground: Withdean Stadium, Tongdean Lane, Brighton BN3 2AF
Tel: 01273 542100

Capacity: 10,000 **Seats:** 6,000 **Cover:** 1,000 **Floodlights**: No

Directions: Off main London - Brighton road

Clubhouse: Pub on ground **Club Shop:** No

HONOURS Sussex Co. Lg Div 3 92-93 (Div 3 Cup 91-92)

PREVIOUS **Leagues:** Brighton Hove & District
Ground: Council pitch

FACT FILE

Founded: 1984
Colours: White with black trim/white/white
Programme Editor: Gary Arnold
Local Newspaper: Brighton Evening Argus

CLUB PERSONNEL

Chairman: Desmond Ralfe
President: Stan Hunt
Manager: Dave Cole

FORESTERS ESSEX SENIOR LEAGUE

President: Arthur Dimond **Chairman & Publicity:** Robert Errington

Secretary: David Walls, Bramley Cottage, Birch Street, Birch, Colchester, Essex CO2 0NW

Tel & Fax: 01206 330146 Email: EssexSenior@wallsd.freeserve.co.uk

FINAL LEAGUE TABLE 2000-01

	P	W	D	L	F	A	Pts	GD		P	W	D	L	F	A	Pts	GD
Brentwood	30	21	3	6	68	26	66	42	Stansted*	30	12	8	10	45	47	44	-2
Saffron Walden*	30	18	3	9	53	24	57	29	Leyton	30	12	7	11	50	43	43	7
Barkingside	30	17	5	8	55	34	56	21	Hullbridge Spts	30	12	4	14	62	60	40	2
Southend Manor	30	17	4	9	71	40	55	31	East Ham Utd	30	12	3	15	52	73	39	-21
Concord Rngrs*	30	17	3	10	57	38	54	19	Sawbridgeworth T	30	10	6	14	41	46	36	-5
Ilford	30	15	5	10	64	48	50	16	Burnham Ramblers	30	7	6	17	44	60	27	-16
Bowers Utd	30	13	8	9	54	46	47	8	Eton Manor	30	3	5	22	39	92	14	-53
Basildon Utd	30	13	6	11	66	48	45	18	Woodford Town*	30	2	2	26	23	119	8	-96

RESULTS CHART 2000-01

		1	2	3	4	5	6	7	8	9	10	11	12	13	14	15	16
1	Barkingside	X	1-4	4-2	1-1	2-0	3-2	2-0	2-2	5-2	1-0	1-0	2-1	1-1	2-1	n/p	3-0
2	Basildon United	1-3	X	1-2	0-1	6-2	3-1	1-1	4-0	4-3	1-1	3-1	0-1	4-0	0-2	2-2	2-2
3	Bowers United	1-1	5-1	X	1-1	2-1	1-1	1-2	2-3	1-2	3-1	1-1	2-0	2-0	2-2	1-2	3-2
4	Brentwood	4-1	2-0	1-0	X	3-2	1-2	4-0	5-1	4-0	0-1	0-1	1-0	2-1	1-0	5-0	3-0
5	Burnham Ramblers	0-3	2-1	1-1	1-5	X	2-0	0-1	3-0	0-0	2-2	1-1	2-3	1-3	1-4	0-2	5-1
6	Concord Rangers	n/p	1-0	2-3	2-1	0-3	X	2-3	2-0	5-0	3-1	0-0	1-0	2-0	3-2	0-2	11-1
7	East Ham United	1-3	1-4	2-4	0-1	4-4	2-1	X	6-4	3-1	2-3	2-4	0-3	2-1	1-6	1-1	2-0
8	Eton Manor	1-3	1-3	0-0	2-5	2-4	0-1	0-1	X	1-8	1-3	3-2	0-1	2-2	2-3	2-2	3-1
9	Hullbridge Sports	1-2	0-0	1-4	1-0	3-0	2-3	6-3	5-1	X	0-3	3-0	0-2	2-0	0-2	0-4	5-0
10	Ilford	1-4	3-2	2-0	1-2	1-0	1-1	3-2	4-0	3-3	X	2-3	2-1	0-2	3-2	1-1	4-1
11	Leyton	2-2	1-2	6-0	1-2	2-1	2-3	3-2	1-0	1-1	0-5	X	0-0	0-0	2-3	1-0	6-0
12	Saffron Walden Town	2-0	2-4	5-2	0-0	1-0	0-1	6-0	3-2	1-2	3-0	2-0	X	n/p	1-0	2-1	6-1
13	Sawbridgeworth Town	3-2	5-2	0-3	2-1	2-2	0-2	2-0	2-2	2-1	3-1	0-1	0-2	X	0-1	2-2	4-1
14	Southend Manor	0-1	2-2	0-1	3-4	2-1	3-1	1-2	6-1	3-2	4-1	2-1	1-0	3-0	X	8-2	3-1
15	Stansted	1-0	0-2	1-1	1-3	2-1	2-1	1-3	4-1	1-4	1-2	1-2	0-0	2-0	1-1	X	4-0
16	Woodford Town	n/p	0-7	0-3	1-5	1-2	0-3	1-3	4-2	2-4	0-9	1-5	0-5	0-4	1-1	1-2	X

Brentwood FC, League Champions. Photo: Margaret Errington

ANCIENT ORDER OF FORESTERS LEAGUE CUP 2000-01

QUARTER-FINALS

Leyton	v	Ilford	3-1	Sawbridgeworth T	v	Barkingside	3-1
Concord Rangers	v	Burnham Ramblers	1-2	Southend Manor	v	East Ham United	4-2

SEMI-FINALS (Two Legs)

Sawbridgeworth Tn	v	Burnham Rmblrs	3-2, 1-1	Leyton	v	Southend Mnr	1-0, 1-5

FINAL

Sawbridgeworth Tn	v	Southend Manor	1-2	at Leslie Field, Burnham Ramblers FC. Att: 220

HARRY FISHER MEMORIAL TROPHY 2000-01

FIRST ROUND

Barkingside	v	Burnham Ramblers	2-1	Concord Rangers	v	East Ham United	5-0
Saffron Walden Tn	v	Stansted	6-0	Hullbridge Sports	v	Brentwood	2*1
Sawbridgeworth Tn	v	Ilford	4-5	Eton Manor	v	Leyton	1-3
Bowers United	v	Woodford Town	4-0	Southend Manor	v	Basildon United	1*2

SECOND ROUND

Barkingside	v	Concord Rangers	2-0	Saffron Walden Tn	v	Hullbridge Spts	2*2, 3-4
Ilford	v	Leyton	1-2	Bowers United	v	Basildon United	2-0

SEMI-FINALS

Barkingside	v	Hullbridge Sports	2-0, 1-1	Leyton	v	Bowers United	4-1, 3-0

FINAL

Barkingside	v	Leyton	2*1

LEADING GOALSCORERS 2000-01

39	Chris Stevens	Ilford	19	Steven Grant	East Ham United
25	Howard Mackler	Hullbridge Sports	19	David Stittle	Brentwood
24	John Doyle	Basildon United	18	Keith Scourfield	Hullbridge Sports
21	Ben Barnett	Southend Manor	17	Micky Boland	Sawbridgeworth Town
20	Damon Miles	Saffron Walden Town	16	Lee Brant	Bowers United
19	C J Emmanuel	Ilford	16	Lee Smith	Basildon United

Southend Manor, AOF Cup Winners. Photo: Margaret Errington

BARKINGSIDE

Secretary: Phil O'Reilly, 102 Luxborough Lane, Chigwell, Essex IG7 5AA
Tel: 020 8559 0709 (H) 020 8504 9618 (B) 07946 317148 (M) Email:PR.O'Reilly@virgin.net
Ground: Oakside, Station Road, Barkingside, Ilford, Essex Tel: 020 8550 3611
Directions: From London A12 Eastern Ave to Green Gate, left into Hurns Rd to Barkingside, right into Craven Gardens, right Carlton Drive to Station Rd, under bridge and grd on right. Next to Barkingside station (Central Line). From Ilford station (BR) take 169 Bus to Craven Gardens
Capacity: 2,500 Seats: 140 Cover: 240 Floodlights: Yes Club Shop: No
Clubhouse: Saturdays 1pm-12. midweeek matchnights 6.30-11pm. Rolls, hotdogs,hamburgers
HONOURS: Spartan Lge. Prem. Div. 96-97, R-up 90-91 (Harry Sunderland Shld 83-84 (R-up 84-85); London Sen. Cup 96-97; S. Essex Lge R-up 46-47, L'don Lg R-up 49-50 (Lg Cup 55-56 (R-up 52-53 62-63)), Gtr L'don Lg 64-65,Spartan S.Mids Premier Champions 98-99
PREVIOUS: **Leagues:** Ilford & Dist. 1898-1925 44-47; Ilford Minor 25-44; Sth Essex 47-48; Walthamstow 48-50; London 50-64; Gtr London 64-71; Metropolitan-London 71-75; Spartan 76- South Midlands 1996-99

FACT FILE
Founded: 1898

Colours: Blue & yellow/blue/blue
Change colours: All yellow
Midweek matchday: Tuesday
Programme: Yes

CLUB PERSONNEL
President: A Smith
Chairman: Michael Woodward
Manager: John Bennett

BASILDON UNITED

Secretary: C.A.Thomas, 52 Conway Gardens, Grays, Essex RM17 6HG
Tel: 01375 390231 (H) Email: clivekaren@bun.co.uk

Ground: Gardiners Close, Gardiners Lane, Basildon, Essex SS14 3AW Tel: 01268 520268

Directions: A176 off Southend arterial (A127), left at r'bout into Cranes FarmRoad, proceed to end of duel carriageway, left at lights, Gardiners Close is 1st left (Football Club signed). Two and a half miles from Basildon BR station
Capacity: 2,000 Seats: 400 Cover: 1,000 Floodlights: Yes
Clubhouse: Open lunchtimes, evenings, weekends. Hot food sold Club Shop: No

HONOURS Isthmian Lge Div 2 83-83; Essex Senior Lge (5) 76-80 94-95, Lg Cup 77-78 94-95 97-98, Res. Cup 92-93; Essex Senior Trophy 78-79; Res. Lge &Shield 94-95
PREVIOUS **Leagues:** Grays & Thurrock; Gtr London 68-70; Essex Snr 70-80; Athenian 80-81; Isthmian 81-91 **Name:** Armada Sports **Ground:** Grosvenor Park 63-69
CLUB RECORDS **Attendance:** 4,000 v West Ham, ground opening 11/8/70

FACT FILE
Founded: 1963
Sponsors: T.B.A.
Colours: Amber & black stripes
Change: Green & white squares/white/white
Midweek Matches: Wednesday
Programme: 16 pages, 50p Editor: T.B.A.

1999-00 Top Scorer: Michael Gore

CLUB PERSONNEL
President: J Oakes
Chairman: John Strange
Press Officer: Frank Ford (01268 552994)
Manager:Steve Wheeler

BOWERS UNITED

Secretary: Lee Stevens,59 Cross Green, Lee Chapel South, Basildon, Essex SS16 5Q
Tel No: 01268 548 493 (H)
Ground: Crown Avenue, off Kenneth Rd, Pitsea, Basildon (01268 452068)
Directions: Turn into Rectory Rd from Old London Rd (B1464) at Pitsea Broadway into Kenneth Rd, right at top Crown Ave. 1.25 miles Pitsea (BR). Bus 5& 42 toRectory Rd, Bowers Gifford
Capacity: 2,000 Seats: 200 Stand: Yes Floodlights: Yes
Clubhouse: Open every night Club Shop: No
PREVIOUSLeagues: Thurrock & Thameside Comb.; Olympian**Ground:** Gun Meadow, Pitsea
HONOURS Thurrock & Thameside Comb. 58-59; Essex Snr Lg 80-81,98-99 R-up 83-84 Div 1 Cup 90-91,Lg Cup Winners 81-82,98-99 R-up (3) Harry Fisher mem Trophy 91-92 R-up (3)
BEST SEASON **FA Cup:** 1st Rd Q 98-99 **FA Vase:** 4th Rd 98-99
CLUB RECORDS **Attendance:** 1,800 v Billericay F.A.Vase
Players progressing: Steve Tilson (Southend Utd)
99-00 P.o.Y.: Steven Chambers **Captain**: Steven Chambers **Top Scorer:** David Hope

FACT FILE
Founded: 1946
Colours: Red & white/black/black
Change colours:All Yellow
Midweek Matches:Tuesday 7.30
Res League; Essex & Herts Border Comb
Programme: 30pages 50p
Editor:Stephen Bond

CLUB PERSONNEL
Chairman:Barry Hubbard
Vice Chairman: Bert Warner
Manager: Brian Horne(07710 103310(M))
2000-01
Captain: Lee Goodwin P.o.Y.: Michael Welsh
Top Scorer: Emmanuel Williams 16

BRENTWOOD

Secretary: Colin Harris, 56 Viking Way, Pilgrims Hatch, Brentwood, Essex CM15 9HY
Tel: 01277 219564 (H) Email Address: khobbs1057@aol.com
Ground: Brentwood Centre, Doddinghurst Rd, Brentwood, Essex. 01277 215151 Ext.713

Directions: From east end High St (Wilsons Corner) turn north into Ongar Rd. 3rd mini-round-about ,Right into Doddinghurst Rd, Centre half mile on right after A12 Bridge, ground far right.
Capacity: !,000 Cover: 100 Seats: Floodlights: Yes
Clubhouse: Open Tues & Thur evening & matchdays Club Shop: No
PREVIOUS **Names:** Manor Ath. 55-70, Brentwood Ath. 70-72
Grounds: King George, Hartswood, `Larkins', Ongar (pre-92), East Thurrock 92/93
Leagues: Romford & Dist., Sth Essex Comb., London & Essex Border,Olympian
HONOURS Olympian Lg Cup 67-68, Essex Inter. Cup 76-77, Essex Lg Cup 75-76 78-79 90-91; Harry Fisher Mem. Trophy 95-96
BEST SEASON **FA Vase:** 3rd Rd Prop 95-96
2000-01 Captain & Top Scorer: Dave Stittle (19) P.o.Y.: Kevin Garneys

FACT FILE
Founded: 1955 Sponsor: CLC Construction
Nickname: Blues
Colours: All sky blue
Change colours: All Yellow
Midweek Matches: Tuesday
Programme: 50p
Club Website:www.brentwoodfc.co.uk

CLUB PERSONNEL

Chairman: K J O'Neale
Manager: Paul Delea (H) 01708 550630

BURNHAM RAMBLERS

Secretary: Chris Dobson, 13 Chapel Rd, Burnham-on-Crouch, Essex CM0 8JB(01621 786334)
Ground: Leslie Field, Springfield Rd, Burnham-on-Crouch CM0 8AU (01621 784383)
Club Website: www.burnhamramblers.co.uk

Directions: On B1010 from South Woodham Ferrers, trt,1/2 mile before town. 10 mins -Burnham (BR)
Capacity: 2,000 Seats:156 Stand: Yes Floodlights: Yes Club Shop: No
Clubhouse: Mon-Fri 7-11pm, Sat 12noon -11pm, Sun 12-3 & 7-9.30pm. Hot meals & snacks available

HONOURS Olympian Lg 65-66; Essex I'mediate Cup R-up 81-82; Essex Snr Lg Cup R-up 86-87 89-90 97-98, (Reserve Cup 89-90 (R-up 92-93), Reserve Shield R-up 90-91; Harry Fisher Mem. Trophy 96-97, R-up 97-98 99-00; Sportsmanship Award 96-97

PREVIOUS **Leagues:** N Essex, Mid-Essex, Olympian, S.E. Essex
Grounds: Wick Rd ,Millfields and Saltcourts
BEST SEASON **FA Vase:** 5th Rd 88-89
CLUB RECORDS **Gate:** 1,500 v Arsenal at opening of new stand

FACT FILE
Founded: 1900 Nickname: Ramblers
Colours: Blue/black/black
Change colours: Yellow/black/yellow
Midweek matches: Tuesday
Reserves' Lge: Essex & Herts Comb.
Prog: 32 pages, 50p Editor: Chris Dobson

CLUB PERSONNEL
Chairman: Ron Hatcher
Vice Chairman: Chris Browne
President: R J Cole, Esq
Press Officer: Nigel Radcliffe, 016217774
Manager Grant Gordon .Physio:Zoe Woolhead
2000-01: Top Scorer: Danny Greaves 16
Captain & P.o.Y: Steven Dobson

CONCORD RANGERS

Secretary: Eddie Crace, 71 Tilburg Road, Canvey Island, Essex, SS8 9ER. Tel: 01268 681868H 07889 904109M 01268 2950288W
Ground: Thames Road, Canvey Island, Essex. SS8 0HP 01268 691780 / 515750
Website: www.concordrangersfc.co.uk Email: ecrace@newholland.com
Directions: Follow A130 onto Canvey Island and turn right into Thorney Bay Road, then right again into Thames Road.
Capacity: 1,500 Cover: Yes Seats: No Floodlights: Yes

HONOURS Southend & Dist. Lge - Lge & Cup 84-85; Southend Alliance - Lge & Cup 87-88; Essex Intermediate Lg Div 2 90-91; Essex Sen Lge 97-98, Cup 96-97; Wirral Programme Award 93-94, Harry Fisher Trophy 99-00

PREVIOUS **Leagues:** Southend & Dist. All., Essex I'mediate (pre-1991) **Ground:** Waterside

CLUB RECORDS **Gate:** 1,500 v Lee Chapel North, FA Sunday Cup 89-90
Win: 12-1 v Woodford, Essex Snr Lge 00-01

FACT FILE
Founded: 1967
Colours:Yellow & Blue/blue/yellow
Change colours: white/black/black
Midweek Matches: Tuesday
Clubhouse: Evenings & weekends
Programme: 20 pages, 50p
Editor: As Secretary

CLUB PERSONNEL
President: Albert Lant
Chairman: Antony Smith
Manager: Steve Knott
2000-01 Top Scorer: Gary Martin
Captain: Roger Gell
P.o.Y.: Danny Clare

ENFIELD TOWN

Enfield Town Football Club, officially formed in June 2001, can trace its existence back to before September 1999, when Isthmian League Enfield F.C. were rendered homeless after the Southbury Road stadium, their home for sixty-three years, was sold for redevelopment. Members of a supporters action group had been invited to join a `Task Force', set up by the local council to find the club a suitable site within the borough, but although several sites were identified the club's chairman appeared reluctant to commit himself. Next, after a year of ground-sharing with no less than six different clubs, the newly-formed Enfield Supporters' Trust stepped up the pressure on the Enfield F.C. chairman to either make progress with his plans to bring the club back to their home borough, or relinquish control. A settlement was almost reached in February 2001 but was further frustrated by an about-turn from the chairman, leading to the dramatic events of June 23rd 2001 when the membership of the Enfield Supporters' Trust voted in favour of breaking away and forming a new club of their own. Enfield Town Football Club was accepted into the Foresters Essex Senior League a mere two days later, having reached an agreement with local Minerva Spartan South Midlands League club Brimsdown Rovers to share their Goldsdown Road ground for one year. A period of intense activity followed, both on and off the pitch, during which the club began to take shape. Popular ex-Enfield manager Jim Chandler agreed to look after the team, whilst several other posts were filled by ex-Enfield personnel, all of whom had left voluntarily to join the new club.
Press Officer: P J Coath, 33 Bertram Rd., Enfield Middx. EN1 1LR Tel: 020 8292 7783
Ground: Brimsdown Sports & Social Club, Goldsdown Road, Enfield, Middlesex Tel: 0181 804 5491 **Directions:** BR from Liverpool Street to Brimsdown (half mile away) or Southbury Road. By road off Green Street, itself off Hertford Road (A1010). Buses 191 or 307

ETON MANOR

Secretary: Mrs Jackie Jones, 31 Greenleafe Drive, Barkingside, Essex (020 8550 9618(H)0956 547220(M)
Ground: Waltham Lodge Sports Ground,Kitchener Rd.,Walthamstowe London E17 4JP(020 8527 2444)
Directions: Sharing with Leyton Pennant (Ryman League).
Capacity: 1,000 Seats: 60 Cover: 60Floodlights: Yes Clubhouse: Yes
HONOURS Essex Snr Cup R-up 37-38, London Lg 33-34 37-38 52-53 53-54 (R-up 48-49 57-58, Lg Cup 55-56 (R-up 46-47 54-55)), Greater London Lg 64-65, Essex Intermediate Cup 64-65, London Intermediate Cup R-up 33-34 66-67, Essex Snr Lg Sportsmanship Award 75-76 (Div 1 Cup 90-91, Res. Div 76-77, Res. Div Cup 91-92).
PREVIOUS **Leagues:** London 33-59; Aetolian 59-64; Greater London 64-69; Metropolitan 69-75.
Grounds: Wildness, Hackney; GUS Sports Ground, Clapton; Walthamstow Ave. FC; Norwegian Ground, Barking; Roding Lane, Buckhurst Hill, ThurrockHotel **Name:** Wilderness Leyton.
CLUB RECORDS **Gate:** 600 v Leyton Orient, opening of floodlights at Roding Lane.
Goalscorer: Dave Sams

FACT FILE
Founded: 1901
Nickname: The Manor
Colours: Sky/navy/navy
Change colours: Maroon & green/maroon/maroon
Midweek Matches: Tuesday
Programme: 12 pages with entry Editor: Secretary

CLUB PERSONNEL
Chairman: Reg Curtis
Manager:Tony Jones
Physio: Alf Jones
00-01 Top Scorer: Jamie Everton

HULLBRIDGE SPORTS

Secretary: Beryl Petre, 58 Grasmere Ave., Hullbridge, Essex SS5 6LF
Tel: 01702 230630 (H) 01702 552211 (B)
Ground: Lower Road, Hullbridge, Hockley, Essex SS5 6BJ Tel: 01702 230420
Directions: Turn into Rawreth Lane from A130 (left if arriving fromChelmsford), down to mini-r'bout, left, across next mini-r'bout, up hill, ground signed on right just past garage
Capacity: 1,500 Seats: No Cover: Yes Floodlights: Yes Club Shop: No
Clubhouse: Lounge bar, function hall with bar & changing rooms - set in 16 acres

HONOURS Essex Intermediate Snr Div Cup 87-88, Southend & District Lg Div 1 65-66 (Div 2 51-52, Div 3 56-57), French Cup 51-52, Essex Snr Lg Sportsmanship Award 91-92 92-93 94-95

PREVIOUS **Leagues:** Southend & Dist., Alliance, Essex I'mediate
Grounds: Pooles Lane Rec

RECORD ATTENDANCE: 800 v Blackburn Rovers F.A.Youth Cup 99-00

FACT FILE
Founded: 1945
Sponsor: Thermo Shield
Colours: Royal Blue & white/blue/blue
Change colours: All yellow
Midweek matches: Tues/Thursday
Programme Editor: T.B.A.
Website: www.sportsworldwide.co.uk
CLUB PERSONNEL
Chairman: Terry Scourfield
Manager: Andy Dixon
2000-01
Capt: Keith Scourfield P.o.Ys: Howard Mackler & John Leek Top Scorer: Howard Mackler

ILFORD

Secretary: Bill Robertson,2 humphrey close,Clayhall,Ilford, Essex JG5 0RW
Tel Nos: 02085506680 (H) 07930 104076 (W)
Ground: Cricklefield Stadium, High Road, Ilford, Essex. IG1 1UB Tel: 0181 514 0019
Directions: 5 min walk from Seven Kings Station. Opposite 'TheCauliflower' publ, Or 86 Bus
Capacity: 5,000 Seats - 216 Cover - Yes Floodlights - Yes
Clubhouse: No, but snackbar available on matchdays
HONOURS: FA Amateur Cup: 28-29 29-30, R-up 35-36 57-58 1973-74 Isthmian Lge Champ. 06-07 20-21 21-22 R-up 11-12 26-27 31-32 37-38 38-39 Essex Senior Cup x13 (record nos. of wins), R-up x5; London Sen. Cup: x7 R-up x 5; London Charity Cup: x 6 R-up x 7: Essex I'mediate Cup R-up x1; London I'mediate Cup R-up x1; Eastern F'lit Comp. Group Winners 96-97
PREVIOUS **League:** Spartan 87-95
BEST SEASON **FA Cup:** 73-74 2nd Rd, 0-2 v Southend Utd. (H)
FA Vase: 99-00 2nd Rd 1-2 v Watton United (a)
CLUB RECORDS **Attendance:** 17,000 Ilford Boys v Swansea Boys (Schools Trophy Final)

FACT FILE
Founded: 1881 Re-Formed: 1987
Sponsor: Kelvin Hughes
Colours: Blue & white hoops/white/blue & white
Change colours: Red & white qtrs/red/red
Midweek matches: Monday
Programme Editor: L Llewellyn
CLUB PERSONNEL
Chairman: George Hogarth
Vice Chairman: Melvin Attwell
President: Lord John Taylor of Warwick
FManager: Joe Simmonds (0208 9895560)
2000-01
Captain: Eddie Nwachokwu
P.o.Y.: & Top Scorer: Chris Stevens (40)

LEYTON

Secretary: Tony Hampford, 282 Lea Bridge Road, Leyton, London E10 7LD
Tel: 0208 556 2665 (H) 0208 539 5405 (B)

Ground: Wingate Leyton Stadium, 282 Lea Bridge Road, Leyton, London E10 7LD
Tel: 0208 539 5405 Email: enquiries@leytonfc.co.uk
Directions: Lea Bridge Rd. is A104, ground next to Hare & Hounds PH.
Leyton (Central Line) thence bus 58 or 158 to Lea Bridge Road.
Clapton (BR) Walk 100 yds to Lea Bridge Rd. roundabout, buses 48, 55, 56 to ground. Bus 48 runs direct to ground from London Bridge (BR) station
Capacity: 2,500 Seats: Yes Cover: Yes Floodlights: Yes

PREVIOUS **Leagues:** Essex Intermediate; Spartan

FACT FILE
Founded: 1868
Nickname: Lilywhite
Colours: Blue & white stripes/blue/blue
Change colours: Red & black halves/red/red
Midweek Matches: Tuesday
Programme Editor: Tony Hampford

CLUB PERSONNEL
Chairman: Phil Foster
Vice Chairman: Doug Digby
President: Peter Lewis
Fixture Sec.: as Secretary
Manager: Rowley Cray

SAFFRON WALDEN TOWN

Secretary: Peter Rule, 48 Church Street, Saffron Walden, Essex, CB10 1VQ (Tel 01799 522417)
Ground: Catons Lane, Saffron Walden, Essex CB10 2DU (01799 522789)
Directions: In Saffron Walden High St turn into Castle St, left at T-junction, 1st left by Victory pub
Capacity: 5,000 Seats: 500 Cover: 2,000 Floodlights: Yes Club Shop: Yes Clubhouse: Yes -
PREVIOUS **Leagues:** Haverhill & Dist.; Stansted & Dist.; Cambridgeshire; Nth Essex; Herts Co.; Spartan 33-49 50-54; Parthenon 49-50; Essex Snr 71-74; Eastern Co's 74-84
HONOURS Essex Snr Lg 73-74, 99-00Lg.Cup 99-00 Eastern Co's Lg 82-83, Spartan Lg Eastern Div 2 36-37,Essex Snr Tphy 82-83 83-84 84-85, Eastern F'lit Comp. 91-92 (R-up 88-89,Nth Thames Group B 82-83), Essex Jnr Cup 1896-97 (R-up 25-26), Cambs Lg R-up 22-23, Essex & Herts Border R-up 25-26(jt), Stansted & Dist. x 7, Haverhill & Dist. x 5 ,Harry Fisher Mem& Uttlesford Ch Cup 98-99,S.Mids Floodlit Cup 99-00 Spoertsmanship Cup: 98-99.99-00
CLUB RECORDS **Scorer:** John Tipputt **Appearances:** Les Page, 700+
Attendance: 6,000 v Rainham Ath., Essex Jun. Cup Final 1926 (played at Crittals, Braintree)
BEST SEASON **FA Cup:** 2nd Qual. Rd replay 84-85, 1-2 v King's Lynn (A)

FACT FILE
Founded: 1872
Nickname: Bloods
Club Sponsors: Tolly Cobbold
Colours: Red & black/black/black
Change cols: Blue & yellow/yellow/yellow
Midweek Matchday: Tuesday
Reserves' League: Essex & Herts Comb
Programme: 24 pages, 40p
Editor: R Smith (01799 500061)
CLUB PERSONNEL
Chairman: Steve Cox
Press Officer: Secretary
Manager: Tim Moylette

Brentwood, Foresters Essex Senior League Champions

Enfield Town. Back Row (l-r): Stuart Snowden, Bradley Brotherton, Kevin Riley, Ricky Antoine, Lee Smart, Bradley Quinn. Front Row: Danny Clarke, John Ridout, Andy Hall, Nicky Morgan, Nathew Negus, Ronnie Watson

SAWBRIDGEWORTH TOWN

Secretary: Barrie Mutimer, 'Ebenezer, 18 Forebury Avenue, Sawbridgeworth, Herts CM21 9BG

Ground: Crofters End, West Road, Sawbridgeworth, Herts. CM21 0DE (01279 722039)

Directions: Three quarters of a mile from the station; up Station Road then into West Road.

Capacity: 1,500 Seats: None Cover: 250 Floodlights: Yes Club Shop: No

HONOURS Essex Olympian Lg 71-72; Essex Snr Lg R-up 92-93 94-95; Harry FisherMem. Cup 87-88; Lg Cup 94-95 R-up 92-93 93-94, Res. Div 91-92 92-93 (R-up 93-94), Res. Shield R-up 92-93); Herts Snr Tphy 90-91 93-94 (R-up 92-93);Herts Charity Shield 92-93 94-95 95-96; Uttlesford Charity Cup 92-93; Herts Intermediate Cup R-up 93-93(res); S. Midlands F'lit Cup R.up 94-95; Res. Sect S.M Lge & Lg.Cup R-Up 94-95
PREVIOUS **Leagues:** Essex Olympian, Spartan 36-53
CLUB RECORDS **Attendance:** 610 v Bishop's Stortford.
PREVIOUS GROUNDS: Hyde Hall, Pishiobury, Hand & Crown.

FACT FILE
Founded: 1890
Nickname: Robins
Colours: Red & black stripes/black/black
Change colours: All blue
Midweek Matchday;
Prog Editor:Gary Bennett (01279 830306)
Wirral programme Award 99-00
CLUB PERSONNEL
Chairman: Anton johnson
President: Ron Alder
Press Officer: Gary Bennett
Manager: John Higley
Physio: Brian Latchford
1999-00 Top Scorer: Roy Smith

SOUTHEND MANOR

Secretary: Dave Kittle, 15 Seymour Rd, Hadleigh, Benfleet, Essex SS7 2HB
Tel: 01702 559581 (H) 01268 752811 (B) 01268 793416 (Fax)
Ground: Southchurch Park Arena, Lifstan Way, Southend-on-Sea. Tel: 01702 615577
Directions: A127 then A1159 for 1 mile turn right at second roundabout by Invisible Man PH, then due south for 1 mile, ground on right near sea front
Capacity: 2,000 Seats: 500 Cover: Yes Floodlights: Yes
Clubhouse: Open every evening Club Shop: No
HONOURS Essex Senior Trophy 92-93; Essex Intermediate Cup 78-79; Essex Senior League 90-91, R-Up: 99-00 Essex Senior League Cup 87-88, R-Up: 99-00,00-01 Challenge Cup 89-90; Harry Fisher Memorial Trophy 90-91 92-93 (R-up 91-92)
PREVIOUS **Leagues:** Southend Borough Combination, Southend Alliance
Grounds: Victory Spts/ Oakwood Rec
RECORDS **Attendance:** 1,521 v Southend Utd, 22/7/91, floodlight opener
BEST SEASON **FA Vase:** 1996-97

FACT FILE
Founded: 1955 Nickname: The Manor
Sponsors: Drum Leisurewear
Colours: Yellow/black/black
Change colours: All white
Midweek Matchday: Tuesday
Reserves Lge: Essex & Herts Border Comb
Programme: 10 pages, 50p
Editor/Press Off: Harry Cooper 01702 308482
Website: www.southendmanor.co.uk
CLUB PERSONNEL
Chairman: Robert Westley
Vice-Chairman: Geoff Gorham
Man: Mark Jenkins Coach: Peter Heathcote
2000-01: Capt: Simon Nicks P.o.Y.: David Manda Top Scorer: Ben Barnett 21

STANSTED

Secretary: Mrs Denise Murnane, 01279 815404 (H&B) 07957 855023 (M) 01279 815780 (F)
Appletree House, Fullers End, Elsenham, Bishops Stortford. CM22 6DU.
Ground: Hargrave Park, Cambridge Road, Stansted, Essex. (01279 812897)
Directions: B1383 north of Bishops Stortford on west side of Cambridge Rd.
Stansted (BR) - 1/2 mile
Capacity: 2,000 Seats: 200 Cover: Yes Floodlights: Yes
Clubhouse: Matchdays till 11pm. Sandwiches available. Club Shop: No

HONOURS FA Vase Winners 83-84; Essex Snr Lg R-up 82-83; Essex Snr Lg Cup 83-84, (R-up 72-73 94-95); Harry Fisher Mem Cup 82-83 84-85 (R-up 92-93 93-94); E. Anglian Cup 83-84; Eastern F/lit Cup 83-84; Uttlesford Char. Cup 93-84 86-87 88-89 94-95 97-98
PREVIOUS **Leagues:** Spartan; London; Herts Co. **Grounds:** Greens Meadow; ChapelHill
RECORDS **Attendance:** 828 v Whickham (FA Vase 83-84)
BEST SEASON **FA Cup:** 97-98 **FA Vase:** Winners 83-84

FACT FILE
Founded: 1902
Nickname: The blues
Sponsor: D C Poultons
Colours: Blue & white/blue/blue
Change: Green & red/green/red
Midweek matches: Tuesday
Reserves League: Cambridgeshire League
Programme Editor: D Murnane

CLUB PERSONNEL
Chairman: Terry Shoebridge
President: Percy Heal
Manager: Tony Mercer

WOODFORD TOWN

Secretary: Bill Robertson, 2 Humphrey Close, Clayhall, Ilford, Essex IG5 0RW
0181 550 6680 (H) 07930 104076 (B&M)

Ground: Clapton FC ground share
Old Spotted Dog Ground, Upton Lane, Forest Gate, London E7
Tel: 0181 472 0822
Directions: BR to Forest Gate,Tube to Plaistow (District Line).
Official entrance in Upton Lane.
Docklands Light Railway to Prince Regent then 325 bus to ground
Buses: Any bus fron Forest Gate station
Capacity: 2,000 Seats: 100 Cover: 180 Floodlights: Yes

FACT FILE

Founded: 1937

Colours: Red, black & white/red/red

Change colours: Blue & white/white/white

CLUB PERSONNEL

Chairman: Mick Wakeling

Fixture Sec. as Secretary

Manager: John Burns

Canvey's Steve Tilson (centre) hammers the ball past Billericay's Gavin King to open the scoring for Canvey. Photo: Alan Coomes

Croydon's Omari Coleman fires in a shot past Dulwich's Al-James Hannigan (3). Photo: Alan Coomes

footballs

SPARTAN SOUTH MIDLANDS FOOTBALL LEAGUE

President: B F Smith **Chairman:** Pat Burns

Hon. Gen. Secretary: M Mitchell, 26 Leighton Court, Dunstable, Beds. LU6 1EW

Tel: 01582 667291

FINAL LEAGUE TABLES 2000-01

PREMIER DIVISION

	P	*W*	*D*	*L*	*F*	*A*	*GD*	*Pts*
Beaconsfield	36	28	4	4	80	36	44	88
London Colney	36	25	6	5	91	36	55	81
Potters Bar Town*	36	25	6	5	82	39	43	78
Brook House	36	22	6	8	64	36	28	72
Somersett A V&E	36	17	9	10	67	47	20	60
Holmer Green	36	18	2	16	58	58	0	56
Hanwell Town	36	13	6	14	67	52	15	54
Hillingdon Boro	36	14	12	10	63	61	2	54
Brache Sparta	36	14	7	15	70	78	-8	49
New Bradwell St P	36	11	12	13	49	52	-3	45
Hoddesdon Town	36	13	5	18	54	60	-6	44
Bedford United	36	11	10	15	49	50	-1	43
St Margaretsbury*	36	9	8	19	45	68	-23	38
Biggleswade Town	36	9	9	18	40	55	-15	36
Ruislip Manor	36	10	6	20	44	60	-16	36
Milton Keynes C	36	9	7	20	50	79	-29	34
Royston Town	36	8	9	19	31	60	-29	33
Haringey Boro	36	6	11	19	33	78	-45	29
Welwyn Garden C	36	6	7	23	25	57	-32	25

SENIOR DIVISION

	P	*W*	*D*	*L*	*F*	*A*	*GD*	*Pts*
Letchworth	36	28	5	3	94	32	62	89
Dunstable Town	36	27	6	3	94	25	69	87
Biggleswade Utd	36	21	6	9	82	46	36	69
Tring Athletic	36	19	10	7	74	27	47	67
Colney Heath	36	19	7	10	86	44	42	64
Cockfosters	36	18	8	10	67	62	5	62
Langford	36	17	7	12	72	57	15	58
Ampthill Town	36	17	5	14	76	54	22	56
Stony Stratford T	36	14	8	14	65	68	-3	50
Leverstock Green	36	14	4	18	38	57	-19	46
Risborough Rngrs	36	12	6	18	57	73	-16	42
Greenacres (H)*	36	10	12	14	46	66	-20	41
Letchworth Brdgr*	36	11	6	19	59	82	-23	41
Brimsdown Rovers	36	12	4	20	53	64	-11	40
Harefield United	36	10	9	17	53	59	-6	39
Amersham Town	36	10	8	18	34	55	-21	38
Harpenden Town	36	7	10	19	51	76	-25	31
Luton Old Boys	36	6	8	22	38	77	-39	26
Totternhoe	36	3	5	28	25	140	-115	14

DIVISION ONE

	P	W	D	L	F	A	Pts	
Pitstone & Ivinghoe	34	26	4	4	91	34	57	82
Flamstead	34	22	5	7	96	46	50	71
The 61 FC (Luton)	34	19	8	7	79	54	25	65
Winslow Utd*	34	20	7	7	81	41	40	64
Kent Athletic	34	18	9	7	83	54	29	63
Old Dunstablians	34	17	7	10	88	58	30	58
Mursley United	34	16	8	10	93	46	47	56
Scot	34	15	7	12	98	76	22	52
Haywood United	34	13	8	13	75	50	25	47
Buckingham Ath	34	11	11	12	61	58	3	44
Milcutt Rovers	34	12	8	14	62	73	-11	44
Abbey Nat (L'ton)*	34	12	4	18	54	58	-4	43
Crawley Green*	34	12	7	15	58	48	10	40
Shillington	34	11	4	19	54	74	-20	37
Caddington	34	10	5	19	44	90	-46	35
Old Bradwell Utd*	34	6	6	22	37	95	-58	27
Markyate	34	6	8	20	36	78	-42	26
North Crawley Utd	34	2	0	32	21	178	-157	6

** points adjustment*

HONOURS LIST 2000-01

Champions	*Runners Up*
PREMIER DIVISION	
Beaconsfield SYCOB	London Colney
SENIOR DIVISION	
Letchworth	Dunstable Town 98
DIVISION ONE	
Pitstone & Ivinghoe	Flamstead
RESERVE SECTION DIVISION ONE	
Tring Athletic	Leverstock Green
RESERVE SECTION DIVISION TWO	
Biggleswade Utd	Harpenden Town
RESERVE SECTION DIVISION THREE	
New Bradwell St Peter	Old Dunstablians

NAPIER ENGLISH ELECTRIC CUP *(Sportsmanship)*

Leverstock Green

HOUGHTON REGIS CUP

(for achievements in competitions outside the League)

Dunstable Town 98

FC CRAIN AWARD *(to club secretaries)*

T Devereux (Harefield United)

ALF JOYCE TROPHY

R Everitt (The 61 FC Luton)

PREMIER DIVISION RESULTS CHART 2000-01

		1	2	3	4	5	6	7	8	9	10	11	12	13	14	15	16	17	18	19
1	Beaconsfield SYCOB	X	1-0	0-0	5-2	4-1	2-1	2-0	1-2	5-2	1-3	2-1	4-0	2-0	0-2	3-0	3-1	3-0	1-0	1-0
2	Bedford United	0-0	X	4-2	1-1	1-2	0-3	3-0	2-1	3-1	2-3	0-3	4-1	1-1	0-3	2-0	0-0	1-2	5-1	1-2
3	Biggleswade Town	0-2	0-2	X	1-1	2-0	1-2	1-2	0-0	2-0	3-0	1-3	2-1	2-3	1-2	3-2	0-2	0-3	0-1	1-1
4	Brache Sparta	3-2	3-3	0-1	X	0-2	2-2	3-1	2-2	0-4	1-0	1-5	2-2	1-2	2-3	0-1	2-1	1-0	2-3	5-1
5	Brook House	0-2	0-2	1-1	1-2	X	0-0	5-0	3-2	6-1	0-0	2-1	4-2	2-1	0-2	2-1	2-1	3-0	1-1	1-0
6	Hanwell Town	1-3	1-2	2-0	3-0	0-1	X	3-2	0-2	3-0	0-3	3-3	2-1	3-2	1-3	5-1	2-3	2-0	0-2	6-1
7	Haringey Borough	2-4	1-1	0-0	2-4	0-1	2-0	X	0-1	2-1	2-0	1-6	1-1	1-0	2-3	0-0	2-7	2-2	0-0	1-1
8	Hillingdon Borough	1-3	1-1	3-0	2-2	1-2	4-3	1-0	X	4-1	2-3	4-3	0-2	2-2	1-1	2-2	2-0	1-1	1-7	2-0
9	Hoddesdon Town	2-3	1-0	1-0	3-4	3-2	1-1	3-1	2-0	X	0-2	0-0	4-1	1-2	1-2	3-0	2-2	1-0	3-0	1-0
10	Holmer Green	2-3	1-0	0-2	1-2	0-2	0-3	4-0	4-2	2-0	X	0-2	4-0	2-3	3-0	0-1	3-2	2-1	1-5	4-2
11	London Colney	1-1	3-1	3-1	6-3	1-4	4-1	8-0	3-0	1-0	2-0	X	1-1	2-1	1-0	1-1	3-1	2-0	2-1	2-0
12	Milton Keynes City	1-3	2-0	4-2	1-0	1-2	0-4	1-1	3-3	3-2	0-2	0-6	X	3-0	2-1	2-3	3-1	1-1	0-2	1-2
13	New Bradwell St Peter	1-2	1-1	0-0	1-2	1-1	0-0	0-0	2-2	2-2	2-0	0-3	2-2	X	4-2	4-0	1-0	0-1	2-1	2-1
14	Potters Bar Town	1-2	4-1	3-2	5-3	1-0	2-2	3-0	1-1	1-1	2-2	4-0	4-2	3-1	X	1-0	3-1	5-1	4-1	1-0
15	Royston Town	1-1	1-0	1-1	5-1	0-4	0-1	0-1	1-2	0-4	0-2	1-2	1-0	0-0	0-0	X	1-2	2-1	0-4	0-1
16	Ruislip Manor	0-1	0-0	1-2	4-3	0-1	1-3	4-0	0-3	1-0	0-2	0-4	2-1	1-1	0-2	2-2	X	1-0	0-1	1-0
17	St Margaretsbury	2-3	2-2	2-4	2-4	1-4	1-3	2-1	1-2	2-1	4-1	0-1	2-3	2-1	0-4	2-1	2-1	X	1-1	1-1
18	Somersett Ambury V & E	2-3	2-1	1-1	0-1	0-1	2-1	2-2	3-3	2-0	6-0	1-1	3-1	4-3	1-3	1-1	3-1	1-1	X	1-0
19	Welwyn Garden City	1-2	0-2	2-1	0-5	1-1	1-0	1-1	0-1	1-2	1-2	0-1	2-1	0-1	0-1	0-1	0-0	2-2	0-1	X

SENIOR DIVISION RESULTS CHART 2000-01

		1	2	3	4	5	6	7	8	9	10	11	12	13	14	15	16	17	18	19
1	Amersham Town	X	2-1	0-1	0-1	0-2	0-1	1-3	0-0	3-1	1-0	1-2	2-3	1-1	1-0	1-1	0-2	1-1	2-2	0-1
2	Ampthill Town	0-0	X	3-2	2-0	0-1	3-2	1-2	6-0	0-2	4-0	0-1	2-0	0-4	1-0	4-2	4-0	8-4	3-0	0-2
3	Biggleswade United	6-1	1-0	X	2-3	4-0	3-2	1-1	4-0	0-0	3-2	3-3	2-3	4-0	2-0	1-2	2-0	3-1	2-1	1-4
4	Brimsdown Rovers	4-0	2-3	1-2	X	0-3	1-2	1-6	0-3	1-2	0-0	1-1	0-2	2-3	2-3	1-0	0-1	3-4	1-0	0-2
5	Cockfosters	1-0	4-4	2-2	1-0	X	1-0	1-5	4-2	1-0	1-3	2-1	1-5	1-4	1-0	3-0	3-2	1-2	6-1	0-2
6	Colney Heath	1-2	1-2	1-2	2-1	2-1	X	1-2	2-0	4-1	3-3	4-1	2-2	6-0	2-0	3-0	3-2	6-0	6-0	0-0
7	Dunstable Town	2-0	3-1	4-0	1-2	1-1	1-2	X	0-1	2-0	2-0	1-0	1-0	6-2	0-0	3-1	0-0	2-1	4-0	3-0
8	Greenacres	0-0	1-1	1-2	3-1	2-2	3-4	0-6	X	1-0	2-2	2-4	0-2	2-2	1-1	2-0	1-1	2-1	2-0	1-1
9	Harefield United	0-1	1-1	1-3	1-3	1-3	1-3	0-1	0-3	X	6-0	1-1	0-6	5-0	0-2	3-1	2-2	2-1	8-0	0-0
10	Harpenden Town	3-1	0-0	0-3	0-2	3-3	0-3	2-2	3-3	2-2	X	1-2	1-3	1-4	1-2	3-1	2-1	1-2	9-0	1-1
11	Langford	0-2	2-4	0-0	0-3	3-3	2-1	1-2	4-0	2-0	3-1	X	0-3	2-3	5-2	6-1	7-1	0-2	3-1	1-0
12	Letchworth	2-1	2-1	2-0	3-1	4-0	2-0	1-2	3-0	2-0	3-2	2-2	X	5-2	1-1	3-2	3-1	2-0	6-0	3-0
13	Letchworth Bridger	1-2	4-3	0-3	1-1	1-3	1-1	0-1	2-2	2-2	1-2	0-3	2-2	X	2-3	3-1	2-1	0-4	6-0	0-2
14	Leverstock Green	0-1	0-3	2-1	0-5	1-3	1-0	0-4	0-2	1-2	0-2	0-1	0-2	1-0	X	3-3	0-2	2-0	4-1	2-1
15	Luton Old Boys	0-2	3-1	1-2	4-5	2-0	2-2	0-6	1-1	0-0	1-0	2-1	0-4	1-0	0-1	X	0-2	1-1	2-4	0-1
16	Risborough Rangers	5-3	1-7	0-5	2-3	2-2	2-2	1-2	1-0	1-2	3-1	2-3	1-2	2-3	2-3	1-0	X	2-1	6-0	0-4
17	Stony Stratford Town	3-1	2-0	2-2	3-2	1-2	1-3	3-3	4-2	2-2	3-0	1-1	1-2	2-0	0-2	2-1	1-1	X	6-1	1-1
18	Totternhoe	1-1	2-1	0-6	2-0	0-2	0-8	0-9	1-1	0-2	0-0	2-4	2-4	2-5	0-1	1-1	0-3	0-2	X	1-7
19	Tring Athletic	3-0	1-2	3-2	0-0	2-2	1-1	0-1	3-0	4-3	5-0	3-0	0-0	3-0	3-0	1-1	0-1	6-0	7-0	X

LEADING GOALSCORERS 2000-01

PREMIER DIVISION

		Lge	CT	DC	Tot
Gary Sippetts	London Colney	29	5	3	37
Kevin Rowlands	Hanwell Town	23	0	3	26
Lee Talbot	Potters Bar Town	22	0	0	22
Steve Smith	Hanwell Town	21	0	1	22
David Ross	London Colney	20	0	1	21
Kevin Hyde	New Bradwell St P	15	3	2	20
Darren Lynch	Milton Keynes C	16	0	0	16
Ryan Harris	Potters Bar Town	14	0	1	15
Jonathon Dobson	Royston Town	13	2	0	15

SENIOR DIVISION

		Lge	*CT*	*DC*	*Tot*
Dave Hewing	Colney Heath	35	0	3	38
Paul Sloley	Stony Stratford	27	0	0	27
Grant Carney	Dunstable T	25	1	0	26
Allan Arthur	Letchworth	24	0	0	24

SENIOR DIVISION cont.

		Lge	*CT*	*DC*	*Tot*
Greg Toyer	Biggleswade U	18	2	1	21
Steve Castleman	Ampthill Town	16	0	0	16
Danny Hutchings	Cockfosters	13	0	2	15
Daniel Griggs	Ampthill Town	12	2	1	15

DIVISION ONE

		Lge	*CT*	*DC*	*Tot*
Scott Covington	Old Dunstablians	33	0	0	33
Anthony Clark	Scot	29	0	0	29
Paul Talbot	Winslow United	27	0	0	27
Shaun Fahy	Kent Athletic	25	0	0	25
Gareth Devoti	Flamstead	23	0	0	23
Richard Pringle	The 61 FC	21	1	0	22
Roy Henney	Pitstone & Iving.	21	0	0	21
Graham Golds	Flamstead	20	0	0	20
Kevin Millington	Scot	19	0	0	19
Michael Lyon	Mursley Utd	17	0	1	18

BEACONSFIELD SYCOB

Secretary: Ken Barrett, 31 Stockey End, Abingdon, Oxon OX14 2NF. Tel: 01235202058 (H), 01235 537080 (B) Email: kj17ox@aol.com

GROUND: Holloway Park, Slough Road, Beaconsfield, Bucks (01494 676868).
Directions: M40 (Jct 2), 1st exit to A355. Club 100yds on right. 1.5 miles from Beaconsfield BR Bus 441 Slough/ High Wycombe
Capacity: 3,000 Cover: 400 Seats:: 250 Floodlights: Yes C lub Shop: Clu
Clubbhouse: Open eves & matchdays. Bar, Committee Room, Hall, Kitchen, Changing Room l
HONOURS: As Slough : Chilt.Lg R-up: 93-4,Lg Cup 92-3 Slough T Cup R-up 91-2
PREVIOUS: **Names:** Slough YCOB & Beaconsfield Utd merged 1994
Leagues: Beaconsfield Utd: Wycombe & District; Maidenhead. Slough YCOB: Windsor, Slough & District; East Berks; Chiltonian (pre 1994) **Previous Grounds:** As Slough: Haymill Community Centre,Burnham Lane,slough (pre 1944)
Record Gate: 300 Beaconsfield Utd v Chesham Utd, Berks & Bucks Sen Cup 1985
BEST SEASON: **FA Cup:** 3rd Q Rd 98-998 **FA Vase:** Beaconsfield: 1st Rd 83-84 85-86 87-88

FACT FILE
Founded: 1994 Nickname: SYCOB
Colours:Red & white quarters/black/red & white
Change colours: Blue with grey stripe
Midweek Matches: Monday or Tuesday
Reserves' League: Suburban
Programme: Yes, £1
Editor: Andy Jackson, 7 Boundary Lane, Chipperfield Rd., Bovingdon, Herts.HP3 0JT
Tel No: 01442 834203

CLUB PERSONNEL
President: D Piercy
Chairman: Fred Deanus
Manager: Simon Delahunty

BEDFORD UNITED

Secretary: Jim McMullen,7 Buttermere Close, Kempston, Bedford MK42 8JU(01234 300765)
GROUND: McMullen Park, Meadow Lane, Cardington, Bedford MK45 3SB (01234 831024)

Directions: M1 jct 13, A421 to Bedford by-pass. Third exit, A603 ground 500 yards on left
Capacity: 5,000 Seats: 25 Cover: 100 Floodlights: Yes
Clubhouse: Open matchdays. Hot & cold snacks and drinks available

HONOURS: Bedford & Dist Lg Premier Division & Division One, County Junior Cup, Biggleswade KO Cup, Butchers Cup(2), Britania Cup, Bedford Charity Cup
PREVIOUS: **Leagues**: Bedford & Dist. Lge (57-70 & 80-89); United Cos. Lge 70-80
Name: Printers Diemer-Reynolds (pre'72)
Grounds: Allen Park (57-80); Fairhill, Clapham Road (80-93); Hillgrounds, Kempston 93-96)

RECORD: Attendance: (at Fairhill) 1500 v Bedford Town, South Midlands Lge Div. 1 26/12/92
Scorer: Neil Tysoe 220 **Appearances:** Simon Fordham 418

Founded: 1957 Nickname: United
Club Sponsors: JDP Finance
Colours: Blue & White/blue/blue
Change colours: Red & black/red/red
Midweek matches: Wednesday
Reserves' League: S. Mids Lge Res. sect
Programme: 24 pages, £1
Editor: Graham Williams (01234 312 982)

Chairman: John Cleverley
Vice Chairman/Press Off Jim McMullen
President: D Rostron
Manager: Cliff Canavan -Smith
Asst. Man.: M Ackroyd
Coach/Physio: Dave Petrie

BIGGLESWADE TOWN

Secretary: Graham Arkwright, 21 Willsheres Rd, Biggleswade, Beds SG18 0BU
Tel: 01767 221574
GROUND: `Fairfield', Fairfield Road, Biggleswade, Beds (01767 312374).
Directions: A1 North r'bout, left immediately after bridge into car park.
10 mins walk from Biggleswade (BR).
Capacity: 2,400 Seats: 50 Cover: 100 Floodlights: Yes Club Shop: No.
Clubhouse: Open all matchdays. , teas, coffees, snacks.
HONOURS:S Mids Lge: Res Div 2 87-88, Res Chall Trophy 88-89, S.M. Floodlit Cup 95-96; Beds Snr Cup 02-03 07-08 46-47 51-52 61-62 62-63 66-67 73-74; Beds Premr Cup 22-23 27-28; N. Beds Charity Cup x13; Utd Co's Lg Cup 73-74; Hinchingbrooke Cup 03-04 12-13 92-93 Hunts Prem Cup 92-93 93-94(joint)00-01 94-95 97-98; Jess Piggott Trophy 87-88 89-90 91-92 92-93
PREVIOUS: Leagues: Biggleswade & Dist. 02-20; Bedford & Dist. 09-12; Utd Co's (prev. Northants Lg) 20-39 51-55 63-80; Spartan 46-51; Eastern Co's 55-63 **Name:** Biggleswade F.C.
RECORD: **Attendance:** 2,000

FACT FILE
Founded: 1874 Nickname: Waders
Club Sponsors: Mantles Ford & LetchworthCouriers
Colours: green/navy/green
Change:orange/black/black
Midweek Matchday: Tuesday
Programme: 32 pages, admission
Editor: Brian Doggett (01767 318307 (H).

CLUB PERSONNEL
Chairman:M.Dorrington V. Chair:M Jarvis
President: R Dorrington
Manager: David Northfield Physio: A.Wellings
2000-01 Captain: Mark Winwood P.o.Y.: Jack Rashid, Top Scorer: Danny Lane 19

BRACHE SPARTA

Secretary: Roy Standring, 37 Taunton Avenue, Luton, Beds. LU2 0LN. Tel: 01582 736574

GROUND: Foxdell Sports Ground, Dallow Rd, Luton LU1 1UP (01582 720751).
Directions: From M1 jct11, take A505 towards Luton. Right at Chaul End roundabout. Across A505 keep B&Q on left, into Dallow Rd. Ground 50 yds on right by Foxdell junior school.
Capacity: 400 Cover: 100 Seats: 25 Floodlights: Yes Club Shop: No
Clubhouse: Open daily 12-3 & 7.30-11. Light snacks & refreshments etc available

HONOURS: South Mids Lg R-up 92-93, 96-97 (Div 1 R-up 83-84 87-88), Lg Cup R-up 75-76 80-81 92-93 97-98, Premier Div Cup Winners 97-98 R-up 91-92, Res Div 2 R-up 75-76, Res Cup R-up 87-88; Luton & Dist. Lg 67-68 69-70 70-71 71-72; William Pease Trophy 66-67 67-68 70-71 71-72; Beds Interm Cup 71-72 (R-up 68-69 70-71), BedsJnr Cup 82-83; Leighton Challenge Cup R-up 69-70 South Mids Lg Prem Div 1 North Champions 97-98, Beds Premier Cup R-up. 97-98

PREVIOUS: **League:** Luton & Dist **Grounds**: Crawley Green Rd, (public park); Hitchin Town FC (share 93-94) **RECORD Attendance :**320

FACT FILE
Founded: 1960
Nickname: The Foxes
Club Sponsors: A & E Engineering
Colours: White/navy/white
Change Colours: All royal
Midweek matches: Tuesday
Prog: 32 pages, £2.50 (incl. admission)
Career Record Goalscorer: Keith Denness

CLUB PERSONNEL
Chairman: Roy Standring **President:** Doug Smith **Manager:** Steve Brinkman
Physio: Chris Garner
Captain: Mark Smith P.o.Y.: Stuart Strange
2000-01Top Scorer: Tommy Doyle 15

BROOK HOUSE

Secretary: Barry Crump, 19 Bradenham Road, Hayes, Middlesex UB4 8LP. Tel: 0208 841 3959 (H), 0966 468029 (B)

Ground: Farm Park, Kingshill Avenue, Hayes, Middlesex (0208 842 1448)
Directions: From North Circular road: A40 Western Ave. to Target r'about, left towards Hayes (A312), over White Hart r'about towards Yeading/Hayes, right at traffic lights in to Kingshill Ave, ground 1 mile on right. Nearest BR stationis Hayes & Harlington, then bus 90 or 195 to Brook House pub. Nearest tube is Northolt (central line), then bus to ground
Capacity: 2,000 Cover: 100 Seats: 120 Floodlights: Yes Club Shop: No
Clubhouse: Open weekdays 7-11pm, Sat noon-11pm, Sun noon-11.00pm

HONOURS: SSM Prem South 97-98, Prem Div R-Up 99-00, Lge Cup 99-00 R-up 91-92.
BEST SEASON: **FA Vase:** 3rd Round Proper 97-98 **FA Cup:** 1st Qual Rd 93-94
Players progressing: Neil Shipperley (Crystal Palace), MarkHyde (Orient), Mark Perry (QPR) David Warner (To Watford for £10,000) and Anthony Charles (To Crewe Alexandrafor £6,000)

FACT FILE
Founded: 1974
Colours: Blue & white stripes/blue/blue
Change colours: All yellow
Midweek matchday: Tuesday
Reserve League: Midd'sex Co Lg
Programme: 28 pages, £3 with entry
Editor: Andrew Gavin (020 8581 8715)

CLUB PERSONNEL
President: Victor Kirby
Chairman: Mick Ralph
Vice-Chairman: JohnHandell
Press Officer: Lawrie Watts
Manager: Mick Harvey Ass Man: B Strutton
Coach: R Leather

DUNSTABLE TOWN

Chairman: Ian Tompkins

Secretary: Colin Howes, 3 Rotherwood Close, Dunstable, Beds LU6 1UA Tel: 01582 478395

Ground: Creasey Park, Brewers Hill Rd, Dunstable

Directions: Travel north on A5, Through centre Dunstable, left at 1st r/about into Brewers Hill Rd, str over mini r/about, grd on right

FACT FILE

Colours:
Blue & white stripes/blue/blue & white

Change Colours:
Red & black hoops/black/red & black

Programme Editor:
Paul Reeves: 0961 951103

HANWELL TOWN

Secretary: John Wake, 38 Warwick Ave., S Harrow, Middx. HA2 8RD. Tel/Fax: 0208 422104822 1048 (H)
GROUND: Reynolds Field, Perivale Lane, Perivale, Greenford, Middx (0181 998 1701)
Directions: A40(M) west from London, leave opp Hoover building (B456 for Ealing), turn left into Argyle Rd, left into Perivale Lane. Grd on left. 500 yards from Perivale tube station (Central line)
Capacity: 2,000 Seats: 90 Cover: 200 Floodlights: Yes Club Shop: No
Clubhouse: Saturday matchdays 2-11pm, Tuesdays 6-11pm, Non-matchdays 7.30-11pm

HONOURS: Spartan Sen Lg R-up 98-99 83-84 (Lg Cup R-up 93-94, London Snr Cup 91-92 92-93 (R-up 93-94), Middx Charity Cup R-up 92-93, 99-00
PREVIOUS: **Leagues:** Dauntless Lge, Harrow, Wembley & District and Middlesex County
RECORDS: **Attendance:** 600 v Spurs, Floodlight opening October 1989
Scorer: Trevor Canoville **Appearances:** Phil Player, 20 seasons, 617 games
BEST SEASON: **FA Cup:** 3rd Rd Qual 97-98
2000-2001: **P.o.Y.:**Steve Smith **Captain:** Chris Beck **Top Scorer:** Keith Rowlands 32

FACT FILE
Founded: 1948 Nickname: The Town
Colours: Black & white stripes/black/black & white
Change colours: White with red trim
Midweek matchday: Tuesday
Reserves' League: S.S.M.Res Lg
Programme: 16 pages, with entry
Editor: Bob Fisher as below

CLUB PERSONNEL
Chairman/Press Officer: Bob Fisher
Tel: 0181 952 4142 (H) 0207 51 4954 (B)
President: Dave Iddiols
Patron: Stephen Pound MP
Manager: Ray Duffy

HARINGEY BOROUGH

Secretary: John Bacon, 7 Everett Close, West Cheshunt, Herts., EN7 6XD Tel: 01707 873187
GROUND: Coles Park, White Hart Lane, Tottenham N17 (020 88891415)
Directions: M25 to J.25 turn south on A10 approx 6 miles, over jnct with N. Circular Rd (A406) Turn R. at T.lght 1 mile into White Hart Lne grd approx 500yds on L. Bus W3 from Finsbury Park. Mainline & Under-grd stn to Northumberland Park mainline station passes grd can be boarded at Alexandra Palace or White Hart Ln. Mainline stations or Wood Green Underground station.
Capacity: 2,500 Seats: 280 Cover: Yes Floodlights: Yes
Clubhouse: Open 7 days a week
HONOURS: FA Amat Cup 19-20; London Sen Cup 12-13, 90-91; Athen Lge 13-14; Div 2 67-68, 68-69; Spartan S. Mids Prem Div 97-98
PREVIOUS: **Leagues:** London 07-14; Isthmian 19-52 84-88; Spartan 52-54; Delphian 54-63; Athenian 63-84
Names: Edmonton; Tufnell Park; Tufnell Park Edmonton; Edmonton & Haringey

FACT FILE
Colours: Green/black/green
Change colours: All Yellow
Midweek Matchday: Tuesday
Reserves League - London Intermediate
Programme Editor: As Secretary

CLUB PERSONNEL
Chairman: Peter Lawlor Tel: 020 8889 2726
Match Secretary : As Secretary

2000-01
Captain: Ian Thurlow

Hanwell Town

Holmer Green FC at Adams Park after winning the Wycombe Senior Cup for the fifth time. Back Row (l-r): Ray Paton (Physio), Jason Quincey, Mel Nwanguma, Richard Dryden, Kevin Blunt, Stuart Glennister, Damian Roscoe, Dave Raleigh (Coach), Steve Ellis, Bo Ivers. Front Row: Stuart Moffat, Andy Duncan, Luke Foulkes, Shaun Martin, Kevin King, Jez Hodges, Brian Stottor, Mark Earaday, Mark Chisholm.

Potters Bar Town. Back Row (l-r): Scott Walton, Steve Hurd (Asst Manager), Ryan Harris, Chris Griggs, John Leahy, Alan Wilkinson, Leon Archer, Jamie Dickie, Jon Meakes (Manager). Front Row: Gary Barth (Capt), Neil Jordan, Matt Chalkley, Andy Martin, Carl Ashton, Brian Simpson (Coach), Steve Smart. Photo: Gordon Whittington

HILLINGDON BOROUGH

Secretary: Garry Grant, 19 Leveret Close,Leavesden, Watford, herts WD2 7AX
Tel Nos: 01923 463602 (H) 0958 409678 (W)
GROUND: Middlesex Stadium, Breakspear Road, Ruislip, Middx HA4 7SB (01895 639544)
Website: www.hillingdonboroughfc.uk.co **E-mail:** alanhbfc@hotmail.com

Directions: From A40 take B467 (signed Ickenham), left at 2nd r'bout into Breakspear Rd South, right after 1 mile by Breakspear pub - ground half mile on left. Nearest station is Ruislip. Bus U1 passes ground
Capacity: 1,500 Seats: 150 Cover: 150 Floodlights: Yes Club Shop: No
Clubhouse: Mon-Fri 7.30-11pm, Sat & Sun lunchtime & 7.30-11.00pm

RECORDS: **Win:** 12-0 v Hanwell T. (H), S.S.M. Prem 97/98
Defeat: 1-11 v St. Albans City (A), FA Cup 2nd Qual. Rd. 24.9.94
Transfer Fee Received: ¨1,000 for Craig Johnson (Wealdstone)
Top goalscoer 2000-01: Andy McCulloch - 18 **Captain:** Kevin Ford **P.o.Y:** Mark Donnelly

FACT FILE
Founded: 1990 Nickname: Boro
Sponsors: Airport Motor Radiator Co
Colours: White/blue/blue
Change colours: All red
Midweek Matches: Tuesday
Reserves' League: Suburban
Programme: 20 pages Editor/Press Off: Alan Taylor (0181 581 0981)

CLUB PERSONNEL
Chairman: Dhally Dhaliwall
Commercial Mgr: Garry grant
Manager: Steve Hawkins
Asst Man.: Ian Lancaster
Physio: Dave Pook

HODDESDON TOWN

Secretary: Brenda Timpson, 82 Tolmers Rd,Cuffley, Herts EN6 4JY (01707 874028)
GROUND: `Lowfield', Park View, Hoddesdon, Herts (01992 463133)
Directions: A10, A1170 into Hoddesdon, over 1st r'about, right at 2nd r'aboutand follow signs to Broxbourne, keeping to the left. Turn right at 1st @mini r-about into Cock Lane and 1st right is Park View. Ground 200yds on the left,entrance opposite Park Rd. BR station is Broxbourne
Capacity: 3,000 Seats: 100 Cover: 250 Floodlights: Yes Club Shop: Scarves,badges,hats &pens
Clubhouse: Bar and well-stocked Tea Bar with hot food. Open at every home game
HONOURS: FA Vase 74-75 (1st winners); S.S.M. Lg Prem Div Plate 97-98 (R-up 96-97, SthMids Lge Lg Cup 85-86 86-87 91-92 (Prem Div Tphy R-up 92-93); Spartan Lg 70-71(R-up(3) 71-74), Div 1 35-36, Div 2 `B' 27-28, Lg Cup(2) 70-72;
PREVIOUS: **Lges:** East Herts 1896-1908, 11-21; Herts Co. 08-25; N Middx Dist 10-22; Spartan 25-75; London Spartan 75-77; Athenian 77-84; South Midlands 84-97
RECORDS: **Attendance:** 3,500 v West Ham, (Floodlight opening friendly), 1975
BEST SEASON: **FA Vase:** Winners 74-75

FACT FILE
Founded: 1879 Nickname: Lilywhites
Colours: White/black/black
Change Colours: All yellow
Midweek matchday: Tuesday
Reserves' Lge: Essex/Herts Border Com
Programme: 100 + pages £1.00
Editor: Mrs Jane Sinden Tel: 01767 631297Fax: 01767 631562

CLUB PERSONNEL
Pres: Peter Haynes Chairman: Roger Merton
Manager: Paul Surridge Gen Man: Jim Briggs
Coach: Don Nicholson
00-01 Capt: Jeff Cross P.o.Y.: Richard Howard
Top Scorer: Richard Howard & Barry White

HOLMER GREEN

Secretary: Stuart Moffat, 40 Broughton Avenue, Aylesbury HP20 1NH
GROUND: Watchet Lane, Holmer Green, High Wycombe (01494 711485)
Directions: From Amersham on A404 High Wycombe Road, after approx 2 miles turn right into Sheepcote Dell Road. Continue until end of road by Bat & Ball PH.Turn right then immediate left, continue approx 1/2 mile until 2 mini roundabouts, turn left in front of the Mandarin Duck into Watchet Lane. The ground is 150 yards on the right
Capacity: 1,000 Seats: 25 Cover:Yes Floodlights:Yes Club Shop:No
Clubhouse: Saturdays 12pm -11 pm midweek 7pm 11pm Badges: Yes (£3)
HONOURS: Berks & Bucks Sen Tr.Finalists 98-99, BB Jun Cup Winners 52-53, 63-64 B&B Inter'iate Cup Winners 76-77; S.Mid Sen Div Winners (2), S.Mid Sen Cup Winners 96-97
Additional Honours: Cheshm Charity Cup Winners (6),Wycombe Sen Cup Winners: (5),Wycombe Lg Winners (4) and Lg Cup Winners 80-8181 Chiltonian League Winners: (3) Lg Cup Winners 94-95, Spartan South Midlands Sen Div Cup Winners: 97-98
PREVIOUS Leagues: 1908--34 Chesham. 34-84 Wyc Comb. 84-95 Chiltonian 95-98 S Mids

FACT FILE
Founded: 1908
Colours: Green & White/ Green/Green
Change colours: All blue
Midweek Matchday: Tuesday (7.45)
Prog: Yes - Inc.Admission
Club Website: www.hgfc1908@freeserve.co.uk

2000-01
Captain & Top Scorer: Shaun Martin 18
P.o.Y.: Jason Quyincey

CLUB PERSONNEL
President: John Anderson
Chairman: Bill Scholes 01494 713867 (H)
Match Secretary: T.B.A. Manager JezHodges

LETCHWORTH

Secretary: Jackie Northcutt, 126 Baldock Road, Letchworth, Herts. SG6 2EL (01462 632637)
Ground: Baldock Road, Letchworth, Herts SG6 2GN (01462 637979)
Directions: Jct 9 (A6141) off A1M straight over large r-about, right at next r-about, ground on right. From Luton (A505) thru Hitchin, ground 3 miles afterHitchin. 2 miles from Letchworth (BR)
Capacity: 3,200 Cover: 400 Seats: 200 Floodlights: Yes Clubhouse: No:
HONOURS: Herts Lg 11-12, Spartan Lg 29-30 35-36 51-52, Delphian Lg 57-58, Athenian Lg 74-75 (Mem. Shield 65-66 66-67), Herts Snr Cup 12-13 35-36 51-52, Herts Charity Shield 22-23 47-48 87-88 91-92, East Anglian Cup 76-77, Woolwich Cup 81-82, Hitchin Cup 81-82
Senior DivisionTrophy Winners: 99-00
PREVIOUS: **Leagues:** Herts Co. 06-07; Biggleswade 07-08; Nth Herts 08-22 , S Mids 22-23 24-29; Spartan 29-56; Athenian 63-77; Isthmian 77-90
Names: Garden City; Letchworth Ath.; Letchworth Town
Grounds: Letchworth Corner; Garth Rd; Cashio Lane
Players progressing to Football League: Imre Varadi, Keith Larner

FACT FILE
Founded: 1906
Nickname: Bluebirds
Colours: All Blue
Change Colours: Red & black/black/black
Midweek matchday: Tuesday
Programme:24 pages,50p
Editor: Nigel Crow
Email: info@letchworthfc.co.uk

CLUB PERSONNEL
Chairman: Graham Hopkins
Match Sec.: T.B.A.
Manager: Kerry Dixon

LONDON COLNEY

Secretary: Dave Brock, 50 Seymour Rd., St Albans, Herts. AL3 5HW. Tel: 01727 761644 (H)

Ground: Cotslandswick, London Colney (01727 822132)
Directions: From London Colney r'bout (junction of A414/A1081) take A414 towards Watford, after layby (300yds) turn left (hidden turning marked `SportsGround') and follow around to gates.
Capacity: 1,000 Cover: 100 Seats: 30 Floodlights: Yes Club Shop:
Clubhouse: Open after games. Hot food available

HONOURS Sth Mids Lg Sen Div 94-95 R-up 93-94 (Chall. Tphy 93-94, Div 1 R-up 92-93, Res.Div 1 92-93), Herts Co. Lg 56-57 59-60 86-87 88-89 (R-up 57-58 58-59). Aubrey Cup 21-22 22-23 56-57 58-59 81-82, Res. Div 1 87-88 88-89 89-90 91-92, Res. Cup 62-63 89-90 91-92 (R-up 70-71)

PREVIOUS **Leagues:** Mid Herts 1907-54; Herts Co. 07-92
Ground: Whitehorse Lane 07-75
Record Attendance: 300 v St Albans City. Herts Senior Cup 98-99

FACT FILE
Founded: 1907 Nickname: Blueboys
Sponsors: City Glass
Colours: All Royal blue
Change Colours: Yellow/ & black/black/yellow
Midweek Matchday: Tuesday
Programme: £1 with entry
Editor: Bill Gash (01727 767556)

CLUB PERSONNEL
Chairman: Bill Gash
Vice Chairman: P Light
President: K.Parsons
Manager: Mick Wright
Physio: J Burt

MILTON KEYNES CITY

Secretary: Peter Baldwin,1 Wantage Close, Hackleton,Nirthants NN7 2AG (01604 870457 (H) 01908 245408 (W) FAX 01908 245088 (Fax at Work)
Ground: Wolverton Park,Old Wolverton Rd.,Wolverton,Milton Keynes MK12 5QH(01908 318317)
Directions: From A5 trunk road exit at Milton Keynes North onto Great Monks Way (V5). Continue over two oundabouts onto Old Wolverton Road. Ground is 1 milwe on right, between two railway arches and next to Wolverton BR station.p
Capacity: 3000 Cover: Yes Seats: 150 Floodlights: Yes Club Shop: No
Clubhouse: On ground and open normal opening hours.Closed Mondays
HONOURS: North Bucks Lge - Div 1 90-91, Prem. Div Cup 92-93, I'mediate Tphy 91-92; Daimler-Benz Austrian International Tournament R-up 1990
S.S.M.Lg Trophy Winners 99-00 **Previous Name:** Mercedes - Benz F.C.
PREVIOUS: **Leagues:** Milton Keynes Sunday/ North Bucks & District (pre'93)
RECORD **Scorer:** Stuart Collard 132 **Appearances:** Stuart Collard 206
Win: 24-2 v Milton Keynes Saints, Berks & Bucks Jun Cup 1st Rd 16/10/93
Defeat: 1-8 v Greenleys, Milton Keynes Sun Lge Cup 1st Rd 22/11/87

FACT FILE
Founded: 1967 Nickname: Blues or City
Sponsors: Wright Tile Centre
Colours: All Royal Blue
Change Colours: Old Gold/Black/Old Gold
Midweek matches: Tuesday
Reserves' league: S.S.M. Reserve Div
Programme: 25 pages,£1.00
Editor: Stuart Collard, 01908 505042 (H), 01908 600394 (B)

CLUB PERSONNEL
Chairman: Bob Flight. President: T.B.A. Manager & Assistant T.B.A. Physio: Andy Nicholls Captain: Mark McCarthy Top Scorer: Darren Lynch (16). P.o.Y.: T.B.A.

NEW BRADWELL St PETER

Secretary: Les Smith,25 Bishopstone,Bradville, Milton Keynes. MK13 7DQ (01908 315736)
Ground: Recreation Ground, Bradwell Road, New Bradwell, Milton Keynes MK13 7AT
Tel.: 01908 313835
Directions: From M1 Jnt 14 go towards Newport Pagnell, left at 1st r-about into H3 (A422 Monks Way). Over 5 r-abouts, right at 6th island into V6 (GraftonSt.), At 1st roundabout go right the way round (back on yourself) then take 1st left at mini-r'about turn left into Bradwell Rd. Go straight over next mini r'about. Ground immediately on left.
Capacity: Seats: 30 Cover: 100 Floodlights: Yes
Clubhouse: Members only (member can sign in 2 guests). Evenings & w/e mid day. No food.
HONOURS: Sth Mids Lg Div 1 76-77 83-84 Sen Div Champs 97-98, (Res Div 2 R-up 76-7), Berks& Bucks Senior Trophy Winners 1999-2000
PREVIOUS: **League:** North Bucks
Names: Stantonbury St James (predecessors were New Bradwell St James); Stantonbury St Peters (until merger with New Bradwell Corinthians in 1946)

FACT FILE
Founded: 1902
Nickname: Peters
Colours: All Maroon
Change: Amber/black/black.
Midweek matches: Tuesday
Programme: 32 pages, £3 with entry
Editor: Paul Smith 01908 550211 (H)

CLUB PERSONNEL
Chairman John Haynes President: J P Booden
Vice-Chairman: R.Creasey
Press Officer: P Smith
Managers:J. Gunn & E.Byrne
2000-01: Captain: gary Flinn
P.o.Y.: Chris Connell Top Scorer:Kevin Hyde

POTTERS BAR TOWN

Secretary: Jeff.Barnes,38 Pinewood Drive, Potters Bar, Herts EN6 2BD Tel/FAX: 01707 660445 Email Address: jibarnes@supanet.com **GROUND:** Parkfield, The Walk, Potters Bar, Herts EN6 1QN, 01707 654833
Directions: M25 jct 24, enter Potters Bar along Southgate Rd (A111), at 1st lights right into the High St (A1000), half mile left into The Walk, grd 200yds on right (opp. Potters Bar Cricket Club)
Capacity: 2,000 Seats: 150 Cover: 100 Floodlights: Yes Club Shop: No Contact Jeff Barnesfor details of pennants,badges, car stickers and hangers etc.
Clubhouse: Sat 12.30-11pm, Sun noon-5pm, Tues & Thurs 7.30-11pm, midweek matchnights
HONOURS: South Midlands Lge. - Prem. Div. 96-97, Plate 96-97; Herts. Sen. Co. Lge. -Prem. Div. 90-91, Div. 1 73-74, 81-82, Div. 2 68-69; North London Comb. - Prem.Div. 67-68, Div. 1 67-68, Div. 2 R-up 65-66;SSMLg R-up 98-99 Prem Div North R-up 97-98 ,SML Floodlight Cup 99-00
PREVIOUS: **Leagues:** Barnet & Dist. 60-65/ N London Comb. 65-68/ Herts Snr Co. 68-91
RECORD: **Attendance:** 4000 v Eastenders XI, 20.4.97. 387 v Barnet, f/light open93
Competitive: 268 v Wealdstone ,F.A.Cup 1998
BEST SEASON: **FA Vase:** 6th Rd 97-98

FACT FILE
Founded: 1960
Nickname: The Grace or The Scholars
Colours: Red & royal stripes/royal/royal
Blue & Yellow stripes/ryellow/yellow
Midweek matchday: Tuesday or Wednesday
Prog Ed: Jonathon Gooding (01483 420731)
Programme: 40pages, £1 and Website-
fotballnews.co.uk/clubs/20/2055/home.page

CLUB PERSONNEL
Chairman: Peter Waller V Chair: Alan Bolt
President: B Wright General Mger: L Eason
Manager: JohnMeakes. Coach:Steve Hurd
Physio: Brian Simpson **00-01** Top Scorer Lee Talbot Capt: Ryan Harris P.o.Y.: Neil Jord

Letchworth with manager Kerry Dixon (far left) celebrate after winning the League title. Photo: Gordon Whittington

Above: Dunstable Town. Back Row (l-r): Ryan Edwards, Mark Kefford, Mick Benham, Paul Turner, Tony Burgess, Darren Croft (Manager), Paul Taylor, Martin Lauder, Andy Judge, Lamine Mohammed Sylla. Front Row: Grant Carney, Craig Sanders (Capt), Andy Draper, Ryan Keebie, Steve Castleman, John Bell (Physio), Gary Capehorn. Photo: Arthur Evans

Right: Spartan South Midlands League President Bill Smith presents the Division One trophy to Pitstone & Ivinghoe skipper Gary Wray. Photo: Gordon Whittington

ROYSTON TOWN

Secretary/Press Officer: Elaine Phillips, 14 Roan walk, Royston, Herts SG8 9HT
Tel No: 01763 241041 (H)
GROUND: Garden Walk, Royston, Herts SG8 7HP (01763 241204).
Directions: FromBaldock, A505 to Royston bypass, right at 2nd island onto A10 towards London, 2nd left is Garden Walk; ground 100 yds on left.
Capacity: 4,000 Seats: 300 Cover: 300 Floodlights: Yes Club Shop: Yes
Clubhouse: Mon-Thurs 7-11, Fri 11-3 & 7-11, Sat 11-3 & 4-11, Sun 12-3.

HONOURS Herts Co. Lg 76-77 (Div 1 69-70 76-77); Sth Mids Lg R-up 79-80 (Div 1 78-79,Chall. Cup R-up 78-79;
PREVIOUS **Leagues:** Buntingford & Dist. 18-28; Cambs 28-50; Herts Co. 50-59 62-77; SthMids 59-62 77-84; Isthmian 84-94
RECORDS **Attendance:** 876 v Aldershot, 13/2/93
Scorer: Trevor Glasscock 289 (1968-82) **Appearances:** Fred Bradley 713
BEST SEASON **FA Cup:** 2nd Qual. Rnd 59-60, 0-9 v Barnet (A), 89-90, 0-3 V Bromley (A)

FACT FILE
Founded: 1875 Nickname: Crows
Res League: Essex & Herts Border Comb
Sponsors: ABA Consultants
Colours: White/black/black
Change colours: Red/white/white
Midweek Matches: Tuesday
Programme: 16 pages, 30p
Editor: Secretary

CLUB PERSONNEL
Chairman: Graham Phillips
Vice-Chairman: Bernard Brown
President: Alan Barlow
Manager: Gavin Head
Asst Mgr: S Salomone Physio: C Mardell

RUISLIP MANOR

Secretary: John Price, 1 Filey Way, Ruislip,Middlesex (01895 631933)
Ground: Grosvenor Vale, off West End Rd, Ruislip, Middx 01895 637487-office,676168-boardroom
Directions: A40 to Ruislip, turn off on A4180, right at r'bout into West EndRd, right into Grosvenor Vale after a 1 1/2 miles - ground at end. From RuislipManor station (Metropolitan Line) turn left out of station, then 1st right intoShenley Ave, 3rd left into Cranley Dr - ground 150 yds on left
Capacity: 3,000 Seats: 250 Cover: 600 Floodlights: Yes Club Shop: Yes
Clubhouse: Mon-Fri 12-3.30 & 5.30-11pm, Sat & Sun 12-3 & 7.30-10.30
HONOURS London Lg R-up 51-52 (Div 1 R-up 47-48), Isthmian Lg Div 2 R-up 92-93 (Associate Members Tphy 90-91), Athenian Lg Div 2 72-73, Middx Snr Cup SF (6), Middx Charity Cup R-up 90-91 95-96
PREVIOUS **Leagues:** Uxbridge 38-39; Middx Snr 39-46; London 46-58; Spartan 58-65; Athenian65-84; Isthmian 84-96
RECORDS **Attendance:** 2,000 v Tooting & Mitcham United, F.A. Amateur Cup 1962
Appearances: Chris Balls, 350 **Goalscorer:** Kevin Quinn, 76
BEST SEASON **FA Cup:** 4th Q Rd 90-91, 2-5 v Halesowen T (A) **F.A.Am.Cup:** 1st Rd 73-74

FACT FILE
Founded: 1938 Nickname: The Manor
Sponsors: Golf Course Management
Colours: Black & White/black/black
Change colours: Blue & yellow/blue/blue.
Midweek Matches: Monday
Reserve League: Suburban Lge (North)
Programme: 24 Price: 50p
Editor/ Press Off.: Chris Thomas
01895 636930

CLUB PERSONNEL
Chairman: David Stock
Vice Chairman: Craig Smith
Manager:Keith Chamberlain
Physio: Gary Strudwick

St MARGARETSBURY

Secretary: Ashley Ward, 1 Village Close, Hoddesdon, Herts. EN11 0GJ (01992 410386)
GROUND: Station Road, Stanstead St Margarets, Nr Ware, Herts (01920 870473)

Directions: Harlow/Chelmsford exit from A10 to A414, take B181 at Amwell roundabout after 300yds towards Stanstead Abotts, ground quarter mile on right. 300yds from St Margaretsbury BR station (Liverpool Str.-Hertford East line)
Capacity: 1,000 Seats: 60 Cover: 60 Floodlights: Yes Club Shop: No

Clubhouse: Bar open every evening 7.30-11, plus Sat 12-2, Sun 12-3. Bar snacks available
HONOURS: Herts Snr Cent Tphy 92-93; Herts Co. Lg Div 2 48-49, Div 3 78-79; Aubrey Cup 48-49 71-72; Res. Div 1 82-83 86-87; Res. Cup 84-85 86-87 87-88); Waltham &Dist Lg 46-47; Spartan Lge 95-96; Roy Bailey Mem Trophy 95-96, Herts Charity Shield 97-98.
PREVIOUS: Lges: East Herts; Hertford & Dist.; Waltham & District 47-48; Herts Co. 48-92
RECORD: Attendance: 327 v Wisbech Town, FA Vase 3rd Round 14/12/85
BEST SEASON **FA Vase:** 3 Rd 1985

FACT FILE
Founded: 1894 Nickname: The Bury
Sponsors: Lawfords Building Supplies
Colours: Red & black/white/white
White/Black/Black
Midweek matchday: Tuesday
Reserve Lg: Essex & Herts Border Comb.
Programme: £3.00 with entry
Editor/Match Sec.: Jon Gooding
Tel:07931 191026

CLUB PERSONNEL
Chairman: Dave Stock
President: R L Groucott
Manager:Martin Gutteridge
Physio: John Elliott

SOMERSETT AMBURY V & E

Secretary: Peter Harris, 30 Lordship Road, Cheshunt, Herts. EN7 5DP
Tel : 01992 429297 (H) 0208 345 1133(W) **Email address:** savefc@fcmail.com
Ground: V & E Club, Goffs lane, Cheshunt, Herts. Tel: 01992 624281

Capacity: 500 Seats: 20 Cover: Yes Floodlights: Yes Club Shop: No

Directions: M25 junct. 25, A10 towards Cheshunt. Take the first left at the first roundabout onto the B198 (Cuffley & Goffs Oak). At the end of the road turn right off roundabout into Goffs lane. Clubhouse on immediate right. Open 11 a.m. 11 p.m. every day.

Previous League: Herts County

2000-01 Captain: Paul Kendall P.o.Y.: Sam Ledger Top Goalscorer: John Dixon 22

Club Website www.savefc.thesportcity.com

FACT FILE
Founded: 1959
Colours: White & blue/blue/blue
Change Colours: Orange/white/orange
Midweek Matchday: Tuesday
Reserves League; Essex ,Herts Border
Programme Editor: Peter Harris
01992 429297 (H) 0181 345 1133 (B)

CLUB PERSONNEL
Chairman:Dave Bidwell
Tel: 01992 428187 (H)
Vice Chairman:Mario Persico
President: Doug Bacon
Manager: Andy Leese
Assistant manager: David Craig

Langford FC. Back Row (l-r): Robert Cook, Jamie Endersby (Asst Mngr), Neil Dowse, Stuart Paul, Jason Wilson, Paul Nigro, Jim Burke (Manager), Colin Roy, Pat Monaghan (Physio), Brad Gillham. Front Row (l-r): James Davis, Dean Bawden, John Hislop, Mark Reed, Paul Damon, Liam Burke (Mascot), Steve Upton. Photo: Gordon Whittington

Walton Casuals. Back Row (l-r): Mark Sullivan (Joint Manager), Neil Campbell, Billy Mead, Dave Fry, Mark Hunter, Geoff Smyrk, Paul Roberts, Grant Woolger, Jamie Reive, Garry Clark (Joint Manager). Front Row: Chris England, Paul Suter, Graham Morrow, Spencer Collins, Lawrence Ennis, Rob Sparkes, Darren Jones (Physio). Photo: Arthur Evans

Welwyn Garden City. Back Row (l-r): Paul Taylor, Danny Milliken (Physio), Mark Anderson, Richard Evans, Nick Miles, Daniel Teixeira, Richard Woodham, Craig Attfield, Neil Conner, Jason Coughlan, Ray Greenall (Assistant Manager). Front Row: Neil Draper, Gregg Somerville, Dave Yeriman, Craig Joyce, Keiran Myles, Matt Kearney, Scott Cox (Capt.). Photo: Arthur Evans

AMERSHAM TOWN

Secretary: Michael Gahagan, 7 Ely Close, Lincoln Pk,Amersham,Bucks.HP7 9HS (01494 24798)
GROUND: Spratley's Meadow, School Lane, Old Amersham, Bucks. (01494 727428)
Directions: From London A413 to Amersham Old town, in front of market hall, right into Church St., first left into School Lane, ground on left past Mill Lane. 1 mile from Amersham Station - BR & underground Metropolitan Line
Capacity: 1,500 Seats: 50 Cover: 100 Floodlights: Yes Club Shop: No
Clubhouse: Open matchdays. Bar facilities. Teas, coffees and light snacks
HONOURS: Hellenic Lg 63-64 (R-up 64-65 65-66, Div 1 62-63, Cup 53-54), Ldn Spartan Lg R-up 79-80, St Marys Cup 89-90 96-97 (R-up 90-91,96-97), B & Bucks Jnr Cup 22-23 (Snr Cup SF 79-80 80-81), Wycombe Chal. Cup 23-24
2000-01 Captain: Trevor Dorrell ScorerToby Francis (7) P.o.Y. Chris Rouse

FACT FILE
Founded: 1890 Nickname: Magpies
Colours: Black & white stripes/black/black
Change colours: All Red
Midweek matches: Tuesday
Reserve's League: S.S Mids.
Prog. Editor: Michael Gahagan
CLUB PERSONNEL
Chairman: David Holdcroft
President: Graham Taylor
Manager: Paul Pitfield Coach: Richard Mount

AMPTHILL TOWN

Secretary: Eric Turner, 34 Dunstable Street, Ampthill, Beds MK45 2JT.
Tel:01525 403128 (H & B)

Ground: Ampthill Park, Woburn Road, Ampthill, Beds. Tel: 01525 404440

Directions: From Ampthill Town Centre follow signs to Woburn then take the first right into Ampthill Park

Chairman: Peter Foxall
Tel: 01525 755041
Manager: Nicholas Burton
Programme Editor: As Secretary
Colours: Yellow & navy blue/navy/navy
Change Colours: Green/black/black
2000-01
Leading goalscorer: Danny Giggs 14
Captain: Carl Page
P.o.Y.: James Slack

BIGGLESWADE UNITED

Secretary: Tracey James, 17 Havelock Road, Biggleswade, Beds SG18 0DB.
Tel: 01767 316270 (H), 020 7270 6045(B), 0771 466 1827(M)
GROUND: Second Meadow, Fairfield Road, Biggleswade, Beds. (01767 600408)
Directions: From A1 Sainsbury's roundabout, cross over iron bridge and take 2nd left into Sun Street.(before Peugot Garage) Take first left into Fairfield Road ground at bottom of road in lane
Capacity: 2,000 Seats: 30 Cover: 130 Floodlights: Yes Club Shop: No
Clubhouse: Open all matchdays, rolls available. Also refreshment hut with hot snacks
HONOURS: Hunts F.A. Prem Cup : 98-99,S.Mids Lg Div 1 96-97 Cup Winners 96-97Beds & District Prtem Div.94-95, 95-96, Div 1. 91-92, Div2 90-91,Div3 88-89 Beds F.A. Inter Cup (2)
Record Crowd: 250 v Biggleswade Town 28.12.98 **Previous Name:**Biggleswade F.C.
Best Season in F.A.Vase: 1st Rd Proper 95-96

Founded: 1959 (original club 1935)
Colours: Red & navy/navy/red
Change : Yellow & Black/black/yellow
Midweek Matchday: Tuesday /Thursday
Prog-With admission Editor: Secretary

Chairman: David McCormick.(01767 316018)
Match Sec.: Mick Brown, (01767 221512)
Manager: 'Snowy' Wright
Physio: Phil Lunceford

BRIMSDOWN ROVERS

Secretary: Mrs Lorraine Winter, 5 Sunnyside Road East, Edmonton, London N9 0SP (Tel & Fax: 020 8807 3666 and Mobile: 07747 681044) Email: lw@brfc.freeserve.co.uk
GROUND: Brimsdown Sports & Social Club, Goldsdown Road, Enfield, Middlesex Tel: 0181 804 5491 **Directions:** BR from Liverpool Street to Brimsdown (half mile away) or Southbury Road. By road off Green Street, itself off Hertford Road (A1010). Buses 191 or307
Capacity: 1,000 Seats: 25Cover: 50Floodlights: Yes Club Shop:
Clubhouse: Large lounge & clubroom, games room & stage. 3 bars (300 capacity)
HONOURS: Spartan Lg 92-93. Spartan Lg Cup 95-96
RECORD: **Gate:** 412 v Chesham Utd, FA Cup 3rd Qual. Rd 12/10/91
BEST SEASON: **FA Vase:** 3rd Rd 93-94 **FA Cup:** 3rd Qual. replay 91-92
PREVIOUS: **Leagues:** Northern Suburban **Names:** Durham Rovers; Brimsdown FC

FACT FILE
Founded: 1947
Colours: Black & white stripes/black/black
Change colours: Yellow/Blue/Yellow
Midweek Matchday: Tuesday
Programme: With admission
Editor: Peter Wade
Chairman: Tony Ashall
Match Secretary: Peter Wade.
5 Goldsdown Rd., Enfield Middlesex EN3
Tel: 0208 804 7053
Manager:Dave Farenden

COCKFOSTERS

Secretary: Graham Bint, 15 Chigwell Park, Chigwell, Essex IG7 5BE (0208 500 7369)
GROUND: Cockfosters Sports Ground, Chalk Lane, Cockfosters, Barnet (0208 449 5833)
Directions: M25 Jct 24 (Potters Bar), take A111 signed Cockfosters - ground 2 miles on right. Adjacent to Cockfosters underground station (Picadilly Line). Bus 298 to Cockfosters station
Capacity: 1,000 Seats: None Cover: 50 Floodlights: Yes Club Shop: No
Clubhouse: 7-11pm Tues & Thurs, 4-11pm Sat, 12-3pm Sun. Hot & cold food onmatchdays
HONOURS: London Interm Cup 70-71 89-90, Herts Snr Co. Lg 78-79 80-81 83-84 R-up 82-83 84-85, Aubrey Cup 78-79 84-85 R-up 70-71 77-78, Herts Interm Cup 78-79 R-up x3
Previous Leagues: Wood Green & Dist. 21-46/ Northern Suburban 46-66/ Herts Snr Co.66-91
BEST SEASON: **FA Vase:** 2nd Round 91-92
RECORDS: **Gate:** 408 v Saffron Walden, Herts Senior County Lg 68-69

Founded: 1921 Nickname: Fosters
Colours: All Red Change colours: All White
Midweek matches: Tuesday
Sponsors: T.S.I.Design
Programme: 12 pages with entry
Editor: A Simmons (0208 440 7998)
Chairman/Press Off.: Frank Brownlie
(0208 500 5930)
President: Les Langdale Manager: Tony Faulkner Physio: John Walsh
2000-01: Captain: Dave Finch . P.o.Y.: Duncan Field . Top Scorer: Danny Hutchings 18

COLNEY HEATH

Secretary: Ann Hutchins,15 Cobmead, Hatfield, Herts AL10 0JF
Tel: 01707 887078 (H) 01795 664978 (B) 07770 803603 (M)

Ground: The Pavillion Recreaton Ground, High St., Colney Heath, St. Albans, Herts.
Tel: 01727 826188

Directions: Turn off the A414 (was A405) into Colney Heath village and the ground is behind the school on the left.

Colours: Black & white stripes/black/black & white
Change cols: Tangerine & black/black/tangerine
Programme: Yes
Editor: Martin Marlborough
Tel: 07960 155463

Chairman: Martin Marlborough
Tel: 07960 155463
Manager: Geoff O'Vell
Tel: 07967 694257

GREENACRES (Hemel Hempstead)

Secretary: Hayley Smith, 437 Barnacres, Hemel Hempstead, Herts. HP3 8JS
Tel No: 01442 214739 (H) 01442 264300 (W)

Ground: Hemel Hempstead FC, Vauxhall Rd., Adeyfield, Hemel Hempstead.
Tel: 01442 259777

Directions: M1 J8; over two roundabouts, then first right off dual carriageway. First left and then right at roundabout

Capacity: 3,000 **Seats:** 100 **Cover:** Yes **Floodlight:** Yes **Club Shop:** No

Clubhouse: as for Hemel Hempstead F.C.

Colours:Green & white hoops/white/gren & white
Change Colours; All Red & White
Midweek Matchday: Wednesday
Programme: £1.00
Editor: William Cain

Chairman: David Boggins 01442 264300 (H)
Match Sec. David Lloyd 01442 259721 (H)
Manager: Paul Burgess

HAREFIELD UNITED

Secretary: Terry Devereux, 72 Williamson Way, Rickmansworth, Herts WD3 2GL.
Tel: 01923 711451 (H/B)
GROUND: Preston Park, Breakespeare Rd North, Harefield, Middx UB9 6DG (01895 823474)
Directions: M25 jct 16 to M40 East, left at 1st roundabout, then 2nd left into Harvill Rd. Follow road up the Church Hill into village, right at mini roundabout, ground on right. Denham (BR)
Capacity: 2,000 Seats: 100 Cover: Yes Floodlights: Yes Club Shop: No
Clubhouse: (01895 823474) Lunchtimes and evenings. Cold snacks (hot on matchdays)
HONOURS: Middx Premier Cup 85-86, Athenian Lg R-up 83-84, Parthenon Lg 64-65 (Div 1 Cup 65-66), Middx Lg 66-67 68-71 (Lg Cup 66-67 68-69)
BEST SEASON: **FA Cup:** 2nd Qual. Rd replay 80-81, 86-87 **F.A.Vase:** 6th Rd 1989-90
RECORD: **Gate:** 430 v Bashley, FA Vase

Founded: 1868 Nickname: Hares
Colours: Red & white stripes/black/red
Change colours: Yellow /green/yellow
Midweek Matches: Tuesday
Reserves' League: Suburban
Programme: 12-40 pages, 30p
Editor: Terry Deveraux (Sec.)

Chairman: Keith Ronald. Tel: 01895 824287
President: Dave West
Manager: Stuart Levy

HARPENDEN TOWN

Secretary: Neil Ludlow, 93 RussellSt.,Luton,Beds LU1 5EB 01582 486802(H) 01582 424233(W)
GROUND: Rothamsted Park, Amenbury Lane, Harpenden (01582 715724)
Directions: A1081 to Harpenden. Turn left/right at George Hotel into Leyton Rd.Turn left into Amenbury Rd, then left again (50yds) into `Pay and Display' carpark - entrance is signposted thru car park to opposite corner
Capacity: 1,500 Seats: 25 Cover: 100 Floodlights: Yes Club Shop: No
Clubhouse: Open matchdays
HONOURS: Sth Mids Lg 61-62 64-65, Ch'ship Shield 67-68, Lg Cup 70-71, Div 1 89-90, Prem Div Tphy 89-90; Mid-Herts Lg 09-10 20-21, Div 1 99-00; Herts Co. Lg 11-12 49-50 51-52 53-54
PREVIOUS: **Leagues:** Mid-Herts; Herts County **Best Seasons:** F.A.Cup: 1st Rd Q
Name: Harpenden FC 1891-1908 F.A.Vase: 2nd Rd

FACT FILE
Founded: 1891
Nickname: The Town
Colours: Yellow/blue/blue
Change:Red & Black Hoops/Black/Black
Midweek matches: Tuesday
Programme: 50pEditor: Chairman
CLUB PERSONNEL
Chairman: Stephen Whiting (01582 761606)
Manager: Martin Forsyth (07887 594687)
2000-01 Captain Simon Foster
Top Scorer: Mark Rainbow 14

KINGS LANGLEY

Secretary: Andy Mackness, 79 Weymouth Street, Apsley, Hemel Hempstead, Herts HP3 9SJ
Tel: 01442 398186 (H) 020 7587 4153 (B) 07976 692801 (M)

Ground: Gaywood Park, Hempstead Road, Kings Langley. Tel: 01923 264489

Directions: From M25 leave at Junction 20. Take A4251 to Kings Langley. The ground is approx. 1 mile on the right.

Colours: Black & white stripes/black/black
Change colours: All white
Programme: Yes
Editor: Adrian Marston Tel: 01923 893320 (H)

Chairman: Derry Edgar
Tel: 01923 268301 (H)

Manager: Colin Jones
Tel: 01442 394986 (H)

LANGFORD

Secretary: Frank Woodward, 4 West View, Langford, Biggleswade. Beds. SG18 9RT
Tel: 01462 701015 (H) Club Email: langfordfc@talk21.com
GROUND: Forde Park, Langford Road, Henlow SG16 6AF Tel: 01462 816106
Directions: Halfway between Langford and Henlow on A6001 Hitchin to Biggleswade road. Bus 177 on main Hitchin-Biggleswade route stops right outside ground
Capacity: 4,000 Seats: 50 Cover: 250 Floodlights: Yes Club Shop: Yes
Clubhouse: Weekday evenings, matchdays 11am-11pm, Sun 12-3pm. Hot food on matchdays
HONOURS: S Mids Lg 88-89 (Lg Cup 73-74 75-76, Prem. Div Tphy 88-89,94-95.O'Brien Div 1 Tphy 84-85), N Beds Charity Cup 27-28 30-31 69-70 75-76 86-87 92-93 94-95 98-99 Bedford & Dist. Lg 30-31 31-32 32-33, Bedford I'mediate Cup 68-69, Hinchingbrooke Cup 72-73
RECORD: **Gate:** 450 v Q.P.R., 75th Anniversary and clubhouse opening, 22/8/85

Founded: 1908 Nickname: Reds
Sponsors:The Codfather / The Boot Pub&Rest
Colours: All red with white trim
Change Colours: Blue & white
Midweek matches: Tuesday
Programme: With admission.
Editors: Bob Reed 01462 700155 (H)
Chairman: Mick Quinlan President: Ted Rutt
Com. Man: Diane Woodward Man: Roy Ryall
2000-01 Leading goalscorer: Mark Reed 15
Captain: Neil Dowse
P.o.Y.: Colin Roy

LETCHWORTH BRIDGER

Secretary: Mark Phillips, 72B Ickneild Way, Letchworth, Herts. SG6 4AT
Tel Nos: 01462 636862 (H) 07977 978426 (M)

Ground: Letchworth Corner Sports Club, Muddy Lane, Letchworth, Herts. SG6 3TB.
Tel: 01462 486459

Directions: A1(M) junc 9 towards Letchworth, over large roundabout, turn left at next roundabout A505 Hitchin, through lights, turn left at pelican crossing into Muddy Lane

Colours: Sky blue & yellow stripes/sky blue/ sky blue & yellow
Change Colours: All claret & blue.

Programme Editor: John Furness
Tel: 01462 627279 (H)

Chairman: Lawrence Bridger

Manager: Dean Cole

LEVERSTOCK GREEN

Secretary: Brian Barter, 11 Curlew Close, Berkhamsted, Herts HP4 2HZ (01442 862322)
GROUND: Pancake Lane, Leverstock Green, Hemel Hempstead. Tel: 01442 246280.
Directions: From M1 leave at A4147 to 2nd r-about. 1st exit to LeverstockGreen, Pancake Lane is on left 300 yrds past the `Leather Bottle' pub
Capacity: Seats: 25 Cover: 100 Floodlights: Yes Club Shop: Yes Clubhouse: Yes, one hour before kick-off but no food

HONOURS: South Midlands Lge - Sen. Div 96-97, Sen Div Cup R-up 93-94, Herts CentenaryTphy R-up 91-92, Herts Charity Shield R-up 91-92, Frank Major Tphy 1991
PREVIOUS: **Leagues:** West Herts (pre-1950); Herts County 50-91
Players progressing to Football League: Dean Austin (Tottenham Hotspur)

Founded: 1895 Nickname: The Green
Sponsor: Sunshine Cabs
Colours: Yellow/Blue/Blue
Change Colours: Green & black/white/black
Midweek Matchday: Tuesday
Prog: 24 pages, 50p Ed: Chairman
Chairman: Bill Dawes, 01442 395748 (H)
Match Sec: Brian Pollard 01442 256720 (H)
Press Officer: Brian Pollard
Manager:Brian Jackson Coach: Brian Howard
2000-01Captain & P.o.Y.: Matt Griffin
Top Goalscorer: Tony Sears 14

PITSTONE & IVINGHOE

Secretary: Jay Adlem, 22 Maud Janes Close, Ivinghoe, Leighton Buzzard. LU7 9ED.
Tel: 01296 668663 (H)

Ground: Pitstone Recreation Ground, Vicarage Road, Pitstone, Bucks Tel: 01296 661271

Directions: Tring Rd (B489) from Dunstable, turn right for Ivinghoe, and continue through to Pitstone r-about; ground left then right. From Aylesbury -left at `Rising Sun' in Aston Clinton, keep on that road to Pitstone r'bout; ground right then right.
Bus 61 from Luton or Aylesbury. Nearest BR stations are Tring or Cheddington.

Colours: Red & black/black/black
Change Colours:
Sky & navy stripes/navy/sky & navy hoops
Programme: Yes
Editor: Rob Adlem Tel: 01296 668663 (H)

Chairman: David Hawkins
Tel: 01296 661456
Manager: Ian Magill
Tel: 01908 639149

RISBOROUGH RANGERS

Secretary: Derrick J Wallace, 42 Ash Road, Princes Risborough, Bucks, HP27 0BQ
Tel: 01844 345179 (H), 01844 345435 (B)
GROUND: `Windsor', Horsenden Lane, Princes Risborough. (01844 274176)
Directions: Rear of Princes Risborough BR Station (Chiltern Line). A4010 fromAylesbury thru Princes Risborough, fork right onto A4009, left by thatched cottage, over railway bridge, immediate right ground 150 yds on right
Capacity: 2,000 Seats: 25 Cover: 100 Floodlights: No Club Shop: No
Clubhouse: Yes. Snacks available matchdays
HONOURS: Berks & Bucks Jnr Cup 85-86, Wycombe & Dist Lg D 2 85-86 D 3 84-85
PREVIOUS: **League:** Wycombe & Dist. 71 -
RECORD: **Gate:** 1,200 v Showbiz XI **Scorer:** Craig Smith

Founded: 1971
Club Sponsors: Systems 3R
Colours: Red & white/black/red
Change Colours: Blue & white/blue/white
Midweek matches: Tuesday
Programme: 20+ pages, £1 with entry
Editor: Richard Woodward
Chairman: Trevor Taylor
Tel: 01844 342202 (H)
Manager: Jon Franklyn

STONY STRATFORD TOWN

Secretary: Maurice J Barber, 26 Boundary Cres., Stony Stratford, Milton Keynes MK11 1DF Tel: 01908 567930 (H)
GROUND: Sports Ground, Ostlers Lane, Stony Stratford (01908 562267).
Directions: From Dunstable use old A5, Watling Street. Approaching Bletchley continue on A5 loop road (Hinkley) to end of dual c'way to A422/A508 r'bout. First exit, thru lights, 2nd right into Ostlers Lane.
Capacity: 600 Seats: 30 Cover: 120 Floodlights: Yes Club Shop: No
Clubhouse: Open evenings & weekends
HONOURS: Sth Mids Lg R-up 70-71 71-72 (Div 1 93-94, Div 1 Cup 93-94)
PREVIOUS: **Leagues:** North Bucks & Dist.; Northampton Combination
RECORD: **Attendance:** 476 v Aston Villa U21, floodlight opening 12.11.96

Reformed: 1953
Sponsor: Keypoint Developments Ltd.
Colours:Sky blue/navy/navy
Change Colours:All yellow
Midweek matches: Tuesday
Reserves' League: SSM Res. Div. One
Programme: 28 pages, £2.00 (Incl. entrance)
Editor: Paul Grimsley Chairman: Mike Judd
Mtch Sec.:Mrs. E. Sartain Man:Chris Johnson
2000-01 Leading goalscorer: Paul Sloley 34
Captain: Brendan Quill
P.o.Y.: Darren Long

THE 61 FC

Secretary: Richard Everitt, 44 Somersby Close, Luton LU1 3XB. Tel: 01582 485095 (H)

Ground: Kingsway, Beverley Road, Luton, Beds. 01582 582965

Directions: M1 jct 11, A505 to Luton centre, right at 1st island, 1st left, Beverley Rd is 3rd left, entrance in Beverley Rd, exactly 1 mile junction 11.All Luton to Dunstable buses pass ground - alight at Beech Hill Bowling Club. 1mile from both Leagrave & Luton BR stations

Colours: Sky blue/royal blue/royal
Change Colours: Red & white/black/red
Programme: Yes
Editor: Richard Everitt Tel: 01582 485095

Chairman: Mark Davis
Tel: 01582 416011
Manager: Richard Everitt
Tel: 01582 485095 (H)

TRING ATHLETIC

Secretary: Ralph Griffiths, 42 Bedgrove, Aylesbury, Bucks HP21 7BD.
Tel: 0129626425 (H), 01296 393363 x 278 (B)
Ground: Miswell Lane, Tring, Herts. (01442 828331) **Directions:** Through Tring on main rd towards Aylesbury, right after Anchor PH into Miswell Lane, grd 500yds on right opposite Beaconsfield Rd. Tring station is several miles outside town, grd by bus ortaxi
Capacity: Seats: 25+ Cover: 100+ Floodlights: No Club Shop: No
Clubhouse: Bar, open matchdays, training nights & Sunday lunchtimes
HONOURS: West Herts Lg R-up 72-73 (Lg Cup 65-66, Div 1 61-62 64-65 65-66 (R-up 71-72 85-86), Div 2 (res) 71-72 (R-up 62-63), Div 3 R-up 83-84, Reserve Cup 72-73,
PREVIOUS: **League:** West Herts 58-88
RECORD **Scorer:** Ian Butler **Appearances:** Alan Sheppard

Founded: 1958 Nickname: Athletic
Sponsors: Heygates
Colours: Red & black/black/black
Change colours: yellow/green/yellow
Midweek matchday: Wednesnay
Programme: 36 pages, 50p Editor: Sec
President: Ralph Griffiths
Chairman: S Thomas Tel: 01442 381633 (H)
Manager: Mick Eldridge
Asst Manager: Ray Brimson
Physio: Jean Adams

WELWYN GARDEN CITY

Secretary: James Bruce, 6 Autumn Grove, Welwyn G.C., Herts AL7 4DB. Tel: 01707331048 (H)
GROUND: Herns Lane, Welwyn Garden City (01707 328470)
Directions: From A1 follow signs for industrial area. Take one-way systemopposite Avdel Ltd (signed Hertford B195), take 2nd exit off one-way system.Ground 400 yards on left. One and a half miles from Welwyn GC (BR)
Capacity: 1,500 Seats: 40 Cover: 120 Floodlights: Yes Club Shop: Yes
Clubhouse: Open every night and weekend lunchtimes. Members Bar, Hall.Steward:Gary Bevan
HONOURS: Herts Snr Centenary Tphy 84-85 (R-up 88-89), Herts Charity Shield 27-28 86-8787-88 94-95 (R-up 48-49), Sth Mids Lg 73-74 (R-up 85-86, Div 1 69-70 81-82, LgCup R-up 74-75 81-82 88-89, Reserve Cup 85-86)
PREVIOUS: **Leagues:** Spartan; Metropolitan; Gtr London. **Ground:** Springfields

Founded: 1921 Nickname: Citizens
Colours: Maroon & blue/blue/maroon
Change Colours: All white
Midweek Matches: Tuesday
Programme: 24 pages, 50p
Editor: Dave Fallon 01438 235701
Local Press: Welwyn & Hatfield Times,
Welwyn & Hatfield Herald & Post
Chairman: Terry Hazel
Manager: David Steedman
Assistant Manager: Ray Greenhall
Physio: Danny Milliken

WINSLOW UNITED

Secretary: David F Ward, 28 Park Road, Winslow, Buckingham MK18 3DL.
Tel: 01296713202 (H), 01865 781210 (B)

Ground: Recreation Ground, Elmfields Gate, Winslow, Bucks. Tel: 01296 713057

Directions: A413 from Aylesbury to Winslow, in High Street turn right into Elmfields Gate, ground on left opp. car park.A421 from Milton Keynes to Buck'ham then thro 'Gt Horwood

Colours: Yellow/blue/yellow
Change colours: Green & white/green/green
Programme: Yes
Editor: David Ward Tel: 01296 713202

Chairman: Jeff Robins
Tel: 01280 814974 (H)

Manager: Peter Miller
Tel: 01908 367832 (H)

The 61 FC. Back Row (l-r): R Everitt (Manager), A Hughes, N Abraham, S Kent, S Wooley, N Tattersall, J Fox, R Peake, M Robinson, L Turney. Front Row: S Simon, I Thomas, M Sapsford, I Dickson, L Kelley< G Perry, D Atkinson. Photo: Martin Wray

Leverstock Green. Back Row (l-r): M Treadwell (Asst Manager), J Milton, S Garnham, S Kempson, J Peppatt, G Woolf, W Cogswell, M Griffin, T Perry, B Jackson (Manager). Front Row: B Chapman (Physio), A Phillips, J Lane, D Fisher, T Sears, C Hewitt, J Juster, J Copson

Winslow FC. Back Row (l-r): P Mcguinis, J Callaghan, D O'Cornnor, N Brown, K Elorid, K Horsler, A Coates, M Swieroski, G Freshwater. Front Row: G Robbins, P Talbot, R Morgan, S Taverner, R Craig, L Boulsh. Photo: Martin Wray

ABBEY NATIONAL (M.K.)

Secretary: Clare O'Connor, 18 Cranwell Close,Shenley Brook End, Milton Keynes MK5 7BU (01908 520370)

Ground: Loughton Sports & Social Club, Lincesdale Grove, loughton, Milton Keynes. Tel: 01908 690668

Directions: From M1 Jct 14 follow H6, Childs Way for 5 miles until V4 Watling Way (Knowlhill r-about), right to Loughton r-about, right along H5 Portway 1st right Linceslade Grove

BUCKINGHAM ATHLETIC

Secretary: Neil Holman, 3 Chandos Close, Buckingham, Bucks. MK18 1AW (o1280 815539)

Ground: Stratford Fields, Stratford Rd, Buckingham Tel: 01280 816945

Directions: From Milton Keynes take the A422 Stony Stratford-Buckingham road -ground on left just before town centre. From Oxford, Aylesbury or Bletchley, take the ring road to the A422 Stony Stratford roundabout, turn left, theground is situated at the bottom of the hill on the left

CADDINGTON

Secretary: Dave Mark, 7 Heathfield Close, Caddington, Luton, Beds. LU1 4HD Tel: 01582 421404 (H) 01797 147968 (B)

Ground: Caddington Recreation Club, Manor Road, Caddington (01582 450151)

Directions: On entering village turn into Manor Road (adjacent to shops andvillage green), proceed 500 metres: Clubhouse and ground on left side next to Catholic Church

CRANFIELD UNITED

Secretary: Ed Frost, 9 Pollys Yard, Newport Pagnell MK16 8YU (01908 210877)

Ground: Crawley Road, Cranfield (01234 751444)

Directions: Take north Crawley/Newport Pagnell road from Cranfield village and ground is on left before leaving speed limit signs.

CRAWLEY GREEN

Secretary: Alan Burgess, 23 Higham Drive, Luton LU2 9SP (01582 483172)

Ground: Crawley Green Recreation Ground, Crawley Green Road, Luton, Beds. 01582 451058

Directions: From M1 jct 10 , to roundabout at end of motorway slip road into Airport Way. At fourth roundabout turn right into Crawley Green Road. Ground is 1/2 mile on left past Ashcroft High School.

FLAMSTEAD

Secretary: Mark McGreevy, 3 White Hill, Flamstead, Herts. AL3 8DN (01582 841 481)

Ground: Flamstead Sports Assoc., Friendless Lane, Flamstead, St Albans, Herts(0582 841307)

Directions: From Dunstable Town Centre travel south on A5 Trunk Roadtowards the M1. Follow for approximately 3 miles then turn right oppositeHertfordshire Moat House Hotel. Ground and parking approximately half a mile onthe corner of the first right turn

HAYWOOD UNITED

Secretary: Lynne Nappin, 6 Evesham Green, Aylesbury, Bucks. HP19 9RX (01296 486924)

Ground: Stocklake Sports & Social Club, Haywards Way, Aylesbury, Bucks. Tel: 01296 423324

Directions: Follow signs to Bicester from Aylesbury ring road . At fifth road island, with Aylesbury Duck Public House on right ,turn right into Jackson Road and then second left into Haywood Way. Club is at bottom of the road.

Previous Leagues: Chiltonian

KENT ATHLETIC

Secretary: Irene Oodian, 9 Gafield Court, Handcross Road,Luton, Beds. LU2 8JZ (01582 483090)

Ground: Kent Social Club, Tenby Drive, Leagrave, Luton (01582 582723)

Directions: M1 jct 11 take A505 towards Luton. Take the first turning on theleft (Stoneygate Road), straight over at the roundabout and turn right attraffic lights into Beechwood Road. Take the first road on the left and then the first right into Tenby Drive. Ground and car park 100 yards on left

LUTON OLD BOYS

Secretary: Larry McGratton,6 Littlechurch Road, Luton , Beds LU2 8JZ (01582 483090)

Ground: Luton Old Boys Association , Dunstable Road, Luton. Tel: 01582 582060

Directions: On the A505 Luton to Dunstable Road towards Luton, between J 11 of the M1 and Chaul End Lane.

NB - there is **NO** right turn approaching from Dunstable direction.

MILLCUTT ROVERS

Secretary: Owen Clark, 108 Manor Road, Barton-le-Clay, Bedford MK45 4NS (01582 882398)

Ground: Barton Rovers FC, Sharpenhoe Road, Barton-le-Clay, Beds. Tel: 01582 707772 Fax: 01582 882398

Directions: Jct 12 M1,turn right. Then second right through Harlington and Sharpenhoe into Barton-le-Clay. Right at Royal Oak Public House onto A6. Ground is 400 yrds on right down concrete drive.

MURSLEY UNITED

Secretary: Geoff Curtis, 26 Berwick Drive, Bletchley, Milton Keynes MK3 7NB (01908 377196)

Ground: Station Road, Mursley, Milton Keynes

Directions: A421 Bletchley to Buckingham Road, first right in village

NORTH CRAWLEY UNITED (previously Newport Athletic)

Secretary: Sharon Stanley, The Chequers , High Street, North Crawley MK16 9LH (01234 391224)

Ground: Willen Rd Sports Ground, Willen Rd, Newport Pagnell

Directions: M1 Junc 14, A509 to Newport Pagnell. 1st r/about turn left A422.1st r/about right into Willen Rd. 1st right Sports Ground 100 yds right

OLD BRADWELL UNITED

Secretary: Paul Mills, 36 Craddocks Close, Bradwell, Milton Keynes MK13 9DX (01908 227520)

Ground: Abbey Road, Bradwell, Milton Keynes (01908 312355)

Directions: M1 junction 14 go towards Newport Pagnell. Turn left at firstroundabout into H3 Honks Way. Go six r'abouts then left onto V6 Grafton Street.Take 1st right at mini-r'about into Rawlins Road and then 2nd left intoLoughton Road. Take 1st right into Primrose Road and at the 'T' junction turnright into Abbey Road

OLD DUNSTABLIANS

Secretary: Craig Renfrew, 75B Princes Street. Dunstable. LU6 3AS. Tel: 01582471794 (H), 01234 265444 (B)

Ground: Lancot Park. Dunstable Road, Totternhoe (01582 663735)

Directions: From Dunstable Town Centre take the B489 Tring Road. At the 4throundabout turn right, signposted Totternhoe. The pitch is located withionDunstable Town Cricket Club which is on the right just before entering thevillage of Totternhoe

PADBURY UNITED

Secretary: James Clarke, 41 Moorhen Way, Buckingham, Bucks. MK18 1GN (01280 824513

Ground: Springfields,Playing Fields, Padbury

Directions: From Buckingham follow ring road with signs,to Aylesbury (A413), then towards Buckingham and Padbury is two miles south of the town A413 and three miles north west of Winslow on A413. Turn off opposite bus shelter on Springfields Estate and follow road forward.

SCOT

Secretary: William Land, 18 Coleridge Close, Bletchley, Milton Keynes MK3 5AF (01908 372228)

Ground: Selbourne Avenue, Bletchley, Milton Keynes (01908 368881)

Directions: Main roads to Bletchley then A421 Buckingham road, at Glen Garageright into Newton Rd, 2nd left into Selbourne Ave., through railway bridge to bottom of road

SHILLINGTON

Secretary: Aubrey Cole, 32 Greenfields, Shillington, Hitchin, Herts. SG5 3NX (01462 711322

Ground: Playing Field, Greenfields, Shillington ()1462 711757)

Directions: From Luton on A6 after bypassing Barton, turn right at learge Roundabout.Through Gobian to Shillington. From Bedfford or Hitchin , A600 to RAF Henlow. At Bird in Hand roundabout take exit to Upper Stondon.

TOTTERNHOE

Secretary: Jim Basterfield, 41 Park Avenue, Totternhoe, Dunstable, Beds LU6 1QF. Tel: 01582 667941 (H)

Ground: Totternhoe Recreation Ground, Dunstable (01582 606738)

Directions: Turn off the main Dunstable to Tring Road B489. Ground on right as you enter Totternhoe. Five miles from Leighton Buzzard (BR), 7 miles fromLuton. Bus 61 Luton-Aylesbury

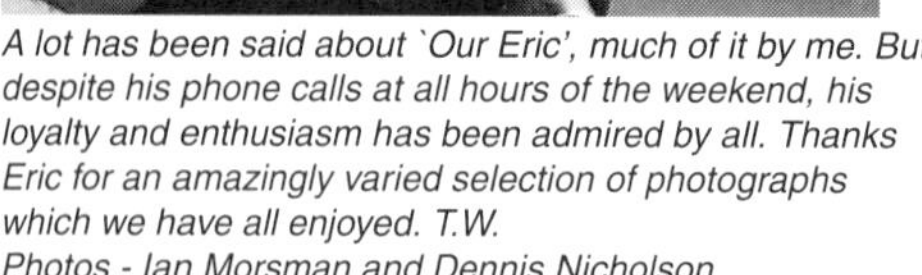

A lot has been said about `Our Eric', much of it by me. But despite his phone calls at all hours of the weekend, his loyalty and enthusiasm has been admired by all. Thanks Eric for an amazingly varied selection of photographs which we have all enjoyed. T.W.
Photos - Ian Morsman and Dennis Nicholson
Turn to page 1006

HERTS SENIOR COUNTY LEAGUE

President: Eric Dear **Chairman:** Cecil T Husdon

General Secretary: Kevin Folds, 6 Lanthony Court, High Street, Arlesey, Beds SG15 6TU
Tel: 01462 734102 Email: KFoldsHSCL@aol.com

Website: www.football.mitoo.co.uk/News.cfm?LeagueCode=HSCL

As for all leagues up and down the country, the Herts Senior County League has had probably the most difficult season in its entire history. Starting with the petrol crisis in September, when the entire weekend programme was cancelled, it failed to have a totally undisrupted weekend until well into April. As a consequence the season was extended from its scheduled finish of 7th May to the end of May. Forecasting the difficulties early, as a non floodlit league the Management Committee introduced double headers (where teams had not previously met) as early as the beginning of February. Despite its unpopularity it proved to be an inspired decision, without which the season would have been impossible to complete. On the field the League welcomed newcomers The Cheshunt Club from the Southern Olympian League, whilst exiting via the pyramid system were Champions Colney Heath.

An intriguing tussle for the Premier title was spoilt by the weather with Kings Langley the only top side able to keep up with their fixtures schedule. As a consequence they looked certain from an early stage to win the Championship and were for long periods double figures ahead of their nearest rivals. Unfortunately for them, they flagged in the latter stages and, having completed their programme the previous weekend, saw the title snatched from them on FA Cup Final weekend when Oxhey Jets completed a double in a double-header encounter with Elliott Star. Only goal difference separated the clubs after a 30 game season. For Oxhey Jets it was a dream turned into reality as the former under-10 club claimed the Premier Division Dewar Shield in their twentieth season in the County League. The icing on the cake was that their Reserves won the Reserve Division One whilst their "A" team won the West Herts League. Consolation for Kings Langley came in the shape of promotion - via the pyramid system - to the Minerva Spartan South Midlands League Senior Division.

At the bottom Benington and Whitewebbs struggled early on with the latter staging a late but unsuccessful revival. Old Parmiterians found life in the Premier Division very hard following the previous season's elevation and eventually slipped into the relegation places.

In Division One newcomers The Cheshunt Club started brilliantly but faded during the run in and finally finished fifth. St Peters once again outscored their rivals but, unlike recent seasons, managed to sustain their form to finish runners up. A revitalised Hatfield Town won the Division One tile and in a great season for the club beat four Premier Division teams on their way to an appearance in the Aubrey Cup Final. That final proved one step too far and Elliott Star picked up the cup for the first time recording a 2-0 success. Hatfield's consolation prize came with victory over the same opponents in the Reserve Cup. Sadly departing the League, as well as Kings Langley, are Agrevo Sports. The Berkhamsted based club are losing their ground although there is a slim possibility of a return in a season or two.

For disciplinary reasons, the Annual General Meeting expelled Whitewebbs, the clubs accepting their Management Committee's recommendation. On a brighter note, joining the League will be Lemsford. The picturesque village on the outskirts of Welwyn and Hatfield has a flourishing youth set up and has for the last couple of seasons operated a mens side in the Mid Herts League.

The second season of the Cherry Red Books sponsored Capital Counties Feeder Leagues' Trophy was washed out with the competition "frozen" at the Quarter Final stage. The Tournament will be finished pre-season and in the early weeks of next campaign. League interest is carried by Bedmond Sports and Social, Oxhey Jets and Wormley Rovers.

Looking to the future the Management Committee has introduced requirements for dry walkways around at least two sides of the pitch at all Premier Division venues and the need for covered spectator accommodation, both by the start of season 2003-04.

Ground hoppers will be pleased to note that all Premier Division clubs are required to produce programmes and, whilst the rule was not rigidly enforced last term, greater emphasis will be placed in the coming season. Also of interest to non-league fans is the publication of the League's history - "Success with Dignity" - which can be purchased through the League's General Secretary.

Kevin Folds, General Secretary

Success with Dignity - The history of the Herts Senior County League (1898-2000)

Over 370 pages (A5 format), including 28 pages of colour and black and white photographs, chart the history of the Herts Senior County League from its conception in January 1898 right up to the end of the 1999-2000 season. All the League tables are included along with all the Aubrey and Reserve Cup Final results and details. In addition, the records of the League's member clubs in the FA Cup, the FA Amateur Cup, the FA Vase and the Cherry Red Book Trophy are included. Price £9.95 (plus £2.00 postage & packing). For a copy send a cheque or postal order payable to the Herts Senior County League for £11.95 to Kevin Folds, General Secretary, HSCL, 6 Lanthony Court, High St, Arlesey, Beds SG15 6TU

FINAL LEAGUE TABLES 2000-01

PREMIER DIVISION

	P	W	D	L	F	A	Pts
Oxhey Jets	30	21	7	2	90	28	70
Kings Langley	30	22	4	4	62	17	70
Wormley Rovers	30	20	5	5	86	38	65
Bedmond S & S	30	15	7	8	51	40	52
Sandridge Rovers	30	14	6	10	53	42	48
Sun Postal Sports	30	14	6	10	50	43	48
Elliott Star	30	12	9	9	55	39	45
London Lions	30	11	8	11	30	36	41
Met Police (Bushey)	30	12	4	14	61	56	40
Cuffley	30	9	7	14	43	45	34
Bovingdon	30	9	4	17	35	55	31
Agrevo Sports	30	9	4	17	50	86	31
Chipperfield Corinth.	30	8	6	16	35	57	30
Whitewebbs*	30	8	4	18	58	85	25
Old Parmiterians	30	6	6	18	22	65	24
Benington	30	4	5	21	20	69	17

DIVISION ONE

	P	W	D	L	F	A	Pts
Hatfield Town	26	19	3	4	77	33	62
St Peters	26	18	3	5	86	31	57
Croxley Guild	26	18	3	5	64	35	57
Evergreen	26	14	8	4	60	37	50
The Cheshunt Club	26	15	3	8	61	48	48
Hadley	26	13	3	10	59	32	41
Bushey Rangers	26	11	3	12	58	63	36
Codicote	26	10	5	11	53	45	35
Welwyn Police	26	9	6	11	28	39	33
North Mymms	26	8	7	11	44	52	31
Mill End S & S	26	8	5	13	57	82	29
Kimpton Rovers	26	4	4	18	60	99	16
Sarratt	26	2	5	19	32	78	11
Standon & Puckeridge	26	3	2	21	29	94	11

* points deducted

PREMIER DIVISION RESULTS CHART 2000-01

		1	2	3	4	5	6	7	8	9	10	11	12	13	14	15	16
1	Agrevo Sports	X	0-3	1-1	2-1	3-0	6-3	1-9	1-3	1-2	2-1	1-1	1-5	2-3	2-2	4-0	0-3
2	Bedmond S & S	1-0	X	7-0	1-1	2-0	0-0	1-0	0-3	2-0	3-0	1-2	0-0	2-1	3-1	4-0	1-5
3	Benington	0-3	1-2	X	0-3	1-2	0A0	2-1	0-1	0-1	1-5	0-2	0-5	3-2	0-1	1-0	0-6
4	Bovingdon	6-5	1-2	1-0	X	1-1	0-1	2-3	0-3	1-1	2-1	1-4	1-6	0-1	0-1	4-3	0-2
5	Chipperfield Corinth	1-2	2-2	2-1	0-1	X	1-0	0-3	0-2	2-0	1-5	3-0	1-1	1-3	1-2	2-0	0-1
6	Cuffley	6-1	0-1	3-2	0-1	1-2	X	0-1	0-1	0-1	1-1	1-1	0-2	1-2	1-1	4-5	2-1
7	Elliott Star	0A0	0A0	0A0	3-0	4-1	1-1	X	0-4	0A0	1-1	0A0	0-7	1-3	3-1	6-1	1-2
8	Kings Langley	4-0	3-1	3-1	1-0	2-0	4-0	0-0	X	1-1	1-0	3-0	1-1	1-0	0-1	5-0	1-1
9	London Lions	0-2	2-1	0A0	2-0	2-0	1-0	1-3	0-3	X	4-2	2-1	1-1	1-1	1-1	1-2	1-3
10	Met Police (Bushey)	4-1	3-1	4-0	1-1	4-1	1-4	1-2	3-5	1-2	X	2-0	1-5	3-6	0-1	5-2	4-2
11	Old Parmiterians	1-3	0-2	0-3	1-0	1-1	0-4	0-6	0-2	0-1	0-3	X	0-0	2-1	0-4	2-6	0-6
12	Oxhey Jets	6-1	2-2	4-2	4-1	1-1	2-0	4-1	3-0	2-0	1-3	2-0	X	3-1	3-2	6-1	2-1
13	Sandridge Rovers	4-1	3-0	1-1	0-1	1-1	1-3	0-2	1-0	2-1	0-1	2-0	2-1	X	1-1	5-2	1-1
14	Sun Postal Sports	4-2	1-2	6-0	2-1	4-2	0-1	2-1	0-2	3-1	0-0	3-0	0-2	0-1	X	2-1	2-2
15	Whitewebbs	5-2	2-2	2-1	1-2	2-4	2-3	3-3	1-2	1-0	3-1	2-2	0-2	4-4	4-1	X	2-3
16	Wormley Rovers	7-0	7-2	2-0	3-2	5-2	3-3	1-0	2-1	0A0	3-0	0-2	4-7	2-0	6-1	2-1	X

AUBREY CUP 2000-01

SEMI-FINALS

Hatfield Town	v	Sandridge Rovers	1-0	Agrevo Sports	v	Elliott Star	1*4

FINAL

Hatfield Town v Elliott Star 0-2 at Baldock Town FC. Att: c450

RESERVE CUP 2000-01

SEMI-FINALS

Met Police Bushey	v	Elliott Star	2*3	Hatfield Town	v	Sun Postal Sports	2-0

FINAL

Elliott Star v Hatfield Town 1-2 at Colney Heath FC. Att: c170

CONSTITUTION FOR 2001-02

PREMIER DIVISION: Bedmond Sports & Social, Bovingdon, Chipperfield Corinthians, Croxley Guild, Cuffley, Elliott Star, Hatfield Town, London Lions, Metropolitan Police Bushey, Oxhey Jets, St Peters, Sandridge Rovers, Sun Postal Sports, Wormley Rovers 14

DIVISION ONE: Benington, Bushey Rangers, Codicote, Evergreen, Hadley, Kimpton Rovers, Lemsford, Mill End Sports & Social, North Mymms, Old Parmiterians, Sarratt, Standon & Puckeridge, The Cheshunt Club, Welwyn 14

MIDDLESEX COUNTY FOOTBALL LEAGUE

Founded 1984

President: Peter Rogers **Chairman:** Reg Johnson

Secretary: Stephen C. Hosmer, 27 St Georges Road, Hanworth, Middx. TW13 6RD
Tel: (H) 020 8894 1244 (Fax) 020 8894 0499 (M) 07831 393559
Email: stephen@hosmer.freeserve.co.uk

The 2000-01 season will be most memorable for the number of matches that were called off due to the weather, and at one stage the league played only three games from the beginning of November to mid-December. We were forced with great reluctance to cancel our main Cup competition, the 'Open Cup', half way through the Group Stages. We had to extend the season along with almost every other League and still found teams in the last few weeks of the season ahving to play eight matches just to complete the fixtures.

The very final match on the last day of the season, Northolt Saints v Technicolour CAV, would decide who won the Premier Division, Northolt Saints needing to win this match by seven clear goals to win the League on goal difference. Northolt Saints, needless to say, won the match by the required difference and won the League.

Two of our clubs, North Greenford United and Spelthorne Sports, took part in the Capital Counties Feeder Leagues Trophies. North Greenford were knocked out by the current holders Tring Athletic (Spartan South Midlands League) 3-1 in extra time. However, both teams were a credit to the League and the competition.

Eddie Cagigao, our secretary, started his new life in Spain in June 2001, but he is starting a League Supporters Club in Spain, and with the advent of email he will stay in touch.

FINAL LEAGUE TABLES 2000-01

PREMIER DIVISION

	P	W	D	L	F	A	GD	Pts
Northolt Saints	24	18	3	3	72	30	42	57
Neasden 2000	24	18	3	3	67	28	39	57
Wraysbury	24	14	5	5	62	30	32	47
North Greenford U	24	13	5	6	47	32	15	44
F.C. Deportivo Gal.	24	12	3	9	47	50	-3	39
Hanworth Villa	24	11	3	10	50	42	8	36
Spelthorne Sports	24	10	6	8	43	43	0	36
Harefield U Res	24	8	5	11	33	49	-16	29
Technicolor C.A.V.	24	6	8	10	33	49	-16	26
Willesden Const.	24	6	5	13	41	45	-4	20
C.B.Hounslow U	24	5	3	16	24	57	-33	18
Broadfields United	24	2	10	12	29	60	-31	13
Brentford New Inn	24	1	5	18	22	55	-33	8

SENIOR DIVISION

	P	W	D	L	F	A	GD	Pts
Pinner Albion Snrs	18	13	1	4	61	30	31	37
Nth Greenford U R	18	11	2	5	43	38	5	35
Neasden 2000 R	18	9	2	7	40	33	7	29
Hanworth V V R	18	9	2	7	43	41	2	29
C.B.Hounslow U R	18	7	6	5	40	38	2	27
Spelthorne Spts R	18	7	5	6	32	27	5	26
Western Command	18	8	1	9	53	42	11	25
Southall T Res	18	6	4	8	41	36	5	22
Southall FC Res	18	3	3	12	30	61	-31	12
Broadfields U Res	18	1	6	11	24	61	-37	9

LEAGUE CONSTITUTION 2001-02

PREMIER DIVISION 14

Brentford New Inn, Broadfields United, C.B.Hounslow United, Edgware Town, F.C.Deportivo Galicia, Hanworth Villa, Harefield United Reserves, Neasden 2000, North Greenford United, Northolt Saints, Spelthorne Sports, Technicolor CAV, Willesden Constantine, Wraysbury

SENIOR DIVISION 13

AC Richmond, Barnesalona FC, Broadfields United Reserves, Hanworth Villa Reserves, Hounslow Wanderers, London Tigers, Neasden 2000 Reserves, North Greenford United Res., Southall FC Reserves, Southall Town Reserves, Spelthorne Sports RReserves, Stonewall FC, Western Command

A QUOTE INSURANCE READING FOOTBALL LEAGUE

President: Leon Summers **Chairman:** John Dell
Secretary: David Jeanes, 6 Hawkesbury Drive, Fords Farm, Calcot, Reading RG31 5ZP
Tel: 01734 413926 (H)
http://www.rdgleague.mcmail.com

FINAL LEAGUE TABLES 2000-01

SENIOR DIVISION

	P	W	D	L	F	A	Pt
Forest Old Boys	22	16	3	3	71	26	51
Mortimer	22	15	6	1	59	25	51
Checkendon Spts	22	14	2	6	49	28	44
Cookham Dean	22	12	4	6	34	30	40
Unity	22	11	4	7	50	36	37
Marlow United	22	10	1	11	40	48	31
Highmoor	22	9	2	11	54	44	29
West Reading	22	7	6	9	32	39	27
Westwood United	22	7	2	13	44	55	23
Sonning Common	22	5	3	14	27	62	18
Roundhead Utd	22	2	6	14	26	51	12
Emmbrook Sports	22	3	3	16	28	70	12

PREMIER DIVISION

	P	W	D	L	F	A	Pt
Royal Mail	20	15	1	4	68	19	46
Forest OB Res.	20	14	2	4	57	37	44
Newtown Henley	20	13	2	5	53	37	41
Goring United	20	10	2	8	48	41	32
Reading YMCA	20	9	3	8	54	44	30
Finchampst'd `A'	20	9	3	8	35	32	30
Reading O. Blues	20	9	1	10	46	50	28
Westwood U Res.	20	8	3	9	50	53	27
REME Arborfield	20	8	2	10	45	57	26
RBC Hamblin	20	2	2	16	31	75	8
IBIS	20	2	1	17	31	73	7

DIVISION 1 KENNET

	P	W	D	L	F	A	Pt
Berks Co. Sports	20	14	5	1	62	30	47
Woodley Town	20	13	3	4	50	36	42
Spencers Wood	20	11	3	6	50	34	36
Rabson Rovers -1	19	9	4	6	56	42	30
Hurst	20	7	8	5	56	35	29
Shinfield	20	8	4	8	50	41	28
Rides United	19	7	2	10	42	43	23
S. Common Res.	20	6	4	10	39	41	22
Woodcote	20	4	4	12	41	89	16
Frilsham/Yatt'don	20	3	6	11	32	58	15
Calcot CA	20	2	7	11	34	63	13

DIVISION 1 THAMES

	P	W	D	L	F	A	Pt
Midgham	20	13	5	2	107	22	44
Stoke Row	20	11	5	4	63	35	38
Reading Univ.	20	11	3	6	59	23	36
AFC Maidenhead	20	11	3	6	56	32	36
Cookham D. Res.	20	9	3	8	47	45	30
Checkendon Res.	20	8	5	7	36	54	29
Victory Gladstone	20	8	3	9	44	53	27
BHM Wokingham	20	7	5	8	42	40	26
Mortimer Res.	20	6	5	9	37	57	23
Westwood U. `A'	20	6	3	11	34	69	21
Whitley Rovers	20	0	0	20	27	122	0

DIVISION 2 KENNET

	P	W	D	L	F	A	Pt
Winkfield	22	16	2	4	112	27	50
Wargrave	22	15	5	2	64	30	50
Highmoor Res.	22	15	3	4	61	28	48
Radstock	22	14	3	5	64	34	45
Wycliffe	22	9	6	7	59	50	33
N. Henley Res.	22	9	2	11	39	44	29
SEB Reading	22	7	4	11	61	69	25
Henley YMCA	22	7	2	13	40	64	23
Frilsham Res.	22	6	3	13	39	62	21
Goring Utd Res.	22	5	5	12	33	65	20
SRCC	22	5	3	14	31	75	18
IBIS Res.	22	3	4	15	32	87	13

DIVISION 2 THAMES

	P	W	D	L	F	A	Pt
Emmbrook Res.	24	19	2	3	87	45	59
Royal Mail Res.	24	16	2	6	86	40	50
Woodley T. Res.	24	15	3	6	66	37	48
Englefield	24	12	4	8	59	49	40
Rabson R. Res.	24	12	4	8	61	50	40
Twyford/R'combe	24	10	4	10	51	46	34
Hurst Res.	24	10	4	10	51	59	34
Sonning	24	9	3	12	49	57	30
Crowthorne Spts	24	9	1	14	50	77	28
REME App'tices	24	7	5	12	63	75	26
Compton	24	5	7	12	49	59	22
Sonning Sports	24	5	4	15	44	78	19
Shinfield Res.	24	4	3	17	34	78	15

READING FOOTBALL LEAGUE CONSTITUTION 2001-02

SENIOR DIVISION

ASCOT UNITED
Ascot Race Course , Winkfield Road , Ascot , Berkshire
CHECKENDON SPORTS
The Playing Fields, Checkendon, Reading, Berkshire
COOKHAM DEAN
Alfred Major Rec Ground, Hillcrest Ave., Cookham Rise, Maidenhead, Berkshire
FOREST OLD BOYS
Holme Park, Sonning Lane, Sonning, Berkshire
01734 690356
IBIS & HIGHMOOR
IBIS Sports Club, Scours Lane, Reading, Berkshire
MARLOW UNITED
Gossmore Park, Gossmore Lane, Marlow, Bucks
MORTIMER
Alfred Palmer Memorial PF, West End Road, Mortimer, Reading, Berkshire
NEWTOWN HENLEY
Harpsden Hall, Harpsden Village, Henley-on-Thames, Oxfordshire
ROYAL MAIL
Kings Meadows, Reading, Berkshire
SONNING COMMON
Peppard Cricket Club, Peppard Common, Stoke Row Road, Peppard, Oxfordshire
UNITY
Cintra Park, Cintra Avenue, Reading, Berkshire
VANSITTART WANDERERS
Slough Grammar School, Lascelles Road, Slough, Berkshire
WEST READING
Victoria Reacreation Ground, Norcot Road, Reading, Berkshire None
WESTWOOD UNITED
Cotswold Sports Centre, Downsway, Tilehurst, Reading, Berkshire

PREMIER DIVISION

BERKS COUNTY SPORTS
Berks Co. Sports & Social Club , Sonning Lane, Sonning , Reading , Berkshire
EMMBROOK SPORTS
Emmbrook Sports Ground, Lowther Road, Emmbrook, Wokingham, Berkshire 01189 780209
FINCHAMPSTEAD 'A'
Memorial Ground, Finchampstead Park, Finchampstead, Berkshire 0118 973 2890
FOREST OLD BOYS RESERVES
Holme Park, Sonning Lane, Sonning, Berkshire
01734 690356
GORING UNITED
Gardiners Recreation Ground, Upper Red Cross Road, Goring-on-Thames, Berkshire
MIDGHAM
Battery End, Wash Common, Newbury, Berkshire
READING OLD BLUES
Sol Joel, Church Road, Reading, Berkshire
READING YMCA
Emmer Green Recreation Ground, Emmer Green, Reading, Berkshire
ROUNDHEAD UNITED
Coley Park, St Saviours Road, Reading, Berkshire
STOKE ROW
Woodcote Recreation Ground, Woodcote, Reading, Berkshire
WESTWOOD UNITED RESERVES
Cotswold Sports Centre, Downsway, Tilehurst, Reading, Berkshire
WOODLEY TOWN
Woodford Park, Haddon Drive, Woodley, Reading, Berkhire

SPRINGBANK VENDING MIDLAND LEAGUE

President: T Myatt Chairman: P Savage
Secretary: M Stokes, 21 Corsican Drive, Pye Green, Cannock, Staffs WS 12 4SZ
Tel: 01543 878075 Fax: 01543 879008

FINAL LEAGUE TABLE 2000-01

	P	W	D	L	F	A	Pts
Norton United	32	22	5	5	85	34	71
Hanford	32	20	7	5	76	38	67
Eccleshall	32	17	9	6	59	36	60
Redgate Clayton	32	15	13	4	57	40	58
Stallington	32	15	10	7	66	50	55
Baddeley Green R	32	15	8	9	62	37	53
Vale Juniors	32	14	8	10	65	47	50
Audley	32	13	7	12	56	48	46
Leoni A G	32	13	6	13	52	55	45
Brocton	32	12	5	15	48	61	41
Milton United	32	10	9	13	37	40	39
Adderley Green	32	10	7	15	48	53	37
Hanley Town	32	8	11	13	41	57	35
Abbey Hulton Utd	32	8	7	17	49	66	31
Ball Haye Green	32	8	4	20	40	70	28
Cheadle Town OB	32	8	3	21	36	75	27
Foley	32	2	5	25	38	108	11

R.S.R. TYRES SURREY COUNTY SENIOR LEAGUE

FINAL LEAGUE TABLES 2000-01

PREMIER DIVISION

	P	W	D	L	F	A	Pt
Worcester Park	30	21	5	4	79	35	68
Colliers Wood U.	30	18	6	6	63	38	60
Virginia Water	30	17	7	6	75	40	58
Guildford	30	15	7	8	56	38	52
Chobham/O'shaw	30	14	9	7	56	42	51
Frimley Green	30	13	9	8	59	47	48
Croydon MO	30	14	5	11	59	50	47
Bookham	30	13	5	12	38	50	44
Bisley Sports -3	30	9	10	11	46	42	34
Ditton -6	30	11	7	12	57	58	34
Netherne Village	30	10	3	17	39	64	33
Hersham RBL	30	8	6	16	33	55	30
Crescent Rovers	30	9	3	18	43	68	30
Farleigh Rvrs	30	8	5	17	44	56	29
Shottermill	30	6	7	17	34	62	25
Sheerwater	30	5	4	21	36	72	19

DIVISION ONE

	P	W	D	L	F	A	Pt
Virginia W. Res.	30	22	5	3	84	28	71
Ditton Res.	30	19	7	4	96	39	64
Crescent Res. -4	30	21	4	5	70	35	64
Netherne V. Res.	30	19	2	9	84	39	59
Colliers W. Res.	30	16	9	5	83	45	57
Farleigh R. Res.	30	14	5	11	59	41	47
Worc. Pk Res. -3	30	14	3	14	53	65	42
Croydon MO Res	30	10	8	12	59	72	38
Frimley G. Res.	30	11	4	15	46	85	37
Chobham Res. -1	30	10	7	13	53	62	36
Hersham Res. -2	30	9	6	15	57	71	31
Sheerwater Res.	30	10	1	19	59	79	31
Bookham Res. -3	30	8	7	15	48	58	28
Guildford Res.	30	7	4	19	51	85	25
Bisley Sports Res.	30	6	4	20	39	68	22
Shottermill Res.	30	4	4	22	34	103	16

LEAGUE CUP 2000-01

FIRST ROUND

Bisley Sports	v	Netherne Village	4-1
Farleigh Rovers	v	Crescent Rovers	1-2
Colliers Wood United	v	Guildford	1-0
Hersham RBL	v	Frimley Green	0-2
Croydon Municipal O	v	Chobham & Ottershaw	3-1
Sheerwater	v	Bookham	0-3
Worcester Park	v	Shottermill	3-0

QUARTER FINALS

Crescent Rovers	v	Bisley Sports	1-3
Frimley Green	v	Colliers Wood United	1-2
Ditton	v	Croydon Municipal O	0- 4
Sheerwater	v	Worcester Park	1-3

SEMI FINALS

Colliers Wood United	V	Bisley Sports	0*0, 2-0
Croydon Municipal O	V	Worcester Park	1-5

FINAL

Colliers Wood United V Worcester Park 2-0 at Walton Casuals

2001-02 CONSTITUTION

BOOKHAM Chrystie Recreation Ground, Dorking Road, Bookham, Surrey 01372 459482

CHOBHAM & OTTERSHAW Chobham Recreation Ground, Station Rd, Chobham, Surrey 01276 857876

COLLIERS WOOD UNITED London Fire Brigade, Banstead Road, Ewell, Surrey 020 8394 1946

CRESCENT ROVERS Wallington Sports/Social Club, Mollison Drive, Wallington, Surrey 020 8647 2558

CROYDON MUNICIPAL OFFICERS Russell Hill Reservoir, Pampisford Rd, Purley, Surrey 020 8660 9720

DITTON Long Ditton Recreation Ground, Windmill Lane, Ditton, Surrey 020 8398 7428

FARLEIGH ROVERS Parsonage Field, Harrow Road, Farleigh, Surrey 01884 626483

FRIMLEY GREEN Frimley Green Road, Frimley Green, Surrey

GUILDFORD Spectrum Leisure Centre, Parkway, Guildford, Surrey 01483 444777

HERSHAM RBL Coronation Playing Field, Molesey Road, Hersham, Surrey 01932 223037

NETHERNE VILLAGE Woodplace Lane, Coulsdon, Surrey 01737 557509

SEELEC DELTA Dorking FC, Meadowbank, Mill Lane, Dorking, Surrey 01306 884112

SHEERWATER Blackmore Crescent, Sheerwater Estate, Woking, Surrey

SHOTTERMILL & HASLEMERE Woolmer Hill Sports Ground, Haslemere, Surrey 01428 643072

VIRGINIA WATER The Timbers, Crown Road, Virginia Water, Surrey 01344 843811

WORCESTER PARK Green Lane, Worcester Park, Surrey 020 8337 4995

SUBURBAN FOOTBALL LEAGUE

Chairman: David Stanley
Chief Executive/Hon. Secretary: Michael Bidmead
55 Grange Road, Chessington, Surrey KT9 1EZ
Tel/Fax: 0208 397 4834 Website: www.suburbanleague.org.uk

The Suburban Football League held its 30th Annual Presentation Dinner and Dance at the palatial Sandown Park Racecourse with over 300 attending, comprising of players, managers, club administrators, wives, girlfriends (and possibly boyfriends) from the 50 member clubs.

During the excellent meal, the diners were introduced to the distinguished array of guests, including Jimmy Hill OBE, David Emery, Editor in Chief of "The Non-League Paper", Alan Wilkes, Disciplinary Manager of the Football Association and representatives from both the Middlesex and Surrey County Football Associaitons.

Jimmy Hill received a warm reception as he proceeded with a brief, but very interesting speech, mentioning that he had mixed emotions the previous week having seen his beloved Coventry City, whom he managed in the top Division, losing its long Premiership status, to be replaced by Fulham, for whom he once played. Jimmy was a personal guest of Corinthian Casuals, and was delighted, as President of their club, that they had just enjoyed a very successful season.

The presentations to the various winners of League competitions were made by the chief guests, Jimmy Hill and David Emery, assisted by the League Chairman. The Premier Division Champions were Berkhamsted Town, with Maidenhead United runners-up. The Divisional Champions were Corinthian Casuals (South) and Marlow (North) with Sutton United and Northwood the respective runners up. Sutton United won the League Cup defeating Yeading 2-0 in an entertaining and competitive final, while Walton & Hersham secured the Champions Cup, defeating Hayes over two legs. Carshalton Athletic were presented with a special award in recognition of their unbroken membership of the League, spanning the 30 full seasons.

Top: David Emery, Editor in Chief of The Non-League Paper together with David Stanley, Chairman of the Suburban Football League present to Berkhamsted Town the Premier Division Winners Trophy at the League's Presentation Dinner.

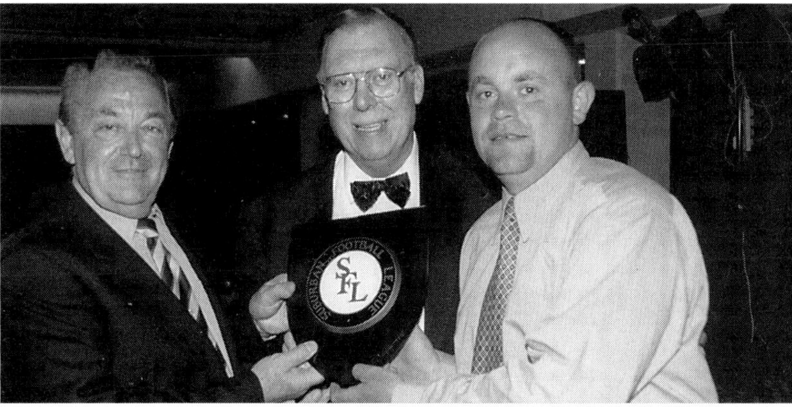

Bottom: The Suburban League's Chief Executive, former Football League referee Michael Bidmead presents a Special Award to Carshalton Athletic's Chief Executive Barry Gartell and Lisison Officer, Vic Thompson, in recognition of the Robins' unbroken membership of the League of 30 years, since its formation in 1971

FINAL LEAGUE TABLES 2000-01

PREMIER DIVISION

	P	W	D	L	F	A	Pts
Berkhamsted T	30	17	4	9	49	37	55
Maidenhead U	30	16	3	11	41	37	51
Basingstoke T	30	13	10	7	75	44	49
Dulwich Hamlet	30	15	4	11	61	48	49
Hayes	30	15	4	11	61	52	49
Met Police	30	12	10	8	50	38	46
Walton & Hersh.	30	14	4	12	64	54	46
Woking	30	14	4	12	52	43	46
Thame United	30	13	6	11	59	55	42
Hendon	30	11	7	12	42	48	40
Oxford City	30	11	7	12	37	43	40
Whyteleafe	30	10	6	14	40	55	36
Kingstonian	30	8	9	13	50	52	33
Uxbridge	30	10	3	17	50	67	33
Chertsey Town	30	8	7	15	37	59	31
Leighton Town	30	8	2	20	35	71	26

SOUTH DIVISION

	P	W	D	L	F	A	Pts
Corinthian Cas.	32	26	4	2	76	28	82
Sutton Utd	32	21	7	4	79	34	70
Crawley Town	32	21	4	7	95	48	67
Carshalton Ath	32	18	10	4	90	41	64
Tooting & Mitcham	32	16	7	9	83	50	55
Aldershot Town	32	15	9	8	74	46	54
Fisher Athletic	32	16	6	10	53	39	54
Ashford Town	32	14	7	11	49	46	49
Tonbridge Angels	32	14	5	13	73	52	47
Croydon Ath	32	10	7	15	54	57	37
Epsom & Ewell	32	10	7	15	47	54	37
Chipstead	32	8	9	15	42	62	33
Reading Town	32	9	4	19	32	74	31
Fleet Town	32	6	7	19	38	89	25
Bracknell Town	32	6	4	22	47	85	22
Molesey	32	5	7	20	40	78	22
Camberley Town	32	3	4	25	26	115	13

NORTH DIVISION

	P	W	D	L	F	A	Pts
Marlow	32	22	3	7	90	42	69
Northwood	32	21	2	9	93	41	65
Hillingdon Boro	32	20	2	10	74	60	62
Brook House	32	18	7	7	92	39	61
Yeading	32	18	6	8	87	43	60
Wembley	32	17	1	14	65	70	52
Burnham	32	14	6	12	56	59	48
Hungerford Town	32	15	3	14	71	76	48
Wingate & Finch.	32	14	4	14	56	68	46
Thatcham Town	32	12	8	12	73	54	44
Kingsbury Town	32	11	7	14	50	57	40
Flackwell Heath	32	11	6	15	55	70	39
Beaconsfield	32	10	3	19	65	82	33
Ruislip Manor	32	9	4	19	38	65	31
Tring Town	32	7	8	17	57	91	29
Abingdon United	32	6	7	19	54	99	25
Abingdon Town	32	7	3	22	33	93	24

SUBURBAN LEAGUE CHALLENGE CUP 2000-01

SECOND ROUND

Sutton United	v	Tring Town	5-1
Tooting & Mitcham	v	Dulwich Hamlet	2*4
Walton & Hersham	v	Beaconsfield SYCOB	0-1
Uxbridge	v	Crawley Town	1-4
Yeading	v	Marlow	2-0
Woking	v	Hayes	2-1
Kingsbury Town	v	Northwood	2-0
Wembley	v	Croydon Athletic	2-0
Leighton Town	v	Abingdon United	6-1
Aldershot Town	v	Staines Town	5-1
Berkhamsted Town	v	Hampton & R Boro	B w/o
Brook House	v	Thatcham Town	7-1
Chertsey Town	v	Hendon	5*2
Kingstonian	v	Whyteleafe	0-1
Maidenhead United	v	Epsom & Ewell	3-1
Met Police	v	Fisher Athletic	2*3

THIRD ROUND

Sutton United	v	Leighton Town	3*1
Beaconsfield SYCOB	v	Berkhamsted Town	2*4
Yeading	v	Chertsey Town	3-0
Kingsbury Town	v	Maidenhead United	1-4
Dulwich Hamlet	v	Aldershot Town	4-1
Crawley Town	v	Brook House	6-2
Woking	v	Whyteleafe	0-2
Wembley	v	Fisher Athletic	3-0

FOURTH ROUND

Sutton United	v	Dulwich Hamlet	1*1, 4p2
Yeading	v	Whyteleafe	2-0
Berkhamsted Town	v	Crawley Town	0-1
Maidenhead United	v	Wembley	2*1

SEMI-FINALS

Sutton United	v	Crawley Town	2-0
Yeading	v	Maidenhead Utd	2-0

FINAL

Sutton United v Yeading 2-0 at Carshalton Athletic FC

ESSEX & HERTS BORDER COMBINATION

Hon Secretary: Fred Hawthorn, PO Box 115,
Upminster, Essex RM14 3AQ Tel: 01708 225451

FINAL LEAGUE TABLES 2000-01

PREMIER DIVISION

		Home			*Away*			*Totals*						
	P	*W*	*D*	*L*	*W*	*D*	*L*	*W*	*D*	*L*	*F*	*A*	*GD*	*Pts*
Braintree Town	24	7	4	1	7	2	3	14	6	4	78	38	40	48
Heybridge Swifts	24	10	0	2	3	5	4	13	5	6	62	34	28	44
Canvey Island	24	8	2	2	5	3	4	13	5	6	51	37	14	44
Ford United	24	7	2	3	5	5	2	12	7	5	55	30	25	43
Hornchurch	24	8	2	2	3	5	4	11	7	6	51	36	15	40
East Thurrock United	24	6	3	3	5	1	6	11	4	9	66	41	25	37
Harlow Town	24	4	6	2	4	0	8	8	6	10	38	31	7	30
St Margaretsbury	24	6	4	2	3	1	8	9	5	10	42	61	-19	*29
Baldock Town	24	4	3	5	4	1	7	8	4	12	47	49	-2	28
Brentwood	24	3	5	4	3	4	5	6	9	9	27	35	-8	27
Ware	24	5	0	7	2	5	5	7	5	12	41	69	-28	26
Witham Town	24	6	3	3	0	3	9	6	6	12	33	59	-26	24
Potters Bar Town	24	0	2	10	2	1	9	2	3	19	21	92	-71	9

DIVISION ONE

	P	W	D	L	W	D	L	W	D	L	F	A	GD	Pts
Cheshunt	28	10	2	2	9	4	1	19	6	3	80	28	52	63
Leyton	28	9	3	2	7	1	6	16	4	8	55	40	15	52
Ilford	28	8	4	2	7	2	5	15	6	7	59	27	32	51
Hullbridge Sports	28	7	4	3	6	5	3	13	9	6	50	32	18	48
Gt Wakering Rovers	28	7	4	3	6	3	5	13	7	8	47	42	5	46
Somersett Ambury VE	28	8	4	2	4	4	6	12	8	8	60	45	15	44
Maldon Town	28	4	5	5	7	3	4	11	8	9	64	53	11	41
Tilbury	28	5	6	3	5	4	5	10	10	8	67	47	20	*39
Basildon United	28	4	3	7	6	2	6	10	5	13	51	60	-9	35
Hoddesdon Town	28	5	5	4	3	3	8	8	8	12	42	49	-7	32
Burnham Ramblers	28	4	5	5	2	6	6	6	11	11	30	54	-24	29
Bowers United	28	3	3	8	3	6	5	6	9	13	36	63	-27	27
Hertford Town	28	4	3	7	1	8	5	5	11	12	33	43	-10	26
Southend Manor	28	4	4	6	2	1	11	6	5	17	44	74	-30	23
Concord Rangers	28	2	2	10	1	5	8	3	7	18	28	89	-61	16

* points deducted

Due to the inclement weather and the requirement of the Club's First Teams to complete their season there were a number of unfulfilled or unresolved fixtures. In each case the match has been declared a 0-0 draw and a point has been awarded to each club.

COMBINATION CUP 2000-01

THIRD ROUND

Canvey Island	v	Ware	3*3, 4p2
Cheshunt	v	Heybridge Swifts	1-0
Leyton	v	Southend Manor	SM w/o
Hoddesdon Town	v	Harlow Town	2-1

SEMI-FINALS

Braintree Town	v	Cheshunt	1*1, 1p3
Southend Manor	v	Hoddesdon Town	1-2

FINAL

Cheshunt	v	Hoddesdon Town	1-0

FRED BUDDEN TROPHY 2000-01

THIRD ROUND

Hornchurch	v	Ford United	1-0
Brentwood	v	Hullbridge	0*0, 3p4
Gt Wakering Rovers	v	Cheshunt	1-2
Braintree Town	v	Heybridge Swifts	2-0

SEMI-FINALS

Hornchurch	v	Hullbridge	2*2, 4p2
Cheshunt	v	Braintree Town	0-2

FINAL

Hornchurch	v	Braintree Town	1-2

WIRRAL PROGRAMME CLUB

The non-profit making Club formed in March 1967

Secretary: I.R.W. Runham

3 Tansley Close, Newton, West Kirby, Wirral CH48 9XH Tel: 0151 625 9554

26th NON-LEAGUE FOOTBALL PROGRAMME OF THE YEAR SURVEY 1999-2000

This season's survey saw 1038 clubs represented, 27 more than last season, and with reserve and youth programmes there were 1103 places, four down on last time.

Again there were many superb programmes with many clubs showing an improvement on last season. It is again pleasing to see clubs issue for the first time plus some after a gap of many seasons. All clubs that issue a programme are to be congratulated, a single sheet is better than nothing. There would be no programmes without the hard work that the editors, plus any helpers they can find, put in, and I'm sure that most supporters and many committee members do not realise the time and effort needed to produce a programme, so our special thanks go to all these people. Our thanks are also due to all those who sent in programmes for the survey and to those who helped spread the word, the clubs themselves, their supporters, our members, other collectors, the Football Association, County Associations, the League Secretaries, the Non League Directory, Team Talk, the Non League Paper, the Football Traveller, Welsh Football, Programme Monthly, and those who lent programmes for the survey. Sincere apologies to anyone inadvertently omitted.

Some clubs only issue for a Saturday game, some for special games, some change the style, content, price, editor, etc, during the season; some have special connections with printers, etc., often we are not aware of these circumstances. Obviously we can only survey the programmes we receive. Some are from early in the season, others from just before the closing date, most from in between. The results always create a lot of interest with varying points being expressed; some of these we hear often second or third hand, but most miss our ears, so if you have any comments on the survey please let us know. I am sure the day will never come when there is complete agreement over the results, however the more discussion there is over the survey the better, as it will keep programmes to the forefront and hopefully encourage clubs at least to maintain or even improve the standards, or better still it may encourage more clubs to issue next season.

The club with the overall winning programme will receive a framed certificate; the winners of each league will also receive a certificate. Please note the programmes have been surveyed, not as many assume voted upon. Marks were awarded to each programme as follows (the maximum marks in each section are given):

Cover 15 (design 10, match details 5), **Page size** 10, **Team layout and position within the programme** 10,
Results 10, **League tables** 10, **Price** 15, **Pictures** 15, **Printing and paper quality** 20, **Frequency of issue** 20,
Value for money 20 (this takes into account the ratio of adverts to content, the club's league etc),
Contents 245 (other than those listed) taking into account their relevance to the club, its league, environs etc, the size of the print used, the spacing between the lines, the size of the margins, and if all the contents are original or reproduced (from League Bulletins, newspapers, magazines etc).

To gain full marks in the Frequency of issue section we needed to receive programmes from six different current season matches for each team entered (allowances were made if six home games were not played by the closing date and we were informed of this). The minimum entry was one programme.

As many programmes varied from issue to issue all programmes were surveyed, the marks in each section being totalled and divided by the number of issues to get the final mark for each section, and the marks from each section were then totalled to get the final score.

A new standard of marks is set each season so this season's total should not be compared with those of earlier seasons, as the comparison will almost certainly be inaccurate; a programme identical to last season's will almost certainly have gained a different points total.

We have already received many entries for the Specials section of the survey (for one-offs, big cup ties, friendlies, testimonials, charity matches, first/last matches at a ground, etc), the closing date for receiving these is 30th June 2001. To receive the results, expected by the end of July, we would appreciate it if you could send a stamped sae. Thank you.

The results of this season's survey are as follows:

Best Non-League Programme Nationally 2000-2001	**1st**	Hoddesdon Town	217 points
	2nd	Northwood	209 points
	=3rd	Langney Sports, Bryntirion Athletic	199 points

NATIONAL TOP 30: 1 Hoddesdon Town 217; **2** Northwood 209; **3=** Langney Sports, Bryntirion Athletic 199; **5=** Hayes, Lancing 185; **7** Aldershot Town; **8** St Andrews U18; **9=** Uxbridge, Glapwell 179; **11** Arlesey Town 177; **12=** Bath City, Yateley Green 175; **14=** Corby Town, Sutton United 174; **16** Arnold Town 173; **17** Woking 172; **18=** Poole Town, Askern Spa Town 171; **20=** Weymouth, Kings Langley, Caersws 169; **23** Hastings Town 168; **24=** Redhill, Colden Common 167; **26=** Morecambe, Chelmsford City, St Leonards, Hemsworth MW 166; **30** Easington United

INDIVIDUAL LEAGUE RESULTS The first number after the club's name is the number of programmes received - 6 shows six or more different programmes were surveyed or every programme if less than six matches were played, the second number is the total points gained. The leagues are in no particular order.

LEAGUE + No of entries			**FIRST**		**SECOND**		**THIRD**	
Nationwide Conference		22	Hayes	6-185	Woking	6-172	Morecambe	1-166
Dr Martens	Overall	62	Langney Sports	6-199	Bath City	6-175	Corby Town	6-174
	Prem Div	22	Bath City	6-175	Weymouth	6-169	Tamworth	6-163
	West Div	22	Shepshed Dynamo	6-156	Hinckley United	6-145	Mangotsfield United	6-141
	East Div	18	Langney Sports	6-199	Corby Town	6-174	Hastings Town	6-168
Rymands	Overall	73	Northwood	6-209	Aldershot Town	6-184	Uxbridge	6-179
	Prem Div	22	Aldershot Town	6-184	Sutton United	6-174	Chesham United	3-155
	Div 1	20	Northwood	6-209	Uxbridge	6-179	Wealdstone	6-161
	Div 2	16	Cheshunt	1-129	Horsham	1-119	Wembley	1-118
	Div 3	15	Arlesey Town	6-177	Croydon Athletic	6-161	Epsom & Ewell	6-149
Unibond	Overall	44	Altrincham	1-160	Hucknall Town	6-153	Leek Town	6-152
	Prem Div	23	Altrincham	1-160	Hucknall Town	6-153	Leek Town	6-152
	Div 1	21	Bradford Park Avenue	4-144	Vauxhall Motors	1-142	Stocksbridge Pk Steels	6-141
Minerva	Overall	46	Hoddesdon Town	6-217	Holmer Green	6-157	Somersett Ambury V&E	1-149
Spartan	Prem Div	20	Hoddesdon Town	6-217	Holmer Green	6-157	Somersett Ambury V&E	1-149
South Mids	Sen Div	T17	Tring Athletic	6-137	Cockfosters	1-131	Letchworth Bridger	1-123
	Div 1	9	Old Dunstablians	1-80	Shillington	1-74	Haywood United	1-71
Comb. Co	Overall	15	Ash United	6-153	Walton Casuals	6-145	Southall	1-137
Kent	Overall	13	Cray Wanderers	6-144	Herne Bay	1-140	Slade Green	6-125
Essex Sen.	Overall	10	Brentwood	1-130	Ilford	1-105	Burnham Ramblers	1-97
Wessex	Overall	20	Blackfield & Langley	6-146	Brockenhurst	6-143	Lymington & New Milton	3-124
Rich City	Overall	31	Lancing	6-185	Redhill	6-167	Ringmer	6-148
Sussex	Div 1	18	Lancing	6-185	Redhill	6-167	Ringmer	6-148
County	Div 2	5	Oving	1-124	Hailsham Town	1-111	Crawley Down	1-103
	Div 3	6	Ifield	6-144	Haywards Heath Town	6-127	Bexhill Town	6-123
Screwfix	Overall	24	Minehead Town	6-137	Taunton Town	6-136	Chippenham Town	3-130
Direct	Prem Div	12	Minehead Town	6-137	Taunton Town	6-136	Chippenham Town	3-130
	Div 1	12	Street	1-125	Calne Town	6-124	Corsham Town	6-114
Jewson	Overall	29	Great Yarmouth Town	6-160	Felixstowe & Walton Utd	6-159	Mildenhall Town	6-151
Eastern	Prem Div	19	Great Yarmouth Town	6-160	Felixstowe & Walton Utd	6-159	Mildenhall Town	6-151
	Div 1	10	Dereham Town	1-121	Downham Town	1-113	Hadleigh United	1-108
United	Overall	24	Eynesbury Rovers	6-159	St Neots Town	6-154	Blackstones	6-146
Counties	Prem Div	17	Eynesbury Rovers	6-159	St Neots Town	6-154	Blackstones	6-146
	Div 1	7	Daventry Town	6-132	Woodford United	6-126	Newport Pagnell Town	1-100
Hellenic	Overall	53	Swindon Supermarine	6-159	Didcot Town	6-137	Wantage Town	5-122
	Prem Div	20	Swindon Supermarine	6-159	Didcot Town	6-137	Wantage Town	5-122
	Div 1 East	17	Penn & Tylers Green	4-116=			Finchampstead	5-112
			Rayners Lane	6-116=				
	Div 1 West	16	Cirencester United	4-120	Purton	6-111	Ardley United	4-106
Mids Alliance		21	Stourbridge	6-162	Boldmere St Michaels	6-156	Knypersley Victoria	6-154
North West	Overall	27	Atherton Laburnam	6-155	Curzon Ashton	6-154	St Helens Town	6-153
Counties	Div 1	17	Curzon Ashton	6-154	St Helens Town	6-153	Clitheroe	=1-142
							Skelmersdale United	=1-142
	Div 2	10	Atherton Laburnam	6-155	Warrington Town	3-145	Daisy Hill	2-144
Northern	Overall	35	Glapwell	6-179	Arnold Town	6-173	Ossett Albion	6-152
Co East	Prem Div	20	Glapwell	6-179	Arnold Town	6-173	Ossett Albion	6-152
	Div 1	15	Pickering Town	5-149	Bridlington Town	=6-142		
					Mickleover Sports	=1-142		
Albany	Overall	30	Newcastle Blue Star	6-140	Brandon United	6-125	Marske United	6-123
	Div 1	20	Newcastle Blue Star	6-140	Brandon United	6-125	Marske United	6-123
	Div 2	10	Horden Colliery Welfare	1-121	Evenwood Town	6-104	Esh Winning	6-97
Middx Co		4	Enfield Reserves	6-90	Technicolour CAV	1-89	CB Hounslow United	1-72
Essex Inter.		8	Manford Way	6-97	Manford Way Reserves	=6-96		
					Upminster Reserves	=4-96		
Hampshire	Overall	11	Yateley Green	6-175	Poole Town	6-171	Colden Common	6-167
	Prem Div	4	Poole Town	6-171	Colden Common	6-167	Amesbury Town	1-135
	Divs 1, 2	7	Yateley Green	6-175	Farnborough North End	6-124	QK Southampton	6-109
Dorset Comb.		13	Flight Refuelling	1-115	Bournemouth Sports	1-102	Portland United	5-96
Kent County		8	Maidstone United	6-142	Tonbridge Rangers	6-115	Norton Sports	4-109
Devon		13	Newton Abbot Spurs	1-142	Buckland Athletic	6-128	Cullompton Rangers	6-112
South Western		18	Penzance	1-149	Saltash United	6-137	Liskeard Athletic	1-99
Anglian	Overall	10	Blofield United	2-103	Acle United	1-100	Cromer United	1-96
Comb.	Prem Div	6	Blofield United	2-103	Acle United	1-100	Cromer United	1-96
	Div 2, 3, 4	4	Watton United	1-86	Poringland Wanderers	1-78	Saham Toney	1-74
Suffolk &	Overall	8	Old Newton United	1-121	Debenham Reserves	1-117	Debenham	1-114
Ipswich	Prem Div	4	Old Newton United	1-121	Ransome Sports	1-87	Capel Plough	1-70
	Other Divs	4	Debenham Reserves	1-117	Debenham	1-114	Stowupland Reserves	1-93
Herts Senior		12	Kings Langley	6-169	Wormley Rovers	1-115	Chipperfield Corinths	1-113
Glos County		6	Highbridge United	6-161	Tytherington Rocks	6-147	Brockworth	6-112
Wiltshire		4	Purton Reserves	6-106	Trowbridge Town	1-91	Shrewton United	3-88

Midland		4	Eccleshall	6-123	Brocton	4-120	Hanford Boys	1-71
Central	Overall	19	Hucknall Rolls Royce	6-153	Long Eaton United	1-130	Sandiacre Town	1-129
Midlands	Sup Div	12	Hucknall Rolls Royce	6-153	Long Eaton United	1-130	Sandiacre Town	1-129
	Prem Div	7	Teversal	1-123	Forest Town	1-116	Bottesford Town	1-114
West Mids	Overall	15	Star	6-152	Shifnal Town Reserves	6-109	Westfields	6-107
	Prem Div	12	Star	6-152	Westfields	6-107	Heath Hayes	1-92
	Div 1 N, S	12	Shifnal Town Reserves	6-109	Bewdley Town	1-73	Lucas Sports	1-71
Mids Comb.	Overall	40	Blackheath Invensys	6-141	Loughborough Athletic	6-131	Alvechurch	=6-130
							Rugby Town	=6-130
	Prem Div	21	Blackheath Invensys	6-141	Alvechurch	6-130	Coventry Sphinx	6-129
	Div 1	8	Loughborough Athletic	6-131	Alvis Oakwood Coventry	6-116	Hams Hall	6-110
	Div 2	7	Rugby Town	6-130	Droitwich Spa	6-103	Malvern Athletic	5-92
	Div 3	4	Loughborough Ath Res	=6-91			Brownhills Town Res.	2-73
			Wilnecote Sports	=3-91				
Cambs.		4	Debden Reserves	6-147	Debden	4-143	Lakenheath	6-135
Leics Senior		8	Coalville Town	6-159	Loughborough Dynamo	6-151	Anstey Nomads	1-106
Notts Alliance		5	Rainworth Miners Welfare	6-141	Wollaton	=2-120		
					Wollaton Reserves	=2-120		
Humberside		3	Easington United	6-165	Barton Town Old Boys	1-78	Beverley Town	1-75
Manchester	Overall	11	Prestwich Heys	6-157	New Mills	6-140	Elton Fold	1-102
	Prem Div	5	Prestwich Heys	6-157	Elton Fold	1-102	Stand Athletic	1-91
	Div 1	3	New Mills	6-140	Ashton Athletic	2-92	Wythenshawe Town	1-88
	Div 2	3	Wilmslow Albion Res.	1-96	Ashton Athletic Res.	1-89	East Manchester Res.	1-52
West Cheshire		3	New Brighton	6-143	New Brighton Res.	6-113	Poulton Victoria	1-72
Northern	Overall	7	West Allotment Celtic	6-112	Newcastle Benfield Saints	1-110	Walker Fosse	1-98
Alliance	Prem Div	4	West Allotment Celtic	6-112	Newcastle Benfield Saints	1-110	Carlisle City	1-96
	Div 1	3	Walker Fosse	1-98	Newbiggin Central Welfare	1-72	Cullercoats	1-64
W Riding Co		4	Hemsworth Miners W	6-166	Brighouse Town	1-112	Littletown	1-83
West Yorks		3	Knaresborough Town	6-130	Beeston St Anthonys	1-101	Wetherby Athletic	1-72
Other Leagues		27	Ifield Reserves	6-145	Rivington	1-142	Thornbury Town	6-137
Youth Clubs/Schools		8	St Andrews U18	6-180	Askern Spa Town	6-171	St Andrews U16	6-144
Club Youth XIs		5	Wotton Bassett Town	6-145	Stowmarket Town	6-128	Hendon	6-103
FA Youth Cup		37	Burscough	1-109	Paget Rangers	1-93	Bilston Town	=1-82
							Ipswich Wanderers	=1-82
Reserves		28	Colden Common	6-162	Debden	6-147	Ifield	6-145
Wales	Overall	65	Bryntirion Athletic	2-199	Caersws	6-169	Rhyl	6-156
Lge of Wales		16	Caersws	6-169	Rhyl	6-156	Carmarthen Town	=6-153
							Llanelli	=6-153
Cymru Allnce		5	Denbigh Town	1-122	Porthmadog	1-120	Airbus UK	1-102
CC Sports	Overall	11	Cwmtillery	6-149	Newport YMCA	6-115	Neath	6-110
Welsh	Div 1	4	Neath	6-110	Cardiff Corinthians	6-101	Caerleon	=1-57
							Gwynfi United	=1-57
	Div 2, 3	7	Cwmtillery	6-149	Newport YMCA	6-115	Newcastle Emlyn	1-77
Gwent Co		13	Abertillery Bluebird	1-121	Abertillery Town	3-91	Blaina West Side	1-80
Welsh Allnce		7	Caerwys	1-113	Prestatyn Town	6-109	Llandudno Junction	1-102
Welsh Nat Wrexham		5	Gresford Athletic	6-150	Hand	6-128	Cefn United Reserves	1-104
Sth Wales Am.		4	Bryntirion Athletic	2-199	Cwmaman	5-144	Trefelin B & G Club	1-94
Other Welsh Leagues		4	AFC Whitchurch	1-92	Penrhyncoch	2-74	Llanrhaeadr	1-53
Scotland	Overall	39	Kirkintilloch Rob Roy	6-164	Haddington Athletic	6-155	Shettleston	6-134
Highland		6	Buckie Thistle	1-121	Fraserburgh	1-113	Forres Mechanics	1-109
East of Scotland		3	Edinburgh City	1-125	Lothian Thistle	1-95	Gala Fairydean	1-75
Central	Overall	10	Kirkintilloch Rob Roy	6-164	Shettleston	6-134	Renfrew	6-98
	Prem Div	7	Renfrew	6-98	Maryhill	1-96	Shotts Bon Accord	1-92
	Div 1	3	Kirkintilloch Rob Roy	6-164	Shetteleston	6-134	Cambuslang Rangers	1-72
Ayrshire		6	Kilwinning Rangers	6-116	Largs Thistle	6-109	Saltcoats Victoria	1-99
Eastern		3	Haddington Athletic	6-155	Dunbar United	6-129	Newtongrange Star	1-102
Fife		5	Newburgh	1-98	Crossgates Primrose	1-96	Thornton Hibs	1-88
Northern		4	Forres Thistle	1-93	Wilsons XI	1-79	Formantine United	1-75
Tayside		2	Tayport	6-131	Coupar Angus	1-50		
Ladies	Overall	53	Langford	4-154	Hampton	6-124	Chelmsford Reserves	=3-107
							Chester City	=1-107
							Loughborough Dynamo	=1-107
FA Premier	Overall	11	Langford	4-154	Wolverhampton Wndrs	1-101	Garswood Saints	1-99
	Nat Div	3	Everton	1-93	Charlton Athletic	1-83	Millwall Lionesses	1-79
	Nth Div	5	Wolverhampton Wndrs	1-101	Garswood Saints	1-99	Oldham Curzon	1-90
	Sth Div	3	Langford	4-154	Barking	1-87	Newport County	1-61
Sth East Comb		6	Hampton	6-124	Chelmsford	4-103	Racers	1-99
Other Ladies Leagues		6	Chelmsford Reserves	3-107	Doncaster Rovers	1-84	Parkgate	1-73
FA Womens Cup		30	Chester City	=1-107			Ambassadors in Sport	1-93
			Loughborough Dynamo	=1-107				
Sunday		49	Orchard Park	1-103	Bradleystoke Sports	1-94	Rolls Royce Celtic	1-92

COUNTY FOOTBALL ASSOCIATIONS

NON-LEAGUE MEDIA Plc

Elvin House, Stadium Way, Wembley, Middlesex, HA9 0DW
Tel: 020 8900 9021 Fax: 020 8900 9023
Email: info@nlfootball.com

Chairman: Graham Gutteridge - Chief Executive: Steve Ireland
Directors: David Emery, Fiaz Ur Rehman, Barry Gold, Bobby Robson CBE

THE NON-LEAGUE PAPER (Sundays)

Hill House, (2nd Floor), Highgate Hill, London, N19 5NA
Tel: 020 7687 7687 Fax: 020 7687 7688
Email: info@nlfootball.com

Editor in Chief: David Emery - Editor:
Editot: Ian Cole Production Editor: John Cleal News Editor: David Watters

THE NON-LEAGUE MAGAZINE (Monthly)

Hill House (2nd floor), Highgate Hill, London, N19 5NA
Tel: 020 7687 7687 Fax: 020 7687 7688
Email: info@nlfootball.com

Managing Editor: Tony Williams - Editor: Stuart Hammonds

THE F.A. NON-LEAGUE CLUB DIRECTORY (Annual)

Helland, North Curry, Taunton, Somerset, TA3 6DU
Tel: 01823 490080 Fax: 01823 490281
Email: tony.williams12@virgin.net

Editor: Tony Williams

'SHE KICKS' (Women's Football Monthly)

Design Works, William Street, Gateshead, Tyne & Wear, NE10 0JP
Tel: 0191 420 8383 Fax: 0191 420 4950
Email: info@shekicks.net

Editor: Jennifer O'Neill

NON-LEAGUE WEEKLY NEWSDESK & ANNUAL

13 Northfield Avenue, Taunton, Somerset, TA1 1XF
Tel: 01823 254071 Fax: 01823 327720
Email: nlnewsdesk@zetnet.co.uk

Editor: James Wright

THE NON-LEAGUE WEBSITE

Rippleffect Studios Ltd., 68A Rodney Street, Liverpool, L1 9AF
Tel: 0151 7096848 Website: www.rippleffect.com
www.thenon-league paper.com (previously www.nlfootball.com)
News Media Manager: Andrew Mullan
News Editor: Steve Whitney - Tel: 01536 515398 Email: stevewhitney@btconnect.com

ADDITIONAL EXECUTIVES FOR ALL PUBLICATONS

Administration: Blanche Dalton (Office) 020 8900 90221
Advertising (Sponsors): Forbes Chapman 07802 237646 or 020 8367 0910
Advertising (General): Launch Pad (Office) 020 7734 7739
Circulation Manager: Brian King (Mobile) 07775 734107
Public Relations: Graham Courtney (Mobile) 07801 833500

BEDFORDSHIRE F.A.

Tel: 01582 565111 (B) Fax: 01582 565222 Email: bedsfa@compuserve.com
Century House, Skimpot Road, Dunstable LU5 4JU

BEDFORDSHIRE FOOTBALL ASSOCIATION

Secretary: Peter D Brown

Executives (Responsibility) Century House for Coaching Exams/Courses, Referees, Womens Football

Number of Affiliated Clubs Senior: 480

President: R Berridge

Number of Affiliated Leagues: Senior: 9 Junior: 4

County Representative Teams: Senior, U18, U16, Intermediate, Womens

Inter County Competitions: East Anglia Counties Intermediate, U18, U16 & Womens, FA County Youth Cup

BEDFORDSHIRE SENIOR CUP 2000-01

(17 ENTRIES)

LAST SEASON'S FINAL: Stotfold v Arlesey Town 2-1

FIRST ROUND

Arlesey Town	v	Caddington	4-0

SECOND ROUND

Kempston Rovers	v	Bedford United	0-2
Potton United	v	Arlesey Town	0-2
Langford	v	Leighton Town	0-1
Barton Rovers	v	Dunstable Town	1-3
Bedford Town	v	Ampthill Town	3-0
Wootton Blue Cross	v	Totternhoe	7-0
Biggleswade United	v	Brache Sparta	5*3
Stotfold	v	Biggleswade Town	1-4

THIRD ROUND

Arlesey Town	v	Dunstable Town	1*1, 0-1
Biggleswade Town	v	Wootton Blue Cross	0-4
Leighton Town	v	Bedford Town (1990)	3-2
Biggleswade United	v	Bedford United	2-0

SEMI-FINALS

Leighton Town	v	Wtn Blue Cross	0*0, 1-2
Biggleswade United	v	Dunstable Town	2*3

FINAL

DUNSTABLE TOWN	v	WTN BLUE CROSS	0*1	at Hitchin Road, Arlesey Town FC

Wootton Blue Cross skipper Jon Hoggett gets his hands on the Bedfordshire Senior Cup, after their 1-0 win over Dunstable. Photo: Gordon Whittington

Top: Bedfordshire Senior Cup Winners, Wootton Blue Cross. Photo: Gordon Whittington

Below: Pitstone & Ivinghoe, winners of the Berks & Bucks Intermediate Cup (left) and SSML Division One (right).
Back Row (l-r): M Jellis, J Law, G Freer, P Saw, F Walcott, D Latham, K Ripley, C Ripley, M Cole, W Bateman, D Fox (Asst Manager), R Adlem, P Pickwick, I Magill (Manager)
Front Row (l-r): C Fox, J Mountford, B Robinson (Coach), C Magill, M Gale, G Wray (Captain), R Henney.
Photo: Gordon Whittington

BERKS & BUCKS F.A. LIMITED

Tel: 01367 242099 Fax: 01367 242158
15a London Street, Faringdon, Oxon SN7 7HD

Secretary: Brian Moore **Press Officer:** Brian Moore

Responsibilities J Kelman (Coaching Exams/Courses)
R J Claridge (Referees)
A Glenny (Womens Football)

Number of Affiliated Leagues: Senior: 17 Junior: 10

President: D J Frost

County Representative Teams: U18, U16 Girls, U14 Girls

Chairman: J A Christopher

Inter County Competitions: South/South West Counties Championship Youth

BERKS & BUCKS SENIOR CUP 2000-01

(18 entries) (FOUNDED 1878-79)

LAST SEASON'S FINAL: Aylesbury United v Reading 2-0

MOST WINS: Wycombe 24 Maidenhead United 16 Marlow 13

FIRST ROUND

Wokingham Town	v	Bracknell Town	3-0

SECOND ROUND

Chalfont St Peter	v	Marlow	0-4	Windsor & Eton	v	Wycombe Ws	W&E W-O
Abingdon Town	v	Wokingham Town	1-4	Maidenhead United	v	Slough Town	2-0
Chesham United	v	Flackwell Heath	5-1	Hungerford Town	v	Burnham	0-3

QUARTER-FINALS

Burnham	v	Wokingham Town	7-0	Windsor & Eton	v	Marlow	3-2
Chesham United	v	Aylesbury United	4-0	Maidenhead United	v	Reading	1-0

SEMI-FINALS

Maidenhead United	v	Windsor & Eton	2-1	Chesham United	v	Burnham	6-2

FINAL

CHESHAM UNITED	v	MAIDENHEAD UTD	1-0	at Slough Town FC

BERKS & BUCKS SENIOR TROPHY 2000-01

LAST SEASON'S FINAL: New Bradwell St Peter v Milton Keynes City 1-1, 3p1 aet

FIRST ROUND

Holmer Green	v	Reading Town	6-1	Milton United	v	Didcot Town	0-2
Wallingford	v	Buckingham Town	8-0	Thatcham Town	v	Wantage Town	2-1
Abingdon United	v	Sandhurst Town	0-1	Newbury	v	Beaconsfield SYCOB	3-2

QUARTER - FINALS

Holmer Green	v	Newbury	2*1	Thatcham Town	v	New Bradwell St Peter	2*3
Didcot Town	v	Milton Keynes City	DT W-O	Wallingford	v	Sandhurst Town	3-1

SEMI-FINALS

Wallingford	v	New Bradwell St Peter	2-1	Holmer Green	v	Didcot Town	1-2

FINAL

DIDCOT TOWN	v	WALLINGFORD	2-1	at Chesham United FC

BIRMINGHAM COUNTY F.A.

Tel: 0121 357 4278 Fax: 0121 358 1661
Ray Hall Lane, Great Barr, Birmingham B43 6JF

Secretary: M Pennick F.F.A. **PR Officer:** A Lacey

Executives (Responsibility) T Stack (Coaching Exams/Courses) G J Southall (Referees)
Natalie Justice (Womens/Girls FDO)

Number of Affiliated Clubs Senior: 1,663 U.18: 484 **President:** J K Horrocks

Number of Affiliated Leagues: Senior: 55 Junior: 14

County Representative Teams: U18, U17, Womens Open, U18, U16

Inter County Competitions: FA County Youth, Midland County Youth (Men & Women)

County Publications: "The Centre Circle" bi-monthly newsletter

BIRMINGHAM SENIOR CUP 2000-01

(42 entries) (FOUNDED 1875-76)

LAST SEASON'S FINAL: Birmingham City v Walsall 1-0

MOST WINS: Aston Villa 19 Birmingham City 9
Kidderminster Harriers 7 Wolverhampton Wanderers 7

FIRST ROUND

Kings Heath	v	West Midlands Police	4-2
Racing Club Warwick	v	Coleshill Town	0*0, 2-1
Highgate United	v	Sutton Coldfield Town	2*4
Stourbridge	v	Brierley Hill Town	3-1
Bolehal Swifts	v	Studley BKL	0-2
Sandwell Borough	v	Wednesfield	2*2, 2*4
Tividale	v	Halesowen Harriers	3*1
Lye Town	v	Gornal Athletic	1*4
Willenhall Town	v	Rugby United	1*2
Stratford Town	v	Handrahan Timbers	3*0
Oldbury United	v	Darlaston Town	4-0
Paget Rangers	v	Evesham United	0-2
Boldmere St M	v	Cradley Town	4-0
Dudley Town	v	Banbury United	0-3

SECOND ROUND

Bedworth United	v	Wednesfield	2-0
Banbury United	v	Moor Green	3-5
Evesham United	v	Hednesford Town	1-0
Solihull Borough	v	Oldbury United @ OU	3-0
Stratford Town	v	Kings Heath	0-1
Rugby United	v	Racing Club Warwick	3-0
Halesowen Town	v	Redditch United	0-1
Tividale	v	Boldmere St Michaels	0-2
Studley BKL	v	Atherstone United	1-0
Tamworth	v	Stourbridge	4-2
Nuneaton Borough	v	Sutton Coldfield Town	2-1
Gornal Athletic	v	Burton Albion	3-1

THIRD ROUND

Walsall	v	Bedworth United	3-0
Moor Green	v	Boldmere St Michaels	3-0
Solihull Borough	v	Tamworth @T	0-2
Nuneaton Borough	v	Gornal Athletic	6-1
Redditch United	v	Birmingham City	1-5
West Bromwich Alb	v	Evesham Utd	WBA W-O
Kings Heath	v	Studley BKL	1-0
Wolverhampton W	v	Rugby United	4-0

QUARTER-FINALS

Kings Heath	v	West Bromwich Alb	0-6
Moor Green	v	Walsall	4-2
Wolverhampton W	v	Tamworth	2-4
Birmingham City	v	Nuneaton Borough	4-2

SEMI-FINALS

Moor Green	v	Birmingham City	3-1
Tamworth	v	West Bromwich Alb	2-0

FINAL

Moor Green	v	Tamworth	3-1

CAMBRIDGESHIRE F.A. LTD

Tel: 01223 576770 Fax: 01223 576780 Email: cambsfa@dial.pipex.com
City Ground, Milton Road, Cambridge CB4 1FA

Secretary: Roger Pawley

Executives (Responsibility) Richard Nichols (Asst Gen Sec, County Referees Sec)
Jim Hill (Football Development Officer)
Phil Mitcham (Competitions Secretary)

Number of Affiliated Clubs Senior: 350 U.18: 50

Number of Affiliated Leagues: Senior: 1 Junior: 6

County Representative Teams: U18, U16, Womens

Inter County Competitions: East Anglian Counties

President: W W Ashton
Chairman: J W Coad

CAMBRIDGESHIRE INVITATION CUP 2000-01

(12 entries) (FOUNDED 1950-51)

LAST SEASON'S FINAL: Cambridge City v Mildenhall Town 3-0

MOST WINS: Wisbech Town 9 Cambridge City 9 Chatteris Town 7

PRELIMINARY ROUND

Chatteris Town	v	Leverington Sports	5-0	Over Sports	v	Histon	2-3
Sawston United	v	Cambridge City @CC	2-5	Wisbech Town	v	Ely City	4-1

FIRST ROUND

March Town United	v	Histon	16/1	Cambridge City	v	Mildenhall Town	0*1
Soham Town Rangers	v	Chatteris Town	4-1	Wisbech Town	v	Newmarket Town	3-2

SECOND ROUND

Mildenhall Town	v	Wisbech Town	0-1	Soham Town Rngrs	v	March/Histon	0-4

FINAL

HISTON v WISBECH TOWN 2-0 at Abbey Stadium, Cambridge United FC att; 152

Huntingdon Town FC won the Cambridgeshire Junior Cup and promotion in the Cambs League.
Photo: Gordon Whittington

CHESHIRE F.A.

Tel: 01606 871166 Fax: 01606 871292 Football Development: 01606 871155

The Cottage, Moss Farm Recreation Centre, Winnington, Northwich CW8 4BG

Secretary & Press Officer: Maureen J Dunford

Executives (Responsibility) John Ackerley (Coaching Exams/Courses)
Bob Cooper (Referees)
Jacci Cooper (Women's Football)

Number of Affiliated Clubs Senior: 816 U.18: 325

President: Alan Burbidge

Number of Affiliated Leagues: Senior: 27 Junior: 13

County Representative Teams: U16 Girls teams

Inter County Competitions: FA County Youth, Northern Counties Youth Cup, Ladies Cup and Senior Cup

CHESHIRE SENIOR CUP 2000-01

(18 entries) (FOUNDED 1879-80)

LAST SEASON'S FINAL: Macclesfield Town v Altrincham 2-1

MOST WINS: Macclesfield Town 20 Northwich Victoria 16 Crewe Alexandra 12 Runcorn 12

PRELIMINARY ROUND

Crewe Alexandra	v	Nantwich Town	9-0	Vauxhall Motors	v	Stalybridge Celtic	0-2

FIRST ROUND

Witton Albion	v	Congleton Town	4-2	Warrington Town	v	Woodley Sports	2*2 0-2
Tranmere Rovers	v	Macclesfield Town	1-2	Northwich Victoria	v	Altrincham	1-0
Runcorn	v	Stockport County	1-4	Winsford United	v	Stalybridge Celtic	0-1
Crewe Alexandra	v	Chester City	2*1	Hyde United	v	Cheadle Town	6-1

SECOND ROUND

Northwich Victoria	v	Hyde United	1-2	Witton Albion	v	Stalybridge Celtic	1-2
Woodley Sports	v	Macclesfield Town	1-5	Stockport County	v	Crewe Alexandra	3-1

SEMI-FINALS

Macclesfield Town	v	Stockport County	5-8	Hyde United	v	Stalybridge Celtic	1-4

FINAL

STALYBRIDGE C	v	STOCKPORT CO	5-1	at Hyde United FC. Att: 855

Cheshire Senior Cup Final: (l-r): J P Damiao, Gary Burgess (Stalybridge), E J Tarry, D Pugh, P Harrison, Glynn Hancock (Stockport) Photo: Keith Clayton

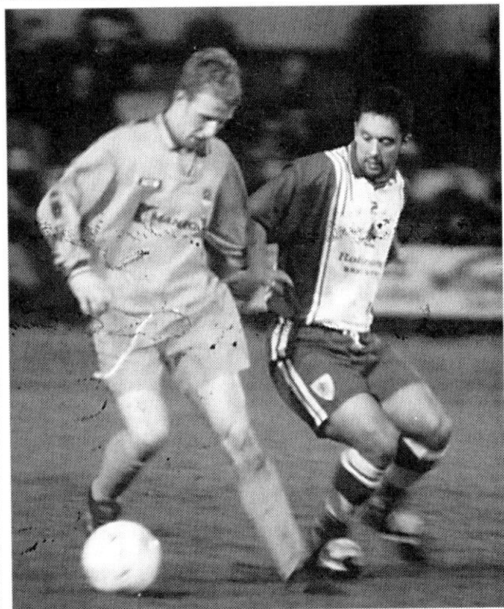

Top: Kevin Parr (Stalybridge) scores his second goal in the Cheshire Senior Cup Final against Stockport.

Centre left: The appreciative Stalybridge crowd.

Centre right: Steve Pickford (Stalybridge) and Dave Smith (Stockport)

Bottom: Gary Bauress and Gary Ingham, Stalybridge, with the Cheshire Senior Cup.

Photos: Keith Clayton

CHESHIRE AMATEUR CUP 2000-01

(FOUNDED 1886-87)

LAST SEASON'S FINAL: BICC Helsby v Barnton 3-1

MOST WINS: ICI Alkali 9 Cammell Laird 7 Poulton Victoria 6

THIRD ROUND (8 matches)

Ashville	v	Christleton	0-1	Barnton	v	Cammell Laird	1-3
Knutsford	v	Heswall	2-2, 4p2	Lymm HSOB	v	Shell	0-2
Pavillions	v	Vauxhall	2-4	Poulton Victoria	v	Dukinfield Town	2-0
Styal	v	Stork	0-1	Upton AA	v	Poynton	1-5

FOURTH ROUND (4 matches)

Christleton	v	Poynton	0-1	Knutsford	v	Cammell Laird	1-2
Poulton Victoria	v	Shell	2-4	Stork	v	Vauxhall	1-1, 1p4

SEMI FINALS

Cammell Laird	v	Poynton	3-0	Shell	v	Vauxhall	3-4

FINAL

CAMMELL LAIRD v VAUXHALL 1-0 at Chester City FC

WIRRAL SENIOR CUP 2000-01

(FOUNDED 1885-86)

LAST SEASON'S FINAL: Cammell Laird v Vauxhall 2-1 aet

MOST WINS: Cammell Laird 10 Tranmere Rovers 9 Poulton Victoria 8
Heswall 7 Ellesmere Port 6 Stork 6

SECOND ROUND (4 matches)

New Brighton	v	Mersey Royal	0-5	Poulton Victoria	v	Cammell Laird	3-2
Shell	v	Castrol Social	2-1	Vauxhall	v	Stork	0-1

SEMI FINALS

Shell	v	Poulton Victoria	0-5	Stork	v	Mersey Royal	3-5

FINAL

POULTON VICTORIA v MERSEY ROYAL 3-2 at Cammell Laird FC

WIRRAL AMATEUR CUP 2000-01

(FOUNDED 1892-93)

LAST SEASON'S FINAL: Cammell Laird Reserves v Charing Cross 3-2

MOST WINS: Heswall 9 Poulton Victoria 5 Stork 5 Cammell Laird 4 Shell 4 West Kirby 4

THIRD ROUND (4 matches)

Ashville Reserves	v	Cammell Laird Res	1-2	Grange Athletic	v	Charing Cross	
Heswall Reserves	v	Mallaby	0-1	Manor Athletic	v	Bronze Social	1-1, 2p4

SEMI FINALS

Cammell Laird Res	v	Bronze Social	4-1	Mallaby	v	Grange Athletic	3-1

FINAL

MALLABY v CAMMELL LAIRD RES 1-0 at Ashville FC

ADDITIONAL 2000-01 CUP FINALS

CHESHIRE SUNDAY CUP

Queens Park v Offerton United 1-1, 3p2

RUNCORN SENIOR CUP

Helsby v Pavilions 3-2

NORTHERN COUNTIES CHAMPIONSHIP

Cheshire FA v Westmorland FA 2-1

WIRRAL SUNDAY PREMIER CUP

Queens Park v The Queens 2-1

WIRRAL JUNIOR CUP

North Star v Abbotsford 2-0

CHESTER SENIOR CUP

Christleton v Blacon Youth Club 2-0

WIRRAL SUNDAY JUNIOR CUP

Christleton Youth v Ashville Youth 1-1. 4p2

CHESHIRE YOUTH CUP

Shaftesbury Boys v Christleton Youth 4-0

CORNWALL F.A.

Tel: 01726 74080 Fax: 01726 76174 E-mail: cfa@btclick.com
1 High Cross Street, St Austell, Cornwall PL25 4AB

Secretary: Barry Cudmore

Executives (Responsibility) John Riley (Coaching Exams/Courses)
Ian Anear (Referees)
Phil Cardew (Football Development Officer)

Number of Affiliated Clubs Senior: 311 U.18: 84

Number of Affiliated Leagues: Senior: 18 Junior: 3

County Representative Teams: Senior, Youth U18

Inter County Competitions: South West Counties Senior & Youth, FA County Youth Cup

President: B F Conyon
Chairman: D G Champion

CORNWALL SENIOR CUP 2000-01

(41 entries) (FOUNDED 1892-93)

LAST SEASON'S FINAL: St Blazey v Porthleven 1*1, 2-1

MOST WINS: Truro City 12 St Austell 11
St Blazey 11 Penzance 10 Torpoint Athletic 10

FIRST ROUND

Helston Athletic	v	Bude Town	1-4
Perranwell	v	Camelford	2-0
Roche	v	Mousehole	6-1
St Dennis	v	Troon	1-0
St Just	v	Padstow United	2-2 5-1
Illogan RBL	v	Ludgvan	2-1
RNAS Culdrose	v	St Breward	2-1
St Agnes	v	Marazion Blues	2-1
St Ives Town	v	Nanpean Rovers	4-1

SECOND ROUND

Bude Town	v	Wendron	3-1
Foxhole Stars	v	Launceston	1-6
Newquay	v	Perranwell	4-1
Penzance	v	RNAS Culdrose	7-0
Probus	v	Wadebridge Town	0-1
St Blazey	v	St Austell	3-0
St Ives Town	v	Goonhaven A	1p4,1-1,2*2
Sticker	v	St Dennis	0-3
Callington Town	v	Saltash United	0-0 rep
Millbrook	v	Falmouth Town	3-1
Penryn Athletic	v	Roche	0-0 0-1
Porthleven	v	Liskeard Athletic	2-0
St Agnes	v	Bodmin Town	4p5 2-2 1*1
St Cleer	v	Torpoint Athletic	0-4
St Just	v	Illogan RBL	1-5
Truro City	v	Mullion	4-1

THIRD ROUND

Bodmin Town	v	Wadebridge Town	0-2
Goonhavern Athletic	v	Newquay	1-4
Penzance	v	Millbrook	1-2
St Dennis	v	Illogan RBL	0-2
Bude Town	v	St Blazey	0-2
Launceston	v	Saltash United	0-1
Roche	v	Porthleven	1-4
Torpoint Athletic	v	Truro City	3-1

QUARTER-FINALS

Illogan RBL	v	St Blazey	0-4
Newquay	v	Saltash United	2-2, 1-2
Millbrook	v	Porthleven	2-2, 2-3
Torpoint Athletic	v	W'bridge T	1p3, 0-0, 1*1

SEMI-FINALS

Porthleven	v	Wadebridge Town	3-1
St Blazey	v	Saltash United	3-0

FINAL

Porthleven	v	St Blazey	2-2, 4-0	at Newquay FC

CUMBERLAND F.A.

Tel: 01900 872310 Fax: 01900 872310
17 Oxford Street, Workington, Cumbria CA14 2AL

Secretary & Press Officer: Geoff Turrell
Executives (Responsibility) Keith Hunton (Coaching Exams/Courses)
Harry Upton & Thomas Jackson (Referees)
Number of Affiliated Clubs Senior: 187 U.18: 186
Number of Affiliated Leagues: Senior: 7 Junior: 4
County Representative Teams: Senior, Youth, Womens
Inter County Competitions: FA County Youth

President: Brian Taylor
Chairman: J Williamson

CUMBERLAND SENIOR CUP 2000-01

(41 entries) (FOUNDED 1960-61)

LAST SEASON'S FINAL: Workington v Carlisle United 2-0

MOST WINS: Penrith 11 Gretna 9 Haig Colliery 3

FIRST ROUND (9 matches)

Langwathby	v	Mirehouse Comm	
Keswick	v	Hearts of Liddlesdale	6-0
Abbeytown	v	Longtown	4-1
British Steel	v	Northbank	2-8
Carleton Rovers	v	Wigton Harriers	1-3
North Lakeland	v	Emperors Palace	w/o NL
Frizington White Star	v	Penrith Rangers	
Egremont St Marys	v	Penrith	0-4
Parton United	v	Carlisle United	0-12

Langwathby and Emperors Palace withdrew

SECOND ROUND (16 matches)

Cleator Moor Celtic	v	Wigton Harriers	6-3
Netherhall	v	Windscale	4-0
Abbeytown	v	Gretna	2-1
Penrith	v	Cleater Moor Celtic	3-1
Cockermouth	v	Carlisle United	W/O C
Windscale	v	Whitehaven	5-0
Whitehaven (NW)	v	Thornhill Bulls	5-0
Mirehouse	v	North Lakeland	11-0
Braithwaite	v	Frizington WS	W/O F
Harraby Catholic	v	Northbank	0-2
St Bees	v	Greystoke	3-2
Silloth	v	Salterbeck United	W/O S
Wetheriggs United	v	Northbank	0-2
Portland	v	Whitehaven Miners S	2-1
Carlisle City	v	Workington	2-1
Keswick	v	Kirkoswald	7-0

Braithwaite expelled. Salterbeck United and Carlisle United withdrew

THIRD ROUND (8 matches)

St Bees	v	Whitehaven	4-2
Keswick	v	Northbank (C & D)	3-4
Carlisle City	v	Mirehouse	2-1
Windscale	v	Cleator Moor Celtic	5-0
Abbeytown	v	Northbank (NA)	0-6
Netherhall	v	Cockermouth	2-1
Penrith	v	Silloth	5-0
Portland	v	Frizington White Star	0-8

FOURTH ROUND (4 matches)

Northbank (NA)	v	Carlisle City	2-1
Netherhall	v	Windscale	0-2
Northbank (C & D)	v	Frizington White Star	1-3
Penrith	v	St Bees	9-1

SEMI-FINALS

Northbank (NA)	v	Frizington White Star	3-0
Penrith	v	Windscale	2-1

FINAL

NORTHBANK (NA) v PENRITH 2-0 Attendance: 318

DERBYSHIRE F.A.

Tel: 01332 361422 Fax: 01332 360130
The Grandstand, Moorways Stadium, Moor Lane, Derby DE24 9HY

Secretary & Press Officer: K Compton
Executives (Responsibility) County Secretary
(Coaching Exams/Courses, Referees, Womens Football)
No. Affiliated Clubs & Leagues 800
Chairman: R F Johnson
County Representative Teams: U16
Inter County Competitions: East Midlands Youth Football Combination

DERBYSHIRE SENIOR CUP 2000-01

(24 entries) (FOUNDED 1883-84)

LAST SEASON'S FINAL: Ilkeston Town v Gresley Rovers 4-0 on aggregate

MOST WINS: Derby County 15 Ilkeston Town 13
Buxton 8 Chesterfield 8 Heanor Town 8

FIRST ROUND

Sth Normanton Ath	v	Mickleover RBL	4-1	Sandiacre Town	v	Blackwel M W	0-1
Graham St Prims	v	Ripley Town	3-2	Long Eaton United	v	Shirebrook Town	2-3

SECOND ROUND

Shirebrook Town	v	Graham St Prims	1*2	Stanton Ilkeston	v	Heanor Town	0-1
Holbrook	v	Sth Normanton Ath	2-1	Shardlow St James	v	Blackwell MW	2-3

THIRD ROUND

Blackwell MW	v	Staveley MW	1-3	Alfreton Town	v	Belper Town	2-1
Stapenhill	v	Glossop N End	GNE T/A	Holbrook	v	Matlock Town	1-2
Gresley Rovers	v	Graham Street Prims	0-2	Glapwell	v	Buxton	3-1
Mickleover Sports	v	Ilkeston Town	1-0	Heanor Town	v	Borrowash Victoria	1-2

QUARTER-FINALS

Matlock Town	v	Alfreton Town	0-4	Borrowash Victoria	v	Staveley MW	3*1

SEMI-FINALS

Glapwell	v	Borrowash Victoria	3-1	Glossop North End	v	Alfreton Town	4-0

FINAL (1st Leg)

GLAPWELL	v	GLOSSOP N END	3-3

FINAL (2nd Leg)

GLOSSOP N END	v	GLAPWELL	2*2, 4p2

DEVON F.A.

Tel: 01626 332077 Fax: 01626 336814
County Headquarters, Coach Road, Newton Abbot, Devon TQ12 1EJ

Secretary & Press Officer: Chris J Davidson
Executives (Responsibility) R Soper (Coaching Exams) C Cox (Referees)
M Lawrence (Womens Football) C Davey (Coaching Courses)
Number of Affiliated Clubs Senior: 161 U.18: 252
Number of Affiliated Leagues: Senior: 50 Junior: 10
Chairman: Brian Williams
County Representative Teams: Senior, U18, Womens
Inter County Competitions: South West Counties Championship
County Publications: "Kick Off" - bi-monthly Newsletter

Per Temps DEVON PREMIER CUP 2000-01
(71 entries)
HOLDERS Vospers Oak Villa

FIRST ROUND

Buckland Athletic	v	Hatherleigh Town	4-1
Galmpton United	v	Seaton Town	2-1
Putford	v	British Aerospace	P W-O
Witheridge	v	Crediton United	3-0
Dolton Rangers	v	Newton Abbot 66	8-0
Mainstone Sports	v	Alphington	0-5
St Peters Jersey	v	Civil Serv S & Leisure	3-0

SECOND ROUND

Alphington	v	Kingsteignton	4-1
Breakwater Brkrs PD	v	Stoke Gabriel	0-1
Buckland	v	Liverton United	2*1
St Peters Jersey	v	Plymouth Parkway	6-0
Dartington Sports	v	Putford	8-1
Dolton Rangers	v	Topsham Town	3-1
Elite Hair	v	Northam Lions	5-1
Galmpton	v	Witheridge	2-4
High Bickington	v	Prince Rock	3-2
Bonne Fenetre	v	Newton Abbot Spurs	1-5
Ottery St Mary	v	Plympton United	4-1
Sidmouth Town	v	Braunton	1-3
St Martins	v	Bishop Steignton Utd	3-1
Tavistock	v	Cullompton Rangers	5*3
Upton Athletic	v	Exeter St Thomas	4-1
Watts Blake Bearne	v	Vospers Oak Villa	1-5
Appledore	v	Newton St Cyres	2-0
Buckfastleigh Rngrs	v	Combe Martin	4-0
Budleigh Salterton	v	Torrington Admirals	3-1
Chudleigh Athletic	v	Holsworthy	0-11
Dartmouth AFC	v	Elmore Res	5-1
Elburton Villa	v	Newton Abbot	1-5
Feniton	v	Okehampton Argyle	3-4
Helle Rovers	v	Exeter Civil Service	3-1
Ivybridge Town	v	Bradworthy United	6-0
Mount Gould BP	v	Jersey Scottish	0-1
Pinhoe	v	Kingskerswell	0-3
South Molton	v	Boca Seniors	0-3
Tap & Barrell	v	Plymouth Civil Service	3*5
Teignmouth	v	Plymstock United	2-1
Victoria Rangers	v	Shamwickshire Rovers	0-1
Willand Rovers	v	Heavitree United	3-1

THIRD ROUND

Upton Athletic	v	Braunton	1-0
Alphington	v	Budleigh Salterton	7-0
Holsworthy	v	Plymouth Civil Serv.	3-2
Vospers Oak Villa	v	Ivybridge Town	2-3
Dartmouth	v	Teignmouth	7-0
Elite Hair	v	Newton Abbot	0-3
Witheridge	v	Hele Rovers	1-0
High Bickington	v	Shamwickshire	4-0
Ottery St Mary	v	St Martins	2-1
Willand Rovers	v	Newton Abbot Spurs	5-3
Dolton Rangers	v	Jersey Scottish	2-6
Appledore	v	Buckfastleigh	4-1
Buckland Athletic	v	Boca Senior	7-3
Okehampton Argyle	v	Tavistock	2-4
Stoke Gabriel	v	Kingkerswell	2-0
Dartington	v	St Peters Jersey	0-5

FOURTH ROUND

Newton Abbott	v	Willand	4-4, 3p2
Witheridge	v	Dartmouth	2-3
Tavistock	v	Stoke Gabriel	1-0
Buckland Athletic	v	High Bickington	9-0
Appledore	v	Upton Athletic	4-1
Ottery St Mary	v	Holsworthy	2-0
Ivybridge Town	v	Jersey Scottish	2-3
Alphington	v	St Peters Jersey	4-0

FIFTH ROUND

Tavistock	v	Ottery St Mary	2-1
Alphington	v	Dartmouth	1-3
Jersey Scottish	v	Buckland Athletic	1-3
Newton Abbot	v	Appledore	1-0

SEMI-FINALS

Buckland Athletic	v	Dartmouth	2-3
Newton Abbot	v	Tavistock	1-0

FINAL

DARTMOUTH	v	NEWTON ABBOT	5p6,3*3

DORSET F.A.

Tel: 01202 682375 Fax: 01202 666577
County Ground, Blandford Close, Hamworthy, Poole BH15 4BF

Secretary: Peter Hough
Deputy Secretary: Colin Chainey
Press Officer: Ian Hallett
Executives (Responsibility) S N Whittle (Referees)
Sue Hough (Football Development)
County Representative Teams: U21, U18, Womens, Womens U18
Inter County Competitions: South West Championship for all the above

President: Spencer Miles
Chairman: Geoff Pike

DORSET SENIOR CUP 2000-01

(37 entries) (FOUNDED 1887-88)

LAST SEASON'S FINAL: Weymouth v Wimborne Town 2-1

MOST WINS: Weymouth 26 Poole Town 10 Portland United 10 Bridport 9

FIRST ROUND

Portland United	v	Okeford United	6-0
Lytchettt Red Triangle	v	Witchampton United	3-2
Hamworthy United	v	Chickerell United	1-2
Dorchester United	v	Poole Town	1*3
Shaftsbury	v	Dorset Knob	2-3
Weymouth United	v	Stourpaine	1v2 WU T-A
Holt United	v	Sturminster Newton U	0-2
Flight Refuelling	v	Dorchester YMCA	9-1
Verwood Town	v	Poole Borough	3*4

SECOND ROUND

St Mary's RC	v	Wareham Rangers	2-5
Flight Refuelling	v	Bournemouth Sports	2-3
St Pauls Jersey	v	Dorset Knob	5-2
Badger Sports	v	Sherborne Town	2-0
Weymouth United	v	Swanage T & H	4*4, 2*3
Stur Newton United	v	Trinidad New Star	3-0
Gillingham Town	v	Chickerell United	3-0
Weymouth Sports	v	Poole Town	1-0
Allendale	v	Hamworthy Recreation	1-4
Blandford United	v	Beaminster	3-0
Poole Borough	v	Lytchett Red Triangle	8-2
Portland United (Parley Sports w/d)			Bye

THIRD ROUND

Weymouth	v	Weymouth Sports	7-2
Wareham Rangers	v	Sturminster Newton U	1-3
Bournemouth Sports	v	Dorchester Town	0-4
Bridport	v	Gillingham Town	0-1
Wimborne Town	v	Poole Boro	2*1
Badger Sports	v	Portland United	1v4 BS T-A
Blandford United	v	St Pauls Jersey	1-2
Hamworthy Rec	v	SwanageT & Herston	3-0

FOURTH ROUND

Dorchester Town	v	Hamworthy Recreation	7-1
Stur Newton United	v	Badger Sports	0-1
Gillingham Town	v	St Pauls Jersey	4-1
Wimborne Town	v	Weymouth	1-2

SEMI-FINALS

Badger Sports	v	Dorchester Town	0-5
Weymouth	v	Gillingham Town	5-1

FINAL

WEYMOUTH v DORCHESTER T 1*2 at Weymouth FC. Att: 618

DURHAM F.A.

Tel: 0191 384 8653 Fax: 0191 384 3234
"Codeslaw', Ferens Park, Durham DH1 1JZ

Secretary: John Topping

Executives (Responsibility) A Philliskirk (Coaching Exams/Courses)
J C Topping (Referees)

Number of Affiliated Clubs Senior: 1100 Junior: 400

Number of Affiliated Leagues: Senior: 50 Junior: 26

President: F D Pattison

Chairman: F D Pattison

County Representative Teams: U18

Inter County Competitions: Association of Northern Counties, FA County Youth

Albany DURHAM CHALLENGE CUP 2000-01

(44 entries) (FOUNDED 1883-84)

LAST SEASON'S FINAL: Darlington v Brandon United 3-1

MOST WINS: Sunderland 21 Spennymoor United 15 Bishop Auckland 14

PRELIMINARY ROUND

Washington Ikeda	v	Easington Colliery	0-1
Washington Nissan	v	Willington	3-2
Horden CW	v	Jarrow Rfng BCA 3p1	1*1
Crook Town	v	Murton	1-0
Annfield Plain	v	Norton & Stcktn A	A W-O
Jarrow	v	Eppleton CW	9-0
Shotton Comrades	v	S'land Ryhope CA	3-0
Evenwood Town	v	Shildon	2-6
Birtley Town	v	Wolviston	1-8
Esh Winning	v	Whickham	3-1
S Sh Harton & West	v	Sth Sh Simonside SC	3-0
Sth Shields Cleadon	v	Horden CW Athletic	10-1

FIRST ROUND

Annfield Plain	v	Tow Law Town	1-3
Bishop Auckland	v	Sth Sh Harton & West	8-0
Esh Winning	v	Darlington Res	1-2
Crook Town	v	Shildon	1-2
Horden CW	v	Sth Shields Cleadon	5-1
Stanley United	v	Dunston Federation	0-4
Billingham Town	v	Wolviston	1-0
Chester le Street Tn	v	Peterlee Newtown	3-1
Hartlepool Utd Res	v	Ryhope CW	3-0
South Shields	v	Spennymoor United	2-0
Hebburn Town	v	Jarrow	3-2
Boldon CA	v	Shotton Comrades	1-5
Seaham Red Star	v	Washington Nissan	0-1
Billingham Synthonia	v	West Auckland Town	1-2
Easington Colliery	v	Brandon United 7p8	0*0
Consett	v	Durham City	2-3

SECOND ROUND

Shildon	v	South Shields	0-4
Washington Nissan	v	Hartlepool United Res	2-0
Billingham Town	v	Dunston F B	3-1
Tow Law Town	v	Durham City	2-1
Chester Le Street Tn	v	Brandon United 3p4	1*1
Darlington Res	v	Hebburn Town	4-3
Shotton Comrades	v	West Auckland Town	0-3
Bishop Auckland	v	Horden	2-0

THIRD ROUND

Washington Nissan	v	Bishop Auckland	0-3
Darlington	v	West Auckland Town	0-1
Tow Law Town	v	South Shields	7-3
Brandon United	v	Billingham Town	2-1

SEMI-FINALS

Bishop Auckland	v	Tow Law Town	5-1
Brandon United	v	West Auckland Town	2-0

FINAL

BISHOP AUCKLAND	v	BRANDON UTD	2-0

at Durham City FC

Bishop Auckland's Danny Mellanby heads clear in the Durham Challenge Cup final against Brandon United.

EAST RIDING F.A. LTD

Tel: 01482 221158 Fax: 01482 221159 E.Mail: secretary@ercfa.freeserve.co.uk
50 Boulevard, Hull HU3 2TB

Secretary & Press Officer: Dennis R Johnson
Football Development Officer: Jonathan Day
Executives (Responsibility) T Mason (Coaching Exams/Courses)
A Youngs (Referees) M Edge (Womens Football)
Number of Affiliated Clubs Senior: 408 U.18: 214
Number of Affiliated Leagues: Senior: 5 Junior: 3
County Representative Teams: Senior, U18, Womens
Inter County Competitions: Association of Northern Counties, FA County Youth, East Midlands U18

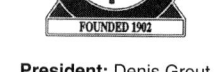

President: Denis Grout
Chairman: M Rawding

EAST RIDING SENIOR CUP 2000-01

(23 entries) (FOUNDED 1902)

LAST SEASON'S FINAL: North Ferriby United v Hall Road Rangers 2-1

MOST WINS: Hull City 25 Bridlington Town 12 North Ferriby United 8

FIRST ROUND

Driffield	v	Sculcoates Amateurs	1-3
Reckitts	v	Hider Foods	2-0
Discount Carpets	v	Nightjar	4-3
Westela & Willerby	v	Hall Rd Rgrs R	WW W-O
Beverley Town	v	Humberstone Chem	1-2
East Hull Amateurs	v	Walkington Wanderers	8-4
North Cave	v	Hedon United	2-0

SECOND ROUND

Bridlington Town	v	Hull City	0-4
Discount Carpets FC	v	East Hull Amat	4-6q
Humberside Chem	v	North Cave	3-2
Reckitts	v	Charleston	4-0
Chisholms	v	Easington United	2p3 2*2
Hall Road Rangers	v	North Ferriby United	0-5
Ideal Standard FC	v	Hutton Cranswick Utd	10-1
Westella & Willerby	v	Sculcoates Amateurs	2-3

THIRD ROUND

North Ferriby United	v	Ideal Standard	2-1
Sculcoates Amateurs	v	East Hull Amateurs	5-2
Reckitts	v	Hull City	1-1, 2p4
Easington United	v	Humberstone Ch	1-1, 5-0

SEMI-FINALS

Easington United	v	Hull City	0-3
Sculcoates Amat.	v	North Ferriby United	1-3

FINAL

HULL CITY	v	NORTH FERRIBY U	0-1	at Boothferry Park, Hull City AFC

EAST RIDING COUNTRY CUP 2000-01

(27 entries)

LAST SEASON'S FINAL: Ward v North Ferriby United Reserves 4-1

FIRST ROUND

Hutton C'wick SRA	v	Greyhound OB	2-1
Shiptonthorpe United	v	Beverley Foresters	5-2
Brandesburton	v	Middleton Rovers	2-1
Nags Head Brid.	v	Mermaid	3-1
Beverley Old Gram	v	Bridlington Rovers	5-2
Holme Rovers	v	Wold Newton	7-0
Hutton Cranswick U	v	Dunnington	D W-O
Ward	v	Horsea Town	5-0
Driffield Town	v	Filey Town	0-9
Bridlington SC Res	v	Hunmanby United	3-0
Pocklington Town	v	North Cave Res	3-0

SECOND ROUND

Brandesburton	v	Crown	0-3
Bridlington S C Res	v	Nags Head Bridlington	1-3
Hutton C'wick SRA	v	Withernsea	3-4
Pocklington Town	v	Ward	0-1
Bridlington S C	v	Filey Town	3-5
Holme Rovers	v	Dunnington	3-5
Long Riston	v	Beverley Gramarians	4-3
Shiptonthorpe Utd	v	Bridlington George	1-2

THIRD ROUND

Withernsea	v	Dunnington	2-3
Crown	v	Filey Town	5-4
Long Riston	v	Ward	1-3
Nags Head Brid.	v	Bridlington George	3-1

SEMI-FINALS

Crown	v	Ward	0-3
Nags Head Brid.	v	Dunnington	1-0

FINAL

WARD v NAGS HEAD BRID. 4-0 at Queensgate, Bridlington Town FC

ESSEX F.A.

Tel: 01245 357727 Fax: 01245 344430
31 Mildmay Road, Chelmsford CM2 0DN

Chief Executive: Philip Sammons
Executives (Responsibility) Steve Goodsell (Coaching Exams/Courses)
Robert Ellis (Referees) Lana Bond (Womens Football)
Number of Affiliated Clubs Senior: 1367 U.18: 463
Number of Affiliated Leagues: Senior: 40 Junior: 15
County Representative Teams: Senior, Intermediate, U18, U16, Womens
Inter County Competitions: East Anglian, Southern Counties

Chairman: R Brooks
Vice -Chairman: E Fairchild

ESSEX SENIOR CUP 2000-01

(42 entries) (FOUNDED 1883-84)

LAST SEASON'S FINAL: Canvey Island v Purfleet 2-0

MOST WINS: Ilford 13 Walthamstow Avenue 12 Grays Athletic 8 Leyton 8

FIRST ROUND

Clapton	v	Bowers United	4-1

SECOND ROUND

Tiptree United	v	Stansted	8-2
Brentwood	v	Aveley	2*3
Southend Manor	v	Burnham Ramblers	3-0
Leyton	v	Hornchurch	0-1
Concord Rangers	v	East Ham United	4p2 0*0
Hullbridge Sports	v	Clapton	4-0
Barkingside	v	Stanway Rovers	3-2
Ilford	v	Waltham Abbey	1-4
Brightlingsea United	v	Saffron Walden Town	1-3

THIRD ROUND

Grays Athletic	v	Leyton Pennant	4-2
Southend United	v	Harwich & Parkeston	3-1
Canvey Island	v	Barkingside	3-0
Hullbridge Sports	v	Billericay Town	2-3
East Thurrock United	v	Braintree Town	7-0
Saffron Walden Town	v	Waltham Abbey	2-3
Barking	v	Halstead Town	1-0
Ford United	v	Maldon Town	1-4
Tiptree United	v	Hornchurch	2-1
Aveley	v	Purfleet	0-4
Great Wakering Rvrs	v	Wivenhoe Town	1-0
Witham Town	v	Romford	0-1
Concord Rangers	v	Southend Manor	3-1
Clacton Town	v	Tilbury	0-1
Heybridge Swifts	v	Chelmsford City	8-0
Dagenham & Red.	v	Harlow Town	4-1

FOURTH ROUND

Heybridge Swifts	v	Tiptree United	4-3
Grays Athletic	v	Great Wak. R	GWR W/O
Purfleet	v	Southend United	4-0
Maldon Town	v	Romford	3-1
East Thurrock Utd	v	Dagenham & Red.	2*3
Barking	v	Canvey Island	2-5
Billericay Town	v	Waltham Abbey	4-1
Concord Rangers	v	Tilbury	0-1

FIFTH ROUND

Purfleet	v	Tilbury	1*0
Heybridge Swifts	v	Tiptree United	2-0
Canvey Island	v	Gt Wakering Rovers	3-1
Dagenham & Red.	v	Maldon Town	4-0

SEMI-FINALS

Dagenham & Red.	v	Heybridge Swifts	2*1
Purfleet	v	Canvey Island	0-1

FINAL

CANVEY ISLAND	v	DAGENHAM & RED.	2*2

Dagenham & Redbridge won 5-4 on penalties

ESSEX THAMES-SIDE TROPHY 2000-01

(24 entries) (FOUNDED 1945-46)

LAST SEASON'S FINAL: Purfleet v Waltham Abbey/Canvey Island

MOST WINS: Ilford 13 Walthamstow Avenue 12 Grays Athletic 8 Leyton 8

FIRST ROUND

Leyton Pennant	v	Witham Town	LP W-O	Ilford	v	Hornchurch	3p4 2*2
Hullbridge Sports	v	Brentwood	^	Clapton	v	Southend Manor	0-5
Concord Rangers	v	Ford United	FU W-O	Basildon United	v	Bowers United	4-2
Great Wakering R	v	Barkingside	1-0	Romford	v	Maldon Town	MT W-O

^ Clubs removed

SECOND ROUND

Burnham Ramblers	v	Barking	3-2	Grays Athletic	v	Leyton Pennant	GA W-O
East Thurrock United	v	Ford United	^	Hullbridge/Brentwood	v	Maldon Town	MT bye
Southend Manor	v	Aveley	SM W-O	Hornchurch	v	Canvey Island	H W-O
Tilbury	v	Purfleet		Basildon United	v	Great Wakering Rvrs	1-2

^ Clubs removed

THIRD ROUND

Hornchurch	v	Grays Athletic	GA W-O	Gt Wakering Rovers	v	Burnham Ramblers	4-0
Maldon Town	v	E Thurrock/Ford	MT Bye	Southend Manor	v	Purfleet	P W-O

SEMI-FINALS

Gt Wakering Rovers	v	Maldon Town	3*1	Grays Athletic	v	Purfleet	6-0

FINAL

GRAYS ATHLETIC v G WAKERING R 3p0, 3*3 at Recreation Ground, Grays Athletic FC

GLOUCESTERSHIRE F.A. LIMITED

Tel: 01454 615888 Fax: 01454 618088
Oaklands Park, Almondsbury, Bristol BS32 4AG

Company Sec. & Press Officer: Paul Britton

Executives (Responsibility) Paul Britton (Coaching Exams/Courses, Womens Football)
J W Hawkins (Referees)

Number of Affiliated Clubs Senior: 868 U.18: 189 **President:** S T Rummins

Number of Affiliated Leagues: Senior: 21 Junior: 10 **Chairman:** CH Willcox MBE JP

County Representative Teams: Senior, U18, Womens, Womens U18

Inter County Competitions: South & South West Counties Championship, FA County Youth Cup

GLOUCESTERSHIRE SENIOR CUP 2000-01

(8 entries) (FOUNDED 1936-37)

LAST SEASON'S FINAL: Forest Green Rovers v Cheltenham Town 2-1

MOST WINS: Cheltenham Town 32 Gloucester City 18 Forest Green Rovers 3

FIRST ROUND

Forest Green Rovers	v	Cinderford Town	0-2	Cirencester Town	v	Bristol Rovers	3-0
Cheltenham Town	v	Mangotsfield United	3-0	Bristol City	v	Gloucester City	2-0

SEMI-FINALS

Cheltenham Town	v	Bristol City	1-2	Cinderford Town	v	Cirencester Town	3-0

FINAL

CINDERFORD TN	v	BRISTOL CITY	1-0

GLOUCESTERSHIRE SENIOR TROPHY 2000-01

(35 entries) (FOUNDED 1978-79)

LAST SEASON'S FINAL: Mangotsfield United v Patchway Town 2-0

MOST WINS: Mangotsfield United 6 Moreton Town 3 Shortwood United 2

FIRST ROUND

Cadbury Heath	v	Winterbourne United	0-1	Hardwicke	v	Bitton	0-4
Oldland Abbotonians	v	Totterdown P O B	5-3				

SECOND ROUND

Yate Town	v	Bristol Manor Farm	2-1	Almondsbury Town	v	Cirencester United	3-0
Axa	v	Pucklechurch Sports	3-1	Patchway Town	v	Harrow Hill	5p4 2*2
Fairford Town	v	Tuffley Rovers	0-1	Winterbourne United	v	Shortwood United	2-0
Viney St Swithens	v	Oldland Abbotonians	0-1	Henbury OB	v	Cheltenham Saracens	2-1
Brockworth	v	Frampton Athletic	3-0	Highridge United	v	Old Georgians	10-1
Gloucester United	v	Bishops Cleeve	8-1	Shirehampton	v	Bitton	0-4
Ellwood	v	Hallen	1-0	Tytherington Rocks	v	Broad Plain House	2-0
D R G	v	Cirencester Academy	2-5	Roman Glass St G	v	Whitminster	3p4 0*0

THIRD ROUND

Tuffley Rovers	v	Henbury O B	2-1	Gloucester United	v	Brockworth	1*0
Whitminster	v	Oldland Abbotonians	3-0	Winterbourne United	v	Tytherington Rocks	1-2
Hallen	v	Highridge United	3-2	Almondsbury Town	v	Axa Sun Life FC	3-4
Patchway Town	v	Cirencester Academy	2-3	Bitton	v	Yate Town	0-3

THIRD ROUND

Whitminster	v	Tuffley Rovers	0-1	Cirencester Academy	v	Tytherington Rocks	4-3
Hallen	v	Axa Sun Life	3-2	Gloucester United	v	Yate Town	1-3

SEMI-FINAL

Yate Town	v	Tuffley Rovers	5*4	Tytherington Rocks	v	Hallen	4-1

FINAL

TYTHERINGTON R	v	YATE TOWN	2-4	at Oaklands Park, Gloucestershire FC. Att: 395

HAMPSHIRE F.A.

Tel: 02380 791110 Fax: 02380 788340
William Pickford House, 8 Ashwood Gardens, off Winchester Road, Southampton SO16 7PW

Chief Executive: L C Jones
Executives (Responsibility) Ms S M Lopez (Coaching Exams/Courses, Womens Football)
L Burgh (Coaching) R G Barnes (Facilities Manager)
Number of Affiliated Clubs: Senior: 2000 U.18: 450
County Representative Teams: Adult, Womens, U21, Girls U16, Boys U18, Girls U18
Inter County Competitions: South West Counties, Hants & Dorset Cup

President: M E Turner
Chairman: E J Ward

HAMPSHIRE SENIOR CUP 2000-01

sponsored by Planet Logo
(45 entries) (FOUNDED 1887-88)

LAST SEASON'S FINAL: Aldershot Town v Andover 9-1

MOST WINS: Southampton 13 Newport 7 Cowes 6

FIRST ROUND

Blackfield & Langley	v	Portsmouth R N	3p0 2*2
Colden Common	v	Hamble ASSC	3-1
Esso Fawley	v	East Cowes Vic Ath	1-3
Liss Athletic	v	West Wight Mayflower	5*7
Pirelli General	v	Locksheath	3-1
Stockbridge	v	New Street	4-0
Whitchurch United	v	Bournemouth	2-3
Brading Town	v	Vosper Th'croft	6p5 3*3
Cove	v	Bishops Waltham Tn	9-1
Horndean	v	Hythe & Dibden	4-2
Petersfield Town	v	R S Basingstoke	1*2
Ringwood Town	v	Lymington Town	2-0
Sylvans Sports	v	Alton Town	3-0

SECOND ROUND

Totton	v	BAT Sports	0-1
Bashley	v	Bournemouth	1*3
Blackfield & Langley	v	Hartley Wintney	1*0
Eastleigh	v	Cowes Sports	2-1
Fleet Town	v	Ringwood Town	3-2
Hamble ASSC	v	Pirelli General	8p7 1*1
Lymington & N Milton	v	Cove	2-1
Sylvans Sports	v	Moneyfields	1-2
Andover	v	RS Basingstoke	3-1
Basingstoke Town	v	East Cowes Vic Ath	4-1
Brockenhurst	v	Farnborough Town	1-4
Fareham Town	v	Christchurch	1*2
Gosport Borough	v	Brading Town	5-0
Havant & W'ville	v	Stockbridge	4-0
Newport IOW	v	Aldershot Town	5-0
West Wight M'flower	v	Horndean	0-2

THIRD ROUND

Andover	v	Moneyfields	3-2
BAT Sports	v	Fleet Town	3*2
Eastleigh	v	Hamble ASSC	4-1
Lymington & N Milton	v	Horndean	6-0
Bournemouth	v	Havant & Waterlooville	1-5
Blackfield & Langley	v	Farnborough Tn	2p3 0*0
Christchurch	v	Gosport Borough	3-1
Newport IOW	v	Basingstoke Town	5-1

FOURTH ROUND

Havant & W'ville	v	Farnborough Town	3-0
Lymington & New M.	v	Newport IOW	4-0
BAT Sports	v	Andover	2-3
Christchurch	v	Eastleigh	1-4

SEMI-FINAL (2 legs)

Eastleigh	v	Andover	0-3, 2-3 = 2-6
Havant & W'looville	v	Lymington	4-0, 2-1 = 6-1

FINAL

HAVANT & W'VILLE v ANDOVER 0-2 at The Dell, Southampton FC

Lee Shearer, (Dover) with son Brenden and Neptune before Kent Senior Cup tie with Gravesend.
Photo: Roger Turner

HEREFORDSHIRE F.A.

Tel: 01432 270308 (H)
1 Muirfield Close, Holmer, Hereford HR1 1QB

Secretary & Press Officer: Jim Lambert

Executives (Responsibility) J Watkins (Football Development Officer)
A Jenkins (Referees) G Stevens (County Coach)
R J Perks (Womens Football)

Number of Affiliated Clubs Senior: 125 U.18: 114

Number of Affiliated Leagues: Senior: 1 Junior: 1

County Representative Teams: Under 18, Under 16

Inter County Competitions: Midland Counties U18, East Midland U16

President: Sir Colin Shepherd

Chairman: E G Powell

HEREFORDSHIRE CHALLENGE CUP 2000-01

(15 entries) (FOUNDED 1973-74)

LAST SEASON'S FINAL: Bromyard Town v Ewyas Harold 4-1 aet

FIRST ROUND

Hinton	v	Weson under Penyard	3-0	Kington Town	v	Ledbury Town	4-1
Westfields	v	Wellington	3-3, 1-2	Ross Town	v	Hereford Civil Service	3-2
Bromyard Town	v	Fownhope	3-2	Ewyas Harold	v	Woofferton	5-0
Pegasus Juniors	v	Leominster Town	6-1				

QUARTER-FINALS

Pegasus Juniors	v	Bromyard Town	3-0	Ross Town	v	Sutton United	7-1
Ewas Harold	v	Kington Town	3-5	Hinton	v	Wellington	0-1

SEMI-FINALS

Wellington	v	Ross Town	0-1	Kington Town	v	Pegasus Juniors	3-2

FINAL

ROSS TOWN v KINGTON TOWN 0-2 at Edgar Street, Hereford United FC. Att: 390

HERTFORDSHIRE F.A.

Tel: 01462 677622 Fax: 01462 677624 E.Mail: competitions@hertsfa.demon.co.uk
County Ground, Baldock Road, Letchworth, Herts S96 2EN

Secretary: R G Kibble **Press Officer:** County HQ

Executives (Responsibility) D Gorringe (Executive Officer)
A Ackrell (Coaching Exams/Courses)
R G Dowden (Referees) M Spacey (Womens Football)

Number of Affiliated Clubs Senior: 860 U.18: 190 **President:** B W A Bayford

Number of Affiliated Leagues: Senior: 24 Junior: 11 **Chairman:** E C Hand

County Representative Teams: Senior, U18, U16

Inter County Competitions: East Anglian, EMYFC

HERTFORDSHIRE SENIOR CUP 2000-01

(22 entries) (FOUNDED 1886-87)

LAST SEASON'S FINAL: St Albans City v Baldock Town 4-1

MOST WINS: Hitchin Town 21 Barnet 16 Watford 14

FIRST ROUND

Cheshunt	v	Watford	0-4	Royston Town	v	Hertford Town	2-0
Hitchin Town	v	Hemel Hempstead T	5-1	Sawbridgeworth Tn	v	Hoddesdon Town	1-5
Somersett Am V&E	v	Berkhamsted Town	2-3	Barnet	v	Bishops Stortford	6-1

SECOND ROUND

Boreham Wood	v	Barnet	3-4	Baldock Town	v	Watford	2-0
Tring Town	v	Potters Bar T 3v2 PB	T-A	Royston Town	v	St Albans City 0v6 RT	T-A
Stevenage Borough	v	Berkhamsted Town	1-0	Welwyn Garden City	v	St Margaretsbury	1-2
Hitchin Town	v	London Colney	7-0	Hoddesdon Town	v	Ware	2-3

Tring Town & St Albans City fielded ineligible players and are therefore removed from the Competition their opponents being reinstated)

THIRD ROUND

Royston Town	v	St Margaretsbury	4-1	Ware	v	Potters Bar Town	1-0
Baldock Town	v	Barnet	3-0	Hitchin Town	v	Stevenage Borough	1-2

SEMI-FINALS

Ware	v	Stevenage Borough	3-1	Royston Town	v	Baldock Town	0-3

FINAL

WARE v BALDOCK TOWN 0-3 at Herts County FA, Letchworth FC

HERTFORDSHIRE SENIOR TROPHY 2000-01

(24 entries)

LAST SEASON'S FINAL: Tring Athletic v Wormley Rovers 2-0

FIRST ROUND

Agrevo Sports	v	de Havilland	2-5	Elliott Star	v	Met Police Bushey	4-2
Bedmond Sports	v	Oxhey Jets	0-1	Sandridge Rovers	v	Benington	7p6 1*1
Bovingdon	v	Greenacres	2-1	Harpenden Town	v	London Lions	2-0
Letchworth Bridger	v	Cuffley	3-0	Chipperfield Corinths	v	Leverstock Green	0-1

SECOND ROUND

Tring Athletic	v	Harpenden Town	3-2	Leverstock Green	v	Sandridge Rovers	1-2
Oxhey Jets	v	Old Parmiterians	7-0	Bovingdon	v	Letchworth	1-2
Whitewebbs	v	Colney Heath	0-6	de Havilland	v	Elliott Star	1-4
Kings Langley	v	Letchworth Bridger	4-1	Wormley Rovers	v	Sun Postal Sports	4-0

THIRD ROUND

Tring Athletic	v	Letchworth	TA W/O	Wormley Rovers	v	Kings Langley	1*0
Sandridge Rovers	v	Elliott Star	3-5	Oxhey Jets	v	Colney Heath	5-2

SEMI-FINALS

Tring Athletic	v	Elliot Star	4-0	Oxhey Jets	v	Wormley Rovers	1-4

FINAL

TRING ATHLETIC v WORMLEY ROVERS 2-0 at Herts County FA, Letchworth FC

Ware defend in depth against Baldock who went on to win the Hertfordshire Senior Cup Final 3-0.
Photo: Gordon Whittington

Hertfordshire Senior Cup Winners, Baldock Town. Photo: Gordon Whittington

HUNTINGDONSHIRE F.A.

Tel: 01480414422 Fax: 01480 412691 Email: info@huntsfa.freeserve.co.uk
Cromwell Chambers, 8 St Johns Street, Huntingdon, Cambs. PE29 3DD

Secretary & Press Officer: Maurice Armstrong
Executives (Responsibility) K J Oldham (Coaching Exams/Courses)
E K Heads (Referees)
S Batchelor (Football Development Officer)
Number of Affiliated Clubs Senior: 130 U.18: 30
Number of Affiliated Leagues: Senior: 1 Junior: 1
County Representative Teams: Senior, Under 18, Under 16, Colts
Inter County Competitions: East Midlands Youth U18 & U16, East Anglian Championship Senior

President: D A Roberts
Chairman: R H Carter

HUNTINGDONSHIRE SENIOR CUP 2000-01

(17 entries) (FOUNDED 1888-89)

LAST SEASON'S FINAL: Eynesbury Rovers v Somersham Town 2-1
MOST WINS: St Neots 34 Eynesbury Rovers 13 Huntingdon Town 12

FIRST ROUND

Alconbury	v	Hemingford United	1-2

SECOND ROUND

Somersham Town	v	Great Paxton	3-2
Bluntisham Rangers	v	Ortonians	2*1
Ramsey Town	v	Eynesbury Rovers	0-1
Hotpoint	v	Godmanchester Rvrs	2-4
St Neots Town	v	St Ives Town	4-0
Yaxley	v	ICA Juventus	5-0
Warboys Town	v	Stilton United	6-0
Hemingford United	v	Huntingdon Utd 2000	3-0

THIRD ROUND

Hemingford United	v	Warboys Town	3-7
Somersham Town	v	Eynesbury Rovers	2-1
Godmanchester Rvrs	v	Yaxley	1-5
Bluntisham Rangers	v	St Neots Town	0-5

SEMI-FINALS

St Neots Town	v	Warboys Town	4-1
Somersham Town	v	Yaxley	5-1

FINAL

SOMERSHAM TN	v	ST NEOTS TOWN	1-0	at Warboys Town FC

Somersham Town, who won the Huntingdonshire Senior Cup 1-0 against St Neots Town. Photo: Gordon Whittington

Top:
Captains and Officials line up before the Kent Senior Cup Final. Dover Athletic v Gravesend & Northfleet.

Centre:
Dover Athletic line up.

Bottom:
Aaron Barnett, Gravesend, takes the wide around Paul Hyde, Dover Athletic's goal-keeper.

Photos:
Roger Turner

KENT F.A. Limited

Tel: 01634 843824 Fax: 01634 815369 E.Mail: Kcfa.Chatham@btinternet.com
69 Maidstone Road, Chatham, Kent ME4 6DT

Chief Executive: K T Masters
Press Officer: Tony Hudd
Executives (Responsibility) Alan Walker (Coaching) John Newson (Referees)
Nici Rice (County Development)
Liz Symons (Girls & Womens Football)
Number of Affiliated Clubs Adult: 1071 U.18: 217
Number of Affiliated Leagues: Senior: 2 Junior: 41
County Representative Teams: U18, U16, Womens, Girls

President: E H Bennett
Chairman: B W Bright

KENT FACIT SENIOR CUP 2000-01
(13 entries) (FOUNDED 1888-89)

LAST SEASON'S FINAL: Gravesend & Northfleet v Folkestone Invicta 3-0
MOST WINS: Maidstone United 15 Dartford 9 Northfleet United 9

FIRST ROUND

Dartford	v	London Fisher Athletic	6-2	Tonbridge Angels	v	Erith & Belvedere	0-2
Margate	v	Sittingbourne	6-0	Bromley	v	Ashford Town	1-0
Welling United	v	Deal Town	4-0				

SECOND ROUND

Folkestone Invicta	v	Erith & Belvedere	3-2	Bromley	v	Dartford	3*1
Dover Athletic	v	Margate	2*1	Gravesend & N'fleet	v	Welling United	3-2

SEMI-FINALS

Dover Athletic	v	Bromley	7-0	Gravesen & N'fleet	v	Folkestone Invicta	5*4

FINAL

DOVER ATHLETIC v GRAVESEND & N 0-4 at Crabble Ground, Dover Athletic FC

KENT PLAAYA SENIOR TROPHY 2000-01
(23 entries) (FOUNDED 1874-75)

LAST SEASON'S FINAL: Deal Town v Chatham Town 5-1
MOST WINS: Ramsgate 3 Alma Swanley 2 Corinthian 2 Faversham Town 2 Fisher Athletic 2

FIRST ROUND

Tunbridge Wells	v	VCD Athletic	1-4	Whitstable Town	v	West Wickham	7-0
Erith Town	v	Faversham Town	1-0	Slade Green	v	Herne Bay	0-3
Maidstone United	v	Snodland	0-1	Greenwich Borough	v	Thames Poly	4-0
Thamesmead Town	v	Chatham Town	2-0				

SECOND ROUND

Erith Town	v	Canterbury City	7-2	Sheppey United	v	Lordswood	0-1
VCD Athletic	v	Milton Athletic	3-0	Knatchbull	v	Beckenham Town	1-0
Ramsgate	v	Cray Wanderers	7*3	Whitstable Town	v	Herne Bay	3*1
Hythe United	v	Snodland	2-1	Thamesmead Town	v	Greenwich Borough	1-0

THIRD ROUND

VCD Athletic	v	Erith Town	2-1	Hythe United	v	Knatchbull	4*2
Whitstable Town	v	Thamesmead Town	3-2	Ramsgate	v	Lordswood	0-1

SEMI-FINALS

VCD Athletic	v	Hythe United	1-0	Lordswood	v	Whitstable Town	0-1

FINAL

VCD ATHLETIC v WHITSTABLE T 9p10, 1*1 at Central Park, Sittingbourne FC

Top:
Aaron Barnett (Gravesend & Northfleet - dark shirt) makes a challenge on Matt Carruthers (Dover) during the Kent Senior Cup Final at The Crabble.

Centre:
A dust up in the penalty area.

Photos:
Roger Turner

Bottom:
Gravesend & Northfleet with the Kent Senior Cup after their 4-0 victory over Dover Athletic.

Photo:
Roger Turner

LANCASHIRE F.A.

Tel: 01772 624000 Fax: 01772 624700

The County Ground, Thurston Road, Leyland PR25 2LF

Secretary & Press Officer J Kenyon, ACIS

Executives (Responsibility) D Egan (Development Officer)
E J Parker (Referees)
Miss J Ashworth (Womens Football Development Officer)

Number of Affiliated Clubs Senior: 1600 U.18: 300 **President:** D J Lewin

County Representative Teams: Senior, U18, Womens

Inter County Competitions: FA County Youth, Northern Counties Senior, U18 & Womens

MARSDEN LANCASHIRE TROPHY 2000-01

(26 entries) (FOUNDED 1885-86)

LAST SEASON'S FINAL: Marine v Bamber Bridge 5-0

FIRST ROUND

Great Harwood Town	v	Fleetwood Freeport	0-6	Southport	v	Darwen	3-0
Rossendale United	v	Atherton Collieries	6*4	Radcliffe Borough	v	Morecambe	1*1, 0-2
Chorley	v	Squires Gate	0-1	Nelson	v	Holker Old Boys	5-1
Lancaster City	v	Blackpool Mechanics	2-1	Colne	v	Ramsbottom	1-5
Bacup Borough	v	Skelmersdale U	1*1, 1-3	Atherton Laburnum R	v	Burscough	1-2

SECOND ROUND

Skelmersdale U	v	Bamber Bridge	1-3	Nelson	v	Morecambe	0-6
Fleetwood Freeport	v	Clitheroe	0-3	Leigh RMI	v	Rossendale United	1-0
Lancaster City	v	Accrington Stanley	5-0	Squires Gate	v	Ramsbottom United	2*1
Barrow	v	Southport	3-5	Marine	v	Burscough	

THIRD ROUND

Clitheroe	v	Bamber Bridge	0-1	Southport	v	Marine	5-0
Lancaster City	v	Leigh RMI	1*1, 3-0	Morecambe	v	Squires Gate	4-1

SEMI-FINALS

Morecambe	v	Southport	1-3	Bamber Bridge	v	Lancaster City	0-1

FINAL

LANCASTER CITY v SOUTHPORT 0-1 at Chorley FC. Att: 779

WHITBREAD LANCASHIRE AMATEUR CUP 2000-01

(FOUNDED 1893-94)

LAST SEASON'S FINAL: Speke v St Dominics 3-2

MOST WINS: Liverpool/Merseyside Police 11 St Dominics 6 Marine 5

FINAL

YORKSHIRE C.T. v PRAIRIE UNITED 2-0

LEICESTERSHIRE & RUTLAND F.A.

Tel: 0116 286 7828 Fax: 0116 286 4858 Email: leicscfa@aol.com
Holmes Park, Dog & Gun Lane, Whetstone LE8 3LJ

Secretary & Press Officer: Paul Morrison
Executives (Responsibility) J Ward (Referees)
Mrs G F Wait (Womens Football)
Number of Affiliated Clubs Senior: 650 U.18: 200
Number of Affiliated Leagues: Senior: 12 Junior: 6
County Representative Teams: Under 18, Under 16, Under 16 Girls
Inter County Competitions: East Midlands Youth Combination U18 & U16

President: G E Cooper
Chairman: J E Bray

LEICESTERSHIRE 'JELSON HOMES' SENIOR CUP 2000-01

(38 entries) (FOUNDED 1887-88)

LAST SEASON'S FINAL: Coalville Town v Holwell Sports 2-1

MOST WINS: Leicester City 27 Enderby Town 6 Shepshed Dynamo 6

FIRST ROUND

Ratby Sports	v	Leics Constab	2p4 2*2	Coalville Town	v	Harborough T Imp	10-0
Barrow Town	v	Thringstone M W	2-1	Castle Donington T	v	Leicester YMCA	2-9
Quorn	v	Holwell Sports	3-0	St Andrews	v	Bardon Hill Sports	4-0

SECOND ROUND

Friar Lane OB	v	Leicester YMCA	3-2	Loughborough Ath	v	St Andrews	0-2
Downes Sports	v	Cottesmore Amateurs	4-1	Asfordby Amateurs	v	Birstall United	0-3
Huncote Sports	v	Narborough & L'thorpe	1*2	Ellistown	v	Leics Constabulary	1-3
Kirby Muxloe	v	Saffron Walden	5-1	Earl Shilton Albion	v	Highfield Rangers	1*3
Anstey Nomads	v	Coalville Town	2*4	Loughborough D'mo	v	Lutterworth Town	0-6
North Kilworth	v	Aylestone Park OB	1-8	Anstey Town	v	Ibstock Welfare	1-5
Fosse Imps	v	Barrow Town	3-2	Thurmaston Town	v	Stoney Stanton	3-1
Thurnaby Rangers	v	Quorn	2-0	Sileby Town	v	Blaby & Whetstone A	1-3

THIRD ROUND

Thurnaby Rangers	v	Ibstock Welfare	0-1	Leics Constabulary	v	Fosse Imps	7p6 1*1
Aylestone Park OB	v	Narborough & L'thorpe	3-1	Thurmaston Town	v	Highfield Rangers	1-4
Birstall	v	Coleshill Town	2-0	St Andrews	v	Downes Sports	7-4
Kirby Muxloe	v	Blaby & Whetstone	2*1	Friar Lane OB	v	Lutterworth Town	3*2

QUARTER-FINALS

Highfield Rangers	v	Kirby Muxloe	0-2	St Andrews	v	Aylestone Park OB	1-0
Leics Constabulary	v	Friar Lane O B	0-4	Ibstock Welfare	v	Birstall United	1-2

SEMI-FINALS

Kirby Muxloe	v	St Andrews	0-2	Friar Lane	v	Birstall United	2*1

FINAL

FRIAR LANE	v	ST ANDREWS	0-2

LEICESTERSHIRE WESTERBY CHALLENGE CUP 2000-01

(12 entries)

LAST SEASON'S FINAL: Leicester City v Barwell 4-0

FIRST ROUND

Kirby Muxloe	v	Downes Sports	0-1	Coalville Town	v	Holwell Sports	0-2
St Andrews	v	Highfield Rangers	2-1	Shepshed Dynamo	v	Quorn	2-1

SECOND ROUND

Oadby Town	v	Leicester City		St Andrews	v	Holwell Sports	3-2
Barwell	v	Shepshed Dynamo	2-0	Downes Sports	v	Hinckley United	1-3

SEMI-FINALS

Oadby Town	v	Hinckley United	0-1	St Andrews	v	Barwell	1*3

FINAL

BARWELL	v	HINCKLEY UNITED	1-2	at Filbert Street

LINCOLNSHIRE F.A.

Tel: 01522 524917 Fax: 01522 528859
PO Box 26, 12 Dean Road, Lincoln LN2 4DP

Secretary:	J Griffin			
Press Officer:	K Weaver			
Executives (Responsibility)	Board of Directors			
Number of Affiliated Clubs	Senior: 911	U.18: 249		**President:** N A Saywell
Number of Affiliated Leagues:	Senior: 19	Junior: 13		**Chairman:** R D Teanby
County Representative Teams:	U18, U16			
Inter County Competitions:	East Midlands Youth Combination, FA County Youth			

LINCOLNSHIRE SENIOR CUP 2000-01

(9 entries) (FOUNDED 1935-36)

LAST SEASON'S FINAL: Grimsby Town v Lincoln United 3-3, 4p2 aet

MOST WINS: Grimsby Town 14 Lincoln City 12 Boston United 5

PRELIMINARY ROUND (1 match)

Gainsborough Trinity	v	Lincoln United	3-1

FIRST ROUND (4 matches)

Grimsby Town	v	Spalding United	0-0, 5p4
Scunthorpe United	v	Boston United	0-1
Gainsborough Trinity	v	Grantham Town	0-2
Stamford AFC	v	Lincoln City	2-1

SEMI-FINALS

Grimsby Town	v	Stamford AFC	0-1
Grantham Town	v	Boston United	0-1

FINAL

BOSTON UNITED	v	STAMFORD AFC	1-2

LINCOLNSHIRE SENIOR 'A' CUP 2000-01

(9 entries) (FOUNDED 1949-50)

LAST SEASON'S FINAL: Brigg Town v Lincoln Moorlands 2-0

MOST WINS: Boston Town 6 Holbeach United 4 Skegness Town 4

PRELIMINARY ROUND (1 match)

Brigg Town	v	Winterton Town	4-1

FIRST ROUND (4 matches)

Louth United	v	Bourne Town	4-2
Boston Town	v	Lincoln Mrlands	1-1, 4p5
Blackstone	v	Nettleham	5-0
Holbeach United	v	Brigg Town	0-3

SEMI-FINALS

Brigg Town	v	Lincoln M'lands	1-1, 9p10
Blackstone	v	Louth United	2-3

FINAL

LINCOLN M'LANDS	v	LOUTH UNITED	0-0, 5p3	at Lincoln City FC

LINCOLNSHIRE SENIOR 'B' CUP 2000-01

(16 entries) (FOUNDED 1949-50)

LAST SEASON'S FINAL: Sleaford Town v Grimsby Imm. Amt. 4-1
MOST WINS: Brigg Town 5 Appleby Frodingham Athletic 4 Lincoln Moorlands 3

FIRST ROUND (8 matches)

Barrowby	v	Limestone Rangers	1-2
Appleby Frodingham	v	Harrowby United	1-3
Hykeham Town	v	Horncastle Town	5-3
Grantham Rangers	v	Grimsby/Imm'ham A	0-1
Epworth Town LC		Walkover	
Alstom Sports	v	Deeping Rangers	1-2
Sleaford Town	v	Bottesford Town	0-2
Barton Town OB	v	Skegness Town AFC	3-1

SECOND ROUND (4 matches)

Harrowby United	v	Barton Town OB	3-2
Grimsby/Imm'ham	v	Hykeham Town	3-2
Deeping Rangers	v	Bottesford Town	3-1
Limestone Rangers	v	Epworth Town LC	2-0

SEMI-FINALS

Deeping Rangers	v	Limestone Rangers	3-2
Harrowby United	v	Grimsby Imm Amt	2-1

FINAL

DEEPING RNGRS v HARROWBY UTD 4-1 at Boston United FC

LINCOLNSHIRE JUNIOR CUP 2000-01

FINAL

MOULTON HARROX v WYBERTON 1-1, 5p6 at Bourne Town FC

LINCOLNSHIRE SUNDAY CUP 2000-01

FINAL

AFC VICTORY v INTERSPORT 1-6 at Grimsby Town FC

LIVERPOOL F.A.

Tel: 0151 523 4488 Fax: 0151 523 4477

Liverpool Soccer Centre, Walton Hall Park, Walton Hall Avenue, Liverpool L4 9XP

Secretary: F L Hunter **Press Officer:** S Catterall

Executives (Responsibility) M McGlyn (Coaching Exams/Courses)
K R Naylor (Referees)
Ms S Gore (Womens Football)

President: J Lawson

Number of Affiliated Clubs	Senior:	900	U.18:	600
Number of Affiliated Leagues:	Senior:	18	Junior:	25
Inter County Competitions:	All FA Competitions			

Nat West LIVERPOOL SENIOR CUP 2000-01

(10 entries) (FOUNDED 1977-78)

LAST SEASON'S FINAL: Marine v Tranmere Rovers 1-0 aet

MOST WINS: Marine 5 Liverpool 3 South Liverpool 3

FIRST ROUND

Burscough	v	Skelmersdale United	5-1	Prescot Cables	v	St Helens Town	1-2

SECOND ROUND

Tranmere Rovers	v	Liverpool	w/d	Burscough	v	Warrington Town	5-1
Marine	v	Everton	3-2	Southport	v	St Helens Town	4-1

SEMI-FINAL

Burscough	v	Marine	6p5, 2-2

FINAL

BURSCOUGH	v	SOUTHPORT	1-0	at Burscough

ADDITIONAL 2000-01 CUP FINALS

LIVERPOOL JUNIOR CUP
Pilkington v Dunningsbridge Park 1-0 at Liverpool FA Soccer Centre

LIVERPOOL INTERMEDIATE CUP
Tapes for Industry v Old Xaverians Res 5-0 at Liverpool FA Soccer Centre

LIVERPOOL SUNDAY PREMIER CUP
Clubmoor Nalgo v Taxi Club 2-1 at Liverpool FA Soccer Centre

LIVERPOOL SUNDAY JUNIOR CUP
Avenue v Windsor Castle 4-2 at Liverpool FA Soccer Centre

LIVERPOOL SUNDAY INTERMEDIATE CUP
Home & Bargain v Phonenett 4-0 at Liverpool FA Soccer Centre

LIVERPOOL YOUTH CUP
Burscough v East Villa 3-2 at Liverpool FA Soccer Centre

PREMIER LEAGUE INTER-COUNTY CHAMPIONSHIP
Merseyside U16 v Oxfordshire U16 1-0 at Derby County FC

WIGAN F.A. CUP
Grange Valley v Charnock Richard 1-0

LIVERPOOL CHALLENGE CUP 2000-01

(40 entries) (FOUNDED 1908-09)

LAST SEASON'S FINAL: Yorkshire CT v Lucas Sports 2-2, 5p4

MOST WINS: Skelmersdale United 8 Prescot Cables 6
New Brighton 5 St Dominics 5 Waterloo Dock 5

FIRST ROUND (8 matches)

BRNESC	v	Stoneycroft	0-3
Garswood United	v	Royal Seaforth	1-5
Manweb	v	Old Xaverians	1-0
REMYCA United	v	St Aloysius	4-4
Burscough Res	v	Merseyside Police	1-2
Maghull	v	Collegiate OB	3-2
Marconi	v	Waterloo Dock	0-2
Warrington Borough	v	Ashton Town	

SECOND ROUND (16 matches)

Aigburth PH	v	Old Cathinians	6-0
Ayone	v	South Liverpool	0-10
Crawfords UB	v	ROMA	3-2
Ford Motors	v	Waterloo GSOB	5-3
Merseyside Police	v	Quarry Bank OB	1-2
Rylands	v	Warbreck	3-2
Sefton & District	v	Marine Reserves	0-5
Stoneycroft	v	Lucas Sports	0-5
Alsop Old Boys	v	Southport Trinity	1-2
Cheshire Lines	v	Manweb	0-1
East Villa	v	St Aloysius	1-3
Maghull	v	Ashton Town	1-0
Old Holts	v	Bootle	3-5
St Dominics	v	Royal Seaforth	3-4
Speke	v	Yorkshire CT	2-7
Waterloo Dock	v	Aintree Villa	1-1, 3p1

THIRD ROUND (8 matches)

Crawfords UB	v	Royal Seaforth	
Lucas Sports	v	Aigburth PH	4-2
Manweb	v	Southport Trinity	4-1
Quarry Bank OB	v	St Aloysius	2-2, 5p4
Ford Motors	v	Waterloo Dock	0-5
Maghull	v	South Liverpool	0-2
Marine Reserves	v	Bootle	7-2
Yorkshire CT	v	Rylands	6-0

FOURTH ROUND (4 matches)

Lucas Sports	v	Royal Seaforth	2-0
Marine Reserves	v	Quarry Bank OB	2-3
Manweb	v	Yorkshire CT	1-2
Waterloo Dock	v	South Liverpool	3-0

SEMI-FINALS

Lucas Sports	v	Quarry Bank OB	2-1
Waterloo Dock	v	Yorkshire CT	2-1

FINAL

WATERLOO DOCK v LUCAS SPORTS 2-1 aet at Liverpool FA Soccer Centre, Walton Hall Park

LONDON F.A.

Tel: 020 8690 9626 Fax: 020 8690 9471 Email: enquiries@londonfa.fsnet.co.uk
6 Aldworth Grove, Lewisham, London SE13 6HY

Secretary:	D G Fowkes			
Executives (Responsibility)	J Drabwell (Coaching Exams) R Jenkins (Referees)			
	C Arundale (Womens Football) D Morrison (Coaching Courses)			
Number of Affiliated Clubs	Adult: 2134	U18: 476		**President:** L A M Mackay
Number of Affiliated Leagues:	Adult: 93	U18: 35		**Chairman:** N R J Moss
County Representative Teams:	Senior, Womens, U16			
Inter County Competitions:	Southern Counties Cup (men), Southern Counties Cup (women), FA County Youth Cup			

LONDON SENIOR CUP 2000-01

(FOUNDED 1882)

LAST SEASON'S FINAL: Bedfont v Erith Town 5-1

FIRST ROUND (4 matches)

Leyton	v	Civil Service	9-0	Brimsdown Rovers	v	Crown & Manor	1-0
Cockfosters	v	Barkingside	1-3	Thames Poly	v	Haringey Borough	2-1

SECOND ROUND (8 matches)

Erith Town	v	Brimsdown Rovers	2-0	Leyton	v	Clapton	4-0
Hornchurch	v	Kingsbury Town	1-3	East Ham United	v	Ilford	2-5
Hoddesdon Town	v	Wingate & Finchley	2-1	Hanwell Town	v	Waltham Abbey	5-3
Woodford Town	v	Thames Poly	1-3	Barkingside	v	Thamesmead Town	1-3

THIRD ROUND (8 matches)

Kingsbury Town	v	Barking	0-2	Metropolitan Police	v	Tooting & Mitcham Utd	5-4
Romford	w/d	Croydon Athletic		Corinthian Casuals	v	Hanwell Town	2-3
Hoddesdon Town	v	Leyton Pennant	2-0	Thamesmead Town	v	Erith & Belvedere	3-1
Leyton	v	Erith Town	2-2, 3p2	Ilford	v	Thames Poly	0-3

FOURTH ROUND (8 matches)

Hanwell Town	v	Met Police	3-3, 6p5	Thamesmead Town	v	Welling United	0-0, 2p3
Fisher Athletic	v	Thames Poly	1-2	Ford United	v	Bedfont	4-1
Hoddesdon Town	v	Barking	1-3	Bromley	v	Dulwich Hamlet	3-6
Leyton	v	Uxbridge	1-7a	Croydon Athletic	v	Croydon	4-3

FIFTH ROUND (4 matches)

Croydon Athletic	v	Welling United	2-2, 3p0	Uxbridge	v	Barking	2-1
Hanwell Town	v	Thames Poly	0-0, 3p5	Ford United	v	Dulwich Hamlet	3-1

SEMI-FINALS

Thames Poly	v	Croydon Athletic	0-1	Uxbridge	v	Ford United	1-2a

FINAL

FORD UNITED	v	CROYDON ATH	3-2	at Leyton Orient FC

OTHER CUP COMPETITIONS

LFA INTERMEDIATE CUP FINAL

Corinthian Casuals	v	Metrogas	2-0	at Dulwich Hamlet FC

LFA JUNIOR CUP FINAL

AFC Saxon	v	Brampton Park	1-1	at Corinthian Casuals FC

(abandoned at half time - no cup presented)

LFA MIDWEEK CUP FINAL

Crown & Manor	v	LITA Sports	2-2, 4p3	at Croydon Athletic FC

LFA SUNDAY CHALLENGE CUP FINAL

Livingstone	v	Mayfair United	3-1	at Dulwich Hamlet FC

LFA SUNDAY INTERMEDIATE CUP FINAL

Sporting Club Tropic	v	Queen Vic Tooting	6-5	at Wingate & Finchley FC

LFA SUNDAY JUNIOR CUP FINAL

Regent Celtic	v	Vista	2-1	at Wingate & Finchley FC

LFA WOMEN'S CUP FINAL

Fulham Ladies	v	Arsenal Ladies	3-0	at Metropolitan Police FC

MANCHESTER F.A.

Tel: 0161 881 0299 Fax: 0161 881 6833 E-mail: mancfa@cs.com
Brantingham Road, Chorlton, Manchester M21 0TT

Secretary & Press Officer: Jon Dutton
Executives (Responsibility) Jason Wright (Education)
Phil Morris (Referees)
Fiona Miley (Womens Football)
Number of Affiliated Clubs Senior: 542 U.18: 154
President: Frank Hannah
Number of Affiliated Leagues: Senior: 29 Junior: 13
County Representative Teams: U18, Womens
Inter County Competitions: FA County Youth, Association of Northern Counties Youth Competition

MANCHESTER PREMIER CUP 2000-01
sponsored by SPARTA SPORTSWEAR
(FOUNDED1979-80)

LAST SEASON'S FINAL: Droylsden v Mossley 2-1

MOST WINS: Curzon Ashton 5 Ashton United 3 Hyde United 3
Droylsden 3 Mossley 2

FIRST ROUND (3 matches)

Curzon Ashton	v	Maine Road	3*2	Ashton United	v	Trafford	3-0
Oldham Town	v	Abbey Hey	4-2				

SECOND ROUND (4 matches)

Curzon Ashton	v	Droylsden	0-1	Flixton	v	Ashton United	0-5
Oldham Town	v	Mossley	0-2	Chadderton	v	Salford City	0-2

SEMI-FINALS

Droylsden	v	Salford City	1*1, 4p3	Ashton United	v	Mossley	2-1

FINAL

DROYLSDEN	v	ASHTON UNITED	0-4

Ashton United (Unibond Division One), winners 4-0 over Droylsden in the Manchester Premier Cup Final played at Oldham Athletic FC. Photo: Colin Stevens

MIDDLESEX COUNTY F.A.

Tel: 0208 424 8524 Fax: 0181 863 0627 E.Mail: association.office@middxfa.org
39 Roxborough Road, Harrow, Middlesex HA1 1NS

Secretary: Peter Clayton Executive Officer: Mark Frost

Executives (Responsibility) P Clayton (Coaching Exams/Courses, Womens Football, Referees)

Number of Affiliated Clubs Snr: 32; Inter: 12; U18 232; Jnr 583; Wmn 19; Other 337 **President:** John Wake

Number of Affiliated Leagues: Adult: 30 Youth: 8 **Chairman:** Derek Mennell

County Representative Teams: Senior, Intermediate, U18, U16, Womens, U16, Womens U16

Inter County Competitions: FA County Yth, Home Counties Yth, Southern Counties (Intermediate, Women)

MIDDLESEX SENIOR CUP 2000-01

(26 entries) (FOUNDED 1888-89)

LAST SEASON'S FINAL: Hayes v Northwood 2-0

MOST WINS: Enfield 14 Southall 12 Wealdstone 11 Hayes 10 Hendon 10

FIRST ROUND

Uxbridge	v	Brook House	4-1	Edgware Town	v	Southall	7-2
Bedfont	v	Southall Town	1-0	Ashford Town	v	Wealdstone	4-1
Waltham Abbey	v	Hillingdon Boro	HB W/O	Kingsbury Town	v	Potters Bar Town	3-2
Hmptn & R'mond B	v	Staines Town	2-3	Harefield United	v	Hanwell Town	0-2
Ruislip Manor	v	Viking Greenford	1*1	Feltham	v	Yeading	0-5

SECOND ROUND

Hendon	v	Wembley	1*1, 2-0	Edgware Town	v	Hillingdon Borough	4-0
StainesTown	v	Hanwell Town	4-0	Yeading	v	Ashford Town	2-1
Harrow Borough	v	Ruislip Manor	7-0	Uxbridge	v	Enfield	3*2
Bedfont	v	Hayes	1-4	Kingsbury Town	v	Northwood	2*3

QUARTER-FINALS

Uxbridge	v	Hendon	2-0	Northwood	v	Staines Town	0-2
Edgware Town	v	Hayes	0-2	Harrow Borough	v	Yeading	6*1

SEMI-FINALS

Staines Town	v	Uxbridge	1-3	Hayes	v	Harrow Borough	1*2

FINAL

HARROW BORO v UXBRIDGE 0-3 at Uxbridge FC, attendance 438

MIDDLESEX SENIOR CHARITY CUP 2000-01

(17 entries) (FOUNDED 1901-02)

LAST SEASON'S FINAL: Ashford Town v Hanwell Town 1-0

MOST WINS: Wealdstone 11 Hayes 10 Southall 10

Competition abandoned due to the adverse weather after just four First Round matches were played

Action from the Norfolk Senior Cup Second Round. Blofield United won the game 3-2 after extra time against Cromer United (striped shirts). Photos: Mike Weston

NORFOLK F.A.

Tel: 01603 717177 Fax: 01603 717187
Plantation Park, Blofield, Norwich NR13 4PL

Secretary & Press Officer: Roger J Howlett
Executives (Responsibility) Through County Office (Coaching Exams/Courses, Referees, Womens Football)
Number of Affiliated Clubs Senior: 487 U.18: 167
Number of Affiliated Leagues: Senior: 16 Junior: 9
County Representative Teams: U18, Womens
Inter County Competitions: FA County Youth, East Anglian Counties

President: R W Kiddell
Chairman: B Woodhouse

NORFOLK SENIOR CUP 2000-01

(30 entries) (FOUNDED 1881-82)

LAST SEASON'S FINAL: Gorleston v Great Yarmouth 4-0

MOST WINS: King's Lynn 19 Great Yarmouth Town 14 Gorleston 13

FIRST ROUND

Anglian Windows	v	Wymondham Town	4-2
Norwich Union	v	Poringland Wndrs	4-1
Sprowston Wndrs	v	Hempnall	3-1

SECOND ROUND

Thetford Town	v	Downham Town	2-4
Loddon United	v	Acle United	1-1 3-4
Lakeford Rangers	v	Swaffham Town	2-4
Mattishall	v	Dereham Town	3-5
Thorpe Village	v	Norwich Union	2-3
Stalham Town	v	Norwich United	2-2 2-3
Sprowston Athletic	v	Sprowston Wanderers	6-0
Anglian Windows	v	St Andrews S C	1-6
North Walsham Tn	v	Wells Town	1-0
Mulbarton United	v	Scole United	0-3
Cromer United	v	Blofield United	2-3

THIRD ROUND

Dereham Town	v	Wroxham	0-1
Gorleston	v	St Andrews	4-1
Norwich United	v	North Walsham T	3A2 0-1
Swaffham Town	v	Blofield United	4-1
Downham Town	v	Scole United	3-0
Great Yarmouth Tn	v	Diss Town	1-0
Sprowston Athletic	v	Fakenham Town	0-4
Acle U	v	Norwich Union	2-2 1-2

FOURTH ROUND

Fakenham Town	v	Downham Town	6-0
Swaffham Town	v	Great Yarmouth T	1*1 0-1
North Walsham Tn	v	Gorleston	0-3
Wroxham	v	Norwich Union	6-0

SEMI-FINALS

Fakenham Town	v	Gorleston	1-2
Great Yarmouth Town	v	Wroxham	2-1

FINAL

GT YARMOUTH TN v GORLESTON 0-4 at Carrow Road, Norwich City FC. Att: 2199

Action from the Norfolk Senior Cup Second Round. Blofield United won the game 3-2 after extra time against Cromer United (striped shirts). Photos: Mike Weston

NORTHAMPTONSHIRE F.A.

Tel: 01604 670741 Fax: 01604 670741
2 Duncan Close, Moulton Park, Northampton

Secretary & Press Officer: B Walden
Executives (Responsibility) N Levett (Football Development Officer)
B Walden (Referees)
Mrs J Jeffrey (Womens Football)
Number of Affiliated Clubs Senior: 466 U.18: 162
Number of Affiliated Leagues: Senior: 12 Junior: 7
County Representative Teams: U18
Inter County Competitions: East Midland Youth Combination

President: D Vernum
Chairman: L Homer

NORTHAMPTONSHIRE 'HILLIER' SENIOR CUP 2000-01
(14 entries) (FOUNDED 1883-84)

LAST SEASON'S FINAL: Kettering Town v Desborough Town 1*1, 3*3, 4p3
MOST WINS: Kettering Town 31 Northampton Town 11 Peterborough United 11

PRELIMINARY ROUND

Long Buckby AFC	v	Bugbrooke St M	2-4	N'ton Spencer	v	Cogenhoe United	1-2
Corby Stewart & L	v	Brackley Town	3-2	Raunds Town	v	Wellingborough Town	3-4

FIRST ROUND

Corby Town	v	Ford Sports	1-0	Cogenhoe United	v	Bugbrook St Michaels	4-0
Rothwell Town	v	Desborough Town	0-3	Wellingborough Town	v	S & L Corby	0-0

SECOND ROUND

Desborough Town	v	Corby Stewart & Lloyds	1-3	Corby Town	v	Cogenhoe United	2-0

SEMI-FINALS

Kettering Town	v	Corby Stewart & Lloyds	2-0	Corby Town	v	Rushden & Diamonds	2-4

FINAL

RUSHDEN & DIAs v KETTERING TOWN 1-3 at Rushden & Diamonds FC

NORTH RIDING F.A.

Tel: 01642 318603 Fax: 01642 318604
Southlands Centre, Ormesby Road, Middlesbrough TS3 0HB

Secretary:	Mark Jarvis			
Football Development Officer:	Andy Clay (01642 321696)			
Executives (Responsibility)	Contact County Office for Coaching Exams/Courses, Referees, Womens Football			
Number of Affiliated Clubs	Senior:	500	U.18:	120
Number of Affiliated Leagues:	Senior:	20	Junior:	10
County Representative Teams:	Senior, U18, Ladies			
Inter County Competitions:	Northern Counties Competitions, FA Youth Competition			

N.R.C.F.A.

President: K Boyer

NORTH RIDING SENIOR CUP 2000-01

(15 entries) (FOUNDED 1881-82)

HOLDERS: York City

MOST WINS: Middlesbrough 46 Scarborough 17 South Bank 8 Stockton 8 York City 8

FIRST PRELIMINARY ROUND

Fishburn Park	v	Bedale	4-1

SECOND PRELIMINARY ROUND

Pickering Town	v	Northallerton Tn	3p5 1*1	Nunthorpe Athletic	v	Thornaby	1-3
York Railway Institute	v	Carlin How	CH W-O	Fishburn Park	v	New Marske SC	1-2

THIRD PRELIMINARY ROUND

Marske United	v	Thornaby	4-3	New Marske	v	Guisborough Town	0-7
Northallerton Town	v	Carlin How	3-1				

FIRST QUALIFYING ROUND

Guisborough Town	v	Whitby Town	1-3	Northallerton Town	v	Marske United	5-2

SECOND QUALIFYING ROUND

Whitby Town	v	Northallerton Town	3-1

SEMI-FINALS

Whitby Town	v	York City	1-1, 5p6	Scarborough	v	Middlesbrough	0-3

FINAL

MIDDLESBROUGH	v	YORK CITY	2-0

NORTHUMBERLAND F.A.

Tel: 0191 236 8020
10 Brenkley Way, Seaton Burn, Newcastle upon Tyne NE13 6DT

Chief Executive: R E Maughan **Press Officer:** Bill Gardner

President: E A Wright

Executives (Responsibility)	B Jones (Coaching Exams/Courses) L Hayden (Referees) G Watson (Mini Soccer & Womens Football)
Number of Affiliated Clubs	Senior: 485 U.18: 426
Number of Affiliated Leagues:	Senior: 21 Junior: 4
County Representative Teams:	Senior, U18
Inter County Competitions:	Northern Counties Senior & Youth Cups, FA County Youth Cup
County Publications:	"The Far Corner" - Bi-monthly Newsletter

NORTHUMBERLAND SENIOR CUP 2000-01

Sponsored by "Absolut"

(FOUNDED 1883-84)

LAST SEASON'S FINAL: Newcastle United Reserves v Newcastle Blue Star 4-1

MOST WINS: Blyth Spartans 21 Newcastle United 21 North Shields 12

FIRST ROUND (4 matches)

Alnwick Town	v	Prudhoe Town	3-0
West Allotment Celtic	v	Blyth Spartans	2-1
Shankhouse	v	Morpeth Town	0-1
Ashington	v	Whitley Bay	2-5

SECOND ROUND (4 matches)

Newcastle Utd Res	v	Whitley Bay	2-1
Newcastle Blue Star	v	Ponteland United	1-1, 1-0
Morpeth Town	v	West Allotment Celtic	2-0
Alnwick Town	v	Bedlington Terriers	1-5

SEMI-FINALS

Bedlington Terriers	v	Morpeth Town	4-4, 5-0
Ponteland United	v	Newcastle Utd Res	0-11

FINAL

BEDLINGTON TERR.	v	NEWCASTLE UTD Rs	10th September 2001

NORTHUMBERLAND BENEVOLENT BOWL 2000-01

Sponsored by "Brother"

(FOUNDED 1975-76)

LAST SEASON'S FINAL: Shankhouse v Benfield Park 3-1

MOST WINS: Morpeth Town 2 Stobswood Welfare 2

FIRST ROUND (4 matches)

Heaton Stannington	v	Amble Town	1-4
Walker Central	v	Newcastle Benfield S	1-5
Percy Main Amat	v	Newbiggin Central W	4-3
Amble Vikings	v	Walker Fosse	2-1

SECOND ROUND (4 matches)

Amble Town	v	North Shields	1-5
Newcastle Benfield S	v	Spittal Rovers	2-0
Coxlodge S C	v	Amble Vikings	2-3
Percy Main Amat	v	Seaton Delaval Amt	3-1

SEMI-FINALS

Percy Main Amateurs	v	North Shields	1-2
Amble Vikings	v	Newcastle B Saints	6-1

FINAL

NORTH SHIELDS	v	AMBLE VIKINGS	2-1

NOTTINGHAMSHIRE F.A. LIMITED

Tel: 0115 941 8954 Fax: 0115 941 5254 Email: NOTTSFA@aol.com
7 Clarendon Street, Nottingham NG1 5HS

Secretary: Mike Kilbee

Executives (Responsibility) Tom Goodwin (Referees Administration Officer)
Helen Bennett (Secretary, Womens Football Committee)

President: John Waterall
Chairman: David Woolrich

Number of Affiliated Clubs Senior: 630 U.18: 193
Number of Affiliated Leagues: Senior: 10 Junior: 4
County Representative Teams: U18
Inter County Competitions: FA County Youth Cup, East Midlands Youth Combination

NOTTINGHAMSHIRE SENIOR CUP 2000-01

(34 entries) (FOUNDED 1883-84)

LAST SEASON'S FINAL: Hucknall Town v Eastwood Town 2-1

MOST WINS: Nottingham Forest 17 Sutton Town 17 Notts County 11

FIRST ROUND

Linby C W	v	Keyworth United	4-5	BRSA Retford	v	Welbeck Colliery	0-4
Kimberley Town	v	Notts Police	1-3	Ruddington United	v	Attenborough	1-4
North Notts	v	Cotgrave C W	5-0	Clifton	v	Kimberley M W	2-1
Teversal	v	Southwell City	2-1	Rainworth M W	v	Pelican	1-0
Ollerton Town	v	IDP Newark	0-4	Clipstone Welfare	v	Siemens	4*2
Greenwood Meadows	v	Blidworth Welfare	3-0	Sneinton	v	Radford	3-1

SECOND ROUND

IDP Newark	v	Rainworth MW	1-0	Notts Police	v	Clifton	3-1
Clipstone Welfare	v	Sneinton	0-5	Attenborough	v	Teversal	3-2
Welbeck C W	v	Keyworth United	2-0	Greenwood Meadows	v	North Notts	1-2

THIRD ROUND

Wollaton	v	North Notts	2-1	Sneinton	v	Attenborough	0-2
Eastwood Town	v	Collingham	3-1	Boots Athletic	v	Notts Police	0-1
Gedling Town	v	Selston	2-1	Arnold Town	v	Welbeck Colliery	0*1
Hucknall Rolls	v	Hucknall Town	0-4	Dunkirk	v	I D P Newark	0-2

FOURTH ROUND

Notts Police	v	Welbeck Miners Welf	0-5	Hucknall Town	v	Eastwood Town	8-0
Gedling Town	v	I D P Newark	3-1	Wollaton	v	Teversal	0-4

SEMI-FINALS

Hucknall Town	v	Welbeck Miners Welf	5-2	Teversal	v	Gedling Town	0-2

FINAL

GEDLING TOWN v HUCKNALL TOWN 0-1 at Notts County FC, attendance 652

OXFORDSHIRE F.A.

Tel: 01993 778586 Fax: 01993 772191 Email: mason@ianj60.freeserve.co.uk
PO Box 62, Witney, Oxon OX28 1HA

Secretary:	Ian Mason
Executives (Responsibility)	Trevor Spindler (Coaching Exams/Courses)
	Paul Faulkner (Referees)
	Bryan Flitter (Womens Football)
Number of Affiliated Clubs	320
Number of Affiliated Leagues:	12
County Representative Teams:	Under 18, Under 16
Inter County Competitions:	Under 18, Under 16

President: J Webb
Chairman: T Williams

OXFORDSHIRE SENIOR CUP 2000-01

(35 entries) (FOUNDED 1884-85)

LAST SEASON'S FINAL: Oxford City v Thame United 2-0

MOST WINS: Oxford City 31 Witney Town 9 Oxford United 8

FIRST ROUND

North Leigh	v	Highmoor	5-1
Bicester Town	v	Ruscote Sports	3-1
Garsington	v	Easington Sports	0-7
Launton Sports	v	Adderbury Park	AP W-O
Wocester College OB	v	Goring United	2-0
Henley Town	v	Kidlington	6-1
Marston Saints	v	Ardley United	2-1
Headington Amateurs	v	Hook Norton	0-3
Old Woodstock Town	v	Clanfield	1-2
Watlington	v	Witney Academy	2*1
Checkendon Sports	v	Carterton Town	0-3
Peppard	v	Charlton United	3-1
Quarry Nomads	v	Chinnor	3-1
Sonning Common	v	Yarnton	7-0
Eynsham Assn	v	Middle Barton	2-3

SECOND ROUND

Carterton Town	v	Clanfield	2-0
Peppard	v	Quarry Nomads	0-1
North Leigh	v	Adderbury Park	4-2
Bicester Town	v	Watlington	3-0
Marston Saints	v	Easington Sports	0-2
Middle Barton	v	Highfield Old Boys	1-3
Worcester College	v	Hook Norton	11p11,1*1,0-1
Sonning Common	v	Henley Town	3-1

THIRD ROUND

Hook Norton	v	Sonning Common	3-1
Quarry Nomads	v	Easington Sports	4-0
Carterton Town	v	Highfield Old Boys	2-1
Bicester Town	v	North Leigh	3-4

FOURTH ROUND

Oxford City	v	Banbury United	0-2
Carterton Town	v	North Leigh	1-4
Thame United	v	Witney Town	5p4, 2*2
Hook Norton	v	Quarry Nomads	0-1

SEMI-FINALS

Thame United	v	North Leigh	1*1, 1-0
Banbury United	v	Quarry Nomads	2-0

FINAL

BANBURY UNITED v THAME UNITED 1-3 at The Manor Ground, Oxford United FC

SHEFFIELD & HALLAMSHIRE F.A.

Tel: 0114 267 0068 Fax: 0114 268 3348
5 Onslow Road, Sheffield S11 7AF

Secretary & Press Officer:	J P Hope-Gill				
Executives (Responsibility)	John Warnock (Coaching Exams/Courses)				
	Peter Jackson (Referees)				
	Julie Callaghan (Womens Football)				
Number of Affiliated Clubs	Senior: 888	U.18:	243		**President:** C L Milner
Number of Affiliated Leagues:	Senior: 17	Junior:	7		**Chairman:** M Matthews
County Representative Teams:	Under 18, Under 16 Girls				
Inter County Competitions:	East Midlands Youth Combination, FA County Youth Cup				

SHEFFIELD & HALLAMSHIRE CUP 2000-01

(48 entries) (FOUNDED 1876-77)

LAST SEASON'S FINAL: Doncaster Rovers v Emley 2-1

SECOND QUALIFYING ROUND (no First)

Penistone Church	v	High Green Villa	3-2
Sheffield Bankers	v	Oughtibridge WMC	0-3
Treeton Welfare	v	Dinnington Town	1-3
Kiveton Park	v	Phoenix	0-1
Sheffield Lane Top	v	The Wetherby	0-2
Mexborough Main St	v	Grapes Roy Hancock	2-1
The Forum	v	South Kirkby Colliery	0-2
Parramore Sports	v	Sheffield Centralians	3-4
Ecclesfield Red Rose	v	Harworth Colliery Inst	3-1
Hemsworth MW	v	Thorpe Hesley	5-0
Davy	v	Caribbean Sports	0-4
NCB Maltby MW	v	Old Edwardians	3-1
Woodhouse W End	v	Yorkshire Main	YM W-O
Swinton Athletic	v	Wombwell Main	0-2
Athersley Recreation	v	Mexborough Town Ath	4-0
Frecheville CA	v	Groves Social	3-1

FIRST ROUND PROPER

Stocksbridge P S	v	Denaby United	3-1
Wombwell Main	v	Frickley Athletic	0-3
Brodsworth Welfare	v	Caribbean Sports	0-1
Worsbrough Bridge	v	South Kirkby Colliery	0-4
Ecclesfield Red Rose	v	Phoenix	2-1
Athersley Recreation	v	Emley	1-3
Rossington Main	v	The Wetherby	0-1
Sheffield Centralians	v	Frecheville CA	1-2
Hemsworth M W	v	Penistone Church	2-0
Mexborough Main St	v	Parkgate	0-3
Dinnington Town	v	Maltby Main	1-0
Sheffield	v	Doncaster Rovers	1-4
Worksop Town	v	Oughtibridge WMC	6-0
Avesta Sheffield	v	Hare & Hounds	2-0
NCB Maltby MW	v	Yorkshire Main	3-5
Hallam	v	Wickersley	2-1

SECOND ROUND

Frickley Athletic	v	Dinnington Town	3*2
Ecclesfield Red Rose	v	Avesta Sheffield	5-2
Parkgate	v	Hallam	3-0
Emley	v	Stocksbridge P S	5-1
Yorkshire Main	v	Doncaster Rovers	0-14
Caribbean Sports	v	The Wetherby	1-3
Worksop Tn (1989)	v	Frecheville C A	5-2
Hemsworth M W	v	South Kirkby Colliery	2-0

THIRD ROUND

Hemsworth MW	v	Worksop Town	1-2
Parkgate	v	Frickley Athletic	0-1
Doncaster Rovers	v	Ecclesfield Red Rose	7-0
Emley	v	The Wetherby	6-0

SEMI-FINALS

Doncaster Rovers	v	Worksop Town	2-1
Frickley Athletic	v	Emley	0-3

FINAL

EMLEY	v	DONCASTER RVRS	1-2	at Hillsborough, Sheffield Wednesday FC

SHROPSHIRE F.A.

Tel: 01743 362769 Fax: 01743 240474
Gay Meadow, Abbey Foregate, Shrewsbury, Shropshire SY2 6AB

Secretary: David Rowe **Press Officer:** Neil Sambrook
Football Development Officer: Mick Murphy
County Reps: Alan Penton (Coaching Exams/Courses)
Eric Adams (Referees)

Number of Affiliated Clubs Senior: 330 U.18: 95
Number of Affiliated Leagues: Senior: 9 Junior: 5
County Representative Teams: U18, Womens, U16
Inter County Competitions: FA County Youth, Midland County Youth, Gilbert Trophy

FLOREAT SALOPIA

President: A W Brett
Chairman: S T Farmer

SHROPSHIRE SENIOR CUP 2000-01

(4 entries) (FOUNDED1877-88)

LAST SEASON'S FINAL: Shrewsbury Town v Shifnal Town 3-0

MOST WINS: Shrewsbury Town 54 Telford United 34 Oswestry Town 11

FIRST ROUND

Bridgnorth Town	v	Telford United	0-2	Shifnal Town	v	Shrewsbury Tn	1-1, 5p4

SEMI-FINALS

Shifnal Town	v	Telford United	0-4

FINAL

TELFORD UNITED v WOLVERHAMPTON W0-2 at Gay Meadow, Shrewsbury Town FC

SHROPSHIRE COUNTY CUP 2000-01

(23 entries)

LAST SEASON'S FINAL: Bandon v Shawbury United 4-3 aet

FIRST ROUND

Broseley Juniors	v	Ironbridge Town	1-5	Oakengates Town	v	Meole Brace	2-1
Wellington Amateurs	v	Shifnal Town Res	0-3	Weston Rhyn	v	Broseley Town	3p1 0*0
Little Drayton Rngrs	v	Clee Hill United	4-0	Shawbury United	v	Star Res	1-0
Whitchurch Alport	v	Newport Town	1-2				

SECOND ROUND

Shifnal Town Res	v	Newport Town	1-6	Shawbury United	v	Oakengates Town	4-1
Belvedere	v	Belle Vue OB	4-1	Weston Rhyn	v	Haughmond	3-0
Ludlow Town	v	Ironbridge Town	7-0	Hanwood United	v	Star	1*4
Tiberton United	v	Little Drayton Rngrs	1-2	Morda United	v	Wem Town	0-4

THIRD ROUND

Little Drayton Rngrs	v	Newport Town	2-0	Ludlow Town	v	Belvedere	2-0
Star	v	Weston Rhyn	2-1	Wem Town	v	Shawbury United	0-1

SEMI-FINALS

Little Drayton Rngrs	v	Ludlow Town	5-0	Star	v	Shawbury United	3p0, 2*2

FINAL

LITTLE DRAYTON	v	STAR	4p3, 0*0

SOMERSET F.A.

Tel: 01761 410280 Fax: 01761 410477 Email: somfa@dial.pipex.com
30 North Road, Midsomer Norton, Bath, Somerset BA3 2QD

Secretary: Mrs H Marchment

Executives (Responsibility) I Tincknell (Coaching Courses/Exams)
J H Day (Referees), K Hodges (Football Development)

Number of Affiliated Clubs Senior: 78 U.18: 407 **President:** F P Hillier

Number of Affiliated Leagues: Senior: 1 Junior: 22 **Chairman:** A J Hobbs

County Representative Teams: Senior, U18, Womens

Inter County Competitions: FA County Youth, South West Counties Championship (Senior, Youth & Womens)

SOMERSET PREMIER CUP 2000-01

(21 entries) (FOUNDED 1948-49)

LAST SEASON'S FINAL: Bristol City v Bath City 3-2

MOST WINS: Bath City 17 Yeovil Town 15 Bristol City 6

FIRST ROUND

Frome Town	v	Bristol Manor Farm	1-2	Bridgwater Town	v	Taunton Town	0-1
Wellington	v	Yeovil Town	0-2	Odd Down Bath	v	Chard Town	1-0
Paulton Rovers	v	Weston Super Mare	4-1				

SECOND ROUND

Backwell United	v	Welton Rovers	1-2	Bristol City	v	Paulton Rovers	1-0
Clevedon Town	v	Keynsham Town	5-0	Bath City	v	Street	5-2
Minehead Town	v	Bishop Sutton	1-3	Brislington	v	Bristol Manor Farm	2-1
Odd Down Bath	v	Mangotsfield Utd	4p3 0*0	Yeovil Town	v	Taunton Town @TT	0-2

THIRD ROUND

Welton Rovers	v	Bath Odd Down	0-1	Bristol City	v	Taunton Town	4-1
Bath City	v	Clevedon Town	0-2	Bishop Sutton	v	Brislington	0-1

SEMI-FINALS

Bath Odd Down	v	Brislington	4p3, 2*2	Bristol City	v	Clevedon Town	0-1

FINAL

CLEVEDON TOWN v BATH ODD DOWN 1-0 at Twerton Park, Bath City FC

SOMERSET SENIOR CUP 2000-01

(52 entries) (FOUNDED 1895-96)

LAST SEASON'S FINAL: Portishead v Radstock Town 2-1

MOST WINS: Paulton Rovers 12 Radstock Town 12 Welton Rovers 9

FIRST ROUND

Cleeve West Town	v	Congresbury	5-1	Odd Down Res	v	Castle Cary	2-4
Clutton	v	Banwell	2*1	Ilminster Town	v	Backwell United Res	1*3
Westland United	v	Imperial	1-2	Watchet Town	v	First Tower United	4*5
Burnham United	v	Radstock Town	1-5	Glastonbury	v	Nailsea United	1-8
Bridgwater Town Res	v	Bishop Sutton Res	4-2	Peasedown Athletic	v	Hartcliffe OB	PA W-O
Fry Club	v	Robinsons	2p3 2*2	Paulton Rovers Res	v	Stockwood Green	1*2
Keynsham Town Res	v	Westland Sports	2*4	Long Sutton	v	Clevedon United	1-2
Hengrove Athletic	v	St George E in G'dano	2-0	Kewstoke	v	Wrington Redhill	3-4
Timsbury Athletic	v	Tunley Athletic	2-1	Brislington Res	v	Winscombe	5-0
Clandown	v	Cutters Friday	1*3	Street Res	v	Shepton Mallet	0-1

SECOND ROUND

Worle St Johns	v	Cutters Friday	4-1	Dundry Athletic	v	Peasedown Athletic	3-10
Clevedon United	v	Wrington-Redhill	9-2	Clutton	v	Cleeve West Town	0-3
Frome Collegeians	v	Frome Town Res	2-4	Imperial	v	Nailsea United	4*4, 3p4
Teyfant Athletic	v	Wells City	0-9	Shepton Mallet	v	Hengrove Athletic	6-1
Radstock Town	v	Welton Rovers Res	0-3	Stockwood Green	v	Timsbury Athletic	3*2
Robinsons	v	Larkhall Athletic	1-2	Backwell United Res	v	Portishead	0-2
Westland Sports	v	First Tower United	3-0	Saltford	v	Cheddar	1-2
Bridgwater T 1984 R	v	Brislington Res	3-0	Nailsea Town	v	Castle Cary	2-1

THIRD ROUND

Worle St Johns	v	Welton Rovers Res	4-1	Wells City	v	Cheddar	2-1
Clutton/Cleeve W T	v	Shepton Mallet	2-1	Larkhall Athletic	v	Stockwood Green	1-2
Bridgwater T 1984 R	v	Portishead	2-1	Westland Sports	v	Nailsea Utd	0-2
Peasedown Athletic	v	Frome Town Res	4-2	Nailsea Town	v	Clevedon U	4V3 CU T/A

QUARTER-FINALS

Bridgwater Town	v	Clevedon United	2-1	Wells City	v	Peasedown Athletic	1-0
Worle St Johns	v	Nailsea United	3-4	Cleeve West Town	v	Stockwood Green	2-1

SEMI-FINALS

Cleeve West Town	v	Bridgwater Town	2*1	Nailsea United	v	Wells City	3-2

FINAL

CLEEVE WEST TN v NAILSEA UNITED 1*2 at Athletic Ground, Paulton Rovers FC

STAFFORDSHIRE F.A.

Tel: 01785 256994 Fax: 01785 224334
County Showground, Weston Road, Stafford ST18 0BD

Secretary: Brian Adshead **Assistant Secretary:** David Shelton

Executives (Responsibility) Andy Weston (Football Development Officer)
Ian Cooper (Coaching Courses), Nick Broad (Referees)

Number of Affiliated Clubs Senior: 567 U18: 553

Number of Affiliated Leagues: Senior: 15 U18: 14

President: P Savage

County Representative Teams: U 18 Boys, U 16 Boys, Ladies, U 16 Girls

Chairman: P Hodgkinson

Inter County Competitions: FA County Youth Challenge Cup, Midland Counties Youth Championship

STAFFORDSHIRE SENIOR CHALLENGE CUP 2000-01
(FOUNDED 1891-92)

LAST SEASON'S FINAL: Tamworth v Blakenall 4-4 on aggregate

MOST WINS: Stoke City 18 Aston Villa 16 West Bromwich Albion 13

FIRST ROUND (5 matches)

Bilston Town	v	Willenhall Town	4-2	Newcastle Town	v	Leek Town	0-2
Pelsall Villa	v	Halesowen Harriers	1-0	Rocester	v	Chasetown	1-1, 3-2
Stafford Town	v	Knypersley Victoria	3-2				

SECOND ROUND (8 matches)

Bloxwich Town	v	Stoke City	1-4	Kidsgrove Athletic	v	Rushall Olympic	1-1, 2-0
Leek CSOB	v	Pelsall Villa	3-1	Rocester	v	Blakenall	3-1
Shifnal Town	v	Leek Town	3-0	Stafford Rangers	v	Bilston Town	4-2
Stafford Town	v	Hednesford Town	0-3	Tamworth	v	Port Vale	0-1

THIRD ROUND (4 matches)

Kidsgrove Athletic	v	Port Vale	0-3	Stoke City	v	Rocester	2-4
Leek CSOB	v	Hednesford Town	2-1	Shifnal Town	v	Stafford Rangers	1-4

SEMI-FINALS

Leek CSOB	v	Rocester	0-1	Stafford Rangers	v	Port Vale	1-1, 3p4

FINAL

PORT VALE	v	ROCESTER	6-1

SUFFOLK F.A.

Tel: 01473 407290 Fax: 01473 407291 Email: suffolkfa.office@dial.pipex.com
Felaw Maltings, 44 Felaw Street, Ipswich, Suffolk IP2 8SJ

Secretary:	William Steward				
Executives (Responsibility)	C Rowe (Coaching Exams/Courses), Brian Thompson (Referees) Angela Locke (Womens Football)				
Number of Affiliated Clubs	Senior: 450		U.18: 200		**President:** Gordon Blake
Number of Affiliated Leagues:	Senior: 13		Junior: 7		**Chairman:** George Whight
County Representative Teams:	Intermediate (adult), U18, U16, Womens				
Inter County Competitions:	All in East Anglian Counties Championships				

SUFFOLK PREMIER CUP 2000-01

(9 entries) (FOUNDED 1958-59)

LAST SEASON'S FINAL: Lowestoft Town v Mildenhall Town 1-0

MOST WINS: Sudbury Town 12 Bury Town 10 Lowestoft Town 6

PRELIMINARY ROUND

Sudbury	v	Woodbridge Town	6-1

FIRST ROUND

Mildenhall Town	v	Ipswich Wanderers	1-0
Sudbury	v	Bury Town	2-1
Stowmarket Town	v	Lowestoft Town	1-2
Newmarket Town	v	Felixstowe & Walton U	2-1

SEMI-FINALS

Mildenhall Town	v	Sudbury	1*2
Lowestoft Town	v	Newmarket Town	1p3, 2*2

FINAL

LOWESTOFT TOWN	v	SUDBURY	4-3	at Felixstowe & Walton United FC

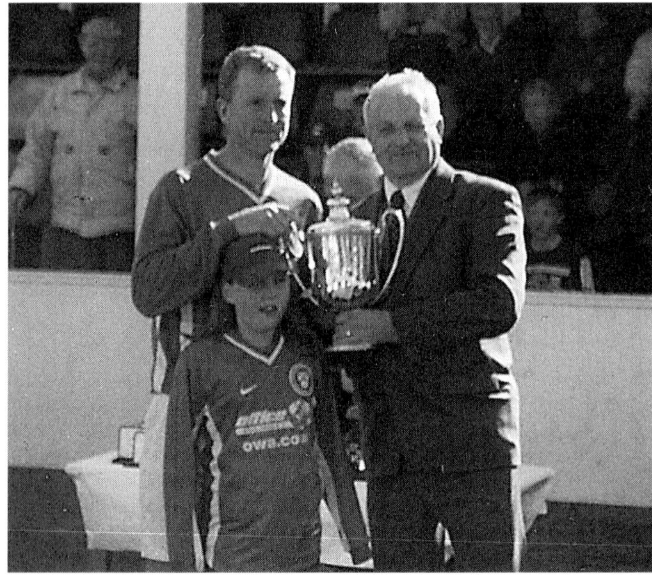

Sean Trail receives the Suffolk Premier Cup from Gordon Raynor, Chairman of the Suffolk County FA at Felixstowe Town FC.

SUFFOLK SENIOR CUP 2000-01

(32 entries) (FOUNDED 1885-86)

LAST SEASON'S FINAL: Grundisburgh v Needham Market 3-1

MOST WINS: Ipswich Town 16 Lowestoft Town 10 Stowmarket Town 8

FIRST ROUND

Whitton United	v	Stonham Aspal	4-2	Sudbury Athletic	v	Beccles Town	0-3
British Sugar	v	Hadleigh United	2-4	Cornard United	v	Framlingham Town	6-0
Bungay Town	v	Walsham le Will	2p4 1*1	Haughley United	v	Ipswich Wanderers Rs	6-4
Woodbridge Athletic	v	Ransomes Sports	2-3	Ipswich Athletic	v	Old Newton United	3-1
Stanton	v	Lowestoft Town Res	1-0	Long Melford	v	Leiston St Margarets	2-1
Leiston FC	v	Brandon Town	4-2	Needham Market	v	Achilles	1-0
Capel Plough	v	Stowmarket Town Rs	0-2	Kirkley	v	Grundisburgh	4p2 1-1
Ashlea	v	East Bergholt United	3-4	Haverhill Rovers	v	Sudbury Res	0-2

SECOND ROUND

Stowmarket Town Rs	v	Beccles Town	4p5 3*3	Needham Market	v	Leiston	2-1
Sudbury Res	v	Walsham le Willows	3-2	Hadleigh United	v	Stanton	2-0
Ransomes Sports	v	Ipswich Athletic	3-4	Long Melford	v	Whitton United	0-2
East Bergholt United	v	Cornard United	3-2	Haughley United	v	Kirkley	9/12

THIRD ROUND

Hadleigh United	v	East Bergholt Utd	4p3 2*2	Kirkley	v	Whitton United	4-3
Ipswich Athletic	v	Beccles Town	3*2	Needham Market	v	Sudbury Res	1-0

SEMI-FINALS

Needham Market	v	Kirkley	2p3, 1*1	Ipswich Athletic	v	Hadleigh United	2*1

FINAL

IPSWICH ATHLETIC	v	KIRKLEY	1-3	at Portman Road, Ipswich Town FC. Att: 1036

SURREY F.A.

Tel: 01372 373543 Fax: 01372 361310
Website: www.surreyfa.co.uk Email: enquiries@surreyfa.co.uk
321 Kingston Road, Leatherhead, Surrey KT22 7TU

Secretary: Ray Ward

Executives (Responsibility)	Larry May (Coaching Exams/Courses)				
	Phil Whatling (Referees) Peter Adams (Womens Football)				
Number of Affiliated Clubs	Senior:	38			**President:** A P Adams
Number of Affiliated Leagues:	Senior:	2	Junior:	20	**Chairman:** R S Lewis
County Representative Teams:	Under 18, Womens				
Inter County Competitions:	Home Counties Womens Competition, FA County Youth Cup				

SURREY SENIOR CUP 2000-01

(36 entries) (FOUNDED 1882-83)

LAST SEASON'S FINAL: Woking v Croydon 1-0

FIRST QUALIFYING ROUND

Epsom & Ewell	v	Raynes Park Vale	3-1	Redhill	v	Cobham	2-0
Chessington United	v	Cranleigh	4-1	Godalming & G'ford	v	Lingfield	6-2
Walton Casuals	v	Ash United	1-5	Chipstead	v	Dorking	1-3
Camberley Town	v	Farnham Town	3-1	Merstham	v	Ch'ton & Hook U	3p4 2*2

SECOND QUALIFYING ROUND

Corinthian Casuals	v	Redhill	2-0	Egham Town	v	Camberley Town	3-2
Ashford Town	v	Croydon Athletic	1-2	Godalming & G'ford	v	Molesey	4-2
Metropolitan Police	v	Epsom & Ewell	2-1	Chess'ton & Hook U	v	Ash United	1-5
Banstead Athletic	v	Westfield	2p4 3*3	Chessington United	v	Dorking	2*1

THIRD QUALIFYING ROUND

Egham Town	v	Ash United	3-1	Metropolitan Police	v	Chessington United	6-2
Westfield	v	Godalming & Guildford	0-1	Croydon Athletic	v	Corinthian Cas	4p3, 0*0

FIRST ROUND PROPER

Walton & Hersham	v	Whyteleafe	1-2	Metropolitan Police	v	Carshalton Athletic	1-4
Kingstonian	v	Croydon Athletic	K W-O	Leatherhead	v	Tooting & Mitcham U	1-3
Sutton United	v	Dulwich Hamlet	1-0	Egham Town	v	Crystal Palace Res	3-4
Godalming & Guildford	v	Woking	1*3	Croydon	v	Chertsey	2-0

SECOND ROUND

Crystal Palace Res	v	Croydon	3-2	Kingstonian	v	Tooting&Mitcham U	3V1
Carshalton Athletic	v	Woking	1-4	Whyteleafe	v	Sutton United	2-0

Kingstonian ineligible player, Tooting & Mitcham United reinstated

SEMI-FINALS

Woking	v	Crystal Palace Res	0-3	Whyteleafe	v	Tooting & Mitcham U	0-3

FINAL

CRYSTAL PALACE v TOOTING & MITCH. 3-1 at Gander Green Lane, Sutton United FC

SUSSEX F.A.

Tel: 01903 753547 Fax: 01903 761608
Website: sussex-fa.org E-mail: sussexfa@dial.pipex.co.uk
Culver Road, Lancing, West Sussex BN15 9AX

Chief Executive Ken Benham
Executives (Responsibility) L Thompson (Coaching Exams)
M Bodenham (Head of Refereeing)
H Millington (Football Development Officer)
Number of Affiliated Clubs Senior: 951 Youth: 246
Number of Affiliated Leagues: Senior: 18 Junior: 10
County Representative Teams: Senior, Inter, U18, U16, Womens, U18, U16
Inter County Competitions: FA County Youth, Home Counties Youth U16's
South West Counties Senior, Womens & U18's, Southern Counties Intermediate

President: John Davey
Chairman: Ron Pavey

Yellow Jersey SUSSEX SENIOR CUP 2000-01

(46 entries) (FOUNDED 1882-83)

LAST SEASON'S FINAL: Brigton & Hove Albion v Hastings Town 1-1, 4p3 aet

MOST WINS: Worthing 20 Eastbourne Town 12 Southwick 10

FIRST ROUND (14 matches)

Ringmer	v	Westfield	3-0	Shoreham	v	East Grinstead Town	4-2
Broadbridge Heath	v	Wick	2-2, 4-2	Shinewater Assn	v	Pagham	1-8
Oakwood	v	Worthing United	1-5	Sidlesham	v	Chichester City Utd	2-3
Eastbourne United	v	Arundel	1-0	Hailsham Town	v	Wealden	2-0
Bosham	v	Lewes	2-4	Withdean 2000	v	Three Bridges	w/o
Lancing	v	Crawley Down	2-1	Crowborough Ath	v	Storrington	2-1
Mile Oak	v	Oving	4-0	Peacehaven & Tels	v	Southwick	2-1

SECOND ROUND (16 matches)

Hassocks	v	Worthing United	3-1	East Preston	v	Bognor Regis Town	1-8
St Leonards	v	Sidley United	0-2	Pagham	v	Mile Oak	2-0
Shoreham	v	Peace & Telscombe	2-1	Eastbourne United	v	Crowborough Athletic	3-0
Horsham YMCA	v	Littlehampton Town	1-0	Three Bridges	v	Broadbridge Heath	0-3
Saltdean United	v	Crawley Town	0-5	Hailsham Town	v	Chichester City Utd	4-2
Hastings Town	v	Langney Sports	1-3	Ringmer	v	Eastbourne Town	3-0
Whitehawk	v	Lancing	4-0	Worthing	v	Horsham	0-2
Lewes	v	Brighton & Hove Alb	3-0	Selsey	v	Burgess Hill Town	w/o

THIRD ROUND (8 matches)

Hassocks	v	Bognor Regis Town	2-3	Sidley United	v	Pagham	0-2
Shoreham	v	Eastbourne Utd	1-1, 1-0	Horsham YMCA	v	Broadbridge Heath	2-1
Crawley Town	v	Hailsham Town	3-0	Langney Sports	v	Ringmer	5-4
Whitehawk	v	Horsham	0-4	Lewes	v	Selsey	4-0

FOURTH ROUND (4 matches)

Bognor Regis Town	v	Pagham	6-4	Shoreham	v	Horsham YMCA	1-3
Crawley Town	v	Langney Sports	2-1	Horsham	v	Lewes	1-1, 1-4

SEMI-FINALS

Bognor Regis Town	v	Horsham YMCA	5-2	at Lancing FC
Crawley Town	v	Lewes	0-3	at Lancing FC

FINAL

BOGNOR REGIS T	v	LEWES	1*2	at Langney Sports FC

Sussex Senior Cup Final
Lewes beat Bognor Regis Town 1-2 after extra time at Langney Sports FC

Top: Michael Birmingham and Marc Cable shake hands before battle commences.

Centre: Aerial battle during the final.

Bottom: Lewes players and officials invade the pitch as the final whistle goes.

Photos: Graham Cotterill

SUSSEX ROYAL ULSTER RIFLES CHARITY CUP 2000-01

(FOUNDED 1896-97)

LAST SEASON'S FINAL: Burgess Hill Town v Saltdean United 3-0

MOST WINS: Horsham 14 Worthing 12 Southwick 10

FIRST ROUND (4 matches)

Arundel	v	Eastbourne Town	3*2
Broadbridge Heath	v	Lancing	1-0
Wick	v	Littlehampton Tn	2-2, 1-3
Crawley Down	v	Peacehaven & Tels	0*1

SECOND ROUND (16 matches)

Ringmer	v	Arundel	1-3
East Preston	v	Pagham	2-5
Eastbourne United	v	Burgess Hill Town	1-2
Hailsham Town	v	Broadbridge Heath	2-4
Storrington	v	Wealden	3-1
Crowborough Ath	v	Oving	4-2
East Grinstead Town	v	Horsham YMCA	1-7
Whitehawk	v	Oakwood	2-2, 3-0
Shoreham	v	Sidley United	0-1
Westfield	v	Lingfield	4-3
Selsey F & S Club	v	Saltdean United	5-2
Worthing United	v	Three Bridges	1-3
Hassocks	v	Shinewater Assn	9-0
Mile Oak	v	Sidlesham	1-4
Chichester City Utd	v	Littlehampton Town	1-3
Redhill	v	Peacehaven & Tels	3-1

THIRD ROUND (8 matches)

Three Bridges	v	Crowborough Athletic	6-2
Storrington	v	Redhill	1-2
Sidlesham	v	Pagham	5-3
Selsey Football & SC	v	Hassocks	1-0
Whitehawk	v	Horsham YMCA	1-2
Littlehampton Town	v	Arundel	1-0
Westfield	v	Sidley United	0-4
Broadbridge Heath	v	Burgess Hill Town	1-3

FOURTH ROUND (4 matches)

Burgess Hill Town	v	Sidley United	3-1
Redhill	v	Three Bridges	2-0
Horsham YMCA	v	Littlehampton Town	4-0
Sidlesham	v	Selsey Football & SC	5-4

SEMI-FINALS

Horsham YMCA	v	Sidlesham	1-0
Burgess Hill Town	v	Redhill	3-0

FINAL

BURGESS HILL T	v	HORSHAM YMCA	0-3

WESTMORLAND F.A.

Tel: 01539 730946 Fax: 01539 730946 E-mail: westfa@dial.pipex.com
Unit 1, Angel Court, 21 Highgate, Kendal, Cumbria LA9 4DA

Executive Officer: P G Ducksbury

Executives (Responsibility) County Office (Football Development, Coaching Exams, Coaching Courses, Girls/Womens Football, Referees)

Number of Affiliated Clubs Senior: 61 U.18: 23

Number of Affiliated Leagues: Senior: 3 Junior: 1

County Representative Teams: Senior, U18

Inter County Competitions: FA County Youth, Association of Northern Counties Senior & Youth Competitions

President: J B Fleming

Chairman: G Aplin

WESTMORLAND CAR SALES SENIOR CUP 2000-01

(FOUNDED 1896-97)

(24 entries)

LAST SEASON'S FINAL: Milnethorpe Corinthians v Wetheriggs United 1-0

MOST WINS: Corinthians 14 Netherfield 12 Burneside 7 Windermere 7

'FIRST ROUND

Esthwaite Vale Utd	v	Ambleside Utd	EVU W-O
Keswick	v	Endmoor KGR	3-2
Victoria SC	v	Arnside	3-2
Windermere SC	v	Kendal Town	3-2
Carvetii United	v	Burneside	1-0
Appleby	v	Burton Thistle	5-1
Kirkby Lonsdale Rgrs	v	Lunesdale United	3-0

SECOND ROUND

Ambleside United	v	Coniston	0-3
Carvetii United	v	Greystoke	6-3
Kirkby Lonsdale Rgrs	v	Dent	5-1
Staveley United	v	Keswick	2-0
Appleby	v	Windermere SC	7-0
Kendal County	v	Shap	5-2
Sedburgh Wndrs	v	Milnethorpe Corinths	2*5
Victoria SC	v	Wetheriggs United	4*2

THIRD ROUND

Carvetii United	v	Kendal County	2-1
Appleby	v	Kirkby Lonsdale Rgrs	2-0
Milnethorpe Corinths	v	Coniston	0-3
Victoria Sporting	v	Staveley United	1-6

SEMI-FINALS

Appleby	v	Coniston	2-1
Staveley United	v	Carvetii United	5-3

FINAL

APPLEBY v STAVELEY UNITED To be played 28 August 2001

WEST RIDING F.A.

Tel: 01132 821222 Fax: 01132 821525 Email: secretary@NRCFA.com
Fleet Lane, Woodlesford, Leeds LS26 8NX

Secretary & Press Officer: G R Carter

Executives (Responsibility) Contact Secretary for:
Coaching Exams/Courses, Referees, Womens Football

Number of Affiliated Clubs Senior: 950 U.18: 300

Number of Affiliated Leagues: Senior: 40 Junior: 12

County Representative Teams: Senior, Junior U18, Womens

Inter County Competitions: Association of Northern Counties Senior, Junior U18 & Womens, FA County Youth

President: A C Taylor
Chairman: G Pawson

WEST RIDING COUNTY CUP 2000-01

(18 entries) (FOUNDED 1924-25)

LAST SEASON'S FINAL: Garforth Town v Eccleshill United 2-0

MOST WINS: Goole Town 11 Farsley Celtic 9 Guiseley 5

FIRST ROUND

Ossett Town	v	Armthorpe Welfare	5-0
Glasshoughton Welf	v	Harrogate Town	2*1

SECOND ROUND

Selby Town	v	Goole	0-2
Liversedge	v	Ossett Town	1-5
Eccleshill United	v	Guiseley	1-2
Tadcaster Albion	v	Thackley	3*3, 2-5
Ossett Albion	v	Harrogate Railway	1-0
Farsley Celtic	v	Hatfield Main	2-1
Yorkshire Amateur	v	Bradford Park Avenue	1-2
Glasshoughton Welf	v	Garforth Town	8-1

THIRD ROUND

Eccleshill/Guiseley	v	Ossett Town	2-3
Glasshoughton Welf	v	Bradford Park Avenue	0-1
Thackley	v	Farsley Celtic	0-1
Ossett Albion	v	Goole	1-0

SEMI-FINALS

Ossett Albion	v	Farsley Celtic	2-5
Bradford Park Ave	v	Ossett Town	0-2

FINAL

Farsley Celtic v Ossett Town 3*2 at County FA Ground, Woodlesford, Leeds. Att: 242

WILTSHIRE F.A.

Tel: 01793 525245 Fax: 01793 692699
16 Robins Green, Covingham, Swindon, Wilts SN3 5AY

Secretary:	Michael Benson
Executives (Responsibility)	Ian Whitehouse (Referees)
	Kelly Simmons (Womens Football)
	B V Stephens (Development Officer)
Number of Affiliated Clubs:	502
Number of Affiliated Leagues:	17
County Representative Teams:	Senior, U21, U18, Womens Senior & U18
Inter County Competitions:	All levels

President: T K Dowty
Chairman: R Gardiner

WILTSHIRE PREMIER SHIELD 2000-01

(12 entries) (FOUNDED 1926-27)

LAST SEASON'S FINAL: Melksham Town v Swindon Town 1-0

MOST WINS: Swindon Town 26 Salisbury City 11 Trowbridge Town 9

FIRST ROUND

Bemerton Hth Hqns	v	Swindon Town	2*1	Swindon S'marine	v	Highworth Town	4p2 1*1
Salisbury City	v	Chippenham Town	1-0	Downton	v	Devizes Town	0-3

SECOND ROUND

Bemerton Hth Hqns	v	Warminster Town	4-0	Calne Town	v	Devizes Town	2-3
Westbury United	v	Salisbury City	0-4	Melksham Town	v	Swindon Supermarine	2-0

SEMI-FINALS

Salisbury City	v	Melksham Town	2-1	Devizes Town	v	Bemerton Heath Hqns	0-1

FINAL

BEMERTON H H	v	SALISBURY CITY	0-1	at Partridge Way, Old Sarum, Salisbury City FC

WILTSHIRE SENIOR CUP 2000-01

(16 entries) (FOUNDED 1886-87)

LAST SEASON'S FINAL:

Pewsey Vale v Purton 0-0, 3p2 aet

MOST WINS:

Devizes Town 14 Swindon Town 10 Chippenham Town 8

FIRST ROUND

Chiseldon Sthbrook	v	Cricklade Town	1-3	Stratton Crosslink	v	Bradford Town	3-0
Purton	v	Marlborough Town	5-0	Aldbourne	v	Shrewton United	0-5
Malmesbury Victoria	v	Biddestone @B	3*1	Wroughton	v	Pewsey Vale	4p5 0*0
Wootton Bassett Town	v	Amesbury Town	6-0	Trowbridge Town	v	Corsham Town	1-5

SECOND ROUND

Malmesbury Victoria	v	Cricklade Town	0-3	Shrewton United	v	Pewsey Vale	5-3
Corsham Town	v	Stratton Crosslink	1-2	Wootton Bassett Tn	v	Purton	4*1

SEMI-FINALS

Wootton Bassett Tn	v	Cricklade Town	2*1	Stratton Crosslink	v	Shrewton United	1-2

FINAL

SHREWTON UTD	v	WOOTTON BASSETT	0-2

WORCESTERSHIRE F.A.

Tel: 01386 443215 Fax:01386 443215
Fermain, 12 Worcester Road, Evesham, Worcestershire WR11 4JU

Company Secretary: M R Leggett
Executives (Responsibility) Andy Norman (Football Development Officer)
Julie Leroux (Girls' & Womens' FDO)
Bill Allsopp (Referees Co-ordinator), Mick Ford (County Coaching Rep)
Dawn Scott (Women's County Coaching Rep)
Number of Affiliated Clubs Senior: 16 Junior: 271 Youth: 108
Womens & Girls: 12 Small-Side: 45
President: P Rushton
Chairman: K J Clifford
Number of Affiliated Leagues: Senior: 7 Junior: 4
County Representative Teams: U18 Youth, U16 Girls'
Inter County Competitions: FA County Youth Cup, Midland Counties Youth Championship

WORCESTERSHIRE SENIOR CUP 2000-01

(8 entries) (FOUNDED 1893-94)

LAST SEASON'S FINAL: Kidderminster Harriers v Solihull Borough 3-0

FIRST ROUND (4 matches)

Redditch United	v	Evesham United	0-1	Kidderminster H	v	Solihull Borough	3-1
Moor Green	v	Bromsgrove Rovers	2-0	Worcester City	v	Halesowen Town	4-1

SEMI-FINALS

Kidderminster Harr	v	Moor Green	0-1	Evesham United	v	Worcester City	2-2, 2-1

FINAL (First Leg)

MOOR GREEN v EVESHAM UNITED 1-1

FINAL (Second Leg)

EVESHAM UNITED v MOOR GREEN 2*4 Moor Green won 5-3 on aggregate

WORCESTERSHIRE SENIOR URN 2000-01

LAST SEASON'S FINAL: Malvern Town v Stourport Swifts 1-1, 4p3 aet

FIRST ROUND (2 matches)

Pershore Town	v	Pegasus Juniors	3-1	Bromsgrove Rvrs Rs	v	Alvechurch	1-2

SECOND ROUND (4 matches)

Malvern Town	v	Pershore Town	2-0	Stourport Swifts	v	Kidderminster H Res	0-3
Feckenham	v	Studley BKL	0-4	Alvechurch	v	Stourbridge	2-1

SEMI-FINALS

Alvechurch	v	Malvern Town	1-2	Studley BKL	v	Kidderminster H Res	0-2

Kidderminster Harriers Reserves fielded ineligible player - tie awarded to Studley BKL

FINAL

MALVERN TOWN v STUDLEY BKL 0-2 at Worcester City FC

RAMESES
MIDLAND INVITATION CUP 2000-01

(53 entries)

LAST SEASON'S FINAL: Bridgnorth Town v Darlaston Town 3-1

FIRST ROUND

Alvechurch	v	Warley Rangers	2*3	Alveston	v	Boldmere St Michaels	0-3
Aylestone Park	v	Downes Sports	1-3	Bolehall Swifts	v	Stratford Town	0-9
Coalville Town	v	Massey Ferguson	1-0	Continental Star	v	Pershore Town	2-1
Gornal Athletic	v	Bridgnorth Town	1-4	Halesowen Harriers	v	Malvern Town	3-4
Handrahan Timbers	v	Pelsall Villa 3A2 4p1	1*1	Ibstock Welfare	v	Chasetown	0-1
Kirby Muxloe	v	Birstall United	3-2	Little Drayton Rngrs	v	Bloxwich Town	1-3
Oadby Town	v	Cheslyn Hay	1-2	Sandwell Borough	v	Anstey Nomads	1-7
St Andrews	v	Thurmaston Town	2-0	Star	v	Cradley Town	0-1
Stourport Swifts	v	Stourbridge	0-2	Studley BKL	v	Shifnal Town	1-2
Thringstone United	v	Barwell	4-3	Wednesfield	v	West Mids Police	0-2
Willenhall Town	v	Leicester YMCA 4p3	2*2	Wolverhampton Cas	v	Rushall Olympic	4-1

SECOND ROUND

Alvechurch/Warley	v	West Mids Police	5-1	Anstey Nomads	v	St Andrews	3-1
Blackheath Invenseys	v	Malvern Town	2-0	Boldmere St M	v	Knypersley Victoria	5-1
Bridgnorth Town	v	Bloxwich Town	3-2	Chasetown	v	Cheslyn Hay	1-3
Cradley Town	v	Brierley Hill Town	0-1	Dudley Town	v	Causeway United	1*2
Kirby Muxloe	v	Coalville Town	3-2	Shifnal Town	v	Thringstone United	2-0
Stourbridge	v	Downes Sports	4*1	Stratford Town	v	Holwell Sports	5-1
Sutton Town	v	Bustleholme	5-1	Tividale	v	Willenhall Town	0-1
Wolverhampton Cas	v	Continental Star	4-0				

THIRD ROUND

Blackheath Invenseys	v	Warley Rangers	1-2	Boldmere St Mich.	v	Kirby Muxloe	4*0
Anstey Nomads	v	Bridgnorth Town	1-8	Wolverhampton Cas.	v	Causeway United	5*1
Brierley Hill Town	v	Sutton Town	0-3	Handrahan Timbers	v	Stratford Town	0-5
Stourbridge	v	Cheslyn Hay	2-0	Willenhall Town	v	Shifnal Town	3-2

FOURTH ROUND

Boldmere St Michaels	v	Willenhall Town	0-2	Wolverhampton Cas.	v	Stourbridge	3-0
Sutton Town	v	Warley Rangers	1*0	Stratford Town	v	Bridgnorth Town	3*5

SEMI-FINALS

Stratford Town	v	Wolverhampton Cas.	2-0	Willenhall Town	v	Warley Rangers	2-1

FINAL

STRATFORD TOWN v WILLENHALL TOWN 0-1

Tony Pennock (Yeovil Town & Wales) also was a canditate for player of the year, now with Rushden & Diamonds.

FA XI v Combined Services. A tremendous save by Services' keeper "Daisy" May foils Neil Gregory.
Photo: Gordon Whittington

Jamie Pitman and Phil Collins are en route to congratulate FA XI goalscorer Leon Braithwaite whilst Services' Alan Pluckrose can only ponder.
Photo: Gordon Whittington

INTER-SERVICE COMPETITION

Each year the best footballers in the armed forces represent their own service in the Inter-Service Competition for the Constantinople Cup. This year's competition was as keenly contested as ever with the RAF beating both the Army and the Royal Navy to retain the Trophy.

ARMY 0 v 5 RAF

at Aldershot Garrison Stadium

ARMY: May, Collins, Watts, Boughen, Tagg, Crow, Bartlett, Bell, Wall, Brown, McCormick, Alford, Wiscombe, K Roberts, Locke, M Roberts
RAF: Sean Cooper, Gary Wotton, Brian Kayll, Mark Mallinson, Ally Christmas, , Andy Dickinson, Daz Bray, Paul Feeley, Mark Preston, Wallace Taylor, Gareth Seddon, Nick Owen, Matt Hopkins, Al Pluckrose, Lenny Brayshaw, Chris Roberts

ROYAL NAVY 3 v 1 ARMY

ROYAL NAVY: from T Price, S Winnan, N Thwaites, J McGall, A Garrett, M Preston, S Riley, L Weatherall, P Gamble, F Quirke, J Delahaye, C Welsby, S Dann, N Haigh, P Willetts, N Geddis, R Evans, R Page, H Richardson, S Mather, A Craven, S O'Neil, P Tickle, P Proctor
ARMY: from D May, P Tagg, D Boughen, P Alford, C Wall, L Ross, E Shannon, S Bell, C Watts, W O'Connor, S McFadden, G Crowe, J Collins, D Hope, L Whittle, W Backhouse, N Bartlett, N Wojtas, K Roberts, M Roberts, S Fraser, J Carver, T McCormick, A Clark, A Brown, G Atkins, M Sellers, N Wiscombe

RAF 3 v 0 ROYAL NAVY

at the RAF Cosford Stadium

RAF: Sean Cooper, Gary Wotton, Brian Kayll, Mark Mallinson, Ally Christmas, , Andy Dickinson, Daz Bray, Paul Feeley, Mark Preston, Wallace Taylor, Gareth Seddon, Nick Owen, Matt Hopkin, Al Pluckrose, Lenny Brayshaw
ROYAL NAVY: from Price, Winnan, Thwaites, McGall, Garrett, Preston, Riley, Weatherall, Gamble, Quirke, Delahaye, Welsby, Dann, Haigh, Willetts, Geddis, Evans, Page, Richardson, Mather, Craven, O'Neil, Tickle, Proctor

INTER-SERVICE COMPETITION TABLE

	P	*W*	*D*	*L*	*F*	*A*	*Pts*
RAF	2	2	1	0	8	0	6
ROYAL NAVY	2	1	0	1	3	4	3
ARMY	2	0	0	2	1	8	0

NAVY PLAYERS FROM NON-LEAGUE CLUBS
Price (Exmouth Town), Winnan (Helston), Riley (Newport IoW), Quirke (Newport IoW), Richardson (Saltash), Proctor (Marine)

RAF PLAYERS FROM NON-LEAGUE CLUBS
Cooper (Gorston), Kayll (Cinderford Town), Dickinson (Carterton Town), Taylor (Carterton Town), Bray (Aylesbury), Feeley (Aylesbury), Brayshaw (Marlow), Roberts (Cemaes Bay, Wales), Seddon (Atherston - now signing for Reading), Preston (Hayes)

Right:
Corporal Gary Wootton lifts the Constantinople Cup

The Navy Squad

The victorious RAF Squad

The Army Squad. Photo: Eric Marsh

MIDDLESEX WANDERERS ASSOCIATION FOOTBALL CLUB

Secretary: Keith Masters, 69 Maidstone Road, Chatham, Kent ME4 6DT
Tel: 01634 403744

The Middlesex Wanderers Association Football Club has been likened at times to Rugby Union's 'Barbarians'. Its main objective is to tour the world promoting the good name of football and good fellowship among National Football Associations and clubs around the world.

What better objective can there be? In its 96 year history the Club has completed well over 100 tours to 43 countries.

The origins of the Club date back to the early 1900's when two brothers, Bob and Horace Allaway, founded Richmond Town Wanderers with the specific purpose of performing what they termed 'Football Missionary Work' by using local amateur players to tour countries where the game was very much in its infancy. The Club's name was changed to Middlesex Wanderers in 1912.

Membership is by invitation and playing membership is available to players of non-league international standard. Such players are very carefully selected and to be invited to play for the Wanderers has been compared with the honour of being invited to represent one's country, such is the prestige.

The Club is unique inasmuch as it is a Full Member of the Football Association but does not play any competitive football in the UK.

Financially the Club is self supporting and organises social events to raise funds to enable tours to continue. The social events take the form of an Annual Dinner and Reunion which takes place at The Cafe Royal in Regent Street, London in November, and a Golf Day in August. This year's dinner will be on Saturday 24th November when the Guest of Honour will be Craig Brown, the Scottish National Coach. Previous Guests of Honour have included such distinguished names as Dave Mackey, Sir Geoff Hurst, Johnny Haynes, Martin O'Neill and Denis Law. The Club also organises a Tour Support Draw with lucrative cash prizes for which further details are available from Terry Moore, 7 School Green Lane, North Weald, Epping, Essex CM16 6EH.

The Wanderers invites members of the football fraternity to join us and become a member of this highly respected and prestigious Club. For further details contact the Club Secretary, Keith Masters, 69 Maidstone Road, Chatham, Kent ME4 6DT. Telephone 01634 403744.

SOUTHERN YOUTH LEAGUE

President: John Denham Chairman: Keith Rivers
Secretary: Graham Preston, 9 Gartmoor Gardens, Southfields SW19 6NX
Tel: 020 8789 2182 (H) 020 7608 8619 (B) Fax: 01493 811972 Email: graham@syl.org.uk

CENTRAL SECTION

	P	W	D	L	F	A	Pts
Sutton United	17	13	4	0	47	19	43
Chipstead	18	8	5	5	39	27	29
Tooting & Mitcham	16	7	5	4	30	18	26
Dulwich Hamlet	17	7	3	7	36	28	24
Walton & Hersham	17	6	6	5	30	31	24
Croydon	15	5	3	7	25	32	18
Banstead Athletic	17	4	6	7	26	34	18
Carshalton Ath	17	4	5	8	22	35	17
Woking	14	3	7	4	13	21	16
Whyteleafe	18	2	4	12	16	38	10

WESTERN SECTION

	P	W	D	L	F	A	PtS
Hampton	20	16	2	2	59	19	50
Aldershot Town	20	15	3	2	55	9	48
Ashford Town	17	11	2	4	30	24	35
Godalming	18	8	1	9	28	34	25
Westfield	16	7	3	6	34	22	24
Greenford Town	17	8	0	9	39	59	24
Cove	17	7	1	9	32	42	22
Walton Casuals	18	5	1	12	20	38	16
Molesey	17	4	0	13	21	40	12
Egham Town	13	2	4	7	12	25	10
Bedfont	17	2	3	12	26	48	9

SOUTHERN SECTION

	P	W	D	L	F	A	Pts
Broadbridge Heath	13	10	2	1	48	15	32
Dorking	14	8	4	2	37	20	28
Colliers Wood	15	9	1	5	29	29	28
Corinthian Casuals	12	7	0	5	37	30	21
Three Bridges	13	5	2	6	24	25	17
Leatherhead	16	4	3	9	24	39	15
Addington	12	4	1	7	28	40	13
Redhill	14	3	2	9	21	36	11
Cobham	13	2	3	8	16	31	9

SOUTHERN YOUTH LEAGUE CUP FINAL

Dulwich Hamlet 4 Woking FC 1

LEADING GOALSCORERS

19 B Jones (Walton & Hersham FC)
19 L Sheekey (Greenford Town FC)

PLAYER OF THE SEASON

D Cooke (Whyteleafe FC)

FAIR PLAY TROPHY

Banstead Athletic FC

SECRETARY OF THE YEAR

Graham Starns (Sutton United FC)

PREVIOUS WINNERS

	LEAGUE	LEAGUE CUP
2000-01	No Play Offs	Dulwich Hamlet
1999-00	Aldershot Town	Tooting & Mitcham
1998-99	Dulwich Hamlet Walton & Hersham (Joint)	Aldershot Town
1997-98	Dulwich Hamlet	Chipstead
1996-97	Ashford Town (Mx)	Croydon
1995-96	Walton & Hersham	Sutton United
1994-95	Welling United	Banstead Athletic

LEAGUE CONSTITUTION 2001-02

CENTRAL
Banstead Athletic FC
Carshalton Athletic FC
Chipstead FC
Croydon FC
Dulwich Hamlet FC
Sutton United FC
Tooting & Mitcham FC
Walton & Hersham FC
Whyteleafe FC
Woking FC

WEST
Aldershot Town FC
Ashford Town FC
Bedfont FC
Chertsey Town FC
Cove FC
Fleet Town FC
Cranleigh Youth FC
Hampton & Richmond FC
Molesey FC
Walton Casuals FC
Westfield FC

SOUTH
Broadbridge Heath FC
Chessington United FC
Cobham FC
Corinthian Casuals FC
Croydon Athletic FC
Dorking FC
Leatherhead FC
Mertsham FC
Redhill FC
Three Bridges FC

BRITISH UNIVERSITIES SPORTS ASSOCIATION

The British Universities Sports Association (BUSA) provides competitive sport to students in higher education through the organisation of championships, representative fixtures and British teams for international events. Football is the largest of the 43 sports that BUSA organise, with 136 first team men's entries and 299 second team and below entries last season. The women's competition had 112 entries.

Bath University won the men's championship, with Luton the runners-up for the third time in four years. In the women's competition, last year's runners-up, Loughborough University, came away from Burton Albion's ground as champions with Crewe and Alsager runners-up. Liverpool University won both the men's and women's Shield competition and Loughborough won the men's Trophy competition.

Scottish Universities men and English Universities women won the annual British University Games, held in Glamorgan in April of this year. English Universities also played some representative matches, the women taking on Arsenal and Fulham in March and the men playing the Prison Officers. Other games for both sides were scheduled, but were hit by the bad weather experienced so often during the season. The women's side, coached by Arsenal captain and Wales manager Sian Williams, were defeated 2-1 by Arsenal and 2-0 by Fulham. The men beat the Prison Officers 3-0.

Bath University, the men's champions, won promotion out of this season's Screwfix League where they play as TeamBath.

A strong GB team will travel to Beijing to take part in the World University Games this month. Second only in size and standard to the Olympic Games, Team GB's Football squad is aiming for a place in the top eight. Graeme Dell, GB Head Coach said, "Our expectations are reasonably high with this squad which has some promising talent within it. Having made tremendous improvements in the past three years with the development squad, improvement on our ninth place in 1999 should be seen as a success."

Britain will face home side China, Nigeria and Mexico in their group. Finishing first or second in their group would be enough to guarantee transition to the knock out stages of the competition and would ensure a placing in the top eight. Team Manager Iain Moir believes China will be the strongest challenge to GB: "China are fielding their Under 21 side who have competed at the World Championships in Argentina. They're on home ground and they should be favourites to win the competition. To qualify for the knock out stages we have to win one game and at least draw another"

These are sentiments shared by Dell: "All of the groups are tough, but by playing to our strengths we should be a match for all three of our first phase opponents." Dell continues that the Great Britain squad should be well prepared for the challenges in China. "Our game against China is probably the biggest any of these lads will ever play in and sharp focus during our preparation phase will ensure that we are physically, tactically and mentally prepared for that challenge."

Most of the team are semi-professional Conference players or are on scholarships in the USA. Simon Travis (West of England) is currently attached to Forest Green Rovers and has represented an FA XI on two occasions, most recently against the Highland League in May 2001.

Kevin Langan is studying Sports Performance and Coaching at Bath University and is a former Bristol City player

(1996-2000). He is looking forward to competing in the World University Games, "It's been my aim to get into the squad and it's been at the back of my mind all season. I'm delighted to have made it through the trials."

This is Langan's first taste of international competition: "Representing Britain is very important for all of us; some of the squad have been sacked from the clubs as they'll miss the start of the season back home to travel to Beijing. They have still chosen to play at the World University Games for their country."

Team GB has played three practice games in this county in a warm up to the Games, winning two and drawing another, and have improved with every game:

Saturday 21st July	GBR	v	Charlton Athletic	1-1	(Bisham Abbey)
Thursday 26th July	GBR	v	Crystal Palace	3-0	(Shenley Sports Ground)
Saturday 30th July	GBR	v	West Ham United	2-1	(Shenley Sports Ground)

The squad flew to a holding camp in Hong Kong to play warm up games against local opposition before moving to Beijing for their opening match against Mexico.

An impressive 1-0 win over Hong Kong's Happy Valley saw Great Britain's Students maintaining their unbeaten run of performances. In the intense 32 degree heat and 90 per cent humidity at the Hong Kong Sports Institute, Britain's footballers were impressive in their team play and against Hong Kong's reigning champions and Cup winners, Happy Valley, who were fielding no fewer than ten full internationals, but never really caused the British defence any major problems, although two first half efforts were well saved by Jim Robinson.

Britain's continued pressure paid off early in the second half when Andrew Murfin latched onto a Ryan Spencer through ball and he slotted home with composure. A clumsy challenge in the 81st minute rewarded Happy Valley with a penalty, but sharp footwork again by Jim Robinson denied the hosts a share of the points.

England's current semi-pro international Nick Roddis and Simon Travis (FA XI) turned in noteworthy performances, as did former England U18 internationals Max Rooke (US) and Andy Hylton (US).

National coach Graeme Dell commented: "This is a pleasing continuation to our preparations; we could have done better in places, but I am pleased with the performances only having arrived yesterday. However, the result is one thing, but our focus over the next few days must ensure that we arrive in Beijing as well prepared as we are able. Already many of these players have shown that they have the ability to survive and cope with international football, which is very pleasing; now we must improve them as a group."

The World University Games are important to the players and both Moir and Dell believe the experience will add tremendously to their development. "This will be a fantastic chance for the players to represent GB and some will go on to play professionally on completion of their studies," Moir says. Echoing these sentiments, Dell continues, "With an increasing number of student players being available to us at the highest level of the domestic game, this unrivalled international experience will contribute significantly towards improvements in their own domestic performances as well as their football careers."

Former World University players who have subsequently had successful international careers include David Weir (Everton), David Weatherall (Bradford City), John Dyson (longest serving player with Huddersfield Town) and John McCarthy (Birmingham City and regular member of the NI squad).

The complete Team GB squad is as follows:

Craig Dootson	Edge Hill	Leigh RMI
James Robinson	University of Wales Institute, Cardiff	Hitchin Town
Andrew Hylton	Barry University, USA	
Kevin Langan	University of Bath	(TeamBath)
Ben Dawson	Pennsylvania State University, USA	
Neil Le Bihan	Kent University	Dover Athletic FC
Simon Travis	University of West of England	Forest Green Rovers
Ryan Spencer	Brunel, West London	Hayes FC
Tom Rutter	Coastal Carolina University, USA	Former Gloucester City
Max Rooke	Mercer University, USA	
Matthew Hayfield	Portsmouth University	Woking
Ellis Wilmott	University of Bath	TeamBath
Jake Sedgemore	Wolverhampton University	Hednesford Town
Luke Anderson	Brunel, West London	Crawley Town
Steve Perkins	St Mary's University College	Woking FC
Nick Roddis	St Mary's University College	Woking FC
Andrew Murfin	Loughborough University	
Philip Denney	Crewe& Alsager Faculty	

Simon Travis
(Forest Green Rovers)

Warren Patmore (Yeovil Town and England) battles Neil O'Brien (Carmarthen Town and Wales) in the first half at Nene Park. Photo: Peter Barnes

England skipper Justin Jackson and Wales captain Andrew York challenge strongly for the ball at Nene Park. Photo: Peter Barnes

LEAGUE OF WALES

President: D W Shanklin

Secretary General: D G Collins
Plymouth Chambers, 3 Westgate Street, Cardiff CF10 1DP
Tel: 029 2037 2325 Fax: 029 2034 3961

THE STRUCTURE OF WELSH FOOTBALL

LEVEL ONE	League of Wales
LEVEL TWO	Welsh Football League Division One, Cymru Alliance
LEVEL THREE	Welsh Football League Division Two, Central Wales League *(abondoned due to Foot & Mouth crisis),* Welsh National League (Wrexham Area) Division One, Welsh Alliance League

FINAL LEAGUE TABLES 2000-01

LEVEL ONE

LEAGUE OF WALES

		Home					*Away*					*Total*						
	P	*W*	*D*	*L*	*F*	*A*	*W*	*D*	*L*	*F*	*A*	*W*	*D*	*L*	*F*	*A*	*Pts*	*GD*
Barry Town	34	14	2	1	54	11	10	3	4	30	19	24	5	5	84	30	77	54
Cwmbran Town	34	13	2	2	38	16	11	0	6	33	18	24	2	8	71	34	74	37
Carmarthen Town	34	10	3	4	39	18	7	4	6	29	21	17	7	10	68	39	58	29
Newton AFC	34	10	0	7	30	22	8	4	5	18	15	18	4	12	48	37	58	11
Caersws FC	34	7	5	5	35	19	9	4	4	37	20	16	9	9	72	39	57	33
Aberystwyth Town	34	9	6	2	41	16	6	4	7	23	26	15	10	9	64	42	55	22
Rhyl	34	10	2	5	45	26	6	4	7	29	26	16	6	12	74	52	54	22
Total Network Solutions	34	8	5	4	29	23	7	4	6	35	24	15	9	10	64	47	54	17
Connah's Quay Nomads	34	7	3	7	20	18	7	5	5	25	29	14	8	12	45	47	50	-2
Haverfordwest County	34	6	3	8	24	31	8	4	5	32	24	14	7	13	56	55	49	1
Afan Lido FC	34	9	5	3	28	16	4	3	10	14	21	13	8	13	42	37	47	5
Rhayader Town	34	6	4	7	23	24	4	6	7	31	41	10	10	14	54	65	40	-11
Flexsys Cefn Druids	34	8	1	8	38	37	3	4	10	22	33	11	5	18	60	70	38	-10
Bangor City	34	5	3	9	28	37	5	4	8	28	47	10	7	17	56	84	37	-28
Oswestry Town	34	4	5	8	19	28	6	1	10	21	46	10	6	18	40	74	36	-34
Port Talbot Athletic	34	4	3	10	19	40	6	2	9	30	37	10	5	19	49	77	35	-28
Llanelli AFC	34	8	1	8	38	33	1	1	15	19	64	9	2	23	57	97	29	-40
UWIC Inter Cardiff	34	2	4	11	18	49	1	0	16	8	55	3	4	27	26	104	13	-78

LEVEL TWO

CC SPORTS WELSH LEAGUE DIVISION ONE

	P	*W*	*D*	*L*	*F*	*A*	*Pts*
Ton Pentre	34	20	11	3	81	28	71
Maesteg Park	34	21	8	5	61	28	71
Fields Pk/Pontllanfraith	34	21	5	8	77	39	68
Goytre United	34	21	5	8	72	52	68
Caedeon	34	17	12	5	55	37	63
Pontardawe	34	13	9	12	64	50	48
Cardiff Corries	34	12	8	14	50	49	44
AFC Rhondda	34	11	10	13	47	54	43
Ammanford	34	11	8	15	45	56	41
Neath	34	10	10	14	49	53	40
Penrhiwceiber	34	11	7	16	62	73	40
Gwynn United	34	12	3	19	47	73	39
Milford United	34	10	8	16	44	58	38
Bridgend Town	34	10	8	16	47	65	38
Cardiff Civil Service	34	8	13	13	47	51	37
Porth Tywyn	34	10	7	17	35	63	37
Briton Ferry	34	9	8	17	49	68	35
Treowen	34	6	6	22	35	72	24

HGF CYMRU ALLIANCE

	P	*W*	*D*	*L*	*F*	*A*	*Pts*
Caernarfon Town	32	24	4	4	105	29	76
Llangefni Town	30	20	5	5	67	34	65
Welshpool Town	32	19	7	6	86	35	64
Cemaes Bay	32	17	9	6	64	38	60
Buckley Town	31	17	7	7	66	29	58
Porthmadog	31	16	6	9	62	37	54
Llandudno Town	32	14	6	12	46	52	48
Lex XI	31	12	4	15	68	84	40
Halkyn United	30	11	6	13	47	55	39
Holywell Town	32	11	6	15	47	69	39
Airbus UK	31	10	7	14	54	63	37
Ruthin Town	32	10	7	15	48	60	37
Holyhead Hotspurs	31	10	6	15	59	76	36
Glantraeth	24	7	5	12	40	60	26
Denbigh Town	32	5	5	22	32	84	20
Brymbo Broughton	30	5	4	21	34	78	19
Flint Town United*	32	6	4	22	43	85	13

** points deducted*

LEVEL THREE

CC SPORTS WELSH LEAGUE DIVISION TWO

	P	W	D	L	F	A	Pts
GARW	30	24	1	5	93	33	73
Llanwern	30	18	5	7	65	37	59
Ely Rangers	30	18	4	8	81	30	58
Porthcawl	30	16	4	10	58	46	52
Chepstow Town*	30	18	3	9	57	48	51
Blaenrhondda	30	14	6	10	48	52	48
Tredegar Town	30	13	4	13	66	54	43
Garden Village	30	11	8	11	50	54	41
Taffs Well	30	10	10	10	49	52	40
Merthyr Saints	30	12	3	16	41	58	38
Aberaman	30	11	3	16	55	64	38
Portos Grange H'quins	30	9	6	15	50	55	33
Morriston Town	30	9	6	15	49	68	33
Risca United	30	8	5	17	46	55	29
Caldicot	30	8	4	18	60	66	28
Albion Rovers	30	3	4	23	22	99	13

WELSH NATIONAL LEAGUE WREXHAM AREA PREMIER DIVISION

	P	W	D	L	F	A	Pts
Gresford Athletic	30	21	6	3	86	34	69
Penycae	30	19	4	7	84	40	61
Castell AC	30	19	3	8	79	55	60
Corwen	30	15	9	6	68	47	54
Bala Town	30	17	3	10	63	50	54
Mold Alexandra	30	15	5	10	85	57	50
Rhos Aelwyd	30	14	5	11	70	58	47
Brickfield Rangers	30	13	6	11	59	51	45
Penley	30	9	10	11	54	56	37
Llangollen	30	11	2	17	66	80	35
Chirk AA	30	9	8	13	46	61	35
Ruthin Town	30	9	7	14	43	51	34
Brymbo Broughton	30	7	7	16	45	74	28
Flexys Cefn Druids	30	8	4	18	52	84	28
Hand Hotel	30	5	6	19	50	98	21
Bradley Villa	30	4	5	21	43	97	17

TY LON VOLVO WELSH ALLIANCE

	P	W	D	L	F	A	Pts
Llanfairpwll	26	18	4	4	75	38	58
Glan Conwy	26	18	2	6	92	49	56
Amlwch Town	26	16	4	6	91	41	52
Bethesda Athletic	26	12	8	6	64	45	44
Rhyl Reserves	26	13	4	9	50	52	43
Prestatyn Town	26	12	4	10	48	56	40
Abergele Town	26	11	6	9	58	52	39
Bangor City	26	9	6	11	48	55	33
Llandudno Junction	26	8	6	12	69	71	30
Colwyn Bay YMCA	26	9	2	15	48	62	29
Loco Llanberis	26	8	4	14	50	56	28
Caerwys	26	4	9	13	35	68	21
Conwy United	26	4	8	14	38	86	20
Pen Phoenix	26	4	5	17	55	90	17

FEEDERS TO LEVEL THREE

CC SPORTS WELSH LEAGUE DIVISION THREE

	P	W	D	L	F	A	Pts
Bettws	30	19	4	7	73	35	61
AFC Llwydcoed	30	18	5	7	66	37	59
Treharris Athletic	30	17	5	8	77	50	56
Dinas Powys	30	17	4	9	72	35	55
Caerao Ely	30	16	6	8	72	48	54
Newport YMCA	30	15	5	10	60	45	50
Pontlottyn	30	14	6	10	54	42	48
Newcastle Emlyn	30	15	3	12	54	55	48
Pontyclun	30	12	11	7	66	40	47
Pontypridd	30	10	10	10	40	47	40
Cwmtillery	30	11	3	16	56	63	36
Abercynon	30	10	5	15	62	80	35
Skewen Athletic	30	8	5	17	48	72	29
Seven Sisters	30	7	6	17	48	69	27
Caerao	30	6	8	16	47	81	28
Abergavenny Thurs.	30	1	2	27	21	138	5

WELSH NATIONAL LEAGUE WREXHAM AREA DIVISION ONE

	P	W	D	L	F	A	Pts
Cefn United	28	23	4	1	143	24	73
Borras Park	28	17	2	9	103	66	53
Llay Welfare*	28	16	4	8	90	55	49
Lead Mills *	28	15	6	7	115	66	48
Buckley Town	27	14	6	7	87	57	48
Ruthin Colts	28	15	3	10	76	48	48
Mynydd Isa*	28	14	4	10	94	72	43
Llanuwchllyn	27	13	3	11	72	60	42
Corwen Res	28	11	1	16	66	80	34
Penycae Res	28	9	6	13	57	62	33
Airbus UK	28	9	4	15	60	74	31
Acrefair	28	9	4	15	62	78	31
Gresford Reserves	28	9	3	16	60	76	30
Glyn Ceiriog	28	5	1	22	58	198	16
Rhostyllen	28	4	1	23	53	180	13

SILVER STAR HOLIDAYS GWYNEDD LEAGUE

	P	W	D	L	F	A	Pts
Felinheli	26	18	6	2	75	27	60
Llanrug United	26	19	3	4	78	33	60
Pwllheli	26	17	5	47	80	38	56
Bodedern	26	16	4	6	87	30	52
Blaenau Ffes	26	13	4	9	52	59	43
Nefyn United	26	12	4	10	64	60	40
Llanrwst United	26	10	7	9	45	44	37
Deiniolen	26	11	1	14	52	68	34
Holyhead Hot	26	10	2	14	55	62	32
Bangor University	26	10	2	14	46	59	32
Caernarfon Town	26	9	4	13	50	44	31
Cemaes Bay	26	7	6	13	43	65	27
Barmouth & Dy	26	4	4	18	36	104	16
Penrhyndeudrth	26	0	0	26	15	116	0
Llangefni Town	0	0	0	0	0	0	0

Revised League table of deletion of Llangefni Town results

CLWYD FOOTBALL LEAGUE

PREMIER DIVISION	P	W	D	L	F	A	Pts
Rhydymywn FC	22	17	2	3	74	37	53
Trefnant Village FC	22	13	6	3	57	27	45
Flint Town Reserves	22	12	4	6	68	40	40
Prestatyn Nova FC	22	12	4	6	66	40	40
Sealand Leisure FC	22	12	3	7	65	47	39
Holywell Town Res	22	11	5	6	47	28	38
Penrhyn United	22	7	4	11	50	58	25
Hawarden Rangers FC	22	7	3	12	44	48	24
Llansannan FC	22	6	4	12	38	58	22
Denbigh Town Res	22	6	2	14	30	55	20
Llandyrnog United FC	22	6	2	14	27	68	20
Point of Ayr	22	2	3	17	23	79	9

SOUTH WALES SENIOR LEAGUE

DIVISION ONE	P	W	D	L	F	A	Pts
Pentwyn Dynamos	30	21	6	3	106	51	69
Cogan Coronation	29	16	7	6	68	45	55
Bridgend Street	30	16	6	8	78	52	54
Lisvane	30	16	5	9	83	68	53
Ynyshir Albions	30	14	10	6	83	66	52
Penrhiwceiber Cons	30	14	5	11	81	64	47
Grange Albion	29	15	6	8	66	40	45
Penydarren BC	29	13	3	13	74	62	42
B P Barry	30	11	8	11	76	72	41
Cwmbach Royal Stars	30	11	8	11	66	76	41
Penrhiwfer	29	10	3	16	62	76	33
Butetown	30	8	8	14	55	67	32
Hopkinstown	30	8	7	15	61	90	31
Arjo Wiggins Trelai	30	9	3	18	62	81	30
AFC Jeff White	30	7	6	17	48	65	27
AFC Rhondda Res	30	2	3	25	29	123	9

VALE OF CONWY LEAGUE

	P	W	D	L	F	A	Pts
Bro Cernyw	12	11	1	0	54	9	34
Llanfairfechan Town	12	7	2	3	30	21	23
Llandudno Reserves	11	6	1	4	31	34	19
Glan Conwy Res	11	3	2	6	14	24	11
Llanrwst Utd Res	12	3	2	7	27	40	40
Mochdre Sports	12	3	1	8	21	31	10
Blaenau Ams Res	12	3	1	8	20	39	10

HERITAGE HOMES CAERNARFON & DISTRICT LEAGUE

DIVISION ONE	P	W	D	L	F	A	Pts
Nanttle Vale	20	17	2	1	92	14	53
Talysarn Celts	20	17	1	2	88	21	52
Porthmadog Reserves	20	16	1	3	85	26	49
Pwllheli Reserves	20	13	0	7	65	36	39
Llanystumdwy	20	12	0	8	62	47	36
Nefyn United	20	8	2	10	46	70	26
Mynydd Llandygai	20	6	4	10	40	73	22
Llanrug United Reserves	20	4	3	13	30	67	15
Talsarnau	20	3	2	15	20	73	9
Harlech Town	20	2	3	15	20	73	9
Pwllheli Youths	20	2	2	16	78	87	8

GEORGE FORD GWENT COUNTY LEAGUE

DIVISION ONE	P	W	D	L	F	A	Pts
Spencer Yth & Boys	30	23	3	4	83	34	72
RTB Ebbw Vale*	30	17	3	10	79	50	63
Abertillery Town	30	17	9	4	77	50	60
Croesyceiliog	30	18	5	7	81	43	59
Aberbargoed Buds*	30	19	2	9	65	51	56
Panteg	30	13	6	11	66	53	45
Fairfield United	30	12	4	14	63	60	40
Pill AFC	30	11	6	13	64	64	39
Blaina West Side	30	12	2	16	55	66	38
Abercarn United*	30	12	4	14	68	64	37
Lucas Cwmbran	30	10	6	14	78	70	36
Clydach Wasps	30	11	2	17	74	72	35
Cromwell Youth*	30	10	7	13	51	59	35
Mardy*	30	12	2	16	70	79	35
Cefn Forest*	30	7	9	14	54	65	32
Newport Civil Service	30	1	0	29	34	182	3

GWENT CENTRAL LEAGUE

DIVISION ONE	P	W	D	L	F	A	Pts
Govilon	28	24	0	3	137	40	72
Usk Town	28	22	2	4	122	38	68
Owens Corning	28	22	2	4	113	39	68
Tranch United*	27	16	5	6	81	53	53
Goytre	28	12	5	11	57	50	41
Fairchild United	27	15	1	11	74	67	40
Gilwern & District	26	11	5	11	70	38	38
Pontypool Town	27	12	2	13	74	71	38
Sebastopol	28	12	0	16	81	79	36
Little Mill United	28	10	3	15	69	102	33
New Inn	27	8	4	15	60	83	28
Panteg	27	8	3	16	38	71	27
mardy	28	6	3	19	57	103	21
Llanarth*	22	5	1	16	43	92	13
Clydach Wasps*	28	2	2	24	30	161	5

SWANSEA SENIOR LEAGUE

DIVISION ONE	P	W	D	L	F	A	Pts
Ragged School	22	14	6	2	70	28	48
West End	22	14	4	4	63	25	46
Farmers Arms	22	12	6	4	51	29	42
Bonymaen Colts	22	11	6	5	46	28	39
PT Stars	22	12	2	8	58	36	38
St Josephs	22	9	7	6	51	30	34
Cwm Press	22	9	5	8	46	40	30
South Gower	22	8	5	9	34	47	29
Malsters Sports	22	7	4	11	31	43	25
North End	22	5	5	12	29	55	20
Mumbles Rangers	22	3	5	14	29	62	14
PT Colts	22	0	1	21	12	97	1

WELSH BREWERS CARMARTHENSHIRE LEAGUE

PREMIER DIVISION	P	W	D	L	Pts
Camford	22	18	2	2	56
Bwich	22	17	1	4	52
Trostre	22	16	2	4	50
Llanelli Steel	22	12	4	6	40
Evans & Williams	22	9	4	9	31
Penyfan	22	9	1	12	28
Trallwm	22	7	5	10	26
Penllergaer	22	6	5	11	23
Pontarddulais	22	6	3	13	21
Pwll	22	5	5	12	20
Gorseinon	22	5	4	13	19
Felinfoel	22	2	4	16	10

L'HIRONDELLE CARDIGANSHIRE LEAGUE

DIVISION ONE	P	W	D	L	F	A	Pts
Cardigan Town	22	17	3	2	71	26	54
Dewi Stars	22	13	4	5	55	31	43
Aberaeron	22	12	7	3	45	27	43
Felinfach	22	12	4	5	56	39	40
Crannog	22	11	3	8	50	36	36
Lampeter	22	10	5	7	39	29	35
Llanbydder	22	11	1	10	52	52	34
Ffostrasol	22	6	4	12	32	54	22
St Dogmaels	22	6	3	13	35	48	21
New Quay	22	5	4	13	33	63	19
Llandysul	22	4	5	13	23	53	17
Pencader	22	3	1	18	33	66	10

ABERDARE VALLEY LEAGUE

PREMIER DIVISION	P	W	D	L	F	A	Pts
Mount Ash Town	22	15	2	5	72	34	47
Aberaman All Stars	22	14	4	4	77	34	46
Aberaman Bt Lgn	22	14	4	4	80	44	46
FC Cwmaman	22	13	3	6	52	37	42
Penywaun FC	22	13	2	7	62	49	41
Tynte Rovers A	22	12	3	7	62	49	39
Glancynon	22	9	3	10	60	48	30
Cwmbach RS	22	9	3	10	47	47	30
Abernant Rovers 97	22	6	5	11	50	55	22
AFC Miskin	22	7	0	15	40	79	21
Bee Hive	22	2	3	17	36	97	9
Mackworth Arms	22	1	3	18	34	96	6

BRIDGEND & DISTRICT LEAGUE

PREMIER DIVISION	P	W	D	L	F	A	Pts
Bettws FC Res	24	17	3	4	72	31	54
Llangynwyd Rgrs Res	24	16	4	4	77	32	52
Tondu Robins	24	14	4	6	58	37	46
Great Western FC	24	13	3	8	59	54	42
Coytrahen FC	24	12	3	9	61	57	39
FC Maesteg	24	12	2	10	48	43	38
Brackla FC	24	10	6	8	57	50	36
Gilfach FC	24	9	4	11	50	66	31
Cefn Cribbwr BC	24	7	6	11	43	55	27
Pantyrawel FC Res	24	7	5	12	53	54	26
Llatwit Major FC Rs	24	7	5	12	50	67	26
Bridgend Corries	24	4	5	15	38	65	17
Pencoed Ath Res	24	2	2	20	47	102	8

ABERYSTWYTH TOWN

Secretary: Rhun Owens, 31 Maesgogerddan, Aberystwyth.
Tel: 01970 623520 (H) 0777 323 0894 (M)
Ground: Park Avenue, Aberystwyth, Ceredigion. Tel: 01970 612122
Directions: From south: A487, 1st right at Trefachan Bridge to r'bout, 1st right with Park Ave. being 3rd right. From north: A487 and follow one-way system to railway station, at r'bout 1st left with Park Avenue being 3rd right. 5 mins walk from Aberystwyth (BR) - follow as above

Capacity: 4,500 Seats: 300 Cover: 1,200 Floodlights: Yes
Clubhouse: Open daily noon-3 & 7-12pm. Snacks available **Club Shop:** Yes

HONOURS Welsh Cup 1899-1900; Welsh I'mediate Cup 85-86 87-88; Mid Wales Lg (11) (Lg Cup(7); Welsh Amtr Cup (3); Welsh Lg Div 2 Sth 51-52; Cambrian Coast Lg (8) Central Wales Chal. Cup(6)

PREVIOUS **League:** Welsh 1896-97; Nth Wales Comb. 99-1900; Montgomeryshire & Dist. 04-20; Central Wales 21-25 81-87; Mid-Wales 26-32 51-81; Cambrian Coast 32-51; Welsh Lg South 51-63; Abacus 87-92

RECORD **Attendance:** 4,500 v Hereford, Welsh Cup 1971
Goalscorer: David Williams 476, 66-83
Appearances: David P Whitney 572, 62-81

FACT FILE
Founded: 1884
Nickname: Seasiders
Sponsors: Continental Cambria Tyres
Colours: Black & green/white/black
Change colours: Yellow/navy/white
Midweek Matchday: Tuesdays
Reserves League: Mid-Wales
Programme: 64 pages, £1.00
Editor: D.Roberts Young (01970 617705)

CLUB PERSONNEL
Chairman: Donald Kane
President: D Jones
Press Officer: Rhun Owens
Manager: Frank Gregan
2000-01
Captain: Gary lewis P.o.Y.: Gary Finlay
Top Scorers: Paul Evans & G.Hughes 17

AFAN LIDO

Secretary: Mr P Robinson, 56 Abbeyville Avenue, Sandfields Estate, Port Talbot SA12 6PY
Tel: 01639 892960 (H) 0411 832169 (M)

Ground: Princess Margaret Way, Aberavon Beach, Port Talbot.
Tel: 01639 892960

Honours: League of Wales R-up 94-95, League of Wales Cup 92-93 93-94

Colours: All red
Change colours: All white
Midweek Rixtures: Tuesday

Chairman: David Dale
Tel: 01639 895524 (H)

Manager: Mark Robinson
Tel: 01639 822026 (H) 0973 638059(M)

BANGOR CITY

Secretary: Alun Griffiths, 12 Lon-Y-Bryn, Menai Bridge, Anglesey, Gwynedd LL575NM
Tel: 01248 712820
Ground: The Stadium, Farrar Road, Bangor, Gwynedd (01248 355852)
Directions: Old A5 into Bangor, 1st left before railway station, ground on leftby garage
Capacity 2,000 Seats: 700 Cover: 1,200 Floodlights: Yes
Clubhouse: Not on ground **Club Shop:** Yes
HONOURS FA Tphy R-up 83-84; Northern Prem. Lg 81-82 (R-up 86-87, Lg Cup 68-69, Presidents Cup 88-89, Chal. Shield 87-88), Cheshire Co. Lg R-up 53-54 58-59,Lancs Comb. R-up 30-31, League of Wales 94-95 (Lg Cup R-up 94-95), WelshNational Lg 27-28 (R-up 26-27), Nth Wales Coast Lg 1895-96, Welsh Cup 1888-89 95-96 1961-62 (R-up 27-28 60-61 63-64 72-73 77-78 84-85), Nth Wales Chal. Cup 26-27 35-36 36-37 37-38 46-47 51-52 57-58 64-65 67-68, Welsh Amtr Cup 1894-9596-96 97-98 98-99 1900-01 02-03 04-05 05-06 11-12, Welsh Jnr Cup 1995-96 97-981919-20, Welsh All. Alves Cup 49-50 59-60 (Cookson Cup 61-62 68-69 84-85 86-87)
RECORD **Attendance:** 10,000 v Wrexham, Welsh Cup final 78-79
PREVIOUS **Leagues:** N Wales Coast 1893-98 1911-12; The Comb 1898-1910; N Wales Comb 30-33; WMids 32-38; Lancs Comb 38-39 46-50; Ches Co 50-68; NPL 68-79 81-82 84-92; AlliancePrem 79-81 82-84, Welsh Cup 97-98,North Wales Challenge Cup 1998-99

FACT FILE
Founded: 1876 Nickname: Citizens
Sponsors: Pentraeth Group
Colours: All blue
Change colours: All white
Midweek Matchedays: Tuesday
Reserve League: Welsh Alliance
Programme: 32 pages, £1.00
Editor: Sam Vilaski
CLUB PERSONNEL
resident: Gwyn Pierce Owen
Marketing Manager: Hayle Meek
Chairman: Ken Jones
Vice Chairman: David Gareth Jones
Press Officer: Alun Griffiths
Manager: Peter Davenport
Assistant Manager: Marc Lloyd Williams
Coach:Stephen Owen Physio: Arwel Jones
2000-01 P.o.Y.: Alen Rowlands
Capt. &Top Scorer: Marc Lloyd- Williams(25)

BARRY TOWN

Secretary: Craig Griffiths, 19 Thistle Close, Barry, South Glam. 01446 733576
Ground: Jenner Park, Barry Tel: 01446 735858
Directions: M4 jct 33 via Wenvoe (A4050) to Barry. Left at 1st 2 r'bouts to Jenner Park. Nearest rail station is Cadoxton
Capacity: 3,000 Seats: 3,000 Cover: Yes Floodlights: Yes
Clubhouse: Open normal licensing hours, 11.00-11.00 daily
HONOURS Welsh Cup (3); Welsh Trophy 94-95; Southern Lg R-up 20-21; Western Lg R-up 11-12, Welsh Lg (7), Lg Cup (4); South Wales Senior Cup (13); SA Brain Cup (3); League of Wales 95-96 96-97 97-98 98-99, R-up 99-00; UEFA Cup 2 Qual Rds 96-97, Prel Rd 97-98 Champs . 2nd . Prelim Rd 01-02

PREVIOUS **Leagues:** Western 08-13; Southern 13-82 89-93; Welsh 82-89 94-95

BEST SEASON **FA Cup**: 2nd Rd 29-30 **FA Trophy** 3rd Qualifying Rd replay 90-91

RECORD **Attendance:** 7,400 v Queens Park Rangers, FA Cup 1st Rd 1961
Goalscorer: Clive Ayres **Appearances:** Basil Bright

Players progressing Chris Simmonds (Millwall) 47, Derek Tapscott/Dai Ward(Arsenal) 53/54, Laurie Sheffield/Gordon Fazer/Phil Green (Newport) 62/66/84,Chris Pike (Fulham) 85, Ian Love (Swansea) 86, Tony Bird/Dave O'Gorman (SwanseaCity) 97, Mark Ovendale (Bournemouth) 98 Eifion Williams (Torquay United) 99

FACT FILE

Founded: 1923
Nickname: Dragons
Sponsors: Tango
Colours: Yellow/yellow/blue
Change: Blue&white
Midweek Matchdays: Tuesday
Programme: Yes

CLUB PERSONNEL

Chairman: Kevin Green
Player Manager: Peter Nicholas

2000-01

Captain: Andrew York
Top Scorer:Jamie Moralee
Player of the Year: Andrew York

CAERNARFON TOWN

Secretary: Geraint Lloyd Owen, c/o club or 01286 830307
Ground: The Oval, Marcus Street, Caernarfon, Gwynedd Tel: 01286 675002
Directions: A55 coast road to A487 bypass to Caernarfon. At inner relief road r'bout follow Beddlegert sign, then 2nd right - ground opposite.
Nearest BR station is 9 miles distant at Bangor. Local buses to Hendre estate
Capacity: 3,678 Seats: 178 Cover: 1,500 Floodlights: Yes
Clubhouse: 2 snooker tables, darts, pool, fruit machines & live entertainment **Club Shop:** Yes

HONOURS N West Co's Lg R-up 84-85 (Div 2 R-up 82-83); Lancs Comb 81-82 (Lg Cup 80-81); Welsh Lg (North)(4) 46-47 65-66 77-79, R-up (4) 56-58 72-73 79-80; Alves Cup(4) 38-39 74-75 77-79; Cookson 56-57 77-78; N Wales Combination 32-33; Welsh National Lg 26-27 29-30 (R-up 28-29); N Wales Coast Lg 11-12
PREVIOUS **Leagues:** North Wales Coast 06-21; Welsh National 26-30; North Wales Comb. 32-33; Welsh Lg (North) 37-76 77-80; Lancs Comb. 80-82; North West Counties 82-85; Northern Premier
BEST SEASON **FA Trophy:** 1st Round replay 87-88
FA Cup : 3rd Rd replay 86-87, 0-1 v Barnsley (A). Also 2nd Rd 29-30
RECORD **Attendance:** 6,002 v Bournemouth, FA Cup 2nd Rd 1929
Goalscorer: W Jones 255 (1906-26) **Appearances:** Walter Jones 306

FACT FILE
Founded: 1876
Nickname: Canaries
Colours: Yellow/green/yellow
Change colours: Sky & claret/claret/claret
Midweek Matchday: Wednesday
Reserve Team: Yes
Programme: 48pgs 70p
Editor: Marc Roberts

CLUB PERSONNEL

President: Jack F Thomas
Chairman: G.Lloyd Owen
Vice-Chairmen: Eilian Angel
Press Officer: Geraint Lloyd Owen
Tel: 01286 830307
Manager: Adie Jones
Coach: Mark Rutter
Physio: Eric Williams

CAERSWS

Secretary: T M B Jones, 3 Hafren Terrace, Caersws, Powys SY17 5ES
Tel: 01686 688103 (H/Fax)

Ground: The Recreation Ground, Caersws, Powys. Tel: 01686 688753
Directions: Entering Caersws, which lies between Newtown & Llanidloes on the A470, the ground entrance is on the left by bridge
Capacity: 3,250 Seats: 250 Cover: 300 Floodlights: Yes **Club Shop:** No
Clubhouse: Not on ground, but in village centre. Normal licensing hours. Food available
HONOURS Welsh Amtr Cup 60-61, I'mediate Cup 88-89 (R-up 91-92); Mid-Wales Lg (9) 59-61 62-63 77-78 82-83 85-86 88-90 96-97 (Lg Cup 79-80 82-83 87-88 89-90); Cent. Wales Chall. Cup 77-78 82-83 87-88 89-90 (Yth Cup 69-70 72-73); Montgomeryshire Chall. Cup (18) 52-53 59-60 62-63 69-72 74-75 76-78 83-89 90-91 94-95 94-95 96-97 97-98 98-99; Montgomeryshire Lg 77-78

PREVIOUS **Leagues:** Mid-Wales (pre-1989)/Cymru Alliance 90-92

RECORD **Attendance:** 2,795 v Swansea City, Welsh Cup 1990
Goalscorer: Gareth Davies

Players progressing: P Woosnam (Leyton O.), M Evans (Wolverhampton W.), KLloyd (Hereford U) Graham Evans (Aston Villa)

FACT FILE
Founded: 1887
Nickname: Bluebirds
Sponsor: Dave Smith
Colours: Blue & white/white/blue
Change colours: Orange/black/black
Midweek Matchday: Tuesday
Reserve League: Mid-Wales
Programme: 44 pages, 50p
Editor: Graham Burrows

CLUB PERSONNEL
Chairman: Garth Williams
Vice Chairman: John Baker
President: Phil Woosnam
Press Officer: Ivor Williams
Manager: Mickey Evans
Asst Manager: Barry Harding
Physio: Wynne Jones

CARMARTHEN TOWN

Secretary: Alan Latham, 3 Maes Dolau, Idole, Carmarthen SA32 8DQ
Tel: 01267 232432 (H), Fax 01267 222851

Ground: Richmond Park, Priory Street, Carmarthen Dyfed
Tel: 01267 232101 Fax: 01267 222851

Directions: Proceed into Carmarthen on A48, pick up A40 to Llandilo at the 1st rounabout and follow town centre signs for 800 meters.Ground on left in Priory Street

Capacity: 3,000 Seats: 500 Cover: 500 Floodlights: Yes

Clubhouse: Yes **Club Shop:** Yes

HONOURS Welsh Lge Div 2 59-60, Div 1 95-96, Cup Winners 95-96

RECORD **Attendance:** 3,000

PREVIOUS **Leagues:** Welsh League

FACT FILE
Founded: 1948
Nickname: The Town
Sponsors: R.S.J. Windows
Colours: Old gold/black/black
Change colours:All white
Midweek Matchday: Tuesday
Reserve League: C C Sports Welsh Lge
Programme: £1.00
Editor: Alun Charles

CLUB PERSONNEL
Chairman: Jeff Thomas
President: Anthony Jenkins
Manager : Tommi Morgan
Physio: Nigel Davies
2000-01
Captain & P.o.Y.: David Barnhouse
Top Scorer: Ryan Nicholls 16

CONNAH'S QUAY NOMADS

Secretary/Press Officer
Robert Hunter, 40 Brookdale Ave., Connah's Quay, Deeside, Clywd CH5 4LU
Tel: 01244 831212 (H) 01244 520299 (B)

Ground: Deeside Stadium Connah's Quay

Directions: On main coast road (A548) from Chester to Rhyl west end of Connah's Quay Deeside College.
Capacity: 3,500 Seats: 500 Cover: 500 Floodlights: Yes
Clubhouse: Yes, in college. **Club Shop:** No

HONOURS Welsh Amtr Cup 52-53 54-55, Nth Wales FA Amtr Cup 52-53 54-55, North Wales Coast Challenge Cup, Welsh Intermediate Cup 80-81, Welsh Alliance CooksonCup 87-88, Welsh Youth Cup 47-48

PREVIOUS **Leagues:** Clywd; Welsh Alliance; Cymru Alliance 90-92

RECORD **Attendance:** 1,500 v Rhyl, Welsh Cup SF 29/3/93

FACT FILE
Founded: 1946
Nickname:Westenders
Sponsors: Copyrite
Colours: White/black/black&white
Change colours: Maroon/white/maroon
Midweek Matchday: Tuesday
Reserve League: Clwyd Premier
Programme: 26 pages, £1.00
Editor: D.Rapson

CLUB PERSONNEL
Chairman: Mr R Morris
President: Mr R Jones
Manager: Neville Powell
Asst Manager: S.Gelder
Physio: M Latter

2000-01
Captain: Carl Smyth P.o.Y.: Craig Hutchinson
Top Scorer: Stuart Rain (13)

CYMBRAN TOWN

Secretary: R L Langley, 1 9 Duffryn Close, Roath Park, Cardiff CF23 6HT
Tel: 029 20764381 (H/Fax) 0771 892 3142 (M)
Ground: Cwmbran Stadium, Henllys Way, Cwmbran, Gwent
Tel: 01633 866192 Fax 01633 863324
Directions: M4 jct 26, follow signs for Cwmbran. At 1st r/about (approx 1.5miles) take 1st exit & proceed along Cwmbran Drive umtil passing Stadium onright. At r/about take 1st exit, then immediately at next r/about take 3rdexit.
Ground entrance 150 yardson right.
One and a half miles from Cwmbran(BR)
Capacity: 8,201 **Seats**: 2,201 **Cover:** 1,857 **Floodlights:** Yes **Club Shop:** Yes
Clubhouse: And clubhouse at 5/7 Commercial Street, Old Cwmbran (01633 483282

HONOURS Lg of W. 92-93; Welsh Lg Div 1 66-67, Welsh Lg Cup 85-86 90-91
PREVIOUS **Leagues:** Monmouthshire Snr 51-59/ Welsh 60-92
RECORD **Attendance:** 8,148 v Manchester Utd Aug 1994
Goalscorer : Graham Reynolds **Appearances:** Mostyn Lewis

Players progressing: Simon King (Newport 1984), Mark Waite (Bristol Rovers1984), Nathan Wigg (Cardiff 1993), Chris Watkins (Swansea 1993)

FACT FILE
Founded: 1951 Nickname: The Town
Sponsors:Colley Hyundas
Colours: All blue.
Change colours: Black & white/black/black
Midweek Matches: Wednesday
Reserves League: Welsh Lge Res Div East
Programme: 40 pages, £1.10
Programme Editor/Press Off: Andrew Havelot
CLUB PERSONNEL
President &Chairman: John Colley
Vice Chairman: Clive Edwrads
General Secretary: Roy Langley
Press Officer: Kevin Morris
Manager: Tony Willcox
Coach: Roger Gibbins Physio: Tommy Cosh
Youth Academy: Delwyn Cheedy
Fitness Coach: Richard Hughes
2000-0
Captain: Nathan Wigg P.o.Y.: Nathan Cotterill
Top Scorer: Jody Jenkins (23)

FLEXSYS CEFN DRUIDS

Secretary: Mr R Davies, 7 Lancaster Terrace, Acrefair, Wrexham LL14 3HP
Tel: 01978 823027 (H) 01978 292931 (B)

Ground: Plas Kynaston lane, Plas Kynaston, Cefn Mawr, Wrexham

FACT FILE
Colours: Black & white/black/black
Change colours: Blue/red/red
Midweek Fixtures: Tuesday

CLUB PERSONNEL

Chairman: Mr M Pritchard
Tel: 01978 812100 (H)
Manager: Gareth Powell
Tel: 01978 755744 (H)

HAVERFORDWEST COUNTY

Secretary: Barry Vaughan Tel: 01437 710805 (H) 01437 764331 (B)
Trem y Gorwel, Chapel Lane, Keston, Haverfordwest, Pembs SA62 6HL

Ground: Bridge Meadow Stadium, Haverfordwest, Pembs.
Tel: 01437 769048 Fax: 01437 762082

Directions: Off the Safeway roundabout near town centre

Capacity: 4,000 Covered Seats: 500 Floodlights: Yes **Club Shop:** Yes

HONOURS West Wales Sen Cup 81-82 88-89 91-92 92-93 97-98 98-99, R-up 37-38 49-50 56-57 60-61 80-81; Welsh Lge 56-57, R-up 67-70 70-71, Prem Div 80-81, National Div 89-90, Div 1 96-97, R-up 94-95 95-96; SA Brains Cup 88-89 R-up 84-85

FACT FILE

Nickname: Bluebirds
Sponsor: Preseli Taxis
Colours: All Blue
Change cols: Orange & black/black/orange & black
Midweek Matchday: Wednesday
Programme: 28 Pages £1.00
Editor: JohnThomas

CLUB PERSONNEL

Chairman: Roger Cottrell
Press Officer: Robert Nesbitt
Manager: Jason Jones

LLANELLI

Secretary: Mr R Davies, 29 Pemberton Park, Llanelli, Carmartenshire SA14 8NN
Tel: 01554 756176 (H) 01554 772973 (B) 01554 772973 (Fax)

Ground: Stebonheath Park, Llanelli, Carmarthenshire SA15 1HF
Tel: 01554 756216. Clubhouse Tel No: 01554 756216

Capacity: 3,700 Cover and seats: 700 Floodlights: Yes Club Shop : No

PREVIOUS
Leagues Welsh League and Southern League

RECORD
Attendance: 15,000 1st Rd F.A.Cup 1950-51

2000-01
Captain & P.o.Y. Mark Dickeson
Top Scorer: Mark Dickeson 30

FACT FILE
Year Formed: 1896
Nickname : Reds
Sponsors : Panda Motors
Colours: All red
Change colours: All white
Midweek Fixtures: Wednesday
Programme: 42 pages Price: £1.00
Editor: Hugh Roberts (01554 750547)

CLUB PERSONNEL
Chairman: Mr R Jones
Tel: 01792 405301 (H)
Press Officer: Hugh Roberts
Manager: Gary Proctor
Tel: 07903 608713 (H)
Coach: Terry Lewis
Physio: Bill Morris

NEWTOWN

Team Secretary: Howard Ellis, 30Court Close, Abermull, Montgomery, Powys (01686 630372 (H) 01686 626121 (W))

Ground: Latham Park, Newtown, Powys Tel: 01686 622666/623120, Fax: 623813
Directions: A43 to Newtown, right at 1st lights into Back Lane & town centre -400yds left into Park St., 500yds right (at Library) into Park Lane - ground at end
Capacity: 5,000 Seats:1,100 Cover: 850 Floodlights: Yes
Clubhouse: Open every evening & matchday afternoons. Hot/cold snacks, pool,darts
Club Shop: Yes

HONOURS League of Wales R-up 95-96 97-98; Welsh Cup 1878-79 94-95 (R-up 85-65 87-88 96-97), Welsh Amtr Cup 1954-55, Central Wales Lg 75-76 78-79 81-82 86-87 87-88 (R-up 51-52 52-53 55-56 56-57 74-75 82-83, Lg Cup 54-55 56-57 74-75 75-76 81-82 83-84), Arthur Barritt Cup 86-87, Central Wales Cup 74-75 80-81 92-93, Emrys Morgan Cup 80-81

PREVIOUS **Leagues:** The Combination/ Central Wales/ Northern Premier

RECORD **Attendance:** 5,002 v Swansea City, Welsh Cup 1954

BEST SEASON **FA Trophy:** 3rd Qual. 89-90
FA Cup: 2nd Rd 1884-85. Also 1st Rd 1885-86

FACT FILE
Founded: 1875Nickname: Robins
Sponsors: ControlTechniques & Elliott Presco
Colours: All red
Change : Blue & yellow/blue/blue & yellow
Midweek Matchdays: Tuesday
Reserves League:Spar Mid Wales
Programme: 36 pages, £1
Editors: Keith Harding/ Nigel Bevan & Barry Gardiner

CLUB PERSONNEL
President: Richard Edwards
Chairman: Keith Harding
Exec Co-Ordinator: Mrs Lyn Barnett
Match Sec/Press Officer: John Annereau
Man : Brian Coyne Asst Man : Richard Pike
Physio: Elwyn Morgan
Res.Team Manager: Jack Watkins
2000-01
Captain: Colin Reynolds P.o.Y,John Cotterill
Top Scorer: Steve McCormick 17

OSWESTRY TOWN

Secretary: Mr C M Lashbrook, 22 Victoria Road, Oswestry, Shropshire SY11 4DS
Tel: 01691 653786 (H) 01952 291359 (B)

Ground: Park Hall Stadium, Burma Road, Park Hall, Oswestry, Shropshire
Tel: 01691 679499

FACT FILE
Colours: Blue & white/blue/blue
Change colours: Green & whire/green/green
Midweek Fixtures: TBA

CLUB PERSONNEL
Chairman: Mr W Jerman
Tel: 01691 661297 (H)
Manager: Ken Swinnerton
Tel: 01978 352301 (H) 01978 310923 (Fax)

PORT TALBOT ATHLETIC

Secretary: Mr J Dawkins, 28 Morrison Road, Port Talbot SA12 6TG
Tel: 01639 791172 (H)

Ground: Victoria Road, Port Talbot

FACT FILE
Colours: Blue & white/blue/blue
Change colours: Yellow & green/green/green
Midweek Fixtures: TBA

CLUB PERSONNEL
Chairman: Andrew Edwards
Tel: 01639 888515 (H)
Manager: David Rees
Tel: 01639 890171 (H)

RHAYADER TOWN

Secretary: Paul Rowe, 9 Glangwy, Rhayader, Powys LD6 5BW
Tel: 01597 810185

Ground: The Weirglodd, Bridge Street, Rhayader, Powys
Tel/Fax: 01597 810067

FACT FILE
Colours: Red & white/red/white
Change Colours: Yellow/yellow & red/yellow
Midweek Matchday: Wednesday

CLUB PERSONNEL
Chairman: M A Pugh (MBE)
Tel: 01597 810234 (H)
Manager: Gary Procter
Tel: 029207 94552 (H) 07974 373311 (M)

RHYL

Secretary: Dennis McNamee, 3 Maes Rhosyn, Rhuddlan. Tel: 01745 591287 (H)
Ground: Belle Vue, Grange Road, Rhyl, Clwyd Tel: 01745 338327
Directions: Leave A55 at the St Asaph/Rhyl turn off and take A525 to Rhuddlan.At roundabout take 2nd turn for Rhyl, then left at next roundabout and over next two roundabouts .After 1mile urn right into Pendyffryn Rd, then left at junction and ground is 300yds on left.

Capacity: 3,800 Cover: 1,200 Seats: 500 Floodlights: Yes
Club Shop: Yes Clubhouse: No

HONOURS Welsh Cup 51-52 52-53 (R-up 29-30 36-37 92-93), Welsh Amateur Cup 72-73, Northern Premier Lg Presidents Cup 84-85, North West Counties Lg R-up 82-83,North Wales Coast Challenge Cup, Cheshire County Lg 47-48 50-51 71-72 (R-up 48-49 49-50 51-52 55-56, Div 2 R-up 81-82, Lg Cup 48-49 51-52 70-71, Div 2 Shield 81-82), Cyrmu Alliance 93-94 (R-up 92-93, Lg Cup 92-93)

PREVIOUS LEAGUES: **North Wales Coast League,** Cheshire County; North West Counties; Northern Premier; Cymru Alliance 92-94
BEST SEASON **FA Cup :** 4th Rd Proper 56-57 (lost 0-3 at Bristol City)
RECORD **Attendance:** 10,000 v Cardiff City, Welsh Cup 1953
Goalscorer: Don Spendlove **Appearances:** Not known

Players progressing:
Ian Edwards, Grenville Millington, Brian Lloyd, Andy Holden, Barry Horne, Andy Jones

FACT FILE
Founded: 1870 (as Rhyl Skull & Crossbones)
Nickname: Lilywhites
Sponsors: Webber Office Solutions of Rhyl
Colours: White/black/black
Change: Blue 7 maroon/ blue/blue
Midweek matches: Tuesday
Programme: 40 pages £1
Editor: Dave Jones (01745 334144)
2000-01
Captain: Danny Barton
Top Scorer: Danny Barton (19)
Player of the Year: Danny Barton
CLUB PERSONNEL
Managing Director; P.Parry
Chairman: David Simmons
Vice Chairmen; N.C.Jones & J.Evans
President: R B G Webster
Company Secretary : David Milner
Press Officer: David .Williams

TOTAL NETWORK SOLUTIONS

Secretary: Gwynfor Hughes, Birch Lea, Porthywaen, Oswestry, Shrops SY10 8LY
Tel: 01691 828645 (H) Fax: 01691 828645

Ground: Recreation Park, Treflan, Llansantffraid Tel: 01691 828112 & Fax 01691 828862
Directions: A483 between Oswestry and Welshpool, right for Llansantffraid (A495) at Llyclys When from North Follow signs to village. Turn opposite Mill silos towards Community Centre. Ground is behind housing estate.
Capacity: 1,500 Seats: 500 Cover:650 Floodlights: Yes Shop: no
Clubhouse: Open every evening except Sunday, plus weekend afternoons.
HONOURS League of Wales Champions 99-00,Welsh Cup 95-96; R-up: 00-01 Welsh Intermediate Cup 92-93; League of Wales Cup 94-95;Cymru Alliance Lge 92-93, R-up 91-92; Central Wales Sen Cup 98-99,R-up 92-93 97-98;Central Wales Lg R-up 90-91 94-95 95-96, Lge Cup 95-96; Montgomeryshire Amtr Lg (7), Village Cup (17); European Champions League 00-01, European Cup Winners Cup Preliminary Rd 96-97 U.E.F.A. Cup: 2000-01

PREVIOUS **League:** Mid-Wales; Cymru Alliance (pre-1993)

RECORD **Attendance:** 2,100 v KS Ruch Chorzow Euro Cup Winners 96(at Wrexham F.C.)
Goalscorer: Adrian Jones **Appearances:** Andy Mulliner

FACT FILE
Founded: 1959
Nickname: The Saints
Sponsors: Total Network Solutions
Colours: Green/white/green
Change: All Blue
Midweek Matchdays: Tuesday
Programme: 40 pages, £1
Editor:Tony Williams
CLUB PERSONNEL
Chairman: Edgar Jones
President: Mike Hughes
Vice-Chairman: Tony Williams
Manager:Ken McKenna
Assistant Manager: John Carroll
Physio: Gordon Evans
2000-01
Captain: Tim Edwards
Top Scorer: John Toner
P.o.Y.: Lee Coathup

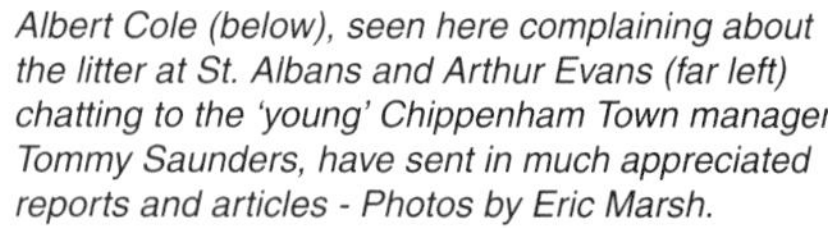

Albert Cole (below), seen here complaining about the litter at St. Albans and Arthur Evans (far left) chatting to the 'young' Chippenham Town manager Tommy Saunders, have sent in much appreciated reports and articles - Photos by Eric Marsh.

Below: Another team group shows - Steve Ayres, Andrew Chitty, Neil Thaler, Eric Marsh standing, Roger Turner, Rosie and Gordon Whittington, Alan Coomes and Garry Letts on board the Riverboat on which Team Talk's 100th Edition was celebrated.

The only obvious deliberate mistake in this photo by Jon Turner was the position of the tea cups. We're not impressed lads - you needn't have taken your pints off the table!

I, unfortunately, wasn't at this get together, but thanks for all the other memories, laughs and, of course, the photos. Let's hope there will be many more in future Directories and other non-League publications.

TONY WILLIAMS

SCOTTISH FOOTBALL

With thanks to Stewart Davidson, Editor of the Scottish Non-League Review of Season 2000/2001, and compiled by Bill Mitchell.

SCOTTISH JUNIOR CUP 2000-01

FIFTH ROUND

Ardeer Thistle 2, 3 Dunbar United 2, 2
Formartine United 4 Petershill 2
Largs Thistle 2 Kirkintilloch Rob Roy 0
Maryhill 2 Auchinleck Talbot 3
Newtongrange Star 2, 3 Kilwinning Rangers 2, 5
Renfrew 5 Dundonald Bluebell 1
Shettleston 1 Arniston Rangers 0
Shotts Bon Accord 0 Carnoustie Panmure 2

SIXTH ROUND

Auchinleck Talbot 2, 1 Ardeer Thistle 2, 0
Carnoustie Panmure 2 Kilwinning Rangers 0
Largs Thistle 2, 1 Shettleston 2, 3
Renfrew 2 Formartine United 0

SEMI-FINALS

Carnoustie Panmure 2 Shettleston 0 *Att: 4,884*
Renfrew 1 Auchinleck Talbot 0 *Att: 3,425*

FINAL

RENFREW 0-0 CARNOUSTIE PANMURE
(After extra-time - Renfrew won 6-5 on penalties)

RENFREW: S Strang; J Hammond, A Foster, N Farquharson, N Shearer (c), J Peacock, B McKeown, S Findlay, A Morrison, J McNally, A Prentice. Substitutes: N MacKinnon for McNally 59 mins, J Ross for Peacock 75 mins, G Elrick for McKeown 82 mins. Not used: S Gilchrist, I Wilson.

CARNOUSTIE PANMURE: R Geddes; G Malone (c), S Kopel, W Morrison, K Galbraith, G Ogilvie, G Miller, G Buick, K Cameron, D Bonella, I MacLeod. Substitutes: I Wilkie for Kopel 46 mins, J Devine for Morrison 79 mins, B Gray for Ogilvie 98 mins. Not used: C Fordyce, M McIlvenny.

Referee: Crawford Allan **Attendance:** 5,252.

TRUTH IS STRANG-ER THAN FICTION! THE SCOTTISH JUNIOR CUP FINAL

The fact that Carnoustie, who dominated this match for long periods, did not take the OVD Scottish Junior Cup back home with them on their first final appearance could largely be attributed to a courageous display by the Renfrew goal-keeper, Scott Strang, who made a string of superb saves, the best of which came when he turned an extra time goal-bound shot by substitute Devine onto a post, from which the ball was eventually cleared after a massive scramble.

History abounds with famous last ditch stands against the odds. In ancient Roman times Horatio held the bridge, the nineteenth century saw the gallant Rorke's Drift siege in Natal and more recently a last day stand at Lord's involving Willie Watson and 'Barnacle' Bailey saved the day for England and paved the way for The Ashes being regained in the Coronation Summer of 1953, but Strang's heroics can be mentioned in the same breath, aided, of course, by some gallant last ditch defending by Foster, skipper Shearer and Farquharson - to name but a few.

Carnoustie attacked constantly and with considerable skill with the silky Iain MacLeod causing havoc whenever he was in possession, while Grant Miller on the other flank with help from skipper Malone also caused numerous problems.

Unfortunately for the Gowfers, the normally prolific Kenny Cameron and the less culpable Darren Bonella were either off target or had to watch Strang block their shots or - as happened towards the end of normal time - turn one over the bar superbly. A goal had to come, but it did not.

Renfrew FC. Back Row (l-r): Stuart Gilchrist, Alan Prentice, Neil Farquharson, Ian Wilson, Scott Strang, Andrew Morrison, Ben Smith, Bobby Tourish. Middle Row: Scott Findlay, Neil Shearer, John Peacock, James Ross, Brian McKeown, Jim Quigley, John Hammond, Neil MacKinnon. Front Row: Jim McNally, Alan Foster, Mick Dunlop (manager), Martin Campbell, Billy Peacock (asst mngr), Gary Elrick, Ryan Conaghan

Carnoustie Panmure. Back Row (l-r): Gary Ogilvie, Iain Macleod, Grant Miller, Michael McIlvenny, Bobby Geddes, Chris Fordyce, Keith Galbraith, Iain Wilkie, Barrie Gray, Darren Bonella. Front Row: Jackie Devine, Scott Kopel, Gus Malone, Garry Buick, Wayne Morrison, Glenn Knox, Kenny Cameron junior.

Renfrew's nearest to a score in their infrequent visits to the Carnoustie end came near the hour mark, when Ogilvie and Geddes had a misunderstanding and the former's back pass almost went in but was cleared off the line by the keeper.

In extra time there was more incessant pressure and that save from Devine, but two hours of thrilling play ended goalless and there were those penalties.

Even then the drama was not over as the luckless Cameron with his side's fifth kick from the spot had the chance to settle matters finally in the Gowfers' favour, but shot wide and the Renfrew team with their ninth spot-kick settled matters through captain Shearer after Strang had also contributed to the tally with a penalty of his own.

Referee Crawford Allan must take credit for the fact that it was excellent entertainment. The 34-year-old bank official was competent but unfussy and the game was played in a good spirit as a result with only three bookings being necessary - most unusual for a game of such importance.

Junior supporters with their passionate and honest local loyalties are usually an absolute delight to meet and these fans were no exception. The Renfrew faithful were openly acknowledging after the match that their team had been 'under the cosh'.

It is also nice to be at Firhill Stadium, the home of newly promoted Partick Thistle, the thinking Glasgow supporters' club. A great day out for the likes of me even through a team from my area of Scotland lost!

Bill Mitchell

JUNIOR INTERNATIONALS

Northern Ireland Tournament

Scotland 1 Republic of Ireland 2 (Limavady)
(Swift)

Northern Ireland 0 **Scotland** 2 (Tobermore)
(Bonella, Currie)

Scotland 2 Isle of Man 0 (Portstewart)
(Gilmour, McCulloch)

The Republic of Ireland won the tournament.

SCOTLAND PARTY: M Graham (Hill of Beath), D Bonella (Carnoustie Panmure), K O'Neill (Pollok), B McMahon (Linlithgow), T Currie (Kilwinning), P Mullin (Kilwinning), S Swift (Benburb), D McCulloch (Auchinleck T), D Flynn (Linlithgow), I McLaughlin (Linlithgow), D Wingate (Benburb), P Kerr (Cumnock), S Ellison (Bonyrigg Rose), I Gallagher (Kilwinning), S Gilmour (Whitburn), J Carruth (Glenafton Ath), G Fields (Auchinleck T), K Biggart (Auchinleck T)

Troon celebrate their South Ayrshire Cup win. They were also Division Two champions and Super Cup finalists. Photo: John B Vass

Troon v Kello Rovers, Ayrshire Division Two. Vital top of the table clash. Troon won the League, Kello were runners up. Photo: John B Vass

Annbank United v Whitletts Victoria, Ayrshire Division Two. Photo: John B Vass

Maybole v Glenafton Athletic in the Irvine Times Ayrshire District Cup Second Round. Photo: John B Vass

Maybole v Formartine United in the OVD Cup Fourth Round. Photo: John B Vass

Craigmark Burntonians v Beith, Ayrshire Division One Photo: John B Vass

Auchinleck Talbot v Hurlford United, Ayrshire Division One, in the last game of the season. Photo: John B Vass

JUNIOR NON-LEAGUE

(West, Central and East Leagues)

AYRSHIRE REGION

DIVISION ONE

	P	W	D	L	F	A	Pts
Kilwinning Rangers	20	14	5	1	50	19	47
Glenafton Athletic	20	11	7	2	44	198	40
Auchinleck Talbot	20	9	6	5	38	23	33
Kilbirnie Ladeside	20	9	5	6	31	22	32
Cumnock	20	10	2	8	36	31	29*
Irvine Meadow	20	7	6	7	40	35	27
Lugar Boswell Thistle	20	5	7	8	24	31	22
Irvine Victoria	20	5	7	8	24	31	22
Hurlford United	20	4	9	7	28	35	21
Beith	20	3	6	11	27	39	15
Craigmark Burnton'n	20	0	6	14	14	56	6

DIVISION TWO

	P	W	D	L	F	A	Pts
Troon	22	18	2	2	78	31	56
Kello Rovers	22	15	3	4	55	25	48
Largs Thistle	22	14	3	5	62	19	45

Troon, Kello Rovers and Largs Thistle promoted.

Other league positions: Muirkirk (39 points), Ardeer Thistle (38), Dalry Thistle (29), Saltcoats Victoria (27), Ardrossan Winton Rovers (22), Maybole (21), Darval (18), Annbank United (13), Whitletts Victoria (9)

AYRSHIRE LEAGUE PLAY-OFF:

Largs Thistle 0 Hurlford United 2
Hurlford United 2 Largs Thistle 2

IRVINE TIMES AYRSHIRE DISTRICT CUP

SEMI-FINALS

Auchinleck Talbot 3, 4p Kilbirnie Ladeside 3, 3p
Irvine Meadow 1 Kilwinning Rangers 3

FINAL

At Beechwood Park, Auchinleck

AUCHINLECK TALBOT 1 *(Lindsay)*
KILWINNING RANGERS 2 *(McTurk, McMillan)*

'ARDROSSAN & SALTCOATS' HERALD AYRSHIRE CUP

SEMI-FINALS

Irvine Meadow 0 Glenafton Athletic 2*
Kilbirnie Ladeside 0 Kilwinning Rangers 4
** Also counted as a league match*

FINAL At Irvine Meadow FC

GLENAFTON ATHLETIC 1 *(Houston)*
KILWINNING RANGERS 0

EAST AYRSHIRE CUP

SEMI-FINAL

Lugar Boswell Thistle 1 Hurlford United 2

FINAL At Cumnock FC

HURLFORD UNITED 2 *(McGregor, Kirkland)*
GLENAFTON ATHLETIC 1 *(Callaghan)*

NORTH AYRSHIRE CUP

SEMI-FINALS

Ardrossan Winton Rovers 0 Largs Thistle 1
Kilwinning Rangers 2 Kilbirnie Ladeside 0

FINAL At Kilbirnie Ladeside FC

KILWINNING RANGERS 1,3p *(Farrell)*
LARGS THISTLE 1,2p *(Sheridan)*

SOUTH AYRSHIRE CUP

SEMI-FINALS

Annbank United 8 Whitletts Victoria 2
Troon 4 Maybole 1

FINAL At Troon FC

TROON 4 *(Ferguson 2, Yair, Harvey)*
ANNBANK UNITED 2 *(Reilly)*

Auchinleck Talbot v Cambuslang Rangers in the Second Round of the Whyte & Mackay West of Scotland Cup. Photo: John B Vass

OVD Cup Quarter Final. Auchinleck Talbot v Ardeer Thistle. Auchinleck went on to the semi finals where they lost to eventual Cup winners Renfrew. Photo: John B Vass

AYRSHIRE SUPER CUP

SEMI-FINALS

Hurlford United 0 Kilwinning Rangers 4
Troon 1 Auchinleck Talbot 0

FINAL At Kilwinning Rangers FC

KILWINNING RANGERS	1,2p	*(Millin)*
TROON	1,4p	*(McLuckie)*

KERR & SMITH AYRSHIRE SECTIONAL LEAGUE CUP

SEMI-FINALS

Beith 0 Kilwinning Rangers 3
Cumnock 1 Hurlford United 0

FINAL At Somerset Park, Ayr. Attendance: 1,331

CUMNOCK	2,5p	*(McGinty 2)*
KILWINNING RNGRS	2,3p	*(Cameron p, Geoghegan)*

WHYTE & MACKAY WEST OF SCOTLAND CUP

(for Ayrshire and Central Region clubs)

QUARTER-FINALS

Beith 2 Lanark United 5
Hurlford United 0, 5p Auchinleck Talbot 0, 6p
Maryhill 2 Bellshill Athletic 0
Renfrew 2, 2p Pollok 2, 3p

SEMI-FINALS

Auchinleck Talbot 1 Pollok 2
Lanark United 1 Maryhill 2

FINAL At Cambuslang Rangers FC

MARYHILL	1	*(McLafferty)*
POLLOK	0	

REEBOK CENTRAL LEAGUE

PREMIER DIVISION

	P	W	D	L	F	A	Pts
Arthurlie	22	16	3	3	57	29	51
Benburb	22	15	4	3	44	19	49
Johnstone Borough	22	12	6	4	44	24	42
Maryhill	22	10	4	8	42	36	34
Renfrew	22	9	3	10	24	36	30
Pollok	22	7	7	8	33	36	28
Neilston Juniors	22	8	4	10	31	36	28
Petershill	22	7	6	9	30	31	27
Larkhall Thistle	22	7	6	9	30	35	27
Rutherglen Glenc'n	22	6	5	11	32	45	23
Shotts Bon Accord	22	5	4	13	27	37	19
Blantyre Victoria	22	3	2	17	18	48	11

DIVISION ONE

	P	W	D	L	F	A	Pts
Lanark United	26	17	5	4	55	35	56
Cambuslang Rangers	26	17	4	5	58	38	55
Cumbernauld United	26	17	3	6	58	30	54

The above were promoted. Other positions: Shettleston (53 points), Greenock (47), Kirkintilloch Rob Roy (37), Carluke Rvrs (37), Kilsyth Rngrs (36) Lesmehagow (32), Vale of Leven (29), Dunipace (25, relegated Port Glasgow (18), Glasgow Perthshire (17), Vale of Clyde (15)

DIVISION TWO	P	W	D	L	F	A	Pts
Bellshill Athletic	24	23	1	0	71	16	70
East Kilbride Thistle	24	16	5	3	56	20	53
St Anthony's	24	14	5	5	44	36	47

The above promoted. Other positions: St Roch's (42), Stonehouse Violet (35), Yoker Ath (31), Ashfield (30), Baillieston (30), Thorniewood Utd (29), Royal Albert (29), Coltness Utd (21), Forth Wndrs (13), Wishaw (11)

EVENING TIMES CUP WINNERS CUP

SEMI-FINALS

Cambuslang Rangers 2, 1p Bellshill Athletic 2, 4p
Lanark United 0, 2p Arthurlie 0, 4p

FINAL At Kirkintilloch Rob Roy FC

ARTHURLIE 2 (*McKenzie 2*)
BELLSHILL ATHLETIC 0

BEATONS LEAGUE CUP

SEMI-FINALS

Benburb 1, 3p Cambuslang Rangers 1, 4p
Shotts Bon Accord 1, 4p Bellshill Athletic 1, 1p

FINAL At Firhill Park, Glasgow

CAMBUSLANG RANGERS 1 (*Daisley*)
SHOTTS BON ACCORD 0

CENTRAL LEAGUE CUP

SEMI-FINALS

Blantyre Victoria 0 Bellshill Athletic 1
Pollok 4 Shotts Bon Accord 0

FINAL At Cambuslang Rangers FC

BELLSHILL ATHLETIC 0
POLLOK 0
(after extra-time. Bellshill Athletic won 3-2 on penalties)

CLYDESDALE CHALLENGE CUP

SEMI-FINALS

Carluke Rovers 1 Forth Wanderers 0
Lanark United 0, 4p Arthurlie 0, 2p

FINAL At Carluke Rovers FC

CARLUKE ROVERS 0
LANARK UNITED 3 (*McBratney 3)*

EAST REGION

DIVISION ONE	P	W	D	L	F	A	Pts
Whitburn	22	16	3	3	51	25	51
Linlithgow Rose	22	12	4	6	42	31	40
Bonnyrigg Rose	22	10	8	4	41	23	38
Newtongrange Star	22	11	3	8	31	22	36
Bo'ness United	22	10	6	6	29	28	36
Camelon	22	9	5	8	35	33	32
Edinburgh United	22	6	6	10	18	27	24
Arniston Rangers	22	4	11	7	23	29	23
Bathgate Thistle	22	5	7	10	26	41	22
Haddington Athletic	22	6	3	13	26	41	21
Harthill Royal	22	4	8	10	26	33	20
Fauldhouse United	22	3	8	11	17	32	17

DIVISION TWO	P	W	D	L	F	A	Pts
Muselburgh Athletic	24	19	1	4	62	23	58
Armadale Thistle	24	18	1	5	58	23	55

The above two were promoted. Other positions: Dalkeith Thistle (52), Broxburn Ath (47), Dunbar U (45), Stoneyburn (40), Pumpherston (36), Bonnybridge (32), West Calder U (18), Blackburn U (17), Sauchie (17), Livingston U (7), Tranent (10)

LEADING GOALSCORERS

39	D McGlynn (Whitburn)
30	S Porteous (Musselburgh Athletic)
29	D Flynn (Linlithgow Rose)
27	S Rixon (Newtongrange Star)
26	K Buckley (Dalkeith Thistle)
21	G Harvey (Bonnyrig Rose)

CARLSBERG LEAGUE CUP

SEMI-FINALS
Newtongrange Star 3 Edinburgh United 0
Bonnyrigg Rose 3 Bo'ness United 2

FINAL At Arniston Rangers FC
BONNYRIGG ROSE 0
NEWTONGRANGE STAR 0
(Bonnyrigg Rose won 8-7 on penalties)

CALDERS EAST OF SCOTLAND CUP

THIRD ROUND
Bo'ness United 2 Edinburgh United 0
Dunbar United 0 Harthill Royal 1
Linlithgow Rose 1, 6 Camelon 1, 1
Pumpherston 1, 0 Bonnyrigg Rose 1, 4

SEMI-FINALS
Bo'ness United 0 Harthill Royal 3
Bonnyrigg Rose 2 Linlithgow Rose 4

FINAL At Livingstone United
HARTHILL ROYAL 0
LINLITHGOW ROSE 5 *(Dickov 2, Logan 2, Flynn)*

DOUG M'AL CUP

(Formerly Brown Cup)

QUARTER-FINALS
Blackburn United 2 Whitburn 4
Fauldhouse United 1 Haddington United 5
Linlithgow Rose 3 Camelon 1
Newtongrange Star 3 Bonnyrigg Rose 0

SEMI-FINALS
Linlithgow Rose 0, 1p Whitburn 0, 4p
Newtongrange Star 3 Haddington United 2

FINAL At Arniston Rangers FC. Att: 1,000
WHITBURN 4 *(McGlynn 2, Hannah, Taylor)*
NEWTONGRANGE STAR 1 *Rixon pen*

CO-OP FUNERAL SERVICES CUP

(Formerly St Michael's Cup)
QUARTER-FINALS
Fauldhouse United 1 Camelon 3
Linlithgow Rose 2 Bathgate Thistle 3
Tranent 0 Dalkeith Thistle 1
Whitburn 4 Haddington Athletic 2

SEMI-FINALS
Bathgate Thistle 0, 4p Dalkeith Thistle 0, 3p
Whitburn 1 Camelon 0

FINAL At Linlithgow Rose FC
BATHGATE THISTLE 1 *(Simpson)*
WHITBURN 0

HEINEKEN FIFE & LOTHIANS CUP

FOURTH ROUND
Arniston Rangers 0 Oakley United 1
Hill of Beath Hawthorn 4 Musselburgh Athletic 2
Stoneyburn 3 Linlithgow Rose 6
Whitburn 3 Bonnyrigg Rose 1

SEMI-FINALS
Linlithgow Rose 4 Hill of Beath Hawthorn 2 aet
Whitburn 2 Oakley United 0

FINAL At Camelon FC. Attendance: 1,500
LINLITHGOW ROSE 5 *(Flynn 3, Corcoran 2)*
WHITBURN 1 *(McGlynn)*

FIFE REGION

FIFE LEAGUE

	P	*W*	*D*	*L*	*F*	*A*	*Pts*
Oakley United	28	23	3	2	83	27	72
Hill of Beath Hawthorn	28	18	7	3	96	29	61
Lochore Welfare	28	19	3	6	94	39	60
Kelty Hearts	28	16	6	6	79	38	54
St Andrews United	28	16	6	6	72	39	54
Thornton Hibs	28	15	7	6	76	25	52
Glenrothes	28	13	10	5	86	31	49
Dundonald Bluebell	28	12	4	12	65	46	40
Crossgates Primrose	28	10	7	11	61	48	37
Newburgh	28	10	6	12	46	45	36
Rosyth Recreation	28	8	4	16	40	58	28
Lochgelly Albert	28	8	4	16	45	75	28
Tulliallan Thistle	28	2	4	22	30	128	10
Kirkcaldy YM	28	2	1	25	19	154	7
Steelend Victoria	28	1	2	25	27	137	5

PEDDIE SMITH MALOCCO CUP

QUARTER-FINALS
Crossgates Primrose 3 Kirkcaldy YM 0
Dundonald Bluebell 5 Lochgelly Albert 0
Glenrothes 3 Newburgh 1
Oakley United 1 Hill of Beath Hawthorn 2

SEMI-FINALS
Dundonald Bluebell 0 Hill of Beath Hawthorn 3
Glenrothes 3 Crossgates Primrose 0

FINAL At Central Park, Crosshill
GLENROTHES 4 *(Hutcheon 2, Mooney, Forrester)*
HILL OF BEATH HAWTHORN 2 *(Walls, Kenny)*

STELLA ARTOIS CUP

SECOND ROUND
Dundonald Bluebell 11 Kirkcaldy YM 0
Glenrothes 2 Lochore Welfare 1
Newburgh 1 Hill of Beath Hawthorn 3
Oakley United 4 Thornton Hibs 0

SEMI-FINALS
Dundonald Bluebell 1 Glenrothes 2
Hill of Beath Hawthorn 1 Oakley United 2

FINAL At Hill of Beath
GLENROTHES 1 *(Andrew)*
OAKLEY UNITED 1 *(Mauchlen)*
(Oakley United won 4-2 on penalties)

INTERBREW CUP

QUARTER-FINALS
Dundonald Bluebell 3, 7p Crossgates Primrose 3, 8p
Kelty Heart 4 Tulliallan Thistle 0
Oakley United 2 Rosyth Recreation 1
St Andrews United 0 Hill of Beath Hawthorn 4

SEMI-FINALS
Crossgates Primrose 0, 3p Oakley United 0, 4p
Hill of Beath Hawthorn 2 Kelty Hearts 0

FINAL At Central Park, Crosshill
OAKLEY UNITED 0
HILL OF BEATH HAWTHORN 2 (*Smart, Thomson)*

NORTH REGION

EAST SECTION

PREMIER DIVISION

	P	*W*	*D*	*L*	*F*	*A*	*Pts*
Longside	22	14	3	5	46	33	45
Sunnybank	22	12	5	5	50	33	41
Formartine United	22	11	7	4	67	38	40
Inverurie Loco Wks	22	12	4	6	52	28	40
Stonehaven	22	12	4	6	53	36	40
Banks O'Dee	22	8	8	6	46	35	32
FC Stoneywood	22	10	2	10	37	54	32
East End	22	7	4	11	43	43	25
Hermes	22	7	3	12	32	42	24
Buchanhaven Hearts	22	7	3	12	29	54	24
Cruden Bay	22	5	1	16	35	68	16
Turriff United	22	4	2	16	23	49	14

NORTH REGION cont.

DIVISION ONE	*P*	*W*	*D*	*L*	*F*	*A*	*Pts*
Culter	22	17	3	2	64	29	54
Wilson's XI	22	15	2	5	54	32	47

The above two clubs promoted. Other positions: Glentanar (46 pts), Fraserburgh U (41), Lads Club (35), Hall Russell U (30), Ellon U (27), Maud (23), Parkvale (21), Lewis U (20), Banchory St Ternan (17), Dyce Jnrs (16)

NORTH REGIONAL PLAY-OFF At Longside
LONGSIDE 2 (*Steven, Bissett)*
DEVERONSIDE 0

GRILL LEAGUE CUP

SEMI-FINALS
Banks O'Dee 2 Formartine United 4
Longside 0 Sunnybank 2

FINAL At Inverurie Loco Works FC
SUNNYBANK 2 (*Cheyne pen, Sutherland)*
FORMARTINE UTD 0

GREAT NORTH REGIONAL CUP

QUARTER-FINALS
Forres Thistle 5 Whitehills 0
Islavale 3 Banks O'Dee 4
Inverurie Loco Works 2 Wilson's XI 1
Stoneywood 0 Sunnybank 2

SEMI-FINALS
Forres Thistle 3 Banks O'Dee 1
Sunnybank 1 Inverurie Loco Works 4

FINAL At Turriff United FC. Attendance: 300
INVERURIE LOCO WORKS 3 (*Davidson, Ross, McKay)*
FORRES THISTLE 1 (*Minty)*

ACORN HEATING CUP

QUARTER-FINALS
Banks O'Dee 2 Dyce 1
Culter 0 Formartine United 1 aet
Longside 2 Lads Club 0
Sunnybank 4 Glentanar 0

SEMI-FINALS
Longside 3 Banks O'Dee 2
Sunnybank 2 Formartine United 3

FINAL At Pittodrie
FORMARTINE UNITED 3 (*Craig 2, Gray)*
LONGSIDE 2 (*Bissett, Main)*

CONSTRUCTION TROPHY

THIRD ROUND
Culter 3 Banks O'Dee 0
Formartine United 1 Sunnybank 3
Hall Russell United 2 Lewis United 1
Longside 4 Dyce Juniors 0

SEMI-FINALS
Culter 5 Sunnybank 0
Longside 5 Hall Russell United 1

FINAL At Hermes FC
CULTER 4 (*McRitchie 3, Small)*
LONGSIDE 1 (*Main)*

ROLLSTUD ARCHIBALD CUP

THIRD ROUND
Cruden Bay 3 0 Longside 6
Formartine United 0 Stoneywood 1
Hermes 0 Inverurie Loco Works 1
Stonehaven 0 Wilson's XI 1

SEMI-FINALS
Inverurie Loco Works 0 Wilson's XI 1
Longside 2 Stoneywood 3 aet

FINAL At Spain Park, Aberdeen
WILSON'S XI 2,2p (*Mowat, Booth)*
STONEYWOOD 2,4p (*Sturton, Jarvie)*

MORRISON TROPHY

SECOND ROUND
Fraserburgh United 2 Dyce Juniors 1
Glentanar 2 Wilson's XI 0
Lads Club 3 Maud 1
Parkvale 4 Ellon United 2

SEMI-FINALS
Fraserburgh United 1 Lads Club 2
Glentanar 2 Parkvale 0

FINAL At Dyce Juniors FC. After extra time
LADS CLUB 3 (*Pirie, McBain, Donaldson)*
GLENTANAR 2 (*O'Driscoll, Mitchell)*

CONCEPT GROUP TROPHY
(for Tayside and North clubs)

FOURTH ROUND
Arbroath SC 1 Banks O'Dee 0
Broughty Athletic 2 Kirrie Thistle 1
Carnoustie Panmure 1, 3p Culter 1, 4p
North End 4 Jeanfield Swifts 1

SEMI-FINALS
Broughty Athletic 4 Arbroath SC 2 aet
North End 2, 4p Culter 2, 2p

FINAL At Strathmore Park, Forfar
BROUGHTY ATHLETIC 2,0p (*Paul og, Ward)*
NORTH END 2,3p (*Davidson, Ferrie)*

SOCIAL BATHING TROPHY

THIRD ROUND
Buchanhaven Hearts 3 Longside 2
Formartine United 3 Glentanar 2
Lads Club 1 Culter 3
Stonehaven 0 Banks O'Dee 1

SEMI-FINALS
Buchanhaven Hearts 2 Banks O'Dee 1
Formartine United 1 Culter 0

FINAL At Longside
BUCHANHAVEN HEARTS 2 (*Buchan, Parsons)*
FORMARTINE UNITED 2 (*Craig 2)*

NORTHERN SECTION

	P	*W*	*D*	*L*	*F*	*A*	*Pts*
Deveronside	24	16	2	5	68	15	54
Forres Thistle	24	15	5	4	79	39	50
Islavale	24	14	7	3	60	27	49
Bishopmill United	24	14	7	3	66	35	49
Strathspey Thistle	24	14	4	6	56	33	46
Nairn St Ninian	24	9	7	8	42	40	34
Whitehills	24	9	6	9	47	47	33
Buckie Rovers	24	9	5	9	44	54	32
New Elgin	24	6	6	12	42	53	24
Burghead Thistle	24	5	6	12	51	52	21
RAF Lossiemouth	24	5	4	15	40	66	19
Kinloss	24	4	3	17	34	81	15
Fochabers	24	2	2	20	21	108	8

ROBERTSON CUP

SEMI-FINALS
Deveronside 2 New Elgin 1
Strathspey Town 1 Forres Thistle 2 aet

FINAL
At Islavale FC. After extra time
DEVERONSIDE 2 (*Findlay, Hepburn)*
FORRES THISTLE 1 (*Pennie)*

STEWART MEMORIAL CUP

SEMI-FINALS
Buckie Rovers 1 Bishopmill United 0
Islavale 2 Nairn St Ninian 0

FINAL
At Burghead
ISLAVALE 2 (*Alexander, Wood)*
BUCKIE ROVERS 0

NICHOLSON CUP

SEMI-FINALS
RAF Lossiemouth 3 Fochabers 4
Whitehills 1, 4p Burghead Thistle 1, 5p

FINAL
At Portgordon
BURGHEAD THISTLE 3 (*Franklin 2, Henderson)*
FOCHABERS 0

MORAYSHIRE ROSEBOWL

SECOND ROUND
Fochabers 0 Deveronside 3
Islavale 6 RAF Lossiemouth aet
New Elgin 2 Bishopmill United 0

SEMI-FINALS
Deveronside 1 Islavale 2
New Elgin 0 Buckie Rovers 2

FINAL
At Burghead Thistle FC
ISLAVALE 5 (*Taylor 3, Alexander 2)*
BUCKIE ROVERS 1 (*Mowat)*

ROBBIE NICOL TROPHY

SECOND ROUND
Fochabers 1 Buckie Rovers 6
Forres Thistle 2 Burghead Thistle 1
Nairn St Ninian 1 Islavale 2
Whitehills 1 New Elgin 2

SEMI-FINALS
Islavale 3, 3p Forres Thistle 3, 5p
New Elgin 3 Buckie Rovers 0

FINAL
At New Elgin FC. After extra time
FORRES THISTLE 5 (*Martin Duncan, Minty, Pennie, Lawrence, Robertson)*
NEW ELGIN 4 (*Mike Duncan, Sim, Wood, Mitchell)*

CLIVE WILLIAMSON CUP

SECOND ROUND
Bishopmill United 4 Whitehills 2
Deveronside 1 Forres Thistle 0
RAF Lossiemouth 2 Islavale 7
Strathspey Thistle 2 New Elgin 2 aet

SEMI-FINALS
Islavale 0 Deveronside 1
New Elgin 2 Bishopmill United 0

FINAL
At Strathspey Thistle FC
DEVERONSIDE 4 (*Hepburn 2, Thorn, McCormack)*
NEW ELGIN 1 (*Webster)*
New Elgin won on penalties

MATTHEW CUP

SECOND ROUND
Burghead Thistle 0 Bishopmill United 4
Deveronside 4 RAF Lossiemouth 1
New Elgin 3, 6p Islavale 3, 5p
Whitehills 1 Forres Thistle 5

SEMI-FINALS
Bishopmill United 1 Deveronside 2
New Elgin 1 Forres Thistle 3

FINAL At Deveronside
DEVERONSIDE 3 (*Cormack, Bowie, Grant)*
FORRES THISTLE 2 (*Esson, Walker)*

TAYSIDE REGION

PREMIER DIVISION

	P	W	D	L	F	A	Pts
Tayport	22	19	2	1	81	11	59
Carnoustie Panmure	22	16	5	1	59	20	53
Dundee North End	22	14	2	6	59	31	44
Kirriemuir Thistle	22	10	4	8	44	38	34
Arbroath SC	22	8	6	8	43	36	30
Forfar West End	22	8	5	9	41	46	29
Dundee Violet	22	6	9	7	24	28	27
Downfield	22	6	7	9	42	53	25
Lochee United	22	7	4	11	33	44	25
Elmwood	22	5	4	13	22	47	19
Forfar Albion	22	4	3	15	25	70	15
Jeanfield Swifts	22	2	3	17	18	67	9

DIVISION ONE

	P	W	D	L	F	A	Pts
Bankfoot Athletic	22	15	4	3	61	28	49
Broughty Athletic	22	13	6	3	50	23	45

The above two clubs are promoted. Other positions: Blairgowrie (43 points), Lochee Harp (42), Kinnoull (35), East Craigie (34), Montrose Roselea (34), Scone Thistle (30), Arbroath Victoria (18), Coupar Angus (17), Luncarty (17), Brechin Victoria (10)

FIFE-TAYSIDE CUP

FOURTH ROUND
Bankfoot Athletic 0 Thornton Hibs 1
Carnoustie Panmure 3 Glenrothes 1
Hill of Beath Hawthorn 4 Arbroath SC Hibs 3
Oakley United 3, 3p Kirrie Thistle 3, 5p

SEMI-FINALS
Hill of Beath Hawthorn 4 Kirrie Thistle 2
Thornton Hibs 1 Carnoustie Panmure 2

FINAL At Glenrothes FC
HILL OF BEATH HAWTHORN 1 (*Thomson)*
CARNOUSTIE PANMURE 0

HERSCHELL TROPHY
At Jeanfield Swifts FC

JEANFIELD SWIFTS 0
TAYPORT 3 (*Corcoran 2, Craik)*

NORTH END CHALLENGE CUP

THIRD ROUND
Downfield 2 Bankfoot Athletic 3 aet
Elmwood 1 Carnoustie Panmure 5
North End 3 Kirrie Thistle 0
Tayport 2 Dundee Violet 1

SEMI-FINALS
Carnoustie Panmure 1 Bankfoot Athletic 2
North End 0 Tayport 4

FINAL
At Dundee North End FC. Attendance: 320
TAYPORT 3 (*Peters, Harris, Kenneth)*
BANKFOOT ATHLETIC 1 (*Ross)*

FINDLAY & COMPANY TROPHY

THIRD ROUND
Broughty Athletic 3 Dundee North End 2
Carnoustie Panmure 1 Arbroath Sports Club 3
Jeanfield Swifts 3 Montrose Roselea 2 aet
Tayport 1 Downfield 0

SEMI-FINALS
Arbroath Sports Club 0 Broughty Athletic 1
Tayport 5 Jeanfield Swifts 1

FINAL
At Lochee United FC
TAYPORT 2 (*Wemyss, Kenneth)*
BROUGHTY ATHLETIC 1 (*Wares pen)*

D J LAING HOMES TROPHY

THIRD ROUND
Arbroath FC 2 Carnoustie Panmure 3
Elmwood 1 Forfar West End 0
Jeanfield Swifts 4 Coupar Angus 1
Tayport 9 Lochee United 1

SEMI-FINALS
Carnoustie Panmure 7 Jeanfield Swifts 0
Tayport 3 Elmwood 2

FINAL
At Glenesk Park, Dundee
CARNOUSTIE PANMURE 1 (*Bonella pen)*
TAYPORT 0

ROSEBANK CAR CENTRE CUP

SECOND ROUND
Blairgowrie Athletic 3 Bankfoot Athletic 1
Coupar Angus 2 Montrose Roselea 3 aet
East Craigie 1 Broughty Athletic 2 aet
Scone Thistle 5 Arbroath Victoria 1

SEMI-FINALS
Blairgowrie 0 Montrose Roselea 2
Scone Thistle 2 Broughty Athletic 3

FINAL At Carnoustie Panmure FC
BROUGHTY ATHLETIC 0
MONTROSE ROSELEA 0
(Broughty Athletic won 5-3 on penalties)

DOWNFIELD SC CUP

SECOND ROUND
Blairgowrie 1, 5p Lochee Harp 1, 6p
East Craigie 3 Kinnoull 1
Montrose Roselea 2 Broughty Athletic 4 aet
Scone Thistle 2 Bankfoot Athletic 3 ST T/A

SEMI-FINALS
Blairgowrie 0 Broughty Athletic 1
East Craigie 4 Scone Thistle 1

FINAL At Downfield
BROUGHTY ATHLETIC 1 *(Heggie)*
EAST CRAIGIE 0

SENIOR NON-LEAGUE

NORTH OF SCOTLAND

HIGHLAND LEAGUE

	P	W	D	L	F	A	Pts
Cove Rangers	26	20	3	3	74	32	63
Huntly	26	19	2	5	61	28	59
Buckie Thistle	26	13	7	6	46	33	46
Clachnacuddin	26	13	5	8	47	35	44
Keith	26	11	9	6	54	43	42
Deveronvale	26	11	8	7	39	32	41
Forres Mechanics	26	10	10	6	44	39	40
Fraserburgh	26	12	3	11	47	38	39
Nairn County	26	8	7	11	44	58	31
Wick Academy	26	8	5	13	39	43	29
Rothes	26	6	5	15	30	45	23
Lossiemouth	26	6	4	16	28	60	22
Brora Rangers	26	4	3	19	41	78	15
Fort William	26	3	5	18	27	57	14

LEADING GOAL SCORERS

47	Beattie (Cove Rangers)
26	Nicol (Keith)
25	Brown (Forres Mechanics)
20	Watt (Deveronvale)
16	Cadger (Deveronvale), Nicol (Huntly), Robertson (Keith), Kellacher (Nairn Co)
15	Still (Keith)

McEWAN'S LAGER NORTH OF SCOTLAND CUP

FIRST ROUND
Clachnacuddin 1 Elgin City 2
Nairn County 2 Inverness Caledonian Thistle 'A' 7 aet
Rothes 1 Golspie Sutherland 2
Wick Academy 1 Forres Mechanics 2 aet

SECOND ROUND
Brora Rangers 1, 6p Ross County 'A' 1, 7p
Elgin City 'A' 1 Forres Mechanics 2
Fort William 0 Lossiemouth 2
Inverness Caledonian Thistle 'A' 4 Golspie Sutherland 1

SEMI-FINALS
Ross County 'A' 0 Lossiemouth 3
Forres Mechanics 4 Inverness Caledonian Thistle 'A' 2

FINAL At Mosset Park, Forres. After extra time
FORRES MECHANICS 1 *(Brown)*
LOSSIEMOUTH 3 *(Hendry (pen), Scott, McIntosh)*

FORRES MECHANICS: McRitchie; Watt, Cameron, Noble, McDonald, Ruickbie, McRae, Sanderson, Brown, Connelly, Reid. Substitutes: Murphy for McRae 73 mins, Bellshaw for Ruickbie 85 mins, Moore for Connelly 111 mins.
LOSSIEMOUTH: Main; Golightly, Rattray, Clark, Fiske, Walker, Milne, Hendry, MacIntosh, Gibson, Moore. Substitutes: Campbell for More 68 mins, Scott for Clark 72 mins, Smith for Gibson 112 mins
Referee: M Ritchie.

INVERNESS CUP

FIRST ROUND
Brora Rangers 0 Clachnacuddin 2
Forres Mechanics 3 Fort William 1 aet
Inverness Caledonian Thistle 'A' 2 Ross County 'A' 4
Nairn County 3 Elgin City 'A' 5

SEMI-FINALS
Clachnacuddin 1 Forres Mechanics 2
Elgin City 'A' 1 Ross County 'A' 3

FINAL At Clachnacuddin FC. Attendance: 220
FORRES MECHANICS 0
ROSS COUNTY 'A' 1 *(Bone)*

ABERDEENSHIRE CUP

FIRST ROUND
Buckie Thistle 2, 0 Fraserburgh 2, 1
Deveronvale 2 Aberdeen 'A' 1
Huntly 3, 2 Keith 3, 1

SEMI-FINALS
Deveronvale 2 Cove Rangers 1
Fraserburgh 2 Huntly 1

FINAL At Balmoor Stadium, Peterhead
DEVERONVALE 2 (*Watt, Cadger)*
FRASERBURGH 1 (*Milne(pen))*

DEVERONVALE: Phimister; Dolan, Kinghorn, Chisholm, Henderson, Montgomery, Singer, Nicol, Cadger, Watt, Urquhart. Substitute: Greig for Urquhart 74 mins. Subs not used: Craigie, McAllister, Stewart, Steven.

FRASERBURGH: Gordon; Milne, Martin, Young, A Stephen, Norris, Murray, McBride, Finnie, Hunter, M Stephen. Substitutes: Keith for Finnie 80 mins, Coutts for Murray 87 mins. Substitutes not used: McLaren, Mackie, Bain.

Referee: G Mitchell.

TENNENTS SCOTTISH QUALIFYING CUP

NORTH

FIRST ROUND
Brora Rangers 1 Cove Rangers 4
Deveronvale 4 Rothes 3
Fort William 0 Buckie Thistle 3
Fraserburgh 1 Forres Mechanics 3
Keith 3 Golspie Sutherland 2
Lossiemouth 2 Nairn County 1
Wick Academy 1 Clachnacuddin 2
Bye Huntly

SECOND ROUND
Cove Rangers 1 Clachnacuddin 0
Deveronvale 3 Forres Mechanics 2
Huntly 0 Keith 3
Lossiemouth 0, 0, 3p Buckie Thistle 0, 0, 4p

SEMI-FINALS
Buckie Thistle 0 Keith 2
Deveronvale 0 Cove Rangers 2

FINAL
At Christie Park, Huntly. Attendance: 747
COVE RANGERS 4 (*Yule (3), Beattie)*
KEITH 2 (*Still, Nicol)*

COVE RANGERS: Coull; Summers (c), McGinley, Megginson, Murphy, Baxter, Brown, Yule, Coutts, Beattie, McCraw. Substitute: Adam for McCraw 97 mins. Substitutes (not used): Pilichos, Mullen, Alexander, Charles.

KEITH: Thain, Craig, Simmers, Maver, McKenzie, Gibson, Still, Presslie, Robertson, Nicol, Hendry. Substitutes: Brown for Hendry 73 mins, Stewart for Robertson 75 mins, Henderson for Craig 105 mins. Substitutes not used: Green, Robb.

Referee: M Ritchie.

For the second time in their short history Cove Rangers grabbed the North Qualifying Cup after a thriller, which went to extra-time and in the process produced two heroes for the winners.

The first was young Coutts, who was a class act on his own and a big future is forecast for the Aberdeen teenager, but the main story of the day involved veteran Ray Yule, who has seen it all before at senior level for various clubs, but still finds a big thrill from playing and managed a monumental hat-trick, all his goals coming from far post headers, one just before half-time, one after 74 minutes and the third in the first period of extra time, after which the prolific Mike Beattie sealed Keith's fate, their fourth Qualifying Final defeat in seven years.

Yule had in fact come off work at a local bakery after a night shift, so he had been allowed little time to shower, have breakfast and join the team coach on its way to Huntly. It would take him a lifetime to earn the kind of money spoilt stars earn in a week, but whom should the readers admire more?

To make this game the spectacle that it was required a brave fight by Keith, who actually took a first half lead through Still and then equalised Yule's second goal, but the better team prevailed on the day.

ABERDEENSHIRE SHIELD

FIRST ROUND
Buckie Thistle 3 Keith 1
Huntly 4 Deveronvale 0

SEMI-FINALS
Buckie Thistle 1 Huntly 0
Cove Rangers 2 Fraserburgh 1 aet

FINAL At Balmoor Stadium, Peterhead. Att: 300
BUCKIE THISTLE 1 (*Thomson)*
COVE RANGERS 2 (*Taylor, Beattie)*

SCOTTISH QUALIFYING CUP

SOUTH

PRELIMINARY ROUND
Dalbeattie Star 5 Preston Athletic 3
Newton Stewart 3, 0 Threave Rovers 3, 3
St Cuthbert Wanderers 4 Girvan 0
Selkirk 0 Edinburgh City 2
Wigtown & Bladnoch 0 Gala Fairydean 3

FIRST ROUND
Burntisland Shipyard 0 Dalbeattie Star 1
Coldstream 5 Glasgow University 2
Edinburgh City 4 St Cuthbert Wanderers 1
Edinburgh University 0 Civil Service Strollers 4
Gala Fairydean 0 Threave Rovers 4
Spartans 3 Annan Athletic 2
Tarff Rovers 2 Whitehill Welfare 3
Vale of Leithen 4 Hawick Royal Albert 2

SECOND ROUND
Civil Service Strollers 0 Spartans 2
Coldstream 0, 2 Vale of Leithen 0, 1
Edinburgh City 1 Threave Rovers 0
Whitehill Welfare 1, 0 Dalbeattie Star 1, 0

SEMI-FINALS
Coldstream 1 Whitehill Welfare 2
Edinburgh City 0, 1 Spartans 0, 2

FINAL In Edinburgh. Attendance: 259

SPARTANS	2	*(Quinn, Rae (pen))*
WHITEHILL WELFARE	3	*(Bird, Samuel, Jardine)*

SPARTAND: Brown; S Thomson, Rae. Hughes, W Thomson, McKeating, Ewing, Knox, Hobbins, Quinn, Middlemiss. Substitutes (not used); Ettles, McDonald, Govan, Campbell, Burns.

WHITEHILL WELFARE: Cantley; Manson Sen, Gowrie, Devine, Steel, Bennett, Jardine, Samuel, Bird, Hope, Manson Jun. Substitutes not used: Bailey, Cunningham, Martin, Temple, Tulloch.

Referee: C Melvinne.

NON-LEAGUE CLUBS IN THE SCOTTISH CUP

FIRST ROUND
Whitehill Welfare 0, 0 Peterhead 0, 3
Edinburgh City 0 Buckie Thistle 1

SECOND ROUND
Buckie Thistle 2 Hamilton Academicals 0
Coldstream 2 Brechin City 6
SECOND ROUND cont.

Montrose 1, 1 Keith 1, 0
Partick Thistle 3 Deveronvale 0
Peterhead 3 Cove Rangers 0
Spartans 1 Stirling Albion 3

THIRD ROUND
Ross County 2 Buckie Thislte 1

HIGHLAND LEAGUE CUP

FIRST ROUND Two Legs
Cove Rangers 1, 0 Forres Mechanics 1, 2
Deveronvale 5, 1 Fort William 0, 1
Huntly 3, 1 Buckie Thistle 0, 0
Lossiemouth 0, 0 Fraserburgh 1, 3
Rothes 3, 4 Clachnacuddin 0, 1
Keith 1, 2 Wick Academy 1, 0

QUARTER-FINALS Two Legs
Forres Mechanics 1, 3 Huntly 1, 1
Nairn County 0, 4 Fraserburgh 1, 1
Rothes 0, 2 Deveronvale 5, 1
Brora Rangers 1, 3 Keith 2, 3

SEMI-FINAL
Nairn County 1 Deveronvale 2 aet
Forres Mechanics 1, 3p Keith 1, 2p

FINAL At Christie Park, Huntly

DEVERONVALE	1	*(More)*
FORRES MECHANICS	2	*(MacDonald, Ross)*

DEVERONVALE: Spiers; Dolan, Kinghorn, Chisholm, Henderson, Montgomery, More, Brown, Cadger, Watt, Urquhart. Substitutes not used: McAllister, Stewart, Craigie, Stephen, Phimister.
FORRES MECHANICS: McRitchie; McGettick, Main, Maguire, MacDonald, Belshaw, Sanderson, Murphy, Brown, Connelly, Ross. Substututes not used: Noble, McIntosh, Moore, Cameron, Reid.
Referee: T Robertson.

EAST OF SCOTLAND LEAGUE

PREMIER DIVISION

	P	W	D	L	F	A	Pts
Annan Athletic	22	13	6	3	48	26	45
Whitehill Welfare	22	13	5	4	47	18	44
Threave Rovers	22	11	6	5	39	28	39
Spartans	22	10	9	4	45	31	38
Craigroyston	22	9	5	8	30	28	32
Edinburgh City	22	8	6	8	37	40	30
Lothian Thistle	22	7	6	8	30	30	27
Vale of Leithen	22	7	3	12	34	42	24
Coldstream	22	7	3	12	28	42	24
Gala Fairydean	22	7	3	12	29	45	24
Civil Service Strol	22	7	2	13	35	43	23
Easthouses	22	5	3	14	21	50	18

DIVISION ONE

	P	W	D	L	F	A	Pts
Pentcaitland/Ormist	20	13	4	3	43	16	43
Edinburgh University	20	12	6	2	35	11	42
Peebles Rovers	20	9	7	4	44	26	34
Hawick Royal Albert	20	8	5	7	41	40	29
Edinburgh Athletic	20	9	2	9	28	43	29
Preston Athletic	20	8	4	8	33	29	28
Eyemouth United	20	8	3	9	30	47	27
Tollcross United	20	5	7	8	25	28	22
Kelso United	20	6	3	11	32	38	21
Selkirk	20	5	1	13	30	49	17
Heriot Watt University	20	3	5	12	23	47	14

LEADING GOAL-SCORERS

27 G Harley (Peebles Rovers)
22 S O'Donnell (Edinburgh City),
C Manson (Whitehill Welfare),
P O'Neill (Lothian Thistle)
16 P Hobbins (Spartans),
P Moffatt (Vale of Leithen),
C McMenamin (Annan Athletic)
15 B Davies (Civil Service Strollers),
David Cheyen (Pencailtand & Ormiston),
J Bird (Whitehill Welfare)

ALEX JACK CUP

SECOND ROUND
Eyemouth United 2 Tollcross 4
Heriot Watt University 0 Craigroyston 3
Kelso United 0, 2, 4p Lothian Thistle 0, 2, 5p
Peebles Rovers 4 Easthouses Lily 1

SEMI-FINALS
Craigroyston 2, 2 Tollcross United 2, 1
Lothian Thistle 4 Peebles Rovers 2

FINAL
LOTHIAN THISTLE 2 *(Ronaldson, Lockhart)*
CRAIGROYSTON 0

IMAGE PRINTERS EAST QUALIFYING CUP

ROUND THREE
Civil Service Strollers 0 Whitehill Welfare 4
Pencaitland & Ormiston 0 Lothian Thistle 2
Spartans 1 Kelso United 2
Vale of Leithen 0 Craigroyston 5

SEMI-FINALS
Kelso United 1, 0 Lothian Thistle 1, 3
Whitehill Welfare 4 Craigroyston 0

FINAL At Preston Athletic FC
WHITEHILL WELFARE 2 *(Manson, Hope pen)*
LOTHIAN THISTLE 0

EAST LEAGUE CUP

THIRD ROUND
Civil Service Strollers 9 Heriot Watt University 1
Edinburgh University 1 Edinburgh City 2
Spartans 2 Coldstream 0
Whitehill Welfare 1, 8p Vale of Leithen 1, 9p

SEMI-FINALS
Spartans 2 Edinburgh City 3
Vale of Leithen 0 Civil Service Strollers 2

FINAL At Whitehill Welfare FC
CIVIL SERVICE STROLLERS 3 *(McLeod, Currie, Langhorn)*
EDINBURGH CITY 1 *(Foster)*

KING CUP

THIRD ROUND
Craigroyston 3 Preston Athletic 0
Edinburgh City 3 Vale of Leithen 6
Peebles Rovers 2, 2 Lothian Thistle 2, 3
Spartans 2 Edinburgh University 0

SEMI-FINALS
Craigroyston 2 Spartans 4
Vale of Leithen 3 Lothian Thistle 1

FINAL At Whitehill Walfare FC
SPARTANS 2 *(McGovern & own goal)*
VALE OF LEITHEN 0

CITY CUP

SEMI-FINAL
Whitehill Welfare 0, 4p Livingston 0, 5p

FINAL At Whitehill Welfare FC
LIVINGSTON 3 *(Baillie, Ormiston, Fairgrieve)*
LOTHIAN THISTLE 0

SOUTH OF SCOTLAND LEAGUE

	P	W	D	L	F	A	Pts
Queen of the South 'A'	14	13	0	1	59	16	39
Tarff Rovers	13	9	2	2	39	19	29
Dalbeattie Star	14	9	1	4	46	24	28
Crichton Royal	13	7	4	2	29	21	25
Dumfries FC	15	7	2	6	34	33	23
St Cuthbert Wndrs	13	6	4	3	33	26	22
Creetown	14	6	2	6	36	39	20
Annan Athletic 'A'	14	6	0	8	33	31	18
Girvan	19	3	6	10	30	63	15
Newton Stewart	9	4	1	4	22	20	13
Threave Rovers 'A'	11	3	0	8	17	34	9
Wigtown & Bladnoch	14	2	2	10	22	46	8
Stranrear Athletic	15	1	2	12	19	47	5

The competition was not completed owing to the Foot & Mouth epidemic and the cups were also seriously disrupted

SOUTH LEAGUE CUP

SECOND ROUND
Creetwon 3, 4p St Cuthbert Wanderers 3, 5p
Dumfries 2 Threave Rovers 1
Newton Stewart 3, 3p Girvan 3, 1p
Tarff Rovers 0, 4p Dalbeattie Star 0, 3p

SEMI-FINALS
Newton Stewart 1 Dumfries 0
Tarff Rovers 1 St Cuthbert Wanderers 2

FINAL At Newton Stewart
NEWTON STEWART 5 (*Davidson 2, McCreadie, McIlwraith, Hughes)*
ST CUTHBERT WANDERERS 0

HAIG GORDON MEMORIAL TROPHY

SECOND ROUND
Creetown 4 Wigtown & Bladnoch 2 aet
Crichton Royal 1 Tarff Rovers 2
Dalbeattie Star 1, 1 Newton Stewart 1, 3
Stranraer Athletic 0 Annan Athletic 5

SEMI-FINAL
Annan Athletic 4 Newton Stewart 2
(Competition incomplete)

CREE LODGE CUP

SECOND ROUND
Dalbeattie Star 1, 4p Dumfries HSFP 1, 5p
Tarff Rovers 7 Crichton Royal 1
Threave Rovers 7 Girvan 1

SOUTH OF SCOTLAND CHALLENGE CUP

SECOND ROUND
Dumfries 1 Tarff Rovers 3
(Competition incomplete)

TWEEDIE CUP

Only the First Round was completed with Annan Ath, Girvan, Tarff Rovers and Newton Stewart advancing.

NORTH CALEDONIAN LEAGUE

	P	W	D	L	F	A	Pts
Alness United	18	15	1	2	68	15	31
Thurso	18	14	1	3	59	22	29
Golspie Sutherland	18	13	0	5	63	20	35
Balintore	18	12	0	6	47	35	24
Halkirk United	18	7	4	7	51	31	18
Invergordon	18	8	2	8	47	41	18
Tain St Duthus	18	5	2	11	27	42	12
Bunillidh Thistle	18	4	1	13	23	56	9
Bonar Bridge	18	3	2	13	22	83	8
Dornoch	18	2	1	15	27	89	5

CHIC ALLAN CUP

SEMI-FINALS
Golspie Sutherland 3 Alness United 2
Halkirk 0 Thurso 3

FINAL At Brora Rangers FC
GOLSPIE SUTHERLAND 3-0 THURSO

PCT CUP

SEMI-FINALS
Alness United 1 Thurso 0
Dornoch 0 Golspie Sutherland 3

FINAL At Balintore
ALNESS UNITED 0-1 GOLSPIE SUTHERLAND

MORRIS NEWTON CUP

SEMI-FINALS
Bonar Bridge 3 Dornoch 1
Golspie Sutherland 3 Thurso 2

FINAL At Ross County FC
GOLSPIE SUTHERLAND 5-2 BONAR BRIDGE

FOOTBALL TIMES CUP

SEMI-FINALS
Golspie Sutherland 2 Invergordon 0
Thurso 1 Alness United 2

FINAL At Brora Rangers FC
ALNESS UNITED 3-1 GOLSPIE SUTHERLAND

OTHER SCOTTISH AMATEUR WINNERS:

SCOTTISH AMATEUR LEAGUE
Premier-Premier: Gartcosh
Premier Division One: Kilbowie
Premier Division Two: Shamrock
Section One - One: Rothesay
Section One - Two: Glencastle

CENTRAL SCOTTISH LEAGUE
Premier: Harestanes
Division 1a: Uddingston
Division 1b: Spartans

CLUB TIES AYRSHIRE LEAGUE
Premier League: Knockintiber
North Division One: Dirrans Athletic
North Division Two: Largs United
South Division One: Cumnock Amateurs
South Division Two: Hurlford Thistle

DUMFRIES AMATEUR LEAGUE
Division One: Kirkconnel
Division Two: Upper Annandale

BORDER AMATEUR LEAGUE
First Division: Gala Rovers
Second Division: Leithen Rovers
Third Division: Newton SB

HIGHLAND AMATEUR CUP
Pentland United

LEWIS & HARRIS LEAGUE
Back

JOHN O'GROATS JOURNAL CAITHNESS COUNTY LEAGUE
Division One: Pentland United
Division Two: Halkirk

STRATHSPEY & BADENOCH WELFARE LEAGUE
Kingussie

GLENDALE PLASTICS KINGDOM CALEDONIAN LEAGUE
Cupar Hearts

LOTHIAN & EDINBURGH AMATEUR FA
Premier: Liberton RM
Lothian West: Oscars
Lothian East: Drumhor
Edinburgh West: Blackridge
Lothian Edinburgh: Tynecastle
Edinburgh East: Scottish Widows

LANARKSHIRE AMATEUR LEAGUE
Premier: Cole United
Division 1a: Orbiston
Division 1b: Eddlewood
Division 1c:Viewpark

SCOTTISH F A AMATEUR CUP

FIFTH ROUND
Drumchapel Amateurs 3 Netherton 1
Newmilns Ves 0, 0 Knockentiber 0, 1
Vale of Clyde 2 St Patrick's FP 3
Welhouse 1, 2 Dalziel HSFP 1, 5

SEMI-FINALS
St Patrick's FP 2 Drumchapel Amateurs 1
Dalziel HSFP 1 Knockintiber Amateurs 0

FINAL At Hampden Park, Glasgow
DALZIEL HIGH SCHOOL FP 2
ST PATRICK'S HIGH SCHOOL FP 1
(after extra-time - score at 90 minutes 0-0)

AMATEUR FOOTBALL ALLIANCE

President: F J Banner
Director (AFA Ltd): W P Goss

General & Company Secretary: Mike Brown, 55 Islington Park Street, London N1 1QB
Tel: 020 7359 3493 Fax: 020 7359 5027
Website: www.amateur-fa.org E-mail: A.F.A@dial.Pipex.com

A F A SENIOR CUP

FIRST ROUND PROPER

Old Manorians	0	v	1	Glyn Old Boys
Parkfield		w/o		Old Malvernians
Hon. Artillery Co	2	v	1	Crch End Vampires
Old Esthameians	1	v	2	U C L Academicals
Old Tenisonians	1	v	6	Old Finchleians
West Wickham	6	v	0	Southgate Olympic
Old Vaughanians	4	v	2	Crdnl Manning O B
Old Lyonians	0	v	2	Nottsborough
Old Salesians	6	v	4	Old Salopians
Old Wokingians	6	v	0	Rugby Clubs
Old Woodhouseians	6	v	0	Wood Green O B
Lensbury	8	v	2	Ealing Association
Shene Old Gramms	0	v	2	Merton
Bank of England	3	v	0	Barclays Bank
Old Kingsburians	0	v	3	Southgate County
Carshalton	6	v	1	Old Dorkinian
Duncombe Sports	4	v	1	Kings Old Boys
Old Suttonians	3	v	2	Old Danes
Queen Mary C OB	0	v	5	Winchmore Hill
Universityof Herts	0	v	5	Alleyn Old Boys
Civil Service	2	v	1	Albanian
Old Foresters	2	v	1	HSBC
Old Stationers	4	v	2	O W'minster Ctzns
Latymer Old Boys	1	v	0	E. Barnet O Grams
Nat West Bank	0	v	6	O Actonians Assn
Old Meadonians	2	v	0	Old Elizabethans
Old Aloysians	3	v	1	Old Bromleians
Polytechnic	5	v	1	Old Buckwellians
Old Salvatorians	2	v	1	Kew Association
Old Owens	4	v	2	Old Bealonians
Chertsey O S'ians	3	v	4	Mill Hill Village

SECOND ROUND PROPER

Glyn Old Boys	1	v	0	Parkfield
Norsemen	1	v	2	Hon. Artillery Co
U C L Academicals	3	v	1	Old Finchleians
West Wickham	1	*	3	Old Vaughanians
Nottsborough	0	v	2	Old Salesians
Old Wokingians	3	v	2	O Woodhouseians
Lensbury	6	v	0	Merton

SECOND ROUND PROPER cont.

Bank of England	2	v	3	Southgate County
Carshalton	5	v	2	Duncombe Sports
Old Suttonians	2	v	0	Winchmore Hill
Alleyn Old Boys	1	v	3	Civil Service
Old Foresters	1	v	0	Old Stationers
Latymer Old Boys	0	v	2	Old Actonians Assn
Old Meadonians	2	v	1	Old Aloysians
Polytechnic	6	v	1	Old Salvatorians
Old Owens	3	v	4	Mill Hill Village

THIRD ROUND PROPER

Glyn Old Boys	0	v	5	Hon Artillery Co
U C L Academicals	1	v	0	Old Vaughanians
Old Salesians	3	v	2	Old Wokingians
Old Meadonians	2	v	1	Old Aloysians
Lensbury	7	v	4	Southgate County
Carshalton	3	v	2	Old Suttonians
Civil Service	1,3p	*	1,2p	Old Foresters
Old Actonians Assn	0	v	3	Old Meadonians
Polytechnic	2	v	0	Mill Hill Village

FOURTH ROUND PROPER

Hon Artillery Co	0	v	1	UCL Academicals
Old Salesians	5	v	3	Lensbury
Carshalton	2	v	3	Civil Service
Old Meadonians	1	v	5	Polytechnic

SEMI-FINALS

UCL Academicals	4	v	1	Old Salesians
Civil Service	1	v	2	Polytechnic

FINAL

UCL Academicals	2	v	1	Civil Service

OTHER AFA CUP FINALS

ESSEX SENIOR

Old Bealonians 2 v 5 Old Brentwoods

MIDDLESEX SENIOR

Old Ignatians 1 v 0 Old Actonians Assn

SURREY SENIOR

HSBC 2 v 3 Old Wokingians

INTERMEDIATE

Crch End Vampires 3,7p * 3,6p O Parmiterians Res

JUNIOR

Old Owens 3rd 0 v 1 Old Challoners Res

MINOR

Mill Hill Village 4th 2 v 1 Albanian 4th

YOUTH

Old Parmiterians 2 v 8 Norsemen

VETERANS

Old Parmitarians A 7 v 1 Old Buckwellians

W E GREENLAND MEMORIAL

Old Actonians Assn 2,1p * 2,4p Old Ignatians

ESSEX INTERMEDIATE

Davenant W OB 1st 2 v 1 Mt Pleasant PO 1st

KENT INTERMEDIATE

Mrgn Guaranty 1st 0 v 6 West Wickham Res

MIDDLESEX INTERMEDIATE

Civil Service Res 0 v 2 Alexandra Park Rs

SURREY INTERMEDIATE

Royal Sun Alliance 4 v 0 Carshalton Res

SENIOR NOVETS

O. Finchleians 5th 2,2p * 2,4p O. Actonians A 5th

INTERMEDIATE NOVETS

Old Aloysians 6th 3 v 1 Phoenix O B 6th

JUNIOR NOVETS

Old Actonians A 8th 2v 1 Old Actonians 7th

ARTHUR DUNN CUP

Old Carthusians v Old Bradfieldians 4-1

ARTHURIAN LEAGUE

(Competition Abandoned)

PREMIER DIVISION	*P*	*W*	*D*	*L*	*F*	*A*	*Pts*
Old Etonians	9	6	3	0	29	16	15
Old Carthusians	13	5	4	4	33	51	14
Old Cholmeleians	8	3	4	1	18	14	10
Old Brentwoods	8	3	3	2	15	15	9
Old Reptonians	9	3	3	3	18	18	9
Old Chigwellians	10	3	2	5	16	19	8
Old Harrovians	6	3	1	2	15	12	7
Old Salopians	9	1	4	4	17	20	6
Lancing Old Boys	10	1	2	7	10	26	4

DIVISION ONE	*P*	*W*	*D*	*L*	*F*	*A*	*Pts*
Old Bradfieldians	10	7	3	1	37	9	16
Old Foresters	8	7	3	1	30	11	14
Old Malvernians	8	5	2	2	26	17	11
Old Haberdashers	9	4	2	3	24	26	10
Old Wellingburians	12	4	2	7	27	37	9
Old Witleians	12	3	1	7	26	38	8
Old Aldenhamians	12	4	2	8	27	44	8
Old Wykehamists	11	2	3	7	25	40	6

DIVISION TWO	*P*	*W*	*D*	*L*	*F*	*A*	*Pts*
Old Carthusians Res	12	8	1	3	52	18	17
Old Westminsters	9	8	0	1	31	8	16
Old Chigwellians Res	10	8	0	2	29	12	16
Old Etonians Res	11	4	2	5	22	26	10
Lancing Old Boys Res	10	4	1	5	16	31	9
Old Brentwoods Res	9	4	0	5	26	22	8
Old Etonians 3rd	13	3	2	8	15	39	8
Old Haberdashers Res	7	0	1	6	11	28	1
Old Salopians Res	5	0	1	4	4	22	1

DIVISION THREE	*P*	*W*	*D*	*L*	*F*	*A*	*Pts*
Old Carthusians 3rd	13	9	0	4	31	19	18
Old Bradfieldians Res	12	7	1	4	32	17	15
Old Cholmeleians Res	8	5	1	2	28	17	11
Old Foresters Res	10	4	2	4	27	21	10
Old Foresters 3rd	10	3	2	5	23	36	8
Old Aldenhamians Res	11	3	1	7	27	51	7
Old Millhillians	7	3	0	4	20	19	6
Old Harrovians Res	9	2	1	6	17	25	5

DIVISION FOUR
Team leading at abandonment Old Haileyburians

DIVISION FIVE
Team leading at abandonment Old Chigwellians 3rd

JUNIOR LEAGUE CUP
Old Westminsters v Old Chigwellians Res 2-1

DERRIK MOORE VETERANS' CUP
Old Brentwoods v Old Cholmeleians 2-1

JIM DIXSON 6-A-S
Won by Old Foresters

LONDON FINANCIAL FOOTBALL ASSOCIATION

DIVISION ONE	P	W	D	L	F	A	Pts
Coutts & Co	16	13	1	2	55	22	40
Morgan Guaranty*	16	10	4	2	40	22	31
Bank of America	16	8	2	6	30	34	26
Dresdner Kleinwort B	16	6	5	5	35	22	23
Granby	16	4	6	6	27	24	18
Mount Pleasant PO	16	2	10	4	11	15	16
Royal Sun Alliance	16	2	9	5	18	29	15
Foreign & C'wealth Off.	16	2	5	9	17	34	11
Citibank	16	3	2	11	22	53	11

DIVISION TWO	P	W	D	L	F	A	Pts
Chase Manhattan Bk	12	12	0	0	63	12	36
Chelsea Exiles	12	8	0	4	47	25	24
Royal Sun Allnce Res	12	7	1	4	34	23	22
Eagle Star	12	5	1	6	34	29	16
Marsh	12	3	2	7	25	31	11
Temple Bar	12	1	4	7	10	46	7
GEFC	12	1	2	9	11	58	5

DIVISION THREE	P	W	D	L	F	A	Pts
Granby Res	18	14	1	3	57	23	43
C Hoare & Co	18	13	2	3	73	29	41
Coutts & Co Res*	18	13	2	3	60	14	29
Marsh Res	18	6	8	4	38	28	26
Royal Bank of Scotland	18	7	2	9	29	32	23
Salomon Smith Barney	18	6	4	8	32	36	22
Customs & Excise	18	6	3	9	26	51	21
ANZ Banking	18	5	3	10	31	51	18
Eagle Star Res	18	4	2	12	19	59	14
UCB Home Loans	18	2	1	15	19	61	7

DIVISION FOUR	P	W	D	L	F	A	Pts
Citibank Res	18	14	2	2	50	14	44
Royal Sun Alliance 3rd	18	13	2	3	79	26	41
Credit Suisse First Bstn	18	11	3	4	52	29	36
Bank of Ireland	18	8	6	4	42	22	30
Granby 3rd	18	8	3	7	29	35	27
Marsh 3rd	18	7	3	8	52	57	24
CGU Cuaco 5th	18	4	7	7	44	69	19
Standard Chartered Bk	18	4	2	12	29	50	14
Temple Bar Res	18	2	6	10	16	49	12
Royal Bank of Scot Res	18	1	2	15	25	67	5

SENIOR CUP
Dresdner Kleinwort Benson v Royal Sun Alliance 2-4

JUNIOR CUP
Customs & Excise v Bank of Ireland 1-0

VETERANS' CUP
Granby v HSBC 1-2

The prolonged winter rainfall prevented 39 games in the competition being played which are entered as 0-0 draws. Some League Cup competitions were also abandoned.

LONDON LEGAL LEAGUE

DIVISION ONE	P	W	D	L	F	A	Pts
Linklaters & Alliance	18	12	3	3	46	18	39
Gray's Inn	18	11	5	2	44	22	38
Denton Wilde Sapte (A)	18	11	2	5	26	20	35
Clifford Chance	18	10	4	4	46	24	34
Slaughter & May	18	8	3	7	26	25	27
Lovells	18	8	0	10	33	48	24
Nabarro Nathanson	18	7	2	9	29	27	23
KPMG ICE	18	7	2	9	38	38	23
CMS Cameron McKenna	18	2	2	14	24	59	8
Norton Rose	18	2	1	15	24	55	7

DIVISION TWO	P	W	D	L	F	A	Pts
Eversheds	18	12	4	2	50	25	40
Rosling King	18	12	3	3	51	17	39
Watson Farley & Wllms	18	11	4	3	32	17	37
Nicholson Graham & J	18	7	5	6	43	43	26
Baker & McKenzie	18	6	4	8	45	38	22
Herbert Smith	18	6	4	8	38	42	22
Simmons & Simmons	18	6	3	9	35	41	21
Taylor Joynson Garrett	18	6	1	11	33	65	19
Pegasus (inner Temple)	18	5	3	10	28	46	18
Freshfields	18	2	3	13	25	46	9

DIVISION THREE	P	W	D	L	F	A	Pts
Allen & Overy	18	13	3	2	78	31	42
Barlow Lyde & Gilbert	18	13	3	2	54	21	42
Titmuss Sainer Dechert	18	11	2	5	45	33	35
S J Berwin & Co	18	9	5	4	53	35	32
London Stock Exchange	18	8	1	9	42	30	25
Richards Butler	18	7	2	9	36	45	23
Denton Wilde Sapte (B)	18	5	4	9	43	46	19
Stephenson Harwood	18	4	3	11	32	64	15
Hammonds Suddards E	18	4	2	11	32	63	14
Macfarlanes	18	3	1	14	27	74	10

LEAGUE CHALLENGE CUP
Denton Wilde Sapte (A) v Gray's Inn 2-0

WEAVERS ARMS CHALLENGE CUP
Lovells v Dechert 3-1

LONDON OLD BOYS CUPS

SENIOR
Old Ignations v Old Vaughanians 1-0
INTERMEDIATE
Albanian Reserves v Old Parmiterians Reserves 0-1
JUNIOR
Latymer Old Boys 3rd v Old Actonians Assn 3rd 0-3
MINOR
Sinjuns 4th v Old Teisonians 4th 0-6
NOVETS
Mill Hill County OB 4th v O Actonians A 5th 0*0,2p4
DRUMMOND
Old Meadonians 6th v Old Aloysians 6th 0-1
NEMEAN
Old Actonians Assn 9th v Old Aloysians 7th 0-6

MIDLAND AMATEUR ALLIANCE

PREMIER DIVISION	P	W	D	L	F	A	Pts
Trent University26	19	6	1	79	33	63	
Lady Bay	26	16	5	5	91	64	53
Old Elizabethans	26	15	5	6	70	31	50
Woodborough United	26	15	5	6	91	55	50
Caribbean Cavaliers	26	14	8	4	75	50	50
Nottinghamshire	26	14	5	7	64	35	47
ASC Dayncourt Res	26	13	1	12	53	55	40
Square Form Stealers	26	10	3	13	70	79	33
Bassingfield	26	8	7	11	48	58	31
Ashland Rovers	26	6	8	12	51	68	26
Wollaton 3rd	26	6	6	14	41	65	24
Horse & Jockey	26	6	4	16	46	90	22
Beeston Old Boys Assn	26	4	2	20	40	88	14
Old Bemrosians	26	3	1	22	52	100	10

DIVISION ONE	P	W	D	L	F	A	Pts
Magdala Amateurs Res	24	18	0	6	99	36	54
Old Elizabethans Res	24	17	2	5	68	39	53
Smithys	24	16	3	5	81	35	51
County NALGO	24	13	2	9	76	53	41
Wollaton 4th	24	10	5	9	59	53	35
Brunts Old Boys	24	11	2	11	52	52	35
Nottinghamshire Res	24	9	7	8	62	49	34
Bassingfield Res	24	9	5	10	55	58	32
Ilkeston Rangers	24	9	5	10	66	82	32
Chilwell	24	7	5	12	53	71	26
Southwell Arms	24	7	3	14	47	74	24
Derbyshire Am Res	24	6	2	16	56	88	20
Dynamo	24	2	3	19	25	109	9

DIVISION TWO	P	W	D	L	F	A	Pts
Pakistan Centre	28	21	4	3	109	36	67
Sherwood Forest	28	19	5	4	87	48	62
FLL Aerospace	28	18	1	9	95	47	55
Old Elizabethans 3rd	28	16	5	7	82	41	53
West Bridgford Utd	28	12	9	7	58	42	45
ASC Dayncourt 3rd	28	13	6	9	59	48	45
Magdala Arms 3rd	28	11	7	10	75	69	40
Edwinstowe FC	28	11	6	11	75	70	39
Tibshelf Old Boys	28	11	4	13	44	65	37
Nottinghamshire 3rd	28	11	3	14	57	53	36
EMTEC	28	10	4	14	65	96	34
Beeston OB Assn 3rd	28	8	5	15	49	79	29
Wollaton 5th	28	9	2	17	65	96	29
Derbyshire Ams 3rd	28	5	4	19	62	99	19
Old Bemrosians Res	28	2	1	25	29	122	7

LEAGUE SENIOR CUP
won by Nottinghamshire v Lady Bay

LEAGUE INTERMEDIATE CUP
won by Old Elizabethan Res v Derbyshire Amtr Res

LEAGUE MINOR CUP
won by FLL Aerospace v Pakistan Centre

OLD BOYS AMATEUR FOOTBALL LEAGUE

PREMIER DIVISION	P	W	D	L	F	A	Pts
Old Meadonians	20	17	0	3	50	19	51
Old Aloysians	20	11	5	4	42	24	38
Old Vaughanians	20	10	4	6	36	32	34
Old Wilsonians	20	9	4	7	34	27	31
Shene Old Gramms	20	9	4	7	48	46	31
Old Ignations	20	6	8	6	33	33	26
Phoenix Old Boys	20	6	6	8	36	31	24
Cardinal Manning OB	20	7	2	11	28	51	23
Old Hamptonians	20	5	6	9	31	33	21
Glyn Old Boys*	20	5	3	12	22	42	16
Old Tenisonians	20	2	4	14	16	38	10

SENIOR DIV ONE	P	W	D	L	F	A	Pts
Old Salvatorians	20	16	3	1	50	9	51
Old Danes	20	15	3	2	65	18	48
Latymer Old Boys	20	15	2	3	64	21	47
Old Dorkinians	20	9	2	9	25	30	29
Old Isleworthians	20	8	2	10	33	44	26
Enfield Old Gramms	20	8	1	11	33	41	25
Old Suttonians	20	7	2	11	25	39	23
Old Manorians	20	6	3	11	40	42	21
Old Minchendenians	20	4	4	12	40	61	16
Old Buckwellians	20	4	4	12	26	50	16
Sinjuns*	20	3	4	13	19	65	7

SENIOR DIV TWO	P	W	D	L	F	A	Pts
Old Tiffinians	20	15	2	3	52	17	47
Chertsey Old Salesians	20	13	1	6	50	28	40
Phoenix Old Boys Res	20	11	5	4	51	35	38
Old Kingsburians	20	9	5	6	59	38	32
John Fisher Old Boys	20	8	3	9	31	36	27
Latymer Old Boys Res	19	8	4	7	38	33	28
Queen Mary College OB	20	7	4	9	42	44	25
Old Sedcopians	20	5	6	9	31	50	21
Old Reigatian	20	4	8	8	24	32	20
Old Vaughanians Res*	19	3	5	11	20	49	12
Clapham Old Xaverians	20	2	5	13	20	56	11

SENIOR DIV THREE	P	W	D	L	F	A	Pts
Old Wokingians	22	21	0	1	81	13	63
Wood Green Old Boys	22	14	4	4	70	31	46
Old Salvatorians Res	22	11	6	5	25	17	39
Old Aloysians Res	22	12	1	9	49	33	37
Old Meadonians Res	22	11	4	7	51	38	37
Old St Marys	22	9	5	8	47	43	32
Old Wilsonians Res	22	8	6	8	34	31	30
Old Hamptonians Res	22	9	3	10	39	40	30
Old Manorians Res	22	7	6	9	40	46	27
Old Tenisonians Res	22	4	3	15	32	60	15
Old Isleworthians Res	22	4	0	18	28	84	12
Phoenix Old Boys 3rd	22	0	6	16	13	73	6

INTERMEDIATE DIVISION NORTH
10 teams won by Old Egbertians

INTERMEDIATE DIVISION SOUTH
10 teams won by Fitzwilliam Old Boys

DIVISION ONE NORTH
11 teams won by Old Egbertians Res

DIVISION TWO NORTH
10 teams won by Old Camdenians

DIVISION THREE NORTH
11 teams won by Old Edmontonians 3rd

DIVISION FOUR NORTH
10 teams won by Royal London Hosp OB Res

DIVISION FIVE NORTH
9 teams won by Old Aloysians 7th

DIVISION SIX NORTH
10 teams won by Old Edmontonians 6th

DIVISION ONE SOUTH
11 teams won by Old Tenisonians 4th

DIVISION TWO SOUTH
10 teams won by Old Tiffinians Reserves

DIVISION THREE SOUTH
11 teams won by Old Josephians Reserves

DIVISION FOUR SOUTH
10 teams won by Old Thorntonians Reserves

DIVISION FIVE SOUTH
12 teams won by Chertsey Old Salesians 3rd

DIVISION SIX SOUTH
10 teams won by Chertsey Old Salesians 4th

DIVISION SEVEN SOUTH
10 teams won by Old Wilsonians 7th

DIVISION EIGHT SOUTH
9 teams won by Old Reigatians 7th

DIVISION ONE WESTERN
10 teams won by Old Hendonians

DIVISION TWO WESTERN
11 teams won by Old Challoners Reserves

DIVISION THREE WESTERN
11 teams won by Mill Hill County OB 3rd

DIVISION FOUR WESTERN
10 teams won by Holland Park Old Boys Res

DIVISION FIVE WESTERN
9 teams won by Old Salvatorians 8th

DIVISION SIX WESTERN
6 teams won by Old Kolsassians

SOUTHERN AMATEUR LEAGUE

SENIOR SECTION

DIVISION ONE

	P	*W*	*D*	*L*	*F*	*A*	*Pts*
Old Actonians Assn	22	16	1	5	57	14	49
Old Owens	22	14	4	4	59	21	46
Old Esthameians	22	11	7	4	47	36	40
Polytechnic	22	11	6	5	57	27	39
Barclays Bank	22	10	4	8	46	32	34
Alleyn Old Boys	22	8	5	9	42	42	29
Norsemen	22	8	5	9	32	38	29
East Barnet Old Gramms	22	7	7	8	35	40	28
Carshalton	22	7	7	8	31	38	28
Crouch End Vampires	22	7	4	11	31	39	25
Old Bromleians*	22	2	3	17	23	66	7
Nat Westminster Bank*	22	4	1	17	27	94	7

DIVISION TWO

	P	*W*	*D*	*L*	*F*	*A*	*Pts*
Broomfield	22	15	4	3	42	20	49
Civil Service	22	13	3	6	38	26	42
Winchmore Hill	22	11	4	7	25	20	37
Old Salesians	22	10	5	7	33	29	35
HSBC	22	10	4	8	41	28	34
Old Stationers	22	7	8	7	44	39	29
West Wickham	22	8	4	10	36	38	28
Lensbury	22	7	6	9	28	30	27
Lloyds TSB Bank	22	7	6	9	44	47	27
Old Finchleians	22	8	1	13	56	62	25
Alexandra Park	22	5	5	12	25	49	20
Old Parmiterians	22	4	4	14	27	51	16

DIVISION THREE

	P	*W*	*D*	*L*	*F*	*A*	*Pts*
Old Lyonians	22	17	4	1	63	17	55
Old Parkonians	22	14	3	5	57	24	45
Bank of England	22	14	2	6	61	21	44
Kew Association	22	13	4	5	66	30	43
Old Westminster Citizens	22	9	4	9	45	52	31
Ibis	22	8	5	9	27	32	29
CGU Cuaco	22	8	4	10	47	42	28
Old Latymerians	22	8	4	10	39	46	28
Merton	22	5	8	9	22	28	23
Southgate Olympic	22	6	1	15	31	65	19
South Bank	22	4	3	15	21	63	15
Brentham	22	2	6	14	24	83	12

RESERVE TEAM SECTION:

DIVISION ONE
12 teams won by HSBC Reserves

DIVISION TWO
12 teams won by Old Parmiterians Reserves

DIVISION THREE
11 teams won by Old Esthameians Reserves

THIRD TEAM SECTION:

DIVISION ONE
12 teams won by Old Owens 3rd

DIVISION TWO
12 teams won by Old Esthameians 3rd

DIVISION THREE
11 teams won by Old Latymerians

FOURTH TEAM SECTION:

DIVISION ONE
12 teams won by Old Actonians Assn 4th

DIVISION TWO
12 teams won by Carshalton 4th

DIVISION THREE
9 teams won by Ibis 4th

FIFTH TEAM SECTION:

DIVISION ONE
11 teams won by Old Actonians Assn 5th

DIVISION TWO
10 teams won by Crouch End Vampires 5th

DIVISION THREE
8 teams won by Old Latymerians 5th

SIXTH TEAM SECTION:

DIVISION ONE
12 teams won by Old Actonians Assn 6th

DIVISION TWO
11 teams won by Civil Service 6th

MINOR SECTION:

DIVISION ONE
10 teams won by Old Actonians Assn 7th

DIVISION TWO
9 teams won by Old Actonians Assn 9th

DIVISION THREE
8 teams won by Kew Association 7th

DIVISION FOUR
7 teams won by Old Parmiterians 9th

SOUTHERN OLYMPIAN LEAGUE

SENIOR SECTION

PREMIER DIVISION

	P	*W*	*D*	*L*	*F*	*A*	*Pts*
UCL Academicals	18	13	4	1	45	17	43
Hale End Athletic	18	11	4	3	45	22	37
Mill Hill Village*	18	10	5	3	44	28	32
Albanian	15	8	6	1	33	16	30
Nottsborough	16	7	3	6	31	35	24
Old Woodhouseians	18	7	1	10	30	32	22
Old Grammarians	16	5	4	7	22	22	19
Ulysses	18	5	1	12	23	38	16
Honourable Artillery Co	17	3	2	12	27	41	11
Wandsworth Borough	18	1	2	15	18	67	5

DIVISION TWO

	P	*W*	*D*	*L*	*F*	*A*	*Pts*
Southgate County	16	10	5	1	37	16	35
Parkfield	15	9	4	2	26	10	31
Pegasus	15	6	7	2	25	21	25
Old Bealonians	15	5	5	5	26	21	20
St Mary's College	15	6	2	7	28	29	20
University of Hertford	15	3	6	6	20	24	15
Kings Old Boys	15	3	6	6	31	47	15
BBC	15	2	5	8	20	28	11
Old Colfeians	15	2	4	9	12	29	10
Duncombe Sports	Record expunged						
City of London	Record expunged						

DIVISION THREE

	P	*W*	*D*	*L*	*F*	*A*	*Pts*
Economicals	19	17	1	1	54	18	52
Brent	20	11	4	5	48	28	37
Ealing Association	20	10	2	8	59	37	32
Centymca	20	9	2	9	48	41	29
The Rugby Clubs	19	9	1	9	48	60	28
Hampstead Heathens	18	8	3	7	48	31	27
Fulham Compton	14	8	1	5	37	30	25
Witan	17	5	5	7	28	32	20
London Welsh	19	6	2	11	32	53	20
The Comets	19	5	1	13	26	41	16
Inland Revenue	19	2	2	15	27	84	8

INTERMEDIATE SECTION:

DIVISION ONE
10 teams won by St Mary's College Reserves

DIVISION TWO
11 teams won by Pegasus Reserves

DIVISION THREE
10 teams won by Kings Old Boys Reserves

SOUTHERN OLYMPIAN LEAGUE cont.

JUNIOR NORTH SECTION:

DIVISION ONE
10 teams won by University of Hertfordshire Res

DIVISION TWO
11 teams won by Albanian 6th

DIVISION THREE
10 teams won by Old Bealonians 6th

JUNIOR SOUTH-WEST SECTION:

DIVISION ONE
10 teams won by Nottsborough

DIVISION TWO
8 teams won by Old Grammarians 4th

DIVISION THREE
9 teams won by Witan 4th

VETERAN'S CUP
won by UCL Academicals

LONDON UNIVERSITY REPRESENTATIVE XI

v Ulysses	won	4-1
v London Legal League	won	4-1
v Oxford University	lost	1-4
v Cambridge University	lost	0-6
v Army Crusaders	won	8-0
v Amateur Football Alliance	cancelled - rain	
v Southern Olympian League	cancelled - rain	

UNIVERSITY OF LONDON

MEN'S COMPETITIONS

PREMIER DIVISION	P	W	D	L	F	A	Pts
King's College	11	11	0	0	36	7	33
London School of Econ	11	7	3	1	29	10	24
University College	11	8	0	3	28	11	24
Royal Holloway College	11	6	2	3	14	11	20
R Free, UC & Mx Hosp	11	6	1	4	35	26	19
Queen Mary Westfield	11	6	0	5	32	25	18
Imperial Coll Sch. of Med	11	5	2	4	35	29	17
Guys, Kings & St Thomas	11	4	2	5	16	25	14
Imperial Coll Sch. of Med	11	3	2	6	10	23	11
Goldsmiths College	11	3	0	8	22	38	9
St Barts & R London Hsp	11	1	0	10	15	33	3
R School of Mines (Imp)	11	0	0	11	9	43	0

UNIVERSITY OF LONDON cont.

DIVISION ONE

	P	W	D	L	F	A	Pts
University College 3rd	11	8	2	1	34	13	26
London Sch Econ Res	11	8	2	1	20	11	26
Imperial College Res	11	6	2	3	30	17	20
University College Res	11	6	1	4	27	15	19
St Georges Hosp MS	11	6	1	4	33	22	19
Imp Coll Sch Med Res	11	5	3	3	23	16	18
Royal Holloway Coll Res	11	5	2	4	19	13	17
Queen Mary W Coll Res	11	3	2	6	16	19	11
Kings College 3rd	11	3	1	7	25	33	10
Kings College Res	11	3	1	7	14	44	10
Goldsmiths Coll Res	11	3	0	8	11	30	9
Royal Veterinary College	11	0	3	8	8	27	3

DIVISION TWO

	P	W	D	L	F	A	Pts
London Sch Econ 3rd	10	8	0	2	26	18	24
Kings College 4th	11	7	2	2	36	22	23
Imperial College 3rd	11	6	2	3	33	16	20
University College 4th	11	5	3	3	37	26	18
Guys, Kings, St Thom Rs	11	5	2	4	24	20	17
Royal Holloway Coll 3rd	10	5	2	3	26	25	17
Qu Mary Westfield C 4th	11	5	1	5	36	29	16
R Free, UC & Mx Hosp Rs	11	4	1	6	26	37	13
Wye College	10	3	3	4	21	21	12
Imperial College 4th	11	3	2	6	26	31	11
Qu Mary Westfield C 3rd	10	2	1	7	26	37	7
London Sch Econ 4th	11	1	1	9	17	52	4

DIVISION THREE

	P	W	D	L	F	A	Pts
Royal Holloway Coll 4th	11	10	1	0	42	9	31
Goldsmiths Coll 3rd	10	8	0	2	47	17	24
Imp Coll Sch Med R 3rd	11	6	2	3	31	16	20
R Free, UC & Mx Hsp 3	10	6	1	3	18	13	19
Goldsmiths Coll 4th	11	5	2	4	23	27	17
Guys, Kings, St Th 4th	11	3	3	5	18	27	12
St Georges Hosp Res	9	3	2	4	13	9	11
St Barts & R London Rs	9	3	1	5	29	22	10
Guys, Kings, St Th 3rd	10	3	1	6	21	30	10
Imp Coll Sch Med 4th	11	3	1	7	17	44	10
St Georges Hosp 3rd	10	2	2	6	15	29	8
St Barts & R London 3rd	11	2	0	9	12	43	6

DIVISION FOUR

	P	W	D	L	F	A	Pts
Sch Oriental/African	24	18	3	3	107	31	57
London Sch Econ 6th	24	15	4	5	88	42	49
Royal Holloway Coll 5th	23	14	3	6	58	39	45
Kings College 6th	23	13	3	7	58	57	42
Birkbeck Coll Students	24	9	6	9	56	34	33
Imperial College 5th	24	10	3	11	44	53	33
School of Pharmacy	21	9	5	7	45	43	32
Kings College 5th	24	9	4	11	33	50	31
London Sch Econ 5th	23	8	6	9	61	47	30
R School Mines Res	24	8	3	13	52	56	27
Qu Mary Westfield 5th	24	6	5	13	57	72	23
University College 5th	24	7	2	15	51	90	23
Qu Mary Westfield 6th	24	2	3	19	22	118	9

DIVISION FIVE

	P	W	D	L	F	A	Pts
Imperial College 6th	24	19	1	4	127	36	58
University College 6th	24	19	1	4	110	48	58
R Coll Science (Imp)	23	19	0	4	95	36	57
University College 7th	24	16	1	7	73	39	49
Heythrop College	23	15	0	8	83	51	45
Sch Slavonic & E Eur.	24	11	2	11	57	82	35
Kings College 7th	24	10	4	10	46	58	34
Royal Vet College Res	23	10	4	9	40	54	34
Guys, Kings, St Th 5th	23	10	1	12	34	69	31
Imperial College 7th	24	7	2	15	46	74	23
London Sch Econ 7th	24	5	2	17	23	79	17
Royal Acad Music	24	3	0	21	18	12	9
Sch Pharmacy Res	24	1	0	23	20	134	3

CHALLENGE CUP
Kings College v Imperial College 0*0, 4p0

RESERVES CHALLENGE CUP
London School Economics Reserves *4
Imperial College School Medicine Reserves *3

RESERVES PLATE
R Free UC & Mx Hosp M S v Imperial College 4th 0-1

VASE
R Holloway 5ths v Royal College of Science 4-1

WOMEN'S LEAGUES

PREMIER DIVISION

	P	W	D	L	F	A	Pts
Qu Mary Westfield Coll	10	7	1	2	50	16	22
Imperial College	10	7	1	2	30	33	22
Guys, Kings, St Thomas	10	5	1	4	43	23	16
London Sch Economics	10	3	2	5	20	31	11
University College	10	2	2	6	23	39	8
Royal Holloway Coll 5th	10	2	1	7	18	42	7

DIVISION ONE

	P	W	D	L	F	A	Pts
Sch Oriental & African	8	8	0	0	46	1	24
Kings College	8	6	0	2	22	11	18
R Free, UC & Mx Hosp	8	3	1	4	1	11	10
Goldsmiths College	8	1	1	6	2	31	4
St Georges Hosp M S	8	1	0	7	3	20	3

DIVISION TWO

	P	W	D	L	F	A	Pts
Royal Veterinary Coll	8	4	1	3	7	4	13
Royal Holloway Coll Rs	8	4	0	4	8	3	12
R Free, UC, Mx Hosp Rs	8	4	0	4	16	18	12
Wye College	8	3	2	3	19	16	11
Guys, Kings, St Thom Rs	8	2	3	3	5	14	9

ENGLISH SCHOOLS' FOOTBALL ASSOCIATION

Publicity: Mike Simmonds, 19 The Spinney, Bulcote, Burton Joyce, Nottingham NG14 5GX
Tel: 0115 931 3299 Fax: 0115 931 2758

THE INTERNATIONAL SEASON

THE E.S.F.A. UNDER 18 SQUAD

The highlight of the 2000-01 season for the Under 18 squad selected from those students still in full time education was a first ever tour to the Far East with games against Malaysia and Singapore. The opening game in Malaysia was played in ninety degree heat and 100 per cent humidity on a pitch carrying surface water from a thunderstorm. Honours deservedly went to the defences in a 0-0 draw with Luke Kitchen and Richard Pell dominant in the central position for the visitors.

In conditions more typical of Europe, England defeated Singapore 2-0 in the second match with midfield players, Paul Honey and Ross Thompson, controlling the game and the goals coming from James Thornby and Graham Hockless, the latter's from the penalty spot.

England returned home with high hopes of taking the Home International Championship (Centenary Shield), but, as has been commonplace in recent seasons, a lack of goals was their problem. Perhaps strikers are such a rare commodity that potential League players are all snapped up by clubs at sixteen and do not continue with their studies.

The opening game against Scotland ended in a 0-0 draw and, although England dominated the game against Northern Ireland, only a far post header from Richard Pell in the 73rd minute prevented another goalless draw. That result left England needing a win in their final match against Wales to regain the Centenary Shield but they were shaken by a fine first half performance from the Welsh team during which they twice struck the woodwork.

Wales deservedly took the lead four minutes into the second half through Dylan Blain. England then took control but it was not until the 74th minute that Paul Honey equalised and, although they in turn struck post and bar three times, the Welsh held out for a 1-1 draw and a share of the Shield with the home side.

INTERNATIONAL CAPS AWARDED TO THE ESFA UNDER 18 SCHOOLBOYS SEASON 2000-01

A	Malaysia	Drew 0-0	**C**	Northern Ireland	Won 1-0	**E**	Scotland	Drew 0-0
B	Singapore	Won 2-0	**D**	Wales	Drew 1-1	**F**	Hungary	Lost 0-2

NAME	A	B	C	D	E	F
Liam Bull (Somerset)	-	1	-	-	-	1
Nathan Jolly (Northumberland)	1	1	1	1	1	1
Andrew Stanford (W Mids)	1	1s	1	1	1	1
Luke Kitchen (Glos)	1+	1+	1+	1+	1+	1+
Richard Pell (Lincs)	1	1	1g	1	1	1
Ben Mortimer (Beds)	-	1	1	1	-	1s
Matthew Kennedy (Shrops)	1s	1	-	-	1s	-
James Thornby (Kent)	1	1g	1s	1	1	1s
Daniel Broxup (Beds)	1s	1	-	-	1s	1

NAME	A	B	C	D	E	F
Alex Porter (Lancs)	1	1s	1	1	1	1
John McGill (Gtr Manch)	1	1s	1	1s	1	-
Tom Griffin (Shrops)	1	1s	-	1s	-	1
Graham Hockless (Humber)	1	1g	1	1	1	1
Paul Honey (Surrey)	1	1	1	1g	1	1
Andrew Grainger (N'berland)	1	-	1	1	1	-
Ross Thompson (Humber)	1s	1	-	-	1	1
William Archer (Gtr Manch)	-	-	1	1	-	-

\+ captain s = substitute g = goalscorer

England Schools' Under 18 International Squad

THE INTER-ASSOCIATION COMPETITIONS

ENGLISH SCHOOLS F.A. HEINZ KETCHUP TROPHY

FINAL	(1st Leg)	Bradford	v	Swindon	1-1	at Bradford City FC
	(2nd Leg)	Swindon	v	Bradford	1-1	at Swindon Town FC

Aggregate 2-2 (Trophy shared)

Bradford's Tom O'Hara and Swindon's Matthew Collins in determined mood during the first leg at the Bradford & Bingley Stadium

When Bradford Under 15's went into a fourth minute lead in the first leg of the final of the premier English Schools' competition, they must have had high hopes of winning the Trophy outright for the first time since 1916. A good move between captain Anthony Doherty and Jarad Peltier ended with Swindon's keeper saving the former's shot but Peltier followed up to score from the rebound. On the stroke of half-time, however, they suffered a blow when Swindon equalised; Justin McKay headed towards goal when Bradford failed to clear a corner and Matthew Axon's attempted clearance hit fellow defender Scott Marsden and rebounded into the net.

The second half saw both sides have chances with Jake Wright and Danny Davis going close for the home side and substitute David Stroud for Swindon. The visitors came closest to breaking the deadlock when James Hambridge hit the post but the sides went into the second leg all square.

At the County Ground, Swindon, it was Bradford's turn to come from behind. In an exciting first half played in torrential rain the highlights were a fantastic save by Daniel Leith in the Swindon goal to deny Doherty and two fine efforts from Hambridge and Chris Taylor for the home side. After the break, a fine header by Scott Ward from Welsh schoolboy international Matthew Collins' corner gave Swindon the lead, but Bradford's determination was rewarded with a fine equaliser from Patrick Carberry. Swindon pressed forward again in a bid to take the Trophy outright and Bradford had keeper James Mann to thank for a superb last minute save from the outstanding Taylor.

Bradford: James Mann, Chris Harris, Luke Richardson, Scott Marsden, Danny Ellis, Ben Kearns, Patrick Carberry, Matthew Axon, Danny Davis, Anthony Doherty, Jarad Peltier, Tom O'Hara, Liam King, Ashley Rosingdale, Jonathan Snowden, Jake Wright, Alex Bluckert.

Swindon: Daniel Leith, Kyle Lapman, Sunny Johal, Matthew Mills, Jack Hazzard, Scott Ward, Matthew Collins, Michael Pook, James Hambridge, Chris Taylor, Liam Barry, Justin McKay, David Stroud, Paddy Slattery, Matthew Gumm, Ian Gill.

Humberside Schools' Under 19 Squad, Winners of the ESFA Inter-County Championship

E.S.F.A./F.A. PREMIER LEAGUE UNDER 19 COUNTY CHAMPIONSHIP

FINAL

Humberside 1 v 0 Gwent

at the Baseball Ground, Derby

Gwent, who like a number of Welsh sides compete in the English Schools' competitions as welcome guests, fielded three members of the Welsh Under 18 squad when they made their first ever appearance in this inter-county final. Humberside, in contrast, were missing one of their two international players. It was the one who did play, Graham Hockless from Hull, who played a crucial part in the goal which settled a closely fought and high quality game seven minutes from time. His pass was collected by another Hull student, Michael Smith, whose cross shot found the far corner of the net to bring Humberside their first success in this competition since 1982.

E.S.F.A./F.A. PREMIER LEAGUE UNDER 16 COUNTY CHAMPIONSHIP

FINAL

Merseyside 1 v 0 Oxfordshire

after extra time, at the Baseball Ground, Derby

Merseyside, despite some indiscipline which saw won of their players sent off, won the Under 16 title for the first time since 1990 when two stars of the future, Robbie Fowler and David Beckham, were on opposing sides as they defeated Essex. Oxfordshire can consider themselves fortunate, as near the end of normal time Michael Alexis had a header cleared off the line. The same player had the ball in the net early in the second half but his effort was ruled out for offside. Merseyside eventually won the game with a goal from Drew Hyland five minutes from the end of the second period of extra time.

E.S.F.A. UNITED NORWEST CO-OP UNDER 16 GIRLS' COUNTY CHAMPIONSHIP

FINAL

Shropshire 3 v 1 Hampshire

at Ewood Park, Blackburn

Hampshire, appearing in their third successive final, were looking for a hat-trick of wins in the competition but were thwarted by a committed Shropshire squad who produced a first ever success for the county at any national level. Shropshire kep the talented Hampshire side at bay in the early stages and then took the lead through Sally Jones midway through the first half. Jones then missed from the spot early in the second half but made amends when she tapped in after a good lay-off from Zoe Carter Rix to make it 2-0. Shropshire went further ahead fifteen minutes from time when a long throw was nodded and Gemma Moss converted from six yards and although Hampshire scored a late consolation effort, Shropshire held out easily enough.

Hampshire Schools' Under 16 Squad, Runners Up in the Under 16 Girls' Championship

E.S.F.A. ADIDAS PREDATOR PREMIER UNDER 11 7-A-SIDE CHAMPIONSHIP

FINAL

Luton 2 v 1 Oxford

THE INDIVIDUAL SCHOOLS' COMPETITIONS

E.S.F.A. GENIE UK UNDER 19 INDIVIDUAL SCHOOLS' CHAMPIONSHIP

FINAL

St Cuthberts High School (Newcastle) 1 v 0 Southend High School for Boys
at The Hawthorns, West Bromwich

A remarkable series of coincidences marked St Cuthbert's first ever outright victory in the oldest of the ESFA Individual Schools' competitions. For Team Manager Dave Stapylton it marked a hat-trick of successes. In 1970, he played as an 18 year old in the team that shared the Trophy with St Michael's College (Leeds) and then in 1981 managed the St Cuthbert's squad who drew in the final with Clapham College (Inner London).

In the recent final, the school's centre half was Ben Summers whose father, Doug, played in the 1981 game; another member of that side was John Carver, now first team coach at Newcastle United, who went back to his former school to present the current squad with their Trophy at a special assembly to mark the occasion. That assembly was overseen by the Headteacher of St Cuthbert's whose son, Chis Murphy, as captain of the side received the Genie Cup. Murphy had an additional reason for pride as he had scored the winning goal in the final.

A soggy pitch made good football difficult but St Cuthbert's bypassed the conditions as early as the tenth minute when Murphy volleyed in at the far post from a floated free kick by Clark Keltie. Since David McArtney had already headed against the bar, St Cuthbert's deserved to take the lead, but it took some good defensive play after the interval from Dryden, Summers and McBride to keep Southend High School at bay.

The St Cuthbert's winning side is pictured as follows: Back Row (l-r): Chris Murphy (capt), David McCartney, Ben Summers, Mick Clennel, Kris McBride, Karl Dryden, Aidan Ames, Martin Johnson, Lee Oliver, Andrew McCartney. Front Row: Michael Sutcliffe, Kevin Walker, Michael Dixon, Clark Keltie, Neil Burke, Craig Johnson, Alex Cook, Stephen Johnson, Mr David Stapylton (Team Manager)

E.S.F.A. GENIE UK UNDER 19 SCHOOLS AND COLLEGES CUP

FINAL

West Suffolk College (Bury St Edmunds) 2 v 1 Ridge Danyers College (Stockport)
at The Hawthorns, West Bromwich

West Suffolk College was only founded in 1999, so it has taken them only two years to make their mark on the English Schools' scene. They came into the final having suffered the disappointment of losing in the semi-final of the British Colleges Cup to Solihull College of the West Midlands and made a slow start to the Genie Final. Andy Hill in the West Suffolk goal did well on a number of occasions and it was largely thanks to his efforts that the first half was goalless. After the break, however, the Bury side had the boost of a first minute goal when Tom Smith's cross from the left was met by man of the match Alex Harrison, who fired home. Ridge Danyers' outstanding player, Dwaine Lyndsay, continued to trouble the West Suffolk defence and three times went close as the game ebbed and flowed. Midway through the half, however, West Suffolk doubled their lead when a slick passing move put Marc Wake clear on the right and his teasing cross was turned into his own net by full back Ben Webber.

Ridge Danyers then showed their spirit and, despite the disappointment of a disallowed effort, reduced the deficit with ten minutes remaining when a powerful shot squirmed under goalkeeper Hill. That set up a grand finale with all eleven Ridge Danyers going forward for corners and throw-ins. West Suffolk somehow survived the pressure and held on for a famous victory.

The winning squad was: Andy Hill, Dale Jones, Jon Oman, Paul Allen, David Proctor, Lee Sim, Matt Curtis, Ian Miller, Alex Harrison, Marc Wake, Tom Smith, Stephen Roberts, Colin Kent, Bradley Rudd, Jon Thorgood, Paul Snowdon

E.S.F.A. SCHOOLSNET UNDER 16 CHAMPIONSHIP

FINAL

Kingsdown School (Swindon) 4 v 1 Cardinal Heenan School (Liverpool)
at Highfield Road, Coventry

Two years ago, Kingsdown School went down 2-0 to Cardinal Newman School from Luton in the first ever Heinz Ketchup Cup final and left Highbury extremely disappointed. This time there was only joy and excitement as they deservedly and convincingly won the Schoolsnet Cup at Highfield Road. They made a dream start with a goal after only six minutes when Kenny Hawkins volleyed in from close range after a flick on from Ross Adams and, although the first half was even, there was greater pattern to Kingsdown's play.

It thus came as little surprise when Ross Adams doubled their lead early in the second half when he out-jumped Heenan's keeper, Steven Smith, to nod in a looping ball. Heenan's hopes were raised four minutes later when Kristian Hall headed in past Hanley in Kingsdown's goal. The Swindon school soon regained their two goal advantage as Aidan Doyle dispossessed a defender on the half way line, ran on and squared the ball to Ross Saville, who had an easy chance to make it 3-1.

This setback seemed to upset some of the Cardinal Heenan players and, as they began to lose their discipline, Kingsdown took full advantage and, after Adams had beaten three men only to stab his shot wide, he made no mistake in the next attack and calmly lobbed over Smith to confirm his side's victory.

The winning Kingsdown squad

E.S.F.A. UNITED NORWEST CO-OP UNDER 16 GIRLS' CUP

FINAL

Bridgnorth Endowed School (Shropshire) 2 v 1 Castle Manor School (Suffolk)
at Gay Meadow, Shrewsbury Town FC

Five of the players who helped Shropshire to win the inter-county title had a double taste of success when Bridgnorth School beat Castle Manor School in a dramatic final. Bridgnorth did things the hard way as they conceded a penalty after only four minutes; keeper Lucy Higgins saved Aimee Rawlings' spot kick but Rawlings netted the rebound. To compound Bridgnorth's misery, Dany Drummond who conceded the penalty was sent off for her offence leaving her school with only ten players for the remainder of the game.

Their re-organised side bravely drew level just before half time through skipper Faye Seeley and then in the second half Gemma Moss, who had scored one of the Shropshire goals in their success at Blackburn, scored the winner for Bridgnorth.

Squads:
Bridgnorth: Lucy Higgins, Katherine Renke, Nicola Puechel, Sally Hinton, Faye Seeley, Dany Drummond, Charlotte Beaman, Beth Jeavons, Zowie Williams, Gemma Moss, Zoe Rix, Carrie Drummond, Nicola Pike, Kate Wall.
Castle Manor: Stacey Spiers, Amie Carr, Fiona Austin, Clare Skinner, Charlene Roach, Zoe Klimicke, Hayley Shaddick, Sam Lovell, Aimee Rawlings, Charlotte Halls, Katie Archer, Zoe Coote, Anna Page

The girls from Bridgnorth Endowed School celebrate their triumph in the English Schools' FA United Co-op Under 16 Cup. They are seen with their rewards and Shrewsbury Town mascot Lennie the Lion.

E.S.F.A. HEINZ KETCHUP UNDER 14 CUP

FINAL

Barlow High School (East Didsbury)	2	v	1	Forest Hill School (Lewisham)

at Stamford Bridge

Birthday boy Daniel Heffernan scored both goals as Barlow High School completed their marathon season by winning the Heinz Ketchup Cup. The game was virtually decided in the first fifteen minutes as Barlow made a storming start. Patrick McFadden, top scorer in the competition with fourteen goals, twice went close in the opening minutes but it was his diminutive colleague Heffernan, who took the honours on this occasion. After eleven minutes he half-volleyed his side ahead and three minutes later he had the simplest of tasks to tap home a cross from McFadden to make it 2-0.

Forest Hill's slow start proved their downfall as they dominated the latter stages of the first period and most of the second. A fine goal ten minutes from half time by Lewis James brought them back into the game, but despite the efforts of captain Anthony Grant, who led by example, and fine efforts from Kelvin Sankoh and Ryan Moore, they couldn't convert their pressure into goals and a gallant Barlow defence held on for a narrow victory.

E.S.F.A. ADIDAS PREDATOR UNDER 11 6-A-SIDE CHAMPIONSHIP

SEMI-FINALS

Cranbourne School (Hertfordshire)	3	v	0	Lyndhurst School (Hampshire)
Talbot School (West Yorkshire)	0	v	0	Lord Scudamore School (Herefordshire)

(Talbot won on corners)

FINAL

Cranbourne School	1	v	1	Talbot Primary School

Trophy shared

THE E.S.F.A. WAGON WHEELS UNDER 12 INDOOR 5-A-SIDE CUPS

BOY'S FINAL

Springfield School (Portsmouth)	2	v	1	George Stephenson School (North Tyneside)

GIRL'S FINAL

All Hallows R.C. High School (Macclesfield)	1	v	4	All Saints R.C. High School (Kirkby-Knowlsley)

E.S.F.A. CAPRI SUN SOCCER SIXES (SMALL PRIMARY SCHOOLS)

SEMI-FINALS

Clarborough School (Nottinghamshire)	2	v	1	Our Lady of the Rosary School (Cumbria)
Englefield School (Berkshire)	0	v	2	Farcet School (Cambridgeshire)

FINAL

Clarborough School	1	v	0	Farcet School

CHANNEL ISLANDS REVIEW

THE SEASON

The highlight of the season was unquestionably Guernsey's gold medal at the prestigious Island Games. The Sarnians stuttered to a less than flattering 3-0 win over the Faithful Islands in their first game and then defeated the hosts, Isle of Man, 3-2 to qualify for the semi-finals, where they beat Isle of Wight. In the final, Guernsey were held to a 0-0 draw by Ynys Mon but won the subsequent penalty shoot out 3-1 to record the most memorable achievement in the 108-year history of the Guernsey Football Association.

Guernsey also won last season's showcase domestic event, the Muratti Vase, with an impressive 4-1 victory over neighbours Jersey. After beating Alderney 6-0 in the semi-final, Matt Falla (2), Micky Smith and Gavin Le Page scored Guernsey's goals in the final at The Track. Jersey now lead the series 42-40.

In the Priaulx League, Sylvans were crowned champions for the eighth successive year. They were pushed hard by St Martins, who only finished three points behind, but their almost impenetrable defending (Sylvans only conceded twelve goals in eighteen league games) ensured them another championship.

In spite of another good domestic season, Sylvans were beaten in an early round of the Hampshire Senior Cup. They did defeat Alton Town 3-0 in the First Round, but were then eliminated in the next stage, losing 2-1 to Moneyfields early in November.

Sylvans were also somewhat humiliated in the Upton Park Trophy (Channel Islands Club Championship). Chasing their first win in the competition since 1998, Guernsey's champions were beaten 5-0 by St Peter of Jersey, who lifted their first ever 'Upton'.

Adie Exall of Sylvans was the season's top goalscorer. He found the net 50 times and thus joined a very select band of local players to reach a half-century in one season.

In other inter-insular football, Guernsey and Jersey shared the honours with two wins apiece. Guernsey won the Under 21 Muratti 2-1 and maintained their 100 per cent record in the Ladies' Muratti by the same scoreline. Jersey retained the Junior Muratti, beating Guernsey 6-2, and won the Star Trophy (Under 15 Schoolboy Muratti) 1-0.

Guernsey's Northerners and Jersey's St Peter won the two big inter-island knock out club competitions. Northerners defeated Sylvans 6-5 on penalties (3-3 after extra time) to win their first Jeremie Cup since 1991 and St Peter beat St Martins 5-2 in the Wheway Cup.

The Stranger Cup, Guernsey's most important cup competition, was won by Northerners for the second successive year and for the sixteenth time overall. They beat Sylvans 1-0 in a close final. Vale Rec, who won the cup seventeen times in eighteen seasons during their golden years of the 1970s and 80s, were again eliminated in the First Round.

At the end of the season, champions Sylvans were left looking for their fifth manager in three years as Alan Le Prevost walked away from the hottest seat in Guernsey football. After an exhausting search for a new manager, Sylvans appointed Rovers' assistant manager Richard Packman to take charge. Packman is a former Egham Town player and coach.

North, too, now have a new manager. They have appointed Geoff Tardif, who in recent years has coached their highly successful youth side, to succeed Mac Gallienne who resigned before the season was out.

Matt Fallaize

GUERNSEY FINAL LEAGUE TABLES 2000-01

PRIAULX LEAGUE

(1st Team)

DIVISION 1	P	W	D	L	F	A	Pts
Sylvans	18	15	0	3	78	12	45
St Martins	18	13	3	2	64	20	42
Northerners	18	11	2	5	56	21	35
Vale REC	18	11	1	6	41	23	34
Belgraves	18	6	0	12	17	43	18
Rovers	18	1	2	15	11	79	5
Rangers	18	1	2	15	12	81	5

JACKSON LEAGUE

(Reserves)

	P	W	D	L	F	A	Pts
Northerners	18	14	1	3	77	19	43
Vale REC	18	11	4	3	60	19	37
St Martins	18	9	5	4	43	24	32
Sylvans	18	8	3	7	45	31	27
Belgraves	18	5	2	11	32	69	17
Rangers	18	5	0	13	27	83	15
Rovers	18	2	3	13	20	59	9

RAILWAY LEAGUE

(3rd Team)

	P	W	D	L	F	A	Pts
Port City	18	14	2	2	91	15	44
Sylvans	18	13	2	3	65	20	41
Bavaria Nomads	18	10	4	4	62	24	34
Northerners	18	10	2	6	64	38	32
Vale REC	18	10	1	7	62	35	31
St Martins	18	8	2	8	49	46	26
Police	18	5	4	9	38	63	19
Belgraves	18	5	1	12	36	59	16
Rovers	18	4	21	12	28	69	14
Rangers	18	1	0	17	14	140	3

CHANNEL ISLANDS CUP FINALS

MURATTI VASE

Guernsey 4 v 1 Jersey

UNDER 21 MURATTI

Guernsey 2 v 1 Jersey

JUNIOR MURATTI

Jersey 6 v 2 Guernsey

STAR TROPHY

Guernsey 0 v 1 Jersey

LADIES MURATTI

Guernsey 2 v 1 Jersey

CARLSBERG VICTORY CUP

Guernsey 1 v 0 Assa Valle du Dropt

MALAYA CUP

Guernsey 4 v 1 Naval Air Command

COMMODORE FERRIES CUP

Guernsey 0 v 0 Royal Navy

Guernsey won 3-2 after penalties

UPTON PARK CUP

St Peter (J) 5 v 0 Sylvans (G)

PORTSMOUTH TROPHY

St Martins (G) 0 v 2 St Pauls (J)

JOHN LEATT MEMORIAL TROPHY

First Tower (J) 0 v 2 Northerners

JEREMIE CUP

Northerners 3 v 3 Sylvans

Northerners won 6-5 after penalties

WHEWAY CUP

St Peter (J) 5 v 2 St Martin

STRANGER CUP

Northerners 1 v 0 Sylvans

JERSEY BRITISH EUROPEAN FOOTBALL COMBINATION

DIVISION ONE	P	W	D	L	F	A	Pts
St Peter	18	17	1	0	65	8	52
St Paul's	18	12	3	3	50	22	39
Scottish	18	11	4	3	64	17	37
First Tower	18	10	1	7	39	21	31
Magpies	18	9	2	7	25	27	29
Wanderers	18	9	1	8	41	39	28
Trinity	18	8	2	8	37	32	26
St Martin	18	4	1	13	21	46	13
Rozel Rovers	18	1	1	16	9	85	4
Sp Academics	18	1	0	17	16	70	3

DIVISION TWO	P	W	D	L	F	A	Pts
St John	16	12	3	1	50	13	39
Grouville	16	11	4	1	40	15	37
Portuguese	16	8	4	4	40	26	28
St Clement	16	6	4	6	34	31	22
SCF	16	5	3	8	22	44	18
St Ouen	16	5	2	9	35	36	17
St Brelade	16	5	2	9	31	38	17
Beeches OB	16	5	1	10	27	42	16
St Lawrence	16	3	1	12	21	55	10

The Jersey team before their successful Bronze medal match against the Isle of Wight
Photo: Gordon Whittington

Sportslines

MATCH REPORTS, BREAKING NEWS AND RESULTS ACROSS THE PYRAMID.

FA Competitions	**09066 555 888**	**Unibond League Newsline**	**09066 555 800**	**Non-League Fixture Line**	**09066 555 950**
Ryman League Newsline	**09066 555 777**	**Dr Martens League ClubCall**	**09068 121 151**	**Womens Football Line**	**09066 555 871**

NATIONWIDE CONFERENCE

Barnet	09068 121 544	Farnborough Town	09068 440 088	Scarborough	09068 121 650
Boston United	09068 121 539	Hayes	09066 555 968	Southport	09066 555 875
Chester City	09068 121 633	Hereford United	09068 121 645	Stevenage Borough	09066 555 959
Dagenham & Redbridge	09066 555 840	Margate	09068 800 665	Telford United	09066 555 982
Doncaster Rovers	09068 121 651	Morecambe	09066 555 966	Woking	09066 555 070
Dover	09066 555 801	Nuneaton Borough	09066 555 848	Yeovil Town	09066 555 850

DR MARTENS LEAGUE

Ashford Town	09066 555 854	Grantham Town	09066 555 975	Rugby United	09066 555 971
Atherstone United	09066 555 905	Gresley Rovers	09066 555 978	Salisbury	09066 555 864
Banbury United	09066 555 906	Halesowen Town	09066 555 818	Stafford Rangers	09066 555 976
Bromsgrove Rovers	09066 555 860	Hastings Town	09066 555 879	Stamford	09066 555 989
Chippenham Town	09066 555 919	Hednesford Town	09066 555 880	Tamworth	09066 555 842
Clevedon Town	09066 555 942	Ilkeston Town	09066 555 980	Tiverton Town	09066 555 876
Corby Town	09066 555 899	Kettering Town	09068 101 567	Welling United	09068 800 654
Crawley Town	09066 555 984	Kings Lynn	09066 555 802	Weymouth	09066 555 830
Dartford	09066 555 846	Moor Green	09066 555 962	Wisbech Town	09066 555 865
Eastbourne Borough	09066 555 894	Rothwell Town	09066 555 829	Worcester City	09066 555 810
Evesham United	09066 555 863				

RYMAN LEAGUE

Aldershot Town	09066 555 855	Chesham United	09068 335 505	Kingstonian	09066 555 965
Aylesbury United	09066 555 811	Croydon Athletic	09066 555 789	Leatherhead	09066 555 861
Basingstoke Town	09066 555 828	Croydon F.C.	09066 555 024	Leyton Pennant	09066 555 819
Bedford Town	09066 555 843	Enfield	09066 555 845	Maidenhead United	09066 555 813
Billericay Town	09066 555 949	Epsom & Ewell	09066 555 916	Purfleet	09066 555 895
Bishops Stortford	09066 555 873	Gravesend & Northfleet	09066 555 844	Romford	09066 555 841
Borehamwood	09066 555 912	Hampton	09066 555 814	Slough Town	09066 555 956
Braintree Town	09066 555 887	Harlow Town	09066 555 889	St Albans City	09066 555 822
Bromley	09066 555 838	Hendon	09066 555 836	Staines Town	09066 555 907
Canvey Island	09066 555 886	Hitchin Town	09066 555 817	Sutton United	09068 121 537
Carshalton Athletic	09066 555 877				

UNIBOND LEAGUE

Altrincham	09066 555 902	Burton Albion	09066 555 883	Hyde United	09066 555 787
Barrow	09066 555 820	Guiseley	09066 555 839	Workington	09066 555 851
Bradford Park Avenue	09066 555 852	Hucknall Town	09066 555 951	Worksop Town	09066 555 977

Eagle Bitter United Counties League		**Rich City Sussex County League**		**Jewson Wessex League**	
Buckingham Town	09066 555 974	East Grinstead	09066 555 823	Fareham Town	09066 555 874
St. Neots Town	09066 555 917				
Hampshire League		**Screwfix Direct League**		**North West Counties League**	
Poole Town	09066 555 884	Taunton Town	09066 555 849	Clitheroe	09066 555 979
Schweppes Essex Senior League					
Enfield Town	09066 555 908				

OTHER LEAGUES & ASSOCIATIONS

Bexley & District League	09066 555 781	Croydon Sunday League	09066 555 862	Sutton Coldfield & District League	09066 555 784
Camberley Sunday League	09066 555 809	Gravesend Boys League	09066 555 869	Tandridge Junior League	09066 555 795
Coronation League	09066 555 859	Kent Schools FA	09066 555 928		

A Quote Insurance Reading Football League	09066 555 868	Eagle Bitter United Counties League	09066 555 885	Midland Combination	09066 555 882
Albany Northern League	09068 121 542	Essex & Herts Border Combination	09066 555 903	Midland Football Alliance	09066 555 866
Bank's Brewery League	09066 555 872	Herts Senior County League	09066 555 832	Minerva Spartan South Midlands League	09066 555 881
Bass Brewers Kent League	09066 555 856	Jewson Eastern Counties League	09068 121 543	North West Counties League	09066 555 944
Cherry Red Records Hellenic League	09066 555 812	Jewson Wessex League	09066 555 870	Screwfix Direct League	09066 555 825
				West Lancashire League	09066 555 831

GENERATE REVENUE FOR YOUR CLUB, LEAGUE OR ASSOCIATION WITH YOUR OWN PREMIUM RATE LINE.
CALL DAVE BODDY ON 01386 550 204 NOW!

On ITV p524

Sportslines ClubCall, Avalon House,
57-63 Scrutton Street, London EC2A 4PJ.
Calls cost 60p per min.

ISLE OF MAN REVIEW

ISLE OF MAN FOOTBALL SEASON 2000-01

Peel continued to keep their place at the top of Manx Football when they won the Division One Title for the second successive season. During the year they were challenged strongly by the St Mary's and Douglas High School Old Boys outfits but the strength in depth of the Western club, who were helped by the experience of former Oldham and Manchester City man Rick Holden, kept Peel ahead.

A number of the Peel players deservedly achieved Island International status during the season and Steve Corkill and Chris Cain were highly rated in the Player of the Year Poll which was won by Chris Higgins.

Peel's new signing Tony Duggan was among the goalscorers, but he and everyone else could not match the superb striking rate of Peter Langridge from the Saints who again won the Golden Boot. St Mary's gained some reward for their season when they won the FA Cup whilst Rushen United, under new manager John Ward, were delighted to take the Hospital Cup where they just outlasted Laxey.

The season was somewhat dominated by the weather, which caused a lot of postponements and a rule change in that no replays were allowed in Cup Competitions, just extra time and penalties. For a long while St George's looked favourites for the drop but in the end they were well clear of two more Douglas sides in Corinthians and Union Mills, who face the coming season in Division Two.

It was a great year for the North in the Second Division as Ayre United go up as champions and they will be joined by Ramsey, whose ground is now probably the best of the local clubs. Ayre added the Woods Cup to their trophies but Colby, who just missed out on promotion, gained some recompense when they won the Paul Henry Knockout Cup.

The Isle of Man side had a disappointing year in that they finished bottom in the Statoil Cup behind Scotland, Northern Ireland and the Irish Republic, after winning it the previous year. They then failed to win a medal in the Island Games and didn't score a goal in the Summer Festival which Wrexham eventually won.

There was, however, a good form shown by the Under 18s who won well in the County Youth Cup, whilst in the Under 17 League it could hardly have been closer with goals scored in the last game ultimately giving Union Mills the title over Peel.

Finally, one big success was Ladies Football with the girls, who only started twelve months ago winning their first game 5-1 over Anglesey and losing out 3-2 to Guernsey in the Bronze Medal Playoff in the Island Games. There are now thirteen Ladies teams on the Island and they will be looking for more competition in the coming year.

Dave Phillips, Manx Sport Information Services

FINAL LEAGUE TABLES 2000-01

DIVISION ONE	P	W	D	L	F	A	Pts
Peel	24	19	3	2	92	25	60
St Marys	24	16	5	3	92	32	53
DHSOB	24	16	3	5	80	46	51
Marown	24	12	8	4	56	37	44
Rushen United	24	11	8	5	55	36	41
Pulrose United	24	12	3	9	82	56	39
Laxey	24	11	5	8	61	55	38
Castletown	24	8	2	14	54	64	26
Gymns	24	7	3	14	53	93	24
Douglas Royal	24	7	2	15	53	63	23
St Georges	24	5	5	14	37	110	20
Corinthians	24	3	5	16	32	77	11
Union Mills	24	2	2	20	35	88	8

DIVISION TWO	P	W	D	L	F	A	Pts
Ayre United	26	23	1	2	100	26	70
Ramsey	26	20	3	3	100	31	63
Colby	26	20	2	4	117	35	62
Foxdale	26	18	1	7	83	45	55
Police	26	16	3	7	110	63	51
Braddan	26	14	3	9	75	61	45
St Johns	26	13	1	12	84	67	40
RYCOB	26	10	2	14	65	68	32
Malew	26	8	2	16	46	78	26
Michael	26	7	4	15	44	60	25
Ronaldsway	26	8	3	15	55	66	24
Barclays	26	5	2	19	54	109	17
Onchan	26	4	4	18	42	102	16
Jurby	26	0	1	25	21	185	1

MANX CUP FINALS

RAILWAY CUP	St Mary's	v	Peel	3-0
F.A. CUP	St Mary's	v	Ayre United	3-0
HOSPITAL CUP	Rushden	v	Laxey	3-2
WOODS CUP	Ayre	v	Foxdale	3-0
PAUL HENRY TROPHY	Colby	v	Ayre	1-0
ALAN HAWLEY TROPHY	DHSOB	v	Union Mills	4-1

THE NATWEST ISLAND GAMES

The 11th Island Games saw 2,100 athletes from as far afield as the Falklands and Rhodes converge on the Isle of Man. First staged in 1985 as the Little Island Games, this multi-sport event is staged biennially, and this year there were 22 islands competing in 15 different sports. And some small islands had teams which are not large enough to even form a football side - Froya (Norway) had two in their team and nearer home, Sark had seven.

After the opening ceremony attended by the Earl and Countess of Wessex, the men's football competition kicked off the following day with twelve teams in four groups of three. Group winners became semi-finalists to determine the medals, while the second-placed teams played off among themselves and similarly the bottom-placed teams. This meant that every team had four games in six days.

GROUP 1	*W*	*D*	*L*	*F*	*A*	*Pts*
Ynys Mon	1	1	0	5	2	4
Shetland	1	1	0	4	3	4
Saameraa	0	0	2	3	7	0

GROUP 2	*W*	*D*	*L*	*F*	*A*	*Pts*
Jersey	2	0	0	14	1	6
Gibraltar	1	0	1	3	2	3
Orkney	0	0	2	0	14	0

GROUP 3	*W*	*D*	*L*	*F*	*A*	*Pts*
I. of Wight	1	1	0	4	1	4
Rhodes	1	0	1	3	4	3
Greenland	0	1	1	0	2	1

GROUP 4	*W*	*D*	*L*	*F*	*A*	*Pts*
Guernsey	2	0	0	6	2	6
I. of Man	1	0	1	11	3	3
Falklands	0	0	2	0	12	0

SEMI-FINALS

Ynys Mon 2 v 2 Jersey aet

Ynys Mon won 6-5 after penalties

Isle of Wight 2 v 3 Guernsey

FINAL

Ynys Mon 0 v 0 Guernsey aet

Guernsey won 3-1 after penalties

Below: We've struck gold! Guernsey savour the moment with keeper hero Jody Bisson to the fore. Photo: Gordon Whittington

Orkney, eventual wooden spoonists

Saaremaa line up before their opening game.

Shetland pose for the cameras in sunny Port Erin before their opening game.

The Isle of Wight team before their Bronze medal game against Jersey.

Photos: Gordon Whittington

A dramatic substitution! Gibralter's Roy Chipolina's first touch wasto flick a corner onto the cross bar, the second to head home the rebound. He added another later as Gibralter beat Orkney 2-0.

Jan Renouf nets Guernsey's equaliser making the score 2-2 midway through the second half against the Isle of Wight. A dramatic last minute winner put them through to the Final.

Ynys Mon (Anglesey) line up before the Final.

Guernsey and Ynys Mon reach the Final with Ynys Mon on the attack.

Photos: Gordon Whittington

WOMEN'S FOOTBALL

Compiled by Jen O'Neill
Editor of She Kicks Magazine (www.shekicks.net)

2000/2001 IN REVIEW

The first full season of the new millennium was a record breaking one for women's football. The number of players shot up to 55,000 (The F.A., July 01) and crowd records for both an international and a domestic match were broken. England's vital Euro play-off against Ukraine at Leyton Orient pulled in over 7,000 fans and the all London FA Cup Final clash between Arsenal and Fulham attracted over 13,000 supporters.

Off the pitch, Fulham, the nation's first professional women's football side helped the continuing rise in media attention for the sport, while on the field it was Arsenal who deserved all of the plaudits with a stunning treble winning effort.

After a successful domestic season, attention turned to the national team as Hope Powell's England squad travelled to Germany to take part in their first major tournament finals for five years. Football aficionados were not surprised when the hosts claimed their third successive European title in front of a packed Donaustadion in Ulm.

Sue Smith hit all four goals for Tranmere in the Premier League Cup semi final as Rovers recorded their first ever win against rivals Everton 4-2, to confirm their first appearance in a major final.

Young Player of the Year, Kate Chapman, had a great season for club (Fulham) and country

AXA F.A. WOMEN'S CUP

QUARTER-FINALS

Fulham 5 v 0 Barnet
at Motspur Park

Arsenal 1 v 0 Doncaster Belles
at Borehamwood FC

Southampton Sts 3 v 2 Charlton Athletic
at AFC Totton

Bristol Rovers 1 v 0 Aston Villa
at Bristol Rovers FC

SEMI-FINALS

Fulham 5 v 0 Southampton Saints
at Kingstonians FC

Fulham's professionals had a 5-0 lead and their place booked in the final by half time. Sanchia Duncan scored a brace, an own goal followed, then Norwegian international Margunn Haugenes and Deena Rahman hit one each. Saints defended in numbers after the break to leave the second half goalless.

Bristol Rovers 0 v 3 Arsenal
at Bristol Rovers FC. Attendance: 3,306

Fifteen shots rained down on the Rovers goal before half time but a combination of woeful shooting and good goal-keeping kept the scoresheet blank. Angela Banks finally broke the deadlock on 65 mins after being put clear. Ten minutes later the game was sealed when Banks pulled the ball back for Jayne Ludlow to finish. Ciara Grant made it 3-0 after latching on to a loose ball in the box. The South West Combination League winners, Rovers, never gave up the fight but made little headway against the Gunners' defence.

FINAL

Arsenal 1- v 0 Fulham
at Crystal Palace FC. Attendance: 13,824

In a clash that pitched Arsenal's amateurs against Fulham, the first professional side in the women's game in England, it was the old order that won through against the new as the fitness and play on display took the women's game a new level.
Fulham, the less experienced on the big stage showed early nerves, but finished stronger in a first half that saw chances at both ends. Arsenal threatened Jody Bowry's goal on the half hour when Kirsty Pealling's cross bounced off Clare Wheatley's back and onto the cross bar.

As Arsenal began to tire a little, Fulham began to press the Gunners into their own half. Eventually their pressure had seemed to pay dividends when Margunn Haugenes' shot from the edge of the area was palmed onto the post by Emma Byrne and Sanchia Duncan followed in and knocked the rebound home. However the referee's assistant raised her flag to give a dubious offside decision against her.

Just two minutes into the second half, Carol Harwood blatantly brought down the speedy Marianne Pettersen inside the box as she broke clear. Harwood was fortunate not to be shown red and EIRE international Byrne was equal to Haugenes' decently struck spot kick, diving to her right to brilliantly turn it wide and again deny the South Londoners the lead.

Fulham were punished for their profligacy when Spacey hit a trademark rasping strike from just over 20 yards out. The rebound off the bar fell to Angela Banks who found space to turn and pulled her left foot shot back across goal to beat Bowry for a 1-0 lead on 52 minutes.
Fulham pushed forward but were ultimately unable to breach the Arsenal back line and the North Londoners held on for a fine victory in a tense match.

Arsenal: (3-5-2) E Byrne – C Harwood, F White, C Stoney - K Pealling, J Ludlow, S Williams, C Grant, C Wheatley – M Spacey (E Maggs, 82 mins), A Banks. Subs not used: L Higgs, S Wooliscroft, C Thorpe, Y Tracy.
Fulham: (4-4-2) J Bowry – R Gibbons, K Petersen, M Phillip, K Jerray-Silver – S Duncan (L R Mork, 77 mins), K Chapman, R McArthur (D Rahman, 81 mins), R Yankey - M Haugenes, M Pettersen. Subs not used: L Young, J Hynes, L Betts.

Referee: Mr. T Parkes
Cautions: S Williams (Arsenal, 20 mins); R Yankey (Fulham, 26 mins); C Harwood (47 mins); K Chapman (56 mins).

Arsenal's Emma Byrne turns Margunn Haugenes' FA Cup Final penalty around the upright.

Angela Banks fires in the FA Cup winner

AXA F.A. WOMEN'S PREMIER LEAGUE 2000-01

FINAL LEAGUE TABLES

NATIONAL DIVISION

	P	W	D	L	F	A	Pts
Arsenal LFC	18	17	1	0	88	9	52
Doncaster Belles LFC	18	15	0	3	58	13	45
Charlton Athletic WFC	18	10	5	3	43	11	35
Everton LFC	18	11	2	5	42	24	35
Tranmere Rovers LFC	18	9	1	8	42	39	28
Barry Town LFC	18	7	2	9	22	39	23
Sunderland AFC	18	5	1	12	29	50	16
Southampton Snts WFC	18	3	6	9	27	52	15
Millwall Lionesses LFC	18	3	2	13	17	55	8
Liverpool LFC	18	0	0	18	13	89	0

Arsenal are Champions, Millwall are relegated to the Southern Division, Liverpool go down to the Northern Division.

NORTHERN DIVISION

	P	W	D	L	F	A	Pts
Leeds United	22	18	2	2	75	18	56
Oldham Curzon LFC	22	17	2	3	61	25	53
Aston Villa LFC	22	12	5	5	52	37	41
Bangor City LFC	22	10	7	5	43	27	37
Wolverhampton W LFC	22	12	1	9	47	42	37
Birmingham City LFC	22	9	5	8	50	42	32
Ilkeston Town LFC	22	8	5	9	39	39	29
Garswood Saints	22	8	1	13	41	60	25
Sheffield Wednesday	22	7	3	12	30	53	24
Coventry City LFC	22	4	5	13	23	48	17
Newcastle Town LFC	22	4	3	15	28	62	15
Huddersfield Town	22	3	1	18	15	51	10

Leeds United are promoted to the National, Newcastle Town are relegated to the Midlands Combination and Huddersfield Town go down into the Northern Combination.

SOUTHERN DIVISION

	P	W	D	L	F	A	Pts
Brighton & Hove Albion	22	18	2	2	56	15	56
Chelsea LFC	22	17	4	1	66	24	55
Wimbledon LFC	22	15	2	5	56	31	47
Barnet LFC	22	13	3	6	66	33	42
Langford LFC	22	12	3	7	47	30	39
Ipswich Town LFC	22	8	3	11	47	57	27
Berkhamsted Town LFC	22	8	1	13	40	51	25
Barking LFC	22	8	0	14	52	54	24
Newport County LFC	22	7	2	13	33	44	23
Wembley Mill Hill LFC	22	6	2	14	35	64	20
Cardiff City LFC	22	6	0	16	32	60	18
Reading Royals LFC	22	2	2	18	25	92	8

Brighton & HA are promoted to the National, both Cardiff City and Reading Royals are relegated into the South West Combination (this is made possible by Chesham United moving across to the South East Combination).

NATIONAL DIVISION REVIEW

Arsenal dominated from the outset. In the three previous season they had suffered early slip ups which had cost them the prize they had not won since 1997 but as the weather, internationals and cup competitions all conspired to interrupt the league programme Arsenal marched on. Doncaster Belles were always their nearest rivals though their challenge was virtually finished when they lost the first of their two league clashes against the Gunners (who also knocked them out of both cup competitions). Charlton Athletic (formerly Croydon WFC) charged into third late on, as they caught up after their delayed start. Everton were not far behind and Tranmere Rovers and surprisingly promoted Barry Town were happily mid-table. The other promoted side Sunderland and Southampton fought off relegation, while Millwall and Liverpool saw their 10 years in the top flight come to an end.

NORTHERN DIVISION REVIEW

Leeds set the early pace their involvement in cup competitions let Oldham Curzon (in their debut season at this level) ahead in terms of points and games played. As the other chasing teams like Bangor, Wolves and Villa were plagued by inconsistency this narrowed the battle for promotion to the two top teams. In the end, Leeds showed their experience, strength of their squad and stayed focused until eventually overtaking Oldham to claim the title.

SOUTHERN DIVISION REVIEW

This was an exciting affair with the weather disrupting fixtures and several strong sides suggesting they might claim the one promotion spot. The extra incentive spurring teams on to try and win the league this time around was the knowledge that professional side Fulham would be the competition for the title in the following season. Brighton were favourites from the outset having just missed out, late on, in the two previous campaigns. Wimbledon, Barnet and particularly Chelsea all gave chase but the Albion made it third time lucky.

AXA F.A. WOMEN'S PREMIER LEAGUE CUP FINAL

at Chester City FC. Attendance: 2,006

Arsenal 3 v 0 Tranmere Rovers

M Spacey 52, 53, A Banks 82

THIRD ANNUAL FA WOMEN'S FOOTBALL AWARDS 2001

AXA PLAYERS' PLAYER OF THE YEAR

NATIONAL DIVISION	Jayne Ludlow	Arsenal
NORTHERN DIVISION	Stacey Daniel	Leeds United
SOUTHERN DIVISION	Kristy Moore	Barnet

THE AXA SPECIAL ACHIEVEMENT AWARD

Maureen Marley, Captain of England and Everton

NATIONWIDE INTERNATIONAL PLAYER OF THE YEAR

Sue Smith, Tranmere Rovers

AXA MANAGER OF THE YEAR AWARD

Vic Akers, Arsenal

WALKERS YOUNG PLAYER OF THE YEAR

Katie Chapman Fulham and England

UMBRO TOP GOALSCORER, AXA F.A.W.P.L

NATIONAL DIVISION	Angela Banks	Arsenal
NORTHERN DIVISION	Kelly Dean	Oldham Curzon
SOUTHERN DIVISION	Kristy Moore	Barnet

SHE KICKS MEDIA AWARD

The Gravesend Messenger

Player of the Year Jayne Ludlow, Arsenal's Welsh midfielder in action

WOMEN'S PYRAMID OF FOOTBALL

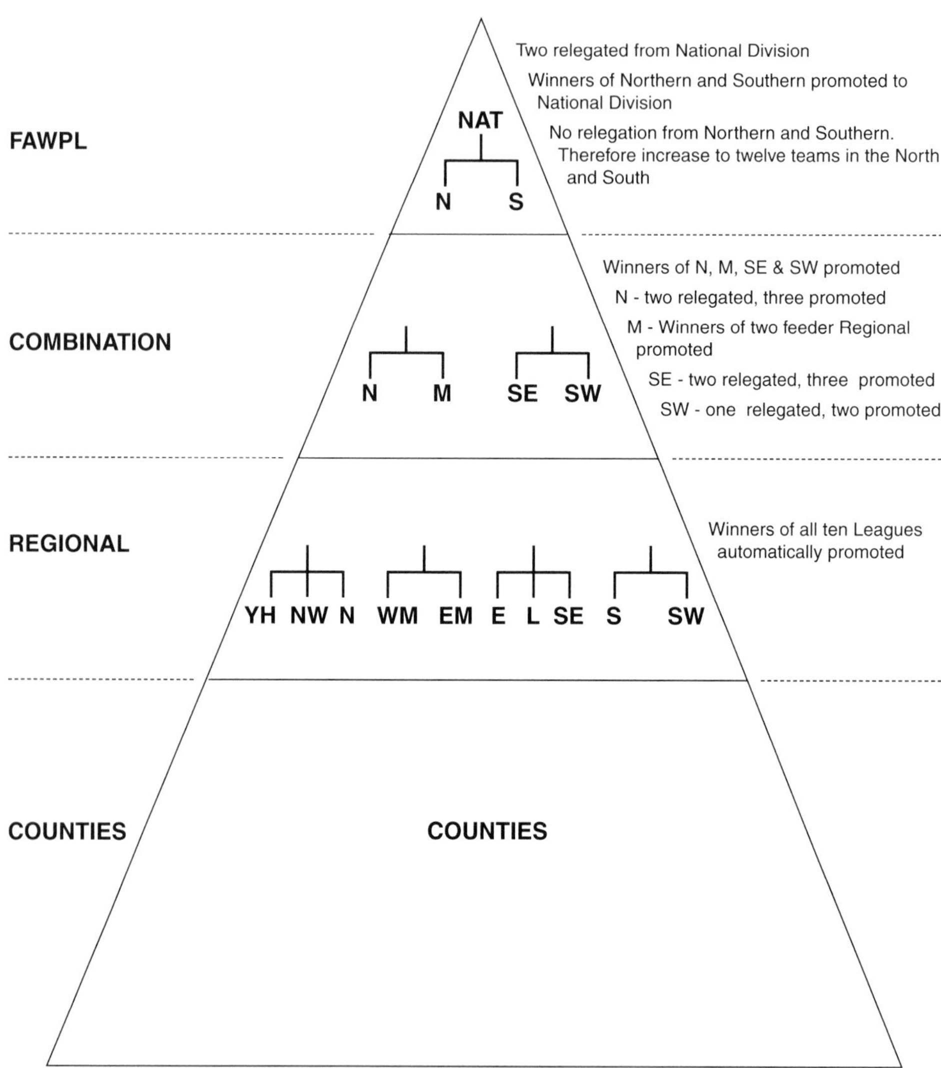

FAWPL
NAT
N
S
Two relegated from National Division
Winners of Northern and Southern promoted to National Division
No relegation from Northern and Southern. Therefore increase to twelve teams in the North and South
COMBINATION
N
M
SE
SW
Winners of N, M, SE & SW promoted
N - two relegated, three promoted
M - Winners of two feeder Regional promoted
SE - two relegated, three promoted
SW - one relegated, two promoted
REGIONAL
YH
NW
N
WM
EM
E
L
SE
S
SW
Winners of all ten Leagues automatically promoted
COUNTIES
COUNTIES

COMBINATION LEAGUES

(Premier League feeders)

NORTHERN COMBINATION

	Pld	W	D	L	F	A	Pts
Manchester City	22	16	2	4	78	34	50
Blackpool Wren Rovers	22	14	4	4	64	33	46
Middlesbrough	22	14	4	4	66	37	46
Newcastle	22	13	5	4	54	38	44
Leeds City Vixens	22	13	2	7	63	46	41
Manchester United	22	9	3	10	48	50	30
Blackburn Rovers	21	9	4	8	51	41	28*
Bradford City	22	7	4	11	41	59	25
Stockport Hatters	22	5	5	12	32	51	20
Chester-le-Street Town	22	5	4	13	44	55	19
Doncaster Rovers	22	5	1	16	51	89	16
Darlington	21	1	2	18	26	83	5

Manchester City are promoted to Northern Division, while Doncaster Rovers and Darlington go down into the Yorkshire & Humberside Regional and Northern Regional Leagues respectively.

SOUTH EAST COMBINATION

	Pld	W	D	L	F	A	Pts
Fulham	20	20	0	0	196	3	60
Enfield	20	12	3	5	50	26	39
Stowmarket	20	10	2	8	54	57	32
Charlton LFC	20	8	5	7	43	69	29
Bedford Town Bells	20	8	4	8	27	43	28
Hampton	20	8	3	9	34	36	27
Chelmsford City	20	7	4	9	43	52	25
Racers	20	7	4	9	34	70	25
Watford	20	6	2	12	30	75	20
Whitehawk	20	5	2	13	29	79	17
Crowborough Athletic	20	4	1	21	21	50	13

Unsurprisingly, Fulham make another step towards to the top by being promoted into the Southern Division, while Crowborough are the only team to face the drop, they go into the Southern East Counties Regional League

MIDLANDS COMBINATION

	Pld	W	D	L	F	A	Pts
Mansfield Town	22	14	2	6	66	37	44
Chesterfield	21	11	6	4	47	27	39
Parkgate	22	11	3	8	58	43	36
Peterborough United	22	10	4	8	40	38	34
Shrewsbury Town	21	11	3	7	42	36	33*
Stafford Rangers	22	8	5	9	41	32	29
Derby County	22	7	8	7	35	40	29
Ilkeston	22	8	4	10	25	30	28
Highfield Rangers	21	8	3	10	41	39	27
Arnold Town	21	6	5	10	27	35	23
Telford United	22	6	5	11	27	53	23
Walsall	18	2	4	12	16	55	10

Mansfield Town (now known as North Notts.) go up to the Northern Division while only Walsall (now Bloxwich Town) are relegated to the West Midlands Regional League after F.A. approves 13 team league forforthcoming season after outstanding games were not played by deadline and it was deemed unfair that either Telford or Arnold should be demoted.

SOUTH WEST COMBINATION

	Pld	W	D	L	F	A	Pts
Bristol Rovers	22	19	2	0	75	5	62
Portsmouth	22	16	2	4	53	26	50
Swindon Town	22	14	4	4	89	38	46
Bristol City	22	12	5	5	43	27	41
Yeovil Town	22	12	4	5	54	33	41
Clevedon Town	22	8	6	8	38	34	30
Reading LFC	22	7	5	10	37	42	25
Cheltenham Town	22	7	4	11	49	59	24*
Saltash Pilgrims	22	5	6	11	27	53	19*
Southampton	22	5	1	16	23	80	16
Denham United	22	3	3	16	32	66	12
Oxford United	22	0	4	18	19	75	4

** points deducted*

Bristol Rovers move up to the Southern Division, while Denham United and Oxford United go the other way into the Southern Regional League.

INTERNATIONAL COMPETITION

FRIENDLY

France 0 –1 England

in Marseilles, France.

FRIENDLY

England 2 – 1 Finland

Karen Burke 1 — *Heidi Kackur 4*

Angela Banks 34

at Leyton Orient FC

UEFA EUROPEAN CHAMPIONSHIP QUALIFIER PLAY OFF 1ST LEG

Ukraine 1 – 2 England

Natalia Zinchenko 90 — *Kelly Smith 58*

Karen Walker 84

in Borispol, nr Kiev, Ukraine

UEFA EUROPEAN CHAMPIONSHIP QUALIFIER PLAY OFF 2ND LEG

England 2 – 0 Ukraine

Sue Smith 63

Rachel Yankey 79

at Leyton Orient FC. Attendance: 7,102.

FRIENDLY

England 4 –2 Spain

Kelly Smith 17

Sue Smith 35, 67, 75

at Luton Town FC. Attendance: 3,602

FRIENDLY

England 1 – 0 Scotland

Angela Banks 45

at Reebok Stadium, Bolton . Attendance: 3,004

England players celebrate their qualification for the Euro Finals after their 4-1 aggregate win over Ukraine.

EUROPEAN CHAMPIONSHIP
FINALS 2000

in Germany

EURO 2001 GROUP A

Russia	1 - 1	England
Svetltskaia 63		*Angela Banks 45*

in Jena. Attendance: 1,253

England: 1. P.Cope, 2. D.Murphy, 3. R.Unitt, 4. B.Easton, 5. M.Marley, 6. K.Chapman, 7. K.Burke, 8. T.Proctor, 9. A.Banks, 10. S.Smith, 11. M.Spacey
Referee: R Ruiz Tacoronte

EURO 2001 GROUP A

Sweden	4 - 0	England
Tornqvist 2		
Bengtsson 26		
Ljungberg 74		
Eriksson 80		

in Jena. Attendance: 1,127

England: 1. P.Cope, 2. D.Murphy, 3. R.Unitt, 4. B.Easton, 5. M.Marley, 6. K.Chapman, 7. K.Burke, 8. T.Proctor, 9. A.Banks, 10. S.Smith, 11. S.Britton
Referee: C Brohet

EURO 2001 GROUP A

England	0 - 3	Germany
		Wimbersky 57
		Wiegmann 65
		Lingor 68

in Jena. Attendance: 11,312

England: 1. P.Cope, 2. K.Chapman, 3. R.Unitt, 4. D.Murphy, 5. F.White, 6. S.Britton, 7. K.Burke, 8. T.Proctor, 9. K.Smith, 10. S.Smith, 11. K.Walker

Referee: Bente Skogvang

FINAL GROUP STANDINGS

Group A		**Group B**	
Germany	9	Denmark	6
Sweden	6	Norway	4
Russia	1	Italy	4
England	1	France	3

SEMI FINALS

In Donaustadion, Ulm. Attendance: 13, 525

Denmark	0 – 1	Sweden
		Nordlund 9
Germany	1 – 0	Norway
Smisek 57		

FINAL

In Donaustadion, Ulm. Attendance: 18,000

Germany	1 – 0	Sweden
Müller 97		

GERMANY are European Champions for THE third successive competition. They keep trophy.

TOURNAMENT TOP SCORERS

3	Sandra SMISEK	Germany
2	Gitte KROGH	Denmark
2	Marinette PICHON	Germany
2	Bettina WIEGMANN	Germany
2	Claudia MÜLLER	Germany
2	Maren MEINERT	Germany
2	Patrizia PANICO	Italy
2	Dagny MELLGREN	Norway
2	Hanna LJUNGBERG	Sweden

Above: The England girls in buoyant mood prior to the Euro 2001 finals.

Scorer of the golden goal for Germany against Sweden in the Euro Championships Final, Claudia Muller, celebrates her second goal in her side's 3-1 group opening win against Sweden.

Tribute to RUSHDEN & DIAMONDS

There may have been some jealousy shown towards Rushden & Diamonds Football Club in their early days, but once the football world got to know Max Griggs and his football philosophy most of the resentment disappeared into genuine admiration.

After all, the Dr. Martens multi millionaire was only doing what we would all do for our clubs if we could only raise the money.

Nene Park became more and more glamourous, the training facilities and general working conditions for their full time squad were just about perfect.

The young Diamonds' supporters, who cannot remember the days of Rushden Town and Irthlingborough Diamonds, are undoubtedly spoilt, but that's not their fault! Hopefully they will realise how lucky they are, as I am sure the older ones do.

If there was a simmering impatience when the club seemed to be stuck near the top of the Conference without actually moving on, well, perhaps it was understandable.

This is where chairman and owner Max Griggs really showed his true character and possibly why he has been so successful. His love of football had not been left behind as his money had set up `the perfect club', he still knew that despite his money being spent on all the right things, results wouldn't just come by right.

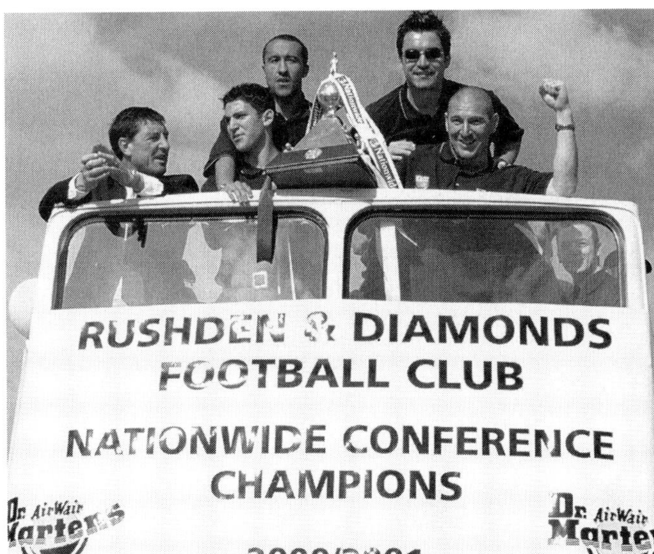

A winning squad had to be built, they must cope with the pressure of success and, of course, a little bit of luck must be there at the right time.

Max stood by manager Brian Talbot when he needed him, and last season, possibly enjoying the lack of pressure as the second favourite chasing the Yeovil youngsters, everything clicked into place.

Chairman, club officials, manager and squad were rewarded, deservedly for all the effort put in, on and off the field.

The majority of the football world celebrated with them and just wished that a fairy godfather would join their clubs. The Diamonds were off to represent our non-league football in the big time, and good luck to them all!

TONY WILLIAMS

RUSHDEN & DIAMONDS

	Date	Comp.	**Opponents**	Gate	Score	**Goalscorers**
1	19/08	Conf.	CHESTER CITY	3966	2 - 0	Darby 47, Jackson 90
2	21/08	Conf.	Hednesford Town	1516	3 - 2	Jackson 22, Darby 35, Burgess 71
3	26/08	Conf.	Dagenham & Redbridge	1686	2 - 0	Burgess 10, Darby 41
4	28/08	Conf.	SOUTHPORT	3574	4 - 0	Darby 12, Jackson 20, Burgess 61, Brady 67
5	02/09	Conf.	Telford United	1510	2 - 1	Brady 48, Darby 81 Worcester City
6	05/09	Conf.	STEVENAGE BOROUGH	4048	2 - 2	Burgess 29, Jackson 48
7	09/09	Conf.	FOREST GREEN ROVERS	3352	0 - 0	
8	12/09	Conf.	Scarborough	1107	3 - 0	Warburton 10, Town 70, Jackson 78
9	16/09	Conf.	Woking	2101	4 - 1	Darby 9 47, Brady 34, Jackson 88[p]
10	23/09	Conf.	KETTERING TOWN	4627	1 - 1	Jackson 64 F
11	26/09	Conf.	DAGENHAM & REDBRIDGE	3069	2 - 1	Burgess 9, Darby 67[p]
12	30/09	Conf.	Kingstonian	1363	4 - 2	Darby 25, Brady 29 84, Jackson 75
13	03/10	Conf.	Leigh RMI	1405	0 - 1	
14	08/10	Conf.	BOSTON UNITED	4570	0 - 0	
15	14/10	Conf.	HEREFORD UNITED	4188	1 - 0	Jackson 55
16	21/10	Conf.	Morecambe	1816	1 - 2	Sigerre 54
17	31/10	Conf.	HAYES	2568	4 - 0	Jackson 13, Wormull 20, Sigerre 29 70
18	04/11	Conf.	YEOVIL TOWN	5283	1 - 2	Jackson 70
19	11/11	Conf.	Doncaster Rovers	3538	2 - 3	Underwood 28, Brady 90
20	02/12	Conf.	Dover Athletic	1407	1 - 4	Underwood 53[p]
21	09/12	Conf.	Hayes	1044	3 - 0	Jackson 24, Underwood 75[p], Setchell 89
22	16/12	Conf.	HEDNESFORD TOWN	2906	5 - 1	Brady 16, Sigerre 48 58, Darby 70 75
23	26/12	Conf.	Nuneaton Borough	2614	1 - 1	Jackson 60
24	01/01	Conf.	NUNEATON BOROUGH	4080	2 - 1	Brady 28, Darby 83
25	06/01	Conf.	Southport	2255	3 - 1	Jackson 13 86, Burgess 55
26	27/01	Conf.	Stevenage Borough	3327	2 - 0	Darby 5 30
27	10/02	Conf.	Forest Green Rovers	1144	0 - 0	
28	17/02	Conf.	SCARBOROUGH	3553	1 - 0	Burgess 72
29	20/02	Conf.	NORTHWICH VICTORIA	2820	2 - 1	Darby 22, Jackson 37
30	03/03	Conf.	WOKING	3667	2 - 0	Darby 46, Carey 65
31	10/03	Conf.	Boston United	3434	1 - 1	Jackson 61
32	13/03	Conf.	Kettering Town	4750	2 - 0	Darby 56[p] 77
33	17/03	Conf.	KINGSTONIAN	3842	2 - 1	Darby 18 73[p]
34	25/03	Conf.	Northwich Victoria	2016	0 - 0	
35	31/03	Conf.	LEIGH RMI	3882	1 - 1	Sigerre 34
36	07/04	Conf.	MORECAMBE	3778	4 - 1	Darby 22 37[p] 54, Brady 63
37	14/04	Conf.	Hereford United	2005	1 - 3	James 61[og]
38	16/04	Conf.	DONCASTER ROVERS	4036	0 - 0	
39	21/04	Conf.	Yeovil Town	8868	0 - 0	
40	24/04	Conf.	TELFORD UNITED	4107	3 - 0	Jackson 45, Brady 52, Butterworth 72
41	28/04	Conf.	DOVER ATHLETIC	5482	2 - 1	Darby 18, Peters 38
42	05/05	Conf.	Chester City	4040	2 - 1	Peters 60, Brady 89

OTHER COMPETITIONS

Date	Comp.	Opponents	Gate	Score	Goalscorers
24/10	Variety CT 2	STEVENAGE BOROUGH	412	2 - 1	Sigerre 25, McElhatton 68
28/10	FA Cup Q4	GRANTHAM TOWN	2685	5 - 4	McElhatton 18 36, Underwood 29[p], Jackson 58, Setchell 64
17/11	FA Cup 1	Luton Town	5771	0 - 1	
28/11	LDV Vans 1S	Barnet	887	0 - 2	
19/12	Variety CT QF	Kingstonian	190	0 - 1	
13/01	FA Trophy 3	Hayes	842	1 - 0	Darby 40
03/02	FA Trophy 4	Marine	965	6 - 0	Darby 21 76, Jackson 60, Burgess 80, Essendoh 90, Rodwell 90
21/02	N'hants SC SF	Corby Town	154	4 - 2	Duffy 17, Sale 18, Wormull 50 90[p]
24/02	FA Trophy 5	Forest Green Rovers	1018	0 - 2	
10/04	N'hants SC F	KETTERING TOWN	1038	1 - 3	Sale

1	2	3	4	5	6	7	8	9	10	11	Substitutes Used
Turley	Mustafa	Rodwell	Warburton	Underwood	Brady	Butterworth	Mills	Burgess	Jackson	Darby	
Turley	Mustafa	Rodwell	Warburton	Underwood	Carey	Butterworth	Brady	Jackson	Darby	Burgess	Setchell (11)
Turley	Mustafa	Rodwell	Warburton	Underwood	Brady	Butterworth	Carney	Burgess	Jackson	Darby	Setchell (5), Sigerre (11)
Turley	Mustafa	Rodwell	Warburton	Underwood	Carey	Butterworth	Brady	Jackson	Darby	Burgess	Setchell (5), Sigerre (10)
Turley	Mustafa	Underwood	Carey	Rodwell	Warburton	Butterworth	Brady	Jackson	Darby	Burgess	Sigerre (9)
Turley	Mustafa	Rodwell	Warburton	Underwood	Carey	Butterworth	Brady	Jackson	Darby	Burgess	
Turley	Mustafa	Underwood	Carey	Rodwell	Warburton	Butterworth	Brady	Jackson	Darby	Burgess	Setchell (3), Sigerre (10)
Turley	Mustafa	Rodwell	Warburton	Underwood	Carey	Butterworth	Brady	Sigerre	Jackson	Burgess	Mills (6), Town (9), Setchell (11)
Turley	Mustafa	Rodwell	Warburton	Underwood	Brady	Carey	Butterworth	Burgess	Jackson	Darby	Setchell (5), Mills (7), Sigerre (11)
Turley	Mustafa	Setchell	Carey	Rodwell	Warburton	Butterworth	Brady	Jackson	Darby	Burgess	Sigerre (9)
Turley	Mustafa	Rodwell	Warburton	Setchell	Carey	Butterworth	Brady	Jackson	Darby	Burgess	
Turley	Mustafa	Setchell	Carey	Rodwell	Warburton	Butterworth	Brady	Jackson	Darby	Burgess	Peters (5)
Turley	Mustafa	Rodwell	Warburton	Setchell	Carey	Butterworth	Brady	Jackson	Darby	Burgess	Mills (6), Sigerre (11)
Turley	Mustafa	Rodwell	Warburton	Setchell	Mills	Butterworth	Brady	Jackson	Darby	Burgess	Collins (11)
Turley	Mustafa	Rodwell	Warburton	Setchell	Brady	Mills	Butterworth	Burgess	Jackson	Darby	
Turley	Mustafa	Setchell	Mills	Rodwell	Warburton	Butterworth	Brady	Jackson	Darby	Burgess	Underwood (3), Sigerre (10, Wormull (11)
Turley	Mustafa	Rodwell	Warburton	Underwood	Mills	Butterworth	Wormull	Sigerre	Setchell	Jackson	Burgess (5), Peters (4), Town (11)
Turley	Mustafa	Underwood	Mills	Rodwell	Warburton	Butterworth	Wormull	Jackson	Darby	Setchell	Brady (8), Sigerre (10), Burgess (11)
Turley	Mustafa	Underwood	Mills	Rodwell	Peters	Butterworth	Wormull	Jackson	Sigerre	Setchell	Naylor (8), Burgess (10), Brady (11)
Turley	Peters	Rodwell	Warburton	Mustafa	Brady	Carey	Butterworth	Underwood	Town	Jackson	Iga (4), Mills (8), Sale (10)
Turley	Mustafa	Mills	Rodwell	Warburton	Underwood	Carey	Burgess	Brady	Jackson	Darby	Setchell (11)
Rogers	Mustafa	Underwood	Mills	Rodwell	Peters	Carey	Brady	Sigerre	Darby	Burgess	Bradshaw (5), Butterworth (9), Setchell (10)
Turley	Mustafa	Rodwell	Underwood	Warburton	Carey	Butterworth	Brady	Jackson	Darby	Burgess	Setchell (10)
Turley	Mustafa	Rodwell	Warburton	Underwood	Carey	Butterworth	Brady	Jackson	Darby	Burgess	
Turley	Mustafa	Rodwell	Warburton	Underwood	Butterworth		Brady	Burgess	Carey	Jackson	Darby
Turley	Mustafa	Underwood	Carey	Peters	Warburton	Butterworth	Brady	Jackson	Darby	Setchell	Essandoh (10)
Turley	Mustafa	Carey	Paters	Setchell	Warburton	Butterworth	Brady	Burgess	Jackson	Darby	
Turley	Mustafa	Peters	Warburton	Underwood	Brady	Carey	Butterworth	Burgess	Darby	Jackson	Wormull (6), Essandoh (10), Setchell (5)
Turley	Mustafa	Peters	Warburton	Setchell	Carey	Butterworth	Brady	Jackson	Darby	Burgess	
Turley	Mustafa	Peters	Warburton	Setchell	Brady	Carey	Butterworth	Burgess	Jackson	Darby	
Turley	Mustafa	Peters	Warburton	Setchell	Brady	Carey	Butterworth	Burgess	Jackson	Darby	
Turley	Mustafa	Peters	Warburton	Setchell	Carey	Butterworth	Brady	Jackson	Darby	Burgess	
Turley	Mustafa	Setchell	Carey	Peters	Warburton	Butterworth	Brady	Jackson	Darby	Burgess	Sigerre (9)
Turley	Mustafa	Peters	Warburton	Setchell	Carey	Butterworth	Brady	Jackson	Darby	Burgess	Mills (6), Sigerre (9)
Turley	Mustafa	Carey	Setchell	Peters	Warburton	Butterworth	Brady	Sigerre	Darby	Burgess	Wormull (9)
Turley	Mustafa	Gray	Carey	Peters	Warburton	Butterworth	Brady	Jackson	Darby	Burgess	Mills (4), Rodwell (6), Sigerre (9)
Turley	Solkhon	Peters	Warburton	Gray	Brady	Carey	Butterworth	Burgess	Darby	Jackson	Mills (2), Wormull (7), Sigerre (9)
Turley	Mustafa	Peters	Warburton	Gray	Carey	Butterworth	Brady	Jackson	Darby	Burgess	Mills (6)
Turley	Mustafa	Peters	Warburton	Gray	Brady	Butterworth	Mills	Burgess	Darby	Jackson	Rodwell (4), Underwood (11)
Turley	Mustafa	Peters	Rodwell	Underwood	Mills	Butterworth	Brady	Jackson	Darby	Burgess	Gray (5), Sigerre (9), Wormull (10)
Turley	Mustafa	Peters	Rodwell	Underwood	Mills	Butterworth	Brady	Jackson	Darby	Burgess	Carey (6)
Turley	Mustafa	Peters	Rodwell	Warburton	Carey	Butterworth	Brady	Jackson	Darby	Burgess	Mills (6), Grays (7), Sigerre (9)

AXA F.A. YOUTH CUP

in association with

THE TIMES

FIRST ROUND QUALIFYING

Home		Away	Score	Att
Chadderton	v	Gretna	4-1	46
Doncaster Rovers	v	Chester City	2-2	95
Chester City	v	Doncaster Rvrs	1-2	58
Ashton United	v	Selby Town	4-1	74
Pontefract Collieries	v	Worksop Town	2-2	90
Worksop Town	v	Pontefract Colls	3-4	75
Burscough	v	Northwich Vic	1-0	60
Guiseley	v	Louth United		

walkover for Guiseley – Louth United withdrawn

Home		Away	Score	Att
Clitheroe	v	Consett	1-4	70
Warrington Town	v	Kendal Town	2-1	18
Scarborough	v	Farsley Celtic	1-0	96
Salford City	v	Runcorn	2-1	52

tie awarded to Runcorn – Salford City played an ineligible player

Home		Away	Score	Att
Emley	v	Stocksbridge P S	1-0	118
Rossendale United	v	Workington	2-5	67
Crook Town	v	Morecambe	0-0	136
Morecambe	v	Crook Town	3-5	70
Frickley Athletic	v	Stalybridge Celtic		

walkover for Frickley Athletic – Stalybridge Celtic withdrawn

Home		Away	Score	Att
Harrogate Town	v	Lancaster City	0-2	57
Holwell Sports	v	Pegasus Juniors	2-0	75
Redditch United	v	Malvern Town	2-1	46
Alvechurch	v	Mickleover Sports	2-0	50
Kettering Town	v	Bridgnorth Town	3*1	89
Congleton Town	v	R C Warwick	1-2	52
Ilkeston Town	v	Boldmere St M	1-1	55
R Boldmere St M	v	Ilkeston Town	4-0	49
Lincoln United	v	Gresley Rovers	9-1	103
Leek Town	v	Telford United	1-2	41
Sutton Coldfield T	v	Bloxwich Town	1-2	55
Handrahan Timbers	v	Willenhall Town	0-4	31
Hednesford Town	v	Glossop N End	6-1	174
Birstall United	v	Burton Albion	1-3	40
Paget Rangers	v	Arnold Town	2-0	108
Grantham Town	v	Rugby United	2-0	68
Bromsgrove Rovers	v	Bedworth United	1-1	114
R Bedworth United	v	Bromsgrove R	5-3	83
Tamworth	v	Hinckley United	4-6	105
Atherstone United	v	Dudley Sports	3-1	61
Newcastle Town	v	Matlock Town	5-1	80
Nuneaton Borough	v	Belper Town	3-1	83

at Belper Town FC

Home		Away	Score	Att
Stevenage Borough	v	Witham Town	5*1	92
Hemel Hempstead T	v	Leyton Pennant	6-0	40
Bury Town	v	Burnham Rmblrs	2-0	65
Southall	v	Tring Town	2-0	26
Ilford	v	Cambridge City	0-10	61

at Cambridge City FC

Home		Away	Score	Att
Hornchurch	v	Banbury United	0-1	26
Wellingborough Tn	v	Braintree Town	3-3	26
Braintree Town	v	Wellingborough T	0-3	51
Brook House	v	Beaconsfield SYCOB		

walkover for Brook House – Beaconsfield SYCOB withdrawn

Home		Away	Score	Att
Enfield	v	Bugbrooke St M	1-0	35

at Cheshunt FC

Home		Away	Score	Att
Wingate & Finchley	v	Harlow Town	1-0	35
Potters Bar Town	v	Leyton	9-1	41
Clacton Town	v	Romford	1-7	76
Wroxham	v	Bowers United	5-0	69
Concord Rangers	v	Long Buckby	1*2	30
Chesham United	v	Maldon Town	2-2	25
R Maldon Town	v	Chesham United	2*2	60

Maldon Town won 4-3 on kicks from the penalty mark

Home		Away	Score	Att
Bedford Town	v	Welwyn Gdn City	6-0	36
Wisbech Town	v	Ware	3-1	70
Southend Manor	v	Waltham Abbey	1*1	39

Southend M won 5-3 on kicks from the penalty mark

Home		Away	Score	Att
Great Wakering Rvrs	v	Uxbridge	1-1	85
R Uxbridge	v	Great Wakering R	1*0	91
Heybridge Swifts	v	Northwood	3-1	72
Wembley	v	Flackwell Heath	6-1	31
Tilbury	v	Ruislip Manor	0-1	35
Ipswich Wanderers	v	St Neots Town	8-0	73
Rushden & Dia	v	Northampton Sp	4-0	159

Canvey Island	v	Bishop's Stortford	2-3	
Histon	v	Soham Town R	3-0	65
Sawbridgeworth T	v	Cogenhoe Utd		

walkover for Cogenhoe United – Sawbridgeworth Town withdrawn

St Albans City	v	Ely City	2-1	71
Marlow	v	Milton Keynes C	7-1	58
Leighton Town	v	Hitchin Town	0-1	84
Staines Town	v	Royston Town	3-1	59
Aylesbury United	v	Clapton	4-0	65

tie awared to Clapton – Aylesbury United played two ineligible players

Eynesbury Rovers	v	Haverhill Rovers	3-1	50
Cheshunt	v	Brentwood	1-2	40
Tiptree United	v	Chelmsford City	5-0	74
Moneyfields	v	Bashley	2-1	74
Littlehampton Town	v	Hillingdon Boro	3-3	42

match abandoned in extra time after 92 mins - floodlight failure – result at 90 mins stands

R Hillingdon Borough	v	Littlehampton T	4-0	40
Folkestone Invicta	v	Erith Town	3-1	62
BAT Sports	v	North Leigh	2-5	33
Whyteleafe	v	Westfield	4-1	38
Deal Town	v	Eastbourne Town		

walkover for Eastbourne Town – Deal Town withdrawn

AFC Lewisham	v	Sandhurst Town	3-2	91

at Sandhurst Town

Didcot Town	v	Maidenhead United		

walkover for Didcot Town – Maidenhead United withdrawn

Kingstonian	v	Lewes	1-4	84
Margate	v	Whitstable Town	1-3	75
Tonbridge Angels	v	Banstead Athletic	0-0	103
R Banstead Athletic	v	Tonbridge Angels	2-6	45
Oxford City	v	Dartford	6-0	75
Saltdean United	v	Godalming & G	4-1	36
Sutton United	v	Aldershot Town	2-2	81
R Aldershot Town	v	Sutton United	4-2	121
Burgess Hill Town	v	Ashford T (Mx)	2-2	48
R Ashford Town (Mx)	v	Burgess Hill T	6*2	39
Basingstoke Town	v	Abingdon United	7-1	86
Lordswood	v	Molesey	2-1	40
Crowborough Athletic	v	Camberley Town	8-2	88
Three Bridges	v	Walton & H'sham	1-2	52
Welling United	v	Tooting & M Utd	0-4	190
Chatham Town	v	Dover Athletic	1-0	62
Bedfont	v	Chipstead	0-3	36
Farnborough Town	v	Chichester C U	0-4	70
Eastleigh	v	Thamesmead T	0-3	69
Ramsgate	v	Reading Town	0-4	29
Herne Bay	v	Croydon	3-2	92
Sittingbourne	v	Leatherhead	2-0	30
Havant & W'ville	v	Bracknell Town	3-1	70
Cobham	v	Gosport Borough	1-0	24
Thame United	v	Fleet Town	6-0	75
AFC Newbury	v	Paulton Rovers	1*1	43

AFC Newbury won 4-1 on kicks from the penalty mark

Cirencester Town	v	Thatcham Town	3-2	
Brislington	v	Street	2-1	20
Salisbury City	v	Newport County	1-4	63
Evesham United	v	Worcester City	3-5	83
Mangotsfield United	v	Yeovil Town	2-0	92
Chippenham Town	v	Gloucester City	2-4	73

SECOND ROUND QUALIFYING

Scarborough	v	Oldham Town	5-2	42
Crook Town	v	Chadderton	5-2	117
Ashton United	v	Lancaster City	3-1	81
Runcorn	v	Pontefract Coll	4-2	53
Guiseley	v	Emley	2-1	50
Burscough	v	Frickley Athletic		

walkover for Burscough – Frickley Athletic withdrawn

Warrington Town	v	Consett	2*2	56

Warrington Town won 4-2 on kicks from the penalty mark

Workington	v	Doncaster Rvrs	1-4	129
Boldmere St Michaels	v	Bloxwich Town	1-3	74
Atherstone United	v	Redditch United	0-1	87
Nuneaton Borough	v	Hednesford Town	1-1	95
R Hednesford Town	v	Nuneaton Boro	1-2	126
Kettering Town	v	Bedworth United	3-2	78
Willenhall Town	v	Hinckley United	0-5	65
Telford United	v	Lincoln United	0-3	45

at Lincoln United FC

Racing Club Warwick	v	Corby Town	1-0	28
Stourbridge	v	Newcastle Town	4-1	56
Paget Rangers	v	Cradley Town	0-4	84
Alvechurch	v	Marconi	1-4	30
Grantham Town	v	Holwell Sports	0*0	81

Holwell Sports won 5-3 on kicks from the penalty mark

Burton Albion	v	Chasetown	4-1	85
Ipswich Wanderers	v	Tiptree United	1-0	51
Hayes	v	St Albans City	1-4	75
Stevenage Borough	v	Staines Town	8-0	83
Bishops Stortford	v	Enfield	2-0	50

Wroxham	v	Kingsbury Town		
walkover to Wroxham – Kingsbury Town withdrawn				
Rushden & Diamonds	v	Brook House	5-2	69
Cogenhoe United	v	Uxbridge	0-3	41
Long Buckby	v	Newmarket Town	1-0	25
Histon	v	Wealdstone	4-2	39
Ford United	v	Wellingborough T	4-1	73
Heybridge Swifts	v	Kempston Rovers	0-1	55
Wembley	v	Wisbech Town	2-1	43
Banbury United	v	Potters Bar Town	1-5	27
Brentwood	v	Hemel H'stead T	1-3	56
Southend Manor	v	Lowestoft Town	3-1	40
Wingate & Finchley	v	Southall	5-1	17
AFC Wallingford	v	Ruislip Manor	2-1	52
Bury Town	v	Bedford Town	3-1	57
Clapton	v	Hitchin Town	1-0	32
Eynesbury Rovers	v	Cambridge City	0-4	79
Romford	v	Purfleet	5*2	66
at Purfleet FC				
Marlow	v	Maldon Town	1*2	40
Moneyfields	v	Crowborough Ath	1-2	47
Walton & Hersham	v	Chatham Town	2-0	50
Whitstable Town	v	Hillingdon Boro	2*3	72
Thame United	v	Tooting & M Utd)	0-1	49
Woking	v	Cobham	5-0	95
Herne Bay	v	Chichester C U	0-4	41
Havant & W'ville	v	Ashford T (Mx)	3-1	61
Eastbourne Town	v	AFC Lewisham	1-5	34
North Leigh	v	Lordswood	0-1	46
Chipstead	v	Saltdean United	3-1	30
Oxford City	v	Reading Town	3-0	85
Carshalton Athletic	v	Thamesmead T	0-4	54
Lewes	v	Sittingbourne	2-4	69
Whyteleafe	v	Aldershot Town	0-3	44
Folkestone Invicta	v	Tonbridge Angels	1-5	62
Basingstoke Town	v	Didcot Town)	3-2	62
Newport County	v	Cinderford Town	2-1	80
Forest Green Rovers	v	Bath City	2-3	53
Cirencester Town	v	AFC Newbury	3-0	34
Worcester City	v	Mangotsfield Utd	2-0	84
Brislington	v	Gloucester City	2-0	38
Pershore Town	v	Hereford United		
walkover for Hereford United – Pershore Town withdrawn				

* = after extra time

THIRD ROUND QUALIFYING

Warrington Town	v	Burscough	0-2	67
Runcorn	v	Guiseley	3-2	42
Ashton United	v	Crook Town	0-2	123
Scarborough	v	Doncaster Rvrs	1-3	90
Kettering Town	v	Burton Albion	0-2	58
Cradley Town	v	Holwell Sports	3-0	63
Redditch United	v	Bloxwich Town	1-1	90
R Bloxwich Town	v	Redditch United	1-0	40
Hinckley United	v	Lincoln United	1-4	94
Nuneaton Borough	v	R C Warwick	3-1	42
Marconi	v	Stourbridge	7-0	52
Rushden & Diamonds	v	Ipswich Wndrs	5-1	134
Wembley	v	Bishop's Stortford	1-0	41
Bury Town	v	Clapton	1-0	43
Hemel Hempstead T	v	Stevenage Boro	2-2	40
R Stevenage Boro	v	Hemel H'stead T	3-1	74
Wingate & Finchley	v	Maldon Town	5-0	37
Ford United	v	Cambridge City	3-1	168
Long Buckby	v	Potters Bar Town	0-2	
AFC Wallingford	v	Uxbridge	2-3	110
Wroxham	v	St Albans City	0-1	57
Romford	v	Kempston Rovers	3-1	32
at Grays Athletic FC				
Southend Manor	v	Histon	0-4	42
Lordswood	v	Basingstoke T	0-2	38
Sittingbourne	v	Crowborough Ath	2-1	86
Hillingdon Borough	v	Tonbridge Angels	5-10	55
Chipstead	v	Tooting & M Utd	1-0	50
Chichester City Utd	v	Oxford City	3-1	63
Woking	v	Aldershot Town	3-2	147
AFC Lewisham	v	Havant & W'ville	6-4	45
ordered to be replayed due to incorrect AFC Lewisham team sheet				
Havant & W'ville	v	AFC Lewisham	1-5	60
Thamesmead Town	v	Walton & Hersham	1-3	21
Worcester City	v	Newport County	2-4	61
Cirencester Town	v	Brislington	1-0	77
Bath City	v	Hereford United	1-6	90

FIRST ROUND PROPER

Oldham Athletic	v	Crook Town	5-2	105
Doncaster Rovers	v	Hull City	1-4	214
Lincoln City	v	Wrexham	0-1	32
Burscough	v	Stoke City	1-3	158

Walsall	v	Notts County	2-0	132
Rochdale	v	Halifax Town	1*1	
Halifax Town won 4-3 on kicks from the penalty mark				
Shrewsbury Town	v	Wigan Athletic	0-2	122
Bury	v	Runcorn	1-3	82
Mansfield Town	v	York City	0-4	97
Darlington	v	Hartlepool Utd	1-1	308
R Hartlepool United	v	Darlington	1-4	294
Blackpool	v	Port Vale	1-2	85
Chesterfield	v	Scunthorpe Utd	1-4	
Rotherham United	v	Carlisle United	1-4	158
Cambridge United	v	Bloxwich Town	7-1	115
Southend United	v	Potters Bar T	1-0	151
Wembley	v	Cradley Town	1-2	49
Histon	v	Marconi	0-4	63
Colchester United	v	Ford United	2-2	196
R Ford United	v	Colchester Utd	1-2	195
Lincoln United	v	Luton Town	2-2	110
R Luton Town	v	Lincoln United	2*1	101
St Albans City	v	Romford	1-2	62
Hullbridge Sports	v	Oxford United	0-7	156
Burton Albion	v	K'derminster H	0-1	97
Peterborough Utd	v	Northampton T	2-3	346
Stevenage Borough	v	Nuneaton Boro	1-0	87
Barnet	v	Wingate & F	2-1	278
Bury Town	v	Uxbridge	3-3	91
Uxbridge	v	Bury Town	2-5	123
Rushden & Diamonds	v	Leyton Orient	1-0	277
Bristol Rovers	v	Tonbridge A	4-0	119
Chipstead	v	Bournemouth	0-2	191
Brentford	v	Torquay United	4-0	148
Basingstoke Town	v	Reading	1-3	173
Swansea City	v	Bristol City	1-0	172
Cheltenham Town	v	Cirencester T	0-4	179
Plymouth Argyle	v	Swindon Town	0-4	172
Woking	v	Sittingbourne	1-1	100
Sittingbourne	v	Woking	1-3	95
Brighton & Hove Alb	v	Wycombe W	1-1	75
(at Bognor Regis Town FC)				
Wycombe Wndrs	v	Brighton & H A	0-2	242
Newport County	v	Hereford Utd	2-2	138
Hereford United	v	Newport Co	1-5	89
Chichester City Utd	v	Cardiff City	2-2	260
R Cardiff City	v	Chichester C U	4-0	182
Walton & Hersham	v	Millwall	0-6	210
(at Millwall FC)				
Exeter City	v	AFC Lewisham	4-2	99

SECOND ROUND PROPER

Carlisle United	v	Wigan Athletic	0*1	123
Halifax Town	v	Hull City	1-3	93
Darlington	v	York City	0-0	209
R York City	v	Darlington	1*1	150
York City won 5-4 on kicks from the penalty mark				
Stoke City	v	Wrexham	2-1	143
Oldham Athletic	v	Port Vale	4-1	31
Scunthorpe United	v	Runcorn	3-2	148
Southend United	v	Cambridge Utd	3-0	160
Luton Town	v	Walsall	4-1	122
Northampton Town	v	Cradley Town	3-0	108
Oxford United	v	Bury Town	6-0	148
Coventry Marconi	v	Stevenage Boro	1-3	117
Colchester United	v	Rushden & Diam	6-2	175
Romford	v	Kidderminster H	0-3	87
(at Barkingside FC)				
Cirencester Town	v	Swansea City	2-5	150
(reversed tie – at Swansea City)				
Barnet	v	Millwall	0-2	320
Bristol Rovers	v	Reading	0-6	167
Bournemouth	v	Cardiff City	2-1	144
Brighton & Hove Alb	v	Brentford	2-2	65
(at Bognor Regis Town FC)				
R Brentford	v	Brighton & H A	1-3	144
Newport County	v	Exeter City	4-1	191
Swindon Town	v	Woking	4-1	120

THIRD ROUND PROPER

Millwall	v	Leeds United	1-3	456
Newcastle United	v	Crystal Palace	2-2	1438
Crystal Palace	v	Newcastle Utd	4-1	162
at Crystal Palace National Sports Centre				
Stevenage Borough	v	Colchester Utd	2-2	269
R Colchester United	v	Stevenage Boro	4-1	138
West Ham United	v	Southend United	3-0	423
Aston Villa	v	Gillingham	0-0	264
Gillingham	v	Aston Villa	2*2	454
Aston Villa won 4-3 on kicks from the penalty mark				
Everton	v	Nottingham F	1-1	374
R Nottingham Forest	v	Everton	3-2	261
Newport County	v	Crewe Alexandra	1-3	249
Norwich City	v	Scunthorpe Utd	0-2	198
York City	v	Huddersfield T	1-1	198
R Huddersfield Town	v	York City	0-1	267

Arsenal	v	Sunderland	1-0	462
Brighton & Hove Alb	v	Oldham Athletic	0-1	78
at Bognor Regis Town FC				
Tranmere Rovers	v	Wigan Athletic	2-0	140
Stoke City	v	Wolverh'ton W	0-0	138
R Wolverhampton W	v	Stoke City	2-0	202
Liverpool	v	Chelsea	1-1	594
R Chelsea	v	Liverpool	1-7	913
Ipswich Town	v	Leicester City	3-2	291
Bolton Wanderers	v	Swindon Town	2-1	379
Manchester City	v	Fulham	1-1	726
R Fulham	v	Manchester City	1-5	59
at Motspur Park				
Swansea City	v	Sheffield United	2-2	300
R Sheffield United	v	Swansea City	2-0	168
Queens Park Rngrs	v	Wimbledon	1-1	342
R Wimbledon	v	Queens Park R	1*1	143
at Sutton United FC				
Wimbledon won 4-2 on kicks from the penalty mark				
West Bromwich Alb	v	Derby County	0-4	306
Tottenham Hotspur	v	Bradford City	4-2	427
Southampton	v	Birmingham City	1-0	365
Coventry City	v	Oxford United	3-1	260
Stockport County	v	Watford	1-1	351
R Watford	v	Stockport County	1-2	212
Northampton Town	v	Blackburn Rovers	0-0	200
Blackburn Rvrs won 5-3 on kicks from the penalty mark				
Reading	v	Manchester Utd	0-1	8894
Luton Town	v	Bournemouth	4-0	155
Burnley	v	Sheffield Wed	0-6	262
Middlesbrough	v	Kidderminster H	4-1	199
Preston North End	v	Charlton Athletic	1-5	201
Hull City	v	Barnsley	0-3	211
Grimsby Town	v	Portsmouth	0-2	105

FOURTH ROUND PROPER

Leeds United	v	Southampton	3-0	708
Blackburn Rovers	v	Colchester Utd	2-2	707
R Colchester United	v	Blackburn Rvrs	0-4	1011
Manchester United	v	Scunthorpe Utd	8-0	2357
at Old Trafford				
Aston Villa	v	Barnsley	2-0	249
Ipswich Town	v	Crystal Palace	3-1	533
Arsenal	v	Middlesbrough	3-1	414
Tranmere Rovers	v	Sheffield United	1-2	271
Coventry City	v	Crewe Alexandra	3-3	323
R Crewe Alexandra	v	Coventry City	1-2	2172
Liverpool	v	Charlton Athletic	4-0	1538
West Ham United	v	Oldham Athletic	0-0	339
Oldham Athletic	v	West Ham Utd	4-2	684
Nottingham Forest	v	Portsmouth	2-1	542
Bolton Wanderers	v	Sheffield Wed	1-1	654
R Sheffield Wed	v	Bolton Wndrs	2*2	374
Bolton Wndrs won 4-2 on kicks from the penalty mark				
Stockport County	v	Tottenham H	2-1	1738
Wimbledon	v	Derby County	0*0	168
Wimbledon won 5-3 on kicks from the penalty mark				
at The Baseball Ground				
Luton Town	v	Manchester City	2-3	372
Wolverhampton W	v	York City	2-1	360

FIFTH ROUND PROPER

Manchester United	v	Nottingham F	1*2	3008
at Nottingham Forest FC				
Wolverhampton W	v	Wimbledon	0-3	324
Liverpool	v	Stockport County	3-1	2040
Aston Villa	v	Leeds United	1-0	453
Manchester City	v	Coventry City	1-2	961
Blackburn Rovers	v	Bolton Wndrs	3-0	1189
Ipswich Town	v	Sheffield United	1-1	
R Sheffield United	v	Ipswich Town	2-4	398
Oldham Athletic	v	Arsenal	1-3	1065

SIXTH ROUND PROPER

Liverpool	v	Wimbledon	2-1	1877
Ipswich Town	v	Nottingham F	2-1	2080
Coventry City	v	Blackburn R	1-2	667
Arsenal	v	Aston Villa	2-0	651

SEMI-FINALS (TWO LEGS)

Arsenal	v	Ipswich Town	3-1
Ipswich Town	v	Arsenal	2-4
Liverpool	v	Blackburn Rovers	1-1
Blackburn Rovers	v	Liverpool	1-1
Blackburn Rovers won 4-3 after penalties			

FINAL (TWO LEGS)

Arsenal	v	Blackburn Rovers	5-0
Blackburn Rovers	v	Arsenal	3-1

THE FOOTBALL ASSOCIATION

FIXTURE LIST 2001-02

(all kick-off times are local)

JULY 2001

01	Sun	UEFA Intertoto Cup 2 (1)
09/10	Sat/Sun	UEFA Intertoto Cup 2 (2)
14/15	Sat/Sun	UEFA Intertoto Cup 3 (1)
21	Sat	UEFA Intertoto Cup 3 (2)
25	Wed	UEFA Intertoto Cup SF (1)
		UEFA Women's U18 Championship Final Round commences

AUGUST 2001

01	Wed	UEFA Intertoto Cup SF (2)
07	Tue	UEFA Intertoto Cup Final (1)
07/08	Tue/Wed	UEFA Champions League 3Q (1)
11	Sat	Football League commences
		F.A. Women's Charity Shield - Arsenal v Doncaster Belles
		(at Kingstonian FC - 12.00)
12	Sun	One 2 One F.A. Charity Shield - Liverpool v Manchester United (at Millennium Stadium, Cardiff - 2pm)
14	Tue	U21 Friendly International - England v Netherlands (at Reading FC - 8.00pm)
15	Wed	Friendly International - England v Netherlands (at Tottenham Hotspur FC - 8pm)
18	Sat	Premier League commences
		Football Conference commences
19	Sun	AXA F.A. Women's Premier League commences
21	Tue	UEFA Intertoto Cup Final (2)
21/22	Tue/Wed	UEFA Champions League 3Q (2)
22	Wed	Worthington Cup 1
23	Thu	Women's Friendly International - England v Denmark (at Northampton Town FC - 7.45)
24	Fri	UEFA Super Cup
25	Sat	F.A. Cup sponsored by AXA EP
31	Fri	UEFA U21 Qualifier -
		Germany v England - 7.30pm (at Dreisam Stadium, Freiburg)

SEPTEMBER 2001

01	Sat	FIFA World Cup Qualifier - Germany v England - 7.30pm (at Olympic Stadium, Munich)
		F.A. Cup sponsored by AXA P
		AXA F.A. Youth Cup 1Q*
04	Tue	UEFA U21 Qualifier - England v Albania - ko tbc (at Middlesbrough FC - 8.00pm)
05	Wed	FIFA World Cup Qualifier - England v Albania - 8.00pm (at Newcastle United FC)
08	Sat	F.A. Carlsberg Vase 1Q
09	Sun	AXA F.A. Women's Cup 1Q
		AXA F.A. Women's Premier League Cup P
11/12	Tue/Wed	UEFA Champions League - Group Stage 1 - Match Day 1
12	Wed	Worthington Cup 2
13	Thu	UEFA Cup 1 (1)
14	Fri	World U17 Championship commences - Trinidad & Tobago
15	Sat	F.A. Cup sponsored by AXA 1Q
18/19	Tue/Wed	UEFA Champions League - Group Stage 1 - Match Day 2
22	Sat	F.A. Carlsberg Vase 2Q
		AXA F.A. Youth Cup 2Q*
23	Sun	AXA F.A. Women's Premier League Cup 1
25/26	Tue/Wed	UEFA Champions League - Group Stage 1 - Match Day 3
27	Thu	UEFA Cup 1 (2)
		FIFA Women's World Cup Qualifier - Germany v England - venue & ko tbc
29	Sat	F.A. Cup sponsored by AXA 2Q
30	Sun	World U17 Championship ends
		AXA F.A. Women's Cup 2Q

OCTOBER 2001

01	Mon	U19 Friendly International - England v Iceland - venue & ko tbc
03	Wed	U17 Friendly International - England v Israel - venue & ko tbc

04	Thu	U19 Friendly International - England v Russia - venue & ko tbc
05	Fri	UEFA U21 Qualifier - England v Greece - ko tbc
		(at Blackburn Rovers FC - 8.00pm)
06	Sat	FIFA World Cup Qualifier - England v Greece
		(at Manchester United FC - 3.00pm)
		AXA F.A. Youth Cup 3Q*
		F.A. County Youth Cup 1*
07	Sun	F.A. Umbro Sunday Cup 1
10	Wed	Worthington Cup 3
12	Fri	U16 Victory Shield - England v Northern Ireland - venue & ko tbc
13	Sat	F.A. Cup sponsored by AXA 3Q
16/17	Tue/Wed	UEFA Champions League - Group Stage 1 - Match Day 4
17	Wed	LDV Vans Trophy 1
18	Thu	UEFA Cup 2 (1)
20	Sat	F.A. Carlsberg Vase 1P
23/24	Tue/Wed	UEFA Champions League - Group Stage 1 - Match Day 5
27	Sat	F.A. Cup sponsored by AXA 4Q
		AXA F.A. Youth Cup 1P*
28	Sun	AXA F.A. Women's Cup 1P
		AXA F.A. Women's Premier League Cup 2
30/31	Tue/Wed	UEFA Champions League - Group Stage 1 - Match Day 6
31	Wed	LDV Vans Trophy 2

NOVEMBER 2001

01	Thu	UEFA Cup 2 (2)
02	Fri	U16 Victory Shield - England v Wales - venue & ko tbc
03	Sat	F.A. Umbro Trophy 1
04	Sun	F.A. Umbro Sunday Cup 2
		FIFA Women's World Cup Qualifier - England v Netherlands venue & ko tbc
07	Wed	UEFA U19 Preliminary Rd - England v Georgia - venue & ko tbc
09	Fri	UEFA U21 Play Offs
10	Sat	FIFA World Cup Play Offs
		F.A. Carlsberg Vase 2P
		AXA F.A. Youth Cup 2P*
		F.A. County Youth Cup 2*
11	Sun	UEFA U19 Preliminary Rd - England v Hungary - venue & ko tbc
		AXA F.A. Women's Cup 2P
		AXA F.A. Women's Premier League Cup 3
13	Tue	UEFA U21 Play Offs
14	Wed	FIFA World Cup Play Offs
17	Sat	F.A. Cup sponsored by AXA 1P
20/21	Tue/Wed	UEFA Champions League - Group Stage 2 - Match Day 7
22	Thu	UEFA Cup 3 (1)
24	Sat	FIFA Women's World Cup Qualifier - Portugal v England - venue & ko tbc
27	Tue	EU/SA Cup
28	Wed	Worthington Cup 4
30	Fri	U16 Victory Shield - Scotland v England - venue & ko tbc

DECEMBER 2001

01	Sat	F.A. Umbro Trophy 2
02	Sun	F.A. Umbro Sunday Cup 3
04/05	Tue/Wed	UEFA Champions League - Group Stage 2 - Match Day 8
05	Wed	LDV Vans Trophy Area QF
06	Thu	UEFA Cup 3 (2)
08	Sat	F.A. Cup sponsored by AXA 2P
		F.A. Carlsberg Vase 3P
		AXA F.A. Youth Cup 3P*
09	Sun	AXA F.A. Women's Cup 3P
12	Wed	Worthington Cup 5
15	Sat	F.A. County Youth Cup 3*
16	Sun	AXA F.A. Women's Premier League Cup SF

JANUARY 2002

01	Tue	New Year's Day
05	Sat	F.A. Cup sponsored by AXA 3P
06	Sun	AXA F.A. Women's Cup 4P
09	Wed	Worthington Cup SF (1)
		LDV Vans Trophy Area SF
12	Sat	F.A. Umbro Trophy 3
13	Sun	F.A. Umbro Sunday Cup 4
19	Sat	F.A. Carlsberg Vase 4P
23	Wed	Worthington Cup SF (2)
26	Sat	F.A. Cup sponsored by AXA 4P
		AXA F.A. Youth Cup 4P*
27	Sun	AXA F.A. Women's Cup 5P
30	Wed	LDV Vans Trophy Area Final 1

FEBRUARY 2002

02	Sat	F.A. Umbro Trophy 4
		F.A. County Youth Cup 4*
03	Sun	F.A. Umbro Sunday Cup 5

09	Sat	F.A. Carlsberg Vase 5P
10	Sun	AXA F.A. Women's Cup 6P
12	Tue	International Friendly dates
12/13	Tue/Wed	International Friendly dates
16	Sat	F.A. Cup sponsored by AXA 5P
		AXA F.A. Youth Cup 5P*
19/20	Tue/Wed	UEFA Champions League - Group Stage 2 - Match Day 9
		LDV Vans Trophy Area Final 2
21	Thu	UEFA Cup 4 (1)
23	Sat	F.A. Umbro Trophy 5
24	Sun	Worthington Cup Final
		FIFA Women's World Cup Qualifier - England v Portugal - venue & ko tbc
26/27	Tue/Wed	UEFA Champions League - Group Stage 2 - Match Day 10
28	Thu	UEFA Cup 4 (2)

MARCH 2002

02	Sat	F.A. Carlsberg Vase 6P
03	Sun	F.A. Umbro Sunday Cup SF
06	Wed	UEFA U17 Preliminary Round - England v Scotland - venue & ko tbc
09	Sat	F.A. Cup sponsored by AXA 6P
		AXA F.A. Youth Cup 6P*
		F.A. County Youth Cup SF*
10	Sun	UEFA U17 Preliminary Round - England v Lithuania - venue & ko tbc
		AXA F.A. Women's Premier League
Cup Final		
12/13	Tue/Wed	UEFA Champions League - Group Stage 2 - Match Day 11
14	Thu	UEFA Cup QF (1)
16	Sat	F.A. Umbro Trophy 6
19/20	Tue/Wed	UEFA Champions League - Group Stage 2 - Match Day 12
20	Wed	U18 Friendly International - Italy v England - venue & ko tbc
21	Thu	UEFA Cup QF (2)
23	Sat	F.A. Carlsberg Vase SF (1)
		FIFA Women's World Cup Qualifier - Netherlands v England venue & ko tbc
24	Sun	LDV Vans Trophy Final
26	Tue	Nationwide U21 Friendly International - England v Italy - venue & ko tbc
27	Wed	Nationwide Friendly International - England v Italy - ko tbc
		(at Leeds United FC)
30	Sat	F.A. Carlsberg Vase SF (2)
		AXA F.A. Youth Cup SF (1)*
31	Sun	AXA F.A. Women's Cup SF

APRIL 2002

02/03	Tue/Wed	UEFA Champions League - QF (1)
04	Thu	UEFA Cup SF (1)
06	Sat	F.A. Umbro Trophy SF (1)
09/10	Tue/Wed	UEFA Champions League - QF (2)
11	Thu	UEFA Cup SF (2)
13	Sat	F.A. Umbro Trophy SF (2)
		AXA F.A. Youth Cup SF (2)*
14	Sun	F.A. Cup sponsored by AXA SF
16/17	Tue/Wed	International Friendly dates
20	Sat	Football League ends
23/24	Tue/Wed	UEFA Champions League - SF (1)
27	Sat	F.A. County Youth Cup Final
28	Sun	Football League Play-Off SF (1)
		AXA F.A. Women's Premier League ends
30/01	Tue/Wed	UEFA Champions League - SF (2)

MAY 2002

01	Wed	Football League Play-Off SF (2)
02	Thu	AXA F.A. Youth Cup Final (1) - o be confirmed
04	Sat	F.A. Cup sponsored by AXA Final
06	Mon	Bank Holiday
		AXA F.A. Women's Cup Final
07	Tue	AXA F.A. Youth Cup Final (2) - to be confirmed
08	Wed	UEFA Cup Final
10-12	Fri/Sun	Football League Play-Off Finals
15	Wed	UEFA Champions League Final
19	Sun	FIFA Women's World Cup Qualifier - England v Germany - venue & ko tbc
31	Fri	World Cup 2002 commences

JUNE 2002

30	Sun	World Cup 2002 Final

To be confirmed: F.A. Umbro Trophy Final
F.A. Carlsberg Vase Final
F.A. Umbro Sunday Cup Final

* closing date of Round

Gary Patterson, England Semi-Professional Captain

LEAGUE INDEX

Leagues are listed alphabetically below with their relevant page numbers. Where a league entry runs to more than one page, the number indicated is that of the first page of the section.
As in previous years, sponsors' names have been omitted to ease reference.
League sponsors, however, get their deserved recognition in the appropriate sections.

VASE & TROPHY CLUBS' INDEX

CLUB	F.A. Competitions	League	County F.A.
Abbey Hey FC	Cup/Vase	N.W.C. Div. 1 (351-370)	Manchester FA
Abingdon Town FC	Cup/Vase	Isthmian Div. 3 (861-870)	Berks & Bucks FA
Abingdon United FC	Cup/Vase	Hellenic Prem. Div. (591-611)	Berks & Bucks FA
Accrington Stanley FC	Cup/Trophy	N.P.L. Prem. Div. (278)	Lancashire FA
AFC Newbury	Cup/Vase	Wessex League (675-686)	Berks & Bucks FA
AFC Sudbury	Cup/Vase	Eastern Prem. Div. (571-588)	Suffolk FA
AFC Totton	Cup/Vase	Wessex League (675-686)	Hampshire FA
AFC Wallingford	Cup/Vase	Combined Counties (871-880)	Berks & Bucks FA
Aldershot Town FC	Cup/Trophy	Isthmian Prem. Div. (776)	Hampshire FA
Alfreton Town FC	Cup/Vase	N.C.E. Prem. Div. (393-410)	Derbyshire FA
Almondsbury Town FC	Vase	Hellenic Prem. Div. (591-611)	Gloucestershire FA
Alnwich Town FC	Vase	Northern Div. 2 (427-445)	Northumberland FA
Alton Town FC	Vase	Hampshire League (687-690)	Hampshire FA
Altrincham FC	Cup/Trophy	N.P.L. Prem. Div. (280)	Cheshire FA
Amesbury Town FC	Vase	Hampshire League (687-690)	Wiltshire FA

Alfreton Town's Craig Atkinson does 'The Bump' with Armthorpe Welfare's D Bennett (left) and Waugh. Photo: Bill Wheatcroft

Alvechurch FC	Vase	Mid. Comb. Prem. Div. (747-754)	Birmingham FA
Andover FC	Cup/Vase	Wessex League (675-686)	Hampshire FA
Anstey Nomads FC	Vase	Leics. Sen. Prem. Div. (764-768)	Leics. & Rutland FA
Arlesey Town FC	Cup/Vase	Isthmian Div. 2 (847-860)	Bedfordshire FA
Armthorpe Welfare FC	Cup/Vase	N.C.E. Prem. Div. (393-410)	West Riding FA
Arnold Town FC	Cup/Vase	N.C.E. Prem. Div. (393-410)	Nottinghamshire FA
Arundel FC	Cup/Vase	Sussex Div. 1 (631-651)	Sussex FA
Ash United FC	Cup/Vase	Combined Counties (871-880)	Surrey FA
Ashford Town FC (Middx)	Cup/Vase	Isthmian Div. 2 (847-860)	Middlesex FA
Ashford Town FC	Cup/Trophy	Southern Eastern Div. (549)	Kent FA
Ashington FC	Cup/Vase	Northern Div. 1 (427-445)	Northumberland FA
Ashton United FC	Cup/Trophy	N.P.L. Div. 1 (327)	Manchester FA
Atherstone United FC	Cup/Trophy	Southern Western Div. (525)	Birmingham FA
Atherton Collieries FC	Cup/Vase	N.W.C. Div. 1 (351-370)	Lancashire FA
Atherton LR FC	Cup/Vase	N.W.C. Div. 1 (351-370)	Lancashire FA
Aveley FC	Cup/Vase	Isthmian Div. 3 (861-870)	Essex FA
Aylesbury United FC	Cup/Trophy	Isthmian Div. 1 (824)	Berks & Bucks FA
Backwell United FC	Cup/Vase	Western Lge. Prem. Div. (696-712)	Somerset FA
Bacup Borough FC	Cup/Vase	N.W.C. Div. 2 (351-370)	Lancashire FA
Bamber Bridge FC	Cup/Trophy	N.P.L. Prem. Div. (282)	Lancashire FA
Banbury United FC	Cup/Trophy	Southern Eastern Div. (550)	Oxfordshire FA
Banstead Athletic FC	Cup/Vase	Isthmian Div. 2 (847-860)	Surrey FA
Barking & East Ham United FC	Cup/Trophy	Isthmian Div. 1 (825)	London FA
Barnet FC	Cup/Trophy	Conference (139)	Hertfordshire FA
Barnstaple Town FC	Cup/Vase	Western Lge. Prem. Div. (696-712)	Devon FA
Barrow FC	Cup/Trophy	N.P.L. Prem. Div. (284)	Lancashire FA
Barrow Town FC	Vase	Leics. Sen. Prem. Div. (764-768)	Leics. & Rutland FA
Barton Rovers FC	Cup/Vase	Isthmian Div. 2 (847-860)	Bedfordshire FA
Barwell FC	Cup/Vase	Midland Alliance (733-745)	Leics. & Rutland FA
Bashley FC	Cup/Trophy	Southern Eastern Div. (551)	Hampshire FA

Beckenham's Joe Westpfel gets in a first time volley despite the attention of Cray's Mark Dudley (4) and Jon Fellows (6). Photo: Alan Coomes

Basingstoke Town FC	Cup/Trophy	Isthmian Prem. Div. (778)	Hampshire FA
BAT Sports FC	Cup/Vase	Wessex League (675-686)	Hampshire FA
Bath City FC	Cup/Trophy	Southern Prem. Div. (476)	Somerset FA
Beaconsfield SYCOB FC	Cup/Vase	Spartan South Mids. Prem. Div. (889-902)	Berks & Bucks FA
Beckenham Town FC	Cup/Vase	Kent League (613-624)	Kent FA
Bedfont FC	Cup/Vase	Combined Counties (871-880)	Middlesex FA
Bedford Town FC	Cup/Trophy	Isthmian Prem. Div. (780)	Bedfordshire FA
Bedford United FC	Cup/Vase	Spartan South Mids. Prem. Div. (889-902)	Bedfordshire FA
Bedlington Terriers FC	Cup/Vase	Northern Div. 1 (427-445)	Northumberland FA
Bedworth United FC	Cup/Trophy	Southern Western Div. (526)	Birmingham FA
Belper Town FC	Cup/Trophy	N.P.L. Div. 1 (328)	Derbyshire FA
Bemerton Heath Harlequins FC	Cup/Vase	Wessex League (675-686)	Wiltshire FA
Berkhamsted Town FC	Cup/Vase	Isthmian Div. 2 (847-860)	Hertfordshire FA
Bicester Town FC	Vase	Hellenic Prem. Div. (591-611)	Oxfordshire FA
Bideford FC	Cup/Vase	Western Lge. Prem. Div. (696-712)	Devon FA
Biggleswade Town FC	Vase	Spartan South Mids. Prem. Div. (889-902)	Bedfordshire FA
Billericay Town FC	Cup/Trophy	Isthmian Prem. Div. (782)	Essex FA
Billingham Synthonia FC	Cup/Vase	Northern Div. 1 (427-445)	Durham FA
Billingham Town FC	Cup/Vase	Northern Div. 1 (427-445)	Durham FA
Bilston Town FC	Cup/Trophy	Southern Western Div. (527)	Staffordshire FA
Birstall United FC	Vase	Leics. Sen. Prem. Div. (764-768)	Leics. & Rutland FA
Bishop Auckland FC	Cup/Trophy	N.P.L. Prem. Div. (286)	Durham FA
Bishop Sutton FC	Cup/Vase	Western Lge. Prem. Div. (696-712)	Somerset FA
Bishop's Stortford FC	Cup/Trophy	Isthmian Div. 1 (826)	Hertfordshire FA
Bitton AFC	Vase	Western Lge. Div. 1 (695-712)	Gloucestershire FA
Blackfield & Langley FC	Vase	Wessex League (675-686)	Hampshire FA
Blackpool Mechanics FC	Cup/Vase	N.W.C. Div. 2 (351-370)	Lancashire FA
Blackstone FC	Cup/Vase	Utd. Counties Prem. Div. (653-673)	Lincolnshire FA
Bloxwich United FC	Cup/Trophy	Southern Western Div. (528)	Staffordshire FA
Blyth Spartans FC	Cup/Trophy	N.P.L. Prem. Div. (288)	Northumberland FA
Bognor Regis Town FC	Cup/Trophy	Isthmian Div. 1 (827)	Sussex FA
Boldmere St Michaels FC	Cup/Vase	Midland Alliance (733-745)	Birmingham FA
Bolehall Swifts FC	Vase	Mid. Comb. Prem. Div. (747-754)	Birmingham FA
Boreham Wood FC	Cup/Trophy	Isthmian Prem. Div. (784)	Hertfordshire FA
Borrowash Victoria FC	Cup/Vase	N.C.E. Prem. Div. (393-410)	Derbyshire FA
Boston Town FC	Cup/Vase	Utd. Counties Prem. Div. (653-673)	Lincolnshire FA
Boston United FC	Cup/Trophy	Conference (145)	Lincolnshire FA
Bottesford Town FC	Vase	Central Mids. Supreme Div. (411-420)	Lincolnshire FA
Bourne Town FC	Cup/Vase	Utd. Counties Prem. Div. (653-673)	Lincolnshire FA
Bournemouth FC	Cup/Vase	Wessex League (675-686)	Hampshire FA
Bowers United FC	Cup/Vase	Essex Senior (881-887)	Essex FA
Brache Sparta FC	Vase	Spartan South Mids. Prem. Div. (889-902)	Bedfordshire FA
Brackley Town FC	Cup/Vase	Hellenic Prem. Div. (591-611)	Northamptonshire FA

Bracknell Town FC	Cup/Vase	Isthmian Div. 3 (861-870)	Berks & Bucks FA
Bradford (Park Avenue) FC	Cup/Trophy	N.P.L. Prem. Div. (290)	West Riding FA
Braintree Town FC	Cup/Trophy	Isthmian Prem. Div. (786)	Essex FA
Brandon United FC	Cup/Vase	Northern Div. 1 (427-445)	Durham FA
Brentwood FC	Cup/Vase	Essex Senior (881-887)	Essex FA
Bridgnorth Town FC	Cup/Vase	Midland Alliance (733-745)	Shropshire FA
Bridgwater Town FC	Cup/Vase	Western Lge. Prem. Div. (696-712)	Somerset FA
Bridlington Town FC	Cup/Vase	N.C.E. Div. 1 (393-410)	EAST RIDING FA
Bridport FC	Cup/Vase	Western Lge. Prem. Div. (696-712)	Dorset FA
Brierley & Hagley Alliance FC	Vase	West Mids. Prem. Div. (755-763)	Birmingham FA
Brigg Town FC	Cup/Vase	N.C.E. Prem. Div. (393-410)	Lincolnshire FA
Brightlingsea United FC	Vase	Eastern Div. 1 (571-588)	Essex FA
Brimsdown Rovers FC	Vase	Spartan South Mids. Div. 1 (889-902)	London FA
Brislington FC	Cup/Vase	Western Lge. Prem. Div. (696-712)	Somerset FA
Bristol Manor Farm FC	Cup/Vase	Western Lge. Prem. Div. (696-712)	Gloucestershire FA
Brockenhurst FC	Cup/Vase	Wessex League (675-686)	Hampshire FA
Brodsworth FC	Cup/Vase	N.C.E. Prem. Div. (393-410)	Sheff. & Hallams. FA
Bromley FC	Cup/Trophy	Isthmian Div. 1 (828)	Kent FA
Bromsgrove Rovers FC	Cup/Vase	Midland Alliance (733-745)	Worcestershire FA
Bromyard Town FC	Vase	West Mids. Prem. Div. (755-763)	Herefordshire FA
Brook House FC	Cup/Vase	Spartan South Mids. Prem. Div. (889-902)	Middlesex FA
Buckingham Town FC	Cup/Vase	Utd. Counties Prem. Div. (653-673)	Berks & Bucks FA
Bugbrooke St Michaels	Cup/Vase	Utd. Counties Prem. Div. (653-673)	Northamptonshire FA
Burgess Hill Town FC	Cup/Vase	Sussex Div. 1 (631-651)	Sussex FA
Burnham FC	Cup/Trophy	Southern Eastern Div. (552)	Berks & Bucks FA
Burnham Ramblers FC	Cup/Vase	Essex Senior (881-887)	Essex FA
Burscough FC	Cup/Trophy	N.P.L. Prem. Div. (292)	Liverpool FA

Borrowash Victoria forward Andy Beckford rifles in a fierce shot against Marconi through a crowded penalty area but his effort goes just wide. Photo: Martin Wray

Burton Albion FC	Cup/Trophy	N.P.L. Prem. Div. (294)	Birmingham FA
Bury Town FC	Cup/Vase	Eastern Prem. Div. (571-588)	Suffolk FA
Buxton FC	Cup/Vase	N.C.E. Prem. Div. (393-410)	Derbyshire FA
Calne Town FC	Cup/Vase	Western Lge. Div. 1 (695-712)	Wiltshire FA
Camberley Town FC	Cup/Vase	Isthmian Div. 3 (861-870)	Surrey FA
Cambridge City FC	Cup/Trophy	Southern Prem. Div. (478)	Cambridgeshire FA
Cammell Laird FC	Vase	West Cheshire (375-378)	Cheshire FA
Canvey Island FC	Cup/Trophy	Isthmian Prem. Div. (788)	Essex FA
Carshalton Athletic FC	Cup/Trophy	Isthmian Div. 1 (829)	Surrey FA
Carterton Town FC	Cup/Vase	Hellenic Prem. Div. (591-611)	Oxfordshire FA
Castleton Gabriels FC	Cup/Vase	N.W.C. Div. 2 (351-370)	Lancashire FA
Causeway United FC	Vase	West Mids. Prem. Div. (755-763)	Birmingham FA
Chadderton FC	Cup/Vase	N.W.C. Div. 2 (351-370)	Manchester FA
Chalfont St Peter FC	Cup/Vase	Isthmian Div. 3 (861-870)	Berks & Bucks FA
Chard Town FC	Vase	Western Lge. Div. 1 (695-712)	Somerset FA
Chasetown FC	Cup/Vase	Midland Alliance (733-745)	Staffordshire FA
Chatham Town FC	Cup/Trophy	Southern Eastern Div. (553)	Kent FA
Cheadle Town FC	Cup/Vase	N.W.C. Div. 2 (351-370)	Cheshire FA
Chelmsford City FC	Cup/Trophy	Southern Prem. Div. (480)	Essex FA
Chertsey Town FC	Cup/Vase	Isthmian Div. 2 (847-860)	Surrey FA
Chesham United FC	Cup/Trophy	Isthmian Prem. Div. (790)	Berks & Bucks FA
Cheshunt FC	Cup/Vase	Isthmian Div. 2 (847-860)	Hertfordshire FA
Cheslyn Hay FC	Vase	Mid. Comb. Prem. Div. (747-754)	Staffordshire FA
Chessington & Hook United FC	Cup/Vase	Combined Counties (871-880)	Surrey FA
Chessington United FC	Vase	Combined Counties (871-880)	Surrey FA
Chester City FC	Cup/Trophy	Conference (151)	Cheshire FA
Chester-le-Street Town FC	Cup/Vase	Northern Div. 1 (427-445)	Durham FA

Chatham's Danny Jeffery fires in a shot past Slade Green's Rob White. Photo: Alan Coomes

Chichester City United FC	Cup/Vase	Sussex Div. 1 (631-651)	Sussex FA
Chippenham Town FC	Cup/Trophy	Southern Western Div. (529)	Wiltshire FA
Chipstead FC	Cup/Vase	Combined Counties (871-880)	Surrey FA
Chorley FC	Cup/Trophy	N.P.L. Div. 1 (329)	Lancashire FA
Christchurch FC	Cup/Vase	Wessex League (675-686)	Hampshire FA
Cinderford Town FC	Cup/Trophy	Southern Western Div. (530)	Gloucestershire FA
Cirencester Town FC	Cup/Trophy	Southern Western Div. (531)	Gloucestershire FA
Clacton Town FC	Cup/Vase	Eastern Prem. Div. (571-588)	Essex FA
Clapton FC	Cup/Vase	Isthmian Div. 3 (861-870)	London FA
Clevedon Town FC	Cup/Trophy	Southern Western Div. (532)	Somerset FA
Clevedon United FC	Vase	Somerset Prem. Div.	Somerset FA
Clitheroe FC	Cup/Vase	N.W.C. Div. 1 (351-370)	Lancashire FA
Cobham FC	Cup/Vase	Combined Counties (871-880)	Surrey FA
Cockfosters FC	Vase	Spartan South Mids. Div. 1 (889-902)	London FA
Cogenhoe United FC	Cup/Vase	Utd. Counties Prem. Div. (653-673)	Northamptonshire FA
Collingham FC	Vase	Central Mids. Supreme Div. (411-420)	Nottinghamshire FA
Colne FC	Vase	N.W.C. Div. 2 (351-370)	Lancashire FA
Colney Heath FC	Vase	Spartan South Mids. Div. 1 (889-902)	Hertfordshire FA
Colwyn Bay FC	Cup/Trophy	N.P.L. Prem. Div. (296)	F.A. of Wales

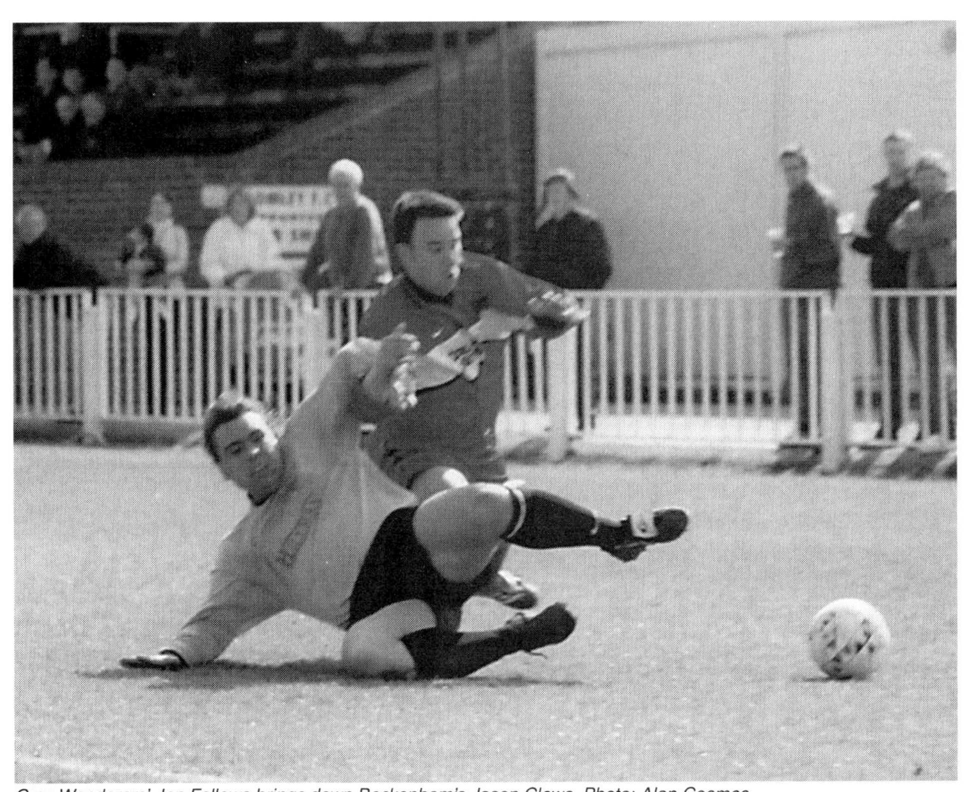

Cray Wanderers' Jon Fellows brings down Beckenham's Jason Clews. Photo: Alan Coomes

Concord Rangers FC	Cup/Vase	Essex Senior (881-887)	Essex FA
Congleton Town FC	Cup/Vase	N.W.C. Div. 1 (351-370)	Cheshire FA
Consett FC	Cup/Vase	Northern Div. 1 (427-445)	Durham FA
Corby Town FC	Cup/Trophy	Southern Eastern Div. (554)	Northamptonshire FA
Corinthian Casuals FC	Cup/Vase	Isthmian Div. 3 (861-870)	London FA
Cornard United FC	Vase	Eastern Div. 1 (571-588)	Suffolk FA
Corsham Town FC	Vase	Western Lge. Div. 1 (695-712)	Wiltshire FA
Cove FC	Cup/Vase	Combined Counties (871-880)	Hampshire FA
Coventry Marconi FC	Vase	Mid. Comb. Prem. Div. (747-754)	Birmingham FA
Cowes Sports FC	Cup/Vase	Wessex League (675-686)	Hampshire FA
Cradley Town FC	Cup/Vase	Midland Alliance (733-745)	Birmingham FA
Crawley Town FC	Cup/Trophy	Southern Prem. Div. (482)	Sussex FA
Cray Wanderers FC	Cup/Vase	Kent League (613-624)	Kent FA
Crook Town FC	Cup/Vase	Northern Div. 2 (427-445)	Durham FA
Crowborough Athletic FC	Vase	Sussex Div. 2 (631-651)	Sussex FA
Croydon FC	Cup/Trophy	Isthmian Prem. Div. (792)	Surrey FA
Croydon Athletic FC	Cup/Vase	Isthmian Div. 3 (861-870)	London FA
Cullompton Rangers FC	Vase	Devon	Devon FA
Curzon Ashton FC	Cup/Vase	N.W.C. Div. 1 (351-370)	Manchester FA
Dagenham & Redbridge FC	Cup/Trophy	Conference (157)	Essex FA
Dartford FC	Cup/Trophy	Southern Eastern Div. (555)	Kent FA
Darwen FC	Cup/Vase	N.W.C. Div. 2 (351-370)	Lancashire FA
Dawlish Town FC	Vase	Western Lge. Prem. Div. (696-712)	Devon FA
Deal Town FC	Cup/Vase	Kent League (613-624)	Kent FA
Deeping Rangers FC	Cup/Trophy	Utd. Counties Prem. Div. (653-673)	Essex FA
Denaby United FC	Cup/Vase	N.C.E. Prem. Div. (393-410)	Sheff. & Hallams. FA
Dereham Town FC	Vase	Eastern Prem. Div. (571-588)	Norfolk FA
Desborough Town FC	Cup/Vase	Utd. Counties Prem. Div. (653-673)	Northamptonshire FA
Devizes Town FC	Cup/Vase	Western Lge. Prem. Div. (696-712)	Wiltshire FA
Didcot Town FC	Cup/Vase	Hellenic Prem. Div. (591-611)	Berks & Bucks FA
Diss Town FC	Cup/Vase	Eastern Prem. Div. (571-588)	Norfolk FA
Doncaster Rovers FC	Cup/Trophy	Conference (163)	Sheff. & Hallams. FA
Dorchester Town FC	Cup/Trophy	Southern Eastern Div. (556)	Dorset FA
Dorking FC	Cup/Vase	Isthmian Div. 3 (861-870)	Surrey FA
Dover Athletic FC	Cup/Trophy	Conference (169)	Kent FA
Downes Sports FC	Vase	Leics. Sen. Prem. Div. (764-768)	Leics. & Rutland FA
Downham Town FC	Vase	Eastern Div. 1 (571-588)	Norfolk FA
Downton FC	Cup/Vase	Wessex League (675-686)	Wiltshire FA
Droylsden FC	Cup/Trophy	N.P.L. Prem. Div. (298)	Manchester FA
Dudley Town FC	Vase	West Mids. Prem. Div. (755-763)	Birmingham FA
Dulwich Hamlet FC	Cup/Trophy	Isthmian Div. 1 (830)	London FA
Dunkirk FC	Vase	Central Mids. Supreme Div. (411-420)	Birmingham FA
Dunstable Town FC	Vase	Spartan South Mids. Prem. Div. (889-902)	Bedfordshire FA

Dunston Federation Brewery FC	Cup/Vase	Northern Div. 1 (427-445)	Durham FA
Durham City FC	Cup/Vase	Northern Div. 1 (427-445)	Durham FA
Easington Colliery FC	Cup/Vase	Northern Div. 2 (427-445)	Durham FA
East Grinstead Town FC	Vase	Sussex Div. 2 (631-651)	Sussex FA
East Preston FC	Cup/Vase	Sussex Div. 2 (631-651)	Sussex FA
East Thurrock United FC	Cup/Vase	Isthmian Div. 2 (847-860)	Essex FA
Eastbourne Borough	Cup/Trophy	Southern Eastern Div. (557)	Sussex FA
Eastbourne Town FC	Cup/Vase	Sussex Div. 2 (631-651)	Sussex FA
Eastbourne United FC	Cup/Vase	Sussex Div. 1 (631-651)	Sussex FA
Eastleigh FC	Cup/Vase	Wessex League (675-686)	Hampshire FA
Eastwood Town FC	Cup/Trophy	N.P.L. Div. 1 (330)	Nottinghamshire FA
Eccleshill United FC	Cup/Vase	N.C.E. Prem. Div. (393-410)	West Riding FA
Edgware Town FC	Cup/Vase	Isthmian Div. 3 (861-870)	Middlesex FA
Egham Town FC	Cup/Vase	Isthmian Div. 3 (861-870)	Surrey FA
Elmore FC	Cup/Vase	Western Lge. Prem. Div. (696-712)	Devon FA
Ely City FC	Cup/Vase	Eastern Prem. Div. (571-588)	Cambridgeshire FA
Emley AFC	Cup/Trophy	N.P.L. Prem. Div. (300)	Sheff. & Hallams. FA
Enfield FC	Cup/Trophy	Isthmian Prem. Div. (794)	Middlesex FA
Epsom & Ewell FC	Cup/Vase	Isthmian Div. 3 (861-870)	Surrey FA
Erith & Belvedere FC	Cup/Trophy	Southern Eastern Div. (558)	Kent FA
Erith Town FC	Cup/Vase	Kent League (613-624)	London FA
Esh Winning FC	Cup/Vase	Northern Div. 2 (427-445)	Durham FA
Evenwood Town FC	Cup/Vase	Northern Div. 2 (427-445)	Durham FA
Evesham United FC	Cup/Trophy	Southern Western Div. (533)	Worcestershire FA
Eynesbury Rovers FC	Cup/Vase	Utd. Counties Div. 1 (653-673)	Huntingdonshire FA

Dudley Town. Back Row (l-r): Ian Cornfield, Brian Carmichael, Keoan Jackson, John Carmichael, Richard Taylor, Tony Higgins, Noel Haye, Albert Johnson, Richard Cooper, Ian Davis. Front Row: Liam Heaton, Stewart Marshall, Martin Hassam, Micky Dixon, Phil Male, Wayne Crumpton, Bernie Gethins, Jason Attwell, Craig Prince.

Fairford Town FC	Vase	Hellenic Prem. Div. (591-611)	Gloucestershire FA
Fakenham Town FC	Cup/Vase	Eastern Prem. Div. (571-588)	Norfolk FA
Falmouth Town AFC	Cup/Vase	South Western (715-722)	Cornwall FA
Fareham Town FC	Cup/Vase	Wessex League (675-686)	Hampshire FA
Farnborough Town FC	Cup/Trophy	Conference (175)	Hampshire FA
Farnham Town FC	Cup/Vase	Combined Counties (871-880)	Surrey FA
Farsley Celtic FC	Cup/Trophy	N.P.L. Div. 1 (331)	West Riding FA
Felixstowe & Walton FC	Cup/Vase	Eastern Prem. Div. (571-588)	Suffolk FA
Fisher Athletic FC	Cup/Trophy	Southern Eastern Div. (559)	London FA
Flackwell Heath FC	Cup/Vase	Isthmian Div. 3 (861-870)	Berks & Bucks FA
Fleet Town FC	Cup/Vase	Wessex League (675-686)	Hampshire FA
Fleetwood Freeport FC	Cup/Vase	N.W.C. Div. 1 (351-370)	Lancashire FA
Flixton FC	Cup/Vase	N.W.C. Div. 1 (351-370)	Manchester FA
Folkestone Invicta FC	Cup/Trophy	Southern Prem. Div. (484)	Kent FA
Ford Sports Daventry FC	Cup/Vase	Utd. Counties Prem. Div. (653-673)	Northamptonshire FA
Ford United FC	Cup/Trophy	Isthmian Div. 1 (831)	London FA
Forest Green Rovers FC	Cup/Trophy	Conference (181)	Gloucestershire FA
Friar Lane OB FC	Vase	Leics. Sen. Prem. Div. (764-768)	Leics. & Rutland FA
Frickley Athletic FC	Cup/Trophy	N.P.L. Prem. Div. (302)	Sheff. & Hallams. FA
Frome Town FC	Cup/Vase	Western Lge. Div. 1 (695-712)	Somerset FA
Gainsborough Trinity FC	Cup/Trophy	N.P.L. Prem. Div. (304)	Lincolnshire FA
Garforth Town FC	Cup/Vase	N.C.E. Prem. Div. (393-410)	West Riding FA
Gateshead FC	Cup/Trophy	N.P.L. Prem. Div. (306)	Durham FA
Gedling Town FC	Cup/Vase	N.C.E. Div. 1 (393-410)	Nottinghamshire FA
Glapwell FC	Cup/Vase	N.C.E. Prem. Div. (393-410)	Derbyshire FA
Glasshoughton Welfare FC	Cup/Vase	N.C.E. Prem. Div. (393-410)	West Riding FA
Glossop North End FC	Cup/Vase	N.W.C. Div. 1 (351-370)	Derbyshire FA
Gloucester City FC	Cup/Trophy	Southern Western Div. (534)	Gloucestershire FA
Gloucester United FC	Vase	Hellenic Prem. Div. (591-611)	Gloucestershire FA
Godalming & Guildford FC	Cup/Vase	Combined Counties (871-880)	Surrey FA
Goole AFC	Cup/Vase	N.C.E. Prem. Div. (393-410)	West Riding FA
Gorleston FC	Cup/Vase	Eastern Prem. Div. (571-588)	Norfolk FA
Gornal Athletic FC	Vase	West Mids. Prem. Div. (755-763)	Birmingham FA
Gosport Borough FC	Cup/Vase	Wessex League (675-686)	Hampshire FA
Grantham Town FC	Cup/Trophy	Southern Eastern Div. (560)	Lincolnshire FA
Gravesend & Northfleet FC	Cup/Trophy	Isthmian Prem. Div. (796)	Kent FA
Grays Athletic FC	Cup/Trophy	Isthmian Prem. Div. (798)	Essex FA
Great Harwood Town FC	Cup/Vase	N.W.C. Div. 1 (351-370)	Lancashire FA
Great Wakering Rovers FC	Cup/Vase	Isthmian Div. 2 (847-860)	Essex FA
Great Yarmouth Town FC	Cup/Vase	Eastern Prem. Div. (571-588)	Norfolk FA
Greenwich Borough FC	Cup/Vase	Kent League (613-624)	Kent FA
Gresley Rovers FC	Cup/Trophy	Southern Western Div. (535)	Derbyshire FA
Gretna FC	Cup/Trophy	N.P.L. Div. 1 (332)	Cumberland FA

Grosvenor Park FC	Vase	Mid. Comb. Prem. Div. (747-754)	Birmingham FA
Guisborough Town FC	Cup/Vase	Northern Div. 1 (427-445)	North Riding FA
Guiseley FC	Cup/Trophy	N.P.L. Div. 1 (333)	West Riding FA
Hadleigh United FC	Vase	Eastern Div. 1 (571-588)	Suffolk FA
Hailsham Town FC	Cup/Vase	Sussex Div. 1 (631-651)	Sussex FA
Halesowen Harriers FC	Cup/Vase	Midland Alliance (733-745)	Birmingham FA
Halesowen Town FC	Cup/Trophy	Southern Western Div. (536)	Birmingham FA
Hall Road Rangers FC	Vase	N.C.E. Div. 1 (393-410)	East Riding FA
Hallam FC	Cup/Vase	N.C.E. Prem. Div. (393-410)	Sheff. & Hallams. FA
Hallen FC	Vase	Western Lge. Div. 1 (695-712)	Gloucestershire FA
Halstead Town FC	Cup/Vase	Eastern Div. 1 (571-588)	Essex FA
Hampton & Richmond Borough FC	Cup/Trophy	Isthmian Prem. Div. (800)	Middlesex FA
Handrahan Timbers FC	Vase	Mid. Comb. Prem. Div. (747-754)	Birmingham FA
Hanwell Town FC	Cup/Vase	Spartan South Mids. Prem. Div. (889-902)	Middlesex FA
Harefield United FC	Vase	Spartan South Mids. Div. 1 (889-902)	Middlesex FA
Haringey Borough FC	Cup/Vase	Spartan South Mids. Prem. Div. (889-902)	London FA
Harlow Town FC	Cup/Trophy	Isthmian Div. 1 (832)	Essex FA
Harpenden Town FC	Vase	Spartan South Mids. Div. 1 (889-902)	Hertfordshire FA
Harrogate Railway FC	Cup/Vase	N.C.E. Prem. Div. (393-410)	West Riding FA
Harrogate Town FC	Cup/Trophy	N.P.L. Div. 1 (334)	West Riding FA
Harrow Borough FC	Cup/Trophy	Isthmian Prem. Div. (802)	Middlesex FA
Harrow Hill FC	Vase	Hellenic Prem. Div. (591-611)	Gloucestershire FA
Harwich & Parkeston FC	Cup/Vase	Eastern Prem. Div. (571-588)	Essex FA
Hassocks FC	Cup/Vase	Sussex Div. 1 (631-651)	Sussex FA
Hastings Town FC	Cup/Trophy	Southern Eastern Div. (561)	Sussex FA
Hatfield Main FC	Cup/Vase	N.C.E. Div. 1 (393-410)	West Riding FA
Havant & Waterlooville FC	Cup/Trophy	Southern Prem. Div. (486)	Hampshire FA
Haverhill Rovers FC	Vase	Eastern Div. 1 (571-588)	Suffolk FA
Hayes FC	Cup/Trophy	Conference (187)	Middlesex FA
Heanor Town FC	Vase	Central Mids. Supreme Div. (411-420)	Derbyshire FA
Heath Hayes FC	Vase	West Mids. Prem. Div. (755-763)	Staffordshire FA
Hebburn FC	Vase	Northern Div. 2 (427-445)	Durham FA
Hednesford Town FC	Cup/Trophy	Southern Prem. Div. (488)	Birmingham FA
Hemel Hempstead Town FC	Cup/Vase	Isthmian Div. 2 (847-860)	Hertfordshire FA
Hendon FC	Cup/Trophy	Isthmian Prem. Div. (804)	Middlesex FA
Henley Town FC	Vase	Hellenic Prem. Div. (591-611)	Oxfordshire FA
Hereford United FC	Cup/Trophy	Conference (193)	Herefordshire FA
Herne Bay FC	Cup/Vase	Kent League (613-624)	Kent FA
Hertford Town FC	Cup/Vase	Isthmian Div. 3 (861-870)	Hertfordshire FA
Heybridge Swifts FC	Cup/Trophy	Isthmian Prem. Div. (806)	Essex FA
Highfield Rangers FC	Vase	Leics. Sen. Prem. Div. (764-768)	Leics. & Rutland FA
Highworth Town FC	Vase	Hellenic Prem. Div. (591-611)	Wiltshire FA
Hillingdon Borough FC	Cup/Vase	Spartan South Mids. Prem. Div. (889-902)	Middlesex FA

Hinckley United FC	Cup/Trophy	Southern Prem. Div. (490)	Leics. & Rutland FA
Histon FC	Cup/Trophy	Southern Eastern Div. (562)	Cambridgeshire FA
Hitchin Town FC	Cup/Trophy	Isthmian Prem. Div. (808)	Hertfordshire FA
Hoddesdon Town FC	Cup/Vase	Spartan South Mids. Prem. Div. (889-902)	Hertfordshire FA
Holbeach United FC	Cup/Vase	Utd. Counties Prem. Div. (653-673)	Lincolnshire FA
Holker Old Boys FC	Vase	N.W.C. Div. 2 (351-370)	Lancashire FA
Holmer Green FC	Cup/Vase	Spartan South Mids. Prem. Div. (889-902)	Berks & Bucks FA
Holwell Sports FC	Vase	Leics. Sen. Prem. Div. (764-768)	Leics. & Rutland FA
Horden CW FC	Cup/Vase	Northern Div. 2 (427-445)	Durham FA
Hornchurch FC	Cup/Vase	Isthmian Div. 3 (861-870)	Essex FA
Horsham FC	Cup/Vase	Isthmian Div. 2 (847-860)	Sussex FA
Horsham YMCA FC	Cup/Vase	Sussex Div. 1 (631-651)	Sussex FA
Hucknall Town FC	Cup/Trophy	N.P.L. Prem. Div. (308)	Nottinghamshire FA
Hullbridge Sports FC	Cup/Vase	Essex Senior (881-887)	Essex FA
Hungerford Town FC	Cup/Vase	Isthmian Div. 2 (847-860)	Berks & Bucks FA
Hyde United FC	Cup/Trophy	N.P.L. Prem. Div. (310)	Cheshire FA
Hythe Town FC	Cup/Vase	Kent League (613-624)	Kent FA
Ibstock Welfare FC	Vase	Leics. Sen. Prem. Div. (764-768)	Leics. & Rutland FA
Ilford FC	Cup/Vase	Essex Senior (881-887)	Essex FA
Ilfracombe Town FC	Vase	Western Lge. Div. 1 (695-712)	Devon FA
Ilkeston Town FC	Cup/Trophy	Southern Prem. Div. (492)	Derbyshire FA
Ipswich Wanderers FC	Cup/Vase	Eastern Prem. Div. (571-588)	Suffolk FA
Jarrow Roofing Boldon CA FC	Cup/Vase	Northern Div. 1 (427-445)	Durham FA
Kempston Rovers FC	Cup/Vase	Utd. Counties Prem. Div. (653-673)	Bedfordshire FA
Kendal Town FC	Cup/Trophy	N.P.L. Div. 1 (335)	Westmorland FA
Kettering Town FC	Cup/Trophy	Southern Prem. Div. (494)	Northamptonshire FA
Keynsham Town FC	Vase	Western Lge. Prem. Div. (696-712)	Somerset FA
Kidsgrove Athletic FC	Cup/Vase	N.W.C. Div. 1 (351-370)	Staffordshire FA
Kimberley Town FC	Vase	Central Mids. Supreme Div. (411-420)	Nottinghamshire FA
Kings Heath FC	Vase	Mid. Comb. Prem. Div. (747-754)	Birmingham FA
King's Lynn FC	Cup/Trophy	Southern Prem. Div. (496)	Norfolk FA
Kingsbury Town FC	Cup/Vase	Isthmian Div. 3 (861-870)	Middlesex FA
Kingstonian FC	Cup/Trophy	Isthmian Prem. Div. (810)	Surrey FA
Kirby Muxloe FC	Vase	Leics. Sen. Prem. Div. (764-768)	Leics. & Rutland FA
Knypersley Victoria FC	Cup/Vase	Midland Alliance (733-745)	Staffordshire FA
Lancaster City FC	Cup/Trophy	N.P.L. Prem. Div. (312)	Lancashire FA
Lancing FC	Cup/Vase	Sussex Div. 2 (631-651)	Sussex FA
Langford FC	Vase	Spartan South Mids. Div. 1 (889-902)	Bedfordshire FA
Leatherhead FC	Cup/Vase	Isthmian Div. 2 (847-860)	Surrey FA
Leek CSOB FC	Cup/Vase	N.W.C. Div. 2 (351-370)	Staffordshire FA
Leek Town FC	Cup/Trophy	N.P.L. Div. 1 (336)	Staffordshire FA
Leigh RMI FC	Cup/Trophy	Conference (199)	Lancashire FA
Leighton Town FC	Cup/Vase	Isthmian Div. 3 (861-870)	Bedfordshire FA

Letchworth FC	Vase	Spartan South Mids. Prem. Div. (889-902)	Hertfordshire FA
Leverstock Green FC	Vase	Spartan South Mids. Div. 1 (889-902)	Hertfordshire FA
Lewes FC	Cup/Vase	Isthmian Div. 2 (847-860)	Sussex FA
Leyton FC	Vase	Essex Senior (881-887)	London FA
Leyton Pennant FC	Cup/Vase	Isthmian Div. 2 (847-860)	Essex FA
Lincoln Moorlands FC	Vase	N.C.E. Div. 1 (393-410)	Lincolnshire FA
Lincoln United FC	Cup/Trophy	N.P.L. Div. 1 (337)	Lincolnshire FA
Littlehampton Town FC	Cup/Vase	Sussex Div. 1 (631-651)	Sussex FA
Liversedge FC	Cup/Vase	N.C.E. Prem. Div. (393-410)	West Riding FA
London Colney FC	Cup/Vase	Spartan South Mids. Prem. Div. (889-902)	Hertfordshire FA
Long Buckby FC	Cup/Vase	Utd. Counties Prem. Div. (653-673)	Northamptonshire FA
Long Eaton United FC	Vase	Central Mids. Supreme Div. (411-420)	Derbyshire FA
Lordswood FC	Cup/Vase	Kent League (613-624)	Kent FA
Louth United FC	Cup/Vase	N.C.E. Div. 1 (393-410)	Lincolnshire FA
Lowestoft Town FC	Cup/Vase	Eastern Prem. Div. (571-588)	Suffolk FA
Ludlow Town FC	Vase	Midland Alliance (733-745)	Shropshire FA
Lymington & New Milton FC	Cup/Vase	Wessex League (675-686)	Hampshire FA
Lymington Town FC	Vase	Hampshire League (687-690)	Hampshire FA
Maidenhead United FC	Cup/Trophy	Isthmian Prem. Div. (812)	Berks & Bucks FA
Maidstone United FC	Vase	Kent League (613-624)	Kent FA
Maine Road FC	Cup/Vase	N.W.C. Div. 1 (351-370)	Manchester FA
Maldon Town FC	Cup/Vase	Eastern Prem. Div. (571-588)	Essex FA
Maltby Main FC	Vase	N.C.E. Div. 1 (393-410)	Sheff. & Hallams. FA
Malvern Town FC	Vase	West Mids. Prem. Div. (755-763)	Worcestershire FA
Mangotsfield United FC	Cup/Trophy	Southern Western Div. (537)	Gloucestershire FA
March Town United FC	Vase	Eastern Div. 1 (571-588)	Cambridgeshire FA
Margate FC	Cup/Trophy	Conference (205)	Kent FA
Marine FC	Cup/Trophy	N.P.L. Prem. Div. (314)	Liverpool FA
Marlow FC	Cup/Vase	Isthmian Div. 2 (847-860)	Berks & Bucks FA
Marske United FC	Cup/Vase	Northern Div. 1 (427-445)	North Riding FA
Matlock Town FC	Cup/Trophy	N.P.L. Div. 1 (338)	Derbyshire FA
Meir KA FC	Vase	Mid. Comb. Prem. Div. (747-754)	Staffordshire FA
Melksham Town FC	Cup/Vase	Western Lge. Prem. Div. (696-712)	Wiltshire FA
Merstham FC	Cup/Vase	Combined Counties (871-880)	Surrey FA
Merthyr Tydfil FC	Cup/Trophy	Southern Prem. Div. (498)	F.A. of Wales
Metropolitan Police FC	Cup/Vase	Isthmian Div. 2 (847-860)	London FA
Mickleover Sports FC	Cup/Vase	N.C.E. Div. 1 (393-410)	Derbyshire FA
Mildenhall Town FC	Cup/Vase	Eastern Prem. Div. (571-588)	Suffolk FA
Milton Keynes City FC	Cup/Vase	Spartan South Mids. Prem. Div. (889-902)	Berks & Bucks FA
Milton United FC	Vase	Hellenic Div. 1 East (591-611)	Berks & Bucks FA
Minehead Town FC	Cup/Vase	Western Lge. Div. 1 (695-712)	Somerset FA
Molesey FC	Cup/Vase	Isthmian Div. 2 (847-860)	Surrey FA
Moneyfields FC	Cup/Vase	Wessex League (675-686)	Hampshire FA

Moor Green FC	Cup/Trophy	Southern Prem. Div. (500)	Birmingham FA
Morecambe FC	Cup/Trophy	Conference (211)	Lancashire FA
Morpeth Town FC	Cup/Vase	Northern Div. 1 (427-445)	Northumberland FA
Mossley FC	Cup/Vase	N.W.C. Div. 1 (351-370)	Manchester FA
Nantwich Town FC	Cup/Vase	N.W.C. Div. 1 (351-370)	Cheshire FA
Needham Market FC	Vase	Eastern Div. 1 (571-588)	Suffolk FA
Nelson FC	Vase	N.W.C. Div. 2 (351-370)	Lancashire FA
Newcastle Benfield Saints FC	Vase	Notts. Alliance (421-425)	Northumberland FA
Newcastle Blue Star FC	Cup/Vase	Northern Div. 1 (427-445)	Northumberland FA
Newcastle Town FC	Cup/Vase	N.W.C. Div. 1 (351-370)	Staffordshire FA
Newmarket Town FC	Cup/Vase	Eastern Prem. Div. (571-588)	Suffolk FA
Newport County FC	Cup/Trophy	Southern Prem. Div. (502)	F.A. of Wales
Newport (IW) FC	Cup/Trophy	Southern Prem. Div. (504)	Hampshire FA
North Ferriby United FC	Cup/Trophy	N.P.L. Div. 1 (339)	East Riding FA
North Leigh FC	Cup/Vase	Hellenic Prem. Div. (591-611)	Oxfordshire FA
Northallerton Town FC	Cup/Vase	Northern Div. 2 (427-445)	North Riding FA
Northampton Spencer FC	Cup/Vase	Utd. Counties Prem. Div. (653-673)	Northamptonshire FA
North Notts FC	Vase	Central Mids. Supreme Div. (411-420)	Nottinghamshire FA
North Shields FC	Vase	Wearside (447-451)	Northumberland FA
Northwich Victoria FC	Cup/Trophy	Conference (217)	Cheshire FA
Northwood FC	Cup/Trophy	Isthmian Div. 1 (833)	Middlesex FA
Norton & Stockton Ancients FC	Vase	Northern Div. 2 (427-445)	Durham FA
Norwich United FC	Vase	Eastern Div. 1 (571-588)	Norfolk FA
Nuneaton Borough FC	Cup/Trophy	Conference (223)	Birmingham FA
Nuneaton Griff FC	Vase	Mid. Comb. Prem. Div. (747-754)	Birmingham FA
Oadby Town FC	Cup/Vase	Midland Alliance (733-745)	Leics. & Rutland FA
Oakwood FC	Vase	Sussex Div. 2 (631-651)	Sussex FA
Odd Down FC	Cup/Vase	Western Lge. Prem. Div. (696-712)	Somerset FA
Oldbury United FC	Cup/Vase	Midland Alliance (733-745)	Birmingham FA
Oldham Town FC	Cup/Vase	N.W.C. Div. 2 (351-370)	Manchester FA
Ossett Albion FC	Cup/Trophy	N.P.L. Div. 1 (340)	West Riding FA
Ossett Town FC	Cup/Trophy	N.P.L. Div. 1 (341)	West Riding FA
Oxford City FC	Cup/Trophy	Isthmian Div. 1 (834)	Oxfordshire FA
Paget Rangers FC	Cup/Vase	Midland Alliance (733-745)	Birmingham FA
Pagham FC	Vase	Sussex Div. 1 (631-651)	Sussex FA
Parkgate FC	Cup/Vase	N.C.E. Div. 1 (393-410)	Sheff. & Hallams. FA
Paulton Rovers FC	Cup/Vase	Western Lge. Prem. Div. (696-712)	Somerset FA
Peacehaven & Telscombe FC	Cup/Vase	Sussex Div. 1 (631-651)	Sussex FA
Pegusus Juniors FC	Vase	Hellenic Prem. Div. (591-611)	Herefordshire FA
Pelsall Villa FC	Cup/Vase	Midland Alliance (733-745)	Staffordshire FA
Penrith FC	Cup/Vase	Northern Div. 2 (427-445)	Cumberland FA
Pershore Town FC	Vase	Mid. Comb. Prem. Div. (747-754)	Worcestershire FA
Peterlee Newtown FC	Cup/Vase	Northern Div. 1 (427-445)	Durham FA

Pickering Town FC	Cup/Vase	N.C.E. Prem. Div. (393-410)	North Riding FA
Pontefract Collieries FC	Cup/Vase	N.C.E. Div. 1 (393-410)	West Riding FA
Porthleven FC	Vase	South Western (715-722)	Cornwall FA
Portland United FC	Vase	Wessex League (675-686)	Dorset FA
Potters Bar Town FC	Cup/Vase	Spartan South Mids. Prem. Div. (889-902)	Hertfordshire FA
Potton United FC	Cup/Vase	Utd. Counties Div. 1 (653-673)	Bedfordshire FA
Poulton Victoria FC	Vase	West Cheshire (375-378)	Cheshire FA
Prescot Cables FC	Cup/Vase	N.W.C. Div. 1 (351-370)	Liverpool FA
Prudhoe Town FC	Vase	Northern Div. 2 (427-445)	Northumberland FA
Purfleet FC	Cup/Trophy	Isthmian Prem. Div. (814)	Essex FA
Quorn FC	Vase	Midland Alliance (733-745)	Leics. & Rutland FA
Racing Club Warwick FC	Cup/Trophy	Southern Western Div. (538)	Birmingham FA
Radcliffe Borough FC	Cup/Trophy	N.P.L. Div. 1 (342)	Lancashire FA
Rainworth MW FC	Vase	Notts. Alliance (421-425)	Nottinghamshire FA
Ramsbottom United FC	Cup/Vase	N.W.C. Div. 1 (351-370)	Lancashire FA
Ramsgate FC	Cup/Vase	Kent League (613-624)	Kent FA
Raunds Town FC	Cup/Vase	Utd. Counties Prem. Div. (653-673)	Northamptonshire FA
Reading Town FC	Cup/Vase	Combined Counties (871-880)	Berks & Bucks FA
Redditch United FC	Cup/Trophy	Southern Western Div. (539)	Birmingham FA
Redhill FC	Cup/Vase	Sussex Div. 1 (631-651)	Surrey FA
Ringmer FC	Cup/Vase	Sussex Div. 1 (631-651)	Sussex FA
Rocester FC	Cup/Trophy	Southern Western Div. (540)	Staffordshire FA
Romford FC	Cup/Vase	Isthmian Div. 2 (847-860)	Essex FA
Rossendale United FC	Cup/Trophy	N.P.L. Div. 1 (343)	Lancashire FA
Rossington Main FC	Cup/Vase	N.C.E. Div. 1 (393-410)	Sheff. & Hallams. FA
Rothwell Corinthians FC	Vase	Utd. Counties Div. 1 (653-673)	Northamptonshire FA
Rothwell Town FC	Cup/Trophy	Southern Eastern Div. (563)	Northamptonshire FA
Royston Town FC	Cup/Vase	Spartan South Mids. Prem. Div. (889-902)	Hertfordshire FA
Rugby United FC	Cup/Trophy	Southern Eastern Div. (564)	Birmingham FA
Ruislip Manor FC	Cup/Vase	Spartan South Mids. Prem. Div. (889-902)	Middlesex FA
Runcorn FC	Cup/Trophy	N.P.L. Prem. Div. (316)	Cheshire FA
Rushall Olympic FC	Cup/Vase	Midland Alliance (733-745)	Staffordshire FA
Saffron Walden Town FC	Cup/Vase	Essex Senior (881-887)	Essex FA
Salford City FC	Cup/Vase	N.W.C. Div. 1 (351-370)	Manchester FA
Salisbury City FC	Cup/Trophy	Southern Prem. Div. (506)	Wiltshire FA
Saltdean United FC	Cup/Vase	Sussex Div. 1 (631-651)	Sussex FA
Sandhurst Town FC	Cup/Vase	Combined Counties (871-880)	Berks & Bucks FA
Sawbridgeworth Town FC	Cup/Vase	Essex Senior (881-887)	Hertfordshire FA
Scarborough FC	Cup/Trophy	Conference (229)	North Riding FA
Seaham Red Star FC	Cup/Vase	Northern Div. 1 (427-445)	Durham FA
Selby Town FC	Cup/Vase	N.C.E. Prem. Div. (393-410)	West Riding FA
Selsey FC	Cup/Vase	Sussex Div. 1 (631-651)	Sussex FA
Shawbury United FC	Vase	West Mids. Prem. Div. (755-763)	Shropshsire FA

Sheffield FC	Cup/Vase	N.C.E. Prem. Div. (393-410)	Sheff. & Hallams. FA
Shepshed Dynamo FC	Cup/Trophy	Southern Western Div. (541)	Leics. & Rutland FA
Shepton Mallet AFC	Vase	Western Lge. Div. 1 (695-712)	Somerset FA
Shifnal Town FC	Cup/Vase	Midland Alliance (733-745)	Shropshire FA
Shildon FC	Cup/Vase	Northern Div. 2 (427-445)	Durham FA
Shirebrook Town FC	Vase	Central Mids. Supreme Div. (411-420)	Derbyshire FA
Shortwood United FC	Cup/Vase	Hellenic Prem. Div. (591-611)	Gloucestershire FA
Shotton Comrades FC	Cup/Vase	Northern Div. 2 (427-445)	Durham FA
Sidley United FC	Vase	Sussex Div. 1 (631-651)	Sussex FA
Sittingbourne FC	Cup/Trophy	Southern Eastern Div. (565)	Kent FA
Skelmersdale United FC	Cup/Vase	N.W.C. Div. 1 (351-370)	Liverpool FA
Slade Green FC	Cup/Vase	Kent League (613-624)	Kent FA
Slough Town FC	Cup/Trophy	Isthmian Div. 1 (835)	Berks & Bucks FA
Soham Town Rangers FC	Cup/Vase	Eastern Prem. Div. (571-588)	Cambridgeshire FA
Solihull Borough FC	Cup/Trophy	Southern Western Div. (542)	Birmingham FA
Somersett Ambury V&E FC	Vase	Spartan South Mids. Prem. Div. (889-902)	Hertfordshire FA
Somersham Town FC	Vase	Eastern Div. 1 (571-588)	Huntingdonshire FA
South Normanton Athletic FC	Vase	Central Mids. Supreme Div. (411-420)	Derbyshire FA
South Shields FC	Cup/Vase	Northern Div. 2 (427-445)	Durham FA
Southall FC	Cup/Vase	Combined Counties (871-880)	Middlesex FA
Southall Town FC	Vase	Hellenic Prem. Div. (591-611)	Middlesex FA
Southam United FC	Vase	Mid. Comb. Prem. Div. (747-754)	Birmingham FA
Southend Manor FC	Cup/Vase	Essex Senior (881-887)	Essex FA
Southport FC	Cup/Trophy	Conference (235)	Lancashire FA
Southwick FC	Cup/Vase	Sussex Div. 1 (631-651)	Sussex FA
Spalding United FC	Cup/Trophy	Southern Eastern Div. (565)	Lincolnshire FA
Spennymoor United FC	Cup/Trophy	N.P.L. Div. 1 (344)	Durham FA
Squires Gate FC	Cup/Vase	N.W.C. Div. 2 (351-370)	Lancashire FA
St Albans City FC	Cup/Trophy	Isthmian Prem. Div. (816)	Hertfordshire FA
St Andrews FC	Vase	Leics. Sen. Prem. Div. (764-768)	Leics. & Rutland FA
St Blazey FC	Cup/Vase	South Western (715-722)	Cornwall FA
St Helens Town FC	Cup/Vase	N.W.C. Div. 1 (351-370)	Liverpool FA
St Ives Town FC	Vase	Utd. Counties Div. 1 (653-673)	Huntingdonshire FA
St Leonards FC	Cup/Trophy	Southern Eastern Div. (567)	Sussex FA
St Margaretsbury FC	Cup/Vase	Spartan South Mids. Prem. Div. (889-902)	Hertfordshire FA
St Neots Town FC	Cup/Vase	Utd. Counties Prem. Div. (653-673)	Huntingdonshire FA
Stafford Rangers FC	Cup/Trophy	Southern Prem. Div. (508)	Staffordshire FA
Stafford Town FC	Cup/Vase	Midland Alliance (733-745)	Staffordshire FA
Staines Town FC	Cup/Trophy	Isthmian Div. 1 (836)	Middlesex FA
Stalybridge Celtic FC	Cup/Trophy	Conference (241)	Cheshire FA
Stamford AFC	Cup/Trophy	Southern Eastern Div. (568)	Lincolnshire FA
Stand Athletic FC	Vase	N.W.C. Div. 2 (351-370)	Lancashire FA
Stansted FC	Vase	Essex Senior (881-887)	Essex FA

Stanway Rovers FC	Vase	Eastern Div. 1 (571-588)	Essex FA
Stapenhill FC	Cup/Vase	Midland Alliance (733-745)	Derbyshire FA
Star FC	Vase	West Mids. Prem. Div. (755-763)	Shropshire FA
Staveley MW FC	Cup/Vase	N.C.E. Div. 1 (393-410)	Derbyshire FA
Stevenage Borough FC	Cup/Trophy	Conference (247)	Hertfordshire FA
Stewarts & Lloyds FC	Cup/Vase	Utd. Counties Prem. Div. (653-673)	Northamptonshire FA
Stocksbridge Park Steels FC	Cup/Trophy	N.P.L. Div. 1 (345)	Sheff. & Hallams. FA
Stotfold FC	Cup/Vase	Utd. Counties Prem. Div. (653-673)	Bedfordshire FA
Stourbridge FC	Cup/Vase	Midland Alliance (733-745)	Birmingham FA
Stourport Swifts FC	Cup/Trophy	Southern Western Div. (543)	Worcestershire FA
Stowmarket Town FC	Cup/Vase	Eastern Prem. Div. (571-588)	Suffolk FA
Stratford Town FC	Cup/Vase	Midland Alliance (733-745)	Birmingham FA
Street FC	Cup/Vase	Western Lge. Div. 1 (695-712)	Somerset FA
Studley BKL FC	Vase	Midland Alliance (733-745)	Birmingham FA
Sutton Coldfield Town FC	Cup/Trophy	Southern Western Div. (544)	Birmingham FA
Sutton United FC	Cup/Trophy	Isthmian Prem. Div. (818)	Surrey FA
Swindon Supermarine FC	Cup/Trophy	Southern Western Div. (545)	Wiltshire FA
Tadcaster Albion FC	Cup/Vase	N.C.E. Div. 1 (393-410)	West Riding FA
Tamworth FC	Cup/Trophy	Southern Prem. Div. (510)	Birmingham FA
Taunton Town FC	Cup/Vase	Western Lge. Prem. Div. (696-712)	Somerset FA
Team Bath FC	Vase	Western Lge. Prem. Div. (696-712)	Somerset FA
Telford United FC	Cup/Trophy	Conference (253)	Shropshsire FA
Thackley FC	Cup/Vase	N.C.E. Prem. Div. (393-410)	West Riding FA
Thame United FC	Cup/Trophy	Isthmian Div. 1 (837)	Oxfordshire FA
Thamesmead Town FC	Cup/Vase	Kent League (613-624)	London FA

Stafford Town. Back Row (l-r): Nick Anthony, Tim Buckley, Alan Somerville, John Gummershall, Neil Walters, Peter Ingram, Russ Dematteo, Kevin Warrilow, Paul Sandlard, Mick Cox. Front Row: Carl Anderson, Mick Stark, Nick Dunne, Warren Campbell, Chris Curtis, Simon Carter, Wesley Morgan

Tunbridge Wells on the attack leaving the Lordswood goalie stranded.

Thatcham Town FC	Cup/Vase	Wessex League (675-686)	Berks & Bucks FA
Thetford Town FC	Vase	Eastern Div. 1 (571-588)	Norfolk FA
Thornaby FC	Cup/Vase	Northern Div. 1 (427-445)	North Riding FA
Three Bridges FC	Cup/Vase	Sussex Div. 1 (631-651)	Sussex FA
Tilbury FC	Cup/Vase	Isthmian Div. 2 (847-860)	Essex FA
Tiptree United FC	Cup/Vase	Eastern Prem. Div. (571-588)	Essex FA
Tiverton Town FC	Cup/Trophy	Southern Prem. Div. (512)	Devon FA
Tividale FC	Vase	West Mids. Prem. Div. (755-763)	Birmingham FA
Tonbridge Angels FC	Cup/Trophy	Southern Eastern Div. (569)	Kent FA
Tooting & Mitcham United FC	Cup/Trophy	Isthmian Div. 1 (838)	Surrey FA
Torrington FC	Cup/Vase	Western Lge. Div. 1 (695-712)	Devon FA
Tow Law Town FC	Cup/Vase	Northern Div. 1 (427-445)	Durham FA
Trafford FC	Cup/Trophy	N.P.L. Div. 1 (346)	Manchester FA
Tring Town FC	Cup/Vase	Isthmian Div. 3 (861-870)	Hertfordshire FA
Tuffley Rovers FC	Cup/Vase	Hellenic Prem. Div. (591-611)	Gloucestershire FA
Tunbridge Wells FC	Cup/Vase	Kent League (613-624)	Kent FA
Uxbridge FC	Cup/Trophy	Isthmian Div. 1 (839)	Middlesex FA
Vauxhall Motors FC	Cup/Trophy	N.P.L. Prem. Div. (318)	Cheshire FA
VCD Athletic FC	Cup/Vase	Kent League (613-624)	Kent FA
Viking Greenford FC	Cup/Vase	Combined Counties (871-880)	Middlesex FA
Walsall Wood FC	Vase	West Mids. Prem. Div. (755-763)	Staffordshire FA
Walton & Hersham FC	Cup/Trophy	Isthmian Div. 1 (840)	Surrey FA

Walton Casuals FC	Cup/Vase	Combined Counties (871-880)	Surrey FA
Wantage Town FC	Vase	Hellenic Prem. Div. (591-611)	Berks & Bucks FA
Warboys Town FC	Cup/Vase	Eastern Div. 1 (571-588)	Huntingdonshire FA
Ware FC	Cup/Vase	Isthmian Div. 3 (861-870)	Hertfordshire FA
Warminster Town FC	Vase	Western Lge. Div. 1 (695-712)	Wiltshire FA
Warrington Town FC	Cup/Vase	N.W.C. Div. 1 (351-370)	Cheshire FA
Washington Ikeda Hoover FC	Vase	Northern Div. 1 (427-445)	Durham FA
Washington Nissan FC	Vase	Northern Div. 2 (427-445)	Durham FA
Wealdstone FC	Cup/Trophy	Isthmian Div. 1 (841)	Middlesex FA
Wednesfield FC	Cup/Vase	Midland Alliance (733-745)	Birmingham FA
Welling United FC	Cup/Trophy	Southern Prem. Div. (514)	London FA
Wellingborough Town FC	Cup/Vase	Utd. Counties Prem. Div. (653-673)	Northamptonshire FA
Wellington Town FC	Vase	Western Lge. Div. 1 (695-712)	Somerset FA
Welton Rovers FC	Cup/Vase	Western Lge. Prem. Div. (696-712)	Somerset FA
Welwyn Garden City FC	Cup/Vase	Spartan South Mids. Div. 1 (889-902)	Hertfordshire FA
Wembley FC	Cup/Vase	Isthmian Div. 2 (847-860)	Middlesex FA
West Allotment Celtic FC	Vase	Northern Alliance	Northumberland FA
West Auckland Town FC	Cup/Vase	Northern Div. 1 (427-445)	Durham FA
West Midlands Police FC	Cup/Vase	Mid. Comb. Prem. Div. (747-754)	Birmingham FA
Westbury United FC	Cup/Vase	Western Lge. Prem. Div. (696-712)	Wiltshire FA
Westfield FC	Vase	Combined Counties (871-880)	Surrey FA
Westfields FC	Vase	West Mids. Prem. Div. (755-763)	Herefordshire FA
Weston Super Mare FC	Cup/Trophy	Southern Western Div. (546)	Somerset FA
Weymouth FC	Cup/Trophy	Southern Prem. Div. (516)	Dorset FA

VCD Athletic

Whickham FC	Vase	Northern Div. 2 (427-445)	Durham FA
Whitby Town FC	Cup/Trophy	N.P.L. Prem. Div. (320)	North Riding FA
Whitchurch United FC	Cup/Vase	Wessex League (675-686)	Hampshire FA
Whitehawk FC	Cup/Vase	Sussex Div. 1 (631-651)	Sussex FA
Whitley Bay FC	Cup/Vase	Northern Div. 1 (427-445)	Northumberland FA
Whitstable Town FC	Cup/Vase	Kent League (613-624)	Kent FA
Whitton United FC	Vase	Eastern Div. 1 (571-588)	Suffolk FA
Whyteleafe FC	Cup/Trophy	Isthmian Div. 1 (842)	Surrey FA
Wick FC	Cup/Vase	Sussex Div. 1 (631-651)	Sussex FA
Willand Rovers FC	Vase	Western Lge. Div. 1 (695-712)	Devon FA
Willenhall Town FC	Cup/Vase	Midland Alliance (733-745)	Birmingham FA
Willington FC	Cup/Vase	Northern Div. 2 (427-445)	Durham FA
Wimborne Town FC	Cup/Vase	Wessex League (675-686)	Dorset FA
Windsor & Eton FC	Cup/Trophy	Isthmian Div. 1 (843)	Berks & Bucks FA
Wingate & Finchley FC	Cup/Vase	Isthmian Div. 3 (861-870)	London FA
Winsford United FC	Cup/Vase	N.W.C. Div. 1 (351-370)	Cheshire FA
Winterton Rangers FC	Vase	N.C.E. Div. 1 (393-410)	Lincolnshire FA
Wisbech Town FC	Cup/Trophy	Southern Eastern Div. (570)	Cambridgeshire FA
Witham Town FC	Cup/Vase	Isthmian Div. 3 (861-870)	Essex FA
Witney Academy FC	Vase	Hellenic Div. 1 West (591-611)	Oxfordshire FA
Witton Albion FC	Cup/Trophy	N.P.L. Div. 1 (347)	Cheshire FA
Wivenhoe Town FC	Cup/Vase	Isthmian Div. 2 (847-860)	Essex FA
Woking FC	Cup/Trophy	Conference (259)	Surrey FA
Wokingham Town FC	Cup/Vase	Isthmian Div. 3 (861-870)	Berks & Bucks FA
Wolverhampton Casuals FC	Vase	West Mids. Prem. Div. (755-763)	Staffordshire FA
Woodbridge Town FC	Cup/Vase	Eastern Prem. Div. (571-588)	Suffolk FA
Woodley Sports FC	Cup/Vase	N.W.C. Div. 1 (351-370)	Cheshire FA
Wootton Bassett Town	Vase	Hellenic Prem. Div. (591-611)	Wiltshire FA
Wootton Blue Cross FC	Cup/Vase	Utd. Counties Prem. Div. (653-673)	Bedfordshire FA
Worcester City FC	Cup/Trophy	Southern Prem. Div. (518)	Worcestershire FA
Workington FC	Cup/Trophy	N.P.L. Div. 1 (348)	Cumberland FA
Worksop Town FC	Cup/Trophy	N.P.L. Prem. Div. (322)	Sheff. & Hallams. FA
Worsbrough Bridge MW FC	Vase	N.C.E. Div. 1 (393-410)	Sheff. & Hallams. FA
Worthing FC	Cup/Trophy	Isthmian Div. 1 (844)	Sussex FA
Wroxham FC	Cup/Vase	Eastern Prem. Div. (571-588)	Norfolk FA
Yate Town FC	Cup/Vase	Hellenic Prem. Div. (591-611)	Gloucestershire FA
Yaxley FC	Cup/Vase	Utd. Counties Prem. Div. (653-673)	Huntingdonshire FA
Yeading FC	Cup/Trophy	Isthmian Div. 1 (845)	Middlesex FA
Yeovil Town FC	Cup/Trophy	Conference (265)	Somerset FA
Yorkshire Amateur FC	Cup/Vase	N.C.E. Div. 1 (393-410)	West Riding FA